T0391260

THE SIXTEENTH
MARCEL GROSSMANN MEETING

On Recent Developments in Theoretical and Experimental
General Relativity, Astrophysics and Relativistic Field Theories

PART B

THE SIXTEENTH
MARCEL GROSSMANN MEETING

On Recent Developments in Theoretical and Experimental
General Relativity, Astrophysics and Relativistic Field Theories

Proceedings of the MG16 Meeting
on General Relativity
Online, 5–10 July 2021

Editors

Remo Ruffini
University of Rome "La Sapienza", Rome, Italy
International Center for Relativistic Astrophysics Network (ICRANet), Pescara, Italy

Gregory Vereshchagin
International Center for Relativistic Astrophysics Network (ICRANet), Pescara, Italy

Series Editor

Remo Ruffini
University of Rome "La Sapienza", Rome, Italy
International Center for Relativistic Astrophysics Network (ICRANet), Pescara, Italy

World Scientific

NEW JERSEY · LONDON · SINGAPORE · BEIJING · SHANGHAI · HONG KONG · TAIPEI · CHENNAI

Published by

World Scientific Publishing Co. Pte. Ltd.

5 Toh Tuck Link, Singapore 596224

USA office: 27 Warren Street, Suite 401-402, Hackensack, NJ 07601

UK office: 57 Shelton Street, Covent Garden, London WC2H 9HE

Library of Congress Cataloging-in-Publication Data
Names: Marcel Grossmann Meeting on General Relativity (16th : 2021 : Online) |
 Ruffini, Remo, editor. | Vereshchagin, Gregory, editor.
Title: The sixteenth Marcel Grossmann meeting on recent developments in theoretical and experimental
 general relativity, astrophysics, and relativistic field theories : proceedings of the MG16 meeting on
 general relativity online, 5–10 July 2021 / editors: Remo Ruffini, University of Rome "La Sapienza",
 Rome, Italy, International Center for Relativistic Astrophysics Network (ICRANet), Pescara, Italy,
 Gregory Vereshchagin, International Center for Relativistic Astrophysics Network (ICRANet), Pescara, Italy.
Other titles: Proceedings of the MG16 meeting on general relativity online, 5–10 July 2021
Description: New Jersey : World Scientific, [2023] | Includes bibliographical references.
Identifiers: LCCN 2022047088 | ISBN 9789811269769 (set ; hardcover) | ISBN 9789811266584 (v. 1) |
 ISBN 9789811266591 (v. 2) | ISBN 9789811266607 (v. 3) | ISBN 9789811266614 (v. 4) |
 ISBN 9789811269776 (set ; ebook)
Subjects: LCSH: General relativity (Physics)--Congresses. | Gravitation--Congresses. |
 Quantum gravity--Congresses. | Cosmology--Congresses. | Astrophysics--Congresses.
Classification: LCC QC173.6 .M37 2021 | DDC 523.01--dc23/eng/20220929
LC record available at https://lccn.loc.gov/2022047088

British Library Cataloguing-in-Publication Data
A catalogue record for this book is available from the British Library.

Copyright © 2023 by Editors

All rights reserved.

This is an Open Access volume published by World Scientific Publishing Company. It is distributed under the terms of the Creative Commons Attribution-Non Commercial 4.0 (CC BY-NC) License. Further distribution of this work is permitted, provided the original work is properly cited.

For any available supplementary material, please visit
https://www.worldscientific.com/worldscibooks/10.1142/13149#t=suppl

Typeset by Stallion Press
Email: enquiries@stallionpress.com

Printed in Singapore

THE MARCEL GROSSMANN MEETINGS
Series Editor: REMO RUFFINI

Publications in the Series of Proceedings

Proceedings of the Sixteenth Marcel Grossmann Meeting on General Relativity
(Virtual Meeting, 2021)
Edited by G. Vereshchagin, R. Ruffini
World Scientific, 2022

Proceedings of the Fifteenth Marcel Grossmann Meeting on General Relativity
(Rome, Italy, 2018)
Edited by E.S. Battistelli, R.T. Jantzen, R. Ruffini
World Scientific, 2022

Proceedings of the Fourteenth Marcel Grossmann Meeting on General Relativity
(Rome, Italy, 2015)
Edited by M. Bianchi, R.T. Jantzen, R. Ruffini
World Scientific, 2017

Proceedings of the Thirteenth Marcel Grossmann Meeting on General Relativity
(Stockholm, Sweden, 2012)
Edited by K. Rosquist, R.T. Jantzen, R. Ruffini
World Scientific, 2015

Proceedings of the Twelfth Marcel Grossmann Meeting on General Relativity
(Paris, France, 2009)
Edited by T. Damour, R.T. Jantzen, R. Ruffini
World Scientific, 2012

Proceedings of the Eleventh Marcel Grossmann Meeting on General Relativity
(Berlin, Germany, 2006)
Edited by H. Kleinert, R.T. Jantzen, R. Ruffini
World Scientific, 2007

Proceedings of the Tenth Marcel Grossmann Meeting on General Relativity
(Rio de Janiero, Brazil, 2003)
Edited by M. Novello, S. Perez-Bergliaffa, R. Ruffini
World Scientific, 2005

Proceedings of the Ninth Marcel Grossmann Meeting on General Relativity
(Rome, Italy, 2000)
Edited by V.G. Gurzadyan, R.T. Jantzen, R. Ruffini
World Scientific, 2002

Proceedings of the Eighth Marcel Grossmann Meeting on General Relativity
(Jerusalem, Israel, 1997)
Edited by T. Piran
World Scientific, 1998

Proceedings of the Seventh Marcel Grossmann Meeting on General Relativity
(Stanford, USA, 1994)
Edited by R.T. Jantzen and G.M. Keiser
World Scientific, 1996

Proceedings of the Sixth Marcel Grossmann Meeting on General Relativity
(Kyoto, Japan, 1991)
Edited by H. Sato and T. Nakamura
World Scientific, 1992

Proceedings of the Fifth Marcel Grossmann Meeting on General Relativity
(Perth, Australia, 1988)
Edited by D.G. Blair and M.J. Buckingham
World Scientific, 1989

Proceedings of the Fourth Marcel Grossmann Meeting on General Relativity
(Rome, Italy, 1985)
Edited by R. Ruffini
World Scientific, 1986

Proceedings of the Third Marcel Grossmann Meeting on General Relativity
(Shanghai, People's Republic of China, 1982)
Edited by Hu Ning
Science Press – Beijing and North-Holland Publishing Company, 1983

Proceedings of the Second Marcel Grossmann Meeting on General Relativity
(Trieste, Italy, 1979)
Edited by R. Ruffini
North-Holland Publishing Company, 1982

Proceedings of the First Marcel Grossmann Meeting on General Relativity
(Trieste, Italy, 1975)
Edited by R. Ruffini
North-Holland Publishing Company, 1977

SPONSORS

International Center for Relativistic Astrophysics Network (ICRANet)
International Center for Relativistic Astrophysics (ICRA)

FREEDOM OF MOVEMENT FOR SCIENTISTS

The Marcel Grossmann Meetings were founded with the premise that scientists of all nations have a right to meet to exchange knowledge independent of national borders.

ACKNOWLEDGEMENTS

We acknowledge the outstanding job done before, during and after the meeting by the ICRANet/ICRA administrative and secretarial staff: Cristina Adamo, Silvia Latorre, Elisabetta Natale, and Cinzia di Niccolo. Finally this meeting and its proceedings could not have functioned without the dedicated IT support of the ICRANet system manager Gabriele Brandolini, with some temporary assistance from Domenico La Selva and Damiano Verzulli. We would like to thank Linda Kwan from World Scientific for valuable assistance during preparation of these proceedings.

ORGANIZING BODIES
OF THE SIXTEENTH MARCEL GROSSMANN MEETING

INTERNATIONAL ORGANIZING COMMITTEE

Blair David, Choquet Bruhat Yvonne, Damour Thibault, De Bernardis Paolo, Everitt C. W. Francis, Fryer Chris, Haensch Theodor, Henneaux Marc, Jones Christine, Kerr Roy, Kleinert Hagen, Kunz Jutta, Laemmerzahl Claus, Longair Malcolm, Mirabel Felix, Mirzoyan Razmik, Piran Tsvi, Rueda Jorge, Ruffini Remo (chair), Sasaki Misao, Sato Humitaka, Sunyaev Rashid, 't Hooft Gerard, Weinberg Steven, Yau Shing-Tung, Zhang Bing

LOCAL ORGANIZING COMMITTEE

Adamo Cristina, Bianco Carlo Luciano, Brandolini Gabriele A., di Niccolo Cinzia, Latorre Silvia, La Selva Domenico, Li Liang, Loppini Alessandro, Natale Elisabetta, Verzulli Damiano, Vereshchagin Gregory (chair), Wang Yu

INTERNATIONAL COORDINATING COMMITTEE

ALBANIA: Hafizi M. - ARGENTINA: Arguelles C., Scoccola C., Reula O., Romero G.E. - ARMENIA: Sahakyan N. - AUSTRALIA: Blair D., Ju L., Lun A., Manchester D., Melatos A., Quinn P., Scott S.M., Steele J.D. - AUSTRIA: Aichelburg P.C., Schindler S. - BELARUS: Kilin S., Prakapenia M., Siutsou I. - BELGIUM: Henneaux M. - BOLIVIA: Aguirre C.B. - BOSNIA: Pasic V. - BRAZIL: Barres de Almeida U., Coelho Goulart J., Dalmolin F.T., de Lima Rafael C.R., Guzzo M., Maia C., Malheiro M., Romero Filho C.A., Shellard R.C., Zen Vasconcellos C. - BULGARIA: Yazadjiev S. - CANADA: Singh D., Smolin L., Turok N. - CHILE: Bauer F., Bunster W.C., Giacomini A. - CHINA (MAINLAND): Cai R., Cai Y., Cao Z., Chang J., Chen J., Chen X., Dai Z., Feng L.-L., Han W., Jing Y., Li T.-P., Lin W., Lou Y.-Q., Luo J., Mei J., Tam T., Wang A., Wang Y., Wu X.-P., Wu Y.-L., Yuan Y.-F., Zhang B.-B., Zhang S.-N., Zhao G. - CHINA (TAIWAN): Chen Chiang-Mei, Chen Pisin, Lee Da-Shin, Lee Wo-Lung, Ni Wei-Tou - COLOMBIA: Bargueño de Retes P., Gonzalez G., Higuera Garzon M.A., Núñez L., Romano A.E., Valenzuela Toledo C.A., Zuluaga J.I. - CROATIA: Dominis Prester D., Karlica M., Milekovic M., Smolcic V., Smolic I., Suric T. - CUBA: Perez Martinez A., Pérez Rojas H. - CZECH REPUBLIC: Bicak J., Stuchlik Z. - DENMARK: Naselsky P. - ECUADOR: Contreras E. - EGYPT: Tawfik A.N., Wanas M.I. - ESTONIA: Einasto J., Saar E. - FINLAND: Poutanen J., Volovik G. - FRANCE: Brillet A., Buchert T., Chardonnet P., Coullet P., de Freitas Pacheco J.A., Deruelle N., Iliopoulos J., Lamanna G., Mignard F. - GEORGIA: Lavrelashvili George, Machabeli Giorgi - GERMANY: Biermann P., Blumlein J., Di Piazza A., Fritzsch H., Genzel R., Gilmozzi R., Hasinger G., Hehl F., Keitel C., Kiefer C., Mirzoyan R.,

Neugebauer G., Nicolai H., Renn J., Ringwald A., Ruediger A. - GREECE: Batakis N.A., Cotsakis S., Vagenas E.C. - HUNGARY: Fodor G., Levai P. - ICELAND: Bjornsson G., Jakobsson P. - INDIA: Chakrabarti S.K., Iyer B., Padmanabhan T., Souradeep T. - IRAN: Baghram S., Bavarsad E., Eslam Panah B., Firouzjahi H., Haghighat M., Mansouri R., Mashhoon B., Shakeri S., Sobouti Y., Taghi Mirtorabi M. - IRELAND: O'Murchada N. - ISRAEL: Milgrom M., Nakar E., Pe'er A., Piran T. - ITALY: Belinski V., Bianchi M., Bianco C.L., Cherubini C., Della Valle M., Falciano S., Filippi S., Haardt F., Menotti P., Merafina M., Pani P., Ricci F., Treves A., Vereshchagin G.V., Vitale S., Xue S.- S. - JAPAN: Fujimoto M.-K., Makishima K., Nakamura T., Sato K., Shibata M. - KAZAKHSTAN: Abishev M., Aimuratov Y., Boshkayev K., Mychelkin E.G., Spitaleri C. - KOREA (PYEONGYANG): Kim J.S. - KOREA (SEOUL): Kim S.P., Kim S.-W., Lee H.K., Lee H.-W., van Putten M. - KYRGYZSTAN: Gurovich V.Ts. - LIBYA: Gadri M. - MEXICO: Breton N., Cervantes-Cota J.L., Fraija Cabrera N.I., García-Diaz A.A., Macías Alvarez A., Mielke Eckehard W., Quevedo H., Rodriguez L.F. - NETHERLANDS: Slagter R. - NEW ZEALAND: Visser M., Wiltshire D. - NORWAY: Elgaroy O., Fonseca Mota D., Knutsen H. - PAKISTAN: Qadir A., Qamar S. - PERU: Vargas T. - POLAND: Belczynski K., Demianski M., Lewandowski Jerzy, Nurowski P., Sokolowski L. - PORTUGAL: Costa M., Da Silva A., Lemos J.P.S., Lobo F., Moniz P., Silva L.O. - ROMANIA: Visinescu M. - RUSSIA: Aksenov A., Arkhangelskaja I., Bisnovatyi-Kogan G., Blinnikov S., Chechetikin V.M., Cherepaschuk A.M., Khriplovich I., Lipunov V.M., Lukash V.N., Novikov I., Rudenko V.N., Starobinsky A.A. - SERBIA: Djordjevic G., Jovanovic P., Knezevic Z., Pankov-Hzvojevic M., Popovic L., Prodanovic T., Sijacki D., Simic S. - SLOVAKIA: Balek V. - SLOVENIA: Cadez A., Gomboc A., Zavrtanik D. - SOUTH AFRICA: Larena J., Maharaj S. - SPAIN: Elizalde E., Ibanez J., Perez M.J., Verdaguer E. - SWEDEN: Abramowicz M.A., Marklund M., Ryde F. - SWITZERLAND: Durrer R., Jetzer P. - TURKEY: Aliev A., Gurses M. - UKRAINE: Novosyadlyj B., Zaslavskii O., Zhuk A. - UNITED ARAB EMIRATES: Fernini I. - UNITED KINGDOM: Cruise A.M., Frenk Carlos S., Green M., Mavromatos N., Perry M., Willingale R. - USA: Abel T., Ashtekar A., Bardeen J., Carlstrom J., Cornish N., Dermer C., Fan X., Flanagan E., Fraschetti F., Fryer C., Incera V., Jantzen R.T. (chairperson), Kolb R., Laguna P., Lousto C., Madau Piero, Mathews Grant, Matzner Richard, Melia Fulvio, Mester John, Michelson Peter, Nordtvedt Kenneth, Parker Leonard, Pretorius F., Pullin J., Shapiro I., Shapiro S., Shoemaker D., Smoot G., Stiavelli M., Teukolsky S., van Nieuwenhuizen P., Zhang B. - UZBEKISTAN: Ahmedov B., Zalaletdinov R.M. - VATICAN CITY: Gionti G. - VENEZUELA: Fuenmayor E. - VIETNAM: Long H.N.

MARCEL GROSSMANN AWARDS

Sixteenth Marcel Grossmann Meeting

Institutional Awards

"for the creation of the world's best X-ray map of the entire sky, for the discovery of millions of previously unknown accreting supermassive black holes at cosmological redshifts, for the detection of X-rays from tens of thousands of galaxy clusters, filled mainly with dark matter, and for permitting the detailed investigation of the growth of the large-scale structure of the universe during the era of dark energy dominance".

S.A. LAVOCHKIN ASSOCIATION
- presented to its Designer General **Alexander Shirshakov**

MAX PLANCK INSTITUTE FOR EXTRATERRESTRIAL PHYSICS (MPE)
- presented to Professor **Peter Predehl**, Principal Investigator of eROSITA

SPACE RESEARCH INSTITUTE (IKI) OF THE RUSSIAN ACADEMY OF SCIENCES
- presented to Professor **Rashid Sunyaev,** Principal Investigator of SRG Observatory in Russia

Individual Awards

DEMETRIOS CHRISTODOULOU
"For his many lasting contributions to the foundation of mathematical physics including the dynamics of relativistic gravitational fields. Notably for: contributing in 1971, at the age of 19, to derive with Remo Ruffini the mass-energy formula of black holes as a function of their angular momentum, charge and irreducible mass. Christodoulou turned then to the study of partial differential equations and mathematical physics, to which he remained dedicated for the rest of his career. Highlights in this area include the theoretical discovery of the nonlinear memory effect of gravitational waves (Phys. Rev. Letters 1991), the monograph (1993) in collaboration with Sergiu Klainerman on the global nonlinear stability of the Minkowski spacetime, the monograph (2009) on the formation of black holes in pure general relativity by imploding gravitational waves, and the monographs (2007 and 2019) on the formation and further development of shocks in fluids."

GERARD 't HOOFT
"for his persistent devotion to the study of the quantum field theory boundary conditions at the black hole horizon".

TSVI PIRAN
"for extending Relativistic astrophysics across international frontiers, a true companion in the search for the deeper meaning of Einstein's great theory".

STEVEN WEINBERG
"for unwavering support for the MG meetings since their inception, a true companion in the search for the deeper meaning of Einstein's great theory".

Each recipient is presented with a silver casting of the TEST sculpture by the artist A. Pierelli. The original casting was presented to His Holiness Pope John Paul II on the first occasion of the Marcel Grossmann Awards.

15th Marcel Grossmann Meeting
July 2018, Rome, Italy

Institutional Awards

PLANCK SCIENTIFIC COLLABORATION (ESA)
"for obtaining important constraints on the models of inflationary stage of the Universe and level of primordial non-Gaussianity; measuring with unprecedented sensitivity gravitational lensing of Cosmic Microwave Background fluctuations by large-scale structure of the Universe and corresponding B-polarization of CMB, the imprint on the CMB of hot gas in galaxy clusters; getting unique information about the time of reionization of our Universe and distribution and properties of the dust and magnetic fields in our Galaxy"

- presented to Jean-Loup Puget, the Principal Investigator of the High Frequency Instrument (HFI)

HANSEN EXPERIMENTAL PHYSICS LABORATORY AT STANFORD UNIVERSITY
"to HEPL for having developed interdepartmental activities at Stanford University at the frontier of fundamental physics, astrophysics and technology"

- presented to Research Professor Leo Hollberg, HEPL Assistant Director

Individual Awards

LYMAN PAGE
"for his collaboration with David Wilkinson in realizing the NASA Explorer WMAP mission and as founding director of the Atacama Cosmology Telescope"

RASHID ALIEVICH SUNYAEV
"for the development of theoretical tools in the scrutinising, through the CMB, of the first observable electromagnetic appearance of our Universe"

SHING-TUNG YAU
"for the proof of the positivity of total mass in the theory of general relativity and perfecting as well the concept of quasi-local mass, for his proof of the Calabi conjecture, for his continuous inspiring role in the study of black holes physics"

14th Marcel Grossmann Meeting
July 2015, Rome, Italy

Institutional Award

EUROPEAN SPACE AGENCY (ESA)
"for the tremendous success of its scientific space missions in astronomy, astrophysics, cosmology and fundamental physics which have revolutionized our knowledge of the Universe and hugely benefited science and mankind"

- presented to its Director General Johann-Dietrich Woerner

Individual Awards

KEN'ICHI NOMOTO
"for heralding the role of binary systems in the evolution of massive stars"

MARTIN REES
"for fostering Research in black holes, gravitational waves and cosmology"

YAKOV G. SINAI
"for applying the mathematics of chaotic systems to physics and cosmology"

SACHIKO TSURUTA
"for pioneering the physics of hot neutron stars and their cooling"

FRANK C.N. YANG
"for deepening Einstein's geometrical approach to physics in the best tradition of Paul Dirac and Hermann Weyl"

T.D. LEE (award received by Yu-Qing Lou on behalf of Prof. T.D. Lee)
"for his work on white dwarfs motivating Enrico Fermi's return to astrophysics and guiding the basic understanding of neutron star matter and fields"

13th Marcel Grossmann Meeting
July 2012, Stockholm, Sweden

Institutional Award

ALBANOVA
for its innovative status as a joint institute established by Stockholm University and the Royal Institute of Technology and for fostering contributions to cosmology and astrophysics in the profound scientific tradition established by Oskar Klein.

- presented to the Rector of Stockholm University, Prof. Kåre Bremer.

Individual Awards

DAVID ARNETT
for exploring the nuclear physics and yet unsolved problems of the endpoint of thermonuclear evolution of stars, leading to new avenues of research in physics and astrophysics.

VLADIMIR BELINSKI and I.M. KHALATNIKOV
for the discovery of a general solution of the Einstein equations with a cosmological singularity of an oscillatory chaotic character known as the BKL singularity.

FILIPPO FRONTERA
for guiding the Gamma-ray Burst Monitor Project on board the BeppoSAX satellite, which led to the discovery of GRB X-ray afterglows, and to their optical identification.

12th Marcel Grossmann Meeting
July 2009, Paris, France

Institutional Award

INSTITUT DES HAUTES ÉSTUDES SCIENTIFIQUE (IHÉS)
for its outstanding contributions to mathematics and theoretical physics, and notably for having renewed basic geometrical concepts, and having developed new mathematical and physical aspects of spacetime.

- presented to Prof. Jean-Pierre Bourguignon

Individual Awards

JAAN EINASTO
for pioneering contributions in the discovery of dark matter and cosmic web and fostering research in the historical Tartu Observatory.

CHRISTINE JONES
for her fundamental contributions to the X-ray studies of galaxies and clusters tracing their formation and evolution and for her role in collaborations using clusters to study dark matter and in analyzing the effects of outbursts from supermassive black holes on the intracluster gas.

MICHAEL KRAMER
for his fundamental contributions to pulsar astrophysics, and notably for having first confirmed the existence of spin-orbit precession in binary pulsars.

11th Marcel Grossmann Meeting
July 2006, Berlin, Germany

Institutional Award

FREIE UNIVERSITÄT BERLIN
for the successful endeavor of re-establishing — in the spirit of the Humboldt tradition — freedom of thinking and teaching within a democratic society in a rapidly evolving cosmos

- presented to Dr. Dieter Lenzen, President of FUB

Individual Awards

ROY KERR
for his fundamental contribution to Einstein's theory of general relativity: "The gravitational field of a spinning mass as an example of algebraically special metrics."

GEORGE COYNE
for his committed support for the international development of relativistic astrophysics and for his dedication to fostering an enlightened relationship between science and religion.

JOACHIM TRUMPER
for his outstanding scientific contributions to the physics of compact astrophysical objects and for leading the highly successful ROSAT mission which discovered more than 200,000 galactic and extragalactic X-ray sources: a major step in the observational capabilities of X-ray astronomy and in the knowledge of our universe.

10th Marcel Grossmann Meeting
July 2003, Rio de Janeiro, Brazil

Institutional Award

CBPF (Brazilian Center for Research in Physics)
for its role as a teaching and research institution and as a place originating fundamental physics ideas in the exploration of the universe.

- presented to its founders Cesar Lattes, Josè Leite Lopez and Jayme Tiomno

Individual Awards

YVONNE CHOQUET-BRUHAT AND JAMES W. YORK, JR.
for separate as well as joint work in establishing the mathematical framework for proving the existence and uniqueness of solutions to Einstein's gravitational field equations.

YUVAL NE'EMAN
for his contributions to science, epistimology, mathematics and physics from subnuclear to space sciences.

9th Marcel Grossmann Meeting
July 2000, Rome, Italy

Institutional Award

SOLVAY INSTITUTES
for identifying and recording in discussions by the protagonists the crucial developments of physics and astrophysics in the twentieth century.

- presented to Jacques Solvay

Individual Awards

CECILLE AND BRYCE DEWITT
for promoting General Relativity and Mathematics research and inventing the "summer school" concept.

RICCARDO GIACCONI
for opening, five successive times, new highways for exploring the Universe.

ROGER PENROSE
for extending the mathematical and geometrical foundations of General Relativity.

8th Marcel Grossmann Meeting
June 1997, Jerusalem

Institutional Award

HEBREW UNIVERSITY

for its role as a cradle of Science and Humanities and for hosting the manuscripts of Albert Einstein.

- presented to M. Magidor, President of the Hebrew University of Jerusalem

Individual Awards

TULLIO REGGE

for his contributions to the interface between mathematics and physics leading to new fields of research of paramount importance in relativistic astrophysics and particle physics.

FRANCIS EVERITT

for leading the development of extremely precise space experiments utilizing superconducting technology to test General Relativity and the Equivalence Principle.

7th Marcel Grossmann Meeting
June 1994, Stanford, USA

Institutional Award

SPACE TELESCOPE SCIENCE INSTITUTE
for its critical role in the direction and operation of the Hubble Space Telescope, a truly unique international laboratory for the investigation and testing of general relativity in the context of modern astrophysics and cosmology.

- presented to Peter Stockman

Individual Awards

SUBRAHMANYAN CHANDRASEKHAR
for his contributions to the analysis of gravitational phenomena from Newton to Einstein and especially for leading the way to relativistic astrophysics with the concept of critical mass for gravitational collapse.

JIM WILSON
for having built on his experience in nuclear physics, thermonuclear reactions, and extensive numerical simulation to create a new testing ground for the novel concepts of relativistic astrophysics.

6th Marcel Grossmann Meeting
June 1991, Kyoto, Japan

Institutional Award

RITP

for keeping alive first in Hiroshima and them in Kyoto research in relativity, cosmology, and relativistic field theory and the development of a school of international acclaim.

- presented to Professor K. Tomita

Individual Awards

MINORU ODA

for participating in the pioneering work of the early sixties in X-ray astronomy and for his subsequent molding of an agile and diversified Japanese scientific space program investigating the deepest aspects of relativistic astrophysics.

STEPHEN HAWKING

for his contributions to the understanding of spacetime singularities and of the large scale structure of the Universe and of its quantum origins.

5th Marcel Grossmann Meeting
August 1988, Perth, Australia

Institutional Award

THE UNIVERSITY OF WESTERN AUSTRALIA
for its contributions to relativistic astrophysics.

- presented to the Vice Chancellor, Professor Robert Smith

Individual Awards

SATIO HAYAKAWA
for his contributions to research in gamma, X-ray and infrared radiation as well as cosmic rays.

JOHN ARCHIBALD WHEELER
for his contributions to geometrodynamics and Einstein's visions.

4th Marcel Grossmann Meeting
July 1985, Rome, Italy

Institutional Award

THE VATICAN OBSERVATORY
for its contributions to the origin and development of astrophysics.

- presented to His Holiness Pope John Paul II

Individual Awards

WILLIAM FAIRBANK
for his work in gravitation and low temperature physics.

ABDUS SALAM
for his work in unifying fundamental interactions.

Institutional Awards for the Spektrum-Roentgen-Gamma (SRG) mission

"for the creation of the world's best X-ray map of the entire sky, for the discovery of millions of previously unknown accreting supermassive black holes at cosmological redshifts, for the detection of X-rays from tens of thousands of galaxy clusters, filled mainly with dark matter, and for permitting the detailed investigation of the growth of the large-scale structure of the universe during the era of dark energy dominance".

S.A. LAVOCHKIN ASSOCIATION
- presented to its Designer General **Alexander Shirshakov**

MAX PLANCK INSTITUTE FOR EXTRATERRESTRIAL PHYSICS (MPE)
- presented to Professor **Peter Predehl**, Principal Investigator of eROSITA

SPACE RESEARCH INSTITUTE (IKI) OF THE RUSSIAN ACADEMY OF SCIENCES
- presented to Professor **Rashid Sunyaev**, Principal Investigator of SRG Observatory in Russia

On Tuesday June 29, 2021, the following 31 astro-ph appeared:

1. https://arxiv.org/abs/2106.14517
2. https://arxiv.org/abs/2106.14518
3. https://arxiv.org/abs/2106.14519
4. https://arxiv.org/abs/2106.14520
5. https://arxiv.org/abs/2106.14521
6. https://arxiv.org/abs/2106.14522
7. https://arxiv.org/abs/2106.14523
8. https://arxiv.org/abs/2106.14524
9. https://arxiv.org/abs/2106.14525
10. https://arxiv.org/abs/2106.14526
11. https://arxiv.org/abs/2106.14527
12. https://arxiv.org/abs/2106.14528
13. https://arxiv.org/abs/2106.14529
14. https://arxiv.org/abs/2106.14530
15. https://arxiv.org/abs/2106.14531
16. https://arxiv.org/abs/2106.14532
17. https://arxiv.org/abs/2106.14533
18. https://arxiv.org/abs/2106.14534
19. https://arxiv.org/abs/2106.14535
20. https://arxiv.org/abs/2106.14536
21. https://arxiv.org/abs/2106.14537
22. https://arxiv.org/abs/2106.14541
23. https://arxiv.org/abs/2106.14542
24. https://arxiv.org/abs/2106.14543
25. https://arxiv.org/abs/2106.14544
26. https://arxiv.org/abs/2106.14545
27. https://arxiv.org/abs/2106.14546
28. https://arxiv.org/abs/2106.14547
29. https://arxiv.org/abs/2106.14548
30. https://arxiv.org/abs/2106.14549
31. https://arxiv.org/abs/2106.14550

S.A. LAVOCHKIN ASSOCIATION
presented to its Designer General **Alexander Shirshakov**

Dr Alexander Shirshakov

S.A. Lavochkin Association created the Navigator space platform carrying German eRosita and Russian ART-XC X-Ray Telescopes, organized the launch of SRG Orbital X-Ray Observatory to the second Lagrangian point of the Sun-Earth system at a distance of 1.5 million km from the Earth and managed the observatory flight and the daily reception of its scientific data on Earth for 23.5 months.

Dr Alexander Shirshakov, Designer General of the S.A. Lavochkin Association, is specialized in design, manufacture, testing, launch and control of S/C for scientific purposes. Among those S/C launched, there are the «Radiostron» Astrophysical Observatory (2011) and the «Spektr-RG» space observatory (2019), while the planned S/C launches are «Luna-25» and «Exomars».

Dr Shirshakov started his career in 1973, working as an engineer of the State Unitary Enterprise «NPO named by S.A. Lavochkin» in Khimki (Russian Federation). Starting from 1989 he has played multiple roles within the Lavochkin Association, been appointed head of the group, head of the sector, head of department, deputy head of the complex, head of the branch, director of the center, deputy head of the Design Bureau, deputy General Designer and deputy General Director.

Dr Shirshakov is an editorial board Member of the reviewed edition of «Vestnik of Lavochkin Association». Since 2017, he is also member of the General Designer council. He has been awarded Honored Mechanical engineer of the Russian Federation as well as Agency-level award of the Russian Federal Space Agency.

MAX PLANCK INSTITUTE FOR EXTRATERRESTRIAL PHYSICS (MPE)
presented to Professor **Peter Predehl**, Principal Investigator of eROSITA

Professor Peter Predehl

eROSITA is the soft X-ray telescope on-board the Russian-German Spektr-RG mission which was successfully launched from Baikonur on July 13, 2019 and placed in a halo orbit around the L2 point. 30 years after ROSAT, eROSITA performs an all-sky survey with an unprecedented sensitivity, spectral and angular resolution. Clusters of galaxies are the largest collapsed objects in the Universe. Their formation and evolution is dominated by gravity, i.e. Dark Matter, while their large scale distribution and number density depends on the geometry of the Universe, i.e. Dark Energy. X-ray observations of clusters of galaxies provide information on the rate of expansion of the Universe, the fraction of mass in visible matter, and the amplitude of primordial fluctuations which are the origin of clusters of galaxies and the whole structure of the universe. eROSITA has been designed to detect at least 100.000 clusters of galaxies and to detect systematically more than 3 million obscured accreting Black Holes. eROSITA will also allow to study the physics of galactic X-ray source populations, like pre-main sequence stars, supernova remnants and X-ray binaries. The eROSITA telescope consists of seven identical Wolter-1 mirror modules. A novel detector system has been developed by MPE on the basis of the successful XMM-Newton pn-CCD technology. MPE is the scientific lead institute of eROSITA, responsible for the development of the instrument, the operation, the analysis software and data archive. Peter Predehl led this development as Principal Investigator of eROSITA and German lead scientist of the SRG mission for more than 15 years until the completion of the first of eight surveys in 2020. At this time eROSITA has already discovered more than 1 million X-ray sources, more than all X-ray observatories of the last 50 years together. This demonstrates that the design goals of the mission will easily be fulfilled.

SPACE RESEARCH INSTITUTE (IKI) OF THE RUSSIAN ACADEMY OF SCIENCES
presented to Professor **Rashid Sunyaev**

Professor Rashid Sunyaev

Space Research Institute (IKI) of the Russian Academy of Sciences was responsible for developing the overall concept and scientific program of the SRG Orbital observatory and played a leading role in developing the ART-XC telescope and the entire SRG observatory as part of the Russian space science program carried out by Roskosmos Corporation in the interests of the Russian Academy of Sciences.

During the flight to the L2 point of the Sun-Earth system, SRG with German (eRosita) and Russian (ART-XC named after Mikhail Pavlinsky) X-ray Telescopes aboard performed calibrations and long duration Performance Verification observations of a dozen of targets and deep fields. Starting in the middle of December 2019, the SRG scanned the whole sky three times. During these scans, SRG discovered two million point X-ray sources: mainly quasars, stars with hot and bright coronae, and more than 30 thousand clusters of galaxies. There is a competition and synergy in the search for clusters of galaxies between SRG and the ground-based Atacama Cosmology and South Pole Telescopes, which are searching for clusters of galaxies in microwave spectral band using Sunyaev-Zeldovich effect. SRG provided the X-Ray map of the whole sky in hard and soft bands, the last is now the best among existing. The huge samples of the X-ray selected quasars at the redshifts up to $z = 6.2$ and clusters of galaxies will be used for well-known cosmological tests and detailed study of the growth of the large scale structure of the Universe during and after reionization. SRG/eRosita is discovering every day several extragalactic objects which increased or decreased their brightness more than 10 times during half of the year after the previous scan of the same one-degree wide strip on the sky. A significant part of these objects has observational properties similar to the Events of Tidal Disruption of a star orbiting in the vicinity of the supermassive black hole. ART-XC discovered a lot of bright galactic and extragalactic transients.

Rashid Sunyaev is the Principal Investigator of SRG mission in Russia, director-emeritus of the Max-Planck Institute for Astrophysics and Maureen and John Hendricks distinguished visiting professor of the Institute for Advanced Study, Princeton.

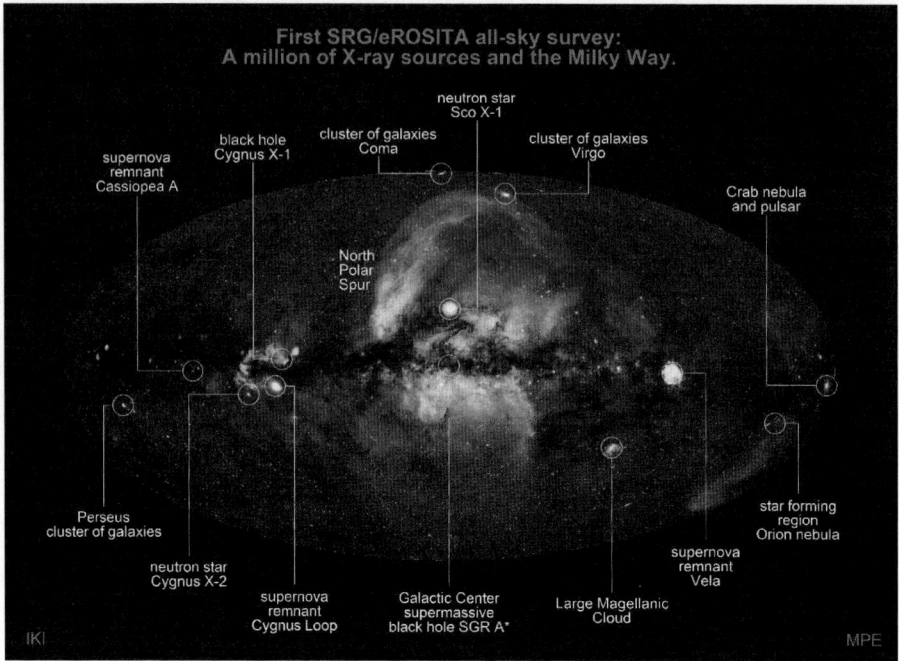

Individual Awards

Professor **DEMETRIOS CHRISTODOULOU**

"For his many lasting contributions to the foundation of mathematical physics including the dynamics of relativistic gravitational fields. Notably for: contributing in 1971, at the age of 19, to derive with Remo Ruffini the mass-energy formula of black holes as a function of their angular momentum, charge and irreducible mass. Christodoulou turned then to the study of partial differential equations and mathematical physics, to which he remained dedicated for the rest of his career. Highlights in this area include the theoretical discovery of the nonlinear memory effect of gravitational waves (Phys. Rev. Letters 1991), the monograph (1993) in collaboration with Sergiu Klainerman on the global nonlinear stability of the Minkowski spacetime, the monograph (2009) on the formation of black holes in pure general relativity by imploding gravitational waves, and the monographs (2007 and 2019) on the formation and further development of shocks in fluids."

Professor Demetrios Christodoulou

It was back in 1967 that Achille Papapetrou mentioned the case of the 16-year-old Demetrios Christodoulou to John Archibad Wheeler. Wheeler interviewed Demetrios in Paris and brought him immediately to Princeton where he was registered as an undergraduate at the university. After one year he entered the graduate school and started collaborating with me. At the time I was working with Wheeler on the effective potential approach to geodesics co-rotating and counter-rotating (see e.g. reference in The Classical Theory of Fields (Landau and Lifshitz, 1980) in the Kerr metric (later renamed as ISCO; see e.g. (Gravitation Misner, Thorne, Wheeler. 1973). In parallel, Frank Zerilli was working on the gravitational radiation emitted by the fall of a test particle in a Schwarzschild black hole (Zerilli 1970). From these limited conceptual arena Charles Misner and later Kip Thorne launched a program for the detection of gravitational waves on the Earth; see e.g. Misner 1974, Abbott et al. 2016, Abbott et al. 2017. See however Davis et al. 1972, Rodriguez et al. 2018 and J.A. Rueda et al. 2018.

A new approach started with the arrival of Demetrios: he was just creating mathematics following his needs. We identified the reversible and irreversible transformations of a Kerr black hole. Wheeler advanced a thermodynamic analogy. I addressed the need of identifying the concept of irreducible mass (from the Italian "irriducibile"), and was Demetrios's contribution to integrate, overnight, the differential equation for infinitesimal reversible transformations which led to the finite mass-energy formula of a Kerr black hole. That evening, while walking back home through IAS woods, I expressed to Wheeler the great relevance of the newly found formula by Demetrios and proposed to let Demetrios be the single author of this article, admiring his great mathematical talent. Wheeler agreed. The Editor of PRL objected since in that two pages article the Fig. 2 by Wheeler and myself was still unpublished. Actually that Fig. 2 followed a discussion I previously had with Penrose in Florence (Penrose 1961) which allowed us to present there, for the first time, a "Penrose Process". Some difficulties in achieving this process were obvious from the example in Fig. 2, which Roger later recognized himself (Penrose & Floyd 1971). The Editor finally agreed on our written request and the paper appeared on September 17, 1970 (Christodoulou, 1970). On January 1971 appeared my article with Johnny introducing the Black Hole (Ruffini & Wheeler, 1971), with the new physics we were developing in Princeton, including the concept of the "ergosphere". On march 1 1971 we submitted the mass formula of the Kerr Newmann metric, including the relation between the surface area of the horizon and the irreducible (Christodoulou & Ruffini, 1971). On March 11, 1971 the same results were independently confirmed by Steven Hawking, extending further the applicability of our equation (Hawking 1971).

The thesis was successfully discussed by a committee including Eugene Wigner (see Fig. 1), one of the closest collaborators of Albert Einstein and David Wilkinson (see Fig. 2), the head of the NASA WMAP mission, and Johnny and myself as supervisors. The new message was clear: Black Holes, far from being a sink of energy, were energy sources emitting "in principle" 50% of their mass energy, being extractable (Christodoulou & Ruffini, 1971).

Fig. 1 and Fig. 2: Demetrios during his thesis presentation with Eugene Wigner (Fig. 1) and David Wilkinson (Fig.2). Johnny and I were supervisors, ready to intervene in case of need, but no need of intervention was necessary! Wigner elaborated the aphorism of Niels Bohr "Interesting = wrong" in the most definite "very interesting if true = totally wrong".

Demetrios turned soon to the study of partial differential equations and mathematical physics, to which he dedicated for the rest of his career and results were published in four monographs: (Christodoulou and Klainerman 1994, Christodoulou 2007, Christodoulou 2009, Christodoulou 2019). In 1968, Johnny proposed to Demetrios the collapse of a "geon" composed of massless scalar field as a second topic for his thesis. It took almost forty years for him to solve this problem, extended by Demetrios to the focusing of gravitational waves leading to black hole formation (Christodoulou 2009).

Fig. 3: Prof. Remo Ruffini receiving the Cressy Morrison Award of the New York Academy of Sciences, 1972 for the discovery of the first Black Hole in our galaxy Cygnus X1.

A "long march" started on 12 December 1970 with the launch of the Uhuru satellite by Riccardo Giacconi. Early in 1971 an almost daily conversation with him and Herb Gursky at the Smithsonian Astrophysical Observatory, leading to the discovery of binary X-ray sources. This was soon followedby the announcement of Cygnus X1 identified as the first black hole in our galaxy (Ruffini 1973); see e.g. Gursky & Ruffini 1975, which contained as well the first publicannouncement of the Discovery of Gamma Ray burst, as well as Giacconi & Ruffini 1980, 2009; see Figs. 3 and 4).

Fig. 4: In the second row, from left to right, there are, among others: E. T. Newman, S. Chandrasekhar (Nobel 1983), R. Giacconi (Nobel 2002), R. Ruffini, A. Treves, A. Hewish (Nobel 1974), D. Arnett, J.H. Taylor (Nobel 1993), J. Wilson, R. Penrose (Nobel 2020), as well as J. Bahcall, T. Damour, T. Piran et al.

Today, after fifty years, this "long march" has reached a definite result: through the grandest observational multi-wavelength effort in the history of mankind, from space, ground and underground observatories, we are finally finding evidence that black holes are "alive" and their "extractable energy" in our mass formula (Christodoulou & Ruffini, 1971), is the energy source of the most energetic cosmological sources: gamma ray bursts (GRBs),the active galactic nuclei (AGNs) as well as the ultra-high energy cosmic rays (UHECRs) (Ruffini et al. 2021 and references therein). Their "inner engine", has three independent components: 1) a Kerr black hole which is neither in a stationary state nor in vacuum, 2) a background magnetic field aligned with the black hole rotation axis, and 3) an extremely diluted fully ionized plasma (Moradi et al. 2021).There is no role in this inner engine for ISCO. Indeed a new electro dynamical field equations describe the synchrotron radiation emitted close to the black hole horizon, they point to a discrete and repetitive emission of "blackholic quanta" in the MeV and in the GeV. The magnitudes and the emission time scales of these quanta, for M87 and GRB 130427A, are expressed as a function of the above three parameters (Rueda & Ruffini, 2021). A long lasting GeV emission with a luminosity decreasing as a temporal power law, allows for the first time in GRBs, the determination of the black hole mass and spin as well as their time evolution perfectly fulfilling our mass energy formula (Christodoulou & Ruffini, 1971): a long lasting emission process profoundly different from the traditional process of continued gravitational contraction.

Remo Ruffini

Professor **GERARD 't HOOFT**

"for his persistent devotion to the study of the quantum field theory boundary conditions at the black hole horizon".

Professor Gerard 't Hooft

Prof. Gerard 't Hooft has been a full Professor at the Utrecht University (the Netherlands), since 1977. Nowadays, he is an Emeritus Professor at that University. During his career, he has paid extended scientific visits to CERN (Geneva), Harvard, Stanford, Princeton and Duke University, NC. In 1999, together with M. Veltman, he received the Nobel Prize in Physics, awarded by The Royal Swedish Academy of Sciences, *"For elucidating the quantum structure of electroweak interactions in physics"*.

Prof. 't Hooft's main subjects of research includes:

– Gauge Theories for the sub-atomic particles and forces, various aspects and ingredients of what is now called "The Standard Model of the sub-atomic particles: renormalizability, topological features such as magnetic monopoles and instantons, 1/N expansions.

– Theories for the quantization of the gravitational force and black holes: producing models for the quantum properties of a black hole, as derived from Standard Model and General Relativity alone; its topological features such as antipodal identification.

– Fundamental theories underlying quantum mechanics, in particular returning determinism and reality to the dynamics of the tiniest material entities in his universe.

Prof. 't Hooft has been awarded the Wolf Prize of the State of Israel (1982), the Pius XI Medal (Vatican City, 1983), the Lorentz Medal (KNAW Amsterdam, 1986) as well as the Spinoza Premium (Netherlands Organization for Scientific Research NWO, 1995).

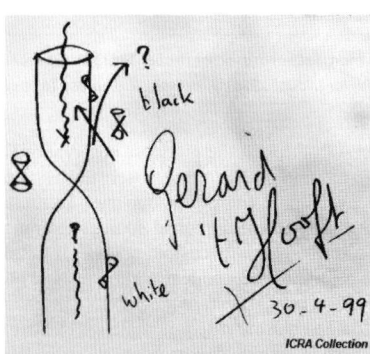

Fig. 2: The signature of Gerard 't Hooft on the wall of ICRA Room 301 (April 4, 1999).

A special event took place at ICRA on April 30, 1999. Prof. Ruffini invited Gerard 't Hooft to Rome to discuss a boundary condition for a quantum field on the black hole horizon, a topic Prof. Ruffini discussed in a previous article "Black-hole evaporation in the Klein-Sauter-Heisenberg-Euler formalism" with Thibault Damour (Phys. Rev. D 14, 332, 1976), but which needed to be examined in more detail. Prof. Ruffini planned to direct Gerard's attention to some specific aspects of this problem. Because we have traditionally been very attentive in spending ICRA travel funds, ICRA offered Gerard to come to Rome on a reduced fare weekend ticket arriving Friday and departing Monday. He had a great relaxing weekend together with Prof. Ruffini following his seminar, which among other things allowed Gerard to sign the wall in our ICRA Room (see Fig. 2), and during this splendid Rome spring weekend he also was able to find a missing factor of 2 in a formula in Prof. Ruffini's 1971 paper with Demetri Christodoulou on the black hole mass formula. The following October, Gerard received the Nobel prize, which meant that we could no longer get away with bringing him to Rome on a cheap ticket! Ever since Gerard has been in our MG IOC helping us with the preparation of the meetings. We are very happy to announce this MG16 Award to Gerard 't Hooft with the motivating phrase *"for his persistent devotion to the study of the quantum field theory boundary conditions at the black hole horizon"*.

Remo Ruffini

Professor **TSVI PIRAN**

"for extending relativistic astrophysics across international frontiers, a true companion in the search for the deeper meaning of Einstein's great theory".

Professor Tsvi Piran

Tsvi Piran is the emeritus Schwartzmann professor at the Hebrew University of Jerusalem. He obtained his PhD in Physics, in 1976 from the Hebrew University working on the collisional Penrose process. Piran returned to the Hebrew University at 1981after being a post doc at Oxford and Texas and a long-term member at the IAS at Princeton. In 1982 he initiated and directed the first ever summer school on Gravitational Waves that took place at Les Houches. Piran was a visiting professor at Harvard, Columbia and New York and a Moore scholar at Caltech.

Piran's research deals with numerous aspects of relativistic astrophysics, ranging from the foundation of numerical relativity to modeling of observer relativistic phenomena and analytic work on the fate of gravitational collapse. Piran's research work focuses mostly on black holes and in particular on gamma-ray bursts. He was among the first to point out their cosmological origin and their association with merging neutron stars and heavy r-process nucleo synthesis. Piran's achievements were recognized in the 2019 EMET prize for Physics.

Professor **STEVEN WEINBERG**

"for unwavering support for the MG meetings since their inception, a true companion in the search for the deeper meaning of Einstein's great theory".

Professor Steven Weinberg. Photo courtesy of Matt Valentine.

Steven Weinberg is a member of the Physics and Astronomy Departments at The University of Texas at Austin. His research has covered a broad range of topics in quantum field theory, elementary particle physics and cosmology. He has been honored with numerous awards, including the Nobel Prize in Physics, the National Medal of Science, the Heinemann Prize in Mathematical Physics and in 2020, the Breakthrough Prize. He is a member of the US National Academy of Sciences, Britain's Royal Society, and other academies in the USA and abroad. The American Philosophical Society awarded him the Benjamin Franklin Medal, with a citation that said he is "considered by many to be the preeminent theoretical physicist alive in the world today." His books for physicists include *Gravitation and Cosmology*, the three-volume work *The Quantum Theory of Fields*, *Cosmology* and published in April of 2021, *Foundations of Modern Physics*. Educated at Cornell, Copenhagen, and Princeton, he also holds honorary degrees from sixteen other universities. He taught at Columbia, Berkeley, M.I.T., and Harvard, where he was Higgins Professor of Physics, before coming to Texas in 1982.

Fig. 1: Chuo Pei Yuan and Cheng Ning Yang at MG2 in Trieste, Italy (1979).

The Sixteenth Marcel Grossmann Meeting (MG16) is a very special one in many respects: it will take place during a pandemic and in spite of the many difficulties, we have decided not to postpone it but to organize it as a virtual meeting. As described on the MG series webpage, these meetings started in 1975 with the first meeting at the International Centre for Theoretical Physics (ICTP) in Trieste (Italy) that I organized with Nobel Prize winner Abdus Salam. A second meeting followed in 1979, with a significantly larger participation including Nobel Laurate Cheng Ning Yang and a Chinese delegation led by Chuo Pei Yuan (see Fig. 1), including Fang Li-Zhi who had accompanied me during my entire first visit to China in 1979. The first truly international MG meeting followed in 1982 in Shanghai (China):this represented an especially important step forward both for the meeting and for China. A multi-millennia *"motto"* in China, which was then proclaimed on banners everywhere, read *"Friends from all over the world are welcomed"*.

We were soon at an impasse over the participation of scientists from Israel, since no diplomatic relations existed between China and Israel at that time and the Israeli scientists were not to be allowed to attend the meeting. A long negotiation began. The boundary conditions were clearly set by Steven Weinberg, a member of the present MG16 IOC: no MG meetings on Einstein's theory of general relativity could occur without the participation of Israeli scientists. The intervention of Yuval Ne'emann, also a member of the MG IOC then as well as the Minister of Science of Israel (see Fig.2), proposed a compromise that would admit at least one Israeli scientist. I went to Beijing alone, meeting every morning for a week with 12 Chinese representatives led by Chuo Pei Yuan going over all possible options. I stayed in an isolated villa not far from Tiananmen Square, accompanied by the 3 volumes of Matteo Ricci (RI MA TO) to keep me company. No solution was in sight the entire week. At the last moment, just before my departure, an agreement was finally reached allowing two Israeli scientists into China. The historic compromise would admit Gerard Tauber and Tsvi Piran into China using a special

Fig. 2: From right to left: Chaim Weizmann, President of Israel; Yuval Ne'emann, Minister of Science of Israel; R. Ruffini.

ICRA travel document I had proposed for them to be able to participate in the meeting, accepted by the Chinese Ambassador in Rome. This modified the thousand-year Chinese *"motto"* to read *"Scientists from all over the world are welcomed"*. The event was extremely beneficial for China and signaled the truly international nature of the MG meetings.

I kept on meeting Tauber in the years which followed (see Fig. 3). Soon after, Yuval Ne'emann visited China. The development of bilateral relations, including military cooperation and economical tights, grow exponentially until the establishment of normal diplomatic relations between Israel and China in 1992.

Fig. 3: From right to left: Arrigo Finzi, Remo Ruffini, Gerard Tauber and Konrad Bleuler.

Fig. 4: Albert Einstein, Hideki Yukawa and John. A. Wheeler with a hand-written dedication to Remo Ruffini "To Remo Ruffini, companion in the search for the deeper meaning of Einstein great theory. With warm regards, John Wheeler 5 April 1968".

Given their key role played in the foundations of the MG meetings, I am very happy to propose on behalf of the MG16 IOC, two special Marcel Grossmann Individual Awards: one to Steven Weinberg for *"for unwavering support for the MG meetings since their inception, a true companion in the search for the deeper meaning of Einstein's great theory"* and another one to Tsvi Piran, *"for extending Relativistic astrophysics across international frontiers, a true companion in the search for the deeper meaning of Einstein's great theory"*, in the words of John A. Wheeler's photo dedication to me (see Fig. 4).

Remo Ruffini

PREFACE

Since 1975, the Marcel Grossmann Meetings on Recent Developments in Theoretical and Experimental General Relativity, Gravitation, and Relativistic Field Theories have been organized in order to provide opportunities for discussing recent advances in gravitation, general relativity and relativistic field theories, emphasizing mathematical foundations, physical predictions and experimental tests. The objective of these meetings is to elicit exchange among scientists that may deepen our understanding of spacetime structures as well as to review the status of ongoing experiments aimed at testing Einstein's theory of gravitation either from the ground or from space. Previous meetings have been held in Trieste (MG1: 1975) and (MG2: 1979), Shanghai (MG3: 1982), Rome (MG4: 1985, MG9: 2000), Perth (MG5: 1988), Kyoto (MG6: 1991), Stanford (MG7: 1994), Jerusalem (MG8: 1997), Rio (MG10: 2003), Berlin (MG11: 2006), Paris (MG12: 2009), Stockholm (MG13: 2012), MG14 in 2015 and MG15 in 2018 both in Rome.

Due to the COVID-19 pandemic spreading in the last two years the decision was taken to organize the Sixteenth Marcel Grossmann meeting for the first time in history entirely online. Despite numerous challenges, related to the organization of large worldwide event, MG16 showed the strongest ever interest from the scientific community with a record-breaking number of almost 1200 registered participants and of more than 1000 speakers.

The traditional six-day schedule has been modified to account for different time zones of the speakers and each day the program of the meeting was divided in three blocks with the reference to the Central European Summer Time. The first block was starting at 06:30 in the morning, allowing comfortable time for speakers from Asia and Oceania. The second block was held in the daytime in Europe and Africa. The third block was starting in the afternoon and ending at 19:30 allowing accommodation of the speakers from the Americas. Each day the blocks of plenary sessions were interchanging with the blocks of about 30 parallel sessions each, making this one of the most intense MG meetings ever. All this was possible thanks to recent developments in communication technologies. The Indico open-source software was selected as a web platform for this meeting, while Zoom platform was adopted for the video-conferencing. The meeting was streamed on ICRANet YouTube channel.

The meeting started on Monday July 5 with the Award ceremony. The individual awards went to Demetrios Christodoulou, Tsvi Piran, Gerard 't Hooft and Steven Weinberg, while the Institutional Awards went to the S.A. Lavochkin Association, to the Max Planck Institute for Extraterrestrial Physics – MPE and to the Space Research Institute IKI of the Russian Academy of Sciences. Overall there were 54 plenary talks, 4 public lectures and 5 roundtables and about 90 parallel sessions. The plenary session "Events in Relativistics Astrophysics" on Monday have seen the contributions from Rashid Sunyaev, Michael Kramer, James Miller-Jones, Felix Mirabel. The public lectures were delivered by Razmik Mirzoyan, Asghar Qadir and Mohammad Bagheri. Plenary talks on Tuesday session "Black holes and the Quantum" by Juan Maldacena, Ahmed Almheiri, Gerard 't Hooft, Mihalis Dafermos, Sergiu Klainerman, Abhay Ashtekar and Frank Wilczek were bracketed by two roundtables on "New results from SRG/eRosita" with the participation of Andrea Merloni, Prof. Rashid Sunyaev, Alexander Lutovinov, Chandreyee Maitra, Esra Bulbul and "Solar neutrinos and Borexino" with the participation of Gianpaolo Bellini and Wick Haxton. Plenary talks on Wednesday in the session "Lambda CDM tensions" by George Efstathiou, Scolnic Daniel, Marc Kamionkowski, Wendy Freedman, Priya Natarajan and Licia Verde were followed by the roundtable "Precision cosmology" with the participation of Licia Verde, Marc Kamionkowski, Piero Rosati, and the public lecture by Francis Halzen. Two blocks of Thursday plenary sessions "Black holes in GRBs" and "Precision tests" included the talks by Roy Kerr, Yuan Ha, Lorenzo Amati, Elena Pian, Carlos Raúl Argüelles, Di Li, Jianglai Liu, Claus Lämmerzahl, Gerhard Heinzel and Ignazio Ciufolini and were followed by the roundtable "GRB 170817A and GRB 190829A" with the participation of Eleonora Troja, Liang Li, Rahim Moradi, Jorge Armando Rueda Hernandez. Two plenary blocks on Friday "Massive stars" and "Physics behind stellar collapse" included the talks by Selma de Mink, Norbert Langer, Jiri Bicak and Tomáš Ledvinka, Ivan De Mitri, Rahim Moradi and Giancarlo Cella. Finally, two plenary blocks on Saturday "Current and future missions" have seen the talks by Shuang-Nan Zhang, Weimin Yuan, Makoto Tashiro, Ruoyu Liu, Jean-Luc Atteia, Jim Hinton and Nicholas White and were followed by the roundtable "What is in our Galactic center" with the participation of Reinhard Genzel, Carlos Raúl Argüelles, Andreas Krut, Jorge Armando Rueda Hernandez, Eduar Becerra Vergara. The program of the meeting can be found at the official website http://www.icra.it/mg/mg16 and at ICRANet Indico website https://indico.icranet.org/event/1/.

These proceedings include about 400 papers containing the results presented at the Sixteenth Marcel Grossmann meeting. The plenary papers from the meeting have been published in International Journal of Modern Physics D as they were submitted. The table of contents includes also the links to YouTube videos with talks given at the meeting and cover plenary talks, public lectures, roundtables and all parallel sessions. The general link to the videos from MG16 is: https://www.youtube.com/watch?v=QFe1lsSid-o&list=PLr5RLbSWSonsaOnZukBDs0qsNIWM8AvRF.

As the editors we would like to express our gratitude to all the chairpersons of the parallel sessions at MG16, who peer-reviewed the papers submitted for these proceedings, as well as to the ICRANet secretariat office and in particular to Cinzia di Niccolo, Elisabetta Natale and Yasmina Di Domizio, as well as to ICRANet system manager Gabriele Brandolini for their help in preparation of this publication.

Remo Ruffini and Gregory Vereshchagin
November 2021

Contents

Publications in this Series	v
Sponsors and Acknowledgements	vii
Organizing Committees	ix
Marcel Grossmann Awards	xi
Preface	xxxvi

PART A
PLENARY SESSIONS

New results from testing relativistic gravity with radio pulsars *Michael Kramer*	3
Dragging of inertial frames by matter and waves *Jiří Bičák and Tomáš Ledvinka*	22
Probes of the progenitors, engines and physics behind stellar collapse *Chris L. Fryer*	39
The observation of high-energy neutrinos from the cosmos: Lessons learned for multimessenger astronomy *Francis Halzen*	59
The first results of PandaX-4T *Jianglai Liu on behalf of the PandaX Collaboration*	85
XRISM: X-ray imaging and spectroscopy mission *Makoto S. Tashiro and the XRISM team*	95
The SVOM mission *J.-L. Atteia, B. Cordier and J. Wei on behalf of the SVOM Collaboration*	104
Quantum field theory with boundary conditions at the horizons *Gerard 't Hooft*	133

The development of general relativity and the cosmological constant
Asghar Qadir 143

The irreducible mass of Christodoulou-Ruffini-Hawking mass formula
Yuan K. Ha 154

Reshaping our understanding on structure formation with the quantum nature of the dark matter
C. R. Argüelles, E. A. Becerra-Vergara, A. Krut et al. 164

First results of LHAASO
Ruo-Yu Liu for the LHAASO Collaboration 180

On the MG16 awards 2021
Remo Ruffini 196

The white dwarf binary merger model of GRB 170817A
J. A. Rueda, R. Ruffini, Liang Li et al. 217

PARALLEL SESSIONS

Accretion

• MHD Processes Near Compact Objects
Chairperson: Sergey Moiseenko
YouTube link: https://youtu.be/2WMTg06ZmV8

A semi-implicit multidimensional unstructured gas dynamical solver for astrophysical applications
Ilya A. Kondratyev and Sergey G. Moiseenko 242

Magnetized neutron stars propagating through a non-uniform ISM
O. D. Toropina, M. M. Romanova and R. V. E. Lovelace 255

Calculation of the kinetic coefficients of arbitrary degenerate electrons in magnetized dense matter
M. V. Glushikhina and G. S. Bisnovatyi-Kogan 264

Modeling of magnetic fields of accretion discs, using no-z- and RZ-approximations
M. V. Pashentseva and E. A. Mikhailov 272

• Accretion Discs and Jets
Chairpersons: Audrey Trova and Shokoufe Faraji
YouTube link: https://youtu.be/29Wj9RCVEKw

Limiting effects in tori clusters
D. Pugliese and Z. Stulchik 280

Hydrodynamical transport of angular momentum in accretion disks
in the presence of nonlinear perturbations due to noise
Subham Ghosh and Banibrata Mukhopadhyay 295

Properties of accretion disc models in the background quadrupole
Shokoufe Faraji 307

Magnetized tori around a uniformly accelerating black hole
Shokoufe Faraji and Audrey Trova 317

Multifrequency behaviour of high mass X-ray binaries
(Time lag between optical and X-ray outbursts)
Franco Giovannelli 321

Active Galactic Nuclei

• The Black Hole in M87
Chairpersons: Brian Punsly and Jorge Rueda
YouTube link: https://youtu.be/l1lTgksyJag

Rotation of the crescent image of M87* and polarization of its ESE hotspot
Krzysztof Nalewajko 339

Magnetic reconnection in jet-accretion disk systems
*Chandra B. Singh, Elisabete M. de Gouveia Dal Pino,
Luis H. S. Kadowaki et al.* 344

• Machine Learning in Astronomy: AGN, Transient Events, Cosmology and Others
Chairpersons: Rahim Moradi and Yu Wang
YouTube link: https://youtu.be/ErqrmMZQsBk

Exact fractal model of the universe and possible machine learning
methods for the verification of the fractality
A. A. Kirillov, E. P. Savelova and P. O. Vladykina 352

Estimating the photometric redshifts of galaxies and QSOs using
regression techniques in machine learning
A. Momtaz, M. H. Salimi and S. Shakeri 368

Deep learning in quasar physics
*F. Rastegar Nia, M. T. Mirtorabi, R. Moradi, Y. Wang
and A. Vafaei Sadr* 382

Cosmological density field emulation and gravitational wave inference
based on dimensionality reduction and supervised machine learning
Miguel Conceição, António da Silva and Alberto Krone-Martins 391

Unsupervised photometric detection of galaxy cluster candidates in
large surveys
Ana Carvalho, Alberto Krone-Martins and Antonio da Silva 409

- **Multiwavelength and Multi-Messenger Observations of Active Galactic Nuclei**

Chairpersons: Paolo Giommi and Narek Sahakyan

YouTube link: https://youtu.be/-Hyu2NQsExg

Time-dependent lepto-hadronic modeling of the emission processes in
blazar jets
S. Gasparyan, D. Bégué and N. Sahakyan 429

Multiwavelength study of high-redshift blazars
G. Harutyunyan and D. Israyelyan 445

Alternative Theories

- **Extended Theories of Gravity and Quantum Cosmology**

Chairpersons: Yi-Fu Cai and Wentao Luo

YouTube links: https://youtu.be/ADRr9DfV5zM
https://youtu.be/eOzpiC1cFkU
https://youtu.be/kYzJds_JIp8

Quantum gravity phenomenology from thermodynamics of spacetime
A. Alonso-Serrano and M. Liška 462

Gauge theory of gravity based on the correspondence between
the 1st and the 2nd order formalisms
David Benisty 479

$U(1)$ local strings in hybrid metric-Palatini gravity
Tiberiu Harko, Francisco S. N. Lobo and Hilberto M. R. da Silva 485

Inflationary supersymmetric FRLW quantum cosmology
N. E. Martínez-Pérez, C. Ramirez and V. M. Vázquez-Báez 499

Effective $f(R)$ actions for modified loop quantum cosmologies
Ana Rita Ribeiro, Daniele Vernieri and Francisco S. N. Lobo 517

Probing multiverse using gravitational wave observations
Moe Kukihara and Kazuhiro Hayama 531

Operator ordering ambiguity in observables of quantum cosmology
Harkirat Singh Sahota and Kinjalk Lochan 538

Decoupled quark stars in self-interacting Brans-Dicke gravity
M. Sharif and Amal Majid 548

Big-bounce in projectively invariant Nieh-Yan models: The Bianchi I case
*Flavio Bombacigno, Simon Boudet, Gonzalo J. Olmo
and Giovanni Montani*. 561

Late time cosmology with derivatives of matter Lagrangian
Shahab Shahidi 576

On the semiclassical and quantum picture of the Bianchi I polymer dynamics
E. Giovannetti, G. Montani and S. Schiattarella 588

Quantum corrections to the Bianchi II transition under local rotational invariance
Sara F. Uria, David Brizuela and Ana Alonso-Serrano 597

- **Mathematical Problems of Relativistic Physics: Classical and Quantum**
Chairpersons: A. Shadi Tahvildar-Zadeh and Michael Kiessling

YouTube links: https://youtu.be/9Dr3M9Kb2jo
https://youtu.be/gMOykpapJ5A

The hypercomplex medium as storage of physical equations
Alexander P. Yefremov 605

The Maxwell-Bopp-Landé-Thomas-Podolsky-Einstein system for a static point source
Érik Amorim 619

On recent developments in the theory of relativistic dissipative fluids
V. Hoang 627

Adiabatic solutions in general relativity as null geodesics on the space of boundary diffeomorphisms
Emine Şeyma Kutluk. 635

The point spectrum of the Dirac Hamiltonian on the zero-gravity Kerr-Newman spacetime
M. Kiessling, E. Ling and A. S. Tahvildar-Zadeh 648

Causal fermion systems: Classical gravity and beyond
Felix Finster 661

Newman-Penrose-Debye formalism for fields of various spins in pp-wave backgrounds
Aleksandr Kulitskii and Elena Yu Melkumova 679

Gravitational geometric phase
Banibrata Mukhopadhyay, Tanuman Ghosh and Soumya Kanti Ganguly 689

Retarded potentials and radiation in odd dimensions
D. V. Gal'tsov and M. Khlopunov 699

Wave propagation in the anti-deSitter optical metric
D. García-Peláez and C. S. López-Monsalvo 713

New approaches to constrained dynamics and Hamilton-Jacobi procedures in general relativity
D. Salisbury, J. Renn and K. Sundermeyer 719

Orientability of space from electromagnetic quantum fluctuations
N. A. Lemos and M. J. Rebouças 725

Essential self-adjointness of Dirac operators under the influence of general-relativistic gravity
Michael K.-H. Kiessling, A. Shadi Tahvildar-Zadeh and Ebru Toprak 736

- **Wormholes, Energy Conditions and Time Machines**
Chairpersons: Francisco Lobo and Diego Rubiera-Garcia

YouTube links: https://youtu.be/tu_3Wqcd9Ys
https://youtu.be/NqN1c-2fv8Y

Relic magnetic wormholes as possible source of toroidal magnetic fields in galaxies
A. A. Kirillov and E. P. Savelova 743

Wormhole geometries induced by action-dependent Lagrangian theories
Ismael Ayuso, Francisco S. N. Lobo and José P. Mimoso 756

Gravitational lensing by wormholes in binary systems
S. Pietroni 774

Hyper-fast positive energy warp drives
E. W. Lentz 779

From black-bounce to traversable wormhole, and beyond
Alex Simpson 787

Tractor beams, pressor beams, and stressor beams within the context of general relativity
Matt Visser, Jessica Santiago and Sebastian Schuster 808

A singularity theorem for evaporating black holes
E.-A. Kontou, B. Freivogel and D. Krommydas 822

Circularly symmetric thin-shell wormholes in F(R) gravity with
(2+1)-dimensions
Cecilia Bejarano, Ernesto F. Eiroa and Griselda Figueroa-Aguirre 831

Warp drive dynamic solutions considering different fluid sources
Osvaldo L. Santos-Pereira, Everton M. C. Abreu and
Marcelo B. Ribeiro 840

Symmetries and geometry of spacetime: Towards a new paradigm
Francisco Cabral, Francisco S. N. Lobo and Diego Rubiera-Garcia 856

- **Theories of gravity: Alternatives to the cosmological and particle standard models**

Chairpersons: Stefano Bellucci and Orlando Luongo

YouTube links: https://youtu.be/-aQcrYoQfBM
https://youtu.be/WsCwPb5OQhY
https://youtu.be/JMnrUfBgqVU
https://youtu.be/pPhZY-bbsew

Thermodynamics of scalar-tensor gravity: A new approach
Valerio Faraoni 876

Two body dynamics in a quadratic modification of general relativity
Soham Bhattacharyya 883

Alternatives to Λ: Torsion, generalized couplings, and scale invariance
C. J. A. P. Martins, C. M. J. Marques, C. B. D. Fernandes et al. 907

Model-independent test of scalar-tensor gravity theory by
reconstructing scalar mode of GW170817
Yuya Gushima and Kazuhiro Hayama 921

Cosmology in the novel scalar-tensor representation of $f(R,T)$ gravity
Tiago B. Gonçalves, João Luís Rosa and Francisco S. N. Lobo 932

On the interaction between electromagnetic, gravitational, and plasma
related perturbations on LRS class II spacetimes
P. Semrén 943

Condition for expansion-collapse duality between Einstein and
Jordan frames
Dipayan Mukherjee, H. K. Jassal and Kinjalk Lochan 958

The model of dark energy based on the quantum-mechanical
uncertainty relation
Yu. V. Dumin 967

- **Conformal Dilaton Gravity and Related Issues**
Chairperson: Reinoud Jan Slagter

YouTube link: https://youtu.be/A3Ygi3YBs5A

Conformal dilaton gravity, antipodal mapping and black hole physics
on a warped spacetime
R. J. Slagter 978

From neutrino masses to the full size of the universe — Some
intriguing aspects of the tetron model
B. Lampe 999

Summary parallel session AT5
Reinoud Jan Slagter 1014

- **Horava-Lifshitz Gravity**
Chairperson: Anzhong Wang

YouTube links: https://youtu.be/vPT1dH1zITE
https://youtu.be/5z7zhpiDOpw

Boundary conditions for the Klein-Gordon field on Lifshitz spacetimes
Lissa de Souza Campos 1017

Dynamical system analysis of Bianchi-I spacetimes in $f(R)$ gravity
Saikat Chakraborty, Kazuharu Bamba and Alberto Saa 1026

Cosmological implications in modified Hořava-Lifshitz gravity
Abdul Jawad, Kazuharu Bamba and Farwa Khurshid 1038

Finite action principle and wormholes
Jan Chojnacki and Jan Kwapisz 1046

Strange quark stars in Hořava gravity
Grigoris Panotopoulos 1054

Shadows of Kerr-like black holes in $4D$ Einstein–Gauss–Bonnet
gravity and constraints from EHT observations
Sushant G. Ghosh and Rahul Kumar Walia 1069

Wormhole interaction in 2d Hořǎva-Lifshitz quantum gravity
Jan Ambjørn, Yuki Hiraga, Yoshiyasu Ito and Yuki Sato 1084

Nature of singularities in vector-tensor theories of gravity
V. H. Satheeshkumar 1095

Hořava-Lifshitz and Einstein-Æther gravity in the light of Event Horizon Telescope observations of M87*
Emmanuel N. Saridakis 1104

Hořava-Lifshitz gravity in $(3+1)$ dimensions coupled with anisotropic matter and possible constraints from GRB 170817A
Tao Zhang and Fu-Wen Shu 1112

Summary of the parallel session AT6
Anzhong Wang 1119

• **Ghost-Free Models of Modified Gravity: Massive Gravity, Horndeski and DHOST Theories, Other Related Models; Their Properties and Solutions**
Chairpersons: Dmitry Gal'tsov and Michael Volkov

YouTube links: https://youtu.be/l8KHUPnT2D8
https://youtu.be/48OHIKpgNqs

Non-local R^2-like inflation, gravitational waves and Non-Gaussianities
K. Sravan Kumar 1124

Palatini kinetic scalar-tensor theory: Analytical and numerical solutions
D. V. Gal'tsov and D. S. Bushuev 1136

PART B

Black Holes: Theory and Observations/Experiments

• **Theoretical and Observational Studies of Astrophysical Black Holes**
Chairperson: Alexander Zakharov

YouTube links: https://youtu.be/fiv_MH-N2kw
https://youtu.be/GYoOb17GvE8

Reconstruction of a star motion in the vicinity of black hole from the redshift of the electromagnetic spectrum
S. O. Komarov and A. K. Gorbatsievich 1151

Shadows of hairy Kerr black holes and constraints from M87*
Sushant G. Ghosh and Misba Afrin 1167

Displacement memory and BMS symmetries
Shailesh Kumar 1179

Physical black holes in semiclassical gravity
Sebastian Murk and Daniel R. Terno 1196

- **Black Hole Thermodynamics**
Chairperson: Hernando Quevedo

YouTube links: https://youtu.be/XmZDf5mrXQk
https://youtu.be/amseL2qykfk

Information recovery from evaporating rotating charged black holes
Zhi-Wei Wang, Samuel L. Braunstein and Saurya Das 1212

Black hole thermodynamics from entanglement mechanics
S. Mahesh Chandran and S. Shankaranarayanan 1223

Thermodynamics of charged black hole
M. Sharif and Amjad Khan 1238

Rindler trajectories and Rindler horizons in the Schwarzschild spacetime
Kajol Paithankar and Sanved Kolekar 1250

Linear growth of the two-point function for the Unruh state in
$1+1$ dimensional black holes
Paul R. Anderson, Zachary P. Scofield and Jennie Traschen 1255

Stress-energy tensor for a quantized scalar field in a four-dimensional
black hole that forms from the collapse of a null shell
*Shohreh Gholizadeh Siahmazg, Paul R. Anderson, Raymond D. Clark
and Alessandro Fabbri* 1265

Microscopic model building for black hole membranes from constraints
of symmetry
Swastik Bhattacharya and S. Shankaranarayanan 1275

Einstein-Maxwell-Dilaton-Axion mass formulas for black holes with
struts and strings
Dmitri Gal'tsov, Gérard Clément and Igor Bogush 1291

- **Black Holes in Alternative Theories of Gravity**
Chairpersons: Jutta Kunz and Kamal Hajian

YouTube links: https://youtu.be/FRNGJKhiw7c
https://youtu.be/Tjfmuut1Eo0

Holography for rotating black holes in $f(T)$ gravity
Masoud Ghezelbash 1308

Infinitely degenerate exact Ricci-flat solutions in $f(R)$ gravity
Semin Xavier, Jose Mathew and S. Shankaranarayanan 1319

Universe in a black hole with spin and torsion
Nikodem Popławski 1327

Asymptotically flat black hole solution in modified gravity
Surajit Kalita and Banibrata Mukhopadhyay 1337

Shadow of a charged black hole surrounded by an anisotropic matter field
Javier Badía and Ernesto F. Eiroa 1343

Constraining modified gravity theories with physical black holes
Sebastian Murk 1351

Penrose suggestion as to pre-Planck-era black holes showing up in present universe data sets discussed, with a possible candidate as to GW radiation which may provide initial CMBR data
A. W. Beckwith 1359

Summary of the parallel session BH3
Kamal Hajian and Jutta Kunz 1372

Binaries

• Explosive Events Associated with Compact-Object Binary Mergers
Chairpersons: Chris Belczynski and Jorge Rueda

YouTube links: https://youtu.be/Dwq1ZU3gKrg
https://youtu.be/nw02ylI6R2M

Uncertainties in kilonova modeling
C. L. Fryer, C. J. Fontes, O. Korobkin et al. 1391

• Post-Newtonian and Post-Minkowskian Corrections for Binary Gravitating Systems
Chairperson: Johannes Bluemlein

YouTube link: https://youtu.be/wfiLG5r08yE

Tutti-Frutti method: Recent developments in the PN/PM/SF treatment of the gravitational two-body problem
Donato Bini and Andrea Geralico 1405

• Multichannel Studies of Nonstationary Relativistic Stars
Chairperson: Vladimir Lipunov

YouTube link: https://youtu.be/usn2PlU_qFA

GRB observations on cubesate satellites in the Universat–SOCRAT project
Sergey I. Svertilov, Michail I. Panasyuk, Vitaly V. Bogomolov et al. 1412

Multiwavelength observations of GRB160625B by MASTER,
Lomonosov, Konus-Wind and three stage collapse
V. M. Lipunov, V. A. Sadovnichy, M. I. Panasyuk et al. 1429

The role of the magnetic fields in GRB outflows
N. Jordana-Mitjans, C. G. Mundell, S. Kobayashi et al. 1449

MASTER optical observations of the blazar TXS0506+056 during the
IC170922A
V. M. Lipunov, K. Zhirkov, V. G. Kornilov et al. 1467

Boson Stars

• Scalar Fields in Cosmology
Chairpersons: Carlos Herdeiro and Alfredo Macias

YouTube links: https://youtu.be/SyLoguueGKk
https://youtu.be/f9nuo8Jvw-w

A short review on nonlinear perturbation theory of structure
formation for modified gravity
Jorge L. Cervantes-Cota and Alejandro Aviles 1474

Testing modified gravity theories with marked statistics
Alejandro Aviles 1494

Dark matter as condensed phase of generic bosons
Elías Castellanos and Jorge Mastache 1513

Cosmic Microwave Background

• Cosmic Backgrounds from Radio to Far-IR
Chairperson: Carlo Burigana

YouTube link: https://youtu.be/4e3Cj5wahck

New Planck tSZ map and its cosmological analysis
H. Tanimura, M. Douspis and N. Aghanim 1527

The CMB dipole: Eppur si muove
R. M. Sullivan and D. Scott 1532

High angular resolution Sunyaev Zel'dovich observations: The case of
MISTRAL
E. S. Battistelli, E. Barbavara, P. de Bernardis et al. 1542

Cosmological and astrophysical results exploiting magnification bias
with high-z sub-millimetre galaxies
L. Bonavera, M. M. Cueli and J. Gonzalez-Nuevo 1557

The impact of the Lorentz symmetry violation on the CMB polarization
Seddigheh Tizchang, Rohoollah Mohammadi and She-Sheng Xue 1571

Cosmic backgrounds from the radio to the far-infrared: Recent results and perspectives from cosmological and astrophysical surveys
Carlo Burigana, Elia Sefano Battistelli, Laura Bonavera et al. 1579

- **New Horizons in Cosmology with CMB Spectral Distortions**

Chairpersons: Jens Chluba and Andrea Ravenni

YouTube links: https://youtu.be/uBYLO4Smw3o
https://youtu.be/5oAPfzAe35k

CMB μT cross-correlations as a probe of PBH scenarios
Ogan Özsoy and Gianmassimo Tasinato 1609

Theoretical and numerical aspects of CMB spectral distortions from non-thermal energy injections
Sandeep Kumar Acharya, Jens Chluba and Abir Sarkar 1628

BISOU: A balloon project to measure the CMB spectral distortions
B. Maffei, M. H. Abitbol, N. Aghanim et al. 1633

Cosmic microwave background spectral distortions constraints on decaying dark matter particles and axion-like particles using *COBE/FIRAS* and *EDGES*
Boris Bolliet 1645

The COSmic Monopole Observer (COSMO)
S. Masi, E. Battistelli, P. de Bernardis et al. 1654

- **Status of the H_0 and σ_8 Tensions: Theoretical Models and Model-Independent Constraints**

Chairpersons: Joan Solà Peracaula and Adrià Gómez-Valent

YouTube links: https://youtu.be/VNWZ1Bzjus4
https://youtu.be/zEBOCwvetKE
https://youtu.be/nzgC7qV9H_Y

Measuring the Hubble constant H_0 from gravitational lensing
Liliya L. R. Williams 1672

Extra components consistency in the Hubble tension and BBN
Osamu Seto and Yo Toda 1686

Gravitational anomalies, axions and a string-inspired running vacuum model in Cosmology
Nick E. Mavromatos 1693

Early and not so early dark energy. What do cosmological observations tell us about them?
Adrià Gómez-Valent, Ziyang Zheng, Luca Amendola, Valeria Pettorino and Christof Wetterich 1713

Renormalized ρ_{vac} without m^4 terms
Cristian Moreno-Pulido and Joan Solà Peracaula 1733

BD-ΛCDM and running vacuum models: Theoretical background and current observational status
Javier de Cruz Pérez, Joan Solà Peracaula, Adrià Gómez-Valent and Cristian Moreno-Pulido 1752

Cosmological tensions: Hints for a new concordance model?
E. Di Valentino 1770

Solving both H_0 and σ_8 tensions in $f(T)$ gravity
Emmanuel N. Saridakis 1783

Precision Cosmology and Hubble tension in the era of LSS surveys
G. Fanizza 1792

- **Effects of Primordial Perturbations Enhancement: From Black Holes Formation to CMB Anomalies**

Chairpersons: Antonio Enea Romano and Krzysztof Turzynski

YouTube link: https://youtu.be/frjjONXbd1M

Primordial black holes arise when the inflaton falls
Keisuke Inomata 1803

Effects of the modification of gravity on the production of primordial black holes
Sergio Andrés Vallejo Peña 1809

Cosmic Strings

- **Cosmic Strings**

Chairpersons: Reinoud Jan Slagter and Batool Imtiaz

YouTube link: https://youtu.be/ZpaU82ZUHzM

$U(1)$ local strings in generalized hybrid metric-Palatini gravity
Hilberto M. R. da Silva, Tiberiu Harko, Francisco S. N. Lobo and João Luís Rosa 1820

New evidence of the azimuthal alignment of quasars spin vector in Large Quasar Groups and cosmic strings
R. J. Slagter 1835

Summary parallel session cosmic strings I
Reinoud Jan Slagter and Batool Imtiaz 1848

- **From Cosmic Strings to Superstrings**
Chairpersons: Carlos Martins and Ivan Rybak
YouTube link: https://youtu.be/LJFtV_4aSAg

Scaling solutions of wiggly cosmic strings
A. R. R. Almeida and C. J. A. P. Martins 1851

High resolution calibration of string network evolution
J. R. C. C. C. Correia and C. J. A. P. Martins 1871

Radiation from Global Cosmic Strings using adaptive mesh refinement
Amelia Drew and E. P. S. Shellard 1891

Analysing the scaling density of axion strings
A. Lopez-Eiguren 1898

Electroweak axion string and superconductivity
Yu Hamada, Yoshihiko Abe and Koichi Yoshioka 1912

Dark Energy and Large Scale Structure

- **Dark Energy and the Accelerating Universe**
Chairpersons: Alexei Starobinky and David Polarski
YouTube links: https://youtu.be/JZEPRS_rqbE
https://youtu.be/3aG_AT4UzWE
https://youtu.be/ZlTWquG-pFk

Hints for the $H_0 - r_d$ tension in uncorrelated Baryon Acoustic Oscillations dataset
Denitsa Staicova 1923

Observational constraints on nonlinear matter extensions of general relativity
E.-A. Kolonia and C. J. A. P. Martins 1935

Constraining the dark energy-dark matter interaction model using low-redshift observations
Archana Sangwan, Joseph P. J. and S. Shankaranarayanan ... 1948

On the evolution of inhomogeneous perturbations in the ΛCDM model and $f(R)$ modified gravity theories
T. Schiavone and G. Montani 1961

Soft dark energy and soft dark matter
Emmanuel N. Saridakis 1970

A simple parametrisation for coupled dark energy
Vitor da Fonseca, Nelson J. Nunes and Tiago Barreiro 1979

- **Cosmography with Gravitational Lensing**
Chairpersons: Claudio Grillo and Mimoza Hafizi
YouTube link: https://youtu.be/FXplIAvUDBM

A tale of two double quasars: Hubble constant tension or biases?
L. J. Goicoechea and V. N. Shalyapin 1990

Dark Matter

- **Interacting Dark Matter**
Chairpersons: Nikolaos Mavromatos
YouTube links: https://youtu.be/zOshKJlwD-Y
https://youtu.be/JR44dh2GYik

Dark energy and dark matter unification from dynamical space time: BBN constraints
D. Benisty 2005

Entropy and irreversible processes in gravity and cosmology
Llorenç Espinosa-Portalés and Juan García-Bellido 2013

LHC experiments for long-lived particles of the dark sector
Vasiliki A. Mitsou 2029

Constraining the interactions in the dark sector with cosmological data
Adrià Gómez-Valent, Valeria Pettorino and Luca Amendola 2050

Running vacuum interacting with dark matter or with running gravitational coupling. Phenomenological implications
Joan Solà Peracaula 2069

Dark matter properties from the Fornax globular cluster timing: Dynamical friction and cored profiles
D. Blas 2089

Growth of linear perturbations in a universe with superfluid dark matter
S. Banerjee, S. Bera and D. F. Mota 2101

Interacting dark sector in the late Universe: Mapping fields and fluids, and observational signatures
Joseph P. J. and S. Shankaranarayanan 2119

The role of self interactions in the cosmological evolution of warm dark matter
R. Yunis, C. R. Argüelles, D. López Nacir et al. 2127

Interaction energy between a charged medium and its electromagnetic field as a dark matter candidate
Mayeul Arminjon 2139

• **Dark Matter Searches with Liquid Xenon and Argon Detectors and Self Gravitating Systems and Dark Matter**
Chairpersons: Marco Merafina and Soroush Shakeri and She-Sheng Xue

YouTube link: https://youtu.be/H9oGYnGq9pI

The maximum mass of dilute axion stars
Pierre-Henri Chavanis 2149

A dark matter solution for the XENON1T electron excess and the galactic center 511 keV line
Yasaman Farzan 2174

Preliminary results of rich galaxy clusters' spatial distribution analysis on CfA2 Redshift Survey data: Compact objects or dark matter presence at redshift less 0.032
I. V. Arkhangelskaja, A. M. Galper, L. N. Khanh and D. N. Dorosheva 2189

• **Dark Matter: Beyond ΛCDM**
Chairpersons: Carlos Argüelles and Andreas Krut

YouTube links: https://youtu.be/hdKeo5L7pYE
https://youtu.be/i0IPHXzmV-s

Probing the nature of dark matter with Milky Way subhaloes
M. R. Lovell 2202

Addressing classical cosmological back-reaction with multiple scales
Yonadav Barry Ginat 2217

Imaging formation process for DM profiles
Omar de J. Cabrera-Rosas and Tonatiuh Matos 2222

The self-gravitating Fermi gas in Newtonian gravity and general relativity
Pierre-Henri Chavanis 2230

• **Dark Matter and Rare Processes**
Chairpersons: Carlos Rita Bernabei and Zurab Berezhiani

YouTube links: https://youtu.be/wheVrbETP_0
https://youtu.be/dVdZ4TIDxt0

The dark matter: DAMA/LIBRA and its perspectives
R. Bernabei, P. Belli, V. Caracciolo et al. 2252

Dark matter directionality approach
R. Bernabei, P. Belli, V. Caracciolo et al. 2272

Collapse models under test by high sensitivity γ-ray and X-ray measurements
C. Curceanu, Kristian Piscicchia, Massimiliano Bazzi et al. 2288

Leptophilic dark matter at linear colliders
P. S. Bhupal Dev 2296

DM6 session: Dark matter and rare processes
R. Bernabei and Z. Berezhiani 2316

- **The Nature of Galactic Halos**
Chairpersons: Francesco De Paolis and Asghar Qadir
YouTube link: https://youtu.be/qIwVnNxi0n0

Primordial black holes as dark matter candidates in the Galactic halo
Lindita Hamolli, Mimoza Hafizi, Francesco De Paolis and Achille A. Nucita 2319

Giant cosmic ray halos around M31 and the Milky Way
S. Recchia, S. Gabici, F. A. Aharonian and V. Niro 2335

A nearly complete census of intergalactic gas using the kinematic Sunyaev-Zel'dovich effect
Chaves-Montero, Jonás 2345

Searching for Intermediate Mass Black Holes in the Milky Way's galactic halo
A. Franco, A. A. Nucita, F. De Paolis, F. Strafella and M. Maiorano . . . 2352

Virial clouds evolution from the last scattering up to the formation of first stars
Noraiz Tahir, Asghar Qadir, Muhammad Sakhi and Francesco De Paolis 2360

Testing Weyl-modified gravity on M31 and Milky Way
Muhammad Bilal and Asghar Qadir 2365

PART C

Education

- **Teaching Einsteinian Physics to School Students**
Chairpersons: David Blair and Matteo Luca Ruggiero
YouTube links: https://youtu.be/W-WV6J8kprg
https://youtu.be/UHYpwKQ09SU

Teaching relativity: A paradigm change
F. Herrmann and M. Pohlig 2371

Teaching relativity: Computer-aided modeling
F. Herrmann and M. Pohlig 2381

Solstices and Equinoxes in 1703 at the meridian line of St. Maria degli Angeli in Rome, and the stellar aberration of Sirius
Costantino Sigismondi and Silvia Pietroni 2388

Positional astrometry at arcsecond accuracy using historical instruments, with light equipment
Costantino Sigismondi and Lorenzo Ricciardi 2398

Daily, seasonal, and equinoctial solar paths on a school soccer field
Costantino Sigismondi 2411

Teaching relativity at the AstroCamp
C. J. A. P. Martins 2415

Sungrazing comets as General Relativistic gravitational probes
Silvia Pietroni and Costantino Sigismondi 2424

The three Summer solstice's markers of 1721 unveiled in the Basilica of Santa Maria degli Angeli in Rome
Costantino Sigismondi 2428

Einstein-First: Bringing children our best understanding of reality
A. Popkova, K. Adams, S. Boublil et al. 2438

Exact Solutions

• Exact Solutions in Four and Higher Dimensions
Chairpersons: David Blair and Matteo Luca Ruggiero
YouTube link: https://youtu.be/GHZUS5-4gVQ

Kundt spacetimes in the Einstein–Gauss–Bonnet theory
R. Švarc, J. Podolský and O. Hruška 2453

Exact decoupled solutions in curvature-matter coupled gravity
M. Sharif and Fizza Furqan 2464

Tolman-Oppenheimer-Volkov conditions beyond spherical symmetry
José P. Mimoso, Alan Maciel and Morgan Le Delliou 2479

A spherically symmetric stiff fluid spacetime in light of cosmic structure formation
Daniele Gregoris 2497

- **Exact Solutions (Including Higher Dimensions)**
  Chairperson: Susan Scott

  YouTube link: https://youtu.be/-hJjJvmmOew

  Three-parameter solution for the null-surface formulation in
  2+1 dimensions
  Tina A. Harriott and J. G. Williams 2510

  New exact stationary cylindrical anisotropic fluid solution of GR
  M.-N. Célérier 2522

Early Universe

- **Quantum Fields**
  Chairperson: Andrei Lebed

  YouTube links: https://youtu.be/BLaTp0r0TkQ
  https://youtu.be/ZifgaSDy5Vc

  Hydrodynamic representation and energy balance for the Dirac and
  Weyl fermions in curved space-times
  Tonatiuh Matos, Omar Gallegos and Pierre-Henri Chavanis 2533

  Breakdown of the Equivalence Principle for a composite quantum body
  A. G. Lebed 2551

  Extended DeWitt-Schwinger subtraction scheme, heavy fields and
  decoupling
  Antonio Ferreiro and Jose Navarro-Salas 2557

  Renormalization and decoupling for the Yukawa model in curved
  spacetime
  Sergi Nadal-Gisbert, Antonio Ferreiro and José Navarro-Salas 2562

  Trace anomaly and evaporation of spherical black holes
  P. Meda 2573

  On decay of the false Unruh vacuum
  A. Shkerin 2587

  Behaviour of noise kernel in de Sitter and FRW space-times
  Ankit Dhanuka and Kinjalk Lochan 2600

  Breaking Buchdahl: Ultracompact stars in semiclassical gravity
  *Julio Arrechea, Carlos Barceló, Raúl Carballo-Rubio and
  Luis J. Garay* 2608

Einstein anomaly with tensors of odd order in six dimensional curved space
Kohei Yamamoto and Satoshi Yajima 2619

Quantum memory and BMS symmetries
Sanved Kolekar and Jorma Louko 2623

• **Topological Methods, Global Existence Problems, and Spacetime Singularities**
Chairperson: Spiros Cotsakis
YouTube link: https://youtu.be/H8Itnc_C10c

Gravitational singularities, scattering maps for bouncing, and structure-preserving algorithms
Philippe G. LeFloch 2630

Brane-world asymptotics in a nonlinear fluid bulk
I. Antoniadis, S. Cotsakis and Ifigeneia Klaoudatou 2645

Primordial synchronization of Mixmaster spatial points
Spiros Cotsakis 2657

• **The Early Universe**
Chairperson: Stefano Ansoldi
YouTube links: https://youtu.be/m80hHWgOlFs
https://youtu.be/6tyaZ8MMVtw

Quintessential inflation from Lorentzian slow roll
David Benisty 2663

Condensed light, quantum black holes and L-CDM cosmology: Experimentally suggested and tested unified approach to dark matter, dark energy, cosmogenesis and two-stage inflation
Victor Borsevici 2672

Helical magnetic fields lead to baryogenesis
Ashu Kushwaha and S. Shankaranarayanan 2692

Polymer Quantization of the Isotropic Universe: Comparison with the Bounce of Loop Quantum Cosmology
G. Barca, E. Giovannetti, F. Mandini and G. Montani 2700

General relativistic evolution equations for density perturbations in open, flat and closed FLRW universes and the problem of structure formation
Pieter G. Miedema 2708

Constraining beyond ΛCDM models with 21cm intensity mapping
forecast observations combined with latest CMB data
M. Berti 2726

Entropy and irreversible processes in gravity and cosmology
Llorenç Espinosa-Portalés and Juan García-Bellido 2737

Fundamental Interactions and Stellar Evolution

• Why and How the Sun and the Stars Shine: The Borexino Experiment
Chairpersons: Giampaolo Bellini, Dmitry Naumov, Gioacchino Ranucci, Gemma Testera

YouTube links: https://youtu.be/hh5wDnM8miU
https://youtu.be/TG-HgBf7W4s
https://youtu.be/HLiis2LFeEs

Experimental detection of the CNO cycle
B. Caccianiga, N. Rossi, G. Testera et al. 2753

Borexino detector performances
A. Caminata, M. Agostini, K. Altenmüller et al. 2765

Study of antineutrinos from the Earth and the Cosmos with the
Borexino detector
Sandra Zavatarelli, M. Agostini, K. Altenmuller et al. 2774

Unveiling the engine of the Sun: Measurements of the pp-chain solar
neutrinos with Borexino
D. Guffanti, A. C. Re and O. Smirnov 2785

Electron neutrino survival probability in the energy range
200 keV–15 MeV
Marco Pallavicini on behalf of the Borexino Collaboration 2804

The relevance of pp-chain and CNO-cycle neutrino measurements for
solar physics
F. L. Villante and A. M. Serenelli 2815

Role of the CNO cycles in stars
A. Ianni 2835

Geoneutrino observation
Tadao Mitsui for the KamLAND Collaboration 2840

Synthesis of the session: Why and how the Sun and the stars shine
Gianpaolo Bellini 2845

- **Rotation in Stellar Evolution**
Chairperson: Georges Meynet

YouTube link: https://youtu.be/9LNoiwa0nv8

The internal rotation of low-mass stars from solar and stellar seismology
G. Buldgen and P. Eggenberger 2848

The rotation of supermassive stars
L. Haemmerlé 2865

Fast Transients

- **What Can We Learn from a Growing Sample of Fast Radio Bursts?**
Chairpersons: Duncan Lorimer, Victoria Kaspi and Bing Zhang

YouTube links: https://youtu.be/yo4n1SgfUrQ
https://youtu.be/NwGooPauhjU

Cosmology with high-redshift FRBs
A. Fialkov 2880

- **Non Standard Cosmological Probes**
Chairpersons: Duncan Lorimer, Victoria Kaspi and Bing Zhang

YouTube links: https://youtu.be/EEFUgiFeMck
https://youtu.be/Ryb15AINfMs

Closing the cosmological loop with the redshift drift
C. J. A. P. Martins, C. S. Alves, J. Esteves, A. Lapel
and B. G. Pereira 2890

Gamma-Ray Bursts as potential cosmological probes
L. Izzo 2906

Surface brightness fluctuations: The method and future applications
Michele Cantiello 2915

Preliminary results of analysis of Ia supernovae redshift distributions
on data of the Asiago Supernova and Open Supernova Catalogues
I. V. Arkhangelskaja 2930

- **Photospheric Emission in GRBs**
Chairpersons: Gregory Vereshchagin and Damien Bégué

YouTube links: https://youtu.be/ZifnzoUXIFc
https://youtu.be/n7vWAVhFXiU

Understanding prompt emission: Where do we stand?
Asaf Pe'er 2946

On explaining prompt emission from GRB central engines with
photospheric emission model
M. Bhattacharya and P. Kumar 2957

Monte Carlo simulations of photospheric emission in Gamma Ray Bursts
T. M. Parsotan and D. Lazzati 2972

The photosphere emission spectrum of hybrid relativistic outflow for
Gamma-Ray Bursts
Yan-Zhi Meng, Jin-Jun Geng and Xue-Feng Wu 2982

On diffusive photospheres in Gamma-Ray Bursts
G. V. Vereshchagin 2989

Summary of the parallel session GB3
G. V. Vereshchagin and D. Bégué 3002

- **High and Very High Energy Emission from Gamma-Ray Bursts**
  Chairpersons: Francesco Longo and Fabian Schüssler

  YouTube links: https://youtu.be/ZUkLyyYowaM
  https://youtu.be/zwN1mNVeUzA

Synchrotron and synchrotron self-Compton emission components in
GRBs detected at very high energies
Jagdish C. Joshi, Vikas Chand and Soebur Razzaque 3009

The VERITAS gamma-ray burst follow-up program
D. Ribeiro for the VERITAS Collaboration 3017

MAGIC view of Gamma-Ray Bursts at very high energies
A. Berti on behalf of the MAGIC Collaboration 3030

Prospects for VHE monitoring of gamma-ray bursts with SWGO
G. La Mura, U. Barres de Almeida, R. Conceição et al. 3041

Theoretical implications on the very high energy emission from
GRB 190114C
*D. Miceli, A. Berti, Z. Bosnjak et al. on behalf of the
MAGIC Collaboration* 3052

AGILE and GRBs: 13 years of observations
A. Ursi on behalf of the AGILE Team 3062

Searching for Gamma-Ray Bursts with the High-Altitude Water
Cherenkov (HAWC) observatory
K. L. Engel for the HAWC Collaboration 3074

- **Electromagnetic Counterparts of Compact Binary Mergers**
  Chairpersons: Jonathan Granot and Paz Beniamini

  YouTube link: https://youtu.be/AS7bwaT48us

  CALET search for gamma-ray counterparts of gravitational wave events
  Masaki Mori for the CALET Collaboration 3084

- **Unusual and New Types of Gamma-Ray Bursts**
  Chairperson: Binbin Zhang

  YouTube link: https://youtu.be/VrF0iU8Q6us

  Off-axis jet scenario for early afterglow emission of low-luminosity
  Gamma-Ray Burst GRB 190829A
  *Yuri Sato, Kaori Obayashi, Ryo Yamazaki, Kohta Murase
  and Yutaka Ohira* 3095

- **Gamma-Ray Burst Correlations: Observational Challenges and Theoretical Interpretation**
  Chairpersons: Maria Giovanna Dainotti and Liang Li

  YouTube links: https://youtu.be/gcEy2h6y1jg
  https://youtu.be/m2pCT6RAmI0
  https://youtu.be/GTCvcVhBjN4

  GRB prompt phase spectra under backscattering dominated model
  Mukesh Kumar Vyas, Asaf Pe'er and David Eichler 3101

  Applying models of pulsar wind nebulae to explain X-ray plateaux
  following short Gamma-Ray Bursts
  L. C. Strang and A. Melatos 3107

  Searching for strange quark planets
  Xu Wang, Yong-Feng Huang and Bing Li 3118

  Probe the universe by using Gamma-Ray Bursts with X-ray plateaus
  Fan Xu and Yong-Feng Huang 3124

  A new perspective on cosmology through Supernovae Ia and
  Gamma Ray Bursts
  B. De Simone, V. Nielson, E. Rinaldi and M. G. Dainotti 3130

  Theory of plateau phase in Gamma-Ray Bursts
  Asaf Pe'er 3141

  Exploring the canonical behaviour of long Gamma-Ray Bursts using
  an intrinsic multi-wavelength afterglow correlation
  S. R. Oates, J. L. Racusin, M. De Pasquale et al. 3150

- **GRB 170817A and Binary Models**
  Chairpersons: Marica Branchesi and Giulia Stratta
  YouTube link: https://youtu.be/FRBvkaLX5WU

Kilonova emission observed so far: A comparison with AT2017gfo
A. Rossi 3162

- **Binary-Driven Hypernovae of Type 1, 2 and 3**
  Chairpersons: Carlo Luciano Bianco, Christian Cherubini and Simonetta Filippi
  YouTube link: https://youtu.be/8IFLfget3C0

Neutrinos and gamma-ray production from proton-proton interactions in binary-driven hypernovae framework
S. Campion, J. D. Melon Fuksman and J. A. Rueda Hernandez 3172

General relativistic turbulence in spherically symmetric core-collapse supernovae simulations
L. Boccioli, G. J. Mathews and E. P. O'Connor 3184

Gravitational Waves

- **Sources of Gravitational Waves**
  Chairperson: Andrew Melatos
  YouTube links: https://youtu.be/Lr8b9nKsFm4
  https://youtu.be/xuqJOXPDyVY
  https://youtu.be/qzOrgojHsMg
  https://youtu.be/KCJoWMd71pE

Mountain formation by repeated, inhomogeneous crustal failure in a neutron star
A. D. Kerin and A. Melatos 3194

Gravitational waves from neutrino mass generating phase transitions
Nobuchika Okada and Osamu Seto 3206

Efficiency of registration of chirp bursts and signals of collapsing stars by the Euro-Asian network of GW interferometers
V. N. Rudenko, S. L. Andrusenko, D. P. Krichevskiy and G. D. Manucharyan 3219

Joint analysis method on gravitational waves and low-energy neutrinos to detect core-collapse supernovae
O. Halim, C. Casentini, M. Drago et al. 3228

- **Mid-frequency Gravitational Waves (0.1–10 Hz): Sources and Detection Methods**
  Chairperson: Wei-Tou Ni
  YouTube link: https://youtu.be/sJ6A7a73Vxw

A cryogenic and superconducting inertial sensor for the Lunar
Gravitational–Wave Antenna, the Einstein Telescope and Selene-physics
F. Badaracco, J. V. van Heijningen, E. C. Ferreira and A. Perali 3245

Space gravitational wave antenna DECIGO and B-DECIGO
S. Kawamura and the DECIGO working group 3254

Summary of the parallel session GW2
Dongfeng Gao, Wei-Tou Ni, Jin Wang et al. 3261

- **Numerical Relativity and Gravitational Wave Observations**
  Chairperson: Nigel Bishop
  YouTube links: https://youtu.be/eZPytAU4Zmk
  https://youtu.be/th-3KqkxDnU

Salient features of the optimised PyCBC IMBH search
Koustav Chandra, Archana Pai, V. Villa-Ortega et al. 3277

Matter shells modifying gravitational wave signals
Monos Naidoo, Nigel T. Bishop and Petrus J. van der Walt 3286

Odd-dimensional gravitational waves from a binary system on
a three-brane
D. V. Gal'tsov and M. Khlopunov 3301

Developments in numerical relativity and gravitational wave observations
Nigel T. Bishop 3309

High Energy

- **Very High Energy Gamma Rays**
  Chairpersons: Razmik Mirzoyan and Alessandro De Angelis
  YouTube link: https://youtu.be/jHM1RH20ZyM

Insights into the Galactic Center environment from VHE gamma-ray
observations with ground-based facilities
C. Fruck 3316

The TAIGA experiment
M. Tluczykont, I. I. Astapov, A. K. Awad et al. 3324

Science perspectives of the Southern Wide-field Gamma-ray
Observatory (SWGO)
K. L. Engel for the SWGO Collaboration 3343

- **Future Missions for High-Energy Astrophysics**
  Chairpersons: Filippo Frontera and Shaolin Xiong
  YouTube link: https://youtu.be/JgDsZX6RUkU

Laue lenses: Focusing optics for hard X/soft Gamma-ray astronomy
L. Ferro, M. Moita, P. Rosati et al. 3355

ASTENA: A mission concept for a deep study of the transient gamma-ray sky and for nuclear astrophysics
E. Virgilli, F. Frontera, P. Rosati et al. on behalf of the ASTENA Collaboration 3368

Polarimetric prospects of a new hard X-soft gamma-ray space mission for next decades
M. Moita, L. Ferro, F. Frontera et al. 3385

• **The SRG Mission: First Results from eROSITA and ART-XC**
Chairperson: Andrea Merloni
YouTube link: https://youtu.be/l0t1B716UcM

Prospect for WHIM detection in the cosmic web by *SRG/eROSITA*
H. Tanimura and N. Aghanim 3400

• **eXTP – Enhanced X-Ray Timing and Polarimetry Mission**
Chairpersons: Marco Feroci and Fangjun Lu
YouTube link: https://youtu.be/3d08eKmsImI

The role of eXTP in the multi-messenger astronomy era
G. Stratta and Gor Oganesyan 3403

• **Observations of HE and UHE Cosmic Rays**
Chairpersons: Ivan De Mitri and Fabio Gargano
YouTube link: https://youtu.be/l9DZyBMWO5c

CALET on the ISS: The first 5 years
Pier Simone Marrocchesi for the CALET Collaboration 3427

The fluxes of charged cosmic rays as measured by the DAMPE satellite
Paolo Bernardini on behalf of the DAMPE Collaboration 3442

Recent results from the Pierre Auger Observatory
E. Roulet for the Pierre Auger Collaboration 3449

The HERD space mission
F.C.T. Barbato on behalf of the HERD Collaboration 3455

PART D

History of Relativity

• **The "Fall and Rise" of Betelgeuse**
Chairperson: Costantino Sigismondi
YouTube link: https://youtu.be/VmbrE2gYmOM

The observation of the stars in daytime and near the horizon
Costantino Sigismondi and Paolo Ochner 3471

Fall and Rise of Betelgeuse: The summary of HR1 session
Costantino Sigismondi and Paolo Ochner 3475

Photometry of Betelgeuse at daylight
Otmar Nickel 3479

Evidence for dynamical changes in Betelgeuse using multi-wavelength data
Sneha Kachhara, Sandip V. George, Ranjeev Misra and G. Ambika 3485

The curious case of Betelgeuse
Jacco Th. van Loon 3494

Variable stars observed from city sites: The 2500 AAVSO-SGQ database
Costantino Sigismondi and Paolo Ochner 3501

Betelgeuse: An introductory course to observational astronomy
Costantino Sigismondi and Tiziana Pompa 3507

The meridian line of the Vatican obelisk to study the stellar aberration
Costantino Sigismondi and Lorenzo Ricciardi 3513

Betelgeuse, Sirius and the stars in the roman *Settecento*
Costantino Sigismondi 3519

- **History of Relativity, Gravitation and Cosmology**
  Chairperson: Luis Crispino
  YouTube link: https://youtu.be/RNbPUSp95PQ

On Einstein's last bid to keep a stationary cosmology
Salvador Galindo-Uribarri and Jorge L. Cervantes-Cota 3536

Jayme Tiomno: Relativity, gravity, cosmology, and the
Marcel Grossmann Meetings
William D. Brewer 3547

A look inside Feynman's route to gravitation
M. Di Mauro, S. Esposito and A. Naddeo 3563

Towards detecting gravitational waves: A contribution by
Richard Feynman
M. Di Mauro, S. Esposito and A. Naddeo 3576

Stellar gravitational collapse, singularity formation and theory breakdown
Kiril Maltsev 3596

The Hamilton-Jacobi analysis by Peter Bergmann and Arthur Komar of classical general relativity
D. Salisbury 3626

- **Time and Philosophy in Physics**
Chairperson: Shokoufe Faraji

YouTube link: https://youtu.be/986v-V5JJEk

The passage of time and top-down causation
Barbara Drossel 3631

Explaining time's passage
Jonathan J. Dickau 3646

A glimpse to Feynman's contributions to the debate on the foundations of quantum mechanics
M. Di Mauro, S. Esposito and A. Naddeo 3657

Summary of the parallel session HR3
Shokoufe Faraji 3671

Neutron Stars

- **Dense Matter in Compact Stars**
Chairpersons: Alessandro Drago and Jorge Rueda

YouTube links: https://youtu.be/U5Yr0oDVhqY
https://youtu.be/MvMDFh-1_bc

Massive compact stars in the two-families scenario
P. Char, A. Drago and G. Pagliara 3677

Quasi-universality of the magnetic deformation of neutron stars in general relativity and beyond
J. Soldateschi, N. Bucciantini and L. Del Zanna 3684

Screening and elastic properties of the NS crust in the OCP approximation
D. Barba González, C. Albertus Torres and M. A. Pérez-García .. 3703

Tidal deformability as a probe of dark matter in neutron stars
D. Rafiei Karkevandi, S. Shakeri, V. Sagun and O. Ivanytskyi .. 3713

Binary neutron star mergers with quark matter equations of state
Atul Kedia, Hee Il Kim, Grant Mathews and In-Saeng Suh 3732

Probing dense matter physics with transiently-accreting neutron stars:
The case of source MXB 1659-29
*Melissa Mendes, Andrew Cumming, Charles Gale and
Farrukh J. Fattoyev* 3736

- **Compact Stars as Laboratories for Testing Strong Gravity**

Chairpersons: Aurora Perez Martinez and César Augusto Zen Vasconcellos

YouTube link: https://youtu.be/C1KGecdNEfs

Vacuum properties and astrophysical implications
*A. Pérez Martínez, M. Pérez-Garcia, E. Rodríguez Querts
and A. Romero Jorge* 3756

Testing extended theories of gravity with GRBs
L. Mastrototaro 3762

- **Pulsar Power in Physics and Astrophysics and Pulsars and Pulsar Systems at High Energies**

Chairpersons: Andrea Possenti and Pak-Hin Tam

YouTube links: https://youtu.be/gAG29DZwUbM
https://youtu.be/ytdUBFrViHI

News and views regarding PSR J1757−1854, a highly-relativistic
binary pulsar
A. D. Cameron, M. Bailes, V. Balakrishnan et al. 3774

On the origin of the unique isolated X-Ray pulsar 1E 161348-5055
with 6.7 hr. spin period
V. Yu. Kim 3785

Advantages of including globular cluster millisecond pulsars in Pulsar
Timing Arrays
M. Maiorano, F. De Paolis, A. A. Nucita and A. Franco 3791

Searching for pulsars in globular clusters with the MeerKAT Radio
Telescope
F. Abbate on behalf of the MeerTIME/TRAPUM Collaboration 3799

Precision Tests

- **Gravitational Lensing and Shadows**

Chairpersons: Perlick Volker and Oleg Tsupko

YouTube links: https://youtu.be/6DXXWpMJ3IQ
https://youtu.be/F-K1gXn71_Y
https://youtu.be/B-V8r2HMztw

Gravitational lensing by rotating Simpson–Visser black holes
Sushant G. Ghosh and Shafqat Ul Islam 3812

Killing tensors in foliated spacetimes and photon surfaces
Igor Bogush, Kirill Kobialko and Dmitri Gal'tsov 3827

Decoding black hole metrics from the interferometric pattern of relativistic images
V. Bozza 3839

Symplectic evolution of an observed light bundle
N. Uzun 3844

Shadow of black holes with a plasma environment in 4D Einstein-Gauss-Bonnet gravity
Javier Badía and Ernesto F. Eiroa 3856

Aspects of neutrino mass hierarchy in gravitational lensing
Himanshu Swami 3865

Photon regions in stationary axisymmetric spacetimes and umbilic conditions
K. V. Kobialko and D. V. Gal'tsov 3874

Gravitational lensing by charged accelerating black holes
Torben C. Frost 3885

- **Experimental Gravitation**
Chairpersons: Angela di Virgilio and Claus Lammerzahl

YouTube link: https://youtu.be/mXcxztQ0nyk
https://youtu.be/tE3gIUBviTc

A manmade experiment aimed to clarify the gravity law in the Solar system
Alexander P. Yefremov and Alexandra A. Vorobyeva 3905

Gravitomagnetic field generation using high permittivity materials in superconducting magnetic energy storage devices
G. V. Stephenson 3910

Large ring laser gyroscopes: Geometry stabilization and laser control
U. Giacomelli, N. Beverini, G. Carelli et al. 3920

Dark gravitomagnetism with LISA and gravitational waves space detectors
A. Tartaglia, M. Bassan, G. Pucacco, V. Ferroni and D. Vetrugno 3929

Light rays in the Solar system experiments: Phases and displacements
Pravin Kumar Dahal and Daniel R. Terno 3942

The Ginger project – preliminary results
C. Altucci, F. Bajardi, A. Basti et al. 3956

• **Variation of the Fundamental Constants, Tests of the Fundamental Symmetries and Probes of the Dark Sector**
Chairpersons: Angela Victor Flambaum and Yevgeny Stadnik
YouTube links: https://youtu.be/NAZA-0tWHak
https://youtu.be/juhDGBJ12Lg
https://youtu.be/zxGgDP2sn60

Varying fundamental constants and dark energy in the ESPRESSO era
C. J. A. P. Martins 3963

• **Dragging is Never Draggy: MAss and CHarge Flows in GR**
Chairperson: Oldrich Semerak
YouTube link: https://youtu.be/ho31IgLNxu8

Testing the general relativistic nature of the Milky Way rotation curve with Gaia DR2
Mariateresa Crosta 3970

Spinning cylinders in general relativity: A canonical form for the Lewis metrics of the Weyl class
L. Filipe O. Costa, José Natário and N. O. Santos 3982

Magnetized black holes: The role of rotation, boost, and accretion in twisting the field lines and accelerating particles
Ondřej Kopáček and Vladimír Karas 3999

Spinning particle: Is Newton-Wigner the only way?
V. Witzany 4010

Gravitomagnetic resonance and gravitational waves
Matteo Luca Ruggiero and Antonello Ortolan 4019

Quantum Gravity

• **Loop Quantum Gravity**
Chairpersons: Marcin Kisielowski and Jerzy Lewandowski
YouTube links: https://youtu.be/VaLPseYWh9E
https://youtu.be/WFIgMqrQ07U

Studying the EPRL spinfoam self-energy
Pietropaolo Frisoni 4026

A spin foam framework for the black-to-white hole transition
Farshid Soltani 4045

Holographic properties of the bulk-to-boundary transmission of information in regions of quantum space
Eugenia Colafranceschi 4062

- **Quantum Gravity Phenomenology**

Chairpersons: Giovanni Amelino-Camelia and Jerzy Kowalski-Glikman

YouTube links: https://youtu.be/vYnVb2zNl0o
https://youtu.be/icK8z80Hm-Y
https://youtu.be/svXLa0yhyYY

Minimal length discretization and properties of modified metric tensor and geodesics
Abdel Nasser Tawfik, Fady T. Farouk, F. Salah Tarabia and Muhammad Maher 4074

The structure of the multiverse from the entanglement entropy
Samuel Barroso Bellido 4082

Effective field theory from relativistic Generalized Uncertainty Principle
Vasil N. Todorinov, Saurya Das and Pasquale Bosso 4088

Stelle gravity as the limit of quantum gravity with maximal momentum
V. Nenmeli, S. Shankaranarayanan, V. Todorinov and S. Das 4107

Baryon asymmetry and minimum length
Saurya Das, Mitja Fridman, Gaetano Lambiase and Elias C. Vagenas . . . 4114

On quantum gravity and quantum gravity phenomenology
Douglas Edmonds, Djordje Minic and Tatsu Takeuchi 4126

WKB approach to the gravity-matter dynamics: A cosmological implementation
G. Maniccia and G. Montani 4146

Natural evidence for fuzzy sphere noncommutative geometry: Super-Chandrasekhar white dwarfs
Surajit Kalita, T. R. Govindarajan and Banibrata Mukhopadhyay 4159

A model of polymer gravitational waves: Theory and some possible observational consequences
Angel Garcia-Chung, James B. Mertens, Saeed Rastgoo, Yaser Tavakoli and Paulo Vargas Moniz 4166

- **Loop Quantum Gravity: Cosmology and Black Holes**

Chairpersons: Jorge Pullin and Parampreet Singh

YouTube links: https://youtu.be/CAuAK31Ukho
https://youtu.be/JlYnEzRiRR0

Primordial power spectrum from a matter-ekpyrotic scenario in loop quantum cosmology *Bao-Fei Li, Sahil Saini and Parampreet Singh*	4178
The primordial power spectra in modified loop quantum cosmology *Bao-Fei Li, Javier Olmedo, Parampreet Singh and Anzhong Wang*	4188
Primordial perturbations in kinetically dominated regimes of classical and quantum cosmology *B. Elizaga Navascués, R. Jiménez-Llamas and G. A. Mena Marugán*	4193
Revisiting the Hamiltonian formalism of the Ashtekar–Olmedo–Singh black hole model *Alejandro García-Quismondo and Guillermo A. Mena Marugán*	4211
A comparison of different choices of clocks in a reduced phase space quantization in loop quantum cosmology with an inflationary potential using effective techniques *Kristina Giesel, Bao-Fei Li and Parampreet Singh*	4228
Initial conditions in LQC/mLQCs *Bao-Fei Li, Parampreet Singh and Anzhong Wang*	4234
Holonomy corrections in effective midisuperspace models *A. Alonso-Bardaji and D. Brizuela*	4239
Infrared signatures of quantum bounce in collapsing geometry *Harkirat Singh Sahota and Kinjalk Lochan*	4247
Effective black hole interior and the Raychadhuri equation *Keagan Blanchette, Saurya Das, Samantha Hergott and Saeed Rastgoo*	4256
Effect of loop quantization prescriptions on the physics of non-singular gravitational collapse *Kristina Giesel, Bao-Fei Li and Parampreet Singh*	4267
Summary of the parallel session QG3 *Jorge Pullin and Parampreet Singh*	4272

Strong Field

• Strong Electromagnetic and Gravitational Field Physics: From Laboratories to Early Universe
Chairpersons: Sang Pyo Kim and She-Sheng Xue

YouTube links: https://youtu.be/kexqTayqFiU
https://youtu.be/laymGp6x9Hg

Reliable equations of state of viscous strong and electroweak matter
A. Tawfik 4277

Neutral fermion pair production by Sauter-like magnetic step
T. C. Adorno, Zi-Wang He, S. P. Gavrilov and D. M. Gitman 4290

On the magnetic field screening in strong crossed electromagnetic field
S. Campion, J. A. Rueda Hernandez, S.-S. Xue and R. Ruffini 4306

Particle creation by strong fields and quantum anomalies
José Navarro-Salas 4317

Constraints on the non-minimal coupling of electromagnetic fields from astrophysical observations
Susmita Jana and S. Shankaranarayanan 4326

New partial resummation of the QED effective action
Silvia Pla and José Navarro-Salas 4337

Can a detector detect soft photons
Sanved Kolekar and Jorma Louko 4347

Breaking of the adiabatic invariance in the production of particles by strong fields
P. Beltrán-Palau, A. Ferreiro, J. Navarro-Salas and S. Pla 4352

Dynamics of relativistic electrons in non-uniform magnetic fields and its applications in quantum computing and astrophysics
Srishty Aggarwal and Banibrata Mukhopadhyay 4362

Validity of the semiclassical approximation in 1+1 electrodynamics: Numerical solutions to the linear response equation
Ian M. Newsome 4374

On Kerr black hole perfect MHD processes in Doran coordinates
C. Cherubini, S. Filippi, A. Loppini et al. 4387

Tadpole contribution to magnetic photon-graviton conversion
N. Ahmadiniaz, F. Bastianelli, F. Karbstein and C. Schubert 4393

- **The Effects of (Non)Linear Electrodynamics on the Properties of Astrophysical/Gravitational Compact Objects**
Chairperson: Seyed Hossein Hendi
YouTube link: https://youtu.be/SAIAXtQhavE

Correspondence of gamma radiation coming from GRBs and
magnetars based on the effects of nonlinear vacuum electrodynamics
Tursynbek Yernazarov, Medeu Abishev and Yerlan Aimuratov 4401

Absorption of massless scalar waves by electrically charged regular
black holes
Marco A. A. de Paula, Luiz C. S. Leite and Luís C. B. Crispino 4410

White Dwarfs

- **White Dwarf Explosions**
Chairpersons: Robert Fisher and María Pilar Ruiz Lapuente
YouTube links: https://youtu.be/ndaW6u2xuOo
https://youtu.be/IwjYaQaqJeI

Modeling Type Ia supernovae with explosions in white dwarfs near
and below the Chandrasekhar mass
Friedrich K. Röpke, Florian Lach, Sabrina Gronow et al. 4420

Type Ia supernovae and their explosive nucleosynthesis: Constraints
on progenitors
Shing-Chi Leung and Ken'ichi Nomoto 4427

Charged polarized white dwarfs with finite temperature as a possible
source of type Ia supernovae
Sílvia P. Nunes, José D. V. Arbañil and Manuel Malheiro 4447

- **White Dwarfs, Magnetic Compact Stars and Nuclear Astrophysics**
Chairpersons: Manuel Malheiro and Jaziel Goulart Coelho
YouTube link: https://youtu.be/onicFElJQnA

CTCV J2056-3014 and other fast-spinning white dwarfs
C. V. Rodrigues, R. Lopes de Oliveira, A. Bruch et al. 4453

Gravitational waves from fast-spinning white dwarfs
M. F. Sousa, J. C. N. de Araujo and J. G. Coelho 4461

Highly magnetized white dwarfs: Implications and current status
B. Mukhopadhyay, M. Bhattacharya, A. J. Hackett et al. 4475

Electron captures and stability of white dwarfs
N. Chamel, L. Perot, A. F. Fantina et al. 4488

Massive hot white dwarfs: Consequences of finite temperature in the
structure and on the onset of instabilities
Sílvia P. Nunes, José D. V. Arbañil and Manuel Malheiro 4508

A study of the infrared emission of SGR/AXPs in a disk scenario and
its implications for their origin
Sarah Villanova Borges 4514

Particle acceleration and high energy emission in the white dwarf
binaries AE Aquarii and AR Scorpii
P. J. Meintjes, S. T. Madzime, Q. Kaplan et al. 4522

Study the effects of anisotropy on the highly magnetized white dwarfs
Debabrata Deb, Banibrata Mukhopadhyay and Fridolin Weber 4532

List of Participants   4545

PART B

PART B

Reconstruction of a star motion in the vicinity of black hole from the redshift of the electromagnetic spectrum

S. O. Komarov* and A. K. Gorbatsievich

Theoretical Physics and Astrophysics Department, Belarusian State University, Minsk, Belarus
E-mail: StasKomarov@tut.by
www.KomarovSO.bsu.by

The problem of calculating the redshift of electromagnetic spectrum of the star, moving in the vicinity of Schwarzschild black hole is solved within the framework of the General Theory of Relativity. The inverse problem — determination the parameters of the motion of a star from observational data of redshift is considered. The approach that gives possibilities to solve the inverse problem is proposed. The approach is tested on the numerical model that gives possibilities to calculate redshift as function of time of observation for a star moving in the vicinity of Schwarzschild black hole. The parameters of the star in numerical model are close to parameters of the S-stars, moving in the vicinity of the Sgr A*.

Keywords: Black hole; gravitational redshift.

1. Introduction

It is well-known from astrophysical observations that supermassive black hole with mass $m_{SBH} \approx 4 \cdot 10^6 m_\odot$,[1,2] where $m_\odot$ is the mass of the Sun, exists in the Galactic Center.[1,3–5] Apart from this, large amount of stars exists in this region. For example, S-cluster includes stars closest to supermassive black hole.[2,6–8]

Astrophysical observations of such stars give possibility to study the structure of the Galactic Center and to test theories of gravity. The main source of information about the motion of these stars is their electromagnetic radiation. In the present work, we have performed theoretical investigation of the redshift of electromagnetic radiation of a star moving in the vicinity of a black hole. This problem includes two parts: the direct problem — calculation the redshift of the electromagnetic radiation of a star moving in external gravitational field and the inverse problem: — determination the motion of the star in external gravitational field if redshift as function of time of observation is known.

The direct problem within the framework of the General Relativity is considered in many papers see, e.g.,[6–12]. The mentioned studies consider different general relativistic effects such as Shapiro delay, gravitational redshift, and Doppler shift. To solve the direct problem, one needs to solve the boundary value problem for the isotropic geodesic that connects the source and the observer. In the cited studies, if the corresponding general relativistic effects are taken into account, this problem is solved using tables of impact parameters that make the accuracy of the solution limited by the step of the data in the tables. In our previous papers,[13–15] we developed a covariant approach that allows one to obtain compact expressions for redshift as a function of observation time. We have solved the boundary value problem by numerically solving a non-linear equation, which allows for much more accurate solutions than table-based methods.

For the solution of inverse problem it is necessary to use statistical methods such us MCMC method.[6,8–10,12] But mentioned studies do not contain any approach for constructing initial guess for the solution of the problem. The method that is presented in this paper gives possibility to obtain such guesses from graphics.

As an example of solving the inverse problem, we consider a mathematical model of a star moving close to a supermassive black hole. For the demonstration purpose, we chose the parameters of motion corresponding to a star on a slightly closer orbit around the black hole than the orbits of known S-stars (see, e.g.,[2,5]). Such orbits allow us to test the approach in the strong-field regime apply to the cases when the sources are on very tight orbits near the Galactic Center. Sources with such orbits may be found with future observations.

In this paper, we use a system of units where the speed of light in the vacuum is equal to unity ($c = 1$), and the metric has signature $- + + +$.

2. Theoretical model

In the present paper consider only the case of spherically symmetric non-charged black hole. In General Relativity such a black hole can be described by the Schwarzschild metric (see, e.g.,[16]):

$$ds^2 = \frac{dr^2}{1 - 2M/r} + r^2 d\theta^2 + r^2 \sin^2\theta d\varphi^2 - \left(1 - \frac{2M}{r}\right) dt^2. \tag{1}$$

Here, $x^i = \{t, r, \theta, \varphi\}$ are Schwarzschild coordinates. Furthermore, $M = Gm_{SBH}$, where G is the gravitational constant. In our model, the mass of the black hole m_{SBH} is much larger than the mass of the star $m_s \sim m_\odot$. Because of this, we model source stars as test particles moving in the external gravitational field of the supermassive black hole. One can obtain the 4-velocity components of the star from the geodesic equation. They have the following form (see, e.g.,[16]):

$$\begin{aligned} u^0 &= \frac{dt}{d\tau} = \frac{E}{(1 - 2M/r)}; \\ u^1 &= \frac{dr}{d\tau} = e_s \sqrt{E^2 - (1 - 2M/r)(1 + L^2/r^2)}; \\ u^2 &= \frac{d\theta}{d\tau} = 0; \\ u^3 &= \frac{d\varphi}{d\tau} = \frac{L}{r^2}, \end{aligned} \tag{2}$$

where we chose the orientation of the spatial part of the coordinate system in such a way that the trajectory of the star lies in the plane $\theta = \pi/2$. Here L is the specific angular momentum of the star (in mass), E is its specific energy (in mass), and τ is its proper time. Factor e_s describes whether the considered part of the trajectory is receding or approaching.

From the system of equations (2), one can find the trajectory of the star in analytic form. In the case of finite motion, it has the following form (see, e.g.,[17]):

$$\frac{1}{r} = \frac{1}{r_s(\varphi, \delta, p_1, p_2)} = \frac{1}{p_1} - \frac{p_2 - p_1}{p_1 p_2} \operatorname{sn}^2 \left[\frac{(\varphi - \delta)}{2} \sqrt{1 - \frac{4M}{p_2} - \frac{2M}{p_1}}, k_s \right], \quad (3)$$

where

$$k_s = \sqrt{\frac{p_2 - p_1}{p_1 p_2 / (2M) - p_2 - 2p_1}},$$

where $\operatorname{sn}[\varphi, k]$ is the Jacobi sine of the first kind (see[18] for definition), δ is the longitude of pericenter, and p_1 and p_2 are pericenter and apocenter distances respectively. They are uniquely related to E and L as follows:

$$L = \frac{p_1 p_2}{\sqrt{\left(1 + \frac{p_1 + p_2}{2M}\right) p_1 p_2 - (p_1 + p_2)^2}}; \quad E = \sqrt{\frac{(p_1 + p_2)\left(2M + \frac{p_1 p_2}{2M} - p_1 - p_2\right)}{\left(1 + \frac{p_1 + p_2}{2M}\right) p_1 p_2 - (p_1 + p_2)^2}}. \quad (4)$$

The proper time of the star τ can be expressed as a function of its angular coordinate φ by using the well-known analytic formula (see, e.g.,[17]):

$$\tau = \tau_s(\varphi, p_1, p_2) + \tau_0. \quad (5)$$

Here, $\tau_s(\delta, p_1, p_2) = 0$. We will not write down this expression explicitly due to cumbersomeness.

Astrophysical observations of stars in the vicinity of the Galactic Center use electromagnetic radiation in the wavelength range of $1\mu m - 10m$ (including observations of pulsars, see, e.g.,[3]). Such wavelengths are small compared to the typical orbit sizes of S-stars, which allows us to use the geometric optics approximation (see, e.g.,[19]). In this approximation, electromagnetic radiation propagates along a null geodesic with tangent vector k_i that satisfies the following relations: $k_j k^j = 0$ and $k_{i;j} k^j = 0$. Here we chose the following coordinate frame $\tilde{K} : \{t, r, \tilde{\theta}, \tilde{\varphi}\}$. Therefore, the observer resides on the axis $\tilde{\theta} = 0$, $\tilde{\varphi} = 0$, we find that the trajectory of the light ray lies in the plane $\tilde{\varphi} = const$ and obtain (see, e.g.,[16]):

$$k^0 = \frac{dt}{d\nu} = \frac{1}{(1 - 2M/r)};$$

$$k^1 = \frac{dr}{d\nu} = e_r\sqrt{1 - (1 - 2M/r)D^2/r^2};$$

$$k^2 = \frac{d\tilde{\theta}}{d\nu} = -\frac{D}{r^2};$$

$$k^3 = \frac{d\tilde{\varphi}}{d\nu} = 0, \quad (6)$$

where ν is an affine parameter along the ray and D is the impact parameter. Factor e_s describes whether the considered light trajectory is receding or approaching.

The sign in the expression for $\tilde{\theta}$ in equation (6) is chosen so that $D > 0$. We only consider zeroth-order trajectories, i.e. trajectories for which the increment of $\tilde{\theta}$ from the source to observer is less then π (see, e.g.,[20,21]).

From equations (6) and by using the boundary condition $r \to \infty$ for $\tilde{\theta} = 0$, we obtain the following analytic expression for the trajectory of the ray:

$$\frac{1}{r} = \frac{1}{r_r(\tilde{\theta}, D)} = \frac{1}{P} - \frac{Qk^2}{2PM} \operatorname{cn}^2\left[\frac{\tilde{\theta}}{2}\sqrt{\frac{Q}{P}} + F\left[\arccos\left(\sqrt{\frac{2M}{Qk^2}}\right), k\right], k\right],$$

where $r_r = r$ is satisfied for the points on the world line of the ray,

$$Q = \sqrt{P^2 + 4PM - 12M^2}; \qquad k = \sqrt{\frac{Q - P + 6M}{2Q}}, \qquad (7)$$

cn $[\varphi, k]$ and F $[\varphi, k]$ are the Jacobi cosine and the elliptic integral of the first kind, respectively (see[18] for definition). If real, P has a physical meaning of the closest approach distance (see, e.g.,[17]). However, whether P is real or complex, it can be expressed through the impact parameter D as follows:

$$P = -\frac{2}{\sqrt{3}} D \sin\left[\frac{1}{3}\arcsin\left(\frac{3\sqrt{3}M}{D}\right) - \frac{\pi}{3}\right].$$

The angular coordinates in both coordinate systems are connected by the following relation (see Fig. 1):

$$\tilde{\theta} = \arccos[\cos(\varphi)\sin(i_0)], \qquad (8)$$

where angle i_0 is the inclination of the orbit of the star.

Redshift of the spectrum of electromagnetic radiation can be calculated from the formula (see, e.g.,[10]):

$$z = \frac{\delta\lambda}{\lambda} = \frac{(u_i)_s (k^i)_s}{(u_j)_o (k^j)_o} - 1. \qquad (9)$$

Here, λ is the wavelength of emitted light, $\delta\lambda$ is the wavelength difference between received and emitted light. $(k_i)_o$ and $(k_i)_s$ denote the wave vector at the location of the observer and source, respectively. Likewise, $(u_i)_o$ and $(u_i)_s$ denote the 4-velocity vector of the observer and the star, respectively.

Consider the case of a stationary observer located at spatial infinity. Therefore, the spacetime around the observer is described to good accuracy by the Minkowsky metric. Therefore, for the observer we have $(u^i)_o = \{1, 0, 0, 0\}$. To calculate the components of the wave vector $(k_i)_s$, it is necessary to solve the boundary value problem for the system of differential equations (6) (see Fig. 2). The zeroth-order trajectory corresponds to the maximal intensity, and one may find it almost in all cases for S-stars (see, e.g.,[20,21]). Because of this, we will consider only light rays of zeroth order. Therefore, the solution is unique. For the chosen assumptions, solving the mentioned boundary value problem reduces to solving the following non-linear ordinary equation for the impact parameter D:

$$r_s(\varphi, p_1, p_2) = r_r(\tilde{\theta}, D). \qquad (10)$$

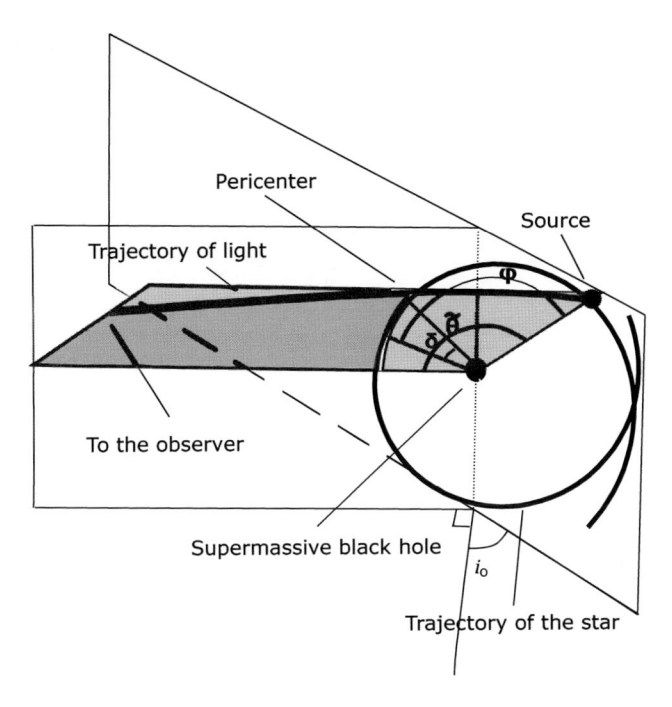

Fig. 1. For the derivation of formula (8)

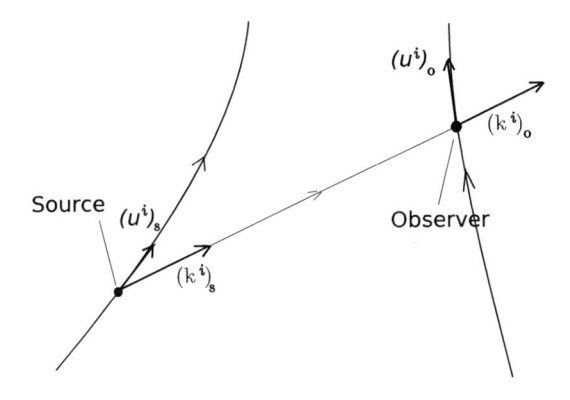

Fig. 2. $(k^i)_o$ and $(k^i)_s$ are tangent vectors to null geodesic that intersect both the worldline of the source and the worldline of the observer

Taking into account the stationarity of the observer, the relation between the angles (8), and substituting expressions (2), (6) into (9), we obtain the redshift in the following form:

$$z = -1 + \frac{E}{q} + \frac{DL}{r^2}\beta - e_s e_r \frac{1}{q}\sqrt{\left(E^2 - q\left(1 + \frac{L^2}{r^2}\right)\right)\left(1 - q\frac{D^2}{r^2}\right)}. \quad (11)$$

Here, we denote $1 - 2M/r = q$ and $\beta = \sin(i_0)\sin(\varphi)/\sin(\tilde{\theta})$. The presented equations allow one to solve the direct problem: calculating the redshift of a star moving in an external gravitational field of a supermassive black hole as a function of observation time. We illustrate the method by using a numerical model as shown in Fig. 3.

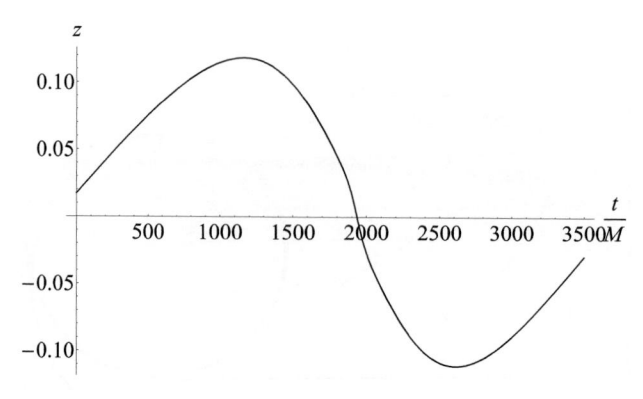

Fig. 3. Redshift of electromagnetic spectrum of a star in an external Schwarzschild gravitational field as a function observation time t. The pericenter distance of the stellar orbit is $p_1 = 60M$, its apocenter distance is $p_2 = 90M$, its inclination is $i_0 = 1.4\,\text{rad}$, the longitude of pericenter is $\delta = 1\,\text{rad}$ and the initial time of pericenter passage is $\tau_0 = 0M$

However, it is more interesting for astrophysical purposes to solve the inverse problem: determining the parameters of motion of a star in the external gravitational field of a supermassive black hole based on its redshift data. In the literature, the inverse problem is solved by minimizing the χ^2 function (see, e.g.,[9,10]):

$$\chi^2 = \sum_{j=1}^{N} \left[\frac{(z_j - z_{\text{obs},j})^2}{\sigma_Z^2} \right], \qquad (12)$$

where z_j and $z_{\text{obs},j}$ are the theoretical and observed values of the redshift, respectively, for the times of observation t_j ($j \in [1, N]$). σ_Z^2 is the dispersion of the redshift observation data. Since function $z_{\text{obs},j}(t)$ has no explicit expression (at least, because D is the solution of non-linear equation 10), minimizing χ^2 can only be performed numerically (for example, using the Metropolis-Hastings algorithm[22]).

In this work, we present another approach based on deriving a system of equations expressed explicitly using elementary or special functions of the parameters of motion of the star. To obtain such equations for the inverse problem, one has to find expressions not only for z but also for $\mathrm{d}z/\mathrm{d}\tau$. We describe this calculation in the following section.

3. Derivative of the redshift function

3.1. *Newman-Penrose null tetrad and optical scalars*

In this section we will use the Newman-Penrose null tetrad (see, e.g.,[23,24]), determined along the world line of the ray emitted by the star:

$$k^i,\, n^i,\, m^i\, \bar{m}^i. \qquad (13)$$

Here k^i is the wave vector of the ray. Symbol ¯ denotes the complex conjugation. All vectors in (13) are null. All scalar products between vectors in (13) are equal to 0 apart from

$$k_i n^i = -1; \quad m_i \bar{m}^i = 1. \tag{14}$$

Consider a congruence of isotropic geodesics that have tangent vectors k^i and intersect the world line of the observer at time t_o. Also, consider the Newman-Penrose tetrad (13) at all points of this congruence. Then the components of the vectors of the tetrad in the coordinate basis of $\tilde{K}$ have the form (we chose the affine parameter ν such that $k_0 = -1$):

$$k_j = \left\{ -1, \, e_r \frac{\sqrt{1-(1-2M/r)D^2/r^2}}{1-2M/r}, \, -D, \, 0 \right\};$$

$$n_j = \left\{ -\frac{1}{2}(1-2M/r), \, -\frac{e_r}{2}\sqrt{1-(1-2M/r)D^2/r^2}, \right.$$
$$\left. \frac{D}{2}(1-2M/r), \, 0 \right\};$$

$$m_j = \frac{1}{\sqrt{2}} \left\{ 0, \, i\frac{D}{r}, \, ie_r r \sqrt{1-(1-2M/r)D^2/r^2}, \, r\sin\tilde{\theta} \right\};$$

$$\hat{m}_j = \frac{1}{\sqrt{2}} \left\{ 0, \, -i\frac{D}{r}, \, -ie_r r \sqrt{1-(1-2M/r)D^2/r^2}, \, r\sin\tilde{\theta} \right\}.$$
$$\tag{15}$$

For the considered congruence, one can obtain the following equations (see, e.g.,[24–26], $\epsilon = k_{[i;j]} = 0$[14])

$$k_{i;j} m^i \bar{m}^j = -\rho, \quad k_{i;j} m^i m^j = -\sigma, \quad k_{i;j} k^j = k_{i;j} k^i = 0. \tag{16}$$

Here, ρ and σ are optical scalars. They are can be found numerically from well-known equations (see, e.g.,[23–26]): Only the sum $\rho + \sigma$ admits an analytical expression (see, e.g.,[25]):

$$\rho + \sigma = -\frac{\frac{d}{d\nu}\left(r\sin\tilde{\theta}\right)}{r\sin\tilde{\theta}} =$$
$$-\frac{e_r}{r}\sqrt{1-\left(1-\frac{2M}{r}\right)\frac{D^2}{r^2}} + \frac{D}{r^2}\cot\tilde{\theta}. \tag{17}$$

We now write down components of the vector of 4-velocity of the star in the basis of the null tetrad (15):

$$u^j = \frac{1}{\sqrt{2}}\left(\bar{A}m^j + A\bar{m}^j\right) + Bk^j + Cn^j. \tag{18}$$

Here A, B, C — are coefficients of decomposition. We obtain $-k_j u^j = (1+z) = C$. Denoting the components of the Killing vector $\frac{\partial}{\partial t}$ as ξ^j, we have

$$\xi^j = \frac{1}{2}\left(1 - \frac{2M}{r}\right)k^j + n^j. \tag{19}$$

Furthermore

$$E = -u^i \xi_i = B + \frac{1}{2}\left(1 - \frac{2M}{r}\right)(1+z). \tag{20}$$

From the relation for the norm of u_i, we obtain

$$u_j u^j = |A|^2 - 2(1+z)B = -1. \tag{21}$$

From (20) and (21), it follows that

$$B = \frac{1+|A|^2}{2(1+z)}, \quad |A|^2 = -1 + 2E(1+z) - (1 - 2M/r)(1+z)^2.$$

Now, we express the time derivative of redshift, using the relation $k_{[j;l]} = 0$ satisfied for the considered congruence in Schwarzschild spacetime (see, e.g.,[14]):

$$\frac{dz}{d\tau} = -k_{j;l} u^j u^l = -|A|^2 k_{j;l} m^j \bar{m}^l - A^2 k_{j;l} m^j m^l -$$
$$\bar{A}^2 k_{j;l} \bar{m}^j \bar{m}^l - 2\bar{A}(1+z)k_{j;l} n^j m^l - 2A(1+z)k_{j;l} n^j \bar{m}^l =$$
$$|A|^2 (\rho + \sigma \cos(2P_A)) - 2\sqrt{2}(1+z)\frac{D}{r^3}|A|\sin(P_A) +$$
$$\frac{e_r}{r^2}(1+z)^2 \sqrt{1 - \left(1 - \frac{2M}{r}\right)\frac{D^2}{r^2}}. \tag{22}$$

Here we use $A = |A|e^{iP_A}$, where $|A|$ and P_A are real. Numerical calculations show that optical scalar σ have very small value comparing to other terms in 22. Due to this will neglect the value of σ in calculations.

From equations (22) and (17) for the time derivative of redshift, we obtain

$$\frac{dz}{d\tau} = \left[2E(1+z) - \left(1 - \frac{2M}{r}\right)(1+z)^2 - 1\right] \times$$
$$\left[-\frac{e_r}{r}\sqrt{1 - \left(1 - \frac{2M}{r}\right)\frac{D^2}{r^2}} + \frac{D}{r^2}\cot\hat{\theta}\right] -$$
$$2\frac{D}{r^3}\sin P_A \sqrt{2E(1+z) - \left(1 - \frac{2M}{r}\right)(1+z)^2 - 1} +$$
$$\frac{e_r}{r^2}(1+z)^2 \sqrt{1 - \left(1 - \frac{2M}{r}\right)\frac{D^2}{r^2}}. \tag{23}$$

To obtain an analytical formula, it is convenient to exclude the impact parameter D from equations (11) and (23). We obtain:

$$\frac{D}{r} = \tag{24}$$

$$\frac{\frac{L}{r}\beta\left((1+z)\left(1-\frac{2M}{r}\right)-E\right) \pm \sqrt{\left(E^2 - \left(1-\frac{2M}{r}\right)\left(1+\frac{L^2}{r^2}\right)\right)\left(|A|^2 + (\beta^2-1)\frac{L^2}{r^2}\right)}}{E^2 - 1 + \frac{2}{r} + \frac{L^2}{r^2}(\beta^2-1)(1-\frac{2}{r})} =$$

$$\mathcal{F}_1(r, z, p_1, p_2, i_0, \tilde{\theta});$$

and $\dfrac{D}{r} = \mathcal{F}_2(r, z, \dfrac{dz}{d\tau}, p_1, p_2, i_0, \tilde{\theta}) =$

$$\frac{r\frac{dz}{d\tau}\left(|A|^2 \cot\tilde{\theta} - \frac{2(1+z)}{r}|A|S\right)}{\left(1-\frac{2M}{r}\right)\left(\frac{(1+z)^2}{r} - |A|^2\right)^2 + \left(|A|^2 \cot\hat{\theta} - \frac{2(1+z)}{r}|A|S\right)^2} \pm$$

$$\frac{\sqrt{\left(1-\frac{2M}{r}\right)\left[\left(\frac{(1+z)^2}{r} - |A|^2\right)^2 - r^2\left(\frac{dz}{d\tau}\right)^2\right] + \left(|A|^2 \cot\tilde{\theta} - \frac{2(1+z)}{r}|A|S\right)^2}}{\left(1-\frac{2M}{r}\right)\left(\frac{(1+z)^2}{r} - |A|^2\right)^2 + \left(|A|^2 \cot\hat{\theta} - \frac{2(1+z)}{r}|A|S\right)^2} \times$$

$$\left(\frac{(1+z)^2}{r} - |A|^2\right). \tag{25}$$

Here, $S = \sin P_A$. To find an exact expression for $\sin P_A$, one may use the law of angular momentum conservation:

$$u_i \Psi^i = L = const, \tag{26}$$

where Ψ^i is the Killing vector field associated with the symmetry of the Schwarzschild metric relative to spatial rotation around an arbitrary axis (we chose it to be orthogonal to the orbit plane). Components of Ψ^i in the coordinate basis of $\hat{K}$ are given by (see, e.g.,[19])

$$\Psi^j = \left\{0, 0, (\cos i + \sin i \cot\tilde{\theta} \cos\tilde{\varphi}), \sin i \sin\tilde{\varphi}\right\}. \tag{27}$$

Equation of the orbital plane has the following form

$$-\sin i \sin\tilde{\theta} \cos\tilde{\varphi} + \cos i \cos\tilde{\theta} = 0. \tag{28}$$

From equations (26), (27), (28), (18) and (15), it follows

$$e_r \frac{l}{r} \frac{1-\beta^2}{|A|\sqrt{1-\left(1-\frac{2M}{r}\right)\frac{D^2}{r^2}}} + e_P \beta \sqrt{1 - \frac{l^2(1-\beta^2)}{r^2}\frac{1}{|A|^2}} =$$

$$\beta \sin P_A + e_r \frac{\sqrt{1-\beta^2}}{\sqrt{1-\left(1-\frac{2M}{r}\right)\frac{D^2}{r^2}}} \cos P_A, \tag{29}$$

where e_P is defined as

$$e_P = \text{sign}\left[e_r\beta l\sqrt{1-\left(1-\frac{2M}{r}\right)\frac{D^2}{r^2}} + e_s D\sqrt{E^2 - \left(1-\frac{2M}{r}\right)\left(1+\frac{L^2}{r^2}\right)}\right]. \tag{30}$$

The exact solution of (29) has the form

$$\sin P_A = e_P \sqrt{1 - \frac{L^2}{r^2}\frac{(1-\beta^2)}{|A|^2}}. \tag{31}$$

4. The inverse problem

4.1. *The surface of parameters of motion*

The main purpose of the present subsection is to obtain the relation between the parameters of motion of the star from one hand and the redshift z and the derivative $dz/d\tau$ for certain moments of proper time from another. From (25) and (25), we obtain:

$$\mathcal{F}_1(r, z(t_o), p_1, p_2, i_0, \tilde{\theta}) = \mathcal{F}_2\left(r, z(t_o), \frac{dz}{d\tau}(t_o), p_1, p_2, i_0, \tilde{\theta}\right). \tag{32}$$

For the known redshift data $z(t_o)$ and $\frac{dz}{d\tau}(t_o) = (z(t_o) + 1)\frac{dz}{d\tau}(t_o)$ (t_o is a certain observation time), equation (32) allows one to implicitly express the constant parameters of motion p_1, p_2 and i_0 in the case, when the radial location of emission r and the angle $\tilde{\theta}$ are known. Therefore, more equations are needed to solve the problem. For this purpose, one can use equations (25) and (10). We express $\tilde{\theta}$ from (10). The impact parameter D in equation (10) can be expressed using (25). This way, we obtain:

$$\tilde{\theta} = f(r, \mathcal{F}_1(r, z(t_o), p_1, p_2, i_0, \tilde{\theta})). \tag{33}$$

Here f is some known explicit function. This equation can be solved for $\tilde{\theta}$ using the iteration method. Because the right-hand side of (33) depends on $\tilde{\theta}$ only through the small optical scalar ρ, it has little influence on the whole expression, and the solution of (33) converges quickly. For our numerical model, we have used only two iterations to obtain the solution in explicit form. Therefore, we obtain the following equation:

$$r = r_s(\varphi(\tilde{\theta}(r, z(t_o), p_1, p_2, i), i) - \delta, p_1, p_2). \tag{34}$$

The system (32), (34 obtained for certain observation time t_o contains 2 equations and 5 unknown variables: p_1, p_2, i_0, δ, r. Because of this, the solution is a 3-surface in a corresponding 5-dimensional space. Since we are only interested in the relations that connect the parameters of motion we must numerically calculate a projection of this space into a 4-dimensional space (with four coordinates: p_1, p_2, i_0, δ). The calculation results for our numerical model of the radiation of the star are presented (see Fig. 4–7) for different points of redshift data. To uniquely visualise the solution, we present it graphically on 2-dimensional sections of the mentioned 4-dimensional space. As seen from Fig. 4–5, the 3-surfaces obtained for each data point do not coincide. Therefore, the intersection point of the surfaces gives an exact value of the parameters of motion of the star. This point can be determined from the obtained figures with high accuracy.

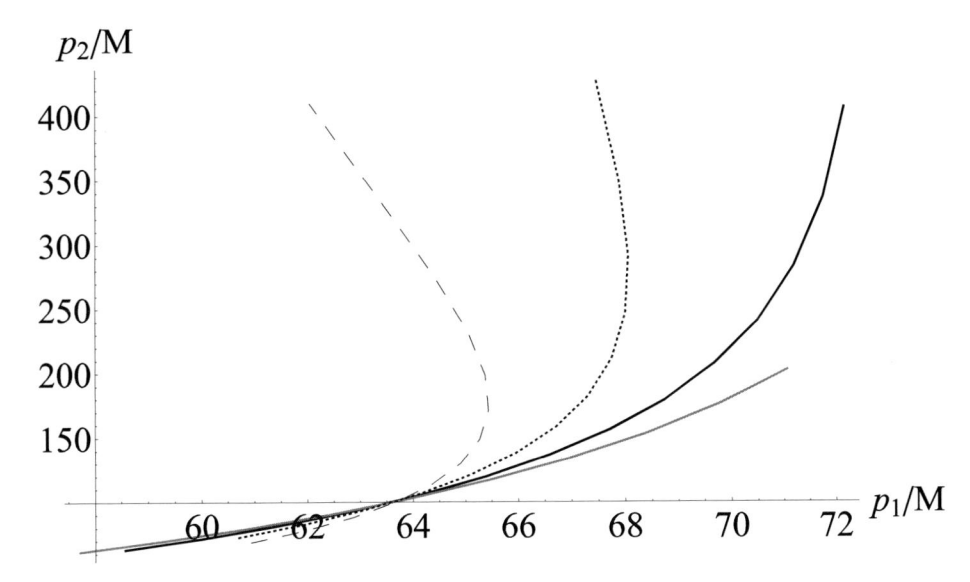

Fig. 4. 2-sections of the solution of (32), (34) for $i_0 = \pi/2$ and $\delta = 1$ by plane p_1, p_2 for different points of data (dashed: $t = 777M$, dotted: $t = 851M$, black: $t = 923M$, gray: $t = 992M$, see also Fig. 3)

Figures 4–7 also illustrate that in the case when the angular parameters are chosen to coincide with the exact solution, sections have a unique point of intersection (Fig. 6) that corresponds to the solution of the inverse problem. At the same time, if the angular parameters are not exact, a unique intersection point does not exist (Fig. 7). This is because the chosen 2-dimensional surface in the last case does not intersect with the solution in the whole 4-dimensional space of motion parameters. By using these figures, one may find if there exists a unique point of intersection in a certain region of the surface. Therefore, an initial approximation to the exact solution of the inverse problem can be found from these figures with a fairly good accuracy.

4.2. Solution of the inverse problem

A further improvement of the results can be obtain using the least squares method. For this purpose, we use functions $\tau_s(\varphi, p_1, p_2)$ and $r_s(\varphi, p_1, p_2)$. From (32), obtain the following equation:

$$\mathcal{F}_1(r_s(\varphi + \delta, E, L), z(\tau_s + \tau_0), p_1, p_2, i, \tilde{\theta}(\varphi, i)) =$$
$$\mathcal{F}_2(r_s(\varphi + \delta, E, L), z(\tau_s + \tau_0), \frac{\mathrm{d}}{\mathrm{d}\tau}z(\tau_s + \tau_0), p_1, p_2, i, \tilde{\theta}(\varphi, i)). \quad (35)$$

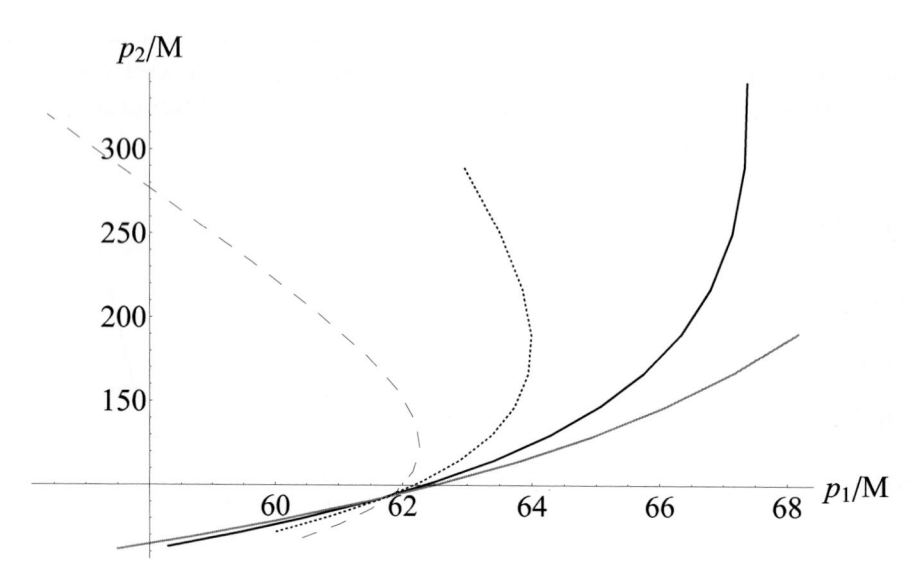

Fig. 5. 2-sections of solution of (32), (34) for $i_0 = \pi/2$ and $\delta = 1,4$ by plane p_1, p_2 for different points of data (dashed: $t = 777M$, dotted: $t = 851M$, black: $t = 923M$, gray: $t = 992M$, see also Fig. 3)

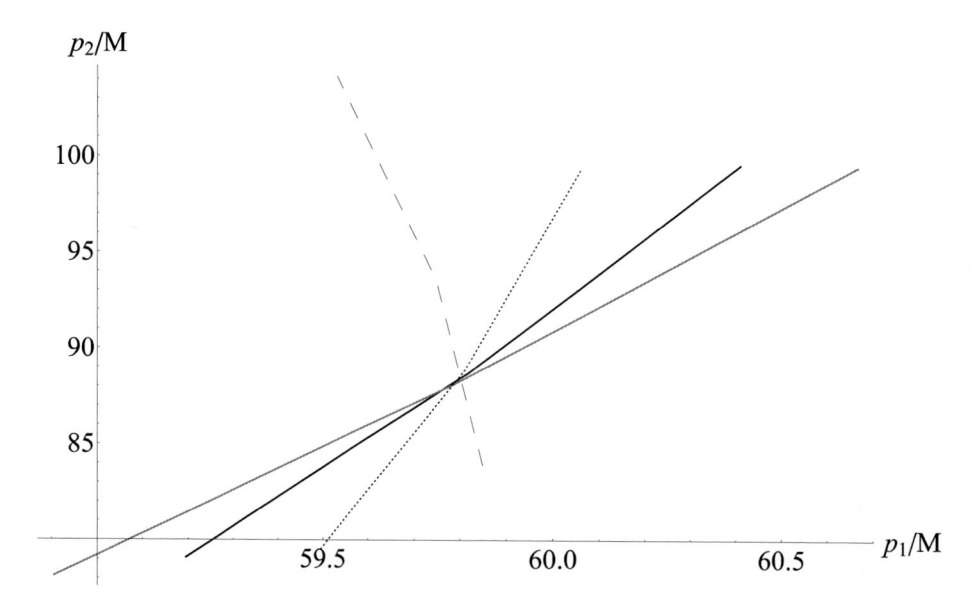

Fig. 6. Magnification of a part of figure (4)

Here, function $z(\tau)$ can be constructed based on the observational data for $z(t)$ and from function $\tau(t)$ given as an implicit function from:

$$\tau(t) = \int_0^t \frac{dt'}{(1+z(t'))}. \tag{36}$$

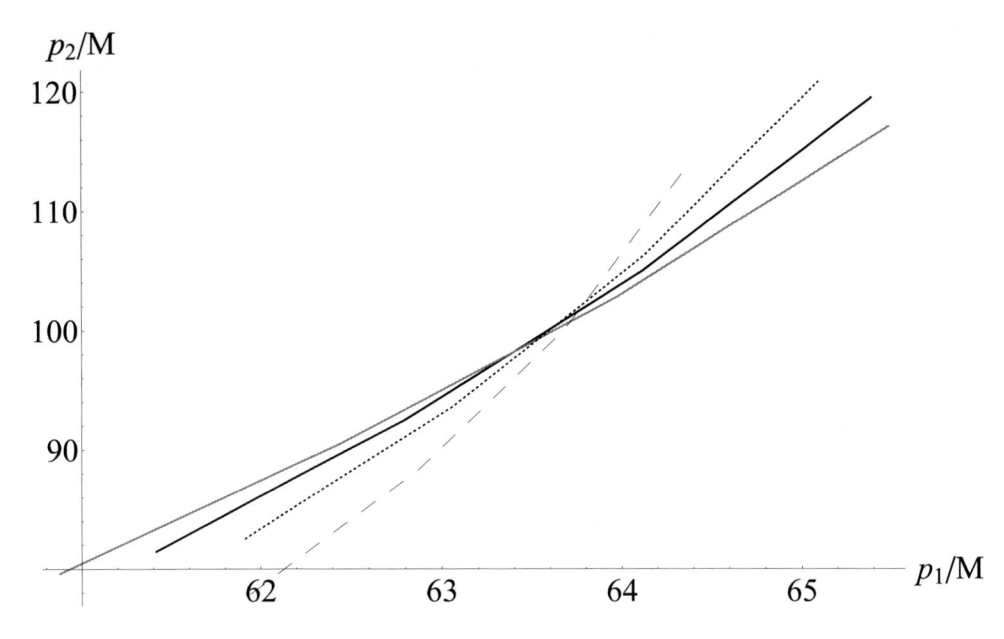

Fig. 7. Magnification of a part of figure (5)

Table 1. Results

Parameter	Initial approximation	Reconstructed value	Exact value
Pericenter distance, p_1/M	62.0	60.1	60.0
Apocenter distance, p_2/M	95.0	89.1	90.0
Orbital inclination, i_0, rad	1.5	1.48	1.4
Initial phase, δ, rad	0.9	1.0	1.0
Initial time of pericenter passage, τ_0/M	–	0.0	0.0

The left-hand side of (35) and the right-hand side of (35) are certain functions of φ. As follows from (35), these functions must be equal for a certain set of unknown parameters E, L, i_0, δ, τ_0. Therefore, one may find these parameters by using the least-squares method. As an example, we choose 10 points for different values of φ in the range [1rad, 1.4rad]. We obtain the initial approximation using the results from the previous subsection. We show the obtained results in Table 1.

5. Conclusion

The presented approach allows one to solve the inverse problem: reconstructing the motion of a star moving in the external gravitational field of a supermassive black hole based on its redshift. The approach uses the properties of congruences of isotropic geodesics to account for the difference between trajectories of light that come to the observer from the different locations of the star during the observation time.

As the main result of the paper, we have provided a method for obtaining good starting values for the parameters of motion of a star. These starting values allow one to solve the inverse problem more accurately by using statistical methods. For this purpose, we used the graphs of the surfaces in the space of parameters of motion. However, the approach may also be formulated in terms of solving a system of equations. If one writes down equations (32) and (34) for four moments of time of observation (t_{o1}, t_{o2}, t_{o3}, t_{o4}), one may obtain a system of 8 equations for 8 unknown variables (p_1, p_2, δ, i_0 and four values of the radius of radiation: r_1, r_2, r_3, r_4). Therefore, one will obtain a complete system of equations. Even numerically, it is not easy to solve a system of 8 non-linear equations. However, in future work, developed mathematical methods will allow one to efficiently solve this system of equations and analyse the conditions for obtaining non-unique solutions. The problem of non-unique solutions can be solved, for instance, by adding more equations to the considered system. The last parameter of motion τ_0 can be determined from the least-squares method. Therefore, in principle, equations (32) and (34) can be used to obtain a unique solution of the inverse problem, rather than the graphic solution presented in our paper.

The obtained equations are exact equations in General Relativity (we only neglect the optical scalar σ). Therefore, one may use the presented approach for all possible sources moving at arbitrary distances from the black hole (if they can be approximated as test particles in an external gravitational field of the black hole).

Furthermore, the approach can be directly applied to pulsar timing data for a pulsar moving in an external gravitational field. A large number of pulsars will likely be detected in the Galactic Center in the near future (see, e.g.,[12]). Pulsars can move closer to the supermassive black hole than S-stars. This way, they may be even more interesting for testing theories of gravity. The arrival times of the radio pulses can be expressed through the redshift by using:

$$t_{TOA}^{(N)} = t_{TOA}^{(N-1)} + T_p(z+1) = t_{TOA}^{(N-1)} + T_p \frac{(k^i u_i)_s}{(k^i u_i)_o}.$$

Here T_p — is the pulsar period in the reference frame of the pulsar, z is the redshift, $t_{TOA}^{(j)}$ — is the time of arrival of the j-th the pulse. In the problem of reconstructing the pulsar motion in the neighbourhood of a supermassive black hole, there exists one more unknown parameter — T_p.

Another interesting application of the results of this paper is reconstructing the motion of a binary star in the vicinity of a black hole. Determining the motion of such objects is a very important problem in astrophysics and stellar mechanics (see, e.g.,[27–31]). An approach for solving the problem of determining only the relative motion of the binary components was presented in our previous paper.[32]

The approach can be applied directly to the redshift data for the stars, moving near the supermassive black hole in the Galactic Center (for example, the S62 star[2]) to test General Relativity. To do this, one may obtain the parameters of motion of a star by using the presented algorithm and calculate the redshift as a function of observation time for future observations. Then, comparing the obtained curve with the observational data will allow one to test the theory.

One may use statistical methods (for example, Metropolis-Hastings algorithm, see[22]) to increase the accuracy of reconstructing the motion of the star. Such methods allow one to calculate the likelihood probability distribution and optimise values of parameters of motion of the star according to the distribution. The approach can be generalised to reconstruct the motion of a star in the vicinity of a rotating black hole. We leave this problem for future work.

Acknowledgments

This research was supported by the Belarusian Republican Foundation for Fundamental Research. Grant №339/02 "Reconstruction of motion of a star in the gravitational field of a supermassive black hole by the redshift of the spectrum of its electromagnetic radiation."

References

1. S. Gillessen, P. Plewa, F. Eisenhauer et. al., An update on monitoring stellar orbits in the galactic center, *Astrophys. J.* **837**, 1 (2017).
2. F. Peibker, A. Eckart and M. Parsa, S62 on a 9.9 yr orbit around Sgr A*, *Astrophys. J.* **889**, 1 (2020).
3. R. Genzel, F. Eisenhauer and S. Gillessen, The Galactic Center massive black hole and nuclear star cluster, *Rev. Mod. Phys.* **82**, 3121 (2010).
4. M. Parsa, A. Eckart, B. Shahzamanian et. al., Investigating the relativistic motion of the stars near the supermassive black hole in the Galactic Center, *Astrophys. J.* **845**, 1 (2017).
5. S. Jia, J. R. Lu, S. Sakai, The Galactic Center: Improved relative astrometry for velocities, accelerations, and orbits near the supermassive black hole, *Astrophys. J.* **873**, 1 (2019).
6. GRAVITY Collaboration: R. Abuter, A. Amorim, N. Anugu et. al., Detection of the gravitational redshift in the orbit of the star S2 near the Galactic Centre massive black hole, *Astron. and Astrophys.* **615**, 1 (2018).
7. GRAVITY Collaboration: R. Abuter, A. Amorim, M. Bauböck et. al., Detection of the Schwarzschild precession in the orbit of the star S2 near the Galactic Centre massive black hole, *Astron. and Astrophys.* **636**, 1 (2020).
8. L. Iorio, Post-keplerian effects on radial velocity in binary systems and the possibility of measuring general relativity with the star S2 in 2018, *MNRAS* **472**, 2249 (2017).
9. M. Grould, F. H. Vincent, T. Paumard and G. Perrin, General relativistic effects on the orbit of the S2 star with GRAVITY, *Astron. and Astrophys.* **608**, A60, 1 (2017).
10. F. Zhang, Y. Lu and Q. Yu, On testing the Kerr metric of the massive black hole in the Galactic Center via stellar orbital motion: full general relativistic treatment, *Astrophys. J.* **809**, p. 27 (2015).

11. R. Angelil et al., Toward relativistic orbit fitting of Galactic Center stars and pulsars, *Astrophys. J.* **720**, 1303 (2010).
12. F. Zhang and P. Saha, Probing the spinning of the massive black hole in the Galactic Center via pulsar timing: A full relativistic treatment, *Astrophys. J.* **849**, p. 15 (2017).
13. A. Gorbatsievich, S. Komarov and A. Tarasenko, Optical appearance of a compact binary system in the neighbourhood of supermassive black hole, *arXiv:1702.08381* (2017).
14. S. Komarov, A. Gorbatsievich, A. Tarasenko, Redshift of a compact binary star in the neighborhood of a supermassive black hole, *Gen. Relativ. and Gravit.* **50**, p. 132 (2018).
15. A. N. Tarasenko, S. O. Komarov, A. K. Gorbatsievich, Redshift of radiation of a point-like source moving in the external Kerr field, *Doklady Natsional'noi akademii nauk Belarusi=Doklady of the National Academy of Sciences of Belarus* **62**, 668 (2018).
16. C. W. Misner, K. S. Thorne and J. A. Wheeler, *Gravitation* (W. H. Freeman and company, San Francisco, 1973).
17. S. Chandrasechar, *The mathematical theory of black holes* (Oxford University press, New York, 1983).
18. G. A. Korn and T. M. Korn, *Mathematical handbook for scientists and engineers; definitions, theorems and formulas; for reference and review* (McGraw-Hill Book company, New York, San Francisco, Toronto, London, Sidney, 1968).
19. H. Stephani, *Relativity. An introduction to Special and General Relativity* (Cambridge University Press, 2004), Third English edition.
20. A. Tarasenko, Reconstruction of a compact object motion in the vicinity of a black hole by its electromagnetic radiation, *Phys. rev. D* **81**, p. 123005 (2010).
21. G. S. Bisnovatyi-Kogan and Y. Tsupko, Strong gravitational lensing by Schwarzschild black holes, *Astrophysics* **51**, 99 (2008).
22. W.K. Hastings, Monte Carlo sampling methods using markov chains and their applications, *Biometrica* **57**, p. 97 (1970).
23. R. Penrose and W. Rindler, *Spinors and space-time. V. 1 Two-spinor calculus and relativistic fields* (Cambridge University Press, 1987), in 2 parts.
24. E. Newman and R. Penrose, An approach to gravitational radiation by a method of spin coefficients, *J. of Math. Phys.* **3**, 566 (1961).
25. S. Pineault and R. C. Roeder, Applications of geometrical optics to the Kerr metric. i. analytical results, *Astrophys. J.* **212**, 541 (1977).
26. I. Novikov and V. Frolov, *Physics of Black Holes* (Springer Netherlands, 1989).
27. S. Naoz, The eccentric Kozai-Lidov effect and its applications, *Annu. Rev. Astron. Astrophys.* **54**, 441 (2016).
28. J. H. Van Landingham, M. C. Miller, D. P. Hamilton, and D. C. Richardson, The role of the Kozai-Lidov mechanism in black hole binary mergers in galactic centers, *Astrophys. J.* **828**, 1 (2016).
29. C. Petrovich and F. Antonini, Greatly enhanced merger rates of compact-object binaries in non-spherical nuclear star clusters, *Astrophys. J.* **846**, 1 (2017).
30. Y. Fang and Q.-G. Huangh, Secular evolution of compact binaries revolving around a spinning massive black hole, *Phys. rev. D* **99**, p. 103005 (2019).
31. F. Antonini and H. B. Perets, Secular evolution of compact binaries near massive black holes: gravitational wave sources and other exotica, *Astrophys. J.* **757**, 1 (2012).
32. S. Komarov, A. Gorbatsievich, Reconstruction of relative motion of a binary star in the vicinity of black hole by its redshift, *International Journal of Modern Physics A* **35**, p. 2040052 (2020).

Shadows of hairy Kerr black holes and constraints from M87*

Sushant G. Ghosh[1,2,*] and Misba Afrin[1,†]

[1] *Centre for Theoretical Physics, Jamia Millia Islamia, New Delhi 110025, India*
[2] *Astrophysics and Cosmology Research Unit, School of Mathematics, Statistics and Computer Science, University of KwaZulu-Natal, Private Bag 54001, Durban 4000, South Africa*
E-mail: sghosh2@jmi.ac.in †E-mail: me.misba@gmail.com

In the wake of the *Event Horizon Telescope* (*EHT*) observations of the supermassive black hole M87*, efforts are underway to distinguish the black holes in general relativity (GR) and modified theories of gravity (MoG). We study the rotating hairy Kerr black holes with a deviation α and primary hair l_0, apart from rotation parameter a and mass M. Interestingly, the hairy Kerr black holes possess smaller sizes but more distorted shadows than the Kerr black holes. We find that, within 1σ uncertainty of the *EHT* observations, the inferred circularity deviation $\Delta C \leq 0.1$ for the M87* black hole is satisfied, whereas the shadow angular diameter $\theta_d = 42 \pm 3 \mu as$, for a given choice of α, places bounds on the parameters a and l_0. Thusfore, the hairy Kerr black holes are inferred to be suitable candidates for astrophysical black holes.

Keywords: Black hole physics, gravitation, strong gravitational lensing, black hole shadow.

1. Introduction

The term "black hole shadow" has come to represent the interior of an "apparent boundary" as termed by Bardeen,[1] the inside of which is dark when the black hole is illuminated by distant, uniform, isotropic emission surrounding it. Indeed, the photons moving in unstable orbits around a black hole form a shadow silhouette that appears as a sharp boundary between bright and dark regions. The seminal work by Synge in 1966[2] gave the critical escape cone of photons from the surface of strong field stars. After that, Cunningham and Bardeen in 1973,[3] using geometrical optics, calculated the apparent position and energy flux of high-frequency radiation emitted by stars in a circular orbit around extremal Kerr black hole and also presented the first image of visible shapes for inner and outer circumferences of accretion disks (cf. Fig. 8[3]). Luminet in 1979[4] investigated the optical appearance of a thin accretion disk around spherically symmetric black holes and obtained the relative intrinsic intensity as well as the gravitational and Doppler spectral shifts of the relativistic photons. The shape and size of a shadow depend entirely upon the black hole parameters and spacetime geometry.[5–8,8–24] However, it is expected that its shape and size will get influenced by the gravity governing a black hole and the matter around it.[5–10,12–18,20,21,25]

The first shadow image of the supermassive black hole M87* has been unveiled by the international *Event Horizon Telescope* (*EHT*) collaboration.[26–28] Using the very long base interferometry (VLBI) technique, the shadow of the M87* – an asymmetric bright emission ring with a diameter of 42 ± 3 μas has been found to harbour an angular gravitational radius 3.8 ± 0.4 μas while also exhibiting a deviation from circularity $\Delta C \leq 0.1$. It is consistent with the shadow of a Kerr black hole as predicted by general relativity (GR). With the detection of the M87* black hole's horizon-scale image[26–28] the black hole shadows have become a physical reality, thus allowing probes into the background theory of gravity as well. The quantitative features are not sufficient to distinguish between black holes in different theories of gravity but using the M87* black hole shadow; one can investigate the viability of black holes in modified theories of gravity (MoG) in explaining the observational data while placing constraints on the black hole parameters using the *EHT* observations.[29]

The shadows cast by black holes in MoG have been found to be smaller and more distorted in comparison with the Kerr black hole shadow.[5,7,9–18] One of the motivations behind the multifarious works on black hole shadow is that by observing the size and deformation of shadow, the spin, mass parameter and possibly other global charges or *hair*-parameters of the black holes can be calculated.[19–22,29–31] The authors in,[23,24] considering the critical impact parameter as an analytical expression of charge, investigated the connection with shadows. In addition, in the context of the Reissner–Nordstrom metric, a tidal charge has been constrained[30] from estimates of shadow done by Doeleman et al.[32] The shadow size in Reissner–Nordstrom spacetime is found to decrease with increasing charge (cf. Figs. 1,2 in,[23] see also a discussion in[25]). Recently, Kocherlakota et al.[33] presented constraints on black hole charge from observations of M87* in 2017. Moreover, the shadows also has a vibrant use in testing theories of gravity.[29,34,35] While the the M87* has been presently inferred to be a black hole via the *EHT* observations,[26–28] there is a possibility that other exotic gravitationally intense objects cast a shadow. The hairy Kerr black holes under consideration are obtained using the gravitational decoupling (GD) approach.[36] It has a source that satisfies the strong energy condition (SEC) thus giving an extended Kerr metric which was termed as Kerr black holes with primary hair by Contreras *et. al.*[36] Hairy black holes are termed as stationary black hole solutions with new global charges, which are not associated with Gauss law.[8,37–39] (See, Ref.[37] for a recent review).

We investigate whether black hole shadow observations can constrain hairy Kerr black holes,[36] which has additional deviation parameter α and primary hair l_0 from the Kerr black hole. Furthermore, the horizons, ergoregions and shadow cast by the hairy Kerr black holes[36] are studied. An investigation of the deviation parameter's effects shows that the hairy Kerr black holes cast smaller and more distorted shadows than the Kerr black hole. Furthermore, within 1σ confidence of the EHT observational data, the parameter space of the hairy Kerr black holes is constrained with the bounds on the shadow observables of M87*.

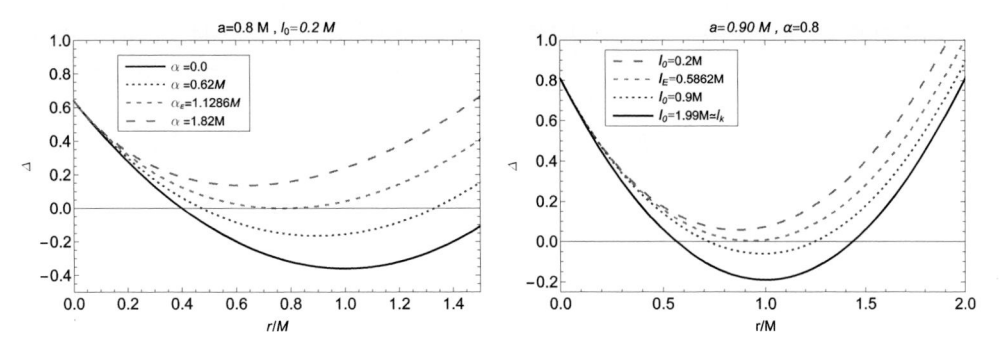

Fig. 1. Horizons of the hairy Kerr black holes are shown with varying α (*left*) and l_0 (*right*) and compared with the Kerr black holes ($\alpha = 0$ or $l \to l_k$).

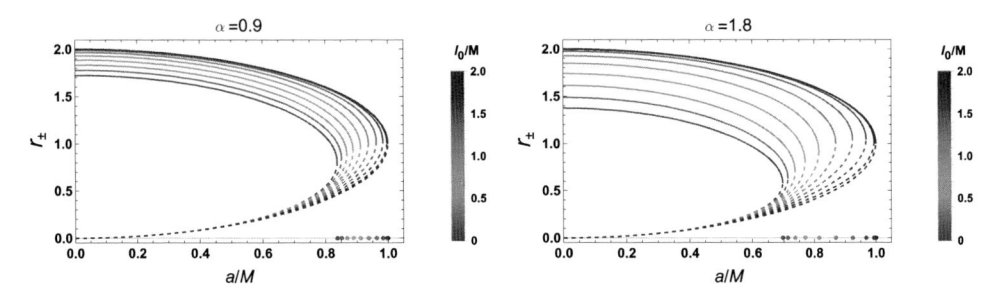

Fig. 2. Event horizon (solid lines) and Cauchy horizon (dashed lines) of hairy Kerr black holes with varying spin a for different values of l_0 and α parameters. The outermost lines are for the Kerr black hole in the limit $l_0 \to l_k$. The extremal spin a_E values are denoted by the colour coded points.

2. Hairy Kerr back holes

The GD approach, which is designed to obtain deformations of the known solutions of GR owing to the additional surrounding sources like dark matter or dark energy,[36,40,41] leads to deformed or hairy Schwarzschild black holes.[36] It has a dimensionless deviation parameter α and primary hair $l_0 \leq 2M$ which also determines the asymptotic flatness. The surrounding matter is described by the conserved stress-energy tensor $S_{\mu\nu}$ that satisfies the SEC. Hence, we consider the rotating counterpart of the spherically symmetric solution described by parameters M, a, l_0 and α, which in the Boyer-Lindquist coordinates reads[36]

$$ds^2 = -\left[\frac{\Delta - a^2 \sin^2\theta}{\Sigma}\right] dt^2 - 2a \sin^2\theta \left[1 - \frac{\Delta - a^2 \sin^2\theta}{\Sigma}\right] dt d\phi$$
$$+ \sin^2\theta \left[\Sigma + a^2 \sin^2\theta \left(2 - \frac{\Delta - a^2 \sin^2\theta}{\Sigma}\right)\right] d\phi^2 + \frac{\Sigma}{\Delta} dr^2$$
$$+ \Sigma d\theta^2, \tag{1}$$

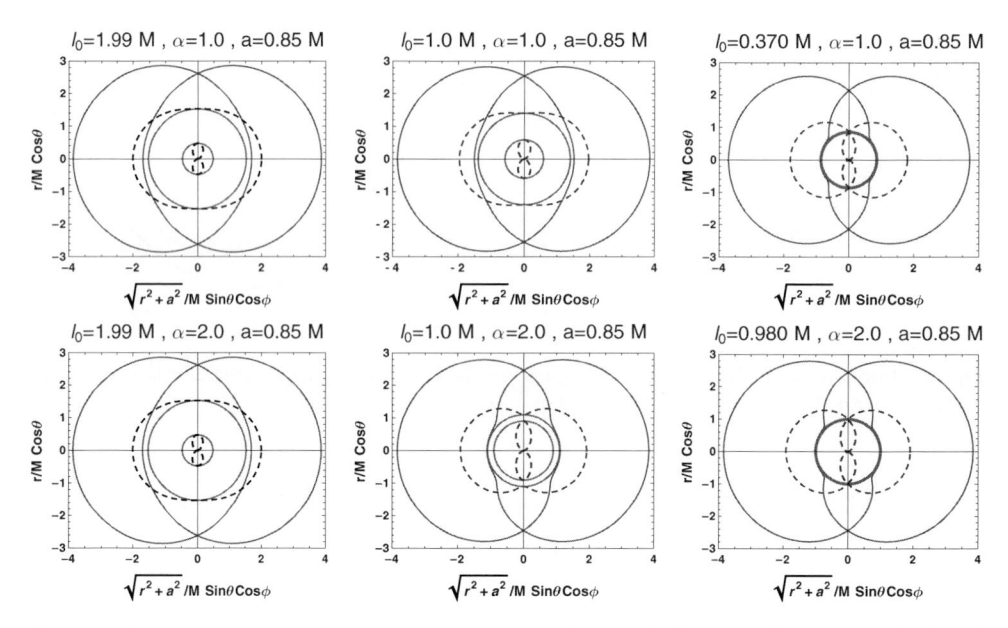

Fig. 3. The cross-section of event horizon (outer red line), SLS (outer blue dotted line) and photon region (bounded within the outer and inner orange lines) of hairy Kerr black holes. The black dotted curves correspond to the event horizon of Kerr black hole ($l_0 \to l_k$).

with $\Delta = r^2 + a^2 - 2Mr + \alpha r^2 e^{-r/(M-\frac{l_0}{2})}$ and $\Sigma = r^2 + a^2 \cos^2\theta$.

Here α is related to l_0 via $l_0 = \alpha l$ and the metric (1) goes to Kerr in the absence of surrounding fluid ($\alpha = 0$). The metric (1) which is termed as hairy Kerr black holes,[36] is same as Kerr black hole with the Kerr mass M replaced by the mass function,

$$m(r) = M - \frac{\alpha}{2} r e^{-r/(M-\frac{l_0}{2})}.$$

Next, we shall investigate how the primary hair l_0 affects the horizons, photon region as well as shadow of the black hole. The horizons of the metric (1) correspond to spacetime points where $\Sigma \neq 0$ and $g^{\alpha\beta} \partial_\alpha r \partial_\beta r = g^{rr} = \Delta = 0$ and is given by the zeros of

$$r^2 + a^2 - 2Mr + \alpha r^2 e^{-r/(M-\frac{l_0}{2})} = 0. \qquad (2)$$

The two roots of Eq. (2) are r_+ outer (event) horizon and r_- the inner (Cauchy) horizon. An analysis of Eq. (2) reveals that, depending on the values of M, a, α and l_0, there can exist a maximum of two distinct real positive roots, or equal roots corresponding respectively to the black holes with Cauchy and event horizons or extremal black holes.

From the horizon structure of the hairy Kerr black holes depicted in Fig. 1, we find that, $l_0 > l_E$ corresponds to hairy Kerr black holes with Cauchy and event horizons whereas $l_0 < l_E$ implies existence of a naked singularity.

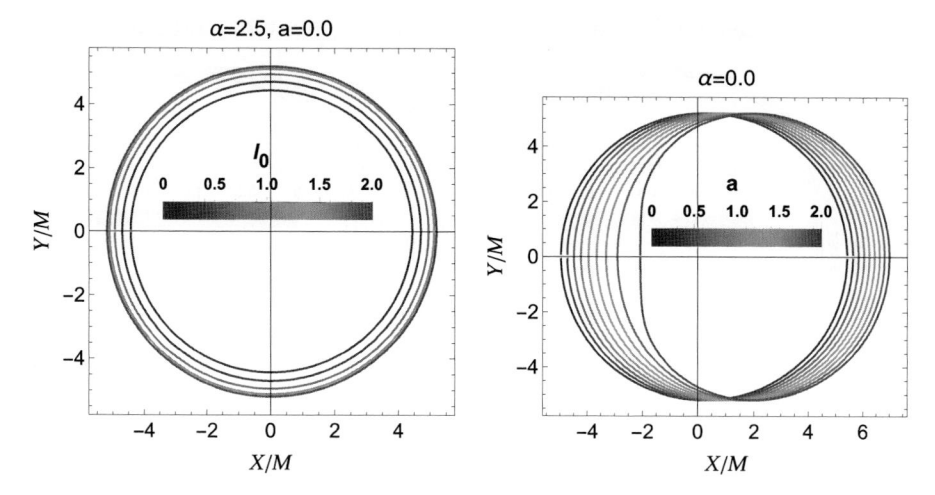

Fig. 4. Shadow geometry of non-rotating hairy black holes with varying l_0 parameter (left) and Kerr black hole ($\alpha = 0$) with varying spin a (right).

Furthermore, the asymptotic time-translational Killing vector, becomes null at the static limit surface (SLS) which yields[9]

$$r^2 + a^2 \cos^2\theta - 2Mr + \alpha r^2 e^{-r/(M-\frac{l_0}{2})} = 0. \tag{3}$$

Thus, the real positive solutions ($r^{\pm}_{SLS}$) of Eq. (3) correspond to the radii of the SLS, the larger of the which corresponds to the outer SLS, denoted by r^{+}_{SLS}. Fig. 3 depicts the ergoregion of the hairy Kerr black hole (1) whereby it can be seen that, the increase in parameter l_0 has a diminishing effect on the ergoregion's size and may thus have consequence in the Penrose energy extraction process.[42]

3. Analytic black hole shadow

We use the Hamilton-Jacobi equation to obtain the geodesic equations in the first-order differential form,[43] which for the metric (1) read[44]

$$\Sigma \frac{dt}{d\lambda} = \frac{r^2+a^2}{\Delta}(E(r^2+a^2) - aL_z) - a(aE\sin^2\theta - L_z), \tag{4}$$

$$\Sigma \frac{dr}{d\lambda} = \pm \sqrt{\mathcal{R}(r)}, \tag{5}$$

$$\Sigma \frac{d\theta}{d\lambda} = \pm \sqrt{\Theta(\theta)}, \tag{6}$$

$$\Sigma \frac{d\phi}{d\lambda} = \frac{a}{\Delta}(E(r^2+a^2) - aL_z) - (aE - \frac{L_z}{\sin^2\theta}), \tag{7}$$

where λ is the affine parameter along the geodesics and the effective potentials $\mathcal{R}(r)$

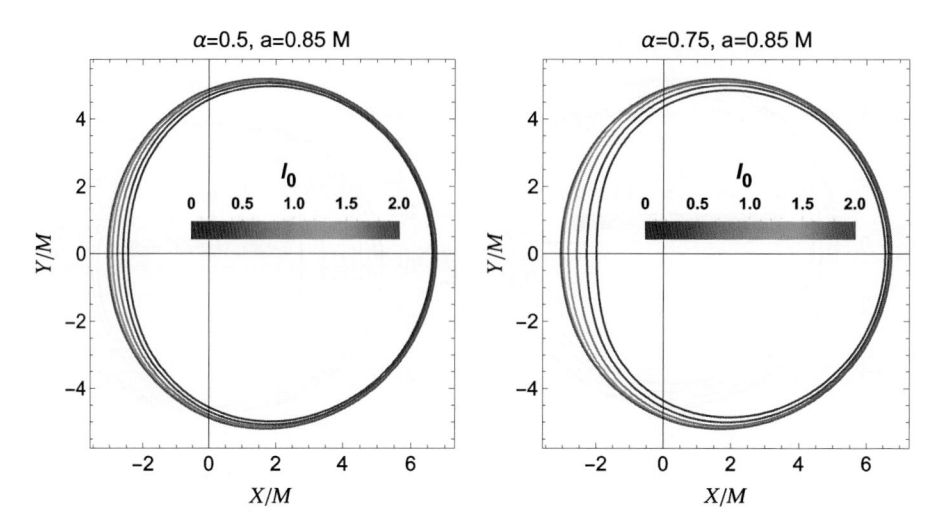

Fig. 5. Shadows of hairy Kerr black holes compared with Kerr black hole shadow (outermost solid curve corresponding to $l_0 \to l_k$).

and $\Theta(\theta)$ for radial and polar motions are given by

$$\mathcal{R}(r) = \Big((r^2 + a^2)E - aL_z\Big)^2 - \Delta\Big(\mathcal{K} + (aE - L_z)^2\Big), \tag{8}$$

$$\Theta(\theta) = \mathcal{K} - \left(\frac{L_z^2}{\sin^2\theta} - a^2 E^2\right)\cos^2\theta. \tag{9}$$

The constant $\mathcal{K}$ is the separability constant related to the Carter constant $\mathcal{Q}$ through $\mathcal{Q} = \mathcal{K} + (aE - L_z)^2$.[44] By introducing reduced quantities called impact parameters[44] $\xi = L_z/E$, $\eta = \mathcal{K}/E^2$, the degrees of freedom of the photon motion reduces from three to two. We are interested in the spherical photon orbits[44] whose radius $r = r_p$ are formed at the local extremum of the radial effective potential outside the horizon such that[44,45]

$$\mathcal{R} = \mathcal{R}' = 0 \text{ and } \mathcal{R}'' \leq 0. \tag{10}$$

Solving Eq. (10) we obtain the critical values of impact parameters (ξ_{crit}, η_{crit}) for the unstable orbits given by,

$$\xi_{crit} = \frac{(a^2 + r^2)\Delta'(r) - 4r\Delta(r)}{a\Delta'(r)},$$

$$\eta_{crit} = \frac{r^2\left(8\Delta(r)\left(2a^2 + r\Delta'(r)\right) - r^2\Delta'(r)^2 - 16\Delta(r)^2\right)}{a^2\Delta'(r)^2}, \tag{11}$$

where $'$ stands for the derivative with respect to the radial coordinate. The Eq. (11) in the limit $\alpha \to 0$ reduces to the critical impact parameter for the Kerr black holes.[19]

The Carter constant is directly related to θ-velocity of the photons and the non-planar or 3D photon orbits only arise for $\eta_{crit} > 0$.[46] The roots of $\eta_{crit} = 0$ give the radii of prograde (r_p^-) and retrograde (r_p^+) orbits. The exterior photon region, $r_+ < r_p^- < r_p < r_p^+$, of the hairy Kerr black holes is depicted in Fig. 3 as the region enclosed between the inner prograde and the outer retrograde orbits (cf. Fig. 3).

The gravitationally lensed image[47–50] of the photon region appears as a dark region outlined by a bright ring to a distant observer is termed the black hole shadow.[51,52] The shadow has been utilized for the measurement of various black hole parameters like its mass, spin angular momentum as well as other *hairs*,[22,29,35] whereby the black hole shadow is evidently a means to test Einstein's GR in the strong-field regime[13] besides the no hair theorem.[29,53] Assuming a distant observer ($r_o \to \infty$) at an inclination angle θ_0 with the rotation axis of the black hole a stereographic projection of the black hole shadow to the celestial image plane gives the shadow outline in the celestial coordinates (X,Y) as,[19]

$$X = -\xi_{crit} \csc\theta_o,$$
$$Y = \pm\sqrt{\eta_{crit} + a^2\cos^2\theta_o - \xi_{crit}^2 \cot^2\theta_o}, \qquad (12)$$

which further gets simplified to $X = -\xi_{crit}$, $Y = \pm\sqrt{\eta_{crit}}$ for an equatorial observer ($\theta_o = \pi/2$). The parametric contour of $(X(r_p),Y(r_p))$ traces the shadow of the hairy Kerr black holes with $m(r) = M - \frac{\alpha}{2}re^{-r/(M-\frac{l_0}{2})}$.

Interestingly, Zakharov et al.[54] carried out an analysis of critical curve $\eta(\xi)$ which separates scatter and capture of a photon in Kerr metric (cf. see Fig. 2[54] and discussion therein) and considering critical values corresponding to multiple roots of the polynomial describing a radial photon motion as functions of ξ (see also the critical curve in Fig. 3[44]). Subsequently, it was shown[31] that for an equatorial observer for any spin parameter $0 \leq a \leq 1$, the maximum absolute value of Y corresponds to $X = -2a$ and hence, in principle, it is possible to estimate a by measuring the position of the maximum value for Y.[31] Moreover, Bardeen[3] and Chadrasekhar[44] considered the apparent shape of a black hole for spin $a = M$, but they do not suggest using the apparent shape of a black hole as GR test perhaps because the dark region (shadow) is too small to be detectable for all known estimates of black hole masses and distances.

We depict the shadows for the non-rotating hairy black hole ($a = 0$) and Kerr black holes ($\alpha = 0$) (1) in Fig. 4 (cf. Fig. 2[31]) . Further, a comparison of the hairy Kerr black hole shadows with that of the Kerr black hole is shown in Fig. 5. There is a decremental effect in the shadow size from that of the Kerr black hole (cf. Fig. 5) with the decrease in l_0 from the Kerr limit $l_0 = l_k$.

4. Constraints on hairy Kerr black hole parameters from *EHT* observation of M87*

The EHT image of M87* is nearly circular and of crescent shape encompassing a central depression in brightness with a flux ratio $\geq 10 : 1$;[26–28] in terms of root-mean-square deviation from the average shadow radius the circularity deviation

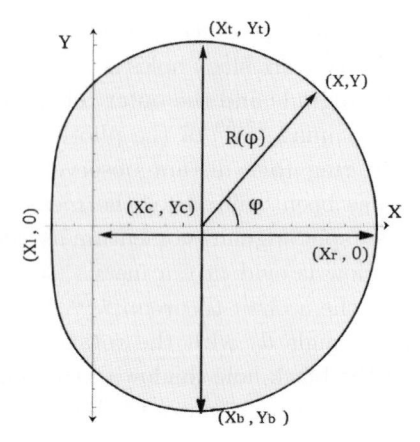

Fig. 6. The coordinates X_l and X_r indicate the most negative and most positive x-coordinates of the shadow while the Y_t, Y_b represent the top most and bottom most points. (X_c, Y_c) is the centre of the shadow and $R(\phi)$ is the polar shadow radius.[55]

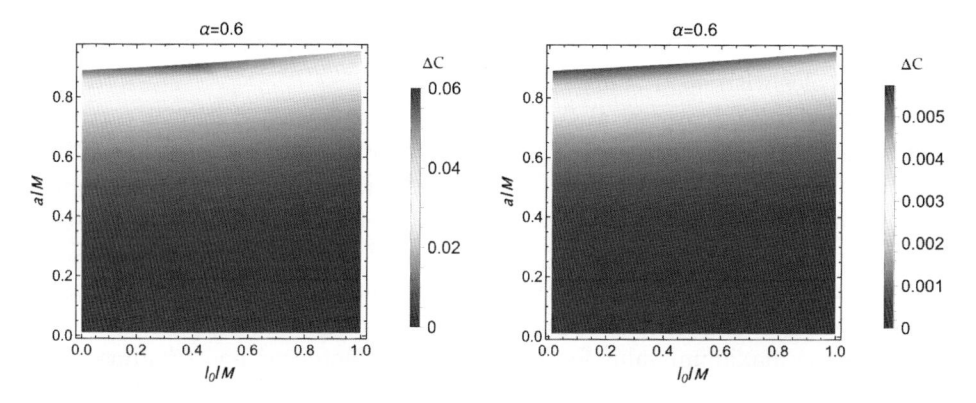

Fig. 7. Circularity deviation observable ΔC for hairy Kerr black hole shadows as a function of parameters (a/M and l_0/M) in agreement with the *EHT* observations of the M87* black hole, $\Delta C \leq 0.1$, is satisfied for the entire parameter space (a/M and l_0/M). The parameters of M87* used are $M = 6.5 \times 10^9 M_\odot$ and $d = 16.8$MPc. The inclination angle is $\theta_0 = 90°$ (*left*) and $17°$ (*right*). The white region is forbidden for (a/M and l_0/M).

$\Delta C \leq 0.10$ (10%) and the angular size θ_d of the bright emission region in the observed image is $42 \pm 3\mu as$.[26–28]

The shadow outline of an axially symmetric black hole is depicted in Fig. 6 with the boundary of the black hole shadow by the polar coordinates $(R(\varphi), \varphi)$, with origin at the shadow centre (X_c, Y_c) such that $X_c = (X_r - X_l)/2$ and $Y_c = 0$ (cf. Fig. 6). The circularity deviation ΔC, which quantifies deviation from a perfect circle, is defined as[56]

$$\Delta C = \frac{1}{\bar{R}}\sqrt{\frac{1}{2\pi}\int_0^{2\pi}\left(R(\varphi)-\bar{R}\right)^2 d\varphi}, \tag{13}$$

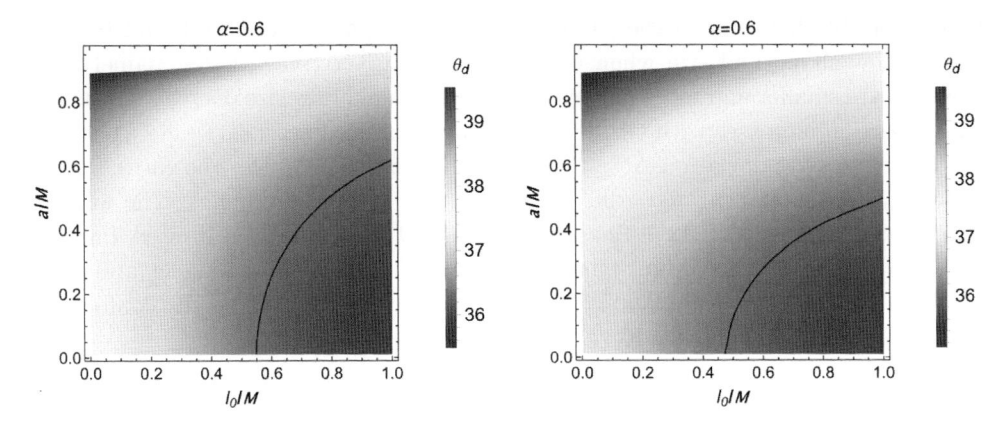

Fig. 8. Angular diameter observable θ_d for hairy Kerr black hole shadows as a function of parameters (a/M and l_0/M). The black solid curve correspond to $\theta_d = 39\mu$as within 1σ region of the measured angular diameter, $\theta_d = 42 \pm 3\mu$as, of the M87* black hole reported by the *EHT*. The parameters of M87* used are $M = 6.5 \times 10^9 M_\odot$ and $d = 16.8$Mpc. The inclination angle is $\theta_0 = 90°$ (*left*) and $17°$ (*right*). The white region is forbidden for (a/M and l_0/M).

with $\bar{R}$ – the average shadow radius.[56] The angular diameter of the shadow θ_d[13] is defined as

$$\theta_d = 2\frac{R_a}{d}, \quad R_a = \sqrt{A/\pi}, \tag{14}$$

Here, φ is the polar angle between the x-axis and the vector connecting the centre (X_c, Y_c) with any point (X, Y) lying on the boundary of the shadow (cf. Fig. 6). where R_a is the areal radius of the shadow. The θ_d together with the ΔC will be useful to perform a comparison between the theoretical predictions for hairy Kerr BH shadows and the *EHT* observations.[56]

Assuming M87* a hairy Kerr black hole, we can calculate ΔC for metric (1) and use the *EHT* observational result $\Delta C \leq 0.1$ to put constraints on the hairy Kerr black hole parameters. The circularity deviation ΔC in the parameter space $(a/M - l_0/M)$ of the hairy Kerr black hole is depicted in Fig. 7. The Fig. 7 clearly indicates that the hairy Kerr black hole shadows of M87* for a given α, satisfy $\Delta C \leq 0.10$ for entire parameter space $(a/M - l_0/M)$ at both the inclination angles. The angular diameter of the shadow is calculated next, which apart from a, l_0, α, θ, depends on mass M and the distance d of the black hole and for the hairy Kerr black holes is depicted in Fig. 8 as function of a and l_0 α taking inclination angle $\theta_0 = 90°, 17°$. The black curves denote the *EHT* bound of 39μas, the 1σ bound of M87* on θ_d, and the region enclosed by it $39\mu as \leq \theta_d \leq 45\mu as$ serves as the parameter space $(a/M - l_0/M)$ consistent with the M87* observations.

5. Conclusions

A thorough analysis reveals that the l_0 and α quantitatively influences the event horizon structure, the ergosphere area, and the spherical photon region around hairy Kerr black holes. Further, both the α and l_0 parameters are found to alter the shadow shape and size when compared to the Kerr black holes, namely, the shadows are smaller and more distorted, besides, the shadow size decreases, whereas the distortion increases with the decreasing value of parameter l_0.

The circularity deviation $\Delta C \leq 0.1$ is satisfied exhaustively for the entire $(l_0 - a)$ parameter space at both $\theta_0 = 90°$ and $\theta_0 = 17°$ inclination angles. The angular diameter satisfies $\theta_d = 42 \pm 3\mu$as within the 1σ region over a limited $(l_0 - a)$ space. However, the accordant parameter space for $\theta_0 = 17°$ is smaller and more constricted than that at $\theta_0 = 90°$. Thus θ_d puts a tighter bound on the conforming parameter space of the hairy Kerr black hole.

Therefore, our results constrain the hairy Kerr black holes parameters to ensure that the M87* shadow observations do not entirely rule out hairy Kerr black holes whereby the Kerr black hole has been studied in a more general setting, thus shedding light on the effect of surrounding dark matter on the Kerr black holes. The current resolution of the M87* black hole shadow angular diameter is of $\mathcal{O}(\mu as)$ makes the distinguishability of the hairy black holes from the Kerr black hole bleak, at least from the present resolution of the *EHT* and the next-generation EHT with higher resolution may pin down the exact constraint. Thus to summarize, with the first direct image of the supermassive black hole M87* *EHT* observation, we have been able to place constraints on the hairy Kerr black hole parameters.

Acknowledgements

M.A. is supported by DST-INSPIRE Fellowship, Department of Science and Technology, Govt. of India

References

1. J. M. Bardeen, Timelike and null geodesics in the Kerr metric, *Les Houches summer school of theoretical physics: Black holes, Gordon and Breach science publishers Inc., United States* (1973).
2. J. L. Synge, The escape of photons from gravitationally intense stars, *Mon. Not. Roy. Astron. Soc.* **131**, 463 (1966).
3. C. T. Cunningham and J. M. Bardeen, The optical appearance of a star orbiting an extreme Kerr black hole, *ApJ* **183**, 237 (1973).
4. J. P. Luminet, Image of a spherical black hole with thin accretion disk, *Astron. Astrophys.* **75**, 228 (1979).
5. L. Amarilla, E. F. Eiroa and G. Giribet, Null geodesics and shadow of a rotating black hole in extended Chern-Simons modified gravity, *Phys. Rev. D* **81**, 124045 (2010).
6. L. Amarilla and E. F. Eiroa, Shadow of a rotating braneworld black hole, *Phys. Rev. D* **85**, 064019 (2012).
7. L. Amarilla and E. F. Eiroa, Shadow of a Kaluza-Klein rotating dilaton black hole, *Phys. Rev. D* **87**, 044057 (2013).
8. C. Herdeiro, E. Radu and H. Rúnarsson, Kerr black holes with Proca hair, *Class. Quantum Gravity* **33**, 154001 (2016).
9. M. Amir, B. P. Singh and S. G. Ghosh, Shadows of rotating five-dimensional charged EMCS black holes, *Eur. Phys. J. C* **78**, 399 (2018).

10. B. P. Singh and S. G. Ghosh, Shadow of Schwarzschild–Tangherlini black holes, *Ann. Phys.* **395**, 127 (2018).
11. Y. Mizuno, Z. Younsi, C. M. Fromm, O. Porth, M. De Laurentis, H. Olivares, H. Falcke, M. Kramer and L. Rezzolla, The current ability to test theories of gravity with black hole shadows, *Nature Astron.* **2**, 585 (2018).
12. S. G. Ghosh, M. Amir and S. D. Maharaj, Ergosphere and shadow of a rotating regular black hole, *Nucl. Phys. B* **957**, 115088 (2020).
13. R. Kumar and S. G. Ghosh, Rotating black holes in $4D$ Einstein-Gauss-Bonnet gravity and its shadow, *JCAP* **07**, 053 (2020).
14. M. Amir and S. G. Ghosh, Shapes of rotating nonsingular black hole shadows, *Phys. Rev. D* **94**, 024054 (2016).
15. R. Kumar, S. G. Ghosh and A. Wang, Gravitational deflection of light and shadow cast by rotating Kalb-Ramond black holes, *Phys. Rev. D* **101**, 104001 (2020).
16. M. Amir and S. G. Ghosh, Rotating Hayward's regular black hole as particle accelerator, *JHEP* **07**, 015 (2015).
17. R. Kumar, B. P. Singh and S. G. Ghosh, Shadow and deflection angle of rotating black hole in asymptotically safe gravity, *Annals Phys.* **420**, 168252 (2020).
18. R. Kumar, B. P. Singh, M. S. Ali and S. G. Ghosh, Shadows of black hole surrounded by anisotropic fluid in Rastall theory, *Phys. Dark Univ.* **34**, 100881 (2021).
19. K. Hioki and K.-I. Maeda, Measurement of the Kerr spin parameter by observation of a compact object's shadow, *Phys. Rev. D* **80**, 024042 (2009).
20. P. V. P. Cunha, C. A. R. Herdeiro and E. Radu, Spontaneously scalarized Kerr black holes in extended scalar-tensor–Gauss-Bonnet gravity, *Phys. Rev. Lett.* **123**, 011101 (2019).
21. P. V. P. Cunha, C. A. R. Herdeiro and E. Radu, EHT constraint on the ultralight scalar hair of the M87 supermassive black hole, *Universe* **5**, 220 (2019).
22. R. Kumar and S. G. Ghosh, Black hole parameter estimation from its shadow, *ApJ* **892**, 78 (2020).
23. A. F. Zakharov, F. de Paolis, G. Ingrosso and A. A. Nucita, Direct measurements of black hole charge with future astrometrical missions, *A&A* **442**, 795 (2005).
24. A. F. Zakharov, Constraints on a charge in the Reissner-Nordström metric for the black hole at the Galactic Center, *Phys. Rev. D* **90**, 062007 (2014).
25. A. F. Zakharov, Constraints on a tidal charge of the supermassive black hole in M87* with the EHT observations in April 2017, *arXiv:2108.01533* (2021).
26. K. Akiyama *et al.*, First M87 Event Horizon Telescope results. I. the shadow of the supermassive black hole, *ApJL* **875**, L1 (2019).
27. K. Akiyama *et al.*, First M87 Event Horizon Telescope results. IV. imaging the central supermassive black hole, *ApJL* **875**, L4 (2019).
28. K. Akiyama *et al.*, First M87 Event Horizon Telescope results. VI. the shadow and mass of the central black hole, *ApJL* **875**, L6 (2019).
29. M. Afrin and S. G. Ghosh, Constraining rotating black holes in Horndeski theory with EHT observations of M87*, *arXiv:2110.05258* (2021).
30. A. F. Zakharov, F. de Paolis, G. Ingrosso and A. A. Nucita, Shadows as a tool to evaluate black hole parameters and a dimension of spacetime, *New Astron. Rev.* **56**, 64 (2012).
31. A. F. Zakharov, A. A. Nucita, F. De Paolis and G. Ingrosso, Measuring the black hole parameters in the Galactic Center with RADIOASTRON, *New Astron.* **10**, 479 (2005).
32. S. S. Doeleman et al., Event-horizon-scale structure in the supermassive black hole candidate at the Galactic Centre, *Nature* **455**, 78 (2008).

33. P. Kocherlakota et al., Constraints on black-hole charges with the 2017 EHT observations of M87*, *Phys. Rev. D* **103**, 104047 (2021).
34. M. Kramer, D. C. Backer, J. M. Cordes, T. J. W. Lazio, B. W. Stappers and S. Johnston, Strong-field tests of gravity using pulsars and black holes, *New Astron. Rev.* **48**, 993 (2004).
35. R. Kumar, A. Kumar and S. G. Ghosh, Testing rotating regular metrics as candidates for astrophysical black holes, *Astrophys. J.* **896**, 89 (2020).
36. E. Contreras, J. Ovalle and R. Casadio, Gravitational decoupling for axially symmetric systems and rotating black holes, *Phys. Rev. D* **103**, 044020 (2021).
37. C. A. R. Herdeiro and E. Radu, Asymptotically flat black holes with scalar hair: a review, *Int. J. Mod. Phys. D* **24**, 1542014 (2015).
38. C. A. R. Herdeiro and E. Radu, Kerr black holes with scalar hair, *Phys. Rev. Lett.* **112**, p. 221101 (2014).
39. Y.-X. Gao and Y. Xie, Gravitational lensing by hairy black holes in Einstein-scalar-Gauss-Bonnet theories, *Phys. Rev. D* **103**, 043008 (2021).
40. J. Ovalle, Decoupling gravitational sources in general relativity: from perfect to anisotropic fluids, *Phys. Rev. D* **95**, 104019 (2017).
41. J. Ovalle, Decoupling gravitational sources in general relativity: the extended case, *Phys. Lett. B* **788**, 213 (2019).
42. R. Penrose and R. M. Floyd, Extraction of rotational energy from a black hole, *Nature* **229**, 177 (1971).
43. B. Carter, Global structure of the Kerr family of gravitational fields, *Phys. Rev.* **174**, 1559 (1968).
44. S. Chandrasekhar, *The mathematical theory of black holes* (Oxford Univ. Press, New York, 1985).
45. V. P. Frolov and A. Zelnikov, *Introduction to black hole physics* (Oxford Univ. Press, Oxford, 2011).
46. E. Teo, Spherical orbits around a Kerr black hole, *Gen. Relativ. Gravit.* **53**, 10 (2021).
47. V. Bozza, Gravitational lensing in the strong field limit, *Phys. Rev. D* **66**, 103001 (2002).
48. S. G. Ghosh, R. Kumar and S. U. Islam, Parameters estimation and strong gravitational lensing of nonsingular Kerr-Sen black holes, *JCAP* **03**, 056 (2021).
49. R. Kumar, S. U. Islam and S. G. Ghosh, Gravitational lensing by charged black hole in regularized $4D$ Einstein–Gauss–Bonnet gravity, *Eur. Phys. J. C* **80**, 1128 (2020).
50. S. U. Islam, R. Kumar and S. G. Ghosh, Gravitational lensing by black holes in the $4D$ Einstein-Gauss-Bonnet gravity, *JCAP* **09**, 030 (2020).
51. A. Grenzebach, V. Perlick and C. Lämmerzahl, Photon regions and shadows of Kerr-Newman-NUT black holes with a cosmological constant, *Phys. Rev. D* **89**, 124004 (2014).
52. P. V. P. Cunha, C. A. R. Herdeiro and M. J. Rodriguez, Does the black hole shadow probe the event horizon geometry?, *Phys. Rev. D* **97**, 084020 (2018).
53. P. V. P. Cunha, C. A. R. Herdeiro, E. Radu and H. F. Runarsson, Shadows of Kerr black holes with scalar hair, *Phys. Rev. Lett.* **115**, 211102 (2015).
54. A. F. Zakharov, Types of unbounded orbits in the Kerr metric, *Zh. Eksp. Teor. Fiz.* **91**, 3 (1986).
55. J. C. S. Neves, Upper bound on the GUP parameter using the black hole shadow, *Eur. Phys. J. C* **80**, 343 (2020).
56. C. Bambi, K. Freese, S. Vagnozzi and L. Visinelli, Testing the rotational nature of the supermassive object M87* from the circularity and size of its first image, *Phys. Rev. D* **100**, 044057 (2019).

Displacement memory and BMS symmetries

Shailesh Kumar

Indian Institute of Information Technology Allahabad,
Devghat, Jhalwa, Uttar Pradesh-211015, India.
E-mail: shaileshkumar.1770@gmail.com

This article reviews one of the most intriguing properties of black hole spacetimes known in the literature- *gravitational memory effect*, and its connection with asymptotic symmetries, also termed as Bondi-van der Burg-Metzner-Sachs (BMS) symmetries, emerging near the horizon of black holes. Gravitational memory is a non-oscillatory part of the gravitational wave amplitude which generates a permanent displacement for freely falling test particles or test detectors. We highlight a model scenario where asymptotic symmetries appear as a soldering freedom in the context of stitching of two black hole spacetimes, and examine the impact of the interaction between test detectors and horizon shells. Further, we provide a more realistic approach of computing displacement memory for near-horizon asymptotic symmetries which is analogous to the conventional memory originally obtained at asymptotic null infinity.

Keywords: Memory, Gravitational waves, BMS symmetries (asymptotic symmetries)

1. Introduction

The observational facets of gravitational waves (GWs)[1,2] have opened a new window to look for various aspects of black hole spacetimes; *gravitational memory*[3–8] is one of such intriguing features that has not been detected yet. GW induces a permanent relative change in the position of test detectors by imparting a memory to the configuration. This permanent relative change is referred to as gravitational memory. The term *memory* implies the information or properties of spacetimes from where it is being generated and carried by gravitational waves. The first practical computation of memory's evolution was done by Marc Favata using post-Newtonian formalism where he accounted for all stages of BBH coalescence.[9–12] In this direction, recently, there have been several implications of detecting GW memory using advanced detectors.[13–20]

On the other hand, it has been shown that the gravitational memory is closely related to the asymptotic symmetries of spacetimes originally discovered by Bondi-van der Burg-Metzner-Sachs (BMS) in the early sixties,[21] and such symmetries can also be recovered near the horizon of black holes which motivated us to probe the near horizon properties of black holes. The recent findings in this direction have provided some strong grounds for the information loss puzzle. In the context of asymptotic symmetries, the existence of soft hair on black holes is necessary for charge conservation of supertranslation and superrotation.[7,22–24] As the conservation principles are derived from the long-distance behaviour of fields close to spatial infinity, the presence of black holes should have no effect on them. We know that the conserved charges can be expressed as bulk integrals over any Cauchy surface. A contribution from the future event horizon should be taken into account for conserved charges as future null infinity is no longer a Cauchy surface in the presence of a classical black hole. In this direction, Strominger and Hawking's latest discovery uses the asymptotic symmetries of the BMS group to prove that information is not lost rather stored in something called as a soft particle. Therefore, soft hair or low-energy quantum excitations may be carried by a black hole and leak information when it evaporates. This brings a direct motivation for the emergence of asymptotic symmetries near the horizon of black holes from conservation perspectives.

Let us understand how memory and BMS symmetries are inter-connected with each other. Classically, for a given spacetime geometry, BMS transformations produce an infinite class of spacetime metrics that are physically unique or distinct. Assume that BMS transformations act on a given metric $g_{\mu\nu}(x^\mu)$ with $x^\mu = (x^0, x^i)$, i.e., one time and three spatial coordinates. Such an action on the metric generates a completely different metric.

$$g_{\mu\nu}(x^\mu) \xrightarrow{\text{BMS transformation}} \tilde{g}_{\mu\nu}(x^\mu).$$

The metric $g_{\mu\nu}(x^\mu)$ and $\tilde{g}_{\mu\nu}(x^\mu)$ are distinct and this relative change implies the generation of *GW memory*, and also motivates us to seek for a connection between memory and BMS symmetries. This change can be understood in the following way- GWs generated from a black hole spacetime carrying information or properties in terms of BMS parameters would interact with the detector setup placed at the asymptotic null infinity, this would induce a permanent relative change in the initial configuration of the setup. A similar setup can also be considered at a place near the horizon of a black hole. A persistent effect similar to that of null-infinity may again be observed. It provides a physical meaning to the inter-connection between GW memory and asymptotic symmetries emerging near the horizon of black holes. Technically, $g_{\mu\nu}(x^\mu)$ can be thought of as a metric of a given asymptotically flat spacetime and $\tilde{g}_{\mu\nu}(x^\mu)$ is the resultant metric appears as a consequence of the interaction between GWs and detectors which implies a net relative change in the configuration and gives a definition to the memory. Briefly, if we have two nearby timelike geodesics or inertial detectors described by the tangent vector T^μ together with a deviation vector s^μ, and let us position them at the future null infinity. The evolution of the deviation vector before and after the interaction with gravitational waves will be captured in the geodesic deviation equation (GDE), written as

$$\frac{D^2 s^\mu}{d\tau^2} = -R^\mu{}_{\delta\sigma\lambda} T^\delta T^\lambda s^\sigma. \tag{1}$$

The solution of the GDE will give us a permanent relative change in the displacement vector s^μ which can further be related to supertranslation and will implicate the achievement of *BMS displacement memory effect*. Our study provides an analogous effect and its connection with asymptotic symmetries for near the horizon of black holes.

There are two methods to recover asymptotic symmetries near the horizon of a black hole. As a recent progress, Donnay et al. showed the first way of obtaining such symmetries near the horizon of a stationary black hole[25] with asymptotic form of the Killing vectors preserving the boundary conditions. It turns out that the near-horizon region of a stationary black hole spacetime induces supertranslations including semi-direct sum with extended asymptotic symmetry superrotations which is being represented by Virasoro algebra. Hence, one can recover asymptotic symmetries that would mimic the ones originally obtained at asymptotic null infinity[25,26] by preserving the near-horizon asymptotic structure of black holes. The second method for recovering asymptotic symmetries deals with the soldering of two spacetimes across a common null hypersurface.[27,28] It has been shown that we can stitch them in infinite ways by demanding that the induced metric remains invariant under the translations generated by the null generators of the shell.[27,28] The freedom for the choice of the intrinsic coordinates on null hypersurface in the null-direction is termed as *soldering freedom*, and also known as *BMS-like soldering freedom*. Since these appear as a metric preserving transformations, hence, known as BMS-like symmetries or BMS-like transformations. We shall discuss the related details in section 2.

The article is organized as follows. In section 2, we discuss the intrinsic formulation of null shells placed at the horizon and how near-horizon asymptotic symmetries are recovered in the context of stitching of two black hole spacetimes. Further, in section 3.1, we show how horizon shells carrying memory affect the displacement between two nearby test detectors or test particles for Schwarzschild and Extreme Reissner Nordström (ERN) black holes. We have also studied the impact of interaction between null geodesics and horizon shells; since we shall be completely focusing on timelike geodesics in this article, we do not include the discussion on null geodesics crossing the horizon shells. However, the study can be found in.[31,32] We further consider a more realistic approach in section 3.2 for determining the displacement memory effect and its connection with near-horizon asymptotic symmetries. In the end, we conclude our findings in section 4 by providing some remarks on possible future outlooks to our studies which might be relevant from theoretical as well as observational perspectives.

2. Horizon shell and asymptotic symmetries

In general relativity, a shell is a geometric configuration that can be used to investigate the propagation of thin distribution of null matter (e.g. neutrino) and impulsive gravitational waves (IGWs). The thin surface layer of null matter together with impulsive waves is precisely referred to as *thin-shell* or *thin null shell*.[29,30] The generated impulsive signals are usually produced during violent astrophysical phenomena like supernova explosions or coalescence of black holes. If we stitch two black hole spacetimes along a common null hypersurface which also happens to be the horizon of black holes, and stitching is consistent with *junction conditions*, we

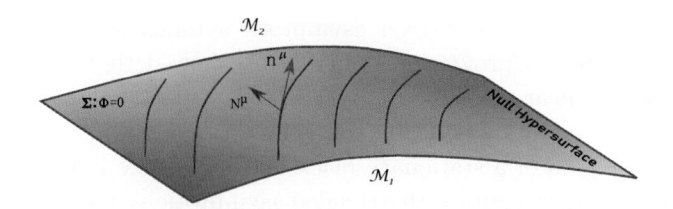

Fig. 1. Null hypersurface Σ separating manifolds $\mathcal{M}_{1,-}$ and $\mathcal{M}_{2,+}$ each with a different metric.

obtain *horizon shell*. The soldering formalism shows that the stess-energy tensor of the stitched spacetime satisfying Einstein field equation carries a singular term proportional to the Dirac delta distribution function, given by

$$T_{\mu\nu} = T_{\mu\nu}^{+}\mathcal{H}(\Phi) + T_{\mu\nu}^{-}\mathcal{H}(-\Phi) + S_{\mu\nu}\delta(\Phi), \qquad (2)$$

where $\mathcal{H}(\Phi)$ is a Heaviside step function for a given null surface $\Sigma \equiv \Phi = 0$. The last term of Eq. (2) corresponds to the stress-energy tensor of the null surface, and further investigation on the same shows the generation of *impulsive gravitational wave* or thin surface layer of null matter or a mixture of both. The null hypersurface, representing the history of impulsive lightlike signals, separates spacetime manifold into two parts $(\mathcal{M}_1, \mathcal{M}_2)$ or $(\mathcal{M}_-, \mathcal{M}_+)$ as depicted in the Fig. 1 each with a different metric. n^μ is a null-normal or a generator of the null hypersurface, and N^μ is a transverse or auxiliary normal which is not tangent to the null surface, satisfying $n \cdot N = -1$. N^μ carries the transversal properties of Σ. One can study the intrinsic quantities of a horizon shell known as surface energy density (μ), surface current (J^A) and surface pressure (p) in terms of *transverse curvature* by analyzing the stress tensor on the null surface. The intrinsic quantities can be written in the following form

$$\mu = -\frac{1}{8\pi}\sigma^{AB}[\mathcal{K}_{AB}] \;\; ; \;\; j^A = \frac{1}{8\pi}\sigma^{AB}[\mathcal{K}_{VB}] \;\; ; \;\; p = -\frac{1}{8\pi}[\mathcal{K}_{VV}], \qquad (3)$$

where '[ ]' denotes the difference between a quantity computed on the null surface Σ for both sides $\mathcal{M}_{1,2}$ separately. We notice that the null shell quantities depend on the induced metric σ^{AB} and jump in the extrinsic curvature $\mathcal{K}_{AB}$[a]. The other related details can be found in.[27,30–32]

An induced tensor field γ_{ab} on Σ is related to the jump of the induced metric g_{ab} and transverse normal N^μ which helps us to examine the intrinsic formulation of the horizon shell. The tensor field γ_{ab} can be written in terms of the jump in the derivative of the induced metric along the auxiliary normal N^μ which can further be written in terms of transverse curvature, i.e., $\gamma_{ab} = N^\mu[\partial_\mu g_{ab}] = 2[\mathcal{K}_{ab}]$. The analysis for intrinsic expression of stress tensor ensures that there is a part of γ_{ab}

---

[a]We have taken Kruskal-like coordinates. Also, Capital Latin letters denote spatial or spherical coordinates of the 2-sphere metric, and lower Latin letters denote hypersurface coordinates.

which does not contribute to stress-energy tensor. We denote this non-contributing part as $\hat{\gamma}_{ab}$. In general, one can write down γ_{ab} containing both null matter ($\bar{\gamma}_{ab}$) and GW degree of freedom ($\hat{\gamma}_{ab}$) in the following way

$$\gamma_{ab} = \hat{\gamma}_{ab} + \bar{\gamma}_{ab}, \qquad (4)$$

with

$$\hat{\gamma}_{ab} = \gamma_{ab} - \frac{1}{2}g_*^{cd}\gamma_{cd}g_{ab} - 2n^d\gamma_{d(a}N_{b)} + \gamma^\dagger N_a N_b \qquad (5)$$

$$\bar{\gamma}_{ab} = 16\pi\left(g_{ac}S^{cd}N_dN_b + g_{bc}S^{cd}N_dN_a - \frac{1}{2}g_{cd}S^{cd}N_aN_b - \frac{2}{2}g_{ab}S^{cd}N_cN_d\right), \qquad (6)$$

where $\gamma^\dagger = \gamma_{cd}n^c n^d$, and g_*^{ab} is the pseudo-inverse of g_{ab}, i.e., $g_*^{ab}g_{bc} = \delta^a_c - n^a N_c$, $g_*^{cd}\gamma_{cd} = g^{AB}\gamma_{AB}$. The $\hat{\gamma}_{ab}$ carries the pure impulsive gravitational wave degree of freedom whereas $\bar{\gamma}_{ab}$ contains the null matter part of the horizon shell. In general, a null shell is being considered the combination of both IGWs and null matter. Further, using the expressions of intrinsic quantities of the null surface together with $\hat{\gamma}_{ab}$ and $\bar{\gamma}_{ab}$, in Kruskal coordinates, one obtains,

$$\bar{\gamma}_{VB} = 16\pi g_{BC}S^{VC} \; ; \; \bar{\gamma}_{AB} = -8\pi S^{VV}g_{AB}. \qquad (7)$$

Now, we shall examine the interaction of such impulsive lightlike signals carrying BMS parameters on timelike geodesics. Let us first investigate the appearance of BMS symmetries in gluing formalism.

2.1. Emergence of asymptotic symmetries

Here, we investigate the emergence of near-horizon asymptotic symmetries in the context of soldering of two black hole spacetimes. This, in gluing formalism, can be achieved via obtaining the freedom in the choice of intrinsic coordinates along the null direction. The soldering freedom of stitching the two spacetimes along a common null surface provides BMS-like transformation on the horizon shell. It emerges as a coordinate transformation which preserves the induced metric on the null hypersurface Σ. This implies us to figuring out the Killing vectors of the hypersurface metric in a suitable coordinate system.[27,28] Therefore, the analysis is based on the Lie derivative of the induced metric along the Killing direction (say $Z^a\partial_a$ with components Z^a). We consider Kruskal coordinates (U, V, x^A) with coordinates (V, x^A) on Σ. Further, we also consider the metric with $g_{aV} = 0$. Therefore, the Killing equation for spatial metric g_{AB} is

$$\mathcal{L}_Z g_{AB} = 0 \implies Z^V\partial_V g_{AB} + Z^C\partial_C g_{AB} + (\partial_A Z^C)g_{CB} + (\partial_B Z^C)g_{AC} = 0. \qquad (8)$$

Now, we may separately examine the emergence of near-horizon BMS symmetries-supertranslation and superrotation.

2.1.1. Supertranslation

The first special case is when metric does not depend on V parameter, i.e., $\partial_V g_{AB} = 0$. This induces a new type of translation which has angle dependent notion, termed as *Supertranslation*. It is similar to the one obtained at asymptotic null infinity for asymptotically flat spacetimes. Keeping in mind the impact of the Z-generated transformations on the null normal n^a of Σ, as a result, Eq. (8) gives

$$\partial_V Z^V = 0 \implies V \longrightarrow V + T(x^A) \quad : \quad BMS \; Supertranslation \qquad (9)$$

This is instantly indentified as a supertranslation in the literature with $T(x^A)$ being a supertranslation parameter, where $x^A = (\theta, \phi)$. It is interpreted as an angle dependent translation, hence named *supertranslation*. The soldering group that keeps this structure preserved is still infinite dimensional. Let us now turn our discussion to investigate the extended form of asymptotic symmetry.

2.1.2. Superrotation

A new type of symmetry labeled as *superrotation* has just been discovered in an extended form of BMS symmetries near the horizon of black holes which mimics the one obtained at asymptotic null infinity.[25,27,28,33,34] It is a local conformal transformation of the spatial slice of the metric, or local conformal transformation of celestial sphere at null infinity.[22,33] Let us determine the extended BMS symmetry by considering the case when the spatial slice of the metric depends on the V parameter, i.e., $\partial_V g_{AB} \neq 0$. The analysis begins with the Eq. (8) in search of possible non-trivial soldering freedoms. If one performs the conformal transformation in spatial coordinates represented in complex coordinates via $z \longrightarrow f(z)$ and $\bar{z} \longrightarrow \bar{f}(\bar{z})$ such that the Eq. (8) can be written in the following way

$$Z^V \partial_V g_{AB} + \Omega(x^A) g_{AB} = 0, \qquad (10)$$

where $x^A = (z, \bar{z})$ and $\Omega(x^A)$ denotes the conformal factor. We have the equation whose feasible solution can be written as, $g_{AB} = r^2(U, V) \tilde{g}_{AB}(x^A)$. It gives a suitable choice along V direction, i.e., $Z^V (= -\frac{V\Omega(x^A)}{2})$ which compensates the conformal transformation. This ensures that the metric remains preserved under such transformations. Thus, the analysis gives rise metric preserving extended BMS transformations known as *superrotation*-like symmetries.

3. Displacement memory and asymptotic symmetries

As a first approach, we wish to examine the relative change in the displacement vector between two nearby timelike geodesics which arises due to interaction with impulsive lightlike signals. We also discuss the appearance of near-horizon asymptotic symmetries in the context of soldering of two ERN and Schwarzschild spacetimes. Second, we would be considering a more realistic approach of computing displacement memory which is analogous to the one obtained at asymptotic null infinity. Let us first start with the case where horizon shell interacts with test detectors.

3.1. *Memory & BMS symmetries due to impulsive lightlike signals*

Cataclysmic processes such as black hole mergers and supernovae explosions produce shockwave type of gravitational radiations. We wish to estimate the finite difference in the displacement vector between two nearby timelike test particles or geodesics upon crossing the horizon shell[b]. It turns out that the asymptotic symmetries, associated with impulsive lightlike signals, leave footprints on test particles upon passing through them. As a result, we studied the effects of horizon shell for Schwarzschild and extreme RN spacetimes on the separation vector of two nearby timelike geodesics. The displacement between the geodesics is identified by supertranslation parameter which gives us *Supertranslation memory effect*. Let us consider a congruence having T^μ to be a tangent vector with $T \cdot T = -1$. A displacement or separation vector between two test particles is X^μ satisfying $T \cdot X = 0$. Thus one can compute the relative change in the separation vector before and the passage of impulsive lightlike signals by analyzing the GDE Eq. (1). Riemann tensor is the memory generating factor for the given configuration. The solution of the GDE will generate a non-vanishing finite change in the deviation vector upon interacting with IGWs. Following the basic framework of the analyses from,[29, 31, 32] we use the expressions written in section 2 and $X^a = \tilde{g}^{ab} X_b$, we obtain components of deviation vectors as

$$X_V = 8\pi U g_{BC} S^{VC} X^B_{(0)} \tag{11}$$

$$X_A = X_{A(0)} + \frac{U}{2} \gamma_{AB} X^B_{(0)} + UV^-_{(0)A}, \tag{12}$$

where $V^-_{(0)a} = \frac{dX^-_a}{dU}\big|_{U=0}$, and $\tilde{g}_{ab} = g_{ab} + (T_{(0)\mu} e^\mu_a)(T_{(0)\nu} e^\nu_b)$ with e_a defined as a triad on the null surface. The $X^B_{(0)}$ is some function evaluated on the null surface, and it is denoted by subscript (0). It is to note that when S^{VC} is nonzero, then we have $X_V \neq 0$. This implies that the particle will be displaced off from the initial two dimensional surface. On the other hand, if $S^{VC} = 0$, the component X_V vanishes which means that the particle will reside on the initial two dimensional surface but with a relative displacement. In this particular consideration, the nonzero displacement vector X_A is written as

$$X_A = (1 - 4\pi U S^{VV})\left(g_{AB} + \frac{U}{2}\hat{\gamma}_{AB}\right) X^B_{(0)}. \tag{13}$$

The factor γ_{AB} is the one which carries the BMS memory part of the wave, and generates the distortion effect on the test particles. This sets our first goal to investigate the memory signal arises in the context of soldering of two black hole spacetimes. Further, we show our studies for extreme RN and Schwarzschild black holes. Let us understand these two cases separately.

---

[b]The study (*B*-memory) of interaction between null congruence and horizon shell can be found in Bhattacharjee et al.[31, 32]

3.1.1. *Extreme RN case (ERN)*

As we know that 70% astrophysical black holes are near extremal and many supermassive black holes are also near extremal.[35–38] Further, Strominger and Vafa[39] determined the Bekenstein-Hawking area-entropy relation for extreme black hole. So extreme black holes are important from experimental as well as theoretical perspectives. Here, we investigate the asymptotic symmetries together with intrinsic properties of the shell and its interaction with test detectors in terms of BMS parameters. It is known that Carter investigated the maximal analytic extension of RN black hole for $e^2 = M^2$.[40] As the Carter's metric is not C^1 i.e. the first derivative of the metric component is discontinuous. Secondly, he certainly did a conceptual analysis without providing the exact Kruskal analogue for the extreme case. For our purpose, it is important to have an exact form of the Kruskal metric which enables us to write $U = 0$ on the horizon. This helps us to perform off-shell extension of the soldering transformation without any obscurities. Therefore, we adopt a Kruskal extension that unambiguously places the shell at $U = 0$, and also better suited for memory effect. The ERN metric in Kruskal coordinates can be written as[41]

$$ds^2 = -\frac{2M}{r^2}\psi(V)'dUdV + r^2(U)(d\theta^2 + \sin^2\theta d\phi^2), \tag{14}$$

where, $\psi(V)'$ is a regular, defined as, $\psi(V) = 4M\left(lnV - \frac{M}{2V}\right)$. Also $U = -(r-M)$ where $r = M$ is the horizon.

Immediately, by looking at the spherical part of the metric, we observe that supertranslation-like symmetries can be recovered, written as: $V \longrightarrow V + T(\theta, \phi)$. We also find that coordinate r is independent of V, thus interestingly, ERN consideration does not induce the superrotation-like symmetries whereas it is not the case with Schwarzschild discussed in section 3.1.2. For explicit details, we refer to Bhattacharjee et al.[32]

Further, we examine some measurable effects on timelike test particles due to interaction with horizon shell of ERN spacetime. In this process, we first extend the soldering transformation off the horizon shell to the linear order in U. The transformations are give by[31]

$$U_+ = UC(V, x^A) \; ; \; V_+ = F(V, x^A) + UA(V, x^A) \; ; \; x_+^A = x^A + UB^A(V, x^A), \tag{15}$$

where $x^A \equiv (\theta, \phi)$, with

$$C = \frac{\partial_V \psi(V)}{\partial_V \psi(F)} \; ; \; A = \frac{M^2}{2}\frac{F_V}{\partial_V \psi(V)}\sigma_{AB}B^A B^B \; ; \; B^A = \partial_V \psi(V)\frac{1}{M^2 F_V}\sigma^{AB}F_B. \tag{16}$$

Here, σ_{AB} denotes the unit 2-sphere metric. One side of the spacetime $\mathcal{M}_-$ is completely ERN and the another side of the spacetime $\mathcal{M}_+$ is off-shell extended with the transformations (15). The process of obtaining the intrinsic quantities is known as *off-shell extension of the soldering transformations*. It is to note here that one can also obtain the intrinsic properties of the horizon shell using *extrinsic curvature algorithm*. Both the results would exactly match. The benefit of the later approach is that it makes the computational algebra significantly simplified. As a result, we find that the surface current (j^A) together with surface energy density (μ) and pressure (p) is nonvanishing, and can be expressed in terms of supertranslation parameter $T(\theta, \phi)$. For example, the surface current is given by

$$j^A = \frac{1}{8M^2\pi} \sigma^{AB} \left(T_B \frac{\psi(T)''}{\psi(T)'} \right). \tag{17}$$

The expressions for μ and p can also be found in.[32] The presence of nonzero surface current induces a finite change in the X_V component of the deviation vector, i.e., $X_V \neq 0$; therefore, test particles get displaced off the initial 2-dimensional surface with a relative change in the displacement vector. The X_θ component is given by

$$X_\theta = X_{\theta(0)} + \frac{U}{2} \left(\gamma_{\theta\theta} X^\theta_{(0)} + \gamma_{\theta\phi} X^\phi_{(0)} \right) + U V^-_{(0)\theta}, \tag{18}$$

where,

$$\gamma_{\theta\theta} = 2\psi(V)' \left(T_{\theta\theta} + \frac{T^2_\theta \psi(T)''}{\psi(T)'} - \frac{M}{\psi(T)'} + \frac{M}{\psi(V)'} \right) \tag{19}$$

$$\gamma_{\theta\phi} = \gamma_{\phi\theta} = 2\psi(V)' \left(\frac{T_\theta T_\phi}{\psi(T)'} \psi(T)'' + T_{\theta\phi} - T_\phi \cot\theta \right). \tag{20}$$

This helps in determining GW degree of freedom γ_{ab}. One can determine X_ϕ component in a similar way. We notice that the deviation is written in terms of supertranslation parameter $T(\theta, \phi)$. The integration with respect to the geodesic parameters would give rise the displacement memory which would mimic the one obtained at null infinity. The Fig. 2 depicts the ultimate result of the test particles getting displaced off from the initial spatial slice with a comparison on Schwarzschild discussed in the section below. This completes our analyses of examining the role of near-horizon asymptotic symmetries on test particles upon interacting with impulsive lightlike signals together with the intrinsic properties of ERN horizon shell.

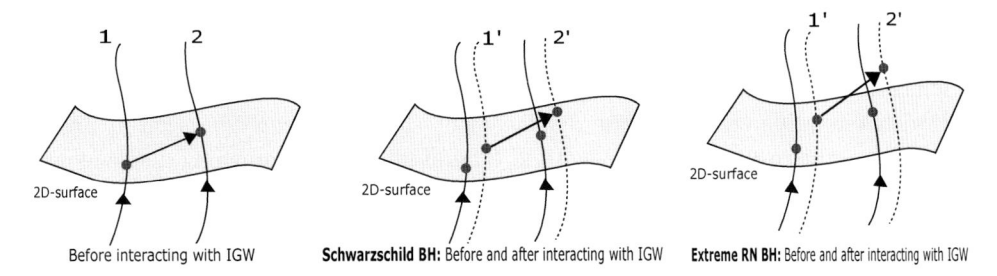

Fig. 2. Timelike geodesics 1 & 2 get displaced upon interacting with IGW, depicted as 1' & 2' with a new relative displacement vector.

3.1.2. *Schwarzschild case*

Now, we start with the Schwarzschild spacetime in order to examine the intrinsic formulation of the horizon shell and study the interaction with test particles.[31] Let us write down the metric in Kruskal coordinates,

$$ds^2 = -2G(r)dUdV + r^2(U,V)(d\theta^2 + \sin^2\theta d\phi^2), \qquad (21)$$

where, $G(r) = \frac{16M^3}{r}$ and $UV = \left(\frac{r}{2M} - 1\right)e^{r/2M}$. The horizon is defined as $U = 0$. One can clearly see the supertranslation-like transformation, written as $V \longrightarrow V + T(\theta,\phi)$. Further, we notice that spherical part of the metric can be written as $\gamma_{\zeta\bar{\zeta}} = r^2 \frac{d\zeta d\bar{\zeta}}{(1+\zeta\bar{\zeta})^2}$, and given the conformal transformations as discussed in (2.1.2), in contrast to ERN spacetime, we obtain superrotations for the null shell placed just outside the horizon $U = \epsilon$ with a compensation along null direction V which makes sure that the soldering transformations also preserve the form of the metric. These transformations mimic the ones originally obtained at asymptotic null infinity. We also compute the intrinsic quantities of the horizon shell which contain supertranslation parameter $T(\theta,\phi)$, can be seen in Bhattacharjee et al.[31]

Next, we show the non-vanishing finite change in the components of the deviation or displacement vector between two nearby timelike geodesics upon passing through the horizon shell. We follow Blau et al.[27] to extend the soldering transformations off the horizon shell in order to compute the induced tensor field γ_{ab}. The computation of the deviation vectors further require the GW degree of freedom which can be expressed as

$$\hat{\gamma}_{\theta\phi} = 2\nabla_\theta^{(2)}\partial_\phi T(\theta,\phi) \; ; \; \hat{\gamma}_{\theta\theta} = 2\Big(\nabla_\theta^{(2)}\partial_\theta T(\theta,\phi) - \frac{1}{\sin^2\theta}\nabla_\phi^{(2)}\partial_\phi T(\theta,\phi)\Big), \qquad (22)$$

where $T(\theta,\phi)$ is a supertranslation parameter. Thus the framework of section 2 and section 3.1 generates the θ-component of the deviation vector,

$$X_\theta = \Big(1 + \frac{U}{8m^2}(\nabla^2 T(\theta,\phi) - T(\theta,\phi))\Big)\Big(\Big(4m^2 + U(\nabla^{(2)}\partial_\theta T(\theta,\phi) \\ - \frac{1}{\sin^2\theta}\nabla_\phi^{(2)}\partial_\phi T(\theta,\phi))\Big)X_{(0)}^\theta + U\nabla_\theta^{(2)}\partial_\phi T(\theta,\phi)X_{(0)}^\phi\Big). \qquad (23)$$

The X_ϕ component can also be computed in the similar way which again carries supertranslation parameter. It turns out that the surface current vanishes, i.e., $J^A = 0$, hence the test particles will remain on the spatial slice of the metric since $X_V = 0$, but with a relative change in the displacement as it can clearly be seen in Fig. 2, and opposes the result of ERN spacetime. Therefore, the nonvanishing displacement vector X_A depicts the BMS displacement memory in the context of soldering of two Schwarzschild spacetime geometries. One can further integrate Eq. (23) with respect to the parameter of the geodesics in order to have the explicit form of the displacement memory. Next, we shall discuss a more realistic approach of estimating the displacement memory which is analogous to the far region analysis.

3.2. *Memory and BMS symmetries: Analogous to far region*

In this section, we adopt a more realistic approach of computing displacement memory near the horizon of black holes and its possible connection with asymptotic symmetries. The analysis of this section is independent of section 2, i.e., it is not based on soldering of black hole spacetimes. We study displacement memory for non-extremal (fixed temperature) and extremal (zero temperature) black holes.[42] This shows an analogous effect of conventional GW-memory which was originally established at asymptotic null infinity (I^+). The emergence of asymptotic symmetries near the horizon of black holes (not in the context of null shell formalism) has been established by.[25,34] In this respect, we are interested in measuring the permanent relative change in the deviation or displacement of the test detectors induced due to the interaction with GW, and its connection with near-horizon BMS symmetries. In this realistic approach, as it can be seen in the schematic diagram below, the detectors are being placed near the horizon of a black hole ($\mathcal{H}^+$), and we estimate a relative change in the deviation vector of configuration before and after the passage of GWs. The displacement vector S^μ between the detector setup or geodesics evolves according to GDE Eq. (1). Let us consider the general form of the 4-dimensional near-horizon metric[26,43]

$$ds^2 = g_{vv}dv^2 + 2\kappa dvd\rho + 2g_{vA}dvdx^A + g_{AB}dx^A dx^B, \qquad (24)$$

with following fall-off conditions for the horizon $\rho = 0$:

$$g_{vv} = -2\kappa\rho + \mathcal{O}(\rho^2) \quad ; \quad k = 1 + \mathcal{O}(\rho^2)$$
$$g_{vA} = \rho\theta_A + \mathcal{O}(\rho^2) \quad ; \quad g_{AB} = \Omega\gamma_{AB} + \rho\lambda_{AB} + \mathcal{O}(\rho^2)$$

where θ_A, Ω and λ^{AB} are functions of (v, x^A). For computational purpose, we consider Ω to be unity. γ_{AB} represents the 2-sphere metric. In stereographic coordinates, $x^A = (\zeta, \bar{\zeta})$, the 2-sphere metric is $\gamma_{AB}dx^A dx^B = \frac{4}{(1+\zeta\bar{\zeta})^2}d\zeta d\bar{\zeta}$. The asymptotic Killing vectors preserving fall-off boundary conditions together with the charges

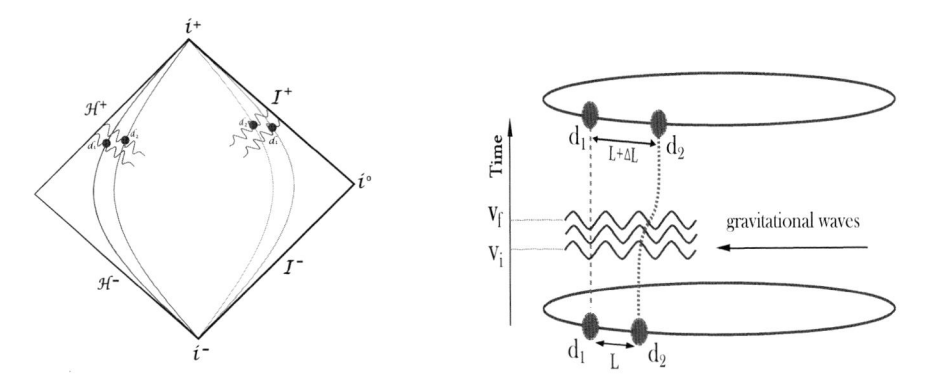

Fig. 3. Schematic diagrams depicting displacement memory effect for the detectors d_1 and d_2. Separation L gets modified permanently before and after the passage of GWs depicted as $L + \Delta L$.

can be found in Donnay et al.[26] It turns out that the variation of κ along Killing direction, when fixed temperature configuration considered, generates a copy of supertranslation together with a superrotation.[25,26] We use this fact in section 3.2.1. Let us consider the fixed temperature configuration first in order to compute displacement memory.

3.2.1. *Memory: Fixed temperature configuration*

The fixed temperature configuration enables us to take κ non-zero but constant. With this consideation, the solution of the GDE for the given metric is[42]

$$\Delta S^{\bar\zeta} = \frac{\rho(1+\zeta\bar\zeta)^2}{4}\left((\Delta\lambda_{\zeta\bar\zeta}S^{\bar\zeta} + \Delta\lambda_{\zeta\zeta}S^\zeta) - \kappa(\Delta v)^2(\mathcal{H}S^{\bar\zeta} + \mathcal{G}S^\zeta)\right) + \mathcal{O}(\rho^2), \quad (25)$$

where $S^{\bar\zeta}$ and S^ζ denote the $\bar\zeta$ and ζ components of the deviation vector. Here, we have also used the vA-component of the Einstein field equation, the $\mathcal{O}(\rho^0)$ term gives $\partial_v\theta_A = 0 \Rightarrow \theta_A = \mathcal{C}(x^A)$. Using vv-component of the Einstein field equation, we replace changes $\Delta\lambda_{AB}$ in Eq. (25) to obtain an explicit form of the memory which also ensures that λ_{AB} can be written in terms of θ_A. The resultant displacement memory is

$$\Delta S^{\bar\zeta} = \frac{\rho(1+\zeta\bar\zeta)^2}{4}\left(\left((\kappa\tilde{G}\Delta v - \frac{2aQ}{(1+\zeta\bar\zeta)^2})S^{\bar\zeta} + \kappa\tilde{B}S^\zeta\right)\Delta v - \kappa(\Delta v)^2(\mathcal{H}S^{\bar\zeta} + \mathcal{G}S^\zeta)\right)$$
$$+ \mathcal{O}(\rho^2), \quad (26)$$

where $\tilde{G}, Q, \tilde{B}, \mathcal{H}$ and $\mathcal{G}$ are functions of $(\zeta, \bar\zeta)$, also $\mathcal{H}$ is written in terms of metric parameter θ_A. Thus the analyses suggest that the displacement memory is restored in terms of metric parameters. This completes our study of achieving the displacement memory near the horizon of non-extremal black holes. Further, we relate it with the asymptotic symmetries.

Relation with BMS symmetry: We show the explicit relation between BMS symmetries and displacement memory. One can obtain the variation of the metric parameters λ_{AB}, θ_A and κ along the Killing direction. Since the the memory (25) or (26) is independent of v coordinate, we only mention the relevant expression of λ_{AB}-variation,[26] given by

$$\mathcal{L}_\chi\lambda_{AB} = f\partial_v\lambda_{AB} - \lambda_{AB}\partial_v f + \mathcal{L}_Y\lambda_{AB} + \theta_A\partial_B f + \theta_B\partial_A f - 2\nabla_A\nabla_B f. \quad (27)$$

On the other hand, the v component of the Killing vector for the fixed temperature configuration generates two sets of supertranslations $T(\phi)$ and $X(\phi)$, i.e.,

$$f(v, x^A) = T(x^A) + e^{-\kappa v}X(x^A). \quad (28)$$

Also, the Lie derivative of g_{vA} along Killing direction yields superrotation $Y^A(x^A)$.[26]

Now, in order to make the variation of λ_{AB} along the killing direction independent of v, we set v coefficients to be zero. Using the general solutions of λ_{AB} from relevant component of Einstein field equations, and for computational simplification switching off the supertranslation parameter T, we obtain $Y^\zeta(\zeta) = \tilde{a} e^{-\int \frac{\tilde{w}}{\tilde{p}} d\zeta}$ as a solution. where, $\tilde{w}$ and $\tilde{p}$ are functions of $(\zeta, \bar{\zeta})$ and $\tilde{a}$ appears as an integration constant; it would be a function of $\bar{\zeta}$ with respect to ζ differential equation. Similarly, one can also find the solution for $Y^{\bar\zeta}(\bar\zeta)$. Therefore, we can find a solution for Y^A that will induce the desired shift in the displacement vector, and serves our purpose of establishing relation between displacement memory and asymptotic symmetries near the horizon of black holes.

3.2.2. *Memory: Zero temperature configuration & BMS symmetries*

We have also provided an explicit approach for zero-temperature configuration (extremal consideration). For this, the metric coefficients remain same as appear in the non-extreme case except the g_{vv} component which becomes $\mathcal{N}(\zeta, \bar\zeta)\rho^2 + \mathcal{O}(\rho^3)$. The displacement memory with this consideration can be achieved by setting $\kappa = 0$ in Eq. (25), and written as

$$\Delta S_E^{\bar\zeta} = \frac{\rho}{4}(1 + \zeta\bar\zeta)^2 (\Delta \lambda_{\zeta\bar\zeta} S_E^{\bar\zeta} + \Delta \lambda_{\zeta\zeta} S_E^\zeta) + \mathcal{O}(\rho^2), \tag{29}$$

where subscript E stands for the change in the displacement vector for *extremal* or *zero temperature* configuration. One can again take the variation of λ_{AB} along Killing direction and obtain set of differential equations similar to the fixed-temperature analyses. The related details can be found in Bhattacharjee et al.[42]

3.2.3. *Memory & BMS symmetries: for a less generic form of the metric*

In this section, we consider a less generic form of the full metric (24) by setting $g_{vA} = 0$ which can be regarded as an asymptotic form of a metric near the horizon of a spherically symmetric black hole deformed in the spatial sector. The displacement memory for this setup can be computed in similar way as obtained for the full metric.

We find that the fixed temperature configuration does not produce very interesting result. However, the displacement memory is written in terms of $\Delta \lambda_{AB}$, and further set of conditions can be obtained in order to have the connection with BMS symmetries. The interesting finding appears if we consider zero temperature configuration. The change in the displacement vector is written in terms of $\Delta \lambda_{AB}$. Using the vv-component of Einstein field equation, the displacement memory is given by

$$\Delta S_E^{\bar\zeta} = \frac{\rho}{4}(1 + \zeta\bar\zeta)^2 H(\zeta, \bar\zeta) \Delta v S_E^{\bar\zeta} + \mathcal{O}(\rho^2). \tag{30}$$

We notice that the displacement memory is proportional to ρ whereas in the far region case[22] the memory is proportional to $\frac{1}{r}$. This implies that the displacement memory near the horizon of black holes is mimicking the one obtained null infinity.

One can further relate it with the BMS symmetries. It turns out that if we freeze off the superrotation, we have an exact solution: $X(\zeta, \bar{\zeta}) = X_1(\zeta) + X_2(\bar{\zeta})$. Hence, there is a supertranslation $X(\zeta, \bar{\zeta})$ that can induce the same shift in the displacement memory. We have also considered the three dimensional analyses for extreme and non-extreme cases, and its connection with near-horizon BMS symmetries in Bhattacharjee et al.[42]

4. Discussion and outlook

The primary motivation of this article is to provide a review study on the displacement memory effect near the horizon of black holes and its connection with asymptotic symmetries which is similar to the one established at null infinity for asymptotically flat spacetimes. In this respect, we started with a brief introduction of the intrinsic formulation of null shell. As a result, we show that the supertranslation-like transformations can be achieved in the context of soldering of two black hole spacetimes. We explicitly provided the results for Schwarzschild and ERN cases. However, interestingly, superrotation can not be recovered for ERN spacetime whereas it can be recovered for Schwarzschild. Further, as a result of interaction between horizon shell and test particles, we find that the particles remain on the initial 2-dimensional surface for Schwarzschild consideration as surface current is zero whereas for ERN spacetime, particles get displaced off from the initial 2-dimensional surface. We compute the components of deviation vectors which carry the supertranslation parameter ensuring that the memory can be obtained in terms of BMS parameters.

We have provided a detailed description of GW memory effect near the horizon of black holes as a more realistic approach which is analogous to the one obtained at null infinity. As a major distinguishing feature in order to establish a connection with asymptotic symmetries, we observed that there are two supertranslation parameters $T(x^A)$ and $X(x^A)$ and one superrotation $Y^A(x^A)$ in near horizon analyses whereas there is only one supertranslation in the far region case. We also notice that $\Delta \lambda_{AB}$ is the data available to be considered in the detection which mimics the data C_{zz} present near the null infinity.[22] The form of the GDE is also quite different with respect to the far region case. These are the brief and major distinguishing features between displacement memory obtained near the horizon of black holes and at asymptotic null infinity, together with its possible connection to BMS symmetries.

The observational features of GW will be extremely useful in investigating the signatures of the asymptotic symmetries in displacement memory effect. As a result, we might be able to look into such symmetries in greater detail as a firm evidence in near future. The theoretical aspects of our study might help as a model framework in the detection prospects of the near-horizon BMS memory effect. It is expected that present-day detectors like LIGO might not be able to play a crucial role in the detection prospects. We hope that advanced detectors like aLIGO or LISA might be able to capture this effect as LISA is looking for a much longer wavelength opening up the detection realm to a wider range of gravitational wave sources. In this direction, building up the theoretical framework of post-Newtonian (PN) formalism having relevance for asymptotic symmetries, it is interesting to investigate the contribution of supertranslation-like symmetries in non-oscillatory signals of the gravitational wave polarizations. This would surely provide a more direct approach to gravitational wave data analysts in order to search for asymptotic symmetries in GW memory signal.

The alternative approach of detecting astrophysical signatures of asymptotic symmetries from gravitational lensing might not be an appropriate direction as supertranslated geometry of the spacetime will not lead to any deviations from standard results in general relativity for static configurations.[44] The underlying reason to the problem is that given a supertranslated Schwarzschild black hole, one can always choose a coordinate patch in a finite solid angular range where the metric will be given by the Schwarzschild. Hence, the signatures of asymptotic symmetries seem to be difficult from gravitational lensing. However, we still have a hope to detect such symmetries in black hole shadows and lensing if we have a dynamically evolving spacetime, and in this consideration, it is not sure whether one can again have some coordinate transformations which would give rise to indistinguishable features. So this might set a stronger grounds for detecting the asymptotic symmetries through deflection angle approach and black hole shadows. Interestingly, it is not difficult to understand that why gravitational memory is suitable for detecting such symmetries, because it appears as a physical effect where initial and final vacua differ by a BMS supertranslation. On another hand, the post-Newtonian tidal environment analysis especially in terms of BMS symmetries can also be explored from BMS-detection prospects.

Furthermore, as we have been investigating the issues from classical perspectives, the quantum memory effect has also got considerable attention in very recent, and it is yet to be explored extensively. This would certainly give a new meaning to the quantum treatment of the memory to catch on to the hawking information paradox. We know that the displacement memory is induced by the radiative energy flux, and it has been shown that there exists a new kind of gravitational memory- *spin memory effect* which is sourced by angular momentum flux.[45] It is interesting to examine the signatures of asymptotic symmetries in the context of spin memory effect near the horizon of black holes from BMS-detection point of view. Further, the algebra of asymptotic symmetries on null surface situated at a finite location of the manifold might determine some fascinating role of symmetries on GW memory.

Acknowledgement

I would like to express my sincere thanks to Srijit Bhattachrajee for proofreading this article and sharing his stimulating ideas during the preparation of the draft. I would also like to thank Arpan Bhattacharyya for illuminating discussions.

References

1. B. P. Abbott, R. Abbott and E. A. Abbott, Observation of gravitational waves from a binary black hole merger, *Phys. Rev. Lett.* **116**, p. 061102 (Feb 2016).
2. R. Abbott, T. D. Abbott and E. A. Abraham, Gw190521: A binary black hole merger with a total mass of 150 $M_\odot$, *Phys. Rev. Lett.* **125**, p. 101102 (Sep 2020).
3. Y. B. Zel'dovich and A. G. Polnarev, Radiation of gravitational waves by a cluster of superdense stars, *Sov. Astron.* **18**, p. 17 (1974).
4. V. B. Braginsky and L. P. Grishchuk, Kinematic Resonance and Memory Effect in Free Mass Gravitational Antennas, *Sov. Phys. JETP* **62**, 427 (1985).
5. D. Christodoulou, Nonlinear nature of gravitation and gravitational wave experiments, *Phys. Rev. Lett.* **67**, 1486 (1991).
6. L. Bieri and D. Garfinkle, Perturbative and gauge invariant treatment of gravitational wave memory, *Phys. Rev. D* **89**, p. 084039 (Apr 2014).
7. A. Strominger and A. Zhiboedov, Gravitational Memory, BMS Supertranslations and Soft Theorems, *JHEP* **01**, p. 086 (2016).
8. A. A. Rahman and R. M. Wald, Black hole memory, *Phys. Rev. D* **101**, p. 124010 (Jun 2020).
9. M. Favata, The Gravitational-wave memory from eccentric binaries, *Phys. Rev. D* **84**, p. 124013 (2011).
10. M. Favata, Post-newtonian corrections to the gravitational-wave memory for quasicircular, inspiralling compact binaries, *Phys. Rev. D* **80**, p. 024002 (Jul 2009).
11. M. Favata, Nonlinear gravitational-wave memory from binary black hole mergers, *The Astrophysical Journal* **696**, L159 (Apr 2009).
12. M. Favata, Gravitational-wave memory revisited: Memory from the merger and recoil of binary black holes, *Journal of Physics: Conference Series* **154**, p. 012043 (Mar 2009).
13. K. Islo, J. Simon, S. Burke-Spolaor and X. Siemens, Prospects for Memory Detection with Low-Frequency Gravitational Wave Detectors (6 2019).
14. P. D. Lasky, E. Thrane, Y. Levin, J. Blackman and Y. Chen, Detecting gravitational-wave memory with LIGO: implications of GW150914, *Phys. Rev. Lett.* **117**, p. 061102 (2016).
15. O. M. Boersma, D. A. Nichols and P. Schmidt, Forecasts for detecting the gravitational-wave memory effect with Advanced LIGO and Virgo, *Phys. Rev. D* **101**, p. 083026 (2020).
16. D. Pollney and C. Reisswig, Gravitational memory in binary black hole mergers, *The Astrophysical Journal* **732**, p. L13 (Apr 2011).
17. A. M. Grant and D. A. Nichols, Persistent gravitational wave observables: Curve deviation in asymptotically flat spacetimes (9 2021).
18. M. Hübner, C. Talbot, P. D. Lasky and E. Thrane, Measuring gravitational-wave memory in the first ligo/virgo gravitational-wave transient catalog, *Phys. Rev. D* **101**, p. 023011 (Jan 2020).
19. T. Islam, S. E. Field, G. Khanna and N. Warburton, Survey of gravitational wave memory in intermediate mass ratio binaries (9 2021).
20. M. Hübner, P. Lasky and E. Thrane, Memory remains undetected: Updates from the second LIGO/Virgo gravitational-wave transient catalog, *Phys. Rev. D* **104**, p. 023004 (2021).
21. H. Bondi, M. G. J. Van der Burg and A. W. K. Metzner, Gravitational waves in general relativity, vii. waves from axi-symmetric isolated system, *Proceedings of the Royal Society of London. Series A. Mathematical and Physical Sciences* **269**, 21 (1962).
22. A. Strominger, Lectures on the infrared structure of gravity and gauge theory (2018).

23. S. W. Hawking, M. J. Perry and A. Strominger, Soft hair on black holes, *Phys. Rev. Lett.* **116**, p. 231301 (Jun 2016).
24. P.-M. Zhang, C. Duval, G. W. Gibbons and P. A. Horvathy, Soft gravitons and the memory effect for plane gravitational waves, *Phys. Rev. D* **96**, p. 064013 (Sep 2017).
25. L. Donnay, G. Giribet, H. A. González and M. Pino, Supertranslations and superrotations at the black hole horizon, *Phys. Rev. Lett.* **116**, p. 091101 (Mar 2016).
26. L. Donnay, G. Giribet, H. A. González and M. Pino, Extended symmetries at the black hole horizon, *Journal of High Energy Physics* **2016**, p. 100 (Sep 2016).
27. M. Blau and M. O'Loughlin, Horizon Shells and BMS-like Soldering Transformations, *JHEP* **03**, p. 029 (2016).
28. S. Bhattacharjee and A. Bhattacharyya, Soldering freedom and bondi-metzner-sachs-like transformations, *Phys. Rev. D* **98**, p. 104009 (Nov 2018).
29. C. Barrabès and W. Israel, Thin shells in general relativity and cosmology: The lightlike limit, *Phys. Rev. D* **43**, 1129 (Feb 1991).
30. C. Barrabes and P. A. Hogan, *Singular Null Hypersurfaces in General Relativity: Light-Like Signals from Violent Astrophysical* (World Scientific Publishing Co. Pte. Ltd., 2003).
31. S. Bhattacharjee, S. Kumar and A. Bhattacharyya, Memory effect and bms-like symmetries for impulsive gravitational waves, *Phys. Rev. D* **100**, p. 084010 (Oct 2019).
32. S. Bhattacharjee and S. Kumar, Memory effect and bms symmetries for extreme black holes, *Phys. Rev. D* **102**, p. 044041 (Aug 2020).
33. G. Barnich and C. Troessaert, Symmetries of asymptotically flat four-dimensional spacetimes at null infinity revisited, *Phys. Rev. Lett.* **105**, p. 111103 (Sep 2010).
34. G. Barnich and C. Troessaert, Supertranslations call for superrotations (2012).
35. M. Volonteri, P. Madau, E. Quataert and M. J. Rees, The distribution and cosmic evolution of massive black hole spins, *The Astrophysical Journal* **620**, 69 (Feb 2005).
36. L. Gou, J. E. McClintock, R. A. Remillard, J. F. Steiner, M. J. Reid, J. A. Orosz, R. Narayan, M. Hanke and J. García, Confirmation via the continuum-fitting method that the spin of the black hole in Cygnus x-1 is extreme, *The Astrophysical Journal* **790**, p. 29 (Jun 2014).
37. J. E. McClintock, R. Shafee, R. Narayan, R. A. Remillard, S. W. Davis and L.-X. Li, The spin of the near-extreme kerr black hole GRS 1915+105, *The Astrophysical Journal* **652**, 518 (Nov 2006).
38. L. W. Brenneman and C. S. Reynolds, Constraining black hole spin via x-ray spectroscopy, *The Astrophysical Journal* **652**, 1028 (Dec 2006).
39. A. Strominger and C. Vafa, Microscopic origin of the bekenstein-hawking entropy, *Physics Letters B* **379**, 99 (Jun 1996).
40. B. Carter, The complete analytic extension of the reissner-nordström metric in the special case e2 = m2, *Physics Letters* **21**, 423 (1966).
41. S. Liberati, T. Rothman and S. Sonego, Nonthermal nature of incipient extremal black holes, *Phys. Rev. D* **62**, p. 024005 (Jun 2000).
42. S. Bhattacharjee, S. Kumar and A. Bhattacharyya, Displacement memory effect near the horizon of black holes, *Journal of High Energy Physics* **2021**, p. 134 (Mar 2021).
43. L. Donnay, G. Giribet, H. A. González and A. Puhm, Black hole memory effect, *Phys. Rev. D* **98**, p. 124016 (Dec 2018).
44. G. Compère and J. Long, Classical static final state of collapse with supertranslation memory, *Classical and Quantum Gravity* **33**, p. 195001 (Sep 2016).
45. S. Pasterski, A. Strominger and A. Zhiboedov, New gravitational memories, *Journal of High Energy Physics* **2016**, p. 53 (Dec 2016).

Physical black holes in semiclassical gravity

Sebastian Murk

Department of Physics and Astronomy, Macquarie University,
Sydney, New South Wales 2109, Australia
and
Sydney Quantum Academy,
Sydney, New South Wales 2006, Australia
E-mail: sebastian.murk@mq.edu.au

Daniel R. Terno

Department of Physics and Astronomy, Macquarie University,
Sydney, New South Wales 2109, Australia
E-mail: daniel.terno@mq.edu.au

We derive and critically examine the consequences that follow from the formation of a regular black or white hole horizon in finite time of a distant observer. In spherical symmetry, only two distinct classes of solutions to the semiclassical Einstein equations are self-consistent. Both are required to describe the formation of physical black holes and violate the null energy condition in the vicinity of the outer apparent horizon. The near-horizon geometry differs considerably from that of classical solutions. If semiclassical physics is valid, accretion into a black hole is no longer possible after the horizon has formed. In addition, the two principal generalizations of surface gravity to dynamical spacetimes are irreconcilable, and neither can describe the emission of nearly-thermal radiation. Comparison of the required energy and timescales with established semiclassical results suggests that if the observed astrophysical black holes indeed have horizons, their formation is associated with new physics.

Keywords: Black holes; white holes; general relativity; semiclassical gravity; quantum aspects of black holes; energy conditions; surface gravity.

1. Introduction

Our current understanding of ultra-compact objects (UCOs) can be summarized as follows: the existence of astrophysical black holes (ABHs) — dark massive compact objects — is established beyond any reasonable doubt. However, it is unclear when, how, or if at all these UCOs develop the standard black hole attributes, such as horizons and singularities. A large number of models, often with deliberately designed features (or lack thereof), purport to describe ABHs. Translating the differences between these models into potentially observable differences between the signals received from the black hole candidates they describe is one of the most exciting topics in gravitational physics research.[1,2]

There is no unanimously agreed upon definition of a black hole.[3] The salient feature of a mathematical black hole (MBH)[4] is the event horizon that separates our outside world from an inaccessible interior. However, event horizons are global teleological entities that are — even in principle — unobservable,[5,6] and observational, numerical, and theoretical studies focus on other characteristics of black holes. A trapped region is a spacetime domain where both ingoing and outgoing future-directed null geodesics emanating from a spacelike two-dimensional surface with spherical topology have negative expansion.[7–9] Its evolving outer boundary is the apparent horizon. This definition captures the most fundamental feature of black holes as spacetime regions that nothing, not even light, can escape. It is also local, and thus physically observable: the escape is not possible now, but the notion of "now" depends on the observer. Following the characterization scheme of Ref. 4, we refer to a trapped spacetime region that is bounded by an apparent horizon as a physical black hole (PBH).[10]

Although it cannot be observed, the event horizon is a useful asymptotic concept, and in many situations it is reasonable to assume that MBHs provide a good description of certain aspects of ABHs. Indeed, the predictions of various alternatives to black holes are most often compared with the standard Schwarzschild/Kerr paradigm.[1,2] However, using this asymptotic concept at finite times is logically unsatisfactory, and in the situations we consider below cannot be sustained.

Another question is whether the asymptotic picture is adequate to describe the relevant geometric and physical properties of black holes. We first formalize the minimal assumptions that underpin the widely used black hole notions presented in Fig. 1, namely regularity of the apparent horizon and its finite-time formation according to the clock of a distant observer. In spherical symmetry, these two assumptions uniquely determine the formation scenario for PBHs and suffice to provide an exhaustive description of their near-horizon geometry. Its properties are the subject of this contribution. We now outline the motivation and justification for these requirements.[10]

In classical general relativity (GR) non-spacelike singularities destroy predictability. According to the weak cosmic censorship conjecture,[16,17] spacetime singularities are concealed by event horizons. Quantum gravitational effects are expected to become important when the spacetime curvature is sufficiently strong,[8,18] i.e. when the Kretschmann scalar $\mathcal{K} := R_{\mu\nu\rho\sigma}R^{\mu\nu\rho\sigma}$ reaches the Planck scale, that is $\mathcal{K} \gtrsim l_{\mathrm{P}}^{-4}$. The near-horizon geometry is believed to be well-described by semiclassical physics. Nontrivial quantum effects are obtained within the framework of quantum field theory in curved spacetime.[18] One of its most spectacular predictions is Hawking radiation: it not only completed black hole thermodynamics,[8,19] but has given rise to the infamous information loss paradox.[12] Regular (singularity-free) black holes were introduced to altogether eliminate singularities in classical gravitational collapse or as a way to resolve the problem of information loss.[4,20,21] Leaving aside the interior structure of black holes, we formulate the regularity criterion as the absence of curvature singularities at the apparent horizon. A precise mathematical formulation[10] is provided in Sec. 2.

To be considered a genuine physical object rather than merely a useful mathematical tool, the horizon must form in finite time of a distant observer, and there

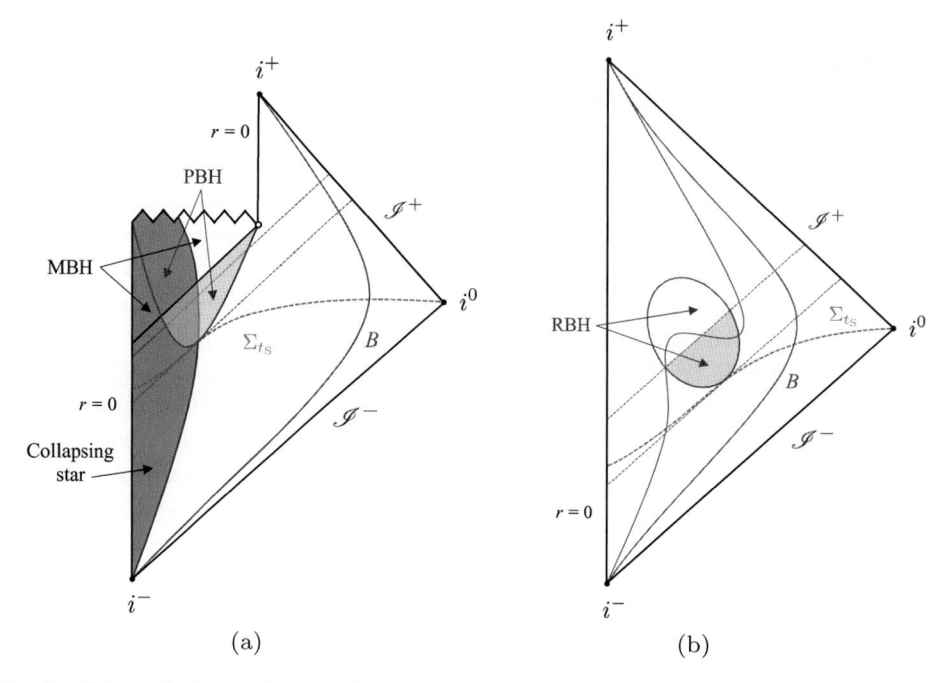

Fig. 1. Schematic Carter–Penrose diagram of the conventional formation and evaporation of (a) a black hole, and (b) a RBH. The outer apparent horizon $r_g(t)$ and the inner apparent horizon $r_{\text{in}}(t)$ form the boundary of a PBH and are shown in blue and red, respectively. The equal time surface Σ_{t_S} is drawn as a dashed orange line. It is null at $(t_S, r_g(t_S))$ and spacelike everywhere else.[11] The trajectory of a distant observer Bob is indicated in green and labeled "B". Dashed grey lines correspond to outgoing radial null geodesics. (a) Diagrams of this type are elaborations of the original sketch by Hawking, see Fig. 5 of Ref. 12. Spacetime regions corresponding to PBH (MBH) solutions are indicated by blue (black) arrows. Light signals emitted from the quantum ergosphere[13] (indicated by the light blue shading), i.e. from within the trapped region, but outside of the event horizon, reach $\mathscr{I}^+$ and are detected by Bob in his finite proper time. The collapsing matter and its surface are shown as in conventional depictions of the collapse. However, the matter in the vicinity of the outer apparent horizon $(t, r_g(t))$ violates the NEC for $t \geqslant t_S$. Moreover, the energy density, pressure, and flux as seen by an infalling observer Alice vary continuously across it, and the equation of state dramatically differs from that of normal matter that may have been used to model the initial EMT of the collapse. (b) The asymptotic structure of a simple RBH spacetime[14] coincides with that of Minkowski spacetime. Conditions for the smooth joining of the inner and outer apparent horizon are described in Ref. 15. An unmarked green line represents a hypersurface $r = $ const that passes through the RBH.

should be some potentially (at least in principle) observable consequences of its formation. Moreover, if black holes do indeed emit Hawking radiation, and their evolution roughly resembles that of Fig. 1(a), then the apparent horizon forms in finite time t_S of a distant observer. We note that, as illustrated in Fig. 1(a), the outer apparent horizon is located outside of the event horizon.[8,12] Hence all signals that are emitted from the so-called quantum ergosphere[13,15] — part of the trapped region that lies outside of the event horizon — reach future null infinity $\mathscr{I}^+$. In addition, models of transient (even if long-lived) regular black holes (RBHs) imply the finite-time formation and disappearance of the trapped region, as depicted in Fig. 1(b). This leads to our second requirement: the finite-time formation of an apparent horizon according to a distant observer.

Working in the framework of semiclassical gravity, we use classical notions (horizons, trajectories, etc.) and describe dynamics via the Einstein equations $G_{\mu\nu} = 8\pi T_{\mu\nu}$. We do not assume any specific matter content nor a specific quantum state ω that produces the expectation values of the energy-momentum tensor (EMT) $T_{\mu\nu} := \langle \hat{T}_{\mu\nu} \rangle_\omega$. Note that this EMT describes the total matter content — both the original collapsing matter and the produced excitations. We do not assume the presence of Hawking-like radiation, an event horizon, or a singularity. To simplify the exposition we work in asymptotically flat spacetimes, even if it is not essential for the resulting near-horizon geometries.

2. Spherically symmetric solutions

It is convenient to use Schwarzschild coordinates to impose the two assumptions described above. Their coordinate singularities allow us to identify the admissible solutions. A general spherically symmetric metric in four spacetime dimensions is given by

$$ds^2 = -e^{2h(t,r)} f(t,r) dt^2 + f(t,r)^{-1} dr^2 + r^2 d\Omega_2. \tag{1}$$

These coordinates provide geometrically preferred foliations with respect to Kodama time, a natural divergence-free preferred vector field.[9,22] In asymptotically flat spacetimes the time t represents the proper time of a distant static observer. Using the advanced null coordinate v, the metric is written as

$$ds^2 = -e^{2h_+} \left(1 - \frac{C_+}{r}\right) dv^2 + 2e^{h_+} dv dr + r^2 d\Omega_2. \tag{2}$$

The Misner–Sharp (MS) mass $C(t,r)/2$[9,23] is invariantly defined via

$$f(t,r) := 1 - C/r := \partial_\mu r \partial^\mu r, \tag{3}$$

and thus $C(t,r) \equiv C_+\bigl(v(t,r), r\bigr)$. The functions $h(t,r)$ and $h_+(v,r)$ play the role of integrating factors in coordinate transformations, such as

$$dt = e^{-h}(e^{h_+} dv - f^{-1} dr). \tag{4}$$

The apparent horizon is located at the Schwarzschild radius $r_g(t) \equiv r_+(v)$ that is the largest root of $f(t,r) = 0$.[9,24] In (v,r) coordinates the tangents to ingoing and outgoing radial geodesics are given by

$$l^\mu_{\text{in}} = (0, -e^{-h_+}, 0, 0), \qquad l^\mu_{\text{out}} = (1, \tfrac{1}{2} e^{h_+} f, 0, 0), \tag{5}$$

respectively. They are normalized to satisfy $l_{\text{in}} \cdot l_{\text{out}} = -1$, and their corresponding expansions are

$$\vartheta_{\text{in}} = -\frac{2e^{-h_+}}{r}, \qquad \vartheta_{\text{out}} = \frac{e^{h_+} f}{r}, \tag{6}$$

thus identifying the domain $r \leqslant r_+ \equiv r_g$ as a PBH.

Using the retarded null coordinate u, the metric is written as

$$ds^2 = -e^{2h_-}\left(1 - \frac{C_-}{r}\right)du^2 - 2e^{h_-}dudr + r^2 d\Omega_2. \tag{7}$$

In (u, r) coordinates the tangents to ingoing and outgoing radial geodesics are given by

$$l^\mu_{\text{in}} = (1, -\tfrac{1}{2}f(u,r)e^{h_-(u,r)}, 0, 0), \qquad l^\mu_{\text{out}} = (0, e^{-h_-(u,r)}, 0, 0), \tag{8}$$

respectively. Again, the tangents are normalized by $l_{\text{in}} \cdot l_{\text{out}} = -1$, and their respective expansions are given by

$$\vartheta_{\text{in}} = -\frac{e^{h_-}f}{r}, \qquad \vartheta_{\text{out}} = \frac{2e^{-h_-}}{r}. \tag{9}$$

As a result, the domain $r \leqslant r_- \equiv r_g$ is a white hole and the Schwarzschild radius is the location of the anti-trapping horizon. As in the case of the maximally extended Schwarzschild solution, these two scenarios describe different physical settings.

The Schwarzschild coordinates become singular as $r \to r_g$. We extract information about the EMT and therefore about the near-horizon geometry by studying how various divergences cancel to produce finite curvature scalars. Singular points are identified through the presence of incomplete geodesics in their vicinity and are excluded from manifolds representing the spacetime. These geodesics are inextendible in at least one direction, but the range of their generalized affine parameter (proper time for timelike geodesics) is bounded.[7,17,25,26] We focus on curvature singularities and formalize the regularity requirement as the demand that curvature scalars built from polynomials of Riemann tensor components are finite. This condition corresponds to the absence of essential scalar curvature singularities. More stringent conditions that involve higher covariant derivatives or regularity of individual components are not imposed.

In a general four-dimensional spacetime, there are 14 algebraically independent scalar invariants that can be constructed from the Riemann tensor.[27] We use two quantities that are expressed straightforwardly from components of the EMT, namely

$$\tilde{\mathrm{T}} := T^\mu{}_\mu, \qquad \tilde{\mathfrak{T}} := T_{\mu\nu}T^{\mu\nu}. \tag{10}$$

The Einstein equations relate them to the curvature scalars as $\tilde{\mathrm{T}} \equiv -\mathcal{R}/8\pi$ and $\tilde{\mathfrak{T}} \equiv R^{\mu\nu}R_{\mu\nu}/64\pi^2$, where $R_{\mu\nu}$ and $\mathcal{R}$ are the Ricci tensor and Ricci scalar, respectively. In spherical symmetry, if the two scalars of Eq. (10) are finite, then the rest are finite as well.[28]

It is convenient to introduce

$$\tau_t := e^{-2h}T_{tt}, \qquad \tau_t{}^r := e^{-h}T_t{}^r, \qquad \tau^r := T^{rr}. \tag{11}$$

The three Einstein equations for G_{tt}, $G_t{}^r$, and G^{rr} can then be written as

$$\partial_r C = 8\pi r^2 \tau_t/f, \tag{12}$$
$$\partial_t C = 8\pi r^2 e^h \tau_t{}^r, \tag{13}$$
$$\partial_r h = 4\pi r \left(\tau_t + \tau^r\right)/f^2. \tag{14}$$

Since $T^\theta{}_\theta \equiv T^\varphi{}_\varphi$ in spherical symmetry, the two scalars have the form

$$\tilde{T} = T + 2T^\theta{}_\theta, \qquad \tilde{\mathfrak{T}} = \mathfrak{T} + 2\left(T^\theta{}_\theta\right)^2, \tag{15}$$

where

$$T := (\tau^r - \tau_t)/f, \qquad \mathfrak{T} := \left((\tau^r)^2 + (\tau_t)^2 - 2(\tau_t{}^r)^2\right)/f^2. \tag{16}$$

The curvature scalars are finite even if the individual terms are divergent in one of the two possible cases. The three effective EMT components τ_a, $a \in \{t, t{}^r, {}^r\}$, may result in finite T and $\mathfrak{T}$, with $T^\theta{}_\theta$ [$G^\theta{}_\theta/8\pi$ with the metric functions that solve Eqs. (12)–(14)] being finite as well, or all four non-zero components $T^\mu{}_\nu$ may diverge, but these divergences cancel to produce the finite scalars of Eq. (15). We first describe the former possibility and then explain why the latter possibility is not realized.

A priori, to ensure that T and $\mathfrak{T}$ remain finite as $r \to r_g$, the effective EMT components τ_a must either diverge according to the same power law f^k, $k < 0$, converge to finite limits ($k = 0$), slowly converge to zero ($0 < k < 1$), or converge to zero with a variety of possible exponents k_a, $k_a \geqslant 1$. It was shown that only two classes of dynamic solutions (with the leading terms in the functions τ_a scaling as f^k, $k = 0, 1$) satisfy the regularity conditions.[29,30] The component $T^\theta{}_\theta$ is either finite due to the Einstein equations (or, possibly, due to some additional constraints on the functions C and h), resulting in admissible solutions, or divergent, indicating the inadmissibility of the solution as $T^\theta{}_\theta$ cannot have the same leading divergence as τ_a/f.[29] Moreover, a slow divergence (or a faster convergence of either τ_t or τ^r) is incompatible with Eqs. (13) and (14). Hence finite values of the two functions of Eq. (16) are a necessary condition to ensure that the curvature scalars are finite. We now briefly summarize the properties of the admissible solutions.

2.1. Generic solution (k = 0)

In principle, the solutions with $k = 0$ allow for $\tau_t \to \tau^r \to \mp \Upsilon^2$, $\tau_t{}^r \to \mp \Upsilon^2$ for some $\Upsilon(t) > 0$, but only

$$\tau_t \approx \tau^r = -\Upsilon^2 + \mathcal{O}(\sqrt{x}), \tag{17}$$
$$\tau_t{}^r = \mp \Upsilon^2 + \mathcal{O}(\sqrt{x}), \tag{18}$$

where $x := r - r_g$ denotes the coordinate distance from the horizon, describe valid solutions: taking $\tau_t \to \tau^r \to +\Upsilon^2$ results in complex-valued solutions of Eqs. (12)–(14) (see Ref. 31 for details).

The negative sign in the leading term of τ_t and τ^r leads to the violation of the null energy condition (NEC)[7,32,33] in the vicinity of the apparent horizon, i.e. a future-directed outward (inward) pointing radial null vector ℓ^μ does not satisfy $T_{\mu\nu}\ell^\mu\ell^\nu \geqslant 0$ for the contracting (expanding) Schwarzschild radius r_g.[31] An immediate consequence of this result is that accreting Vaidya black hole solutions in (v, r) coordinates cannot describe PBHs as they satisfy the NEC.[31]

The metric functions that solve Eqs. (12) and (14) are

$$C = r_g - 4\sqrt{\pi} r_g^{3/2} \Upsilon \sqrt{x} + \mathcal{O}(x), \tag{19}$$

$$h = -\frac{1}{2} \ln \frac{x}{\xi} + \mathcal{O}(\sqrt{x}), \tag{20}$$

where $\xi(t)$ is determined by the choice of time variable and the higher-order terms depend on the higher-order terms in the EMT expansion.[34] Eq. (13) must then hold identically. Both sides contain terms that diverge as $1/\sqrt{x}$, and their identification results in the consistency condition

$$r'_g/\sqrt{\xi} = 4\varepsilon_\pm \sqrt{\pi r_g}\, \Upsilon, \tag{21}$$

which describes the expansion or contraction of the Schwarzschild sphere depending on the sign of $\varepsilon_\pm = \pm 1$.

Useful information can be obtained by working with retarded and advanced null coordinates that result in regular metric functions.[31] If $r'_g > 0$, this is achieved by using the retarded null coordinate u. For $r'_g < 0$, the advanced null coordinate v leads to

$$C_+(v,r) = r_+(v) + \sum_{i\geqslant 1}^{\infty} w_i(v)(r - r_+)^i, \tag{22}$$

$$h_+(v,r) = \sum_{i\geqslant 1}^{\infty} \chi_i(v)(r - r_+)^i, \tag{23}$$

for some functions $w_i(v)$, $\chi_i(v)$, where $w_1 \leqslant 1$ due to the definition of r_+. This is the general form of the metric functions in (v, r) coordinates that ensures finite curvature scalars at the apparent horizon if $r'_g < 0$.[29] The components of the EMT in (v, r) and (t, r) coordinates are related by

$$\theta_v := e^{-2h_+} \Theta_{vv} = \tau_t, \tag{24}$$

$$\theta_{vr} := e^{-h_+} \Theta_{vr} = (\tau_t{}^r - \tau_t)/f, \tag{25}$$

$$\theta_r := \Theta_{rr} = (\tau^r + \tau_t - 2\tau_t{}^r)/f^2, \tag{26}$$

where $\Theta_{\mu\nu}$ labels the EMT components in (v, r) coordinates, which are finite. Hence $r'_g < 0$ corresponds to an evaporating PBH. Similarly, (u, r) coordinates are regular at the anti-trapping horizon r_g of an expanding white hole, $r'_g > 0$.[10,31]

The limiting form of the (tr) block of the EMT as $r \to r_g$ is

$$T^a{}_b = \begin{pmatrix} \Upsilon^2/f & -\varepsilon_\pm e^{-h}\Upsilon^2/f^2 \\ \varepsilon_\pm e^h \Upsilon^2 & -\Upsilon^2/f \end{pmatrix}, \quad T_{\hat{a}\hat{b}} = \frac{\Upsilon^2}{f}\begin{pmatrix} -1 & \varepsilon_\pm \\ \varepsilon_\pm & -1 \end{pmatrix}, \tag{27}$$

where the second expression is written in the orthonormal frame. It makes the violation of the NEC particularly transparent.

In the test-field limit[18] quantum fields propagate on a given gravitational background, but the resulting EMT is not permitted to backreact on the geometry via the Einstein equations. It is instructive to compare the tensor of Eq. (27) with explicit results obtained in the test-field limit. Out of the three popular choices for the vacuum state,[8,18] only the Unruh vacuum results in an EMT with nonzero T_{tr} components. The state itself corresponds to the requirement that no particles impinge on the collapsing object from infinity.[35] In the context of a static maximally extended spacetime, its counterpart is a state with unpopulated modes at past null infinity and the white hole horizon.[8,18] Using various semi-analytical and numerical methods that are based on conformally coupled fields[36] and minimally coupled scalar field,[37] the expectation values of the renormalized components T_{tt}, $T_t{}^r$, and T^{rr} have been determined explicitly. They approach the same negative value as $r \to r_g$.

The experiences of observers in the vicinity of the apparent horizon depend on their trajectories. A static observer finds that the energy density $\rho := T_{\mu\nu} u^\mu u^\nu = -T^t{}_t$, pressure $p := T_{\mu\nu} n^\mu n^\nu = T^r{}_r$, and flux $\phi := T_{\mu\nu} u^\mu n^\nu$ diverge at the apparent horizon, where u^μ denotes the four-velocity and n^μ the outward-pointing radial spacelike vector. The experience of a radially-infalling observer Alice moving on the trajectory $x_A^\mu(\tau) = (t_A, r_A, 0, 0)$ is different, and also differs from the infall into a classical eternal black hole.

First, crossing the apparent horizon of a PBH happens not only at some finite proper time τ_0, but also at a finite time $t_0(\tau_0)$, $r_g(t_0(\tau_0)) = r_A(\tau_0)$ according to the clock of a distant Bob. This is particularly easy to see for radial null geodesics, where

$$\frac{dt}{dr} = -\frac{e^{-h(t,r)}}{f(t,r)} \to \pm \frac{1}{|r'_g|} \tag{28}$$

at $r = r_g$, the rhs is obtained using Eqs. (19)–(21),[29] and the upper (lower) signature corresponds to an outgoing (ingoing) null ray. We use this result in our estimate of the formation time in Sec. 4, and in showing that the simple generalizations of surface gravity to nonstationary spacetimes fail for PBHs (Sec. 3.2).

It is possible to find explicit relations between (t, r) and (v, r) coordinates in the vicinity of the apparent horizon,[30] namely

$$x(r_+ + y, v) = r_+ + y - r_g(t(v, r_+ + y)) = -r''_g y^2/(2r'^2_g) + \mathcal{O}(y^3), \tag{29}$$

which relates the coordinates $x := r - r_g(t)$ and $y(r, v) := r - r_+(v)$. Another useful relation[38] is

$$w_1 = 1 - 2\sqrt{2\pi r_g^3 |r''_g|} \frac{\Upsilon}{|r'_g|}. \tag{30}$$

For an evaporating PBH ($r'_g < 0$) the energy density, pressure, and flux in Alice's frame are finite. However, upon approaching the anti-trapping horizon of an expanding white hole ($r'_g > 0$), Alice encounters a firewall,

$$\rho_A = T_{\mu\nu} u_A^\mu u_A^\nu = -\frac{\dot{r}_A^2}{4\pi r_g X} + \mathcal{O}(1/\sqrt{X}), \tag{31}$$

where $X := r_A(\tau) - r_g(t_A(\tau))$,[28] which may be another indication of the instability[8] of such objects.

Violations of the NEC are bounded by quantum energy inequalities.[33,39] Outside of the singularities the lower bounds were shown to exist for the energy density $\langle \hat{T}_{\mu\nu} \rangle_\omega u^\mu u^\nu$ and its smeared averages. These are known to be state-independent for free fields. For spacetimes of small curvature, explicit bounds for a geodesic observer were derived in Ref. 40. A finite bound is violated by the $1/f^2$ divergence of the energy density that results in the logarithmic divergence of its smeared time average provided that the radial velocity does not go to zero.[11,29] However, this is not true for geodesics, and thus the inequality of Ref. 40 is inapplicable.

Observers that have crossed the apparent horizon but change their mind before traversing the quantum ergosphere can exit the black hole before it evaporates. Their experiences at the apparent horizon are more involved: for a geodesic observer that attempts to cross the apparent horizon from the inside, the energy density also diverges. However, it does so according to a weaker $1/f$ law, and thus the integrated energy density remains finite.

2.2. Extreme solution ($k = 1$)

The static solution with $k = 0$ is impossible, as in this case $\mathfrak{T}$ would diverge at the apparent horizon. Consequently, EMT components that allow for static solutions must behave differently. Many models of static nonsingular black holes assume finite values of energy density and pressure at the horizon.[4,21] With respect to the scaling behavior f^k of the effective EMT components of Eq. (11) this is the $k = 1$ solution, with

$$\tau_t{}^t \to E(t)f, \qquad \tau_t{}^r \to \Phi(t)f, \qquad \tau^r{}_r \to P(t)f, \tag{32}$$

where $\rho = E$ and $p = P$ at the apparent horizon. Any two functions can be expressed algebraically in terms of the third, and $8\pi r_g^2 E \leqslant 1$ to ensure that $C(t,r) - r_g > 0$ for $r > r_g$.

Only the extreme value of $E = (8\pi r_g^2)^{-1}$ corresponds to non-extreme dynamic black holes (i.e. those with $r_g \neq$ const whose trapped regions have nonzero volume).[30] As a result

$$C(t,r) = r - c_{32}(t) x^{3/2} + \mathcal{O}(x^2) \tag{33}$$

for some coefficient $c_{32}(t) > 0$, setting via Eq. (32) the scaling of other leading terms in the EMT. Consistency of Eqs. (13) and (14) implies $P = -E = -1/(8\pi r_g^2)$ and $\Phi = 0$. From the next-order expansion we obtain

$$h = -\frac{3}{2} \ln \frac{x}{\xi} + \mathcal{O}(\sqrt{x}), \tag{34}$$

as well as the consistency relation

$$r'_g = \varepsilon_\pm c_{32} \xi^{3/2}/r_g, \qquad (35)$$

where the case $\varepsilon_\pm \equiv -1$ ($\varepsilon_\pm \equiv +1$) describes an evaporating PBH (an expanding white hole). The NEC violation is more subtle than in the $k = 0$ case. At $r = r_g(t)$ itself the NEC is marginally satisfied, as

$$T_{\hat a \hat b} = \frac{1}{8\pi r_g^2} \begin{pmatrix} 1 & 0 \\ 0 & -1 \end{pmatrix}. \qquad (36)$$

However, the NEC is violated for some $x > 0$, as for both incoming and outgoing directions $l_{\rm in}$, $l_{\rm out}$, we have

$$T_{\hat a \hat b} l^{\hat a} l^{\hat b} = -\frac{3 c_{32} \sqrt{x}}{8\pi r_g^2} + \mathcal{O}(x). \qquad (37)$$

Solutions with a time-independent apparent horizon or general static solutions do not require $w_1 = 1$ to satisfy Eqs. (24)–(26). Since $r_+(v) = r_g(t) = {\rm const}$, it is possible to have non-extreme solutions. Then Eq. (13) implies $\Phi = 0$ and the identity $E = -P$ follows from Eq. (26), leading to a regular function $h(t,r)$. However, in this case Eq. (4) indicates that the apparent horizon cannot be reached in finite time t.

The curvature scalars of the solutions we have considered so far were rendered finite thanks to the constraint that Eq. (13) imposes on the dynamic behavior via Eqs. (21) and (35). For example, the Ricci scalar of the solution with $C(t,r)$ given by Eq. (33) includes the potentially divergent term

$$R_{\rm div} = \frac{3}{4\sqrt{x}} \left(\frac{r_g r'^2_g}{c_{32} \xi^3} - \frac{c_{32}}{r_g} \right) \qquad (38)$$

that vanishes upon substitution of Eq. (35). However, a metric with $C(t,r) = r + c_2 x^2 + \ldots$ and the same $h(t,r)$ of Eq. (34), while being a solution of the Einstein equations, has a finite value of the Ricci scalar only in the static case $r'_g = 0$, as in this case

$$R_{\rm div} = -\frac{3 r_g r'^2_g}{c_2 \xi^3 x}. \qquad (39)$$

3. Implications

The solutions described in Sec. 2 have many remarkable properties, and their near-horizon geometry differs considerably from that of Schwarzschild black hole spacetimes. First, we mention an immediate mathematical consequence of the firewall that we have described. The divergence of ρ_A [see Eq. (31)] points to the presence of a matter singularity. As a result, we observe that if an apparent/anti-trapping horizon forms, it is a surface with an intermediate singularity. The appearance of a negative energy firewall is the counterpart to arbitrarily large tidal forces that could tear apart an observer falling into such a singularity. In these cases the fate of an observer depends on the integrated tidal stress.[8,41]

Consider observers attempting to enter an expanding white hole or exit an evaporating PBH.[10] In the former case, the radial velocity $\dot R < 0$ on a geodesic trajectory reverses the sign at some finite $R - r_g$ due to the divergent radial acceleration, and in fact the energy density remains finite. On the other hand, a massive test particle exits a PBH with $\dot R = 0$ and the energy density diverges, but its integrated smeared version remains finite.[11]

Since all curvature scalars remain finite, it is instructive to check the Ricci spinors

$$\Phi_{00} = \tfrac{1}{2} R_{11}, \quad \Phi_{22} = \tfrac{1}{2} R_{22}, \quad \Phi_{11} = \tfrac{1}{4}(R_{12} + R_{34}). \qquad (40)$$

Using the natural Newman–Penrose tetrad that is built from the two null vectors of Eq. (5) and a pair of complex-conjugate vectors m^μ and $\bar m^\mu := m^{\mu*}$,

$$m = \frac{1}{\sqrt{2}r} \partial_\theta + \frac{i}{\sqrt{2} r \sin\theta} \partial_\phi, \quad m \cdot \bar m = 1, \qquad (41)$$

we find that the values of all nonzero spinors are finite at the apparent horizon. However, given the freedom of choice of these vectors $l^\mu_{\text{out}} \to A l^\mu_{\text{out}}$, $l^\mu_{\text{in}} \to l^\mu_{\text{in}}/A$, the values of the spinors Φ_{00} and Φ_{22} depend on this choice. By choosing $A = f(v,r)$ (this form of the tangent vectors may appear more natural in (t,r) coordinates), we find

$$\Phi_{00} \propto f, \quad \Phi_{22} \propto f^{-1}, \qquad (42)$$

again demonstrating that the apparent/anti-trapping horizon is a surface of intermediate singularity.[11]

3.1. *Black hole formation*

Consider now possibilities for horizon formation. The properties of the self-consistent solutions of the Einstein equations that we have described above lead to the identification of a unique scenario for black hole formation.[29,30] We consider only evaporating PBHs ($r'_g < 0$) due to the implications of the results presented in Sec. 2.1. Working in (v,r) coordinates, we assume that the first marginally trapped surface appears at some v_S at $r_+(v_S)$ that corresponds to a finite value of t_S. For $v \leqslant v_S$, the MS mass in its vicinity can be described by modifying Eq. (22) as

$$C(v,r) = \Delta(v) + r_*(v) + \sum_{i \geqslant 1} w_i(v)(r - r_*)^i, \qquad (43)$$

where $r_*(v)$ corresponds to the maximum of $\Delta_v(r) := C(v,r) - r$, and the deficit function $\Delta(v) := C(v, r_*) - r_*(v) \leqslant 0$. At the advanced time v_S, the location of the maximum corresponds to the first marginally trapped surface, $r_*(v_S) = r_+(v_S)$, and $\sigma(v_S) = 0$. For $v \geqslant v_S$, the MS mass is described by Eq. (22). For $v \leqslant v_S$, the (local) maximum of $\Delta_v(r)$ is determined by $\Delta_v(r)/dr = 0$, hence $w_1(v) - 1 \equiv 0$.

There are no *a priori* restrictions on the evolution of r_* before the PBH is formed. However, since an expanding Schwarzschild sphere describes white hole solutions $r'_+(v_S) < 0$. For $v > v_S$, the maximum of $C(v,r)$ does not coincide with $r_+(v)$ since the trapped region is of finite size. As a result, $w_1(v) < 1$ for $v > v_S$.

This means that at its formation a PBH is described by a $k=1$ solution, which can be seen from Eq. (30), as $w_1 = 1$ implies $\Upsilon = 0$. It then immediately switches to the $k=0$ solution, with matching decrease in $w_1(v)$ and increase in $\Upsilon(t(v,r_+))$, and $w_1 < 1$ at all subsequent stages. The transition from f^1 to f^0 behavior is continuous as $\Upsilon(t_S) \equiv 0$ for the $k=1$ solution and it increases thereafter.[30] A detailed discussion can be found in Ref. 10.

3.2. *Surface gravity*

The surface gravity κ plays an important role in GR and semiclassical gravity.[7–9] However, it is unambiguously defined only in stationary spacetimes (for a Schwarzschild black hole $\kappa = (2r_g)^{-1}$), where it is proportional to the Hawking temperature.

Generalizations of surface gravity to dynamical spacetimes are related to two (equivalent in stationary spacetimes) definitions of κ that are based on the peeling off properties and the inaffinity of null geodesics at the horizon, respectively.[9,42] For sufficiently slowly evolving horizons with properties sufficiently close to their classical counterparts, these different generalizations of surface gravity are practically indistinguishable.[42] This agreement is important. Emission of Hawking-like radiation does not require the formation of an event or even an apparent horizon.[43–46] The role of the Hawking temperature is captured in various derivations either by the peeling[47] or the Kodama[48] surface gravity.

For PBHs, however, these quantities are very different. Here we consider only one version of the peeling surface gravity.[38] In Schwarzschild coordinates κ_{peel} is defined from the near-horizon behavior of null geodesics[9,42] as the linear coefficient in the Taylor expansion of

$$\frac{dr}{dt} = \pm e^h f(t,r) \tag{44}$$

in powers of x as $x \to 0$ (i.e. $r \to r_g$). However, such an expansion is impossible for the metric functions of Eqs. (22)–(23). Alternatively, to be compatible with Eq. (28), κ_{peel} should be infinite, as we now demonstrate.

For differentiable C and h, the result is

$$\kappa_{\text{peel}} = \frac{e^{h(t,r_g)}(1 - C'(t,r_g))}{2r_g}. \tag{45}$$

This quantity is undefined for $k=0$ solutions as for a radial geodesic [Eq. (28)] it implies

$$\frac{dr}{dt} = \pm|r'_g| + \mathcal{O}(\sqrt{x}), \tag{46}$$

and κ_{peel} diverges (for both $k=0$ and $k=1$ solutions).[30]

The Kodama vector field has many useful properties of the Killing field to which, modulo possible rescaling, it reduces in the static case.[9,22,42] Similar to the Killing vector, it is most conveniently expressed in (v, r) coordinates,

$$K^\mu = (e^{-h_+}, 0, 0, 0). \tag{47}$$

It is covariantly conserved, and generates the conserved current

$$\nabla_\mu K^\mu = 0, \tag{48}$$

$$\nabla_\mu J^\mu = 0, \quad J^\mu := G^{\mu\nu} K_\nu, \tag{49}$$

thereby giving a natural geometric meaning to the Schwarzschild coordinate time t. The MS mass is its Noether charge.

Since $K_{(\mu;\nu)} \neq 0$, the generalized Hayward–Kodama surface gravity is defined via[49]

$$\frac{1}{2} K^\mu (\nabla_\mu K_\nu - \nabla_\nu K_\mu) := \kappa_K K_\nu, \tag{50}$$

evaluated on the apparent horizon. Hence

$$\kappa_K = \frac{1}{2} \left(\frac{C_+(v,r)}{r^2} - \frac{\partial_r C_+(v,r)}{r} \right) \bigg|_{r=r_+} = \frac{(1-w_1)}{2r_+}, \tag{51}$$

where Eq. (22) was used to obtain the final result. Thus at the formation of a black hole (i.e. of the first trapped surface) this version of surface gravity is zero. At the subsequent evolution stages that correspond to a $k = 0$ solution, κ_K is nonzero. However, it approaches the static value $\kappa = 1/(4M)$ only if the metric is close to the pure Vaidya metric with $w_1 \equiv 0$. This in turn contradicts the semiclassical results.[38]

4. Discussion

The solutions we have described follow from commonly obtained or assumed, but not always sufficiently articulated requirements: the formation of a minimally regular horizon in finite time of a distant observer. The two classes of spherically symmetric solutions that satisfy these requirements must violate the NEC in the vicinity of the outer apparent horizon, and the matter content is dominated by a null fluid. Unless we accept that semiclassical physics breaks down at the horizon scale, accretion is no longer possible after the horizon has formed: the solutions describe either evaporating black holes or expanding white holes.

It is still not clear how the collapsing matter actually behaves, and how the continuous transition from f^1 to f^0 behavior immediately after PBH formation (Sec. 3.1) can be realized in nature. A mechanism that converts the original matter into the exotic matter present in the vicinity of the forming apparent horizon is required to violate the NEC. However, the emission of collapse-induced radiation[43–45] is a nonviolent process that approaches at latter times the standard Hawking radiation and Page's evaporation law[8,50] $r'_g = -\alpha/r_g^2$, $\alpha \sim 10^{-3} - 10^{-4}$.

In addition, there is no obvious way to reconcile the two standard definitions of surface gravity that underpin different derivations of Hawking radiation to dynamical spacetimes (Sec. 3.2): the peeling surface gravity κ_{peel} diverges, whereas the Kodama surface gravity κ_{K} is zero at the instant of PBH formation and in contradiction with established semiclassical results thereafter. This has interesting repercussions for the formulation of the information loss paradox[38] and indicates that the Hawking radiation that is obtained on the Schwarzschild background is not an asymptotic form of the radiation that is emitted by a PBH.

Our results indicate that the observed ABHs may be horizonless UCOs rather than genuine PBHs with a horizon — not due to some exotic supporting matter or dramatic variation in the laws of gravity, but simply because the conditions for the formation of a horizon have not been met at the present moment of t. Even if no new physics is required to produce the mandatory NEC violation, the process may be too slow to transform the UCOs that we observe into PBHs. Eq. (28) of Sec. 2.1 sets the timescale of the last stages of infall according to Bob. Assuming that it is applicable through the radial interval of the order of r_g, we find $t_{\text{in}} \sim r_g/r_g'$. For an evaporating macroscopic PBH, this is of the same order of magnitude as the Hawking process decay time $t_{\text{evp}} \sim 10^3 r_g^3$. Such behavior was found in thin shell collapse models, where the exterior geometry is modeled by a pure outgoing Vaidya metric.[34] For a solar mass black hole, this time is about 10^{67} yr, indicating that it is simply too early for the horizon to form. It is also conceivable that the conditions are not met before evaporation is complete or before effects of quantum gravity become dominant.[8] Horizon avoidance may therefore occur due to the absence of new physics, and not because of it.

A more detailed understanding of the near-horizon geometry as well as the behavior of matter during gravitational collapse and PBH formation is needed to resolve all of the remaining questions. Coming of age of multimessenger astronomy and controversies surrounding the direct observation of ABHs make it a particularly timely project.

Acknowledgments

SM is supported by an International Macquarie University Research Excellence Scholarship and a Sydney Quantum Academy Scholarship. The work of DRT is supported by the ARC Discovery project grant DP210101279.

References

1. L. Barack, V. Cardoso, S. Nissanke, and T. P. Sotiriou (eds.), Class. Quantum Gravity **36**, 143001 (2019).
2. V. Cardoso and P. Pani, Living Rev. Relativ. **22**, 4 (2019).
3. E. Curiel, Nat. Astron. **3**, 27 (2019).
4. V. P. Frolov, J. High Energy Phys. **05**, 049 (2014).
5. M. Visser, Phys. Rev. D **90**, 127502 (2014).

6. V. Cardoso and P. Pani, Nat. Astron. **1**, 586 (2017).
7. S. W. Hawking and G. F. R. Ellis, *The Large Scale Structure of Space-Time* (Cambridge University Press, Cambridge, England, 1973).
8. V. P. Frolov and I. D. Novikov, *Black Hole Physics: Basic Concepts and New Developments* (Kluwer, Dordrecht, 1998).
9. V. Faraoni, *Cosmological and Black Hole Apparent Horizons* (Springer, Heidelberg, 2015).
10. R. B. Mann, S. Murk, and D. R. Terno, Int. J. Mod. Phys. D **31**, 2230015 (2022).
11. P. K. Dahal, S. Murk, and D. R. Terno, AVS Quantum Sci. **4**, 015606 (2022).
12. S. W. Hawking, Commun. Math. Phys. **43**, 199 (1975).
13. J. W. York, Jr., Phys. Rev. D **28**, 2929 (1983).
14. R. Carballo-Rubio, F. Di Filippo, S. Liberati, and M. Visser, Phys. Rev. D **101**, 084047 (2020).
15. P. Binétruy, A. Helou and F. Lamy, Phys. Rev. D **98**, 064058 (2018).
16. J. M. M. Senovilla and D. Garfinkle, Class. Quantum Gravity **32**, 124008 (2015).
17. Y. Choquet-Bruhat, *General Relativity and the Einstein Equations* (Oxford University Press, Oxford, England, 2009).
18. N. D. Birrel and P. C. W. Davies, *Quantum Fields in Curved Space* (Cambridge University Press, Cambridge, England, 1984).
19. R. M. Wald, Living Rev. Relativ. **4**, 6 (2001).
20. T. A. Roman and P. G. Bergman, Phys. Rev. D **28**, 1265 (1983).
21. S. A. Hayward, Phys. Rev. Lett. **96**, 031103 (2006).
22. G. Abreu and M. Visser, Phys. Rev. D **82**, 044027 (2010).
23. C. W. Misner and D. H. Sharp, Phys. Rev. **136**, B571 (1964).
24. V. Faraoni, G. F. R. Ellis, J. T. Firouzjaee, A. Helou, and I. Musco, Phys. Rev. D **95**, 024008 (2017).
25. R. Penrose, *Structure of space-time*, in C. DeWitt, J. A. Wheeler (eds.), *Batelle Rencontres: 1967 Lectures in Mathematics and Physics*, pp. 121–235 (W. A. Benjamin, San Francisco, 1968).
26. F. J. Tipler, C. J. S. Clarke, and G. R. F. Ellis, *Singularities and horizons: A review article*, in A. Held (ed.), *General relativity and gravitation: One hundred years after the birth of Albert Einstein*, vol. 2, p. 97 (Plenum, New York, 1980).
27. H. Stephani, D. Kramer, M. MacCallum, C. Hoenselaers, and E. Herlt, *Exact Solutions of Einstein's Field Equations*, 2nd edn. (Cambridge University Press, Cambridge, England, 2003).
28. D. R. Terno, Phys. Rev. D **100**, 124025 (2019).
29. D. R. Terno, Phys. Rev. D **101**, 124053 (2020).
30. S. Murk and D. R. Terno, Phys. Rev. D **103**, 064082 (2021).
31. V. Baccetti, R. B. Mann, S. Murk, and D. R. Terno, Phys. Rev. D **99**, 124014 (2019).
32. P. Martín-Moruno and M. Visser, *Classical and Semi-classical Energy Conditions*, in *Wormholes, Warp Drives and Energy Conditions,* edited by F. N. S. Lobo (Springer, New York, 2017), p. 193.
33. E.-A. Kontou and K. Sanders, Class. Quantum Gravity **37**, 193001 (2020).
34. V. Baccetti, S. Murk, and D. R. Terno, Phys. Rev. D **100**, 064054 (2019).
35. W. G. Unruh, Phys. Rev. D **14**, 870 (1976).
36. M. Visser, Phys. Rev. D **56**, 936 (1997).
37. A. Levi and A. Ori, Phys. Rev. Lett. **117**, 231101 (2016).
38. R. B. Mann, S. Murk, and D. R. Terno, Phys. Rev. D **105**, 124032 (2022).
39. C. J. Fewster, *Quantum Energy Inequalities*, in *Wormholes, Warp Drives and Energy Conditions*, edited by F. N. S. Lobo (Springer, New York, 2017), p. 215.

40. E.-A. Kontou and K. D. Olum, Phys. Rev. D **91**, 104005 (2015).
41. G. F. R. Ellis and A. R. King, Commun. Math. Phys. **38**, 119 (1974).
42. B. Cropp, S. Liberati, and M. Visser, Class. Quantum Gravity **30**, 125001 (2013).
43. P. Hájíček, Phys. Rev. D **36**, 1065 (1987).
44. C. Barceló, S. Liberati, S. Sonego, and M. Visser, Class. Quantum Gravity **23**, 5341 (2006).
45. T. Vachaspati, D. Stojkovic, and L. M. Krauss, Phys. Rev. D **76**, 024005 (2007).
46. A. Paranjape and T. Padmanabhan, Phys. Rev. D **80**, 044011 (2009).
47. C. Barceló, S. Liberati, S. Sonego, and M. Visser, Phys. Rev. D **83**, 041501(R) (2011).
48. F. Kurpicz, N. Pinamonti, and R. Verch, Lett. Math. Phys. **111**, 110 (2021).
49. S. A. Hayward, Class. Quantum Gravity **15**, 3147 (1998).
50. D. N. Page, Phys. Rev. D **13**, 198 (1976).

Information recovery from evaporating rotating charged black holes

Zhi-Wei Wang

Department of Physics and Astronomy, University of Lethbridge,
4401 University Drive, Lethbridge, Alberta T1K 3M4, Canada
zhiweiwang.phy@gmail.com

Samuel L. Braunstein

Computer Science, University of York, York YO10 5GH, United Kingdom
sam.braunstein@york.ac.uk

Saurya Das*

Department of Physics and Astronomy, University of Lethbridge,
4401 University Drive, Lethbridge, Alberta T1K 3M4, Canada
saurya.das@uleth.ca

In classical gravity, nothing can escape from a black hole, not even light. In particular, this happens for stationary black holes because their horizons are null. We show, on the other hand, that the apparent horizon and the region near $r = 0$ of an *evaporating* charged, rotating black hole are both timelike. This implies that there exists a channel, via which classical or quantum information can escape to the outside, as the black hole evaporates. Since astrophysical black holes have at least some rotation, our results apply to all black holes in nature. We discuss implications of our result.

Keywords: Black hole information loss; Hawking radiation; evaporating black holes; rotating black holes; Vaidya metric.

1. Introduction

In classical general relativity, a black hole is a region of spacetime from which nothing escapes. This result underwent a change with the discovery of Hawking radiation.[1,2] Studying the evolution of a vacuum quantum state in curved spacetime with a horizon, Hawking showed that the ingoing vacuum state has a probability to yield a non-vacuum outgoing state when the former enters the horizon of a black hole. This means that a black hole can radiate energy to infinity via this quantum mechanism.

Now, both classical and quantum information can enter the horizon of a black hole. However, as Hawking's work showed, only thermal Hawking radiation carrying very little information emerges from it.[3] Therefore, when the black hole evaporates completely, all information carried by the matter that was used to create the black hole is apparently lost forever. This violates unitarity in quantum theory which

---

*Author for correspondence (saurya.das@uleth.ca)

requires the information of a quantum system be conserved during its evolution. Further study of this apparent information loss paradox led to the idea of black hole complementarity,[4–6] the firewall paradox[7,8] etc.

When discussing the above problem, people often overlook an implicit hypothesis that the causal structure of a black hole is not disturbed by Hawking radiation itself. Parikh and Wilczek were the first to examine this assumption and show that the singularity of an evaporating charged black [white] hole may be accessible for an observer outside when the metric is time-dependent.[9] However, the metric used in their paper in fact seems to represent a white hole, contrary to their claim that it is a black hole (see Appendix A for a detailed analysis). Recently, numerical simulation also shows that the horizon of a charged black hole may be timelike.[10] We know on the other hand, that much like other astronomical objects, all black holes in nature are rotating and uncharged, and the probability of finding a black hole with zero rotation is practically nil.

Motivated by the above, in this work,[11] we show that for a rotating and charged black hole which is Hawking radiating, there is a classical channel through which information can escape, and following the above reasoning, it provides an extended window of information recovery from its interior. In the process, the black hole shrinks of course, but presumably at a faster rate than predicted by Hawking radiation, because of the additional outflow of information and associated matter.

We demonstrate the above rigorously by constructing the Penrose diagram for the above process. In particular, we prove that the region immediately surrounding $r = 0$ is timelike, and the apparent horizon is timelike as well. These two results and the Penrose diagram all together imply null geodesics originating from anywhere near the centre of the black hole to the apparent horizon may emerge to the outside Universe. This in turn provides a route for classical or quantum information to escape from the black hole. This escape of potentially a large amount of information must be taken into account in any attempt to resolve the information loss problem. What is most significant is perhaps the fact that the escaping information need not be thermal.

2. Coordinates for an evaporating rotating charged black hole

Since we are interested in evaporating black holes, we will start with the following time-dependent metric, which represents a rotating and charged Vaidya-type black hole,[12,13] as shown in Appendix B

$$ds^2 = -\left(1 - \frac{2Mr - Q^2}{\sigma^2}\right)du^2 + 2du\,dr + \sigma^2 d\theta^2 - 2a\sin^2\theta\,dr\,d\phi$$
$$- \frac{2(2Mr - Q^2)a}{\sigma^2}\sin^2\theta\,du\,d\phi + \left(\frac{2Mr - Q^2}{\sigma^2}a^2\sin^2\theta + r^2 + a^2\right)\sin^2\theta\,d\phi^2,$$

(1)

where $\sigma^2 \equiv r^2 + a^2 \cos^2\theta$, and $M = M(u)$, $Q = Q(u)$ and $a = a(u)$ denote smooth decreasing functions of the retarded time u.

Next, to construct a two-dimensional Penrose diagram for the above metric, we restrict ourselves to the symmetry axis along $\theta = 0$.[14] Then one gets, from Eq. (1):

$$ds^2 = -\left(1 - \frac{2Mr - Q^2}{r^2 + a^2}\right)du^2 + 2\,du\,dr = -\left[\frac{r^2 - 2Mr + a^2 + Q^2}{r^2 + a^2}\,du - 2\,dr\right]du. \tag{2}$$

We also assume without loss of generality that M, a and Q are proportional to each other and linear functions of u

$$M(u) = M_0 \text{ (constant)}, \qquad u < u_0 \tag{3}$$
$$ = \mu u + b \equiv \tilde{u}, \qquad u_0 < u \leq -b/\mu, \mu < 0 \tag{4}$$
$$ = 0, \qquad -b/\mu < u \tag{5}$$
$$a(u) = \lambda_1 M(u), \qquad 0 \leq \lambda_1 \leq 1 \tag{6}$$
$$Q(u) = \lambda_2 M(u), \qquad 0 \leq \lambda_2 \leq 1. \tag{7}$$

This means that the black hole starts its process of evaporation at time $u = u_0$, and undergoes a mass decrease at a constant rate μ. Contrary to Ref. [13], where the angular momentum was held fixed, in this work we make it time-dependent. This is because on the one hand, the form of the metric continues to hold with that generalization and moreover, the condition $\lambda_1, \lambda_2 \leq 1$ ensures that there are no naked singularities.

The following points may be noted here. First, continuity of the functions $M(u), a(u), Q(u)$ in Eqs. (3-7) guarantees that the various patches of the Penrose diagram that will smoothly join to each other.[9] Second, considering arbitrary decay rates (i.e. not constant over time) is also straightforward. In this case, one can simply break down the non-linear decay function such as $M(u)$ into a series of linear functions of the form $M(u) = \sum_{i=1}^{N}(\mu_i u + b_i)\left[\Theta(u_i + \frac{1}{2}) - \Theta(u_i + \frac{1}{2})\right]$ $(u_0 \leq u_i)$, and similarly for $a(u)$ and $Q(u)$, for $N \gg 1$.

Now, following Ref. [9] and details presented in Ref. [11], we find a set of coordinates which are smooth across the horizon. To this end, we first write metric (2) in the so-called 'double null' form:

$$ds^2 = -\frac{g(\tilde{u}, r)}{\mu} d\tilde{u}\,dv, \tag{8}$$

where,

$$dv \equiv \frac{1}{g(\tilde{u}, r)}\left[\left(\frac{r^2 - 2Mr + (\lambda_1^2 + \lambda_2^2)M^2}{r^2 + \lambda_1^2 M^2}\right)\frac{d\tilde{u}}{\mu} - 2dr\right]. \tag{9}$$

with the integrating factor

$$g(\tilde{u}, r) = \left(\frac{r^2 - 2Mr + (\lambda_1^2 + \lambda_2^2)M^2}{r^2 + \lambda_1^2 M^2}\right)\frac{\tilde{u}}{\mu} - 2r. \tag{10}$$

We may then read off

$$\frac{\partial v}{\partial r} = \frac{r^2 + \lambda_1^2 \tilde{u}^2}{-r[r^2 + \lambda_1^2 \tilde{u}^2] + \frac{\tilde{u}}{2\mu}[r^2 - 2\tilde{u}r + (\lambda_1^2 + \lambda_2^2)\tilde{u}^2]} \tag{11}$$

$$\frac{\partial v}{\partial \tilde{u}} = \frac{\frac{1}{2a}(r^2 - 2Mr + (\lambda_1^2 + \lambda_2^2)\tilde{u}^2)}{-r[r^2 + \lambda_1^2 \tilde{u}^2] + \frac{\tilde{u}}{2\mu}[r^2 - 2\tilde{u}r + (\lambda_1^2 + \lambda_2^2)\tilde{u}^2]} . \tag{12}$$

As one can see, the common denominators $D(r)$ of the above expressions are cubic in r, which may be rewritten as

$$\begin{aligned} D(r) &= -r[r^2 + \lambda_1^2 \tilde{u}^2] + \frac{\tilde{u}}{2\mu}[r^2 - 2\tilde{u}r + (\lambda_1^2 + \lambda_2^2)\tilde{u}^2] \\ &= -r^3 - \lambda_1^2 \tilde{u}^2 r + \frac{\tilde{u}}{2\mu}r^2 - \frac{\tilde{u}^2}{\mu}r + \frac{\tilde{u}^3}{2\mu}(\lambda_1^2 + \lambda_2^2) \\ &= -r^3 + \frac{\tilde{u}}{2\mu}r^2 - (\lambda_1^2 \tilde{u}^2 + \frac{\tilde{u}^2}{\mu})r + \frac{\tilde{u}^3}{2\mu}(\lambda_1^2 + \lambda_2^2). \end{aligned} \tag{13}$$

Since $D(-\infty) > 0$, $D(+\infty) < 0$, and $D(0) = \frac{\tilde{u}^3}{2\mu}(\lambda_1^2 + \lambda_2^2) < 0$ because of $\mu < 0$ and $\tilde{u} > 0$ ($\tilde{u} = 0$ represents a flat spacetime and hence is ignored here), the scenarios with positive roots for the cubic equation $D(r) = 0$ are well described by Fig. 1. No other scenario has a positive root.

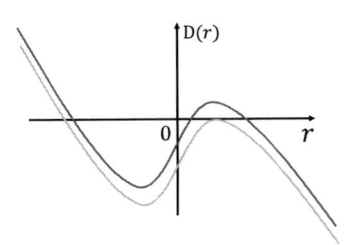

Fig. 1. Scenarios caused singularities for Eqs. (11) and (12).

For the case represented by the red line in Fig. 1, the denominators have three roots r_1, r_2, r_3, (with $r_1 > r_2 > 0 > r_3$) where v has coordinate singularities, and

$$v = \sum_{i=1}^{3} A_i \ln(r - r_i) , \tag{14}$$

with

$$A_1 = \frac{r_1^2}{(r_1 - r_2)(r_1 - r_3)} + \lambda_1 \tilde{u}^2, \quad A_2 = \frac{-r_2^2}{(r_1 - r^2)(r_2 - r_3)} + \lambda_1 \tilde{u}^2,$$

$$A_3 = \frac{r_3^2}{(r_1 - r_3)(r_2 - r_3)} + \lambda_1 \tilde{u}^2 . \tag{15}$$

Then the complete set of singularity free coordinates for the two patches may be defined as:

$$V_2(v) \equiv e^{v/A_1}$$
$$= (r-r_1)(r-r_2)^{A_2/A_1}(r-r_3)^{A_3/A_1}, \qquad r_2 \leq r < \infty \quad (16)$$
$$V_1(v) \equiv k_1 - (-V_2)^{A_1/A_2}$$
$$= k_2 + (r_1-r)^{A_1/A_2}(r_2-r)(r-r_3)^{A_3/A_2}, \qquad 0 \leq r < r_2 \quad (17)$$

The constants k_i are determined by matching V_2 with V_1 in $r_2 < r < r_1$. If the denominator $D(r)$ of Eq. (11) is described by the gold line in Fig. 1, it has a negative root r_3 and a positive double root r_1 such that it can be factored as $(r-r_3)(r-r_1)^2$. This is nothing but a special case that $r_1 = r_2$ in the red-line scenario in Fig. 1.

3. Timelike regions

With the results in last section, it is easy to show that $r = 0$ and its immediate neighbourhood is *timelike*. For example, in the case of Eqs. (14-17) above,

$$ds^2 = -\frac{g(\tilde{u},r)A}{V(\tilde{u},r)\mu} d\tilde{u}\, dV \quad (18)$$
$$\xrightarrow{r \to 0} -\left(\frac{\lambda_1^2 + \lambda_2^2}{\lambda_1^2}\right) du^2 < 0. \quad (19)$$

It may be noted that the 'ring singularity' of the metric is at $r = 0$ and $\theta = \pi/2$. It follows that except for that singular point, the region in the neighbourhood of $r = 0$ is regular and of finite curvature, except perhaps at the end of the evaporation process.

We now consider the apparent horizon and show that it is timelike as well. We follow the procedure of Ref. [15], and define the function:

$$f(u,r) = r - R_\pm, \quad (20)$$

where $R_\pm$ represents the outer and inner apparent horizons of the evaporating rotating charged black hole. A rigorous calculations for $R_\pm$ yields

$$R_\pm = r_\pm + \frac{a\lambda_1(r_\pm^2 + a^2)}{r_\pm^2 - (M + 2a\mu\lambda_1)r_\pm}\mu + O(\mu^2), \quad (21)$$

where

$$r_\pm = M \pm (M^2 - Q^2 - a^2)^{1/2} \quad (22)$$

(see Appendix B for more details).

We assume that the evaporating process is sufficiently slow and that $|\mu|$ is sufficiently small. Therefore, we focus on the leading term in Eq. (21) for our future calculations. Thus, Eq. (20) reduces to

$$f(u,r) = r - M \mp (M^2 - Q^2 - a^2)^{1/2}, \quad (23)$$

such that the apparent horizons are at

$$f(u,r) = 0, \ r_\pm = M \pm (M^2 - Q^2 - a^2)^{1/2}. \quad (24)$$

Now since M, Q and a are functions of u the vector n_a, normal to the surface $f(u,r) = 0$, will have components given by

$$n_u = f_{,u} = -\mu \mp \frac{\mu \, (M - \lambda_1 a - \lambda_2 Q)}{(M^2 - Q^2 - a^2)^{1/2}} \,, \qquad n_r = f_{,r} = 1 \,, \qquad (25)$$

and norm

$$n^2 = g^{ab} n_a n_b = 2\mu[-1 \mp (1 - \lambda_1^2 - \lambda_2^2)^{1/2}] > 0 \,, \qquad (26)$$

where we have used $\mu < 0$ from Eq. (4). Therefore, n_a is spacelike and the apparent horizon is timelike.

4. Penrose diagram

The information loss problem may be easily described using Penrose diagrams. The Penrose diagram in Fig. 2 depicts a static Schwarzschild (non-rotating, uncharged) black hole. In this case, the singularity is spacelike, and it is clear that information, from within the horizon, propagating along null or timelike geodesics cannot reach the outside Universe. The Penrose diagram in Fig. 3 describes an evaporating

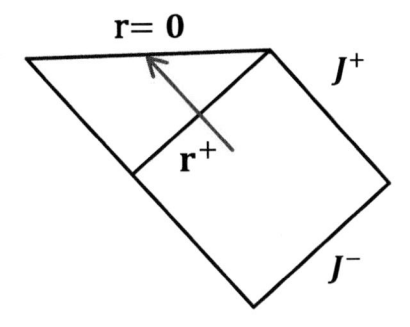

Fig. 2. Penrose diagram of a static Schwarzschild black hole.

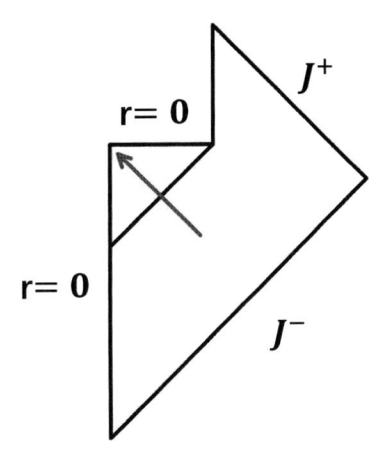

Fig. 3. Penrose diagram of an evaporating Schwarzschild black hole.

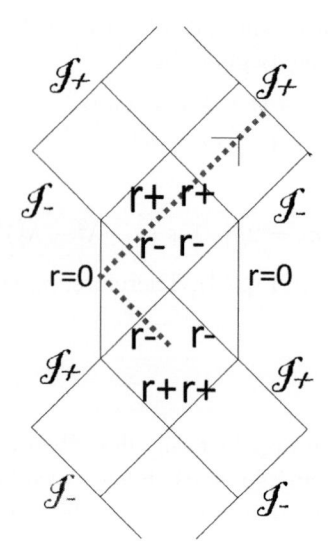

Fig. 4. Penrose diagram for stationary Kerr black hole.

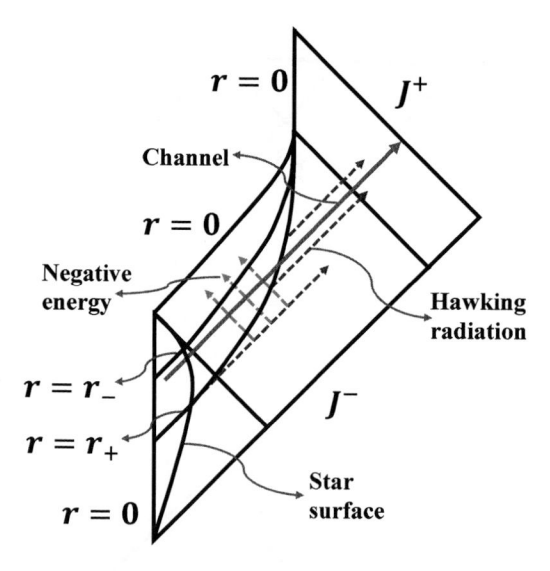

Fig. 5. Penrose diagram for an evaporating rotating (charged) black hole. This Penrose diagram describes a rotating (charged) star first collapsing into a rotating (charged) black hole. Then the black hole begins to evaporate, and both its inner and outer horizons at $\theta = 0$ follow timelike trajectories. After the black hole completely evaporates away, the spacetime is connected with a flat spacetime.

Schwarzschild black hole. The evaporating procedure of a Schwarzschild black hole does not change the fact that the horizon is along a null direction and hence does not improve the situation.

Similarly, Fig. 4 is the Penrose diagram of a maximally extended rotating black hole whose singularity is timelike. Although information propagating along null rays in such a Penrose diagram can exit a future horizon, it does so only by entering another Universe. Therefore, the information loss problem is not resolved in the present Universe.

Based on the results of Eqs. (19), (21), and (26), we can draw the Penrose diagram for the evaporating charged, rotating black hole (Fig. 5). As one can see, there is a channel (outgoing null rays in red) which can carry classical as well as quantum information all the way from the interior to infinity, crossing the timelike horizon along the way.

We assume $\theta = 0$ in Eq. (2) to simplify our calculations, it does not restrict our conclusion that there exists at least one such outgoing information channel. Even if future work shows that this channel is unique because its special azimuth, there is no limit in principle to the amount of information that can exit through this channel. Since our major calculations are carried out for a specific azimuth $\theta = 0$, its generalization to black holes in higher-dimensional spacetimes should be straightforward.

5. Discussion

We have shown in this article that the apparent horizon and the region close to $r = 0$ of an evaporating charged rotating black hole follow timelike trajectories. This implies that there exists a channel through which classical or quantum information can escape. Since proposals such as the fuzzball and firewall deal purely with quantum information, and in the context of Hawking radiation, there is no contradiction between those and our results here.[7,8,19] On the contrary, our approach complements the others.

It is known that matter flowing into the dynamic charged and rotating black hole may cause instability due to mass-inflation, resulting in the nature of the singularity changing.[20,21] However, we do not anticipate such a problem in our case since (a) our results pertain to the region of low curvature (not singularity), and (b) we have outgoing as opposed to infalling matter. That said a careful study of the effect for the spacetime under consideration is warranted and we hope to report on this in the future.

Since the horizon of a stationary black hole is null and the evaporating procedure is a quantum effect, emergence of such a classical channel is not a pure classical phenomenon. If the evaporation process stops for any reason before the black hole evaporates completely, our Fig. 5 would change and revert back to Fig. 4. However, since the Hawking temperature remains non-zero throughout, we do not consider this possibility.

Although our work does not completely resolve the problem of information loss, it complements other approaches in opening up a new information recovery channel. More work needs to be done to determine the extent of information that can be extracted via this channel, and its interplay with the quantum resolution of the singularity.

Appendix A. The metric in Parikh and Wilczek's paper represents a white hole

To our knowledge, such an analysis was first done by in[9] for non-rotating black holes. However, contrary to their assuming the metric that they used to be that of an evaporating black hole, it is in fact that of a charged white hole. They study the metric[9]

$$ds^2 = -\left(1 - \frac{2Mr - Q^2}{r^2}\right)du^2 - 2du\,dr + r^2(d\theta^2 + \sin^2\theta\,d\phi^2), \quad (A.1)$$

where $M = M(u)$ and $Q = Q(u)$ denote smooth decreasing functions of the retarded time u. It is easy to see that Eq. (A.1) represents a white hole by taking $Q = 0$.[22] To show that Eq. (A.1) is the metric of a white hole, we now calculate the expansion of the null normal vector of this metric.

Since this metric is spherically symmetric, it is easy to figure out that the outward null normal vector l^μ and the inward null normal vector n^μ for this metric are

$$l^\mu = (0, 1, 0, 0) \quad \text{and} \quad n^\mu = \left(1, -\frac{r^2 - 2Mr + Q^2}{2r^2}, 0, 0\right). \quad (A.2)$$

It is easy to check that

$$l^\mu l_\mu = 0, \quad n^\mu n_\mu = 0 \quad \text{and} \quad l^\mu n_\mu = -1. \quad (A.3)$$

Finally, we calculate the expansion for both l^μ and n^μ by $\theta^{(A)} = A_{\mu;\nu}\sigma^{\mu\nu}$, where $\sigma^{\mu\nu} = g^{\mu\nu} + l^\mu n^\nu + n^\mu l^\nu$, to obtain

$$\theta^{(l)} = \frac{2}{r} \quad \text{and} \quad \theta^{(n)} = -\frac{r^2 - 2Mr + Q^2}{r^3}. \quad (A.4)$$

From Eq. (A.4) we know that $\theta^{(l)} > 0$ and $\theta^{(n)} < 0$ when r is larger than the apparent horizon. However, it is the vanishing of $\theta^{(n)}$ that defines an apparent horizon. Thus, the Vaidya-type metric in Parikh and Wilczek's paper represents a white hole.

Appendix B. The metric in our manuscript represents a black hole

To show that our metric represents an evaporating black hole, we calculate the expansion of the null normal vectors for the rotating charged Vaidya-type black hole, see Eq. (1) in the manuscript.

Suggested by the rotating charged stationary black hole,[23] we may conjecture that the outward null vector l^μ and the inward null vector n^μ for the rotating charged Vaidya-type black hole are

$$l^\mu = \left(\frac{r^2 + a^2}{\sigma^2}, \frac{\Delta}{2\sigma^2}, 0, \frac{a}{\sigma^2}\right) \quad \text{and} \quad n^\mu = (0, -1, 0, 0). \quad (B.1)$$

where $\sigma^2 = r^2 + a^2 \cos^2\theta$ and $\triangle = r^2 + a^2 - 2Mr + Q^2$. It is easy to check that

$$l^\mu l_\mu = 0, \quad n^\mu n_\mu = 0 \quad \text{and} \quad l^\mu n_\mu = -1 \tag{B.2}$$

for the Vaidya-type metric in our manuscript. Then we calculate the expansion for both l^μ and n^μ by $\theta^{(A)} = A_{\mu;\nu}\sigma^{\mu\nu}$, where $\sigma^{\mu\nu} = g^{\mu\nu} + l^\mu n^\nu + n^\mu l^\nu$. Finally, we obtain

$$\theta^{(l)} = \frac{r\triangle + 2\,a\,a'(u)(r^2 + a^2\cos^2(\theta))}{(r^2 + a^2\cos^2(\theta))^2} \quad \text{and} \quad \theta^{(n)} = -\frac{2r}{r^2 + a^2\cos^2(\theta)}. \tag{B.3}$$

From Eq. (B.3) we see that $\theta^{(l)} > 0$ and $\theta^{(n)} < 0$ when r is larger than the apparent horizon and $\theta^{(l)} = 0$ defines the apparent horizon. Thus, the Vaidya-type metric in our manuscript represents a black hole.

The apparent horizon for a stationary rotating charged black hole is defined by $\triangle = 0$. Here, our calculations show that the time dependence of the angular momentum $a(u)$ makes the apparent horizon shift slightly from the stationary case with the size of the shift depending on the rate of change of $a(u)$ with respect to u.

If we insert our linear functions for M, Q and a, Eqs. (3-6) in the manuscript, into the expansion of the outward null normal vector and suppose the rate of change is very slow (μ is very small), we can obtain the corrected apparent horizon for $\theta = 0$ as

$$R_\pm = r_\pm + \frac{a\lambda_1(r_\pm^2 + a^2)}{r_\pm^2 - (M + 2a\mu\lambda_1)r_\pm}\mu + O(\mu^2). \tag{B.4}$$

Since we have proved $r_\pm$ is timelike, the apparent horizon of a slowly evaporating rotating charged black hole should also be timelike.

References

1. S. W. Hawking, Black hole explosions? *Nature* **248**, 30–31 (1974).
2. S. W. Hawking, Particle creation by black holes, *Communications in Mathematical Physics* **43**, 199–220 (1975).
3. S. W. Hawking, Breakdown of predictability in gravitational collapse, *Physical Review D* **14(10)**: 246 (1976).
4. G. 't Hooft, On the quantum structure of a black hole, *Nuclear Physics B* **256**: 727-745 (1985).
5. G. 't Hooft, The black hole interpretation of string theory, *Nuclear Physics B* **335**: 138–154 (1990).
6. L. Susskind, L. Thorlacius, J. Uglum, The stretched horizon and black hole complementarity, *Physical Review D* **48**: 3743 (1993).
7. S. L. Braunstein, Black hole entropy as entropy of entanglement, or it's curtains for the equivalence principle, *arXiv preprint* arXiv:0907.1190 (2009).
8. A. Almheiri, D. Marolf, J. Polchinski, J. Sully, Black holes: complementarity or firewalls?, *Journal of High Energy Physics* **2013(2)**: 1-20 (2013).
9. M. Parikh, F. Wilczek, Global structure of evaporating black holes. *Physics Letters B* **449** (1999) 24-29.

10. J. C. Schindler, A. Aguirre, A. Kuttner, Understanding black hole evaporation using explicitly computed Penrose diagrams, *Physical Review D* **101**: 024010 (2020).
11. S. L. Braunstein, S. Das, Z.-W. Wang, Information recovery from evaporating black holes, *International Journal of Modern Physics D* 2150069 (2021).
12. P. C. Vaidya, Curr. Sci. **12**, 183 (1943); Proc. Ind. Ac. Sci. A **33**, 264 (1951); Nature **171**, 260 (1953).
13. J. Jing and Y. Wang, Int. J. Theor. Phys. **35**, 1481 (1996).
14. B. Carter, Phys. Rev. **141**, 1242 (1966).
15. Y. Kaminaga, Class. Quant. Grav. **7**, 1135 (1990).
16. L. Susskind, *An Introduction To Black Holes, Information And The String Theory Revolution: The Holographic Universe*, World Scientific (2004).
17. A. Ashtekar, J. Phys.: Conf. Ser. **189** 012003 (2009).
18. S. Das, Phys. Rev. **D89** (2014) 084068 [arXiv:1311.6539].
19. S. D. Mathur, Fortsch.Phys. 53 (2005) 793-827 [arXiv:hep-th/0502050].
20. C. Barrabès, W. Israel, E. Poisson, Class. Quant. Grav. **7**, L273–L278 (1990).
21. D. Rossi, *Reissner-Nordström Black Holes and Mass Inflation*, thesis, University of Bologna (2019).
22. E. Poisson, *A Relativist's Toolkit The Mathematics of Black-Hole Mechanics*, Cambridge University Press (2004) p.167.
23. E. T. Newman, R. Penrose, *Spin-coefficient formalism*, Scholarpedia, **4**(6):7445 (2009).

Black hole thermodynamics from entanglement mechanics

S. Mahesh Chandran* and S. Shankaranarayanan[†]

*Dept. of Physics, IIT Bombay,
Mumbai, Maharashtra-400076, India*
E-mail: maheshchandran@iitb.ac.in
[†] *E-mail: shanki@iitb.ac.in*

Since its inception, the Bekenstein-Hawking area relation for black-hole entropy has been the primary testing ground for various theories of quantum gravity. However, a key challenge to such theories is identifying the microscopic structures and explaining the exponential growth of microstates, providing a fundamental understanding of thermodynamic quantities. Since entropy is a single number, we explore other quantities to provide complete information about the black-hole microstates. We establish a one-to-one correspondence between entanglement energy, entropy, and temperature (quantum entanglement mechanics) and the Komar energy, Bekenstein-Hawking entropy, and Hawking temperature of the horizon (black-hole thermodynamics), respectively. We also show that this correspondence leads to the Komar relation and Smarr formula for generic 4-D spherically symmetric space-times. While offering an independent derivation of black-hole thermodynamics from field observables, the universality of results suggests that quantum entanglement is a *fundamental building block of space-time*.

Keywords: Entanglement Entropy; Black Hole Thermodynamics; Field Theory in Curved Space-times.

1. Introduction

Black holes are fascinating entities that typically arise from gravitationally collapsing bodies, such as stars at the end of their life cycle or star collisions. Despite their violent origin, black holes relax to a stationary state, which can then be fully described by a mere handful of variables such as their mass, charge and angular momentum. This makes it easier to probe various quantum and gravitational phenomena that come with it, further making it an ideal testing ground for ongoing research on quantum gravity.

Interestingly, like ordinary matter systems such as ideal gases, black holes also obey an equation of state. The physical parameters describing stationary black-holes satisfy what is known as the Komar relation[1–3]:

$$E_{\text{Komar}} = 2\, T_{\text{H}}\, S_{\text{BH}}, \tag{1}$$

where E_{Komar} is related to the Hamiltonian of the Einstein-Hilbert action,[4] T_{H} is the Hawking temperature[5] and S_{BH} is the Bekenstein-Hawking entropy.[6] The above relation is a by-product of the Smarr formula[7,8]:

$$M = 2T_H\, S_{\text{BH}} + 2\Omega_H J + \Phi_H Q \tag{2}$$

that relates the mass (M), angular momentum (J), entropy ($S_{\rm BH}$), electric charge (Q) of black-holes, angular velocity Ω_H, and Φ_H which is the potential difference between the horizon and infinity. It was shown that the Smarr formula, in its differential form and subject to certain assumptions, gives rise to the first law of black hole thermodynamics.[9] At the heart of this law is the analogy that connects thermodynamic entropy to surface area, and temperature to surface gravity.

Most of the effort in literature has been to understand the microscopic statistical origin of black-hole entropy,[10–13] and in extension, black hole thermodynamics. However, black-hole entropy has the problem of Universality[14]— wherein up to the leading order, several approaches using completely different microscopic degrees of freedom lead to Bekenstein-Hawking entropy.[10,13,14] The inability to conclusively distinguish such approaches, along with the fact that entropy is a single number, suggests that it may be impossible to identify the true degrees of freedom that give rise to black hole entropy. Therefore, it requires us to also identify other physical quantities corresponding to black hole thermodynamics, if we were to attempt resolving the universality problem.

Over the last decade or so, one such approach that has grown increasingly crucial to understanding black-hole physics, and quantum gravity in general, is quantum entanglement.[15–19] A fundamental feature of entanglement is the *Area law* — the entanglement entropy of blocks of low energy states of local Hamiltonian is often proportional to the measure of the boundary separating the block from its setting.[13,20–22] The area law has not only established a direct link between entanglement entropy and black hole entropy, but also led to the conjecture that space-time fabric might itself be built upon entanglement.[17] If entanglement is a necessity for the existence of space-time, then the *litmus-test* is to derive all the quantities of black-hole thermodynamics from entanglement.

In this talk, we show that the quantum scalar fields in a $(3 + 1)$-dimensional black-hole space-times with one or more horizons, provide a way to obtain the physical quantities from entanglement *aka entanglement mechanics*. We relate these quantities to black-hole thermodynamics, and further show that these quantities satisfy Smarr formula (2).[23]

2. Modeling scalar field in a background space-time

In this section, we recapitulate the procedure for probing entanglement mechanics of a minimally coupled scalar field against a static, spherically symmetric background space-time with one or more horizons. The line-element for such a space-time can in general be written as follows:

$$ds^2 = -f(r)dt^2 + \frac{1}{f(r)}dr^2 + r^2 d\Omega^2. \tag{3}$$

Depending on the form of $f(r)$, there is usually a handful of coordinate settings that help us understand the system better. Suppose the space-time in question has a horizon (r_h), such as in the Schwarzschild case, it is useful to rewrite the metric in terms of proper-length coordinates[24]:

$$ds^2 = -f(r)dt^2 + d\rho^2 + r^2 d\Omega^2 \, ; \qquad \rho = \int_{r_h}^{r} \frac{dr}{\sqrt{f(r)}}. \qquad (4)$$

Before modeling the scalar field in this setting, we have to address two fundamental aspects — i) Since entanglement entropy diverges in the continuum limit, the field has to be *regularized*. The regularisation provided by the more rigorous definition of quantum fields in terms of operator-valued distributions is difficult to calculate even for simple free theories.[25] We therefore resort to regularisation by discretization,[21, 22] i.e., we treat quantum fields on a lattice, with the lattice spacing a fixed in units of proper length as depicted in Fig 1. (ii) To capture entanglement of the field across a space-time horizon, the field must be treated as a *bipartite* system made up of subsystems on either sides of the horizon. However, the proper length co-ordinates only capture the region on that side of the horizon where $f(r) > 0$. The physics in the region $f(r) < 0$ will hence remain inaccessible. The bipartition will then have to be performed as close to the horizon as possible, i.e., by tracing out a single degree of freedom along proper length co-ordinate. This is in fact a valid approximation for large horizon radius and/or small lattice spacing of discretized field.[23]

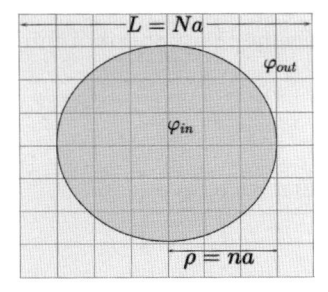

Fig. 1. Discretization scheme for a scalar field in proper length co-ordinates. The field essentially is replaced by a network of coupled harmonic oscillators placed at every grid point.

To set the model up, we begin with the action for a massive scalar field in an arbitrary space-time[26, 27]:

$$S = \frac{1}{2} \int d^4x \sqrt{-g} \left[g^{\mu\nu} \partial_\mu \varphi \partial_\nu \varphi - m_f^2 \varphi^2 \right]. \qquad (5)$$

For the proper-length coordinate (4), we use the following spherical decomposition of the scalar field with appropriate scaling:

$$\dot\varphi(\rho,\theta,\phi) = \frac{f^{1/4}(r)}{r} \sum_{lm} \dot\varphi_{lm}(\rho) Z_{lm}(\theta,\phi) \qquad (6)$$

$$\varphi(\rho,\theta,\phi) = \frac{f^{1/4}(r)}{r} \sum_{lm} \varphi_{lm}(\rho) Z_{lm}(\theta,\phi). \tag{7}$$

Substituting these in the action (5), leads to the following effective $(1+1)$-D Lagrangian:

$$L = \frac{1}{2}\sum_{lm} \int d\rho \left[\dot{\varphi}_{lm}^2 - r^2\sqrt{f(r)}\left\{\partial_\rho\left(f^{1/4}(r)\frac{\varphi_{lm}}{r}\right)\right\}^2 - f(r)\left\{m_f^2 + \frac{l(l+1)}{r^2}\right\}\varphi_{lm}^2 \right] \tag{8}$$

With the help of canonical conjugate momenta defined as $\pi_{lm} = \dot{\varphi}_{lm}$, we can now write down the Hamiltonian of the system. To regularize this Hamiltonian, we introduce lattice spacing a in the proper length co-ordinate as $\rho = ja$. The IR cut-off here is on the proper length, which is fixed to be $\rho_L = (N+1)a$. For each lattice point j, we obtain the corresponding lattice point in rescaled radial co-ordinate $r' = r/a$, by inverting the following expression for r_j:

$$j = \int_{\Delta_h}^{r_j} \frac{dr'}{\sqrt{f(r')}}. \tag{9}$$

where we have introduced the dimensionless parameters $\Delta_h = r_h/a$ and $r_j = r/a|_{\rho=ja}$. For convenience, we further define $f_j = f(r)|_{\rho=ja}$. It should be noted that the lattice points in radial co-ordinate $\{r_j\}$ are not equally spaced. On employing the midpoint discretization scheme,[13] we obtain a fully regularized Hamiltonian:

$$H = \frac{1}{2a}\sum_{lmj}\left[\pi_{lm,j}^2 + r_{j+\frac{1}{2}}^2 f_{j+\frac{1}{2}}^{1/2}\left\{f_j^{1/4}\frac{\varphi_{lm,j}}{r_j} - f_{j+1}^{1/4}\frac{\varphi_{lm,j+1}}{r_{j+1}}\right\}^2 \right.$$
$$\left. + f_j\left\{\Lambda^2 + \frac{l(l+1)}{r_j^2}\right\}\varphi_{lm,j}^2\right], \tag{10}$$

where $\Lambda = a^2 m_f^2$. Let us now factorize the Hamiltonian as $H = \tilde{H}/a$ and consider the following scaling transformations:

$$a \to \eta a; \quad m_f \to \eta^{-1} m_f; \quad r_h \to \eta r_h \tag{11}$$

Under these transformations, the parameters Λ and Δ_h remain invariant. The Hamiltonian H has therefore been factorized into a scale-dependent part $1/a$ and a scale-independent part $\tilde{H}$. Since the relations between entanglement measures of H and $\tilde{H}$ are well established,[23] it is sufficient to work with the scale-invariant part $\tilde{H}$. It can be seen that $\tilde{H} = \sum_{lm} \tilde{H}_{lm}$ exactly resembles a network of coupled harmonic oscillators:

$$\tilde{H}_{lm} = \frac{1}{2}\left[\sum_i \pi_{lm,i}^2 + \sum_{ij} \varphi_{lm,i} K_{ij} \varphi_{lm,j}\right] \tag{12}$$

Here, K_{ij} is the coupling matrix, which contains all the relevant information about the interactions, and in which all information about entanglement entropy is encoded. To simplify further, we will focus on the massless case ($\Lambda = 0$), and also impose the Dirichlet boundary condition $\varphi_{lm,N+1} = 0$ to obtain a non-divergent scaling behavior. The coupling matrix will therefore have the following non-zero elements:

$$K_{11} = f_1 \frac{l(l+1)}{r_1^2} + \frac{r_{3/2}^2}{r_1^2}\sqrt{f_1 f_{3/2}}$$

$$K_{jj \neq 1} = f_j \frac{l(l+1)}{r_j^2} + \frac{\sqrt{f_j}}{r_j^2}\left\{r_{j+\frac{1}{2}}^2 \sqrt{f_{j+\frac{1}{2}}} + r_{j-\frac{1}{2}}^2 \sqrt{f_{j-\frac{1}{2}}}\right\} \quad (13)$$

$$K_{j,j+1} = K_{j+1,j} = -\frac{r_{j+\frac{1}{2}}^2}{r_j r_{j+1}}\left\{f_{j+\frac{1}{2}}^2 f_j f_{j+1}\right\}^{1/4}$$

Having fully described the model, we now introduce quantities associated with entanglement mechanics, namely, the entanglement entropy and entanglement energy, of a quantum field in a 4-D spherically symmetric space-time with at least one horizon[23, 28]:

$$S_{\text{ent}} = -\operatorname{Tr} \rho_{red} \log \rho_{red} \quad ; \quad E_{\text{ent}} = \epsilon \operatorname{Tr}\left[\rho : H_{in} :\right], \quad (14)$$

where $: H_{in} :$ is the normal-ordered Hamiltonian corresponding to the reduced subsystem, ρ is the density matrix, and ρ_{red} is the reduced density matrix obtained by tracing over the field outside the horizon. The constant prefactor ϵ in the definition of entanglement energy accounts for the fact that it is not a unique measure;[23] it may be obtained *uniquely* by comparing with physical quantities of black-holes. While entanglement entropy (S_{ent}) essentially captures change in information content in the presence of the horizon, we may define entanglement energy (E_{ent}) as the disturbed vacuum energy or the *correlation energy* in the presence of the horizon. We further invoke the Komar relation(1) to define entanglement temperature as $T_{ent} = E_{ent}/2S_{ent}$.[23] Having formulated the quantities that describe entanglement mechanics for a given field, we proceed to simulate them in various space-times to infer its fundamental structure.

3. Entanglement mechanics of the field near space-time horizon

In this section, we discuss results from numerical simulations of entanglement mechanics in a variety of static, spherically symmetric space-times with one or more horizon(s).

3.1. *Schwarzschild Black Hole*

In the Schwarzschild space-time, $f(r) = 1 - r_h/r$, and the proper length (4) takes the form:

$$\rho = r\sqrt{1 - \frac{r_h}{r}} + \frac{r_h}{2}\ln\left[\frac{r}{r_h}\left\{1 + \sqrt{1 - \frac{r_h}{r}}\right\}^2\right]. \quad (15)$$

where the horizon radius is $r_h = 2M$. On discretizing $\rho = ja$, we get a scale-invariant expression that connects lattice-points in the proper length and radial co-ordinates as follows:

$$j = r_j \sqrt{1 - \frac{\Delta_h}{r_j}} + \frac{\Delta_h}{2} \ln\left[\frac{r_j}{\Delta_h}\left\{1 + \sqrt{1 - \frac{\Delta_h}{r_j}}\right\}^2\right], \qquad (16)$$

where $\Delta_h = 2M/a$ and $r_j = r/a$ are dimensionless. We also see that $f_j = 1 - \Delta_h/r_j$. This confirms that the Hamiltonian in (10) is characterized by dimensionless parameters Λ and Δ_h, and is therefore invariant under the transformations:

$$a \to \eta a; \quad m_f \to \eta^{-1} m_f; \quad M \to \eta M \qquad (17)$$

Now we focus on the scale-invariant Hamiltonian $\tilde{H}$, wherein we vary the rescaled horizon Δ_h, and assume that the entanglement mechanics of the field at the horizon can be approximated by tracing out the closest oscillator near the horizon. This approximation is reasonable for large values of Δ_h, wherein the radial distance of the closest oscillator from horizon is negligible ($r_1 \sim \Delta_h$).

From Fig 2, we observe the following scaling relations:

$$\tilde{S} = c_s \Delta_h^2; \quad \tilde{E} = c_e \Delta_M, \qquad (18)$$

where a linear fit fixes the values $c_s \sim 0.3$ and $c_e \sim 0.06$. For the original Hamiltonian H, we then have:

$$S = c_s \frac{r_h^2}{a^2}; \quad E = c_e \frac{M}{a^2}; \quad T = \frac{c_e}{4 c_s r_h} = \frac{\pi c_e}{c_s} T_H \qquad (19)$$

where T_H is the Hawking temperature. From the above relations, we see that (i) entanglement entropy exhibits an area law whereas entanglement energy scales linearly with horizon radius—the latter is fundamentally different from an area-law scaling observed in Minkowski space-time, (ii) entanglement temperature is independent of the UV cut-off a, and (iii) The entanglement mechanics follows the same laws of black-hole mechanics.[10] In the following sections, we will see if these observations extend for other space-times as well.

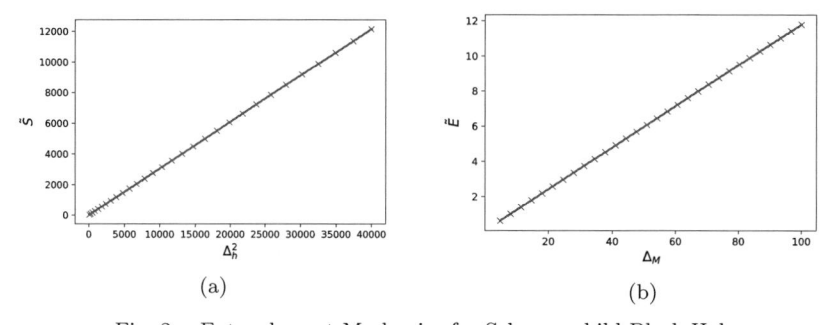

Fig. 2. Entanglement Mechanics for Schwarzschild Black Hole.

3.2. Reissner-Nordström

We will now probe entanglement mechanics of the field in an asymptotically flat space-time with multiple horizons. The line-element for Reissner-Nordström black hole is given by (4), where

$$f(r) = 1 - \frac{2M}{r} + \frac{Q^2}{r^2}.$$

For $Q < M$, the roots are given by $r_\pm = M \pm \sqrt{M^2 - Q^2}$ where r_+ corresponds to the event-horizon and r_- refers to the internal Cauchy horizon. Thus, $f(r)$ is positive in two regions: 1. $0 < r < r_-$ and 2. $r_+ < r < \infty$.

3.2.1. Cauchy horizon

In terms of the dimensionless variable (χ), the Cauchy horizon is

$$r_- = Q\{\chi - \sqrt{\chi^2 - 1}\} \text{ where } \chi = M/Q \in (1, \infty).$$

To ensure that the proper length is positive definite quantity, we reverse the limits of integration in Eq. (4), i.e.,

$$\rho = \int_r^{r_h} \frac{dr}{\sqrt{f(r)}} = -\sqrt{Q^2 + r(r - 2\chi Q)} + \chi Q \ln\left[\frac{Q\sqrt{\chi^2 - 1}}{\chi Q - 2\left\{r + \sqrt{Q^2 + r(r - 2\chi Q)}\right\}}\right] \tag{20}$$

On discretizing $\rho = ja$, we convert the above expression into a dimensionless form:

$$j = -\sqrt{\Delta_Q^2 + r_j(r_j - 2\chi\Delta_Q)} + \chi\Delta_Q \ln\left[\frac{\Delta_Q\sqrt{\chi^2 - 1}}{\chi\Delta_Q - 2\left\{r_j + \sqrt{\Delta_Q^2 + r_j(r_j - 2\chi\Delta_Q)}\right\}}\right], \tag{21}$$

where $\Delta_Q \equiv Q/a$ and $r_j \equiv r/a$ are both dimensionless. We also see that

$$f_j = 1 - \frac{2\chi\Delta_Q}{r_j} + \frac{\Delta_Q^2}{r_j^2}. \tag{22}$$

The resulting Hamiltonian H is factorized into a scale-dependent part $1/a$ and a scale-independent part $\tilde{H}$. The latter is completely characterized by dimensionless parameters Λ, Δ_Q and χ, all of which are invariant under the scaling transformations:

$$a \to \eta a; \quad m_f \to \eta^{-1} m_f; \quad M \to \eta M; \quad Q \to \eta Q \tag{23}$$

The IR cut-off on proper length is fixed at $r = 0$, leading to a certain discretization relation:

$$\Delta_Q \left[\chi \ln\sqrt{\frac{\chi+1}{\chi-1}} - 1\right] = N + 1 \tag{24}$$

The above relation tells us that if we fix Δ_q, then χ is discretized and vice versa. Here, we will consider the scenario where horizon changes on account of varying Δ_Q while keeping χ fixed. Physically, this corresponds to varying both mass and charge of the black hole proportionately to account for particles with a fixed mass-charge ratio (χ) that are entering the event horizon. As a result, both mass and charge have equally spaced discrete spectra:

$$Q_N = \frac{(N+1)a}{\left(\chi \ln \sqrt{\frac{\chi+1}{\chi-1}} - 1\right)}; \quad M_N = \chi Q_N; \quad (25)$$

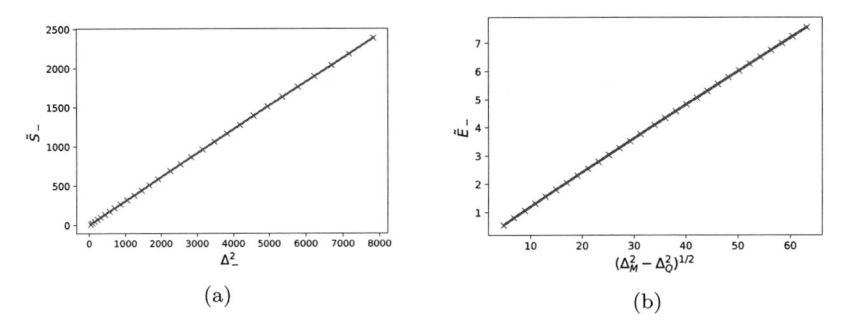

Fig. 3. Entanglement Mechanics at RN Cauchy horizon, when $\chi = 1.1$.

3.2.2. Event horizon

In terms of the dimensionless variable (χ), the event horizon is

$$r_+ = Q(\chi + \sqrt{\chi^2 - 1}).$$

From Eq. (4), we obtain:

$$\rho = \sqrt{Q^2 + r(r - 2\chi Q)} + \chi Q \ln\left[\frac{r - \chi Q + \sqrt{Q^2 + r(r - 2\chi Q)}}{Q\sqrt{\chi^2 - 1}}\right]. \quad (26)$$

On discretizing $\rho = ja$, we convert the above expression into a dimensionless form:

$$j = \sqrt{\Delta_Q^2 + r_j(r_j - 2\chi \Delta_Q)} + \chi \Delta_Q \ln\left[\frac{r_j - \chi \Delta_Q + \sqrt{\Delta_Q^2 + r_j(r_j - 2\chi \Delta_Q)}}{\Delta_Q \sqrt{\chi^2 - 1}}\right] \quad (27)$$

where $\Delta_Q \equiv Q/a$ and $r_j \equiv r/a$ are both dimensionless. From Figs 3 and 4, we obtain the following scaling relations for scale-invariant system $\tilde{H}$:

$$\tilde{S}_\pm = c_s \Delta_\pm^2; \quad \tilde{E}_\pm = c_e \sqrt{\Delta_M^2 - \Delta_Q^2}, \quad (28)$$

where a linear fit fixes the values $c_s \sim 0.3$ and $c_e \sim 0.12$ for both horizons. It can also be seen from here that in the limit $\Delta_Q \to 0$, we recover the values of c_e and c_s for Schwarzschild (18). As discussed above, $\tilde{S}_-$ and $\tilde{E}_-$ have discrete spectra. Since the entanglement energy is identical for both the horizons, we may therefore write for the total Hamiltonian (H):

$$S_\pm = c_s \frac{r_\pm^2}{a^2}; \quad E_+ = c_e \frac{\sqrt{M^2 - Q^2}}{a^2}; \quad T^{(\pm)} = \frac{\pi c_e}{c_s} T_H^{(\pm)} \qquad (29)$$

where $T_H^{(-)}$ and $T_H^{(+)}$ are the Hawking temperatures of Cauchy and event horizon, respectively.

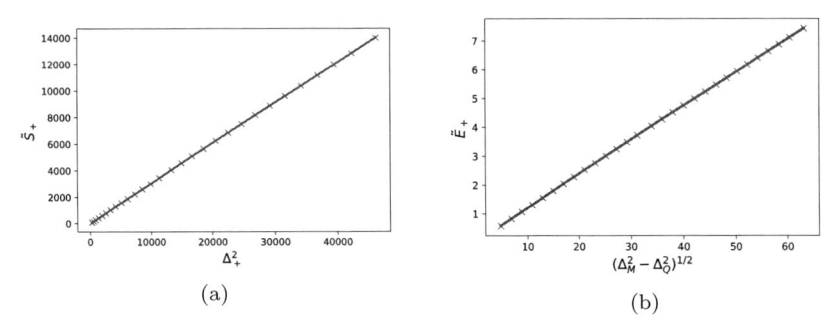

Fig. 4. Entanglement Mechanics at RN event horizon, when $\chi = 1.1$.

3.3. *Schwarzschild de-Sitter*

We now move on to a space-time with multiple horizons that is asymptotically non-flat. A Schwarzschild black hole (of mass M) in a de-Sitter space-time (of radius l) is described by:

$$f(r) = 1 - \frac{2M}{r} - \frac{r^2}{l^2},$$

This space-time also has two horizons — r_b (event horizon) and r_c (cosmological horizon)[29]:

$$r_- = -\frac{2l}{\sqrt{3}} \cos \frac{\theta}{3}; \quad r_b = \frac{2l}{\sqrt{3}} \cos \frac{\pi + \theta}{3}; \quad r_c = \frac{2l}{\sqrt{3}} \cos \frac{\pi - \theta}{3} \qquad (30)$$

where r_- is the third negative root, $\theta = \cos^{-1}(3\sqrt{3}\chi)$ and $\chi = M/l \in [0, 1/(3\sqrt{3})]$. $f(r)$ is positive in the region between the two horizons. Hence, in this region, we have two definitions for proper length — one w.r.t. the event horizon r_b which we refer to as ρ_b and the second w.r.t. the cosmological horizon r_c which we refer to as ρ_c.

3.3.1. Event horizon

The proper length with respect to the event horizon r_b is obtained as follows[23]:

$$\rho_b = \frac{2r_b l}{\sqrt{r_c(r_b - r_-)}} \Pi\left(\vartheta, \alpha^2, k\right), \tag{31}$$

where,

$$\vartheta = \sin^{-1}\sqrt{\frac{r_c(r - r_b)}{r(r_c - r_b)}}; \quad \alpha^2 = 1 - \frac{r_b}{r_c}; \quad k^2 = \frac{r_-(r_b - r_c)}{r_c(r_b - r_-)}. \tag{32}$$

On discretizing proper length $\rho_b = ja$, we convert the above expression into a dimensionless form:

$$j = \frac{2\Delta_b \Delta_l}{\sqrt{\Delta_c(\Delta_b - \Delta_-)}} \Pi\left(\vartheta, \alpha^2, k\right). \tag{33}$$

In terms of the dimensionless variables $\Delta_l = l/a$ and $r_j = r/a$, we have

$$f_j = 1 - \frac{2\Delta_M}{r_j} - \frac{r_j^2}{\Delta_l^2}, \tag{34}$$

and,

$$\Delta_- = -\frac{2\Delta_l}{\sqrt{3}}\cos\frac{\theta}{3}; \quad \Delta_b = \frac{2\Delta_l}{\sqrt{3}}\cos\frac{\pi + \theta}{3}; \quad \Delta_c = \frac{2\Delta_l}{\sqrt{3}}\cos\frac{\pi - \theta}{3};$$

$$\vartheta = \sin^{-1}\sqrt{\frac{\Delta_c(r_j - \Delta_b)}{r_j(\Delta_c - \Delta_b)}}; \quad \alpha^2 = 1 - \frac{\Delta_b}{\Delta_c}; \quad k^2 = \frac{\Delta_-(\Delta_b - \Delta_c)}{\Delta_c(\Delta_b - \Delta_-)}. \tag{35}$$

As a result, the Hamiltonian $\tilde{H}$ is fully characterized by dimensionless parameters Δ_l and Δ_M, both of which are invariant under the scaling transformations:

$$a \to \eta a; \quad m_f \to \eta^{-1} m_f; \quad M \to \eta M; \quad l \to \eta l \tag{36}$$

In the case of SdS, the IR cut-off on proper length is automatically fixed as we restrict ourselves to the region $\tilde{r}_b \leq r_j \leq \tilde{r}_c$:

$$N + 1 = \frac{2\tilde{r}_b \Delta_l}{\sqrt{\tilde{r}_c(\tilde{r}_b - \tilde{r}_-)}} \Pi\left(\frac{\pi}{2}, \alpha^2, k\right) \tag{37}$$

This is a discretization relation similar to what was obtained for RNBH. We will consider the case where we fix Δ_M and vary Δ_l by varying N. This is to ensure that χ is always between $[0, 1/(3\sqrt{3}]$. From Fig 5, we obtain the following scaling relations for the scale-invariant Hamiltonian ($\tilde{H}$):

$$\tilde{S}_b \sim c_s \Delta_b^2; \quad \tilde{E}_b \sim c_e(3\Delta_M - \Delta_b) \tag{38}$$

where, $c_s \sim 0.3$ and $c_e \sim 0.12$ are the best-fit numerical values. In the limit $\Delta_l \to \infty$, we recover the prefactors of the Schwarzschild black hole (18). For the total Hamiltonian (H), the scaling relations become:

$$S_{b,N} \sim c_s \frac{r_{b,N}^2}{a^2}; \quad E_{b,N} \sim c_e \frac{3M - r_{b,N}}{a^2}; \quad T^{(b)} = \frac{\pi c_e}{c_s} T_H^{(b)} \tag{39}$$

where $T_H^{(b)}$ is the Hawking temperature of the event horizon in SdS.[29,30]

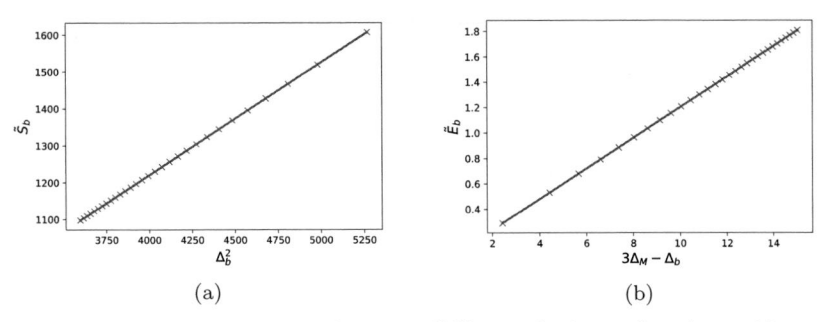

Fig. 5. Entanglement Mechanics at SdS event horizon, when $\Delta_M = 25$.

3.3.2. *Cosmological horizon*

To explore the scaling properties of cosmological horizon, we define proper distance r_c as follows[31]:

$$\rho_c = \frac{2l}{\sqrt{r_c(r_b - r_-)}} \left[r_- F(\vartheta, k) - (r_c - r_-) \Pi\left(\vartheta, \alpha^2, k\right) \right], \tag{40}$$

where,

$$\sin\vartheta = \sqrt{\frac{(r_b - r_-)(r_c - r)}{(r_c - r_b)(r - r_-)}}; \quad \alpha^2 = \frac{r_b - r_c}{r_b - r_-}, \tag{41}$$

and the definition of k is the same as Eq. (32). On discretizing proper length $\rho_c = ja$, we convert the above expression into a dimensionless form:

$$j = \frac{2\Delta_l}{\sqrt{\Delta_c(\Delta_b - \Delta_-)}} \left[\Delta_- F(\vartheta, k) - (\Delta_c - \Delta_-) \Pi\left(\vartheta, \alpha^2, k\right) \right], \tag{42}$$

where in terms of dimensionless variables $\Delta_l = l/a$ and $r_j = r/a$, we can also rewrite:

$$\sin\vartheta = \sqrt{\frac{(\Delta_b - \Delta_-)(\Delta_c - r_j)}{(\Delta_c - \Delta_b)(r_j - \Delta_-)}}; \quad \alpha^2 = \frac{\Delta_b - \Delta_c}{\Delta_b - \Delta_-}, \tag{43}$$

Except for ϑ and α given above, the parameters used here follow the same definition as in (35). Now we impose an IR cut-off on proper length to restrict ourselves in the region $\tilde{r}_b \leq r_j \leq \tilde{r}_c$:

$$N + 1 = \frac{2\Delta_l}{\sqrt{\Delta_c(\Delta_b - \Delta_-)}} \left[\Delta_- K(k) - (\Delta_c - \Delta_-) \Pi\left(\frac{\pi}{2}, \alpha^2, k\right) \right] \tag{44}$$

This expression relates the number of oscillators N, Δ_l and χ, and we only need to fix two of these to fix the third. We will fix Δ_M here as we did for the event horizon, which leaves Δ_l with a discrete spectrum. From Fig 6, we see that the spectra for Δ_l obtained from ρ_b and ρ_c coincide exactly, and therefore the two discretization relations (37) and (44) are identical.

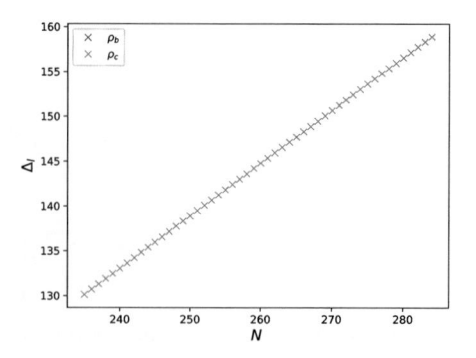

Fig. 6. Discretization of Δ_l from the cutoffs on proper lengths ρ_b and ρ_c, for $\Delta_M = 25$.

From Fig. 7, we obtain the following scaling relations for the scale-invariant system $\tilde{H}$:

$$\tilde{S}_c \sim c_s \Delta_c^2; \qquad \tilde{E}_c \sim c_e \left[\Delta_c - 3\Delta_M\right] \tag{45}$$

where $c_s \sim 0.3$ and $c_e \sim 0.12$ are the best-fit numerical values. For the total Hamiltonian H, the scaling relations become:

$$S_{c,N} \sim c_s \frac{r_{c,N}^2}{a^2}; \qquad E_{c,N} \sim c_e \frac{r_{c,N} - 3M}{a^2}; \qquad T^{(c)} \sim \frac{\pi c_e}{c_s} T_H^{(c)}, \tag{46}$$

where $T_H^{(c)}$ is the Hawking temperature of the cosmological horizon in SdS.

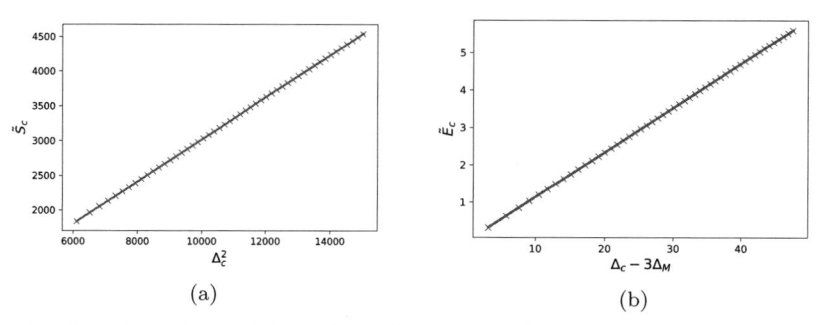

Fig. 7. Entanglement Mechanics at SdS cosmological horizon, when $\Delta_M = 25$.

4. Black hole thermodynamics from entanglement mechanics

On numerically simulating the quantum entanglement mechanics near the horizon r_h for a variety of such space-times, we observe some universal properties associated with their scaling relations. Before we proceed, we first invoke the definition of entanglement energy wherein the pre-factor ϵ was introduced. Here, we may fix this pre-factor as $\epsilon \sim 1.26$ upon imposing the condition that the entanglement temperature is identical to Hawking temperature ($T_{ent} = T_H$). While this rescales the proportionality constant c_e obtained numerically, the simulations nevertheless capture a universal one-to-one correspondence[23] between entanglement mechanics and black hole thermodynamics:

$$E_{\text{ent}} = \frac{c_e}{a^2} E_{\text{Komar}}; \quad S_{\text{ent}} = \frac{c_s}{\pi a^2} S_{\text{BH}}; \quad T_{\text{ent}} = T_H. \tag{47}$$

Note that E_{ent} and S_{ent} depend on the UV cut-off (a), where as the temperature does not. Moreover, even with the pre-factor ϵ being assigned a new value, the constants of proportionality are found to be universal across all black-hole space-times, irrespective of whether they are asymptotically flat or non-flat:

$$c_e \sim 0.0955; \quad c_s \sim 0.3. \tag{48}$$

Let us put these results in perspective: We have related quantum scalar fields near the horizon with the thermodynamic observables that describe any black-hole space-time (cf. Table 1). The fact that this is true for all 4-D spherically symmetric space-time suggests that entanglement of the quantum fields near the horizon carries crucial information about the black-hole thermodynamics. The above relations (47) go further and lead to the following universal and cut-off independent (a) result:

$$E_{\text{ent}} = 2T_{\text{ent}} S_{\text{ent}} \quad \Longleftrightarrow \quad E_{\text{Komar}} = 2T_H S_{\text{BH}} \tag{49}$$

It is important to note that the above relation does not imply equality of their respective counterparts. On rearranging this relation further, we obtain the generalized Smarr formula of black hole thermodynamics, as summarized in Table 1.

Table 1. Generalized Smarr formula.

Space-time	Entanglement Structure	Thermodynamic Structure	Smarr formula	Pressure	Potential
Schwarzschild	$S_{\text{ent}} = (c_s/a^2) r_h^2$	$S_{BH} = \pi r_h^2$	$M = 2T_H S_{BH}$	—	—
	$E_{\text{ent}} = (c_e/a^2) M$	$E_{\text{Komar}} = M$			
Reissner-Nordström	$S_+ = (c_s/a^2) r_+^2$	$S_{BH} = \pi r_+^2$	$M = 2T_H S_{BH} + Q^2/r_+$	—	Q/r_+
	$E_+ = (c_e/a^2)\sqrt{M^2 - Q^2}$	$E_{\text{Komar}} = \sqrt{M^2 - Q^2}$			
Schwarzschild-AdS	$S_{\text{ent}} = (c_s/a^2) r_h^2$	$S_{BH} = \pi r_h^2$	$M = 2T_H S_{BH} - r_h^3/l^2$	$3/8\pi l^2$	—
	$E_{\text{ent}} = (c_e/a^2)[3M - r_h^2]$	$E_{\text{Komar}} = 3M - r_h^2$			
Schwarzschild-dS	$S_b = (c_s/a^2) r_b^2$	$S_{BH} = \pi r_+^2$	$M = 2T_H S_{BH} + r_b^3/l^2$	$-3/8\pi l^2$	—
	$E_b = (c_e/a^2)[3M - r_b^2]$	$E_{\text{Komar}} = 3M - r_b^2$			

5. Conclusion

The Smarr formula for asymptotically flat and non-flat space-times is generally derived using Komar integral relations[32] or via the first law of thermodynamics with the help of scaling relations,[33] both of which makes use of Killing potential. In this talk, we developed an independent approach towards the derivation of the generalized Smarr formula, which essentially describes the equation of state for black holes. The intrinsically quantum phenomenon of entanglement pertaining to the field near a horizon, gives rise to not just the thermodynamic quantities associated with the space-time, but also the exact relation connecting the same. This in turn gives entanglement mechanics an upper hand in addressing the universality problem of black hole entropy. While a wealth of other approaches may explain black-hole entropy, entanglement mechanics *alone* expands the analogy to include other thermodynamic quantities as well.

The results further complements two earlier results: First, Jacobson argued that entanglement provides a link between the presence of matter and the space-time geometry.[34] Second, in quantum gravity, Perez conjectured that degrees of freedom hidden from the classical space-time description but correlated to matter fields are necessary to maintain unitarity in the global evolution and prevent the information loss.[35] Our analysis here provides a crucial link to these results, placing entanglement at the center of a fundamental connection between space-time and matter, thereby holding the key to understanding black-hole horizons.

Acknowledgements

SMC is supported by Prime Minister's Research Fellowship offered by the Ministry of Education, Govt. of India. The work is supported by the MATRICS SERB grant.

References

1. D. Kastor, S. Ray and J. Traschen, Enthalpy and the mechanics of AdS black holes, *Classical Quantum Gravity* **26**, p. 195011 (2009).
2. T. Padmanabhan, Equipartition energy, noether energy and boundary term in gravitational action, *General Relativity and Gravitation* **44**, 2681 (2012).
3. T. Padmanabhan, General relativity from a thermodynamic perspective, *General Relativity and Gravitation* **46**, p. 1673 (2014).
4. P. T. Chruściel, On the relation between the einstein and the komar expressions for the energy of the gravitational field, *Annales de l'I.H.P. Physique théorique* **42**, 267 (1985).
5. S. W. Hawking, Particle creation by black holes, *Communications in Mathematical Physics* **43**, 199 (1975).
6. J. D. Bekenstein, Black holes and entropy, *Phys. Rev. D* **7**, 2333 (Apr 1973).
7. L. Smarr, Mass formula for kerr black holes, *Phys. Rev. Lett.* **30**, 71 (Jan 1973).
8. P. C. W. Davies, Thermodynamics of black holes, *Reports on Progress in Physics* **41**, 1313 (Aug 1978).
9. J. M. Bardeen, B. Carter and S. W. Hawking, The four laws of black hole mechanics, *Commun. Math. Phys.* **31**, 161 (1973).
10. R. M. Wald, The thermodynamics of black holes, *Living Reviews in Relativity* **4** (Jul 2001).
11. D. N. Page, Hawking radiation and black hole thermodynamics, *New Journal of Physics* **7**, 203 (Sep 2005).
12. S. Carlip, *Black Hole Thermodynamics and Statistical Mechanics*, in *Physics of Black Holes: A Guided Tour*, ed. E. Papantonopoulos (Springer Berlin Heidelberg, Berlin, Heidelberg, 2009), Berlin, Heidelberg, pp. 89–123.

13. S. Das, S. Shankaranarayanan and S. Sur, *Black hole entropy from entanglement: A review* (Nova Publishers, 2010), ch. 6.
14. S. Carlip, Black hole entropy and the problem of universality, *Journal of Physics: Conference Series* **67**, p. 012022 (May 2007).
15. G. Vidal, Entanglement renormalization, *Phys. Rev. Lett.* **99**, p. 220405 (Nov 2007).
16. B. Swingle, Entanglement renormalization and holography, *Phys. Rev. D* **86**, p. 065007 (Sep 2012).
17. M. Van Raamsdonk, Building up spacetime with quantum entanglement, *General Relativity and Gravitation* **42**, 2323 (2010).
18. C. Cao, S. M. Carroll and S. Michalakis, Space from hilbert space: Recovering geometry from bulk entanglement, *Phys. Rev. D* **95**, p. 024031 (Jan 2017).
19. K. Hyatt, J. R. Garrison and B. Bauer, Extracting entanglement geometry from quantum states, *Phys. Rev. Lett.* **119**, p. 140502 (Oct 2017).
20. L. Bombelli, R. K. Koul, J. Lee and R. D. Sorkin, Quantum source of entropy for black holes, *Phys. Rev. D* **34**, 373 (Jul 1986).
21. M. Srednicki, Entropy and area, *Phys. Rev. Lett.* **71**, 666 (Aug 1993).
22. J. Eisert, M. Cramer and M. B. Plenio, Colloquium: Area laws for the entanglement entropy, *Rev. Mod. Phys.* **82**, 277 (Feb 2010).
23. S. M. Chandran and S. Shankaranarayanan, One-to-one correspondence between entanglement mechanics and black hole thermodynamics, *Phys. Rev. D* **102**, p. 125025 (Dec 2020).
24. S. Mukohyama, M. Seriu and H. Kodama, Thermodynamics of entanglement in schwarzschild spacetime, *Phys. Rev. D* **58**, p. 064001 (Jul 1998).
25. E. Witten, APS Medal for Exceptional Achievement in Research: Invited article on entanglement properties of quantum field theory, *Rev. Mod. Phys.* **90**, p. 045003 (2018).
26. N. D. Birrell and P. C. W. Davies, *Quantum Fields in Curved Space*, Cambridge Monographs on Mathematical Physics (Cambridge University Press, 1982).
27. T. Jacobson, *Introduction to Quantum Fields in Curved Spacetime and the Hawking Effect*, in *Lectures on Quantum Gravity*, eds. A. Gomberoff and D. Marolf (Springer US, Boston, MA, 2005), Boston, MA, pp. 39–89.
28. S. Mukohyama, M. Seriu and H. Kodama, Can the entanglement entropy be the origin of black-hole entropy?, *Phys. Rev. D* **55**, 7666 (Jun 1997).
29. S. Shankaranarayanan, Temperature and entropy of schwarzschild–de sitter spacetime, *Phys. Rev. D* **67**, p. 084026 (Apr 2003).
30. G. W. Gibbons and S. W. Hawking, Cosmological event horizons, thermodynamics, and particle creation, *Phys. Rev.* **D15**, 2738 (1977).
31. P. F. Byrd and M. D. Friedman, *Handbook of Elliptic Integrals for Engineers and Scientists* (Springer Berlin Heidelberg, 1971).
32. A. Komar, Covariant conservation laws in general relativity, *Phys. Rev.* **113**, 934 (Feb 1959).
33. G. W. Gibbons, M. J. Perry and C. N. Pope, The First law of thermodynamics for Kerr-anti-de Sitter black holes, *Class. Quant. Grav.* **22**, 1503 (2005).
34. T. Jacobson, Thermodynamics of spacetime: The einstein equation of state, *Phys. Rev. Lett.* **75**, 1260 (Aug 1995).
35. A. Perez, No firewalls in quantum gravity: the role of discreteness of quantum geometry in resolving the information loss paradox, *Classical and Quantum Gravity* **32**, p. 084001 (Mar 2015).

Thermodynamics of charged black hole

M. Sharif* and Amjad Khan

Department of Mathematics, University of the Punjab,
Quaid-e-Azam Campus, Lahore-54590, Pakistan
* E-mail: msharif.math@pu.edu.pk
www.pu.edu.pk

This paper investigates thermodynamics as well as thermal stability of the Reissner-Nordström black hole with the effects of non-linear electrodynamics. We first calculate the expressions for Hawking temperature, Helmholtz free energy, internal energy, enthalpy and Gibbs free energy of this black hole and then study their graphical behavior in the presence of non-linear electrodynamic effects. We also investigate thermal stability of the considered system with two different methods, i.e., through heat capacity and through Hessian matrix. It is found from both the methods that the considered system is thermodynamically stable in the presence of non-linear electrodynamic parameter (α). Finally, we analyze the phase transitions of Hawking temperature as well as heat capacity in terms of entropy for different values of charge (q), horizon radius (r_+) and coupling parameter. We obtain that Hawking temperature changes its phase from positive to negative for increasing values of q and r_+ while it shows opposite trend for higher values of α. The heat capacity changes its phase from negative to positive for large values of charge, horizon radius and coupling parameter.

Keywords: Thermodynamics; Stability; Phase transitions.

1. Introduction

The study of final outcomes of self-gravitating objects is one of the most important subjects in general relativity. Black hole (BH) is a completely collapsed structure of massive stars which is defined as a thermodynamical object with very strong gravitational field such that anything even light cannot escape from it. Black hole thermodynamics has resemblance with classical thermodynamics in which mass is related to energy, surface area to entropy and surface gravity to temperature. This resemblance motivated Bekenstein[1] to find out the relation between entropy and area of the event horizon of BH. In this regard, he found that entropy is proportional to the area of event horizon of BH. Hawking's discovery[2] of black body radiations further confirmed the validity of this relation. Consequently, it is impossible to obtain thermal equilibrium between BH and thermal radiations leading to the concept of holographic principle.[3]

Hawking[4] evaluated the expressions of surface gravity, angular frequency and electric potential for any BH having mass, angular momentum and charge. He also discussed generalized second law of BH thermodynamics as well as thermal equilibrium condition for BHs. Motivated by the work of Hawking, Davies[5] discussed about the entropy, thermal stability, phase transition and third law of BH thermodynamics. He also discussed quantum effects of BHs as well as nature and origin of

BH thermal radiations. Wald[6] reviewed the laws of BH thermodynamics, physical correspondence among laws of BH as well as classical thermodynamics, derivation of Hawking radiations, formula for entropy of BH and validity of generalized second law of thermodynamics.

In literature, there is a wide discussion about thermodynamics of different BH geometries. Balart and Vagenas[7] proposed the exact solutions of various regular charged BHs in the presence of non-linear electrodynamic effects and observed that the behavior of some BHs asymptotically coincide to RN BH. Tharanath et al.[8] studied thermal quantities of four regular BHs and observed second order phase transition. Faizal and Khalil[9] found leading order corrections to the thermodynamic quantities of RN, Kerr as well as charged-AdS BHs and concluded that in all three cases, these BHs create remnants. Pradhan[10] investigated local thermal stability as well as logarithmic corrections for entropy of charged accelerating BHs and observed that these BHs undergo second order phase transitions. Sharif and Zunaira[11] investigated the effects of thermal fluctuations on thermodynamics of charged BH with Weyl corrections and concluded that in the presence of logarithmic corrections small BHs are unstable. Sinha[12] discussed thermodynamics as well as stability of asymptotically flat RN BH and observed that this BH exhibits phase transition which is different from the phase transition of Schwarzschild BH.

Davies[13] developed thermodynamical theory of BHs and found that phase transition occurs in the Kerr-Newman BH. Hawking and Page[14] determined the presence of phase transition in the Schwarzschild-AdS BH. Biswas and Chakraborty[15] investigated that whether phase transition is possible in Horava-Lifshitz gravity under the consideration of classical and topological choices of BH thermodynamics. They concluded that phase transition occurs in Horava-Lifshitz gravity from stable to unstable phase for increasing values of radius. Kubiznak and Mann[16] analyzed the first order small-large BHs phase transition in charged AdS BH which is analogous to liquid-gas phase transitions of fluids.

Chaturvedi et al.[17] investigated phase transition in the framework of thermodynamic geometry for charged AdS BH and found first order phase transition for fixed electric charge. Wei et al.[18] studied thermodynamics and found first order phase transition for charged AdS BHs in five-dimensions. Ovgun[19] studied thermodynamics as well as phase transition of a specific charged AdS type BH in $f(R)$ gravity coupled with Yang-Mills field by considering cosmological constant as thermal pressure. Wei and Liu[20] discussed a relation between phase transition and null geodesics of charged AdS BH. Saleh et al.[21] examined thermodynamics as well as phase transition of Bardeen BH surrounded by quintessence and found that the presence of quintessence induces phase transition in the considered BH. Kuang et al.[22] evaluated thermal quantities of AdS non-linear electrodynamic BH. Bhatacharya et al.[23] provided a general criteria to get information and other various results with an extremal limit of BH spacetime. They also evaluated critical values of second order phase transition without considering any specific BH and showed that these values are in agreement with those of any specific BH cases.

Gonzalez et al.[24] studied thermodynamics and stability of charged BHs with non-linear electrodynamics and found that small BHs are stable locally. Dayyani[25] explored thermodynamical properties and phase transition of dilaton BH with non-linear electrodynamics and observed zeroth order phase transition. Yu and Gao[26] derived the exact solutions of RN BH with non-linear electrodynamics. Javed et al.[27] observed the effect of non-linear electrodynamics on weak field deflection angle of RN BH. Recently, Fauzi and Ramadhan[28] discussed thermodynamics of charged BHs with non-linear electrodynamics and verified the first law of BH thermodynamics.

In this paper, we study thermodynamical quantities, thermal stability and phase transition for RN BH with non-linear electrodynamic effects. The paper is outlined as follows. In section **2**, we discuss thermodynamic quantities and their graphical behavior for this BH. Section **3** is devoted to investigate thermal stable configuration and section **4** analyzes phase transitions in terms of entropy. In the last section, we conclude all the results.

2. Thermodynamics

In this section, we discuss thermodynamic quantities such as Hawking temperature, entropy, Helmholtz-Gibbs free energy, internal energy and enthalpy of RN BH with non-linear electrodynamic effects. The line element of this BH is given as[26]

$$ds^2 = f(r)dt^2 - \frac{dr^2}{f(r)} - r^2\left(d\theta^2 + \sin^2\theta d\phi^2\right), \tag{1}$$

with

$$f(r) = 1 + \frac{q^2}{r^2} - \left(\frac{2M}{r} + \frac{\alpha^2 r^2}{3}\right) + 2\alpha q, \tag{2}$$

where q, M and α represent charge, mass of BH and coupling constant, respectively. The line element (1) reduces to the RN BH when $\alpha = 0$, $q \neq 0$, Schwarzschild metric for $\alpha = 0$, $q = 0$ and it becomes Schwarzschild BH with the effects of non-linear electrodynamics for $\alpha \neq 0$, $q = 0$. Figure 1 shows the graphical analysis of the metric function (2) indicating the appearance of naked singularities for the increasing values of the coupling parameter. Setting $f(r_+) = 0$, the mass of BH in terms of r_+ can be obtained as

$$M = \frac{1}{6r_+}\left(3q^2 + r_+^2(6\alpha q - \alpha^2 r_+^2 + 3)\right), \tag{3}$$

where r_+ represents horizon radius of BH. To obtain the expression for Hawking temperature, we first evaluate surface gravity of the BH

$$\kappa = -\frac{\left(q + r_+ - \alpha r_+^2\right)\left(q - \alpha r_+^2 - r_+\right)}{2r_+^3}.$$

Consequently, the Hawking temperature ($T = \frac{\kappa}{2\pi}$) is

$$T = -\frac{\left(q + r_+ - \alpha r_+^2\right)\left(q - \alpha r_+^2 - r_+\right)}{4\pi r_+^3}. \tag{4}$$

The graphical sketch of Hawking temperature versus α is shown in Figure 2. It is found that Hawking temperature increases with the increasing values of coupling parameter throughout the considered domain.

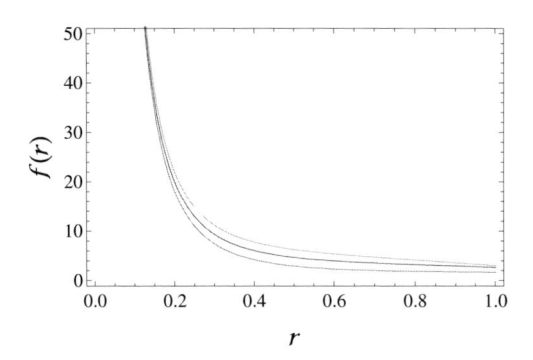

Fig. 1. Plot of the metric function versus r for $M = 1 = q$ with $\alpha = 1$(red), 2(blue) and 3(green).

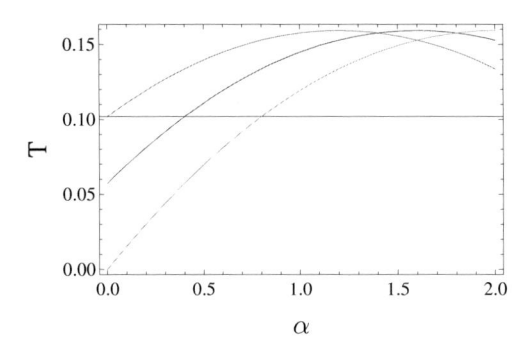

Fig. 2. Plot of Hawking temperature versus α for $r_+ = 0.5$ with $q = 0.3$(red), 0.4(blue) and 0.5(green).

According to Bekenstein area-entropy relation, the entropy of BH can be evaluated as[29]

$$S = \int_0^{2\pi}\int_0^{\pi} \sqrt{g_{\theta\theta}g_{\phi\phi}}d\theta d\phi = \pi r_+^2. \tag{5}$$

Now we calculate other thermal quantities by using the expressions of entropy and Hawking temperature. The expression of Helmholtz free energy can be calculated as

$$F = \frac{1}{16}\left(4q^2 \log(r_+) + r_+^2\left(-4\alpha q + \alpha^2 r_+^2 - 2\right)\right).$$

Figure 3 shows the graphical representation of Helmholtz free energy for different values of the coupling parameter. It is noted that Helmholtz free energy is an increasing function of r_+ and for increasing values of the coupling constant, it increases more rapidly. The increasing trend of Helmholtz free energy depicts that the reactions occurring inside the considered system are non-spontaneous and work done is required to make the system thermodynamically stable. The internal energy $(U = F + ST)$ of the considered system can be obtained as

$$U = \frac{4q^2 r_+ \log(r_+) - 4q^2 - 4\alpha q(r_+ - 2)r_+^2 + \alpha^2(r_+ - 4)r_+^4 - 2(r_+ - 2)r_+^2}{16 r_+}.$$

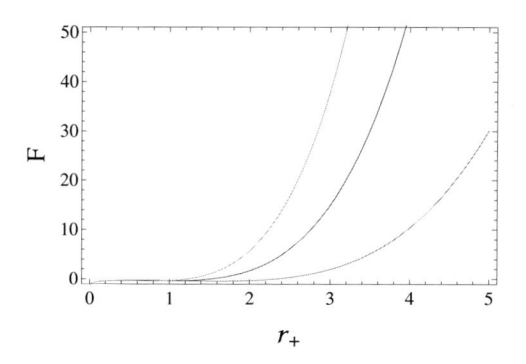

Fig. 3. Plot of Helmholtz free energy versus r_+ for $q = 1$ with $\alpha = 1$(red), 2(blue) and 3(green).

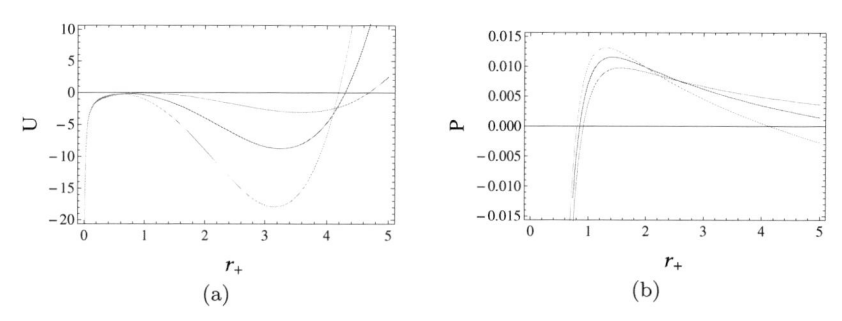

Fig. 4. (a) Plots of internal energy versus r_+ for $q = 1$ with $\alpha = 1$(red), 2(blue), 3(green). (b) Plot of pressure versus r_+ for $q = 1$ with $\alpha = 0.1$(red), 0.2(blue), 0.3(green).

The graphical representation of internal energy in terms of horizon radius is shown in Figure 4(a). It is observed that internal energy of the system fluctuates for increasing values of r_+ and becomes positive towards the boundary of event horizon. The negative behavior of internal energy shows that the considered system is releasing heat for small values of r_+. The corresponding volume is given as[24]

$$V = \frac{4\pi r_+^3}{3}.$$

The pressure for the above calculated volume can be obtained by the relation

$$P = -\frac{dF}{dV} = -\frac{dF}{dr_+}\frac{dr_+}{dV},$$

which gives

$$P = -\frac{\left(q - \alpha r_+^2 + r_+\right)\left(q - r_+(\alpha r_+ + 1)\right)}{16\pi r_+^3}.$$

Figure 4(b) shows the graphical structure of pressure versus r_+ for different values of the coupling parameter. It is noted that pressure of the considered system firstly increases for certain values of horizon radius and then decreases monotonically for large radii. However, for increasing values of the coupling constant, the pressure of BHs with small radii increases slightly while shows opposite trend for large radii.

The expression of enthalpy ($H = VP + U$) can be calculated as follows

$$H = -\left(4q^2(r_+ + 3) - 12q^2 r_+ \log(r_+) + 4\alpha q(r_+ - 6)r_+^2 + \alpha^2(r_+ + 12)r_+^4 + 2(r_+ - 6)r_+^2\right)(48r_+)^{-1}.$$

The graphical analysis of enthalpy in terms of horizon radius is represented in Figure 5(a). It is observed that enthalpy of the considered system is an increasing function of horizon radius. The increasing values of the coupling parameter do not affect the enthalpy for BHs of both small as well as large radii. It is concluded that the considered system is absorbing heat from its surroundings. The Gibbs free energy ($G = H - ST$) of the considered system is obtained as

$$G = \frac{1}{48}\left(12q^2 \log(r_+) - \left(2q + \alpha r_+^2\right)^2 - 2r_+^2\right).$$

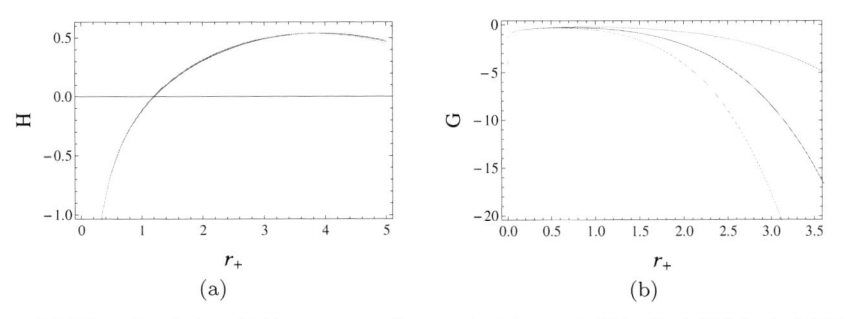

Fig. 5. (a) Plot of enthalpy (left) versus r_+ for $q = 1$ with $\alpha = 0.01$(red), 0.02(blue), 0.03(green). (b) Plot of Gibbs free energy (right) versus r_+ for $q = 1$ with $\alpha = 1$(red), 2(blue), 3(green).

Figure 5(b) represents the graphical structure of Gibbs free energy in terms of r_+ for different values of the coupling constant. It is noted that the Gibbs free energy of the system is inversely proportional to the horizon radius. The increasing values of the coupling parameter do not affect the Gibbs free energy of BHs with $r_+ < 1$ while for $r_+ \geq 1$, the Gibbs free energy is affected significantly and decreases more rapidly.

3. Thermal Stability

In this section, we discuss thermal stable configuration of RN BH with non-linear electrodynamic effects through the following two different methods:

- Heat Capacity;
- Hessian Matrix.

3.1. *Through Heat Capacity*

In order to analyze thermal stability of the considered system, the expression of heat capacity $(T\frac{\partial S}{\partial T})$ can be calculated as follows

$$C = \frac{\pi r_+^2 \left(q + r_+ - \alpha r_+^2\right)\left(q - \alpha r_+^2 - r_+\right)}{r_+^2 - 2\left(q^2 - \alpha q r_+^2\right)}. \tag{6}$$

The graphical analysis of heat capacity represents that it diverges at $r_+ = 0.56$ and this divergent point is known as Davies point (Figure 6). It is also noted that heat capacity changes its phase from negative to positive for increasing values of horizon radius which shows that the considered system is stable in the presence of non-linear electrodynamic effects.

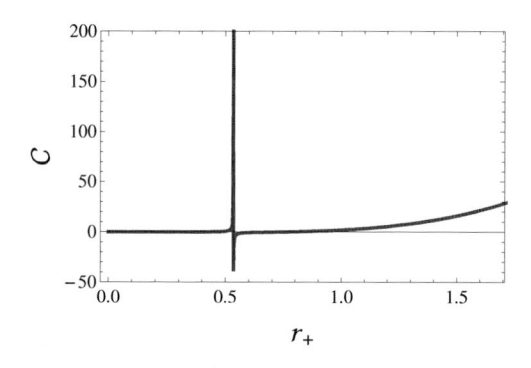

Fig. 6. Plot of heat capacity versus r_+ for $q = 1$ and $\alpha = 3$.

3.2. Through Hessian Matrix

We can also use Hessian matrix to investigate thermal stability of the considered system which contains second order partial derivatives of Helmholtz free energy and is defined as[30]

$$H = \begin{pmatrix} H_{mm} & H_{mn} \\ H_{nm} & H_{nn} \end{pmatrix} = \begin{pmatrix} \frac{\partial^2 F}{\partial T^2} & \frac{\partial^2 F}{\partial T \partial v} \\ \frac{\partial^2 F}{\partial v \partial T} & \frac{\partial^2 F}{\partial v^2} \end{pmatrix},$$

with $m \neq n$, and

$$H_{mm} = \frac{\partial^2 F}{\partial T^2}, \quad H_{mn} = \frac{\partial^2 F}{\partial T \partial v}, \quad H_{nm} = \frac{\partial^2 F}{\partial v \partial T}, \quad H_{nn} = \frac{\partial^2 F}{\partial v^2}.$$

It is noted that $H_{mm}H_{nn} = H_{mn}H_{nm}$, which implies that one of the eigenvalues of the Hessian matrix is zero. Therefore, to determine the stability of the considered geometry, we use trace of the Hessian matrix as

$$Tr(H) = H_{mm} + H_{nn},$$

where

$$H_{mm} = -\left(4\pi^2 r_+^6 \left(9q^4 - 32\alpha q^3 r_+^2 + 2q^2 r_+^2 \left(17\alpha^2 r_+^2 - 8\right) + 4\alpha q r_+^4 \left(3 - 2\alpha^2 r_+^2\right) - 3\alpha^4 r_+^8 - 4\alpha^2 r_+^6 + 3r_+^4\right)\right) \left(\left(-3q^2 + 2\alpha q r_+^2 + \alpha^2 r_+^4 + r_+^2\right)^3\right)^{-1},$$

$$H_{nn} = \left(r_+^2 \left(3\alpha + \left(q - \alpha r_+^2\right)^{-1}\right) + q \left(2r_+^2 \left(q - \alpha r_+^2\right)^{-2} - 1\right)\right) \times \left(4\left(\alpha - q r_+^{-2}\right)\right)^{-1},$$

hence

$$Tr(H) = \left(r_+^2 \left(3\alpha + \left(q - \alpha r_+^2\right)^{-1}\right) + q \left(2r_+^2 \left(q - \alpha r_+^2\right)^{-2} - 1\right)\right)$$
$$\times \left(4\left(\alpha - q r_+^{-2}\right)\right)^{-1} - \left(4\pi^2 r_+^6 \left(9q^4 - 32\alpha q^3 r_+^2 + 2q^2 r_+^2 \left(17\alpha^2 r_+^2 - 8\right)\right.\right.$$
$$\left.\left. + 4\alpha q r_+^4 \left(3 - 2\alpha^2 r_+^2\right) - 3\alpha^4 r_+^8 - 4\alpha^2 r_+^6 + 3r_+^4\right)\right)$$
$$\times \left(\left(-3q^2 + 2\alpha q r_+^2 + \alpha^2 r_+^4 + r_+^2\right)^3\right)^{-1}.$$

A thermodynamical system is said to be stable if $Tr(H) \geq 0$.[31] Figure 7 shows the graphical analysis of the Hessian trace in terms of r_+ for different values of the coupling parameter. It is observed that the trace of Hessian matrix is not defined in the interval $0.5 < r_+ < 0.59$. It is also observed that the Hessian trace shows similar behavior to heat capacity and hence shows that the considered system is stable in the presence of non-linear electrodynamic effects.

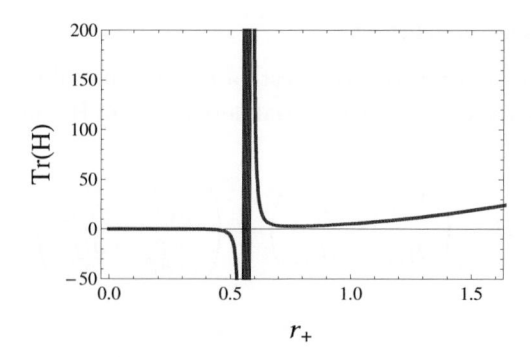

Fig. 7. Plot of Hessian trace versus r_+ for $q = 1$ and $\alpha = 3$.

4. Phase Transitions

Here we examine the phase transitions of Hawking temperature as well as heat capacity of RN BH with non-linear electrodynamic effects in terms of entropy. The Hawking temperature evaluated in Eq. (4) can be written in the form of entropy as

$$T = -\frac{\left(q - \alpha r_+^2 + r_+\right)\left(q - r_+(\alpha r_+ + 1)\right)}{4r_+ S}.$$

Figure 8(a),(c),(e) represents the phase transitions of Hawking temperature in terms of S for different values of q, r_+ and α. It is noted that the Hawking temperature changes its phase from positive to negative for increasing values of q and r_+, respectively (Plot (a) and (c)). However, for increasing values of non-linear electrodynamic parameter, the Hawking temperature changes its phase from negative to positive (plot (c)). The expression of heat capacity for RN BH with non-linear electrodynamic effects in terms of entropy can be obtained from Eq. (6) as

$$C = \frac{S\left(q - \alpha r_+^2 + r_+\right)\left(q - r_+(\alpha r_+ + 1)\right)}{-2q^2 + 2\alpha q r_+^2 + r_+^2}.$$

The phase transitions of heat capacity versus entropy for different values of q, r_+ and α is shown in Figure 8(b),(d),(f). It is noted that heat capacity of the considered BH changes its phase from negative to positive for the increasing values of q, r_+ and α. It is also observed that the considered system is unstable for small values of the considered parameters while it shows stable behavior for large values of q, r_+ and α.

5. Concluding Remarks

In this paper, we have derived thermodynamical quantities for RN BH with non-linear electrodynamic effects and observed their behavior graphically. We have also discussed thermal stable configuration of this BH using both heat capacity as well as Hessian matrix and compared the results graphically. Firstly, we have calculated

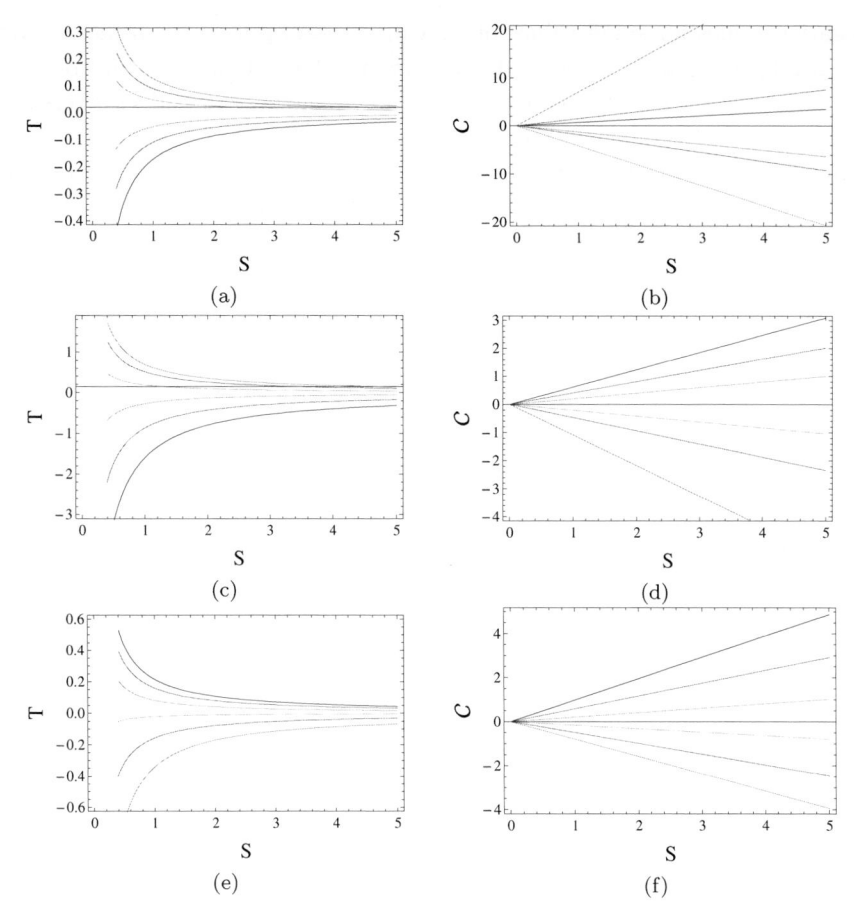

Fig. 8. Hawking temperature ((a), (c), (e)) versus S for $\alpha = 1$, $r_+ = 1$. We take $q = 1.7$(red), 1.8(blue), 1.9(green), 2.1(orange), 2.2(purple), 2.3(black) for plot (a), $\alpha = 1$, $q = 1$ with $r_+ = 0.4$(red), 0.5(blue), 0.6(green), 0.7(orange), 0.8(purple), 0.9(black) for plot (e) and $r_+ = 3$, $q = 1$ with $\alpha = 0.2$(red), 0.3(blue), 0.4(green), 0.5(orange), 0.6(purple), 0.7(black) plot (e). Heat capacity ((b), (d), (f)) versus S with $r_+ = 1$, $\alpha = 1$. We take $q = 1.1$(red), 1.2(blue), 1.3(green), 1.4(orange), 1.5(purple), 1.6(black) for plot (b), $\alpha = 2$, $q = 1$ with $r_+ = 0.7$(red), 0.8(blue), 0.9(green), 1.1(orange), 1.2(purple), 1.3(black) for plot (d) and $r_+ = 3$, $q = 1$, $\alpha = 0.2$(red), 0.3(blue), 0.4(green), 0.5(orange), 0.6(purple), 0.7(black) for plot (f).

the expressions of Hawking temperature with the help of surface gravity ($T = \frac{\kappa}{2\pi}$) and then Helmholtz free energy for the considered BH. The graphical representation of Helmholtz free energy shows that it is an increasing function of r_+ and the presence of non-linear electrodynamic effects only affect the Helmholtz free energy of BHs with large radii while BHs of small radii are unaffected. It is also noted that for increasing values of the coupling constant, it increases more rapidly. The increasing trend of Helmholtz free energy depicts that the reactions occurring inside the considered system are non-spontaneous. The internal energy of the system fluctuates and has negative values for small values of r_+ which shows that the considered system is releasing heat. It is also observed that larger values of the coupling parameter induces large fluctuations in the internal energy of the system and vice-versa.

The enthalpy of the considered system is increasing continuously and showing that the considered system is absorbing heat while the increasing values of coupling parameter do not affect the enthalpy for BHs of both small as well as large radii (Figure 4(a)). Figure 5(a) shows that Gibbs free energy of the considered system is inversely proportional to the horizon radius. The increasing values of coupling parameter do not affect the Gibbs free energy of BHs with $r_+ < 1$ while for $r_+ \geq 1$, this free energy is affected significantly and decreases more rapidly.

Secondly, we have discussed thermal stability of the considered system with the help of heat capacity as well as Hessian matrix by observing their graphical behavior. It is noted that the heat capacity has Davies point at $r_+ = 0.56$ and changes its phase from negative to positive for increasing values of horizon radius which shows that the considered system is stable in the presence of coupling parameter (Figure 6). It is observed from Figure 7 that the trace of Hessian matrix is not defined in the interval $0.5 < r_+ < 0.59$ and shows similar behavior to heat capacity. It is concluded from both the methods that our system is thermodynamically stable in the presence of non-linear electrodynamic effects.

Finally, we have investigated the phase transitions of Hawking temperature as well as heat capacity in terms of entropy for the considered BH. It is found that Hawking temperature changes its phase from positive to negative for increasing values of both charge and horizon radius. This shows that BHs with small charge and radii are more hotter than the BHs with large charge and radii while it shows opposite behavior for increasing values of the coupling parameter. The heat capacity changes its phase from negative to positive for increasing values of the considered parameters which shows that BHs with small values of q, r_+ and α are unstable while BHs with large values are stable throughout the considered domain. We would like to mention here that all our results reduce to the RN BH for $\alpha = 0$.[9]

References

1. J. D. Bekenstein, Black holes and entropy, *Phys. Rev. D* **7**, 2333 (1973).
2. S. W. Hawking, Black hole explosions?, *Nature* **248**, 30 (1974).
3. R. Easther, D. Lowe, Holography, Cosmology and the Second Law of Thermodynamics, *Phys. Rev. Lett.* **82**, 4967 (1999).
4. S. W. Hawking, Black holes and thermodynamics, *Phys. Rev. D* **13**, 191 (1976).
5. P. C. Davies, Thermodynamics of black holes, *Rep. Prog. Phys.* **41**, 1313 (1978).
6. R. M. Wald, The Thermodynamics of black holes, *Living Rev. Relativ.* **4**, 1 (2001).
7. L. Balart, E. C. Vagenas, Regular black holes with a nonlinear electrodynamics source, *Phys. Rev. D* **90**, 124045 (2014).
8. R. Tharanath, J. Suresh, V. C. Kuriakose, Phase transitions and geometrothermodynamics of regular black holes, *Gen. Relativ. Gravit.* **46**, 47 (2015).
9. M. Faizal, M. M. Khalil, GUP-Corrected thermodynamics for all black objects and the existence of remnants, *Int. J. Mod. Phys. A* **30**, 1550144 (2015).

10. P. Pradhan, Horizon Areas and logarithmic correction to the charged accelerating black hole entropy, *Universe* **5**, 57 (2019).
11. M. Sharif, Z. Akhtar, Quasi-normal modes and thermal fluctuations of charged black hole with Weyl corrections, *Phys. Dark Universe* **29**, 100589 (2020).
12. A. K. Sinha, Thermodynamics of asymptotically flat Reissner–Nordstrom black hole, *Mod. Phys. Lett. A* **36**, 2150071 (2021).
13. P. C. W. Davies, The thermodynamic Theory of black holes, *Proc. Roy. Soc. Lond. A* **499**, 353 (1977).
14. S. W. Hawking, D. N. Page, Thermodynamics of black holes in anti-de Sitter space, *Comm. Math. Phys.* **87**, 577 (1983).
15. R. Biswas, S. Chakraborty, Black hole thermodynamics in Horava Lifshitz gravity and the related geometry, *Astrophys. Space Sci.* **193**, 332 (2011).
16. D. Kubiznak, R. B. Mann, P-V criticality of charged AdS black holes, *J. High Energy Phys.* **1207**, 033 (2012).
17. P. Chaturvedi, A. Das, G. Sengupta, Thermodynamic geometry and phase transitions of dyonic charged AdS black holes, *Eur. Phys. J. C* **110**, 77 (2017).
18. S. W. Wei, B. Liang, Y. X. Liu, Critical phenomena and chemical potential of charged AdS black hole, *Phys. Rev. D* **96**, 124018 (2017).
19. A. Ovgun, P-V criticality of a specific black hole in $f(r)$ gravity coupled with Yang-Mills field, *Ad. High Energy Phys.* **2018**, 8153721 (2018).
20. S. W. Wei, Y. X. Liu, Photon orbits and thermodynamic phase transition of d-dimensional charged AdS black holes, *Phys. Rev. D* **97**, 104027 (2018).
21. M. Saleh, B. B. Thomas, T. C. Kofane, Thermodynamics and phase transition from regular Bardeen black hole surrounded by quintessence, *Int. J. Theor. Phys.* **57**, 2640 (2018).
22. X. M. Kuang, B. Liu, A. Ovgun, Nonlinear electrodynamics AdS black hole and related phenomena in the extended thermodynamics, *Eur. Phys. J. C* **78**, 1 (2018).
23. K. Bhattacharya, et al., A general framework to study the extremal phase transition of black holes, *Phys. Rev. D* **99**, 124047 (2019).
24. H. A. Gonzalez, M. Hassaine, C. Martinez, Thermodynamics of charged black holes with a nonlinear electrodynamics source, *Phys. Rev. D* **80**, 104008 (2009).
25. Z. Dayyani, et al., Critical behavior and phase transition of dilaton black holes with nonlinear electrodynamics, *Eur. Phys. J. C* **78**, 152 (2018).
26. S. Yu, C. Gao, Exact black hole solutions with non-linear electrodynamic field, *Int. J. Mod. Phys. D* **29**, 2050032 (2020).
27. W. Javed, J. Abbas, A. Ovgun, Deflection angle of photon from magnetized black hole and effect of nonlinear electrodynamics, *Eur. Phys. J. C* **79**, 1 (2019); W. Javed, A. Hamza, A. Ovgun, Effect of non-linear electrodynamics on weak field deflection angle by black hole, *Phys. Rev. D* **101**, 103521 (2020).
28. M. I. Fauzi, H. S. Ramadhan, Nonlinear electrodynamics black holes: Study of thermodynamic properties, *AIP Conf. Proc.* **2234**, 040009 (2020).
29. S. Das, et al., General logarithmic corrections to black-hole entropy, *Class. Quantum Grav.* **19**, 2355 (2002).
30. B. Pourhassan, M. Faizal, Thermodynamics of a sufficient small singly spinning Kerr-AdS black hole, *Nucl. Phys. B* **913**, 834 (2016).
31. B. Cuadros-Melgar, et al., Late-time tails, entropy aspects, and stability of black holes with anisotropic fluids, *Eur. Phys. J. C* **80**, 848 (2020).

Rindler trajectories and Rindler horizons in the Schwarzschild spacetime

Kajol Paithankar

UM-DAE Centre for Excellence in Basic Sciences,
Mumbai 400098, India
E-mail: kajol.paithankar@cbs.ac.in

Sanved Kolekar

Indian Institute of Astrophysics,
2nd Block, Koramangala, Bengaluru 560034, India
E-mail: sanved.kolekar@iiap.res.in

We investigate radial linear uniformly accelerated trajectories and their corresponding Rindler horizons in the black hole geometry. In a curved spacetime, a covariant definition for Rindler trajectories is provided in the context of the generalised Letaw-Frenet equations for trajectories with constant curvature scalar and vanishing torsion and hypertorsion. Interestingly, we arrive at a bound on magnitude of acceleration for Rindler trajectories such that, for acceleration greater than the bound value, the Rindler trajectory always falls into the black hole and the distance of closest approach for the trajectory to turn away is always greater than the Schwarzschild radius for all finite boundary data. We further investigate the past and future Rindler horizons using the analytical solution for the trajectories and discuss their features.

Keywords: Rindler trajectory, Schwarzschild spacetime, Letaw-Frenet equations.

1. Introduction

In a flat spacetime, Rindler trajectories are a special class of hyperbolic trajectories, moving along orbits of the boost Killing vector and lying in the right or left Rindler quadrant constrained by the future and past null Rindler horizons.[1] The investigation of quantum fields in this background leads to the Unruh effect, which states that the Minkowski vacuum appears as thermal to Rindler observer.[2] It has also been demonstrated that the Rindler observer in an inertial thermal bath with temperature T_B is unable to distinguish between the background thermal and quantum fluctuations as the corresponding reduced density matrix turns out to be symmetric in the two temperatures, the inertial bath temperature T_B and the acceleration temperature T_{unruh}.[3] An analogous case to be investigated would be in curved spacetime case of a black hole with Hawking radiation and an uniformly accelerated observer with arbitrary acceleration.

In this talk, we obtain a solution for radial Rindler trajectories in the Schwarzschild spacetime. In a curved spacetime, the flat spacetime hyperbolic trajectories are replaced by linearly uniformly accelerated (LUA) trajectories which are locally hyperbolic at every point along the trajectory. We use the covariant definition in the context of the generalised Letaw-Frenet equations in curved spacetime for trajectories with constant curvature scalar and vanishing torsion and hyper-torsion. The accompanying Rindler horizons and the Rindler quadrant is expected to get modified in this case due to the presence of background curvature. We determine the causal past and future of the intercepts of the LUA trajectory at future and past null infinity respectively to analyse the corresponding Rindler horizons in the Schwarzschild background for such trajectories.

2. Rindler trajectories in Schwarzschild spacetime

In a curved spacetime, a generalisation of the Rindler trajectory involves, in addition to the constancy condition on the magnitude of acceleration, a further constraint on the trajectory that it must be *linear* with vanishing torsion and hyper-torsion. Such a construction is based on the generalised Letaw-Frenet equations in curved spacetime and the corresponding geometrical scalar invariants which lead to a covariant definition of the linear uniformly accelerated (LUA) trajectory.[4,5] For the LUA trajectory, the Letaw-Frenet equations take the following form of a constraint equation

$$w^i - |a|^2 u^i = 0 \tag{1}$$

where $w^i = u^j \nabla_j a^i$ with u^i and a^i being the velocity and acceleration vectors along the trajectory.

For the Schwarzschild spacetime,

$$ds^2 = \left(1 - \frac{r_s}{r}\right) dt^2 - \left(1 - \frac{r_s}{r}\right)^{-1} dr^2 - r^2 d\theta^2 - r^2 \sin^2\theta \, d\phi^2 \tag{2}$$

we consider radial trajectories which start from the boundary $r \to \infty$, travel towards the black hole and then turn back to infinity. The equation for radial LUA trajectory consistent with the constraint equation is

$$\frac{dt}{dr} = \pm \left(1 - \frac{r_s}{r}\right)^{-1} \frac{(|a|\, r + h)\, \sqrt{r}}{|a|\, \sqrt{(r - r_{min})(r - r_{max})(r - r_n)}} \tag{3}$$

where $|a|$ is the constant magnitude of acceleration, h specifies the initial data at spatial infinity which accounts for the nonlinear shift in the trajectory along the radial direction, and r_{min}, r_{max} and r_n are the roots of the cubic polynomial, $r(|a|r + h)^2 - r + r_s$. The roots r_{min} and r_{max} are the turning points of the LUA trajectories initially moving towards and away from the black hole respectively. The root r_n being negative does not have any physical significance.

These turning points are positive real only when the magnitude of acceleration satisfies the following bound $|a|_b$

$$|a| \le |a|_b = \frac{2\left(-9h + h^3 + \sqrt{(3 + h^2)^3}\right)}{27\, r_s}. \tag{4}$$

A LUA trajectory violating the acceleration bound always falls into the black hole. The turning point r_{min} corresponding to $|a|_b$ gives the lower bound on the distance of closest approach r_b for the return trajectory,

$$r_b = \frac{2}{3|a|_b}\left(\frac{\sqrt{3+h^2}}{2} - h\right). \quad (5)$$

The bound $|a|_b$ has a positive real value only when $h < 1$. Hence, altogether, in the Schwarzschild spacetime for a radial LUA trajectory to turn back at r_{min} it should have initial data $h < 1$ and magnitude of acceleration $|a| < |a|_b$. For all finite boundary data $h < 1$, the distance of closest approach r_b is found to be greater than the Schwarzschild radius r_s.

3. Rindler horizons in Schwarzschild spacetime

For a radially inward moving LUA trajectory satisfying all the conditions to escape back to infinity, the explicit solution $t(r)$ is obtained by integrating Eq. (3) in terms of the elliptic integrals (For details, see[6]). The constant of integration is fixed by choosing $t = 0$ when the trajectory is at its turning point $r = r_{min}$. The nature of trajectories is well explained by this solution in whole spacetime except at radial infinity where the elliptic integral of third kind, encountered in solution, is ill-defined.

This problem is circumvented by re-deriving the solution $t(r)$ as a series expansion. For a LUA trajectory starting from $r_i > r_{min}$, the relevant factors appearing in the denominator of Eq. (3) are expanded around r_{max} and r_s to get

$$\frac{dt}{dr} = \pm \frac{1}{|a|} \sum_{i=0}^{\infty} \sum_{j=0}^{\infty} \binom{-1}{i}\binom{-1/2}{j} \frac{(-r_s)^i (-r_{max})^j}{(r)^{i+j}} \frac{(|a|r + h)}{\sqrt{(r - r_{min})(r - r_n)}} \quad (6)$$

where the notation $\binom{x}{y}$ refers to binomial coefficients. Integrating this equation we get the solution $t(r)$ in terms of the Appell Hypergeometric functions $\mathbf{F_1}$ as,

$$t(r) = \pm \frac{2}{|a|}\sqrt{\frac{r_{min}(r - r_{min})}{r(r_{min} - r_n)}} \sum_{i=0}^{\infty}\sum_{j=0}^{\infty} G(i,j)$$
$$\left(|a|(r_{min} - r_n)\mathbf{F_1}\left[\frac{1}{2}, 2-i-j, \frac{-1}{2}, \frac{3}{2}; \frac{r - r_{min}}{r}, \frac{-r_n(r - r_{min})}{r(r_{min} - r_n)}\right]\right.$$
$$\left. + (h + |a|r_n)\mathbf{F_1}\left[\frac{1}{2}, 1-i-j, \frac{1}{2}, \frac{3}{2}; \frac{r - r_{min}}{r}, \frac{-r_n(r - r_{min})}{r(r_{min} - r_n)}\right]\right) \quad (7)$$

where the coefficients $G(i,j)$ are defined to be

$$G(i,j) = \binom{-1}{i}\binom{-1/2}{j}\left(\frac{-r_s}{r_{min}}\right)^i\left(\frac{-r_{max}}{r_{min}}\right)^j. \quad (8)$$

This solution satisfies the boundary condition $t(r_{min}) = 0$ and has a well defined asymptotic value denoted by $\mathcal{C}$. Using the properties of Hypergeometric functions the solution $t(r)$ for $r \to \infty$ is written in the form, $t(r) = \pm (r + r_s \log(r/r_s) + \mathcal{C})$, with $\mathcal{C}$ determined to be

$$\mathcal{C} = \frac{h}{|a|} + \frac{r_{max}}{2} + \frac{h(r_{max} + 2r_s)}{|a|\sqrt{-r_n r_{min}}} \sin^{-1}\left(\sqrt{\frac{-r_n}{r_{min} - r_n}}\right)$$
$$+ r_s \log\left(\frac{4r_s}{r_{min} - r_n}\right) + \frac{\sqrt{\pi}}{|a|} \sqrt{\frac{r_{min}}{r_{min} - r_n}} (S_d + S_s) \quad (9)$$

where S_d and S_s are double and single convergent summation series respectively expressed as,

$$S_d = \sum_{i=1}^{\infty} \sum_{j=1}^{\infty} G(i,j) \left[|a|(r_{min} - r_n) H_1(i+j) + (h + |a| r_n) H_2(i+j) \right] \quad (10)$$

$$S_s = \sum_{k=2}^{\infty} (G(k,0) + G(0,k)) \left[|a|(r_{min} - r_n) H_1(k) + (h + |a| r_n) H_2(k) \right] \quad (11)$$

with the functions being defined as

$$H_1(k) = \frac{\Gamma(k-1)}{\Gamma\left(k - \frac{1}{2}\right)} \mathbf{F}\left[\frac{1}{2}, \frac{-1}{2}, k - \frac{1}{2}; \frac{-r_n}{r_{min} - r_n}\right]$$

$$H_2(k) = \frac{\Gamma(k)}{\Gamma\left(k + \frac{1}{2}\right)} \mathbf{F}\left[\frac{1}{2}, \frac{1}{2}, k + \frac{1}{2}; \frac{-r_n}{r_{min} - r_n}\right]$$

The LUA trajectory asymptotes to null trajectories near radial infinity as expected, since away from the black hole the scenario becomes asymptotically flat. The asymptotic expansion of LUA trajectory $t(r)$ matches to the form of the null trajectories representing the future and past Rindler horizons,

$$r + r_s \log\left|\frac{r}{r_s} - 1\right| \mp t = \mathcal{C}^{\pm}$$

where we then have the intercepts at radial infinity, $\mathcal{C}^+ = \mathcal{C}^- = \mathcal{C}$ due to the symmetry about the $t = 0$ axis.

The Rindler quadrant for the radial LUA trajectories in the Schwarzschild spacetime is then the union of the past and future null infinity with the past and future horizons in the Penrose diagram. The intersection points of these are the spatial infinity i^0, the past and future intercepts $\mathcal{C}^-$ and $\mathcal{C}^+$ and the bifurcation point of the past and future horizons, which is found to be,

$$r_{null} = r_s \left(1 + W\left[e^{-1-\frac{\mathcal{C}}{r_s}}\right]\right) \quad (12)$$

where $W[x]$ is the productlog function. Thus, unlike in the case of the Rindler quadrant in the flat spacetime, for the Schwarzschild case, the bifurcation point r_{null} is dependent on the asymptotic initial data h as well as the acceleration magnitude $|a|$ and the Schwarzschild radius r_s.

4. Discussion

For the case of Schwarzschild black hole the following observations are made, in comparison with flat spacetime, regarding the Rindler trajectories: In the flat spacetime, all the Rindler trajectories with the magnitude of acceleration in range 0 to ∞ lie in the same Rindler quadrant. This is due to the reason that the corresponding intercept $\mathcal{C}$, the Rindler horizons and the bifurcation point are independent of $|a|$ and just depend on h. In fact, for the limiting case $|a| \to \infty$, the turning point r_{min} is the bifurcation point as the Rindler trajectory coincides with the past and future null horizons. However, in the Schwarzschild case, the intercepts $\mathcal{C}$, the corresponding Rindler horizons and the bifurcation points are all functions of $|a|$ as well. Hence, increasing $|a|$ decreases not just the turning point r_{min} but also the bifurcation point r_{null}. However, it turns out that the turning point does not catch up with the bifurcation point. These observations provide an alternate perspective to look at the acceleration bounds $|a|_b$. The lowest possible value for r_{null} is limited by the black hole horizon to being the Schwarzschild radius r_s, which in turn limits the lowest possible value of r_{min} to $r_{min} = r_b$ and hence a maximum value for the acceleration $|a|$.

References

1. W. Rindler, Hyperbolic Motion in Curved Space Time, *Phys. Rev.* **119**, 2082 (1960).
2. W. G. Unruh, Notes on black-hole evaporation, *Phys. Rev. D* **14**, 870 (1976).
3. Sanved Kolekar and T. Padmanabhan, Indistinguishability of thermal and quantum fluctuations, *Class. Quant. Grav.* **32**, 202001 (2015).
4. J. Letaw, Stationary world lines and the vacuum excitation of noninertial detectors, *Phys. Rev. D* **23**, 1709 (1981).
5. Sanved Kolekar and Jorma Louko, Gravitational memory for uniformly accelerated observers, *Phys. Rev. D* **96**, 024054 (2017).
6. Kajol Paithankar and Sanved Kolekar, Bound on Rindler trajectories in a black hole spacetime, *Phys. Rev. D* **99**, 064012 (2019).
7. Kajol Paithankar and Sanved Kolekar, Rindler horizons in a Schwarzschild spacetime, *Phys. Rev. D* **100**, 084029 (2019).

Linear growth of the two-point function for the Unruh state in 1 + 1 dimensional black holes

Paul R. Anderson* and Zachary P. Scofield

Department of Physics, Wake Forest University,
Winston-Salem, NC 27109, USA
* E-mail: anderson@wfu.edu

Jennie Traschen

Department of Physics, University of Massachusetts,
Amherst, MA 01003, USA
E-mail: traschen@umass.edu

The symmetric two-point function for a massless, minimally coupled scalar field in the Unruh state is examined for Schwarzschild-de Sitter spacetime in two dimensions. This function grows linearly in terms of a time coordinate that is well-defined on the future black hole and cosmological horizons, when the points are split in the space direction. This type of behavior also occurs in two dimensions for other static black hole spacetimes when the field is in the Unruh state, and at late times it occurs in spacetimes where a black hole forms from the collapse of a null shell. The generalization to the case of the symmetric two-point function in two dimensions for a massive scalar field in Schwarzschild-de Sitter spacetime is discussed.

Keywords: Black hole, quantum field theory in curved space

1. Introduction

Hawking[1] predicted that black holes that form from collapse evaporate and at late times the particles are in a thermal distribution with a temperature that is proportional to the surface gravity of the black hole. In four dimensions (4D) it is very difficult to compute quantities such as the two-point function and the stress-energy tensor for a quantum field in the spacetime of a black hole that forms from collapse. Instead, it is significantly easier, although not easy, to do such computations in eternal black hole spacetimes which are either static or stationary. It is easier yet to work with a massless minimally coupled scalar field in spacetimes with two dimensions (2D) that have similar structures to the 4D black hole spacetimes.

Unruh[2] showed that, for an isolated eternal black hole in an asymptotically flat spacetime, there is a particular state for a quantum field that has the same properties as the *in* state for that field has at late times in a spacetime where the black hole forms from collapse. In particular, this state, called the Unruh state, has the same flux of particles at infinity for an eternal black hole as occurs at late times for a black hole that forms from collapse. Thus computations of various quantities for a quantum field in the Unruh state can give insight into the late time behaviors of these quantities in spacetimes where a black hole forms from collapse.

The simplest 4D black hole spacetimes to compute quantum effects in are those which are static and spherically symmetric outside of the event horizon where the metric has the general form

$$ds^2 = -f(r)dt^2 + f^{-1}(r)dr^2 + r^2 d\Omega^2 \,. \tag{1}$$

These are easily changed to 2D spacetimes by dropping the last term on the right. All 2D spacetimes are conformally flat and the massless, minimally coupled scalar field is conformally invariant in such spacetimes making it possible to analytically solve the mode equation in coordinates for which the metric is conformally flat.

In Ref. 3, the Hadamard Green's function, which is the symmetric two-point function, was computed and studied for a massless, minimally coupled scalar field in the Unruh state in 2D for Schwarzschild-de Sitter(SdS) spacetime, Schwarzschild spacetime, de Sitter space, a class of Bose-Einstein condensate analog black hole spacetimes, and a spacetime in which a null shell collapses to form a black hole. It was shown that in all of these cases there is linear growth in terms of a time coordinate T that is regular on the future horizon(s) when the points are split in the spatial direction.

In this proceeding we summarize some of the results of Ref. 3 for black holes. We also discuss the computation of the symmetric two-point function for a massive, minimally coupled scalar field in SdS. In this case, the mode functions and the two-point function must be computed numerically.

In Sec. 2, some properties of 2D SdS are reviewed along with the Unruh state for a massless, minimally coupled scalar field. The Hadamard Green's function for this field is displayed in Sec. 3 and its linear growth in time is discussed. Ongoing work related to the massive scalar field in 2D SdS is discussed in Sec. 4. In Sec. 5 the computation of the symmetric two-point function for a massless, minimally coupled scalar field in a 2D collapsing null shell spacetime is reviewed. Our results are summarized in Sec. 6. Throughout, our units are $\hbar = c = G = 1$.

2. Massless, Minimally Coupled Scalar Field in SdS

A Penrose diagram for SdS is given in Fig. 1. The 2D SdS metric is given by

$$ds^2 = -f(r)dt^2 + \frac{dr^2}{f(r)}, \tag{2a}$$

$$f(r) = 1 - \frac{2M}{r} - H^2 r^2 = -\frac{H^2}{r}(r - r_c)(r - r_b)(r + r_c + r_b) \,. \tag{2b}$$

Here $r_c > r_b$ are the locations of the cosmological and black hole horizons respectively, and $\frac{1}{3}\Lambda = H^2$. The two parameterizations are related by

$$M = \frac{r_b r_c (r_b + r_c)}{2(r_b^2 + r_c^2 + r_b r_c)}, \qquad H^2 = \frac{1}{r_b^2 + r_c^2 + r_b r_c} \tag{3}$$

It is useful to define the tortoise coordinate

$$r_*(r) = \int \frac{dr}{f} \,. \tag{4}$$

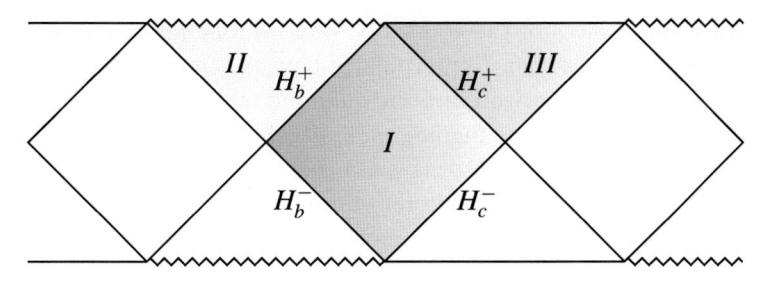

Fig. 1. Penrose diagram for SdS. Region I is the static patch between the black hole horizons and cosmological horizons, Region II is the interior of the black hole, and Region III is the cosmological region.

The ingoing and outgoing radial null coordinates are

$$u = t - r_*, \quad v = t + r_*. \tag{5}$$

One can define two sets of Kruskal coordinates, one for each horizon. The ones we are concerned with are

$$U_b = \frac{1}{\kappa_b} e^{-\kappa_b u}, \quad r < r_b, \quad U_b = -\frac{1}{\kappa_b} e^{-\kappa_b u}, \quad r > r_b \tag{6}$$

$$V_c = -\frac{1}{\kappa_c} e^{-\kappa_c v}, \quad r < r_c, \quad V_c = \frac{1}{\kappa_c} e^{-\kappa_c v}, \quad r > r_c.$$

The surface gravities for the two horizons are

$$\kappa_b = \frac{H^2}{2r_b}(r_c - r_b)(r_c + 2r_b),$$

$$\kappa_c = \frac{H^2}{2r_c}(r_c - r_b)(2r_c + r_b), \tag{7}$$

where for a horizon at $r = r_h$ we set $2\kappa_h = |f'(r_h)|$ so that each of the surface gravities is a positive quantity.

A set of coordinates that are good across $\mathcal{H}_b^+$ and $\mathcal{H}_c^+$ was found in Refs. 4, 5. Let

$$T = t + h(r), \quad \text{where} \quad \frac{dh}{dr} = \frac{j}{f}, \quad j(r) = -\gamma r + \frac{\beta}{r^2}, \tag{8}$$

and

$$\gamma = \frac{r_c^2 + r_b^2}{r_c^3 - r_b^3}, \quad \beta = \frac{r_c^2 r_b^2 (r_b + r_c)}{r_c^3 - r_b^3}. \tag{9}$$

Then the 2D SdS metric becomes

$$ds^2 = -f(r)dT^2 + 2j(r)drdT + \frac{1-j^2}{f}dr^2. \tag{10}$$

Note that for these choices of the constants γ and β, one finds that $j(r_b) = 1$ and $j(r_c) = -1$, which ensures that T interpolates between the ingoing null coordinate v at the future black hole horizon and the outgoing null coordinate u at the future cosmological horizon. These are ingoing and outgoing Eddington-Finklestein coordinates respectively. The metric (10) is well behaved in the static and cosmological regions and has the Eddington-Finklestein form on both the future black hole and future cosmological horizons. The coordinate T stays timelike and r stays spacelike beyond the cosmological horizon.

The definitions of r_* and T each contain an arbitrary constant which can be chosen such that

$$T = u \text{ on } \mathcal{H}_c^+, \quad \text{and} \quad T = v \text{ on } \mathcal{H}_b^+. \quad (11)$$

The result is[3]

$$T = t + h(r) \quad (12)$$
$$= t + \frac{1}{2\kappa_b} \log \frac{|r - r_b|}{r_c - r_b} + \frac{1}{2\kappa_c} \log \frac{|r - r_c|}{r_c - r_b} + \frac{1}{2}\left(\frac{r_c}{r_b \kappa_b} - \frac{1}{\kappa_N}\right) \log \frac{r + r_c + r_b}{r_c + 2r_b}$$
$$- \frac{r_b r_c}{2(r_c - r_b)} \log \frac{r^2}{r_c r_b} + \frac{r_c}{4 r_b \kappa_b} \log \frac{r_c + 2r_b}{2r_c + r_b},$$

and

$$r_*(r) = \frac{1}{2\kappa_b} \log \frac{|r - r_b|}{r_c - r_b} - \frac{1}{2\kappa_c} \log \frac{|r - r_c|}{r_c - r_b} + \frac{1}{2\kappa_N} \log \frac{|r + r_c + r_b|}{r_c + 2r_b} \quad (13)$$
$$- \frac{r_c}{4 r_b \kappa_b} \log \frac{2r_c + r_b}{r_c + 2r_b} - \frac{r_b r_c}{2(r_c - r_b)} \log \frac{r_b}{r_c},$$

where

$$\kappa_N = \frac{H^2}{2(r_c + r_b)}(2r_c + r_b)(r_c + 2r_b). \quad (14)$$

To relate the Kruskal coordinates to T and r, note that $u = T - (h(r) + r_*)$ and $v = T - h(r) + r_*$. Substitution gives

$$V_c = \frac{1}{\kappa_c} e^{-\kappa_c T} \tilde{V}_c, \quad \text{and} \quad U_b = \frac{1}{\kappa_b} e^{-\kappa_b T} \tilde{U}_b, \quad (15)$$

where $\tilde{V}_c$ and $\tilde{U}_b$ only depend on r and are given by

$$\tilde{V}_c = e^{\kappa_c(h - r_*)} = \frac{r - r_c}{r_c - r_b}\left(\frac{r + r_c + r_b}{r_c + 2r_b}\right)^{r_b/2r_c}\left(\frac{r_b}{r}\right)^{H^2 r_b(2r_c + r_b)/2}, \quad (16)$$

$$\tilde{U}_b = -e^{\kappa_b(h + r_*)} = -\frac{(r - r_b)}{r_c - r_b}\left(\frac{r + r_b + r_c}{2r_c + r_b}\right)^{r_c/2r_b}\left(\frac{r_c}{r}\right)^{H^2 r_c(r_c + 2r_b)/2}.$$

Note that these expressions work both inside and outside the black hole and cosmological horizons.

The complete set of modes that comprise the Unruh state consist of modes that are positive frequency with respect to U_b on the past black hole horizon and modes that are positive frequency with respect to V_c on the past cosmological horizon.[6–8]

$$p_\omega^b = \frac{e^{-i\omega U_b(u)}}{\sqrt{4\pi\omega}} \quad \text{and} \quad p_\omega^c = \frac{e^{-i\omega V_c(v)}}{\sqrt{4\pi\omega}} \quad (17)$$

Expanding the massless minimally coupled scalar field in terms of these gives

$$\phi = \int_0^\infty d\omega \left[a_\omega^b p_\omega^b + a_\omega^c p_\omega^c + a_\omega^{b\dagger} p_\omega^{b*} + a_\omega^{c\dagger} p_\omega^{c*} \right], \quad (18)$$

where $a^{(b,c)}$ are the annihilation operators.

3. Symmetric Two-Point Function in SdS

For a massless, minimally coupled scalar field in 2D SdS in the Unruh state, the symmetric two-point function for an arbitrary splitting of the points is[3]

$$\begin{aligned}
G^{(1)}(x,x') &= \langle U | \left(\phi(x)\phi(x') + \phi(x')\phi(x) \right) | U \rangle \\
&= \int_0^\infty d\omega [p_\omega^b(x) p_\omega^{b*}(x') + p_\omega^c(x) p_\omega^{c*}(x') + \text{c.c.}] \\
&= \frac{1}{2\pi} \int_{\omega_0}^\infty \frac{d\omega}{\omega} \left\{ \cos[\omega(U_b - U_b')] + \cos[\omega(V_c - V_c')] \right\} \\
&= -\frac{1}{2\pi} \left\{ ci[\omega_0 |U_b - U_b'|] + ci[\omega_0 |V_c - V_c'|] \right\}. \quad (19)
\end{aligned}$$

Here ci is the cosine integral function which has the expansion $ci(z) = \gamma_E + \log z + O(z^2)$, and ω_0 is a small infrared cutoff.

Let x be on H_+^b and x' on H_+^c and take $T' = T$. Note that on H_b^+, $U_b = 0$, $v = T$ and on H_c^+, $V_c = 0$, $u = T$. Then

$$U_b - U_b' = -\kappa_b^{-1} e^{-\kappa_b T}, \quad V_c - V_c' = \kappa_c^{-1} e^{-\kappa_c T},$$
$$2\pi G^{(1)}(T,r;T,r') = (\kappa_b + \kappa_c)T - \log\left[(\kappa_b \kappa_c)^{-1} \omega_0^2\right] - 2\gamma_E. \quad (20)$$

Thus one sees an unexpected linear growth in the time coordinate T for this separation of the points. For a more general separation

$$2\pi G^{(1)}(T,r;T,r') = T(\kappa_b + \kappa_c) - \log\left(\frac{\omega_0^2}{\kappa_b \kappa_c} |\Delta \tilde{U}_b \Delta \tilde{V}_c| \right) - 2\gamma_E, \quad (21)$$

where $\Delta \tilde{U}_b$ and $\Delta \tilde{V}_c$ are functions of r and r', but not T.

In Ref. 3 a similar linear growth in a time coordinate for $G^{(1)}(x,x')$ in 2D for a massless minimally coupled scalar field was found in Schwarzschild spacetime for the Unruh state, de Sitter spacetime for the Bunch-Davies state, and a class of Bose-Einstein condensate analog black hole spacetimes for the Unruh state. A general argument was also given that linear growth should occur whenever there is a past horizon and no scattering for the Unruh state.

One may ask what these situations have in common. In each case the symmetric two-point function is computed for a massless minimally coupled scalar field in 2D in the Unruh state or its analog, the two-point function has an infrared divergence which requires an infrared cutoff, and each spacetime has a static patch and at least one past horizon. In the next two sections, two cases are discussed in which one or more of these conditions does not occur.

4. Massive Scalar Field in 2D SdS

One way to investigate the generality of the linear growth in time is to work with a massive scalar field. Work is in progress to compute the symmetric two-point function for this field. It is significantly more difficult than for the massless scalar field because the mode equation contains an effective potential term and does not have simple closed form solutions. Instead, when separation of variables is used, the radial part of the mode equation can be solved numerically.

The mode equation cannot be separated in Kruskal coordinates but it can be separated in terms of the coordinates t and r in (2b). The mode equation in this case is

$$-\frac{\partial^2 h}{\partial t^2} + \frac{\partial^2 h}{\partial r_*^2} - m^2 f = 0 \,. \tag{22}$$

The relevant solutions are of the form

$$h(t,r) = \frac{e^{-i\omega t}}{\sqrt{4\pi\omega}} \chi_\omega(r) \,, \tag{23}$$

with

$$\frac{d^2\chi}{dr_*^2} + (\omega^2 - m^2 f)h = 0 \,. \tag{24}$$

A complete set of modes that specify the Boulware state can be obtained by combining modes which on the past black hole horizon have the form

$$h^b_\omega = \frac{e^{-i\omega u}}{\sqrt{4\pi\omega}} \,, \tag{25}$$

and those which on the past cosmological horizon have the form

$$h^c_\omega = \frac{e^{-i\omega v}}{\sqrt{4\pi\omega}} \,. \tag{26}$$

The modes that specify the Unruh state can be expanded in terms of these modes with the result

$$p^{(b,c)}_\omega = \int_0^\infty d\omega' \, [\alpha^{(b,c)}_{\omega\omega'} h^{(b,c)}_{\omega'} + \beta^{(b,c)}_{\omega\omega'} h^{(b,c)*}_{w'}] \,. \tag{27}$$

Since the mode equation reduces to its massless form on the past horizons, the initial conditions for the Unruh state are exactly the same as in the massless case (17).

Using the usual scalar product,[9] one finds[10]

$$\alpha_{\omega\omega'}^{(b,c)} = \frac{1}{2\pi}\sqrt{\frac{\omega'}{\omega}}\left(\kappa_{(b,c)}\right)^{-1-i\frac{\omega'}{\kappa_{(b,c)}}}\frac{\Gamma(-i\frac{\omega'}{\kappa_{(b,c)}})}{(-i\omega)^{-i\frac{\omega'}{\kappa_{(b,c)}}}},$$

$$\beta_{\omega\omega'}^{(b,c)} = \frac{1}{2\pi}\sqrt{\frac{\omega'}{\omega}}\left(\kappa_{(b,c)}\right)^{-1+i\frac{\omega'}{\kappa_{(b,c)}}}\frac{\Gamma(i\frac{\omega'}{\kappa_{(b,c)}})}{(-i\omega)^{i\frac{\omega'}{\kappa_{(b,c)}}}}. \quad (28)$$

Note that these are divergent in the limit $\omega' \to 0$ due to the poles in the Gamma functions. However, we have shown that because of scattering effects, these divergences are canceled in the integrand of Eq. (27). Also, it is important to note that the limit $\omega' \to 0$ needs to be taken before the limits $r \to r_b$ and $r \to r_c$. They cannot be interchanged.

At present, work is in progress to compute p_ω^b and p_ω^c numerically. It is not yet known whether the divergence that exists for the massless case for these mode functions continues to be present in the massive case.

5. Collapsing Null Shell Spacetime

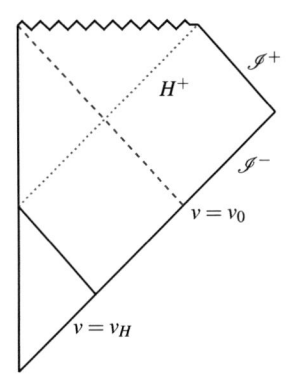

Fig. 2. Penrose diagram for a 2D spacetime in which a null shell collapses to form a black hole and there is a perfectly reflecting mirror at the origin. The trajectory of the shell is given by the dashed blue line and the event horizon is given by the dotted red line.

Another calculation that was done in Ref. 3 was to compute the two-point function for a massless scalar field in a 2D spacetime in which a null shell collapses to form a Schwarzschild black hole. Inside the shell the metric is the flat space metric

$$ds^2 = -dt^2 + dr^2, \quad (29)$$

and outside it is Eq. (2b) with $H = 0$, which is the Schwarzschild metric. If one puts in a perfectly reflecting mirror and requires that the field vanish at the surface of the mirror then one obtains the same conditions on the mode functions at $r = 0$ as in the 4D case. The Penrose diagram for this spacetime is shown in Fig. 2.

Inside the shell, the usual null coordinates are

$$u = t - r, \qquad v = t + r, \qquad (30)$$

and outside the shell they are

$$u_s = t_s - r_*, \qquad v = t_s + t_*. \qquad (31)$$

The coordinates r and v are continuous across the trajectory of the shell which is $v = v_0$, for some v_0. At the null shell surface one finds[11,12]

$$u(u_s) = v_H - 4MW\left[\exp\left(\frac{v_H - u_s}{4M}\right)\right], \qquad (32)$$

where $v_H = v_0 - 4M$ and W is the Lambert W function. On past null infinity both u_s and u are equal to $-\infty$. On the future horizon of the black hole $u_s = \infty$ and $u = v_H$.

Because of the mirror, the mode functions must vanish at $r = 0$. For the *in* state, at past null infinity they have the form

$$f_\omega^{\text{in}} \to \frac{e^{-i\omega v}}{\sqrt{4\pi\omega}}. \qquad (33)$$

The solution that satisfies these two conditions is

$$f_\omega^{\text{in}} = \frac{1}{\sqrt{4\pi\omega}}(e^{-i\omega v} - e^{-i\omega u}). \qquad (34)$$

Since there is no scattering in 2D for the massless, minimally coupled scalar field, outside the shell the solution is

$$f_\omega^{\text{in}} = \frac{1}{\sqrt{4\pi\omega}}(e^{-i\omega v} - e^{-i\omega u(u_s)}). \qquad (35)$$

Note that $f_\omega^{\text{in}} = 0$ at $\omega = 0$. Thus there is no infrared divergence in the two-point function for this state and no infrared cutoff is necessary. One finds that[3]

$$2\pi G^{(1)}(x, x') = \log\left[\frac{|v - u(u_s')||v' - u(u_s)|}{|v - v'||u(u_s) - u(u_s')|}\right]. \qquad (36)$$

Using $v = T - h(r) + r_*$ and $u = T - h(r) - r_*$, one finds for $T = T'$ and fixed values of r and r', that at late times

$$2\pi G(T, r;, T, r') \to \kappa T + \log(\kappa^2 T^2) + (r, r' \text{dependent terms}). \qquad (37)$$

Thus, there is not only a linear growth in T as there is for the Unruh state, but there is also a secondary logarithmic growth.

6. Conclusions

In Ref. 3, the behavior of the two point function was investigated for a massless, minimally coupled scalar field in the Unruh state in certain 2D spacetimes. It was found that linear growth in time of the form

$$2\pi G^{(1)}(T,r;T,r') = T \sum_J \kappa_J + (r, r' \text{dependent terms}) \tag{38}$$

occurs, where the sum is over the surface gravities of the past horizons and T is a time coordinate that is regular on the future horizons. Along with the existence of one or two past horizons, the Green's function for each spacetime is infrared divergent and thus requires an infrared cutoff to regularize this divergence.

The two-point function for this field in a 2D spacetime in which a null shell collapses to form a black hole was also computed. In this case there is no past horizon and thus no Unruh state. Instead, since the spacetime is asymptotically flat, the state for the massless, minimally coupled scalar field was chosen to be the initial vacuum state. By putting a perfectly reflecting mirror at the origin and requiring that the mode functions vanish there, the same type of condition that one finds in the 4D collapsing null shell spacetime if the shell is spherically symmetric was imposed. As a result of this condition, the two-point function has no infrared divergences.

It was found that at early times there is no linear growth in time of the form (38), however at late times there is growth of this form. There is also a subleading term that diverges logarithmically in time at late times. Thus, the linear growth in time found in the eternal black hole calculations also occurs, at least in 2D, for a black hole that forms from the collapse of a null shell. Perhaps this is not surprising since the Unruh state is supposed to give the leading order, late time behavior of quantities such as the two-point function and stress-energy tensor for the quantum field in the case of a black hole that forms from collapse. However, it does show that the linear growth in time does not depend on the existence of either a past horizon or an infrared divergence in the two-point function.

To see whether the linear growth in time only occurs for the massless scalar field, the case of a massive scalar field in the Unruh state in 2D SdS is being investigated. It has been shown that, when the mode functions for the Unruh state are expanded in terms of those for the Boulware state, an infrared diverge that occurs in the massless case is not present in the massive one. Work is in progress to determine whether the linear growth in time of the two-point function also occurs for a massive scalar field.

Acknowledgments

P.R.A. and J.T. would like to thank David Kastor for useful conversations. P.R.A. would also like to thank Alessandro Fabbri and Ian Moss for useful conversations. This work came about as a result of conversations at the NORDITA Gravitational

Physics with Lambda Workshop 2018. We would like to thank NORDITA for their generous support. This work was supported in part by the National Science Foundation under Grants No. PHY-1505875 and PHY-1912584 to Wake Forest University.

References

1. S. W. Hawking, *Commun. Math. Phys.* **43**, 199 (1975), Erratum: [*Commun. Math. Phys.* **46**, 206 (1976)].
2. W. G. Unruh, *Phys. Rev. D* **14**, 870 (1976).
3. P. R. Anderson and J. Traschen, arXiv:2012.08494 [hep-th].
4. R. Gregory, D. Kastor and J. Traschen, JHEP **1710**, 118 (2017).
5. R. Gregory, D. Kastor and J. Traschen, *Class. Quant. Grav.* **35**, 155008 (2018).
6. S. Tadaki and S. Takagi, *Prog. Theor. Phys.* **83**, 941 (1990).
7. S. Tadaki and S. Takagi, *Prog. Theor. Phys.* **83**, 1126 (1990).
8. D. Markovic and W. G. Unruh, *Phys. Rev.* D **43**, 332 (1991).
9. N. D. Birrell and P. C. W. Davies, *Quantum fields in Curved Space* (Cambridge University Press, Cambridge, UK, 1982).
10. P. R. Anderson, S. Gholizadeh Siahmazgi, R. D. Clark, and A, Fabbri, *Phys. Rev.* D **102**, 125035 (2020).
11. S. Massar and R. Parentani, *Phys. Rev.* D **54**, 7444 (1996).
12. A. Fabbri and J. Navarro-Salas, *Modeling black hole evaporation* (Imperial College Press, London, UK, 2005).

Stress-energy tensor for a quantized scalar field in a four-dimensional black hole that forms from the collapse of a null shell

Shohreh Gholizadeh Siahmazg*, Paul R. Anderson† and Raymond D. Clark

Department of Physics, Wake Forest University,
Winston Salem, North Carolina 27109, USA
* E-mail: ghols18@wfu.edu
† E-mail: anderson@wfu.edu

Alessandro Fabbri

Departamento de Física Teórica and IFIC, Universidad de Valencia-CSIC
C. Dr. Moliner 50, 46100 Burjassot
E-mail: afabbri@ific.uv.es

A method is presented which allows for the numerical computation of the stress-energy tensor for a quantized massless minimally coupled scalar field in the region outside the event horizon of a 4D Schwarzschild black hole that forms from the collapse of a null shell. This method involves taking the difference between the stress-energy tensor for the *in* state in the collapsing null shell spacetime and that for the Unruh state in Schwarzschild spacetime. The construction of the modes for the *in* vacuum state and the Unruh state is discussed. Applying the method, the renormalized stress-energy tensor in the 2D case has been computed numerically and shown to be in agreement with the known analytic solution. In 4D, the presence of an effective potential in the mode equation causes scattering effects that make the the construction of the in modes more complicated. The numerical computation of the *in* modes in this case is given.

Keywords: Black holes; Quantum field theory in curved space; Stress-energy tensor.

1. Introduction

The expectation value of the renormalized stress-energy tensor operator for a quantized field is a useful way to study quantum effects curved space. It can also be used in the context of semiclassical gravity to compute the backreaction of the quantum field on the background geometry. In the case of four-dimensional, 4D, black holes, this quantity has to date only been computed for static black holes[1-4,6-15] and Kerr black holes.[16,17] However, to our knowledge, a full numerical computation of this quantity has not been done for a quantized field in a 4D spacetime in which a black hole forms from the collapse of a null shell, which is probably the simplest model for the formation of a black hole.

In Ref. 18, we developed a method to numerically compute the full renormalized stress-energy tensor for a massless minimally coupled scalar field in the case of a spherically symmetric black hole in 4D that forms from the collapse of a null shell. This method can be used in the region outside the null shell and future horizon, where by Birkhoff's theorem, the geometry is described by the Schwarzschild metric.

In this proceeding, we review this method with a focus on the computation of a complete set of *in* modes that can be used to construct the quantum field in the region outside the null shell. We also present new numerical results for a low frequency *in* mode on the future horizon and for a mode with relatively high frequency on the part of the future horizon close to the null shell trajectory.

In Sec. 2, we review the null shell spacetime and the metrics describing the geometry inside and outside of the null shell. In Sec. 3, we discuss the quantization of the massless minimally coupled scalar field in the null shell spacetime. In Sec. 4, we present our method to expand the *in* modes in terms of a complete set of modes in pure Schwarzschild spacetime and present our numerical results for the high and low frequency modes on the future horizon. In Sec. 5, a proper method for the renormalization of the stress-energy tensor is given. In this section, we summarize the application of our method in Ref. 18 to the case of a collapsing null shell spacetime which has a perfectly reflecting mirror at the spatial origin.

2. Collapsing null shell

The model we consider is a spherically symmetric null shell whose collapse results in the formation of a black hole. The Penrose diagram of the spacetime is depicted in Fig. 1 The spacetime inside the null shell is described by the flat metric

$$ds^2 = -dt^2 + dr^2 + r^2 d\Omega^2 ,$$

and from Birkhoff's theorem, the metric outside the shell is the Schwarzschild metric

$$ds^2 = -\left(1 - \frac{2M}{r}\right) dt_s^2 + \left(1 - \frac{2M}{r}\right)^{-1} dr^2 + r^2 d\Omega^2$$

with $d\Omega^2 = d\theta^2 + \sin^2\theta d\phi^2$. It is more convenient to use radial null coordinates to match the geometries inside and outside of the shell. In the interior,

$$u = t - r , \quad v = t + r .$$

and in the exterior region,

$$u_s = t_s - r_* , \quad v = t_s + r_* ,$$

where $r_* = r + 2M \ln\left(\frac{r-2M}{2M}\right)$ is the tortoise coordinate in Schwarzschild spacetime. The null shell trajectory is $v = v_0$. We match the two spacetimes so that the v coordinate and the angular coordinates are continuous across the null shell trajectory. Applying this condition gives the following relation between the u an u_s coordinates[19,20]

$$u_s = u - 4M \log\left(\frac{v_H - u}{4M}\right) ,$$

where $v_H = v_0 - 4M$.

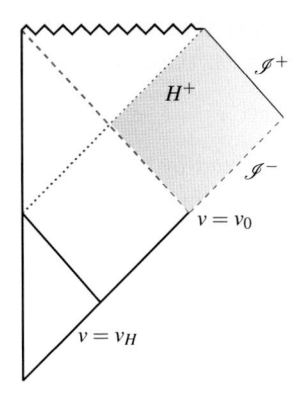

Fig. 1. Penrose diagram for a spacetime in which a null shell collapses to form a spherically symmetric black hole. The vertical line on the left corresponds to the surface $r = 0$ which is also the surface where $u = v$. The dashed red line on $v = v_0$ is the trajectory of the null shell. The horizon, H^+ is the dotted blue curve. Inside the shell trajectory H^+ corresponds to the surface $u = v_H$ and outside the shell trajectory it corresponds to $u_s = \infty$. A Cauchy surface is shown by the dashed line. It is the union of the surface $v = v_0$ with the part of $\mathscr{I}^-$ with $v > v_0$.

3. Massless minimally coupled scalar field

We consider a massless minimally coupled scalar field in the null shell spacetime. In a general static spherically symmetric spacetime, it can be expanded in the following way,

$$\phi = \sum_{\ell=0}^{\infty} \sum_{m=-\ell}^{\ell} \int_0^{\infty} [a_{\omega\ell m} f_{\omega\ell m} + a^{\dagger}_{\omega\ell m} f^*_{\omega\ell m}]$$

with $\Box f_{\omega\ell m} = 0$. In the region inside the null shell, $v < v_0$, separation of variables gives

$$f_{\omega\ell m} = \frac{Y_{\ell m}(\theta, \phi)}{r\sqrt{4\pi\omega}} \psi_{\omega\ell}(t, r) = \frac{Y_{\ell m}(\theta, \phi)}{r\sqrt{4\pi\omega}} e^{-i\omega t} \chi_{\omega\ell}(r), \quad (1)$$

while in the region outside the null shell, $v > v_0$, it gives

$$f_{\omega\ell m} = \frac{Y_{\ell m}(\theta, \phi)}{r\sqrt{4\pi\omega}} \psi_{\omega\ell}(t_s, r) = \frac{Y_{\ell m}(\theta, \phi)}{r\sqrt{4\pi\omega}} e^{-i\omega t_s} \chi_{\omega\ell}(r). \quad (2)$$

In the regions $v < v_0$ and $v > v_0$ respectively, the radial parts of the mode functions satisfy the differential equations

$$\frac{d^2 \chi_{\omega\ell}}{dr^2} = -\left[\omega^2 - \frac{\ell(\ell+1)}{r^2}\right] \chi_{\omega\ell}. \quad (3)$$

$$\frac{d^2 \chi_{\omega\ell}}{dr_*^2} = -\left[\omega^2 - \left(1 - \frac{2M}{r}\right)\left(\frac{2M}{r^3} + \frac{\ell(\ell+1)}{r^2}\right)\right] \chi_{\omega\ell}. \quad (4)$$

The *in* state is fixed by requiring that $\psi_{\omega\ell} = e^{-i\omega v}$ on past null infinity and it vanishes at $r = 0$. The solution with these properties has the form

$$\psi_{\omega\ell}^{in}(r,t) = C_\ell e^{i\omega t} \omega r j_\ell(\omega r) \tag{5}$$

inside the null shell, where C_ℓ is fixed by the aforementioned condition on past null infinity. Here j_ℓ is a spherical bessel function of the first kind. It is not possible for this solution to have the form $e^{-i\omega t_s}\chi_{\omega\ell}(r)$ outside the null shell. The solution in this region is more complicated.

4. Computation of $f_{\omega\ell m}^{in}$

We can compute $f_{\omega\ell m}^{in}$ outside the null shell and the event horizon by expanding it in terms of a complete set of modes since the geometry here is the Schwarzschild geometry. This problem can be mapped to the shaded part of pure Schwarzschild spacetime shown in Fig. 2. We choose a complete sets of modes that consists of the union of the modes $f_{\omega\ell m}^{H^+}$ that are positive frequency on future horizon and zero on future null infinity, and the modes $f_{\omega\ell m}^{\mathscr{I}^+}$ that are positive frequency on the future null infinity and zero on the future horizon, *i.e.*,

$$f_{\omega\ell m}^{in} = \sum_{\ell'=0}^{\infty}\sum_{m'=-\ell'}^{\ell'}\int_0^\infty d\omega' \Big[A_{\omega\ell m\omega'\ell'm'}^{\mathscr{I}^+} f_{\omega'\ell'm'}^{\mathscr{I}^+} + B_{\omega\ell m\omega'\ell'm'}^{\mathscr{I}^+} (f_{\omega'\ell'm'}^{\mathscr{I}^+})^* \\ + A_{\omega\ell m\omega'\ell'm'}^{H^+} f_{\omega'\ell'm'}^{H^+} + B_{\omega\ell m\omega'\ell'm'}^{H^+} (f_{\omega'\ell'm'}^{H^+})^* \Big]. \tag{6}$$

The matching coefficients $A_{\omega\ell m\omega'\ell'm'}^{\mathscr{I}^+}$, $B_{\omega\ell m\omega'\ell'm'}^{\mathscr{I}^+}$, $A_{\omega\ell m\omega'\ell'm'}^{H^+}$, and $B_{\omega\ell m\omega'\ell'm'}^{H^+}$ can be found using the following scalar products on the Cauchy surface shown in Fig. 2.

$$A_{\omega\ell m\omega'\ell'm'}^{(\mathscr{I}^+,H^+)} = (f_{\omega\ell m}^{in}, f_{\omega'\ell'm'}^{(\mathscr{I}^+,H^+)}), \tag{7}$$

$$B_{\omega\ell m\omega'\ell'm'}^{(\mathscr{I}^+,H^+)} = -(f_{\omega\ell m}^{in}, (f_{\omega'\ell'm'}^{(\mathscr{I}^+,H^+)})^*). \tag{8}$$

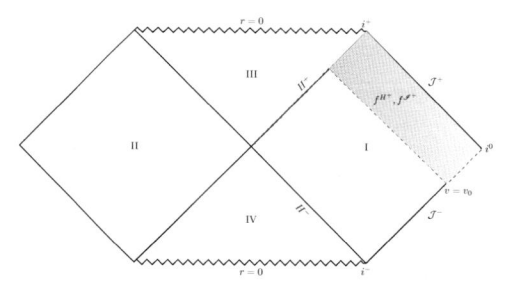

Fig. 2. Penrose diagram for Schwarzschild spacetime showing the Cauchy surface used for matching the in modes in the null shell spacetime to a complete set of modes in Schwarzschild spacetime in the region outside the past and future horizons. The Cauchy surface is denoted by the dashed red curve.

The reason one can expand the *in* modes in this way is that the same differential equations govern the evolution of the *in* modes in the shaded region in Fig. 1 and the shaded region in Fig. 2 because the metric is the same in both regions. However, one may notice that the union of the part of past null infinity with $v > v_0$ and the null shell surface does not form a Cauchy surface in pure Schwarzschild spacetime. We resolve this issue by adding the part of the future horizon with $-\infty < v < v_0$ to the union of $\mathscr{I}^-$ with $v > v_0$ and the null shell surface $v = v_0$, as shown in Fig. 2. We also need to specifity $\psi^{in}_{\omega\ell}$ on the Cauchy surface to evaluate the scalar products in Eqs. 7 and 8. On the part of the Cauchy surface with $v > v_0$ on past null infinity, $\psi^{in}_{\omega\ell} = e^{-i\omega v}$ and on the part where $v = v_0$, $\psi^{in}_{\omega\ell}$ is given by Eq. 5. For the part with $v < v_0$ on the future horizon, we can specify $\psi^{in}_{\omega\ell}$ any way we like so long as it is continuous at $v = v_0$.

Before computing the matching coefficients, we introduce a different complete set of modes that are defined by two linearly independent solutions to the radial mode equation in Schwarzschild spacetime with the following properties

$$\chi_R^\infty \to e^{i\omega r_*}, \qquad r_* \to \infty, \tag{9}$$

$$\chi_L^\infty \to e^{-i\omega r_*}, \qquad r_* \to \infty. \tag{10}$$

Near the horizon, they have the behaviors[21]

$$\chi_R^\infty \to E_R(\omega)e^{i\omega r_*} + F_R(\omega)e^{-i\omega r_*}, \qquad r_* \to -\infty, \tag{11}$$

$$\chi_L^\infty \to E_L(\omega)e^{i\omega r_*} + F_L(\omega)e^{-i\omega r_*}, \qquad r_* \to -\infty. \tag{12}$$

where E_R, E_L, F_R, and F_L are scattering parameters that can be determined numerically.

Evaluating the scalar products in Eqs. 7 and 8 gives the following results for the matching coefficients[18]

$$A^{H^+}_{\omega\omega'l} = -\frac{i}{2\pi}\sqrt{\frac{\omega'}{\omega}}\frac{e^{i\omega' v_0}}{\omega' - i\epsilon}\psi^{in}_{\omega\ell}(v_H, v_0) + \frac{i}{2\pi}\sqrt{\frac{\omega'}{\omega}}\frac{1}{F_L^*(\omega',\ell)}\frac{e^{i(\omega'-\omega)v_0}}{\omega' - \omega + i\epsilon}$$
$$+ \frac{i}{2\pi\sqrt{\omega\omega'}}\int_{-\infty}^{v_H} du\, [\partial_u \psi^{in}_{\omega\ell}(u,v_0)]\, \psi^{H^+*}_{\omega'\ell}(u_s(u), v_0), \tag{13}$$

$$B^{H^+}_{\omega\omega'l} = \frac{i}{2\pi}\sqrt{\frac{\omega'}{\omega}}\frac{e^{-i\omega' v_0}}{\omega' + i\epsilon}\psi^{in}_{\omega\ell}(v_H, v_0) - \frac{i}{2\pi}\sqrt{\frac{\omega'}{\omega}}\frac{1}{F_L(\omega',\ell)}\frac{e^{-i(\omega+\omega')v_0}}{\omega' + \omega - i\epsilon}$$
$$- \frac{i}{2\pi\sqrt{\omega\omega'}}\int_{-\infty}^{v_H} du\, [\partial_u \psi^{in}_{\omega\ell}(u,v_0)]\, \psi^{H^+}_{\omega'\ell}(u_s(u), v_0). \tag{14}$$

$$A^{\mathscr{I}^+}_{\omega\omega'l} = -\frac{i}{2\pi}\sqrt{\frac{\omega'}{\omega}}\frac{F_R^*(\omega',\ell)}{F_L^*(\omega',\ell)}\frac{e^{-i(\omega-\omega')v_0}}{\omega'-\omega+i\epsilon}$$

$$-\frac{i}{2\pi\sqrt{\omega\omega'}}\int_{-\infty}^{v_H}du\,\left[\psi^{\text{in}}_{\omega\ell}(u,v_0)-e^{-i\omega v_0}\right]\partial_u\psi^{\mathscr{I}^+\,*}_{\omega'\ell}(u_s(u),v_0), \quad (15)$$

$$B^{\mathscr{I}^+}_{\omega\omega'l} = \frac{i}{2\pi}\sqrt{\frac{\omega'}{\omega}}\frac{F_R(\omega',\ell)}{F_L(\omega',\ell)}\frac{e^{-i(\omega+\omega')v_0}}{\omega'+\omega-i\epsilon}$$

$$+\frac{i}{2\pi\sqrt{\omega\omega'}}\int_{-\infty}^{v_H}du\,\left[\psi^{\text{in}}_{\omega\ell}(u,v_0)-e^{-i\omega v_0}\right]\partial_u\psi^{\mathscr{I}^+}_{\omega'\ell}(u_s(u),v_0). \quad (16)$$

In the case $\ell=0$, the *in* mode functions have the form $f^{in}_{\omega 00}=\frac{\psi^{in}_{\omega 00}}{r\sqrt{4\pi\omega}}$ where $\psi^{in}_{\omega 0}=e^{-i\omega v}-e^{-i\omega u}$ for $v\leq v_0$. Note that the terms with closed form in Eqs. 13–16 (v-dependent terms) are the only terms that contribute to the v-dependent part of $f^{in}_{\omega 00}$ and the integral terms contribute to the u-dependent part of $f^{in}_{\omega 00}$. We used the v-dependent terms in the matching coefficients to construct $f^{in}_{\omega 00}$ on H^+. The numerical results are shown in Fig. 3 and Fig. 4. In Fig. 3, the real and imaginary parts of the v-dependent part of the *in* mode function have been numerically computed on H^+. The results show that *in* mode function is continuous across the null shell as expected. For large values of ω, the effective potential in the mode equation is always small compared to ω^2 and one can ignore the scattering effects. Hence, one should expect to see the same behaviour as in the 2D case where there are no scattering effects. This is shown to be correct in Fig. 4. where the real and imaginary parts of $f^{in}_{\omega 00}$ are plotted for $M\omega=9$.

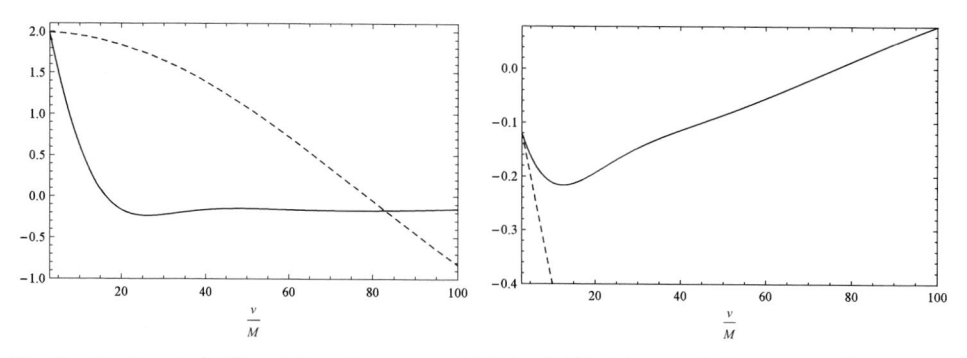

Fig. 3. Real part (left) and imaginary part (right) of $\psi^{in}_{\omega 00}(v)$ on H^+ for $v>v_0$. $\frac{v_0}{M}=3$ and $M\omega=0.02$. The dashed lines and solid lines correspond to the *in* modes in the 2D and the 4D cases respectively.

5. Stress-energy tensor and renormalization

One can renormalize the stress-energy tensor by subtracting from the unrenormalized expression for the stress-energy tensor for the in vacuum state, the unrenor-

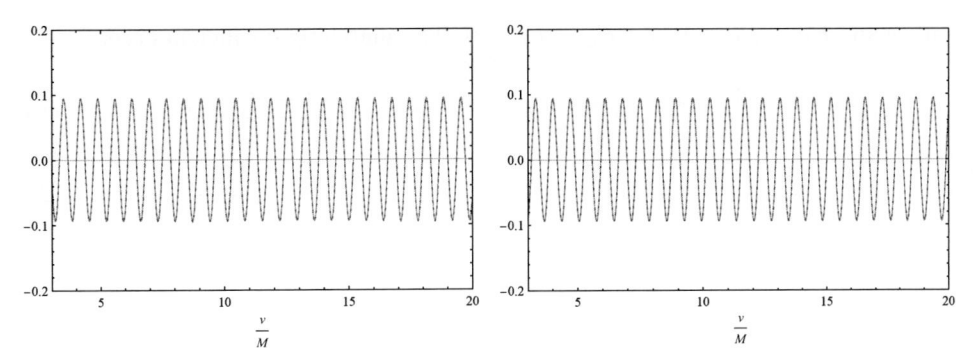

Fig. 4. Real part (left) and imaginary part (right) of $\psi^{in}_{\omega 00}(v)$ on H^+ for $v > v_0$. $\frac{v_0}{M} = 3$ and $M\omega = 9$. The dashed blue lines and solid yellow lines correspond to the *in* modes in the 2D and the 4D cases respectively.

malized stress-energy tensor for the Unruh state. Since the renormalization counterterms are local and thus do not depend on the state of the quantum field, this quantity will be finite. Then one can add back the unrenormalized stress-energy tensor for the Unruh state and subtract from it the renormalization counter terms. Schematically one can write

$$\langle in|T_{ab}|in\rangle_{\text{ren}} = \Delta\langle T_{ab}\rangle + \langle U|T_{ab}|U\rangle_{\text{ren}}, \tag{17}$$

where $\Delta\langle T_{ab}\rangle = \langle in|T_{ab}|in\rangle_{\text{unren}} - \langle U|T_{ab}|U\rangle_{\text{unren}}$. Note that the Unruh state is defined by a set of modes that are positive frequency on the past horizon with respect to the Kruskal time coordinate and the set of modes that have the form $\psi_{\omega\ell} = e^{-i\omega v}$ on past null infinity. The quantity $\langle U|T_{ab}|U\rangle_{\text{ren}}$ has been numerically computed for a massless minimally coupled scalar field in Schwarzschild spacetime. Thus what remains is to compute the difference between the unrenormalized expressions.

The unrenormalized stress-energy tensor can be computed by taking derivatives of the Hadamard Green's function as follows,[22]

$$\langle T_{ab}\rangle_{\text{unren}} = \frac{1}{4} \lim_{x' \to x} \left[\left(g_a^{c'} G^{(1)}_{;c';b}(x,x') + g_b^{c'} G^{(1)}_{;a;c'}(x,x') \right) - g_{ab} g^{cd'} G^{(1)}_{;c;d'}(x,x') \right], \tag{18}$$

where the quantity $g_a^{b'}$ parallel transports a vector from x' to x and is called the bivector of parallel transport.

5.1. *Stress-energy tensor in 2D*

In this section, we show how our method can be applied to the case of a 2D null shell spacetime which has a perfectly reflecting mirror at $r = 0$. There is no scattering that means $E_R = F_L = 1$ and $E_L = F_R = 0$. The matching coefficients are,[18]

$$A^{\mathscr{I}^+}_{\omega\omega'} = -\frac{1}{2\pi}\sqrt{\frac{\omega}{\omega'}}(4M)^{i4M\omega'}e^{-i(\omega-\omega')v_H}\frac{\Gamma(1-i4M\omega')}{[-i(\omega-\omega')+\epsilon]^{1-i4M\omega'}}, \qquad (19)$$

$$B^{\mathscr{I}^+}_{\omega\omega'} = \frac{1}{2\pi}\sqrt{\frac{\omega}{\omega'}}(4M)^{-i4M\omega'}e^{-i(\omega+\omega')v_H}\frac{\Gamma(1+i4M\omega')}{[-i(\omega+\omega')+\epsilon]^{1+i4M\omega'}}. \qquad (20)$$

The expression for f^{in}_ω can be obtained by substituting Eqs. 19 and 20 into Eq. 6. Those for f^{Unruh}_ω can be obtained using similar expressions. See Ref. 18 for more details. Next, we construct the Hadamard form of the Green's function which in 2D is

$$G^{(1)}_{in}(x,x') = \int_0^\infty d\omega \, [f^{in}_\omega(x)f^{in*}_\omega(x') + f^{in*}_\omega(x)f^{in}_\omega(x')] \,. \qquad (21)$$

We subtract off the corresponding expression for the Unruh state to obtain

$$\Delta G(x,x') = G^{(1)}_{in}(x,x') - G^{(1)}_{\text{Unruh}}(x,x'),$$

which gives

$$\Delta\langle T_{tt}\rangle = -(1-\frac{2M}{r})\lim_{x'\to x}\frac{1}{4}(\Delta G_{;t';r} + \Delta G_{;t;r'}). \qquad (22)$$

Our method results in a complicated operation for $\Delta\langle T_{tt}\rangle$ which initially contains a triple integral. One of the integrals can be computed in closed form with the result[18]

$$\Delta\langle T_{tt}\rangle = \Re\left\{\frac{i}{8\pi^3}\int_0^\infty d\omega_1\int_0^\infty d\omega_2 \, e^{-2\pi M(\omega_1+\omega_2)}\right.$$
$$\times\left\{e^{i(\omega_2-\omega_1)u_s}\frac{(4M\omega_1 e^{\frac{v_H}{4M}})^{4iM\omega_1}}{(4M\omega_2 e^{\frac{v_H}{4M}})^{4iM\omega_2}}\frac{\Gamma(1-4iM\omega_1)\Gamma(1+4iM\omega_2)}{4M(\omega_1-\omega_2-i\epsilon)}\right.$$
$$+ e^{-i(\omega_2+\omega_1)u_s}(4M\omega_1 e^{\frac{v_H}{4M}})^{4iM\omega_1}(4M\omega_2 e^{\frac{v_H}{4M}})^{4iM\omega_2}$$
$$\left.\left.\times\frac{\Gamma(1-4iM\omega_1)\Gamma(1-4iM\omega_2)}{4M(\omega_1+\omega_2)}\right\}\right\}. \qquad (23)$$

This quantity has been computed numerically and the results are shown in Fig. 5. The stress-energy tensor for a massless minimally coupled scalar field in the 2D collapsing null shell spacetime has been previously computed analytically using a different method[19,20,23–25] and the stress-energy tensor for the Unruh state has also been computed analytically.[19,20,23–30] Our results are shown with the dots in Fig. 5 and the result found by using previous methods is shown with a solid curve. They agree to more than ten digits. It is worth mentioning that in 2D, once $\Delta\langle T_{tt}\rangle$ is numerically computed, $\Delta\langle T_{rr}\rangle$ and $\Delta\langle T_{rt}\rangle$ can be easily determined.[18]

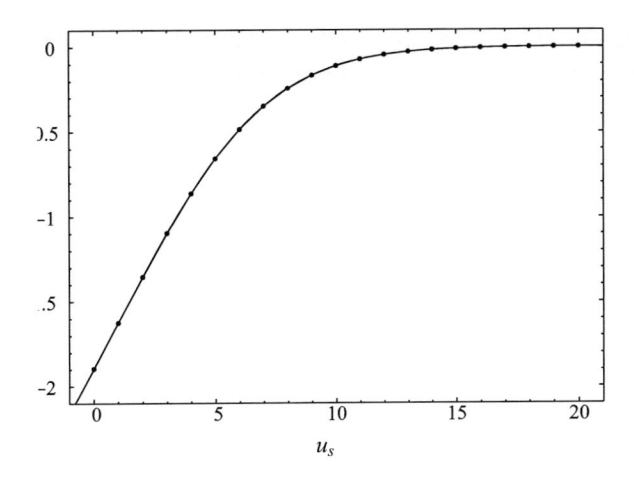

Fig. 5. The quantity $10^4 M^2 \langle T_{tt} \rangle$ is plotted for the massless minimally coupled scalar field in the region exterior to the null shell and to the event horizon. The dots correspond to the results of the numerical computations. The solid curve represents the analytic results in (reference).

6. Summary

We have reviewed a method of computing the stress-energy tensor for a massless minimally-coupled scalar field in a spacetime in which a spherically symmetric black hole is formed by the collapse of a null shell. This method primarily involves two parts. One part is the expansion of the *in* mode functions in terms of a complete set of modes in the part of a Schwarzschild black hole that is outside the event horizon. The matching coefficients of the expansion have been found in terms of the integrals of the mode functions and closed form terms. These matching coefficents have been used to numerically compute part of the *in* mode function on the future horizon of the black hoe.

The second part of the method is the renormalization of the stress-energy tensor which involves taking the difference between the stress-energy tensor for the "in" state in the collapsing null shell spacetime and that for the Unruh state in the Schwarzschild spacetime. Finally, we reviewed the computation of the stress-energy tensor in the corresponding 2D case using aformentioned method.

Acknowledgment

P. R. A. would like to thank Eric Carlson, Charles Evans, Adam Levi, and Amos Ori for helpful conversations and Adam Levi for sharing some of his numerical data. A.F. acknowledges partial financial support from the Spanish Ministerio de Ciencia e Innovación grant FIS2017-84440-C2-1-P and from the Generalitat Valenciana grant PROMETEO/2020/079. This work was supported in part by the National Science Foundation under Grants No. PHY-1308325, PHY-1505875, and PHY-1912584 to Wake Forest University. Some of the numerical work was done using the WFU DEAC cluster; we thank the WFU Provost's Office and Information Systems Department for their generous support.

References

1. M. S. Fawcett, Commun. Math. Phys **89**, 103 (1983).
2. K. W. Howard and P. Candelas, Phys. Rev. Lett. **53**, 403 (1984).
3. K. W. Howard, Phys. Rev. D **30**, 2532 (1984).
4. B. P. Jensen and A. Ottewill, Phys. Rev. D **39**, 1130 (1989).
5. B. P. Jensen, J. G. McLaughlin, and A. C. Ottewill, Phys. Rev. D **43**, 4142 (1991).
6. B. P. Jensen, J. G. Mc Laughlin, and A. C. Ottewill, Phys. Rev. D **45**, 3002 (1992).
7. P. R. Anderson, W. A. Hiscock, and D. A. Samuel, Phys. Rev. Lett. **70**, 1739 (1993).
8. P. R. Anderson, W. A. Hiscock, and D. A. Samuel, Phys. Rev. D **51**, 4337 (1995).
9. P. R. Anderson, W. A. Hiscock, and D. J. Loranz, Phys. Rev. Lett. **74**, 4365 (1995).
10. E. D. Carlson, W. H. Hirsch, B. Obermayer, P. R. Anderson, and P. B. Groves, Phys. Rev. Lett. **91**, 051301 (2003).
11. P. R. Anderson, R. Balbinot, and A. Fabbri, Phys. Rev. Lett. **94**, 061301 (2005).
12. C. Breen and A. C. Ottewill, Phys. Rev. D **85**, 084029 (2012).
13. A. Levi and A. Ori, Phys. Rev. Lett. **117**, 231101 (2016).
14. A. Levi, Phys. Rev. D **95**, 025007 (2017).
15. N. Zilberman, A. Levi, A. Ori, Phys. Rev. Lett. **124**, 171302 (2020).
16. G. Duffy and A. C. Ottewill, Phys. Rev. D **77**, 024007 (2008).
17. A. Levi, E. Eilon, A. Ori, and M. van de Meent, Phys. Rev. Lett. **118**, 141102 (2017).
18. P. R. Anderson, S Gholizadeh Siahmazgi, R. D. Clark, and A. Fabbri, Phys. Rev. D **102**, 125035 (2020).
19. A. Fabbri and J. Navarro-Salas, *Modeling black hole evaporation* (Imperial College Press, London, UK, 2005).
20. S. Massar and R. Parentani, Phys. Rev. D **54**, 7444 (996).
21. P. R. Anderson, A. Fabbri, and R. Balbinot, Phys. Rev. D **91**, 064061 (2015).
22. S. M. Christensen, Phys. Rev. D **14**, 2490 (1976).
23. M. R. R. Good, P. R. Anderson, and C. R. Evans, Phys. Rev. D **94**, 065010 (2016).
24. P. R. Anderson, R. D. Clark, A. Fabbri, and M. R. R. Good, Phys. Rev. D **100**, 061703(R) (2019).
25. W. A. Hiscock, Phys. Rev. D **23**, 2813 (1981).
26. S. W. Hawking, Commun. Math. Phys. **43** 199 (1975).
27. W. G. Unruh, Phys. Rev. D **14**, 870 (1976).
28. T. Elster, Phys. Lett. **94A**, 205 (1983).
29. E. T. Akhmedov, H. Godazgar, and F. K. Popov, Phys. Rev. D **93**, 024029 (2016).
30. P. C. W. Davies, S. A. Fulling, and W. G. Unruh, Phys. Rev. D **13**, 2720 (1976).
31. P. R. Anderson, R. Balbinot, A. Fabbri, and R. Parentani, Phys. Rev. D **87**, 124018 (2013).

Microscopic model building for black hole membranes from constraints of symmetry

Swastik Bhattacharya

Department of Physics, BITS Pilani Hyderabad;
Hyderabad 500078, Telangana State, India
E-mail: swastik@hyderabad.bits-pilani.ac.in

S. Shankaranarayanan

Department of Physics, Indian Institute of Technology Bombay,
Mumbai 400076, India
E-mail: shanki@phy.iitb.ac.in

Einstein equations projected on black-hole horizons give rise to the equations of motion of a viscous fluid. This suggests a way to understand the microscopic degrees of freedom on the black-hole horizon by focusing on the physics of this fluid. In this talk, we shall approach this problem by building a crude microscopic model for the Horizon-fluid(HF) corresponding to asymptotically flat black-holes in 3+1 dimensions. The symmetry requirement for our model is that it should incorporate the S1 diffeo-symmetry on the black-hole horizon. The second constraint comes from the demand that the correct value of the Coefficient of the Bulk Viscosity of the HF can be deduced from the model. Both these requirements can be satisfied by an adoption of the eight vertex Baxter model on a S2 surface. We show that the adiabatic entropy quantisation proposed by Bekenstein also follows from this model. Finally, we argue the results obtained so far suggest that a perturbed black-hole can be described by a CFT perturbed by relevant operators and discuss the physical implications.

Keywords: Black Hole; Horizon-fluid; Bulk Viscosity; deformed CFT.

1. Introduction

Gravity, quantum theory, and thermodynamics[1–3] are related at some fundamental level. The laws of black-hole mechanics are formally similar to the Laws of Thermodynamics and suggest that black-holes have entropy and temperature.[4–8] A satisfactory explanation of black-hole thermodynamics requires a statistical mechanical origin of entropy. It has been argued that most of the black-hole degrees of freedom (DOF) reside on the horizon, as the black-hole entropy scales as area.[1,9] Also, black-hole thermodynamics deals only with equilibrium states.

Gravity causes the non-stationary black-hole horizon to interact with external fields (perturbations) continually. These interactions lead to the transfer of energy from the external fields to black-hole degrees of freedom. If we compute observables involving black-hole, we observe *dissipative* effects corresponding to interaction with fields. In macroscopic black-hole physics, this can be explicitly seen by projecting the equations of motion of external fields and gravity theory on the black-hole event horizon leading to dissipative equations. In these scenarios, fluid dynamics description is useful as only average quantities resulting from the interactions at the microscopic level are observed on macroscopic scales.[10] Interestingly, it was shown black-hole horizon behaves like a viscous fluid and satisfies Damour-Navier-Stokes equation.[11–13]

Since we do not have a consistent model of quantum gravity, we explore here the viability of certain ideas in the context of a toy model for the non-stationary black-hole horizon that is slightly perturbed from stationarity. The toy model we construct takes into account *two different aspects of the black-hole horizon*. First, the model incorporates near-horizon symmetries of the stationary black-hole.[14–20] Second, the model accounts for the physics of transport phenomena of horizon-fluid.[21,22]

The first aspect is the constraint of symmetry on the microscopic theory. Thus, for example, we demand that the model must incorporate near-horizon symmetries. The second aspect can be viewed as the expectation that the transport phenomena exhibited by the horizon-fluid corresponding to a black-hole in the hydrodynamic limit should follow from this model.

A Conformal Field Theory (CFT) on the black-hole horizon can partly incorporate the near-horizon symmetries and is a natural candidate for the microscopic theory of stationary black-holes. We extend the analysis and show that a perturbed CFT can also incorporate this symmetry. Thus in our model, a non-stationary black-hole can be viewed as interacting with external fields. For the microscopic description, this means adding interaction terms to the stationary black-hole described by CFT. We can see this process as a perturbed black-hole relaxing to a stationary black-hole by emitting QNMs.[23] In practice, we shall deform the CFT by introducing only a mass term. However, it plays a vital role by determining the infra-red cutoff for the theory and, as a consequence, also determining the value of the coefficient of Bulk Viscosity, ζ.

We focus only on the Bulk Viscosity here, which means we only consider homogeneous processes, e.g., the increase of black-hole area in a spherically symmetric space-time due to infalling spherical mass shell. Modeling such processes is comparatively easier. Stationary, non-extremal black-holes in 4-dimensional general relativity exhibit an infinite-dimensional symmetry in the near-horizon region.[14–20,24,25] Thus, the near-horizon possess infinite-dimensional algebra such as $\mathcal{S}1$ diffeomorphism[19,20] or (near) BMS.[25–28] The CFT describing a stationary black-hole can incorporate the $\mathcal{S}1$ diffeosymmetry[19,20] as it possesses a representation of the Virasoro algebra.[20,29]

The perturbed CFT we choose possesses symmetries that lead to a representation of the Virasoro algebra.[30] These are *Integrable field theories* with an infinite number of conserved charges corresponding to an infinite number of symmetries.[31] The crucial point that allows us to model the black-hole horizon-fluid by such a perturbed CFT model is that one of the representations of the Virasoro algebra corresponding to the perturbed CFT is also a representation of the $\mathcal{S}1$

diffeomorphism symmetry. Throughout what follows, we use natural units setting $\hbar = c = G = k_B = 1$.

2. The microscopic model

We consider here the *Eight-vertex Baxter model*[32–37] for our purpose. We show that this model exhibits both the two aspects discussed above. The model has the following properties that form crucial ingredients for the microscopic model building of the horizon-fluid: First, it possesses *lattice* Virasoro algebra corresponding to $S1$ diffeomorphism symmetry.[38,39] Second, it consists of two staggered 2D Ising lattices, and its free energy density is the same as that of the 2D Ising model. However, the two-sublattice symmetry is very different from that of the usual Ising model. Hence, the Baxter solution's critical indices are, in general, different from that of Ising.[38] Third, it exhibits a second-order phase transition. In the continuum limit, it is an Integrable Field Theory near the critical point and is a CFT at the critical point.[39–41]

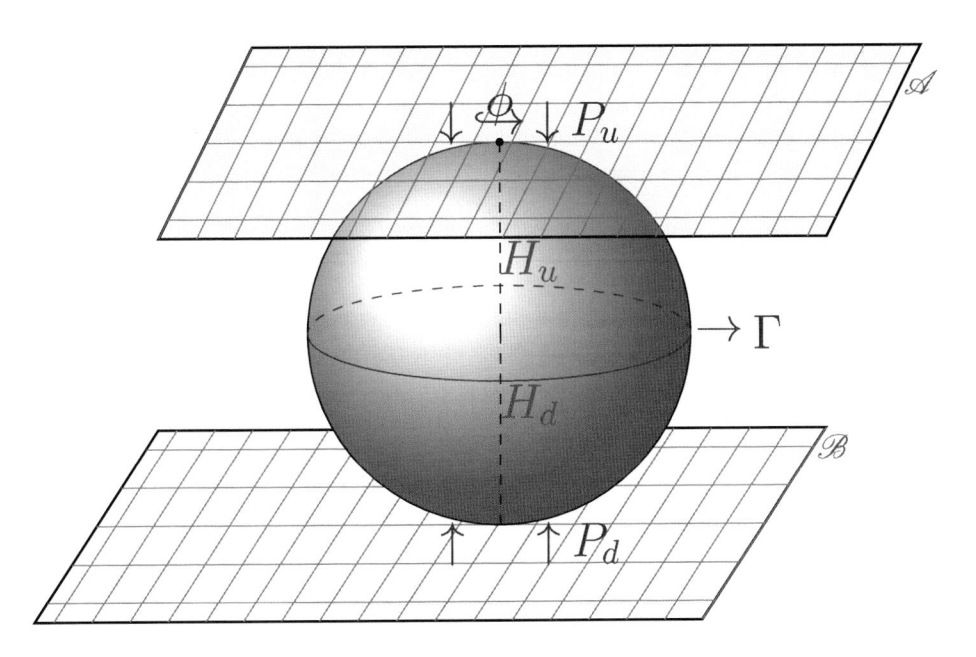

Fig. 1. The projection of the 8-vertex Baxter model from the two sub-lattices to S^2 surface of the horizon.

The Baxter model can be adapted to the cross-section of a black-hole event-horizon, a S^2 surface. As shown in 1, this model can be adopted on the two hemispheres of the S^2 surface through projection from two Baxter lattices. Let P_u (P_d) denote the map corresponding to the projection $\mathcal{A} \to H_u$ ($\mathcal{B} \to H_d$). For the consistency of the model, we need to impose the condition $P_u^{-1} \circ \{\Gamma\} \equiv P_d^{-1} \circ \{\Gamma\}$, where, P^{-1} denotes the inverse map and Γ is equatorial plane of the S^2 surface.

The above condition retains the periodic boundary condition of the Baxter model. The projection allows relating the Euclidean boost parameter of the Baxter model[41] to the azimuthal angle in the spherical polar coordinate. We can then relate the Virasoro algebra (corresponding to the $\mathcal{S}1$ diffeomorphism) of the Euclidean boost parameter to the $\mathcal{S}1$ diffeomorphism of the azimuthal angle in the horizon-fluid model. Thus, the projection retains the model's main physical features[41] and *directly* incorporates a representation of the $S1$ diffeosymmetry in the model. *It is simply the diffeosymmetry of the azimuthal angle for the black-hole system.*

3. Eight-vertex model and deformed CFT

The Eight-vertex model has eight possible arrangements of arrows at a vertex with four distinct Boltzmann weights a, b, c, d. These satisfy two constraints:[37]

$$\frac{cd}{ab} = \frac{1-\Gamma}{1+\Gamma} \; ; \; \frac{a^2+b^2-c^2-d^2}{2(ab+cd)} = \Delta \tag{1}$$

For constant Γ and Δ, there exists a one-parameter family of Boltzmann weights (w) which satisfy the star–triangle relations and, hence, the eight-vertex model has a one-parameter family of commuting transfer matrices.[37] This allows one to parameterize the Boltzmann weights explicitly in terms of *spectral variable* (u):

$$\begin{aligned} a &= \operatorname{snh}(\lambda - u) \quad b = \operatorname{snh} u \\ c &= k \operatorname{snh} \lambda, \qquad d = k \operatorname{snh}(\lambda - u) \end{aligned} \tag{2}$$

where, k is the elliptic modulus, and snh is the hyperbolic analogue of sn and is given by $\operatorname{snh} u = -i \operatorname{sn}(iu)$. It has been shown that the transfer matrix of the eight-vertex model commutes with the XYZ Hamiltonian:[43]

$$H_{\text{XYZ}} = -\frac{1}{2} \sum_{j=1}^{N} J_\sigma \sigma_j^\sigma \sigma_{j+1}^\sigma \quad \text{where} \quad \sigma = x, y, z \,. \tag{3}$$

The coupling constants are related to the weights by the relation: $J_x : J_y : J_z = 1 : \Gamma : \Delta$. The spins σ_n's are related to the vertex weights by the vertex operator (V_n):

$$V_n = \frac{1}{2} \left[a + c + [a-c]\sigma_n^z \sigma_{n+1}^z + [b+d]\sigma_n^x \sigma_{n+1}^x + \sigma_n^y \sigma_{n+1}^y \right]$$

where,

$$\begin{aligned} a &= \exp\left[K_1 + K_2 + K'''\right], \\ b &= \exp\left[-K_1 + K_2 + K'''\right], \\ c &= \exp\left[-K_1 + K_2 - K'''\right], \\ d &= \exp\left[K_1 - K_2 - K'''\right]. \end{aligned} \tag{4}$$

The Hamiltonian of the Baxter model is:

$$H_{\text{Baxter}} = \sum_\sigma [K_1\, \sigma_1\sigma_3 + K_2\, \sigma_2\sigma_4 + K''\, \sigma_1\sigma_2\sigma_3\sigma_4] \tag{5}$$

where σ_1, σ_3 (σ_2, σ_4) are the lattice spins in one (second) Ising sublattice with coupling constant K_1 (K_2) as shown in 2, and K'' refers to the four-spin coupling that connects the two sublattices.

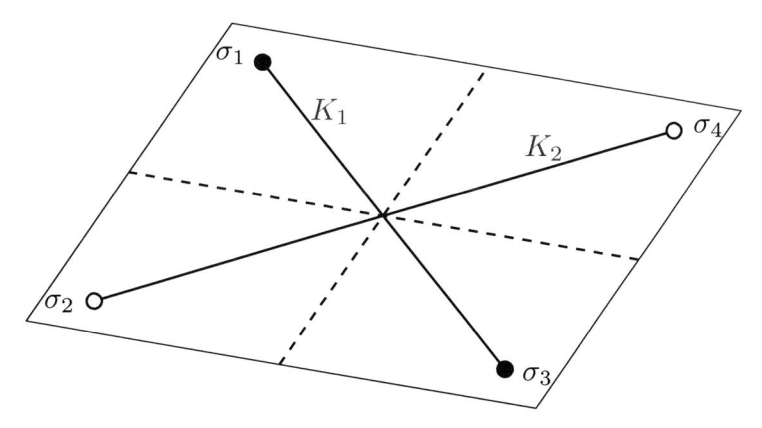

Fig. 2. A single face of the 8-Vertex Baxter model in the spin formulation. K_1 and K_2 are the horizontal and vertical spin-spin couplings of the two Ising sublattices.

It is possible to obtain the statistical weight (partition function) in the row-to-row transfer matrix and corner transfer matrix formulations.[37] In our case, it is convenient to use the corner transfer matrix (CTM) formulation as it directly connects the algebra with the conserved charges.

CTM can be expressed conveniently in terms of Fermions described by the following XYZ spin-chain Hamiltonian.[37,39–41] In this formulation, the partition function is evaluated by choosing a spin in the middle of the lattice and fixing the spins along the vertical and horizontal axes while summing over all spins in the interior of each quadrant.[37] The final sum over the spins along the axes may be interpreted as the trace of a product of four corner transfer matrices.

Thus we see that the eight vertex Baxter model is closely related to the XYZ spin chain. Now we can map it to a theory of Fermions by introducing the Corner Transfer Matrix(CTM).

The CTM operator can be viewed physically as connecting semi-infinite rows of arrows with a semi-infinite column of arrows of one quadrant of the lattice. In the thermodynamic limit, the following relation holds:[37]

$$\mathcal{A}(u) = \exp\left[-\frac{\pi u}{2K}\mathcal{L}_0\right], \tag{6}$$

where K is a complete elliptic integral associated with modulus k and

$$\mathcal{L}_0 = \frac{2K}{\pi} \sum_{j=-\infty}^{\infty} j \mathcal{H}_{XYZ}(j, j+1). \tag{7}$$

$\mathcal{H}_{XYZ}$ corresponds to the Hamiltonian of a spin chain with nearest neighbour (3) To keep the calculations transparent, we set $\Gamma = 0$, i.e., $cd = ab$ in (1). This corresponds to the condition $J_z = 0$ in the Hamiltonian (3) which is the well-known XY model.[37] $\mathcal{L}_0$ in Eq. (7) is diagonalized by the operators:

$$\Psi(l) = N_l \int d\alpha \, e^{-\imath \alpha l \pi / 2K} \chi(\alpha) \tag{8}$$

where N_l is the normalization constant, and $\chi(\alpha) = \operatorname{sn}\alpha \, a^{\alpha}(\alpha) + \imath \sqrt{k} \operatorname{cn}\alpha \, a^y(\alpha)$. The integration over α is over one complete real period of the elliptic functions from $-2K + \imath K'/2$ to $2K + \imath K'/2$. Itoyama and Thacker showed that $\mathcal{L}_0$ could be expressed as

$$\mathcal{L}_0 = \sum_l l : \bar{\Psi}(l)\Psi(l) : + h, \tag{9}$$

where, h is a constant. $\mathcal{L}_0$ is embedded into a Virasoro algebra as a central element.[39–41] The normal ordering is defined by the relations, $\Psi(l)|h\rangle = 0 (\forall\, l \geq 1)$, $\overline{\Psi}(l)|h\rangle = 0, (\forall\, l \leq 1)$. Other Virasoro operators $\mathcal{L}_n$ can be constructed from these momentum space operators.[41] From (8), it follows that,

$$[\mathcal{L}_n, \mathcal{L}_m] = (n - m)\mathcal{L}_{n+m} + \frac{1}{12}c(n^3 - n)\delta_{n+m,0}. \tag{10}$$

As noted in Ref.,[41] the physical Hilbert space built from the state $|h\rangle$, forms the highest weight representation of the Virasoro algebra. Since the eigenvalues of $\mathcal{L}_0$ are doubled due to the zero modes of the operator $\Psi(0)$ and $\overline{\Psi}(0)$, the highest weight vector forms a two-dimensional representation under parity conjugation. At the critical point, the central charge $c = 1$ and $h = \frac{1}{8}$.

Using the following classical generators (l_n^{Diff}),

$$l_n^{Diff} = -\frac{1}{2}\zeta^{n+1}\frac{d}{d\zeta} - \frac{1}{2}\frac{d}{d\zeta}\zeta^{n+1}. \tag{11}$$

we can obtain other Virasoro algebra, different from the one described above. The difference is that l_n^{Diff} are generators of diffeo-transformation of the spectral rapidity parameter or the Euclidean boost parameter (α).[41,44] We can then construct the corresponding Virasoro algebra by defining the following $\mathcal{L}_n^{diff}$:

$$\mathcal{L}_n^{diff} = : \int_{-K}^{3K} \frac{d\beta}{2\pi} B(\beta + 2K - \imath K') l_n B(\beta) : + h\delta_{n,0}$$

$$= \sum_l \left(l + \frac{n-1}{2}\right) : \bar{\psi}(l)\psi(l+n) : + h\delta_{n,0}. \tag{12}$$

This demonstrates that the eight-vertex model possesses the Virasoro algebra given by (12), which holds the key to incorporating near-horizon $S1$ diffeo-symmetry in the model of the horizon-fluid. The 2-D Euclideanized space-time (τ, q) can be identified with the 2-D Euclidean space (x_1, x_2) on which the horizon-fluid resides. The rapidity or the boost parameter in a Euclideanized space-time corresponds to an angle of rotation. A closer look reveals that in our case, the rapidity is the azimuthal angle (See (1)). Thus, l_n^{Diff} diffeomorphism algebra of the spectral rapidity corresponds to the l_n^{Diff} diffeomorphism symmetry on the black-hole horizon. Thus we see that the microscopic modelling of the horizon-fluid with a mass gap incorporates the l_n^{Diff} diffeomorphism symmetry on the black-hole horizon.

4. Continuum limit and modelling horizon-fluid

Long-range effects dominate the critical properties of this model; hence, a continuum approximation will suffice for our purpose. The eight-vertex model's continuum limit is a theory of massive Dirac Fermions (Ψ_1, Ψ_2)[41]

$$\mathcal{S}_{\text{Dirac}} = \int d\tau dq \left[\frac{1}{2} i \bar{\Psi}_1 \left(\frac{\overleftrightarrow{\partial}}{\partial \tau} + \frac{\overleftrightarrow{\partial}}{\partial q} \right) \Psi_1 + \frac{1}{2} i \bar{\Psi}_2 \left(\frac{\overleftrightarrow{\partial}}{\partial \tau} - \frac{\overleftrightarrow{\partial}}{\partial q} \right) \Psi_2 - m(\bar{\Psi}_1 \Psi_2 + \bar{\Psi}_2 \Psi_1) \right]. \tag{13}$$

The above action possesses an infinite sequence of conserved densities. Physically, this implies that besides the total angular momentum, the entire momentum distribution is conserved.[41] We can rewrite these operators as integrals of local densities in coordinate space:

$$\mathcal{L}_n = \int dq \, J_0^{(n)}(q), \tag{14}$$

where J_0 is the zeroth component of a conserved current. $J_0^{(-1)}$ is the Hamiltonian plus the momentum operator, and $J_0^{(0)}$ (at $\tau = 0$) is the first moment of the Dirac Hamiltonian.[41] Integrability ensures the operators are related to the infinite sequence of conserved charges, with one for each new $\mathcal{L}_n$.[41]

The action (13) is useful to identify the infinite number of conserved charges. However, for our purpose here, starting from the action (13) it is cumbersome to look at the hydrodynamic or long-wavelength properties. Hence, to derive ζ, we will not make direct use of the action (13). Instead, to make contact with the macroscopic level, i.e., Damour's fluid description, we turn to the fact that the Free-energy density of the Baxter model is the same as that of a classical Ising model in 2-dimensions near the critical point.[37] On the other hand, the theory of the 2-dimensional Ising model can be described by a theory of a free massive scalar field φ in a two-dimensional Euclidean spacetime.[45] The key is to identify the microscopic field with the phenomenological order parameter.

The task of identifying the microscopic field with the phenomenological order parameter is non-trivial. For the transport theory, we need to describe the dynamics of the black-hole horizon, starting from a $(2 + 1)$-dimensional Hamiltonian.

However, the microscopic model we have constructed is characterized by the *2-D Euclidean space-time Hamiltonian*. This means that the microscopic model suffices to describe the quantum states for a system in thermal equilibrium with the desired accuracy but is inadequate if we consider how the system evolves with time. In other words, such Hamiltonians do not contain information about the dynamics of the black-hole horizon.

There are two ways to tackle this issue. Both approaches keep the thermal states the same but provide different inputs about the dynamics of the system. One way is to assume that a phenomenological Langevin equation gives the dynamics. From this, one can work out the transport theory and compute the correct coefficient of Bulk Viscosity for the Horizon-fluid. The other approach is to construct a $(2+1)$−dimensional Hamiltonian with the same symmetries as the mass gap possessed by the 2-D Euclidean space-time Hamiltonian. For a general process, this is a challenging problem. Fortunately, this difficulty is bypassed for the processes describing bulk viscosity of the fluid using the mean-field theory description. We should emphasize that in this case also, the thermal states remain the same. (The collection of the thermal states of the $(2+1)$−dimensional theory is equivalent to collecting the quantum states of the $1+1$ dimensional Euclideanized theory subject to appropriate boundary conditions.) We shall only discuss the second approach here as a Langevin-type equation can also be derived from the dynamical quantum theory under suitable approximation.

The mean-field description will not capture all the details of the symmetries of the quantum states of the model or can reproduce the correct scaling exponents; however, it works satisfactorily to describe horizon-fluid properties. Thus, the 2-D mean-field theory Hamiltonian of the microscopic model can be extended to the following $2+1$ dimensional space-time Hamiltonian:

$$H_{\text{eff}}(\varphi) = \int \left[\frac{1}{2}(\frac{\partial \varphi}{\partial t})^2 + \frac{1}{2}(\nabla \varphi)^2 + \frac{m_{eff}^2}{2}\varphi^2 \right] dA, \tag{15}$$

where the integral is over the area of the event horizon. The above Hamiltonian satisfies the essential requirement of possessing $Z2$ symmetry. Still, it suffers from the weakness that there is very little guidance otherwise in terms of symmetry requirements. One can view the above Hamiltonian as a Mean-Field description of the horizon-fluid near a critical point.

We are now in a position to identify the above Hamiltonian (15) with the horizon-fluid. As a first step, we write down the Landau-Ginzburg expression for the entropy functional corresponding to the horizon-fluid instead of using the Free Energy functional.[46] This is because the black-hole (of horizon area A) constantly interacts with the environment, leading to energy flow. Thus, we need a framework in which the energy density and the order parameter appear in the formalism on the same footing. As shown in Ref.,[46] the appropriate thermodynamic potential to consider in such a case, is the entropy functional and not free energy. The stationary state of the black-hole corresponds to the thermodynamic equilibrium state of the black-hole with maximum entropy. The quasi-stationary state of a black-hole corresponds to the vacuum of the deformed CFT.

Following,[21] we assume that the entropy density of the horizon-fluid is homogeneous. We focus on a macroscopically small but finite element of the black-hole horizon area, denoted as $\mathcal{A}$. $\mathcal{A}$ satisfies the condition $\mathcal{A}/A \ll 1$. The order parameter (η) is taken to be:

$$\eta = C\sqrt{\mathcal{A}}.$$

We can fix the value of the constant C only by relating it to a macroscopic quantity. The entropy functional ($\mathcal{S}$) of the horizon-fluid of this finite element about $(T, \mathcal{A})$ is given by:[46]

$$\mathcal{S} = \mathcal{S}_0(T, \mathcal{A}) - a\,\eta^2 - b\,\eta^4, \tag{16}$$

where a, b are constants. Let the value of the entropy functional $\mathcal{S}$ in the quasi-stationary state by $\mathcal{S}_{QS}$ and the stationary state by $\mathcal{S}_S$, respectively. Note that $\mathcal{S}_S$ is the global maximum for entropy functional $\mathcal{S}$. We assume that the process of going from $\mathcal{S}_{QS}$ to $\mathcal{S}_S$ is a slow physical process so that we can use equilibrium thermodynamics to describe the quasi-stationary state. For the microscopic model of the horizon-fluid, this means that the ground state of the deformed CFT evolves slowly into a state of CFT. The slow evolution implies that the deformed CFT vacuum is likely to possess some of the symmetries of a CFT state. This is reminiscent of the adiabatic evolution of a quantum state.

Rewriting (16) in terms of the horizon-area at equilibrium, we get,

$$S_{\max} = \frac{\mathcal{A}_{\max}}{4} = \mathcal{S}_0 - a\,C^2 \mathcal{A}_{\max} - b\,C^4 \mathcal{A}_{\max}^2,$$
$$\text{where} \quad a = -\frac{1}{4C^2}; \quad \mathcal{S}_0 - b\,C^4\,\mathcal{A}^2 = 0. \tag{17}$$

Denote the deviation of any variable from its equilibrium value by a prefix δ. The change in the entropy functional is related to the change in the energy density of the horizon-fluid:

$$\delta\mathcal{H}(\delta\eta) = -T\,\delta\mathcal{S} = \frac{T}{2C^2}\delta\eta^2. \tag{18}$$

where we have $k_B = 1$. [Expansion around the maximum implies that the terms proportional to $\delta\eta$ cancel out as the expansion is being done around a maximum value of the entropy function. This leads to the condition $2b\eta_{max}^2 = -a$. Substituting this in the terms quadratic in $\delta\eta$, i.e. $(a + 2b\eta_{max}^2)\delta\eta^2$) leads to the above expression.]

Using the above expression, we can relate the order parameter (η) with the scalar field (φ) and the change in the energy density of the horizon fluid ($\delta\mathcal{H}(\delta\eta)$) with $H_{\text{eff}}(\varphi)$ (15), i.e.

$$\delta H = \int dA\,\delta\mathcal{H} = \delta H_{\text{eff}}. \tag{19}$$

For the homogeneous process, the spatial gradient terms in the Hamiltonian (15) can be ignored. Also, the field is taken to vary slowly so the kinetic term in the Hamiltonian (15) can be ignored. Using the universality near critical point, we have:[37,41]

$$\langle \varphi_* \rangle = \frac{\delta \eta}{\sqrt{\mathcal{A}}}, \qquad (20)$$

where, $\langle \varphi_* \rangle$ is the average value of the field φ_* in the area $\mathcal{A}$. As seen from the above expression, φ_* is dimensionless, and is related to φ as follows: $\varphi = \sqrt{\Upsilon}\varphi_*$ where Υ has the dimensions of energy. The change in the energy of the horizon fluid is given by:

$$\delta H = \frac{\Upsilon}{2} \int dA\, m_*^2\, \varphi_*^2, \quad \text{where} \quad m_* = \frac{1}{C} \quad \text{and} \quad \Upsilon = T \qquad (21)$$

Thus, we have made the connection between the microscopic model with black-hole thermodynamics. m_* has the dimensions of energy, i.e., $m_* = 1/(l_P^2 C)$, l_P being the Planck length. C is dimensionless. Note that we have set $l_P = 1$. In the next section, we evaluate the correlations for this process (bulk viscosity). The thermal correlations considered here remain the same for Hamiltonian corresponding to action (13) and H_{eff}.

5. Bulk viscosity from the microscopic model

We use the above mean-field theory description to calculate the viscosity coefficient of the horizon-fluid from the correlations of the energy-momentum tensor of the scalar field given by the Hamiltonian (15). Jeon has developed such a description.[42] First, however, we need to make suitable changes to apply to the horizon-fluid.

According to Jeon, the coefficient of bulk-viscosity (ζ) of a viscous-fluid with stress-tensor is:[42]

$$\zeta = \frac{\beta}{2} \lim_{\omega \to 0} \lim_{\mathbf{q} \to 0} \sigma_{\bar{P}\bar{P}}, \qquad (22)$$

where, $\sigma_{\bar{P}\bar{P}}$ is given by

$$\sigma_{\bar{P}\bar{P}}(\omega, \mathbf{q}) = \frac{1}{2\pi\mathcal{A}} \int d^2\mathbf{x} \int_{-\infty}^{\infty} dt\, e^{-i\mathbf{q}\cdot\mathbf{x}+i\omega t} \langle \bar{P}(t,\mathbf{x})\bar{P}(0) \rangle, \qquad (23)$$

where $\mathcal{A}$ is the area normalization of the spatial part,

$$\bar{P}(t,\mathbf{x}) = P(t,\mathbf{x}) - v_S^2 \rho(t,\mathbf{x}) = \frac{1}{2} T_i^i(x^\mu) - v_S^2 T_{00}(x^\mu). \qquad (24)$$

and v_S is the speed of sound of the field.

To apply this formalism to horizon-fluid, we need to make suitable changes in the formulation. As mentioned earlier, the stress-tensor of the horizon-fluid vanishes as the infalling matter-energy reaches the horizon and the horizon becomes quasi-stationary.[11–13] In other words, when the matter reaches an equilibrium at a given temperature, the stress-tensor of the horizon-fluid is zero. Thus, the field-theoretic description of the horizon-fluid corresponds to the deviation of the energy-momentum tensor of the field ($T^H_{\mu\nu}$) from its thermal average at the thermal state ($\langle T^H_{\mu\nu}\rangle_{\text{equilibrium}}$). In the case of normal-fluid, we use the stress-tensor (cf. 23). For the horizon-fluid on the other hand, the key quantity is the deviation of the energy-momentum tensor of the field, i.e.,

$$\delta T^H_{\mu\nu} = T^H_{\mu\nu} - \langle T^H_{\mu\nu}\rangle_{\text{equilibrium}}.$$

Physically, this corresponds to the state when the expectation value of the stress-energy tensor of the perturbed CFT on the horizon is the thermal average. Thus, for the horizon-fluid, Eqs. (23) and (24) become:

$$\delta P(\bar{t},\mathbf{x}) = \frac{1}{2}\delta T^i_i(x^\mu) - \delta T_{00}(x^\mu) \qquad (25)$$

$$\sigma_{\delta\bar{P},\delta\bar{P}}(\omega,\mathbf{q}) = \frac{1}{2\pi\mathcal{A}}\int d^2\mathbf{x}\int_{-\infty}^{\infty} dt\, e^{-i\mathbf{q}\cdot\mathbf{x}+i\omega t}\langle\delta\bar{P}(t,\mathbf{x})\delta\bar{P}(0)\rangle_0. \qquad (26)$$

For the horizon-fluid, v_S is equal to the speed of light ($c=1$). For the Hamiltonian (15), we have:

$$\bar{P} = -\frac{1}{2}(\nabla\phi)^2 - m^2_{\text{eff}}\phi^2. \qquad (27)$$

We can ignore contributions from the ($\nabla\phi$) term for the homogeneous perturbations responsible for the bulk viscosity. We can determine $\delta T_{\mu\nu}$ by systematically tracking the deviation of the field ϕ from its average value at equilibrium state, i.e.,

$$\phi = \langle\phi\rangle_0 + \delta\phi$$

where $\langle\rangle_0 \equiv \phi_0$ denotes the ensemble average of the density matrix.

For a field at a temperature T, the density matrix is the thermal density matrix at T. In the hydrodynamic limit, ϕ_0 is given by:

$$\phi_0^2 = \frac{\sum e^{-\beta H}\phi^2}{\sum e^{-\beta H}} = \frac{\int\mathcal{D}\phi\,\phi^2 e^{-\beta\int\frac{m^2_{\text{eff}}}{2}\phi^2 d^2 x}}{\int\mathcal{D}\phi\, e^{-\beta\int\frac{m^2_{\text{eff}}}{2}\phi^2 d^2 x}} = \frac{1}{2m^2_*}, \qquad (28)$$

where star denotes that rescaled variables [see the discussion below Eq. (33)]. Writing $\phi = \phi_0 + \delta\phi$, (27) can be written as

$$\delta\bar{P} = -2m^2_*\phi_0\delta\phi = -2\frac{m_*}{\sqrt{2}}\delta\phi = \sqrt{2}m_*\delta\phi = \frac{\sqrt{2}}{C}\delta\phi. \qquad (29)$$

The Coefficient of Bulk Viscosity is given by,

$$\zeta = 2\pi\,\text{Im}\left[\frac{1}{4\pi\mathcal{A}}\lim_{\mathbf{q}\to 0}\lim_{\omega\to m_*}\int d^3x\, e^{-i\mathbf{q}\cdot\mathbf{x}+i\omega t}\langle[\delta\bar{P}(t,\mathbf{x}),\delta\bar{P}(0)]\rangle\theta(-t)\right]. \qquad (30)$$

Substituting (29) in (30), and keeping in mind that the perturbations are homogeneous, one gets,

$$\zeta = \text{Im}\left[\lim_{\omega\to m_*}\frac{1}{C^2}\int_{-\infty}^{\infty} dt\, e^{i\omega t}\langle[\delta\hat{\phi}(t),\delta\hat{\phi}(0)]\rangle\theta(-t)\right]. \qquad (31)$$

$\langle[\delta\hat{\phi}(t,\mathbf{x}),\delta\hat{\phi}(0)]\rangle\theta(-t)$ corresponds to the advanced Green's function that appears because of the teleological nature of the event horizon [for detailed discussion, see[12, 13, 21]], and

$$[\delta\hat{\phi}(t),\delta\hat{\phi}(0)] = [\hat{\phi}(t),\hat{\phi}(0)] \qquad (32)$$

To obtain the above commutation relation of the field operator, we write the Hamiltonian (15) as

$$H_{\text{HF}} = \frac{T}{2}\int\left[(\frac{\partial\varphi_*}{\partial t})^2 + (\nabla\varphi_*)^2 + m_*^2\varphi_*^2\right]dA. \qquad (33)$$

where $\phi = \sqrt{T}\phi_*$, and ϕ_* is the rescaled (dimensionless) effective scalar field and T is taken to be a constant for convenience. Rewriting $\hat{\varphi}_*$ (also $\hat{\varphi}$) in terms of the creation and annihilation operators, i.e.,

$$\hat{\varphi}_*(t,\mathbf{x}) = \sum_{\mathbf{k}_*}[\hat{a}_{\mathbf{k}_*}u_{\mathbf{k}_*}(t,\mathbf{x}) + \hat{a}^\dagger_{\mathbf{k}_*}u^*_{\mathbf{k}_*}(t,\mathbf{x})], \qquad (34)$$

where,

$$u_{\mathbf{k}_*}(t,\mathbf{x}) = \frac{1}{\sqrt{2\pi}}\frac{1}{\sqrt{2\omega_*}}e^{i(\mathbf{k}_*\cdot\mathbf{x}-\omega_*t)} \qquad (35)$$

and $\mathbf{k}_*$, ω_*, $\mathbf{x}$ and t are dimensionless variables. Expressing the dimensionless part of the above Hamiltonian (33) in the frequency domain, we have:

$$H_{\text{eff}}(\varphi) = T\sum_{\mathbf{k}_*}(\hat{a}^\dagger_{\mathbf{k}_*}\hat{a}_{\mathbf{k}_*} + \frac{1}{2})\omega_*, \qquad (36)$$

where the dispersion relation is given by:

$$\omega_*^2 = \mathbf{k}_*^2 + \frac{1}{C^2} \quad \text{and} \quad C = \frac{1}{m_*}. \qquad (37)$$

In the hydrodynamic limit ($\mathbf{k}_* \to 0$), the above expression reduces to $\omega_{*H} = 1/C$. Substituting Eq. (32) in Eq. (31) and after a little algebraic manipulation in terms of dimensionless variables, we have:[47]

$$\zeta[\omega_{*H}] = \text{Im}\left[-\frac{i}{4C^2}\frac{T\omega_{*H}}{E_\beta(\omega_{*H})}\int_{-\infty}^{\infty}\langle\hat{\varphi}(0)\hat{\varphi}(t) + \hat{\varphi}(t)\hat{\varphi}(0)\rangle e^{-i\omega_{*H}t}\theta(-t)dt\right], \qquad (38)$$

where $E_\beta(\omega_{*H})$ is the average energy of excitation in the mode with frequency ω_{*H} at temperature T. The above integral exhibits a pole at $\omega'_* = \omega_{*H}$, which is the well-known pole at the hydrodynamical limit. Using the fact that the process corresponding to bulk viscosity is homogeneous, we have

$$\langle\hat{\varphi}^2_{\omega_H}(0)\rangle = \frac{1}{(2\pi)^2}\frac{1}{4m_*^2} = \frac{1}{(2\pi)^2}\frac{C^2}{4} \qquad (39)$$

In the hydrodynamic limit, we get:

$$\zeta[\omega_{*H}] = -\frac{1}{128\pi^2}\frac{T\omega_{*H}}{E_\beta(\omega_{*H})} = -\frac{1}{128\pi^2}2\tanh\frac{1}{2C}. \qquad (40)$$

Demanding that the above expression matches with the expression derived by Damour[11]:

$$\zeta = -\frac{1}{16\pi},$$

we have

$$\tanh\frac{1}{2C} = \frac{1}{4\pi}. \tag{41}$$

Solving this equation numerically, we get, $C = 6.2696$ and hence, $m_* = 0.1595$. The negative sign of a transport coefficient arises due to $\theta(-t)$ in the response function of the black-hole horizon.[21]

6. Discussion

The minimal microscopic model for the horizon-fluid discussed here incorporates three simple ideas. First, the model contains an infinite-dimensional symmetry algebra, namely the Virasaro algebra, corresponding to black-holes' near-horizon $S1$ diffeo-symmetry. Second, the model describes a perturbed CFT that possesses a representation of the Virasoro algebra. The deformation is characterized by a mass term and is supposed to address the perturbed nature of the non-stationary black-hole horizon. Finally, the mass gap provides a simple derivation of ζ and area quantization, thus demonstrating that in the long-wavelength limit, it can connect with the known semiclassical Physics of black-holes. Historically, Bekenstein was the first to derive the quantization of area using adiabatic quantization. We obtained quantization of entropy by slowly evolving the black-hole horizon. Adiabatic quantization of a system is applicable when some of the parameters characterizing the system evolve slowly.

In this talk, only the homogeneous perturbations of the stationary black-hole have been considered. We need to construct a microscopic model, including general perturbations, which can describe the horizon-fluid. This complete theory would, of course, be richer than the toy model we have put forward. So the Baxter model serves only as an illustration in this sense. Nonetheless, an improved model should also share the first three critical features of the current model mentioned above. Thus, we expect a more comprehensive microscopic future model of the horizon-fluid to describe a system close to the critical point. It should represent the near-horizon symmetry algebra and a mass gap with a fixed, known value.

Our results also lead to an interesting suggestion. The twin requirements of the theory incorporating near-horizon symmetries($S1$ diffeomorphism) and possessing length scales due to external perturbations can be naturally satisfied if the theory on the non-stationary black-hole horizon is a deformed CFT. Similar types of arguments also lead to the expectation that the theory on the stationary black-hole horizon is a CFT.[19] Since the non-stationary black-hole eventually becomes stationary, it is reasonable to assume that the deformed CFT flows into a CFT as the black-hole horizon dynamically evolves. Note that the above argument does not depend on any specific model. This leads us to conjecture that *the low energy theory on the black-hole horizon flows towards a critical point as the perturbed black-hole ultimately becomes stationary*. We think that this conjecture may be a good starting point to construct quantum theory models of the black-hole horizon.

References

1. Robert M. Wald. The thermodynamics of black holes. *Liv. Rev. Rela.*, 4:6, 2001.
2. Ted Jacobson and Renaud Parentani. Horizon entropy. *Found. Phys.*, 33(2):323–348, 2003.
3. Steven Carlip. Black Hole Thermodynamics and Statistical Mechanics. *Lect. Notes Phys.*, 769:89–123, 2009.
4. James M. Bardeen, B. Carter, and S. W. Hawking. The four laws of black hole mechanics. *Commun. Math. Phys.*, 31:161–170, 1973.
5. Ted Jacobson. Thermodynamics of space-time: The Einstein equation of state. *Phys. Rev. Lett.*, 75:1260–1263, 1995.
6. T. Padmanabhan. Thermodynamical aspects of gravity: new insights. *Rep. Prog. Phys.*, 73(4):046901, April 2010.
7. T. Padmanabhan. Distribution Function of the Atoms of Spacetime and the Nature of Gravity. *Entropy*, 17:7420–7452, October 2015.
8. S. W. Hawking. Particle creation by black holes. *Commun. Math. Phys.*, 43:199–220, 1975.
9. Saurya Das and S. Shankaranarayanan. Where are the black hole entropy degrees of freedom? *Class. Quant. Grav.*, 24:5299–5306, 2007.
10. Paul Romatschke and Ulrike Romatschke. *Relativistic Fluid Dynamics In and Out of Equilibrium*. Cambridge Monographs on Mathematical Physics. Cambridge University Press, 2019.
11. T. Damour. Surface Effects in Black-Hole Physics. In R. Ruffini, editor, *Marcel Grossmann Meeting: General Relativity*, 1982.
12. R. H. Price and K. S. Thorne. Membrane viewpoint on black holes: Properties and evolution of the stretched horizon. *Phys. Rev. D.*, 33:915–941, February 1986.
13. Kip S Thorne, Richard H Price, and Douglas A Macdonald. *The Membrane Paradigm*, volume 19. Yale University Press, New Haven, 1986.
14. Romesh K. Kaul and Parthasarathi Majumdar. Quantum black hole entropy. *Phys. Lett.*, B439:267–270, 1998.
15. Romesh K. Kaul and Parthasarathi Majumdar. Schwarzschild horizon dynamics and SU(2) Chern-Simons theory. *Phys. Rev.*, D83:024038, 2011.
16. Jun-ichirou Koga. Asymptotic symmetries on Killing horizons. *Phys. Rev. D*, D64:124012, 2001.
17. M. Hotta, K. Sasaki, and T. Sasaki. Diffeomorphism on horizon as an asymptotic isometry of Schwarzschild black hole. *Class. Quant. Grav.*, 18:1823–1834, 2001.
18. M. Hotta. Holographic charge excitations on horizontal boundary. *Phys. Rev.*, D66:124021, 2002.
19. S. Carlip. Black hole entropy from conformal field theory in any dimension. *Phys. Rev. Lett.*, 82:2828, 1999.
20. Steven Carlip. Effective Conformal Descriptions of Black Hole Entropy. *Entropy*, 13:1355–1379, 2011.
21. Swastik Bhattacharya and S. Shankaranarayanan. Fluctuations in horizon-fluid lead to negative bulk viscosity. *Phys. Rev. D*, D93(6):064030, 2016.

22. Bethan Cropp, Swastik Bhattacharya, and S. Shankaranarayanan. Hints of quantum gravity from the horizon fluid. *Phys. Rev. D.*, D95(2):024006, 2017.
23. S. Chandrasekhar. *The mathematical theory of black holes*. Oxford Univ. Press, Oxford, 1992.
24. Glenn Barnich and Cedric Troessaert. Symmetries of asymptotically flat 4 dimensional spacetimes at null infinity revisited. *Phys. Rev. Lett.*, 105:111103, 2010.
25. Laura Donnay, Gaston Giribet, Hernan A. Gonzalez, and Miguel Pino. Supertranslations and Superrotations at the Black Hole Horizon. *Phys. Rev. Lett.*, 116(9):091101, 2016.
26. H. Bondi, M. G. J. van der Burg, and A. W. K. Metzner. Gravitational waves in general relativity. 7. Waves from axisymmetric isolated systems. *Proc. Roy. Soc. Lond.*, A269:21–52, 1962.
27. R. K. Sachs. Gravitational waves in general relativity. 8. Waves in asymptotically flat space-times. *Proc. Roy. Soc. Lond.*, A270:103–126, 1962.
28. Andrew Strominger. Lectures on the Infrared Structure of Gravity and Gauge Theory. 2017.
29. Geoffrey Compére. The Kerr/CFT correspondence and its extensions. *Living Rev. Rel.*, 15:11, 2012.
30. AB Zamolodchikov. Higher-order integrals of motion in two-dimensional models of the field theory with a broken conformal. *JETP Lett*, 46(4), 1987.
31. Alexander B Zamolodchikov. Integrable field theory from conformal field theory. In *Integrable Systems and Quantum Field Theory*, pages 641–674. Elsevier, 1989.
32. Rodney J Baxter. Eight-vertex model in lattice statistics. *Physical Review Letters*, 26(14):832, 1971.
33. RJ Baxter and FY Wu. Exact solution of an ising model with three-spin interactions on a triangular lattice. *Physical Review Letters*, 31(21):1294, 1973.
34. R. J. Baxter. Corner transfer matrices of the eight-vertex model. i. low-temperature expansions and conjectured properties. *Journal of Statistical Physics*, 15(6):485–503, Dec 1976.
35. R. J. Baxter. Corner transfer matrices of the eight-vertex model. ii. the ising model case. *Journal of Statistical Physics*, 17(1):1–14, Jul 1977.
36. Rodney J Baxter. Variational approximations for square lattice models in statistical mechanics. *Journal of Statistical Physics*, 19(5):461–478, 1978.
37. Rodney J Baxter. *Exactly solved models in statistical mechanics*. Elsevier, 2016.
38. Leo P Kadanoff and Franz J Wegner. Some critical properties of the eight-vertex model. *Physical Review B*, 4(11):3989, 1971.
39. H. Itoyama and H. B. Thacker. Lattice Virasoro Algebra and Corner Transfer Matrices in the Baxter Eight Vertex Model. *Phys. Rev. Lett.*, 58:1395, 1987.
40. HB Thacker. Corner transfer matrices and lorentz invariance on a lattice. *Physica D: Nonlinear Phenomena*, 18(1-3):348–359, 1986.
41. H. Itoyama and H. B. Thacker. Integrability and Virasoro Symmetry of the Noncritical Baxter-Ising Model. *Nucl. Phys.*, B320:541–590, 1989.
42. S. Jeon, Phys. Rev. D **52**, 3591-3642 (1995) doi:10.1103/PhysRevD.52.3591 [arXiv:hep-ph/9409250 [hep-ph]].
43. Bill Sutherland. Two-dimensional hydrogen bonded crystals without the ice rule. *Journal of Mathematical Physics*, 11(11):3183–3186, 1970.
44. J.-L. Gervais. Infinite family of polynomial functions of the virasoro generators with vanishing poisson brackets. *Physics Letters B*, 160(4):277–278, 1985.
45. A M. Polyakov. *Gauge Fields and Strings*. Contemporary concepts in physics. Taylor & Francis, 1987.

46. Oliver Penrose and Paul C Fife. Thermodynamically consistent models of phase-field type for the kinetic of phase transitions. *Physica D*, 43(1):44–62, 1990.
47. R. Kubo. The fluctuation-dissipation theorem. *Reports on Progress in Physics*, 29:255–284, January 1966.
48. R. Kubo, J. Phys. Soc. Jap. **12**, 570-586 (1957) doi:10.1143/JPSJ.12.570
49. J. D. Bekenstein. The quantum mass spectrum of the kerr black hole. *Lettere al Nuovo Cimento (1971-1985)*, 11(9):467–470, 1974.

Einstein-Maxwell-Dilaton-Axion mass formulas for black holes with struts and strings

Dmitri Gal'tsov[a,*], Gérard Clément[b,†] and Igor Bogush[a,‡]

[a] *Faculty of Physics, Moscow State University, 119899, Moscow, Russia*
[b] *LAPTh, Université Savoie Mont Blanc, CNRS, France*
Email: [*]galtsov@phys.msu.ru, [†]gclement@lapth.cnrs.fr, [‡]igbogush@gmail.com

Mass formulas are obtained for stationary axisymmetric solutions of the Einstein-Maxwell dilaton-axion theory, which have a regular rod structure on the axis of symmetry. Asymptotic mass, angular momentum and charge are expressed as the sums of masses, angular momenta and charges of rods dressed with field contributions. The calculation is based on a three-dimensional sigma model representation of the stationary EMDA system and the Tomimatsu approach proposed for the Einstein-Maxwell system. Our results provide an alternative interpretation of mass formulas and thermodynamics for black holes with Dirac and Misner strings. It is also applicable to aligned multiple black holes with struts.

Keywords: Black hole mass formulas, Dirac string, Misner string, therodynamics of black holes with NUT

1. Introduction

Mass formulas for black holes and the concept of irreversible mass were proposed by Christodoulou,[1] Hawking,[2] Christodoulou and Ruffini,[3] and Smarr[4] in the early 1970s, shortly before Hawking discovered the evaporation of a black hole.[5] They have played an important role in understanding the energy extraction from rotating black holes and the energy balance of merging black holes, which was brilliantly confirmed in the recent experiments of Ligo. The thermodynamics of black holes[6–9] then gave them a deep quantum interpretation. The mathematical foundations and detailed derivation of mass formulas in the Einstein-Maxwell theory were given by Carter.[10]

The original integral Smarr's mass formula[4] relates the total values of mass, angular momentum and electric charge of black holes in Einstein-Maxwell theory with the horizon area. The area term in this formula was originally interpreted mechanically as the work of *stresses* of the horizon. Further, this interpretation was forgotten in favor of the thermodynamic one. When interest turned to solutions with NUT, it was immediately found,[11–14] that the Misner string also contributes to the Smarr mass formula, and this contribution was included in the entropy term. This interpretation was revived recently in slightly different terms in a series of papers,[15–19] based on the Bonnor interpretation of the Misner strings as mild physical singularities.[20]

In our opinion, the most natural description of solutions with Misner and Dirac strings as well as aligned multicenter solutions with struts can be given in terms of the rod structure, introduced by Harmark,[21] developing earlier ideas of Emparan and Reall.[22] The main novelty of this approach is the derivation of separate formulas for the partial masses for each component of the entire system, represented by a set of rods. In this interpretation, Misner's strings appear as independent components on the same base and as black holes.

Using the representation of vacuum stationary axisymmetric solutions in Weyl coordinates, we consider the solutions as generated by data on the polar axis, which look like distributional matter objects that are sources of the Poisson equation for the gravitational potential.[23] Accordingly, the total gravitational field can be viewed as a nonlinear superposition of the components such as black holes, struts, Misner and Dirac strings. Despite the nonlinearity of Einstein's equations, the total mass, angular momentum (and electric charge in the case of an electrovacuum) can be represented as the sum of the individual contributions of the constituents. This simple additivity is associated with conservation laws for the Komar and Gauss integrals. The magnetic charge and magnetic mass (NUT) in this description are due to the Misner and Dirac strings, which correspond to the individual elements in the rod system, so these charges do not enter the black hole horizon mass. Their contribution enters the asymptotic Komar mass as the proper masses of the Dirac and Misner strings along with the black hole contribution.

The difference between the horizon and the string rods is that the directions of the former are timelike, and the directions of the latter are spacelike. Both rods are Killing horizons and have an associated surface gravity. But the entropic interpretation of the surface contribution of spacelike rods (often encountered) does not seem convincing. An alternative interpretation may be similar to Smarr's original point of view.

This programme was previously performed for the Einstein-Maxwell system,[24,25] and here it is extended to Einstein-Maxwell-dilaton-axion gravity (EMDA). We show that Tomimatsu's proposal within the context of electrovacuum[26,27] on calculating Komar integrals over rods in terms of the boundary values of Ernst's potentials can be generalized to the sigma model representation of stationary dilaton-axion gravity. Surprisingly, the obtained mass formulas are very similar to the formulas obtained in the case of Einstein-Maxwell.

2. Stationary EMDA gravity

The EMDA gravity can be viewed as a consistent truncation of a toroidal reduction of the heterotic string,[28] or as a truncation of $N = 4$ four-dimensional supergravity.[29,30] Rotating electrically charged black hole solution of EMDA theory was obtained by Sen[28] within the first approach and independently, with the inclusion of NUT and magnetic charge, by Gal'tsov and Kechkin[31] in the second context. Recently, these solutions have attracted attention as an alternative to the Kerr metric in an effort to find astrophysical evidence for new physics.[32–34]

The mass formulas and thermodynamics of EMDA black holes have been discussed frequently in the past, though not in full generality, see, for example[35,36] (a more complete list of references prior to 2008 can be found in[36]). Our discussion here, based on generalization of,[25] covers solutions with Misner and Dirac strings, and is also applicable to hitherto unknown solutions for double black holes with struts that are expected to exist.

The EMDA action in our conventions reads:

$$S = \frac{1}{16\pi} \int \left\{ R - 2\partial_\mu \phi \partial^\mu \phi - \frac{1}{2} e^{4\phi} \partial_\mu \kappa \partial^\mu \kappa - e^{-2\phi} F_{\mu\nu} F^{\mu\nu} - \kappa F_{\mu\nu} \tilde{F}^{\mu\nu} \right\} \sqrt{-g} d^4 x, \tag{1}$$

where $\tilde{F}^{\mu\nu} = \frac{1}{2} E^{\mu\nu\lambda\tau} F_{\lambda\tau}$. Dilaton ϕ and axion κ parameterize a coset $SL(2,R)/SO(2)$, and the $SL(2,R)$ group is the symmetry of the full action. To see this, one can introduce the complex scalar

$$\zeta = \kappa + i e^{-2\phi} \tag{2}$$

and the self-dual Maxwell field $\mathcal{F} = \left(F + i\tilde{F} \right)/2$. Then the action takes the form

$$S = \frac{1}{16\pi} \int \left\{ R - 2|\partial \zeta (\zeta - \bar{\zeta})^{-1}|^2 + (i\zeta \mathcal{F}_{\mu\nu} \mathcal{F}^{\mu\nu} + c.c.) \right\} \sqrt{-g} d^4 x, \tag{3}$$

which is invariant under the $SL(2,R)$ transformations

$$\zeta \to \frac{\alpha\zeta + \beta}{\gamma\zeta + \delta}, \qquad \alpha\beta - \gamma\delta = 1,$$
$$F \to (\gamma\kappa + \delta)F + \gamma e^{-2\phi} \tilde{F}, \tag{4}$$

which interchange the modified Maxwell equations and the Bianchi identity

$$\nabla_\nu G^{\mu\nu} = 0, \quad \nabla_\nu \tilde{F}^{\mu\nu} = 0, \tag{5}$$
$$G^{\mu\nu} = e^{-2\phi} F^{\mu\nu} + \kappa \tilde{F}^{\mu\nu}. \tag{6}$$

The Einstein equations are

$$R_{\mu\nu} = 2\phi_{,\mu}\phi_{,\nu} + \frac{1}{2} e^{4\phi} \kappa_{,\mu} \kappa_{,\nu} - e^{-2\phi} \left(2 F_{\mu\lambda} F^\lambda{}_\nu + \frac{1}{2} F^2 g_{\mu\nu} \right). \tag{7}$$

For stationary and axisymmetric configurations the axion and dilaton kinetic term disappear from the Einstein equations in the $t - \varphi$ sector, and the dilaton enters only through the scale factor $e^{-2\phi}$ in front of the Maxwell energy-momentum tensor. This is crucial for our derivation.

Assuming the existence of the Killing vector $k = \partial_t$, the metric can be represented as

$$ds^2 = g_{\mu\nu} dx^\mu dx^\nu = -f(dt - \omega_i dx^i)^2 + \frac{1}{f} h_{ij} dx^i dx^j, \tag{8}$$

where three-dimensional metric h_{ij}, three-dimensional rotation vector ω_i, $(i,j = 1,2,3)$ and the scale factor f depend only on the space coordinates x^i. The spatial parts of the Bianchi identities and the modified Maxwell equations can be solved by introducing electric v and magnetic u potentials

$$F_{i0} = \frac{1}{\sqrt{2}} \partial_i v, \qquad (9)$$

$$G^{ij} = -\frac{f}{\sqrt{2h}} \epsilon^{ijk} \partial_k u. \qquad (10)$$

The mixed R_0^i Einstein equations are solved by introducing the twist potential χ obtained by dualizing the rotation two-form:

$$f^2 h_{il} \frac{\epsilon^{ljk}}{\sqrt{h}} \partial_j \omega_k = \partial_i \chi + v \partial_i u - u \partial_i v. \qquad (11)$$

The remaining equations reduce to those of three-dimensional gravitating sigma-model equations for six scalars $X^A = f, \chi, v, u, \phi, \kappa$, $A = 1, \ldots, 6$, and the three-dimensional metric h_{ij}:

$$S = \int \left[\mathcal{R}(h) - \mathcal{G}_{AB}(X) \partial_i X^A \partial_j X^B h^{ij} \right] \sqrt{h} \, d^3 x, \qquad (12)$$

where the target space metric $\mathcal{G}_{AB}$ can be presented as

$$dl^2 = \frac{1}{2} f^{-2} [df^2 + (d\chi + v du - u dv)^2] - f^{-1} [e^{2\phi}(du - \kappa dv)^2 + e^{-2\phi} dv^2]$$
$$+ 2 d\phi^2 + \frac{1}{2} e^{4\phi} d\kappa^2. \qquad (13)$$

The isometry group of this metric is $SO(3,2)$, as was identified in.[37] Based on isomorphism $SO(3,2) \sim Sp(4,R)$, a convenient 4×4 matrix representation of the coset $Sp(4,R)/SO(1,2)$ was suggested,[38] suitable for the generation technique. In terms of complex coordinates, one of which is (2) and two other are the following generalization of the Ernst potentials[39]

$$\Psi = u - \zeta v, \quad \mathcal{E} = if - \chi + v\Psi, \qquad (14)$$

the target space is a three-dimensional Kähler space.

3. Rod structure

Consider the spacetime metric, admitting two commuting Killing vectors k, m corresponding to stationarity and axial symmetry. Let t, φ be chosen so that $k = \partial_t$, $m = \partial_\phi$ with $t \in R$ and $\varphi \in [0, \pi]$. The remaining coordinates will be primarily assumed of the Boyer-Lindquist type, r, θ with $0 < r < \infty$ and $\theta \in [0, \pi]$. We assume that the spacetime manifold has no strong naked curvature singularities, but can have visible line singularities along (a part of) the polar axis in the sense of Israel.[23] These includes cosmic strings (conical singularities), struts in aligned multiple black hole solutions (conical singularities of both positive or negative tension) and Misner strings in spacetimes with NUTs, without time periodicity being imposed. We also assume that spacetime is asymtotically flat, or asymptotically locally flat. To such a spacetime one can ascribe a *rod structure* following Harmark.[21]

Let γ_{ab}, $x^a = t$, φ is the two-dimensional Lorentzian metric of the subspace spanned by the Killing vectors. Introduce the Weyl cordinates ρ, z such that ρ is

$$\rho = \sqrt{|\det \gamma|}, \tag{15}$$

and z to ensure the metric form:

$$ds^2 = \gamma_{ab}(\rho, z)dx^a dx^b + e^{2\nu}(d\rho^2 + dz^2), \tag{16}$$

where ν is a function of (ρ, z). To find the rod structure, one has to solve the equation

$$\rho(r, \theta) = 0. \tag{17}$$

Generically, the solution splits the polar axis into a certain number of finite or semi-infinite intervals $(-\infty, z_1], [z_1, z_2], \ldots, [z_N, +\infty)$ called rods (we will label two semi-infinite rods by $n = \pm$, and the remaining finite ones by an index n corresponding to the left bound of the interval). Each rod can be equipped with a two-dimensional vector, called *rod direction*, via the following reasoning. At $\rho = 0$ the matrix $\gamma_{ab}(0, z)$ is degenerate by virtue of the definition (15), so it must have zero eigenvalues. For quasiregular spacetimes, such that on the symmetry axis there are no strong curvature singularities these eigenvalues must be non-degenerate except, perhaps, for a discrete set of "turning" points z_n which mark the ends of rods. The eigenvector v_n^a, satisfying the equation

$$\gamma_{ab}(0, z)v_n^b = 0 \tag{18}$$

on any segment $z \in [z_n, z_{n+1}]$, is called the *n*-s rod direction. By continuity, this vector can be extended to small $\rho \neq 0$, and a more accurate analysis shows that, in the leading order in ρ, its 2D norm behaves as

$$v_n^2 = \gamma_{ab} v_n^a v_n^b \sim \pm a(z)\rho^2, \qquad e^{2\nu} \sim c^2 a(z), \tag{19}$$

where c is some constant and the sign $\pm$ corresponds to *spacelike* and *timelike* rod respectively.

Normalization of directional vectors can be chosen in different ways. One possibility, *Killing* normalization, relates to preferred normalisation an associated Killing vector in spacetime: $V = v^0 k + v^1 m$, namely, $v_0 = 1$ in the timelike case, and $v_1 = 1$ in spacelike. In view of behavior near the axis (19), in both cases the rod itself (i.e. the submanifold $\rho = 0$) will be the Killing horizon for so defined Killing vector. Another possibility is to choose the scale factor in such a way as to ensure the finiteness of its norm at $\rho \to 0$:

$$l_n^a = \lim_{\rho \to 0} \rho^{-1} e^{-\nu} v_n^a, \tag{20}$$

again with an option of further constant rescaling. An important property of so defined rod direction is its constancy (in view of (19) along the rod, i.e.,

$$\partial_z l_n^a = 0. \tag{21}$$

Timelike rods of finite length correspond to black hole horizons, infinite timelike rods describe acceleration horizons. The constant components of such a horizon rod are connected with its angular velocity Ω_H and the surface gravity $\varkappa_H$ of the Killing vector

$$\xi = k + \Omega_H\, m\,. \tag{22}$$

The surface gravity

$$\varkappa_H = (-\xi_{\mu;\nu}\xi^{\mu;\nu}/2)^{1/2} \tag{23}$$

can be expressed in the Weyl coordinates as

$$\varkappa_H = \lim_{\rho\to 0}\left(-\rho^{-2}e^{-2\nu}\gamma_{ab}v^a v^b\right)^{1/2}, \tag{24}$$

with $v^0 = 1$, $v^1 = \Omega_H$. It may be convenient to choose a canonical normalization of the directional vectors that corresponds to the unit surface gravity:

$$l_H = (1/\varkappa_H,\ \Omega_H/\varkappa_H)\,. \tag{25}$$

Spacelike rods correspond to line defects, such as cosmic strings, struts, Misner strings, which can be also Dirac strings associated with the corresponding vector potentials. These rods are Killing horizons for some spacelike Killing vectors. For them one also has constant angular velocities Ω_n and *spacelike* surface gravities

$$\varkappa_n = \lim_{\rho\to 0}\left(\rho^{-2}e^{-2\nu}\gamma_{ab}v_n^a v_n^b\right)^{1/2}, \tag{26}$$

so that the normalized directional vectors will be

$$l_n = (1/\varkappa_n,\ \Omega_n/\varkappa_n)\,. \tag{27}$$

Here $v_n^1 = 1$. With the normalized spacelike directional vector, the period (28) will be 2π. If the coordinate η associated with the spacelike rod Killing vector $l = \partial_\eta$, conical singularity is absent with perdiocity of η with

$$\Delta\eta = 2\pi \lim_{\rho\to 0}\left(\rho^2 e^{2\nu}\left(\gamma_{ab}l_n^a l_n^b\right)^{-1}\right)^{1/2}. \tag{28}$$

This is important in the situation when two spacelike rods meet at the turning point, where potentially a mismatch of periodicities may lead to *orbifold* singularities. This may happen for instantons.[41]

4. Komar charges

Following,[25] we start with the Komar definition[40] of the asymptotic mass and angular momentum:

$$M_\infty = \frac{1}{4\pi}\oint_{\Sigma_\infty} D^\nu k^\mu d\Sigma_{\mu\nu}, \quad J_\infty = -\frac{1}{8\pi}\oint_{\Sigma_\infty} D^\nu m^\mu d\Sigma_{\mu\nu}. \tag{29}$$

We also need a conserved electric charge as the surface integral. The definition of a conserved electric charge in EMDA follows from the modified Maxwell equations:

$$Q_\infty = \frac{1}{4\pi}\oint_{\Sigma_\infty} G^{\mu\nu} d\Sigma_{\mu\nu}. \tag{30}$$

Consider some stationary axisymmetric solution with an arbitrary rod structure z_n, l_n. Each rod must be surrounded by a thin cylinder Σ_n. Using Ostrogradski formula one can transform the asymptotic total mass to the sum of the local Komar masses M_n^d of rods ("direct" masses) and the bulk contribution coming from the fields: $M = \sum_n M_n^d + M_F$, where

$$M_n^d = \frac{1}{4\pi}\oint_{\Sigma_n} D^\nu k^\mu d\Sigma_{\mu\nu}, \quad M_F = \frac{1}{4\pi}\int D_\nu D^\nu k^\mu dS_\mu, \tag{31}$$

where Σ_n are the spacelike surfaces bounding the various sources[a], and the second integral is over the bulk. Similarly, the asymptotic angular momentum will read $J = \sum_n J_n^d + J_F$, where

$$J_n^d = -\frac{1}{8\pi}\oint_{\Sigma_n} D^\nu m^\mu d\Sigma_{\mu\nu}, \quad J_F = -\frac{1}{8\pi}\int D_\nu D^\nu m^\mu dS_\mu, \tag{32}$$

Using the well-known Killing lemma for k,

$$D_\nu D^\nu k^\mu = -[D_\nu, D^\mu]k^\nu = -R^\mu{}_\nu k^\nu, \tag{33}$$

and similarly for m, and an explicit form for the Ricci tensor in EMDA theory (7), one can express the bulk integrals as

$$M_F = -\frac{1}{4\pi}\int e^{-2\phi}\left(F_{it}F^{it} - F_{i\varphi}F^{i\varphi}\right)\sqrt{|g|}d^3x, \tag{34}$$

$$J_F = \frac{1}{4\pi}\int e^{-2\phi} F_{i\varphi}F^{it}\sqrt{|g|}\,d^3x. \tag{35}$$

Using the identities

$$F_{it}\tilde{F}^{it} - F_{i\varphi}\tilde{F}^{i\varphi} = 0, \quad F_{i\varphi}\tilde{F}^{it} = 0 \tag{36}$$

---

[a] We use the metric signature (-+++) and the convention $d\Sigma_{\mu\nu} = 1/2\sqrt{|g|}\,\epsilon_{\mu\nu\lambda\tau}dx^\lambda dx^\tau$ with $\epsilon_{t\rho z\varphi} = 1$ in Weyl coordinates. We will label t, φ by an index a, and the remaining coordinates ρ, z by i, j. The two-dimensional Levi-Civita symbol ϵ_{ij} is defined with $\epsilon_{\rho z} = 1$ and $\epsilon_{xy} = 1$ respectively.

one can rewrite (34) and (35) as

$$M_F = -\frac{1}{4\pi} \int \left(F_{it} G^{it} - F_{i\varphi} G^{i\varphi}\right) \sqrt{|g|} d^3x, \qquad (37)$$

$$J_F = \frac{1}{4\pi} \int F_{i\varphi} G^{it} \sqrt{|g|}\, d^3x. \qquad (38)$$

In view of the modified Maxwell equations, these expressions can be presented in the full divergence form

$$M_F = -\frac{1}{4\pi} \int \partial_i \left[\sqrt{-g}\left(A_t G^{it} - A_\varphi G^{i\varphi}\right)\right] d^3x, \qquad (39)$$

$$J_F = \frac{1}{4\pi} \int \partial_i \left(\sqrt{|g|} A_\varphi G^{it}\right) d^3x, \qquad (40)$$

suggesting the representation of the asymptotic mass and angular momentum as the surface integrals over the rods[b]:

$$M_\infty = \sum_n M_n, \quad M_n = \frac{1}{8\pi} \oint_{\Sigma_n} \left(g^{ij} g^{ta} \partial_j g_{ta} + 2\left(A_t G^{it} - A_\varphi G^{i\varphi}\right)\right) d\Sigma_i \qquad (41)$$

$$J_\infty = \sum_n J_n, \quad J_n = -\frac{1}{16\pi} \oint_{\Sigma_n} \left(g^{ij} g^{ta} \partial_j g_{\varphi a} + 4 A_\varphi G^{it}\right) d\Sigma_i, \qquad (42)$$

where we have also rewritten the direct Komar integrals in an explicit form. Thus we have succeeded in presenting the EMDA bulk contributions in the form of the integrals over the rods in the same was as it was done in[25] for the Einstein-Maxwell system. This procedure can be regarded as rod's dressing by the bulk field. So the resulting Smarr formulas for the asymptotic mass and angular momentum were written as sums of the dressed rod's contributions. Note, that in the general case, this is the only representation for the global M, J that can be found, since different forms of rod's contribution do not allow one to write asymptotic quantities directly in terms of physical charges as was possible for a single black hole.

From now on we assume the standard Weyl-Papaperou parametrization of the metric

$$ds^2 = -f(dt - \omega d\varphi)^2 + f^{-1}[e^{2k}(d\rho^2 + dz^2) + \rho^2 d\varphi^2], \qquad (43)$$

and represent the four-potential as

$$\sqrt{2}\, A_\mu dx^\mu = v dt + A d\varphi, \qquad (44)$$

(note that v, u, A in this paper differs from these in[25] by $\sqrt{2}$ to be consistent with the EMDA literature). Computation of the direct rod Komar integrals integrals was given in.[4] It amounts to dualizing the rotation three-form

$$\partial_i \chi = -f^2 \rho^{-1} \epsilon_{ij} \partial_j \omega + (u\partial_i v - v\partial_i u), \qquad (45)$$

---

[b]We assume that the integrals over in infinite sphere vanish, otherwise they must be added too. This happens if the North and South Misner and Dirac strings are arranged non-symmetrically, by adding suitable constants to the asymptotic values of the rotation function ω and the azimuthal component of the four-potential A_φ.

and leads to

$$M_n^d = \frac{1}{8\pi} \int_n \omega \left[\partial_z \chi + (v\partial_z u - u\partial_z v)\right] dz d\varphi \qquad (46)$$

Similarly for the angular momentum

$$J_n^d = -\frac{1}{16\pi} \int_n \omega \left\{2 - \omega \left[\partial_z \chi + (v\partial_z u - u\partial_z v)\right]\right\} dz d\varphi \qquad (47)$$

Note the appearance of the electromagnetic potentials in the expressions for direct rod mass and angular momentum due to use of dualized twist potential, i.e., implicit use of Einstein equations. These terms will be exactly canceled by the field contributions to the same quantities.

To continue, we show that, apart from constancy (i.e. z-independence) of the rod angular velocity $\Omega = 1/\omega$ and the generalized surface gravity $\varkappa$, one can prove for any rod the following relations:

$$\lim_{\rho \to 0} \left(G^{\rho t} - \omega G^{\rho \varphi}\right) \sqrt{|g|} = 0, \qquad (48)$$

$$\lim_{\rho \to 0} (v + A/\omega) \equiv -\sqrt{2}\Phi = \text{const}, \qquad (49)$$

where Φ can be interpreted as an electric potential of the rod. Together with constancy of ω, the last relation gives also

$$\partial_z A = -\omega \partial_z v, \qquad (50)$$

as $\rho \to 0$.

Using (48-50), and the EMDA dualization equation (10) one can rewrite the field contribution to the dressed rod mass (34) as

$$M_n^F = -\frac{1}{8\pi} \oint_{\Sigma_n} \left[\omega \left(v\partial_z u - u\partial_z v\right) - \partial_z(uA)\right] dz d\varphi. \qquad (51)$$

Combining this with the direct Komar mass (46) we obtain the dressed rod's mass

$$M_n = \frac{1}{8\pi} \int_{\Sigma_n} \left[\omega \partial_z \chi + \partial_z(A\,u)\right] dz d\varphi. \qquad (52)$$

It may seem surprising that this formula does not differ from that for Einstein-Maxwell system. No explicit scalar terms are seen.

For the bulk contribution to the angular momentum, one also applies the Eq. (48) and then magnetic dualization equation (10). The subsequent transformations are the same as in[25] and lead to the same result

$$J_n^F = \frac{1}{8\pi} \int_H \left[\omega^2 u \partial_z v + \omega \partial_z(Au)\right] dz d\varphi. \qquad (53)$$

Combining with the direct Komar momentum, we obtain for the dressed rod:

$$J_n = \frac{1}{16\pi} \int_H \omega \left[-2 + \omega \partial_z \chi + \partial_z(A\,u) - \sqrt{2}\omega \Phi_n \partial_z u\right] dz d\varphi, \qquad (54)$$

this expression also does not contain the dilaton and axion. Now consider Komar electric charge of a rod (30). Explicitly, it is given by the flux

$$Q_n = \frac{1}{4\pi} \int_{\Sigma_n} \sqrt{|g|} G^{t\rho} dz d\varphi. \tag{55}$$

Manipulating with indices and using dualization equation (10)

$$G^{t\rho} = \frac{g^{\rho\rho}}{g_{tt}} G_{t\rho} - \frac{g_{t\varphi}}{g_{tt}} G^{\varphi i} = e^{-2k} \left[G_{t\rho} + \frac{f\omega}{\rho} \partial_z u \right], \tag{56}$$

one finds that in the limit $\rho \to 0$ only the second term contributes, so

$$Q_n = \frac{1}{4\sqrt{2}\pi} \int_{\Sigma_n} \omega \partial_z u \, dz d\varphi. \tag{57}$$

After integration over φ

$$M_n = \frac{\omega_n}{4} \chi \Big|_{z_n}^{z_{n+1}} + \frac{1}{4} (Au) \Big|_{z_n}^{z_{n+1}} \tag{58}$$

Similarly, for the angular momentum (54) one finds

$$J_n = \frac{\omega_n}{8} \left\{ -2(z_{n+1} - z_n) + \left[\omega_n \left(\chi - \sqrt{2} \Phi_n u \right) + Au \right] \Big|_{z_n}^{z_{n+1}} \right\}. \tag{59}$$

Finally, the electric charge will be

$$Q_n = \frac{\omega_n}{2\sqrt{2}} u \Big|_{z_n}^{z_{n+1}}. \tag{60}$$

The angular velocity of a rod is defined as a limit

$$\Omega_n = \lim_{\rho \to 0} \omega^{-1}(\rho, z), \qquad z_n < z < z_{n+1}. \tag{61}$$

Combining the above formulas we obtain rod Smarr mass

$$M_n = \frac{L_n}{2} + 2\Omega_n J_n + \Phi_n Q_n, \tag{62}$$

where $L_n = z_{n+1} - z_n$ is the n-s rod length (for infinite rods some length regularization is needed). Please note that this formula is identical; it is valid for any rod, regardless of the specific parameter values.

5. Length versus entropy

Although it looks like a one-dimensional object, any rod with finite surface gravity has a finite surrounding cylindrical area:

$$\mathcal{A}_n = \oint d\varphi \int_{z_n}^{z_{n+1}} \sqrt{|g_{zz} g_{\varphi\varphi}|} dz = 2\pi \int_{z_n}^{z_{n+1}} \sqrt{|e^{2k}|} |\omega| dz. \tag{63}$$

The surface gravity (by definition, positive) in Weyl coordinates reads

$$\kappa_n = |\Omega_n| \sqrt{|e^{-2k}|}. \tag{64}$$

Thus the integral (63) is simply proportional to the rod's length:

$$\frac{\kappa_n}{2\pi}\mathcal{A}_n = z_{n+1} - z_n = L_n. \tag{65}$$

This is true for both timelike rods (horizons) and spacelike ones (defects). In the first case, the surface gravity is proportional to the Hawking temperature, and the area of the horizon is proportional to the entropy.

$$T_H = \kappa_H/2\pi, \qquad S_H = \mathcal{A}_H/4, \tag{66}$$

therefore

$$T_H S_H = \frac{\kappa_H}{8\pi}\mathcal{A}_H = \frac{L_H}{4}, \tag{67}$$

and the Smarr formula can be rewritten as[4]

$$M_H = 2\Omega_H J_H + 2T_H S_H + \Phi_H Q_H. \tag{68}$$

For spacelike rods such an identification does not seem justified, so we prefer to leave Smarr formua in its "length" form (62).

For multicenter solutions this mass relation holds separately for each black hole constituent. As stated in,[24,25] this is also true when black holes have magnetic and/or NUT charges. In our interpretation, the contribution of these parameters to the total asymptotic mass comes from individual rods representing the Dirac and Misner strings.

6. EMDA rotating dyon with NUT

The metric of the EMDA dyon with the NUT parameter constructed in 1994[31] can be represented in the Kerr form:

$$ds^2 = -\frac{\Delta - a^2 \sin^2\theta}{\Sigma}(dt - \omega d\varphi)^2 + \Sigma\left(\frac{dr^2}{\Delta} + d\theta^2 + \frac{\Delta \sin^2\theta}{\Delta - a^2 \sin^2\theta}d\varphi^2\right), \tag{69}$$

with the modified coefficient functions:

$$\Delta = (r - r_-)(r - 2M) + a^2 - (N - N_-)^2,$$
$$\Sigma = r(r - r_-) + (a\cos\theta + N)^2 - N_-^2,$$
$$\omega = \frac{-2w}{\Delta - a^2\sin^2\theta}, \quad w = N\Delta\cos\theta + a\sin^2\theta\left(M(r - r_-) + N(N - N_-)\right).$$

Two new parameters r_-, N_- depend on mass M, NUT parameter N, electric and magnetic charges Q, P as follows:

$$r_- = \frac{M(Q^2 + P^2)}{M^2 + N^2}, \qquad N_- = \frac{N(Q^2 + P^2)}{2(M^2 + N^2)}, \tag{70}$$

and a is the rotation parameter. The electric and magnetic potentials and the complex axidilaton scalar (2) depend also on the asymptotic values of dilaton and axion $\zeta_\infty = \kappa_\infty + ie^{-2\phi_\infty}$:

$$v = -\frac{\sqrt{2}e^{\phi_\infty}}{\Sigma}\text{Re}\left[\mathcal{Q}(r - r_- + i\delta)\right], \qquad u = -\frac{\sqrt{2}e^{\phi_\infty}}{\Sigma}\text{Re}\left[\mathcal{Q}\zeta_\infty(r - r_- + i\delta)\right]$$

$$\zeta = \frac{\zeta_\infty R + \mathcal{D}\zeta_\infty^*}{R + \mathcal{D}}, \qquad R = r - \frac{\mathcal{M}^* r_-}{2\mathcal{M}} + i\delta, \qquad \delta = a\cos\theta + N - N_-,$$

where the complex mass, electromagnetic and axidilaton charges are introduced

$$\mathcal{M} = M + iN, \qquad \mathcal{Q} = Q + iP, \qquad \mathcal{D} \equiv D + iA = -\frac{\mathcal{Q}^{*2}}{2\mathcal{M}}. \tag{71}$$

The explicit expressions for the axion and dilaton fields are

$$\kappa = \kappa_\infty - e^{-2\phi_\infty}\frac{2\text{Im}(R\mathcal{D}^*)}{|R + \mathcal{D}|^2}, \qquad e^{-2(\phi - \phi_\infty)} = \frac{\Sigma}{|R + \mathcal{D}|^2}, \tag{72}$$

where $|R|^2 - |\mathcal{D}|^2 = \Sigma$. The dilaton asymptotics renormalizes the electric and magnetic charges, and the axion determines their mixing. Indeed, for $r \to \infty$, the electric and magnetic potentials are read as follows:

$$v \sim -\frac{\sqrt{2}Q e^{\phi_\infty}}{r}, \qquad u \sim \frac{\sqrt{2}\left(P e^{-\phi_\infty} - \kappa_\infty Q e^{\phi_\infty}\right)}{r}. \tag{73}$$

The axion and dilaton asymptotics $r \to \infty$ read as follows:

$$\zeta \sim \zeta_\infty - 2ie^{-2\phi_\infty}\frac{\mathcal{D}}{r}, \qquad \kappa \sim \kappa_\infty + 2e^{-2\phi_\infty}\frac{A}{r}, \qquad \phi \sim \phi_\infty + \frac{D}{r}. \tag{74}$$

Combining electric and magnetic potentials, the complex potential Ψ reads

$$\Psi = \frac{\sqrt{2}e^{\phi_\infty}}{\Sigma}\left[(\zeta - \kappa_\infty)\text{Re}\left[\mathcal{Q}(r - r_- + i\delta)\right] + e^{-2\phi_\infty}\text{Im}\left[\mathcal{Q}(r - r_- + i\delta)\right]\right] \tag{75}$$

Applying the inverse dualization equations (10), we find the azimuthal component of the Maxwell four-potential For the four-potential one-form $\text{A} = A_\mu dx^\mu$ we obtain:

$$A_\mu dx^\mu = \frac{e^{\phi_\infty}}{\Sigma}\left(-Q(r - r_-) + P\delta\right)\left(dt + \left(2Ny - a(1 - y^2)\right)d\varphi\right) - e^{\phi_\infty}Pyd\varphi. \tag{76}$$

Its norm diverges on the Misner strings $\cos\theta = \pm 1$:

$$A_\mu A^\mu\big|_{\cos\theta \to \pm 1} \sim \frac{-e^{2\phi_\infty}P^2}{\Sigma \sin^2\theta}, \tag{77}$$

thus, Misner rods are also Dirac string loci.

Gravitational dualization equation (11) gives the metric twist potential

$$\chi = 2\frac{M\delta - N(r - r_-)}{\Sigma}. \tag{78}$$

The ergosphere boundary is given by

$$r_E = M + r_-/2 + \sqrt{|\mathcal{M}|^2\left(1 - r_-/2M\right)^2 - a^2\cos^2\theta}, \tag{79}$$

and the event horizon radius (the outermost root of $\Delta = 0$) is equal to

$$r_H = M + r_-/2 + \sqrt{|\mathcal{M}|^2 (1 - r_-/2M)^2 - a^2}, \qquad (80)$$

so that the horizon two-surface touches the ergosphere at the polar axis.

The transformation to the Weyl coordinates ρ, z is given by

$$\rho^2 = \Delta \sin^2 \theta,$$
$$z = (\Delta'/2) \cos \theta = (r - M - r_-/2) \cos \theta.$$

Solving the equation $\rho = 0$, we find that the rod system consists of three rods:

- l_+ : northern Misner string $r \in (r_H, \infty)$, $\cos \theta = 1$;
- l_H the horizon rod $r = r_H$, $\theta \in [0, \pi]$;
- l_+ southern Misner string $r \in (r_H, \infty)$, $\cos \theta = -1$.

The normalized directional vectors are given by the formulas (25), (27) in terms of the corresponding surface gravities and angular velocities.

It is also useful to represent the solution in terms of prolate spheroidal coordinates x, y definied as

$$r = \sigma x + M + r_-/2, \qquad \cos \theta = y, \qquad (81)$$

$$\sigma^2 = |\mathcal{M}|^2 - |\mathcal{D}|^2 - |\mathcal{Q}|^2 - a^2, \qquad (82)$$

One obtains:

$$ds^2 = -f(dt - \omega d\varphi)^2 + f^{-1}\left[\sigma^2 e^{2k}(x^2 - y^2)\left(\frac{dx^2}{x^2-1} + \frac{dy^2}{1-y^2}\right) + \rho^2 d\varphi^2\right], \qquad (83)$$

where the metric functions now read

$$\Sigma = (\sigma x + M)^2 - |\mathcal{D}|^2 + (ay + N)^2,$$
$$\Sigma f = \sigma^2(x^2 - 1) - a^2(1 - y^2), \qquad e^{2k} = \frac{f\Sigma}{\sigma^2(x^2 - y^2)},$$
$$f\Sigma\omega = -2\left[N\sigma^2(x^2 - 1)y + a(1 - y^2)\left(M\sigma x + |\mathcal{M}|^2 - |\mathcal{Q}|^2/2\right)\right].$$

The South segment of the Misner string is $x > 1$, $y = -1$, the horizon rod is $x = 1, -1 \leq y \leq 1$ and the North Misner string is $x > 1$, $y = 1$. As expected, the inverse rotation function on the rods is constant on them and represents their angular velocities. It is easy to find

$$\Omega_H = \frac{2a}{\nu^2}, \qquad \Omega_\pm = \mp \frac{1}{2N}. \qquad (84)$$

where a new parameter is introduced

$$\nu^2 = 2M\sigma + 2|\mathcal{M}|^2 - |\mathcal{Q}|^2, \qquad (85)$$

such that the boundary values of $\Sigma(x, y)$ are

$$\Sigma_\pm \equiv \Sigma(1, \pm 1) = \nu^2 \pm 2aN. \qquad (86)$$

The other ingredients of the mass formulas depend on the values of electric and magnetic potentials $v_\pm$ and $u_\pm$ of the defect rods $l_\pm$. The magnetic potential in spheroidal coordinates is

$$u = \frac{\sqrt{2}}{\Sigma}\left\{e^{\phi_\infty}\kappa_\infty[-Q(\sigma x + M - r_-/2) + P\delta] + e^{-\phi_\infty}[P(\sigma x + M - r_-/2) + Q\delta]\right\} \quad (87)$$

Using it, we obtain:

$$v_\pm = -\frac{\sqrt{2}e^{\phi_\infty}}{\nu^2 \pm 2aN}\mathrm{Re}\left[\mathcal{Q}(\sigma \pm ia + \mathcal{M}(1 - |\mathcal{Q}|^2/2|\mathcal{M}|^2))\right], \quad (88)$$

$$u_\pm = -\frac{\sqrt{2}e^{\phi_\infty}}{\nu^2 \pm 2aN}\mathrm{Re}\left[\mathcal{Q}\zeta(\sigma \pm ia + \mathcal{M}(1 - |\mathcal{Q}|^2/2|\mathcal{M}|^2))\right] \quad (89)$$

For surface gravities it is convenient to use Eq. (64). One finds:

$$\varkappa_H = \frac{\sigma}{\nu^2}, \qquad \varkappa_n = \mp\frac{1}{2N}. \quad (90)$$

Note that the angular velocities and surface gravities of Misner strings coincide similarly to the case of Kerr-Newman-NUT.[25] But they enter into the mass formula in a different way, so on should not consider this coincidence as a matter of interpretation.

The electric charges of the rods are given by (57). One finds the Gauss charges of the horizon and strings as:

$$Q_H = \frac{\omega_H}{2\sqrt{2}}(u_+ - u_-) = \frac{e^{-\phi_\infty}\nu^2\left(2\sigma N^2 + M\nu^2\right)\mathrm{Im}\left[\zeta_\infty e^{2\phi_\infty}\mathcal{M}\mathcal{Q}\right]}{|\mathcal{M}|^2\left(\nu^4 - 4a^2N^2\right)}, \quad (91)$$

$$Q_\pm = \frac{Nu_\pm}{\sqrt{2}}. \quad (92)$$

Combining them together, we obtain

$$Q_H + Q_+ + Q_- = Qe^{-\phi_\infty} + P\kappa_\infty e^{\phi_\infty}. \quad (93)$$

This coincides with the true asymptotic charge of the configuration, with account of axion mixing and dilaton renormalization.

The electric potential on the horizon and on the strings are

$$\Phi_H = e^{\phi_\infty}\frac{\nu^2(QM - NP) + 2\sigma N(QN + MP)}{2\nu^2|\mathcal{M}|^2}, \qquad \Phi_\pm = -e^{\phi_\infty}\frac{P}{2N}. \quad (94)$$

Rod masses can be expressed in the form (58), using the corresponding values of the twist potential (78). One obtains

$$M_H = \nu^2 \cdot \frac{M\nu^2 + 2\sigma N^2}{\nu^4 - 4a^2N^2} + \frac{1}{4}(2N(v_+u_+ + v_-u_-) - \sqrt{2}e^{\phi_\infty}P(u_+ + u_-)), \quad (95)$$

$$M_\pm = N\frac{-N\sigma \pm Ma}{\nu^2 \pm 2aN} + \frac{1}{4}(2Nv_\pm - \sqrt{2}Pe^{\phi_\infty})u_\pm, \quad (96)$$

where the boundary values of electric and magnetic potentials are given by (88), (89). One can distinguish Dirac string contributions to the masses of defects as the parts non-vanishing for $N = 0$. Other terms are due to Misner strings. Direct substitution of (88-89) leads to long expressions, but the one can show that the Maxwell contributions to the total mass cancel out, while the remaining part non-trivially leads to the identity

$$M_\infty = M_H + M_+ + M_- = M.$$

Now we turn to the angular momentum balance, using the rod's momenta the expression (59). The length of the horizon rod is $L_H = 2\sigma$. Other rod lengths diverge. As it was shown in Ref.,[25] to overcome this issue, one can regularize the angular momentum as follows:

$$\tilde{J}_\pm = J_\pm + \frac{\omega_\pm L_\pm}{4} \qquad (97)$$

We then obtain the angular momenta of the three rods as

$$J_H = \frac{\omega_H}{2}\left(-\sigma + M_H - Q_H \Phi_H\right), \qquad \tilde{J}_\pm = N^2 \left(\frac{\pm N\sigma - Ma}{\nu^2 \pm 2aN} \mp \frac{v_\pm u_\pm}{2}\right). \qquad (98)$$

We have explicitly checked that

$$\tilde{J}_\infty = J_H + \tilde{J}_+ + \tilde{J}_- = aM.$$

Therefore, we have constructed horizon mass, angular momentum and charge in terms of the global parameters and checked their total balance.

7. Conclusion

We have shown that the derivation of mass formulas using the Tomimatsu approach for calculating Komar integrals around rods in electrovacuum can be generalized to the EMDA theory containing scalar fields coupled to the graviphoton. Using a three-dimensional reduction of the EMDA equations, we construct magnetic and twist potentials, which allow to express the integrals over the rods in the same way as in the Einstein-Maxwell theory, where Tomimatsu used for this purpose the Ernst potentials. It should be noted that the scalar dilaton and axion fields do not contribute to the resulting mass formulas, and their asymptotics only rotates electric and magnetic charges in the parameter space. For regular asymptotically flat configurations, the dilaton and axion charges are secondary and their variations do not enter the Smarr-type formulas.

In this approach, the magnetic and NUT charges do not affect the mass and angular momentum of the black hole calculated as Komar's integrals over the horizon. They contribute to the asymptotic mass and angular momentum via the respective individual rods representing the Dirac and Misner strings. As an illustration, we considered the case of a rotating EMDA dyon equipped with NUT. In this case, as in the case of dyonic Kerr-Neumann-NUT, the Dirac string contributes to the asymptotic mass, but not to the asymptotic angular momentum, while the Misner string contributes to both.

The work is supported by the Russian Foundation for Basic Research on the project 20-52-18012Bulg-a, and the Scientific and Educational School of Moscow State University "Fundamental and Applied Space Research". I.B. is also grateful to the Foundation for the Advancement of Theoretical Physics and Mathematics "BASIS" for support.

References

1. D. Christodoulou, "Reversible and irreversible transforations in black hole physics," Phys. Rev. Lett. **25** (1970), 1596-1597.
2. S. W. Hawking, "Black holes in general relativity," Commun. Math. Phys. **25** (1972), 152-166.
3. D. Christodoulou and R. Ruffini, "Reversible transformations of a charged black hole," Phys. Rev. D **4** (1971), 3552-3555.
4. L. Smarr, "Mass formula for Kerr black holes," Phys. Rev. Lett. **30** (1973), 71-73 [erratum: Phys. Rev. Lett. **30** (1973), 521-521].
5. S. W. Hawking, "Black hole explosions," Nature **248** (1974), 30-31.
6. J. D. Bekenstein, "Black holes and the second law," Lett. Nuovo Cim. **4** (1972), 737-740.
7. J. M. Bardeen, B. Carter and S. W. Hawking, "The Four laws of black hole mechanics," Commun. Math. Phys. **31** (1973) 161.
8. S. W. Hawking, "Black Holes and Thermodynamics." Phys. Rev. D **13** (1976) 191.
9. G. W. Gibbons and S. W. Hawking. "Action Integrals and Partition Functions in Quantum Gravity," Phys. Rev. D **15** (1977) 2752.
10. B. Carter, "Black Hole Equilibrium States, Part 2: General Theory of Stationary Black Hole States", in Black Holes (Les Houches 1972) ed B and C. DeWitt, (Gordon Breach, New York 1973)) 125-214.
11. C. J. Hunter. "The Action of instantons with nut charge," Phys. Rev. D **59** (1999) 024009, [gr-qc/9807010].
12. S. W. Hawking and C. J. Hunter. "Gravitational entropy and global structure," Phys. Rev. D **59** (1999) 044025, [hep-th/9808085].
13. S. Carlip, "Entropy from conformal field theory at Killing horizons," Class. Quantum Grav. **16** (1999) 3327, [gr-qc/9906126].
14. R. B. Mann, "Misner string entropy," Phys. Rev. D **60** (1999) 104047, [hep-th/9903229].
15. R. A. Hennigar, D. Kubizňák and R. B. Mann, "Thermodynamics of Lorentzian Taub-NUT spacetimes," Phys. Rev. D **100** (2019) no. 6, 064055, [arXiv:1903.08668 [hep-th]].
16. R. Durka, "The first law of black hole thermodynamics for Taub-NUT spacetime," [arXiv:1908.04238 [gr-qc]].
17. S. Q. Wu and D. Wu, "Thermodynamical hairs of the four-dimensional Taub-Newman-Unti-Tamburino spacetimes," Phys. Rev. D **100** (2019) no. 10, 101501, [arXiv:1909.07776 [hep-th]].
18. Z. Chen and J. Jiang, "General Smarr relation and first law of a NUT dyonic black hole," Phys. Rev. D **100** (2019) no. 10, 104016, [arXiv:1910.10107 [hep-th]].
19. A. Ballon Bordo, F. Gray and D. Kubizňák, "Thermodynamics of Rotating NUTty Dyons," JHEP **05** (2020), 084, [arXiv:2003.02268 [hep-th]].

20. G. Clément, D. Gal'tsov and M. Guenouche, "Rehabilitating space-times with NUTs," Phys. Lett. B **750** (2015) 591, [arXiv:1508.07622 [hep-th]].
21. T. Harmark, "Stationary and axisymmetric solutions of higher-dimensional general relativity," Phys. Rev. D **70**(2004) 124002, [hep-th/0408141].
22. R. Emparan and H. S. Reall, "Generalized Weyl solutions," Phys. Rev. D **65** (2002), 084025, [arXiv:hep-th/0110258 [hep-th]].
23. W. Israel, "Line sources in general relativity," Phys. Rev. D **15** (1977) 935.
24. G. Clément and D. Gal'tsov, "On the Smarr formula for rotating dyonic black holes," Phys. Lett. B **773** (2017) 290, [arXiv:1707.01332 [gr-qc]].
25. G. Clément and D. Gal'tsov, "On the Smarr formulas for electrovac spacetimes with line singularities," Phys. Lett. B **802** (2020), 135270, [arXiv:1908.10617 [gr-qc]].
26. A. Tomimatsu, "On Gravitational Mass and Angular Momentum of Two Black Holes in Equilibrium," Prog. Theor. Phys. **70** (1983), 385.
27. A. Tomimatsu, "Equilibrium of Two Rotating Charged Black Holes and the Dirac String," Prog. Theor. Phys. **72** (1984), 73.
28. A. Sen, "Rotating charged black hole solution in heterotic string theory," Phys. Rev. Lett. **69** (1992), 1006-1009, [arXiv:hep-th/9204046 [hep-th]].
29. G. W. Gibbons, "Antigravitating Black Hole Solitons with Scalar Hair in N=4 Supergravity," Nucl. Phys. B **207** (1982), 337-349.
30. R. Kallosh, D. Kastor, T. Ortin and T. Torma, "Supersymmetry and stationary solutions in dilaton axion gravity," Phys. Rev. D **50** (1994), 6374-6384, [arXiv:hep-th/9406059 [hep-th]].
31. D. V. Galtsov and O. V. Kechkin, "Ehlers-Harrison type transformations in dilaton - axion gravity," Phys. Rev. D **50** (1994), 7394-7399, [arXiv:hep-th/9407155 [hep-th]].
32. A. Narang, S. Mohanty and A. Kumar, "Test of Kerr-Sen metric with black hole observations," [arXiv:2002.12786 [gr-qc]].
33. I. Banerjee, B. Mandal and S. SenGupta, "Implications of Einstein-Maxwell dilaton-axion gravity from the black hole continuum spectrum," Mon. Not. Roy. Astron. Soc. **500** (2020) no. 1, 481-492, [arXiv:2007.13980 [gr-qc]].
34. I. Banerjee, B. Mandal and S. SenGupta, "Signatures of Einstein-Maxwell dilaton-axion gravity from the observed jet power and the radiative efficiency," Phys. Rev. D **103** (2021) no. 4, 044046, [arXiv:2007.03947 [gr-qc]].
35. M. Rogatko, "Extrema of mass, first law of black hole mechanics and staticity theorem in Einstein-Maxwell axion dilaton gravity," Phys. Rev. D **58** (1998), 044011, [arXiv:hep-th/9807012 [hep-th]].
36. T. Ghosh and S. SenGupta, "Thermodynamics Of dilaton-axion black holes," Phys. Rev. D **78** (2008), 124005, [arXiv:0811.3679 [hep-th]].
37. D. V. Gal'tsov, "Integrable systems in stringy gravity," Phys. Rev. Lett. **74** (1995), 2863-2866, [arXiv:hep-th/9410217 [hep-th]].
38. D. V. Gal'tsov and O. V. Kechkin, "Matrix dilaton - axion for heterotic string in three-dimensions," Phys. Lett. B **361** (1995), 52-58, [arXiv:hep-th/9507164 [hep-th]].
39. D. V. Gal'tsov and S. A. Sharakin, "Matrix Ernst potentials for EMDA with multiple vector fields," Phys. Lett. B **399** (1997), 250-257, [arXiv:hep-th/9702039 [hep-th]].
40. A. Komar, "Covariant conservation laws in general relativity," Phys. Rev. **113** (1959), 934-936.
41. Y. Chen and E. Teo, "Rod-structure classification of gravitational instantons with U(1)xU(1) isometry," Nucl. Phys. B **838** (2010) 207, [arXiv:1004.2750 [gr-qc]].

Holography for rotating black holes in $f(T)$ gravity

Masoud Ghezelbash

Department of Physics and Engineering Physics,
University of Saskatchewan
Saskatoon, Saskatchewan, Canada
E-mail: amg142@campus.usask.ca
www.usask.ca

We extend the black hole holography to the case of an asymptotically anti–de Sitter (AdS) rotating charged black holes in $f(T) = T + \alpha T^2$ gravity, where α is a constant. We find that the scalar wave radial equation at the near-horizon region implies the existence of the 2D conformal symmetries. We show that choosing proper central charges for the dual CFT, we produce exactly the macroscopic Bekenstein-Hawking entropy from the microscopic Cardy entropy for the dual CFT. These observations suggest that the rotating charged AdS black hole in $f(T)$ gravity is dual to a 2D CFT at finite temperatures.[*]

Keywords: $f(T)$ gravity, Black holes, Holography

1. Introduction

The idea of AdS/CFT correspondence was extended to the case of extremal rotating black holes, namely, the Kerr/CFT correspondence which was proposed by Guica et al.[6] The correspondence states that the physics of the extremal Kerr black holes, which are rotating with maximum angular velocity, can be described by a 2D CFT, living on the near-horizon region of the black holes. The correspondence was established by showing that one can microscopically reproduces the Bekenstein-Hawking entropy, using the CFT Cardy entropy formula. As one would expect, the Kerr/CFT correspondence is not only a peculiar property of extremal black holes but also non-extremal Kerr black holes. However, at the near-horizon region of the non-extremal Kerr black holes, one cannot indicate any conformal symmetries. In other words, the conformal symmetries are not the symmetries of the non-extremal Kerr black hole geometry (as they are for the case of the extremal Kerr black holes). However, it turns out that the "hidden" conformal symmetries can be revealed by looking at the solution space of the radial part of the Klein-Gordon equation, for a massless scalar probe in the near-horizon region of the Kerr black holes.[7] In this case, the radial equation, can be written as the $SL(2, R)_L \times SL(2, R)_R$ Casimir eigen-equation. Subsequently, the Kerr/CFT correspondence can be established by matching the microscopic CFT Cardy entropy to the macroscopic Bekenstein-Hawking entropy

---

[*]This presentation is entirely based on the published paper in *Phys. Rev.* **D 101**, 024020 (2020) by C. Bernard and M. Ghezelbash.

of the Kerr black holes with general angular momentum and mass parameters. The correspondence has been studied for several black holes solutions, for instance, in Refs.[8–12,12–18].

The usual theory of gravity, based on the Riemannian geometry, has been extended through several gravity theories. One of them is the teleparallel gravity (TG) theory, where the Ricci scalar R, is replaced by the teleparallel torsion scalar T. Moreover, the TG has been generalized to $f(T)$ gravity by replacing the torsion scalar T, with an arbitrary function of T, such as $f(T)$. In,[19] Awad et al. find an asymptotically rotating charged AdS black hole solution, in quadratic $f(T)$ gravity, where $f(T) = T + \alpha T^2$. A very natural question to be asked, is "Do we have any $f(T)$/Hidden CFT correspondence?", that we address in this article.

The outline of this presentation is organized as follows. In Sec. 2, we review the $f(T)$-Maxwell gravity theory as well as the rotating charged AdS black hole solutions, and its thermodynamics aspects. We also consider the massless Klein-Gordon wave equation, in the background of the rotating charged AdS black holes, in quadratic $f(T)$ gravity. In Sec. 3, we study the radial wave equation in the near-horizon region of the black holes, and rewrite it as the $SL(2,R)_L \times SL(2,R)_R$ Casimir equation. We also find the central charges of the dual CFT by matching the Cardy entropy for the dual CFT to the macroscopic Bekenstein-Hawking entropy. Therefore, we present evidence that the rotating charged AdS black holes in quadratic $f(T)$ gravity, can be considered holographically dual to the CFT. In the final section, we summarize our results and address some future works. We use the Planck units, in which $c = G = \hbar = k_B = 1$.

2. f(T) Rotating Black Holes

The basic variables in TG are tetrad fields $e_a{}^\mu$, where $a = (0,1,2,3)$ is the index of internal space and $\mu = (0,1,2,3)$ is the index of spacetime. The tetrad fields satisfy

$$e_a{}^\mu e^a{}_\nu = \delta^\mu_\nu, \quad e_a{}^\mu e^b{}_\mu = \delta^b_a. \tag{1}$$

The tetrad fields are related to the spacetime metric and its inverse

$$g_{\mu\nu} = \eta_{ab} e^a{}_\mu e^b{}_\nu, \quad g^{\mu\nu} = \eta^{ab} e_a{}^\mu e_b{}^\nu, \tag{2}$$

respectively, where $\eta_{ab} = \text{diag}(-,+,+,+)$ is the metric of 4D Minkowski spacetime. Also, it can be shown that $e = \det(e_{a\mu}) = \sqrt{-g}$, where g is the determinant of the metric. In TG, we use the Weitzenbock connection

$$W^\alpha{}_{\mu\nu} = e_a{}^\alpha \partial_\nu e^a{}_\mu = -e^a{}_\mu \partial_\nu e_a{}^\alpha, \tag{3}$$

to define the covariant derivative, by

$$\nabla_\nu e_a{}^\mu = \partial_\nu e_a{}^\mu + W^\mu{}_{\rho\nu} e_a{}^\rho = 0. \tag{4}$$

The Weitzenbock connection is curvature-free, but it has a non vanishing torsion

$$T^\alpha{}_{\mu\nu} = W^\alpha{}_{\nu\mu} - W^\alpha{}_{\mu\nu} = e_i{}^\alpha \left(\partial_\mu e^i{}_\nu - \partial_\nu e^i{}_\mu \right). \tag{5}$$

We define the torsion scalar by
$$T = T^\alpha{}_{\mu\nu} S_\alpha{}^{\mu\nu}, \tag{6}$$
where the superpotential tensor is
$$S_\alpha{}^{\mu\nu} = \frac{1}{2}\left(K^{\mu\nu}{}_\alpha + \delta^\mu_\alpha T^{\beta\nu}{}_\beta - \delta^\nu_\alpha T^{\beta\mu}{}_\beta\right). \tag{7}$$
We note that the Contortion tensor $K_{\alpha\mu\nu}$ is given by
$$K_{\alpha\mu\nu} = \frac{1}{2}\left(T_{\nu\alpha\mu} + T_{\alpha\mu\nu} - T_{\mu\alpha\nu}\right). \tag{8}$$

We consider a four-dimensional rotating charged AdS black hole solution in $f(T)$-Maxwell theory with a negative cosmological constant where
$$f(T) = T + \alpha T^2. \tag{9}$$
The dimensional negative parameter α is the coefficient of the quadratic term of the scalar torsion. The action of the $f(T)$-Maxwell theory in 4D, for an asymptotically AdS spacetimes, is given by
$$\mathcal{S} = \frac{1}{2\mathfrak{K}} \int d^4x\, |e|\, (f(T) - 2\Lambda - F \wedge {}^*F), \tag{10}$$
where $\Lambda = -3/l^2$ is the 4D cosmological constant, l is the length scale of AdS spacetime. The constant $\mathfrak{K}$ in (10) is related to the 4D Newton's gravitational constant G_4, by $\mathfrak{K} = 2\Omega_2 G_4$, where $\Omega_2 = 2\pi^{3/2}/\Gamma(3/2)$, is the volume of 2D unit sphere, and $\Gamma(3/2) = \frac{1}{2}\sqrt{\pi}$.

In the action (10), $F = d\tilde{\Phi}$, where $\tilde{\Phi} = \tilde{\Phi}_\mu dx^\mu$ is the gauge potential one-form.

Varying action (10) with respect to the tetrad fields and the Maxwell potential Φ_μ, one finds the field equations for gravity
$$S_\mu{}^{\rho\nu} \partial_\rho T f''(T) + \left[e^{-1} e^a{}_\mu \partial_\rho (e e_a{}^\alpha S_\alpha{}^{\rho\nu}) - T^\alpha{}_{\lambda\mu} S_\alpha{}^{\nu\lambda}\right] f'(T)$$
$$-\frac{\delta^\nu_\mu}{4}\left(f(T) + \frac{6}{l^2}\right) = -\frac{\mathfrak{K}}{2}\mathcal{T}_{\text{em}}{}^\nu{}_\mu, \tag{11}$$
and the Maxwell's equations
$$\partial_\nu\left(\sqrt{-g} F^{\mu\nu}\right) = 0. \tag{12}$$
respectively.

In equation (11), $\mathcal{T}_{\text{em}}{}^\nu{}_\mu = F_{\mu\alpha} F^{\nu\alpha} - 1/4\delta_\mu{}^\nu F_{\alpha\beta} F^{\alpha\beta}$, is the energy-momentum tensor of the electromagnetic field. The rotating charged AdS black hole solution, is given by[19]
$$ds^2 = -A(r)(\Xi dt - \Omega d\phi)^2 + \frac{dr^2}{B(r)} + \frac{r^2}{l^4}(\Omega dt - \Xi l^2 d\phi)^2 + \frac{r^2}{l^2} dz^2, \tag{13}$$
where the range of coordinates are given by $-\infty < t, z < \infty$, $0 \leq r < \infty$ and $0 \leq \phi < 2\pi$.

In metric (13), we have

$$A(r) = r^2 \Lambda_{eff} - \frac{M}{r} + \frac{3Q^2}{2r^2} + \frac{2Q^3\sqrt{6|\alpha|}}{6r^4}, \qquad (14)$$

$$B(r) = A(r)\beta(r), \qquad (15)$$

$$\beta(r) = \left(1 + Q\sqrt{6|\alpha|}/r^2\right)^{-2}, \qquad (16)$$

$$\Xi = \sqrt{1 + \frac{\Omega^2}{l^2}}, \qquad (17)$$

where $\Lambda_{eff} = \frac{1}{36|\alpha|}$, and M, Q, and Ω are the mass parameter, the charge parameter, and the rotation parameter, respectively. The parameter α cannot be zero, since the effective cosmological constant Λ_{eff}, and the metric functions $A(r)$ and $B(r)$ become singular. The gauge potential one-form $\tilde{\Phi}$ is given by

$$\tilde{\Phi}(r) = -\Phi(r)\left(\Omega d\phi - \Xi dt\right). \qquad (18)$$

where $\Phi(r) = \frac{Q}{r} + \frac{Q^2\sqrt{6|\alpha|}}{3r^3}$. We note that the torsion scalar T, for the black hole solution (13), is given by

$$T(r) = \frac{4A'(r)B(r)}{rA(r)} + \frac{2B(r)}{r^2}, \qquad (19)$$

where $A(r)$ and $B(r)$, in equations (14) and (15).

We notice that setting the rotational parameter $\Omega = 0$, we find the static charged black hole configuration, as in Ref.[20]. Moreover, turning off the mass parameter M and Q, the metric (13) reduces to, the 4D AdS metric in an uncommon coordinate system.

The horizons of the black holes are the positive roots of $A = 0$, among which, the outer one is denoted by r_+. The non-vanishing components of the contravariant metric tensor are given by

$$g^{tt} = \frac{l^4\left(A(r)\Omega^2 - r^2\Xi^2\right)}{A(r)r^2(\Xi^2 l^2 - \Omega^2)^2}, \quad g^{rr} = B(r), \quad g^{zz} = \frac{l^2}{r^2},$$

$$g^{\phi\phi} = \frac{A(r)\Xi^2 l^4 - r^2\Omega^2}{A(r)r^2(\Xi^2 l^2 - \Omega^2)^2}, \quad g^{t\phi} = g^{\phi t} = \frac{\Xi\Omega l^2\left(A(r)l^2 - r^2\right)}{A(r)r^2(\Xi^2 l^2 - \Omega^2)^2}, \qquad (20)$$

and the determinant of the metric is

$$\sqrt{-g} = \sqrt{\frac{A(r)}{B(r)}} \frac{r^2\left(\Xi^2 l^2 - \Omega^2\right)}{l^3}. \qquad (21)$$

We find the area of the outer horizon $\mathcal{A}$, by setting $dt = dr = 0$ in the metric (13), and find

$$\mathcal{A} = \int_0^{2\pi} d\phi \int_0^L dz \sqrt{-g}|_{dt=dr=0} = \frac{2\pi r_+^2 \Xi L}{l}. \qquad (22)$$

We discuss now the first law of black hole thermodynamics in $f(T)$ gravity. Generally, the first law of black hole thermodynamics

$$\delta \mathcal{Q} = \tau \delta S, \qquad (23)$$

where $\delta \mathcal{Q}$ and δS are the heat flux and the entropy change, respectively, is violated in $f(T)$ gravity. The Hawking temperature $\tau = \kappa/2\pi$ in $f(T)$ gravity, where κ is the surface gravity, is the same as one in the Einstein gravity, since it is independent of dynamics of gravity. The black hole solutions in $f(T)$ gravity, violate the Clausius relation $dS = d\mathcal{Q}/\tau$, which suggest that black hols in $f(T)$ gravity, even in a static spacetime, are in non-equilibrium state and produce an intrinsic entropy production.[21]

The heat flux $\delta \mathcal{Q}$ along a Killing vector ξ^μ, is given by

$$\delta \mathcal{Q} = \frac{\kappa}{2\pi} \left(\frac{f'(T) \, d\mathcal{A}}{4} \right) \Big|_0^{d\lambda} + \frac{1}{8\pi} \int_H k^\nu \partial^\mu f'(T) \left(\xi^\rho S_{\rho\nu\mu} - \partial_\nu \xi_\mu \right) d\mathcal{A} d\lambda, \qquad (24)$$

where H is the black hole horizon, λ is the affine parameter, $k^\mu = dx^\mu/d\lambda$ is the tangent vector to H, and κ is the surface gravity of the surface H. The first term in the right-hand side of equation (24) provides the first law of black hole thermodynamics Ref.[21]. However, the second term, in general, is not equal to zero. This term maybe regarded as a contribution to the intrinsic entropy production δS_i, where

$$\frac{1}{8\pi} \int k^\nu \partial^\mu f'(T) \left(\xi^\rho S_{\rho\nu\mu} - \partial_\nu \xi_\mu \right) d\mathcal{A} d\lambda = -\tau \delta S_i. \qquad (25)$$

The equation (25) suggests that the $f(T)$ black holes are in non-equilibrium thermodynamics, where

$$\delta \mathcal{Q} = \tau \delta S - \tau \delta S_i. \qquad (26)$$

Miao et al.[21] showed that the first law of thermodynamics for the $f(T)$ black holes can be recovered approximatively, if $f''(T) \ll 1$. In this approximation, the intrinsic entropy production term in equation (24) can be neglected, and the entropy of black holes in $f(T)$ gravity becomes

$$S = \frac{f'(T) \mathcal{A}}{4}. \qquad (27)$$

We note that in the case of $f'(T) = 1$, the entropy production δS_i vanishes, and the entropy (27) reduces to the Bekenstein-Hawking entropy in Einstein gravity. Using equations (9) and (22) in (27), we find the entropy of black holes in equation (13), as

$$S = \frac{\pi \Xi L \left(7r_+^6 + 9\sqrt{6|\alpha|} Q r_+^4 + 18M|\alpha| r_+^3 - 54Q^2 |\alpha| r_+^2 - 42\sqrt{6|\alpha|}^3 Q^3 \right)}{9l \left(Q\sqrt{6|\alpha|} + r_+^2 \right)^2}. \qquad (28)$$

We consider a massless scalar field ψ, in the background of the rotating charged AdS black holes (13), in quadratic $f(T)$ gravity. The scalar wave equation is given by[22]

$$\frac{1}{\sqrt{-g}}\partial_\mu\left(\sqrt{-g}g^{\mu\nu}\partial_\nu\psi\right) = 0. \tag{29}$$

We consider the following ansatz for the scalar field

$$\psi(t,r,z,\phi) = e^{-i\omega t + ikz + im\phi}R(r), \tag{30}$$

where ω is the frequency of the scalar field, m is the azimuthal harmonic index, and k is the wave number. Substituting equations (20), (21), and (30) into equation (29), we find the radial equation

$$B(r)\frac{d^2R(r)}{dr^2} + \left(rB(r)\frac{dA(r)}{dr} + rA(r)\frac{dB(r)}{dr} + 4A(r)B(r)\right)\frac{dR(r)}{dr} + V(r)R(r) = 0, \tag{31}$$

where the potential $V(r)$, is given by

$$V(r) = \frac{r^2\left(\Xi l^2\omega - \Omega m\right)^2 - A(r)l^2\left\{k^2l^4\Xi^4 + k^2\Omega^4 + l^2\left[m^2\Xi^2 - 2m\Xi\Omega\omega + \Omega^2\left(\omega^2 - 2\Xi^2 k^2\right)\right]\right\}}{A(r)r^2(\Xi^2l^2 - \Omega^2)^2}. \tag{32}$$

In the near-horizon region, we expand the metric function $A(r)$ as a quadratic polynomial in $(r - r_+)$, such as

$$A(r) \simeq K(r - r_+)(r - r_*), \tag{33}$$

where

$$K = 15r_+^4\Lambda_{eff} - 3Mr_+ + \frac{3Q^2}{2}, \tag{34}$$

$$r_* = r_+ - \frac{2r_+\left(2r_+^4\Lambda_{eff} - Mr_+ + Q^2\right)}{10r_+^4\Lambda_{eff} - 2Mr_+ + Q^2}. \tag{35}$$

We note that r_* is not necessarily any of the black hole horizons. In the near-horizon region, we consider the low-energy limit for the scalar fields, where $r_+ \ll \frac{1}{\omega}$. Moreover, we consider a limit where the outer horizon r_+ is very close to r_*, in which, $|r_+ - r_*| \ll r_+$. Using these two approximations, we find that the radial equation (31) simplifies to

$$\frac{d}{dr}\{(r - r_+)(r - r_*)\frac{d}{dr}R(r)\} + \left[\left(\frac{r_+ - r_*}{r - r_+}\right)\mathcal{A} + \left(\frac{r_+ - r_*}{r - r_*}\right)\mathcal{B} + \mathcal{C}\right]R(r) = 0, \tag{36}$$

where the constants $\mathcal{A}$, $\mathcal{B}$ and $\mathcal{C}$ are given by

$$\mathcal{A} = \frac{\mathcal{D}m^2 + \mathcal{E}m\omega}{K^2 r_+{}^2 r_*{}^3 (\Xi^2 l^2 - \Omega^2)^2 (r_+ - r_*)^2 \beta} + \frac{\mathcal{F}\omega^2}{K r_+{}^2 (\Xi^2 l^2 - \Omega^2)^2 (r_+ - r_*)^2 \beta} - C_1, \tag{37}$$

$$\mathcal{B} = \frac{\mathcal{G}m^2 + \mathcal{I}m\omega}{K^2 r_+{}^3 r_* (\Xi^2 l^2 - \Omega^2)^2 (r_+ - r_*)^2 \beta} + \frac{\mathcal{J}\omega^2}{K r_+{}^2 (\Xi^2 l^2 - \Omega^2)^2 (r_+ - r_*)^2 \beta} + C_2, \tag{38}$$

$$\mathcal{C} = -\frac{2m\Omega \left(\Xi l^2 \omega - \Omega m/2 \right)^2 \left(r_+{}^2 + r_+ r_* + r_*{}^2 \right)}{(\Xi^2 l^2 - \Omega^2)^2 K^2 r_+{}^3 r_*{}^3 \beta}. \tag{39}$$

In equations (37)-(39), the constants C_1 and C_2 are given by $C_1 = C_2 = k^2 l^2 / K\beta (r_+ - r_*)^2 r_+{}^2$, and

$$\mathcal{D} = \Omega^2 \left(r_+{}^3 + 2 r_+{}^2 r_* + 3 r_*{}^2 r_+ \right) - l^4 \Xi^2 r_*{}^3 K, \tag{40}$$

$$\mathcal{E} = 2\Omega \Xi l^2 \left(K l^2 r_*{}^3 - r_+{}^3 - 2 r_+{}^2 r_* - 3 r_+ r_*{}^2 \right), \tag{41}$$

$$\mathcal{F} = -l^4 \Omega^2, \tag{42}$$

$$\mathcal{G} = K \Xi^2 l^4 r_+ r_* - \Omega^2 \left(3 r_+{}^2 + 2 r_+ r_* + r_*{}^2 \right), \tag{43}$$

$$\mathcal{I} = 2 l^2 \Xi \Omega \left[3 r_+{}^2 - r_+ r_* \left(K l^2 - 2 \right) + r_*{}^2 \right], \tag{44}$$

$$\mathcal{J} = l^4 \Omega^2. \tag{45}$$

3. Holography for $f(T)$ Rotating Black Holes

To find the existence of the possible hidden symmetry, we introduce the following conformal coordinates ω^+, ω^- and y, in terms of the black hole coordinates t, r and ϕ

$$\omega^+ = \sqrt{\frac{r - r_+}{r - r_*}} e^{2\pi T_R \phi + 2 n_R t}, \tag{46}$$

$$\omega^- = \sqrt{\frac{r - r_+}{r - r_*}} e^{2\pi T_L \phi + 2 n_L t}, \tag{47}$$

$$y = \sqrt{\frac{r_+ - r_*}{r - r_*}} e^{\pi (T_L + T_R)\phi + (n_L + n_R) t}, \tag{48}$$

where T_L, T_R, n_L and n_R are constants. We also define the sets of *local* vector fields

$$H_1 = i\partial_+, \tag{49}$$

$$H_0 = i\left(\omega^+ \partial_+ + \frac{1}{2} y \partial_y \right), \tag{50}$$

$$H_{-1} = i(\omega^{+2} \partial_+ + \omega^+ y \partial_y - y^2 \partial_-), \tag{51}$$

as well as
$$\bar{H}_1 = i\partial_-, \tag{52}$$
$$\bar{H}_0 = i\left(\omega^-\partial_- + \frac{1}{2}y\partial_y\right), \tag{53}$$
$$\bar{H}_{-1} = i(\omega^{-2}\partial_- + \omega^- y\partial_y - y^2\partial_+). \tag{54}$$

The vector fields (49)-(54) obey the $sl(2,R)_L \times sl(2,R)_R$ algebra, as
$$[H_0, H_{\pm 1}] = \mp i H_{\pm 1}, \quad [H_{-1}, H_1] = -2i H_0, \tag{55}$$
$$[\bar{H}_0, \bar{H}_{\pm 1}] = \mp i \bar{H}_{\pm 1}, \quad [\bar{H}_{-1}, \bar{H}_1] = -2i \bar{H}_0. \tag{56}$$

The quadratic Casimir operators of $sl(2,R)_L \times sl(2,R)_R$ algebra, are given by
$$\mathcal{H}^2 = \bar{\mathcal{H}}^2 = -H_0^2 + \frac{1}{2}(H_1 H_{-1} + H_{-1} H_1) = \frac{1}{4}(y^2\partial_y^2 - y\partial_y) + y^2\partial_+\partial_-. \tag{57}$$

We notice that the Casimir operators (57), can be rewritten in terms of (t,r,ϕ) coordinates, as
$$\mathcal{H}^2 = (r-r_+)(r-r_*)\frac{\partial^2}{\partial r^2} + (2r - r_+ - r_*)\frac{\partial}{\partial r}$$
$$+ \left(\frac{r_+ - r_*}{r - r_*}\right)\left[\left(\frac{n_L - n_R}{4\pi G}\partial_\phi - \frac{T_L - T_R}{4G}\partial_t\right)^2 + C_2\right]$$
$$- \left(\frac{r_+ - r_*}{r - r_+}\right)\left[\left(\frac{n_L + n_R}{4\pi G}\partial_\phi - \frac{T_L + T_R}{4G}\partial_t\right)^2 - C_1\right], \tag{58}$$

where $G = n_L T_R - n_R T_L$.

The Casimir operator (58) reproduces the radial equation (36), by choosing the right and left temperatures, as
$$T_R = \frac{r_+ K(r_+ - r_*)\left(\Xi^2 l^2 - \Omega^2\right)\sqrt{\beta r_+ r_* \delta}}{4\pi\delta}, \tag{59}$$
$$T_L = \frac{r_+ K(\Xi^2 l^2 - \Omega^2)[r_+^4 + 2r_+^3 r_* + 6r_+^2 r_*^2 - 2r_*^3 r_+(Kl^2 - 1) + r_*^4]\sqrt{\beta r_+ r_* \delta}}{4\pi(r_+ + r_*)^3 \delta}, \tag{60}$$

respectively, and
$$n_R = 0, \tag{61}$$
$$n_L = \frac{r_*^2 r_+ K\left(\Omega^2 - \Xi^2 l^2\right)\sqrt{\beta r_+ r_* \delta}}{2\Omega l^2 \Xi (r_+ + r_*)^3}. \tag{62}$$

The constant δ which appears in equations (59), (60), (61) and (62), is given by $\delta = 3\Omega^2 r_+^2 - r_+ r_*\left(K\Xi^2 l^4 - 2\Omega^2\right) + \Omega^2 r_*^2$. Moreover, we find two constraints for the parameters of the black hole solutions (13), such as

$$\frac{\Omega^2\Xi^2 l^4\left[-3r_+^2 + r_* r_+ \left(Kl^2 - 2\right) - r_*^2\right]^2}{K^2 \beta r_+^3 r_*(r_+ - r_*)^2 (\Xi^2 l^2 - \Omega^2)^2} = \frac{l^4 \Omega^2}{r_+^2 K (\Xi^2 l^2 - \Omega^2)^2 (r_+ - r_*)^2 \beta}, \quad (63)$$

and

$$\frac{\Omega^2 \Xi^2 l^4 \left(Kl^2 r_*^3 - r_+^3 - 2r_* r_+^2 - 3r_*^2 r_+\right)^2}{K^2 \beta r_+ r_*^5 (r_+ - r_*)^2 (\Omega^2 - \Xi^2 l^2)^2 \left(Kl^4 \Xi^2 r_* r_+ - 3\Omega^2 r_+^2 - 2\Omega^2 r_* r_+ - \Omega^2 r_*^2\right)}$$
$$= \frac{l^4 \Omega^2}{r_+^2 K (\Xi^2 l^2 - \Omega^2)^2 (r_+ - r_*)^2 \beta}. \quad (64)$$

We note that equations (63) and (64) restrict the black hole parameters, in accord with existence of the real positive values for the outer horizon (and any other horizons), as the roots of the tri-quadratic algebraic equation

$$A(r) = 0, \quad (65)$$

where $A(r)$ is given in (14).

We note that both right and left temperatures (59) and (60) are positive definite.[23] We emphasize that $SL(2,R)_L \times SL(2,R)_R$ is a *local* hidden symmetry, for the solution space of massless scalar field in the near region of the rotating charged AdS black holes (13), in quadratic $f(T)$ gravity. The *local* hidden symmetry is generated by the vector fields (49)–(54), which are not periodic under the angular identification $\phi \sim \phi + 2\pi$. These symmetries can't be used to generate new global solutions from the old ones. This can be interpreted as a statement that the $SL(2,R)_L \times SL(2,R)_R$ symmetry is spontaneously broken down to $U(1)_L \times U(1)_R$ subgroup under the angular identification $\phi \sim \phi + 2\pi$. As a result, we can identify the left and right temperatures of the dual CFT. We recall the Cardy entropy formula for the dual 2D CFT with temperatures T_L and T_R

$$S_{CFT} = \frac{\pi^2}{3}\left(c_L T_L + c_R T_R\right), \quad (66)$$

where c_L are c_R are the corresponding central charges for the left and right sectors. The central charges can be derived from the *asymptotic symmetry group* of the near-horizon (near-)extremal black hole geometry. There is no derivation for the central charges of the CFT dual to the non-extremal black holes, that we consider in this article. Of course, we expect that the conformal symmetry of the extremal black holes connects smoothly to those of the non-extremal black holes, for which the central charges are the same. The near-horizon extremal geometry for the spacetime (13) is still unknown, and it is not a straightforward task to find that, due to the tri-quadratic behaviour of the metric function $A(r)$. As a result, we turn the logic around and consider the favourite holographic situation, in which, the Cardy entropy (66) produces exactly the macroscopic entropy (27). Substituting equations (28),

(59), and (60) into equation (66), we find the central charges

$$c \equiv c_L = c_R$$
$$= \frac{12 \Xi \delta L \varpi (r_+ + r_*)^3}{lKr_+{}^2(\Xi^2 l^2 - \Omega^2)(r_+{}^3 + 2r_+{}^2 r_* + 3r_+ r_*{}^2 - l^2 K r_*{}^3)(Q\sqrt{6|\alpha|} + r_+{}^2)^2 \sqrt{\beta r_+ r_* \delta}}, \quad (67)$$

where $\varpi = r_+{}^2 \left(r_+{}^2 Q \sqrt{6|\alpha|}/2 + 7r_+{}^4/18 + M|\alpha| r_+ - 3Q^2 |\alpha| \right) - 7\sqrt{6|\alpha|}^3 Q^3/3$.
We note that we only consider CFTs, in which the left and right central charges are equal, $c \equiv c_L = c_R$.[24,25]

4. Conclusions

In this presentation which is based entirely on the published paper,[23] we extend the concept of black hole holography to the non-extremal 4D rotating charged AdS black holes in $f(T)$-Maxwell theory with a negative cosmological constant. We explicitly construct the hidden conformal symmetry for the rotating black holes in $f(T)$-Maxwell theory with a negative cosmological constant. We mainly consider the near-horizon region, as the metric function which determines the event horizon, is a triple-quadratic equation. In this region, we show that the radial equation of the scalar wave function could be written as the $SL(2,R)_L \times SL(2,R)_R$ squared Casimir equation, indicating a *local* hidden conformal symmetry acting on the solution space. The conformal symmetry is spontaneously broken under the angular identification $\phi \sim \phi + 2\pi$, which suggests the rotating charged AdS black holes in quadratic $f(T)$ gravity, should be dual to the finite temperatures T_L and T_R mixed state, in the 2D CFT. Instead of calculating the central charges using the *asymptotic symmetry group*, we calculated the central charges by assuming the Cardy entropy for the dual CFT, matches the macroscopic Bekenstein-Hawking entropy. These results suggest that rotating charged AdS black holes in quadratic $f(T)$ gravity with particular values of M, Ω, Q, and $|\alpha|$, are dual to a 2D CFT.

It is an open question to find the near-horizon (near-)extremal geometry of the rotating charged AdS spacetime in quadratic $f(T)$ gravity. We may calculate the central charges using the *asymptotic symmetry group* to confirm our results in this article. We can also study on various kinds of superradiant scattering off the near-extremal black hole as a further evidence to support the holographic picture for the non-extremal 4D rotating charged AdS black holes in $f(T)$-Maxwell theory with a negative cosmological constant. We leave addressing these open questions for future articles.

Acknowledgments

The author would like to acknowledge the financial support by the Natural Sciences and Engineering Research Council of Canada.

References

1. G. 't Hooft, *Conf. Proc.* **C930308**, 284 (1993).
2. L. Susskind, *J. Math. Phys.* **36**, 6377 (1995).
3. J. D. Bekenstein, *Phys. Rev. D* **7**, 2333 (1973).
4. S. W. Hawking, *Commun. Math. Phys.* **43**, 199 (1975).
5. J. M. Maldacena, *Int. J. Theor. Phys.* **38**, 1113 (1999), *Adv. Theor. Math. Phys.* **2**, 231(1998).
6. M. Guica, T. Hartman, W. Song and A. Strominger, *Phys. Rev. D* **80**, 124008 (2009).
7. A. Castro, A. Maloney and A. Strominger, *Phys. Rev. D* **82**, 024008 (2010).
8. A. M. Ghezelbash, *JHEP* **08**, 045 (2009).
9. A. M. Ghezelbash, *Mod. Phys. Lett. A* **27**, 1250046 (2012).
10. B. Chen and J. Long *JHEP* **08**, 065 (2010).
11. B. Chen, A. M. Ghezelbash, V. Kamali and M. R. Setare, *Nucl. Phys. B* **848**, 108 (2011).
12. A. M. Ghezelbash, V. Kamali and M. R. Setare, *Phys. Rev. D* **82**, 124051(2010).
13. A. M. Ghezelbash and H. M. Siahaan, *Class. Quant. Grav.* **30**, 135005 (2013).
14. Y.-Q. Wang and Y.-X, Liu, *JHEP* **08** 087 (2010).
15. B. Chen, J. Long, and J.-j. Zhang, *Phys. Rev. D* **82**, 104017 (2010).
16. A. M. Ghezelbash and H. M. Siahaan, *Gen. Rel. Grav.* **46**, 1783 (2014).
17. H. M. Siahaan, *Class. Quant. Grav.* **33**, 155013 (2016).
18. H. M. Siahaan, *Class. Quant. Grav.* **35**, 155002 (2018).
19. A. M. Awad, G. G. L. Nashed and W. El Hanafy, arXiv:1903.12471[gr-qc].
20. A. M. Awad, S. Capozziello, and G. G. L. Nashed, *JHEP* **07**, 136 (2017).
21. R.-X. Miao, M. Li and Y.-G. Miao, *JCAP* **1111**, 033 (2011).
22. C. Bernard, *Phys. Rev. D* **96**, 105025 (2017).
23. C. Bernard and M. Ghezelbash, *Phys. Rev. D* **101**, 024020 (2020).
24. S. El-Showk and K. Papadodimas, *JHEP* **10**, 106 (2012).
25. G. Compère, *Living Rev. Rel.* **15**, 11 (2012).

Infinitely degenerate exact Ricci-flat solutions in $f(R)$ gravity

Semin Xavier

Department of Physics, Indian Institute of Technology, Mumbai, Maharashtra 400076
E-mail: seminxavier@iitb.ac.in

Jose Mathew

Department of Physics, The Cochin College, Kochi, Kerala, India
E-mail: josecherukara@gmail.com

S. Shankaranarayanan

Department of Physics, Indian Institute of Technology, Mumbai, Maharashtra 400076
E-mail: shanki@phy.iitb.ac.in

The evidence is mounting that the universe is currently undergoing a phase of accelerated expansion. One possible alternative is the modification in gravity in the largest possible scales. This leads to the many questions related to black-holes: violation of Birkhoff theorem and no-hair theorem. To confirm/infirm, we need to obtain exact black-hole solutions in these modified gravity theories. In this talk, we focus on the exact spherically symmetric solutions in $f(R)$ theories of gravity. We explicitly show that some $f(R)$ models contain an infinite number of exact static, Ricci-flat spherically symmetric vacuum solutions and, hence, violate Birkhoff's theorem in $f(R)$ theories. We analytically derive two exact vacuum black-hole solutions for the same class of $f(R)$ theories. The two black-hole solutions have the event-horizon at the same point; however, their asymptotic features are different. Our results suggest that the no-hair theorem may not hold for generic modified gravity theories. We discuss the implications to distinguish modified gravity theories from general relativity.

Keywords: $f(R)$ theory, no-hair theorem, based on the work[1]

1. Introduction

General Relativity (GR) is a successful description of gravity and is in excellent agreement with experiments and observations. However, paradoxically, the very success of GR suggests that GR might have classical and quantum corrections in the strong gravity regime.[2–6] Recently, strong gravity diagnostic parameters have been proposed to distinguish GR and modified gravity theories.[7]

In GR, static black-hole solutions are the final stage of gravitationally collapsed objects. As a consequence of the no-hair theorem,[8] GR predicts that the Kerr metric represents the most general astrophysical black holes.[9] In the case of spherical symmetry, Birkhoff's theorem ensures that the most general spherically symmetric, electrovac solution of the Einstein-Maxwell equations is the static Reissner-Nordstrom solution.[10,11] The absence of spin-0 modes in the linearized field equations leads to this result. However, there is no Birkhoff theorem for the Kerr metric. Outside a rotating star, the metric is not described by Kerr. In comparison, the Schwarzschild solution describes the space-time outside a non-rotating star.

In this talk, we show that the Schwarzschild solution is not an unique solution for $f(R)$ theories of gravity. More specifically, we show that there exists an infinite number of spherically symmetric vacuum solutions in 4-D $f(R)$ theories of gravity *without* transforming to a conformal frame.

$f(R)$ theories of gravity are the most straightforward modifications to GR.[6] The higher-order Ricci scalar terms encapsulate modifications to GR. Although the equations of motion are higher-order, they do not suffer from Oströgradsky instability.[12] A deviation from general relativity may introduce changes in both the generation and the propagation of gravitational waves. Unlike GR, $f(R)$ theories have an extra field equation and longitudinal mode.[7,13]

Although Schwarzschild black-hole is a solution to vacuum $f(R)$ theories of gravity. The additional dynamical equation by the trace equation in $f(R)$ theories may give rise to new solutions other than GR. The reason for such assumption is that, in $f(R)$ gravity has 11 dynamical variables — 10 metric variables $(g_{\mu\nu})$ and the Ricci scalar (R). In other words, in $f(R)$ theories, the scalar curvature R, plays a non-trivial role in determining the metric itself. Recently, the effects on the extra mode are used to obtain diagnostic parameters to distinguish GR and modified gravity theories using the Quasi-normal mode spectrum of the identical black-hole solutions in the two theories.[7] Here, the focus is to test the validity of this assumption. In other words, to verify whether the black-hole solutions in the two theories are indeed identical. We show that $f(R)$ admits multiple space-time geometries with the horizon for the same stress-tensor configuration (vacuum in this case).

We use $(-,+,+,+)$ signature for the 4-D space-time metric,[14] Greek alphabets for the 4-D space-time, and $\kappa^2 = 8\pi G/c^4$ where G is the Newton's constant. We shall denote the derivative of any function with r by an overprime, and overdot denotes the partial derivative w.r.t Ricci scalar (R).

2. $f(R)$ theory and the model

The modified vacuum action for $f(R)$ gravity is:[6]

$$S[g_{\mu\nu}] = \frac{1}{2\kappa^2} \int d^4x \sqrt{-g}\, f(R) \tag{1}$$

where $f(R)$ is arbitrary function of the Ricci scalar R. Using the metric formalism[6] the modified Einstein tensor $(\mathcal{G}_{\mu\nu})$ is obtained, i.e.,

$$\mathcal{G}_{\mu\nu} \equiv \dot{f}(R)\, R_{\mu\nu} - \nabla_\mu \nabla_\nu \dot{f}(R) + g_{\mu\nu} \Box \dot{f}(R) - \frac{f(R)}{2} g_{\mu\nu} = 0, \tag{2}$$

where $\dot{f}(R) = \partial f/\partial R$ and $\Box = \nabla^\mu \nabla_\mu$. For the above $f(R)$ action (1), the trace of the field equation (2) is dynamical:

$$R\, \dot{f}(R) + 3\Box \dot{f}(R) - 2\, f(R) = 0 \tag{3}$$

In $f(R)$, the scalar curvature R, plays a non-trivial role in determining the metric itself. In general, the field equations for $f(R)$ gravity (2) are fourth-order partial differential equations, instead of second-order partial differential equations of GR. Hence, we expect more class of solutions in $f(R)$ theories of gravity.

One may still find the trivial solution where for which $R = R_0 =$ constant. In such a case, the field equations reduce to the Einstein field equations with an effective cosmological constant and an effective gravitational constant.[15] This includes the case where $R = 0$. However, our interest in this talk is to look for non-trivial solutions.

In our model, we consider $f(R)$ to be a polynomial in R, i.e.,

$$f(R) = \beta_0 + \beta_1 R + \beta_2 R^2 + \cdots, \quad (4)$$

where β_i's ($i = 0, 1, 2 \cdots$) are constants having appropriate dimensions. The above form of $f(R)$ can be written in a binomial form, i.e.,

$$f(R) = (\alpha_0 + \alpha_1 R)^p, \quad (5)$$

where, p is the power index, we are interested in the strong-gravity corrections to GR, we take $p > 1$. In principle, p need not be an integer. The α_0 and α_1 being positive constants related to the β_i's in (4). For simplicity consider $p = 1$, the above from (3) reduces to:

$$f(R) = \alpha_0 + \alpha_1 R. \quad (6)$$

Thus, α_0 acts like the cosmological constant and α_1 is a dimensionless constant that modifies Newton's constant. [Note that α_1 is dimensionless and α_0 has dimensions of $[L]^{-2}$.]

3. A class of exact solutions for $f(R)$ theory

Consider the static, spherically symmetric metric of the form,

$$ds^2 = -A(r)e^{\delta(r)}dt^2 + \frac{dr^2}{A(r)} + r^2\left(d\theta^2 + \sin^2\theta\, d\phi^2\right) \quad (7)$$

where $A(r)$ and $\delta(r)$ are arbitrary functions of the Schwarzschild radial coordinate r. Substituting the above metric in the modified Einstein's equations (2) for the model $f(R)$ (5), leads to the following three field equations:

$$\mathcal{G}_t^t \equiv T_3[A(r), \delta(r)] = 0 \quad (8a)$$
$$\mathcal{G}_r^r \equiv T_4[A(r), \delta(r)] = 0 \quad (8b)$$
$$\mathcal{G}_\theta^\theta = \mathcal{G}_\phi^\phi \equiv T_5[A(r), \delta(r)] = 0 \quad (8c)$$

where T_3, T_4 and T_5 are functions of $A(r)$ and $\delta(r)$, and their derivatives. More specifically, (i) T_3 and T_5 are non-linear, and *contain up to 4th order derivatives* of $A(r)$ and $\delta(r)$, and (ii) T_4 is non-linear and *contain up to 3rd order derivatives* of

$A(r)$ and $\delta(r)$. (iii) Even in the special case of $\delta(r) = 0$, $\mathcal{G}_t^t \neq \mathcal{G}_r^r$. Hence, we do not expect to get identical solutions as in GR.

The field equations (8) contain up to fourth-order derivatives in $A(r)$ and $\delta(r)$. Thus, an exact solution to these equations will contain up to four independent constants.

Ref. 1 contains the details of the procedure used to reduce these highly non-trivial equations into a product of two second-order non-linear differentials in $A(r)$ and $\delta(r)$. Interestingly, both the procedures lead to the following equation:

$$\frac{2}{r} \frac{(p - \frac{1}{2})}{p(p-1)} \frac{T_1[A(r), \delta(r)]}{(\Phi(r) + 4)} \frac{T_2[A(r), \delta(r)]}{(\Phi(r) - 2)} = 0 \tag{9}$$

where $\Phi(r) = r\left(\delta'(r) + [\ln A(r)]'\right)$ and prime denotes derivative w.r.t r.

At this point, we would like to stress the following points: First, we have obtained the Eq. (9) using two different approaches. This implies that Eq. (9) is a unique differential equation for this $f(R)$ model with the metric (7). Second, Eq. (9) is a product of two second-order non-linear differentials of $T_1[A(r), \delta(r)]$ and $T_2[A(r), \delta(r)]$.[1] It simplifies the procedure to obtain the exact black-hole solutions for any value of p using $T_1[A(r), \delta(r)]$ or $T_2[A(r), \delta(r)]$. Third, the above equation imposes constrains on p, $A(r)$ and $\delta(r)$. More specifically, if for a non-trival solution,

$$p \neq 0, \frac{1}{2}, 1; \; \Phi(r) \neq -4 \text{ or } 2. \tag{10}$$

Since $p = 1$ is not allowed. It means we are looking for non-trivial solutions valid for modified theories of gravity, where $p = 1$ will give solutions of GR. While $p = 0$ and 1 will lead to divergence, $p = 1/2$ will lead to trivial solutions. Fourth, the above condition of $\Phi(r)$ implies that

$$\delta(r) + \ln A(r) \neq \ln(r^2) \text{ or } \ln(r^{-4}) \tag{11}$$

If we assume $\delta(r) = $ constant, then $A(r) \neq c_0 r^2 + c_1 r^{-4}$, where c_0, c_1 are constants. Lastly, non-trivial solutions for the above equation (9) are possible if T_1 or T_2 vanish, i.e.,

$$T_1[A(r), \delta(r)] = 0 \quad \text{or} \quad T_2[A(r), \delta(r)] = 0 \tag{12}$$

In principle, from Eq. (12) we can identity that for a given $A(r)$, we can have two functional forms of $\delta(r)$. Either $T_1 = 0$ or $T_2 = 0$ will give two choices of $\delta(r)$. While, the functional form of $A(r)$ can be obtained from the condition (10) on $\Phi(r)$, we get

$$\delta'(r) + (\ln[A(r)])' = \mu(r) \quad \mu(r) \neq \frac{-4}{r} \text{ or } \frac{2}{r} \tag{13}$$

Thus, for a given $\mu(r)$, we have a functional relation between $A(r)$ and $\delta(r)$. Substituting this relation in the constraint relation (12), we obtain two set of differential equation in terms of $A(r)$ or $\delta(r)$.

Thus, Eq. (12) give two branches of solutions for $A(r)$ and $\delta(r)$ by setting $T_1 = 0$ or $T_2 = 0$. Using the arbitrary function $\mu(r)$, we can obtain an infinite solutions for the spherically symmetric metric (7).

At this point, it is important to validate whether any arbitrary function $\mu(r)$ satisfying $T_1 = 0$ or $T_2 = 0$ is indeed a solution to the vacuum field equations (8)?

To address this, for any p, we write a formal solution to the above equation Eq. (13) as

$$A(r) = e^{-\delta(r)}\gamma(r) \quad \text{where} \quad \gamma(r) = \exp\left(\int \mu(r) dr\right). \quad (14)$$

Substituting $A(r)$ in-terms of $\delta(r)$ in $T_2[A(r), \delta(r)] = 0$, we obtain a differential equation in $\delta''(r)$. Substituting these in Eq. (8), we get,

$$T_3[\delta(r), \gamma(r)] = 4\alpha_1 p(p-1)(p-2)\gamma^7(r) e^{-\delta(r)} [\delta'(r) r - 8]^2 \, T_2[\delta(r), \gamma(r)]^2$$
$$= T_5[\delta(r), \gamma(r)] \quad (15\text{a})$$
$$T_4[\delta(r), \gamma(r)] = -2\alpha_1 p(p-1)\gamma^5(r) e^{-\delta(r)} [\delta'(r) r - 8] (r \ln[\gamma(r)]' + 4) \, T_2[\delta(r), \gamma(r)] \quad (15\text{b})$$

Since, we have obtained the above expressions using the condition $T_2[A(r), \delta(r)] = 0$, we have $\mathcal{G}_t^t = \mathcal{G}_r^r = \mathcal{G}_\theta^\theta = \mathcal{G}_\phi^\phi = 0$. This implies that $A(r)$ given by Eq. (14) satisfying $T_2[A(r), \delta(r)] = 0$ is an exact solution for the $f(R)$ model (5). Since $A(r)$ depends on the arbitrary function $\mu(r)$, for the same observer with Schwarzschild time t, there are *infinite number of exact static, spherically symmetric solutions* for this model.

This is the key result of this talk. The Birkhoff theorem in GR guarantees that static Schwarzschild solution[11] is the most general spherically symmetric vacuum solution. However, the trace equation (3) provides a non-trivial dynamical structure in $f(R)$ theories. This provides an infinite set of static solutions for $f(R)$ theories of gravity. To our knowledge, such an explicit calculation is new for any modified theories of gravity. All the earlier analyses, either restrictive or use a conformal frame to confirm/infirm Birkhoff theorem.[16,17] Here, we have not made any approximation or performed a conformal transformation. Our results point that the Birkhoff theorem is not valid for all modified gravity theories.

As noted in Eq. (12), we can obtain non-trivial solutions if T_1 or T_2 vanish. Until now, we have shown that $T_2 = 0$ yields an infinitely many vacuum spherically symmetric solutions. Unlike T_2, T_1 is not a common factor of the field equations (15); hence, $T_1 = 0$ alone can not provide valid solutions. Thus, beside $T_1 = 0$, we must use either of the three equations (8) to obtain a unique solution.

4. Two vacuum black-hole solutions

In the earlier section, we showed that there exists an infinite number of spherically symmetric vacuum solutions for the $f(R)$ model (5). In this section, we obtain two black-hole solutions which satisfy the condition $T_2[A(r), \delta(r)] = 0$.

As we have mentioned earlier, $\delta(r) = 0$ is a trivial solution. Hence, setting $\delta(r) = 0$, we obtain the following solution for $A(r)$

$$A(r) = 1 + C_2 r^2 - \frac{C_3}{r^2} \quad \text{where} \quad C_2 = \frac{\alpha_0}{12\alpha_1} \tag{16}$$

which satisfies the null-energy condition.[14] C_3 is a constant of integration and can take any real value. We like to list the following important points regarding the above solution: First, it is easy to verify that the above solution satisfies the modified Einstein's equations (8). Second, C_2 is a positive constant, since, α_0 and α_1 are positive constants. Physically, C_2 acts like an effective cosmological constant. For $C_3 > 0$, the metric (7) has a horizon at

$$r_h = \sqrt{\frac{\sqrt{1 + 4C_2 C_3} - 1}{2C_2}} \tag{17}$$

In the limit of $\alpha_0 \to 0$, $C_2 \to 0$, the metric (7) has a horizon at $r = \sqrt{C_3}$. Thus, $\alpha_0 \to 0$ is a smooth limit. Third, the term c_3/r^2 is a reminiscence of the charge in the Reissner-Nordström solution in GR.[14] In our case, the $1/r^2$ term is present in the absence of the $1/r$ term. While in GR, C_3/r^2 term can not exist without the mass term. This result is similar to the one obtained sometime back in the context of black-holes on the brane.[18] Physically, C_3 corresponds to the mass of the black-hole. Lastly, it is easy to verify that the above solution satisfies the modified Einstein's equations (8). The Kretschmann scalar for the above form of $A(r)$ is

$$R^{\alpha\beta\gamma\delta} R_{\alpha\beta\gamma\delta} = \frac{\alpha_0^2}{6\alpha_1^2} + \frac{56 C_3^2}{r^8}. \tag{18}$$

Thus, the metric has a singularity at $r = 0$ and is finite everywhere else. For finite α_0, the Kretschmann scalar is a positive constant at asymptotic infinity, which corresponds to asymptotic de Sitter space-times in GR.[14]

To obtain second solution, assume $A(r)$ in Eq. (16) and $\delta(r) \neq 0$. Now $A(r)$ in Eq. (16) in $T_2[A(r), \delta(r)] = 0$, this leads to the following differential equation for $\delta(r)$:

$$\delta''(r) + \frac{1}{2}\delta'(r)^2 + \frac{(5 C_2 r^4 + 2r^2 + C_3)}{(C_2 r^4 + r^2 - C_3)} \frac{\delta'(r)}{r} = 0 \tag{19}$$

This differential equation is highly non-linear; however, it has the following exact solution:

$$e^{\delta(r)/2} = \frac{C_4}{2} - \frac{C_5}{2(12\alpha_1)^{3/2}} \frac{(2C_2 r^2 + 1)}{(4 C_2 C_3 + 1)} \frac{1}{(C_2 r^4 + r^2 - C_3)^{1/2}} \tag{20}$$

where C_4 and C_5 are arbitrary constants. [C_4 is dimensionless while C_5 has dimension of $[L]$.] The horizon for this new solution is given by (17). The Kretschmann scalar again can be evaluated, and near origin is singular, i.e.

$$R^{\alpha\beta\gamma\delta} R_{\alpha\beta\gamma\delta} \sim \frac{\Gamma(C_2, C_3, C_4, C_5)}{r^8} \tag{21}$$

and is finite everywhere else. Thus, the constants C_4 and C_5 determine the behavior of the second black-hole solution. Thus, we have reconfirmed the results in the earlier section and shown that at least two black-hole solutions correspond to the same matter configuration (in this case, vacuum). To our knowledge, this is a novel result for any modified theories of gravity and confirms that Birkhoff's theorem is not valid for all modified gravity theories.

5. Conclusions and Discussion

In this talk, we obtained many exact static spherically symmetric vacuum solutions for $f(R)$ gravity. We obtained two exact vacuum black-hole solutions to the $f(R)$ model to emphasize this unique feature. We showed that two solutions have the event-horizon at the same point; however, their asymptotic features are different. Our results point that the Birkhoff theorem is not valid for all modified gravity theories. The two black-hole solutions have a space-time singularity at the origin.

Unlike in the literature, we have obtained the exact solutions *without* transforming to a conformal frame. Our analysis shows the deficiency of finding solutions in the conformally transformed frame.[1] The conformal transformations are not well-defined near $T_2 \to 0$ and, hence, the conformal frame will not be able to pick off the solutions we have obtained. However, the solution corresponding to $T_1[A(r), \delta(r)] = 0$ will be well-defined in the conformal frame.

One of the prospects of gravitational wave observations is to find signatures for the modified gravity theories. We have shown that if the modified theories belong to one of the degenerate classes with $T_2 = 0$, then our analysis shows that the prospect of detection needs different methodologies than the one that is currently used.[19]

Acknowledgments

This work was made possible by the use of GRTensor 3 package for MAPLE. SX is financially supported by the MHRD fellowship at IIT Bombay. The work is supported by the MATRICS SERB grant.

References

1. S. Xavier, J. Mathew and S. Shankaranarayanan, Infinitely degenerate exact ricci-flat solutions in f(r) gravity, *Class. Quant. Grav.* **37**, p. 225006 (2020).
2. K. S. Stelle, Renormalization of higher-derivative quantum gravity, **16**, 953.
3. S. Capozziello and M. D. Laurentis, Extended theories of gravity (August 2011).
4. T. Clifton, P. G. Ferreira, A. Padilla and C. Skordis, Modified gravity and cosmology, *Physics Reports 513, 1 (2012), 1-189* (June 2011).
5. S. Nojiri, S. D. Odintsov and V. K. Oikonomou, Modified gravity theories on a nutshell: Inflation, bounce and late-time evolution (May 2017).
6. T. P. Sotiriou and V. Faraoni, f(r) theories of gravity, *Rev. Mod. Phys. 82:451-497,2010* (May 2008).
7. S.Shankaranarayanan, Strong gravity signatures in the polarization of gravitational waves, *Int. J. Mod. Phys. D* **28**, p. 1944020 (2019).

8. J. D. Bekenstein, Novel "no-scalar-hair" theorem for black holes, *Phys. Rev. D* **51**, p. R6608 (1995).
9. P. T. Chruściel, J. L. Costa and M. Heusler, Stationary black holes: Uniqueness and beyond, *Living Rev. Relativity 15, (2012),* 7 (May 2012).
10. N. Voje Johansen and F. Ravndal, On the discovery of birkhoff's theorem, *Gen. Rel. Grav.* **38**, 537 (2006).
11. H.-J. Schmidt, The tetralogy of birkhoff theorems, *Gen. Rel. Grav.* **45**, 395 (2013).
12. R. P. Woodard, Avoiding dark energy with 1/r modifications of gravity, *Lect. Notes Phys.* **720**, 403 (2007).
13. S. Bhattacharyya and S. Shankaranarayanan, Quasinormal modes as a distinguisher between general relativity and f(r) gravity, *Phys. Rev. D 96, 064044 (2017)* (April 2017).
14. C. W. Misner, K. S. Thorne and J. A. Wheeler, *Gravitation* (W. H. Freeman, San Francisco, 1973).
15. P. Cañate, L. G. Jaime and M. Salgado, Spherically symmetric black holes in $f(r)$ gravity: Is geometric scalar hair supported ? (September 2015).
16. J. Oliva and S. Ray, Birkhoff's theorem in higher derivative theories of gravity, *Class. Quant. Grav. 28:175007,2011* (April 2011).
17. S. Capozziello and D. Sáez-Gómez, Scalar-tensor representation of $f(r)$ gravity and birkhoff's theorem (July 2011).
18. N. Dadhich, R. Maartens, P. Papadopoulos and V. Rezania, Black holes on the brane, *Phys. Lett. B* **487**, 1 (2000).
19. L. Barack *et al.*, Black holes, gravitational waves and fundamental physics: a roadmap, *Class. Quant. Grav.* **36**, p. 143001 (2019).

Universe in a black hole with spin and torsion

Nikodem Popławski

Department of Mathematics and Physics, University of New Haven,
West Haven, CT 06516, USA
E-mail: NPoplawski@newhaven.edu
www.newhaven.edu

We consider gravitational collapse of a spherically symmetric sphere of a fluid with spin and torsion into a black hole. We use the Tolman metric and the Einstein–Cartan field equations with a relativistic spin fluid as a source. We show that gravitational repulsion of torsion prevents a singularity and replaces it with a nonsingular bounce. Quantum particle production during contraction strengthens torsion in opposing shear. Particle production during expansion can produce enormous amounts of matter and generate a finite period of inflation. The resulting closed universe on the other side of the event horizon may have several bounces. Such a universe is oscillatory, with each cycle larger in size then the previous cycle, until it reaches the cosmological size and expands indefinitely. Our universe might have therefore originated from a black hole existing in another universe.

Keywords: Einstein-Cartan theory; torsion; gravitational collapse.

1. Einstein–Cartan gravity and spin fluid

In general relativity (GR), the affine connection $\Gamma^{\,k}_{i\,j}$ is constrained to be symmetric. Einstein–Cartan–Sciama–Kibble (EC) gravity removes this constraint by regarding the antisymmetric part of the connection, the torsion tensor $S^k{}_{ij} = \Gamma^{\,k}_{[i\,j]}$, as a variable.[1] The total Lagrangian density is $-\frac{1}{2\kappa}R\sqrt{-g} + L_{\rm m}$, where R is the Ricci scalar constructed from the connection and $L_{\rm m}$ is the Lagrangian density of matter, as in GR.[2]

Varying the Lagrangian with respect to the contortion tensor $C_{ijk} = S_{ijk} + S_{jki} + S_{kji}$ gives the Cartan equations:

$$S^j{}_{ik} - S_i\delta^j_k + S_k\delta^j_i = -\frac{1}{2}\kappa s_{ik}{}^j,$$

where $S_i = S^k{}_{ik}$ and $s^{ijk} = 2(\delta L_{\rm m}/\delta C_{ijk})/\sqrt{-g}$ is the spin tensor. Varying the Lagrangian with respect to the metric tensor g_{ik} gives the Einstein equations with the Ricci tensor. They can be put into a GR form with the modified energy–momentum tensor:

$$G^{ik} = \kappa T^{ik} + \kappa^2\Big(-s^{ij}{}_{[l}s^{kl}{}_{j]} - \frac{1}{2}s^{ijl}s^k{}_{jl} + \frac{1}{4}s^{jli}s_{jl}{}^k + \frac{1}{8}g^{ik}(-4s^l{}_{j[m}s^{jm}{}_{l]} + s^{jlm}s_{jlm})\Big).$$

Dirac spinors, representing fermions, couple to torsion through the covariant derivative in the Lagrangian and therefore are the source of torsion. At macroscopic

scales, Dirac fields can be averaged and described as a spin fluid:[3]
$$s_{ij}{}^k = s_{ij}u^k, \quad s_{ij}u^j = 0.$$
The terms in the effective energy–momentum tensor that are quadratic in the spin tensor do not vanish after averaging:
$$G^{ij} = \kappa\left(\epsilon - \frac{1}{4}\kappa s^2\right)u^i u^j - \kappa\left(p - \frac{1}{4}\kappa s^2\right)(g^{ij} - u^i u^j),$$
where
$$s^2 = \frac{1}{2}s_{ij}s^{ij} > 0 \propto n_f^2$$
is the averaged square of the spin density.[4] The Einstein–Cartan equations for a spin fluid are therefore equivalent to the GR Einstein equations for a perfect fluid with:
$$\tilde{\epsilon} = \epsilon - \alpha n_f^2, \quad \tilde{p} = p - \alpha n_f^2,$$
where ϵ and p are the thermodynamic energy density and pressure, n_f is the number density of fermions, and $\alpha = \kappa(\hbar c)^2/32$ with $\kappa = 8\pi G/c^4$.

2. Gravitational collapse of a fluid sphere

A spherically symmetric gravitational field is given by the Tolman metric:[5]
$$ds^2 = e^{\nu(\tau,R)}c^2 d\tau^2 - e^{\lambda(\tau,R)}dR^2 - e^{\mu(\tau,R)}(d\theta^2 + \sin^2\theta\, d\phi^2),$$
where ν, λ, and μ are functions of a time coordinate τ and a radial coordinate R. Coordinate transformations $\tau \to \tilde{\tau}(\tau)$ and $R \to \tilde{R}(R)$ do not change the form of the metric. The components of the Einstein tensor corresponding to this metric that do not vanish identically are:
$$G_0^0 = -e^{-\lambda}\left(\mu'' + \frac{3\mu'^2}{4} - \frac{\mu'\lambda'}{2}\right) + \frac{e^{-\nu}}{2}\left(\dot{\lambda}\dot{\mu} + \frac{\dot{\mu}^2}{2}\right) + e^{-\mu},$$
$$G_1^1 = -\frac{e^{-\lambda}}{2}\left(\frac{\mu'^2}{2} + \mu'\nu'\right) + e^{-\nu}\left(\ddot{\mu} - \frac{\dot{\mu}\dot{\nu}}{2} + \frac{3\dot{\mu}^2}{4}\right) + e^{-\mu},$$
$$G_2^2 = G_3^3 = -\frac{e^{-\nu}}{4}(\dot{\lambda}\dot{\nu} + \dot{\mu}\dot{\nu} - \dot{\lambda}\dot{\mu} - 2\ddot{\lambda} - \dot{\lambda}^2 - 2\ddot{\mu} - \dot{\mu}^2)$$
$$- \frac{e^{-\lambda}}{4}(2\nu'' + \nu'^2 + 2\mu'' + \mu'^2 - \mu'\lambda' - \nu'\lambda' + \mu'\nu'),$$
$$G_0^1 = \frac{e^{-\lambda}}{2}(2\dot{\mu}' + \dot{\mu}\mu' - \dot{\lambda}\mu' - \dot{\mu}\nu'),$$
where a dot denotes differentiation with respect to $c\tau$ and a prime denotes differentiation with respect to R.

In the comoving frame of reference, the spatial components of the four-velocity u^μ vanish. The nonzero components of the energy–momentum tensor for a spin fluid, $T_{\mu\nu} = (\tilde{\epsilon} + \tilde{p})u_\mu u_\nu - \tilde{p}g_{\mu\nu}$, are: $T_0^0 = \tilde{\epsilon}$, $T_1^1 = T_2^2 = T_3^3 = -\tilde{p}$. The Einstein field equations $G_\nu^\mu = \kappa T_\nu^\mu$ in this frame of reference are:
$$G_0^0 = \kappa\tilde{\epsilon}, \quad G_1^1 = G_2^2 = G_3^3 = -\kappa\tilde{p}, \quad G_0^1 = 0.$$

The covariant conservation of the energy–momentum tensor gives

$$\dot{\lambda} + 2\dot{\mu} = -\frac{2\dot{\tilde{\epsilon}}}{\tilde{\epsilon} + \tilde{p}}, \quad \nu' = -\frac{2\tilde{p}'}{\tilde{\epsilon} + \tilde{p}},$$

where the constants of integration depend on the allowed transformations $\tau \to \tilde{\tau}$ and $R \to \tilde{R}$.

If the pressure is homogeneous (no pressure gradients), then $\tilde{p}' = 0$, which gives $\nu' = 0$. Therefore, $\nu = \nu(\tau)$ and a transformation $\tau \to \tilde{\tau}$ can bring ν to zero and $g_{00} = e^\nu$ to 1. The system of coordinates becomes synchronous. Defining $r(\tau, R) = e^{\mu/2}$ turns the metric into[5]

$$ds^2 = c^2 d\tau^2 - e^{\lambda(\tau, R)} dR^2 - r^2(\tau, R)(d\theta^2 + \sin^2\theta\, d\phi^2).$$

Every particle in a collapsing fluid sphere is represented by a value of R that ranges from 0 (at the center) to R_0 (at the surface). The Einstein field equations reduce to

$$\kappa\tilde{\epsilon} = -\frac{e^{-\lambda}}{r^2}(2rr'' + r'^2 - rr'\lambda') + \frac{1}{r^2}(r\dot{r}\dot{\lambda} + \dot{r}^2 + 1),$$

$$-\kappa\tilde{p} = \frac{1}{r^2}(-e^{-\lambda}r'^2 + 2r\ddot{r} + \dot{r}^2 + 1),$$

$$-2\kappa\tilde{p} = -\frac{e^{-\lambda}}{r}(2r'' - r'\lambda') + \frac{\dot{r}\dot{\lambda}}{r} + \ddot{\lambda} + \frac{1}{2}\dot{\lambda}^2 + \frac{2\ddot{r}}{r},$$

$$2\dot{r}' - \dot{\lambda}r' = 0.$$

Integrating the last equation gives

$$e^\lambda = \frac{r'^2}{1 + f(R)}, \tag{1}$$

where f is a function of R satisfying a condition $1 + f > 0$.[6] Substituting this relation into the second field equation gives $2r\ddot{r} + \dot{r}^2 - f = -\kappa\tilde{p}r^2$, which is integrated to

$$\dot{r}^2 = f(R) + \frac{F(R)}{r} - \frac{\kappa}{r}\int \tilde{p}r^2\, dr,$$

where F is a positive function of R. Substituting the last two equations into the first field equation gives a relation $\kappa(\tilde{\epsilon} + \tilde{p}) = F'(R)/(r^2 r')$, leading to

$$\dot{r}^2 = f(R) + \frac{\kappa}{r}\int_0^R \tilde{\epsilon} r^2 r'\, dR. \tag{2}$$

If the mass of the sphere is M, then the Schwarzschild radius $r_g = 2GM/c^2$ of the black hole that forms from the sphere is equal to

$$r_g = \kappa \int_0^{R_0} \tilde{\epsilon} r^2 r'\, dR.$$

These two equations give $\dot{r}^2(\tau, R_0) = f(R_0) + r_g/r(\tau, R_0)$. If $r_0 = r(0, R_0)$ is the initial radius of the sphere and the sphere is initially at rest, then $\dot{r}(0, R_0) = 0$. Consequently, the value of R_0 is determined by

$$f(R_0) = -\frac{r_g}{r_0}.$$

Substituting $r = e^{\mu/2}$ and (1) into the first conservation law gives the first law of thermodynamics for the effective energy density and pressure:

$$\frac{d}{d\tau}(\tilde{\epsilon} r^2 r') + \tilde{p}\frac{d}{d\tau}(r^2 r') = 0. \tag{3}$$

3. Collapse of a spin fluid sphere

If we assume that the spin fluid is composed of an ultrarelativistic matter in kinetic equilibrium, then $\epsilon = h_\star T^4$, $p = \epsilon/3$, and $n_\mathrm{f} = h_{n\mathrm{f}} T^3$, where T is the temperature of the fluid, $h_\star = (\pi^2/30)(g_\mathrm{b} + (7/8)g_\mathrm{f})k^4/(\hbar c)^3$, and $h_{n\mathrm{f}} = (\zeta(3)/\pi^2)(3/4)g_\mathrm{f} k^3/(\hbar c)^3$. For standard-model particles, $g_\mathrm{b} = 29$ and $g_\mathrm{f} = 90$. The effective energy density and pressure are thus:

$$\tilde{\epsilon} = h_\star T^4 - \alpha h_{n\mathrm{f}}^2 T^6, \quad \tilde{p} = \frac{1}{3} h_\star T^4 - \alpha h_{n\mathrm{f}}^2 T^6.$$

Since the pressure has no gradient, the temperature only depends on τ, and so does the energy density. This scenario describes a homogeneous sphere. The first law of thermodynamics (3) gives

$$r^2 r' T^3 = g(R), \tag{4}$$

where g is a function of R. Putting this relation into (2) gives

$$\dot{r}^2 = f(R) + \frac{\kappa}{r}(h_\star T^4 - \alpha h_{n\mathrm{f}}^2 T^6) \int_0^R r^2 r' dR. \tag{5}$$

Equations (4) and (5) give the function $r(\tau, R)$, which with (1) gives $\lambda(\tau, R)$.[7] The integration of (5) also contains the initial value $\tau_0(R)$. The metric therefore depends on three arbitrary functions: $f(R)$, $g(R)$, and $\tau_0(R)$.

We seek a solution of (4) and (5) as

$$f(R) = -\sin^2 R, \quad r(\tau, R) = a(\tau)\sin R, \tag{6}$$

where $a(\tau)$ is a nonnegative function of τ. For this choice of functions, (4) gives $a^3 T^3 \sin^2 R \cos R = g(R)$, in which separation of the variables τ and R leads to

$$g(R) = \mathrm{const} \cdot \sin^2 R \cos R, \quad a^3 T^3 = \mathrm{const}.$$

Consequently,

$$aT = a_0 T_0, \quad \frac{\dot{T}}{T} + \frac{H}{c} = 0, \tag{7}$$

where $a_0 = a(\tau = 0)$ and $T_0 = T(\tau = 0)$ are the values at the initial time, and $H = c\dot{a}/a$. Substituting (6) into (5) gives

$$\dot{a}^2 + 1 = \frac{\kappa}{3}(h_\star T^4 - \alpha h_{n\mathrm{f}}^2 T^6)a^2, \tag{8}$$

which has a form of the Friedmann equation for the scale factor a as a function of the cosmic time τ in a closed, homogeneous universe. The quantity H is the Hubble parameter of this universe. Using (7) in (8) yields[8]

$$\dot{a}^2 = -1 + \frac{\kappa}{3}\left(\frac{h_\star T_0^4 a_0^4}{a^2} - \frac{\alpha h_{\rm nf}^2 T_0^6 a_0^6}{a^4}\right). \tag{9}$$

The relations (6) determine the constants:

$$\sin R_0 = \left(\frac{r_g}{r_0}\right)^{1/2}, \quad a(0) = \left(\frac{r_0^3}{r_g}\right)^{1/2}.$$

Substituting the initial values $a(0)$ and $\dot{a}(0) = 0$ into (8), in which the second term on the right-hand side is negligible, gives $Mc^2 = (4\pi/3)r_0^3 h_\star T_0^4$. This relation indicates the equivalence of mass and energy of a fluid sphere with radius r_0 and determines T_0. An event horizon for the entire sphere forms when $r(\tau, R_0) = r_g$, which is equivalent to $a = (r_g r_0)^{1/2}$. Equation (9) has two turning points, $\dot{a} = 0$, if

$$\frac{r_0^3}{r_g} > \frac{3\pi G \hbar^4 h_{\rm nf}^4}{8 h_\star^3} \sim l_{\rm Planck}^2,$$

which is satisfied for astrophysical systems that form black holes.[9]

Substituting (6) into (1) gives $e^{\lambda(\tau, R)} = a^2$. Consequently, the square of an infinitesimal interval in the interior of a collapsing spin fluid is given by

$$ds^2 = c^2 d\tau^2 - a^2(\tau) dR^2 - a^2(\tau)\sin^2 R(d\theta^2 + \sin^2\theta\, d\phi^2).$$

This metric has a form of the closed Friedmann–Lemaître–Robertson–Walker metric and describes a part of a closed universe with $0 \leq R \leq R_0$ (like dust).

4. Nonsingular bounce

Equation (9) can be solved analytically in terms of an elliptic integral of the second kind, giving the function $a(\tau)$ and then $r(\tau, R) = a(\tau)\sin R$. The value of a never reaches zero because as a decreases, the right-hand side of (9) becomes negative, contradicting the left-hand side. The change of the sign occurs when $a < (r_g r_0)^{1/2}$, that is, after the event horizon forms. Consequently, all particles with $R > 0$ fall within the event horizon but never reach $r = 0$ (the only particle at the center is the particle that is initially at the center, with $R = 0$). A singularity is replaced with a nonsingular bounce.[7] Nonzero values of a give finite values of T and thus finite values of ϵ, p, and $n_{\rm f}$.

After the bounce, the matter expands on the other side of the event horizon as a new universe. This universe has a closed geometry (constant positive curvature). The quantity $a(\tau)$ is the scale factor. The universe is oscillatory: the value of a oscillates between the two turning points. The value of R_0 does not change. A turning point at which $\ddot{a} > 0$ is a bounce, and a turning point at which $\ddot{a} < 0$ is a crunch. This universe has an infinite number of identical cycles.

The Raychaudhuri equation for a congruence of geodesics without four-acceleration and rotation is $d\theta/ds = -\theta^2/3 - 2\sigma^2 - R_{\mu\nu}u^\mu u^\nu$, where θ is the expansion scalar, σ^2 is the shear scalar, and $R_{\mu\nu}$ is the Ricci tensor. For a spin fluid, the last term in this equation is equal to $-\kappa(\tilde{\epsilon}+3\tilde{p})/2$. Consequently, the necessary and sufficient condition for avoiding a singularity in a black hole is $-\kappa(\tilde{\epsilon}+3\tilde{p})/2 > 2\sigma^2$. For a relativistic spin fluid, $p = \epsilon/3$, this condition is equivalent to

$$2\kappa\alpha n_f^2 > 2\sigma^2 + \kappa\epsilon. \tag{10}$$

Without torsion, the left-hand side of (10) would be absent and this inequality could not be satisfied, resulting in a singularity. Torsion may provide a necessary condition for preventing a singularity.[10] In the absence of shear, this condition would be also sufficient.[11]

The presence of shear opposes the effects of torsion. The shear scalar σ^2 grows with decreasing a like $\sim a^{-6}$, which is the same power law as that for n_f^2. Therefore, if the initial shear term dominates over the initial torsion term in (10), then it will dominate at later times during contraction and a singularity will form. To avoid a singularity if the shear is present, n_f^2 must grow faster than $\sim a^{-6}$. Consequently, fermions must be produced in a black hole during contraction.

The production rate of particles in a contracting or expanding universe[12] can be phenomenologically given by

$$\frac{1}{c\sqrt{-g}}\frac{d(\sqrt{-g}n_f)}{dt} = \frac{\beta H^4}{c^4}, \tag{11}$$

where $g = -a^6 \sin^4 R \sin^2\theta$ is the determinant of the metric tensor and β is a nondimensional production rate. With particle production, the second equation in (7) turns into[8]

$$\frac{\dot{T}}{T} = \frac{H}{c}\left(\frac{\beta H^3}{3c^3 h_{nf}T^3} - 1\right). \tag{12}$$

Particle production changes the power law $n_f(a)$:

$$n_f \sim a^{-(3+\delta)},$$

where δ varies with τ. Putting this relation into (11) gives

$$\delta \sim -a^\delta \dot{a}^3.$$

During contraction, $\dot{a} < 0$ and thus $\delta > 0$. The term $n_f^2 \sim a^{-6-2\delta}$ grows faster than $\sigma^2 \sim a^{-6}$ and a singularity is avoided. Particle production and torsion together reverse the effects of shear, generating a bounce.[7]

5. Closed universe in a black hole

The dynamics of the nonsingular, relativistic universe in a black hole is described by equations (8) and (12), where $H = c\dot{a}/a$. These equations, with the initial conditions $a(0) = (r_0^3/r_g)^{1/2}$ and $\dot{a}(0) = 0$, give the functions $a(\tau)$ and $T(\tau)$.

The shear would enter the right-hand side of the first equation as an additional positive term that is proportional to a^{-4}. When the universe becomes nonrelativistic, the term $h_\star T^4$ changes into a positive term proportional to a^{-1}. The cosmological constant enters as a positive term proportional to a^2.

Particle production increases the maximum size of the scale factor that is reached at a crunch. Consequently, a new cycle is larger and lasts longer then the previous cycle. R_0 is given by $\sin^3 R_0 = r_g/a(0)$, where $a(0)$ is the maximum scale factor in the first cycle. Since the maximum scale factor in the next cycle is larger, the value of $\sin R_0$ decreases. As cycles proceed, R_0 approaches π (the value for a completely closed universe).

A parent black hole creating a new, baby universe becomes an Einstein–Rosen bridge (unidirectional wormhole) to that universe.[13] If the universe is closed, it is analogous to the 2-dimensional surface of a 3-dimensional baloon (sphere). The universe would be mathematically the 3-dimensional hypersurface of a 4-dimensional hypersphere. The 3-dimensional space in which the balloon expands is not analogous to any higher dimensional space. Points off the surface of the balloon are not in the universe in this analogy. The balloon radius represents the scale factor a. The universe expands, which can be described locally by the Hubble law.

This scenario occurs also if the fermionic matter is described by the Dirac Lagrangian density instead of the spin fluid.[14]

6. Inflation and oscillations

During expansion ($H > 0$), if β is too big, then the right-hand side of (12) could become positive. In this case, the temperature would grow with increasing a, which would lead to eternal inflation. Consequently, there is an upper limit to the production rate: the maximum of the function $(\beta H^3)/(3c^3 h_{nf} T^3)$ must be lesser than 1.

If $(\beta H^3)/(3c^3 h_{nf} T^3)$ increases after a bounce to a value that is slightly lesser than 1, then T would become approximately constant. Accordingly, H would be also nearly constant and the scale factor a would grow exponentially, generating inflation.[8] Since the energy density would be also nearly constant, the universe would produce enormous amounts of matter and entropy. Such an expansion would last until the right-hand side of drops below 1. Consequently, inflation would last a finite period of time. After this period, the effects of torsion weaken and the universe smoothly enters the radiation-dominated expansion, followed by the matter-dominated expansion.

Torsion and particle production can therefore generate finite inflation without scalar fields and reheating, which is consistent with the astronomical data.[15] If quantum effects in the gravitational field near a bounce do not produce enough matter, then the closed Universe reaches the maximum size and then contracts to another bounce, beginning the new cycle. Because of matter production, a new cycle reaches larger size and last longer than the previous cycle.[16] When the Universe reaches a size at which the cosmological constant becomes dominant, it avoids another contraction and expands to infinity.[17]

7. Our universe in a black hole

These results suggest that every black hole may create a new, closed, baby universe. Accordingly, our Universe may be closed and may have born in the interior of a black hole existing in a parent universe.[13,18] Its energy would be equal to zero minus the energy of the wormhole connecting the Universe to the parent universe.[19] This hypothesis could solve the black hole information paradox: the information goes through the Einstein–Rosen bridge to the baby universe on the other side of the black hole's event horizon. The motion of matter through an event horizon is unidirectional: it defines the past and future. Time asymmetry at the event horizon may induce time asymmetry everywhere in the baby universe and could explain why time flows in one direction. Recent astronomical data seem to favor the closed geometry of the Universe,[20] thus providing some support for the black-hole cosmology.

8. Summary

The conservation law for total angular momentum in curved spacetime, consistent with Dirac equation, may require torsion.[2] The simplest theory with torsion, the Einstein–Cartan gravity, has the same Lagrangian as GR, but the affine connection contains the torsion tensor, generated by spin. Gravitational collapse of a sphere of a spin fluid creates an event horizon. The matter within the horizon collapses to extremely high densities, at which torsion acts like gravitational repulsion. Semiclassically and without shear, torsion prevents a singularity and replaces it with a nonsingular bounce. With shear, torsion prevents a singularity if the number of fermions increases during contraction through quantum particle production.[7] Particle production during expansion produces enormous amounts of matter and can generate a finite period of inflation. The resulting closed universe on the other side of the event horizon may have several bounces. Such a universe is oscillatory, with each cycle larger in size then the previous cycle, until it reaches a size at which the cosmological constant dominates, and then expands indefinitely.

In addition to eliminating gravitational singularities, torsion may also remove loop divergences in Feynman diagrams in quantum electrodynamics, resulting in finite values of bare (before renormalization) quantities such as the mass and electric charge of the electron.[21] Consequently, torsion may be a physical phenomenon that ensures physics is finite.

Acknowledgments

This work was funded by the University Research Scholar program at the University of New Haven. The author is thankful to Michael Del Grosso, Jordan Cubero, Gabriel Unger, and Shantanu Desai for valuable discussions.

References

1. L. P. Eisenhart, *Non-Riemannian Geometry* (American Mathematical Society, 1927); E. Schrödinger, *Space-time Structure* (Cambridge University Press, 1954); J. A. Schouten, *Ricci-Calculus* (Springer-Verlag, 1954).
2. D. W. Sciama, Proc. Camb. Phil. Soc. **54**, 72 (1958); T. W. B. Kibble, J. Math. Phys. **2**, 212 (1961); D. W. Sciama, in *Recent Developments in General Relativity*, p. 415 (Pergamon, 1962); Rev. Mod. Phys. **36**, 463 (1964); Rev. Mod. Phys. **36**, 1103 (1964); F. W. Hehl and B. K. Datta, J. Math. Phys. **12**, 1334 (1971); F. W. Hehl, Gen. Relativ. Gravit. **4**, 333 (1973); Gen. Relativ. Gravit. **5**, 491 (1974); F. W. Hehl, P. von der Heyde, G. D. Kerlick, and J. M. Nester, Rev. Mod. Phys. **48**, 393 (1976); V. de Sabbata and M. Gasperini, *Introduction to Gravitation* (World Scientific, 1985); F. W. Hehl and J. D. McCrea, Found. Phys. **16**, 267 (1986); V. de Sabbata and C. Sivaram, *Spin and Torsion in Gravitation* (World Scientific, 1994); N. Popławski, *Classical Physics: Spacetime and Fields*, arXiv:0911.0334; N. J. Popławski, Phys. Lett. B **690**, 73 (2010); Phys. Lett. B **727**, 575 (2013).
3. K. Nomura, T. Shirafuji, and K. Hayashi, Prog. Theor. Phys. **86**, 1239 (1991).
4. F. W. Hehl, P. von der Heyde, and G. D. Kerlick, Phys. Rev. D **10**, 1066 (1974).
5. R. A. Tolman, Proc. Natl. Acad. Sci. USA **20**, 169 (1934); J. R. Oppenheimer and H. Snyder, Phys. Rev. **56**, 455 (1939).
6. L. D. Landau and E. M. Lifshitz, *The Classical Theory of Fields* (Pergamon, 1975).
7. N. Popławski, Zh. Eksp. Teor. Fiz. **159**, 448 (2021); J. Exp. Theor. Phys. **132**, 374 (2021).
8. N. Popławski, Astrophys. J. **832**, 96 (2016); Int. J. Mod. Phys. D **27**, 1847020 (2018).
9. G. Unger and N. Popławski, Astrophys. J. **870**, 78 (2019).
10. F. W. Hehl, Abh. Braunschw. Wiss. Ges. **18**, 98 (1966); A. Trautman, Bull. Acad. Polon. Sci., Serie Sci. Math. Astr. Phys. **20**, 185 (1972); W. Kopczyński, Phys. Lett. A **39**, 219 (1972); W. Kopczyński, Phys. Lett. A **43**, 63 (1973); A. Trautman, Symp. Math. **12**, 139 (1973); Nature Phys. Sci. **242**, 7 (1973).
11. B. Kuchowicz, Gen. Relativ. Gravit. **9**, 511 (1978); M. Gasperini, Phys. Rev. Lett. **56**, 2873 (1986); Y. N. Obukhov and V. A. Korotky, Class. Quantum Grav. **4**, 1633 (1987); N. J. Popławski, Phys. Lett. B **694**, 181 (2010); Phys. Lett. B **701**, 672 (2011); Gen. Relativ. Gravit. **44**, 1007 (2012).
12. L. Parker, Phys. Rev. Lett. **21**, 562 (1968); Phys. Rev. **183**, 1057 (1969); Y. B. Zel'dovich, J. Exp. Theor. Phys. Lett. **12**, 307 (1970); L. Parker, Phys. Rev. D **3**, 346 (1971); Phys. Rev. D **3**, 2546 (1971); Y. B. Zel'dovich and A. A. Starobinskii, J. Exp. Theor. Phys. Lett. **26**, 252 (1977); V. A. Beilin, G. M. Vereshkov, Y. S. Grishkan, N. M. Ivanov, V. A. Nesterenko, and A. N. Poltavtsev, J. Exp. Theor. Phys. **51**, 1045 (1980).
13. N. J. Popławski, Phys. Lett. B **687**, 110 (2010).
14. N. Popławski, Phys. Rev. D **85**, 107502 (2012); J. Magueijo, T. G. Zlosnik, and T. W. B. Kibble, Phys. Rev. D **87**, 063504 (2013); J. L. Cubero and N. J. Popławski, Class. Quantum Grav. **37**, 025011 (2020).
15. S. Desai and N. J. Popławski, Phys. Lett. B **755**, 183 (2016).
16. J. D. Barrow and M. P. Dąbrowski, Mon. Not. Roy. Astron. Soc. **275**, 850 (1995); J. D. Barrow and C. Ganguly, Int. J. Mod. Phys. D **26**, 1743016 (2017).
17. H. Bondi, *Cosmology* (Cambridge University Press, 1960); E. A. Lord, *Tensors, Relativity and Cosmology* (McGraw-Hill, 1976).
18. I. D. Novikov, J. Exp. Theor. Phys. Lett. **3**, 142 (1966); R. K. Pathria, Nature **240**, 298 (1972); V. P. Frolov, M. A. Markov, and V. F. Mukhanov, Phys. Lett. B **216**, 272 (1989); Phys. Rev. D **41**, 383 (1990); L. Smolin, Class. Quantum Grav. **9**, 173 (1992);

S. Hawking, *Black Holes and Baby Universes and other Essays* (Bantam Dell, 1993); W. M. Stuckey, Am. J. Phys. **62**, 788 (1994); D. A. Easson and R. H. Brandenberger, J. High Energ. Phys. **06**, 024 (2001); J. Smoller and B. Temple, Proc. Natl. Acad. Sci. USA **100**, 11216 (2003).
19. N. J. Popławski, Class. Quantum Grav. **31**, 065005 (2014); N. Popławski, Mod. Phys. Lett. A **33**, 1850236 (2018).
20. E. Di Valentino, A. Melchiorri, and J. Silk, Nature Astron. **4**, 196 (2020).
21. N. Popławski, Found. Phys. **50**, 900 (2020); M. Del Grosso and N. Popławski, arXiv:2107.01612.

Asymptotically flat black hole solution in modified gravity

Surajit Kalita[1] and Banibrata Mukhopadhyay[2]

Department of Physics, Indian Institute of Science, Bangalore-560012, India
[1] *E-mail: surajitk@iisc.ac.in*
[2] *E-mail: bm@iisc.ac.in*

From time to time, different observations suggest that Einstein's theory of general relativity (GR) may not be the ultimate theory of gravity. Various researchers have suggested that the $f(R)$ theory of gravity is the best alternative to replace GR. Using $f(R)$ gravity, one can elucidate the various unexplained physics of compact objects, such as black holes, neutron stars, and white dwarfs. Researchers have already put effort into finding the vacuum solution around a black hole in $f(R)$ gravity. However, for a long time, they could not find an asymptotically flat vacuum solution. In this article, we show that the asymptotically flat vacuum solution of $f(R)$ gravity is possible and thereby use it to explain the spherical accretion flow around the black hole.

Keywords: Black hole, modified gravity, spherical accretion.

1. Introduction

Einstein's theory of general relativity (GR) is undoubtedly the most beautiful theory to explain gravity. It can easily explain a large number of phenomena where Newtonian gravity falls short, such as the deflection of light in strong gravity, generation of the gravitational waves, perihelion precession of Mercury's orbit, gravitational redshift of light, to mention a few. However, following several recent observations in cosmology and the high-density regions in the universe, such as the vicinity of compact objects, it seems that GR may not be the ultimate theory of gravity. Starobinsky first used one of the modified theories of gravity, namely R^2-gravity,[1] to explain the cosmology of the very early universe. Eventually, researchers have proposed different modifications of GR, e.g., various models of $f(R)$ gravity, to elaborate on various unexplained physics related to compact objects. Capozziello and his collaborators used different forms of $f(R)$ gravity to explain the massive neutron stars.[2] Similarly, Kalita & Mukhopadhyay used $f(R)$ gravity to unify the physics of all white dwarfs, including those possessing sub- and super-Chandrasekhar limiting masses,[3] and show that they can be detected by various proposed gravitational wave detectors.[4]

According to Birkhoff's theorem, the spherically symmetric vacuum solution in GR is static, which is the famous Schwarzschild solution. In the same context, the vacuum solution of $f(R)$ gravity is also an interesting problem. Multamäki & Vilja first obtained the solutions for a static, spherically symmetric vacuum spacetime in $f(R)$ gravity,[5] and argued that for a large class model, Schwarzschild-de Sitter metric is an exact solution of the field equations. Eventually, many researchers have obtained several solutions for different modified theories of gravity in various spacetime geometries. Capozziello and his collaborators obtained spherically symmetric as well as axially symmetric vacuum solutions in $f(R)$ gravity using Noether symmetry.[6,7] These new solutions alter the black hole's event horizon, thereby various critical orbits, such as marginally stable, marginally bound, and photon orbits. In this way, modified theories of gravity change the dynamics of the particles moving around the black hole.

The above-mentioned solutions, introduced in these literatures, always contain some diverging terms in the metric components. Hence these solutions never reduce to the Minkowski metric at the asymptotically flat limit. This asymptotic flatness is essential in the context of physical problems such as accretion disc, as a disc is expected to extend in a vast region around the compact object. Therefore, at the outermost portion of the disc, which is very far from the compact object, no physics should be violated as given by the Schwarzschild/Minkowski metric. Many of the models mentioned above assume scalar curvature, $R \neq 0$ throughout the spacetime, which is again questionable as for the Schwarzschild metric, $R = 0$, which needs to be satisfied at the asymptotic flat limit. Kalita & Mukhopadhyay, for the first time, obtained the spherically symmetric asymptotically flat vacuum solution in the premise of $f(R)$ gravity.[8] In this article, we primarily discuss this solution and its applications in the spherical accretion flow around a black hole.

2. Basic formalism

The 4-dimensional action for $f(R)$ gravity in vacuum is given by[9]

$$S = \frac{c^4}{16\pi G} \int \sqrt{-g}\, f(R)\, \mathrm{d}^4 x, \tag{1}$$

where c is the speed of light, G is Newton's gravitational constant, R is the scalar curvature, and $g = \det(g_{\mu\nu})$ is the determinant of the metric $g_{\mu\nu}$. Varying this action with respect to $g_{\mu\nu}$, with appropriate boundary conditions, we obtain the modified Einstein equation for the $f(R)$ gravity, given by

$$f'(R)G_{\mu\nu} + \frac{1}{2}g_{\mu\nu}\left[Rf'(R) - f(R)\right] - \left(\nabla_\mu \nabla_\nu - g_{\mu\nu}\Box\right) f'(R) = 0, \tag{2}$$

where $\Box$ is the d'Alembertian operator given by $\Box = \nabla^\mu \nabla_\mu$ and ∇_μ is the covariant derivative. For $f(R) = R$, Equation (2) reduces to the well-known Einstein field equation in GR.

3. Asymptotically flat vacuum solution in $f(R)$ gravity

To obtain the spherically symmetric solution of the modified Einstein equation, we first assume $g_{\mu\nu} = \mathrm{diag}(s(r), -p(r), -r^2, -r^2 \sin^2\theta)$, where s, p are the functions of the radial coordinate r only. We know that far from the compact objects, the metric should reduce first to the Schwarzschild metric, and at very far from the compact object, it should reduce to the Minkowski metric as the effect of gravity is negligible there. Using these conditions at the asymptotic limit, one can show that for $f'(R) = 1 + \beta/r$ with β being a constant, in $c = G = M = 1$ unit, the temporal and radial components of the metric are given by[8]

$$g_{tt} = s(r) = 1 - \frac{2}{r} - \frac{\beta(\beta-6)}{2r^2} + \frac{\beta^2(13\beta-66)}{20r^3} - \frac{\beta^3(31\beta-156)}{48r^4} + \ldots, \quad (3)$$

$$g_{rr} = -p(r) = -\frac{16r^4}{(\beta+2r)^4}\frac{1}{s(r)}. \quad (4)$$

It is, of course, obvious from the above expressions that as $\beta \to 0$, it reduces to the Schwarzschild metric, and as $r \to \infty$, it reduces to the Minkowski metric, i.e., the flat spacetime.

(a) temporal component

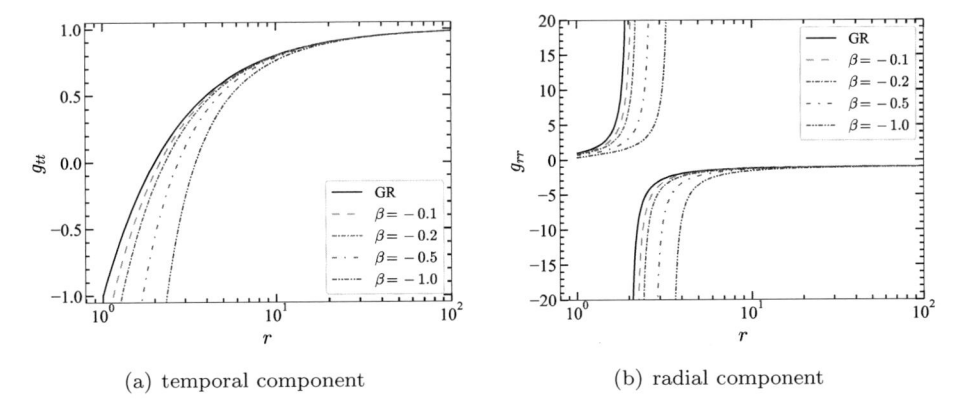

(b) radial component

Fig. 1. Variation of temporal and radial metric elements as functions of distance r. All the quantities are in dimensionless units of $c = G = M = 1$.

From Equations (3) and (4), it is observed that in $f(R)$ gravity, the vacuum solution is different from the Schwarzschild metric. This deviation indicates the violation of Birkhoff's theorem, which states that any spherically symmetric vacuum solution is essentially the Schwarzschild solution. Figure 1 describes the variations of the metric elements g_{tt} and g_{rr} with respect to r for different β. It is evident from the figure that as $r \to \infty$, the solutions reduce to the flat Minkowski metric, which, however, deviates near the black hole. $\beta = 0$ represents the Schwarzschild solution, with the radius of the event horizon $r_H = 2$. In $f(R)$ gravity, as β deviates from 0, the solution is no longer the Schwarzschild solution, and the physics related to these solutions alter. For example, one can easily obtain the event horizon from Equations (3) and (4) by solving $g_{rr} \to \infty$, which shows that r_H shifts from 2 as β deviates from 0. Not only the radius of the event horizon, but one can also obtain the various marginal orbits in $f(R)$ gravity from Equations (3) and (4). Table 1 shows the radii of various orbits and their critical angular momenta for different β. We choose β to be negative because it guarantees that gravity is always attractive.

Table 1. Various characteristic parameters of spacetime for different values of β: r_H is the event horizon, r_{MB} the marginally bound orbit, r_{MS} the marginally stable orbit, L_{MB} and L_{MS} are their corresponding specific angular momenta, and r_{ph} is the photon orbit. All the values are in dimensionless unit considering $c = G = M = 1$.

β	r_H	r_{MB}	r_{MS}	r_{ph}	L_{MB}	L_{MS}
0 (GR)	2.00	4.00	6.00	3.00	4.00	3.46
-0.1	2.15	4.30	6.45	3.20	4.15	3.61
-0.2	2.30	4.60	6.90	3.40	4.29	3.75
-0.5	2.74	5.52	8.28	3.98	4.71	4.15
-1.0	3.47	7.07	10.64	4.94	5.37	4.78
-1.5	4.18	8.66	13.08	5.89	5.99	5.37

4. Spherical accretion flow in $f(R)$ gravity

The vacuum solution for the $f(R)$ gravity can be used to understand the physics of black hole accretion. Here we explore the simplest class of it, i.e., spherical accretion flow around a black hole. In the Newtonian framework, such a flow is known as the Bondi accretion flow.[10] Since this flow is spherically symmetric, it does not possess any angular momentum, i.e., the flow is not rotating. The equations for conservation of energy and mass flux are respectively given by

$$T^\mu_{0;\mu} = 0, \quad \text{and} \quad (\rho U^\mu)_{;\mu} = 0, \qquad (5)$$

where T^μ_ν is the stress-energy tensor, ρ is the density, and U^μ is the four-velocity of the fluid. Using these equations, for a spherically symmetric metric, $g_{\mu\nu} = \text{diag}(-e^{2\phi(r)}, e^{2\lambda(r)}, r^2, r^2 \sin^2\theta)$, the radial velocity ($u$) gradient equation for such flow is given by[8,11]

$$\frac{du}{u}\left[V^2 - \frac{u^2}{u^2 + e^{-2\lambda}}\right] + \frac{dr}{r}\left[2V^2 + r(V^2 - 1)(\phi' + \lambda') + \frac{r\lambda' e^{-2\lambda}}{u^2 + e^{-2\lambda}}\right] = 0, \qquad (6)$$

where $u = \mathrm{d}r/\mathrm{d}t$, $V^2 = 4T/3(1+4T)$ with T being the temperature of the fluid. The general idea of an accretion disc is that there is a Keplerian disc outside, where the matter has a minimal radial velocity. As the Keplerian disc terminates at a smaller distance from the black hole, the matter has a significant radial velocity, and it starts falling faster to the black hole. We assume that in this region, matter starts exhibiting spherical accretion flow. In other words, we assume that as the matter comes close enough to the black hole, it loses all its angular momentum, resulting in radial fall to the black hole (in reality, matter exhibits some angular momentum, even if sub-Keplerian). Figure 2 shows the accretion and wind flows for the spherical accretion flow in $f(R)$ gravity, which are obtained by solving the Equation (6). It is evident from the figure that the velocity is highly dependent on the outside temperature (T_out), where matter starts behaving as a spherical accretion flow. The flow reaches the speed of light at the event horizon. As the event horizon shifts in the presence of $f(R)$ gravity, the flow reaches this maximum speed at different radii for different values of β. However, since the solution is asymptotically flat, both the accretion and wind curves match the well-known case for the Schwarzschild solution far from the black hole.

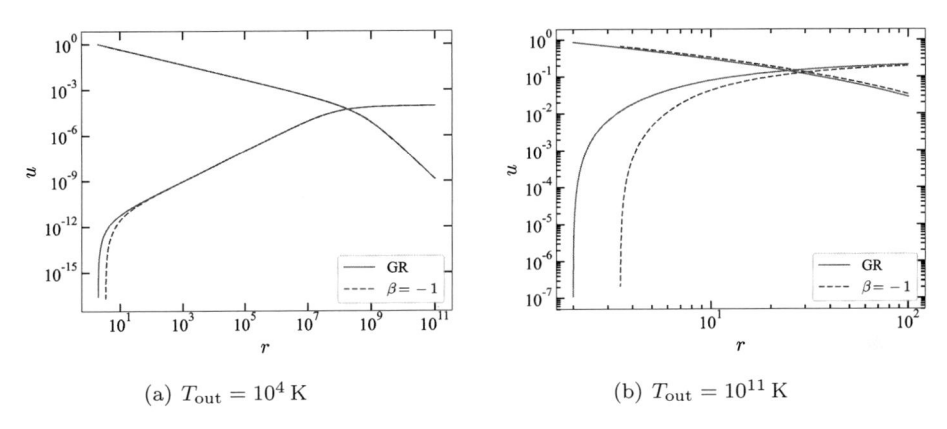

(a) $T_{\text{out}} = 10^4$ K

(b) $T_{\text{out}} = 10^{11}$ K

Fig. 2. Spherical accretion flow in modified gravity: red solid line corresponds to the Schwarzschild spacetime and blue dashed line corresponds to the $f(R)$ gravity with $\beta = -1$.

5. Conclusions

$f(R)$ gravity is one of the best bets to replace GR, and researchers have already proposed different models to explain various exciting phenomena related to cosmology and compact objects. For more than a decade, various researchers have put effort into obtaining the vacuum solution of $f(R)$ gravity. However, none of those solutions are asymptotically flat, which means they do not reduce to the Minkowski metric as one moves very far from any gravity source, and hence they may not be applicable to astrophysical phenomena. In this article, we have argued that asymptotically flat vacuum spacetime is also possible in $f(R)$ gravity. We have shown here that the vacuum solution in $f(R)$ gravity is not the Schwarzschild solution, which indicates the violation of Birkhoff's theorem in the presence of the modified gravity. Since the solution is no longer the Schwarzschild solution, the quantities related to the event horizon and marginal orbits also alter, which further affects the spherical accretion flow around a black hole.

References

1. A. A. Starobinsky, A new type of isotropic cosmological models without singularity, *Physics Letters B* **91**, 99 (March 1980).
2. A. V. Astashenok, S. Capozziello and S. D. Odintsov, Maximal neutron star mass and the resolution of the hyperon puzzle in modified gravity, *Phys. Rev. D* **89**, p. 103509 (May 2014).

3. S. Kalita and B. Mukhopadhyay, Modified Einstein's gravity to probe the sub- and super-Chandrasekhar limiting mass white dwarfs: a new perspective to unify under- and over-luminous type Ia supernovae, *J. Cosmology Astropart. Phys.* **9**, p. 007 (September 2018).
4. S. Kalita and B. Mukhopadhyay, Gravitational Wave in f(R) Gravity: Possible Signature of Sub- and Super-Chandrasekhar Limiting-mass White Dwarfs, *ApJ* **909**, p. 65 (March 2021).
5. T. Multamäki and I. Vilja, Spherically symmetric solutions of modified field equations in $f(R)$ theories of gravity, *Phys. Rev. D* **74**, p. 064022 (September 2006).
6. S. Capozziello, A. Stabile and A. Troisi, Spherically symmetric solutions in $f(R)$ gravity via the Noether symmetry approach, *Classical and Quantum Gravity* **24**, 2153 (April 2007).
7. S. Capozziello, M. De Laurentis and A. Stabile, Axially symmetric solutions in $f(R)$-gravity, *Classical and Quantum Gravity* **27**, p. 165008 (August 2010).
8. S. Kalita and B. Mukhopadhyay, Asymptotically flat vacuum solution in modified theory of Einstein's gravity, *European Physical Journal C* **79**, p. 877 (October 2019).
9. A. De Felice and S. Tsujikawa, $f(R)$ Theories, *Living Reviews in Relativity* **13**, p. 3 (June 2010).
10. H. Bondi, On spherically symmetrical accretion, *MNRAS* **112**, p. 195 (1952).
11. F. C. Michel, Accretion of Matter by Condensed Objects, *Ap&SS* **15**, 153 (January 1972).

Shadow of a charged black hole surrounded by an anisotropic matter field

Javier Badía[1,2,*] and Ernesto F. Eiroa[1,†]

[1]*Instituto de Astronomía y Física del Espacio (IAFE, CONICET-UBA),*
Casilla de Correo 67, Sucursal 28, 1428, Buenos Aires, Argentina
[2]*Departamento de Física, Facultad de Ciencias Exactas y Naturales,*
Universidad de Buenos Aires, Ciudad Universitaria Pab. I, 1428, Buenos Aires, Argentina
* E-mail: jbadia@iafe.uba.ar
† E-mail: eiroa@iafe.uba.ar

A certain type of matter with anisotropic pressures can add to the Reissner-Nordström metric a term proportional to a power of the radial coordinate. Using the standard method of separating variables for the Hamilton-Jacobi equation, we study the shadow of the corresponding rotating solution, obtained through the Newman-Janis algorithm. We define and calculate three observables in order to characterize the position, size and shape of the shadow.

Keywords: Black hole shadow; anisotropic fluid; electromagnetic field.

1. Introduction

There has been a renewed interest in the study of black hole shadows since the release of the first reconstructed image of the surroundings of the supermassive black hole M87* by the Event Horizon Telescope (EHT) collaboration.[1,2] While the shadow of a non-rotating black hole is a circle, a rotating black hole has an asymmetric shadow[3] whose shape depends on the black hole mass and spin, as well as the inclination angle of the observer. In alternative theories of gravity the shadow also presents characteristics that depend on the parameters of the specific model.[4]

Anisotropic fluids in general relativity have been studied in the context of compact objects such as stars or black holes, and in particular spherically symmetric black holes surrounded by an anisotropic fluid have recently been introduced.[5] The anisotropy allows the matter around the black hole to remain static by means of a negative radial pressure, and the resulting metric has a very general form, also being found in some alternative theories of gravity.[6] In this work we study the shadows of the charged and rotating version[7] of these black holes. We adopt units such that $G = c = 1$.

2. Black hole solution

The energy-momentum tensor corresponding to the anisotropic fluid adopted by Cho & Kim[5] has the form

$$T_\mu{}^\nu = \mathrm{diag}(-\rho, p_1, p_2, p_2) \tag{1}$$

in spherical coordinates, with a radial pressure p_1 and an angular pressure p_2. A barotropic equation of state

$$p_i = w_i \rho \qquad (2)$$

is assumed. It can be shown that in order to have a static black hole solution the value $w_1 = -1$ must be chosen, leaving w_2 as the only free parameter, which we will simply name w. It is also possible to add to the black hole an electric charge,[8] leading to the solution

$$ds^2 = -f(r)dt^2 + f(r)^{-1}dr^2 + r^2(d\theta^2 + \sin^2\theta\, d\varphi^2), \qquad (3)$$

with

$$f(r) = 1 - \frac{2m(r)}{r}, \qquad (4)$$

$$m(r) = M - \frac{Q^2}{2r} + \frac{K}{2r^{2w-1}}, \qquad (5)$$

where M, Q, and K are integration constants. M and Q are the mass and the electric charge of the black hole, respectively, while K is related to the energy density of the anisotropic fluid. It can be seen that by changing the equation of state of the fluid—that is, by changing w—one arrives at a different power of r in the last term of $f(r)$. The squared charge Q^2 is clearly positive; however, there is no impediment to continuing the solution to negative values, replacing Q^2 by a parameter q which may take either sign, and we will do so in the following. When q is negative the second term in $m(r)$ can no longer be interpreted as arising from an electric charge, but it can be found for example in some braneworld models.[9]

Applying the Newman-Janis algorithm to the spherically symmetric solution (3) leads to the corresponding axisymmetric metric

$$ds^2 = -\frac{\rho^2 \Delta}{\Sigma}dt^2 + \frac{\Sigma \sin^2\theta}{\rho^2}(d\varphi - \Omega\, dt)^2 + \frac{\rho^2}{\Delta}dr^2 + \rho^2 d\theta^2, \qquad (6)$$

where

$$\rho^2 = r^2 + a^2 \cos^2\theta, \qquad (7)$$

$$\Delta = r^2 - 2m(r)r + a^2, \qquad (8)$$

$$\Sigma = (r^2 + a^2)^2 - a^2 \Delta \sin^2\theta, \qquad (9)$$

$$\Omega = \frac{2am(r)r}{\Sigma}, \qquad (10)$$

and

$$m(r) = M - \frac{q}{2r} + \frac{K}{2r^{2w-1}}, \qquad (11)$$

as in the spherically symmetric case. When $K = 0$ the Kerr-Newman metric is recovered, with q replaced by Q^2. It is important to keep in mind that outside of general relativity, the metric obtained through the Newman-Janis algorithm may correspond to a different energy-momentum tensor than that of the original spherically symmetric metric.[10] We will assume throughout this work that $w > 0$ so that the spacetime is asymptotically flat. The weak, strong and dominant energy conditions impose various restrictions[5,7] on the allowed values of w and K, but since they do not affect the calculation of the shadow we will not take them into account.

We require the presence of an event horizon, so that the spacetime does not contain a naked singularity. The event horizon is located at the largest solution of $\Delta(r) = 0$, so that its disappearance corresponds to parameter values for which $\Delta(r)$ has a double root. The values of w and K for which this happens can be found parametrically as functions of the radius r of the double root,[11] and are given by

$$w = \frac{a^2 + q - Mr}{\Delta_{\text{KN}}} \tag{12}$$

and

$$K = \frac{\Delta_{\text{KN}}}{r^2 r(r-M)/\Delta_{\text{KN}}}, \tag{13}$$

where $\Delta_{\text{KN}} = r^2 - 2Mr + a^2 + q$ is the functional form of Δ in a Kerr-Newman-like spacetime. Plotting these curves for various values of $a^2 + q$ shows the regions in parameter space for which an event horizon exists, as seen in Figure 1, in which we have set $M = 1$ for simplicity. It can be seen from the figure that unlike for the Kerr-Newman spacetime, where $a^2 + q \leq M^2$ is a necessary condition for the existence of an event horizon, the presence of the fluid allows for black holes with $a^2 + q > M^2$.

3. The black hole shadow

We will briefly review the standard method for finding the null geodesics for photons and the shadow, adapted to our selected spacetime.[3,11] The metric (6) is independent of the t and φ coordinates, leading to the conserved quantities $E = -p_t$ and $L = p_\varphi$; however, there is an additional hidden symmetry with an associated conserved quantity, the Carter constant $\mathcal{Q}$. This constant can be found by assuming a separable solution for the Hamilton-Jacobi equation, leading to the first-order equations of motion

$$\rho^2 \dot{t} = \frac{r^2 + a^2}{\Delta} P(r) + aL - a^2 \sin^2\theta \, E, \tag{14}$$

$$\rho^2 \dot{\varphi} = \frac{aP(r)}{\Delta} + \frac{L}{\sin^2\theta} - aE, \tag{15}$$

$$(\rho^2 \dot{r})^2 = \mathcal{R}(r), \tag{16}$$

$$(\rho^2 \dot{\theta})^2 = \Theta(\theta), \tag{17}$$

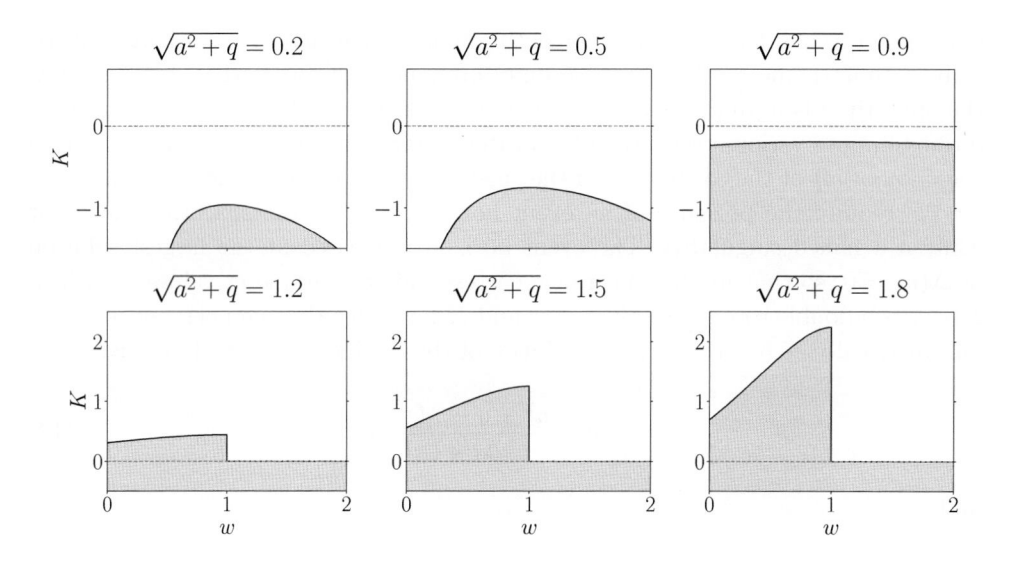

Fig. 1. Presence of an event horizon for our adopted metric. The shaded regions indicate the parameter values for which the spacetime contains a naked singularity, while in the white regions there is an event horizon. The solid curves separating them are described parametrically by Eqs. (12) and (13). We have set $M = 1$, so that all parameters are dimensionless.

where

$$P(r) = E(r^2 + a^2) - aL, \tag{18}$$

$$\mathcal{R}(r) = P(r)^2 - \Delta[(L - aE)^2 + \mathcal{Q}], \tag{19}$$

$$\Theta(\theta) = \mathcal{Q} + \cos^2\theta \left(a^2 E^2 - \frac{L^2}{\sin^2\theta}\right). \tag{20}$$

For convenience, we define the impact parameters $\xi = L/E$ and $\eta = \mathcal{Q}/E^2$. The trajectories that make up the shadow contour have the same impact parameters as the spherical photon orbits—that is, the solutions of the equations of motion that stay at a constant value of r. These can be found by solving $\mathcal{R}(r) = 0 = \mathcal{R}'(r)$, and the corresponding impact parameters are given parametrically by

$$\xi = \frac{4m(r)r^2 - (r + m(r) + m'(r)r)(r^2 + a^2)}{a(r - m(r) - m'(r)r)} \tag{21}$$

$$\eta = r^3 \frac{4a^2(m(r) - m'(r)r) - r(r - 3m(r) + m'(r)r)^2}{a^2(r - m(r) - m'(r)r)^2}. \tag{22}$$

A distant observer at an inclination angle $\theta = \theta_o$ can use the celestial coordinates (α, β), which are given by

$$\alpha = -\frac{\xi}{\sin\theta_o}, \tag{23}$$

$$\beta = \pm\sqrt{\eta + \cos^2\theta_o\left(a^2 - \frac{\xi^2}{\sin^2\theta_o}\right)}; \tag{24}$$

they correspond to horizontal and vertical displacement in the image plane, respectively.

Figure 2 shows the shadows produced by a black hole with spin $a/M = 0.9$ as seen by a distant equatorial observer, for various values of the parameters w, K and q. We find the expected behaviors from the Kerr and Kerr-Newman spacetimes: the shadow is asymmetrical and displaced as a consequence of the spin of the black hole, and its size decreases as the charge increases.

To better characterize the size and shape of the shadow, we define three observables[11,12] that can be calculated from a given shadow contour: the area of the shadow, its oblateness, and its horizontal displacement. The area is simply

$$A = 2\int \beta\, d\alpha, \tag{25}$$

where the plus sign in Eq. (24) has been chosen; the oblateness measures the deviation of the shadow from circularity and is defined as

$$D = \frac{\Delta\alpha}{\Delta\beta}, \tag{26}$$

where $\Delta\alpha$ and $\Delta\beta$ are the extent of the shadow in the horizontal and vertical directions respectively; finally, the horizontal displacement is more properly described as the α-coordinate of the centroid, given by

$$\alpha_c = \frac{1}{A}\int 2\alpha\beta\, d\alpha. \tag{27}$$

Working with observables has the benefit of making it easier to explore larger areas of parameter space at once; this can be seen in Figs. 3, 4 and 5, showing the values of A, D and α_c for $a/M = 0.9$ and various values of the other parameters. All plots are shown as functions of q, whose maximum value is determined by the requirement that there exist an event horizon.

It is clear from Fig. 3 that the shadow becomes smaller as q increases or as K decreases. This is to be expected, since both parameters appear with opposite signs in the metric. The oblateness and horizontal displacement show more interesting features. For $w < 1$ we see that the shadow becomes more compressed and more displaced as the charge increases. For $w = 2$ and $K > 0$, though, the charge can become large enough to reach a region where the behavior reverses, with D becoming greater than one and α_c becoming greater than zero, reflecting a shadow

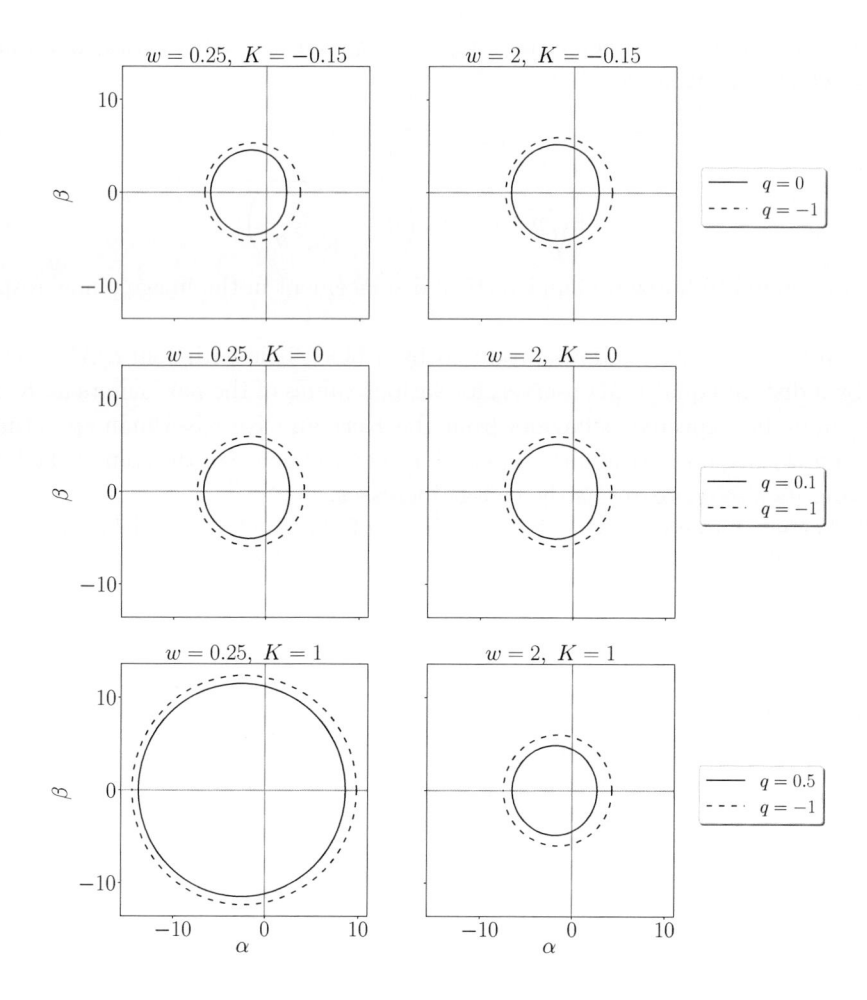

Fig. 2. The shadows of a black hole with $a/M = 0.9$ for an observer at $\theta_o = \pi/2$, for various values of the parameters. All quantities have been adimensionalized by setting $M = 1$.

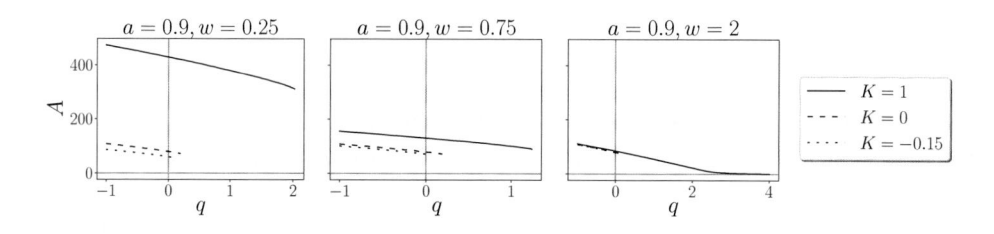

Fig. 3. The area of the black hole shadow for some values of the parameters. We set $M = 1$, so that all quantities are dimensionless.

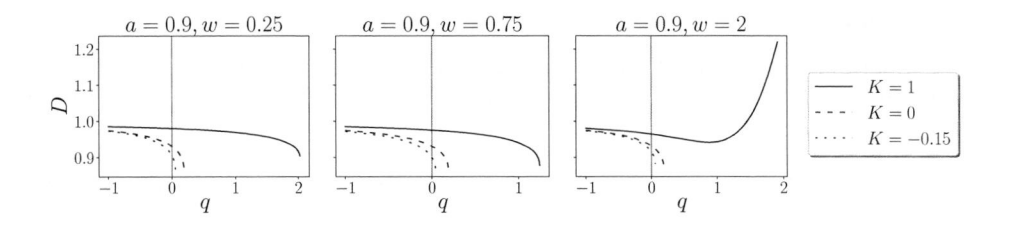

Fig. 4. The oblateness of the black hole shadow for some values of the parameters. We set $M = 1$.

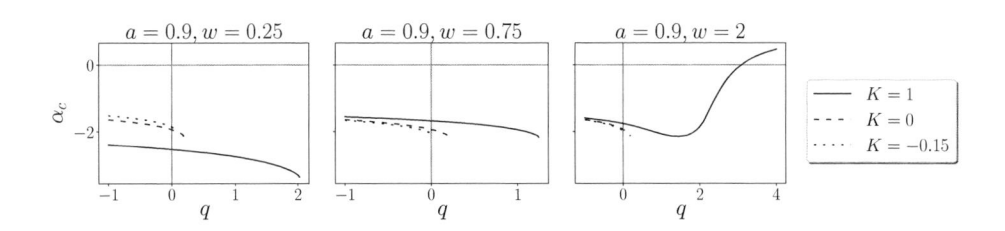

Fig. 5. The horizontal position of the shadow centroid for some values of the parameters. We set $M = 1$.

that is wider than it is tall—unlike the Kerr shadow—and displaced in the opposite direction. However, the energy-momentum tensor of the fluid can have the physically undesirable property of having negative energy[7,11] in this region of parameter space, so the corresponding shadows should be interpreted with care.

4. Discussion

In this work we have considered the effect of a fluid with anisotropic pressure on the shadow of a charged and rotating black hole. The fluid makes a contribution to the gravitational field of the black hole, and the resulting Hamilton-Jacobi equation for the geodesics is separable, so that a standard method for finding the shadow contour can be used. We have produced plots of the shadow for various values of the charge as well as the fluid anisotropy and density, and we have found that for many values of the parameters the shadow is qualitatively similar to the well known Kerr-Newman case, exhibiting the typical deviation from circularity due to the spin and shrinking as the charge increases or the energy density of the fluid decreases. However, in some regions of parameter space where the fluid has negative energy, the opposite behavior is seen, with the shadow becoming narrow and displaced in the opposite direction.

Acknowledgments

This work has been supported by CONICET and Universidad de Buenos Aires.

References

1. K. Akiyama *et al.* (Event Horizon Telescope), First M87 Event Horizon Telescope Results. I. The Shadow of the Supermassive Black Hole, *Astrophys. J. Lett.* **875**, L1 (2019).
2. K. Akiyama *et al.* (Event Horizon Telescope), First M87 Event Horizon Telescope Results. V. Physical Origin of the Asymmetric Ring, *Astrophys. J. Lett.* **875**, L5 (2019).
3. J. Bardeen, *Black Holes*, Proceedings of École d'été de Physique Théorique, Les Houches 1972, 215-240, edited by C. De Witt and B.S. De Witt (Gordon and Breach Science Publishers, New York, 1973).
4. V. Perlick and O. Y. Tsupko, Calculating black hole shadows: review of analytical studies, arXiv:2105.07101 [gr-qc]
5. I. Cho and H. Kim, Simple black holes with anisotropic fluid, *Chinese Phys. C* **43**, 025101 (2018).
6. R. Kumar, S. G. Ghosh, and A. Wang, Gravitational deflection of light and shadow cast by rotating Kalb-Ramond black holes, *Phys. Rev. D* **101**, 104001 (2020).
7. H. Kim, B. Lee, W. Lee, and Y. Lee, Rotating black holes with an anisotropic matter field, *Phys. Rev. D* **101**, 064067 (2020).
8. V. V. Kiselev, Quintessence and black holes, *Class. Quant. Grav.* **20**, 1187 (2003).
9. A. N. Aliev and A. E. Gümrükçüoglu, Charged rotating black holes on a 3-brane, *Phys. Rev. D* **71**, 104027 (2005).
10. D. Hansen and N. Yunes, Applicability of the Newman-Janis algorithm to black hole solutions of modified gravity theories, *Phys. Rev. D* **88**, 104020 (2013).
11. J. Badía and E. F. Eiroa, Influence of an anisotropic matter field on the shadow of a rotating black hole, *Phys. Rev. D* **102**, 024066 (2020).
12. R. Kumar and S. G. Ghosh, Black Hole Parameter Estimation from Its Shadow, *Astrophys. J.* **892**, 78 (2020).

Constraining modified gravity theories with physical black holes

Sebastian Murk

Department of Physics and Astronomy, Macquarie University,
Sydney, New South Wales 2109, Australia
and
Sydney Quantum Academy,
Sydney, New South Wales 2006, Australia
E-mail: sebastian.murk@mq.edu.au

We review the constraints modified theories of gravity must satisfy to be compatible with the spherically symmetric black hole solutions of semiclassical gravity that describe the formation of an apparent horizon in finite time of a distant observer. The constraints are satisfied in generic modified gravity theories with up to fourth-order derivatives in the metric, indicating that the semiclassical solutions correspond to zeroth-order terms in perturbative solutions of these theories. As a result, it may not be possible to distinguish between the semiclassical theory and modifications including up to fourth-order derivatives based on the observation of an apparent horizon alone.

Keywords: Black holes; general relativity; modified gravity; alternative theories of gravity; quantum aspects of black holes.

1. Introduction

The predictions of general relativity (GR) have been confirmed in numerous experiments and are so far compatible with all currently available astrophysical and cosmological data. In particular, strong evidence for the existence of astrophysical black holes (ABHs) — massive dark compact objects — has accumulated over the last few decades. The precise nature of ABHs is still under debate, but contemporary models describe them as ultra-compact objects (UCOs) with or without a horizon.[1] Due to their compactness, they provide excellent opportunities to probe strong gravity.[2]

The development of alternative theories of gravity has received much attention in recent years in an attempt to alleviate some of the perceived shortcomings of GR (such as the presence of singularities) and incorporate quantum gravitational effects.[3,4] As a preliminary test, any modified theory of gravity (MTG) should be compatible with the observed ABHs candidates and provide a model to describe them. Present-day astrophysical observations such as the detection of gravitational waves from coalescing compact systems[5,6] and measurements of the M87 black hole shadow[7] probe the (dynamic) strong-field regime of gravity and limit the extent to which MTG can deviate from GR while still being compatible with observational data.

There is no single, unanimously agreed upon definition of what exactly constitutes a black hole as different lines of research focus on different aspects. Consequently, the most useful and/or practical definition of a black hole depends on the context and highlights the relevant features. Nevertheless, a widely accepted feature of black holes is the presence of a trapped spacetime region from which nothing can escape.[8] We adapt the terminology of Ref. 9 and refer to a trapped region that is bounded by an apparent horizon as a physical black hole (PBH). The definition of an apparent horizon (see Sec. 2) is an observer-dependent notion that is, at least in principle, physically observable (in contrast to the global, observer-independent notion of an event horizon).[10] It is therefore possible that GR and various MTG can be distinguished observationally based on distinct properties of PBHs and their horizons in these models.

2. Mathematical preliminaries

We work in units where $\hbar = c = G = 1$, use the $(-+++)$ signature of the metric, and describe dynamics using the semiclassical Einstein equations $G_{\mu\nu} = 8\pi T_{\mu\nu}$ or modifications thereof, where $T_{\mu\nu} \equiv \langle \hat{T}_{\mu\nu} \rangle_\omega$ on the rhs denotes the expectation value of the renormalized energy-momentum tensor (EMT) that describes both the collapsing matter and the produced excitations. No assumptions are made about the matter content or the quantum state ω.

The field equations of a generally covariant metric theory of gravity can be derived from its action.[11] Here, we omit discussions of the matter Lagrangian and boundary conditions and focus on the gravitational action

$$S = \int \sqrt{-g}\, \mathcal{L}_\text{g}\, d^4x \tag{1}$$

determined by the gravitational Lagrangian density $\mathcal{L}_\text{g}(g^{\mu\nu}, R_{\mu\nu\rho\sigma})$. In classical GR and semiclassical gravity, it is strictly linear in the Ricci scalar, i.e. $\mathcal{L}_\text{g}(g^{\mu\nu}, R_{\mu\nu\rho\sigma}) = R$. Modifications typically include higher-order curvature corrections, which we organize according to powers of derivatives in the metric, i.e.

$$\begin{aligned}\mathcal{L}_\text{g}\sqrt{-g} &= \frac{M_\text{Pl}^2}{16\pi}\left(R + \lambda\mathcal{F}(g^{\mu\nu}, R_{\mu\nu\rho\sigma})\right) \\ &= \frac{M_\text{Pl}^2}{16\pi}R + a_1 R^2 + a_2 R_{\mu\nu}R^{\mu\nu} + a_3 R_{\mu\nu\rho\sigma}R^{\mu\nu\rho\sigma} + \ldots,\end{aligned} \tag{2}$$

where λ sets the scale of the perturbative analysis, the cosmological constant term was omitted, M_P denotes the Planck mass, and the coefficients a_1, a_2, a_3 are dimensionless.

We limit our exposition to spherical symmetry and work with a general spherically symmetric metric in Schwarzschild coordinates given by

$$ds^2 = -e^{2h(t,r)}f(t,r)dt^2 + f(t,r)^{-1}dr^2 + r^2 d\Omega, \tag{3}$$

where
$$f(t,r) := \partial_\mu r \partial^\mu r \equiv 1 - C(t,r)/r \tag{4}$$

provides a coordinate-independent definition of the Misner–Sharp mass[12] $C(t,r)/2$, r denotes the areal radius, and the function $h(t,r)$ plays the role of an integrating factor in coordinate transformations, such as

$$dt = e^{-h}\left(e^{h_+} dv - f^{-1} dr\right). \tag{5}$$

Explicit calculations can be simplified by introducing the effective EMT components

$$\tau_t := e^{-2h} T_{tt}, \qquad \tau_t{}^r := e^{-h} T_t{}^r, \qquad \tau^r := T^{rr}. \tag{6}$$

The apparent horizon plays a central role in our analysis. Its outer component is located at the Schwarzschild radius $r_g(t)$ that is defined as the largest root of $f(t,r) = 0$.[13] Albeit an observer-dependent notion in general, it is unambiguously defined in spherical symmetry. To be of physical relevance, it must form in finite time according to the clock of a distant observer.[14,15] Moreover, to maintain predictability of the theory, it must be a regular surface,[16,17] i.e. the curvature scalars

$$\mathrm{T} := T^\mu{}_\mu = -R/8\pi + \mathcal{O}(\lambda), \qquad \mathfrak{T} := T^{\mu\nu} T_{\mu\nu} = R^{\mu\nu} R_{\mu\nu}/64\pi^2 + \mathcal{O}(\lambda^2), \tag{7}$$

must be finite at $r = r_g$. Mathematically, this requirement is expressed as

$$\mathrm{T} = (\tau^r - \tau_t)/f \to g_1(t) f^{k_1}, \tag{8}$$

$$\mathfrak{T} = \left[(\tau_t)^2 - 2(\tau_t{}^r)^2 + (\tau^r)^2\right]/f^2 \to g_2(t) f^{k_2}, \tag{9}$$

for some functions $g_{1,2}(t)$ and $k_{1,2} \geqslant 0$. While there a infinitely many solutions in principle, only two distinct classes of dynamic solutions that satisfy the regularity requirement were found to be self-consistent.[18,19] With respect to the scaling behavior $\tau \sim f^k$ of the effective EMT components of Eq. (6), they correspond to the values $k \in \{0, 1\}$, where $k \equiv k_1 \equiv k_2$. Both of them violate the null energy condition (NEC) in the vicinity of the outer apparent horizon.[15,18,20] We briefly summarize their properties in what follows.

3. Semiclassical PBH solutions in spherical symmetry

In spherical symmetry, the relevant components G_{tt}, $G_t{}^r$, G^{rr} of the semiclassical Einstein equations can then be written as

$$\partial_r C = 8\pi r^2 \tau_t / f, \tag{10}$$

$$\partial_t C = 8\pi r^2 e^h \tau_t{}^r, \tag{11}$$

$$\partial_r h = 4\pi r (\tau_t + \tau^r) / f^2, \tag{12}$$

respectively.

3.1. $k = 0$ solutions

Close to the horizon (i.e. as $r \to r_g$), the limiting form of the effective EMT components is given by

$$\tau_t = -\Upsilon^2 + \sum_{j \geq \frac{1}{2}}^{\infty} e_j x^j, \qquad \tau_t{}^r = \pm \Upsilon^2 + \sum_{j \geq \frac{1}{2}}^{\infty} \phi_j x^j, \qquad \tau^r = -\Upsilon^2 + \sum_{j \geq \frac{1}{2}}^{\infty} p_j x^j \qquad (13)$$

for some time-dependent function $\Upsilon(t) > 0$, where $j \in \mathbb{Z}_{\frac{1}{2}}^{1}$ labels half-integer and integer coefficients and powers of the coordinate distance $x := r - r_g$ from the apparent horizon, and the lower signature of $\tau_t{}^r$ corresponds to evaporation (accretion). Taking $\tau_t \to \tau^r \to +\Upsilon^2 + \mathcal{O}(\sqrt{x})$ results in complex-valued solutions of the Einstein equations Eqs. (10)–(12).[20] The leading terms of the metric functions that solve Eqs. (10) and (12) are given by

$$C = r_g - c_{12}\sqrt{x} + \sum_{j \geq 1}^{\infty} c_j x^j, \qquad (14)$$

$$h = -\frac{1}{2} \ln \frac{x}{\xi} + \sum_{j \geq \frac{1}{2}}^{\infty} h_j x^j, \qquad (15)$$

where the leading coefficient $c_{12} = 4\sqrt{\pi} r_g^{3/2} \Upsilon$, $\xi(t)$ is determined by the choice of time variable, and higher-order terms must be matched with those of the EMT expansion. Eq. (11) then necessitates that the dynamic behavior of the horizon is governed by

$$r_g' = \pm c_{12} \sqrt{\xi}/r_g \qquad (16)$$

where the lower (upper) sign corresponds to evaporation (accretion).

3.2. $k = 1$ solution

For $k = 1$, the limiting form of the effective EMT components close to the horizon (i.e. as $r \to r_g$) is given by

$$\tau_t = Ef + \sum_{j \geq 2}^{\infty} e_j x^j, \qquad \tau_t{}^r = \Phi f + \sum_{j \geq 2}^{\infty} \phi_j x^j, \qquad \tau^r = Pf + \sum_{j \geq 2}^{\infty} p_j x^j, \qquad (17)$$

where E, Φ, and P denote energy density, flux, and pressure at the horizon. The metric functions that solve Eqs. (10) and (12) are given by

$$C = r - c_{32} x^{3/2} + \mathcal{O}(x^2), \qquad (18)$$

$$h = -\frac{3}{2} \ln \frac{x}{\xi} + \mathcal{O}(\sqrt{x}), \qquad (19)$$

where the leading coefficient $c_{32} = 4r_g^{3/2} \sqrt{-\pi e_2/3}$, and e_2 denotes the $\mathcal{O}(x^2)$ coefficient of τ_t, see Eq. (17). According to Eq. (11), the dynamic behavior of the

horizon is governed by
$$r'_g = \pm c_{32}\xi^{3/2}/r_g. \qquad (20)$$
where the lower (upper) sign corresponds to evaporation (accretion). For $k = 1$, only one solution is self-consistent. It describes PBHs at the instant of their formation[19] and is uniquely defined by the energy density $E := -T^t_t$ and pressure $P := T^r_r$ at the horizon, which take on their maximal possible values $E = -P = 1/(8\pi r_g^2)$. Hence, we refer to it as extreme-valued $k = 1$ solution.

4. Modified Einstein equations in spherical symmetry

The modified Einstein equations are obtained through variation of the gravitational action[11] [cf. Eqs. (1)–(2)], and can be represented schematically as
$$G_{\mu\nu} + \lambda \mathcal{E}_{\mu\nu} = 8\pi T_{\mu\nu}, \qquad (21)$$
where the terms $\mathcal{E}_{\mu\nu}$ denote deviations from the Einstein equations that result from the variation of $\mathcal{F}(g^{\mu\nu}, R_{\mu\nu\rho\sigma})$ [cf. Eq. (2)]. The explicit form of the Einstein equations in MTG then immediately follows from Eqs. (10)–(12):
$$fr^{-2}e^{2h}\partial_r C + \lambda \mathcal{E}_{tt} = 8\pi T_{tt}, \qquad (22)$$
$$r^{-2}\partial_t C + \lambda \mathcal{E}_t^{\ r} = 8\pi T_t^{\ r}, \qquad (23)$$
$$2f^2 r^{-1}\partial_r h - fr^{-2}\partial_r C + \lambda \mathcal{E}^{rr} = 8\pi T^{rr}. \qquad (24)$$

The metric functions that solve the modified Einstein equations Eq. (21) are
$$C_\lambda =: \bar{C}(t, r) + \lambda \Sigma(t, r), \qquad (25)$$
$$h_\lambda =: \bar{h}(t, r) + \lambda \Omega(t, r), \qquad (26)$$
where Σ and Ω denote the perturbative corrections, and the bar labels the semiclassical metric functions introduced in Sec. 3. Schematically, substitution of Eqs. (25)–(26) into the modified Einstein equations Eq. (21) yields an equation of the form
$$\bar{G}_{\mu\nu} + \lambda \tilde{G}_{\mu\nu} + \lambda \bar{\mathcal{E}}_{\mu\nu} = 8\pi \left(\bar{T}_{\mu\nu} + \lambda \tilde{T}_{\mu\nu} \right), \qquad (27)$$
where objects labeled by the tilde correspond to first-order terms in the expansion of λ that involve the perturbative corrections Σ and Ω, and terms of order $\mathcal{O}(\lambda^2)$ and higher have been omitted. The modified gravity contributions can be expressed solely in terms of unperturbed quantities, i.e. $\bar{\mathcal{E}}_{\mu\nu} \equiv \mathcal{E}_{\mu\nu}(\bar{C}, \bar{h})$. For a detailed account of the perturbative analysis, the reader is referred to Ref. 21.

5. Constraints for modified gravity theories

Any arbitrary MTG must satisfy several constraints[21] to be compatible with the spherically symmetric PBH solutions of semiclassical gravity described in Sec. 3. The constraints are twofold: first, the terms $\bar{\mathcal{E}}_{\mu\nu}$ that encode deviations from the semiclassical theory must follow a particular structure when expanded in terms of the coordinate distance $x := r - r_g$ from the apparent horizon. Second, several identities between their coefficients must hold.

To be compatible with PBH solutions of the $k = 0$ type (Sec. 3.1), the MTG terms $\bar{\mathcal{E}}_{\mu\nu}$ must conform to the expansion structures prescribed by

$$\bar{\mathcal{E}}_{tt} = \frac{\text{æ}_{\bar{1}}}{x} + \frac{\text{æ}_{\overline{12}}}{\sqrt{x}} + \text{æ}_0 + \sum_{j \geq \frac{1}{2}}^{\infty} \text{æ}_j x^j, \tag{28}$$

$$\bar{\mathcal{E}}_t{}^r = \frac{\text{œ}_{\overline{12}}}{\sqrt{x}} + \text{œ}_0 + \sum_{j \geq \frac{1}{2}}^{\infty} \text{œ}_j x^j, \tag{29}$$

$$\bar{\mathcal{E}}^{rr} = \text{ø}_0 + \sum_{j \geq \frac{1}{2}}^{\infty} \text{ø}_j x^j, \tag{30}$$

and the three identities

$$\text{æ}_{\bar{1}} = \sqrt{\bar{\xi}} \text{œ}_{\overline{12}} = \bar{\xi} \text{ø}_0, \qquad \text{æ}_{\overline{12}} = 2\sqrt{\bar{\xi}} \text{œ}_0 - \bar{\xi} \text{ø}_{12}, \tag{31}$$

between their lowest-order coefficients must be satisfied.

Similarly, to be compatible with the extreme-valued $k = 1$ solution (Sec. 3.2), the MTG terms must follow the expansion structures prescribed by

$$\bar{\mathcal{E}}_{tt} = \frac{\text{æ}_{\overline{32}}}{x^{3/2}} + \frac{\text{æ}_{\bar{1}}}{x} + \frac{\text{æ}_{\overline{12}}}{\sqrt{x}} + \text{æ}_0 + \sum_{j \geq \frac{1}{2}}^{\infty} \text{æ}_j x^j, \tag{32}$$

$$\bar{\mathcal{E}}_t{}^r = \text{œ}_0 + \sum_{j \geq \frac{1}{2}}^{\infty} \text{œ}_j x^j, \tag{33}$$

$$\bar{\mathcal{E}}^{rr} = \sum_{j \geq \frac{3}{2}}^{\infty} \text{ø}_j x^j, \tag{34}$$

and the two identities

$$\text{æ}_{\overline{32}} = 2\bar{\xi}^{3/2} \text{œ}_0 - \bar{\xi}^3 \text{ø}_{32}, \qquad \text{æ}_{\bar{1}} = 2\bar{\xi}^{3/2} \left(h_{12} \text{œ}_0 + \text{œ}_{12} \right) - \bar{\xi}^3 \left(2h_{12} \text{ø}_{32} + \text{ø}_2 \right). \tag{35}$$

between their lowest-order coefficients must hold.

For both types of solutions $k \in \{0, 1\}$, no additional constraints can be obtained through the consideration of higher-order terms ($\geq \mathcal{O}(x^{3/2})$) in the metric functions as in this case the modified Einstein equations contain too many additional independent variables. A comprehensive analysis of this result and a detailed derivation of Eqs. (28)–(35) is provided in Ref. 21.

If a particular MTG does not satisfy the constraints for one or both classes of semiclassical PBHs, the theory in question may still possess solutions corresponding to PBHs, but their underlying mathematical description must then differ from that of Sec. 3.1 and/or Sec. 3.2, which may or may not lead to observable differences based on properties of the associated near-horizon geometry.

So far, the constraints imposed by Eqs. (28)–(35) have been investigated in MTG with up to fourth-order derivatives in the metric.[22] In particular, it has been demonstrated that

(1) generic $\mathfrak{f}(R)$ theories, where $\mathcal{L}_\mathrm{g} = \mathfrak{f}(R)$, $\mathfrak{f}(R) =: R + \lambda \mathcal{F}(R)$ [cf. Eq. (2)], $\mathcal{F}(R) = \beta R^q$, and $\beta, q \in \mathbb{R}$
(2) generic MTG with up to fourth-order derivatives in the metric, where the particular choice of $\mathcal{L}_\mathrm{g} = (-\alpha R_{\mu\nu} R^{\mu\nu} + \beta R^2 + \gamma \kappa^{-2} R)$ in the action is motivated by the desire to avoid ghosts (massive states of negative norm that result in an apparent lack of unitarity),[23,24] and $\kappa^2 = 32\pi$

satisfy all of the constrains identically (i.e. without requiring any additional conditions) and are thus compatible with the existence of spherically symmetric semiclassical PBHs. The procedure for obtaining explicit expressions for the MTG terms $\bar{\mathcal{E}}_{\mu\nu}$ in terms of unperturbed quantities is outlined in Ref. 22, and explicit expressions for the relevant MTG coefficients of Eqs. (31) and (35) in these two theories are provided in the following linked Github repository.

6. Discussion

We have outlined a procedure to test the compatibility of arbitrary metric MTG with the PBH solutions of semiclassical gravity, which are characterized by the formation of a regular apparent horizon in finite time of a distant observer. We find that generic MTG with up to fourth-order derivatives in the metric identically satisfy all of the constraints for both classes of solutions, indicating that the semiclassical PBHs correspond to zeroth-order terms in perturbative solutions of these models. As a result, the observation of an apparent horizon by itself is insufficient to distinguish between the semiclassical theory and modifications including up to fourth-order derivatives in the metric. A detailed analysis of the response of the near-horizon geometry to perturbations is required, and may allow to identify potentially observable differences between PBHs of various theoretical frameworks.

Acknowledgments

I would like to thank Daniel Terno for useful discussions and helpful comments. This work was supported by an International Macquarie University Research Excellence Scholarship and a Sydney Quantum Academy Scholarship.

References

1. L. Barack, V. Cardoso, S. Nissanke, and T. P. Sotiriou (eds.), Class. Quantum Gravity **36**, 143001 (2019).
2. V. Cardoso and P. Pani, Living Rev. Relativ. **22**, 4 (2019).
3. C. P. Burgess, Living Rev. Relativ. **7**, 5 (2004).
4. J. F. Donoghue and B. R. Holstein, J. Phys. G: Nucl. Part. Phys. **42**, 103102 (2015).

5. LIGO Scientific Collaboration and Virgo Collaboration, Phys. Rev. Lett. **116**, 061102 (2016).
6. LIGO Scientific Collaboration and Virgo Collaboration, Astrophys. J. Lett. **882**, L24 (2019).
7. Event Horizon Telescope Collaboration, Phys. Rev. Lett. **125**, 141104 (2020).
8. E. Curiel, Nat. Astr. **3**, 27 (2019).
9. V. P. Frolov, J. High Energy Phys. **05**, 049 (2014).
10. M. Visser, Phys. Rev. D **90**, 127502 (2014).
11. T. Padmanabhan, Phys. Rev. D **84**, 124041 (2011).
12. C. W. Misner and D. H. Sharp, Phys. Rev. **136**, B571 (1964).
13. V. Faraoni, G. F. R. Ellis, J. T. Firouzjaee, A. Helou, and I. Musco, Phys. Rev. D **95**, 024008 (2017).
14. S. Murk and D. R. Terno, arXiv:2110.12761 (2021).
15. P. K. Dahal, S. Murk, and D. R. Terno, arXiv:2110.00722 (2021).
16. B.-L. B. Hu and E. Verdaguer, *Semiclassical and Stochastic Gravity: Quantum Field Effects on Curved Spacetime* (Cambridge University Press, 2020).
17. L. Parker and D. Toms, *Quantum Field Theory in Curved Spacetime* (Cambridge University Press, 2009).
18. D. R. Terno, Phys. Rev. D **101**, 124053 (2020).
19. S. Murk and D. R. Terno, Phys. Rev. D **103**, 064082 (2021).
20. V. Baccetti, R. B. Mann, S. Murk, and D. R. Terno, Phys. Rev. D **99**, 124014 (2019).
21. S. Murk and D. R. Terno, Phys. Rev. D **104**, 064048 (2021).
22. S. Murk, arXiv:2110.14973 (2021).
23. K. S. Stelle, Gen. Relativ. Gravit. **9**, 353 (1978).
24. T. P. Sotiriou and V. Faraoni, Rev. Mod. Phys. **82**, 451 (2010).

Penrose suggestion as to pre-Planck-era black holes showing up in present universe data sets discussed, with a possible candidate as to GW radiation which may provide initial CMBR data

A. W. Beckwith

Physics Department, College of Physics, Chongqing University,
City, State ZIP/Zone, People's Republic of China
E-mail: rwill9955b@gmail.com, abeckwith@uh.edu

What we are doing is three-fold. First, we examine the gist of the Penrose suggestion as to signals from a prior universe showing up in the CMBR. That is, this shows up as data in the CMBR. Second, we give a suggestion as to how super massive black holes could be broken up s of a prior universe cycle by pre-big-bang conditions, with say millions of pre-Planck black holes coming up out of a breakup of prior universe black holes. Three, we utilize a discussion as to Bose–Einstein condensates set as gravitons as to composing the early universe black holes. The BEC formulation gives a number N of gravitons, linked to entropy, per black hole, which could lead to contributions to the alleged CMBR perturbations, which were identified by Penrose et al.

Keywords: Minimum scale factor, Cosmological constant, Space-time bubble, Penrose singularity, Prior universe black holes.

1. First, What Does Penrose Suggest About the CMBR Data Set and Preuniverse Massive Black Holes?

The abstract has a clue, as part of Ref. 1 states as to what we want to explain in the CMBR, i.e., circular rings in the CMBR "data."

In Ref. 1 there is a well crafted suggestion by Gurzadyan and Penrose as to an initial quote:

> The significance of individual low-variance circles in the true data has been disputed; yet a recent independent analysis has confirmed CCC's expectation that CMB circles have a non-Gaussian temperature distribution. Here we examine concentric sets of low-variance circular rings in the WMAP data, finding a highly nonisotropic distribution.

Here is the nuts and bolts as to what Penrose cosmology is about Ref. 2.

1.1. *There is initial inflationary expansion of the universe, but the caveat is that matter–energy is sucked up in super-massive black holes*

That is, rather than have a purported infinite expansion, and we see the following dynamic. We connect a countable sequence of open Friedmann–Lemaître–Robertson–Walker metric (FLRW) spacetimes, each representing a big bang followed by an infinite future expansion. Penrose noticed that the past conformal boundary of one copy of FLRW spacetime can be "attached" to the future conformal boundary of another, after an appropriate conformal rescaling. result g_{ab} reset in a conformal reset with matter from black holes collected and reset to a new value of g_{ab} at the start of cosmological expansion with matter–energy from black holes being recycled conformally to a new expansion cycle.[2]

1.2. *Next, let us view the Penrose suggestion as to black holes from a prior universe*

In order to see this, consider a suggestion as to black holes, being the template for a start to the present universe,[2] and also Ref. 3 which has the Penrose suggestion of an imprint of a prior universe black holes having an effect upon the CMBR spectrum. The CMBR spectrum is a real datum, but the worth of getting this information would be in terms of having what was said in Ref. 3 as to the "ghost" of prior universe black hole radiation. To get a glimpse of where this is going the author invites readers to look at Ref. 4 as to the cosmic maelstrom such "signals" would have to pass through.

> Figure 1 shows a conformal diagram representing the effect of a highly energetic event occurring at the space-time point H. In CCC, H is taken to be a Hawking point, where virtually the entire Hawking radiation of a previous-aeon supermassive black hole is concentrated at H by the conformal compression of the hole's radiating future. The horizontal line at the bottom stands for the crossover surface dividing the previous cosmic aeon from our own and describes our conformally stretched big bang. In conventional inflationary cosmology, X would represent the graceful exit turn-off of inflation. In each case, the future light cone of H represents the outer causal boundary of physical effects initiated at H, and such effects can reach D only within the roughly 0.08 radian spread indicated at the top of the diagram.[3]

2. What Can We Expect from the Transition from a Prior Universe to the Planckian Regime of Micro Black Holes? A Transition from Initially Gigantic Black Holes to Micro Black Holes

2.1. *In a word, we would likely have in the prior universe a massive black hole, which would be broken up into millions (billions?) of Planck-sized black holes*

In a word the GW radiation and thermal/photonic input would have to fight through a thicket of pairs of micro black holes which would be in binary configuration generating their OWN GW background.

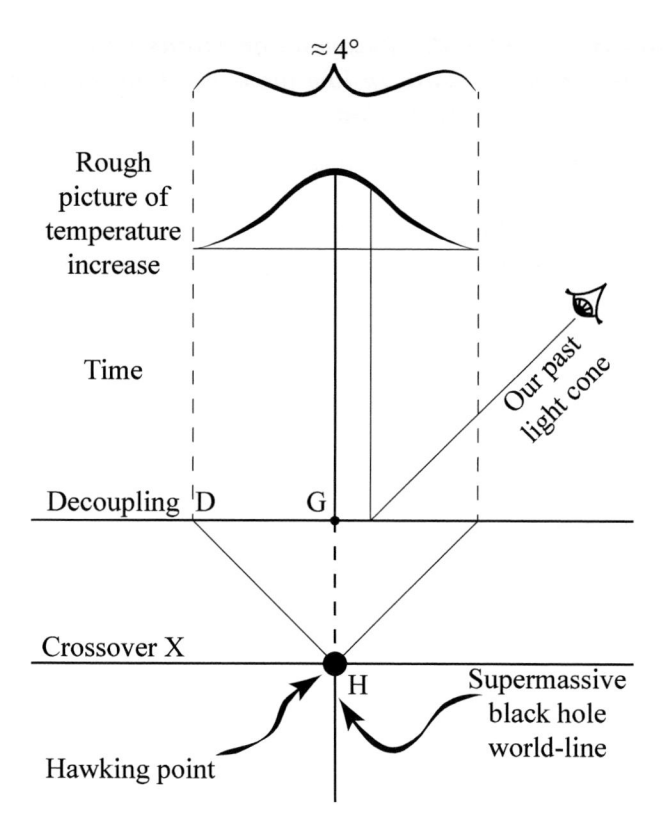

Fig. 1. Competing black hole radiation, and can we see this today in the CMBR?

We first will discuss this "binary black holes" signal background which the Planckian early universe stars would have to impinge upon, in order to come to our attention.

Now for the discussion of the millions (more than that) of micro-sized black hole pairs which would create a generalized GW signature.

To evaluate the above in terms of our model, we need to refer to a formula given in Ref. 4, 18, on page 16 of that document which reads as a change in power from rotating Planck-sized black holes separated say by a Planck length.

$$\dot{E} = GW - (\Delta \text{ in energy}) = \frac{32(M_1 M_2)^2 (M_1 + M_2)}{5R^2 M_{\text{Planck}}^5} \xrightarrow{M_1 = M_2 = M_{\text{Planck}}} \frac{64}{5 R_{\text{Planck}}^2}$$
$$\equiv (\Delta \text{ in power from rotating binary black holes}). \tag{1}$$

For M about the size of a Planck-sized black hole, it likely would fade out almost too quickly to be very measurable.

2.2. We also can consider the following gravitons as a Bose–Einstein condensate in low mass black holes, and its relevance to signal propagation

This is a way to get measurable GW signals from a black hole, which have a chance of being detected.

We will be looking at Ref. 5, specifically page 181, where we have the following scaling arguments to work through, if gravitons are Bose–Einstein condensates (BECs) for small black holes. The following are scaling value to consider, if we want BEC.

Why we consider BECs and Eq. (2)–Eq. (6), i.e., if there is a break up of massive black holes into say Planck mass-sized black holes, as or about the Planck era, very likely will not have a surviving signal which has a chance of being measurable in the CMBR data. That is, the discussion of Eq. (2)–Eq. (6) below uses the device of having BEC condensation in gravitons for masses up to about 10 grams or so, and in doing so a dodge as to getting entropy counts per black hole.

That is after the black hole masses, as given in Eq. (2)–Eq. (6) are likely built up by the consolidation of two mini black holes going through an inspiral collapse, as has been modeled in GW.

$$m \approx \frac{M_P}{\sqrt{N_{graviton}}} \tag{2}$$

$$M_{BH} \approx \sqrt{N_{graviton}} \cdot M_P \tag{3}$$

$$R_{BH} \approx \sqrt{N_{graviton}} \cdot l_P \tag{4}$$

$$S_{BH} \approx k_B N_{graviton} \tag{5}$$

$$T_{BH} \approx \frac{T_P}{\sqrt{N_{graviton}}}. \tag{6}$$

Here, the first term, m, is in the effective mass of a graviton. This is my take as to how to make all this commensurate as to special relativity.

$$m \approx \frac{m_g}{\sqrt{1 - \left(\frac{v_g}{c}\right)^2}} \approx \frac{M_P}{\sqrt{N_{graviton}}} \approx 10^{-10} \, g \tag{7}$$

$$\therefore N_{graviton} \approx 10^{10} \tag{8}$$

With this, if say one has a 1 gram black hole, about 10^5 times larger than a Planck mass, one would be having say an entropy generated this way of about 10^{10}, assuming Planck normalization.

3. So, Then What are the Number of Gravitons Emitted via a Spinning Planck-Sized Black Holes Component Binary in Terms of Gravitons?[6] What Does This Say About an Optimal Black-Hole Size as to Perhaps See Measurable GW/Graviton Generation Effects

Likely from the situation in Ref. 6 for items as of about a Planck length, and involving Planck-sized masses, we would see the following equation for a rotating rod, of mass M, and of velocity V, of its end, for graviton production.

$$N_g \approx \frac{32G}{45\hbar c} M_{\text{rod}}^2 \cdot \left(\frac{V_{\text{tip}}}{c}\right)^4 \propto 7.5 \times 10^{-8} M_{\text{rod}}^2 \Rightarrow N_g \geq 1 \text{ iff } M_{\text{rod}} \geq 4 \times 10^6 \text{ g}. \quad (9)$$

If we have an equivalent situation with respect to two black holes in a binary state, we would likely need to have approximately black holes of masses 10^5 g to 10^6 g—i.e., 10^{10} to 10^{11} times larger than Planck mass—to have a measurable GW/Graviton signal which would be commensurate with experimental data sets. If we had say 10^5 to 10^6 g black holes, then the value of gravitons released per second, from a BEC condensate of gravitons for a mini black hole would me many times larger than Eq. (8) above.

We don't know the exact values, but this leads to our next point, which is the stages of black holes, before the Planckian era, to at the point of time (and space) where 1 to 10^5 g black holes would be composed of gravitons by BEC condensation of gravitons, for a release in.

Considering this, what can we say about the regimes of black-hole masses, just before the Planckian era, during the Planckian era, and right after the Planckian era?

We are assuming the following. A moderately large number (10^6 or more) of super massive black holes which would be in the center of galaxies, and which would be broken up and recycled in the CCC cosmology regime, with masses dropping from about 10^{41} g, down to about 10^{-4} to 10^{-5} g, before recombination by Planck era recombination into a tier of black holes which would be at least 1 gram in mass, scaling up to 10^5 g in mass so as to allow for BEC generation of gravitons through entropy production as in Eq. (2)–Eq. (7) above.

In doing so, we purport to use the datum given in Ref. 6 that masses of say much lower than 10^5 to 10^6 g for black holes likely do not have much chance of producing gravitons which would be detectable in the present era. Indeed, a minimum mass of about 1 to 10 grams for a black hole would be needed for a Bose–Einstein condensation via gravitons for a "light, low-mass" black hole which would be able to by Eq. (2)–Eq. (6), Eq. (8), and Eq. (9) to have at least 10^{10} gravitons per second generated (entropy for a BEC black hole).

We then would to a round off approximation state this hierarchy of black-hole behavior and size to consider.

Table 1. Scaling of mass of black holes, and their purported number, If CCC cosmology (Penrose) assumed for GW radiation release (may affect the CMBR)

End of prior universe time frame	Super massive end-of-time black hole 10^{41} to 10^{44} g.	10^6 to 10^9 of black holes, usually from centers of galaxies
Planck era black hole formation assuming merging of micro black-hole pairs	Micro black holes 10^{-5} to 10^{-4} g (approximately the Planck mass value).	10^{40} to 10^{45} black holes, assuming not too much destruction of matter–energy from pre-Planck to Planck conditions
Post-Planck era black holes: Can use Eq. (2)–Eq. (6) to have 10^{10} gravitons/second released per black hole	Normal-sized black holes 10 g to 10^6 g	10^{20} to, at most, 10^{25} black holes with repeated black-hole pairs forming a single black hole multiple times.

4. Why We Would Have the Figures from Table 1 to Consider for Contributions to the CMBR and the Penrose Suggestion

The formula which is for luminosity from a black hole and in page 16 of Ref. 4 the text states that the two black holes emit GW with a wave frequency 2 times the rotation frequency of the orbit of the two black holes to each other.

If we assume that we are still using this approximation above,[4] we can see support for our choice of Planck length as the minimum separation distance between the two black holes via using Planck units normalized to 1 as yielding

$$R \text{ (separation)} \simeq r_g^{\text{eff}} = \frac{M_1 + M_2}{M_{\text{Planck}}^2} \xrightarrow{M_1 = M_2 = M_{\text{Planck}} = 1} 1 \equiv R_{\text{Planck}}. \qquad (10)$$

Going to Clifford Will,[7] we see on page 252 a loss or shrinkage of the period for the rotating black hole pair defined by P

$$\frac{\dot{P}}{P} = \frac{dP}{dt} \cdot \frac{1}{P} = -\frac{3}{2}\frac{\dot{E}}{E}. \qquad (11)$$

Whereas, with the mechanics version of P for a sphere to be defined by, where M is a mass of a star, and we assume a binary system with two masses of equal mass M, so that, if R is the separation between the two masses[8] on page 188 would be

$$P = R\sqrt{\frac{2\pi^2 R}{GM}} \xrightarrow{M_1 = M_2 = M_{\text{Planck}} = 1} R_{\text{Planck}} \sqrt{\frac{2\pi^2 R_{\text{Planck}}}{GM_{\text{Planck}}}}. \qquad (12)$$

For Planck-sized masses, this means that the period of the binary Planck mass black hole pair would be vanishingly small.

The frequency of rotation would be half that of the GW emitted by these two Planck mass black holes which would collapse into each other. Note that the frequency we have stated for this last step, is given in Eq. (13). That is, could we have the following quantization contribution to initial frequency?

Our final concluding point to this chapter is to review the physics of Fig. 1, and then to ask, can we ascertain the GW radiation of Planck era black hole stars in a binary configuration contributing to a buildup of generating frequency getting. If

$$\Delta E \Delta t \approx \hbar \Rightarrow \hbar \omega \Delta t \approx \hbar \omega \left(\frac{2}{3 a_{\min}}\right)^{\frac{1}{\gamma}} \Rightarrow \omega \approx \hbar^{-1} \left(\frac{2}{3 a_{\min}}\right)^{-\frac{1}{\gamma}}. \qquad (13)$$

We claim that if we take the energy as consistent with a change in value as given by Eq. (1) that this will lead to a frequency which may, if $a_{\min} \approx 10^{-25}$–$10^{-20}$ (range from 10^{-25} to 10^{-20}) lead to

$$\omega \approx \hbar^{-1} \left(\frac{3}{2}\right)^{\frac{1}{\gamma}} \cdot 10^{\frac{25}{\gamma}} \propto \left(\frac{3}{2}\right)^{\frac{1}{\gamma}} \cdot 10^{\frac{25}{\gamma}} \text{ Hz}. \qquad (14)$$

Whereas note that the frequency is, say dependent upon the choice of γ and that this could be very different from the Planck frequency

$$\omega_{\text{P}} \approx 1.885 \times 10^{43} \text{ Hz}. \qquad (15)$$

We have then that if one had a redshift, of $z \approx 10^{25}$, that this would mean a present value of frequency as of about 1 Hz, whereas we can consider what would be gained by looking at the contribution near the CMBR, $z \approx 1{,}100$ or so for the CMBR, whereas this would mean roughly that we would be looking in the regime of the CMBR:

$$\omega_{\text{signal from Planck to CMBR}} \propto \left(\frac{3}{2}\right)^{\frac{1}{\gamma}} 10^{\frac{25}{\gamma}} \times 10^{-3} \text{ Hz}. \qquad (16)$$

However, we have in doing this, that the duration of this frequency signal would be very minimal, due to the decay of the period, this would be going on for less than a nanosecond.

If so then we would need to refer to Eq. (2)–Eq. (6) and the value of

$$E_{\text{BEC–Graviton}} \approx \frac{k_B T_{\text{BH}}}{2} \approx \frac{k_B \times 10^{-5} \times T_{\text{P}}}{2}$$

$$\Rightarrow \omega_{\text{BEC–Graviton}} \approx 10^{38} \text{ Hz} \Rightarrow \omega_{\text{BEC–Graviton-to-CMBR}} \approx 10^{38} \text{ Hz}. \qquad (17)$$

Needless to state, that unlike the case of (12), one would likely have the duration of the signal last long enough as to imprint directly on the CMBR. That is, look at Ref. 8. Also, for this I refer to the Zeldovich 4 conference Abhay Ashtekar presentation.[9] Ashtekar referred to a removal of bogus data points in the CMBR (Figure 1[9]).

Now looking at what was discussed by Abhay Ashtekar in Zeldovich 4, on September 7, 2020.[9]

In our Fig. 2, we copy what was done by Ashtekar, in Zeldovich 4 as to what was part of anisotropic fits to the E and B polarization, as given is made easier, if there is a nonsingular start to the universe which I discussed in detail in Ref. 10, and that further polarization states which may be analyzed in detail could be ascertained in Ref. 11.

If one has a nonsingular start to the universe, modeled on a multiverse generalization of Penrose CCC cosmology[10] then the details of a break up of black holes

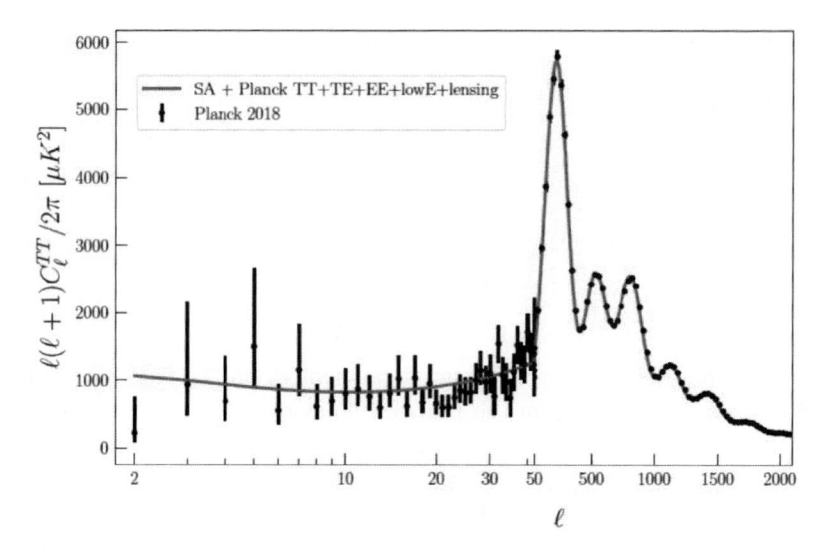

Fig. 2. Filling in the data points left out in terms of CMBR cosmic microwave background[9]

would not be so startling, i.e., these are the details from Ref. 10 as given by the following generalization of CCC cosmology.[10]

4.1. *Looking now at the modification of the Penrose CCC (cosmology)*

We now outline the generalization for Penrose CCC (Cosmology) just before inflation which we state we are extending Penrose's suggestion of cyclic universes, black hole evaporation, and the embedding structure our universe is contained within. This multiverse has black holes and may resolve what appears to be an impossible dichotomy. The text following is largely from Ref. 10 and has serious relevance to the final part of the conclusion. That there are N universes undergoing Penrose "infinite expansion"[2] contained in a mega universe structure. Furthermore, each of the N universes has black hole evaporation, with Hawking radiation from decaying black holes. If each of the N universes is defined by a partition function, called $\{\Theta_i\}_{i=N}^{i=1}$, then there exist an information ensemble of mixed minimum information correlated about 10^7–10^8 bits of information per partition function in the set $\{\Theta_i\}_{i=N}^{i=1}\big|_{\text{before}}$, so minimum information is conserved between a set of partition functions per universe.[12]

$$\{\Theta_i\}_{i=N}^{i=1}\big|_{\text{before}} \equiv \{\Theta_i\}_{i=N}^{i=1}\big|_{\text{after}} \tag{18}$$

However, there is nonuniqueness of information put into partition function $\{\Theta_i\}_{i=N}^{i=1}$. Also Hawking radiation from black holes is collated via a strange attractor collection in the mega universe structure to form a new inflationary regime for each of the N universes represented.

Our idea is to use what is known as CCC cosmology,[12] which can be thought of as the following. First. Have a big bang (initial expansion) for the universe which is represented by $\{\Theta_i\}_{i=N}^{i=1}$. Verification of this mega structure compression and expansion of information with stated nonuniqueness of information placed in each of the N universes favors ergodic mixing of initial values for each of N universes expanding from a singularity beginning. The n_f stated value, will be $S_{\text{entropy}} \approx n_f$.[12,13] How to tie in this energy expression, as in Eq. (16) will be to look at the formation of a nontrivial gravitational measure as a new big bang for each of the N universes as by $n(E_i)$. The density of states at energy E_i for partition function.[12,14]

$$\{\Theta_i\}_{i=1}^{i=N} \propto \left\{ \int_0^\infty dE_i \cdot n(E_i) \cdot e^{-E_i} \right\}_{i=1}^{i=N}. \tag{19}$$

Each E_i identified with Eq. (13) above, are with the iteration for N universes.[2,12] Then the following holds, by asserting the following claim to the universe, as a mixed state, with black holes playing a major part.

4.1.1. *Claim 1*

See the below representation[12] of mixing for assorted N partition function per CCC cycle.

$$\frac{1}{N} \sum_{j=1}^{N} \Theta_j \big|_{j \text{ before nucleation regime}} \xrightarrow{\text{vacuum-nucleation transfer}} \Theta_i \big|_{i \text{ fixed after nucleation regime}} \tag{20}$$

For N number of universes, with each $\Theta_j\big|_{j \text{ before nucleation regime}}$ for $j = 1$ to N being the partition function of each universe just before the blend into the right-hand side of Eq. (20) above for our present universe. Also, each independent universes as given by $\Theta_j\big|_{j \text{ before nucleation regime}}$ is constructed by the absorption of one to ten million black holes taking in energy.[2] Furthermore, the main point is done in Ref. 10 in terms of general ergodic mixing.[12]

4.1.2. *Claim 2*

$$\Theta_j\big|_{j \text{ before nucleation regime}} \approx \sum_{k=1}^{\max} \widetilde{\Theta}_k \bigg|_{\text{black holes } j\text{th universe}} \tag{21}$$

What is done in Claims 1 and 2[10] is to come up as to how a multi dimensional representation of black hole physics enables continual mixing of spacetime largely as a way to avoid the anthropic principle,[10] as to a preferred set of initial conditions.

5. Conclusion

If one has a nonsingular start of expansion of the universe and ergodic mixing of initial conditions of space-time from other universes, how does this relate to the breaking up of black holes from Table 1? In Ref. 10 in order to do away with the anthropic principle, the following references in terms of ergodic mixing of the partition function of the universe was utilized, as far as a multiverse. But there is one final piece. Assume that we have

$$\omega_{\text{Earth}} \leq 10^{-25} \omega_{\text{initial}}. \tag{22}$$

We will be of course assuming an equivalence between a graviton count and information,[16] and we can in future work compare this with the Rosen[3] value of energy for a mini universe of (from a Schrödinger equation) with ground state mass of $m = \sqrt{\pi} M_{\text{Planck}}$ and an energy of

$$E_{\hat{n}} = \frac{-Gm^5}{2\pi^2 \hbar^2 \hat{n}^2}. \tag{23}$$

Our preliminary supposition is that Eq. (23) could represent the initial energy of a pre-Planckian universe and that Eq. (24) would be thermally based energy dumped into the space-time bubble assumed in Ref. 10. That is,

$$E_{\text{universe}} = 10^{41} \times E_{\text{BEC-Graviton}} \approx 10^{41} \times \left(\frac{k_B T_{\text{BH}}}{2} \approx \frac{k_B \times 10^{-5} \times T_P}{2} \right) \tag{24}$$

is the thermal energy dumped in due to the use of cyclic conformal cosmology. Here we specify that initially it would have that the value of Eq. (24) would exactly counter balance the energy given in a negative form by Rosen as of Eq. (23).

Now use the following approximation of the universe, initially having the entropy of a black hole. That is, we are using Ng infinite quantum statistics,[18] while area denotes the surface area of the regime of space-time:

$$S_{\text{universe}} \propto S_{\text{BH}} \simeq \frac{A}{4 l_{\text{Planck}}^2} \approx \frac{9 n_Q}{4} \approx n_{\text{graviton}}. \tag{25}$$

This way of noting entropy and the signals of the prior universe black holes being generated secondarily is a surface area which is commensurate with the utilization of Eq. (2)–Eq. (6) for BEC condensation by gravitons for early-universe black holes. This is in tandem with the quantum fluctuations as seen in Figure 2 below. Also see Appendix A as well as the physics.[3,17,18]

The bubble nucleation, plus the details of cosmology leading to black holes from a prior universe showing up:

> For thirty years Oxford mathematician Roger Penrose has challenged one of the key planks of cosmology, namely the concept of inflation, now over 40 years old, according to which our universe expanded at an enormous rate immediately after the big bang. Instead, fifteen years ago, Penrose proposed a counterconcept of conformal cyclic cosmology by which inflation is moved to before the big bang and which introduces the idea of preceding eons. The concept has been disputed by most physicists, but Penrose and colleagues believe that new evidence has come to light which requires closer inspection

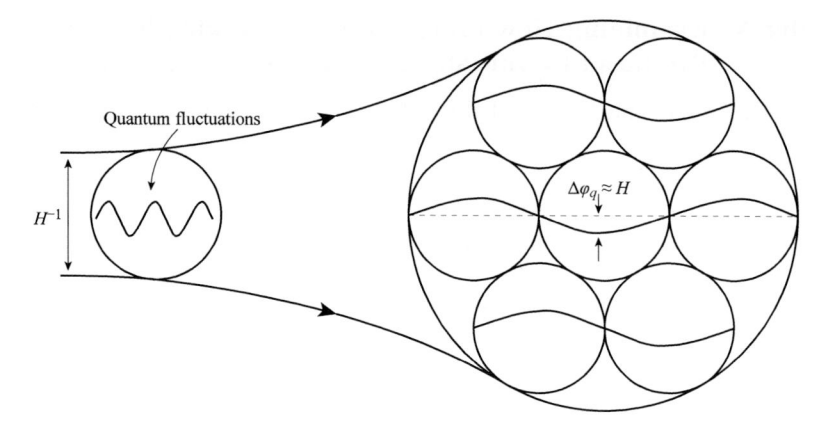

Fig. 3. We here are examining how the universe has self replicating regimes of spacetime[10,14]

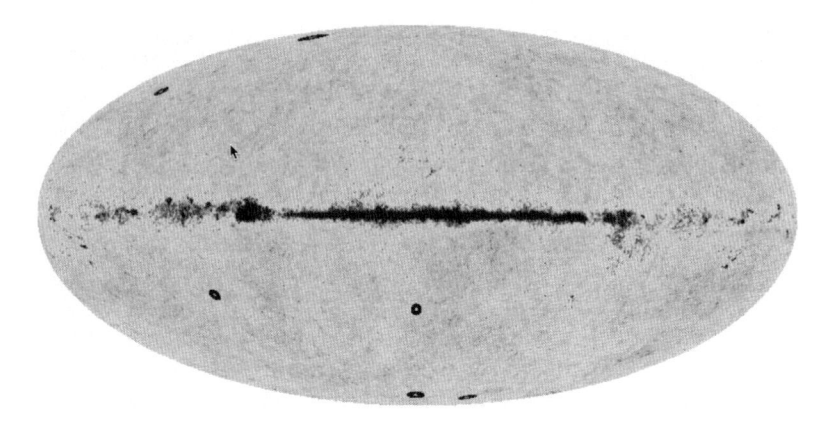

Fig. 4. Mollweide view showing how the CMBR spectrum has "rings" in it from black holes from a prior universe

Source: This from Ref. 19 with Ref. 3 having the data points used to construct this image in.

and argument—the research is published today in the Monthly Notices of the Royal Astronomical Society.[19]

Recent analysis of the cosmic microwave background (CMB) by Penrose, An, Meissner, and Nurowski has revealed, both in the Planck and WMAP satellite data (at 99.98% confidence), a powerful signal that had never been noticed previously, namely numerous circular spots ≈ 8 times the diameter of the full moon. The brightest six (Figure 1) are ≈ 30 times the average CMB temperature variations seen at precisely the same locations in the Planck and WMAP data. These spots were overlooked previously owing to a belief that the very early exponentially expanding *inflationary* phase of standard cosmology should have obliterated any such features.

Judicious application of Eq. (2)–(6) plus Table 1 above leads to this phenomenon.

Appendix A. Examining How Many Gravitons Might Be Produced by Initially Planck-Sized Black Holes

Alexander D. Dolgov and Damian Ejlli[4] inform us that a mass of a primordial black hole is

$$M_{\text{early black hole}} \approx 4 \times 10^{38} t \frac{\text{g}}{\text{s}}. \tag{26}$$

A Planck mass is of the value 10^{-5} g, i.e., almost, is then obtainable when

$$t_{\text{formation}} \approx 10^{-43}\,\text{s} \Rightarrow M_{\text{early black hole}} \approx 10^{-5}\text{g}. \tag{27}$$

Note that $t_{\text{formation}} \approx 10^{-43}$ sec $\geq 5.39 \times 10^{-44}$ s leads to almost a Planck mass, $2.176434(24) \times 10^{-5}$ g $= M_{\text{Planck}}$.

The mechanism of how Planck-sized black holes could generate GW comes from,[4] initial friction in the early universe environment, leading to coupling of early primordial binary black hole systems which in turn would collapse and form larger black holes—i.e., in fact the argument in Ref. 18 is stated on page 15 as follows.

> For PBH masses below a few grams dynamical friction would be an efficient mechanism of PBH cooling leading to frequent binary formation. Moreover, dynamical friction could result in the collapse of small PBHs into much larger black holes with the mass of the order of Mb (18). This process would be accompanied by a burst of GW emission

> What is called Mb in this situation is given in Ref. 4 on page 4.

> As we see in what follows, generation of gravitational waves would be especially efficient from such high density clusters of primordial black holes. Let us assume that the spectrum of perturbations is the flat Harrison–Zeldovich one and that a perturbation with some wavelength λ crossed horizon at moment t_{in}. The mass inside horizon at this moment was

$$Mb(t_{\text{in}}) = m_2 Pl t_{\text{in}}.\,(4) \tag{28}$$

> It is the mass of the would-be high density cluster of PBHs.

We then from here have the mechanism of black hole formation comes from binary pair formation of small black holes which collapse into a larger set of black holes. This chain of black-hole pair production and collapse would then lead to an accretion procedure along the lines of Eq. (25). Eventually these black hole clusters would form the mega black holes as seen in the center of spiral galaxies.

References

1. V. G. Gurzadyan and R. Penrose, On CCC-predicted concentric low-variance circles in the CMB sky, *Eur. Phys. J. Plus* **128**, Article 22 (2013). https://doi.org/10.1140/epjp/i2013-13022-4.

2. R. Penrose, Before the big bang: An outrageous new perspective and its implications for particle physics *Proc. EPAC 2006* (Edinburgh, Scotland, 2006) pp. 2759–2762, http://accelconf.web.cern.ch/accelconf/e06/PAPERS/THESPA01.PDF
3. D. An, K. A. Meissner, P. Nurowski, and R. Penrose, *Apparent Evidence for Hawking Points in the CMB Sky* (2020), https://arxiv.org/abs/1808.01740.
4. A. D. Dolgov and D. Ejlli, Relic gravitational waves from light primordial black holes, *Phys. Rev. D* **84**, Article 024028 (2011). https://doi.org/10.1103/PhysRevD.84.024028.
5. P.-H. Chavanis, Self gravitating Bose–Einstein condensates, in *Quantum Aspects of Black Holes*, ed. X. Calmet, Fundamental Theories of Physics, Vol. 178 (Springer Nature, Cham, Switzerland, 2012), pp. 151–194, https://doi.org/10.1007/978-3-319-10852-0_6.
6. G. L. Murphy, Gravitons from a spinning rod, *Aust. J. Phys.* **31**, 205–207 (1978), https://www.publish.csiro.au/ph/pdf/PH780205.
7. C. M. Will, *Theory and Experiment in Gravitational Wave Physics*, 2nd edn. (Cambridge University Press, New York, 2018).
8. S. Passaglia, W. Hu, and H. Motohashi, Primordial black holes and local non-Gaussianity in canonical inflation, *Phys. Rev. D* **99**, Article 043536 (2019), https://arxiv.org/abs/1812.08243.
9. A. Ashtekar, Quantum gravity in the sky? Alleviating tensions in the CMB using Planck scale physics, Zeldovich 4, (2020), http://www.icranet.org/images/stories/Meetings/ZM4/presentations/Ashtekar.pdf.
10. A. W. Beckwith, A Solution of the cosmological constant, using multiverse version of Penrose CCC cosmology, and enhanced quantization compared, *J. High Energy Phys. Gravit. Cosmol.* **7**, 559–571 (2021), https://doi.org/10.4236/jhepgc.2021.72032.
11. N. Poplawski, Cosmological constant from QCD vacuum and torsion, *Ann. Phys.* **523**, 291–295 (2011) https://doi.org/10.1002/andp.201000162.
12. H. Dye, On the ergodic mixing theorem, *Trans. Amer. Math. Soc.* **118**, 123–130 (1965), http://www.ams.org/journals/tran/1965-118-00/S0002-9947-1965-0174705-8/S0002-9947-1965-0174705-8.pdf.
13. P. D. Naselsky, D. Novikov, and I. Novikov, *The Physics of the Cosmic Microwave Background* (Cambridge University Press, Cambridge, UK, 2006).
14. V. Mukhanov, *Physical Foundations of Cosmology* (Cambridge University Press, New York, 2005), https://doi.org/10.1017/CBO9780511790553.
15. N. Rosen, Quantum mechanics of a miniuniverse, *Int J. Theor. Phys.* **32** (8), 1435–1440 (1993), https://doi.org/10.1007/BF00675204.
16. I. Haranas and I. Gkigkitzis, The mass of graviton and its relation to the number of information according to the holographic principle, *Int. Sch. Res. Notices* **2014**, Article 718251, https://doi.org/10.1155/2014/718251.
17. Y. J. Ng, Holographic foam, dark energy and infinite statistics, *Phys. Lett. B*, **657**, 10–14 (2007), https://doi.org/10.1016/j.physletb.2007.09.052.
18. R. Letzter, *Physicists Think They've Spotted the Ghosts of Black Holes from Another Universe*, Live Science (2018), https://www.livescience.com/63392-black-holes-from-past-universes.html.
19. R. Penrose, *Hawking Points in the Cosmic Microwave Background—A Challenge to the Concept of Inflation*, University of Oxford Mathematical Institute (2018). https://www.maths.ox.ac.uk/node/36137.

Summary of the parallel session BH3

Kamal Hajian

*Hanse-Wissenschaftskolleg Institute for Advanced Study, Lehmkuhlenbusch 4, 27733
Delmenhorst, Germany
E-mail: kamalhajian@ipm.ir*

Jutta Kunz

*Institute of Physics, University of Oldenburg, 26111 Oldenburg, Germany
E-mail: jutta.kunz@uni-oldenburg.de*

We summarize the talks presented at the BH3 session (Black Holes in Alternative Theories of Gravity) of the 16th Marcel Grossmann Meeting held online on July 5-10 2021.

Keywords: Gravity; Alternative theories; Black holes.

1. Introduction

Black holes have received tremendous interest in recent years, originating on the one hand from the discovery of gravitational waves, generated in the merger of stellar black holes, by the LIGO collaboration,[1] and on the other hand from the observation of the shadow of the supermassive black hole at the center of M87 by the EHT collaboration.[2] The analysis of observational data of black holes is typically based on the *Kerr hypothesis*, namely the assumption that rotating black holes are well described by the Kerr solution of General Relativity. Just like General Relativity itself, also the *Kerr hypothesis* is still consistent with all available data.

However, there are a number of reasons suggesting that General Relativity will be superseded by a new theory of gravity, which would reduce to General Relativity in a limit. From a theoretical side these reasons include the problem of quantization of gravity and the presence of singularities in solutions of General Relativity, while from an observational side the need for *Dark Matter* and *Dark Energy* in a cosmological context seem most provoking.

All these reasons have led to a large number of suggestions for alternative theories of gravity based on deep theoretical reasoning or simply phenomenological modelling, see e.g.,[3-6] While alternative theories of gravity should be consistent with observations in the weak gravity regime, thus in particular, with observations in the solar system, the strong gravity regime is so far much less constrained. In the strong gravity regime there exist certainly high precision data from pulsar observations (see, e.g.[7]), but the unknown equation of state of matter at extreme densities and pressures may lead to degeneracies with the unknown theory of gravity. Therefore black holes may present cleaner probes of the strong gravity regime.

In General Relativity black holes are remarkably simple objects in terms of the characterization of the space-times, as expressed by the *no-hair theorem* (see, e.g.[8]). Consequently, Kerr black holes are uniquely determined by their mass and their angular momentum, and all their higher multipole moments can be fully expressed by these two lowest moments. Moreover, when considering the fields of the Standard Model of Particle Physics, no astrophysical rotating black holes other than the *bald* Kerr black holes arise. Only microscopic black holes might carry fields of the Standard Model as hair (see, e.g.[9,10]). However, if one allows for a hypothetical complex massive scalar field or Proca field, then General Relativity allows for rotating Kerr black holes with scalar or Proca hair that might be of astrophysical relevance.[11,12]

Alternative theories of gravity typically introduce further degrees of freedom, often in the form of gravitational scalar or vector fields.[3–6] Prominent theories with additional scalar fields are Horndeski and beyond Horndeski theories,[13–16] while their counterparts with vector fields are generalized Proca and beyond generalized Proca theories.[17–20] But further degrees of freedom may also be present when the tensorial part of gravity is modified, yielding, for instance, de Rham-Gabadadze-Tolley massive gravity[21] and bigravity theories.[22,23] While General Relativity can be formulated in terms of curvature, torsion or non-metricity, as expressed by the *geometrical trinity of gravity*,[24] the associated generalizations of these formulations are no longer equivalent.

Up to now most work on black holes in alternative theories of gravity has been done in metric theories. Here the recent years have witnessed the emergence of new types of black holes due to newly discovered phenomena. These are, for instance, curvature-induced spontaneously scalarized black holes that arise in certain Horndeski models with higher curvature terms, when curvature is sufficiently strong to induce a tachyonic instability in the background of a Schwarzschild or Kerr black hole solution.[25–29] Similarly, spin-induced spontaneously scalarized black holes emerge in the presence of sufficient curvature and spin.[30–33] While these solutions satisfy circularity, this is not necessarily true for rotating black holes in beyond Horndeski theories, where also so-called disformed black holes with a non-circular geometry can arise (see, e.g.[34,35]).

A very important aspect of black holes in alternative theories of gravity is of course their stability and their response to perturbations. In particular, the study of quasi-normal modes (QNMs) is very valuable here, since these are also of relevance for the analysis of the ringdown phase of black hole mergers. Whereas the QNMs of the Schwarzschild and Kerr black holes are known since quite some time (see, e.g.[36–40]), the study of the QNMs of black holes in alternative theories of gravity is still in its infancy. While some work has been done for static black holes (see, e.g.[41]), very little is known so far even for the case of slow rotation only. The presence of additional degrees of freedom in alternative theories of gravity, yields a much more intricate spectrum, though, since various modes forbidden in General Relativity will be present in alternative theories of gravity.

In the following we will summarize the progress on black holes in alternative theories of gravity reported in our session of the 16th Marcel Grossmann Meeting.

2. Summary of the presentations

The 16th Marcel Grossmann Meeting was held online on July 5-10 2021. This was the first time that the meeting was held completely online, mainly because of the COVID-19 pandemic around the world. In the parallel session "Black Holes in Alternative Theories of Gravity" abbreviated as BH3, 16 physicists presented their recent research activities in two days, Tuesday 06 July 2021 09:30-12:30 and Thursday 08 July 2021 16:30-19:30 CEST. Here we recall the main points of the talks in BH3, and provide a summary of the presentations.

2.1. *Asymptotically flat hairy black holes in massive bigravity*

Presented by: Mikhail Volkov
In collaboration with: Romain Gervalle
Based on the Ref.[42].

The ghost-free theories of bigravity were first introduced by Hassan and Rosen in Ref.[43]. In these theories, there are two metrics denoted by $g_{\mu\nu}$ and $f_{\mu\nu}$. Both of the metrics have the usual Einstein-Hilbert action, and there is an interaction term between the two metrics. The metric $g_{\mu\nu}$ can be coupled to some matter, while $f_{\mu\nu}$ is not coupled to any matter. Analyzing the propagating degrees of freedom, there are two gravitons in such theories, one massive and one massless. These family of theories have been shown to be able to describe the accelerating expansion of the universe without a cosmological constant.

Any black hole as a vacuum solution in general relativity is a solution to bigravity theories by the choice of $g_{\mu\nu} = f_{\mu\nu}$. For example, the Schwarzschild metric is a solution to these theories if one chooses $g_{\mu\nu} = f_{\mu\nu}$ be equal to the Schwarzschild metric. However, this solution is not a stable solution in these theories. An interesting question arises here: if one relaxes the constraint $g_{\mu\nu} = f_{\mu\nu}$, is it possible to have spherically symmetric asymptotically flat solutions other than the Schwarzschild. The terminology "hairy black holes" has been used for such solutions in bigravity, and the "bald Schwarzschild" for the special case of $g_{\mu\nu} = f_{\mu\nu}$ to be Schwarzschild. It has been a debate to answer this question[44–46] whether there are hairy black holes in ghost-free bigravity or not. Romain Gervalle and Mikhail Volkov in Ref.[42] have tried to answer this interesting question by constructing spherically asymptotically flat black hole solutions numerically. They have found that there exist such black hole solutions (as pairs of solutions, one for $g_{\mu\nu}$ and one for $f_{\mu\nu}$) with the same horizon and surface gravity. Free parameters of the Schwarzschild hairy black holes are constrained by studying the stability of the solution. To this end, the $g_{\mu\nu}$ metric should be close to the Schwarzschild metric, the $f_{\mu\nu}$ metric should not be coupled to the matter, and the mass of the black hole should be between $0.2 M_\odot$ and $0.3 \times 10^6 M_\odot$.

2.2. An overview of quasinormal modes in modified and extended gravity

Presented by: Aurélien Barrau
In collaboration with: Flora Moulin and Killian Martineau
Based on the Ref.[47].

Quasi-normal modes (QNMs) are dissipative perturbations around a black hole background solution. They satisfy purely outgoing and ingoing boundary conditions at infinity and at the event horizon respectively. The oscillatory time dependence of these modes is described by

$$\psi \propto e^{i\omega t} = e^{i(\omega_R + i\omega_I)t}. \tag{1}$$

The frequency ω_R characterizes the oscillatory behavior of the mode, while for the $\omega_I > 0$ and $\omega_I < 0$ the mode grows or decays exponentially, respectively. The main question in the QNM analysis is to find the behavior of the complex function ω.

In this talk, Aurélien Barrau provided an overview on QNMs, and presented their results for perturbations around a spherically symmetric black hole in some alternative theories of gravity. Their analysis is based on Wentzel-Kramers-Brillouin (WKB) approximation method.[48–50] The theories under consideration have been chosen to be the massive gravity,[21,22,51,52] Modified Scalar-Tensor-Vector (STV) Gravity,[53] Horava-Lifshitz,[54–57] $\hbar$-correction (quantum correction),[58] and loop quantum gravity (based on the model presented in Ref.[59]). For each one of these choices, the diagrams of ω_R and ω_I for some suitable multipole number ℓ and overtone number n were illustrated and compared qualitatively.

2.3. Constraining modified gravity theories with physical black holes

Presented by: Sebastian Murk
In collaboration with: Daniel R. Terno
Based on the Ref.[60].

In this work, the authors emphasize that a physical black hole is a celestial object which has a smooth apparent horizon and trapped surface.[61] Requesting the smoothness of these surfaces constrains the gravitational models which govern the dynamics of such solutions. To be more accurate, the existence of semiclassical physical black holes in modified theories of gravity induces some necessary conditions.

In order to find such necessary conditions, Sebastian Murk as a PhD student and his colleague have focused on the spherically symmetric black hole solutions which are presented as expansions in the coordinate distance from the apparent horizon and do not require a General Relativity solution as the zeroth-order perturbative solution of the modified theory. The only condition which they impose is the regularity of apparent horizon for black hole solutions. They pick finiteness of T^μ_μ and $T^{\mu\nu}T_{\mu\nu}$ as the regularity condition on the trapped horizon. By perturbing the Einstein equation with a new term $G_{\mu\nu} + \lambda\epsilon_{\mu\nu} = 8\pi T_{\mu\nu}$ and a generic ansatz for a spherically symmetric black hole metric, the necessary conditions on the component of the $\epsilon_{\mu\nu}$ are investigated. In the end, the results are studied more for a special modified gravity, the Starobinsky model.[62]

2.4. Black holes, stationary clouds and magnetic fields

Presented by: Nuno Santos
In collaboration with: Carlos A.R. Herdeiro
Based on the Ref.[63].

Stationary bosonic clouds are stable configuration of scalar fields around a black hole resulting in a bound state. Suggested by many examples, in order to have such a bound state, two conditions are necessary: (1) the possibility for superradiance, (2) a confinement mechanism. The former is necessary to synchronize the bosonic cloud with the black hole rotation, and the latter is needed to make the configuration stable. Interestingly, stationary clouds are characterized by a discrete number of nodes in the radial direction, n, the orbital angular momentum, ℓ, and the azimuthal harmonic index m. In this regard, they resemble orbital configurations in a Hydrogen atom.[11,12,64,65]

In this presentation, the bosonic clouds are studied around a Reissner-Nordström black hole immersed in a magnetic field. These family of black hole solutions are called Reissner-Nordström-Melvin black holes.[66] They are solutions to Einstein-Maxwell theory, and their asymptotics resemble a magnetic Melvin universe. These black holes are stationary and axially symmetric. The presence of an external magnetic field provides both of the conditions for the stability of a bosonic cloud, i.e., the ergoregion and the confinement mechanism. The scalar field in this analysis has been considered to be complex, massless and minimally coupled to gravity. So, the theory is described by the action:

$$\mathcal{I} = \frac{1}{4\pi} \int d^4x \sqrt{-g} \Big[\frac{R}{4} - \frac{F^2}{4} - (\nabla^\mu \Psi^*)(\nabla_\mu \Psi)\Big]. \tag{2}$$

The bosonic clouds in this model, and on the Reissner-Nordström-Melvin solution are studied, and it is shown that for specific mass to charge ratios, there exist stable bosonic clouds.

2.5. Bardeen black hole from a self-dual radius in spacetime

Presented by: Michael Florian Wondrak
In collaboration with: Marcus Bleicher, Piero Nicolini, and Euro Spallucci
Based on the Ref.[67,68].

String T-duality is an equivalence between two string theories on spacetimes with at least one compactified extra dimension – provided that the compactification radii are inversely related to each other, i.e. $R_1 = R$ and $R_2 = \frac{(R^\star)^2}{R}$. The special case of $R = R^\star$ is called self-dual radius. Beginning from T-duality in bosonic string theory, Michael Florian Wondrak first gave an overview on how quantum field propagators are deformed.[69] The scalar propagator obtained via Schwinger's proper time formalism is read to be

$$G(k) = -\frac{\ell_0 K_1(\ell_0\sqrt{k^2+m^2})}{\sqrt{k^2+m^2}}. \tag{3}$$

In this relation, $K_\nu(x)$ is the Modified Bessel function of second kind, and ℓ_0 is the zero point length.[70] Studying the potential induced by this propagator, a spherically symmetric black hole solution was derived,

$$ds^2 = -f(r)dt^2 + \frac{dr^2}{f(r)} + r^2 d\Omega^2, \quad f(r) = 1 - \frac{2Mr^2}{(r^2+\ell_0^2)^{3/2}}. \tag{4}$$

This metric resembles the Bardeen black hole with a new interpretation of the UV cut-off in terms of the zero point length ℓ_0 instead of a magnetic monopole charge. Then, the thermodynamics of this black hole was studied and it was shown that at the end of evaporation process, the evaporation stops with a cold remnant instead of a final explosion. The remnants of these black holes were investigated regarding a possible fraction of dark matter. With a mass below $5 \times 10^{-8}\, M_\odot$, they comply with recent constraints on primordial black holes.[71] In the rest of the talk, observability of ℓ_0 was discussed: From the hydrogen energy spectrum, an upper bound of 4×10^{-19} meter was deduced.

2.6. *Asymptotically flat black hole solution in modified gravity*

Presented by: Surajit Kalita
In collaboration with: Banibrata Mukhopadhyay
Based on the Ref.[72].

$f(R)$ gravities are among alternative theories of gravity which have observational motivations to be studied. In these theories, one replaces the Ricci scalar R in the Lagrangian of General Relativity by a function of R, which is called $f(R)$.

$$\mathcal{I} = \frac{1}{16\pi}\int d^4x \sqrt{-g} f(R). \tag{5}$$

Although the equations of motion are higher-order in derivatives, they do not suffer from Ostrogradsky instability. In this presentation, Surajit Kalita presented the construction of spherically symmetric asymptotic flat black hole solutions to a subset of $f(R)$ theories. This subset is parametrized by a constant B in the relation $\frac{df}{dR} = 1 + \frac{B}{r}$. The metric ansatz is chosen to be $g_{\mu\nu} = \text{diag}(g_{tt}, g_{rr}, r^2, r^2\sin^2\theta)$. By inserting this ansatz in the equations of motion of $f(R)$ gravities, the unknown components (g_{tt}, g_{rr}) are found as an expansion if powers of B and $\frac{1}{r}$. Then, some properties of these solutions are analyzed, including marginally stable and bound orbits, and spherical accretion flows. Moreover, from these solutions it is deduced that the Birkhoff theorem can be violated in $f(R)$ gravities.

2.7. Infinitely degenerate exact Ricci-flat solutions in $f(R)$ gravity

Presented by: Semin Xavier
In collaboration with: Jose Mathew and S. Shankaranarayanan
Based on the Ref.[73].

In this talk, Semin Xavier presented their results for an infinite number of solutions to a subset of $f(R)$ gravities. The theory is described by the action

$$\mathcal{I} = \frac{1}{16\pi} \int d^4x \sqrt{-g} f(R), \qquad f(R) = (\alpha_0 + \alpha_1 R)^p, \tag{6}$$

for a real number $p > 1$, and constants α_0 and α_1. The metric ansatz is chosen to be spherically symmetric:

$$ds^2 = -A(r) e^{\delta(r)} dt^2 + \frac{dr^2}{A(r)} + r^2 (d\theta^2 + \sin^2\theta d\varphi^2). \tag{7}$$

Solving the equations of motion for the unknown functions $A(r)$ and $\delta(r)$ it is shown that there are an infinite number of possibility for these functions. As a result, it is discussed that in $f(r)$ gravities the Birkhoff theorem may be violated. In order to show this explicitly, two black hole solutions are constructed and studied.

2.8. Does the Penrose suggestion as to black holes from a prior universe showing up in today's universe have credibility? Examined from a singular, and nonsingular beginning of cosmological expansion

Presented by: Andrew Walcott Beckwith
Based on the Ref.[74].

Conformal Cyclic Cosmology (CCC) is a cosmological model in the framework of General Relativity, which is proposed by Roger Penrose.[75] In this model of cosmology, the universe iterates through infinite cycles, with the future timelike infinity of each previous iteration being identified with the past timelike infinity of the next universe. From the observational point of view, it has been suggested that the black holes in the previous universe can have implications in our universe, imprinted in the cosmic microwave background (CMB).[76,77]

In this talk, Andrew Walcott Beckwith discussed on the feasibility and credibility of the proposed methods for checking CCC using CMB data. He discussed the Penrose singularity theorem, and investigated the two cases of the CCC: cycling through singular or non-singular starting/ending points.

2.9. Analytical computation of quasi-normal modes of slowly-rotating black-holes in dCS gravity

Presented by: Manu Srivastava
In collaboration with: Yanbei Chen and S. Shankaranarayanan
Based on the Ref.[78].

Gravitational waves have provided interesting data about the inspiral and ring-down phases of black hole mergers. The waves in the ring-down phase are quasi-normal modes of the black hole merger. Therefore, by studying the data in the ring-down phase we can investigate the quasi-normal modes of the system.[36,37,40] However, quasi-normal mode frequencies depend on the gravitational theory. So, they provide a new tool to distinguish and examine alternative theories of gravity.

In this line of research, Manu Srivastava and his collaborators have focused on dynamical Chern-Simons gravity (dCS), which is described by the following action:[79]

$$\mathcal{I} = \frac{1}{16\pi} \int d^4x \sqrt{-g} R - \frac{\beta}{2} \int d^4x \sqrt{-g} (\nabla_\mu \vartheta \nabla^\mu \vartheta + V(\vartheta))$$
$$+ \frac{\alpha}{4} \int d^4x \sqrt{-g} \vartheta * RR + \mathcal{I}_{\text{matter}}, \quad (8)$$

in which ϑ is a pseudo-scalar field, and $*RR$ is the Pontryagin density

$$*RR \equiv \frac{1}{2} \epsilon^{cdef} R^a{}_{bef} R^b{}_{acd}. \quad (9)$$

where ϵ^{cdef} is the Levi-Civita tensor. The background is chosen to be a slowly rotating black hole introduced in Ref.[80]. The parameter of slow rotation is denoted by a. In the analysis, quasi-normal modes in the axial and polar sectors are studied up to linear order in a and quadratic order in α. The results of this study, along with the data from gravitational wave observations, can be used as a test for dCS gravity and to constrain coupling parameters.

2.10. Scalar perturbations of Kerr black-holes in hybrid metric-Palatini gravity

Presented by: João Luís Rosa
In collaboration with: José P. S. Lemos and Francisco S. N. Lobo
Based on the Ref.[81].

In General Relativity, the connection $\Gamma^\lambda_{\mu\nu}$ is assumed to be the metric connection, which is related to the metric by the relation

$$\Gamma^\lambda_{\mu\nu} = \frac{1}{2} g^{\lambda\sigma} (\partial_\mu g_{\sigma\nu} + \partial_\nu g_{\sigma\mu} - \partial_\sigma g_{\mu\nu}). \quad (10)$$

However, in the Palatini formulation of gravity (see a review in Ref.[82]), the connection $\hat{\Gamma}^\lambda_{\mu\nu}$ is considered independent of the metric. If we denote the Ricci scalar which is built upon $\hat{\Gamma}$ by $\mathcal{R}$, then the generalized hybrid metric-Palatini (GHMP) gravity[83–85] (see a review in Ref.[86]) is described by the following action:

$$\mathcal{I} = \frac{1}{16\pi} \int d^4x \sqrt{-g} f(R, \mathcal{R}) + \mathcal{I}_{\text{matter}}. \quad (11)$$

By the equations of motion, it turns out that the $\mathcal{R}$ is the Ricci scalar calculated for a metric which is conformal to $g_{\mu\nu}$. Motivated by this, João Luís Rosa and his collaborators have shown that for any vacuum solution to GR, there is a non-trivial function $f(R,\mathcal{R})$ such that it is a solution to the GHMP too.

In this context, the Kerr black hole can also be considered as a solution to the GHMP. The stability of the Kerr constrains the $f(R,\mathcal{R})$, and this is analyzed in this presentation by studying massive scalar perturbations around the Kerr black hole. In particular, it is shown that the Kerr black hole is stable for some specific $f(R,\mathcal{R})$ theories and masses for the scalar perturbation.

2.11. *Emergent magnetic monopoles in degenerate theory*

Presented by: Suvikranth Gera
In collaboration with: Sandipan Sengupta
Based on the Ref.[87].

Magnetic monopoles are theoretical counterparts for electric charges in electric-magnetic duality.[88,89] Although they have been studied extensively, there is not yet observational evidence for their existence in nature.

In this talk, Suvikranth Gera presented a non-invertible metric which resembles a magnetic monopole in the first-order formulation of gravity.[90–92] Unlike the usual metric formulations, the non-invertible metric is well-defined in the tetrad formulations. In the presentation, he first presented the metric explicitly, and then followed by the calculation the spin-connection and its field strength in the first-order formulation. The magnetic charge is calculated, and the topological origin and its observability is discussed at the end, and it is mentioned that this solution has not any curvature singularity. Moreover, for the observers moving on timelike geodesics, this emergent magnetic charge is not accessible observationally, although it affects the curvature of the space-time.

2.12. *Black holes in metric-affine gravity: properties and observational discriminators*

Presented by: Diego Rubiera-Garcia
Based on the Ref.[93].

A generic connection $\Gamma^\lambda_{\mu\nu}$ can be independent of the metric (see the review in Ref.[82]). Such a generic connection is called affine connection. Accordingly, it can be regarded as an independent field in the Lagrangian. These models of gravity are called metric-affine gravities. In a subset of such models, which is called "Ricci based gravities," the connection $\Gamma^\lambda_{\mu\nu}$ appears in the Lagrangian only through a symmetric Ricci tensor $R_{\mu\nu}$,

$$\mathcal{I} = \frac{1}{16\pi}\int d^4x \sqrt{-g}\mathcal{L}_G[g_{\mu\nu},R_{\mu\nu}(\Gamma)] + \mathcal{I}_{\text{matter}}[g_{\mu\nu},\psi_m]. \qquad (12)$$

In this talk, Diego Rubiera-Garcia presented an overview on recent results for the black holes in these models of gravity. It is shown that for spherically symmetric black holes, the curvature singularity can be smoothed out, and the geodesic completeness is restored. Moreover, for such solutions there exist "double critical curves." This feature makes the shadow of the black hole to appear as two or more bright rings.

2.13. *Holography for rotating black holes in $f(T)$ gravity*

Presented by: Masoud Ghezelbash
In collaboration with: Canisius Bernard
Based on the Ref.[94].

General relativity is based on the Riemann curvature, while the torsion and non-metricity are considered to vanish. However, it is equivalent to make gravitational theories solely based on torsion, or non-metricity. These equivalent formulations in the literature are referred as Teleparallel and Symmetric Teleparallel (or coincident) gravities respectively. Similar to the Ricci scalar R which is made from the Riemann tensor, one can appropriately define the torsion scalar T, or the non-metricity scalar Q. According to the equivalence alluded to above, one can have analogous theories for $f(R)$, namely $f(T)$ or $f(Q)$.

It is useful to study gravitational features in GR, in the Teleparallel gravity or Symmetric Teleparallel gravity. In this talk, Masoud Ghezelbash has focused on the Kerr/CFT correspondence in $f(T)$ gravities. Kerr/CFT is a correspondence between the near horizon region of extremal black holes (originally Kerr black hole[95]) with a (chiral) two dimensional CFT. In this correspondence, the entropy of the black hole is calculated via the Cardy-formula for the entropy in a CFT:[96,97]

$$S = \frac{\pi^2}{3}(c_L T_L + c_R T_R), \qquad (13)$$

in which the c's are the central charge of the left and right sectors, and the T's are Frolov-Thorne temperatures.[98] The result of such analyses shows that the entropy is proportional to the angular momentum associated with the axial symmetry which eventually enhances to the Virasoro sectors in the CFT (a review on Kerr/CFT and its extensions can be found in Ref.[99]). Besides, there are many works attempting to realize black hole microstates from the CFT using the Kerr/CFT correspondence (see e.g.[100–108]).

In this study, the model of gravity has been chosen to be

$$\mathcal{I} = \frac{1}{16\pi} \int d^4x \sqrt{-g} \left(f(T) - 2\Lambda - F^2\right), \qquad (14)$$

in which Λ is the cosmological constant, and F^2-term is the Maxwell theory. A rotating charged black hole as a solution to this theory (introduced in Ref.[109]) is chosen to be studied, and the wave equation for a massless scalar field is approximated in the near horizon geometry of this black hole. Instead of a chiral Virasoro, a full Virasoro algebra is reported in this near horizon, and the Cardy formula (13) is used to reproduce the black hole entropy.

2.14. Universe in a black hole with spin and torsion

Presented by: Nikodem Poplawski
Based on the Ref.[110].

The Einstein-Cartan theory (EC) of gravity[111–115] is the simplest theory with torsion and curvature. In this theory, the Lagrangian is the same as the Einstein gravity

$$\mathcal{I} = \frac{1}{2\kappa} \int d^4x \sqrt{-g}(R + \mathcal{L}_{\text{matter}}), \tag{15}$$

but in addition to the metric, the torsion is considered as a dynamical field. In this talk, Nikodem Poplawski studies the collapse of spherically symmetric fermionic matter to form a black hole in EC. He explains that if a fermionic field is considered as a perfect fluid with energy density ϵ and pressure p as the matter in this theory, the effect of the dynamics of torsion can be absorbed in the energy-momentum tensor[116] by

$$T_{\mu\nu} = \epsilon u_\mu u_\nu - p(g_{\mu\nu} - u_\mu u_\nu) \quad \rightarrow \quad \tilde{T}_{\mu\nu} = \tilde{\epsilon} u_\mu u_\nu - \tilde{p}(g_{\mu\nu} - u_\mu u_\nu), \tag{16}$$

in which

$$\tilde{\epsilon} = \epsilon - \alpha n_f^2, \qquad \tilde{p} = p - \alpha n_f^2. \tag{17}$$

In this relation, u_μ is the four-velocity, n_f is the number density of fermions, and $\alpha = \frac{\kappa}{32}$. Using $\tilde{T}_{\mu\nu}$, the equation of motion can be written as the usual Einstein equation:

$$G_{\mu\nu} = \kappa \tilde{T}_{\mu\nu}. \tag{18}$$

In this setup, the collapse is studied by the Tolman ansatz[117] for the metric:

$$ds^2 = e^{\nu(\tau,R)}d\tau^2 - e^{\lambda(\tau,R)}dR^2 - e^{\mu(\tau,R)}(d\theta^2 + \sin^2\theta d\varphi^2), \tag{19}$$

and solved for the unknown functions (ν, μ, λ). The results show that in this collapse, the singularity is prevented by the effects of the torsion. The geometry of the universe on the other side of the horizon is calculated, and it is shown that the geometry is an oscillating FLRW metric and it describes a closed universe. It is also calculated that due to the pair particle production, the frequency of the oscillation is reduced in time.

2.15. Absorption by deformed black holes

Presented by: Renan B. Magalhães
In collaboration with: Luiz C.S. Leite and Luís C.B. Crispino
Based on the Ref.[118].

The usual way to study alternative theories of gravity is to change the Lagrangian or the dynamical fields. Then, the equations of motion follow, and one can study the solutions to the new equations. However, in Ref.[119], Johannsen and

Psaltis introduced a parametric deviation approach, which is the reverse of the procedure mentioned above. They deform black holes by some parameters such that the black holes remain smooth, free of pathology, and have some suitable properties. Then, the equations of motion which could have such solutions are investigated. Following this method, Konoplya and Zhidenko in Ref.[120] have deformed the Kerr black hole by some parameters, while keeping its suitable features intact.

In this talk, Renan B. Magalhães presented the analysis of the absorption cross section of a massless scalar field for the static Konoplya-Zhidenko black hole. The metric of this black hole is similar to the Schwarzschild black hole with a deformed mass:

$$ds^2 = -fdt^2 + \frac{dr^2}{f} + r^2 d\Omega^2, \qquad f = 1 - \frac{2M}{r}, \qquad M \to M + \frac{1}{2}\sum_i \frac{\eta_i}{r^i}, \qquad (20)$$

with the special choice of $\eta_i = \delta_{i2}$. So, the f is chosen to be $f = 1 - \frac{2M}{r} + \frac{\eta}{r^3}$ for some parameter η. In order to have a horizon, $\eta_{\min} < \eta < 0$ in which $\eta_{\min} = \frac{-32}{27M^3}$. On this specific background, Renan B. Magalhães and his collaborators have studied the wave equation for a scalar field $\Box\psi = 0$. He presented the result of the radial potential for different spherical harmonic modes, illustrating them from numerical calculations. Moreover, the absorption cross sections are derived numerically.

2.16. *Shadow of a charged black hole surrounded by an anisotropic matter field*

Presented by: Javier Badía
In collaboration with: Ernesto F. Eiroa
Based on the Ref.[121].

Observation of the shadow of a supermassive black hole at the center of galaxy M87 has been one of the main progresses in black hole physics in recent years.[122] In parallel with this observation, theoretical studies of black hole shadows have been one of the active lines of research (see Ref.[123] for a review). Especially, the presence of matter fields surrounding black holes, and its effect on their shadows has been investigated (see e.g.[124–127]).

In this talk, Javier Badía presents the results of the calculation of shadows for rotating charged black holes surrounded by an anisotropic matter field.[128,129] In the spherical coordinates (t, r, θ, φ) the anisotropic matter is considered to be a perfect fluid which is described by the energy-momentum tensor

$$T_\mu^\nu = \text{diag}(-\rho, p_1, p_2, p_2), \qquad p_1 = -\rho, \qquad p_2 = \text{w}\rho. \qquad (21)$$

The rotating charged black hole surrounded by this matter is derived by the Newman-Janis algorithm to the following spherically symmetric spacetime:

$$ds^2 = -f(r)dt^2 + \frac{dr^2}{f(r)} + r^2 d\Omega^2, \qquad f(r) = 1 - \frac{2m(r)}{r}, \qquad m(r) = M - \frac{Q^2}{2r} + \frac{K}{2r^{2\text{w}-1}}. \qquad (22)$$

The M, Q, and K are integration constants, and w is restricted to be $\frac{1}{2} < w < 1$ by physical energy conditions. The resulting metric by the Newman-Janis algorithm is the Kerr metric in which $M \to m(r)$, i.e.

$$ds^2 = -(1-f)dt^2 + \frac{\rho^2}{\Delta}dr^2 + \rho^2 d\theta^2 - 2fa\sin^2\theta\, dtd\varphi$$
$$+ \left(r^2 + a^2 + fa^2\sin^2\theta\right)\sin^2\theta\, d\varphi^2,$$
$$\rho^2 = r^2 + a^2\cos^2\theta, \quad \Delta = r^2 - 2m(r)r + a^2, \quad f = \frac{2m(r)r}{\rho^2}, \quad (23)$$

and $m(r) = M - \frac{Q^2}{2r} + \frac{K}{2r^{2w-1}}$.

On this background, the Hamilton-Jacobi equation for the null geodesics is separable, and reduces to ordinary differential equations with radial derivatives. The result of the shadow calculations for an asymptotic observer on the equator is presented by illustrations. Moreover, three observables which characterize the shadows, named as the area, oblateness, and centroid of the shadows are discussed.[121,130]

Acknowledgments

We would like to thank the organizers of MG16 for making this interesting meeting with numerous inspiring talks and discussions possible in spite of the pandemic, and we would like to thank the speakers of our session for their notable contributions and for sharing with us their latest results. K.H. thanks also the administration of Hanse-Wissenschaftskolleg (Institute for Advanced Study) for the extension of his fellowship. J.K. gratefully acknowledges support by the DFG Research Training Group 1620 *Models of Gravity* and the COST Actions CA15117 *CANTATA* and CA16104 *GWverse*.

References

1. B. P. Abbott *et al.*, Observation of Gravitational Waves from a Binary Black Hole Merger, *Phys. Rev. Lett.* **116**, p. 061102 (2016).
2. K. Akiyama *et al.*, First M87 Event Horizon Telescope Results. I. The Shadow of the Supermassive Black Hole, *Astrophys. J.* **875**, p. L1 (2019).
3. C. M. Will, The Confrontation between general relativity and experiment, *Living Rev. Rel.* **9**, p. 3 (2006).
4. V. Faraoni and S. Capozziello, *Beyond Einstein Gravity: A Survey of Gravitational Theories for Cosmology and Astrophysics* (Springer, Dordrecht, 2011).
5. E. Berti *et al.*, Testing General Relativity with Present and Future Astrophysical Observations, *Class. Quant. Grav.* **32**, p. 243001 (2015).
6. E. N. Saridakis *et al.*, Modified Gravity and Cosmology: An Update by the CANTATA Network (5 2021).
7. L. Shao *et al.*, Testing Gravity with Pulsars in the SKA Era, *PoS* **AASKA14**, p. 042 (2015).
8. P. T. Chrusciel, J. Lopes Costa and M. Heusler, Stationary Black Holes: Uniqueness and Beyond, *Living Rev. Rel.* **15**, p. 7 (2012).

9. M. S. Volkov and D. V. Gal'tsov, Gravitating nonAbelian solitons and black holes with Yang-Mills fields, *Phys. Rept.* **319**, 1 (1999).
10. B. Kleihaus, J. Kunz and F. Navarro-Lerida, Rotating black holes with non-Abelian hair, *Class. Quant. Grav.* **33**, p. 234002 (2016).
11. C. A. R. Herdeiro and E. Radu, Kerr black holes with scalar hair, *Phys. Rev. Lett.* **112**, p. 221101 (2014).
12. C. Herdeiro, E. Radu and H. Rúnarsson, Kerr black holes with Proca hair, *Class. Quant. Grav.* **33**, p. 154001 (2016).
13. G. W. Horndeski, Second-order scalar-tensor field equations in a four-dimensional space, *Int. J. Theor. Phys.* **10**, 363 (1974).
14. C. Charmousis, E. J. Copeland, A. Padilla and P. M. Saffin, General second order scalar-tensor theory, self tuning, and the Fab Four, *Phys. Rev. Lett.* **108**, p. 051101 (2012).
15. T. Kobayashi, M. Yamaguchi and J. Yokoyama, Generalized G-inflation: Inflation with the most general second-order field equations, *Prog. Theor. Phys.* **126**, 511 (2011).
16. J. Gleyzes, D. Langlois, F. Piazza and F. Vernizzi, Healthy theories beyond Horndeski, *Phys. Rev. Lett.* **114**, p. 211101 (2015).
17. G. Tasinato, Cosmic Acceleration from Abelian Symmetry Breaking, *JHEP* **04**, p. 067 (2014).
18. L. Heisenberg, Generalization of the Proca Action, *JCAP* **05**, p. 015 (2014).
19. G.-P. Nicosia, J. Levi Said and V. Gakis, Generalised Proca theories in teleparallel gravity, *Eur. Phys. J. Plus* **136**, p. 191 (2021).
20. L. Heisenberg, R. Kase and S. Tsujikawa, Beyond generalized Proca theories, *Phys. Lett. B* **760**, 617 (2016).
21. C. de Rham, G. Gabadadze and A. J. Tolley, Resummation of Massive Gravity, *Phys. Rev. Lett.* **106**, p. 231101 (2011).
22. S. F. Hassan and R. A. Rosen, On Non-Linear Actions for Massive Gravity, *JHEP* **07**, p. 009 (2011).
23. S. F. Hassan and R. A. Rosen, Exact Solution to the 'Auxiliary Extra Dimension' Model of Massive Gravity, *Phys. Lett. B* **702**, 90 (2011).
24. J. B. Jiménez, L. Heisenberg and T. S. Koivisto, The Geometrical Trinity of Gravity, *Universe* **5**, p. 173 (2019).
25. D. D. Doneva and S. S. Yazadjiev, New Gauss-Bonnet Black Holes with Curvature-Induced Scalarization in Extended Scalar-Tensor Theories, *Phys. Rev. Lett.* **120**, p. 131103 (2018).
26. H. O. Silva, J. Sakstein, L. Gualtieri, T. P. Sotiriou and E. Berti, Spontaneous scalarization of black holes and compact stars from a Gauss-Bonnet coupling, *Phys. Rev. Lett.* **120**, p. 131104 (2018).
27. G. Antoniou, A. Bakopoulos and P. Kanti, Evasion of No-Hair Theorems and Novel Black-Hole Solutions in Gauss-Bonnet Theories, *Phys. Rev. Lett.* **120**, p. 131102 (2018).
28. P. V. P. Cunha, C. A. R. Herdeiro and E. Radu, Spontaneously Scalarized Kerr Black Holes in Extended Scalar-Tensor–Gauss-Bonnet Gravity, *Phys. Rev. Lett.* **123**, p. 011101 (2019).
29. L. G. Collodel, B. Kleihaus, J. Kunz and E. Berti, Spinning and excited black holes in Einstein-scalar-Gauss–Bonnet theory, *Class. Quant. Grav.* **37**, p. 075018 (2020).
30. A. Dima, E. Barausse, N. Franchini and T. P. Sotiriou, Spin-induced black hole spontaneous scalarization, *Phys. Rev. Lett.* **125**, p. 231101 (2020).

31. S. Hod, Onset of spontaneous scalarization in spinning Gauss-Bonnet black holes, *Phys. Rev. D* **102**, p. 084060 (2020).
32. C. A. Herdeiro, E. Radu, H. O. Silva, T. P. Sotiriou and N. Yunes, Spin-induced scalarized black holes (9 2020).
33. E. Berti, L. G. Collodel, B. Kleihaus and J. Kunz, Spin-induced black-hole scalarization in Einstein-scalar-Gauss-Bonnet theory (9 2020).
34. T. Anson, E. Babichev, C. Charmousis and M. Hassaine, Disforming the Kerr metric, *JHEP* **01**, p. 018 (2021).
35. J. Ben Achour, H. Liu, H. Motohashi, S. Mukohyama and K. Noui, On rotating black holes in DHOST theories, *JCAP* **11**, p. 001 (2020).
36. K. D. Kokkotas and B. G. Schmidt, Quasinormal modes of stars and black holes, *Living Rev. Rel.* **2**, p. 2 (1999).
37. H.-P. Nollert, TOPICAL REVIEW: Quasinormal modes: the characteristic 'sound' of black holes and neutron stars, *Class. Quant. Grav.* **16**, R159 (1999).
38. L. Rezzolla, Gravitational waves from perturbed black holes and relativistic stars, *ICTP Lect. Notes Ser.* **14**, 255 (2003).
39. E. Berti, V. Cardoso and A. O. Starinets, Quasinormal modes of black holes and black branes, *Class. Quant. Grav.* **26**, p. 163001 (2009).
40. R. A. Konoplya and A. Zhidenko, Quasinormal modes of black holes: From astrophysics to string theory, *Rev. Mod. Phys.* **83**, 793 (2011).
41. J. L. Blázquez-Salcedo, Z. Altaha Motahar, D. D. Doneva, F. S. Khoo, J. Kunz, S. Mojica, K. V. Staykov and S. S. Yazadjiev, Quasinormal modes of compact objects in alternative theories of gravity, *Eur. Phys. J. Plus* **134**, p. 46 (2019).
42. R. Gervalle and M. S. Volkov, Asymptotically flat hairy black holes in massive bigravity, *Phys. Rev. D* **102**, p. 124040 (2020).
43. S. F. Hassan and R. A. Rosen, Bimetric Gravity from Ghost-free Massive Gravity, *JHEP* **02**, p. 126 (2012).
44. M. S. Volkov, Hairy black holes in the ghost-free bigravity theory, *Phys. Rev. D* **85**, p. 124043 (2012).
45. R. Brito, V. Cardoso and P. Pani, Massive spin-2 fields on black hole spacetimes: Instability of the Schwarzschild and Kerr solutions and bounds on the graviton mass, *Phys. Rev. D* **88**, p. 023514 (2013).
46. F. Torsello, M. Kocic and E. Mortsell, Classification and asymptotic structure of black holes in bimetric theory, *Phys. Rev. D* **96**, p. 064003 (2017).
47. F. Moulin, A. Barrau and K. Martineau, An overview of quasinormal modes in modified and extended gravity, *Universe* **5**, p. 202 (2019).
48. B. F. Schutz and C. M. Will, BLACK HOLE NORMAL MODES: A SEMIANALYTIC APPROACH, *Astrophys. J. Lett.* **291**, L33 (1985).
49. S. Iyer and C. M. Will, Black Hole Normal Modes: A WKB Approach. 1. Foundations and Application of a Higher Order WKB Analysis of Potential Barrier Scattering, *Phys. Rev. D* **35**, p. 3621 (1987).
50. S. Iyer, BLACK HOLE NORMAL MODES: A WKB APPROACH. 2. SCHWARZSCHILD BLACK HOLES, *Phys. Rev. D* **35**, p. 3632 (1987).
51. C. de Rham and G. Gabadadze, Generalization of the Fierz-Pauli Action, *Phys. Rev. D* **82**, p. 044020 (2010).
52. C. de Rham, Massive Gravity, *Living Rev. Rel.* **17**, p. 7 (2014).
53. J. W. Moffat, Black Holes in Modified Gravity (MOG), *Eur. Phys. J. C* **75**, p. 175 (2015).
54. P. Horava, Quantum Gravity at a Lifshitz Point, *Phys. Rev. D* **79**, p. 084008 (2009).

55. E. O Colgain and H. Yavartanoo, Dyonic solution of Horava-Lifshitz Gravity, *JHEP* **08**, p. 021 (2009).
56. A. Kehagias and K. Sfetsos, The Black hole and FRW geometries of non-relativistic gravity, *Phys. Lett. B* **678**, 123 (2009).
57. H. Lu, J. Mei and C. N. Pope, New Black Holes in Five Dimensions, *Nucl. Phys. B* **806**, 436 (2009).
58. P. Bargueño, S. Bravo Medina, M. Nowakowski and D. Batic, Quantum Mechanical Corrections to the Schwarzschild Black Hole Metric, *EPL* **117**, p. 60006 (2017).
59. E. Alesci and L. Modesto, Hawking radiation from loop black holes, *J. Phys. Conf. Ser.* **360**, p. 012036 (2012).
60. S. Murk and D. R. Terno, Spherically symmetric black holes in metric gravity, *Phys. Rev. D* **104**, p. 064048 (2021).
61. V. P. Frolov, Information loss problem and a 'black hole' model with a closed apparent horizon, *JHEP* **05**, p. 049 (2014).
62. A. A. Starobinsky, A New Type of Isotropic Cosmological Models Without Singularity, *Phys. Lett. B* **91**, 99 (1980).
63. N. M. Santos and C. A. R. Herdeiro, Black holes, stationary clouds and magnetic fields, *Phys. Lett. B* **815**, p. 136142 (2021).
64. W. E. East, F. M. Ramazanoğlu and F. Pretorius, Black Hole Superradiance in Dynamical Spacetime, *Phys. Rev. D* **89**, p. 061503 (2014).
65. C. A. R. Herdeiro and E. Radu, Dynamical Formation of Kerr Black Holes with Synchronized Hair: An Analytic Model, *Phys. Rev. Lett.* **119**, p. 261101 (2017).
66. G. W. Gibbons, A. H. Mujtaba and C. N. Pope, Ergoregions in Magnetised Black Hole Spacetimes, *Class. Quant. Grav.* **30**, p. 125008 (2013).
67. P. Nicolini, E. Spallucci and M. F. Wondrak, Quantum Corrected Black Holes from String T-Duality, *Phys. Lett. B* **797**, p. 134888 (2019).
68. M. F. Wondrak and M. Bleicher, Constraints on the String T-Duality Propagator from the Hydrogen Atom, *Symmetry* **11**, p. 1478 (2019).
69. M. Fontanini, E. Spallucci and T. Padmanabhan, Zero-point length from string fluctuations, *Phys. Lett. B* **633**, 627 (2006).
70. T. Padmanabhan, Duality and zero point length of space-time, *Phys. Rev. Lett.* **78**, 1854 (1997).
71. B. Carr and F. Kühnel, Primordial Black Holes as Dark Matter: Recent Developments, *Ann. Rev. Nucl. Part. Sci.* **70**, 355 (2020).
72. S. Kalita and B. Mukhopadhyay, Asymptotically flat vacuum solution in modified theory of Einstein's gravity, *Eur. Phys. J. C* **79**, p. 877 (2019).
73. S. Xavier, J. Mathew and S. Shankaranarayanan, Infinitely degenerate exact Ricci-flat solutions in f(R) gravity, *Class. Quant. Grav.* **37**, p. 225006 (2020).
74. A. W. Beckwith, Does the penrose suggestion as to black holes from a prior universe showing up in today's universe have credibility? examined from a singular, and nonsingular beginning of cosmological expansion, *Journal of High Energy Physics, Gravitation and Cosmology* **7**, 149 (2021).
75. R. Penrose, Before the big bang: An outrageous new perspective and its implications for particle physics, *Conf. Proc. C* **060626**, 2759 (2006).
76. D. An, K. A. Meissner, P. Nurowski and R. Penrose, Apparent evidence for Hawking points in the CMB Sky, *Mon. Not. Roy. Astron. Soc.* **495**, 3403 (2020).
77. N. J. Popławski, Black Hole Genesis and origin of cosmic acceleration (12 2019).
78. M. Srivastava, Y. Chen and S. Shankaranarayanan, Analytical computation of quasi-normal modes of slowly rotating black holes in dynamical Chern-Simons gravity, *Phys. Rev. D* **104**, p. 064034 (2021).

79. R. Jackiw and S. Y. Pi, Chern-Simons modification of general relativity, *Phys. Rev. D* **68**, p. 104012 (2003).
80. N. Yunes and F. Pretorius, Dynamical Chern-Simons Modified Gravity. I. Spinning Black Holes in the Slow-Rotation Approximation, *Phys. Rev. D* **79**, p. 084043 (2009).
81. J. a. L. Rosa, J. P. S. Lemos and F. S. N. Lobo, Stability of Kerr black holes in generalized hybrid metric-Palatini gravity, *Phys. Rev. D* **101**, p. 044055 (2020).
82. G. J. Olmo, Palatini Approach to Modified Gravity: f(R) Theories and Beyond, *Int. J. Mod. Phys. D* **20**, 413 (2011).
83. T. Harko, T. S. Koivisto, F. S. N. Lobo and G. J. Olmo, Metric-palatini gravity unifying local constraints and late-time cosmic acceleration, *Phys. Rev. D* **85**, p. 084016 (Apr 2012).
84. S. Capozziello, T. Harko, T. S. Koivisto, F. S. N. Lobo and G. J. Olmo, Hybrid metric-palatini gravity, *Universe* **1**, 199 (2015).
85. N. Tamanini and C. G. Böhmer, Generalized hybrid metric-palatini gravity, *Phys. Rev. D* **87**, p. 084031 (Apr 2013).
86. T. Harko and F. S. N. Lobo, *Extensions of f(R) Gravity: Curvature-Matter Couplings and Hybrid Metric-Palatini Theory* (Cambridge University Press, 11 2018).
87. S. Gera and S. Sengupta, Magnetic monopole as a spacetime defect, *Phys. Rev. D* **104**, p. 044038 (2021).
88. P. A. M. Dirac, Quantised singularities in the electromagnetic field, *Proc. Roy. Soc. Lond. A* **133**, 60 (1931).
89. P. A. M. Dirac, The Theory of magnetic poles, *Phys. Rev.* **74**, 817 (1948).
90. A. A. Tseytlin, On the First Order Formalism in Quantum Gravity, *J. Phys. A* **15**, p. L105 (1982).
91. R. K. Kaul and S. Sengupta, Degenerate spacetimes in first order gravity, *Phys. Rev. D* **93**, p. 084026 (2016).
92. R. K. Kaul and S. Sengupta, New solutions in pure gravity with degenerate tetrads, *Phys. Rev. D* **94**, p. 104047 (2016).
93. D. Rubiera-Garcia, From fundamental physics to tests with compact objects in metric-affine theories of gravity, *Int. J. Mod. Phys. D* **29**, p. 2041007 (2020).
94. C. Bernard and M. Ghezelbash, Hidden conformal symmetry of the rotating charged AdS black holes in quadratic $f(T)$ gravity, *Phys. Rev. D* **101**, p. 024020 (2020).
95. M. Guica, T. Hartman, W. Song and A. Strominger, The Kerr/CFT Correspondence, *Phys. Rev. D* **80**, p. 124008 (2009).
96. J. L. Cardy, Operator Content of Two-Dimensional Conformally Invariant Theories, *Nucl. Phys. B* **270**, 186 (1986).
97. H. W. J. Bloete, J. L. Cardy and M. P. Nightingale, Conformal Invariance, the Central Charge, and Universal Finite Size Amplitudes at Criticality, *Phys. Rev. Lett.* **56**, 742 (1986).
98. V. P. Frolov and K. S. Thorne, Renormalized Stress - Energy Tensor Near the Horizon of a Slowly Evolving, Rotating Black Hole, *Phys. Rev. D* **39**, 2125 (1989).
99. G. Compère, The Kerr/CFT correspondence and its extensions, *Living Rev. Rel.* **15**, p. 11 (2012).
100. H. Afshar, D. Grumiller, W. Merbis, A. Perez, D. Tempo and R. Troncoso, Soft hairy horizons in three spacetime dimensions, *Phys. Rev. D* **95**, p. 106005 (2017).
101. H. Afshar, D. Grumiller and M. M. Sheikh-Jabbari, Near horizon soft hair as microstates of three dimensional black holes, *Phys. Rev. D* **96**, p. 084032 (2017).
102. H. Afshar, S. Detournay, D. Grumiller, W. Merbis, A. Perez, D. Tempo and R. Troncoso, Soft Heisenberg hair on black holes in three dimensions, *Phys. Rev. D* **93**, p. 101503 (2016).

103. G. Compère, K. Hajian, A. Seraj and M. M. Sheikh-Jabbari, Wiggling Throat of Extremal Black Holes, *JHEP* **10**, p. 093 (2015).
104. G. Compère, K. Hajian, A. Seraj and M. M. Sheikh-Jabbari, Extremal Rotating Black Holes in the Near-Horizon Limit: Phase Space and Symmetry Algebra, *Phys. Lett. B* **749**, 443 (2015).
105. K. Hajian, M. M. Sheikh-Jabbari and H. Yavartanoo, Extreme Kerr black hole microstates with horizon fluff, *Phys. Rev. D* **98**, p. 026025 (2018).
106. K. Hajian and A. Seraj, Symplectic Structure of Extremal Black Holes, *Springer Proc. Phys.* **208**, 61 (2018).
107. B. Chen, A. M. Ghezelbash, V. Kamali and M. R. Setare, Holographic description of Kerr-Bolt-AdS-dS Spacetimes, *Nucl. Phys. B* **848**, 108 (2011).
108. A. M. Ghezelbash, V. Kamali and M. R. Setare, Hidden Conformal Symmetry of Kerr-Bolt Spacetimes, *Phys. Rev. D* **82**, p. 124051 (2010).
109. A. M. Awad, G. G. L. Nashed and W. El Hanafy, Rotating charged AdS solutions in quadratic $f(T)$ gravity, *Eur. Phys. J. C* **79**, p. 668 (2019).
110. N. Popławski, Gravitational Collapse of a Fluid with Torsion into a Universe in a Black Hole, *J. Exp. Theor. Phys.* **132**, 374 (2021).
111. D. Sciama, On a Nonsymmetric theory of the pure gravitational field, *Proc. Cambridge Phil. Soc.* **54**, p. 72 (1958).
112. D. W. Sciama, The Physical structure of general relativity, *Rev. Mod. Phys.* **36**, 463 (1964), [Erratum: Rev. Mod. Phys. 36, 1103–1103 (1964)].
113. T. W. B. Kibble, Lorentz invariance and the gravitational field, *J. Math. Phys.* **2**, 212 (1961).
114. F. W. Hehl and B. K. Datta, Nonlinear spinor equation and asymmetric connection in general relativity, *J. Math. Phys.* **12**, 1334 (1971).
115. F. W. Hehl, P. Von Der Heyde, G. D. Kerlick and J. M. Nester, General Relativity with Spin and Torsion: Foundations and Prospects, *Rev. Mod. Phys.* **48**, 393 (1976).
116. F. W. Hehl, G. D. Kerlick and P. Von Der Heyde, General relativity with spin and torsion and its deviations from einstein's theory, *Phys. Rev. D* **10**, 1066 (1974).
117. R. C. Tolman, Effect of imhomogeneity on cosmological models, *Proc. Nat. Acad. Sci.* **20**, 169 (1934).
118. R. B. Magalhães, L. C. S. Leite and L. C. B. Crispino, Absorption by deformed black holes, *Phys. Lett. B* **805**, p. 135418 (2020).
119. T. Johannsen and D. Psaltis, A Metric for Rapidly Spinning Black Holes Suitable for Strong-Field Tests of the No-Hair Theorem, *Phys. Rev. D* **83**, p. 124015 (2011).
120. R. Konoplya and A. Zhidenko, Detection of gravitational waves from black holes: Is there a window for alternative theories?, *Phys. Lett. B* **756**, 350 (2016).
121. J. Badía and E. F. Eiroa, Influence of an anisotropic matter field on the shadow of a rotating black hole, *Phys. Rev. D* **102**, p. 024066 (2020).
122. K. Akiyama *et al.*, First M87 Event Horizon Telescope Results. I. The Shadow of the Supermassive Black Hole, *Astrophys. J. Lett.* **875**, p. L1 (2019).
123. V. Perlick and O. Y. Tsupko, Calculating black hole shadows: review of analytical studies (5 2021).
124. V. Perlick, O. Y. Tsupko and G. S. Bisnovatyi-Kogan, Influence of a plasma on the shadow of a spherically symmetric black hole, *Phys. Rev. D* **92**, p. 104031 (2015).
125. O. Y. Tsupko, Deflection of light rays by a spherically symmetric black hole in a dispersive medium, *Phys. Rev. D* **103**, p. 104019 (2021).
126. V. Perlick and O. Y. Tsupko, Light propagation in a plasma on Kerr spacetime: Separation of the Hamilton-Jacobi equation and calculation of the shadow, *Phys. Rev. D* **95**, p. 104003 (2017).

127. O. Y. Tsupko and G. S. Bisnovatyi-Kogan, Gravitational lensing in the presence of plasmas and strong gravitational fields, *Grav. Cosmol.* **20**, 220 (2014).
128. I. Cho and H.-C. Kim, Simple black holes with anisotropic fluid, *Chin. Phys. C* **43**, p. 025101 (2019).
129. H.-C. Kim, B.-H. Lee, W. Lee and Y. Lee, Rotating black holes with an anisotropic matter field, *Phys. Rev. D* **101**, p. 064067 (2020).
130. J. Badia and E. F. Eiroa, Shadow of axisymmetric, stationary and asymptotically flat black holes in the presence of plasma (6 2021).

Uncertainties in kilonova modeling

C. L. Fryer*, C. J. Fontes, O. Korobkin, M. Mumpower and R. Wollaeger

Center for Theoretical Astrophysics, Los Alamos National Laboratory,
Los Alamos, NM 87545, USA
*E-mail: fryer@lanl.gov
https://ccsweb.lanl.gov/astro/index.html

E.M. Holmbeck

The Observatories of the Carnegie Institute for Science,
Pasadena, CA, 91101, USA

R. O'Shaugnessy

Rochester Institute of Technology,
Rochester, NY 14623

The detection of the merger of a neutron star binary in both gravitational waves and a broad spectrum of electromagnetic waves (GW170817) provided the most compelling evidence to date that such mergers produce heavy r-process elements. The inferred rate of these mergers coupled to the estimated r-process production suggests that these mergers could produce nearly all of the r-process elements in the universe. However, uncertainties in the merger rate and the amount of r-process production per merger means that scientists can not constrain the fraction of the merger r-process contribution to better than 1–100% of the total amount in the universe. The total r-process mass synthesized is best constrained by the observations themselves and uncertainties in the inferred production quantity follows from the uncertainties in modeling the emission from the NSM ejecta. In this paper, we review these modeling uncertainties.

Keywords: Neutron Stars; Gravitational Waves, r-Process

1. Kilonovae, a Key to Understanding r-Process

Many of the heaviest elements in the universe are produced through a process of rapid neutron capture (r-process), building isotopes far from stability that then decay to the long-lived heavy isotopes observed in the universe. This rapid neutron capture requires extreme conditions with high densities and large fractions of free neutrons. Scientists identified neutron star mergers (NSMs) as a potential source of these r-process elements over 40 years ago[1,2] and evidence has been growing steadily to argue that these mergers could dominate the r-process production.

Although the evolution of the ejecta from these mergers reaches ideal conditions (high densities, temperatures and neutron fractions) for the production of r-process elements, observational validation of r-process production in NSMs has been much more difficult to obtain. Until recently, theoretical and observational evidence relied on galactic chemical evolution arguments and their associated uncertainties.[3,4]

This situation changed with the joint electromagnetic- and gravitational-wave observations of NSM GW170817.[5] Between the gamma-, x-, optical, infra-red, and radio emission, it became clear that the NSM in GW170817 produced both a relativistic jet and a lower-velocity mass ejecta that argued for both neutron-rich dynamical ejecta and higher electron-fraction wind ejecta components.

Although initial analyses argued strongly that GW170817 produced a large fraction of r-process ($0.04M_\odot$), as more studies were completed, uncertainties in the inferred r-process production from GW170817 grew.[6] Many of these differences arose from different assumptions about the properties of the outflow material and a difference in which observations were used to constrain the data. But these are just some of the uncertainties in the analysis of the optical and infra-red emission from NSMs. In this paper, we review these uncertainties. In section 2, we review the uncertainties in the properties (distributions of the velocity, density, entropy and neutron fraction) of the outflow from these mergers. Section 3 reviews some of the microphysics uncertainties in these calculations. Section 4 details alternative power sources that can alter the mass inferred from observations.

2. Uncertainties in the Outflows

The emission from astrophysical transients depends upon the ejecta properties (e.g. composition, velocity and angular distributions). Unlike many transients that are produced by a single outburst, the ejecta from NSMs arises from multiple components including ejecta from the initial tidal tails produced in the dynamical merger and a outflow arising from a disk. The disk outflow is driven by viscous forces and neutrino emission from a post-disruption torus of material (Figure 1). We will refer to the former as *dynamical* ejecta and the latter as *wind* ejecta. The bulk of the dynamical material is ejected along the orbital plane. This material has a high-neutron fraction, ideally suited for the production of the most massive elements (heavy r-process). In contrast, the wind ejecta is more isotropic and consists of material spanning a broad range of neutron fractions that depend on both the properties of the disk and the fate of the merged core.

Many of the initial studies of GW170817 used spherically-symmetric models, varying the fraction of heavy r-process to lighter elements.[6] Some of these initial models used two components to differentiate between the dynamical ejecta primarily flowing along the orbital plane and a more symmetric or axis-aligned wind outflow[7] shown in Figure 1. However, even these two-component models made simplifying assumptions using a single composition for each component and a fixed velocity distribution of the ejecta. These assumptions oversimplify the nature of the ejecta and can have order-of-magnitude effects on the inferred mass of r-process ejecta. Before we study how these two components fit together, we first review some of the outflow uncertainties in the individual dynamical and wind components.

Although models of the dynamical ejecta have produced a range of ejecta masses, e.g. compare the results in,[8,9] these numerical differences are slowly diminishing as

disk / NS-driven wind **dynamical ejecta**

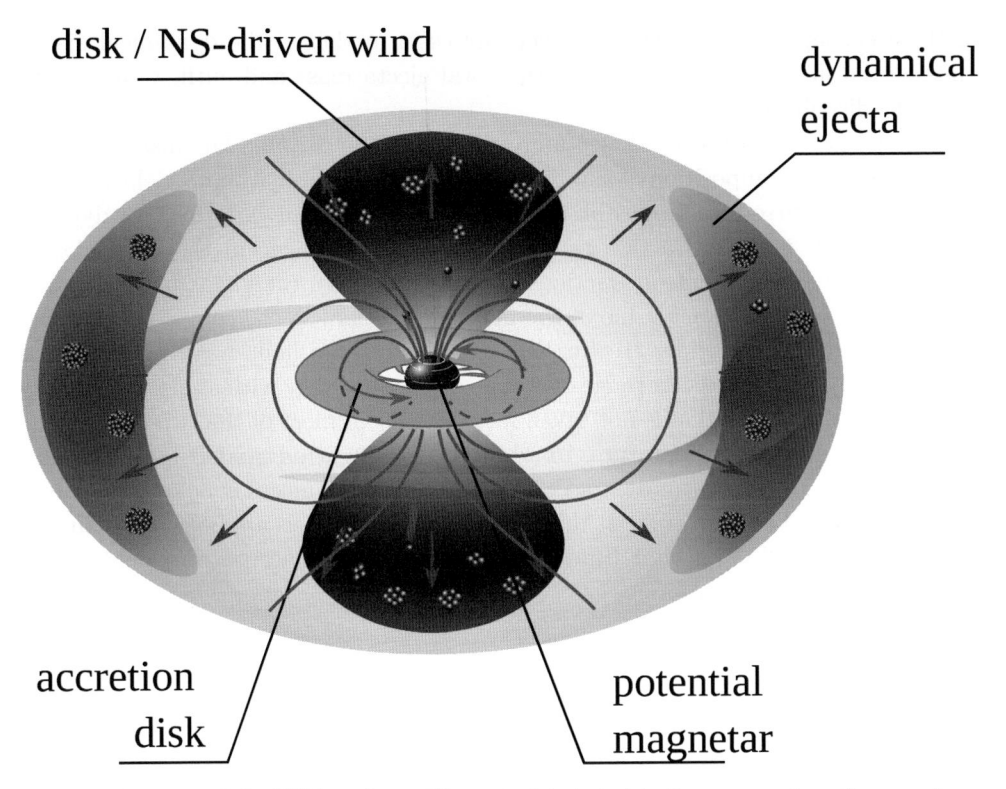

accretion disk **potential magnetar**

Fig. 1. Anatomy of the NSM outflows. The material ejected in the merger phase flows predominantly along the orbital plane and is very neutron rich. The merged object produces a neutron star or black hole core surrounded by a torus of high angular-momentum material. Outflows driven by viscous forces in this disk, coupled with neutrino emission, produce the "wind" ejecta with its lower neutron fraction. These outflows produce the observed kilonova light-curve emission from the ultra-violet to the infra-red powered by radioactive decay. When material falls back on this merged core and/or if a magnetar forms, an additional power source can contribute additional energy to the observed transient.

computational methods improve. Even with this convergence, the ejecta mass will vary with the individual masses of the merging compact objects.[8] The composition of this ejecta is much better constrained than the ejecta mass. At high neutron fractions (above 0.8), the final composition does not depend sensitively on the neutron fraction. Because of this, the small variation in the neutron fraction does not alter the Lanthanide composition considerably and the composition of this ejecta is fairly stable. In addition, the final composition is also less sensitive to the details of the outflow (density and temperature evolution). For this reason, the composition of this ejecta is well-understood with the dominant uncertainties depending on our lack of understanding of the nuclear physics (Sec. 3). Finally, due to the dense forest of absorption lines in the opacity produced by the heavy r-process lanthanides and actinides, the light curves do not depend sensitively on the exact relative abundance of these elements.[10] The primary uncertainties in models of the dynamical ejecta emission lie in our understanding of the total ejecta mass and outflow properties (velocity distribution).

The properties of the wind ejecta are much more uncertain. The mass, velocity distribution and composition of this ejecta varies considerably from model to model. Whereas the neutron fraction is high and exhibits only small variations for dynamical ejecta, the neutron fraction ranges across a broad range in the wind ejecta. Further, at the lower neutron fractions (between 0.5-0.8), the yields become much more sensitive to the exact value of the neutron fraction, so the composition of the wind ejecta can vary wildly. To further complicate these light-curve models, disk models of this wind predict a range of compositions that vary with angle and time.[11] This composition variation is not taken into account in most of the two-component models currently in the literature. In addition, current wind models typically only follow the wind out to, at most, 1 second and much of the ejecta is below the escape velocity (but still accelerating) at this time. Although models are being constructed to follow this outflow to later times, we still do not have accurate models of this ejecta's velocity distribution.

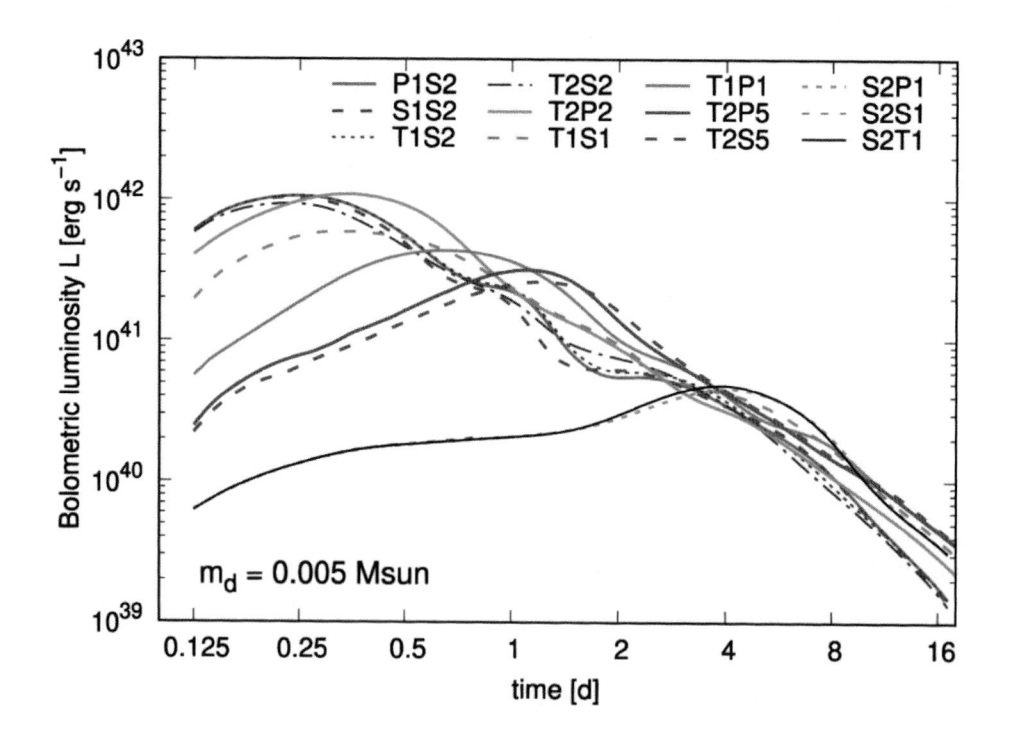

Fig. 2. Bolometric Light curves versus time for a broad range of models varying the morphology of the two components in a dynamical plus wind model.[12] Varying the morphology alone can change the bolometric luminosity by over an order of magnitude.

Although we have mostly discussed the role of the composition, the morphology of the ejecta (velocity and angular distribution) may be even more important. Figure 2 shows a broad set of models with the same explosion energy and mass, but varying the angular morphology of the ejecta.[12] In this study, two-component models were developed, each with a different morphology. In these models, although the energy of the ejecta is the same, the velocity distribution of the ejecta can vary. Changing the morphology alters both the peak luminosity and the time of that peak, varying both by an order of magnitude.

At this time, a complete study of all the outflow uncertainties has not been done. We end this section with the discussion of a final study varying ejecta mass and velocity of a two-component model.[13] This grid of models used a single dynamical ejecta composition and one of two wind compositions. It focused on a primary pair of morphologies for these two components, using a default r-process composition for the dynamical ejecta and two different compositions for the wind. But the compositions were fixed for each component. Although the peak velocity was changed, the velocity distribution was unaltered. Depending on the relative velocities of the two components, the dynamical ejecta, with its high-opacity lanthanides, can obscure the wind ejecta. In these cases, the luminosity can depend sensitively on the viewing angle. In other cases, the wind ejecta is sufficiently fast that the light-curve is similar, regardless of viewing angle. Although more massive ejecta models are, on average, brighter, lower mass models can be brighter than higher mass models based on this viewing angle.

3. Uncertainties in the Microphysics and its Implementation

The outflow models depend on detailed general-relativistic, magneto-hydrodynamic models including neutrino transport (and the related neutrino microphysics). We do not have enough space to discuss all of this microphysics in detail. Instead we focus on the uncertainties in the nuclear physics and atomic physics with a brief discussion on each.

Unstable neutron-rich nuclei participating in the r-process have many unmeasured properties that consequently influence kilonova signals.[14,15] Uncertainties in nuclear binding energies and reaction rates impact the flow of material to heavier mass regions as well as the subsequent flow back towards lighter mass regions in ejecta with low electron fraction.[16] Properties that depend on excited nuclear states, including half-lives and branching ratios, additionally control the timescale over which energy is released as well as potentially stored.[17,18] The creation of the heaviest elements in merger events[19] may produce distinct observable signals, e.g. via the production of long-lived species like ^{254}Cf or via unique electromagnetic signatures.[20,21,21,22] Central to the reduction of large nuclear uncertainties that impact kilonovae are experimental studies undertaken at radioactive beam facilities around the world, see e.g.[23,24]

A major uncertainty in the application of atomic physics to the modeling of kilonovae concerns the bound-bound (line absorption) contribution to the radiative opacity. While photons traveling through a plasma can be absorbed in a number of atomic processes, line absorption is the dominant mechanism in the dynamical ejecta due to the dense forest of lines associated with near-neutral lanthanide and actinide elements. Complete sets of lanthanide opacities have been recently produced for the purpose of kilonova modeling[25–27] using different atomic physics methods, which is another potential source of uncertainty. In an effort to mitigate this issue, we have made available to the public our lanthanide opacites[28] so that kilonova modelers can use a consistent set of opacities, thereby ruling out emission differences that could arise from atomic physics implementations. As a specific illustration of these concepts, we present in Figure 3 the opacity of Nd, calculated under the assumption of local thermodynamic equilibrium (LTE), at a temperature of $T = 0.5$ eV and mass density $\rho = 10^{-13}$ g/cm^3, using four different models (see[26] for details). Note that the line features enhance the opacity by six to eight orders of magnitude compared to what would occur if only free-electron processes were included. The Planck mean opacity, κ^P, is also displayed for each model, indicating a maximum discrepancy of about 40% between the various models for this integrated quantity. Detailed light-curve and spectral comparisons were carried out with these four models.[26] Only

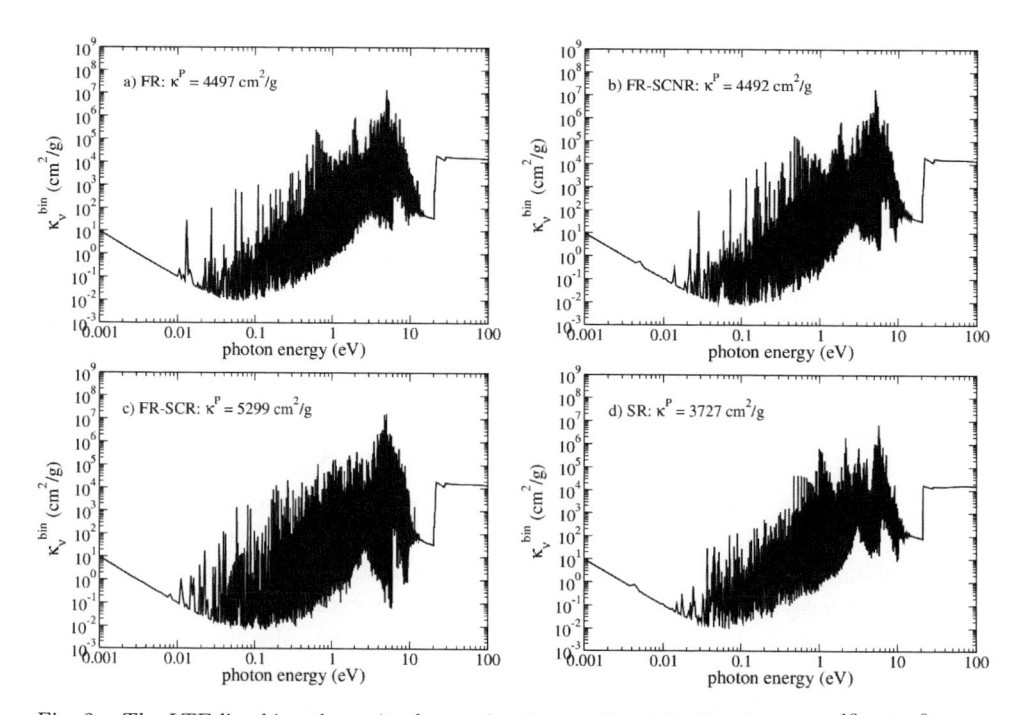

Fig. 3. The LTE line-binned opacity for neodymium at $T = 0.5$ eV and $\rho = 10^{-13}$ g/cm^3 using four different models described in:[26] a) FR, b) FR-SCNR, c) FR-SCR, and d) SR. The Planck mean opacity, obtained via integration of the line-binned opacity, is also listed in each panel.

modest differences were noted in the light-curves, i.e. differences of 10–20% in the peak of the light curve and a maximum shift of half a day in the time of peak luminosity. Similar, modest differences were observed in the spectra produced with these models, i.e. certain spectral features are shifted redward are blueward, but the overall spectral characteristics are similar.

From a more general perspective, we note that opacities are typically calculated from first principles, rather than measured. The line contribution depends on quantities such as transition energies, line strengths (quantum mechanical matrix elements) and atomic level populations. While it is beyond the scope of this article to provide a detailed discussion of these concepts, we mention that recent work[29,30] has been performed to compare calculated energies with benchmark values in the NIST Atomic Spectra Database[31] for a number of important, low-lying levels of the lanthanides. Also, most simulations employ the LTE approximation when calculating the level populations. This assumption is expected to be valid up to about one week post merger. But, as with many astrophysical transients, the LTE conditions become less and less valid as the expansion continues and the density becomes so low that the thermalization timescale from collisions becomes long compared to evolutionary timescales of the ejecta. A recent study[32] explores the possibility that non-thermal, β-decay electrons, produced from the radioactive decay of r-process nuclei, are primarily responsible for the heating and collisional ionization in the ejecta.

With the large number of atomic levels, the number of line features is enormous (in the 10s of millions). Implementing these opacities into a numerical calculation is intractable even from a computational memory standpoint. In addition, because of the high velocities in the ejecta, modeling radiation transport becomes even more difficult. For a single strong line, the Sobolev approximation can be used to determine the likelihood of a photon to both be absorbed as it expands out of a medium and its likelihood of escaping this line when re-emitted. Transient explosions exhibit homologous outflow conditions where the velocity of the ejecta is proportional to the radius. As a photon moves out through this ejecta, its energy spans a broad range with respect to the rest frame of the outflow. Even if the photon does not interact with a line feature at one radius, it may interact with this feature at a different radius.

This treatment includes the fact that the velocity of the ejecta spans a range such that, even if a photon does not interact with an absorption feature in the rest frame of the outflowing material at one position, it may, as it transports outward, interact with other material. Hence, a single line feature can affect a larger energy band of photons. On the other hand, if most of the re-emitted photons arise from a direct de-excitation of the absorption feature, the photons remain trapped in a line feature in material moving at a constant velocity. For the homologous outflow of astrophysical transients, the photon can escape more quickly, effectively reducing the opacity. Implementing the Sobolev approximation is already difficult, but in

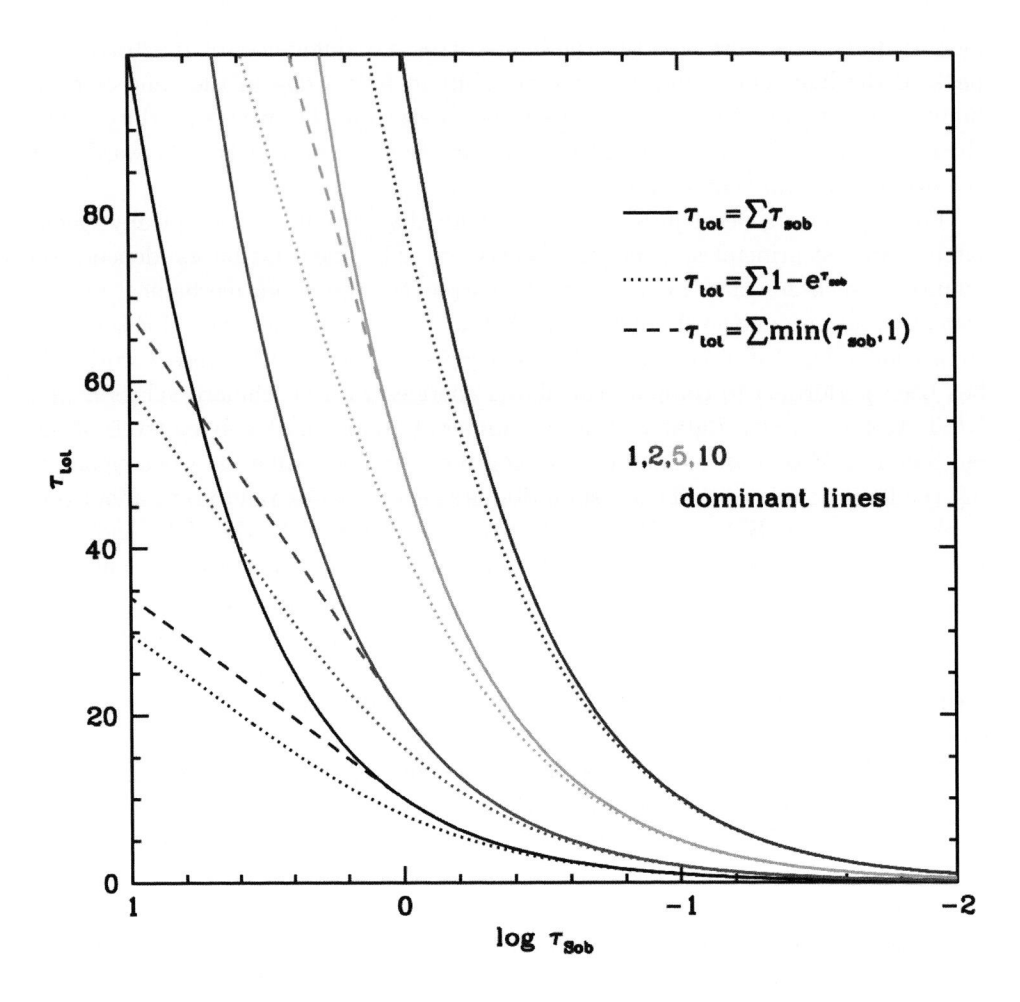

Fig. 4. A number of prescriptions have been proposed to model the expansion opacities. This figure shows the total optical depth using three different prescriptions for different numbers of dominant line features as a function of the optical depth of the line feature. There is some convergence with large number of lines, showing why a simple averaged opacity can work nearly as well as a more complicated expansion procedure.

a medium where a forest of lines exists, producing an accurate model for spectra becomes increasingly difficult. The deficiencies of the Pinto & Eastman expansion opacity[33] were outlined in its inception and a number of alternative approaches have been developed (for a review, see[34]). A number of methods have been developed to calculate the optical depth and these different models produce a range of results based on these prescriptions (Figure 4). For a simplified model with pure neodymium, Figure 5 compares the bolometric luminosity for different approaches: Sobolev, expansion opacity and a simple binned treatment. Compared to many of our other uncertainties, the opacity implementation errors seem low.

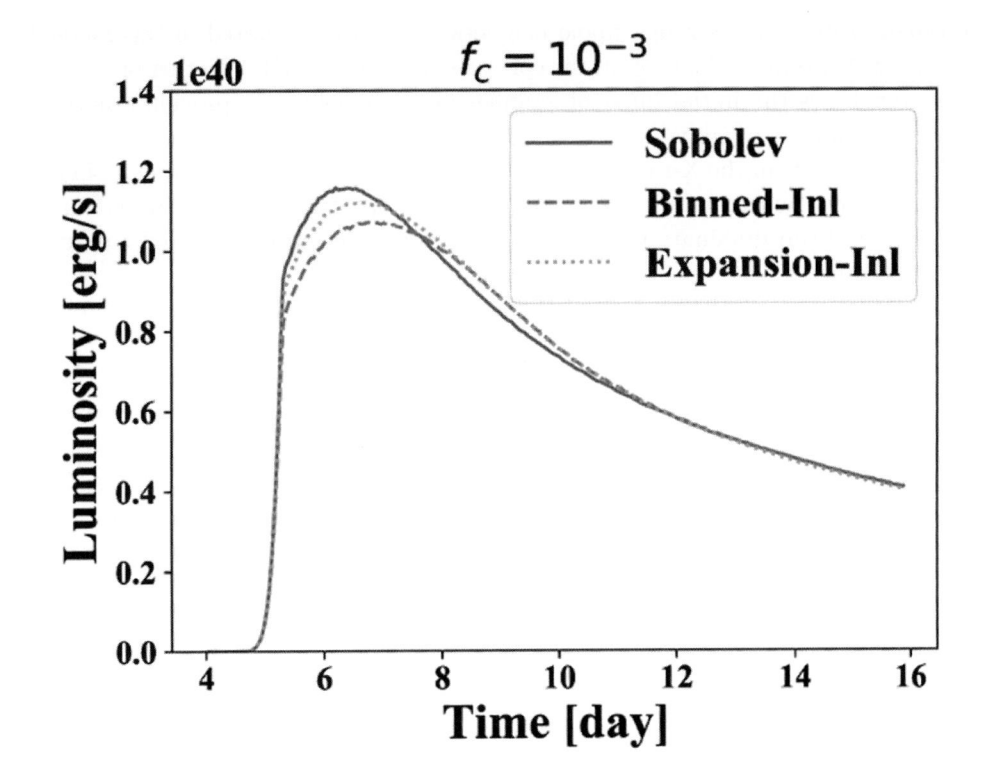

Fig. 5. Bolometric light curves using three different implementations of the opacity. The quantity $f_c = 10^{-3}$ indicates the cut off value for retaining oscillator strengths in the atomic physics model.

4. Alternative Energy Sources

Most calculations assume that the power source behind the kilonova emission arises solely from radioactive decay. But, just as with core-collapse supernovae, the light-curves and spectra can be powered by a variety of sources. For kilonovae, a number of additional power sources have been proposed to drive the observed emission: magnetar emission, shock heating in the ejecta, and fallback accretion. In this section, we will discuss each of these energy sources in turn, reviewing both their basic physics and expected features.

The black hole accretion disk engine paradigm argued that long-duration bursts are produced in stellar collapse, while short-duration GRBs are produced by the merger of compact remnants. Under this paradigm, scientists predicted that short-duration GRBs should be offset from their formation region due to the momentum imparted on compact binaries at birth.[35,36] Although other power sources do not differentiate between short- and long-duration bursts in this manner, magnetar engines for short-duration bursts have remained a competitive model for these bursts. The basic idea behind this engine is that the merged core of a NSM is expected to be rapidly rotating. If strong, dipole magnetic fields are generated in this merged core, then the rotational energy in the core can power the GRB. Whether or not the magnetar drives the initial burst of gamma-rays, magnetars do provide a natural explanation for the roughly hall of all short-duration bursts that exhibit a long-lived ("plateau") phase in the X-ray that can last up to 10^5s.[37] The magnetar emission, if reprocessed by the expanding ejecta, can power the optical and even infra-red emission,[38,39] and can dominate the observed emission, altering the inferred r-process yield in the merger.

In supernovae, shock heating is believed to dominate the heating in type II supernovae, shock breakout events, and many superluminous supernovae. Shock heating may also play a role in kilonova emission. Shocks between the jet and the wind ejecta have been invoked to explain additional emission at early times (first day) in the kilonova emission.[40] At later times (beyond a day), material falls back onto the compact remnant, likely forming a disk and further outflows. The potential energy released in this fallback can be tapped to provide an additional power source. Depending upon the timing of the fallback, this accretion emission

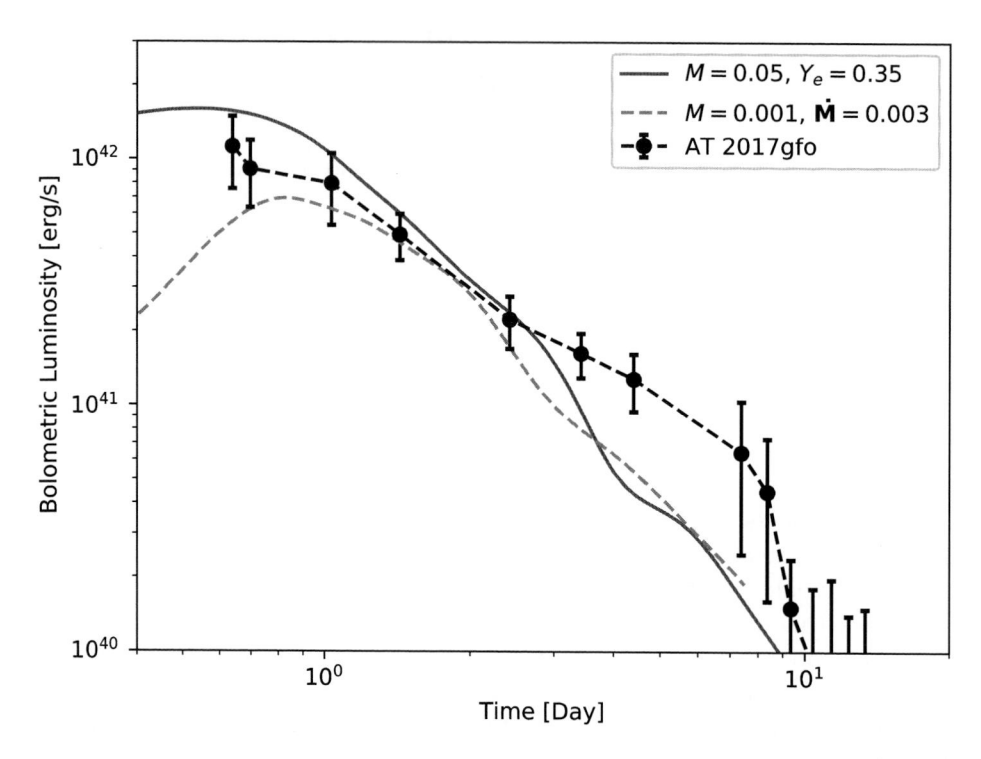

Fig. 6. Bolometric luminosity versus time for a 0.05 $M_\odot$ 1D spherical wind model (blue), a 0.001 $M_\odot$ 1D spherical model with a $\dot{M} = 0.003$ $M_\odot$/s central fallback luminosity source (dashed orange), and the EM counterpart of GW170817, AT 2017gfo (dashed black, with error bars).

can play a major role in the emission after the first day (Figure 6). The accretion luminosity is proportional to the potential energy released:

$$L_{\text{acc}} \propto GM_{\text{core}}\dot{M}_{\text{fallback}}/r_{\text{ISCO}} \qquad (1)$$

where G is the gravitational constant, M_{core} is the mass of the merged core, r_{ISCO} is its innermost stable circular orbit if the core is a black hole or the neutron star radius if it is a neutron star, and $\dot{M}_{\text{fallback}}$ is the fallback accretion rate. Whether the merged core is a black hole or a neutron star, the fallback material is likely to have sufficient angular momentum to initially be centrifugally supported in an accretion disk, providing a mechanism by which a fraction of the potential energy released in the infall can be converted to both energy and mass ejection.

5. Conclusions

In addition to being the primary mechanism behind short-duration gamma-ray bursts, NSMs have the potential to be the dominant source of r-process elements in the universe. To validate this claim, scientists must be able to accurately infer the mass and abundances from observations of the ejecta-driven transient from these mergers (a.k.a. kilonovae). In this paper, we reviewed a broad set of uncertainties affecting the modeling of kilonova light-curves and the current status of our efforts to characterize and, hopefully constrain, them. Much more work must be done to infer accurate r-process masses from these observations.

In this short paper, we focused mostly on broad-band light-curves. Spectra are key to constraining the different models and a number of studies have focused on trying to find line features in the kilonova observations e.g.[41]. Gamma-ray decay lines, particularly in the remnants of the NSM ejecta, also have the potential to probe detailed yields.[21,42] So despite the difficulties that face astronomers in understanding the yields from these mergers, the future is looking bright.

References

1. J. M. Lattimer and D. N. Schramm, Black-Hole-Neutron-Star Collisions, *ApJ Letters* **192**, p. L145 (September 1974).
2. J. M. Lattimer and D. N. Schramm, The tidal disruption of neutron stars by black holes in close binaries., *ApJ* **210**, 549 (December 1976).
3. P. Beniamini, K. Hotokezaka and T. Piran, r-process Production Sites as Inferred from Eu Abundances in Dwarf Galaxies, *ApJ* **832**, p. 149 (December 2016).
4. M. Safarzadeh and E. Scannapieco, Simulating neutron star mergers as r-process sources in ultrafaint dwarf galaxies, *MNRAS* **471**, 2088 (October 2017).
5. B. P. Abbott and a. et, Multi-messenger Observations of a Binary Neutron Star Merger, *ApJ Letters* **848**, p. L12 (October 2017).
6. B. Côté, C. L. Fryer, K. Belczynski, O. Korobkin, M. Chruślińska, N. Vassh, M. R. Mumpower, J. Lippuner, T. M. Sprouse, R. Surman and R. Wollaeger, The Origin of r-process Elements in the Milky Way, *ApJ* **855**, p. 99 (March 2018).

7. R. T. Wollaeger, O. Korobkin, C. J. Fontes, S. K. Rosswog, W. P. Even, C. L. Fryer, J. Sollerman, A. L. Hungerford, D. R. van Rossum and A. B. Wollaber, Impact of ejecta morphology and composition on the electromagnetic signatures of neutron star mergers, *MNRAS* **478**, 3298 (August 2018).
8. O. Korobkin, S. Rosswog, A. Arcones and C. Winteler, On the astrophysical robustness of the neutron star merger r-process, *MNRAS* **426**, 1940 (November 2012).
9. M. Shibata and K. Hotokezaka, Merger and Mass Ejection of Neutron Star Binaries, *Annual Review of Nuclear and Particle Science* **69**, 41 (October 2019).
10. W. Even, O. Korobkin, C. L. Fryer, C. J. Fontes, R. T. Wollaeger, A. Hungerford, J. Lippuner, J. Miller, M. R. Mumpower and G. W. Misch, Composition Effects on Kilonova Spectra and Light Curves. I, *ApJ* **899**, p. 24 (August 2020).
11. J. M. Miller, T. M. Sprouse, C. L. Fryer, B. R. Ryan, J. C. Dolence, M. R. Mumpower and R. Surman, Full Transport General Relativistic Radiation Magnetohydrodynamics for Nucleosynthesis in Collapsars, *ApJ* **902**, p. 66 (October 2020).
12. O. Korobkin, R. T. Wollaeger, C. L. Fryer, A. L. Hungerford, S. Rosswog, C. J. Fontes, M. R. Mumpower, E. A. Chase, W. P. Even, J. Miller, G. W. Misch and J. Lippuner, Axisymmetric Radiative Transfer Models of Kilonovae, *ApJ* **910**, p. 116 (April 2021).
13. R. T. Wollaeger, C. L. Fryer, E. A. Chase, C. J. Fontes, M. Ristic, A. L. Hungerford, O. Korobkin, R. O'Shaughnessy and A. M. Herring, A Broad Grid of 2D Kilonova Emission Models, *ApJ* **918**, p. 10 (September 2021).
14. Y. L. Zhu, K. A. Lund, J. Barnes, T. M. Sprouse, N. Vassh, G. C. McLaughlin, M. R. Mumpower and R. Surman, Modeling Kilonova Light Curves: Dependence on Nuclear Inputs, *ApJ* **906**, p. 94 (January 2021).
15. J. Barnes, Y. L. Zhu, K. A. Lund, T. M. Sprouse, N. Vassh, G. C. McLaughlin, M. R. Mumpower and R. Surman, Kilonovae Across the Nuclear Physics Landscape: The Impact of Nuclear Physics Uncertainties on r-process-powered Emission, *ApJ* **918**, p. 44 (September 2021).
16. B. Côté, M. Eichler, A. Yagüe López, N. Vassh, M. R. Mumpower, B. Világos, B. Soós, A. Arcones, T. M. Sprouse, R. Surman, M. Pignatari, M. K. Pető, B. Wehmeyer, T. Rauscher and M. Lugaro, ^{129}I and ^{247}Cm in meteorites constrain the last astrophysical source of solar r-process elements, *Science* **371**, 945 (February 2021).
17. M. R. Mumpower, T. Kawano and P. Möller, Neutron-γ competition for β-delayed neutron emission, *PRC* **94**, p. 064317 (December 2016).
18. G. W. Misch, T. M. Sprouse and M. R. Mumpower, Astromers in the Radioactive Decay of r-process Nuclei, *ApJ Letters* **913**, p. L2 (May 2021).
19. E. M. Holmbeck, A. Frebel, G. C. McLaughlin, M. R. Mumpower, T. M. Sprouse and R. Surman, Actinide-rich and Actinide-poor r-process-enhanced Metal-poor Stars Do Not Require Separate r-process Progenitors, *ApJ* **881**, p. 5 (August 2019).
20. Y. Zhu, R. T. Wollaeger, N. Vassh, R. Surman, T. M. Sprouse, M. R. Mumpower, P. Möller, G. C. McLaughlin, O. Korobkin, T. Kawano, P. J. Jaffke, E. M. Holmbeck, C. L. Fryer, W. P. Even, A. J. Couture and J. Barnes, Californium-254 and Kilonova Light Curves, *ApJ Letters* **863**, p. L23 (August 2018).
21. O. Korobkin, A. M. Hungerford, C. L. Fryer, M. R. Mumpower, G. W. Misch, T. M. Sprouse, J. Lippuner, R. Surman, A. J. Couture, P. F. Bloser, F. Shirazi, W. P. Even, W. T. Vestrand and R. S. Miller, Gamma Rays from Kilonova: A Potential Probe of r-process Nucleosynthesis, *ApJ* **889**, p. 168 (February 2020).
22. X. Wang, N3AS Collaboration, N. Vassh, FIRE Collaboration, T. Sprouse, M. Mumpower, R. Vogt, J. Randrup and R. Surman, MeV Gamma Rays from Fission: A Distinct Signature of Actinide Production in Neutron Star Mergers, *ApJ Letters* **903**, p. L3 (November 2020).

23. A. Spyrou, S. N. Liddick, F. Naqvi, B. P. Crider, A. C. Dombos, D. L. Bleuel, B. A. Brown, A. Couture, L. Crespo Campo, M. Guttormsen, A. C. Larsen, R. Lewis, P. Möller, S. Mosby, M. R. Mumpower, G. Perdikakis, C. J. Prokop, T. Renstrøm, S. Siem, S. J. Quinn and S. Valenta, Strong Neutron-γ Competition above the Neutron Threshold in the Decay of ^{70}Co, *Physical Review Letters* **117**, p. 142701 (September 2016).
24. O. Hall, T. Davinson, A. Estrade, J. Liu, G. Lorusso, F. Montes, S. Nishimura, V. H. Phong, P. J. Woods, J. Agramunt, D. S. Ahn, A. Algora, J. M. Allmond, H. Baba, S. Bae, N. T. Brewer, C. G. Bruno, R. Caballero-Folch, F. Calviño, P. J. Coleman-Smith, G. Cortes, I. Dillmann, C. Domingo-Pardo, A. Fijalkowska, N. Fukuda, S. Go, C. J. Griffin, R. Grzywacz, J. Ha, L. J. Harkness-Brennan, T. Isobe, D. Kahl, L. H. Khiem, G. G. Kiss, A. Korgul, S. Kubono, M. Labiche, I. Lazarus, J. Liang, Z. Liu, K. Matsui, K. Miernik, B. Moon, A. I. Morales, P. Morrall, M. R. Mumpower, N. Nepal, R. D. Page, M. Piersa, V. F. E. Pucknell, B. C. Rasco, B. Rubio, K. P. Rykaczewski, H. Sakurai, Y. Shimizu, D. W. Stracener, T. Sumikama, H. Suzuki, J. L. Tain, H. Takeda, A. Tarifeño-Saldivia, A. Tolosa-Delgado, M. Wolińska-Cichocka and R. Yokoyama, β-delayed neutron emission of r-process nuclei at the N = 82 shell closure, *Physics Letters B* **816**, p. 136266 (May 2021).
25. D. Kasen, B. Metzger, J. Barnes, E. Quataert and E. Ramirez-Ruiz, Origin of the heavy elements in binary neutron-star mergers from a gravitational wave event, *Nature* **551**, 80 (November 2017).
26. C. J. Fontes, C. L. Fryer, A. L. Hungerford, R. T. Wollaeger and O. Korobkin, A line-binned treatment of opacities for the spectra and light curves from neutron star mergers, *MNRAS* **493**, 4143 (April 2020).
27. M. Tanaka, D. Kato, G. Gaigalas and K. Kawaguchi, Systematic opacity calculations for kilonovae, *MNRAS* **496**, 1369 (August 2020).
28. K. Olsen, C. J. Fontes, C. L. Fryer, A. L. Hungerford, R. T. Wollaeger and O. Korobkin. NIST-LANL Opacity Database (ver. 1.0), [Online]. Available: [Online]. Available: https://nlte.nist.gov/OPAC. National Institute of Standards and Technology, Gaithersburg, MD., (2020).
29. G. Gaigalas, D. Kato, P. Rynkun, L. Radžiūtė and M. Tanaka, Extended Calculations of Energy Levels and Transition Rates of Nd II-IV Ions for Application to Neutron Star Mergers, *ApJ Supp* **240**, p. 29 (February 2019).
30. L. Radžiūtė, G. Gaigalas, D. Kato, P. Rynkun and M. Tanaka, Extended Calculations of Energy Levels and Transition Rates for Singly Ionized Lanthanide Elements. I. Pr-Gd, *ApJ Supp* **248**, p. 17 (May 2020).
31. A. Kramida, Yu. Ralchenko, J. Reader and and NIST ASD Team. NIST Atomic Spectra Database (ver. 5.8), [Online]. Available: https://physics.nist.gov/asd [2021, October 1]. National Institute of Standards and Technology, Gaithersburg, MD., (2020).
32. K. Hotokezaka, M. Tanaka, D. Kato and G. Gaigalas, Nebular emission from lanthanide-rich ejecta of neutron star merger, *MNRAS* **506**, 5863 (October 2021).
33. P. A. Pinto and R. G. Eastman, The Physics of Type IA Supernova Light Curves. II. Opacity and Diffusion, *ApJ* **530**, 757 (February 2000).
34. J. I. Castor, *Radiation Hydrodynamics* 2004.
35. C. L. Fryer, S. E. Woosley and D. H. Hartmann, Formation Rates of Black Hole Accretion Disk Gamma-Ray Bursts, *ApJ* **526**, 152 (November 1999).
36. J. S. Bloom, S. Sigurdsson and O. R. Pols, The spatial distribution of coalescing neutron star binaries: implications for gamma-ray bursts, *MNRAS* **305**, 763 (May 1999).

37. L. C. Strang, A. Melatos, N. Sarin and P. D. Lasky, Inferring properties of neutron stars born in short gamma-ray bursts with a plerion-like X-ray plateau, *MNRAS* **507**, 2843 (October 2021).
38. R. T. Wollaeger, C. L. Fryer, C. J. Fontes, J. Lippuner, W. T. Vestrand, M. R. Mumpower, O. Korobkin, A. L. Hungerford and W. P. Even, Impact of Pulsar and Fallback Sources on Multifrequency Kilonova Models, *ApJ* **880**, p. 22 (July 2019).
39. L. Piro, E. Troja, B. Zhang, G. Ryan, H. van Eerten, R. Ricci, M. H. Wieringa, A. Tiengo, N. R. Butler, S. B. Cenko, O. D. Fox, H. G. Khandrika, G. Novara, A. Rossi and T. Sakamoto, A long-lived neutron star merger remnant in GW170817: constraints and clues from X-ray observations, *MNRAS* **483**, 1912 (February 2019).
40. H. Klion, P. C. Duffell, D. Kasen and E. Quataert, The effect of jet-ejecta interaction on the viewing angle dependence of kilonova light curves, *MNRAS* **502**, 865 (March 2021).
41. D. Watson, C. J. Hansen, J. Selsing, A. Koch, D. B. Malesani, A. C. Andersen, J. P. U. Fynbo, A. Arcones, A. Bauswein, S. Covino, A. Grado, K. E. Heintz, L. Hunt, C. Kouveliotou, G. Leloudas, A. J. Levan, P. Mazzali and E. Pian, Identification of strontium in the merger of two neutron stars, *Nature* **574**, 497 (October 2019).
42. M.-R. Wu, P. Banerjee, B. D. Metzger, G. Martínez-Pinedo, T. Aramaki, E. Burns, C. J. Hailey, J. Barnes and G. Karagiorgi, Finding the Remnants of the Milky Way's Last Neutron Star Mergers, *ApJ* **880**, p. 23 (July 2019).

Tutti-Frutti method: Recent developments in the PN/PM/SF treatment of the gravitational two-body problem

Donato Bini* and Andrea Geralico[†]

Istituto per le Applicazioni del Calcolo "M. Picone," CNR I-00185 Rome, Italy
* E-mail: donato.bini@gmail.com
[†] E-mail: andrea.geralico@gmail.com

We review some recent results obtained at the sixth Post-Newtonian level of approximation for the Hamiltonian description of a two-body system, by using several methods whose combination has led to the so-called "Tutti-Frutti" approach.

Keywords: Two-body system; Post-Newtonian and Post-Minkowskian approximation; Scattering angle

1. Introduction

The two-body gravitational interaction is a fundamental physics problem whose descriptions necessitates a fully general relativistic treatment. The latter, in turn, is much difficult and over the years several approximation methods have been implemented for the mathematical treatment of this problem, ranging from weak-field and slow-motion (Post-Newtonian (PN) approximation[1]), weak-field but eventually relativistic motions (Post-Minkowskian (PM) approximation[2,3]), extreme-mass-ratio limit (i.e., the condition in which the mass of one of the two bodies is much larger of the other, discussed in the framework of perturbation theory and gravitational self-force (GSF)[4]), Effective Field Theory (EFT),[5] numerical relativity (NR).[6]

All these analytical (and semi-analytical) treatments have been used to build up a Hamiltonian description of the system. Since as soon as one raises the level of approximation considered the number of terms entering this Hamiltonian raises as well, in 1999 A. Buonanno and T. Damour[7,8] introduced the so-called Effective One-Body (EOB) approach aiming at a partial resummation of the Hamiltonian itself. Indeed, the EOB is especially useful since it condensates in a few gravitational potentials the essential characteristics of the interaction, and can be also continuously (and easily) updated as soon as new results become available in the literature by using whatever approximation scheme.

Let us recall also that 1) the gravitational interaction of two bodies is actually compatible with two basic scenarios: capture (the more massive of the two attracts and then swallows the other; the system in this case spirals undergoing ellipticlike motions) and scattering (the two bodies can be close enough but they have enough energy to resist the attraction; the system in this case undergoes hyperboliclike or paraboliclike motions). 2) Both cases are of particular importance in view of the possibility to detect gravitational wave signals from Earth-based interferometers operating now (e.g., Ligo[9] and Virgo[10]) and also (more likely) by future, forthcoming satellite missions involving space-based interferometers (Lisa[11]). 3) The mathematical description of the dynamics by any available approximation method has strong limitations when the gravitational field becomes too strong, as for example in the case of the capture. In this condition one is only left with NR.

To add fuel to fire one should also take into account that new difficulties arise when taking into account the emission of gravitational radiation (energy, angular momentum and linear momentum) by the system as soon as a purely conservative scenario is no more possible. Indeed, starting from the 2.5PN level of approximation the problem is no more conservative, so that one has to deal with radiation-reaction effects. Furthermore, starting from the 4PN order the Hamiltonian of the system also includes a nonlocal part, which accounts for the past history of the system.

This picture clearly explains the difficulties which one encounters when trying to reach the 5PN (and beyond) level of accuracy in the model. Luckily, the various concomitant effects can be still computed separately so one can decide to limit to the study of the conservative and local part of the Hamiltonian, and later including nonlocal effects and radiation-reaction induced effects. This is the spirit of the recently developed "Tutti-Frutti" (TF) method, which combines several theoretical formalisms: PN, PM, multipolar-post-Minkowskian (MPM), EFT, GSF, EOB, and Delaunay averaging.[12–16]

2. EOB Hamiltonian

The EOB approach rewrites the (real, conservative) two-body Hamiltonian $H(r, p_r, p_\phi)$ in terms of an effective Hamiltonian $H_{\text{eff}}(r, p_r, p_\phi)$ (ϕ is an ignorable coordinate in the conservative case)

$$H = M\sqrt{1 + 2\nu(\hat{H}_{\text{eff}} - 1)}, \qquad (1)$$

with

$$M = m_1 + m_2, \qquad \mu = \frac{m_1 m_2}{m_1 + m_2}, \qquad \nu = \frac{m_1 m_2}{(m_1 + m_2)^2} \qquad (2)$$

the total mass of the system (M), the reduced mass (μ) and the symmetric mass ratio (ν). The effective Hamiltonian (per unit of reduced mass, μ) $\hat{H}_{\text{eff}}$ written in the standard p_r-gauge or DJS gauge[17] involves several potentials: A, $\bar{D}$, $\hat{Q}$, etc.,

$$\hat{H}_{\text{eff}}^2 = A(u,\nu)[1 + p_\phi^2 u^2 + A(u,\nu)\bar{D}(u,\nu)p_r^2 + \hat{Q}(u,\nu;p_r)], \qquad (3)$$

where $u = GM/r$ and

$$\hat{Q}(u,\nu;p_r) = p_r^4 q_4(u,\nu) + p_r^6 q_6(u,\nu) + p_r^8 q_8(u,\nu) + \ldots. \qquad (4)$$

The various potentials 1) have a polynomial structure in terms of the symmetric mass-ratio ν, e.g.,

$$A(u,\nu) = 1 - 2u + \nu a^{\nu^1}(u) + \nu^2 a^{\nu^2}(u) + \nu^3 a^{\nu^3}(u) + \ldots,$$
$$\bar{D}(u,\nu) = 1 + \nu \bar{d}^{\nu^1}(u) + \nu^2 \bar{d}^{\nu^2}(u) + \nu^3 \bar{d}^{\nu^3}(u) + \ldots,$$
$$q_4(u,\nu) = 1 + \nu q_4^{\nu^1}(u) + \nu^2 q_4^{\nu^2}(u) + \nu^3 q_4^{\nu^3}(u) + \ldots, \tag{5}$$

etc., with the degree of the polynom increasing with PN approximation order; 2) have both a local part and a nonlocal part

$$A(u,\nu) = A_{\text{loc}}(u,\nu) + A_{\text{nl}}(u,\nu),$$
$$\bar{D}(u,\nu) = \bar{D}_{\text{loc}}(u,\nu) + \bar{D}_{\text{nl}}(u,\nu),$$
$$\hat{Q}(u,\nu;p_r) = \hat{Q}_{\text{loc}}(u,\nu;p_r) + \hat{Q}_{\text{nl}}(u,\nu;p_r), \tag{6}$$

the nonlocal part starting at 4PN.

3. The Tutti-Frutti approach and the determination of the conservative dynamics at 6PN

The starting point of the TF approach is to consider the total two-body conservative action, which at the 6PN accuracy has both a local-in-time part and a nonlocal-in-time part (starting at 4PN)

$$S_{\text{tot}}^{\leq 6\text{PN}} = S_{\text{loc}}^{\leq 6\text{PN}} + S_{\text{nonloc}}^{\leq 6\text{PN}}. \tag{7}$$

The main steps are summarized below.

(1) Fix completely the nonlocal part of the Hamiltonian by using Delaunay averaging along ellipticlike orbits.
The nonlocal action is given by

$$S_{\text{nonloc}}^{4+5+6\text{PN}} = -\int dt\, H_{\text{nonloc}}^{4+5+6\text{PN}}(t), \tag{8}$$

with

$$H_{\text{nonloc}}^{4+5+6\text{PN}}(t) = \frac{G\mathcal{M}}{c^3} \text{Pf}_{2r_{12}/c} \int \frac{dt'}{|t-t'|} \mathcal{F}_{2\text{PN}}^{\text{split}}(t,t'). \tag{9}$$

Here, $\mathcal{M}$ denotes the total ADM conserved mass-energy of the binary system, r_{12} entering the timescale of the the *partie finie* (Pf) operation is the harmonic-coordinate radial distance, and $\mathcal{F}_{2\text{PN}}^{\text{split}}(t,t')$ is the time-split version of the fractionally 2PN-accurate gravitational-wave energy flux, i.e.,

$$\mathcal{F}_{2\text{PN}}^{\text{GW}}(t) \propto I_{ab}^{(3)}(t) I_{ab}^{(3)}(t) + O(\eta^2) \quad \to \quad \mathcal{F}_{2\text{PN}}^{\text{split}}(t,t') \propto I_{ab}^{(3)}(t) I_{ab}^{(3)}(t') + O(\eta^2), \tag{10}$$

with $\eta \equiv \frac{1}{c}$, the superscript in parenthesis denoting repeated time-derivatives of the quadrupole moment I_{ab}. Taking then the (Delaunay) time average of the harmonic-coordinates Hamiltonian (9) gives a gauge-invariant function of two orbital parameters

$$\langle \delta H_{\text{nonloc,h}}^{4+5+6\text{PN}} \rangle = \frac{1}{\oint dt_h} \oint \delta H_{\text{nonloc,h}}^{4+5+6\text{PN}}(t_h) dt_h \,. \tag{11}$$

Next, do the same computation in EOB coordinates. Comparison between the two results allows fixing the nonlocal parts of the EOB potentials.

(2) Use SF information about small-eccentricity ellipticlike motion to determine (part of) the local EOB Hamiltonian.

Compute the averaged redshift factor, z_1, i.e., a (first) gauge-invariant variable associated with the conservative dynamics of the two-body system, along ellipticlike orbits by using first-order SF techniques in a small-eccentricity expansion limit, including but high powers of the eccentricity (up to the eighth order). $z_1 \sim \langle \partial_{m_1} H \rangle$ incorporates both local and nonlocal contributions in the Hamiltonian, but it is limited from the fact that analytic computations are possible only at first-order in the symmetric mass-ratio ν. Combining this result with the information about the nonlocal part of the EOB Hamiltonian specified at the point 1 will allow one to determine all the linear-in-ν local EOB potentials. The remaining (i.e., higher order in ν) coefficients are still undetermined.

(3) Compute another gauge-invariant quantity, the scattering angle, χ, along hyperboliclike orbits to determine most of the remaining coefficients.

The total scattering angle $\chi^{\text{tot}} = \chi^{\text{loc}} + \chi^{\text{nonloc}}$ can be expressed as a large-angular momentum (or equivalently large-eccentricity) expansion, with coefficients having a precise mass-structure (or ν-structure) as recently shown by Damour.[18] Therefore, one needs to separately compute both the local and the nonlocal contributions to the scattering angle. The latter is defined by

$$\chi^{\text{nonloc}}(E, J, \nu) = \frac{\partial W^{\text{nonloc}}(E, J, \nu)}{\partial J} \,, \tag{12}$$

where E and J are the total energy and angular momentum in the c.m. frame, respectively, and

$$W^{\text{nonloc}}(E, J; \nu) \equiv \int_{-\infty}^{+\infty} dt\, H^{\text{nonloc}}(t) \,, \tag{13}$$

is the integrated nonlocal action. In order to compute the local contribution χ^{loc}, instead, it is convenient to convert the local EOB Hamiltonian into the so-called energy-gauge.[19] Imposing then that χ^{tot} satisfies the prescribed ν-structure will fix most of the parametrizing coefficients of the EOB potentials.

All the above steps used jointly have lead to the determination of most of the coefficients entering the conservative Hamiltonian of the two-body system. More precisely at 5PN there remain only 2 quantities to be determined ($\bar{d}_5^{\nu^2}$ and $a_6^{\nu^2}$) and at 6PN there remain only 4 more quantities to be determined ($q_{45}^{\nu^2}$, $\bar{d}_6^{\nu^2}$, $a_7^{\nu^2}$, and $a_7^{\nu^3}$).

Within the EFT approach, the conservative scattering angle can be decomposed into a potential-graviton contribution, and a radiation-graviton one.[5] The $O(G^4)$ potential-graviton contribution to the radial action has been recently derived in Ref.,[20] whereas Ref.[21] has computed the potential-graviton contribution to the 5PN two-body Hamiltonian. Although the TF decomposition of the two-body dynamics into local-in-time and non-local-in-time parts is closely linked to the EFT decomposition, one cannot simply identify the TF time-symmetric local-in-time dynamics to the EFT time-symmetric potential-graviton dynamics. However, one can compare the total conservative scattering angle derived within the two approaches. This allows one to complete the result of Ref.[20] by providing the explicit expression (at the 6PN accuracy) of the complementary radiation-graviton contributions to the scattering angle, or equivalently, to the radial action. Furthermore, adding the radiation-graviton contributions to the 5PN Hamiltonian obtained in Ref.[22] yields explicit expressions for the two 5PN undetermined $O(G^5)$ and $O(G^6)$ TF parameters $\bar{d}_5^{\nu^2}$ and $a_6^{\nu^2}$, involving either π^2 terms and rational coefficients entering various (local-in-time) radiation-graviton contributions to the conservative effective 5PN action.[22] Our results are in agreement (for the π^2 contributions) with those of Ref.[21] A comparison with the results of Ref.[22] is currently under consideration.

4. Radiation-reaction effects

The presence of a radiation-reaction force implies a modification of Hamilton equations as

$$\dot{\mathbf{q}} = \frac{\partial H}{\partial \mathbf{p}}, \qquad \dot{\mathbf{p}} = -\frac{\partial H}{\partial \mathbf{q}} + \boldsymbol{\mathcal{F}}_{\mathrm{rr}}. \tag{14}$$

The work done by this force on the system implies energy, angular momentum and linear momentum losses by the system itself, as well as to the fact that the four-velocity of the center-of-mass is no more conserved, leading to recoil effects. For instance, the scattering angle will be modified as

$$\chi = \chi^{\mathrm{cons}} + \delta^{\mathrm{rr}}\chi, \tag{15}$$

where the radiation-reaction corrections to the conservative value can be written as

$$\delta^{\mathrm{rr}}\chi = -\frac{1}{2}\left[\frac{\partial \chi^{\mathrm{cons}}}{\partial E} E^{\mathrm{rad}} + \frac{\partial \chi^{\mathrm{cons}}}{\partial J} J^{\mathrm{rad}}\right], \tag{16}$$

in terms of the energy and angular momentum losses E^{rad} and J^{rad}. The latter include instantaneous and tail (i.e. hereditary) contributions, and admit a double PM and PN expansion. At the fractional 2PN order they read

$$\begin{aligned} E_{\mathrm{2PN}}^{\mathrm{rad}} &= \nu^2\left(E_{\mathrm{N}} + \eta^2 E_{\mathrm{1PN}} + \eta^3 E_{\mathrm{1.5PN}}^{\mathrm{tail}} + \eta^4 E_{\mathrm{2PN}}\right), \\ J_{\mathrm{2PN}}^{\mathrm{rad}} &= \nu^2\left(J_{\mathrm{N}} + \eta^2 J_{\mathrm{1PN}} + \eta^3 J_{\mathrm{1.5PN}}^{\mathrm{tail}} + \eta^4 J_{\mathrm{2PN}}\right), \end{aligned} \tag{17}$$

where tails start at the 1.5PN order. For example, the Newtonian values are given by

$$E_\mathrm{N} = \frac{37}{15}\pi\frac{p_\infty^4}{j^3} + \frac{1568}{45}\frac{p_\infty^3}{j^4} + \frac{122}{5}\pi\frac{p_\infty^2}{j^5} + O\left(\frac{1}{j^6}\right),$$

$$J_\mathrm{N} = \frac{16}{5}\frac{p_\infty^3}{j} + \frac{28}{5}\pi\frac{p_\infty^2}{j^2} + \frac{176}{5}\frac{p_\infty}{j^3} + O\left(\frac{1}{j^4}\right), \quad (18)$$

where $j \equiv cJ/(GM\mu)$ is a dimensionless angular momentum parameter, and the linear momentum at infinity, p_∞, is related to the binding energy by $\bar{E} \equiv (E - Mc^2)/(\mu c^2) = \frac{1}{2}p_\infty^2$, at the Newtonian level. At higher PN orders the coefficients of the above expansion become functions of ν: linear functions of ν at 1PN, quadratic at 2PN, etc., but the structure of the PM expansion is exactly the same.

We have computed in Ref.[23] the changes of 4-momentum during the scattering process (between the two asymptotic states of the two bodies labelled by $a = 1, 2$) which are linear order in radiation-reaction, i.e.,

$$\Delta p_{a\mu} \equiv p_{a\mu}^+ - p_{a\mu}^- = \Delta p_{a\mu}^{\mathrm{cons}} + \Delta p_{a\mu}^{\mathrm{rr}}, \quad (19)$$

where the radiation-reacted contribution $\Delta p_{a\mu}^{\mathrm{rr}}$ is the sum of a relative-motion term and a recoil one, which are linear in the radiative losses of energy, linear-momentum, and angular momentum. We have also shown how the polynomial dependence of $\Delta p_{a\mu}^{\mathrm{rr}}$ can be exploited to yield some identity relating the various radiative losses. Adding radiation-reaction effects at higher PN orders is an open issue for challenging future works.

References

1. L. Blanchet, "Gravitational Radiation from Post-Newtonian Sources and Inspiralling Compact Binaries," Living Rev. Rel. **17**, 2 (2014) [arXiv:1310.1528 [gr-qc]].
2. L. Bel, T. Damour, N. Deruelle, J. Ibanez and J. Martin, "Poincaré-invariant gravitational field and equations of motion of two pointlike objects: The postlinear approximation of general relativity," Gen. Rel. Grav. **13**, 963 (1981).
3. K. Westpfahl, "High-Speed Scattering of Charged and Uncharged Particles in General Relativity," Fortsch. Phys. **33**, 417 (1985).
4. S. L. Detweiler, "Perspective on gravitational self-force analyses," Class. Quant. Grav. **22**, S681 (2005) [gr-qc/0501004].
5. W. D. Goldberger and I. Z. Rothstein, "An Effective field theory of gravity for extended objects," Phys. Rev. D **73**, 104029 (2006) [arXiv:hep-th/0409156 [hep-th]].
6. F. Pretorius, "Numerical relativity using a generalized harmonic decomposition," Class. Quant. Grav. **22**, 425 (2005) [gr-qc/0407110].
7. A. Buonanno and T. Damour, "Effective one-body approach to general relativistic two-body dynamics," Phys. Rev. D **59**, 084006 (1999) [gr-qc/9811091].
8. A. Buonanno and T. Damour, "Transition from inspiral to plunge in binary black hole coalescences," Phys. Rev. D **62**, 064015 (2000) [gr-qc/0001013].
9. See the LIGO website at http://www.ligo.org
10. See the VIRGO website at http://www.virgo-gw.eu
11. See the LISA website at https://lisa.nasa.gov/

12. D. Bini, T. Damour and A. Geralico, "Novel approach to binary dynamics: application to the fifth post-Newtonian level," Phys. Rev. Lett. **123**, no.23, 231104 (2019) [arXiv:1909.02375 [gr-qc]].
13. D. Bini, T. Damour and A. Geralico, "Binary dynamics at the fifth and fifth-and-a-half post-Newtonian orders," Phys. Rev. D **102**, no.2, 024062 (2020) [arXiv:2003.11891 [gr-qc]].
14. D. Bini, T. Damour and A. Geralico, "Sixth post-Newtonian local-in-time dynamics of binary systems," Phys. Rev. D **102**, no.2, 024061 (2020) [arXiv:2004.05407 [gr-qc]].
15. D. Bini, T. Damour and A. Geralico, "Sixth post-Newtonian nonlocal-in-time dynamics of binary systems," Phys. Rev. D **102**, no.8, 084047 (2020) [arXiv:2007.11239 [gr-qc]].
16. D. Bini, T. Damour, A. Geralico, S. Laporta and P. Mastrolia, "Gravitational scattering at the seventh order in G: nonlocal contribution at the sixth post-Newtonian accuracy," Phys. Rev. D **103**, no.4, 044038 (2021) [arXiv:2012.12918 [gr-qc]].
17. T. Damour, P. Jaranowski, and G. Schäfer, "On the determination of the last stable orbit for circular general relativistic binaries at the third post-Newtonian approximation," Phys. Rev. D **62**, 084011 (2000) [arXiv:gr-qc/0005034].
18. T. Damour, "Classical and quantum scattering in post-Minkowskian gravity," Phys. Rev. D **102**, no.2, 024060 (2020) [arXiv:1912.02139 [gr-qc]].
19. T. Damour, "High-energy gravitational scattering and the general relativistic two-body problem," Phys. Rev. D **97**, no. 4, 044038 (2018) [arXiv:1710.10599 [gr-qc]].
20. Z. Bern, J. Parra-Martinez, R. Roiban, M. S. Ruf, C. H. Shen, M. P. Solon and M. Zeng, "Scattering Amplitudes and Conservative Binary Dynamics at $\mathcal{O}(G^4)$," Phys. Rev. Lett. **126**, no.17, 171601 (2021) [arXiv:2101.07254 [hep-th]].
21. J. Blümlein, A. Maier, P. Marquard and G. Schäfer, "The fifth-order post-Newtonian Hamiltonian dynamics of two-body systems from an effective field theory approach: potential contributions," Nucl. Phys. B **965**, 115352 (2021) [arXiv:2010.13672 [gr-qc]].
22. S. Foffa and R. Sturani, "Hereditary terms at next-to-leading order in two-body gravitational dynamics," Phys. Rev. D **101**, no.6, 064033 (2020) [erratum: Phys. Rev. D **103**, no.8, 089901 (2021)] [arXiv:1907.02869 [gr-qc]].
23. D. Bini, T. Damour and A. Geralico, "Radiative contributions to gravitational scattering," Phys. Rev. D **104**, no.8, 084031 (2021) [arXiv:2107.08896 [gr-qc]].

GRB observations on cubesate satellites in the Universat–SOCRAT project

Sergey I. Svertilov[1], Michail I. Panasyuk, Vitaly V. Bogomolov[2] and Mikhail I. Prokhorov[3]

Skobeltsyn Institute of Nuclear Physics, Lomonosov Moscow State University,
Moscow, 119234, Russia
Department of Physics, Lomonosov Moscow State University,
Moscow, 119234, Russia
Email: [1] *sis@coronas.ru,* [2] *bogovit@rambler.ru,* [3] *prokhorov.mi17@physics.msu.ru*

Anatoly F. Iyudin[4], Pavel A. Klimov[5], Vladislav I. Osedlo[6], Vasily L. Petrov[7], Oleg Yu. Peretyat'ko[8], Yury K. Zaiko[9] and Ivan V. Yashin[10]

Skobeltsyn Institute of Nuclear Physics, Lomonosov Moscow State University,
Moscow, 119234, Russia
Email: [4] *aiyudin@srd.sinp.msu.ru,* [5] *pavel.klimov@gmail.com,* [6] *osedlo@mail.ru,*
[7] *vas@srd.sinp.msu.ru,* [8] *pouoleg@mail.ru,* [9] *zaikoiurii@yandex.ru,* [10] *iv_n@bk.ru*

Vladimir M. Lipunov

Department of Physics, Lomonosov Moscow State University,
Moscow, 119234, Russia
Sternberg Astronomical Institute, Lomonosov Moscow State University,
Moscow, 119234, Russia
Email: lipunov2007@gmail.com

Vitaliy Yu. Prokopyev and Alexey S. Styuf

Division for Aerospace Research, Novosibirsk State University,
Novosibirsk, 630090, Russia
Email: vprok@cosmos.nsu.ru

Multi-channel astronomy is one of the most important and rapidly developing field of modern physics. The well known result of multi-channel observations is simultaneous detection of gravitational wave and gamma ray bursts associated with neutron star merger event. This observation open a new window to study the Universe, and actually triggered the broad scale study of astrophysical phenomena in hard X-Rays and gamma rays by orbital experiments together with ground based observations of gravitational waves, neutrino and ultra-high energy cosmic rays. From this perspective it appears that small satellites of CubeSat type are quite appropriate for multi-channel observations of astrophysical transients because it is the cheapest way to realize all-sky monitoring observations by orbital instruments. Presently at D.V. Skobeltsyn Institute of Nuclear Physics of the M.V. Lomonosov Moscow State University (SINP MSU) a new project named Universat–SOCRAT is under development which is intended for operational monitoring of near-Earth's radiation environment and monitoring of electromagnetic transients in the optical, UV, X-ray and gamma ranges. Here we discuss the first results of charged particles, gamma quanta fluxes and UV-emission measurements from the upper atmosphere in several CubeSat missions, which were successfully launched in 2019, 2020.

Keywords: Multimessenger astronomy; Universat-SOCRAT project.

1. Introduction

One of the most important and interesting fields of modern physics and astrophysics is the study of extreme processes and phenomena leading to the most powerful explosions, acceleration of particles to the maximum possible energies, generation of superstrong gravitational and electromagnetic fields. Such phenomena include cosmic gamma-ray bursts (GRBs) associated with the collapse of massive stars (hypernovae), merging of relativistic compact objects (neutron stars and black holes), leading to the generation of gravitational waves and short-term increases in gamma-ray fluxes, nonstationary processes in neutron stars with a superstrong magnetic field (magnetars), dynamic processes in the nuclei of active galaxies, pulsars and close binary systems, which can be associated with the acceleration of particles to high and extremely high energies and the generation of high and ultrahigh energy neutrinos.

Despite the fact that these extreme phenomena have been studied very intensively in recent years, there are still many unsolved problems. As for GRBs, this is, first of all, the definition of the mechanism of functioning of the "central engine", the formation of relativistic jets and the propagation of relativistic shock waves in them, the so-called shells. The related problems concern with the study of the possibility of particle acceleration on relativistic shock waves, and of the conditions for generation of polarized electromagnetic radiation. In this regard, especially important information can be obtained as a result of multi-wavelength observations of the so-called intrinsic emission of a GRB, especially in the optical and gamma ranges. Among the observational tasks, it should be noted that it is necessary to observe GRBs with the maximum possible temporal and spectral resolution, as well as at a high level of sensitivity, which will make it possible to expand the range of observed burst sources up to the most distant objects in the Universe ($z \sim 10-12$). The study of the fine temporal structure of GRB intrinsic emission, as well as of the so-called precursors, including their observations in the optical range, is very actual.

An important task is studying of the so-called short hard GRBs, includes the need to discover their intrinsic optical emission. It is known, that such bursts are associated with the processes of neutron stars merging in close binaries; therefore, their study is particularly relevant after recent discovery of gravitational-waves bursts generated during the merger of relativistic compact objects.

Considering the relevance of studying extreme astrophysical phenomena, it should be emphasized that for further progress in understanding their nature, multi-wave (at least simultaneous in the optical, X-ray and gamma ranges), multi-channel and multi-satellite observations are required. Multi-channel observations mean the simultaneous detection of events by space-based and ground-based facilities, including ground-based optical, radio and gamma telescopes, gravitational-wave antennas, and facilities designed to detect neutrinos and ultra-high energy cosmic rays. Multi-satellite observations are necessary to ensure the detection of each GRB on several spacecraft in order to localize the GRB source using the triangulation technique.

2. Advantages of CubeSat constellation for GRB observations

The main success of multi-channel astrophysical observations is connected with simultaneous detection of gravitation wave and gamma-ray burst in August 17, 2017 from neutron star merging.[1] It seems that one of the cheapest and very effective ways of multi-channel and multi-satellite observations of such events and GRBs in general is use of small satellites grouping, in particular the CubeSat constellations. Due to the relatively low cost and ease of manufacture, it is possible to carry out more, or less regular launches of CubeSat satellites as a by-pass mission. Thus, a constellation of nano-satellites can be created, which will significantly increase the efficiency of space radiation and electromagnetic transient monitoring.

The solution for the localization problem can be achieved by applying the triangulation method for observations of the selected area with different satellites. For this purpose the number of CubeSats should be launched for the joint observations of a given burst. To realize the triangulation technique in minimal variant 3-4 CubeSats are necessary (see Fig. 1). Optimally they should be launched as by-pass mission together with the main spacecraft of multi-satellite group, i.e. on the near circular solar-synchronous orbits with altitude about 400 – 600 km, inclination about 98° and longitude deviation of the ascending node $< 5°/year$. The error box of GRB source localization is defined by time delay of signals detected on each satellite. The longer delay the more accurate will be localization. Delay itself depends on distance between satellites, i.e. the larger distance corresponds to the longer delay. In the case of near-Earth orbits the distance between satellites is limited by about 10 000 – 15 000 km, because all satellites should be from one side of the Earth to avoid the screening of GRB source. By this the necessity of maintaining of given distance between satellites is a separate technical problem. It can be solved by the use of thrusters. Off cause CubeSat constellation can be used also for observations of transient events from the Earth atmosphere, including Terrestrial Gamma Ray Flashes (TGF) and monitoring of space radiation. However, there will be other requirements to the distance between satellites in the case of triangulation technique application for TGFs. In the last case the given area of Atmosphere should be observed by all satellites of grouping, thus the maximal distance should be no more than about 1000 km. For successive realization of multi-satellite mission for GRB observations certain conditions should be met:

- presence of satellite Internet (global star/iridium) plus high frequency transmitter;
- stabilization better than $1°/s$, satellite orientation on the "Zenith–Nadir" axis and velocity vector with accuracy $+/-10°$, information on satellite axes orientation with accuracy $0.1°$;
- possibility of quasi-autonomous navigation, in particular with the use of millisecond pulsars as beacons;

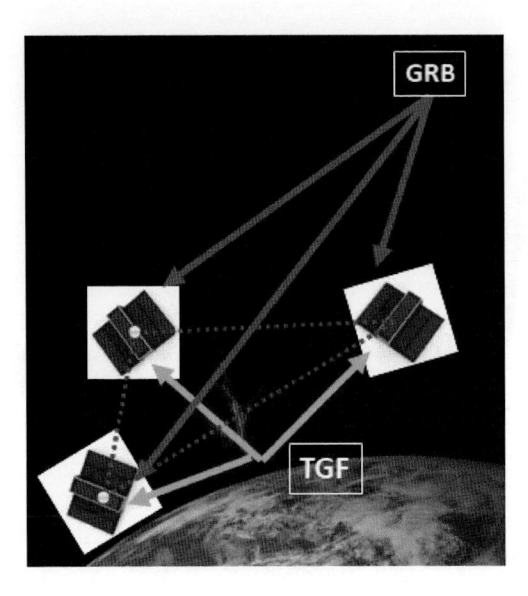

Fig. 1. The CubeSat constellation in minimal configuration.

- different data types, such as monitoring, event-by-event, telegrams about burst triggers (GCN);
- data daily volume no less 100 Mb;
- exact timing is needed;
- orientation accuracy $\sim 1°$ is useful;
- fast telegrams are needed;
- necessity of charge particle variation control.

The last demand is particularly actually if the satellites are launched to the polar orbit because of the problem of false triggering by electron precipitation rises. It can be solved by monitoring of electron flux with the use of special electron detectors or instruments which are able to select true gamma-quantum flux rises on the background of electron precipitation. The last is illustrated by Figs 2, 3, on which the examples of GRB imitations by electron precipitation and the map with such imitation distributions from the BDRG/Lomonosov data[2] are presented.

For instruments, that can be used for GRB detection on-board CubeSats one of the main criteria is the detector area, that is sufficient for GRB registration, should be larger $\sim 50 cm^2$ in the energy range of photons from ~ 20 keV up to several MeV. Such detector units can also be used to detect TGFs and X-ray and gamma ray emission of solar flares.

We note, that presently the space project of Moscow University Universat-SOCRAT is under realization. In the frame of this project the launches of a number of satellites including CubeSats, that can be used as the base of constellation for GRB study, is foreseen.

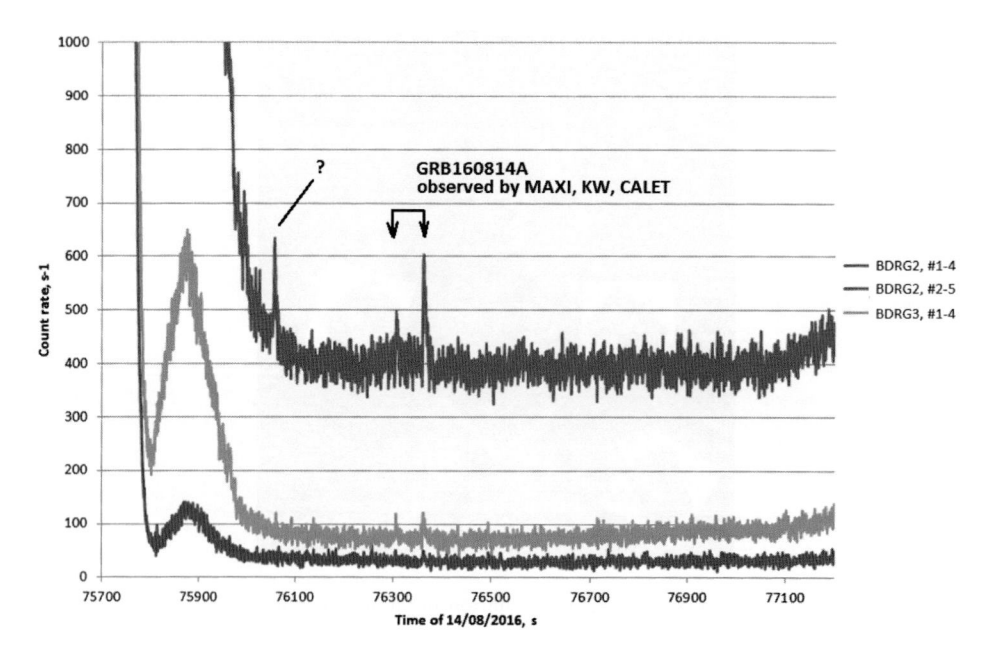

Fig. 2. Example of GRB and burst imitations by magnetosphere electron precipitation detected BDRG/Lomonosov near radiation belts.

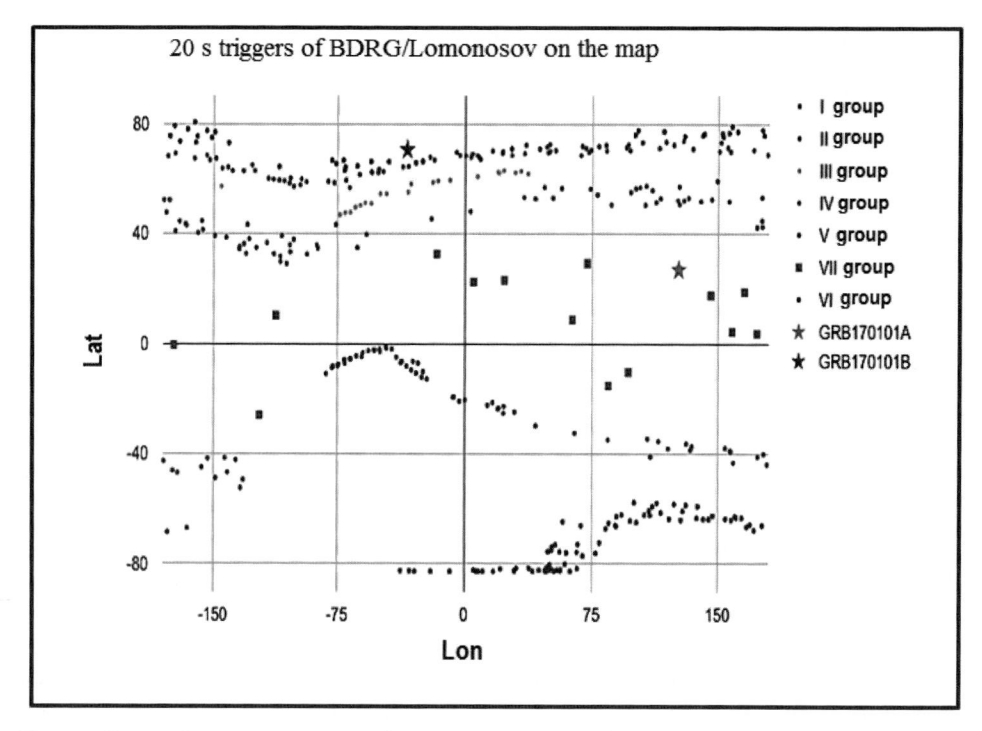

Fig. 3. Geographic distribution of different types of BDRG/Lomonosov triggers. By stars the real GRBs are marked.

2.1. *Universat–SOCRAT space project*

Under the Universat–SOCRAT project it is planned to create a grouping of small satellites for real time monitoring in the near-Earth space of potentially dangerous hazards, i.e. the radiation environment; dangerous objects of the natural (asteroids, meteors) and technogenic origin (space debris), as well as electromagnetic transients (cosmic gamma-ray bursts, optical, ultraviolet and gamma ray flashes from the Earth's atmosphere.[3,4])

Within the framework of the Universat–SOCRAT project several small spacecraft should be launched on specially selected orbits. In the minimal version, the group of satellites should consist of three spacecraft. One spacecraft of medium mass (small satellite) should be launched on a low solar-synchronous orbit with a height of about 500–650 km and an inclination of 97–98°. Two other satellites of lower mass (micro satellites) should be launched on an orbit close to circular with a height of about 1500 km and an inclination of $\sim 80°$ and on an elliptical orbit with an apogee of about 8000 km, a perigee of 600–700 km, inclination 63.4° and argument of perigee $\sim 310°$.

The small satellite payload should include instruments for monitoring of space radiation, a set of instruments for optical monitoring of hazardous objects, a set of instruments for studying of atmospheric phenomena in the optical range, a set of instruments for monitoring in gamma- range, and special unit for data collection. The payload should also include three-component magnetometer. The payload of each micro satellite should include instruments for space radiation monitoring, a compact gamma spectrometer, a wide field of view optical camera, an ultraviolet detector and an electronics unit for data collection. Payload of all three satellites also should include the special electronic unit for data collection from detector units, its transmission to the board systems and feeding too the instruments power supply and commands.

The basic multi-satellite group can be supplemented with nano-satellites of the CubeSat type. Due to the relative cheapness and ease of manufacture, it is possible to carry out more or less regular launches of satellites as a by-pass mission. Thus, a constellation of nanosatellites can be created, which will significantly increase the efficiency of space radiation and electromagnetic transient monitoring.

The use of several nano-satellites of CubeSat type equipped with several multi-directional spectrometers of energetic protons and electrons will provide a solution of the problem of elaboration of a three-dimensional dynamic model of radiation in near-Earth space. For this, the satellites should be launched onto specially selected orbits and provide measurements that will allow us to calculate the current distribution of particle fluxes in a large volume of near-Earth space, i.e. from low orbits to geostationary, and, as a result, determine the current levels of radiation doses for a wide range spacecraft orbits, and also give a forecast of the radiation situation at low altitudes. Simultaneous measurements of particle fluxes on several spacecraft located at different points in near-Earth space will also allow sufficiently reliable separation of temporal and spatial effects in detected variations of the instrument output readings.

The nano-satellite constellation also gives advantages for GRB and TGF study. As it was mentioned above, the crucial point from this view is necessity of good localization of the transient source. This can be achieved with the use of triangulation technique. In the case of GRB observations about 3–4 satellites will be enough. As for TGF study, optimally the spacecraft grouping should consist of 16 satellites pairwise launched in 8 double orbits, i.e. for each pair of orbits the angle between the planes of the orbits should be about For the all constellation spacecraft the main operational mode of the most instruments is on duty mode when the all instruments are switched-on and operate continuously. Instrument switching between the operational modes is carried out by commands from the Earth or by the internal programs. To optimize the payload energy consumption, the data exchange between instrument electronic and satellite board should be foreseen, including information on changing the parameters of the spacecraft power system and payload switching into energy-saving modes (changes in the instrument operating modes or their partial switching-off).

2.2. *Instruments for gamma transient monitoring*

Instruments for study of gamma transients in the Universat-SOCRAT project will include gamma-ray flash monitor (GFM), and a tracking gamma-ray spectrometer (TGS) of the high resolution and sensitivity, that will be sensitive also to neutrons with energies from about 1 MeV up to dozens of MeV.[5] The separate unit for data analysis and control of GFM and TGS should be also foreseen in the payload. This unit should contain digital electronics unit that will provide the record of data stream with a time resolution of $\sim 10\mu s$, and generate the triggers enabling the detection of different type events, including GRB/TGF flux increases. The data record must be referenced to the UTC time with an accuracy of $\sim 10\mu s$ to allow the positioning of the burst, if observed simultaneously by several space missions, using triangulation, and for the comparison with the data of ground based lightning nets.

To realize the triangulation technique sufficiently light X-ray and gamma-ray detectors aimed for the GRB/TGF detection only, without spectrometer capabilities, will be used on the CubeSats. The composition of each spacecraft of small satellite constellation of the cubesat type should include gamma-ray detectors in the amount of:
— Cubesat 1U – 1 instrument;
— Cubesat 3U – at least 1 instrument;
— Cubesat 6U – at least 3 instruments.

If one instrument is installed on the satellite, its axis should be directed along the nadir - zenith axis to nadir, and the field of view should not be obscured within ±60° from the axis of the instrument in the nadir direction. If two instruments are installed on the spacecraft, their axes should be normal to each other, while the axis of one detector should be directed along the nadir—zenith axis to nadir, and the axis of the other detector should be directed along the spacecraft velocity vector in the case of the orbital orientation of the spacecraft (along the line "zenith - nadir" and the velocity vector), while the field of view should not be obscured within $\pm 60°$ from the axis of the detector. If three instruments are installed on the spacecraft, their detector axes should be normal to each other, directed along mutually perpendicular edges of the cube, as if forming a Cartesian coordinate system, while the axis of one detector should be directed to the nadir, the other along the velocity vector, the axis of the third should complement the three-axial coordinate system to complete. Each gamma detector should be placed in a cubesat-type spacecraft in such a way that the surface of its input window coincides with the surface of one of the side faces of the satellite. The instrument should consist of detector assemblies and electronics boards. Various options for the use of detector units are considered. In the simplest version there are considered 4 detector units each from scintillation crystals with a size of $45 \times 45 \times 5$ mm, viewed by a photo-sensor. There are considered as possible scintillators CsI(Tl) crystals (a cheap option) or Ce:GAGG (an optimal option). For signal pickup, photodetectors such as tube photomultiplier tubes (PMTs) or silicon PMT arrays (Si-PM) can be used.

To provide identification of different types of space radiation (electrons, gamma-quanta), a variant with a fosphich detector can be used when a combination of a plastic scintillator/inorganic scintillator (CsI(Tl) or Ce:GAGG), viewed by a single photodetector, is used while the separation of signals from different scintillators is carried out by analyzing the time profiles of the PMT output signals.

A multi-pixel version of the detector can be also considered when it consists of individual crystals (pixels) of a relatively small size, each of which is viewed by its own photodetector. In this case, a variant can be considered both using standard arrays of silicon PMTs, and using original photodetectors and corresponding non-standard electronics.

2.3. *Instruments for electromagnetic transient monitoring in ultraviolet and optics*

Instruments for study transient luminous events (TLEs) in UV and optical bands should include position sensitive spectrometer, i.e. small lens telescope with high time resolution for spectral measurements of TLE and lightning and UV and infrared (IR) detector-photometer, which is similar to that used in Tatiana-2 and Vernov missions.[6] This instrument will be added by channels in far UV range. It allows comparison with data of previous experiments on study UV flashes in the Atmosphere. Spectral measurements are necessary to determine the type and altitude of TLE generation as well as to reveal lightning discharges by typical 777 nm line and by the absence of signal in the range of oxygen absorption lines about 762 nm. Axes of both instruments should be directed toward Nadir with open angles about 90°.

For the TLE observations on the CubeSats will be used compact UV detector with a wide field of view (AURA-2) or its improved version, i.e. telescope (AURA-2T).[7] These instruments are the development of the AURA (Atmospheric Ultraviolet Radiation) detector already launched on board the VDNH-80 satellite. In this instrument SiPM MicroFC-60035-SMT silicon photomultipliers with a sensitive area of 6 × 6 mm, spectral sensitivity from 300 to 800 nm, a maximum spectral sensitivity at 420 nm, and a quantum efficiency of about 41% at 420 nm are used as photodetectors. Silicon photomultiplier tubes, unlike traditional PMTs used for fast photometry, have a number of advantages that are significant for experiments on small spacecraft. It is compact (thickness about 1 mm), low voltage (25 − 70 V) and low weight. The main advantages of the new detector options are high temporal resolution ($1\mu s - 10ms$) and spatial resolution, higher sensitivity due to an increase in the area of the optical system.

The operation of the detectors in the monitoring mode under the condition of simultaneous operation on several spacecraft will make it possible to control transient activity in the Earth's atmosphere, both of thunderstorm and extra-thunderstorm nature with a large exposure. Cartography and monitoring of UV transients is an important task for understanding the interconnections of various energetic processes in the atmosphere. Also, the quasi-stationary UV glow of the atmosphere can be an additional indicator of the state of the geomagnetic situation and the effect of the solar wind on the atmosphere and magnetosphere of the Earth.

3. First results of Moscow University CubeSat missions

The first stage of the Universat–SOCRAT program began to be implemented on July 5, 2019 after a successful launch from the Vostochny cosmodrome of three nanosatellites of the cubesat type (SOCRAT, AmurSat, VDNH-80). These satellites are equipped with instruments DéCoR (Detector of Cosmic Radiation) for monitoring space radiation, as well as prototypes of instruments for observing transient phenomena in the Earth's atmosphere. In particular, scintillation fosphich detectors, which are prototype of the instrument intended for gamma transient observation on cubsats, are installed on two satellites (AmurSat, VDNH-80). These instruments detect charged particles and gamma rays in the energy release range of 0.1 - 2.0 MeV. The geometric factor of these instruments is $\sim 50 cm^2 sr$. One of the cubesats (VDNH-80) also contains an optical photometer AURA, consisting of four silicon photomultipliers, whose input windows are covered by different light filters. Thus, the instrument provides observations of the Earth's atmosphere in the range from ultraviolet to red. The satellites were launched into a sun-synchronous orbit with an altitude of ~ 800 km. This creates favorable conditions for monitoring space radiation in various areas of near-Earth space, including zones of captured radiation, areas of precipitation, etc. Such an orbit also allows observations of flash phenomena both in the near-equatorial atmosphere and at high latitudes.

The implementation of the Universat-SOCRAT program was continued by the successful launch on 28 September 2020 of three more spacecraft of the cubesat type, on which DeCoR and AURA-2 instruments are installed. One of them, the DECART 6U satellite, contains three identical DeCoR instruments installed in such a way that their axes are mutually normal to each other, which makes it possible to estimate the angular distributions of the detected fluxes. DeCoR devices are also installed on the Norbi 6U satellite, developed jointly with the Novosibirsk State University, as well as on the Yarilo-2 spacecraft of the 1.5U format, developed jointly with the N.E. Bauman Moscow State Technical University. The AURA-2 instrument is operated on-board of DECART satellite.

3.1. *Parameters, structure and functioning principles of DeCoR payload*

The DéCoR payload is an instrument for measuring the fluxes and spectra of charged particles and gamma rays in the energy release range of 0.1 - 2 MeV. The main scientific goals are the study of fast variations of electron fluxes in the areas of precipitation and the slot between radiation belts, as well as the study of the dynamics of particle fluxes and gamma rays at low orbits in dependence on geomagnetic conditions. An important factor that allows more efficient scientific research is the installation of the instrument on two satellites, sequentially flying through the same region of near-Earth space. A photo of the instrument and sketch of detector unit are shown in Fig. 4.

The DeCoR instrument is adapted in order to be mounted in the cubesat satellite body. Its detector is a two-layer assembly of a plastic scintillator and a CsI (Tl) crystal (see Fig. 4b). The detector has a sensitive area of $\sim 18 cm^2$. The assembly is viewed by two PMTs. Separate digitization of the initial and final parts of the PMT output pulse ("Fast component" and "Slow component") from each PMT allows determining the scintillator in which the interaction took place from the pulse shape analysis pulse and, thus allows separate measuring of electrons and gamma ray fluxes. Data and commands are exchanged with the satellite's on-board systems by the instrumentmicrocontroller of the device using the UART protocol. For the accumulation and storage of scientific data non-volatile memory with a capacity of 16 MB is foreseen in the instrument. For transmission to the Earth, the DeCoR instrument generates both monitoring data (particle counting rates 1 time per second) and detailed data about all interactions in the detector with a time resolution of $20 \mu s$ (so call event by event mode), which are accumulated in the instrument's memory by a command that determines the moment of interesting time from the view of the researcher . The main way to conduct a scientific experiment is to regularly collect and transmit monitoring data to the Earth, as well as activate from time to time the detailed recording mode on pre-calculated sections of the satellite trajectory passing through the zones of possible variations of the trapped and quasi-trapped particle fluxes.

a

b

Input window (Al, 0.1 mm + polymer, 0.1 mm)

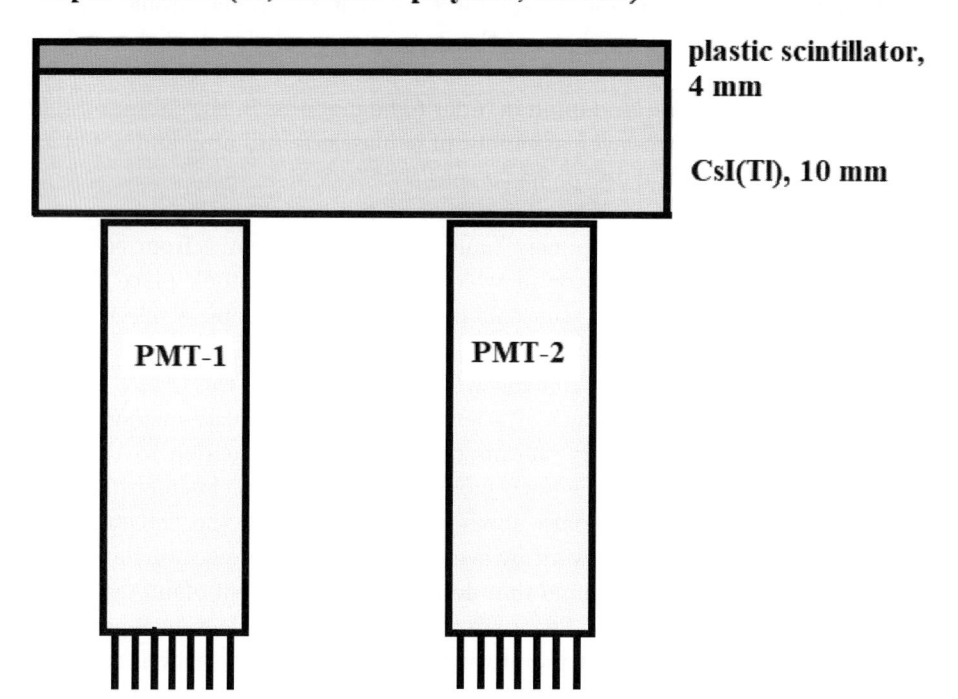

plastic scintillator, 4 mm

CsI(Tl), 10 mm

PMT-1

PMT-2

Fig. 4. The photo (a) and general view (b) of DeCoR instrument.

After viewing data of the "Monitoring" type, the researcher identifies the time points at which the flow variations of interest actually occurred. For these moments, detailed data is requested for transmission to Earth. The used data transfer rate allows you to transmit detailed data about an interesting phenomenon, for example, about the precipitation of magnetosphere electrons lasting several minutes, for A magnetometer is also installed in the DeCoR instrument, which makes it possible to measure the magnitude of the magnetic field along three mutually perpendicular axes. Using the outputs of this magnetometer allows taking into account spacecraft rotation in the study of trapped and precipitating electrons and even use it to estimate the pitch-angle distribution of particles. The magnetometer data are included directly in the monitoring information frames containing the parameters of the measured radiation.

3.2. *The results of observations with DeCoR instrument on-board AmurSat and VDNH-80 satellites*

Space missions with AmurSat and VDNH-80 satellites were the first Moscow University experience of monitor observations on cubesats. Due to technical problems, first of all connected with necessity of solar battery charging and limited transmitter capabilities, during both missions data were obtained from DeCoR instrument for about hundred and a half orbits. Taking into account that background conditions appropriate for GRB observations were on about a half of orbit, real instrument field of view about 1 sr and GRB detection threshold about $5 \cdot 10^{-7} erg/cm^2$, the expected number of detecting GRBs was no more than one. Really there were no detected any significant gamma-quantum flux increasing, which can be discussed as GRB candidates. Nevertheless sufficiently rich experience was obtained in view of radiation monitoring, especially of electron flux variation study by two spacecraft.

As noted above, an important advantage of multi-satellite experiments is the possibility of simultaneous measurements at different points in the near-Earth space on the one hand and measurements in the same regions with sequential passage of satellites through them on the other. Such measurements are illustrated in Fig. 5, 6, which show the orbital projections of the AmurSat and VDNKh-80 satellites and the outputs of two DeCoR instruments installed on these satellites, which were recorded on March 18, 2020. The difference in the positions of the satellites was about half of the orbit, so at the same time one spacecraft was taking measurements in the North Polar Region, and the other in the South.

Instruments on both satellites were switched on over Kaluga-city, when the satellites were moving in the direction of the northern polar region. At the moment of switching on the DeCoR instrument on the VDNH-80 satellite, the AmurSat cubesat was in the southern hemisphere, so the DeCoR instrument on it was switched on after ~ 45 minutes. At the same time, the AmurSat satellite continued to move along a similar trajectory with the VDNH-80 spacecraft.

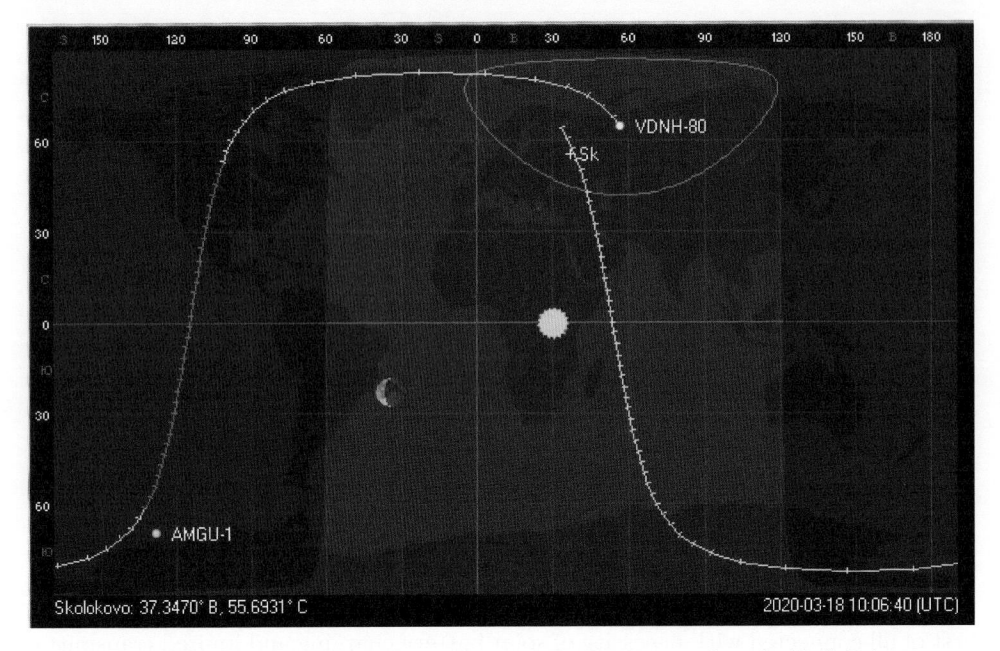

Fig. 5. Projection of VDNH-80 satellite orbit onto the Earth map when the DeCoR instrument was switched on March 18, 2020.

The orbital projection of the VDNH-80 satellite during the switching on of the DeCoR instrument on March 18, 2020 is shown in Fig. 5. It also shows the position of the AmurSat satellite at the moment when the DeKoR instrument was switched on the VDNH-80 satellite. The DeCoR instrument on the AmurSat satellite was switched on in $\sim$ 45 minutes above the communication point in Kaluga, thus, the data array transmitted from the AmurSat satellite corresponds to a trajectory close to that shown in the figure.

The time variation of the counting rate of electrons with energy $>$ 300 keV along the orbit of the VDNH-80 satellite, recorded in the monitor mode with a time resolution of 5 s are shown in Fig. 6a. The maxima are clearly visible at the moments when the satellite is in the outer radiation belt of the Earth, as well as some small increases in the polar region. Significant increases in the counting rate near the geomagnetic equator are also clearly visible.

The counting rates in a similar channel of the DeCoR instrument installed on the AmurSat satellite are shown in Fig. 6b. Noteworthy is the repeatability of the features visible when two satellites pass the same polar region with an interval of $\sim$ 45 minutes. During the flight of the geomagnetic equator, a smooth increase in the electron counting rate is also seen. The moving average line shows modulation with a period of $\sim$ 40 s associated with the rotation of the satellite. As noted above, the presence of such modulation indicates that the electron flux is non-isotropic in the near-equatorial regions.

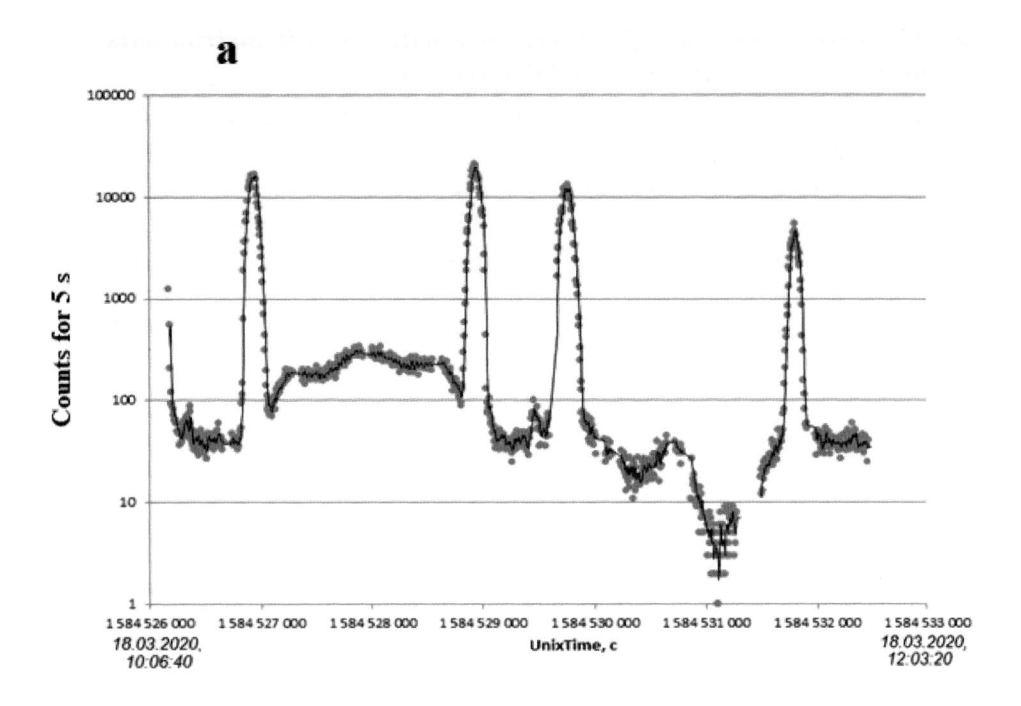

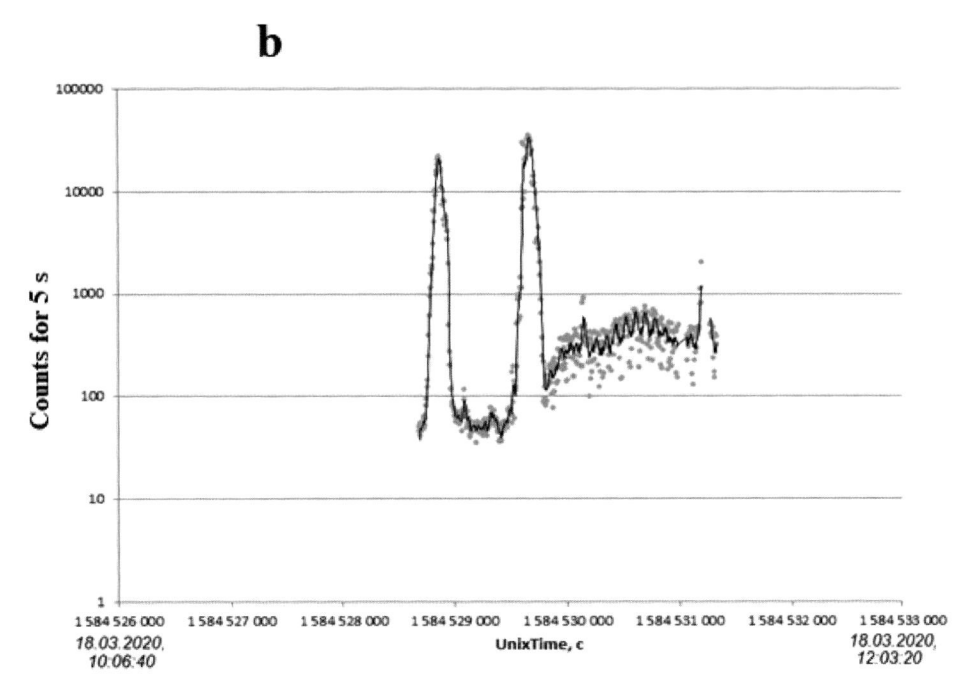

Fig. 6. Time variation of the count rate for electrons with energy > 300 keV, recorded in the monitor mode of the DeCoR instrument operated on-board VDNH-80 satellite on March 18, 2020 (a), similar readings of the DeCoR instrument on -board AmurSat satellite (b).

3.3. *The first experience of observations with DéCoR instruments on-board Norbi and DEKART satellites*

Just now the stage of flight tests of Norbi and DEKART missions was completed and regular observations were begun. The example of DeCoR instrument data obtained from Norbi CubeSat on July 14, 2021 is presented in Fig. 7. There it can be seen the monitor time dependent (with 5 s time resolution) count rates in plastic detector (mainly electrons) and CsI(Tl) (mainly gamma quanta) recorded for several consequent orbits. All typical variations caused by the near-Earth radiation flux distribution can be seen. There are seen peaks connected with the crossing of the outer belt regions and South–Atlantic Anomaly, as well, as in precipitation areas.

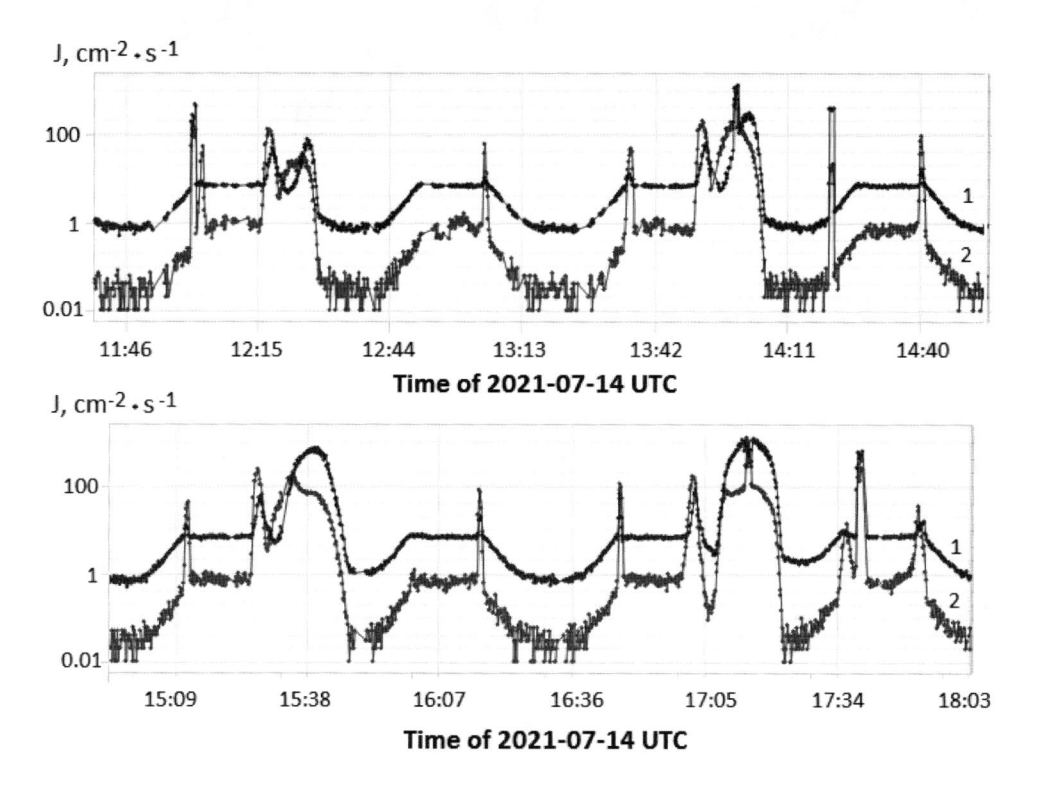

Fig. 7. Time variation of the count rate for electrons with energy > 300 keV (red curve) and for gamma-quanta (dark blue curve), recorded in the monitor mode of the DeCoR instrument operated on-board Norbi satellite on July 14, 2021.

It is necessary to note that gamma quantum count rate dependence along the orbit contains the intervals of quasi-constant background that correspond near-equatorial and polar cup regions. These intervals are quite appropriate for GRB detection. Nevertheless on these intervals flux increasing caused by electron precipitation can be observed. The example of such event detected on 04:49 September 28, 2021 is presented in Fig. 8.

The example of output data from one detector unit of DéCoR instrument on-board DEKART satellite is presented in Fig. 9. As it could be seen, time dependent gamma quantum and electron count rates, recorded with 0.5 s time resolution along the orbit, are quite similar to those obtained by Norbi satellite. Thus, it gives opportunity for multi-satellite measurements of time effects in near-Earth radiation fluxes and increase probability of GRB detection, including possibility of simultaneous GRB observation on two satellites.

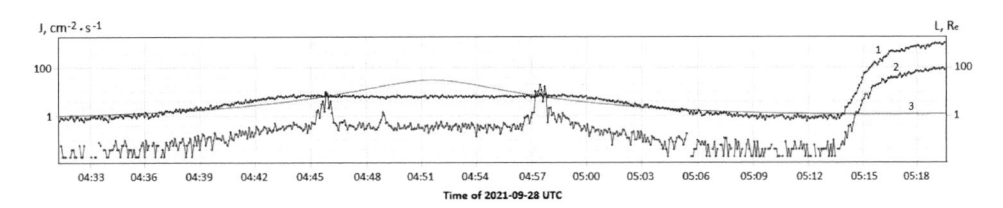

Fig. 8. Time variation of the count rate for electrons with energy > 300 keV (red curve), and gamma-quanta (dark blue curve), and L values (violet curve) recorded in the monitor mode of the DeCoR instrument operated on-board Norbi satellite on September 28, 2021.

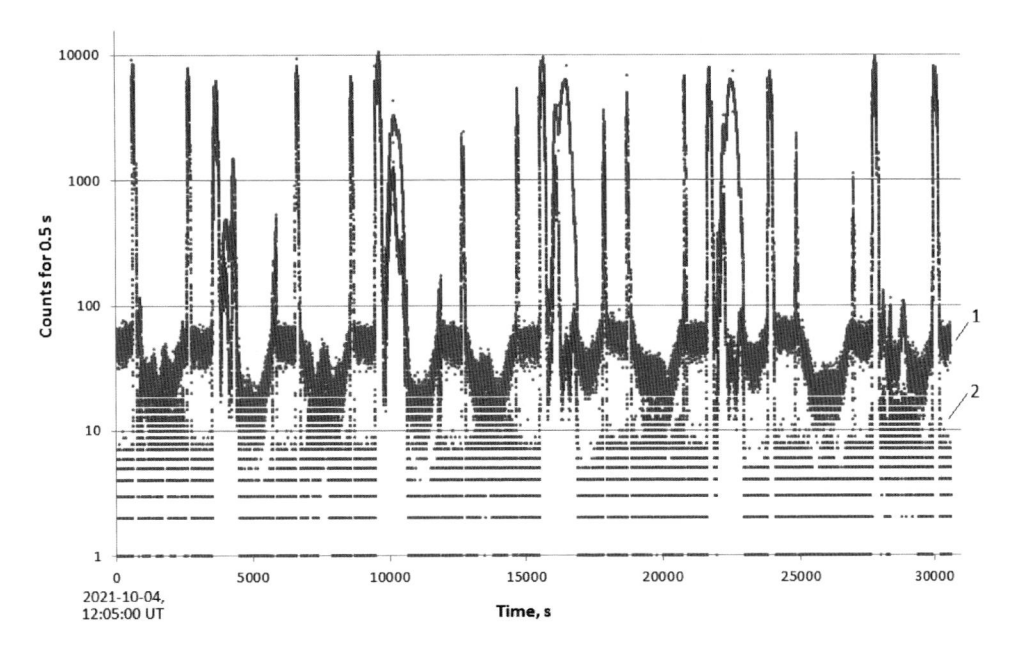

Fig. 9. Time variation of the count rate for electrons with energy > 300 keV (red curve) and for gamma-quanta (dark blue curve) recorded in the monitor mode of the DeCoR detector on-board DEKART satellite on October 4, 2021.

4. Conclusion

The successful realization of the CubeSat missions in frame of Universat–SOCRAT project make it possible for the first time to create a prototype of nano-satellite constellation a space system for monitoring of space radiation and electromagnetic transients including GRBs.

The first stage of this project was beginning from the launching of three CubeSats in July, 2019 and then three CubeSats in September, 2020. The prototypes of the instruments, which should be used in future Universat–SOCRAT missions were tested in these orbital experiments with CubeSats. Results of these tests confirmed that instruments operate well as in terms of command control as in terms of detector parameters. The particle flux measurements carried out during flight tests demonstrate the presence of variations corresponding to the expected changes in outputs at low polar orbit. During flight tests, both monitoring data with a time resolution of ~ 0.5, 1 and 5 s and event by event data with a time resolution of $\sim 20\mu s$ were successfully obtained from both DeCoR instruments installed on-board launched cubesats. Obtaining and processing of these data allows us to analyze both slow and fast particle flux variations. Thus, flight tests have confirmed the suitability of the instruments for the scientific research for which they were intended including principal possibility of GRB observation.

References

1. Abbott B. P., Abbott R., Abbott T. D., et al., "Multi-messenger Observations of a Binary Neutron Star Merger", *The Astrophysical Journal Letters*, V.848, Iss. 2, article id. L12, 59 pp., 2017.
2. Svertilov S.I., Panasyuk M.I., Bogomolv V.V., et al., "Wide-Field Gamma-Spectrometer BDRG: GRB Monitor on-board the Lomonosov Mission", *Space Science Review*, article id. V.214, 8, 22 pp., 2018.
3. Osedlo V.I., Sadovnichii V.A., Panasyuk M.I. et al., "Multi-satellite project "Universat-Socrat" for natural and artificial hazards monitoring", *Advances in the Astronautical Sciences*, V.163, pp. 45-52, 2018.
4. Sadovnichiy V.A., Panasyuk M.I., Lipunov V.M., et al., "Project "Universat-SOCRAT" of Multiple Small Satellites for Monitoring of Natural and Technogenic Space Hazards", *Open Astronomy*, V.27. Iss. 1, pp. 126-131, 2018.
5. Panasyuk M.I., Klimov P.A., Svertilov S.I., et al., "Universat-SOCRAT multi-satellite project to study TLEs and TGFs", *Progress in Earth and Planetary Science*, V.6, pp. 35-54, 2019.
6. Panasyuk M.I., Svertilov S.I., Bogomolov V.V., et al., "RELEC mission: Relativistic electron precipitation and TLE study on-board small spacecraft", *Advances in Space Research*, V.57, pp. 835–849, 2016.
7. Svertilov S.I., Panasyuk M.I., Petrov V.L., et al., "Multi-Satellite Project UNIVERSAT-SOCRAT of Cubesat Grouping for Spacecraft and Aviation Radiation Hazard Warning System and First Experience of Moscow University Cubesat Missions", *Advances in the Astronautical Sciences*, V.173, pp. 171-188, 2018.

Multiwavelength observations of GRB160625B by MASTER, Lomonosov, Konus-Wind and three stage collapse

V. M. Lipunov[1,2,*], V. A. Sadovnichy[3], M. I. Panasyuk[1,4], I. V. Yashin[4], S. I. Svertilov[1,4],
D. Svinkin[5], E. Gorbovskoy[2], S. G. Simakov[2], G. V. Lipunova[2], V. G. Kornilov[1,2], D. Frederiks[5],
V. Topolev[1,2], R. Rebolo[6], M. Serra[6], N. Tiurina[2], E. Minkina[1,2], V. V. Bogomolov[1,4],
A. V. Bogomolov[4], A. F. Iyudin[4], A. Chasovnikov[1,2], A. Gabovich[8], N.M. Budnev[7],
O. A. Gress[2,7], G. Antipov[2], D. Vlasenko[1,2], P. Balanutsa[2], R. Podesta[5], K. Zhirkov[1,2],
A. Kuznetsov[2], V. Vladimirov[2], F. Podesta[5], C. Francile[5], Yu. Sergienko[8], A. Tlatov[9],
O. Ershova[7], D. Cheryasov[2] and V. Yurkov[8]

[1] *Lomonosov Moscow State University, Physics Department, Vorobievy Hills, 1, Moscow 119991, Russia*

[2] *Lomonosov MSU, SAI, Universitetsky, 13, Moscow 119234, Russia*

[3] *Lomonosov Moscow State Universit, GSP-1, Vorobievy Hills, 1, Moscow, 119991, Russia*

[4] *Lomonosov Moscow State University, Skobeltsyn Institute of Nuclear Physics (SINP MSU), Vorobievy Hills, 1, Moscow, 119991, Russia*

[5] *Ioffe Institute of theoretical physics, 26 Politekhnicheskaya, St Petersburg 194021, Russia*

[6] *Instituto de Astrofísica de Canarias, Lactea, E38205, LaLaguna, Tenerife, Spain*

[7] *Irkutsk State University, 20, Gagarin, Irkutsk 664003, Russia*

[8] *Blagoveschensk State Pedagogical University, Lenin, 104, Amur, Blagoveschensk 675000, Russia*

[9] *Kislovodsk Solar Station Pulkovo Observatory, Gagarina 100, Kislovodsk 357700, Russia*

*E-mail: lipunov@sai.msu.ru

The detailed continuous fast optical photometry analysis obtained by MASTER Global Network for the GRB160625B optical counterpart MASTER OT J203423.51+065508.0 is presented. There are also hard X-ray and gamma-ray emission obtained by the Lomonosov and Konus-Wind spacecrafts detectors. We detected quasiperiodic emission components in the intrinsic optical emission of GRB160625B and propose a three-stage collapse scenario for this long and bright GRB. We associate quasiperiodic fluctuations with forced precession of a Spinar, i.e. self-gravitating rapidly rotating super dense body, whose evolution is determined by a powerful magnetic field. The spinar's mass lead it to collapse into a black hole at the end of an evolution.

Keywords: Gamma-ray burst

1. Introduction

Gamma-ray bursts (GRB) still remain a mysterious phenomenon. We proceed from the assumption believe that long gamma-ray burst occurs as a result of the collapse of the rapidly rotating core of a massive star. The fast rotation of the core slows down the collapse and extends time available to produce electromagnetic radiation. Two scenarios are possible here. In the first scenario (MacFadyen & Woosley, 2000),[1] a black hole first forms, and then the fallback of the supernova envelope, which has a supercritical torque, forms a heavy superdense disk. Due to the generation of magnetic fields by this disk, axial jets with a large gamma factor are generated, which we observe. In another scenario, a rapidly rotating magnetized object, a Spinar, is first formed, which is slowly compressed due to the dissipation of the rotational moment (Lipunov & Gorbovskoy, 2007).[2] In this case, a jet with a Poynting-Umov energy flow is formed along the rotation axis. The operating time of the central gamma-ray burst engine changes depending on the dissipation rate. In general, both scenarios require a fairly large torque in the collapsing stellar core. And here the authors are impressed by a binary scenario in which fast rotation occurs due to the tidal influence of the second component in a very close binary system (Tutukov & Cherepashchuk, 2016).[3] In this scenario, the centrifugal barrier is a consequence of the large torque acquired as a result of the natural evolution of the binary system. In the case of GRB160625B our attention was attracted by the quasiperiodic brightness fluctuations during the time of the central engine operation, and below we try to interpret them as a consequence of a Spinar Paradigm at work (Lipunova & Lipunov, 1997; Lipunov & Gorbovskoy, 2007;2008; Lipunova et al., 2009)[2,4–6]

In this paper, we present multiwavelength observations of GRB160625B, one of the brightest gamma-ray bursts in the history of their study. We have concentrated on the temporal behavior of itsintrinsic electromagnetic radiation. We present optical and gamma-ray data, recorded during the time of the operation of the central engine of GRB160625B. We made an attempt to find traces of the duality of the GRB system. We have suspected traces of the dual nature of long GRBs. Of course, we do not have one hundred percent proof of this scenario, but this study can serve as an example of searching for and finding the dual nature of long GRBs.

2. Observations

GRB160625B was observed by the large number of space and ground telescopes in a wide range of electromagnetic waves from gamma-ray to radio. For the first time in the GRB study history, the polarization of its own prompt optical emission synchronous with the gamma one was discovered (Troja et al., 2017a).[7] Now we present the details of synchronous observations in the optical (MASTER OT J203423.51+065508.0) and gamma-ray ranges.

GRB 160625B triggered Fermi observatory at 2016-06-25 22:40:16UT , firstly as a short pulse (Fermi-GBM trigger 488587220, Burns et al.2016),[8] then the

Fermi-LAT triggered (Dirirsa et al. 2016)[9] at 22:43:24.82UT, at 22:51:16.03 Fermi-GBM triggered again (trigger 488587880).The GBM light curve consists of multiple peaks over approximately 700 seconds, the first one being 1 second long soft peak. The main peak, corresponding to the LAT trigger, was very hard and about 25 seconds long. The peak that triggered GBM for the second time was soft and about 30 seconds long (Burns et al. 2016).[8] Swift has initiated a series of observations and discovered uncatalogued X-ray sources at R.A.,Dec.(2000)=20:34:23.25 +06:55:10.5 with an uncertainty of 3.8 arcsec (Melandri et al. 2016), publishied it at 2016-06-26 06:54:13UT.

This long, extremely bright GRB 160625B also triggered BDRG detectors onboard Lomonosov Space Observatory of Moscow State University (Sadovnichii et al. 2017)[10](Fig. 1) and Konus-Wind at 22:40:19.875UT (Svinkin et al. 2016)[11](Fig. 1) as well as the CALET Gamma-ray Burst Monitor (CGBM) at 22:40:15.49 (Nakahira et al. 2016).[12]

The optical counterpart was discovered by RATIR (Troja et al. 2017b)[14] starting 8.53h after LAT trigger. MASTER started observation in polarization filters (Lipunov 2010, 2019, Kornilov 2012)[17–19] 31 sec after GBM notice time (57 sec after GBM, i.e. 131 sec before LAT Trigger, Dirirsa et al.2016)[9] at 2016-06-25 22:41:13UT (Gorbovskoy et al. 2016),[20] but published the circular in GCN (Barthelmy et al. 1998ab)[21, 22] at 16/06/28 14:05:38. The GCN publication was delayed by the installation of the new MASTER telescope in Argentina at this time (MASTER-OAFA). MASTER measurements probed the structure of the magnetic field at an early development stage of the jet, closer to a central black hole, and show that the prompt emission phase is produced via fast-cooling synchrotron radiation in a large-scale magnetic field that was advected from the black hole and distorted by dissipation processes within the jet (Troja et al. 2017a).[7] The optical data obtained by MASTER telescopes-robots (Lipunov et al. 2010,2019)[17, 18] have the best temporal resolution with the minimum exposure time of 5 seconds. This resolution made it possible to suspect quasiperiodic variability in the optical range, which we try to associate with the dual nature of the long GRB.

The detection of a substantial (8.3 ± 0.8 per cent from our most conservative estimation) variable linear polarization of a prompt optical flash that accompanied the extremely energetic and long prompt γ-ray emission from GRB 160625B was discovered by MASTER (Gorbovskoy et al. 2016a, Lipunov et al. 2016a, Troja et al. 2017a).[7, 15, 16]

2.1. *MASTER*

MASTER Global Robotic Net of Lomonosov Moscow State University in 2016 consisted of orbital MASTER-Shok detectors on-board Lomonosov spacecraft and of 8 ground observatories with identical scientific equipment distributed all over the Earth: MASTER-Amur, -Tunka, -Ural, -Kislovodsk, -Tavrida in Russia, -SAAO (South African Astronomical Observatory), -IAC (Tenerife, Spain, Teide observatory of Institute of Astrophysics of the Canary Islands), -OAFA (Argentina, San Juan National University Astronomical Observatory named by Felix Aguilar), see Lipunov 2010, 2019[17,18](Fig. 1). Identical equipment includes twin wide-field (MASTER-II, 4-8 square degrees up to 20m unfiltered limit at 180s exposition) and very wide field (MASTER-VWFC, 800 square degrees, up to 15m at summary image) optical channels (Kornilov et al. 2012)[19] which allows us to follow a target 24h per day in one photometric channel. MASTER-VWFC are the ground-based analogue of the MASTER-SHOCK cameras, that were installed on board the Lomonosov space observatory (Sadovnichy et al. 2017,2018, Lipunov et al. 2018, Svertilov et al.2018, Park et al. 2018).[10,23,25,37,38] Observations by MASTER-VWFC are unfiltered.

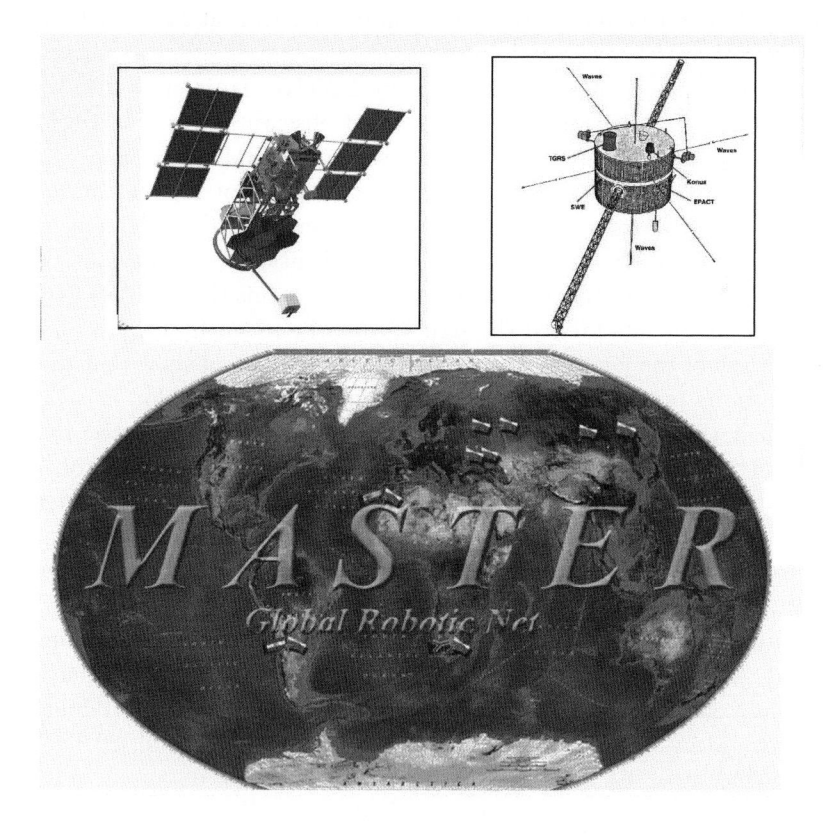

Fig. 1. MASTER Global Robotic Net. The upper left part shows Lomonosov satellite and the upper right part shows Konus-Wind. The flags indicate equipped sites of network stations.

MASTER own developed photometer can observe simultaneously in 2 orthogonally oriented polarization filters in both tubes of twin MASTER telescope

(Kornilov et al. 2012)[19] or in BVRI filters and unfiltered. Mount has fast positioning with the speed up to 30 deg/s.

MASTER key factors is own software for real-time reduction. It includes full robotization of all processes: hardware control, weather control, efemerides, central planner, automatic evening/morning calibration,and primary image reduction, astrometry and photometry, extraction of new optical sources and notification of the main station of them). Such features let us to discover significant and variable linear polarization during the prompt optical flash of GRB 160625B (Troja et al. 2017a),[7] to discover GRB optical counterparts (Lipunov et al. 2016, Gorbovskoy et al. 2016, Sadovnichy et al. 2018, Laskar et al. 2019),[20,24–27] to discover Smooth Optical Self-similar Emission of GRB subclass (Lipunov et al. 2017),[28] to make the most optical support to GW150914 event (Abbott et al. 2016ab, Lipunov et al. 2017,2018),[29–31] to independently discover Kilonova GW170817(Abbott et al. 2017, Lipunov et al. 2017),[32,33] to make the most optical support to the follow-up of a rare IceCube neutrino multiplet (Aartsen et al. 2017),[34] to discover V404Cygni polarization variability (Lipunov et al. 2017),[35] to make optical observationsthat revealed a strong evidence for a high-energy neutrino progenitor - blazar TXS 0506+056 for IC170922A (Lipunov et al. 2020)[36] , to discover more than 2000 optical transients of 10 different types and other.

2.2. *MASTER GRB160625B observation*

MASTER-IAC robotic telescope pointed to the GRB 160625B at 2016-06-25 22:41:13UT, and observed Swift X-ray error box (Melandri et al., 2016)[13] by MASTER-IAC wide field camera with a 5 second exposition time without filter and imaged several thousand frames.

MASTER-Tavrida started first frame exposition 12 seconds after LAT notice time (66s after trigger time) at 22:44:30UT.

MASTER-Tavrida and MASTER-IAC very wide field of view cameras (VWFC) observed GRB error-box when the Fermi-LAT detected the main impulse of GRB with a high coordinate accuracy of 0.5 degrees, 131 seconds after the first message.

MASTER OT J203423.51+065508.0 optical counterpart was detected at 22:43:30UT (+2.5 sec of exposition) UT with m_{OT}=8.60 and was getting brighter up to a maximum of 7.86m(see Fig. 2). The prompt optical emission strongly correlated with Konus-Wind gamma ray light curve (Svinkin et al., 2016).[11]

MASTER-IAC robotic telescope started observation of the error box 43 sec after LAT notice time or 95 sec after trigger time at 2016-06-25 22:44:59UTby main MASTER-II telescope in two polarizations. The OT was 8.6m at the moment.

As a result, MASTER not only registered the entire event of the GRB explosion in the optical range with the best time resolution (2.5 sec), but for the first time in the history of gamma-ray burst research, it detected the polarization of prompt optical emission from the gamma-ray burst while the flash was still going on (Troja et al. 2017a).[7]

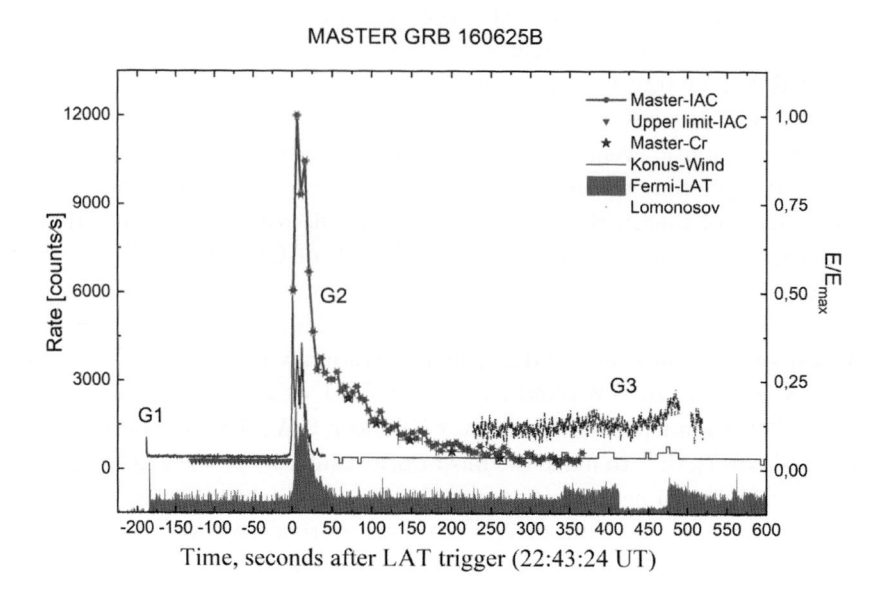

Fig. 2. Red curve - observations of the very wide-field MASTER-IAC cameras, reduced to the proper time of the system (compression of the burst time scale relative to the observed one). The purple dots corresponds to the MASTER-Tavrida measurements taken with a lower temporal resolution. The gray curve corresponds to the emission detected by Fermi-LAT (see Toja et al. 2017a.[7]

The gamma-ray burst GRB160625B turned out to be one of the most powerful cosmic explosions of this type, which appeared as a narrow jet of relativistic particles accelerated by the electromagnetic field of a rapidly rotating black hole at the other end of the Universe forming before our eyes.

An analysis of the MASTER's polarization observations made it possible for the first time to detect the polarization of GRB's intrinsic optical radiation and directly showed that the muzzle of the most powerful space gun was formed by an ordered powerful magnetic field of a forming black hole (Troja et al., 2017).[7]

This magnificent astrophysical experiment succeeded thanks to the interaction of scientists from several countries, who created unique robotic equipment to detect gamma rays, infrared radiation, and photons in the optical range born by the GRB event.

2.3. *LOMONOSOV Observations*

The GRB monitor (BDRG) aboard the Lomonosov (Sadovnichii et al. 2017)[10] observatory (hereafter BDRG/Lomonosov (Svertilov et al., 2018)[37] was built for the early detection of GRBs in the gammas of 0.01-3.0 MeV energy range and for generation of triggers for those events. The BDRG consisted of 3 identical detector units connected to the electronic unit. The BDRG instrument detector units (blocks) were mounted on the spacecraft payload platform in such a way that their axes are oriented 90° to each other. Each detector has a cosine angular dependence for a sensitive area not shaded by satellite construction elements within $\sim 60°$ of its axis. The monitor's central axis, relative to which the detector axes are inclined, is directed toward to the local zenith. Thus, the total field of view for all three detectors is about 2π sr; and one quarter of this field, i.e. $\pi/2$ sr, is the value of a solid angle, within which limits the GRB position error can be estimated with sufficiently good accuracy through the comparison of all three detector outputs.

BDRG operates in two main observational modes: the monitor or continuous mode, and the burst mode. In the monitor mode all instrument outputs were recorded and stored continuously with time resolutions adjustable by commands from Earth. On the other hand, the burst mode was activated by on-board instrument triggers to record detailed information of each photon during the before-burst, burst, and after-burst time intervals. The BDRG trigger initiated the estimation of GRB positions and relayed the trigger not only to other GRB observation instruments onboard the Lomonosov spacecraft, i.e. SHOK optical cameras (Lipunov et al., 2018)[23] and Ultrafast Flash Observatory (Park et al., 2018),[38] but to the ground telescopes as well through the Gamma-ray Coordinates Network (GCN, Barthelmy et al. 1998ab)[21] viathe Global Star transmitter.

Each BDRG detector unit consisted of a thin layer (0.3 cm) of NaI(Tl) crystals optically coupled to a considerably thicker layer (1.7 cm) of CsI(Tl) crystals situated underneath. The diameter of the detectors is 13 cm, and both layers are read by a single photomultiplier tube (PMT). Thus, the overall detector area is about 130 cm2. The thickness of the NaI(Tl) layer is optimized for the soft part of energy range, and the working ranges of the units are 0.01-0.5 MeV for the NaI(Tl) layer and 0.05-3 MeV for CsI(Tl). As such, the NaI(Tl) layer serves as the main detector for hard X-ray timing, while the CsI(Tl) operates as an active shield against background gamma-rays. Additionally, the CsI(Tl) crystals can also detect gamma-rays with energies up to a few MeV. The difference in decay times for the NaI(Tl) ($\sim$0.25 ms) and CsI(Tl) ($\sim$2.0 ms) crystals permits the separation of light flashes in the scintillators through special electronic circuits that differentiate pulse shapes.

The information provided by the BDRG units consisted of a number of different categories for the data frames generated continuously (continuous mode) as well as irregularly by various triggers (burst mode). The continuous data stream included three types of frame corresponding to the instruments' monitoring, spectrum, and event. Monitoring frames provided count rates in 8 energy channels for the NaI(Tl) and CsI(Tl) scintillator crystals for each of the BDRG detector units, while spectrum frames contain 724 channel spectra for NaI(Tl) and CsI(Tl), separately. Event frames gave the primary values for energy release within the NaI(Tl) and CsI(Tl) crystals, combined with time data for a fixed number of detected gamma-quanta. Likewise, information about the main parameters for all GRB triggers was stored and transferred in the form of "trigger logs". There are three trigger types categorized as "fast," "slow" and "super-slow," with characteristic times of 10 ms, 1 s, and 20 s, respectively. Corresponding to each trigger type, three data frame sequences for the monitoring, spectrum, and event were generated continuously in a manner similar to the continuous mode discussed above. A portion of data collected before the trigger was always included for all trigger types.

On 25 June 2016 near the GRB160625B trigger, the BDRG/Lomonosov operated in monitoring mode. The background environment at the time of event was very complicated. The Lomonosov satellite was flying through the radiation belts.

The count rate variations in the BDRG/Lomonosov gamma-quanta channels are illustrated by the curves in the upper panel of Fig. 3, in which count-rates of three BDRG-1 NaI detector channels 10 – 35, 35 – 170, 170 – 650 keV shown with the time resolution of 0.1 s are plotted. Full data is available on the link(http://master.sai.msu.ru/static/MG16MASTER/BDRG160625B.txt)

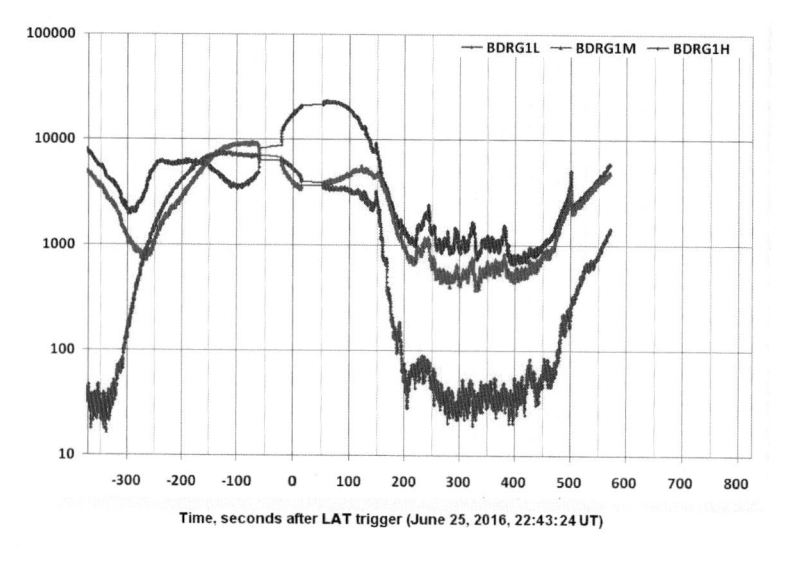

Fig. 3. GRB160626B γ-ray light curves.The BDRG-1(NaI detector) counts vs time in the 10-35keV (BDRG1L), 35-170 keV (BDRG1M), 170-650 keV (BDRG1H) ranges.

The clear count-rate increases in the time interval from about -150 to 350 seconds relative to the Swift trigger time (-300 to 200 seconds relative to the LAT trigger time) corresponds to the satellite crossing outskirts of the external radiation belt. After that the satellite flew into the region of the South polar cap, where the background is smaller, and after that it began to cross the outer belt again and the background began to increase. Thus, due to such background variations the main pulse (G2) as well as the precursor (G1) could not be observed on by the

Lomonosov satellite detectors. Only the "last tail" (G3) could be observed. However, during the corresponding time interval (from about 350 to 550 seconds from LAT trigger time) count variations in the BDRG/Lomonosov were in reality combination of GRB counts plus variations caused by unstable electron fluxes in the polar cap. The last component can give the significant input in gamma ray channels of the instrument due to electron bremsstrahlung. Thus, to obtain the real GRB light curve it is necessary to clean the detector outputs from electron background variations.

To realize this procedure we used the outputs from different BDRG detectors. Because of different BDRG detector orientation the given GRB source was observed by separate detectors at different angles. In the case of GRB160625B only BDRG1 detector unit was illuminated, the angle between the detector axis and direction toward the GRB source was about 56°, while for BDRG2 and BDGR3 these angles were about 136° and 116° respectively. It means that GRB source was out of field of view (FOV) of both latter detector units. On the other hand, since counting rate of the irregular variations observed in the polar cap regions are mainly due to the quasi-trapped electron fluxes having an anisotropic but rather wide pitch-angle distribution, they will exhibit similar temporal behavior in separate, although differently oriented detectors. It allows us to use regression analysis of detector unit count rates obtained for two detectors during time interval of GRB observation to estimate regression coefficients, which then can be used for rejection of the part of counting rate variations caused by electron fluxes. Because during the time of GRB160625B observation BDRG2 unit was switched-off, for regression analysis only the BDRG1 and BDRG3 unit outputs were used. To be exact, we selected time interval from 200 to 450 seconds after LAT trigger (22:43:24UTC) to estimate regression coefficients, which corresponds to the time between G2 and G3 events, when expected input to detectors counting rates from GRB160625B was negligible.

2.4. *Konus-Wind observations*

GRB 160625B triggered Konus-Wind GRB spectrometer (KW, Aptekar et al. 1995)[41] at T0= 81619.875 s UT (22:40:19.875; Svinkin et al., 2016).[11] The burst was detected by the S2 detector, which observes the Northern ecliptic hemisphere; the incident angle was 65.2 deg. The propagation delay from Earth to WIND is 3.356 s for this GRB; correcting for this factor, the KW trigger time corresponds to the Earth-crossing time 81616.519 s UT (22:40:16.519).

2.4.1. *Time history*

Count rates for Konus-Wind are recorded in three energy bands in the triggered mode: 17–70 keV (B1), 70–300 keV (B2), and 300–1170 keV (B3). The record starts at T0 - 0.512 s and continues to T0 + 229.376 s with an accumulation time varying from 2 to 256 ms. Waiting-mode count rate data are available up to T0 + 250 s in the same energy bands with a coarse temporal resolution of 2.944 s. A source activity after time interval T0 + 250 s may be traced in the housekeeping mode with temporal resolution of 3.68s for the 70–300 keV energy range.

The prompt-emission light curve (Fig. 4) can be divided into three episodes. It starts, at $\sim$ T0 - 0.3 s, with a short, spectrally-soft initial pulse (precursor) which has duration of about 1 s. The precursor is followed, starting at $\sim$ T0 + 180s, by the main, extremely bright and spectrally-hard emission episode lasting for about 40 s. The final episode observed by KW in the housekeeping mode starts at $\sim$ T0 + 530 s and has duration of about 150 s. The total burst duration is about 680 s.

The first episode was localized only by Fermi (GBM) with a position uncertainty of about 2 deg (statistical only). The difference in the arrival time of the gamma-ray signals at Fermi-GBM and Konus-Wind provides additional significant constraints on the gamma-ray localization of the episode (Zhang et al., 2018).[42] The triangulation of the first episode is consistent with the source position determined by Swift-XRT in the main episode, supporting the association of the precursor and the burst.

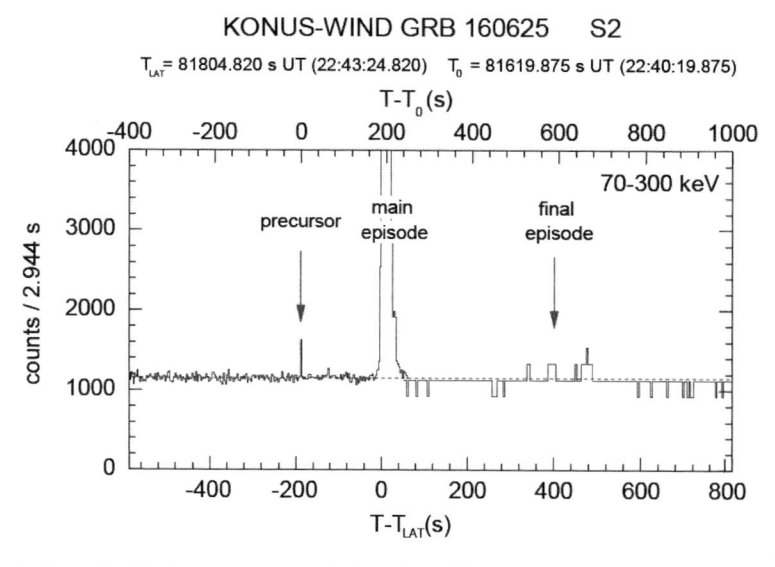

Fig. 4. GRB 160625B light curve recorded in the KW waiting and housekeeping modes in the 70-300 keV band (B2).

Let us discuss the time-resolved spectral analysis. In the triggered mode, Konus-WIND measures 64 energy spectra in 128 channels of two overlapping energy bands: 20–1170 keV (PHA1) and 244 keV–15 MeV (PHA2). The first four spectra have a fixed accumulation time of 64 ms; after that, the accumulation time varies over 0.256-8.192 s, depending on the current intensity of the burst. Five initial energy spectra covered the precursor (T0 – T0+8.448 s) and 35 covered the main episode (T0+180.480 - T0 + 237.824 s).

The spectral analysis was performed with XSPEC version 12.9.0i (Arnaud 1996)[43] with the three model: Band GRB function (Band et al. 1993):[44] $f(E) \sim E^\alpha exp(-(2+\alpha)E/Epeak)$ for $E < Epeak(\alpha - \beta)/(2+\alpha)$, and $f(E) \sim E^\beta$ for $E > Epeak(\alpha - \beta)/(2+\alpha)$, where α is the power law photon index at low energies, Epeak is the peak energy in the EF(E) spectrum, and β is the high-energy photon index; a cutoff power law model (CPL): $f(E) \sim E^\alpha exp(-(2+\alpha)E/Epeak)$; and a simple power law. The spectral models were normalized to the energy flux in the 20 keV – 10 MeV range, a standard band for the KW GRB spectral analysis.

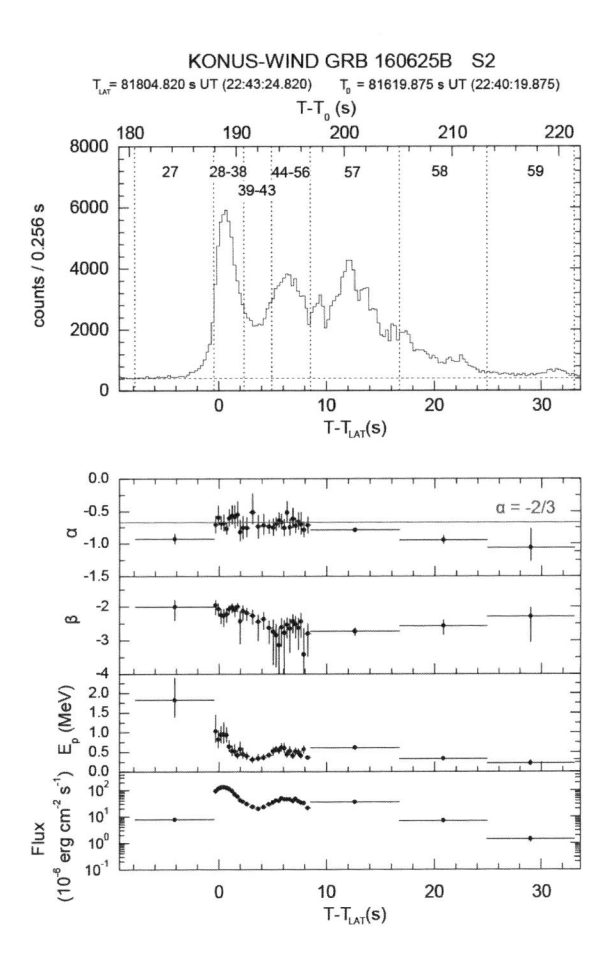

Fig. 5. Spectral evolution of the gamma-ray emission during the prompt phase of the burst main episode. The Konus-WIND light curve in the combined B1+B2+B3 energy band (17-1170 keV) is shown with 256 ms resolution, along with the temporal behavior of the Band spectral model parameters Epeak, α, and β obtained from the time-resolved fits.

Typically, the spectral channels are rebinned to have at least 10 counts per energy bin to ensure Gaussian-distributed errors and the correctness of the χ^2 statistic.

For the precursor, constrained spectral parameters of the CPL model are available only for the sum of the first four spectra, while for the main episode, a good count statistic is achieved for 35 individual spectra between T0+180.480 s and T0+237.824 s, the spectrum between T0+ 229.632 s and T0+237.824 s is well described by a simple power law. The good spectral coverage enables us to construct the temporal behavior of the model parameters (α, β, Epeak) and to trace in detail the evolution of the spectral composition of radiation over the course of the main episode (Fig. 5).

Spectrum 27 was measured at the onset of the very intense initial pulse of the main episode (Fig. 5). The emission at this moment is hard; Epeak reaches the highest value for the burst ($\sim$ 1.8 MeV). After the summit of the brightest pulse, Epeak starts to decrease gradually (spectra 28-38), down to $\sim$ 300 keV in spectra (39-43), and then grows up to $\sim$ 600 keV at the time of the second peak (spectra 44-56), staying at this level during the last peak (spectrum 57). Spectra 58-60 describe the decay of the main episode showing the typical decrease in Epeak. During the brightest part of the main episode the low-energy spectral index is approximately constant and is consistent with the synchrotron emission in the slow-cooling regime $\alpha = -2/3$ (Preece et al., 1998).[45] The high-energy index β shows no significant correlation with energy flux and is typical for long GRBs ($\beta \sim$ -2).

Spectrum 1-4 (time –averaged), corresponding to the peak of the initial pulse is well fitted with a CPL model with $\alpha \sim$ -0.4, and Epeak $\sim$ 70 keV ($\chi^2/dof =$ 16.5/29). The fit with a single blackbody (BB) component yields kT= 17.3 (-1.6, +1.6) keV, energy flux 1.92 (-0.19,+0.19) $10^{-6} erg/cm^2/s$, with $\chi^2/dof = 32.1/30$; the fit underestimates count rate at energies below $\sim$ 30 keV. Thus, despite the BB kT is consistent with the value found by Zhang et al., 2018,[42] we argue that BB model cannot be favoured for the spectrum.

3. Modeling

Looking at the optical light curve starting from 20 seconds relative to the main pulse and up to 200 - 250 seconds, one can suspect quasiperiodic brightness oscillations with an amplitude significantly exceeding the random brightness measurement error. Recall that a five-second exposure on ultra-wide field cameras is practically without delay. Such variability at times of the order of ($\tau \sim$ 10-20 seconds) is caused by internal physical processes in the operation of the central engine. However, it would be tempting to associate this phenomenon with the interaction of a relativistic jet with quasiperiodic inhomogeneous layers in the radial distribution of the progenitor's stellar wind. This type of inhomogeneity can be caused by the presence of a close second component in the collapsing star's binary system. Calculations carried out earlier (Lipunova et al. 2009)[6] show that in systems with an orbital period of less than 1 - 2 hours, tidal forces lead to a critical increase in the spin moment of the collapsar. As a result, it is under these conditions that the formation of a massive accretion disk (Woosley 1993)[46] or a spinar (Lipunov & Gorbovskoy, 2007)[2] prolongs the magneto-rotational collapse, which leads to the phenomenon of a gamma-ray burst.

First of all, we will discuss the possible reasons for the quasiperiodic optical emission, which is an intrinsic emission at the stage of the central engine operation and must reflect some quasiperiodic oscillations of the central engine. This circumstance is supported by the fact that we detect oscillations after 30 seconds (in our own frame of reference) from the trigger, that is, at the same time when the optical and gamma spectra become one. Recently, Suvorov and Kokkotas (2021)[47] discussed quasiperiodic pulsations of X-rays from some short GRBs in the magnetar model. Actually, the only property of the magnetars used here is the one inherent to all radio transmitters they loose energy approximately according to the magnetic dipole law (Pacini, 1967)[48] and their total power changes over time $L \sim t^{-2}$. In connection with the gamma-ray bursts, this circumstance was expressed by Lipunova & Lipunov (1998).[4] The merit of the works of Suvorov and Kokkotas (2021)[47] is the attraction of the idea that the observed quasiperiodic oscillations are associated with the free precession of a neutron star with an anomalously strong magnetic field. In fact, the magnetar model is only a special case of a more general model of the magnetorotational collapse - Spinar Paradigm (Lipunov & Lipunov, 1998; Lipunov & Gorbovskoy, 2007, 2008; Lipunova et al., 2009).[2,4–6] In the framework of Spinar Paradigm, it is assumed that the initial rotational moment of the body is so great that centrifugal forces have a significant effect on the collapse process. In particular, this model successfully explains not only the plateau phenomenon, but also a sharp (by several orders of magnitude) cliff at the end of the plateau (Lipunov & Gorbovskoy, 2007).[2] In fact, an approximate non-stationary model of gravitational-rotational collapse (Lipunov & Gorbovskoy, 2008)[5] includes all relativistic effects plus the contribution of the nuclear forces of the neutron liquid. The collapse character depends on three main parameters: the core mass M of the collapsing star, the generalized Kerr parameter $a_0 = I\omega_0 c/GM^2$ and the ratio of magnetic and gravitational energy $\alpha_m = U_m/U_{gr} << 1$ which remains constant in the approximation of the conservation of the magnetic flux. A black hole or a neutron star can also be the end product of the collapse (Lipunova et al., 2009).[6] In the process of formation of both types of objects, an intermediate object is formed - a spinar - which can experience not only free, but also forced precession. In addition, if a neutron star can only slow down, decreasing the overall luminosity, the spinar can accelerate as it evolves, and this will even be accompanied at certain stages by an increase in luminosity. It is precisely by the spinar precession that we propose to explain the suspected oscillations of the intrinsic optical emission of the GRB160625B gamma burst. Remarkably, the magneto-rotational collapse model naturally explains the existence of the precursor, with which we begin.

In the spinar model, the precursor of the gamma-ray bursts occurs during the first abrupt stop of the collapse due to the increase in centrifugal force (Fig. 6).

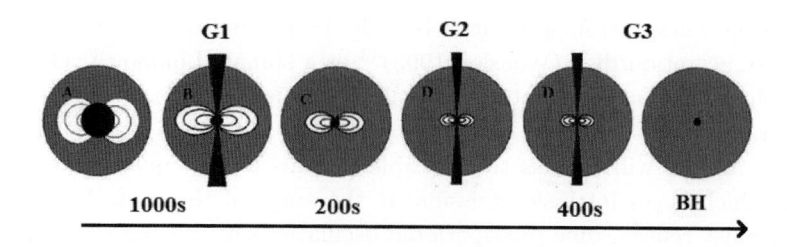

Fig. 6. Scheme of the three-stage magneto-rotational collapse in the Spinar Paradigm.

At this moment, half of the gravitational energy accumulated by the free-falling progenitor core is converted into heat. The second half of the work of gravitational forces turns into the energy of the spinar rotation. In other words, the centrifugal forces stop the collapse and a spinar is formed - which continues to slowly contract, losing its extreme moment and constantly increasing its radiation power (see Fig. 6). This is the formation of the precursor! Its maximum power $E_{precursor} \approx GM^2/2R_{sp}$ is determined by the radius of the formed spinar (Lipunov & Gorbovskoy, 2007)[2] $R_{sp} \approx a_0^2 R_g/2$, where R_g – Shwarcshild radius:

$$E_{precursor} \approx GM^2/2R_{sp} \approx (1/2a_0^2)Mc^2 \tag{1}$$

If the core torque is not too high $a_0 < 5 - 10m^{-1}(m = M/M_0)$, then this energy directed mainly along the spinar rotation axis will pierce the progenitor shell and we will see the precursor (Lipunov & Gorbovskoy, 2007).[2] However, immediately after the formation of the Spinar, the energy released by the spinar will already be determined by the magnitude of the magnetic energy $L_{sp} = U_m\omega \approx \alpha_m U_{gr}\omega$. Accordingly, the energy released by the spinar in one spin period and the corresponding pressure impulse on the shell will be reduced by a factor of $\alpha_m << 1$, hence the jet breakdown will happen. But if the torque is lost, the luminosity of the spinar will grow $L_{sp} = U_m\omega \approx \varepsilon_m U_{gr}\omega$ and finally break through the shell. This will be the time close to the beginning of the gamma-ray burst t_{GRB}. However, the time elapsed from the precursor to the start of the gamma-ray burst will be determined by the rate of loss of the spinar torque at the moment of its formation: $\Delta t \approx I\omega/U_m$. We can express the magnetic energy through the magnetic flux $\Phi = \pi B R^2 = \Phi_{28} 10^{28} Gs\, cm^2$, thus normalizing the flux to the characteristic of magnetars the does not change during the collapse, according to our assumption. Then we get the precursor time:

$$\Delta t_1 \approx -800s\, \Phi_{28}^{-2} m_{10}^3 a_0^3 \tag{2}$$

Kerr Black Hole released energy can reach 44% (Kip Thorne, 1974),[49] we get another important ratio of precursor fluence to gamma-ray burst fluence $E_{pre}/E_{GRB} \approx a_0^{-2}$. Usually there is a ratio $E_{pre}/E_{GRB} \approx 1 - 10\%$ (Troja, 2007),[50] corresponding to the generic Kerr parameter $a_0 \sim$ 3-10 . For the masses of nuclei close to M $\sim M_{OV}$, a larger Kerr parameter is required. However, in this case, it is necessary to include the contribution of nuclear forces (Lipunova et al., 2009).[6]

After the formation of the spinar, the direction of the magnetic flux of course does not have to coincide with its axis of rotation. We recall that we are considering the case of the conservation of the magnetic flux without an accompanying generation of the type of the dynamo mechanism. Therefore, a spinar can participate in a free precession, especially when it turns into a magnetar. However, a spinar is not a neutron star, whose surface is a hard boundary, beyond which there is a vacuum, or a highly discharged magnetosphere with a Julian-Goldreich density (Lipunov, 1992).[51] Spinar is an idealization of a superdense rotating body surrounded by a gas-dynamic plasma. Its evolution can be described by the equation:

$$dI\omega/dt = K_\parallel + K_\perp \tag{3}$$

On the right is the moment of forces, the parallel component of which leads to a change in the spinar's rotational moment in magnitude, and the perpendicular component leads to forced precession. It is clear that the spinar is not a rigid body, but the experience of studying the precession of accretion disks under the action of the magnetic moments of the seat shows that even thin disks successfully precess, though in a differential way (Lipunov & Shakura, 1980).[52] The maximum value of both moments of forces in equation 3 is determined as $|K| \approx U_m = \varepsilon_m U_{gr}$. The forced precession frequency turns out to be of the order of $\Omega = |K_\perp/I\omega| \approx \varepsilon_m \omega$. As the spinar radius approaches the event horizon $R \to R_g/2$ spinar frequency tends to the $\omega \to c/R_g$ as $R \to R_g$. So far as $U_m \to \varepsilon_m M c^2$ we get an estimate of the precession period:

$$T = 2\pi/\Omega = (2\pi/\omega)\varepsilon_m^{-1} \approx 5000s\, \Phi_{28}^{-2} m_{10}^3 r^{3/2} \tag{4}$$

Here $r = R/R_g$.

For the precursor GRB160725B in its own frame of reference $\Delta t_{pre} \approx -70s$ (we took z = 1.406 (GCN circular №19600), and the characteristic time of variations is T $\approx$ 10 sec. From 2 and 4 we obtain the estimate $a \approx 10$ and $\Phi_{27}^{-2} m^3$. Accordingly, the magnetic flux turns out to be quite reasonable $\Phi_{27}^{-2} \approx 140 m^{3/2}$.

After the main pulse (G2), the luminosity of the spinar begins to decrease. This is a sure sign that the role of nuclear forces is becoming important. The role of nuclear forces can become important only if the mass of the collapsing nucleus does not greatly exceed the Oppenheimer-Volkov limit. Let us recall that the Oppenheimer-Volkov limit essentially depends on the contribution of centrifugal forces to the equilibrium of the neutron star. So if the fraction of the rotational energy in the virial theorem is 10-20%, the Openhemer Volkov limit can increase by 2-3 times, depending on the equation of state of the neutron star (Lipunov, 1992).[51] With a mass of 4-5 solar masses, the spinar will be supported by nuclear forces until it freezes. This will happen during the after

$$\Delta t_3 \approx I\omega/U_m \approx 6I\omega R/\Phi^2 \approx 10s\, m^2 \Phi_{27}^{-2} r^2$$

So far as $r \to 1/2$ relativistic effects should be taken into account immediately.

Next, we applied a dynamic model of gravimagnetic collapse, which allows us to describe the evolution of a collapsing spinar from the moment of the loss of stability to the collapse into a black hole (Lipunov & Gorbovskoy, 2008; Lipunova et al., 2009).[5,6] In this formulation, a simple non-stationary three-parameter model of collapse is obtained with the decisive role of the rotation and the magnetic field. The input parameters of the theory are the mass, angular momentum and magnetic field of the collapsar. The approximate model includes: centrifugal force, relativistic effects of the Kerr metric, pressure of nuclear matter, dissipation of angular momentum under the influence of a spinar magnetic field, decrease in the dipole magnetic moment as a result of compression and the effects of general relativity (a black hole has no hair), neutrino cooling, time dilation due to gravitational redshift.

In Fig. 7 the results of calculating our approximate model are shown, the parameters of which are given in Fig. 1. Obviously, the main time intervals between the events of the gamma-ray burst G1, G2, G3 are in good agreement with observations. Of course, we do not pretend to describe a detailed light curve within the framework of our approximate model. We can only compare with observations the total energy release of the central engine at times G1, G2 and G3.

Table 1. Core collapse with the mass $M = 3.52 M_\circ, M_{OV} = 2.5 M_\circ$, effective Kerr parameter $a_0 = 4.9$ and magnetic parameter $a_m = 10^{-4}$.

Stage	Time(obs),s	E(obs)/E90	Time,s	E/E90	R/Rg	B,Gs	a_0
G1	-180	0.02	-75	0.03	37	10^{13}	4.9
G2	0	0.88	0.93	2	3	$2*10^{14}$	2.4
G3	~450	190	0.04	0.04	3	$1.2*10^{15}$	1

We associate a slight increase in the gamma flux in G3 with an increase in the power of the central engine at the moment when the spinar loses its stability and collapses into a black hole. Note that such a three-stage collapse occurs only when the mass of the collapsing nucleus exceeds but is comparable with the Oppenheimer – Volkov limit.

4. Discussion

We presented multi-wavelength observations of GRB160625B, one of the brightest gamma-ray bursts in the history of their study. The authors of the article have already published a paper, concerning the first in the history discovery of variable polarization of the intrinsic emission of gamma-ray bursts (Troja et al., 2017).[7] Here we have concentrated on the temporal behavior of itsintrinsic electromagnetic radiation and presented optical and gamma-ray data, recorded during the time of the operation of the central engine of GRB160625B. We made an attempt to find

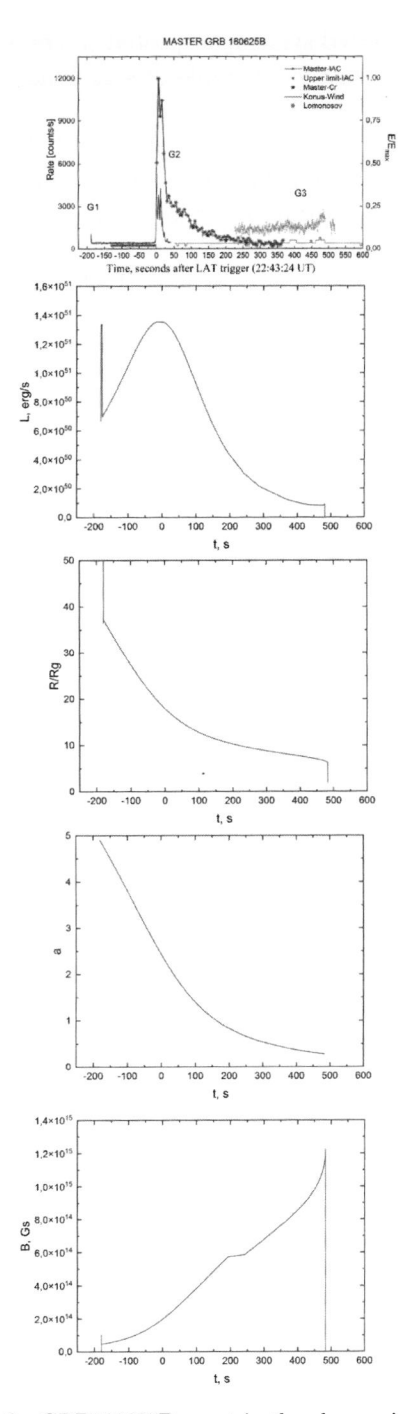

Fig. 7. In the diagram of the GRB160625B event in the observer's frame of reference is shown. In the top diagram, we have shown three principal G1 events - the position of the precursor ($\Delta t = -200$ s), the main peak of the G2 pulse (t = 0) and finally the last episode of increased G3 activity ($\Delta t = 400$–500 s).

traces of the duality of the GRB system, suspected traces of the dual nature of long GRBs. This study can serve as an example of searching for and finding the dual nature of long GRBs.

Long bright GRB160625B is rare, but not unique. GRB 080319B (Racusin et al., 2008)[53] also had a significant gap between the optical flux and the flux obtained by extrapolating the standard spectrum to the low frequency range. For GRB 080319B Kumar and Narayan (Kumar, Narayan 2009)[54] (see also Lazar et al 2009)[55] proposed a relativistic turbulence model to explain the fine structure of the light curve observed in the gamma range. It is assumed that the matter of the dropped shell is divided into two phases: the turbulent cells and everything in between. In this case, gamma emission is generated in both phases (reverse Compton), and synchrotron radiation of electrons in the inter-cell space is responsible for the radiation flux in the optics.

This explains a number of observed properties of gamma-ray bursts and, what is important in the context of this work, the huge excess of the flux in the optical range over what is dictated by the Band function. However, the natural consequence of this theory is a diminishing of the polarization over time, since the assumed turbulence entangles the magnetic field, leading to depolarization. In fact, the MASTER polarization observations (see Troja et al., 2017)[7] show an increase in polarization. Thus, in the case of GBR 160625B, the relativistic turbulence model does not work.

We interpret the features of the GRB160625B radiation within the framework of the model of a three-stage magnetorotational collapse of the core of a massive star whose mass exceeds but is comparable to the Oppenheimer-Volkov limit. In this model, the first G1 event in Spinar Paradigm will be explained by an abrupt stop of the nucleus collapse at the centrifugal barrier and the formation of a spinar. In this case, half of the accumulated gravitational energy is converted into rotational energy, and the second can be converted into jet energy along the spinar's axis of rotation. Further, as the rotational moment is lost, the spinar is compressing, gradually increasing its rotational energy, mainly emitted along the axis of rotation with a power of the proportional to the Umov-Poynting vector electromagnetic energy flow $E_{G1} = U_m \omega$. Of course, the observer will not see a smooth curve, since the jet must accumulate enough energy to pierce the progenitor shell (Lipunov & Gorbovskoy, 2007).[2] Naturally, in a model based on the conservation laws with an approximate description of the torque dissipation, one should not rely on the exact repetition of the light curve at the moment of the mainpulse G2. Therefore, we only achieved the coincidence of the moment of the maximum energy release with observations and the interval preceding the collapse of a heavy spinar with a powerful magnetic field and a mass exceeding the Oppenheimer-Volkov limit for a non-rotating neutron star.

MASTER and Lomonosov Space Observatory are supported by Lomonosov Moscow State University Development program (equipment). VL, PB are supported by RFBR grant 19-29-11011. NB is supported by FZZE-2020-0017).

References

1. MacFadyen A. I., Woosley S. E., 2001, ApJ 550, 410
2. Lipunov V., Gorbovskoy E., 2007, ApJ, 665L, 97L
3. Tutukov, A. V., Cherepashchuk, A. M., 2016, ARep, 60, 461
4. Lipunova G.V. and Lipunov V.M., 1998, A&A, 329, L29
5. Lipunov V., Gorbovskoy E., 2008, MNRAS, 383, 1397L
6. Lipunova G. et al. 2009, MNRAS,397,1695
7. Troja et al., 2017a, Natur, 547, 425T
8. Burns et al. 2016, GCN Circular, 19581,1
9. Dirirsa et al., 2016, GCN 19580, 1
10. Sadovnichii V., Panasyuk M. et al. 2017, SSRv, 212, 1705S
11. Svinkin et al. 2016, GCN, 19604, 1
12. Nakahira et al. 2016, GCN Circular, 19617,1
13. Melandri et al. 2016, GCN Circular, 19585,1
14. Troja et al. 2017b, GCN Circuar, 19588,1
15. Gorbovskoy et al. 2016a, GCN Circular, 19612,1
16. Lipunov et al. 2016a, GCN Circular, 19683,1
17. Lipunov V. et al. 2010, Advances in Astronomy, 2010, 30L
18. Lipunov et al. 2019, ARep, 63, 293L
19. Kornilov V. et al. 2012, ExpAst, 33, 173
20. Gorbovskoy et al. 2016b, MNRAS, 455, 3312
21. Barthelmy S. D. et al. 1998a, AIP Conference Proceedings, 428, 129
22. Barthelmy S. D. et al. 1998b, AIP Conference Proceedings,428, 99
23. Lipunov V. et al. 2018, Space Sci Rev, 214, 6
24. Lipunov et al. 2016b, ApJ, 833, 198L
25. Sadovnichy, V., Panasyuk M. et al. 2018, ApJ, 861, 48S
26. Ershova et al., 2020, ARep, 64, 126
27. Laskar et al. 2019, ApJ, 884, 121
28. Lipunov et al. 2017d, ApJ, 845, 52L
29. Lipunov et al. 2017a, MNRAS, 465, 3656L
30. Abbott B. P. et al. 2016, ApJL, 826, 13
31. Lipunov et al. 2018, NewA, 63, 48L GW
32. Abbott B. P. et al. 2017a, ApJL, 848, 12
33. Lipunov et al2017c, ApJL, 850, 1
34. Aartsen M. et al. 2017, A&A, 607A, 115I
35. Lipunov et al. 2019, NewA, 72, 42
36. Lipunov V. et al. 2020, ApJ, 896L, 19L
37. Svertilov S.I., Panasyuk M.I.et al. 2018, SSRv, 214, 1
38. Park I.H., M.I., etal.. 2018 Space Sci Rev, 214, 14
39. Mazaeva et al. 2016, GCN Circular, 19605, 1
40. von Kienlin et al.2003, A&A 411, L299-L305
41. Aptekar et al.. 1995,SSRv, 71, 265A
42. Zhang, B. et al. 2018, NatAstron 2, 69
43. Arnaud 1996 ASPC, 101, 17A
44. Band D.,1993, ApJ, 413, 281
45. Preece et al. 1998 ApJ, 506L, 23
46. Woosley, S. E. 1993, ApJ, 405, 273
47. Suvorov A.G., Kokkotas K.D., 2021, MNRAS, 502, 2482-2494
48. Pacini, F. 1967, Natur 216, 567-568

49. Kip S. Thorne 1974, ApJ, 191, 507-519
50. Troja, E., et al. 2007, ApJ, 665, 599
51. Lipunov V. M. 1992, Astrophysics of Neutron Stars, Springer
52. Lipunov V. M., Shakura N. I., SvAL, 6, 14L
53. Racusin, J.et al. 2008, Nature 455, 183
54. Pawan Kumar, Ramesh Narayan, 2009, MNRAS, 395 (1), 472
55. Lazar M., Poedts S. 2009, A&A, 494, 311-315

The role of the magnetic fields in GRB outflows

Jordana-Mitjans, N.[1,*]; Mundell, C. G.[1]; Kobayashi, S.[2]; Smith, R. J.[2]; Guidorzi, C.[3,4,5]; Steele, I. A.[2]; Shrestha, M.[2]; Gomboc, A.[6]; Marongiu, M.[7]; Martone, R.[3]; Lipunov, V.[8]; Gorbovskoy, E. S.[8]; Buckley, D. A. H.[9]; Rebolo, R.[10]; Budnev, N. M.[11]

[1] *Department of Physics, University of Bath, Claverton Down, Bath, BA2 7AY, UK*
[2] *Astrophysics Research Institute, Liverpool John Moores University, 146 Brownlow Hill, Liverpool, L3 5RF, UK*
[3] *Department of Physics and Earth Science, University of Ferrara, via Saragat 1, I-44122, Ferrara, Italy*
[4] *INFN – Sezione di Ferrara, Via Saragat 1, 44122 Ferrara, Italy*
[5] *INAF – Osservatorio di Astrofisica e Scienza dello Spazio di Bologna, Via Piero Gobetti 101, 40129 Bologna, Italy*
[6] *Center for Astrophysics and Cosmology, University of Nova Gorica, Vipavska 13, 5000 Nova Gorica, Slovenia*
[7] *INAF – Osservatorio Astronomico di Cagliari - via della Scienza 5 - I-09047 Selargius, Italy*
[8] *Lomonosov Moscow State University, SAI, Physics Department, 13 Univeristetskij pr-t, Moscow 119991, Russia*
[9] *South African Astronomical Observatory PO Box 9, Observatory 7935, Cape Town, South Africa*
[10] *Instituto de Astrofísica de Canarias (IAC), Calle Vía Láctea s/n, E-38200 La Laguna, Tenerife, Spain*
[11] *Applied Physics Institute, Irkutsk State University, 20, Gagarin blvd, 664003, Irkutsk, Russia*
* E-mail: N. Jordana@bath.ac.uk

Gamma-ray bursts (GRBs) are bright extragalactic flashes of gamma-ray radiation and briefly the most energetic explosions in the Universe. Their catastrophic origin —the merger of compact objects or the collapse of massive stars— drives the formation of a newborn compact remnant (black hole or magnetar) that powers two highly relativistic jets. As these jets continue to travel outwards, they collide with the external material surrounding the dying star, producing a long-lasting afterglow that can be seen across the entire electromagnetic spectrum, from the most energetic gamma-ray emission to radio wavelengths. But how can such material be accelerated and focused into narrow beams? The internal shock model proposes that repeated collisions between material blasted out during the explosion can produce the gamma-ray flash. The competing magnetic model credits primordial large-scale ordered magnetic fields that collimate and accelerate the relativistic outflows. To distinguish between these models and ultimately determine the power source for these energetic explosions, our team studies the polarization of the light during the first minutes after the explosion (using novel instruments on fully autonomous telescopes around the globe) to directly probe the magnetic field properties in these extragalactic jets. This technology allowed the detection of highly polarized optical light in GRB 120308A[1] and confirmed the presence of mildly magnetized jets with large-scale primordial magnetic fields in a reduced sample of GRBs (e.g. GRB 090102,[2] GRB 110205A,[3] GRB 101112A,[3] GRB 160625B[4]). Here we discuss the observations of the most energetic and first GRB detected at very high TeV energies, GRB 190114C,[5] which opens a new frontier in GRB magnetic field studies suggesting that some jets can be launched highly magnetized and that the collapse and destruction of these magnetic fields at very early times may have powered the explosion itself.

Additionally, our most recent polarimetric observations of the jet of GRB 141220A[6] indicate that, when the jetted ejected material is decelerated by the surrounding environment, the magnetic field amplification mechanisms at the front shock —needed to generate the observed synchrotron emission— produce small magnetic domains. These measurements validate theoretical expectations and contrast with previous observations that suggest large magnetic domains in collisionless shocks (i.e. GRB 091208B[7]).

Keywords: High energy astrophysics; Gamma-ray bursts; Magnetic fields; Polarimetry; Shocks; Jets

Gamma-ray bursts (GRBs) are briefly the most intense sources of gamma-ray photons in the Universe to the extent that they outshine any other kind of gamma-ray emitter present in the sky map. The amount of energy released in a matter of milliseconds to hundreds of seconds provides a unique opportunity to study physics in extreme environments (e.g., GRB central engines, jet composition, energy dissipation, acceleration, collimation, shock physics) and test the physical models regarding the nature of their progenitors.[8,9] Additionally, their brightness and cosmological distances make them useful for probing the composition of the early Universe.[10,11]

GRBs with long duration (typically > 2 s; see Ref. 12) are related to the death of massive stars as single collapsars[13,14] or in binary systems,[15] and short GRBs (< 2 s) to mergers from an old population of degenerate compact stars. Possible merger candidates include neutron star binaries[16,17] or binaries containing a stellar black hole and a neutron star companion.[18–20] Due to their inspiral and coalescence, they are emitters of gravitational waves[21] and they are also promising candidate sources of high-energy neutrinos.[22]

GRBs are produced when the central engine (a black hole or magnetar) drives out two bipolar relativistic jets that burrow through the stellar ejecta and emit the characteristic prompt gamma-ray emission via internal dissipation mechanisms[23] —i.e. internal shocks[24] or reconnection.[25] Later on, the relativistic ejecta are decelerated by the circumburst medium by a pair of external shocks:[26,27] a short-lived reverse shock[28,29] and a forward shock (see Fig. 1). This lagging emission called the afterglow radiates via synchrotron emission and can be detected seconds to years after the burst at wavelengths across the electromagnetic spectrum.[30,31] In this context, a variety of afterglow light curves are expected depending on the relative contributions of the reverse and forward shock.

1. Magnetic fields in GRBs

Magnetic fields play an important role in the physics of GRBs by affecting how the jet is launched (formation, acceleration, collimation and composition of the jet) and in shaping the afterglow emission (particle acceleration by the shock). Depending on the driving mechanism of the relativistic outflow —if dominated by kinetic or magnetic energy— GRBs jets can be launched as baryonic (also named hydrodynamical jets[32]) or magnetized jets (i.e., Poynting-flux jets[33,34]). The degree

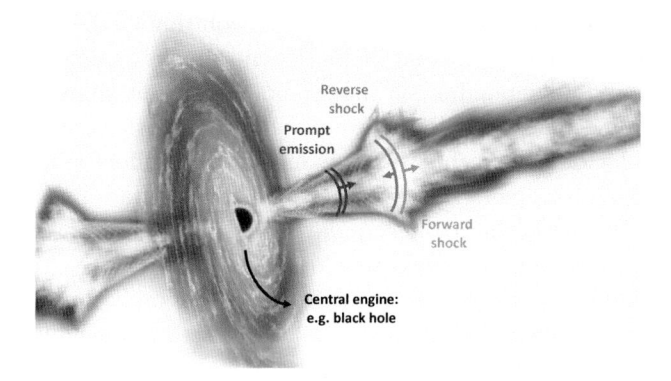

Fig. 1. Schematic representation of a GRB outflow. The steps for the formation of a GRB are: (1) an extragalactic massive star collapses or two compact objects merge, (2) there is accretion onto a newborn black hole, and (3) the ejecta are collimated and accelerated to relativistic speeds along the narrow beam of a jet. Note that the emission we detect (prompt gamma-ray emission and afterglow) comes from sites at different distances from the central engine. Additionally, the afterglow (reverse and forward shock) is formed at the contact discontinuity between the outflow and the circumburst medium.

of magnetization of an outflow is usually characterized by the parameter σ, which is defined as the ratio of magnetic to kinetic energy flux.[35]

In a baryonic jet ($\sigma \ll 1$), neutrino annihilation at the polar region of a hyper-accreting system would launch a thermally-driven fireball that accelerates the material.[13,36] In this model, tangled magnetic fields are locally generated in shocks.[37]

In a magnetized jet ($\sigma \gg 1$), large-scale magnetic fields extract rotational energy from the black hole, accretion disk or magnetar (in a magnetohydrodynamic extraction[33,38,39]), which accelerates the material. The magnetization parameter σ influences the dynamics of the jet and it is thought to decrease with increasing distance from the central engine.[40] In this scenario, the magnetic field configuration is likely toroidal far from the black hole.[41] The detection or non-detection of this large-scale magnetic field remnant is crucial to support or discard the magnetic jet model. Furthermore, a plausible scenario is that GRB outflows are launched with a combination of both hot-baryonic and cold-magnetic components, leading to a broad range of magnetization degrees σ with consequences in the prompt and afterglow emission phase.[34,35,42]

2. The polarization of GRBs

GRBs are extragalactic collimated sources that are not possible to spatially resolve. Polarization offers a tool to study the magnetic field properties and the jet geometry on length scales orders of magnitude smaller than what imaging can probe. Additionally, it can give an extra dimension of information on the jet physics and underlying emission processes and provide complementary information that can break degeneracies in the temporal and spectral evolution of the emission. Overall, the expected polarization signals in GRBs depend on the magnetic field topology (i.e. ordered or random depending on the jet model), the jet angular geometry,[43,44] and the emission mechanisms. While the emission mechanisms for the prompt emission are still under debate,[45] the afterglow emission is widely assumed to be synchrotron.[46] In the lab frame, synchrotron-emitted photons are linearly polarized,[47] with $P \approx 70\%$. However, the intrinsic polarization from synchrotron emission can be averaged out if the magnetic field topology is random.

During the afterglow stage, the forward shock emission is produced by shocked ambient medium, with tangled magnetic fields locally produced and amplified by e.g., a two-stream magnetic instability (Weibel instability[37,48]). Consequently, the forward shock emission is insensitive to the magnetic field structure of the original ejecta and it is expected to be unpolarized (see Section 2.2). In contrast, the prompt and reverse shock emission is still sensitive to the properties of the central engine ejecta and measuring the polarization allows discriminating between competing jet models (see Section 2.1).

2.1. *The polarization of baryonic and magnetized jets*

Distinct polarization signatures are predicted for magnetized and baryonic jet models. We expect unpolarized emission if the jet is baryonic[37] and polarized emission in a magnetized jet[49] from large-scale ordered magnetic fields advected from the central engine (see Fig. 2). Even if the magnetic fields become slightly distorted during the internal shocks, a mildly magnetized jet is still expected to produce large polarization levels, as only a small area of the jet is observed due to the relativistic beaming. However, note that the maximum synchrotron polarization is reduced to $P \approx 50\%$ due to relativistic aberration effects —i.e., the rotation of the polarization vectors.[50] In the case of a highly magnetized jet (see Fig. 2), reconnection mechanisms are thought to power the prompt emission,[25,51] which would in principle distort the order in the magnetic fields.

2.1.1. *Prompt gamma-ray emission*

Polarization studies of the prompt gamma-ray emission offer great prospects for the study of jet models.[52] However, current studies have yielded a wide range of polarization results,[52–59] i.e. $P = 0\% - 100\%$, with the discrepancy usually related to data with low signal-to-noise, instrumental bias or selection effects in the data analysis.[52,54] Furthermore, time-resolved analyses suggest that the polarization degree in time-integrated studies has been averaged out given that the polarization angle evolves through single pulses (see Refs. 60–62). More importantly, the interpretation of these results is complex given that the underlying physics of the prompt emission remain unknown.[45]

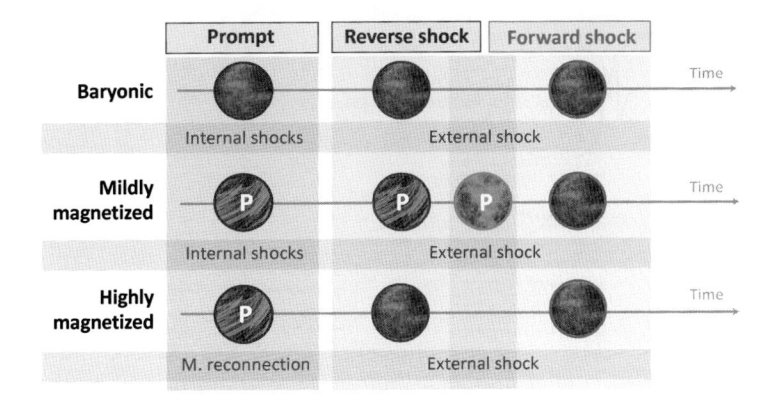

Fig. 2. Summary of the magnetic field structures expected in each jet model (baryonic and magnetized) for the different shocks (internal and external) and assuming synchrotron as the emitting mechanism. The white **P** letter denotes those magnetic field structures that would give rise to significant polarization (large-scale ordered or locally tangled magnetic fields). Note that emission from different origins can be blended into the overall received; e.g. in a mildly magnetized jet, the polarization can be reduced from the maximum expected given a mix of reverse and unpolarized forward shock emission.

2.1.2. *The early optical afterglow*

At optical bands, the polarization measurements from the early afterglow are the domain of robotic telescopes with rapid follow-up capabilities[69–72] (see Fig. 3). The first robust evidence of large-scale ordered magnetic fields in the fireball was the detection of $P = 10\% \pm 1\%$ polarization during the steep decay of GRB 090102 bright reverse shock.[2] This result suggested that primordial magnetic fields do play a role in GRBs outflows and that they can persist at great distances from the central source —up to the external shock radius. The GRB 120308A measurements further proved this idea with a time-resolved polarimetric light curve during a reverse-forward shock interplay[1] (see Fig 4); the polarization decayed steadily from $P = 28\% \pm 4\%$ to $P = 16^{+5}_{-4}\%$ with constant polarization angle due to the increase of unpolarized forward shock photons. Additionally, polarization degrees of $P = 13^{+13}_{-9}\%$ and $P \approx 6\%$ were also detected in GRB 110205A and GRB 101112A.[3]

Overall, current observations of polarized reverse shocks and the modelling of the early GRB afterglow suggest mildly magnetized jets at the deceleration radius,[35,73] with magnetization degrees $\sigma = 0.1 - 1$. These intermediate values of magnetization allow the existence of bright reverse shocks and are also consistent with the measurements of polarized reverse shocks (see Fig. 2). However, we note that some observations suggest higher magnetization at different stages of the jet. The $P < 8\%$ constraint during the fireball deceleration of GRB 060418[74] implies that the reverse shock could have been suppressed due to high magnetization in the fireball at the external shock radius, with $\sigma \geq 1$. Additionally, the optical emission

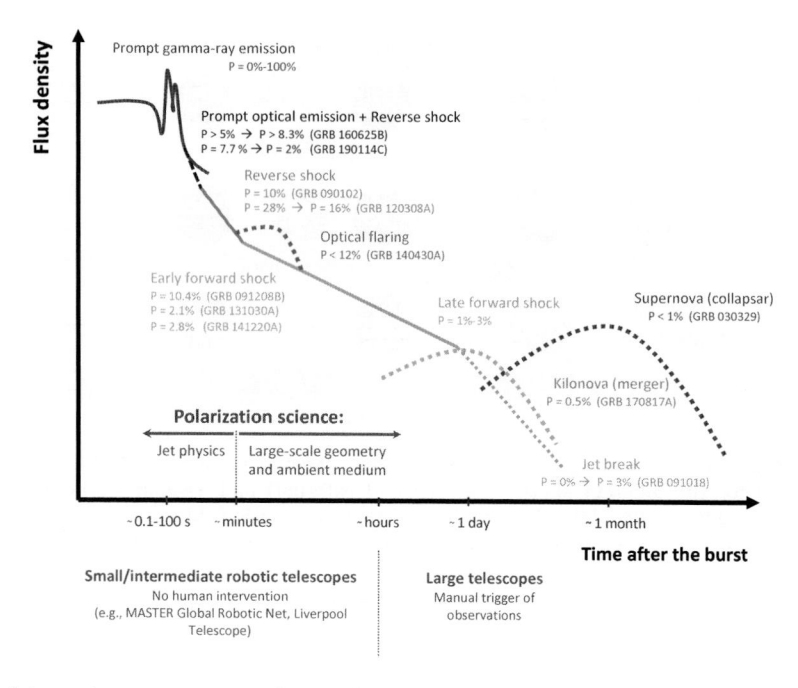

Fig. 3. Schematic representation of the different types of GRB emission and relevant polarization measurements. Note that, with the exception of the prompt gamma-ray emission, the represented "canonical" light curve refers to optical wavelengths. *References:* GRB 030329[63] GRB 090102,[2] GRB 091018,[64] GRB 091208B,[7] GRB 120308A,[1] GRB 131030A,[65] GRB 140430A,[66] GRB 141220A[6] GRB 160625B,[4] GRB 170817A,[67] GRB 190114C,[5] late-time forward shocks[68] and the AstroSat CZT/POLAR gamma-ray polarization catalogues.[52,59]

in between gamma-ray pulses of GRB 160625B[4] was interpreted as reverse shock and presented a significant increase from $P > 5.2\% \pm 0.6\%$ to $P > 8.3\% \pm 0.5\%$ simultaneous to a gamma-ray pulse —implying that polarized prompt emission photons contributed at optical wavelengths. The polarization lower limits were quite low through observations, which led to speculations regarding distorting mechanisms during the prompt gamma-ray emission, such as reconnection.[25,51]

2.1.3. *The highly magnetized jet of GRB 190114C*

Both MASTER II from the Master Global robotic net and RINGO3 instrument from the Liverpool Telescope observed GRB 190114C, the first GRB detected at very high energies (in the TeV domain[76]). Interestingly, the afterglow emission decay rate presented a steep to shallow transition, which suggested reverse shock contribution.[5] Our observations report remarkably low polarization just after the end of the gamma-ray flash ($P = 7.7\%$), a sharp drop of polarization one minute later ($P = 2\%$) and constant levels during the following half an hour. In Ref. 5, we suggest that the $P \approx 2\%$ constant polarization is due to differential dust absorption

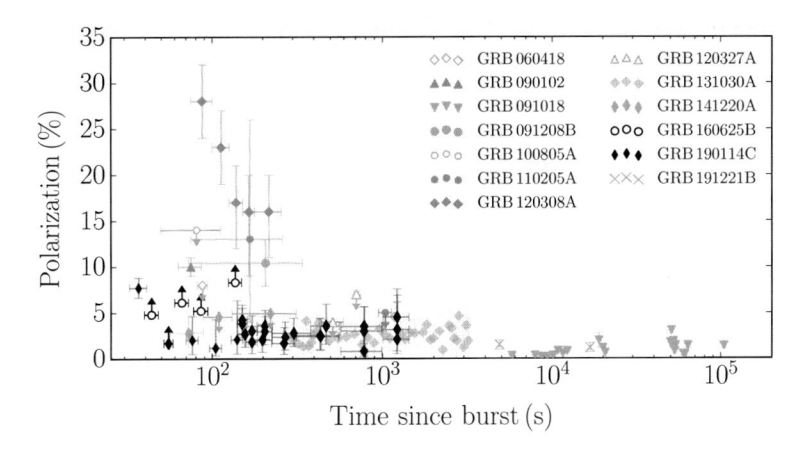

Fig. 4. Rest-frame polarization measurements of GRBs at optical bands —adapted from Ref. 1. Overall, the polarization dependency with time indicates that the regime in which we can infer the jet physics corresponds to observations before ~ 5 min postburst. In contrast, the polarization at later times gives information about the jet geometry and dust. *References:* GRB 060418,[74] GRB 090102,[2] GRB 091018,[64] GRB 091208B,[7] GRB 110205A,[3] GRB 100805A,[3] GRB 120308A,[1] GRB 120327A,[3] GRB 131030A,[65] GRB 141220A,[6] GRB 160625B,[4] GRB 190114C,[5] and GRB 191221B.[75]

in the line of sight —mainly due to the highly obscured environment in which the GRB was formed— which means that the intrinsic polarization of the jet is very small for reverse shock emission. Our low optical polarization measurements are also consistent with $P = 0.87\% \pm 0.13\%$ measured 2.2 h later at millimetre frequencies, during the reverse shock emission.[77]

The temporal and spectral modelling of GRB 190114C emission indicates a clear interplay between the reverse and forward shock and more magnetization in the reverse shock, which suggests the existence of a primordial large-scale magnetic field ejected from the rotating black hole. However, GRB 190114C polarimetric observations reveal that the magnetic field in the ejecta was mostly random oriented in space, which does not agree with what we expect from previous measurements of reverse shocks[1,2] (see Fig. 4).

In Ref. 5, we propose that the polarization was low because the large-scale magnetic field catastrophically collapsed during the first tens of seconds of the gamma-ray flash via magnetic reconnection mechanisms and that the $P = 7.7\%$ measurement is a relic from this emission.[25,51] As opposed to previous polarization measurements,[1,2] these findings suggest that at least some energetic GRBs can be launched highly magnetized and that magnetic dissipation mechanisms can power a bright gamma-ray prompt. Additionally, it opens a debate about the nature of the bright early-time steep emission, which could be a reconnection tail instead of a reverse shock. That is because the reverse shock emission could have been suppressed if, at the deceleration radius, the outflow was still in the highly magnetized regime.[42]

These results pin down timescales and distances for which large-scale magnetic fields survive in astrophysical jets and challenge the current models for the production of GRBs.

2.2. *The polarization from collisionless shocks*

Polarimetric studies of the late afterglow have measured low degrees of polarization at optical wavelengths during the decay of the long-lived forward shock[68] and have provided information on the angular structure of jets[43] and the dust properties of GRB host galaxies[78] (see Fig. 4). Additionally, these polarization levels agree with theoretical predictions and suggest that forward shocks are intrinsically unpolarized due to tangled magnetic fields locally generated in shocks.[37]

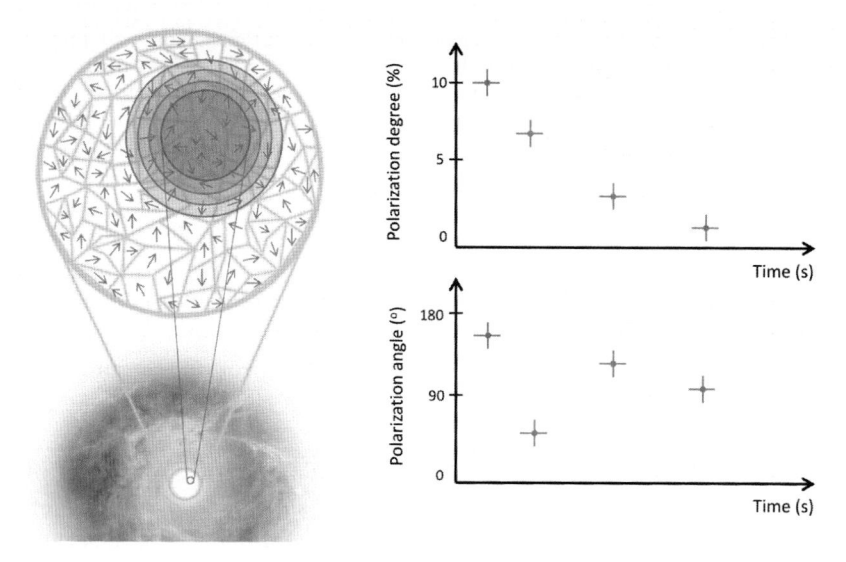

Fig. 5. Schematic representation of the evolution of the polarization degree and angle in the patches model.[79]

However, Ref. 7 observations set a debate on the intrinsic polarization of forward shocks at early times given the detection of significant polarization in the GRB 091208B forward shock ($P = 10.4\% \pm 2.5\%$), which favoured the patches model.[79] Phenomenologically, the patches model implies that as the outflow decelerates and the visible emitting region increases, more patches with coherent magnetic fields (i.e., highly polarized; $P \approx 50\%$) are visible. As the orientation of the magnetic field is random from one domain to another, the overall observed polarization decreases with time (see Fig. 5). Consequently, GRB 091208B measurement still agrees with the $P \approx 1\% - 3\%$ polarization found in late-time forward shocks. Physically, the patches model proposes that the amplification mechanism of the magnetic field at the shock front —needed to increase the magnetic energy density from interstellar to the observed levels— leads to the formation of large magnetic domains (i.e. large coherent length scales for the magnetic field).

The GRB 091208B measurement gives rise to new possible mechanisms for magnetic field amplification, as well as adding a problematic degeneracy in early-time polarimetric studies. Note that the GRB 091208B polarization level is comparable to that measured in the reverse shock of GRB 090102.[2] If forward shocks are polarized at early times, it becomes difficult to disentangle the possible polarized components that probe the jet physics from the contribution of the shocked ambient material. Consequently, a good understanding of the typical polarization levels of early-time forward shocks is crucial.

2.2.1. *The polarization of the early-time classical forward shock of GRB 141220A*

In Ref. 6, we report the early-time observations of GRB 141220A forward shock. Interestingly, this afterglow presented temporal and spectral properties typical of late-time forward shocks but starting as soon as 1.4 min postburst. Furthermore, our polarimetric observations at 2.2-3.4 min postburst are earlier than GRB 091208B measurement (2.5-11.8 min), which allow us to probe smaller emitting regions. If the length scale of the magnetic field was the same as in GRB 091208B, we would expect $P = 20\%$ polarization for GRB 141220A at the time of observations (as predicted by the patches model; see Fig 5). Instead, we measure $P = 2.8^{+2.0}_{-1.6}\%$ in GRB 141220A, which we find is compatible with that induced by dust in the GRB environment and agrees with theoretical predictions of unpolarized forward shocks,[37,80] i.e. $P_{\text{th}} = 0\% - 2\%$ (but see Refs. 81, 82).

The GRB 141220A and current early-time forward shock polarization measurements suggest that GRB 091208B is an outlier (see Fig. 4). We speculate that GRB 091208B scenario could be similar to the reverse-forward shock interplay in GRB 120308A.[1] As the polarization measurement was integrated over a large time window, we suggest the presence of a more stable underlying polarized component and ordered large-scale magnetic fields in the fireball.

3. Outlook

After 15 years of progress in early-time polarization studies of GRBs afterglows, we can confidently confirm the presence of large-scale ordered magnetic fields in a subset of bright afterglows, suggesting that the magnetic field ejected from the central source does play a role in the jet launching. In general, we have not measured the maximum polarization allowed by theory in reverse shocks ($P = 50\%$) and polarization observations indicate that highly polarized emission at $P = 28\%$ level is not that common (GRB 120308A;[1] see Fig. 4). Therefore, mechanisms that can change the magnetic field topology might play an important role at the early stages of GRB jets.

Observations of reverse shocks remain rare,[73] and a way to overcome the lack of reverse shocks in the optical is to look at millimetre and radio wavelengths. The predictions are that, if the forward shock peaks at optical bands, the reverse shock will peak at $1 - 100\,\text{GHz}$ bands and $\sim 0.01 - 0.1\,\text{days}$ postburst with fluxes of $0.01 - 0.1\,\text{mJy}$.[83] However, if the magnetization is high at the external shock radius, the reverse shock would be suppressed.[42] The lack of reverse shocks at optical and radio wavelengths would indirectly imply that jets are still highly magnetized at large distances from the central source. Consequently, the rate and the polarization of reverse shocks at optical[1–5] and lower frequencies[77] can greatly constrain the magnetization of GRB jets and further test the mildly and highly magnetized jet regimes.

Great advancement will be made on constraining GRB jet models with a faster target acquisition and the increase of the polarimeters' sensitivity.[84] This will allow gathering a large polarimetric dataset of measurements at early times, sampling most of the GRB population at lower luminosities. Furthermore, other TeV GRBs have been discovered[85–88] —something we did not expect before the Cherenkov Telescope Array (CTA). With the start of the CTA era, we will be able to track the earliest stages of the magnetic field and its evolution in the most energetic systems. Consequently, we will need new polarization technology to optimize CTA follow-up as well as other multimessenger triggers from gravitational waves and possibly neutrinos.

References

1. C. G. Mundell, D. Kopač, D. M. Arnold, I. A. Steele, A. Gomboc, S. Kobayashi, R. M. Harrison, R. J. Smith, C. Guidorzi, F. J. Virgili, A. Melandri and J. Japelj, Highly polarized light from stable ordered magnetic fields in GRB 120308A, *Nature* **504**, 119 (December 2013).
2. I. A. Steele, C. G. Mundell, R. J. Smith, S. Kobayashi and C. Guidorzi, Ten per cent polarized optical emission from GRB090102, *Nature* **462**, 767 (December 2009).
3. I. A. Steele, D. Kopač, D. M. Arnold, R. J. Smith, S. Kobayashi, H. E. Jermak, C. G. Mundell, A. Gomboc, C. Guidorzi, A. Meland ri and J. Japelj, Polarimetry and Photometry of Gamma-Ray Bursts with RINGO2, *ApJ* **843**, p. 143 (Jul 2017).
4. E. Troja, V. M. Lipunov, C. G. Mundell, N. R. Butler, A. M. Watson, S. Kobayashi, S. B. Cenko, F. E. Marshall, R. Ricci and A. Fruchter, Significant and variable linear polarization during the prompt optical flash of GRB 160625B., *Nature* **547**, 425 (Jul 2017).
5. N. Jordana-Mitjans, C. G. Mundell, S. Kobayashi, R. J. Smith, C. Guidorzi, I. A. Steele, M. Shrestha, A. Gomboc, M. Marongiu, R. Martone, V. Lipunov, E. S. Gorbovskoy, D. A. H. Buckley, R. Rebolo and N. M. Budnev, Lowly Polarized Light from a Highly Magnetized Jet of GRB 190114C, *ApJ* **892**, p. 97 (April 2020).
6. N. Jordana-Mitjans, C. G. Mundell, R. J. Smith, C. Guidorzi, M. Marongiu, S. Kobayashi, A. Gomboc, M. Shrestha and I. A. Steele, Coherence scale of magnetic fields generated in early-time forward shocks of GRBs, *MNRAS* **505**, 2662 (August 2021).
7. T. Uehara, K. Toma, K. S. Kawabata, S. Chiyonobu, Y. Fukazawa, Y. Ikejiri, T. Inoue, R. Itoh, T. Komatsu, H. Miyamoto, T. Mizuno, O. Nagae, H. Nakaya, T. Ohsugi,

K. Sakimoto, M. Sasada, H. Tanaka, M. Uemura, M. Yamanaka, T. Yamashita, R. Yamazaki and M. Yoshida, GRB 091208B: First Detection of the Optical Polarization in Early Forward Shock Emission of a Gamma-Ray Burst Afterglow, *ApJ* **752**, p. L6 (June 2012).

8. B. Zhang, Open questions in GRB physics, *Comptes Rendus Physique* **12**, 206 (April 2011).
9. P. Kumar and B. Zhang, The physics of gamma-ray bursts & relativistic jets, *Phys. Rep.* **561**, 1 (February 2015).
10. R. Salvaterra, M. Della Valle, S. Campana, G. Chincarini, S. Covino, P. D'Avanzo, A. Fernández-Soto, C. Guidorzi, F. Mannucci, R. Margutti, C. C. Thöne, L. A. Antonelli, S. D. Barthelmy, M. de Pasquale, V. D'Elia, F. Fiore, D. Fugazza, L. K. Hunt, E. Maiorano, S. Marinoni, F. E. Marshall, E. Molinari, J. Nousek, E. Pian, J. L. Racusin, L. Stella, L. Amati, G. Andreuzzi, G. Cusumano, E. E. Fenimore, P. Ferrero, P. Giommi, D. Guetta, S. T. Holland, K. Hurley, G. L. Israel, J. Mao, C. B. Markwardt, N. Masetti, C. Pagani, E. Palazzi, D. M. Palmer, S. Piranomonte, G. Tagliaferri and V. Testa, GRB090423 at a redshift of z~8.1, *Nature* **461**, 1258 (October 2009).
11. A. Cucchiara, A. J. Levan, D. B. Fox, N. R. Tanvir, T. N. Ukwatta, E. Berger, T. Krühler, A. Küpcü Yoldaş, X. F. Wu, K. Toma, J. Greiner, F. E. Olivares, A. Rowlinson, L. Amati, T. Sakamoto, K. Roth, A. Stephens, A. Fritz, J. P. U. Fynbo, J. Hjorth, D. Malesani, P. Jakobsson, K. Wiersema, P. T. O'Brien, A. M. Soderberg, R. J. Foley, A. S. Fruchter, J. Rhoads, R. E. Rutledge, B. P. Schmidt, M. A. Dopita, P. Podsiadlowski, R. Willingale, C. Wolf, S. R. Kulkarni and P. D'Avanzo, A Photometric Redshift of z ~9.4 for GRB 090429B, *ApJ* **736**, p. 7 (July 2011).
12. C. Kouveliotou, C. A. Meegan, G. J. Fishman, N. P. Bhat, M. S. Briggs, T. M. Koshut, W. S. Paciesas and G. N. Pendleton, Identification of two classes of gamma-ray bursts, *ApJ* **413**, L101 (August 1993).
13. S. E. Woosley, Gamma-ray bursts from stellar mass accretion disks around black holes, *ApJ* **405**, 273 (March 1993).
14. A. I. MacFadyen and S. E. Woosley, Collapsars: Gamma-Ray Bursts and Explosions in "Failed Supernovae", *ApJ* **524**, 262 (October 1999).
15. C. L. Fryer, P. A. Mazzali, J. Prochaska, E. Cappellaro, A. Panaitescu, E. Berger, M. van Putten, E. P. J. van den Heuvel, P. Young, A. Hungerford, G. Rockefeller, S.-C. Yoon, P. Podsiadlowski, K. Nomoto, R. Chevalier, B. Schmidt and S. Kulkarni, Constraints on Type Ib/c Supernovae and Gamma-Ray Burst Progenitors, *PASP* **119**, 1211 (November 2007).
16. B. Paczynski, Gamma-ray bursters at cosmological distances, *ApJ* **308**, L43 (September 1986).
17. D. Eichler, M. Livio, T. Piran and D. N. Schramm, Nucleosynthesis, neutrino bursts and gamma-rays from coalescing neutron stars, *Nature* **340**, 126 (July 1989).
18. B. Paczynski, Cosmological gamma-ray bursts., *Acta Astronomica* **41**, 257 (January 1991).
19. R. Narayan, B. Paczynski and T. Piran, Gamma-Ray Bursts as the Death Throes of Massive Binary Stars, *ApJ* **395**, p. L83 (August 1992).
20. S. E. Woosley and J. S. Bloom, The Supernova Gamma-Ray Burst Connection, *ARA&A* **44**, 507 (September 2006).
21. B. P. Abbott, R. Abbott, T. D. Abbott, F. Acernese, K. Ackley, C. Adams, T. Adams, P. Addesso, R. X. Adhikari, V. B. Adya and et al., GW170817: Observation of Gravitational Waves from a Binary Neutron Star Inspiral, *Physical Review Letters* **119**, p. 161101 (October 2017).

22. S. S. Kimura, K. Murase, P. Mészáros and K. Kiuchi, High-energy Neutrino Emission from Short Gamma-Ray Bursts: Prospects for Coincident Detection with Gravitational Waves, *ApJ* **848**, p. L4 (October 2017).
23. R. Sari and T. Piran, Variability in Gamma-Ray Bursts: A Clue, *ApJ* **485**, 270 (August 1997).
24. M. J. Rees and P. Meszaros, Unsteady Outflow Models for Cosmological Gamma-Ray Bursts, *ApJ* **430**, p. L93 (August 1994).
25. B. Zhang and H. Yan, The Internal-collision-induced Magnetic Reconnection and Turbulence (ICMART) Model of Gamma-ray Bursts, *ApJ* **726**, p. 90 (Jan 2011).
26. R. Sari, Hydrodynamics of Gamma-Ray Burst Afterglow, *ApJ* **489**, L37 (November 1997).
27. T. Piran, Gamma-ray bursts and the fireball model, *Phys. Rep.* **314**, 575 (June 1999).
28. R. Sari and T. Piran, Predictions for the Very Early Afterglow and the Optical Flash, *ApJ* **520**, 641 (Aug 1999).
29. S. Kobayashi, Light Curves of Gamma-Ray Burst Optical Flashes, *ApJ* **545**, 807 (Dec 2000).
30. E. Costa, F. Frontera, J. Heise, M. Feroci, J. in't Zand, F. Fiore, M. N. Cinti, D. Dal Fiume, L. Nicastro, M. Orlandini, E. Palazzi, M. Rapisarda#, G. Zavattini, R. Jager, A. Parmar, A. Owens, S. Molendi, G. Cusumano, M. C. Maccarone, S. Giarrusso, A. Coletta, L. A. Antonelli, P. Giommi, J. M. Muller, L. Piro and R. C. Butler, Discovery of an X-ray afterglow associated with the γ-ray burst of 28 February 1997, *Nature* **387**, 783 (June 1997).
31. J. van Paradijs, P. J. Groot, T. Galama, C. Kouveliotou, R. G. Strom, J. Telting, R. G. M. Rutten, G. J. Fishman, C. A. Meegan, M. Pettini, N. Tanvir, J. Bloom, H. Pedersen, H. U. Nørdgaard-Nielsen, M. Linden-Vørnle, J. Melnick, G. Van der Steene, M. Bremer, R. Naber, J. Heise, J. in't Zand, E. Costa, M. Feroci, L. Piro, F. Frontera, G. Zavattini, L. Nicastro, E. Palazzi, K. Bennett, L. Hanlon and A. Parmar, Transient optical emission from the error box of the γ-ray burst of 28 February 1997, *Nature* **386**, 686 (April 1997).
32. A. Shemi and T. Piran, The Appearance of Cosmic Fireballs, *ApJ* **365**, p. L55 (December 1990).
33. V. V. Usov, Millisecond pulsars with extremely strong magnetic fields as a cosmological source of gamma-ray bursts, *Nature* **357**, 472 (June 1992).
34. S. S. Komissarov, N. Vlahakis, A. Königl and M. V. Barkov, Magnetic acceleration of ultrarelativistic jets in gamma-ray burst sources, *MNRAS* **394**, 1182 (April 2009).
35. B. Zhang and S. Kobayashi, Gamma-Ray Burst Early Afterglows: Reverse Shock Emission from an Arbitrarily Magnetized Ejecta, *ApJ* **628**, 315 (July 2005).
36. M. A. Aloy, H. T. Janka and E. Müller, Relativistic outflows from remnants of compact object mergers and their viability for short gamma-ray bursts, *A&A* **436**, 273 (June 2005).
37. M. V. Medvedev and A. Loeb, Generation of Magnetic Fields in the Relativistic Shock of Gamma-Ray Burst Sources, *ApJ* **526**, 697 (Dec 1999).
38. R. D. Blandford and R. L. Znajek, Electromagnetic extraction of energy from Kerr black holes., *MNRAS* **179**, 433 (May 1977).
39. R. D. Blandford and D. G. Payne, Hydromagnetic flows from accretion disks and the production of radio jets., *MNRAS* **199**, 883 (June 1982).
40. Zhang, Gamma-Ray Burst Prompt Emission, *International Journal of Modern Physics D* **23**, p. 1430002 (December 2014).
41. H. C. Spruit, F. Daigne and G. Drenkhahn, Large scale magnetic fields and their dissipation in GRB fireballs, *A&A* **369**, 694 (Apr 2001).

42. D. Giannios, P. Mimica and M. A. Aloy, On the existence of a reverse shock in magnetized gamma-ray burst ejecta, *A&A* **478**, 747 (Feb 2008).
43. E. M. Rossi, D. Lazzati, J. D. Salmonson and G. Ghisellini, The polarization of afterglow emission reveals γ-ray bursts jet structure, *MNRAS* **354**, 86 (Oct 2004).
44. R. Gill, J. Granot and P. Kumar, Linear polarization in gamma-ray burst prompt emission, *MNRAS* **491**, 3343 (January 2020).
45. K. Toma, T. Sakamoto, B. Zhang, J. E. Hill, M. L. McConnell, P. F. Bloser, R. Yamazaki, K. Ioka and T. Nakamura, Statistical Properties of Gamma-Ray Burst Polarization, *ApJ* **698**, 1042 (June 2009).
46. R. Sari, T. Piran and R. Narayan, Spectra and Light Curves of Gamma-Ray Burst Afterglows, *ApJ* **497**, L17 (April 1998).
47. G. B. Rybicki and A. P. Lightman, *Radiative processes in astrophysics* 1979.
48. E. S. Weibel, Spontaneously Growing Transverse Waves in a Plasma Due to an Anisotropic Velocity Distribution, *Phys. Rev. Lett.* **2**, 83 (Feb 1959).
49. J. Granot and A. Königl, Linear Polarization in Gamma-Ray Bursts: The Case for an Ordered Magnetic Field, *ApJ* **594**, L83 (September 2003).
50. M. Lyutikov, V. I. Pariev and R. D. Blandford, Polarization of Prompt Gamma-Ray Burst Emission: Evidence for Electromagnetically Dominated Outflow, *ApJ* **597**, 998 (Nov 2003).
51. W. Deng, H. Zhang, B. Zhang and H. Li, Collision-induced Magnetic Reconnection and a Unified Interpretation of Polarization Properties of GRBs and Blazars, *ApJ* **821**, p. L12 (Apr 2016).
52. M. Kole, N. De Angelis, F. Berlato, J. M. Burgess, N. Gauvin, J. Greiner, W. Hajdas, H. C. Li, Z. H. Li, A. Pollo, N. Produit, D. Rybka, L. M. Song, J. C. Sun, J. Szabelski, T. Tymieniecka, Y. H. Wang, B. B. Wu, X. Wu, S. L. Xiong, S. N. Zhang and Y. J. Zhang, The POLAR gamma-ray burst polarization catalog, *A&A* **644**, p. A124 (December 2020).
53. W. Coburn and S. E. Boggs, Polarization of the prompt γ-ray emission from the γ-ray burst of 6 December 2002, *Nature* **423**, 415 (May 2003).
54. R. E. Rutledge and D. B. Fox, Re-analysis of polarization in the γ-ray flux of GRB 021206, *MNRAS* **350**, 1288 (June 2004).
55. C. Wigger, W. Hajdas, K. Arzner, M. Güdel and A. Zehnder, Gamma-Ray Burst Polarization: Limits from RHESSI Measurements, *ApJ* **613**, 1088 (October 2004).
56. D. Götz, P. Laurent, F. Lebrun, F. Daigne and Ž. Bošnjak, Variable Polarization Measured in the Prompt Emission of GRB 041219A Using IBIS on Board INTEGRAL, *ApJ* **695**, L208 (April 2009).
57. D. Götz, S. Covino, A. Fernández-Soto, P. Laurent and Ž. Bošnjak, The polarized gamma-ray burst GRB 061122, *MNRAS* **431**, 3550 (June 2013).
58. D. Yonetoku, T. Murakami, S. Gunji, T. Mihara, K. Toma, Y. Morihara, T. Takahashi, Y. Wakashima, H. Yonemochi, T. Sakashita, N. Toukairin, H. Fujimoto and Y. Kodama, Magnetic Structures in Gamma-Ray Burst Jets Probed by Gamma-Ray Polarization, *ApJ* **758**, p. L1 (October 2012).
59. T. Chattopadhyay, S. V. Vadawale, E. Aarthy, N. P. S. Mithun, V. Chand, A. Ratheesh, R. Basak, A. R. Rao, V. Bhalerao, S. Mate, B. Arvind, V. Sharma and D. Bhattacharya, Prompt Emission Polarimetry of Gamma-Ray Bursts with the AstroSat CZT Imager, *ApJ* **884**, p. 123 (October 2019).
60. J. M. Burgess, M. Kole, F. Berlato, J. Greiner, G. Vianello, N. Produit, Z. H. Li and J. C. Sun, Time-resolved GRB polarization with POLAR and GBM. Simultaneous spectral and polarization analysis with synchrotron emission, *A&A* **627**, p. A105 (July 2019).

61. V. Sharma, S. Iyyani, D. Bhattacharya, T. Chattopadhyay, A. R. Rao, E. Aarthy, S. V. Vadawale, N. P. S. Mithun, V. B. Bhalerao, F. Ryde and A. Pe'er, Time-varying Polarized Gamma-Rays from GRB 160821A: Evidence for Ordered Magnetic Fields, *ApJ* **882**, p. L10 (September 2019).
62. S.-N. Zhang, M. Kole, T.-W. Bao, T. Batsch, T. Bernasconi, F. Cadoux, J.-Y. Chai, Z.-G. Dai, Y.-W. Dong, N. Gauvin, W. Hajdas, M.-X. Lan, H.-C. Li, L. Li, Z.-H. Li, J.-T. Liu, X. Liu, R. Marcinkowski, N. Produit, S. Orsi, M. Pohl, D. Rybka, H.-L. Shi, L.-M. Song, J.-C. Sun, J. Szabelski, T. Tymieniecka, R.-J. Wang, Y.-H. Wang, X. Wen, B.-B. Wu, X. Wu, X.-F. Wu, H.-L. Xiao, S.-L. Xiong, L.-Y. Zhang, L. Zhang, X.-F. Zhang, Y.-J. Zhang and A. Zwolinska, Detailed polarization measurements of the prompt emission of five gamma-ray bursts, *Nature Astronomy* **3**, 258 (January 2019).
63. K. S. Kawabata, J. Deng, L. Wang, P. Mazzali, K. Nomoto, K. Maeda, N. Tominaga, H. Umeda, M. Iye, G. Kosugi, Y. Ohyama, T. Sasaki, P. Höflich, J. C. Wheeler, D. J. Jeffery, K. Aoki, N. Kashikawa, T. Takata, N. Kawai, T. Sakamoto, Y. Urata, A. Yoshida, T. Tamagawa, K. Torii, W. Aoki, N. Kobayashi, Y. Komiyama, Y. Mizumoto, J. Noumaru, R. Ogasawara, K. Sekiguchi, Y. Shirasaki, T. Totani, J. Watanabe and T. Yamada, On the Spectrum and Spectropolarimetry of Type Ic Hypernova SN 2003dh/GRB 030329, *ApJ* **593**, L19 (August 2003).
64. K. Wiersema, P. A. Curran, T. Krühler, A. Meland ri, E. Rol, R. L. C. Starling, N. R. Tanvir, A. J. van der Horst, S. Covino, J. P. U. Fynbo, P. Goldoni, J. Gorosabel, J. Hjorth, S. Klose, C. G. Mundell, P. T. O'Brien, E. Palazzi, R. A. M. J. Wijers, V. D'Elia, P. A. Evans, R. Filgas, A. Gomboc, J. Greiner, C. Guidorzi, L. Kaper, S. Kobayashi, C. Kouveliotou, A. J. Levan, A. Rossi, A. Rowlinson, I. A. Steele, A. de Ugarte Postigo and S. D. Vergani, Detailed optical and near-infrared polarimetry, spectroscopy and broad-band photometry of the afterglow of GRB 091018: polarization evolution, *MNRAS* **426**, 2 (Oct 2012).
65. O. G. King, D. Blinov, D. Giannios, I. Papadakis, E. Angelakis, M. Balokovic, L. Fuhrmann, T. Hovatta, P. Khodade, S. Kiehlmann, N. Kylafis, A. Kus, I. Myserlis, D. Modi, G. Panopoulou, I. Papamastorakis, V. Pavlidou, B. Pazderska, E. Pazderski, T. J. Pearson, C. Rajarshi, A. N. Ramaprakash, A. C. S. Readhead, P. Reig, K. Tassis and J. A. Zensus, Early-time polarized optical light curve of GRB 131030A., *MNRAS* **445**, L114 (November 2014).
66. D. Kopač, C. G. Mundell, J. Japelj, D. M. Arnold, I. A. Steele, C. Guidorzi, S. Dichiara, S. Kobayashi, A. Gomboc, R. M. Harrison, G. P. Lamb, A. Melandri, R. J. Smith, F. J. Virgili, A. J. Castro-Tirado, J. Gorosabel, A. Järvinen, R. Sánchez-Ramírez, S. R. Oates and M. Jelínek, Limits on Optical Polarization during the Prompt Phase of GRB 140430A, *ApJ* **813**, p. 1 (November 2015).
67. S. Covino, K. Wiersema, Y. Z. Fan, K. Toma, A. B. Higgins, A. Melandri, P. D'Avanzo, C. G. Mundell, E. Palazzi, N. R. Tanvir, M. G. Bernardini, M. Branchesi, E. Brocato, S. Campana, S. di Serego Alighieri, D. Götz, J. P. U. Fynbo, W. Gao, A. Gomboc, B. Gompertz, J. Greiner, J. Hjorth, Z. P. Jin, L. Kaper, S. Klose, S. Kobayashi, D. Kopac, C. Kouveliotou, A. J. Levan, J. Mao, D. Malesani, E. Pian, A. Rossi, R. Salvaterra, R. L. C. Starling, I. Steele, G. Tagliaferri, E. Troja, A. J. van der Horst and R. A. M. J. Wijers, The unpolarized macronova associated with the gravitational wave event GW 170817, *Nature Astronomy* **1**, 791 (October 2017).
68. S. Covino, G. Ghisellini, D. Lazzati and D. Malesani, *Polarization of Gamma-Ray Burst Optical and Near-Infrared Afterglows*, in *Gamma-Ray Bursts in the Afterglow Era*, eds. M. Feroci, F. Frontera, N. Masetti and L. Piro, Astronomical Society of the Pacific Conference Series, Vol. 312 2004, p. 169.

69. V. M. Lipunov, A. V. Krylov, V. G. Kornilov, G. V. Borisov, D. A. Kuvshinov, A. A. Belinsky, M. V. Kuznetsov, S. A. Potanin, G. A. Antipov, N. V. Tyurina, E. S. Gorbovskoy and I. Chilingaryan, MASTER: The Mobile Astronomical System of Telescope-Robots, *Astronomische Nachrichten* **325**, 580 (October 2004).
70. I. A. Steele, The Liverpool telescope, *Astronomische Nachrichten* **325**, 519 (October 2004).
71. K. S. Kawabata, O. Nagae, S. Chiyonobu, H. Tanaka, H. Nakaya, M. Suzuki, Y. Kamata, S. Miyazaki, K. Hiragi, H. Miyamoto, M. Yamanaka, A. Arai, T. Yamashita, M. Uemura, T. Ohsugi, M. Isogai, Y. Ishitobi and S. Sato, Wide-field one-shot optical polarimeter: HOWPol, **7014**, p. 70144L (July 2008).
72. A. N. Ramaprakash, C. V. Rajarshi, H. K. Das, P. Khodade, D. Modi, G. Panopoulou, S. Maharana, D. Blinov, E. Angelakis, C. Casadio, L. Fuhrmann, T. Hovatta, S. Kiehlmann, O. G. King, N. Kylafis, A. Kougentakis, A. Kus, A. Mahabal, A. Marecki, I. Myserlis, G. Paterakis, E. Paleologou, I. Liodakis, I. Papadakis, I. Papamastorakis, V. Pavlidou, E. Pazderski, T. J. Pearson, A. C. S. Readhead, P. Reig, A. Słowikowska, K. Tassis and J. A. Zensus, RoboPol: a four-channel optical imaging polarimeter, *MNRAS* **485**, 2355 (May 2019).
73. J. Japelj, D. Kopač, S. Kobayashi, R. Harrison, C. Guidorzi, F. J. Virgili, C. G. Mundell, A. Melandri and A. Gomboc, Phenomenology of Reverse-shock Emission in the Optical Afterglows of Gamma-Ray Bursts, *ApJ* **785**, p. 84 (Apr 2014).
74. C. G. Mundell, I. A. Steele, R. J. Smith, S. Kobayashi, A. Melandri, C. Guidorzi, A. Gomboc, C. J. Mottram, D. Clarke, A. Monfardini, D. Carter and D. Bersier, Early Optical Polarization of a Gamma-Ray Burst Afterglow, *Science* **315**, p. 1822 (March 2007).
75. D. A. H. Buckley, S. Bagnulo, R. J. Britto, J. Mao, D. A. Kann, J. Cooper, V. Lipunov, D. M. Hewitt, S. Razzaque, N. P. M. Kuin, I. M. Monageng, S. Covino, P. Jakobsson, A. J. van der Horst, K. Wiersema, M. Böttcher, S. Campana, V. D'Elia, E. S. Gorbovskoy, I. Gorbunov, D. N. Groenewald, D. H. Hartmann, V. G. Kornilov, C. G. Mundell, R. Podesta, J. K. Thomas, N. Tyurina, D. Vlasenko, B. van Soelen and D. Xu, Spectropolarimetry and photometry of the early afterglow of the gamma-ray burst GRB 191221B, *MNRAS* **506**, 4621 (September 2021).
76. MAGIC Collaboration, V. A. Acciari, S. Ansoldi, L. A. Antonelli, A. Arbet Engels, D. Baack, A. Babić, B. Banerjee, U. Barres de Almeida, J. A. Barrio, J. Becerra González, W. Bednarek, L. Bellizzi, E. Bernardini, A. Berti, J. Besenrieder, W. Bhattacharyya, C. Bigongiari, A. Biland, O. Blanch, G. Bonnoli, Ž. Bošnjak, G. Busetto, A. Carosi, R. Carosi, G. Ceribella, Y. Chai, A. Chilingaryan, S. Cikota, S. M. Colak, U. Colin, E. Colombo, J. L. Contreras, J. Cortina, S. Covino, G. D'Amico, V. D'Elia, P. da Vela, F. Dazzi, A. de Angelis, B. de Lotto, M. Delfino, J. Delgado, D. Depaoli, F. di Pierro, L. di Venere, E. Do Souto Espiñeira, D. Dominis Prester, A. Donini, D. Dorner, M. Doro, D. Elsaesser, V. Fallah Ramazani, A. Fattorini, A. Fernández-Barral, G. Ferrara, D. Fidalgo, L. Foffano, M. V. Fonseca, L. Font, C. Fruck, S. Fukami, S. Gallozzi, R. J. García López, M. Garczarczyk, S. Gasparyan, M. Gaug, N. Giglietto, F. Giordano, N. Godinović, D. Green, D. Guberman, D. Hadasch, A. Hahn, J. Herrera, J. Hoang, D. Hrupec, M. Hütten, T. Inada, S. Inoue, K. Ishio, Y. Iwamura, L. Jouvin, D. Kerszberg, H. Kubo, J. Kushida, A. Lamastra, D. Lelas, F. Leone, E. Lindfors, S. Lombardi, F. Longo, M. López, R. López-Coto, A. López-Oramas, S. Loporchio, B. Machado de Oliveira Fraga, C. Maggio, P. Majumdar, M. Makariev, M. Mallamaci, G. Maneva, M. Manganaro, K. Mannheim, L. Maraschi, M. Mariotti, M. Martínez, S. Masuda, D. Mazin, S. Mićanović, D. Miceli, M. Minev, J. M. Miranda, R. Mirzoyan, E. Molina, A. Moralejo, D. Morcuende, V. Moreno, E. Moretti, P. Munar-Adrover,

V. Neustroev, C. Nigro, K. Nilsson, D. Ninci, K. Nishijima, K. Noda, L. Nogués, M. Nöthe, S. Nozaki, S. Paiano, J. Palacio, M. Palatiello, D. Paneque, R. Paoletti, J. M. Paredes, P. Peñil, M. Peresano, M. Persic, P. G. Prada Moroni, E. Prandini, I. Puljak, W. Rhode, M. Ribó, J. Rico, C. Righi, A. Rugliancich, L. Saha, N. Sahakyan, T. Saito, S. Sakurai, K. Satalecka, K. Schmidt, T. Schweizer, J. Sitarek, I. Šnidarić, D. Sobczynska, A. Somero, A. Stamerra, D. Strom, M. Strzys, Y. Suda, T. Surić, M. Takahashi, F. Tavecchio, P. Temnikov, T. Terzić, M. Teshima, N. Torres-Albà, L. Tosti, S. Tsujimoto, V. Vagelli, J. van Scherpenberg, G. Vanzo, M. Vazquez Acosta, C. F. Vigorito, V. Vitale, I. Vovk, M. Will, D. Zarić and L. Nava, Teraelectronvolt emission from the γ-ray burst GRB 190114C, *Nature* **575**, 455 (November 2019).
77. T. Laskar, K. D. Alexander, R. Gill, J. Granot, E. Berger, C. G. Mundell, R. Barniol Duran, J. Bolmer, P. Duffell, H. van Eerten, W.-f. Fong, S. Kobayashi, R. Margutti and P. Schady, ALMA Detection of a Linearly Polarized Reverse Shock in GRB 190114C, *ApJ* **878**, p. L26 (Jun 2019).
78. S. Klose, E. Palazzi, N. Masetti, B. Stecklum, J. Greiner, D. H. Hartmann and H. M. Schmid, Prospects for multiwavelength polarization observations of GRB afterglows and the case GRB 030329, *A&A* **420**, 899 (Jun 2004).
79. A. Gruzinov and E. Waxman, Gamma-Ray Burst Afterglow: Polarization and Analytic Light Curves, *ApJ* **511**, 852 (February 1999).
80. T. Inoue, K. Asano and K. Ioka, Three-dimensional Simulations of Magnetohydrodynamic Turbulence Behind Relativistic Shock Waves and Their Implications for Gamma-Ray Bursts, *ApJ* **734**, p. 77 (June 2011).
81. J. Mao and J. Wang, Application of Jitter Radiation: Gamma-Ray Burst Prompt Polarization, *ApJ* **776**, p. 17 (October 2013).
82. J. Mao and J. Wang, Linear Polarization, Circular Polarization, and Depolarization of Gamma-ray Bursts: A Simple Case of Jitter Radiation, *ApJ* **838**, p. 78 (April 2017).
83. D. Kopač, C. G. Mundell, S. Kobayashi, F. J. Virgili, R. Harrison, J. Japelj, C. Guidorzi, A. Melandri and A. Gomboc, Radio Flares from Gamma-ray Bursts, *ApJ* **806**, p. 179 (June 2015).
84. C. M. Gutiérrez, D. Arnold, D. Copley, C. M. Copperwheat, E. Harvey, H. Jermak, J. Knapen, A. McGrath, A. Oria, R. Rebolo, I. A. Steele and M. Torres, The new 4-m robotic telescope, *Astronomische Nachrichten* **340**, 40 (January 2019).
85. H. Abdalla, R. Adam, F. Aharonian, F. Ait Benkhali, E. O. Angüner, M. Arakawa, C. Arcaro, C. Armand, H. Ashkar, M. Backes, V. Barbosa Martins, M. Barnard, Y. Becherini, D. Berge, K. Bernlöhr, E. Bissaldi, R. Blackwell, M. Böttcher, C. Boisson, J. Bolmont, S. Bonnefoy, J. Bregeon, M. Breuhaus, F. Brun, P. Brun, M. Bryan, M. Büchele, T. Bulik, T. Bylund, M. Capasso, S. Caroff, A. Carosi, S. Casanova, M. Cerruti, T. Chand, S. Chandra, A. Chen, S. Colafrancesco, M. Curyło, I. D. Davids, C. Deil, J. Devin, P. deWilt, L. Dirson, A. Djannati-Ataï, A. Dmytriiev, A. Donath, V. Doroshenko, J. Dyks, K. Egberts, G. Emery, J. P. Ernenwein, S. Eschbach, K. Feijen, S. Fegan, A. Fiasson, G. Fontaine, S. Funk, M. Füßling, S. Gabici, Y. A. Gallant, F. Gaté, G. Giavitto, L. Giunti, D. Glawion, J. F. Glicenstein, D. Gottschall, M. H. Grondin, J. Hahn, M. Haupt, G. Heinzelmann, G. Henri, G. Hermann, J. A. Hinton, W. Hofmann, C. Hoischen, T. L. Holch, M. Holler, D. Horns, D. Huber, H. Iwasaki, M. Jamrozy, D. Jankowsky, F. Jankowsky, A. Jardin-Blicq, I. Jung-Richardt, M. A. Kastendieck, K. Katarzyński, M. Katsuragawa, U. Katz, D. Khangulyan, B. Khélifi, J. King, S. Klepser, W. Kluźniak, N. Komin, K. Kosack, D. Kostunin, M. Kreter, G. Lamanna, A. Lemière, M. Lemoine-Goumard, J. P. Lenain, E. Leser, C. Levy, T. Lohse, I. Lypova, J. Mackey, J. Majumdar,

D. Malyshev, V. Marandon, A. Marcowith, A. Mares, C. Mariaud, G. Martí-Devesa, R. Marx, G. Maurin, P. J. Meintjes, A. M. W. Mitchell, R. Moderski, M. Mohamed, L. Mohrmann, C. Moore, E. Moulin, J. Muller, T. Murach, S. Nakashima, M. de Naurois, H. Ndiyavala, F. Niederwanger, J. Niemiec, L. Oakes, P. O'Brien, H. Odaka, S. Ohm, E. de Ona Wilhelmi, M. Ostrowski, I. Oya, M. Panter, R. D. Parsons, C. Perennes, P. O. Petrucci, B. Peyaud, Q. Piel, S. Pita, V. Poireau, A. Priyana Noel, D. A. Prokhorov, H. Prokoph, G. Pühlhofer, M. Punch, A. Quirrenbach, S. Raab, R. Rauth, A. Reimer, O. Reimer, Q. Remy, M. Renaud, F. Rieger, L. Rinchiuso, C. Romoli, G. Rowell, B. Rudak, E. Ruiz-Velasco, V. Sahakian, S. Sailer, S. Saito, D. A. Sanchez, A. Santangelo, M. Sasaki, R. Schlickeiser, F. Schüssler, A. Schulz, H. M. Schutte, U. Schwanke, S. Schwemmer, M. Seglar-Arroyo, M. Senniappan, A. S. Seyffert, N. Shafi, K. Shiningayamwe, R. Simoni, A. Sinha, H. Sol, A. Specovius, M. Spir-Jacob, Ł. Stawarz, R. Steenkamp, C. Stegmann, C. Steppa, T. Takahashi, T. Tavernier, A. M. Taylor, R. Terrier, D. Tiziani, M. Tluczykont, C. Trichard, M. Tsirou, N. Tsuji, R. Tuffs, Y. Uchiyama, D. J. van der Walt, C. van Eldik, C. van Rensburg, B. van Soelen, G. Vasileiadis, J. Veh, C. Venter, P. Vincent, J. Vink, H. J. Völk, T. Vuillaume, Z. Wadiasingh, S. J. Wagner, R. White, A. Wierzcholska, R. Yang, H. Yoneda, M. Zacharias, R. Zanin, A. A. Zdziarski, A. Zech, A. Ziegler, J. Zorn, N. Żywucka, F. de Palma, M. Axelsson and O. J. Roberts, A very-high-energy component deep in the γ-ray burst afterglow, *Nature* **575**, 464 (November 2019).
86. O. Blanch, F. Longo, A. Berti, S. Fukami, Y. Suda, S. Loporchio, S. Micanovic, J. G. Green, V. Pinter, M. Takahashi and MAGIC Collaboration, GRB 201216C: MAGIC detection in very high energy gamma rays, *GRB Coordinates Network* **29075**, p. 1 (December 2020).
87. V. A. Acciari, S. Ansoldi, L. A. Antonelli, A. Arbet Engels, K. Asano, D. Baack, A. Babić, A. Baquero, U. Barres de Almeida, J. A. Barrio, J. Becerra González, W. Bednarek, L. Bellizzi, E. Bernardini, M. Bernardos, A. Berti, J. Besenrieder, W. Bhattacharyya, C. Bigongiari, A. Biland, O. Blanch, G. Bonnoli, Ž. Bošnjak, G. Busetto, R. Carosi, G. Ceribella, M. Cerruti, Y. Chai, A. Chilingarian, S. Cikota, S. M. Colak, E. Colombo, J. L. Contreras, J. Cortina, S. Covino, G. D'Amico, V. D'Elia, P. da Vela, F. Dazzi, A. de Angelis, B. de Lotto, M. Delfino, J. Delgado, C. Delgado Mendez, D. Depaoli, F. di Pierro, L. di Venere, E. D. Souto Espiñeira, D. Dominis Prester, A. Donini, D. Dorner, M. Doro, D. Elsaesser, V. Fallah Ramazani, A. Fattorini, G. Ferrara, L. Foffano, M. V. Fonseca, L. Font, C. Fruck, S. Fukami, R. J. García López, M. Garczarczyk, S. Gasparyan, M. Gaug, N. Giglietto, F. Giordano, P. Gliwny, N. Godinović, J. G. Green, D. Green, D. Hadasch, A. Hahn, L. Heckmann, J. Herrera, J. Hoang, D. Hrupec, M. Hütten, T. Inada, S. Inoue, K. Ishio, Y. Iwamura, J. Jormanainen, L. Jouvin, Y. Kajiwara, M. Karjalainen, D. Kerszberg, Y. Kobayashi, H. Kubo, J. Kushida, A. Lamastra, D. Lelas, F. Leone, E. Lindfors, S. Lombardi, F. Longo, R. López-Coto, M. López-Moya, A. López-Oramas, S. Loporchio, B. Machado de Oliveira Fraga, C. Maggio, P. Majumdar, M. Makariev, M. Mallamaci, G. Maneva, M. Manganaro, K. Mannheim, L. Maraschi, M. Mariotti, M. Martínez, D. Mazin, S. Mender, S. Mićanović, D. Miceli, T. Miener, M. Minev, J. M. Miranda, R. Mirzoyan, E. Molina, A. Moralejo, D. Morcuende, V. Moreno, E. Moretti, V. Neustroev, C. Nigro, K. Nilsson, D. Ninci, K. Nishijima, K. Noda, S. Nozaki, Y. Ohtani, T. Oka, J. Otero-Santos, S. Paiano, M. Palatiello, D. Paneque, R. Paoletti, J. M. Paredes, L. Pavletić, C. Peñil, C. Perennes, M. Persic, P. G. Prada Moroni, E. Prandini, C. Priyadarshi, I. Puljak, W. Rhode, M. Ribó, J. Rico, C. Righi, A. Rugliancich, L. Saha, N. Sahakyan, T. Saito, S. Sakurai, K. Satalecka, F. G. Saturni, B. Schleicher, K. Schmidt, T. Schweizer, J. Sitarek, I. Šnidarić, D. Sobczynska,

A. Spolon, A. Stamerra, D. Strom, M. Strzys, Y. Suda, T. Surić, M. Takahashi, F. Tavecchio, P. Temnikov, T. Terzić, M. Teshima, N. Torres-Albà, L. Tosti, S. Truzzi, A. Tutone, J. van Scherpenberg, G. Vanzo, M. Vazquez Acosta, S. Ventura, V. Verguilov, C. F. Vigorito, V. Vitale, I. Vovk, M. Will, D. Zarić, MAGIC Collaboration and L. Nava, MAGIC Observations of the Nearby Short Gamma-Ray Burst GRB 160821B, *ApJ* **908**, p. 90 (February 2021).

88. H. E. S. S. Collaboration, H. Abdalla, F. Aharonian, F. Ait Benkhali, E. O. Angüner, C. Arcaro, C. Armand, T. Armstrong, H. Ashkar, M. Backes, V. Baghmanyan, V. Barbosa Martins, A. Barnacka, M. Barnard, Y. Becherini, D. Berge, K. Bernlöhr, B. Bi, E. Bissaldi, M. Böttcher, C. Boisson, J. Bolmont, M. de Bony de Lavergne, M. Breuhaus, F. Brun, P. Brun, M. Bryan, M. Büchele, T. Bulik, T. Bylund, S. Caroff, A. Carosi, S. Casanova, T. Chand, S. Chandra, A. Chen, G. Cotter, M. Curyło, J. Damascene Mbarubucyeye, I. D. Davids, J. Davies, C. Deil, J. Devin, L. Dirson, A. Djannati-Ataï, A. Dmytriiev, A. Donath, V. Doroshenko, L. Dreyer, C. Duffy, J. Dyks, K. Egberts, F. Eichhorn, S. Einecke, G. Emery, J. P. Ernenwein, K. Feijen, S. Fegan, A. Fiasson, G. Fichet de Clairfontaine, G. Fontaine, S. Funk, M. Füßling, S. Gabici, Y. A. Gallant, G. Giavitto, L. Giunti, D. Glawion, J. F. Glicenstein, M. H. Grondin, J. Hahn, M. Haupt, G. Hermann, J. A. Hinton, W. Hofmann, C. Hoischen, T. L. Holch, M. Holler, M. Hörbe, D. Horns, D. Huber, M. Jamrozy, D. Jankowsky, F. Jankowsky, A. Jardin-Blicq, V. Joshi, I. Jung-Richardt, E. Kasai, M. A. Kastendieck, K. Katarzyński, U. Katz, D. Khangulyan, B. Khélifi, S. Klepser, W. Kluźniak, N. Komin, R. Konno, K. Kosack, D. Kostunin, M. Kreter, G. Lamanna, A. Lemière, M. Lemoine-Goumard, J. P. Lenain, F. Leuschner, C. Levy, T. Lohse, I. Lypova, J. Mackey, J. Majumdar, D. Malyshev, D. Malyshev, V. Marandon, P. Marchegiani, A. Marcowith, A. Mares, G. Martí-Devesa, R. Marx, G. Maurin, P. J. Meintjes, M. Meyer, A. Mitchell, R. Moderski, L. Mohrmann, A. Montanari, C. Moore, P. Morris, E. Moulin, J. Muller, T. Murach, K. Nakashima, A. Nayerhoda, M. de Naurois, H. Ndiyavala, J. Niemiec, L. Oakes, P. O'Brien, H. Odaka, S. Ohm, L. Olivera-Nieto, E. de Ona Wilhelmi, M. Ostrowski, S. Panny, M. Panter, R. D. Parsons, G. Peron, B. Peyaud, Q. Piel, S. Pita, V. Poireau, A. Priyana Noel, D. A. Prokhorov, H. Prokoph, G. Pühlhofer, M. Punch, A. Quirrenbach, S. Raab, R. Rauth, P. Reichherzer, A. Reimer, O. Reimer, Q. Remy, M. Renaud, F. Rieger, L. Rinchiuso, C. Romoli, G. Rowell, B. Rudak, E. Ruiz-Velasco, V. Sahakian, V. Sailer, H. Salzmann, D. A. Sanchez, A. Santangelo, M. Sasaki, M. Scalici, J. Schäfer, F. Schüssler, H. M. Schutte, U. Schwanke, M. Seglar-Arroyo, M. Senniappan, A. S. Seyffert, N. Shafi, J. N. S. Shapopi, K. Shiningayamwe, R. Simoni, A. Sinha, H. Sol, A. Specovius, S. Spencer, M. Spir-Jacob, Ł. Stawarz, L. Sun, R. Steenkamp, C. Stegmann, S. Steinmassl, C. Steppa, T. Takahashi, T. Tam, T. Tavernier, A. M. Taylor, R. Terrier, J. H. E. Thiersen, D. Tiziani, M. Tluczykont, L. Tomankova, M. Tsirou, R. Tuffs, Y. Uchiyama, D. J. van der Walt, C. van Eldik, C. van Rensburg, B. van Soelen, G. Vasileiadis, J. Veh, C. Venter, P. Vincent, J. Vink, H. J. Völk, Z. Wadiasingh, S. J. Wagner, J. Watson, F. Werner, R. White, A. Wierzcholska, Y. W. Wong, A. Yusafzai, M. Zacharias, R. Zanin, D. Zargaryan, A. A. Zdziarski, A. Zech, S. J. Zhu, J. Zorn, S. Zouari, N. Żywucka, P. Evans and K. Page, Revealing x-ray and gamma ray temporal and spectral similarities in the GRB 190829A afterglow, *Science* **372**, 1081 (June 2021).

MASTER optical observations of the blazar TXS0506+056 during the IC170922A

V. M. Lipunov[1,2,*], K. Zhirkov[1,2], V. G. Kornilov[1,2], E. Gorbovskoy[2], N. M. Budnev[3], D. A. H. Buckley[4], R. Rebolo[5], M. Serra[5], R. Podesta[6], C. Francile[6], V. Topolev[1,2], N. Tiurina[2], O. A. Gress[2,3], P. Balanutsa[2], A. Chasovnikov[1,2], D. Vlasenko[1,2], E. Minkina[1,2], A. Gabovich[7], G. Antipov[2], A. Kuznetsov[2], V. Vladimirov[2], S. Svertilov[8], F. Podesta[6], V. Grinshpun[1,2], A. Tlatov[9], D. Cheryasov[2] and V. Senik[2]

[1] *Lomonosov Moscow State University, Physics Department, Vorobievy Hills, 1, Moscow 119991, Russia*

[2] *Lomonosov MSU, SAI, Universitetsky, 13, Moscow 119234, Russia*

[3] *Irkutsk State University, 20, Gagarin, Irkutsk 664003, Russia*

[4] *South African Astrophysical Observatory, PO Box 9, 7935 Observatory, Cape Town, South Africa*

[5] *Instituto de Astrofísica de Canarias, Lactea, E38205, LaLaguna, Tenerife, Spain*

[6] *Observatorio Astronomico Felix Aguilar(OAFA), San Juan National University, Avda Benavides s/n, Rivadavia, El Leonsito, Argentina;*

[7] *Blagoveschensk State Pedagogical University, Lenin, 104, Amur, Blagoveschensk 675000, Russia*

[8] *Lomonosov Moscow State University, Skobeltsyn Institute of Nuclear Physics (SINP MSU), Vorobievy Hills, 1, Moscow, 119991, Russia*

[9] *Kislovodsk Solar Station Pulkovo Observatory, Gagarina 100, Kislovodsk 357700, Russia*

E-mail: lipunov@sai.msu.ru

We present MASTER Global Robotic Net (Lipunov et al. 2010) earliest optical alert observations of IceCube-170922A error box. We discovered fast variability of blazar TXS 0506+056 27 sec after notice time (73s after the trigger time) at 2017-09-22 20:55:43 UT by MASTER-Tavrida robotic telescope. MASTER found the blazar TXS 0506+056 to be in the off-state after one minute and then switched to the on-state no later than two hours after the event. The effect is observed at a 50-sigma significance level. We also analysed own unique 16-years light curve of blazar TXS 0506+056 (518 data set).

Keywords: Gamma-ray burst

1. Introduction

High energy cosmic neutrinos sources are still mysterious. MASTER Global Robotic Net (Lipunov et al. 2010)[19] starts Ice Cube alert and follow up observations a few years ago. On 22 September 2017 the robotic telescope of the MASTER global network automatically imaged the error box of the high-energy neutrino event IceCube-170922A (Kopper et al. 2017). Observations were carried out 27 seconds after receiving the alert, i.e., 73 seconds after the IceCube-170922A neutrino event was detected by the IceCube observatory at the South Pole (Lipunov et al. 2018a).[23] Observations started at 84 degree zenith distance (MASTER has fully opened roof as alert telescope).

We calibrated these images using the Gaia (Brown et al. 2018) catalog as the source of reference stars, and found the BL Lacertae type blazar TXS 0506+056 (IceCube et al. 2017) to be in the off-state after one minute and then switched to the on-state no later than two hours after the event. The effect is observed at *delta* m =0.790+-0.016 (a 50-*sigma* significance level).[27]

IceCube registered events with error regions, whose sizes are currently comparable to one square degree. Therefore finding a blazar within the error box of a VHE neutrino event cannot be considered sufficient to prove that blazars are actually progenitors of these particles. Detecting some non-standard event from the supposed source at a time close to the neutrino event is required. For example, a blazar emitting gamma and cosmic rays and showing a sharp flux variation near the neutrino detection time would provide compelling evidence of the association of the neutrino event with a known astrophysical object. The first candidate object for an astrophysical neutrino event was the blazar TXS 0506+056 (IceCube et al. 2017)[14,15] found inside the error box of the IceCube-170922A neutrino event. This blazar turned out to be located at a distance of $\tilde{3}.7$ billion light years (its redshift is z = 0.3365+/- 0.0010) (Paiano et al. 2018).[29]

TXS 0506+056 blazar was registered in the gamma-ray active state several months before the neutrino event. Detection of high-energy particles (175Gev) began one week after, and the optical, x-ray, and gamma-ray emission was observed with low temporal resolution and showed no appreciable variations near the detection time . Therefore although when combining the available data suggested that TXS 0506+056 was a very promising high energy neutrino source optical candidate, the temporal resolution of multi-messenger data did not provide conclusive evidence at the time and the object remained just a likely, but still debatable, candidate. In this letter we report conclusive detection of light variation of the blazar TXS 0506+056 just several minutes after the neutrino event, which ended no later than after two hours. For comparison, nearest ASAS-SN, Kiso/KWFC and Kanata/HONIR optical observations do not show the same decrease in optical brightness (because they started 18 hours after MASTER observations when effect disappeared. Although the blazar was in the gamma-ray active state, this state started several months before the neutrino event. Detection of high-energy particles (175Gev) began one week after, and the optical, x-ray, and gamma-ray emission was observed with low temporal resolution and showed no appreciable variations near the detection time. Therefore although when combining the available data suggested that TXS 0506+056 was a very promising high energy neutrino source optical candidate, the temporal resolution of multi-messenger data did not provide conclusive evidence at the time and the object remained just a likely, but still debatable, candidate . In this letter we report conclusive detection of light variation of the blazar TXS 0506+056 just several minutes after the neutrino event, which ended no later than after two hours. For comparison, nearest ASAS-SN, Kiso/KWFC and Kanata/HONIR optical observations do not show the same decrease in optical brightness (because they started 18 hours after MASTER observations when effect disappeared.

2. MASTER alert optical observations of IceCube-170922A error box

MASTER Global Robotic Net, as the leader of early gamma-ray burst observations (Troja et al. 2017; Ershova et al. 2020, Lipunov et al. 2016, Lipunov et al. 2017, Gorbvoskoy et al. 2016)[10, 11, 18, 20, 21, 32] has an almost 20-year long experience with real-time rapid pointings to GRB alerts within the first minute of the alert . In 2015 MASTER started actively participation in the program of fast optical support of major physical and astrophysical experiments, such as detection of very high energy neutrinos (ANTARES (Dornic et al. 2015;[9] Gress et al. 2019[12]), IceCube (Aartsen et al. 2017)[1] , Baksan (Lipunov et al. 2019a),[25] gravitational waves (LIGO/VIRGO collaboration (Abbott et al. 2016),[2] and Fast Radio Bursts (FRB (Lipunov et al. 2018b)[24]). The favorable arrangement of MASTER sites makes it possible to inspect all gravitational-wave error boxes. MASTER made the crucial contribution to the optical support of the first gravitational-wave event GW 150914 by inspecting the most part of the error box (Abbott et al. 2016, Lipunov et al. 2017).[3, 21] On 17 August 2017 MASTER, together with 5 other telescopes, performed the first ever optical localization of a gravitational-wave source independently discovered Kilonova from GW 170817 (Abbot et al. 2017, Lipunov et al. 2017).[3, 22]

At the 22nd of September, 2017, MASTER received an alert from IceCube event and MASTER-Tavrida telescope acquired the first three images, starting from 2017-09-22 20:55:43UT 27 sec after notice time (i.e.73s after the trigger time). The field of view of the MASTER telescope has a size of four square degrees (Lipunov et al. 2010)[19] and fully covers the final field of view of IceCube (Lipunov et al. 2020[27]).

MASTER limiting magnitude was 19.0m at 180-second frames, despite the large zenith distance (84 degrees). Hence the TXS 0506+056 blazar at the time of the alert was a 15.12 +- 0.01 magnitude object in all three frames acquired over $\tilde{1}5$ minutes (the light curve is shown in Fig. 2). There was the faintest blazar brightness over the full period of this alert. After 2 hours, at 2017-09-22 23:11:36 UT, the flux from the blazar increased in brightness by a factor of two and reached 14.33m+-0.01m. We emphasize that here in the text we give the averaged values for the triples of frames in the first minutes and after two hours (compare[27]). Hence our observations show at an extremely high confidence level of 50 sigma that within several minutes of the neutrino event, the blazar was in an anomalously extinguished state. This conclusion

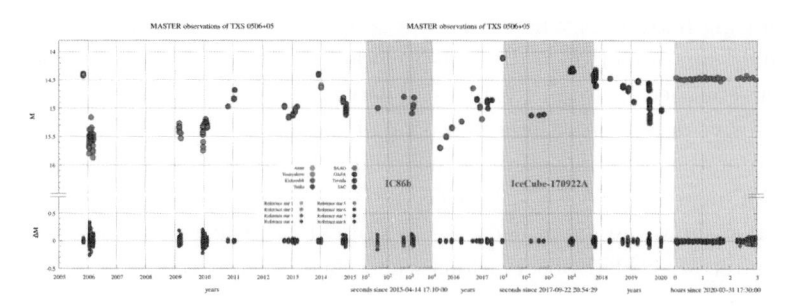

Fig. 1. MASTER light curve of the TXS 0506+056 blazar for the 16 years. Archive light curve of the TXS 0506+056 blazar based on observations made by MASTER Global Net robotic telescope of from 2005 until now (red point). Below we see the photometry of 8 reference stars, to the pink and blue panels represent three very narrow episodes in time. The first of these is April 2015 when IceCube IC86b saw a 3.5 sigma excess of the neutrino flux over the background (IceCube 2017) . The second is the 22 September 2017 event (IceCube 2017). Logarithmic time is shown in seconds from the neutrino trigger. It is easy to easily see the rapid change in the luminosity of the blazar in $\tilde{2}$ times. Finally, the third episode is a uniform blazar monitoring timeline in the first quarter of 2020. With these new observations, the total number of observations submitted reached 518 (See the photometry table)[27]

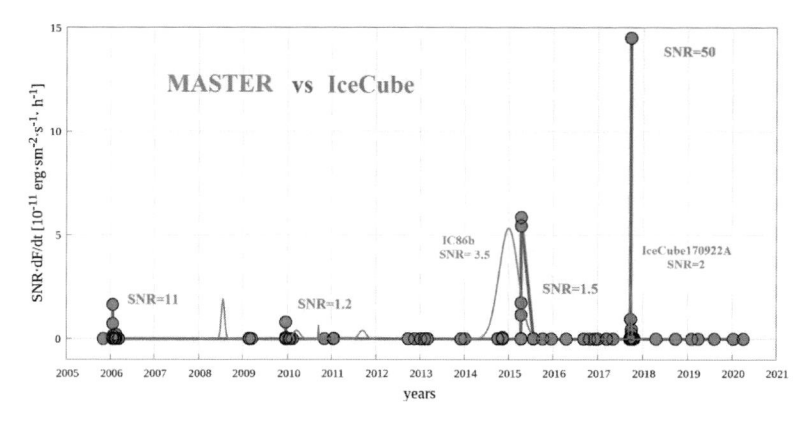

Fig. 2. MASTER optical variability rate history for blazar TXS0506+056. Flux deriviation the multiplied by the signal-to-noise ratio (blue). The orange curves schematically show the Gaussian analysis of the archive data of IceCube.[27]

was fully confirmed during the two days after the alert, when the MASTER-SAAO robotic telescope joined the blazar observation campaign (Lipunov et al. 2018)[23, 24]

To undestand, was it a unique event for the TXS 0506+056 blazar or no, we analysed 518 2x2 square-degrees images in MASTER Global Robotic Net database, starting from 2005, when we had only one MASTER I telescope located near Moscow (Lipunov et al. 2010,[19] MASTERVostryakovo).[27] All MASTER telescopes has identical equipment, that gives us possibility to make photometry in one system (Lipunov et al. 2010, 2019b).[19, 26]

Fig. 1 shows our photometry of the blazar over the last 16 years. We chose 8 Gaia catalog stars, having the brightness and color similar to those of the blazar, as photometric reference stars, and estimated the errors of individual photometric measurements from the scatter of the magnitudes of these reference stars. We also checked these stars for rapid and long-term variability and found them to be quite stable. We found three times when the brightness of the blazar varied $\tilde{0}.5$m more than 1-3 significance level. The first such time was in 2006, when IceCube neutrino observatory was not yet operating. The second time was in April 2015 (substantial increase of neutrino signal IC86b). The MASTER observation date is in April but statistically close to Gaussian IceCube half year window 9/2014 to 3/2015. And the third time was in September 2017, when the IceCube-170922 (IC86C) event occurred.[27]

The event of September 22, 2017 has outstanding characteristics in terms of flux derivation and signalto- noise ratio. Recently, we conducted detailed blazar monitoring over several nights at the right end of Fig. 2. As we see in the usual state, the blazar is stable at times of several hours and even days with an accuracy of $\tilde{0}.02$ mag. This means that the instability we discovered on 22 September 2017, a few minutes after the neutrino alert, has a reliability of 50 sigma by this criterion(Fig. 2). This result shows the power of fast alert observations of sources of ultrahigh energy particles.

The event of September 22, 2017 has outstanding characteristics in terms of flux derivation and signal-to- noise ratio. Recently, we conducted detailed blazar monitoring over several nights. In the usual state, the blazar is stable at times of several hours and even days with an accuracy of $\tilde{0}.02$ mag. This means that the instability we discovered on 22 September 2017, a few minutes after the neutrino alert, has a reliability of about 40 sigma, and by this criterion. This result shows the power of fast alert observations of sources of ultrahigh energy particles.

3. Discussion

We find for the adopted set of Hubble cosmological parameters (Planck Collaboration et al. 2016)[4] H0 = 67.8 km/s/Mpc (the Hubble constant), $Omega_m = 0.308$, $\Omega_\Lambda = 0.692$ (the matter and vacuum density) that several minutes after the neutrino event the optical isotropic luminosity of the blazar was L_{opt} $4.3*10^{45}$ erg/s and after two hours it returned to the typical level within several weeks of the neutrino event, $9.7 * 10^{45}$ erg/s (we include galactic absorbtion AB=0.4 (Schlegel et al. 1998)[31]). The generally accepted picture (Schlegel et al. 1998)[31] is that blazar radiation arises from relativistic jet directed toward us. The boosted jet gamma factor is moderate Γ 10. In the shock wave at the front of the jet there is an acceleration of protons to ultrahigh energies, which in turn collide with target photons and generate pion production. The decay of pions, in turn, gives rise to a muon neutrino which registers an IceCube detection and high gamma photons detected by the Fermi gamma-ray observatory.

During the period within ~2 weeks around the neutrino event detection time the 0.1 – 100 Gev gamma-ray luminosity was $1.3 * 10^{47}$ erg/s (IceCube et al 2017). Note that the neutrino luminosity of the quasar was equal to about $4 * 10^{47}$ erg/s, which is appreciably higher and, evidently, closer to the gamma-ray luminosity. However, this is not surprising because neutrinos and gamma-ray emission have the same source of energy — that of high-energy protons accelerated by the central supermassive black hole.

The event that we discovered, namely the decrease of the brightness of the TXS 0506+056 blazar near the neutrino detection time, provides complementary and very compelling evidence for the link between the blazar and the IceCube-170922 neutrino event. We analyzed archival data (MASTER unique 518 photometry data for 16 years), which we found to be consistent with this fact. We also propose a hypothesis explaining the anti correlation of the optical and neutrino flux. An increase in neutrino flux means that up to half of the protons disappear. If we assume that these protons produce synchrotron optical radiation, then any increase in neutrino luminosity will lead to a decrease in the optical brightness of the blazar.

MASTER and Lomonosov Space Observatory are supported by Lomonosov Moscow State University Development program (equipment). VL, PB are supported by RFBR grant 19-29-11011. NB is supported by FZZE-2020-0017).

References

1. Aartsen M. et al., 2017, A&A 607, A115
2. Abbott B.P. et al. 2016, ApJL, 826, 13A
3. Abbot B. P. et al. 2017, ApJL, 848 (2), L12
4. Planck Collaboration et al. 2016, A&A, 594, A13
5. Ageron M.et al. 2011, NIMPh, 656, 11
6. Balkanov V. et al. 2002, NuPhS, 110, 504B
7. Boliev M.M. et al. 2018, PPN , 49 (4), 585
8. Brown A.G.A. et al. 2018, A&A, 616, A1
9. Dornic D. et al. 2015, ATel, 7987, 1
10. Ershova O. et al. 2020, ARep, 64 (2), 126
11. Gorbovskoy et al. 2016, MNRAS, 455, 3312
12. Gress O. et al. 2019, RMxAA, 51, 89
13. Hayakava S., Yamamoto Y. 1963, PThPh, 30, 71
14. IceCube Collaboration et al. 2017, Sci, 361, eaat1378
15. IceCube Collaboration. 2017, Sci, 361, 147
16. Kopper C.et al. 2017, GCN Circ, 21916, 1
17. Kornilov V. et al. 2012, ExpAst, 33, 173
18. Laskar et al. 2019, ApJ, 884, 121
19. Lipunov V. et al. 2010, AdAst, 2010, 30L
20. Lipunov V. et al. 2016, MNRAS, 455, 3312
21. Lipunov V. et al. 2017, MNRAS , 465 (3), 3656
22. Lipunov V. et al. 2017, ApJL, 850, 1L
23. Lipunov V.M. et al. 2018a, GCN Circ, 22942, 1
24. Lipunov V. et al. 2018b,ATel, 11902, 1
25. Lipunov V. et al. 2019a, GCN Circ, 26539, 1

26. Lipunov V. et al. 2019b, ARep, 63,293
27. Lipunov V. et al. 2020, ApJ, 896L, 19L
28. ORiordan M., Pe'er A., McKinney J. C. 2017, ApJ, 843, 2, id. 81
29. Paiano S. et al. 2018, ApJ, 854, L32
30. Paliya V.S.et al. 2020, a-ph: 20034.060112v2 , htttps://arxiv.org/abs/2003.06012
31. Schlegel D., Finkbeiner D., Davis M. 1998, ApJ, 843, 525
32. Troja et al., 2017a, Natur, 547, 425T

A short review on nonlinear perturbation theory of structure formation for modified gravity

Jorge L. Cervantes-Cota

Departamento de Física, Instituto Nacional de Investigaciones Nucleares, Carretera México Toluca Km. 36.5, Ocoyoacac, C.P. 52750, Edo. Mex., México.
E-mail: jorge.cervantes@inin.gob.mx

Alejandro Aviles

Departamento de Física, Instituto Nacional de Investigaciones Nucleares, Apartado Postal 18-1027, Col. Escandón, Ciudad de México,11801, México. and
Consejo Nacional de Ciencia y Tecnología, Av. Insurgentes Sur 1582, Colonia Crédito Constructor, Del. Benito Juárez, 03940, Ciudad de México, México
E-mail: avilescervantes@gmail.com

In this proceedings contribution we summarize a series of results on nonlinear perturbation theory for modified gravity models, in which a scalar field changes the gravitational dynamics at cosmic scales. We discuss its effects on large scale structure, focusing on screenings and the power spectrum of matter fields and tracers. We also discuss a redshift space distortions model for modified gravity and the departures from the LCDM model.

Keywords: Perturbation theory; modified gravity.

1. Introduction

In recent years we have witnessed important developments on the understanding of large scale structure (LSS) formation. The experimental confirmation of baryon acoustic oscillation (BAO) feature and measurements of redshift space distortions (RSD) have boosted the search for an increasing accuracy in the determination of the cosmological parameters from the LSS side, apart from those of the cosmic microwave background (CMB) measurements, and other probes.

On the other hand, there is a growing interest to test gravity at cosmological scales. One the one hand, because we do not really know the origin of dark energy (being this a constant or a field), so it can be due to some modified gravity (MG). On the other hand, because the level of understanding of the LSS phenomena mentioned in the previous paragraph opens the possibility to test gravity at cosmic scales at high precision. Due to these facts, a natural interest arose to develop perturbation theory (PT) for MG models. At the same time, MG simulations have been carried out, see for example Cautun et al.[1] Both PT theory and simulations allow us to understand the role that gravity plays to form structure.

Nonlinear PT for LSS in MG models have been developed in the last decade or so, beginning with approach proposed by Koyama et al[2] for standard perturbation theory (SPT) to one-loop. Later, we and other collaborators developed the formalism for Lagrangian perturbation theory (LPT).[3-6] Nonlinear PT is limited to weakly nonlinear scales, but it is nevertheless important because of the BAO and RSD effects are manifested in these scales. Non-linearities in MG show special features such as screening mechanisms due to the fifth force of the scalar degree of freedom present in these models.[7]

Since our goal is to test gravity at cosmic scales, one employs toy MG models, such as f(R) or Dvali-Gabadadze-Porrati (DGP) models to achieve a percent-level of precision in the power spectrum (PS) or two point correlation function, that will allow to describe the physics that new generation of stage IV experiments will be able to reach soon, such as DESI,[8] EUCLID[9] and LSST,[10] among others. Therefore, a whole machinery of tools are being developed, including precision theory, mocks, simulations, emulators, among other technical improvements, see for instance Alam et al.[11]

There are a few pieces to be understood to study LSS in PT, and that we tackle in the present work: description of the dynamics of density fields composed of dark matter particles, and here one has LPT and SPT; then, one has to deal with biased tracers; to understand how the RSD description is modelled in MG; to add the small-scale effective field theory (EFT) corrections coming from UV-cutoffs of PT; and finally, to apply a IR-resummation of modes to cancel out unwanted features in the power spectrum.

Our primer to PT for MG is organized as follows: We first explain, in section 2, how LPT is obtained and the role of growth functions is emphasized, and in section 3 we discuss their use to screen the fifth force. In section 4, we explain how LPT results can be used to obtain SPT ones, establishing a bridge between these two formalisms. In section 5, we present the power spectra for matter fields and in section 6 we introduce the bias parameter that contributes to power spectra for tracers. In section 7 we review recent results in which we modeled RSD for MG models. Finally, in section 8, EFT and IR-resummation explanations are shortly addressed, before we conclude in section 9.

2. LPT for MG

At the large scales we are working, baryons behave essentially as cold dark matter. So, from now on we consider the whole matter that follows trajectories with Eulerian comoving coordinates $\mathbf{x}$. The Lagrangian displacement vector field $\boldsymbol{\Psi}$ relates the initial (Lagrangian) $\mathbf{q}$ and Eulerian $\mathbf{x}$ positions of particles as $\boldsymbol{\Psi}(\mathbf{q}, t) = \mathbf{x}(\mathbf{q}, t) - \mathbf{q}$, chosen such that $\mathbf{x}(\mathbf{q}, t_{ini}) = \mathbf{q}$, with t_{ini} an early time where the evolution of all scales of interest remains linear and the overdensities are quite small, $\delta(\mathbf{x}, t_{ini}) = \delta(\mathbf{q}) \ll 1$. We consider $\boldsymbol{\Psi}$ a longitudinal field, since it is the only contribution to 1-loop. Using matter conservation,

$$(1 + \delta(\mathbf{x}, t))d^3 x = (1 + \delta(\mathbf{q}))d^3 q, \tag{1}$$

one gets the known relation between density and Lagrangian fields

$$\delta(\mathbf{x},t) = \frac{1+\delta(\mathbf{q})-J}{J} \simeq \frac{1-J}{J}, \qquad (2)$$

where $J_{ij} = \partial x_i/\partial q^j = \delta_{ij} + \Psi_{i,j}$ is the Jacobian matrix of the coordinate transformation and J its determinant. Since $\mathbf{\Psi}$ is a potential field, the Jacobian matrix is symmetric.

The fundamental field in LPT is the displacement field, and its equation of motion is given by the geodesic equation,

$$\hat{\mathcal{T}}\mathbf{\Psi}(\mathbf{q},t) = -\frac{1}{a}\nabla_{\mathbf{x}}\psi(\mathbf{x},t)|_{\mathbf{x}=\mathbf{q}+\mathbf{\Psi}}. \qquad (3)$$

where $\hat{\mathcal{T}} \equiv \frac{d^2}{dt^2} + 2H\frac{d}{dt}$. We use $\nabla_{\mathbf{x}} = \partial/\partial \mathbf{x}$ to denote partial differentiation with respect to Eulerian coordinates, and $\nabla = \partial/\partial \mathbf{q}$ for differentiation with respect to Lagrangian coordinates. The two scalar gravitational potentials of the metric are related by $\phi - \psi = \varphi/2$, assuming Newtonian gauge, where φ is the scalar field mediating the fifth force.

The gravity model can be set out in the Einstein frame, where the Ricci scalar in the Lagrangian is not coupled to the scalar field, but the couplings are given by the scalar field and the matter Lagrangian, such as in Symmetron gravity.[12] Another possibility is to lay out the theory in the Jordan frame, where explicit couplings exist between the Ricci and the scalar field, such as Brans-Dicke type of couplings, and in addition, couplings to matter may exist. For the sake of concreteness, we opt for the latter approach here, but we will show below some results for the former, as well. Then, the Poisson equation is

$$\frac{1}{a^2}\nabla_{\mathbf{x}}^2\psi = A_0\delta(\mathbf{x},t) - \frac{1}{2a^2}\nabla_{\mathbf{x}}^2\varphi. \qquad (4)$$

clearly, the scalar field modifies the Newtonian potential (ψ), and then the force upon to test particles. The Klein-Gordon equation in the quasi-static limit takes the form[2]

$$(3+2\omega_{\text{BD}})\frac{1}{a^2}\nabla_{\mathbf{x}}^2\varphi = -8\pi G\bar{\rho}\delta + \text{NL}, \qquad (5)$$

where NL contains all nonlinear terms to be defined next that will encode the mode couplings.

It is useful to consider PT in the Fourier space, in which modes are decoupled for LCDM and become simple for MG models at first order approximation. The full expansion for Klein-Gordon equation becomes

$$-\frac{k^2}{2a^2}\varphi(\mathbf{k}) = -(A(k)-A_0)\tilde{\delta}(\mathbf{k}) + \frac{k^2/a^2}{6\Pi(k)}\delta I(\mathbf{k})$$
$$-\frac{(3+2\omega_{\text{BD}})k^2/a^2}{3\Pi(k)}\frac{1}{2a^2}[(\nabla_{\mathbf{x}}^2\varphi - \nabla^2\varphi)](\mathbf{k}), \qquad (6)$$

where $[(\cdots)](\mathbf{k})$ means Fourier transform of $(\cdots)(\mathbf{q})$ and we defined

$$A(k) = A_0 \left(1 + \frac{k^2/a^2}{3\Pi(k)}\right), \tag{7}$$

$$\Pi(k) = \frac{1}{3a^2}\left((3 + 2\omega_{\rm BD})k^2 + M_1 a^2\right), \tag{8}$$

$$A_0 = A(k=0,t) = 4\pi G\bar{\rho}. \tag{9}$$

$A(k)$ is the gravitational strength in the MG cases, while A_0 is for GR. In Brans-Dicke type theories we identify $3 + 2\omega_{\rm BD} = 1/2\beta^2$, allowing us to recognize the β parameter as the strength of the matter to scalar field coupling.

There are two nonlinear terms in eq. (6), the second and third terms of the right hand side (r.h.s.). The second term encodes the nonlinear gravity model, given by

$$\delta I(\mathbf{k}) = \frac{1}{2}\int \frac{d^3k_1 d^3k_2}{(2\pi)^3}\delta_{\rm D}(\mathbf{k} - \mathbf{k}_1 - \mathbf{k}_2)M_2(\mathbf{k}_1, \mathbf{k}_2)\varphi(\mathbf{k}_1)\varphi(\mathbf{k}_2)$$
$$+ \frac{1}{3}\int \frac{d^3k_1 d^3k_2 d^3k_3}{(2\pi)^6}\delta_{\rm D}(\mathbf{k} - \mathbf{k}_1 - \mathbf{k}_2 - \mathbf{k}_3)M_3(\mathbf{k}_1, \mathbf{k}_2, \mathbf{k}_3)\varphi(\mathbf{k}_1)\varphi(\mathbf{k}_2)\varphi(\mathbf{k}_3). \tag{10}$$

The M_i functions carry the gravitational properties of particular MG models. It is convenient to insert eq. (6) into eq. (10) to obtain an equation in terms of δ expansions that is useful to find the final expression for the displacements.

The third term accounts for the difference of the Laplacian in x- and q- coordinates, the so called frame-lagging term:

$$[(\nabla_{\mathbf{x}}^2\varphi - \nabla^2\varphi)](\mathbf{k}) = [-2\Psi_{i,j}\varphi_{,ij} - \Psi_{i,ij}\varphi_{,j} + 3\Psi_{i,j}\Psi_{j,k}\varphi_{,ki} + 2\Psi_{i,j}\Psi_{j,ik}\varphi_{,k}$$
$$+ \Psi_{l,li}\Psi_{i,j}\varphi_{,j}](\mathbf{k}), \tag{11}$$

computed up to third-order PT. This term contributes at different scales, but it is more important at large scales, especially if the theory is expected to reduce to GR in that limit.

It is convenient to recast eq. (3) in terms of only Lagrangian coordinates, then by taking the $\mathbf{x}$-divergence and transforming to Lagrangian coordinates with the aid of $\nabla_{\mathbf{x}i} = (J^{-1})_{ji}\nabla_i$, we get in Fourier space

$$[(J^{-1})_{ij}\hat{\mathcal{T}}\Psi_{i,j}](\mathbf{k}) = -A(k)\tilde{\delta}(\mathbf{k}) + \frac{2\beta^2 k^2}{k^2 + m^2 a^2}\delta I(\mathbf{k}) + \frac{1}{2}\frac{m^2}{k^2 + m^2 a^2}[(\nabla_{\mathbf{x}}^2\varphi - \nabla^2\varphi)](\mathbf{k}), \tag{12}$$

and

$$\tilde{\delta}(\mathbf{k}) = \int d^3q\, e^{-i\mathbf{q}\cdot\mathbf{k}}\delta(\mathbf{x}) = \left[\frac{1 - J(\mathbf{q})}{J(\mathbf{q})}\right](\mathbf{k}). \tag{13}$$

Eq. (12) is solved perturbatively using $(J^{-1})_{ij} = \delta_{ij} - \Psi_{i,j} + \Psi_{i,k}\Psi_{k,j} + \cdots$. One obtains the following equation for the displacement at third order PT:

$$(\hat{\mathcal{T}} - A(k))[\Psi_{i,i}](\mathbf{k}) = [\Psi_{i,j}\hat{\mathcal{T}}\Psi_{j,i}](\mathbf{k}) - \frac{A(k)}{2}[\Psi_{i,j}\Psi_{j,i}](\mathbf{k}) - \frac{A(k)}{2}[(\Psi_{l,l})^2](\mathbf{k})$$
$$- [\Psi_{i,k}\Psi_{k,j}\hat{\mathcal{T}}\Psi_{j,i}](\mathbf{k}) + \frac{A(k)}{6}[(\Psi_{l,l})^3](\mathbf{k})$$
$$+ \frac{A(k)}{2}[\Psi_{l,l}\Psi_{i,j}\Psi_{j,i}](\mathbf{k}) + \frac{A(k)}{3}[\Psi_{i,k}\Psi_{k,j}\Psi_{j,i}](\mathbf{k})$$
$$+ \frac{k^2/a^2}{6\Pi(k)}\delta I(\mathbf{k}) + \frac{M_1}{6\Pi(k)}\frac{1}{a^2}[(\nabla_{\mathbf{x}}^2\varphi - \nabla^2\varphi)](\mathbf{k}). \quad (14)$$

One then can analyze solutions at different PT orders. To linear order one has

$$(\hat{\mathcal{T}} - A(k,t))[\Psi_{i,i}^{(1)}] = 0, \quad (15)$$

which is the same equation for the linear matter overdensity. Hence, the first order solution is

$$\Psi_i^{(1)}(\mathbf{k},t) = i\frac{k_i}{k^2}\delta_L(\mathbf{k},t) = i\frac{k_i}{k^2}D_+(k,t)\delta_L(\mathbf{k},t_0), \quad (16)$$

where we notice the normalization is fixed by eq. (1), and we choose the growth function such that $D_+(k \to 0, t_0) = 1$, where t_0 denotes present time. More generally, Lagrangian displacements are expanded as

$$\Psi_i(\mathbf{k}) = \sum_{n=0}^{\infty}\Psi^{(n)} = \sum_{n=1}^{\infty}\frac{i}{n!}\int_{\mathbf{k}_{1\cdots n}=\mathbf{k}} L_i^{(n)}(\mathbf{k}_1,...,\mathbf{k}_n)\delta_L(\mathbf{k}_1)\cdots\delta_L(\mathbf{k}_n). \quad (17)$$

Hereafter we make use of the shorthand notation

$$\int_{\mathbf{k}_{1\cdots n}=\mathbf{k}} = \int\frac{d^3\mathbf{k}_1}{(2\pi)^3}\cdots\frac{d^3\mathbf{k}_n}{(2\pi)^3}(2\pi)^3\delta_D(\mathbf{k} - \mathbf{k}_{1\cdots n}), \quad (18)$$

and $\mathbf{k}_{1\cdots n} = \mathbf{k}_1 + \cdots + \mathbf{k}_n$ denotes the sum of arbitrary number of momenta.

The LPT kernels $L_i^{(n)}$ are obtained order by order using eq. (12). At first order, reading eq. (16) above, we have

$$L_i^{(1)}(\mathbf{k}) = \frac{k_i}{k^2}, \quad (19)$$

while to second order we obtain[3]

$$L_i^{(2)}(\mathbf{k}_1,\mathbf{k}_2) = \frac{3}{7}\frac{k_i}{k^2}\left(\mathcal{A}(\mathbf{k}_1,\mathbf{k}_2) - \mathcal{B}(\mathbf{k}_1,\mathbf{k}_2)\frac{(\mathbf{k}_1\cdot\mathbf{k}_2)^2}{k_1^2 k_2^2}\right), \quad (20)$$

with $\mathbf{k} = \mathbf{k}_1 + \mathbf{k}_2$,

$$\mathcal{A}(\mathbf{k}_1,\mathbf{k}_2) = \frac{7D_{\mathcal{A}}^{(2)}(\mathbf{k}_1,\mathbf{k}_2)}{3D_+(k_1)D_+(k_2)}, \quad \mathcal{B}(\mathbf{k}_1,\mathbf{k}_2) = \frac{7D_{\mathcal{B}}^{(2)}(\mathbf{k}_1,\mathbf{k}_2)}{3D_+(k_1)D_+(k_2)}, \quad (21)$$

and the second order growth functions are the solutions to equations

$$(\hat{\mathcal{T}} - A(k))D_{\mathcal{A}}^{(2)} = \left[A(k) + (A(k) - A(k_1))\frac{\mathbf{k}_1 \cdot \mathbf{k}_2}{k_2^2} + (A(k) - A(k_2))\frac{\mathbf{k}_1 \cdot \mathbf{k}_2}{k_1^2}\right.$$
$$\left. - \left(\frac{2A_0}{3}\right)\frac{k^2}{a^2}\frac{M_2(\mathbf{k}_1\mathbf{k}_2)}{6\Pi(k)\Pi(k_1)\Pi(k_2)}\right]D_+(k_1)D_+(k_2), \quad (22)$$

$$(\hat{\mathcal{T}} - A(k))D_{\mathcal{B}}^{(2)} = \left[A(k_1) + A(k_2) - A(k)\right]D_+(k_1)D_+(k_2), \quad (23)$$

with appropriate initial conditions. The second and third terms in the r.h.s. of eq. (22) stem from the frame-lagging contributions. The fourth term is the second order contribution of δI, which in MG is responsible of the screening mechanism. Since $\mathcal{A}$ and $\mathcal{B}$ depend on $\mathbf{k}_1$ and $\mathbf{k}_2$, the decomposition in eq. (20) is arbitrary and we adopt it because they take values of order unity and the connection to ΛCDM is direct. For this case we obtain

$$D_{\mathcal{A}}^{(2)}(t) = D_{\mathcal{B}}^{(2)}(t) = (\hat{\mathcal{T}} - A_0)^{-1}\left[\frac{3}{2}\Omega_m H^2 D_+^2\right]$$
$$= \frac{3}{7}D_+^2(t) + \frac{4}{7}(\hat{\mathcal{T}} - A_0)^{-1}\left[\frac{3}{2}\Omega_m H^2 D_+^2\left(1 - \frac{f^2}{\Omega_m}\right)\right], \quad (24)$$

thus $\mathcal{A} = \mathcal{B}$ are only time dependent. For $f = \Omega_m^{1/2}$ we get $\mathcal{A}^{\text{EdS}} = \mathcal{B}^{\text{EdS}} = 1$ and the standard kernels in Einstein-de Sitter (EdS) are recovered.

The third order kernel $L_i^{(3)}(\mathbf{k}_1, \mathbf{k}_2, \mathbf{k}_3)$ and many more details are provided in Aviles & Cervantes,[3] therefore we do not reproduce them here.

3. Screenings by the growth functions

As explained above, MG models introduce a fifth force that changes the Newtonian collapse at cosmic scales. A known effect in nonlinear MG is that its spherical solutions show the screening of fifth force, to drive the solution to the Newtonian one. This happens in large density regions that produce an effective weak coupling that effectively cancels the fifth force; there are other screening mechanisms stemming from different theoretical reasons; see, e.g., K. Koyama.[13] Although screenings are more usually studied in the highly non-linear regime, they also leave imprints in quasi-linear scales that can be captured by cosmological PT.

3.1. *Einstein frame: Symmetron case*

The previous LPT formalism was done in the Jordan frame, but it can be equally well translated to the Einstein frame, for example to study PT within Symmetron fields.

The Symmetron achieves its screening through the coupling of the scalar field to the matter Lagrangian, generating an effective potential with two parameters (using $\hat{n} = \hat{m} = 1/2$): the scalar field mass (m) and the strength of the coupling (β), see details in reference.[12]

To convert theories posed in the Einstein frame to the Jordan frame, it is convenient to define a rescaled field:

$$\chi(\mathbf{q}, t) \equiv -\frac{2\beta}{C} \frac{\varphi(\mathbf{q}, t)}{M_{\text{Pl}}}, \qquad (25)$$

hereafter we denote $C \equiv C(\bar{\varphi})$ unless otherwise is explicitly stated. And again, this new scalar field follows a similar Klein Gordon equation

$$-\frac{k^2}{2a^2}\chi(\mathbf{k}) = -(A(k) - A_0)\tilde{\delta}(\mathbf{k}) + \frac{k^2/a^2}{6\Pi(k)}\delta\mathcal{I}(\chi)$$
$$- \frac{C}{2\beta^2}\frac{k^2/a^2}{3\Pi(k)}\frac{1}{2a^2}[(\nabla_{\mathbf{x}}^2\chi - \nabla^2\chi)](\mathbf{k}), \qquad (26)$$

and the contribution from screenings is given by

$$\delta\mathcal{I}(\mathbf{k}) = \sum_{n=2}^{\infty}\frac{(-1)^{n+1}}{2^n n!}\frac{C^n \kappa_{n+1}}{\beta^{n+1}}[\chi^n](\mathbf{k})$$
$$+ \sum_{n=1}^{\infty}\frac{(-1)^{n+1}}{2^n n!}\frac{2A_0 C^n \beta_{n+1}}{\beta^{n+1}}[\chi^n \delta](\mathbf{k}), \qquad (27)$$

where $3 + 2\omega_{\text{BD}}(a) = \frac{C}{2\beta^2}$.

Solutions to first order are formally the same as eq. (16). To second order one can write the solutions as:

$$\Psi^{i(2)}(\mathbf{k}) = \frac{ik^i}{2k^2}\int_{\mathbf{k}_{12}=\mathbf{k}}\frac{3}{7}\left(\bar{D}_{\text{NS}}^{(2)}(\mathbf{k}_1, \mathbf{k}_2) - \bar{D}_{\text{S}}^{(2)}(\mathbf{k}_1, \mathbf{k}_2)\right)\delta_1\delta_2, \qquad (28)$$

where we denote $\delta_{1,2} \equiv \delta_L(\mathbf{k}_{1,2})$ and where we split the second order growth in non-screened (NS) and screening (S) pieces. These growth functions $D^{(2)}$ are solutions to the equations:

$$(\hat{\mathcal{T}} - A(k))D_{\text{NS}}^{(2)}(\mathbf{k}_1, \mathbf{k}_2) = \left(A(k) - (A(k_1) + A(k_2) - A(k))\frac{(\mathbf{k}_1 \cdot \mathbf{k}_2)^2}{k_1^2 k_2^2}\right.$$
$$\left. + (A(k) - A(k_1))\frac{\mathbf{k}_1 \cdot \mathbf{k}_2}{k_2^2} + (A(k) - A(k_2))\frac{\mathbf{k}_1 \cdot \mathbf{k}_2}{k_1^2}\right)D_+(k_1)D_+(k_2) \qquad (29)$$

$$(\hat{\mathcal{T}} - A(k))D_{\text{S}}^{(2)}(\mathbf{k}_1, \mathbf{k}_2) = \left(\frac{2A_0}{3}\right)^2 \frac{k^2}{a^2}\frac{M_2(\mathbf{k}_1, \mathbf{k}_2)D_+(k_1)D_+(k_2)}{6\Pi(k)\Pi(k_1)\Pi(k_2)}, \qquad (30)$$

and the normalized growth functions are defined as

$$\bar{D}_{\text{S,NS}}^{(2)}(\mathbf{k}_1, \mathbf{k}_2, t) = \frac{7}{3}\frac{D_{\text{S,NS}}^{(2)}(\mathbf{k}_1, \mathbf{k}_2, t)}{D_+(k_1)D_+(k_2)}. \qquad (31)$$

In an EdS universe one obtains the well known result $\bar{D}_{NS}^{(2)} = 1 - (\hat{\mathbf{k}}_1 \cdot \hat{\mathbf{k}}_2)^2$, while in ΛCDM one gets the same result multiplied by a function that varies slowly with time, such that nowadays $\bar{D}_{NS}^{(2)\Lambda CDM} \simeq 1.01 \bar{D}_{NS}^{(2)EdS}$. As expected, the screening second order growth, $\bar{D}_S^{(2)}$, is zero in both EdS and ΛCDM models.

The function $\bar{D}_S^{(2)}$ encodes the non-linearities of the effective potential of the scalar field and it yields the second order screening effects that drive the theory to GR at small scales. The total second-order growth function, as can be read from eq. (28), is given by $D^{(2)} = D_{NS}^{(2)} - D_S^{(2)}$, such that negative values of $D_S^{(2)}$ enhance the growth of perturbations (*anti-screening effects*), while positive values of it yield the standard suppression of the fifth force. In the Symmetron case there are configurations of interacting wave modes that instead of driving the theory towards GR, they drive the theory away from it. In fact, from eq. (30), all triangular configurations with

$$k_1^2 + k_2^2 < k_{AS}^2(a), \qquad (32)$$

where the anti-screening wavenumber is defined as

$$k_{AS}^2(a) \equiv \frac{\kappa_3 \beta a^2}{\beta_2} - 2m^2 a^2, \qquad (33)$$

will contribute with a negative source to the second order screening as long as the r.h.s. of the above equation is positive.

Analogously, each higher perturbative order carries its own screening and it is efficient over a certain k interval. We emphasize that $\bar{D}_S^{(2)}$ and $\bar{D}_S^{(3)}$ with positive values will screen the fifth force, while negative values will anti-screen it instead. Given this, the M_i MG functions of each model will determine their screening properties. We plot in Fig. 1 the normalized second and third order screening growth functions $\bar{D}_S^{(2)}(\mathbf{k}_1, \mathbf{k}_2)$ and $\bar{D}_S^{(3)}(\mathbf{k}_1, \mathbf{k}_2, \mathbf{k}_3)$ for the Symmetron, again for different triangle configurations.

The vertical lines correspond to the *screening wavenumber*

$$k_{M_1} = a\sqrt{M_1(a)}, \qquad (34)$$

that characterizes the scale at which the screening is present; in fact it is close to the maximum screening growth of the largest triangular contribution (squeezed modes). This scale might serve to parametrize the nonlinear growth to eventually make (e.g. N-point statistics) computations more efficient.

3.2. Jordan frame: the f(R) case

As it is known, a f(R) Lagrangian can be transformed into the Jordan frame, and so we can use the formalism of section 2 and, in fact, also the screening/non-screened division of the previous subsection. Here we consider the HS n=1 model for different $f_{R0} = -10^{-4}, -10^{-8}, -10^{-12}$ corresponding to F4, F8, and F12 models. In the

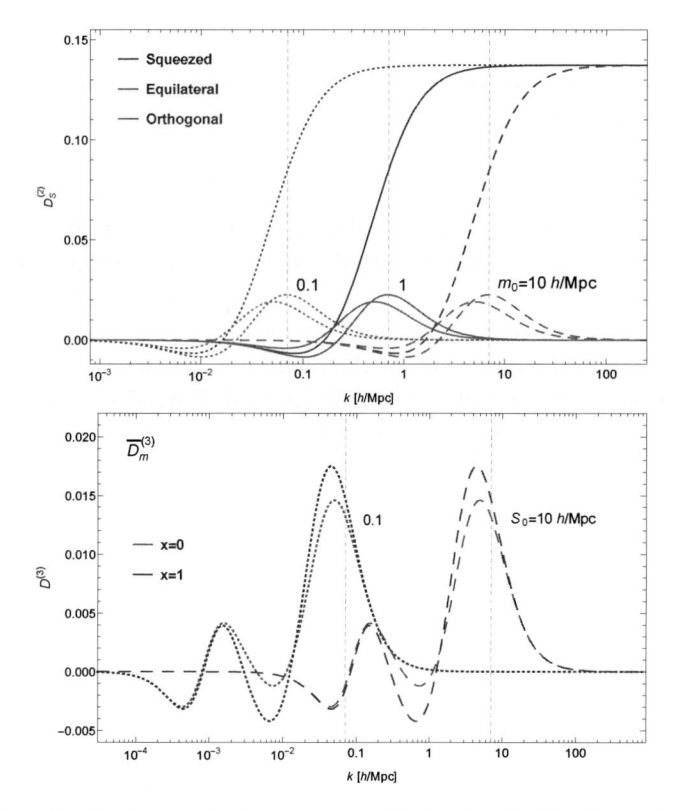

Fig. 1. We show the displacements at second and third order, for the Symmetron model with $a_{ssb} = 0.33$, $\beta_0 = 1$ and different values of m_0, and considering different triangle configurations; results are shown for $z = 0$. The vertical lines are located at $k = a\sqrt{M_1}$, showing the characteristic scale at which the screenings are present. In the upper plot we show the $\bar{D}_S^{(2)}$ functions. The plot below shows $\bar{D}_S^{(3)}(\mathbf{k}, -\mathbf{p}, \mathbf{p})$ for two values of cosine angle $x = \hat{\mathbf{k}} \cdot \hat{\mathbf{p}}$. In both plots one observes regions of antiscreening behavior ($\bar{D}_S < 0$).

upper panel of Fig. 2 we show plots for the second order screening growth functions, $\bar{D}_S^{(2)}$, evaluated at redshift $z = 0$ and for different triangular configurations.

Note that in f(R) the screening scale, eq. (34), goes as $k_{M_1} \propto \sqrt{1/|f_{R0}|}$. The lower panel of Fig. 2 shows the growth $D_S^{(3)}(\mathbf{k}, -\mathbf{p}, \mathbf{p})$ for the double squeezed configuration with additionally $|\mathbf{k}| = |\mathbf{p}|$ and for different values of the cosine angle $x = \hat{\mathbf{k}} \cdot \hat{\mathbf{p}}$.

In order to study the effects of the background evolution on the screening growth, in Fig. 3 we show it for the F4 model at different redshifts $z = 0, 3$, and 10. The upper panel uses a ΛCDM background cosmology and the lower panel an EdS background evolution. In ΛCDM the screening curves are narrower and reach smaller maxima, this is expected because the cosmic acceleration attenuates the clustering of dark matter, and hence the nonlinear effects. Instead, in an EdS background the pattern of the growth is preserved. The vertical lines again denote the scale k_{M_1}, which are in ΛCDM slightly shifted in comparison with the EdS results.

It is worthy to observe that in f(R) the nonlinearities of the Klein-Gordon equation lead to screening for any configuration. This is manifested in Figs. 2 and 3 because the screening growth functions always take positive values.

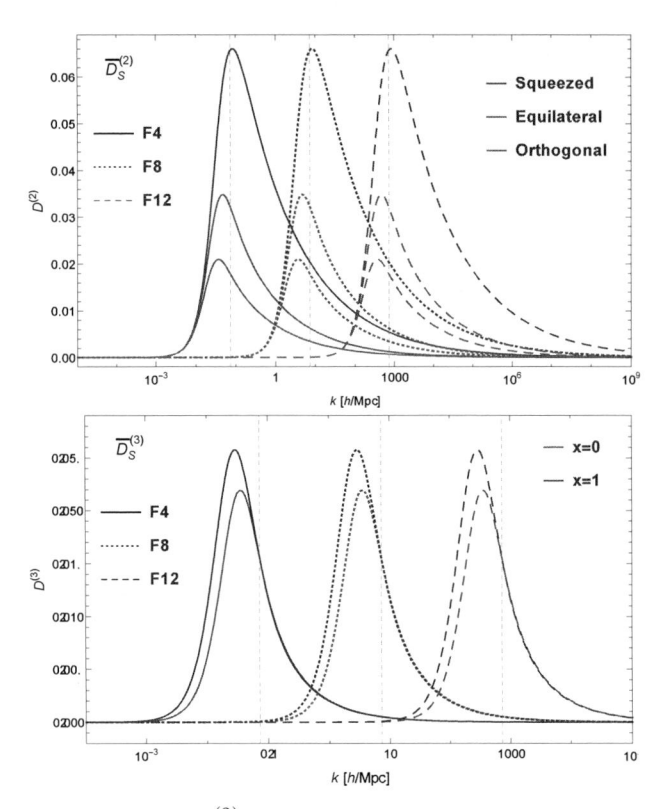

Fig. 2. The upper plot shows the $\bar{D}_S^{(2)}$ functions for F4, F8, and F12 models, considering different triangle configurations. The vertical lines are located at $k = a\sqrt{M_1}$, showing the characteristic scale at which the screenings are present. The lower panel shows the third order growth $\bar{D}_S^{(3)}$ for different angles $x = \hat{\mathbf{k}} \cdot \hat{\mathbf{p}}$ and with $k = p$. The f(R) n=1 shows no antiscreening.

We have considered other models that show different screening mechanisms, such as DGP based on the Vainshtein mechanism. In this case, the second and third order screening growths always act to attenuate the fifth force that modifies Newtonian gravity: no antiscreening is found. We refer to further details on the screening treatment to reference.[7]

4. From Lagrangian to standard PT

The formalism presented above was developed for LPT. However, one can demonstrate that from the kernel solutions of LPT one can obtain the kernels in SPT,

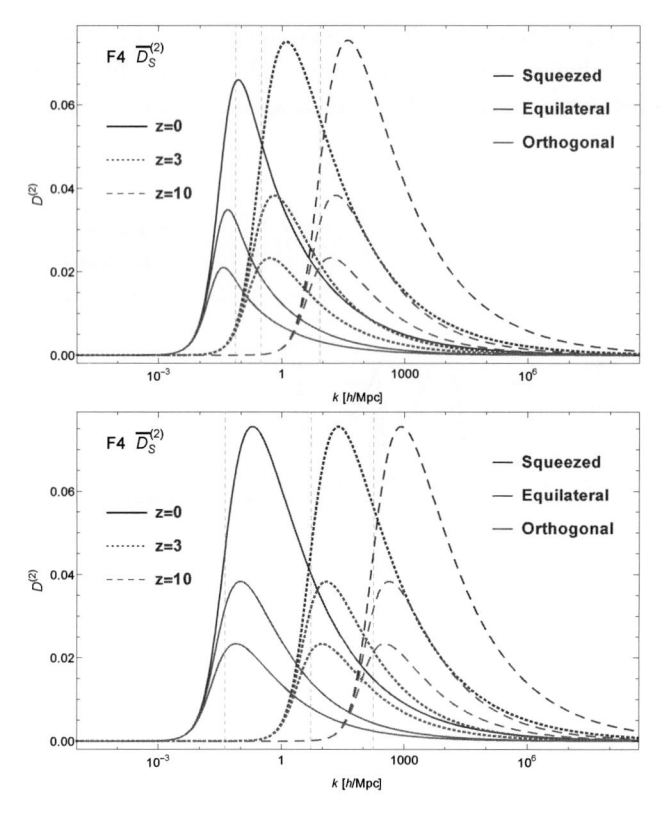

Fig. 3. $\bar{D}_S^{(2)}$ functions for the F4 for redshifts $z = 0, 3, 10$, and considering different triangle configurations. The vertical lines are located at $k = a\sqrt{M_1}$, showing the characteristic scale at which the screenings are present. The upper panel shows a ΛCDM background evolution while the bottom panel an EdS background evolution.

so establishing a formal connection between these two formalisms. This was done for general cosmologies in reference,[4] where it is shown that the SPT power spectrum computed from the LPT formalism coincides with the Eulerean, SPT power spectrum. Here omit details that can be found in the above reference, where it is shown that one can express the overdensities as

$$\delta^{(n)}(\mathbf{k}) = \sum_{\ell=1}^{n} \sum_{m_1+\cdots+m_\ell=n} \frac{k_{i_1}\cdots k_{i_\ell}}{\ell! m_1! \cdots m_\ell!}$$
$$\times \int_{\mathbf{p}_{1\cdots n}=\mathbf{k}} L_{i_1}^{(m_1)}(\mathbf{p}_1,...,\mathbf{p}_{m_1}) \cdots L_{i_\ell}^{(m_\ell)}(\mathbf{p}_{m_{\ell-1}+1},...,\mathbf{p}_{m_\ell})$$
$$\times \delta_L(\mathbf{p}_1)\cdots\delta_L(\mathbf{p}_n). \tag{35}$$

This expression provides the SPT F_n kernels out of the LPT kernels (L_n):

$$F_n(\mathbf{k}_1, \ldots, \mathbf{k}_n) = \sum_{\ell=1}^{n} \sum_{m_1+\cdots+m_\ell=n} \frac{k_{i_1}\cdots k_{i_\ell}}{\ell! m_1! \cdots m_\ell!} \times L_{i_1}^{(m_1)}(\mathbf{k}_1,...,\mathbf{k}_{m_1}) \cdots L_{i_\ell}^{(m_\ell)}(\mathbf{k}_{m_{\ell-1}+1},...,\mathbf{k}_{m_\ell}) \quad (36)$$

with $\mathbf{k} = \mathbf{k}_1 + \cdots + \mathbf{k}_n$.

As an example of these results here we show the $n=2$ kernel:

$$F_2(\mathbf{k}_1, \mathbf{k}_2) = \frac{1}{2} + \frac{3}{14}\mathcal{A} + \left(\frac{1}{2} - \frac{3}{14}\mathcal{B}\right)\frac{(\mathbf{k}_1 \cdot \mathbf{k}_2)^2}{\mathbf{k}_1^2 \mathbf{k}_2^2} + \frac{\mathbf{k}_1 \cdot \mathbf{k}_2}{2}\left(\frac{1}{k_1^2} + \frac{1}{k_2^2}\right). \quad (37)$$

and, analogously, for the velocity field kernels one finds a similar relation general relationship. For $n=2$ we obtain:

$$G_2(\mathbf{k}_1, \mathbf{k}_2) = \frac{3}{14}\mathcal{A}(f_1+f_2) + \frac{3\dot{\mathcal{A}}}{14H} + \left(\frac{f_1+f_2}{2} - \frac{3}{14}\mathcal{B}(f_1+f_2) - \frac{3\dot{\mathcal{B}}}{14H}\right)\frac{(\mathbf{k}_1 \cdot \mathbf{k}_2)^2}{\mathbf{k}_1^2 \mathbf{k}_2^2}$$
$$+ \frac{\mathbf{k}_1 \cdot \mathbf{k}_2}{2}\left(\frac{f_2}{k_1^2} + \frac{f_1}{k_2^2}\right), \quad (38)$$

where $f_{1,2} = f(k_{1,2})$ are growth rates for two arbitrary modes. $\mathcal{A}$ and $\mathcal{B}$ are given by eq. (21).

In Fig. 4 we plot the ratios of the SPT 1-loop to linear matter power spectra, for the ΛCDM model, as well as for HS n=1 F4, and the normal branch of DGP with crossover scale fixed by the Hubble constant, $r_c = H_0^{-1}$. We fixed the cosmological parameters to $\Omega_m = 0.281$, $\Omega_b = 0.046$, $h = 0.697$, $n_s = 0.971$, and $\sigma_8 = 0.82$, corresponding to WMAP 9 years best fit to ΛCDM.[14] For F4 model, the background cosmology is indistinguishable to that in ΛCDM. This is not the case for DGP. However, as it is usual in the literature, for DGP we fix to a ΛCDM background. In such a way we can compare the differences in the growth of perturbations due to the fifth force and not to a different Hubble flow. Despite this, the power spectrum in DGP suffers a scale independent shift because $A(k,t) = A(t) \neq A_0$. We plot the the power spectra with and without screenings; the later are achieved by setting $M_2 = M_3 = 0$ in eq. (10).

5. Matter power spectra

We now construct the power spectra for STP for general cosmologies. We follow the approach developed in Aviles et al.[15] As described in section 2, the Poisson equation is given by eq. (4), whereas the fluid equations are:

$$\partial_t \delta(\mathbf{x},t) + \frac{1}{a}\partial_i\left[(1+\delta)v^i\right] = 0, \quad (39)$$

$$\partial_t v^i(\mathbf{x},t) + \frac{1}{a}v^j\partial_j v^i + Hv^i + \frac{1}{a}\partial_i\psi = 0, \quad (40)$$

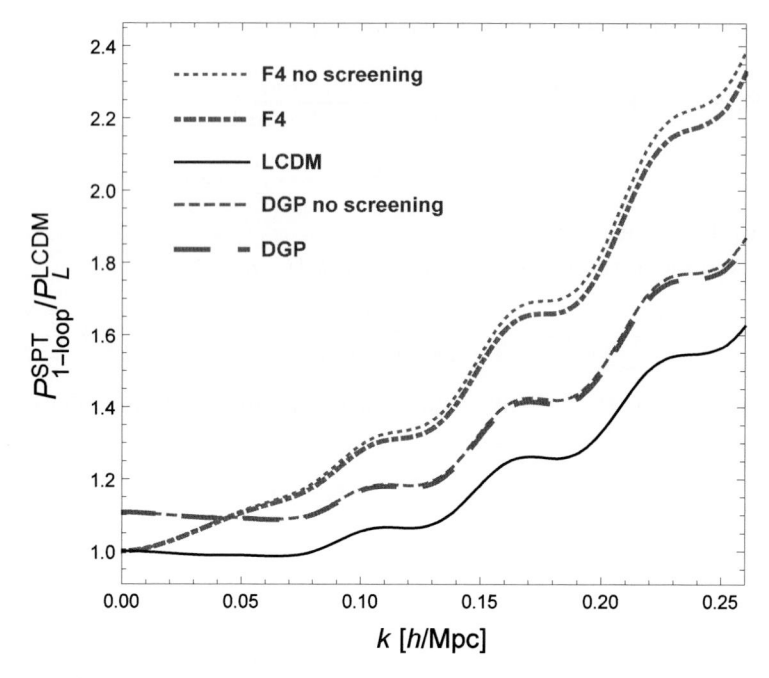

Fig. 4. Ratio of 1-loop SPT to ΛCDM linear matter power spectra for ΛCDM, F4, and DGP models at redshift $z = 0$. The role of screening is self evident at nonlinear scales. We fix cosmological parameters to the best fit of the WMAP Nine-year results.[14]

where $v^i(t) = \frac{dx^i(t)}{d\tau} = a\dot{x}^i(t)$ is the CDM fluid's element peculiar velocity; $\mathbf{x}$ is its comoving coordinate, t the cosmic time, and $d\tau = \frac{1}{a}dt$ the conformal time, such that the total velocity is $v_T^i = aHx^i + v^i$.

We use the (dimensionless) velocity divergence

$$\theta(\mathbf{x}, t) = -\frac{\partial_i v^i}{aH f_0}, \qquad (41)$$

where $f_0(t)$ is an arbitrary function of time that will be fixed to be the logarithmic growth rate at a convenient scale. We assume the transverse piece of the velocity is negligible at large scales, hence it is a longitudinal field fully specified by θ.

In Fourier space the continuity and Euler equations can be written as

$$\frac{1}{H}\frac{\partial \delta(\mathbf{k})}{\partial t} - f_0 \theta(\mathbf{k}) = f_0 \int_{\mathbf{k}_{12}=\mathbf{k}} \alpha(\mathbf{k}_1, \mathbf{k}_2) \theta(\mathbf{k}_1) \delta(\mathbf{k}_2), \qquad (42)$$

$$\frac{1}{H}\frac{\partial f_0 \theta(\mathbf{k})}{\partial t} + \left(2 + \frac{\dot{H}}{H^2}\right) f_0 \theta(\mathbf{k}) - \frac{A(k)}{H^2}\delta(\mathbf{k}) - \frac{S(\mathbf{k})}{H^2} = f_0^2 \int_{\mathbf{k}_{12}=\mathbf{k}} \beta(\mathbf{k}_1, \mathbf{k}_2) \theta(\mathbf{k}_1) \theta(\mathbf{k}_2), \qquad (43)$$

with
$$\alpha(\mathbf{k}_1, \mathbf{k}_2) = 1 + \frac{\mathbf{k}_1 \cdot \mathbf{k}_2}{k_1^2}, \qquad \beta(\mathbf{k}_1, \mathbf{k}_2) = \frac{k_{12}^2(\mathbf{k}_1 \cdot \mathbf{k}_2)}{2k_1^2 k_2^2}. \tag{44}$$

where $S(k)$ is related to eq. (10), see Aviles et al.[15] One finds perturbative solutions at the different orders according to eqs. (42, 43) and the nonlinear expansion (10). The solutions are same those given in eqs. (37) and (38), and so for higher orders.

Having found the kernels up to third order, we can now construct spectra and cross-spectra of the velocity and density fields. At 1-loop in PT, one can use the general expressions

$$P_{ab}(k) = P_{ab}^L(k) + P_{ab}^{22}(k) + P_{ab}^{13}(k), \tag{45}$$

where a and b refer to δ or θ fields, and linear power spectra $P_{ab}^L(k)$

$$P_{\delta\delta}^L(k) \equiv P_L(k), \quad P_{\delta\theta}^L(k) = \frac{f(k)}{f_0} P_L(k), \quad P_{\theta\theta}^L(k) = \left(\frac{f(k)}{f_0}\right)^2 P_L(k), \tag{46}$$

and leading nonlinear contributions

$$P_{\delta\delta}^{22}(k) = 2 \int_{\mathbf{p}} \left[F_2(\mathbf{p}, \mathbf{k} - \mathbf{p})\right]^2 P_L(p) P_L(|\mathbf{k} - \mathbf{p}|), \tag{47}$$

$$P_{\delta\theta}^{22}(k) = 2 \int_{\mathbf{p}} F_2(\mathbf{p}, \mathbf{k} - \mathbf{p}) G_2(\mathbf{p}, \mathbf{k} - \mathbf{p}) P_L(p) P_L(|\mathbf{k} - \mathbf{p}|), \tag{48}$$

$$P_{\theta\theta}^{22}(k) = 2 \int_{\mathbf{p}} \left[G_2(\mathbf{p}, \mathbf{k} - \mathbf{p})\right]^2 P_L(p) P_L(|\mathbf{k} - \mathbf{p}|), \tag{49}$$

$$P_{\delta\delta}^{13}(k) = 6 P_L(k) \int_{\mathbf{p}} F_3(\mathbf{k}, -\mathbf{p}, \mathbf{p}) P_L(p), \tag{50}$$

$$P_{\delta\theta}^{13}(k) = 3 P_L(k) \int_{\mathbf{p}} \left[F_3(\mathbf{k}, -\mathbf{p}, \mathbf{p}) G_1(\mathbf{k}) + G_3(\mathbf{k}, -\mathbf{p}, \mathbf{p})\right] P_L(p), \tag{51}$$

$$P_{\theta\theta}^{13}(k) = 6 P_L(k) \int_{\mathbf{p}} G_3(\mathbf{k}, -\mathbf{p}, \mathbf{p}) G_1(\mathbf{k}) P_L(p). \tag{52}$$

The above expressions are valid for any cosmological model such as MG models, dark energy, or massive neutrinos—in general, for models that introduce a new degree of freedom to the dynamics. For the different models, these expressions for power spectra and kernels are the same, the difference being the corresponding growth solutions through $\mathcal{A}$ and $\mathcal{B}$ (see e.g. eq. 37) that are inside the kernels.

6. Bias Expansion and tracer's power spectra

We now turn to the description of dark matter halos and galaxies, instead of only matter fields. That is, we go into tracers, that are more closely related to observations.

We expand the tracer densities in terms of a set of operators, including the leading curvature operators, labeled with "m" to make reference to matter fields, in a manner similar to McDonald and Roy[16]:

$$\delta(\mathbf{x}) = c_\delta \delta_m + c_{\nabla^2\delta}\nabla^2\delta_m + \frac{1}{2}c_{\delta^2}\delta_m^2 + \frac{1}{2}c_{s^2}s^2$$
$$+ \frac{1}{6}c_{\delta^3}\delta_m^3 + \frac{1}{2}c_{\delta s^2}\delta s^2 + c_\psi \psi + c_{st} st + \frac{1}{2}c_{s^3}s^3, \quad (53)$$
$$\theta(\mathbf{x}) = \theta_m + c_{\nabla^2\theta}\nabla^2\theta_m. \quad (54)$$

Since for MG models an additional scale shows up, the bias coefficients are re-scaled. The first order terms are:

$$\delta^{(1)}(\mathbf{k}) = (c_\delta - c_{\nabla^2\delta}k^2)\delta_m^{(1)}(\mathbf{k}), \text{ and} \quad (55)$$
$$\theta^{(1)}(\mathbf{k}) = (1 - c_{\nabla^2\theta}k^2)\theta_m^{(1)}(\mathbf{k}). \quad (56)$$

The expansion goes to third order that can be found in Aviles et al.[15]

One can now find the tracers' power spectra, that will be given in terms of the above biases and matter power spectra of the previous section. We obtain:

$$P_{\delta\delta}(k) = (b_1 - b_{\nabla^2\delta}k^2)^2 P_L(k) + b_1^2 P_{m,\delta\delta}^{\text{loop}}(k) + 2b_1 b_2 P_{b_1 b_2}(k) + 2b_1 b_{s^2} P_{b_1 b_{s^2}}(k)$$
$$+ b_2^2 P_{b_2^2}(k) + 2b_2 b_{s^2} P_{b_2 b_{s^2}}(k) + b_{s^2}^2 P_{b_{s^2}^2}(k) + 2b_1 b_{3nl}\sigma_3^2(k)P_L(k), \quad (57)$$

$$P_{\delta\theta}(k) = (b_1 - b_{\nabla^2\delta}k^2)(1 - b_{\nabla^2\theta}k^2)\frac{f(k)}{f_0}P_L(k) + b_1 P_{m,\delta\theta}^{\text{loop}}(k) + b_2 P_{b_2,\theta}(k)$$
$$+ b_{s^2} P_{b_{s^2},\theta}(k) + b_{3nl}\sigma_3^2(k)\frac{f(k)}{f_0}P_L(k), \quad (58)$$

$$P_{\theta\theta}(k) = (1 - b_{\nabla^2\theta}k^2)^2 \left(\frac{f(k)}{f_0}\right)^2 P_L(k) + P_{m,\theta\theta}^{\text{loop}}(k), \quad (59)$$

with

$$P_{b_1 b_2}(k) = \int_{\mathbf{k}_{12}=\mathbf{k}} F_2(\mathbf{k}_1,\mathbf{k}_2)P_L(\mathbf{k}_1)P_L(\mathbf{k}_2), \quad (60)$$

$$P_{b_1 b_{s^2}}(k) = \int_{\mathbf{k}_{12}=\mathbf{k}} F_2(\mathbf{k}_1,\mathbf{k}_2)S_2(\mathbf{k}_1,\mathbf{k}_2)P_L(\mathbf{k}_1)P_L(\mathbf{k}_2), \quad (61)$$

$$P_{b_2^2}(k) = \frac{1}{2}\int_{\mathbf{k}_{12}=\mathbf{k}} P_L(\mathbf{k}_1)\left[P_L(\mathbf{k}_2) - P_L(\mathbf{k}_1)\right], \quad (62)$$

$$P_{b_2 b_{s^2}}(k) = \frac{1}{2}\int_{\mathbf{k}_{12}=\mathbf{k}} P_L(\mathbf{k}_1)\left[P_L(\mathbf{k}_2)S_2(\mathbf{k}_1,\mathbf{k}_2) - \frac{2}{3}P_L(\mathbf{k}_1)\right], \quad (63)$$

$$P_{b_{s^2}^2}(k) = \frac{1}{2}\int_{\mathbf{k}_{12}=\mathbf{k}} P_L(\mathbf{k}_1)\left[P_L(\mathbf{k}_2)[S_2(\mathbf{k}_1,\mathbf{k}_2)]^2 - \frac{4}{9}P_L(\mathbf{k}_1)\right], \quad (64)$$

and

$$P_{b_2,\theta}(k) = \int_{\mathbf{k}_{12}=\mathbf{k}} G_2(\mathbf{k}_1,\mathbf{k}_2)P_L(\mathbf{k}_1)P_L(\mathbf{k}_2), \tag{65}$$

$$P_{b_{s^2},\theta}(k) = \int_{\mathbf{k}_{12}=\mathbf{k}} G_2(\mathbf{k}_1,\mathbf{k}_2)S_2(\mathbf{k}_1,\mathbf{k}_2)P_L(\mathbf{k}_1)P_L(\mathbf{k}_2), \tag{66}$$

with renormalized bias parameters

$$b_1 = c_\delta + \left[\frac{31}{24}c_{\delta^2}\mathcal{C}_{\delta^2} + \frac{1}{2}c_{\delta^3}\mathcal{C}_{\delta^3} + \frac{1}{3}c_{\delta s^2}\mathcal{C}_{\delta s^2} + \frac{68}{63}c_{s^2}\mathcal{C}_{s^2} - \frac{16}{63}c_{st}\mathcal{C}_{st}\right]\sigma^2, \tag{67}$$

with $\mathcal{C}_\mathcal{O}$ constants of order unity and they are required in cosmologies beyond EdS, as we have seen for $\mathcal{C}_{s^2}$ and $\mathcal{C}_{st}$. At 1-loop in the PS the rest of biasing parameters remain equal after renormalization: $b_2 = c_{\delta^2}$ and $b_{s^2} = c_{s^2}$.

7. Redshift space distortions in MG

We now introduce a model for RSD in alternative cosmologies. An object located at a comoving distance $\mathbf{x}$ is observed to be at an apparent position $\mathbf{s}$, such that the map between real and redshift space positions is given by the non-relativistic, longitudinal Doppler effect,

$$\mathbf{s} = \mathbf{x} + \mathbf{u}, \tag{68}$$

where $\mathbf{u}$ is given in terms of the divergence field $\mathbf{u}(\mathbf{k}) = if_0\hat{\mathbf{n}}\frac{\mathbf{k}\cdot\hat{\mathbf{n}}}{k^2}\theta(\mathbf{k})$.

Clearly, the map to redshift coordinates conserves the number of tracers, $[1+\delta_s(\mathbf{s})]d^3s = [1+\delta(\mathbf{x})]d^3x$, yielding

$$(2\pi)^3\delta_D(\mathbf{k}) + \delta_s(\mathbf{k}) = \int d^3x\big(1+\delta(\mathbf{x})\big)e^{-i\mathbf{k}\cdot(\mathbf{x}+\mathbf{u}(\mathbf{x}))}, \tag{69}$$

and the redshift-space PS becomes[17,18]

$$(2\pi)^3\delta_D(\mathbf{k}) + P_s(\mathbf{k}) = \int d^3x e^{-i\mathbf{k}\cdot\mathbf{x}}\Big[1+\mathcal{M}(\mathbf{J}=\mathbf{k},\mathbf{x})\Big], \tag{70}$$

with the velocity moments generating function

$$1 + \mathcal{M}(\mathbf{J},\mathbf{x}) = \big\langle\big(1+\delta(\mathbf{x}_1)\big)\big(1+\delta(\mathbf{x}_2)\big)e^{-i\mathbf{J}\cdot\Delta\mathbf{u}}\big\rangle, \tag{71}$$

where $\Delta\mathbf{u} = \mathbf{u}(\mathbf{x}_2) - \mathbf{u}(\mathbf{x}_1)$ and $\mathbf{x} = \mathbf{x}_2 - \mathbf{x}_1$. Function $\mathcal{M}$ (or its Fourier transform) plays a central role in RSD. Different expansion procedures of eq. (71) yield different approaches to RSD modeling, grouped in Vlah et al[18] as: direct Lagrangian, moment expansion, streaming model, and smoothing kernel. We will follow here the moment expansion (ME) approach, in which the exponential in the generating function is expanded and the moments are evaluated.

The m-th density weighted velocity field moment of the generating function is an m-rank tensor defined as[17,18]

$$\Xi^m_{i_1\cdots i_m}(\mathbf{x}) \equiv i^m \frac{\partial^m}{\partial J_{i_1}\cdots \partial J_{i_m}}\left[1+\mathcal{M}(\mathbf{J},\mathbf{x})\right]\bigg|_{\mathbf{J}=0} = \langle(1+\delta_1)(1+\delta_2)\Delta u_{i_1}\cdots \Delta u_{i_m}\rangle, \tag{72}$$

with $\delta_1 = \delta(\mathbf{x}_1)$ and $\delta_2 = \delta(\mathbf{x}_2)$. The PS in the moment expansion approach becomes

$$(2\pi)^3\delta_D(\mathbf{k}) + P_s(\mathbf{k}) = \sum_{m=0}^{\infty}\frac{(-i)^m}{m!}k_{i_1}\cdots k_{i_m}\tilde{\Xi}^m_{i_1\cdots i_m}(\mathbf{k}), \tag{73}$$

where the $\tilde{\Xi}^m_{i_1\cdots i_m}(\mathbf{k})$ are the Fourier moments of the generating function —the Fourier transforms of their configuration space counterparts, $\Xi^m_{i_1\cdots i_n}(\mathbf{x})$.

Now, to compute the moments we make the following ansatz:

$$P^m(k,\mu) \equiv \frac{(-i)^m}{m!}k_{i_1}\cdots k_{i_m}\tilde{\Xi}^m_{i_1\cdots i_m}(\mathbf{k}) = \sum_{n=0}^{m}\mu^{2n}f_0^m I_n^m(k), \tag{74}$$

such that the total PS in redshift coordinates (s) is

$$P_s^{\text{ME}}(k,\mu) = \sum_{m=0}^{\infty} P^m(k,\mu), \tag{75}$$

up to a Dirac delta function localized at $\mathbf{k}=0$. Whereas the first equality (definition) in eq. (74) depends on $\mathbf{k}$, implicitly on k and $\mu \equiv \hat{\mathbf{k}}\cdot\hat{\mathbf{n}}$, the second equality is an ansatz with explicit angular dependence as even powers of μ. This ansatz has been shown to work, at least for moments m = 0, ..., 4, in Aviles et al,[15] where the functions $I_n^m(k)$ are given for the momenta necessary to compute the 1-loop expansion.

8. Considering UV and IR modes

There are still two important ingredients before we have a final model: EFT counterterms and infrared (IR) resummation of modes.

- As it is known, UV modes need to be cut off in the integrals, since small scale modes are not properly captured in PT, so it will not otherwise render the correct dynamics. The EFT for large scale structure formalism, see for instance Baumann et al[19] and Hertzberg et al,[20] cuts-off the loop integrals, by directly smoothing the overdensity fields by an arbitrary scale, and introduces counterterms necessary to remove the cut-off dependence on the final expressions. In redshift space, the situation is more complex, because the counterterms not only model small scales, non-perturbative physics, but also the non-linear mathematical map between real space and redshift space densities, see various authors.[21–23] In our case, the final expression turns to:

$$P_s^{\text{EFT}}(k,\mu) = P_s^{\text{ME}}(k,\mu) + (\alpha_0 + \alpha_1\mu^2 + \cdots)k^2 P_L(k) + \tilde{c}(\mu k f_0)^4 P_s^K(k,\mu) + P_{\text{shot}}, \tag{76}$$

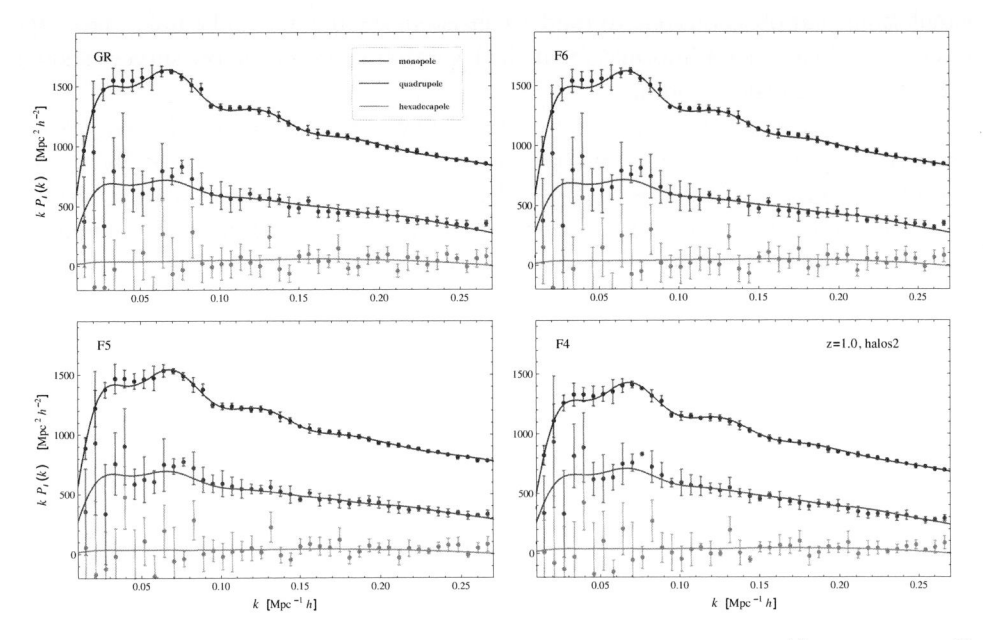

Fig. 5. Redshift-space power spectrum multipoles for halo catalogue 2 ($4.5 \times 10^{12} < M_h < 1 \times 10^{13}$ $M_\odot h^{-1}$) at redshift $z = 1$.

where the α_i stem from the nonlinear mathematical map between real space and redshift space densities and the $\tilde{c}$ from nonlinearities from the Fingers of God (FoG) that couple velocities and density fields. P_{shot} models the stochastic terms, uncorrelated with long wave-length fluctuations.

• Despite the success of SPT-EFT in modeling the broadband PS, the theory yet gives poor results in modeling the BAO since long-wavelength displacement fields, though being essentially linear, stream largely contributing to damp features in the PS in a manner that is non-perturbative under an SPT scheme. Then, in order to model the spread and degradation of the BAO oscillations due to large scale bulk flows, we employ IR-resummations[24] as implemented by Ivanov et al.[22,25]

The final result is a complete PS model for RSD that can be compared to dark matter halos or galaxies. In Fig. 5 we plot our analytical results against RSD multipoles for the HS n=1 model, extracted from **ELEPHANT** simulations,[1] with halo masses in the interval $4.5 \times 10^{12} < M_h < 1 \times 10^{13}$ $M_\odot h^{-1}$ evaluated at $z = 1$. These results show that theory renders precise results for wave modes as big as $k = 0.25$ h/Mpc.

9. Conclusions

In the last few years the PT for LSS has been developed to a point that most problems have been tackled, and it seems now ready to be feasibly compared against simulations and observations, to render consistent results and to be able to extract cosmological parameter information at the level that stage-IV galaxy surveys should provide, among other probes.

The present contribution presents some PT developments for models that possess an extra degree of freedom, that is, models of MG, dynamical dark energy, or considering massive neutrinos within LCDM.[26,27] We explained mainly our results, but, because of the limited space here, we did not provide a full list of references, however, this can be found in the our cited papers in the bibliography.

Acknowledgments

The authors acknowledge support by CONACyT project 283151.

References

1. M. Cautun, E. Paillas, Y.-C. Cai, S. Bose, J. Armijo, B. Li and N. Padilla, The Santiago–Harvard–Edinburgh–Durham void comparison – I. SHEDding light on chameleon gravity tests, *Mon. Not. Roy. Astron. Soc.* **476**, 3195 (2018).
2. K. Koyama, A. Taruya and T. Hiramatsu, Non-linear Evolution of Matter Power Spectrum in Modified Theory of Gravity, *Phys. Rev. D* **79**, p. 123512 (2009).
3. A. Aviles and J. L. Cervantes-Cota, Lagrangian perturbation theory for modified gravity, *Phys. Rev. D* **96**, p. 123526 (2017).
4. A. Aviles, M. A. Rodriguez-Meza, J. De-Santiago and J. L. Cervantes-Cota, Nonlinear evolution of initially biased tracers in modified gravity, *JCAP* **11**, p. 013 (2018).
5. G. Valogiannis and R. Bean, Convolution Lagrangian perturbation theory for biased tracers beyond general relativity, *Phys. Rev. D* **99**, p. 063526 (2019).
6. G. Valogiannis, R. Bean and A. Aviles, An accurate perturbative approach to redshift space clustering of biased tracers in modified gravity, *JCAP* **01**, p. 055 (2020).
7. A. Aviles, J. L. Cervantes-Cota and D. F. Mota, Screenings in Modified Gravity: A perturbative approach, *Astron. Astrophys.* **622**, p. A62 (2019).
8. A. Aghamousa *et al.*, The DESI Experiment Part I: Science,Targeting, and Survey Design (10 2016).
9. L. Amendola *et al.*, Cosmology and fundamental physics with the Euclid satellite, *Living Rev. Rel.* **21**, p. 2 (2018).
10. A. Abate *et al.*, Large Synoptic Survey Telescope: Dark Energy Science Collaboration (11 2012).
11. S. Alam *et al.*, Testing the theory of gravity with DESI: Estimators, predictions and simulation requirements (11 2020).
12. P. Brax and P. Valageas, Impact on the power spectrum of Screening in Modified Gravity Scenarios, *Phys. Rev.* **D88**, p. 023527 (2013).
13. K. Koyama, Cosmological Tests of Modified Gravity, *Rept. Prog. Phys.* **79**, p. 046902 (2016).
14. G. Hinshaw, D. Larson, E. Komatsu, D. N. Spergel, C. L. Bennett, J. Dunkley, M. R. Nolta, M. Halpern, R. S. Hill, N. Odegard, L. Page, K. M. Smith, J. L. Weiland, B. Gold, N. Jarosik, A. Kogut, M. Limon, S. S. Meyer, G. S. Tucker, E. Wollack and E. L. Wright, Nine-year Wilkinson Microwave Anisotropy Probe (WMAP) Observations: Cosmological Parameter Results, *APJS* **208**, p. 19 (October 2013).

15. A. Aviles, G. Valogiannis, M. A. Rodriguez-Meza, J. L. Cervantes-Cota, B. Li and R. Bean, Redshift space power spectrum beyond Einstein-de Sitter kernels, *JCAP* **04**, p. 039 (2021).
16. P. McDonald and A. Roy, Clustering of dark matter tracers: generalizing bias for the coming era of precision LSS, *JCAP* **08**, p. 020 (2009).
17. R. Scoccimarro, Redshift-space distortions, pairwise velocities and nonlinearities, *Phys. Rev. D* **70**, p. 083007 (2004).
18. Z. Vlah and M. White, Exploring redshift-space distortions in large-scale structure, *JCAP* **1903**, p. 007 (2019).
19. D. Baumann, A. Nicolis, L. Senatore and M. Zaldarriaga, Cosmological Non-Linearities as an Effective Fluid, *JCAP* **1207**, p. 051 (2012).
20. M. P. Hertzberg, Effective field theory of dark matter and structure formation: Semi-analytical results, *Phys. Rev. D* **89**, p. 043521 (2014).
21. A. Perko, L. Senatore, E. Jennings and R. H. Wechsler, Biased Tracers in Redshift Space in the EFT of Large-Scale Structure (10 2016).
22. M. M. Ivanov, M. Simonović and M. Zaldarriaga, Cosmological Parameters from the BOSS Galaxy Power Spectrum, *JCAP* **05**, p. 042 (2020).
23. S.-F. Chen, Z. Vlah and M. White, Consistent Modeling of Velocity Statistics and Redshift-Space Distortions in One-Loop Perturbation Theory, *JCAP* **07**, p. 062 (2020).
24. L. Senatore and M. Zaldarriaga, The IR-resummed Effective Field Theory of Large Scale Structures, *JCAP* **02**, p. 013 (2015).
25. M. M. Ivanov and S. Sibiryakov, Infrared Resummation for Biased Tracers in Redshift Space, *JCAP* **07**, p. 053 (2018).
26. A. Aviles and A. Banerjee, A Lagrangian Perturbation Theory in the presence of massive neutrinos, *JCAP* **10**, p. 034 (2020).
27. A. Aviles, A. Banerjee, G. Niz and Z. Slepian, Clustering in Massive Neutrino Cosmologies via Eulerian Perturbation Theory (6 2021).

Testing modified gravity theories with marked statistics

Alejandro Aviles

Consejo Nacional de Ciencia y Tecnología,
Av. Insurgentes Sur 1582, Colonia Crédito Constructor, Del. Benito Juárez, 03940,
Ciudad de México, México,
and
Departamento de Física, Instituto Nacional de Investigaciones Nucleares
Apartado Postal 18-1027, Col. Escandón, Ciudad de México,11801, México
E-mail: avilescervantes@gmail.com

In the last two decades, Modified Gravity (MG) models have been proposed to explain the accelerated expansion of the Universe. However, one of the main difficulties these theories face is that they must reduce to General Relativity (GR) at sufficiently high energy densities, such as those found in the solar system. To achieve this, MG theories typically employ so-called screening mechanisms: nonlinear effects that bring them to GR at the appropriate limits. For this reason, low-energy regions where the screenings do not operate efficiently, such as cosmic voids, are identified as ideal laboratories for testing GR. Hence, the use of *marked* statistics that up-weight low energy densities have been proposed for being implemented with data from future galaxy surveys. In this proceeding note, we show how to construct theoretical templates for such statistics and test their accuracy with the use of N-body simulations.

Keywords: Modified Gravity; Cosmic Large Scale Structure; Testing General Relativity.

1. Modified gravity in Cosmology: a very brief introduction

The standard model of Cosmology, the so-called ΛCDM, is the most successful theory to date for describing the large-scale behaviour of our Universe. The outstanding way this model fits the cosmic background radiation (CMB) anisotropies measurements from the Planck satellite[1]—and prior to that from the WMAP and COBE experiments—leaves small room for modifications of it. However, among other drawbacks in Cosmology, nowadays cosmic acceleration is still not well understood, and in models that modify the background history of the Universe at late times, the CMB differs mainly because the journey of photons from the last-scattering surface to us is affected. This is a secondary effect called the integrated Sachs-Wolfe effect and its influence over the CMB is mainly localized at small multipoles, where the error on measurements is nonetheless large because of the cosmic variance—the fact that we have only one universe and hence a small number of long wave-length modes to average over. Such a liberty has led to a lot of proposals (literally hundreds of them) as alternatives to the cosmological constant to explain the speeding up of the expansion of the Universe. Unfortunately, there is much more literature proposing new gravity models or that makes simple tests to them (the vast majority focusing only on the homogeneous and isotropic cosmology; I will come back to this in a moment), than literature that explore methods to probe the clustering due to gravity at cosmological scales. Of course, this is a highly unbalanced situation and observational cosmologists cannot test each of the proposed models. These alternatives can be categorized into two big branches: dark energy (DE) and Modified Gravity (MG); though, one should be careful since there is not a well defined boundary between them. In this proceedings note, we will focus on the latter assuming well defined, and to the particular case of chameleon fields[2,3] although the techniques described here have been applied to other kinds of theories.

Perhaps the most difficult aspect of modifying gravity is the following. Observations indicate that the *true* model of the universe should be close to ΛCDM, at least from the epoch of the primordial ("Big-Bang") Nucleosynthesis until now. In particular the expansion history should be close to that of ΛCDM, perhaps with small differences with the aim of, for example, resolving the Hubble tension.[4] However, as a rule of thumb, MG models that slightly depart from ΛCDM at the background level, become quite different at the perturbative level.[5,6] That is, two models that have almost the same expansion history, typically predict a completely different clustering. This is because in MG the two scalar gravitational potentials of the metric, thinking of in Newtonian gauge, are different even in the absence of anisotropic stresses, which makes GR a very special theory and not easy to mimic. This would mean that the gravitational potential appearing in the geodesic potential is not the same to the gravitational potential sourced by the energy density fields in the Poisson equation; and what is particularly important to this discussion is that the homogeneous and isotropic expansion is completely insensitive to this. For example, take a look at figure 1, where we show the power spectrum of matter density fluctuations in GR and in the F5 gravitational model (we will define what is F5 in appendix A). The F5 gravitational model is indistinguishable for any practical purpose from GR at the background level, but their predicted matter power spectra differ by a lot. This is the reason why it does not make too much sense to test MG models at the background level only, for example using supernovae data only. However, for the sake of fairness we must say there are exceptions to this rule, for example the recently proposed No-Slip gravity,[7] tailored with the specific purpose that the two scalar gravitational potentials become equal.

When gravity is modified, in particular in the infrared, one should be careful to not spoil the well-tested regimes of validity of GR, as for example in the solar system or regions with much larger densities,[a] but at the same time provide the accelerated expansion of the Universe. In order to deal with this unquestionable observational constriction, MG models often invoke mechanisms that yield the theory to GR in the appropriate limits. These are generically called *screening* mechanisms: non-linear effects that drive MG theories to GR when either the environmental energy

---

[a]It is perhaps surprising to consider the solar system a high energy density region, but it is very large compared to the mean background energy density $3H_0^2/8\pi G \sim 10^{-29}$ g/cm^3. The latter is the one that is important at the largest cosmological scales, and hence drives the background history of the Universe.

density is large, or there are large gravitational tidal fields, among other scenarios. The most popular is the *chameleon* mechanism,[2,3] in which a scalar field mediates a universal fifth force, but its mass depends on the environmental density where it resides: as larger is the ambient density, the lighter is the mass of the scalar field and smaller the range of the force. For example, in successful theories, and for human-like densities (~ 1 gram per cubic centimeter) the range of the fifth-force becomes so ridiculously small that it becomes effectively invisible to any experiment. On the other hand, at extremely low ambient densities the range of the fifth-force becomes quite large, with cosmological scope.

The most studied MG theory in Cosmology, one can affirm with high confidence, is the $f(R)$ gravity,[8–10] and in particular the Hu-Sawicki model.[11] Although, these theories were first understood as higher-order gravity theories, it was soon recognized that under a few assumptions they can be described as second order differential equations for the metric plus a scalar field[12,13] which propagates only an additional massive mode. In this proceeding note we will lead with the Hu-Sawicki model to exemplify our analytical results and to take advantage of the fact that we have good, *state-of-the-part* N-body simulations for them—the Extended LEnsing PHysics using ANalaytic ray Tracing `Elephant` cosmological suite of simulations.[14,15] Even though $f(R)$ is not a representative model of the vast universe of MG models (or more narrowly of Hordenski theories), the techniques reviewed here can be applied to different models and can be beneficial to study MG that rely on screening mechanisms. The material presented in this note is extracted mainly from Refs. 16–19; we refer the reader to these works for further details.

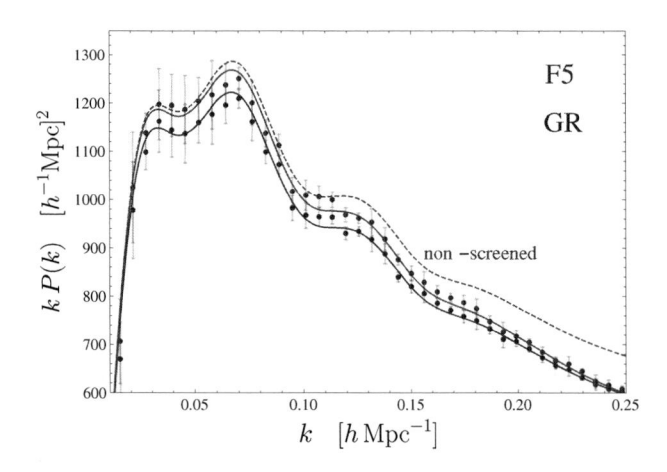

Fig. 1. Matter power spectrum in the models GR (blue line) and Hu-Sawicki F5 (red lines). The latter is further shown with and without screenings with solid and dashed lines, respectively. To generate this analytical results we use the Standard Perturbation Theory with effective field theory counterterms and infrared-resummations of Refs. 20, 21. The mock data is extracted from the `Elephant` simulations.

2. The importance of up-weight low energy density regions

In figure 1 we show the chameleon screening in action. The black line is the analytical power spectrum of the ΛCDM. The red coloured lines show the matter power spectrum in the Hu-Sawicki F5 model with screenings (solid line) and without screenings (dashed line), together with data from the `Elephant` simulations. We note the screening mechanism drives the theory to GR, more evident at small scales (high wave-numbers k), while without the screenings the differences between the two models are larger. This behaviour raises the question if the power spectrum, and its counterpart in configuration space, the correlation function, are the most clever way to test the gravitational theories from its cosmological clustering. After all, by construction these statistics give more weight to high density regions, since they sum over all tracers evenly (either particles, halos, galaxies...), and tracers tend to clump together by gravitational attraction. Meanwhile, cosmological voids are underrepresented by the power spectrum—as well as by the correlation function and their N-points generalizations—even though they are the largest regions in our universe, and as such, they contain a significant share of the total energy budget. But clumpy regions of space, being denser, behave very close to GR due to the screenings mechanism. Hence, the standard statistics used in Cosmology may not be the best option to test infrared modifications of GR.

With the above ideas in mind, M. White proposed in Ref. 16 to use *marked correlation functions*[b] to test gravity at cosmological scales. The proposal consists in weighting the tracer field density fluctuations with a function (the mark) whose value depends on the environmental density, such that objects residing in low density regions become up-weighted in 2-point statistics, while objects residing in high density become down-weighted. In this way, statistics of such marked density fields will probe low density regions where gravitational fifth-force screenings are inefficient and the effects of hypothetical MG theories would be more pronounced.

The construction of a marked density field $\delta_M(\mathbf{x}, t)$ is a three step process, depicted in figure 2. It goes as follows,

(1) One starts with the matter fluctuations field $\delta(\mathbf{x}, t)$ and convolve it with a window function $W_R(\mathbf{x})$ of width R (a Gaussian is used in this work) to obtain the smoothed density

$$\delta_R(\mathbf{x}, t) = \int d^3y \, W_R(|\mathbf{x} - \mathbf{y}|)\delta(\mathbf{y}, t). \tag{1}$$

The scale R is chosen from the beginning and it determines the size of the region which is used to define the environmental density of the tracers. In this sense,

---

[b]Marked statistics have a long history;[22] they have been used to assign properties to objects, such as the luminosity, color, and morphology of galaxies,[23,24] and to break degeneracies between Halo Occupation Distribution (HOD; a semi-analytical method to populate halos from N-body simulations with galaxies) and cosmologies.[25]

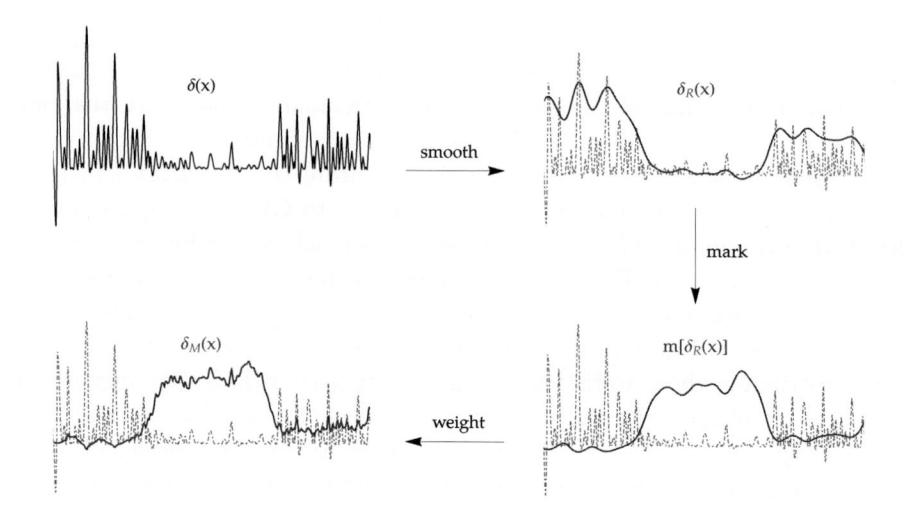

Fig. 2. 1-dimensional cartoon for the construction of the marked density field.

it is good to have sufficiently large values for R, typically comparable to, or a little bit smaller than, the size of cosmic voids. Here we use $R = 10\,h^{-1}\,\mathrm{Mpc}$.

(2) Construct the mark function $m(\delta_R(\mathbf{x}))$. We choose a function that decays with the environmental (or smoothed) density, such that low density regions are up-weighted, as required. For example, a simple exponential $m = \exp[-\alpha(1 + \delta_R(\mathbf{x}))]$ can do the job. However it is better to have more free parameters such that we have more liberty to find an optimal mark for a particular MG model. The most used weight is the White-mark[16]

$$m(\delta(\mathbf{x}), R) = \left(\frac{1+\delta_*}{1+\delta_* + \delta_R(\mathbf{x})}\right)^p, \qquad (2)$$

with $p > 0$ and $\delta_* > 0$ dimensional parameters. It was find with numerical simulations that the choices $p = 10$ and $\delta_* = 4$ maximize both the Fisher information and the signal-to-noise.[26] However, these parameters are not good for perturbative analysis, so we will use the parameters $p = 7$ and $\delta_* = 10$, unless otherwise is stated. Other authors working with simulations have used different parameters and mark functions.[18,26–28]

(3) Weight the density field of tracers $1 + \delta_X(\mathbf{x})$ with the mark function $m(\delta(\mathbf{x}), R)$ to obtain the marked density field

$$1 + \delta_M(\mathbf{x}, t) = \big(1 + \delta_X(\mathbf{x}, t)\big) m[\delta_R(\mathbf{x})]. \qquad (3)$$

The density field can be that of any tracer of the underlying matter density, it can even be the matter density field itself. But we observe tracers, as galaxies for example, in the sky. These are related through a biasing function F to the dark matter as

$$1 + \delta_X(\mathbf{x}) = F_\mathbf{x}[\delta(\mathbf{x}), \nabla^2\delta(\mathbf{x}), ...; \mathbf{x}] \tag{4}$$

where the stochasticity of this relation is emphasized by writing $\mathbf{x}$ as an additional argument. The dependence on the non-local curvature operator $\nabla^2\delta(\mathbf{x})$ is expected to be small in GR, but a well defined bias expansion within chameleon theories must contain higher-order derivative operators.[29,30]

3. Marked correlation function

A marked correlation function (mCF)[16,22–25,31,32] is defined as the sum of pairs of objects (i,j) separated by a distance r, and weighted by the ratio of the mark function value to the mean mark $m_i/\bar{m}$ at each point and divided by the number of pairs $n(r)$,

$$\mathcal{M}(r) = \sum_{i,j|r_{ij}=r} \frac{m_i m_j}{n(r)\bar{m}^2}, \tag{5}$$

so it quantifies the deviation of a pair of objects to have the mean mark $\bar{m}$ subjected to be located at a separation r. By construction it can be written as

$$\mathcal{M}(r) = \frac{1 + W(r)}{1 + \xi(r)} \tag{6}$$

where $\xi(r)$ is the standard 2-point correlation function of tracers

$$1 + \xi(r) = \left\langle \left(1 + \delta_X(\mathbf{x}+\mathbf{r})\right)\left(1 + \delta_X(\mathbf{x})\right) \right\rangle, \tag{7}$$

and $W(r)$ is the 2-point correlation function of marked fields:

$$1 + W(r) = \frac{1}{\bar{m}^2} \left\langle \left(1 + \delta_M(\mathbf{x}+\mathbf{r})\right)\left(1 + \delta_M(\mathbf{x})\right) \right\rangle. \tag{8}$$

At large scales both ξ and W are small and one gets

$$\mathcal{M}(r) = 1 + W(r) - \xi(r). \tag{9}$$

Now, one may show that $\xi(r) \in W(r)$,[17] hence the mark function becomes a 2-point statistic of the clustering of marks with the clustering of objects effectively factorized out. The presence of the mean mark is not necessary to estimate the mCF, but it plays an important role in the analytical renormalization of the theory.

4. Perturbative treatment of the marked correlation function

It is well known that a good modeling of N-point statistics of density fields in configuration space requires the use of Lagrangian Perturbation Theory (LPT),[33] since the spread and degradation of the BAO oscillations is due to large scale bulk flows, long wave-length Lagrangian displacement fields that are well described in the Lagrangian framework, even at the linear order.[34] However the derivation of the marked correlation function within the Lagrangian framework is quite large and technical, so we prefer to omit it in this note; the interested reader can find it in Ref. 17, and later on we will display the main results. However, in this section we develop the Standard Perturbation Theory (SPT) approach to the marked correlation function, which is easier, but yet shows the main ingredients and insights of the theory.

We start by expanding the mark in a power series of δ_R

$$m(\delta_R; C_i) = C_0 + C_1 \delta_R + \frac{1}{2} C_2 \delta_R^2 + \cdots \qquad (10)$$

with $C_i = m^{(i)}[0]$, the i-th derivative of $m[\delta_R]$ evaluated at $\delta_R = 0$. The fewer parameters are needed to model the mark, the better the convergence will be. We notice that $C_1 < 0$ enhances low density regions.

For the sake of simplicity we will assume a local relation between matter and tracer overdensities

$$1 + \delta_X(\mathbf{x}) = c_0 + c_1 \delta(\mathbf{x}) + \frac{c_2}{2} \delta^2(\mathbf{x}) + \cdots, \qquad (11)$$

with $c_i = \partial F_\mathbf{x}^{(i)}[\delta_R = 0]/\partial \delta_R$ the bare bias parameters and $F_\mathbf{x}$ given by eq. (4). A Taylor expansion is an unnatural and restrictive assumption for biased tracers, but being pragmatic we note that it works at the level of precision required by our simulations.

The mean mark is given by the mark weighted by the tracer density field

$$\bar{m} = \langle m[\delta_R(\mathbf{x})](1 + \delta_X(\mathbf{x})) \rangle$$
$$= \left\langle \left(C_0 + C_1 \delta_R(\mathbf{x}) + \frac{C_2}{2} \delta_R^2(\mathbf{x}) + \cdots \right) \left(c_0 + c_1 \delta(\mathbf{x}) + \frac{c_2}{2} \delta^2(\mathbf{x}) + \cdots \right) \right\rangle$$
$$= c_0 C_0 + c_1 C_1 \sigma_R^2 + \frac{1}{2} c_0 C_2 \sigma_{RR}^2 + \frac{1}{2} C_0 c_2 \sigma^2 + \cdots, \qquad (12)$$

with zero-lag correlators defined as

$$\sigma^2 \equiv \langle (\delta(0))^2 \rangle, \quad \sigma_R^2 \equiv \langle \delta_R(0)\delta(0) \rangle, \quad \sigma_{RR}^2 \equiv \langle (\delta_R(0))^2 \rangle. \qquad (13)$$

We will use also the correlation and cross-correlation functions

$$\xi(r) \equiv \langle \delta(\mathbf{x})\delta(\mathbf{x}+\mathbf{r}) \rangle, \qquad (14)$$
$$\xi_R(r) \equiv \langle \delta_R(\mathbf{x})\delta(\mathbf{x}+\mathbf{r}) \rangle, \qquad (15)$$
$$\xi_{RR}(r) \equiv \langle \delta_R(\mathbf{x})\delta_R(\mathbf{x}+\mathbf{r}) \rangle. \qquad (16)$$

We have to write eq. (12) in terms of renormalized bias parameters,[35]

$$b_n^E = \int \frac{d\lambda}{2\pi} e^{-\lambda^2 \sigma^2/2} \tilde{F}_{\mathbf{x}}(\lambda)(i\lambda)^n, \qquad (17)$$

where $\tilde{F}_{\mathbf{x}}(\lambda)$ is the Fourier transform of $F_{\mathbf{x}}$ with spectral parameter λ (dual to δ). We are using the label "E" to distinguish Eulerian from Lagrangian biases. Equation (17) leads to the relation between bare bias c_n and renormalized bias b_n^E parameters:[36, 37]

$$b_n^E = \sum_{k=0}^{\infty} \frac{\sigma^{2k}}{2^k k!} c_{n+2k}. \qquad (18)$$

Analogously, we introduce the "resummed" expansion parameters B_n as

$$B_n = \frac{B_n^*}{B_0^*} \quad \text{with} \quad B_n^* = \int \frac{d\Lambda}{2\pi} e^{-\Lambda^2 \sigma_{RR}^2/2} \tilde{m}(\Lambda)(i\Lambda)^n, \qquad (19)$$

where $\tilde{m}(\Lambda)$ is the Fourier transform of $m(\delta_R)$, and Λ is a spectral parameter, dual to δ_R. One easily finds[17] the following relation between the expansion parameters B_n and the Taylor coefficients of the mark function C_n

$$B_n(C_n, \sigma_{RR}^2) = \frac{\sum_{k=0}^{\infty} C_{n+2k} \sigma_{RR}^{2k}/(2^k k!)}{\sum_{k=0}^{\infty} C_{2k} \sigma_{RR}^{2k}/(2^k k!)}. \qquad (20)$$

Inserting the b_n^E and B_n parameters in eq. (12) we get

$$\bar{m} = B_0^* \left[1 + b_1^E B_1 \sigma_R^2 + \cdots\right]. \qquad (21)$$

We compute now

$$\bar{m}^2(1 + W(r)) = \langle m[\delta_R(\mathbf{x}_1)](1 + \delta_X(\mathbf{x}_1))m[\delta_R(\mathbf{x}_2)](1 + \delta_X(\mathbf{x}_2))\rangle$$

$$= \int \frac{d\lambda_1 d\lambda_2 d\Lambda_1 d\Lambda_2}{(2\pi)^4} \langle e^{i(\lambda_1 \delta_1 + \Lambda_1 \delta_{R,1} + \lambda_2 \delta_2 + \Lambda_2 \delta_{R,2})}\rangle \tilde{F}_{\mathbf{x}}(\lambda_1)\tilde{F}_{\mathbf{x}}(\lambda_2)\tilde{m}(\Lambda_1)\tilde{m}(\Lambda_2)$$

$$= \int \frac{d\lambda_1 d\lambda_2 d\Lambda_1 d\Lambda_2}{(2\pi)^4} \tilde{F}_{\mathbf{x}}(\lambda_1)\tilde{F}_{\mathbf{x}}(\lambda_2)\tilde{m}(\Lambda_1)\tilde{m}(\Lambda_2) e^{-\frac{1}{2}(\lambda_1^2 + \lambda_2^2)\sigma^2 - \frac{1}{2}(\Lambda_1^2 + \Lambda_2^2)\sigma_{RR}^2}$$

$$\times \left[1 - (\lambda_1 \Lambda_1 + \lambda_2 \Lambda_2)\sigma_R^2 - \lambda_1 \lambda_2 \xi(r) - \Lambda_1 \Lambda_2 \xi_{RR}(r) - (\lambda_1 \Lambda_2 + \lambda_2 \Lambda_1)\xi_R(r) + \cdots\right]$$

$$= \bar{m}^2 \left[1 + (b_1^E)^2 \xi(r) + B_1^2 \xi_{RR}(r) + 2b_1^E B_1 \xi_R(r) + \cdots\right], \qquad (22)$$

where the ellipsis denotes second order terms in $\xi_{,R,RR}(r)$. In the second equality, we have shifted to Fourier space ($\delta \to \lambda$, $\delta_R \to \Lambda$) and in the third equality we used the cumulant expansion theorem,

$$\langle e^{iX}\rangle = \exp\left[\sum_{N=1}^{\infty} \frac{i^N}{N!}\langle X^N\rangle_c\right], \qquad (23)$$

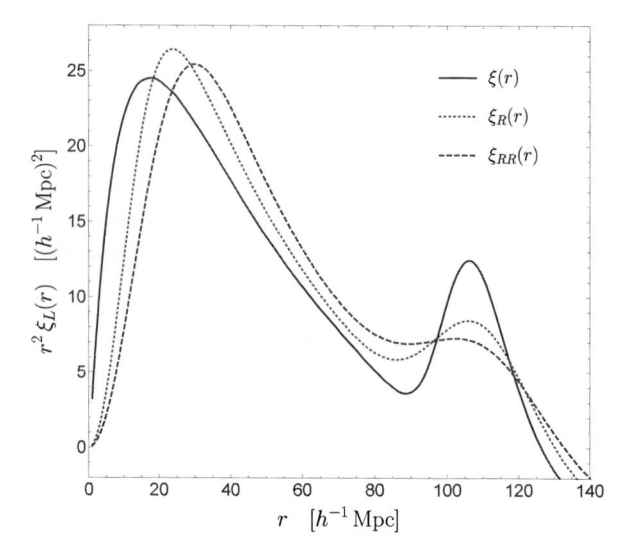

Fig. 3. Smoothed correlation functions defined in defined in eqs. (14)-(16) and appearing in the Eulerian marked correlation function [Eq. (24)]. We use a Gaussian damping kernel W_R of width $R = 10\,h^{-1}$Mpc to smooth the density fields.

and expanded out of the exponential all terms but those containing σ^2 and σ^2_{RR}, such that we can use Eqs. (17) and (19) to get biases from spectral parameters, as we did in the last equality. The mCF becomes

$$\mathcal{M}^E(r) = \frac{1+W(r)}{1+\xi_X(r)} = \frac{1+(b_1^E)^2\xi(r) + B_1^2\xi_{RR}(r) + 2b_1^E B_1 \xi_R(r) + \cdots}{1+(b_1^E)^2\xi(r) + \cdots}. \quad (24)$$

In figure 3 we show the correlation functions defined in eqs. (14)-(16) and used to construct the above mCF. We use a Gaussian smoothing kernel W_R with width $R = 10\,h^{-1}$Mpc.

We notice that the zero-lag correlators σ^2 and σ^2_{RR} do not appear in the mCF as is guaranteed because we are using renormalized b and B parameters. Meanwhile, the cross-covariance σ^2_R is canceled out by the mean mark squared appearing in the definition of the mCF in eq. (5). We remark that a process of renormalization of the Taylor expansion coefficients C is not strictly necessary because the scale R is physical, and chosen from the beginning by the observer to mark the tracers, so there is no impediment for σ^2_{RR} to appear in the final expressions. However, the use of parameters B instead of the Taylor coefficients leads to simpler final equations. Furthermore, in real applications, we have to use a mark computed by the number density of galaxies. Another advantage of using the renormalized B parameters is that the effect of this reassignment can be included simply by re-scaling the B parameters. For the application to dark matter halos and galaxies, one should treat them as free parameters and fit them with simulations.

5. Lagrangian space

In Lagrangian space one considers regions of space, at an initial early time with spatial coordinates $\mathbf{q}$. We relate matter and tracers overdensities, in an analogous way to eq. (4), by

$$1 + \delta_X(\mathbf{q}) = F[\delta(\mathbf{q})], \quad (25)$$

with the difference that the overdensity fields are taken at an initial early time.[c] Assuming number conservation of tracers, $(1 + \delta_X(\mathbf{x}))d^3x = (1 + \delta_X(\mathbf{q}))d^3q$, one can relate the function $F_\mathbf{x}$, introduced in eq. (4), and F through

$$F_\mathbf{x}[\delta(\mathbf{x})] = \int \frac{d^3k}{(2\pi)^3} \int d^3q \, e^{i\mathbf{k}\cdot(\mathbf{x}-\mathbf{q})} \int \frac{d\lambda}{2\pi} \tilde{F}(\lambda) e^{i\lambda\delta(\mathbf{q}) - i\mathbf{k}\cdot\mathbf{\Psi}(\mathbf{q},t)}, \quad (26)$$

with $\mathbf{\Psi}(\mathbf{q})$ the Lagrangian displacement vector, that maps Lagrangian coordinates $\mathbf{q}$ to Eulerian coordinates $\mathbf{x}$ as $\mathbf{x}(\mathbf{q},t) = \mathbf{q} + \mathbf{\Psi}(\mathbf{q},t)$. Equivalently to eq. (17), we introduce the renormalized Lagrangian local biases[35] with

$$b_n = \int \frac{d\lambda}{2\pi} e^{-\lambda^2 \sigma^2/2} \tilde{F}(\lambda)(i\lambda)^n. \quad (27)$$

The next step is to evolve initially biased tracers with overdensity $\delta_X(\mathbf{q})$ using Convolution Lagrangian perturbation theory[38,39] and thereafter assign them a mark $m[\delta_R(\mathbf{x})]$ at the moment of observation. The use of the Lagrangian approach has some advantages with respect to the Eulerian. In the first place it is well known that the two-point correlation function is poorly modeled within the Eulerian approach, particularly at the BAO peak position; second, the (renormalized) Lagrangian bias parameters are obtained through the peak background split prescription,[40–43] and hence are physically appealing. But the price to pay is that the mCF is cumbersome to compute, since it becomes a double Gaussian convolution:[17]

$$1 + W(r) = \int \frac{d^3q \, e^{-\frac{1}{2}(\mathbf{r}-\mathbf{q})^T \mathbf{A}^{-1}(\mathbf{r}-\mathbf{q})}}{(2\pi)^{3/2} |\mathbf{A}|^{1/2}} \int \frac{d^3Q \, e^{-\frac{1}{2}(\mathbf{R}-\mathbf{Q})^T \mathbf{C}^{-1}(\mathbf{R}-\mathbf{Q})}}{(2\pi)^{3/2} |\mathbf{C}|^{1/2}} \quad (28)$$

$$\times \left(1 + \mathcal{I}^0(\mathbf{r},\mathbf{q},\mathbf{R},\mathbf{Q}; b_i, B_i)\right), \quad (29)$$

with $\mathcal{I}^0$ a function, whose expression is quite large and not very illuminating, and contains the information of the mark (through the expansion parameters B_i) and of the tracers (through the bias parameters b_i). It can be found in eq. (B.8) of Ref. 17. The matrices $\mathbf{A}$ and $\mathbf{C}$ are given by

$$A_{ij}(\mathbf{q}) = 2\int \frac{d^3p}{(2\pi)^3} \left(1 - e^{i\mathbf{p}\cdot\mathbf{q}}\right) \frac{p_i p_j}{p^4} P_L(p), \quad (30)$$

---

[c]This initial time is taken early enough that all scales of interest are still in the linear regime and one can safely take $\delta(\mathbf{q}) \ll 1$, but late enough that the background universe is already in the Einstein-de Sitter phase.

and

$$C_{ij}(\mathbf{q}) = -\frac{1}{4}A_{ij}(\mathbf{q}) + \frac{1}{6\pi^2}\int_0^\infty P_L(p)dp\,\delta_{ij}, \qquad (31)$$

with $P_L(p)$ the linear matter power spectrum. We notice that if $1+\mathcal{I}$ is not a function of $\mathbf{Q}$, it can be pulled out of the $\mathbf{Q}$ integral and due to that C_{ij} depends only on $\mathbf{q}$, the integration over $\mathbf{Q}$ gives 1. This is the case of the "standard" correlation function in Convolution Lagrangian Perturbation Theory (CLPT),[38] reducing the double Gaussian convolution in eq. (28), to a single three-dimensional convolution.

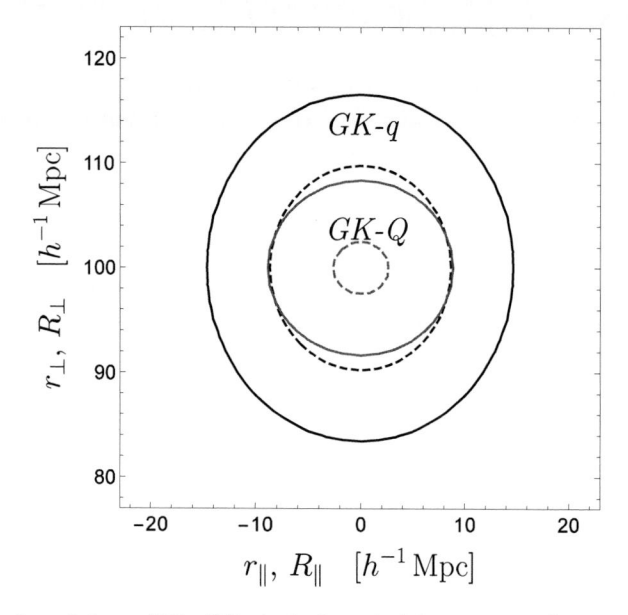

Fig. 4. Gaussian kernels in eq. (28). $GK\text{-}q$ is the kernel of the q-integral (black curves) and $GK\text{-}Q$ the kernel of the Q-integral (red curves). Dashed and solid curves show the regions that enclose the 68% and 95% of the volume respectively. A similar plot can be found in Ref. 44. Figure adapted from Ref. 17.

In figure 4 we show level plots for the Gaussian kernels appearing in eq. (28). $GK\text{-}q$ is the kernel of the q-integral and $GK\text{-}Q$ the kernel of the Q-integral. These are shown as a function of $r_\parallel$ ($R_\parallel$) and $r_\perp$ ($R_\perp$), the components of $\mathbf{r}$ ($\mathbf{R}$) parallel and perpendicular to the Lagrangian coordinate $\mathbf{q}$ ($\mathbf{Q}$) with $Q = q = 100\,h^{-1}\,\text{Mpc}$ fixed. To have a sense of the meaning of this plot, consider that the kernel $GK\text{-}q$ is the probability distribution of finding two dark matter particles separated by a distance $\mathbf{r}$ at the redshift of evaluation ($z = 0.5$ in the plot), given that they were separated by a distance $\mathbf{q}$ at the early initial time.[44] We notice that both kernels have their maximum value at $Q = q = 100\,h^{-1}\,\text{Mpc}$, but the $GK\text{-}Q$ is more sharply peaked because $|\mathbf{C}| < |\mathbf{A}_L|$. This observation suggests to approximate

$$\frac{e^{-\frac{1}{2}(\mathbf{R}-\mathbf{Q})^T\mathbf{C}^{-1}(\mathbf{R}-\mathbf{Q})}}{(2\pi)^{3/2}|\mathbf{C}|^{1/2}} \approx \delta_D(\mathbf{R}-\mathbf{Q}). \tag{32}$$

By doing so, one arrives at

$$1 + W^{W16}(r) = \int \frac{d^3q}{(2\pi)^{3/2}|A_L|^{1/2}} e^{-\frac{1}{2}(\mathbf{r}-\mathbf{q})^T A_L^{-1}(\mathbf{r}-\mathbf{q})} \left(1 + J^0(\mathbf{q},\mathbf{r};b_i,B_i)\right) \tag{33}$$

which is the generalization of the Zeldovich approximation (ZA) result obtained in Ref. 16. The expression for $J^0(\mathbf{q},\mathbf{r};b_i,B_i)$ is given by eq. (4.18) of Ref. 17.

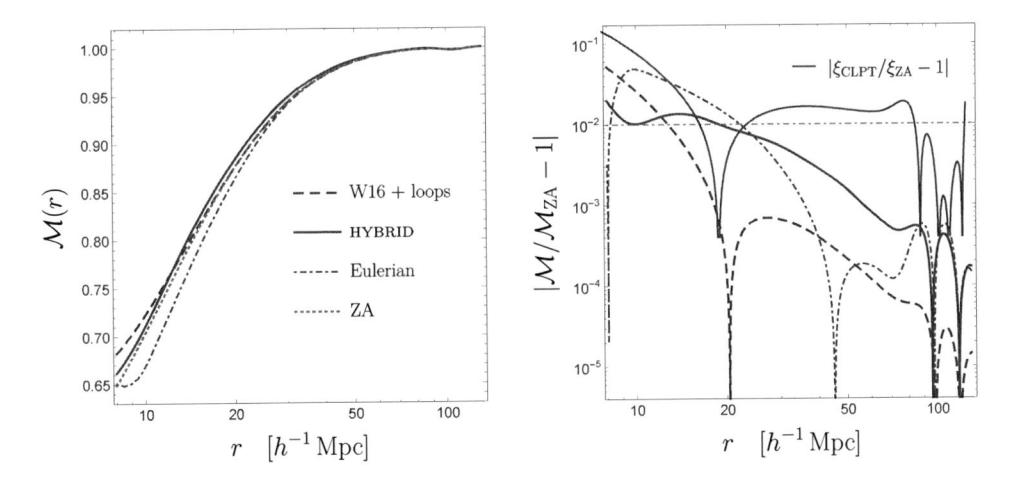

Fig. 5. Marked correlation function modeling comparison. The left panel shows the mCF with parameters $b_1 = 1.2$, $b_2 = 0.2$, $B_1 = -0.7$, $B_2 = B_1^2$, for the different methods: solid red curve is the HYBRID model presented in Ref. 17; dashed blue the method of Eq. (33), which is the method introduced in Ref. 16, plus 1-loop nonlinear contributions; in dotted gray, the ZA; and in dot-dashed green, the Eulerian linear model of eq. (24). The right panel shows the relative differences with respect to the ZA. The gray dot-dashed horizontal line denotes the 1% differences. The solid black curve in the right panel shows the relative differences between the CLPT 1-loop and ZA standard correlation functions. Figure adapted from Ref. 17.

Figure 5 shows the mCF using different analytical methods for the MG Hu-Sawicki F5 model: solid red curve is the one presented above and developed in Ref. 17—called HYBRID from now on, because it evolves the tracers using LPT but marks the tracers using the Eulerian smoothed matter overdensity fields at the moment of observation. The dashed blue is the method of eq. (33), which is that introduced in Ref. 16 with the addition of leading non-linear (loop) corrections; in dotted gray, the Zeldovich Approximation, which in this work means the linear model of Ref. 16; and, in dotdashed green, the Eulerian linear model of eq. (24).

We are using Lagrangian local biases $b_1 = 1.2$ and $b_2 = 0.2$, and mark parameters $B_1 = -0.7$, $B_2 = B_1^2$. In the right panel we show the relative difference between the models and the ZA. The agreement between them is very good, even for the linear Eulerian theory, below 1% for scales above $\sim 20\, h^{-1}$ Mpc. The relative differences between the CLPT standard correlation function with and without loop contributions (ξ_{CLPT} and ξ_{ZA}, respectively) is shown in the right panel (black curve); by comparing it with the dashed blue curve (which shows the relative differences of the W16+1-loop and ZA mCFs) we confirm that mCFs which efficiently enhance low density regions in the sky are indeed more linear than the standard correlation function.

6. Comparison to simulations

We use the `Elephant` suite of simulations run with the `ECOSMOG` code.[14] This suite contains five realisations of the initial conditions and for each realisation we have one simulation of ΛCDM (GR) together with three simulations of the Hu-Sawicki $f(R)$ model with parameters $f_{R0} = -10^{-4}$ (F4), $f_{R0} = -10^{-5}$ (F5) and $f_{R0} = -10^{-6}$ (F6). It also contains galaxy mock catalogs that were made with a Halo Occupation Distribution (HOD) method. The HOD parameters for the ΛCDM model are the best-fit parameter values from the CMASS data.[45] For the $f(R)$ models, we tune the HOD parameters so that we reproduce the correlation function in the ΛCDM model. The simulations were ran in a box of size $L = 1024\, h^{-1}$ Mpc with $N = 1024^3$ particles and the cosmological parameters used to make the initial conditions were $\Omega_b = 0.046$, $\Omega_\Lambda = 0.719$, $\Omega_m = 0.281$, $h = 0.697$, $\sigma_8 = 0.82$ and $n_s = 0.971$, and for our analysis we choose snapshots at redshift $z = 0.5$. To compute the mark for each of our tracers (dark matter particles, halos or mock galaxies) we binned the particles/halos/mock galaxies to a grid with gridsize of $20\, h^{-1}$ Mpc (corresponding to a $N = 52^3$ grid) using a Nearest Grid Point assignment scheme to get an estimate for the density for which the mark depends on.

Both, the standard and weighted 2-point correlation functions were computed using the Correlation Utilities and Two-point Estimates (CUTE)[46] code.[d] From this the marked correlation function follows simply as $\mathcal{M}(r) = (1 + W(r))/(1 + \xi(r))$.

We consider the White-mark with $\rho_* = 10$, $p = 7$, corresponding to coefficients $C_0 = 1$, $C_1 = -0.64$, $C_2 = 0.46$ in the Taylor expansion of the mark function in eq. (10). In our analytical models we smooth the matter fields that assign the mark with a top-hat filter W_R of radius $R = 10\, h^{-1}$ Mpc.

We first confront different analytical methods against matter data, since in this case the mCF does not suffer from biasing-marking degeneracies and we can observe more neatly the effects of the weights. The expansion parameters B are obtained from eq. (20): $B_1^{\text{GR}} = -0.6495$, $B_1^{\text{F6}} = -0.6497$, $B_1^{\text{F5}} = -0.6505$, $B_1^{\text{F4}} = -0.6522$,

---

[d]https://github.com/damonge/CUTE

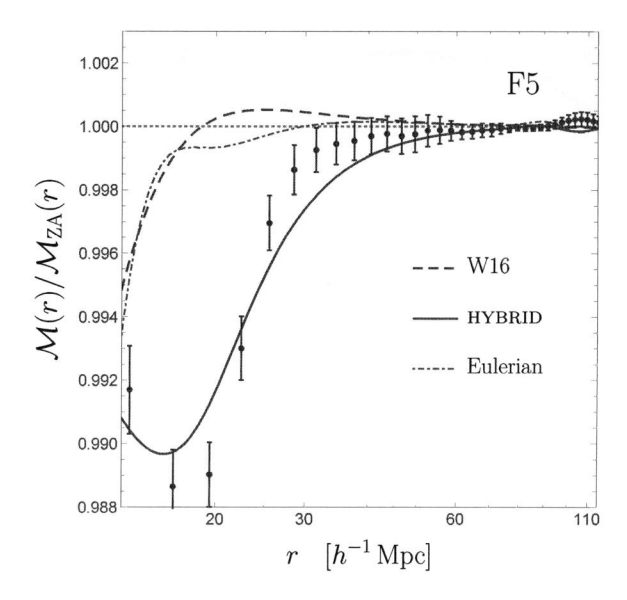

Fig. 6. Ratios of different mCFs analytical models to the ZA mCF for the F5 gravity (we obtain similar results for F4, F6 and GR). We show the W16 model plus 1-loop corrections (dashed blue); the HYBRID model (solid red); and the linear Eulerian model of eq. (24) (dot-dashed green). Figure adapted from Ref. 17.

$B_2^{GR} = 0.4628$, $B_2^{F6} = 0.4502$, $B_2^{F5} = 0.4495$, $B_2^{F4} = 0.4480$; which are numerically very close to C_1 and C_2 values because $C_0 = 1$ and the variances σ_{RR}^2 are small.

In figure 6 we show the ratios of the different analytical methods to the ZA model. We do it for the Hu-Sawicki F5 gravity model, and we have checked also the gravity theories GR, F4 and F6, and obtained similar results. The dashed blue curve shows the analytical result with the W16 model plus 1-loop corrections; solid red, the HYBRID method; and dot-dashed green, the linear Eulerian model of eq. (24). The differences between the analytical methods are apparent but small, being lesser than the 1%. At scales $r > 40\,h^{-1}\,\text{Mpc}$, all analytic models are indistinguishable and they are within the errors of the simulation data. At smaller scales, the method HYBRID outperforms the other perturbative approaches and captures reasonably the trend of the data all the way up to the smoothing scale $R = 10\,h^{-1}\,\text{Mpc}$.

Finally, in figure 7 we use the HYBRID model to fit the data for halos and galaxies (HOD), finding very good agreement between simulations and theory for $r > 30\,h^{-1}\,\text{Mpc}$. In the left panel we show that the MG models are differentiated by the data and the analytical curves in the interval $30 < r < 50\,h^{-1}\,\text{Mpc}$, with the exception of the F5 and F6 models, which become indistinguishable within the error bars. However, we notice that the HOD mCFs for the different MG models do not look differently enough to be distinguished by our data. We think that the use of different parameters δ_* and p or different mark functions can help to discern between different gravitational patterns; see, for example, Ref. 18.

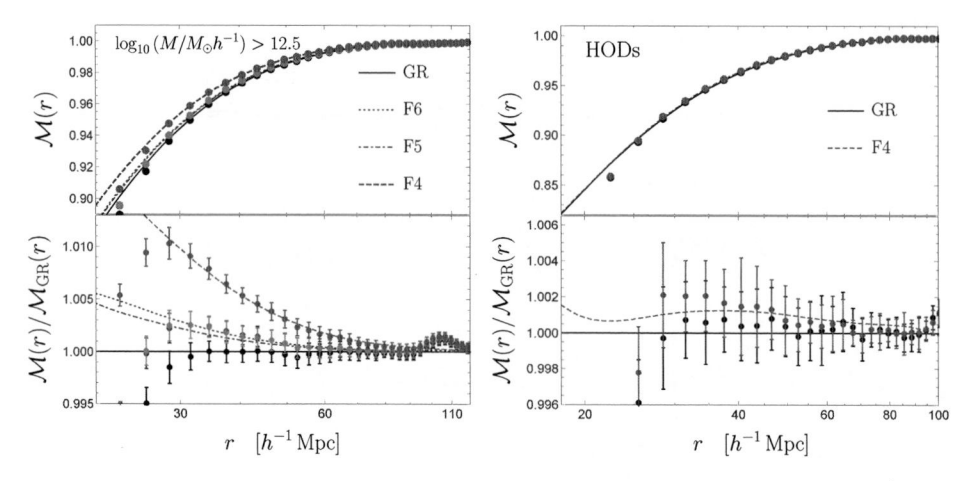

Fig. 7. Halos and galaxies mCFs. Left panel is for halo masses $12.5 < \log_{10}[M/(M_\odot h^{-1})] < 15$ and gravitational models F4, F5, F6 and GR. Right panel is for HOD and shows only the F4 and GR models. The linear local biases are fitted by using the ZA correlation function. Figure adapted from Ref. 17.

7. Marked power spectrum

Recently, it was discovered that the marked statistics can be very useful for the estimation of cosmological parameters, particularly the mass scale of the primordial neutrinos.[47] The reason is that given the large velocity dispersion of neutrinos, they do not contribute to the small scale clustering (see, e.g. Ref. 48). But instead, they free-stream over large distances, allowing them to populate the cosmic voids considerably. On the other hand, the influence of neutrinos on high density regions, for example halos, is quite marginal because their contribution to the total matter density is very small. Thus, statistics that up-weight low density regions can be very beneficial for parameter estimation. In fact, the Fisher formalism results are quite impressive: the marked power spectrum of the matter field outperforms the constraining power of the standard power spectrum by at least a factor of 2 on all cosmological parameters, and in particular of up to 80 times for the sum of the neutrino masses, when a combination of two different mark functions is used.

The analytical description of the marked power spectrum has been studied in detail in a couple of recent works. First, for matter in real space[49] and later for tracers in redshift space.[19] The main complication of such studies is that the mark parameters optimal for improving the cosmological parameter estimation are not able for a perturbative treatment, and the linear theory fails at all scales. The large-scale theory contains non-negligible contributions from all perturbative orders; in Ref. 19 a reorganization of the theory that contains all terms relevant on large-scales is proposed, with an explicit form at one-loop and the following structure at infinite-loop:

$$\mathcal{M}(k,\mu) = \left[C_0 - C_1 W_R(k)\right]\left[(\tilde{a}_0 + \tilde{a}_2\mu^2)P_L(k) + \tilde{b}_0\right] + \text{EFT} + \text{shot noise}$$

with $\tilde{a}_0$, $\tilde{a}_2$ and $\tilde{b}_0$ free parameters of the theory. EFT refers to the standard 1-loop corrections to the linear power spectrum and the effective field theory terms, while the shot noise includes the stochastic contributions.

8. Summary

We have reviewed the analytical study of marked statistics that up-weight low density regions in the Universe.[16–19] The idea behind marked statistics is to assign a value (the mark) to each entity in a catalogue and perform statistics over the resulting weighted objects. An efficient way to suppress non-linearities is by choosing a mark that gives more weight to objects that reside in low density regions, which become less important as one consider higher density regions. This marking process can be particularly useful for testing general relativity with cosmological probes, since modified gravity models that provide cosmic acceleration, often rely on screening mechanisms to hide its range and strength on high density environments, and the screenings switch off in regions that are more depleted of matter, like cosmic voids. Therefore, the effects of an hypothetical MG are expected to be more pronounced in low density regions. It is then natural to search for such marked statistics, as proposed in Ref. 16. Further, these statistics can potentially improve the constraining power of all cosmological parameters, in particular the mass of the primordial neutrinos, as it was shown in Ref. 47.

Acknowledgments

I want to thank Alfredo Macias and Carlos Herdeiro for inviting me to give a talk in the BS1 parallel session "Scalar fields in Cosmology" of the Sixteenth Marcel Grossmann Meeting – MG16, July 5-10 2021. I also want to thank Jorge L. Cervantes-Cota, Baojiu Li, Kazuya Koyama, Hans Winther, Elisa Massara, Oliver Philcox and Martin White for their collaboration in developing the material that led to this work. I acknowledge support by CONACyT project 283151 and CONACyT Ciencia de Frontera grant No. 102958. I would like to thank the DiRAC Data Centric system at Durham University (www.dirac.ac.uk) for computational facilities.

Appendix A. Hu-Sawicki MG model

The Hu-Sawicki model[11] is a particular realisation of $f(R)$ gravity that is able to evade the strong constraints coming from local test of gravity and still give rise to interesting observable signatures on cosmological scales. $f(R)$ theories consist on replace the Einstein-Hilbert Lagrangian density $\sqrt{-g}R$ by a general function of the Ricci scalar $\sqrt{-g}(R + f(R))$; see Ref. 50 for a review. The Hu-Sawicki model is defined by the function

$$f(R) = -M^2 \frac{c_1(R/M^2)^n}{c_2(R/M^2)^n + 1} \qquad (A.1)$$

where the energy scale is chosen to be $M^2 = \Omega_m H_0^2$. In this parametrized model, at high curvature ($R \ll M^2$) the function $f(R)$ approaches a constant, recovering GR with cosmological constant, while at low curvature it goes to zero, recovering GR; the manner these two behaviors are interpolated is dictated by the free parameters. Given that $d^2 f(R)/dR^2 > 0$ for $R > M^2$, the solutions are stable and the scalar tensor gravity description is possible.[12] In order to be have a similar background evolution than the ΛCDM model it is also necessary that $c_1/c_2 = 6\Omega_\Lambda/\Omega_m$, thus leaving two parameters to fix the model. One choose these parameters to be n and $f_{R0} \equiv df(R)/dR|_{R=R_0}$, with $R_0 = 3H_0^2(\Omega_m + 4\Omega_\Lambda)$ the Ricci scalar of the background cosmological metric evaluated nowadays.

In this work we have considered a fixed value $n = 1$, and hence the model has only one free parameter f_{R0}. Taking this parameter to zero we recover GR. The three choices for the parameters we are considering in this paper (F4, F5 and F6) are such that they lie in the region around where the best constraints lie today. The F4 model corresponds to $|f_{R0}| = 10^{-4}$ (is in tension with local experiments), the F5 model to $|f_{R0}| = 10^{-5}$ (agrees with most experiments and observations, but are in tension with others) and the F6 model to $|f_{R0}| = 10^{-6}$ (which is still allowed). All these models are completely compatible with observations of the expansion history of the Universe, but present large deviations from the ΛCDM in the clustering and formation of structures.

References

1. N. Aghanim et al., Planck 2018 results. VI. Cosmological parameters (2018).
2. J. Khoury and A. Weltman, Chameleon fields: Awaiting surprises for tests of gravity in space, *Phys. Rev. Lett.* **93**, p. 171104 (2004).
3. J. Khoury and A. Weltman, Chameleon cosmology, *Phys. Rev.* **D69**, p. 044026 (2004).
4. L. Verde, T. Treu and A. G. Riess, Tensions between the Early and the Late Universe, *Nature Astron.* **3**, p. 891 (7 2019).
5. E. Bertschinger, On the Growth of Perturbations as a Test of Dark Energy, *Astrophys. J.* **648**, 797 (2006).
6. E. Bertschinger and P. Zukin, Distinguishing Modified Gravity from Dark Energy, *Phys. Rev.* **D78**, p. 024015 (2008).
7. E. V. Linder, No Slip Gravity, *JCAP* **03**, p. 005 (2018).
8. A. A. Starobinsky, A New Type of Isotropic Cosmological Models Without Singularity, *Phys. Lett.* B **91**, 99 (1980).
9. S. M. Carroll, V. Duvvuri, M. Trodden and M. S. Turner, Is cosmic speed - up due to new gravitational physics?, *Phys. Rev.* **D70**, p. 043528 (2004).
10. S. Capozziello, Curvature quintessence, *Int. J. Mod. Phys.* **D11**, 483 (2002).
11. W. Hu and I. Sawicki, Models of f(R) Cosmic Acceleration that Evade Solar-System Tests, *Phys. Rev.* **D76**, p. 064004 (2007).

12. G. Magnano and L. M. Sokolowski, On physical equivalence between nonlinear gravity theories and a general relativistic selfgravitating scalar field, *Phys. Rev. D* **50**, 5039 (1994).
13. L. G. Jaime, L. Patino and M. Salgado, Robust approach to f(R) gravity, *Phys. Rev. D* **83**, p. 024039 (2011).
14. B. Li, G.-B. Zhao, R. Teyssier and K. Koyama, ECOSMOG: an Efficient COde for Simulating MOdified Gravity, *JCAP* **2012**, p. 051 (Jan 2012).
15. M. Cautun, E. Paillas, Y.-C. Cai, S. Bose, J. Armijo, B. Li and N. Padilla, The Santiago–Harvard–Edinburgh–Durham void comparison – I. SHEDding light on chameleon gravity tests, *Mon. Not. Roy. Astron. Soc.* **476**, 3195 (2018).
16. M. White, A marked correlation function for constraining modified gravity models, *JCAP* **1611**, p. 057 (2016).
17. A. Aviles, K. Koyama, J. L. Cervantes-Cota, H. A. Winther and B. Li, Marked correlation functions in perturbation theory, *JCAP* **01**, p. 006 (2020).
18. S. Alam, C. Arnold, A. Aviles *et al.*, Testing the theory of gravity with DESI: estimators, predictions and simulation requirements (11 2020).
19. O. H. E. Philcox, A. Aviles and E. Massara, Modeling the Marked Spectrum of Matter and Biased Tracers in Real- and Redshift-Space, *JCAP* **03**, p. 038 (2021).
20. A. Aviles and J. L. Cervantes-Cota, Lagrangian perturbation theory for modified gravity, *Phys. Rev.* **D96**, p. 123526 (2017).
21. A. Aviles, G. Valogiannis, M. A. Rodriguez-Meza, J. L. Cervantes-Cota, B. Li and R. Bean, Redshift space power spectrum beyond Einstein-de Sitter kernels, *JCAP* **04**, p. 039 (2021).
22. C. Beisbart and M. Kerscher, Luminosity- and morphology-dependent clustering of galaxies, *Astrophys. J.* **545**, p. 6 (2000).
23. R. K. Sheth, The halo-model description of marked statistics, *Mon. Not. Roy. Astron. Soc.* **364**, p. 796 (2005).
24. R. K. Sheth, A. J. Connolly and R. Skibba, Marked correlations in galaxy formation models, *Submitted to: Mon. Not. Roy. Astron. Soc.* (2005).
25. M. White and N. Padmanabhan, Breaking Halo Occupation Degeneracies with Marked Statistics, *Mon. Not. Roy. Astron. Soc.* **395**, p. 2381 (2009).
26. G. Valogiannis and R. Bean, Beyond δ: Tailoring marked statistics to reveal modified gravity, *Phys. Rev.* **D97**, p. 023535 (2018).
27. C. Hernández-Aguayo, C. M. Baugh and B. Li, Marked clustering statistics in $f(R)$ gravity cosmologies, *Mon. Not. Roy. Astron. Soc.* **479**, 4824 (2018).
28. J. Armijo, Y.-C. Cai, N. Padilla, B. Li and J. A. Peacock, Testing modified gravity using a marked correlation function, *Mon. Not. Roy. Astron. Soc.* **478**, 3627 (2018).
29. V. Desjacques, D. Jeong and F. Schmidt, Large-Scale Galaxy Bias, *Phys. Rept.* **733**, 1 (2018).
30. A. Aviles, M. A. Rodriguez-Meza, J. De-Santiago and J. L. Cervantes-Cota, Nonlinear evolution of initially biased tracers in modified gravity, *JCAP* **1811**, p. 013 (2018).
31. S. Gottloeber, M. Kerscher, A. V. Kravtsov, A. Faltenbacher, A. Klypin and V. Mueller, Spatial distribution of galactic halos and their merger histories, *Astron. Astrophys.* **387**, p. 778 (2002).
32. R. Skibba, R. K. Sheth, A. J. Connolly and R. Scranton, The luminosity-weighted or 'marked' correlation function, *Mon. Not. Roy. Astron. Soc.* **369**, 68 (2006).
33. M. White, The Zel'dovich approximation, *Mon. Not. Roy. Astron. Soc.* **439**, 3630 (2014).
34. T. Baldauf, M. Mirbabayi, M. Simonović and M. Zaldarriaga, Equivalence Principle and the Baryon Acoustic Peak, *Phys. Rev.* **D92**, p. 043514 (2015).

35. T. Matsubara, Nonlinear perturbation theory with halo bias and redshift-space distortions via the Lagrangian picture, *Phys. Rev.* **D78**, p. 083519 (2008), [Erratum: Phys. Rev.D78,109901(2008)].
36. A. Aviles, Renormalization of Lagrangian bias via spectral parameters, *Phys. Rev.* **D98**, p. 083541 (2018).
37. A. Eggemeier, R. Scoccimarro and R. E. Smith, Bias Loop Corrections to the Galaxy Bispectrum, *Phys. Rev.* **D99**, p. 123514 (2019).
38. J. Carlson, B. Reid and M. White, Convolution Lagrangian perturbation theory for biased tracers, *Mon. Not. Roy. Astron. Soc.* **429**, p. 1674 (2013).
39. Z. Vlah, M. White and A. Aviles, A Lagrangian effective field theory, *JCAP* **1509**, p. 014 (2015).
40. N. Kaiser, On the Spatial correlations of Abell clusters, *Astrophys. J.* **284**, L9 (1984).
41. H. J. Mo, Y. P. Jing and S. D. M. White, High-order correlations of peaks and halos: A Step toward understanding galaxy biasing, *Mon. Not. Roy. Astron. Soc.* **284**, p. 189 (1997).
42. R. K. Sheth and G. Tormen, Large scale bias and the peak background split, *Mon. Not. Roy. Astron. Soc.* **308**, p. 119 (1999).
43. F. Schmidt, D. Jeong and V. Desjacques, Peak-Background Split, Renormalization, and Galaxy Clustering, *Phys. Rev.* **D88**, p. 023515 (2013).
44. S. Tassev, Lagrangian or Eulerian; Real or Fourier? Not All Approaches to Large-Scale Structure Are Created Equal, *JCAP* **1406**, p. 008 (2014).
45. M. Manera, R. Scoccimarro, W. J. Percival, L. Samushia, C. K. McBride, A. J. Ross, R. K. Sheth, M. White, B. A. Reid, A. G. Sánchez, R. de Putter, X. Xu, A. A. Berlind, J. Brinkmann, C. Maraston, B. Nichol, F. Montesano, N. Padmanabhan, R. A. Skibba, R. Tojeiro and B. A. Weaver, The clustering of galaxies in the SDSS-III Baryon Oscillation Spectroscopic Survey: a large sample of mock galaxy catalogues, *Mon. Not. Roy. Astron. Soc.* **428**, 1036 (Jan 2013).
46. D. Alonso, CUTE solutions for two-point correlation functions from large cosmological datasets, *arXiv e-prints* , p. arXiv:1210.1833 (Oct 2012).
47. E. Massara, F. Villaescusa-Navarro, S. Ho, N. Dalal and D. N. Spergel, Using the Marked Power Spectrum to Detect the Signature of Neutrinos in Large-Scale Structure, *Phys. Rev. Lett.* **126**, p. 011301 (2021).
48. J. Lesgourgues and S. Pastor, Massive neutrinos and cosmology, *Phys. Rept.* **429**, 307 (2006).
49. O. H. E. Philcox, E. Massara and D. N. Spergel, What does the marked power spectrum measure? Insights from perturbation theory, *Phys. Rev. D* **102**, p. 043516 (2020).
50. K. Koyama, Cosmological Tests of Modified Gravity, *Rept. Prog. Phys.* **79**, p. 046902 (2016).

Dark matter as condensed phase of generic bosons

Elías Castellanos

Mesoamerican Centre for Theoretical Physics
Universidad Autónoma de Chiapas. Ciudad Universitaria,
Carretera Zapata Km. 4, Real del Bosque (Terán), 29040,
Tuxtla Gutiérrez, Chiapas, México
E-mail: ecastellanos@mctp.mx

Jorge Mastache

Consejo Nacional de Ciencia y Tecnología,
Av. Insurgentes Sur 1582, Col Crédito Constructor,
Del. Benito Juárez, CP 03940. Mexico, and

Mesoamerican Centre for Theoretical Physics
Universidad Autónoma de Chiapas. Ciudad Universitaria,
Carretera Zapata Km. 4, Real del Bosque (Terán), 29040,
Tuxtla Gutiérrez, Chiapas, México
E-mail: jhmastache@mctp.mx

We analyze the properties of a generic bosonic cloud that we interpreted as a condensed phase of generic bosons or a Bose–Einstein condensate (BEC) type halo surrounding a Schwarzschild–type black hole. We model the halo as a condensed phase of generic bosons in terms of a massive scalar field that satisfies a self–interacting Klein–Gordon equation. To model the density of particles of the corresponding cloud, we apply the so–called Thomas–Fermi approximation that allows us to extract relevant properties of the system. By using galaxy data from a subsample of SPARC data base, we find the best fits of the BEC model by using the Thomas–Fermi approximation. We show that in the centre of galaxies we must have a supermassive compact central object, i.e., supermassive black hole, additionally the cloud or the halo behaves as a weakly interacting BEC composed of ultralight bosons.

Keywords: Dark matter; Bose–Einstein condensate.

1. Introduction

Bose–Einstein condensates (BECs) play a fascinating role in modern physics, relating many models spreading from microscopic well proved behavior of ultracold quantum gases to galactic and cosmological scales. Nevertheless, there is an issue not well understood in this scenario that deserves more in-depth study, i.e., the non–trivial conditions in which scalar fields can form BECs. However, it seems to be that scalar fields in the form of a BEC formed by generic bosons can describe the basic properties of dark matter (DM) in the universe.[1–5] According to this line of thought, DM consists of a particular type of spin–zero bosons, such as ultra–light scalar field dark matter or fuzzy dark matter, weakly interacting massive particles, axions, etc., (depending on the specific model under consideration) which have not yet been observed. The bosonic character of these particles, by using the theory of relativistic Bose gases,[6,7] also opens the door for the existence of scalar field dark matter in the form of BECs.[8,9]

The relation between scalar fields and (relativistic) condensates (BEC's) has already a long history, which is non trivial field of study even in flat space time, see for instance[6,7,10–14] and references therein. The aforementioned relation remains a very important topic that must be still fully understood.

Let us remark that in the core of the current astrophysics and cosmology, scalar fields seem to be a relevant candidate to describe dark matter (DM).[1–4,15] Nowadays, the observations suggest that the amount of dark matter in the universe is around 26% of the total energy density. In other words, the existence of dark matter can be found in the following observations, for instance, from the kinematic of galaxies and clusters,[16,17] the physics of the cosmic microwave background radiation (CMBR) and baryon acoustic oscillations (BAO),[18,19] as well as observations from Supernovae Type Ia (SNIa) and Gravitational Lensing (GL).[20,21]

Moreover, dark matter could consist of some type of generic scalar field(–particle) of spin–zero, for instance, Weakly Interacting Massive Particles (WIMPs), axions and others. Although these particles have been not yet observed, scalar fields interpreted as dark matter open up a very interesting model to confront observations. On the other hand, the theory of relativistic bosonic gases and its transitions, under certain circumstances as BEC's open the door to the interpretation of dark matter in the form of a condensate of generic bosonic particles.[8,9,22]

At this point is important to mention that there are some models related to the above ideas in the literature, for instance, the so–called hairy wigs models.[23,24] In the above mentioned approach it is shown that these systems can form stable structures for enough time, make them plausible candidates to describe dark matter galactic halos. Even more, since it is generally accepted that almost all the galaxies host a supermassive black hole at the center, and together with the assumption that dark matter is some kind of scalar field, this leads to the analysis of the existence of bound or quasi–bound scalar field configurations surrounding these compact objects. In fact, in the case of a Schwarzschild black hole and a massive scalar field without self–interactions, it was found that such quasi–bound states exist.[25]

Furthermore, when self-interactions are present for these scalar field configurations surrounding black holes and when quasi–bound states exist, the system can be also analyzed from the Bose–Einstein condensation point of view.[5,26,27] It is quite interesting that in the aforementioned scenario a Gross–Pitaevskii like–equation can be deduced from the corresponding Klein–Gordon equation. In other words, it is possible to study the system by using the formalism behind the Bose–Einstein condensation to extract relevant information. More precisely, in the formalism developed in refs.[5,26,27] it was shown that for a spherically symmetric test–scalar field configurations surrounding different types of black holes, the system can be interpreted as a trapped BEC. In other words, the corresponding Klein–Gordon equation can be rewritten in a form of a Gross–Pitaevskii equation, which describes the dynamics of usual laboratory BEC's, under certain circumstances. Additionally, in the three quoted references, it was analyzed the limit of validity of the so–called Thomas–Fermi approximation which is capable to give us an approximated solution (in principle, by using a simple algebraic procedure) for the system under consideration.

Here it is important to mention that in the standard theory of condensates (for instance, ref.[28]) the Thomas–Fermi approximation is an algebraic procedure that is useful for exploring relevant properties associated with the system when interactions are present. Moreover, the Thomas–Fermi approximation is valid when the kinetic energy is negligible with respect to the potential and interaction ones. Then, the kinetic energy can be neglected from the very beginning in the corresponding Gross–Pitaevskii equation. As a consequence, the non–linear differential equation becomes an algebraic equation for the order parameter, which in principle, is easy to solve. Additionally, the Thomas–Fermi approximation is valid when the corresponding scattering length, which describes the interaction among the particles within the system, is much smaller than the mean inter–particle spacing for sufficient large clouds. In other words, when the system is diluted enough and contains a large number of particles. Finally, we must add that the Thomas–Fermi approximation fails for trapped condensates near the edge of the cloud, due to the divergent behavior of the kinetic energy (i.e. the total kinetic energy per unit area diverges on the boundary of the system[28]). The last assertion can be used to define the validity of the Thomas–Fermi approximation and sets the limit in which we can extract information from the system. Therefore, in the case of the scalar field configurations viewed as BEC's surrounding black holes, the divergent behavior of the kinetic energy on the predicted boundary of the system can be used to test the region in which the Thomas–Fermi approximation is valid. In other words, we are not able to extract information beyond the region in which the approximation is valid. Deeper research is needed to support the description of these systems as dark matter. In addition, according to the results obtained in refs.,[5,26] observable features related to the *scalar cloud* within the Thomas–Fermi approximation, for discriminating between different types of black holes are tiny.

The main goal of the present manuscript is to identify the particle density distribution obtained from the Thomas–Fermi approximation (or the BEC density distribution) as a DM density profile surrounding galaxies (i.e., we restrict our analysis to the region in which the Thomas–Fermi approximation is valid).

Galaxy rotation curves cannot be explained by luminous matter alone and we have to appeal to an extra matter component, i.e. DM or BEC–DM in our scenario, to explain the observations.[29,30] Several DM density profiles have been proposed, we can categorize the profiles by its central behavior. Profiles whose densities grow with a power law of $\rho \sim r^{-1}$ are known as cuspy profiles, i.e. Navarro–Frenk–White.[31,32] Profiles whose density tends to a constant value at the center of the galaxy are know as core profiles, i.e. isothermal, Burket profiles.[33,34] Most cuspy profiles come from numerical simulations while the later are phenomenological proven, but must of them do not offer a clear explanation for the DM fundamental nature. Moreover, there is a tension between cores and cusp profiles because, on one hand, cuspy profiles are the one predicted from numerical simulations, on the other hand, observations seem to prefer cored profiles, the so called core–cusp problem.[35]

We are able to constrain the parameters of the BEC–DM model within the Thomas–Fermi approximation by using a total of 20 high resolution, circular galaxies, see reference.[27] The mass density of the BEC is given in terms of the mass of the bosonic particles M_Φ, a frequency ω, the coupling constant λ (which describes the interparticle interaction within the system) and, the only astronomical parameter, the mass of the black hole M. Except for the mass of the black hole, the profile is only given by the underlying particle model, the BEC indeed, which we expect to be equal for all galaxies, leaving the mass of the black hole as the only astronomical parameter that may vary from one galaxy to other.

2. Rotation Curves and Bose–Einstein Condensates

In this section, we summarize some important results obtained in refs. [5, 26, 27] In the aforementioned references a Gross–Pitaevskii like–equation is deduced from the corresponding Klein–Gordon equation in spherically symmetric and static black hole spacetimes. Also, a self–interacting scalar potential is assumed, allowing to link the system with the BEC's point of view. It is important to mention that both equations contain the same information related to the system. After the deduction of the Gross–Pitaevskii like–equation we apply the Thomas–Fermi approximation, which allows us to deduce with a very simple procedure, the corresponding density profile that we assume as a galactic dark matter halo.

In order to deduce the density profile we consider a test scalar field(–particle) in a spherically symmetric and static spacetime where the metric which in standard spherical coordinates is given by

$$ds^2 = -f(r)c^2 dt^2 + \frac{1}{f(r)}dr^2 + r^2(d\theta^2 + \sin^2\theta d\phi^2). \quad (1)$$

Thus, the Klein–Gordon equation for a complex test–scalar field Φ with a scalar potential $V(\Phi)$ in a spacetime with metric $g_{\mu\nu}$ can be written as follows:

$$\frac{1}{\sqrt{-g}}\partial_\mu\left(\sqrt{-g}g^{\mu\nu}\partial_\nu\Phi\right) - \frac{dV(\Phi\Phi^*)}{d\Phi^*} = 0, \quad (2)$$

where the star is complex conjugation and g is the determinant of the metric. If we want to link the system with a weakly interacting Bose–Einstein condensate of some generic bosonic particles, we assume a scalar potential of the form

$$V(\Phi\Phi^*) = \mu^2\Phi\Phi^* + \frac{\lambda}{2}(\Phi\Phi^*)^2, \quad (3)$$

where μ is the scalar mass parameter which is related to the mass of the bosonic particles M_Φ through the inverse of the Compton wavelength of the particles $\mu = \frac{M_\Phi c}{\hbar}$.

Additionally, λ is the self–interaction coupling constant which is interpreted as the scattering length of the particles.

We can find solutions of the Klein–Gordon equation by using the following ansatz

$$\Phi(t,r) = e^{i\omega t}\frac{u(r)}{r}, \qquad (4)$$

where we assume that the frequency ω is *real*. Notice that in general the function $u(r)$ is a complex–valued classical function that can be interpreted as the macroscopical wave function of the system or the order parameter as in standard theory of condensates. By using the ansatz (4) the corresponding Klein–Gordon equation reduces to a Gross–Pitaevskii–like equation of the form

$$\left(-\frac{d^2}{dr_*^2} + V_{\text{eff}}(r) + \lambda_{\text{eff}}(r)\frac{|u(r)|^2}{r^2}\right)u(r) = \frac{\omega^2}{c^2}u(r), \qquad (5)$$

where we have also introducing the r_* coordinate defined as $dr_* = \frac{dr}{f(r)}$, i.e., the so–called tortoise coordinate.

Notice that in equation (5) we define the effective trapping potential as

$$V_{\text{eff}}(r) = f(r)\left(\mu^2 + \frac{f'(r)}{r}\right) \qquad (6)$$

where the prime indicates derivatives respect to the r coordinate, together with an effective self–interaction parameter with the following functional form

$$\lambda_{\text{eff}}(r) = \lambda f(r). \qquad (7)$$

Here is important to mention that the effective potential in equation (6) is caused by the curvature of the spacetime itself, together with the contribution of the mass parameter μ. In other words, the effective potential V_{eff} allows the bosonic cloud to admit the existence of quasi–bound states. Additionally, λ is *modulated* by the influence of the spacetime geometry, i.e., the interactions show a position-dependent behavior as was shown in refs.[5,26] Finally, we must mention that the term ω^2/c^2 can be also identified with effective chemical potential.

As was mentioned in the introduction, the Thomas–Fermi approximation assumes that the kinetic energy is negligibly small in comparison to the potential energy and the self-interaction energy. Then, we can neglect the kinetic energy in equation (5) from the very beginning, with the result of an algebraic equation, from which we can obtain the density of particles $\rho(r) \equiv \frac{|u(r)|^2}{r^2}$.

The solution for the Gross–Pitaevskii–like equation (5) within the Thomas–Fermi approximation is then given by

$$\frac{|u(r)|^2}{r^2} \equiv \rho(r) = \left(\frac{\omega^2}{c^2} - V_{\text{eff}}(r)\right)\frac{1}{\lambda_{\text{eff}}(r)}. \qquad (8)$$

Notice that the above equation is well defined as long as the right-hand side is positive. The value of $\rho(r)$ is zero outside the region delimited by the equation

$V_{\text{eff}}(r) = \omega^2/c^2$. Moreover, the equation $V_{\text{eff}}(r) = \omega^2/c^2$ sets the size of the cloud within de Thomas–Fermi approximation. The region in which the condensate lies is a spherical shell of inner radius r_{min} and outer radius r_{max}, where r_{min} and r_{max} are precisely the solutions of the equation $V_{\text{eff}}(r) = \omega^2/c^2$. Additionally, as was point it out in,[26] the Thomas–Fermi approximation becomes arbitrarily good if λN (with N the total number of particles within the condensate) becomes sufficiently big. In the present case, λN increases if the ω/c is chosen very close to the mass parameter μ. Then we expect that the Thomas–Fermi approximation becomes quite good if the corresponding parameters are chosen properly.

For simplicity, let us assume that the function $f(r)$ in the metric (1) in ordinary units is given by:

$$f(r) = \left(1 - \frac{\alpha}{r}\right), \qquad (9)$$

where $\alpha \equiv 2GM/c^2$ for the Schwarzschild metric, where G is the gravitational constant and M the mass of the black hole.

Let us remark that the model under consideration comes from *first principles* in the sense that we only assume a scalar distribution in a form of some kind of Bose–Einstein condensate composed of generic bosonic particles surrounding a black hole. Then, we can obtain the density of particles or the density profile that we interpreted as a galactic dark matter halo by using the so–called Thomas–Fermi approximation.

The SPARC catalog have an observing data sample of 175 galaxies from $HI/H\alpha$ studies with large range of luminosities and Hubble types.[36] Our sample consist on galaxies with large number of observational data points, preferably with observations close to the galactic center, their rotation curve is smooth, with no relevant wiggles and extended to large radii, have none or small bulge. The total rotational velocity is computed taken the values for the gas and the stars from the mass model of the SPARC catalog. The bulge and the stellar disk model is given by the catalog.

The mass model include the four main components of a galaxy: the budge (when is present), V_b, the gas disk, V_g, the stellar disk, $V_\star$, and the BEC halo, V_{bec}. The total gravitational potential of the galaxy is the sum of each component of the galaxy, thus the observed rotation velocity is,

$$V_{\text{tot}}^2 = V_g^2 + \Upsilon_b V_b^2 + \Upsilon_\star V_\star^2 + V_{\text{bec}}^2, \qquad (10)$$

where $\Upsilon_\star$ and Υ_b are the mass-to-light ratio of the star and bulge disk, respectively. We take the mass-to-light ratio of the star, $\Upsilon_\star$, as free parameter. We assume an heuristic relation between the bulge and the stellar disk so $\Upsilon_b = 1.4\Upsilon_\star$ is assumed.[36] Is well know that the value of $\Upsilon_\star$ is model dependent which precise value rely on extinction, star formation history, IMF, among others. We ignore a priori any knowledge of the IMF and treat $\Upsilon_\star$ as an extra free parameter.

The halo model that we are proposing have four free parameters, the mass of the black hole, M, the mass parameter of the scalar field μ, the frequency of the field, ω and the self–interaction parameter, λ. The mass of the black hole is the only galactic parameter that can change from one galaxy to another.

We assume that galaxies with a central black hole could possibly create enough gravitational potential well in order to create a condensate cloud of almost non–interactive particles that could affect the dynamics of the galaxy. In the present work, we estimate the parameters of the scalar field(–particle) from rotation curves. It is worth pointing out that this in principle is an *universal profile* extracted from a particle model in which only the astronomical parameter is the mass of the black hole, other parameters are inherent of the particle which means should be the same for all galaxies.

The density profile is simple enough in order to compute the mass as function of the radius, the integral over the volume is given by

$$M(r) = \frac{\mu}{\lambda}\left[\alpha^2\omega^2 r + \frac{1}{2}\alpha\omega^2 r^2 - \frac{1}{3}\left(\mu^2 - \omega^2\right)r^3 \right.$$
$$\left. -\alpha\log(r) + \alpha^3\omega^2\log(r-\alpha)\right] \quad (11)$$

This expression should be evaluated between $r_{\min}$ and $r_{\max}$. Dimensional analysis of the expression for the mass let us conclude that the r^3 term is negligible because $\mu \sim \omega$, therefore the two most relevant terms are the ones proportional to $\log r$ and r^2, that dominates at small and large radii, respectively. And because $\alpha \gg \omega$ we can approximate the mass as,

$$M(r) \approx \frac{\mu\alpha}{\lambda}\left[\frac{1}{2}\omega^2 r^2 - \log(r)\right], \quad (12)$$

from the last expression we clear see that $r_{\min}$ can be approximately computed when $M(r) = 0$, which gives $r_{\min}^2 \approx -\mathcal{W}(-\omega^2)/\omega^2$, where $\mathcal{W}$ is the Lambert function. The value of $r_{\max}$ can also be approximated when the term proportional to r^3 gets bigger to the r^2 term in equation (11), which would lead to a negative values for the mass. Thus, $r_{\max} \sim 3\alpha/2(1-\mu^2/\omega^2)$, given the bound we fix for ω, this would lead to $r_{\max} \sim \mathcal{O}(\alpha 10^{14})$. Then, the region where the Thomas–Fermi approximation is valid is given by

$$\frac{3}{2}\frac{\alpha}{1-\mu^2/\omega^2} \gtrsim r \gtrsim \frac{[-\mathcal{W}(-\omega^2)]^{1/2}}{\omega} \quad (13)$$

Notice that if we do not have observation for $r \sim \mathcal{O}(r_{\min})$ then the parameters μ, ω and λ will be degenerate for the fitting, this is, we can find any combination of $\mu\omega^2/\lambda = $ cte to valid for one galaxy. We can break the degeneracy with α because $r_{\max}$ highly depends on its value.

We assume circular rotation velocities of test particles in the plane of the galaxy and also spherical DM halos and BEC distributions. For this distribution of matter the circular velocity at radius r is given by $V_H^2(r) = GM(r)/r$. From this last expression and equation (12) we see that in the case of the BEC at large radii the velocity grows as $v \propto r^{1/2}$. Our objective is to test the realization of the BEC model, equation (11), through rotation curves of a sample of high-resolution galaxies. Form Fig. 1 notice that we may have no presence of BEC at the center of the galaxy (i.e. for $r < r_{\min}$), which make sense if we have a central super-massive object as a black hole. Thus, this profile is neither core or cuspy, we may call it null central profile. The extension of the condensate reaches up to $r_{\max}$, which is a finite value close to the observational limit of the galaxy.

Let us now do an analysis of the equations in order to found bounds to the parameters. The frequency ω is particularly important because the region where the Tomas–Fermi approximation is valid is given by the condition $V_{\text{eff}}(r) = \omega^2/c^2$. The region $r_{\max} > r > r_{\min}$ where the condensate could form is given by the roots of the polynomial $(\mu^2 - \omega^2)r^4 - \alpha\mu^2 r^3 - \alpha r + \alpha^2 = 0$. The extreme case where $\omega \to \mu$ gives a region where $r_{\max} \to \infty$. The closer the value of ω is to μ the larger the potential well of the condensate. For instance, assuming a black hole of $M = 10^{13} M_\odot$ and $\mu = \mu_{\max}$, if ω is just 10% less than μ then $r_{\max} \sim 4$ pc, which will make the model not testable for currents observations. However, if the percentile difference is of the order $\mathcal{O}(10^{-4})$ then $r_{\max} \sim 50$ kpc, enough extension for a Milky Way galaxy size. If we assume that all galaxies are surrounded for a dark matter halo then the frequency parameter is the most constrained of all four parameters.

The maximum radius at which the approximation is valid, at least the maximum observed radius, also depends on the value of ω, the smaller the value of ω the smaller is the region. We find out that if $1 - \mu/\omega < 10^{-5}$ the maximum radius is of the order of $r_{\max} \sim \mathcal{O}(10)$ kpc. Therefore we fix the value of ω such that $1 - \mu/\omega = 10^{-7}$ in order to make sure that the maximum observed galaxy rotation curve is well inside the region where the Thomas–Fermi approximation is valid.

A special case is to compute the maximum value of the mass parameter $\mu_{\max}$, which is defined when $V_{\text{eff}}(r_\wedge) = \mu_{\max}^2$ at the radius $r_\wedge$, from this condition we obtain that $\mu_{\max}^2 = f(r_\wedge)/r_\wedge^2$. Using the equation of the corresponding V_{eff} is quite to easy to compute that $f(r_\wedge) = 1/3$. Therefor $r_\wedge = 3GM/c^2$. For instance, for a black hole of $M_{\text{bh}} = 10^{13} M_\odot$, the radii where the potential is maximum is $r_\wedge \sim 1.4$ pc. Is important to notice that the maximum value of $\mu_{\max}$ is given only in terms of the mass of the black hole.

We take the ansatz $V_{\text{eff}}(r_\vee) = 0.95\, \mu_{\min}^2$ in order to compute $\mu_{\min}$, which range $(0.7 - 0.85)\, \mu_{\max}$. Taking $V_{\text{eff}}(r_\vee) = \mu_{\min}^2$ makes no physical sense because there will be no potential well where the condensate could form.

The scattering length (or the self–interacting parameter λ) acts as a weight parameter, this should be or the order of $\mathcal{O}(10^{-70})$ 1/m to fit current observational velocities. The smaller the value of λ the higher velocities we can compute, this will also mean that the scalar field is behaving almost as an ideal condensate. Heuristically speaking, we found that the bounds should be the order of $10^{-50} > \lambda[\text{m}^{-1}] > 10^{-90}$.

We use the observed rotation curve, stellar, and gas component as an input for the numerical code, in order to obtain the properties of the BEC. When fitting

Eq. (10) to the observed rotation curves, we apply a non-linear least-squares method to perform the fit, minimizing the residual sum of the χ^2-test. The χ^2-goodness-of-fit test, that tell us how close are the theoretical to the observed values. In general the χ^2-test statistics is of the form:

$$\chi^2 = \sum_{i=1}^{n} \left(\frac{V_{\text{obs}_i} - V_{\text{model}_i}(r, \rho_0, r_s, r_c)}{\sigma_i} \right)^2, \quad (14)$$

where σ is the standard deviation, and n is the number of observations. Comparison of the fits derived can tell us which of the DM models is preferred. More important are the differences between the reduced $\chi^2_{\text{red}} = \chi^2/(n-p-1)$ values, where n is the number of observations and p is the number of fitted parameters. The uncertainties in the rotation velocity are reflected in the uncertainties in the model parameters.

Table 1. Numerical fits for the BEC model by using the SPARC data base. For each Galaxy we reported the values of: Υ relation total mass-to-light ratio on luminosity, the reduced χ^2 in terms of the degree of freedom for the BEC model χ^2/dof, which correspond to 3 and 4 dof, respectively. The small χ^2 values are mainly due to the large data error bars. $\log_{10} M_{\text{BH}}/M_\odot$ is the mass of the black hole given in solar units $M_{BH} = 10^x M_\odot$. The free parameters for the BEC model are: λ and μ. The last column is the $\ln B$ factor in comparison with the NFW model.

Galaxy ID	BEC model in the Thomas–Fermi approximation					$\ln B$
	$\Upsilon^{\text{bec}}_\star$	χ^2/dof	$\log_{10} M_{\text{BH}}/M_\odot$	$\log_{10} \lambda \text{ pc}^{-1}$	$\mu[\text{pc}^{-1}]$	
IC2574	$0.21^{+1.07}_{-0.21}$	5.37	12.00 ± 0.73	-89.83 ± 0.78	4.06 ± 0.97	4.44
NGC2403	0.68 ± 0.46	14.14	10.64 ± 0.51	-91.88 ± 0.96	4.12 ± 0.30	4.42
NGC2841	0.95 ± 0.16	2.50	11.20 ± 0.10	-91.43 ± 0.17	4.01 ± 1.00	2.23
NGC2903	$0.44^{+1.39}_{-0.44}$	5.75	10.72 ± 0.94	-92.77 ± 0.42	2.34 ± 0.97	1.47
NGC3198	0.73 ± 0.04	2.58	10.96 ± 0.16	-91.30 ± 0.47	4.24 ± 1.00	1.40
NGC3521	0.54 ± 0.10	0.21	11.71 ± 1.35	-89.99 ± 1.49	7.87 ± 0.95	1.61
NGC4559	$0.52^{+2.16}_{-0.52}$	0.24	10.78 ± 0.97	-91.03 ± 0.91	5.89 ± 1.64	1.24
NGC6015	0.94 ± 0.05	7.16	11.08 ± 0.40	-91.35 ± 0.54	3.60 ± 1.03	1.35
NGC6503	0.63 ± 0.10	5.09	10.72 ± 0.34	-91.58 ± 0.51	4.33 ± 0.46	1.10
NGC6946	0.50 ± 0.06	1.91	10.77 ± 0.61	-90.59 ± 0.98	9.79 ± 1.54	2.06
NGC7331	0.38 ± 0.03	0.90	11.05 ± 0.25	-90.36 ± 0.46	10.20 ± 0.94	1.37
NGC7793	$0.71^{+1.18}_{-0.71}$	0.78	10.70 ± 7.54	-90.79 ± 42.99	7.54 ± 4.65	1.39
UGC02953	$0.67^{+1.08}_{-0.67}$	14.86	11.12 ± 1.00	-91.58 ± 1.59	4.01 ± 0.45	1.54
UGC03205	0.25 ± 0.16	5.10	10.78 ± 0.47	-91.32 ± 0.19	3.74 ± 1.19	2.54
UGC03580	0.81 ± 0.07	3.11	10.78 ± 0.47	-91.57 ± 0.84	4.23 ± 0.98	1.92
UGC05253	$0.52^{+0.98}_{-0.52}$	6.56	11.05 ± 0.95	-91.54 ± 1.62	4.30 ± 1.01	1.47
UGC07524	$1.11^{+2.64}_{-1.11}$	0.59	10.54 ± 1.05	-90.66 ± 1.86	8.42 ± 1.02	1.96
UGC08699	0.56 ± 0.01	1.44	10.73 ± 0.25	-92.16 ± 0.34	3.51 ± 0.05	1.29
UGC09133	$0.58^{+0.97}_{0.58}$	23.93	11.35 ± 2.36	-90.65 ± 2.61	5.21 ± 1.60	1.57
UGC11455	0.54 ± 0.08	3.60	11.67 ± 1.12	-89.78 ± 1.24	8.56 ± 1.00	2.95
UGC11914	$0.64^{+0.84}_{-0.64}$	2.16	12.01 ± 0.99	-90.83 ± 2.16	3.96 ± 0.95	0.92

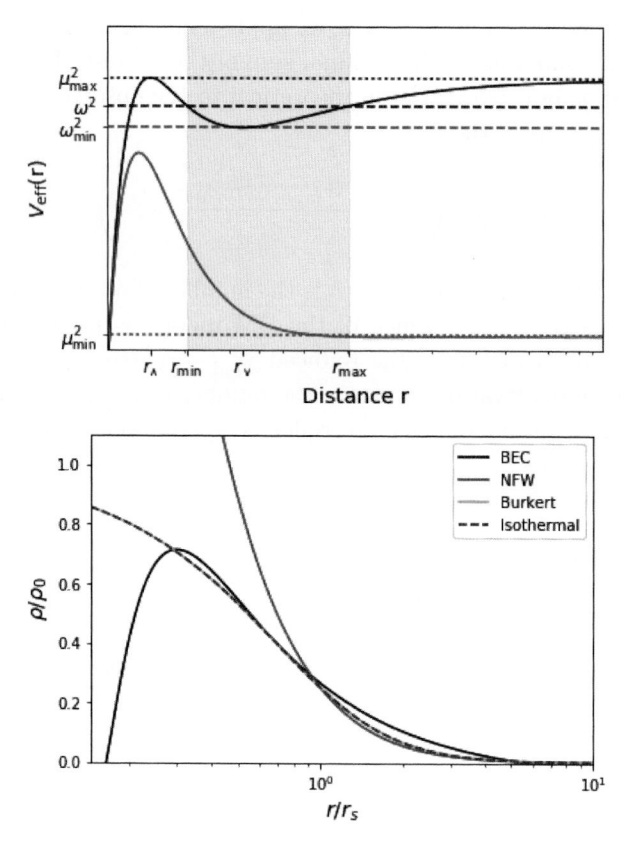

Fig. 1. *Up:* Plot of the potential V_{eff}, Eq. (6). Solid lines are two examples for different values of mass parameter μ, the black lines is given $\mu_{\max} = V_{\text{eff}}(r_\wedge))$ and the red line is given $\mu_{\min}$. The ω parameter defines the the region where the Thomas-Fermi approximation is valid, $r_{\max} > r > r_{\min}$ and could take the value $\omega_{\max}(=\mu_{\max}) > \omega > \omega_{\min}(= V_{\text{eff}}(r_\vee))$. *Down:* Plot of the profile density of BEC (solid black), NFW (solid red), Burkert (solid yellow) and isothermal (dashed blue).

3. Discussion

According to the results summarized in the present work, it seems to be that the interpretation of dark matter as some kind of BEC is, in fact, a good model to describe the kinematics of the galaxy rotation curves. Even more, we have shown that the corresponding Thomas–Fermi approximation can give insights in a simple way that match with the observations of rotation curves in galaxies. From the simple analysis, we notice that density is proportional $\rho \propto r^{-1}$ for all radii, in contrast with most DM profiles that behave as $\rho \propto r^{-3}$ at large radii. The mass of the BEC behaves as $m_{\text{bec}} \propto r^2$, and therefore $v_{\text{bec}} \propto r^{1/2}$, this coincides with NFW in the limit $r \ll r_{\max}$ where $v_{\text{nfw}} \propto r^{1/2}$, with $r_{\max} \sim 2.163 r_s$.

We have obtained an average $\mu = 5.43 \pm 2.24$ pc^{-1} which corresponds to an average boson mass of $M_\Phi = (3.47 \pm 1.43) \times 10^{-23}$ eV. Previous analysis has found

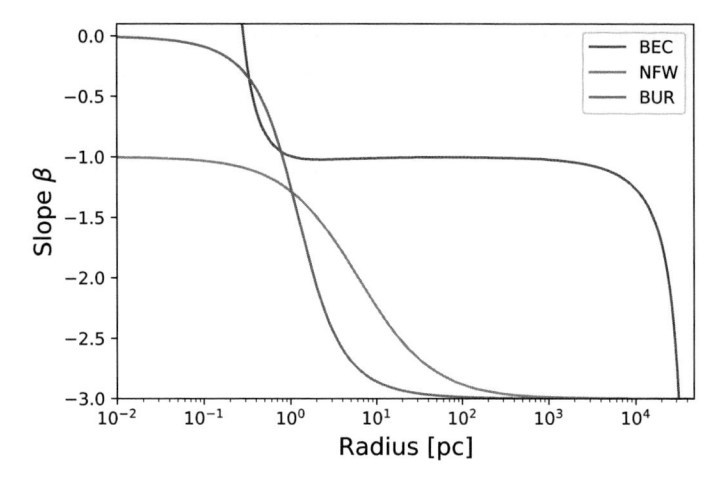

Fig. 2. The slope for different profiles. For BEC (blue line) notice that the density is bounded between some $r_{\min}$ and $r_{\max}$, in this region the slope is almost constant with value $\beta = -1$. For NFW (orange line) we notice its cuspy behavior close to the galactic centre and then dilutes as $\rho \propto r^{-3}$, while core profiles as Burkert (green line) reach constant value in the centre $\beta = 0$ and $\rho \propto r^{-3}$ at large radii.

masses for ultralight dark matter (see[42] for a compilation of results), which constrain the mass of the boson in the order of 10^{-22} eV. Notice that the latter result agrees with the one obtained in the present work. For the self–interacting parameter we get the values $\log_{10}(\lambda \, [\text{pc}^{-1}]) = -91.09 \pm 0.74$. In other words, the halo viewed as a Bose–Einstein condensate can be interpreted almost as an ideal condensate of some generic bosons, which also agree with the results reported in.[26,27]

Thus, the corresponding mass of the black holes at the galaxy centre is given by $\log_{10} M/M_\odot = 11.08 \pm 0.43$. This kind of scenarios, e.g Abell 85 and Holm 15A, has been reported in[43,44] with a core that host supermassive black holes of mass 10^9–10^{11} $M_\odot$. Although recent observation of supermassive black holes in galaxies supports our fitting for the mass of the black hole, we could also think of the possibility that the black hole may not be the only option to trap the boson cloud. In future works, we could use a weak field approximation to also include the mass of stars, bulge, and gas in the center of the galaxy, even more, the self-gravitating effect of the bosonic halo or the effects caused by the rotation of the halo as a contribution to the gravitational potential and therefore reduce the contribution of the black hole as the only source of the potential. Indeed, the BEC model on average fits quite well and is not a bad fitting at all given the simplicity of the model is something that must be taken into account. The above results are sumarized in Table (1).

The BEC model in the Thomas–Fermi approximation is strong enough as the NFW model to describe galaxy rotation curves. More important, we cannot ignore that the BEC model comes from first principles and that makes use the Thomas–Fermi approximation and assume that is only a compact central object that condensates the relativistic bosonic cloud. This model can be extended and generalized to include bulge and central stars contribution that may diminish the mass of the central black hole, or the self gravitating nature of the halo and also with rotation (and maybe charged). The good fitting of the BEC model using galaxy rotation curves may be indicating that the nature of dark matter may be close to be unveiled.

The fit in this model helps us to set physical bounds to the parameters of the Bose–Einstein dark matter approach. These bounds can be used to extend the analysis in bigger samples of galaxies. Finally, more general scenarios can be taken into account in order to study the corresponding rotation curves, for instance, in charged and rotating black holes spacetimes and perhaps as discrimination criteria of the nature of supermassive black holes. Even more, we are able to extend also the analysis reported in the present manuscript in order to study the eventual relation between dark matter and the so–called boson stars from the Bose–Einstein condensation point of view, in the relativistic and non–relativistic regime.[39–41]

Acknowledgments

This work was partially supported by CONACyT México under Grant No. 304001. J.M. acknowledges CONACYT Cátedras program and the support of the MCTP/UNACH.

References

1. S. J. Sin, *Late-time phase transition and the galactic halo as a Bose liquid*, Phys. Rev. D 50 (1994) 3650.
2. F. S. Guzmán, T. Matos and H. Villegas, *Scalar fields as dark matter in spiral galaxies: comparison with experiments*, Astron. Nachr. 320 (1999) 97
3. F. S. Guzmán and T. Matos, *Quintessence at Galactic Level?* Class. Quantum Grav. 17 (2000) L9
4. J. Magaña, T. Matos, *A brief review of the scalar field dark matter model*, J. Phys. Conf. Ser. 378 (2012) 012012
5. E. Castellanos, C. Escamilla–Rivera, C. Lämmerzahl and A. Macías, *Scalar field as a Bose-Einstein condensate in a Schwarzschild-de Sitter spacetime*, Int. J. Mod. Phys. D 26 (2017) 1750032
6. J. Bernstein and S. Dodelson, *Relativistic Bose gas*, Phys. Rev. Lett. 66 (1991) 683
7. L. Parker and Y. Zhang, *Ultrarelativistic Bose-Einstein condensation in the Einstein universe and energy conditions*, Phys. Rev. D 44 (1991) 2421
8. C. G. Boehmer and T. Harko, *Can dark matter be a Bose-Einstein condensate?* JCAP (2007) 025
9. L.A. Ureña–López, *Bose-Einstein condensation of relativistic scalar field dark matter*, JCAP (2009) 014
10. L. Dolan and R. Jackiw, Phys. Rev. D 9 (1974) 3320.
11. Weinberg, Phys. Rev. D 9 (1974) 3357.
12. E. Castellanos and T. Matos, Int. J. Mod. Phys. B 27 (2013) 11.
13. M. Grether, M. de Llano and G. A. Baker, Jr., Phys. Rev. Lett. 99 (2007) 200406.
14. Tonatiuh Matos, Elías Castellanos and Abril Suárez, *Bose–Einstein Condensation and Symmetry Breaking of a Complex Charged Scalar Field*, Eur. Phys. J. C 77:500 (2017).

15. S. U. Ji and S. J. Sin, *Late-time phase transition and the galactic halo as a Bose liquid. II. The effect of visible matter*, Phys. Rev. D50 (1994) 3656
16. F. Zwicky, Helv. Phys. Acta **6**, 110 (1933) [Gen. Rel. Grav. 41 207 (2009)]. doi:10.1007/s10714-008-0707-4
17. V. C. Rubin, N. Thonnard and W. K. Ford, Jr., Astrophys. J. 238 471 (1980). doi:10.1086/158003
18. N. Aghanim et al. [Planck Collaboration], arXiv:1807.06209 [astro-ph.CO].
19. D. J. Eisenstein et al. [SDSS Collaboration], Astrophys. J. 633 560 (2005) doi:10.1086/466512 [astro-ph/0501171].
20. P. Astier et al. [SNLS Collaboration], Astron. Astrophys. 447 31 (2006) doi:10.1051/0004-6361:20054185 [astro-ph/0510447].
21. N. Kaiser and G. Squires, Astrophys. J. 404 441 (1993). doi:10.1086/172297
22. A. Suárez, V. Robles and T. Matos, *A Review on the Scalar Field/Bose-Einstein Condensate Dark Matter Model*, Astrophys. Space Sci. Proc. 38 (2014) 107
23. J. Barranco et al., Phys. Rev. Lett. 109 (2012) 081102.
24. N. Sanchis-Gual, J. C. Degollado, P. J. Montero and J. A. Font, *Quasistationary solutions of self-gravitating scalar fields around black holes*, Phys. Rev. D 91 (2015) 043005.
25. J. Barranco, A. Bernal, J. C. Degollado, A. Diez-Tejedor, M. Megevand, D. Núñez and O. Sarbach, *Self-gravitating black hole scalar wigs* [arXiv:1704.03450]
26. Elías Castellanos, Juan Carlos Degollado, Claus Lämmerzahl, Alfredo Macías and Volker Perlick, *Bose–Einstein condensates in charged black–hole spacetimes* JCAP 01(2018) 043.
27. Elías Castellanos, Celia Escamilla–Rivera and Jorge Mastache, *Is a Bose–Einstein condensate a good candidate for dark matter? A test with galaxy rotation curves*, Int. J. Mod. Phys. D. 29 9 (2020) 2050063.
28. C. J. Pethick and H. Smith, *Bose–Einstein Condensation in Dilute Gases*, Cambridge University Press, Cambridge (2002)
29. P. Salucci, Astron. Astrophys. Rev. 27 no. 1, 2 (2019) doi:10.1007/s00159-018-0113-1 [arXiv:1811.08843 [astro-ph.GA]].
30. P. Salucci, Found. Phys. 48 no. 10, 1517 (2018) doi:10.1007/s10701-018-0209-5 [arXiv:1807.08541 [astro-ph.GA]].
31. J. F. Navarro, C. S. Frenk and S. D. M. White, Astrophys. J. 462 563 (1996) doi:10.1086/177173 [astro-ph/9508025].
32. B. Moore, T. R. Quinn, F. Governato, J. Stadel and G. Lake, Mon. Not. Roy. Astron. Soc. 310 1147 (1999) doi:10.1046/j.1365-8711.1999.03039.x [astro-ph/9903164].
33. J. E. Gunn and J. R. Gott, III, Astrophys. J. 176 1 (1972). doi:10.1086/151605
34. A. Burkert, IAU Symp. **171**, 175 (1996) [Astrophys. J. 447 L25 (1995)] doi:10.1086/309560 [astro-ph/9504041].
35. W. J. G. de Blok, Adv. Astron. 789293 (2010) doi:10.1155/2010/789293 [arXiv:0910.3538 [astro-ph.CO]].
36. Federico Lelli et al. 2016 AJ 152 157.
37. F. C. van den Bosch and R. A. Swaters, Mon. Not. Roy. Astron. Soc. 325 1017 (2001) doi:10.1046/j.1365-8711.2001.04456.x [astro-ph/0006048].
38. Elías Castellanos, Guillermo Chacón-Acosta and Jorge Mastache, Non-relativistic Boson Stars as N-Body Quantum Systems, arXiv:2012.03445 [gr-qc] (2020).
39. F. Schunck and E. Mielke, Class. Quantum Grav. 20 (2003) R301–R356.
40. F. Schunck and E. Mielke, General relativistic boson stars, Class. Quantum Grav. 20 (2003) R301-R356.

41. J. Eby, et al., Approximation methods in the study of boson stars, Phys. Rev. D 98
42. P. H. Chavanis, arXiv:1810.08948 [gr-qc].
43. O. Lopez-Cruz, et al. The Brightest Cluster Galaxy in Abell 85: The Largest Core Known so far DOI:10.1088/2041-8205/795/2/L31
44. K. Mehrgan, et al. A 40-billion solar mass black hole in the extreme core of Holm 15A, the central galaxy of Abell 85 arXiv:1907.10608

New Planck tSZ map and its cosmological analysis

H. Tanimura*, M. Douspis and N. Aghanim

*Université Paris-Saclay, CNRS, Institut d'Astrophysique Spatiale,
Bâtiment 121, 91405 Orsay, France
E-mail: hideki.tanimura@ias.u-psud.fr

We constructed a new all-sky Compton parameter map (y-map) of the thermal Sunyaev-Zel'dovich (tSZ) effect by applying the MILCA component separation algorithm to the 100 to 857 GHz frequency channel maps from the Planck data release 4. The Planck team performed several improvements for the new channel maps in terms of noises and systematics, and it allowed us to produce a new y-map with reduced noises by $\sim 7\%$ and minimal survey strips compared to the previous version released in 2015. We computed the tSZ angular power spectrum of the new y-map and performed a cosmological analysis. The results showed $S_8 = 0.764^{+0.015}_{-0.018}$ (stat) $^{+0.031}_{-0.016}$ (sys), including systematic uncertainties from a hydrostatic mass bias and pressure profile model. The value is fully consistent with recent KiDS and DES weak-lensing observations. It is also consistent with the Planck CMB's result within 2σ, while our result is slightly lower.

Keywords: Clusters; intracluster medium; large-scale structure of Universe; cosmic background radiation

1. S_8 tension

The current standard cosmological model called the Λ cold dark matter (ΛCDM) model, mainly consisting of dark energy and dark matter, provides a wonderful fit to many cosmological data. However, a slight discrepancy was found in the latest data analyses between the CMB anisotropies ($z \sim 1100$) and other low-redshift ($z \sim 0-1$) cosmological probes for the $S_8 (\equiv \sigma_8 (\Omega_m/0.3)^{0.5})$ cosmological parameter representing the amplitude of the structure growth in the Universe. For example, the S_8 value was precisely measured to be $S_8 = 0.830 \pm 0.013$ with the Planck CMB observation.[1] However, a lower value of $S_8 \sim 0.77 \pm 0.03$ was measured using the population of galaxy clusters detected by Planck at low redshift ($z < 0.6$),[2,3] thus called "S_8 tension". Furthermore, other low-redshift observations with gravitational lensing by the Kilo-Degree Survey[4] (KiDS) and the Dark Energy Survey[5,6] (DES) experiments also found lower S_8 values. These results indicate that the cosmic structure growth is slower than the prediction based on the CMB measurement and may demand modifications to the standard cosmological model to explain all these measurements.

We use the thermal Sunyaev Zel'dovish (tSZ) effect to investigate the value of the S_8 parameter. The tSZ signals provide independent constraints on cosmological parameters. In particular, it is sensitive to the normalization of the matter power spectrum, commonly parameterized by σ_8, and to the total matter density, Ω_m. It is also sensitive to other cosmological parameters, e.g., the baryon density parameter Ω_b, the Hubble constant H_0, and the primordial spectral index n_s. However, these variations are small relative to those of Ω_m and σ_8.[7] Thus, in our analysis, we varied only Ω_m and σ_8, and other cosmological parameters were fixed to the fiducial values obtained from the Planck CMB measurements.[1]

2. New all-sky tSZ map

The tSZ signal is subdominant relative to the CMB and other foreground emissions in the Planck bands. Thus a tailored component separation algorithm is required to reconstruct the tSZ map. We adopted the MILCA (Modified Internal Linear Combination Algorithm)[8] used for the Planck y-map reconstruction in 2015 and applied it to the 100 to 857 GHz frequency channel maps from the Planck data release 4 (PR4).

The Planck PR4 data implemented several improvements from the previous version: the usage of foreground polarization priors during the calibration stage to break scanning-induced degeneracies, the correction of bandpass mismatch at all frequencies, and the inclusion of 8% of data collected during repointing maneuvers, etc. These improvements allowed us to produce a new y-map with reduced noises by ~7% and minimal survey strips than the previous version released in 2015 (Fig. 1).

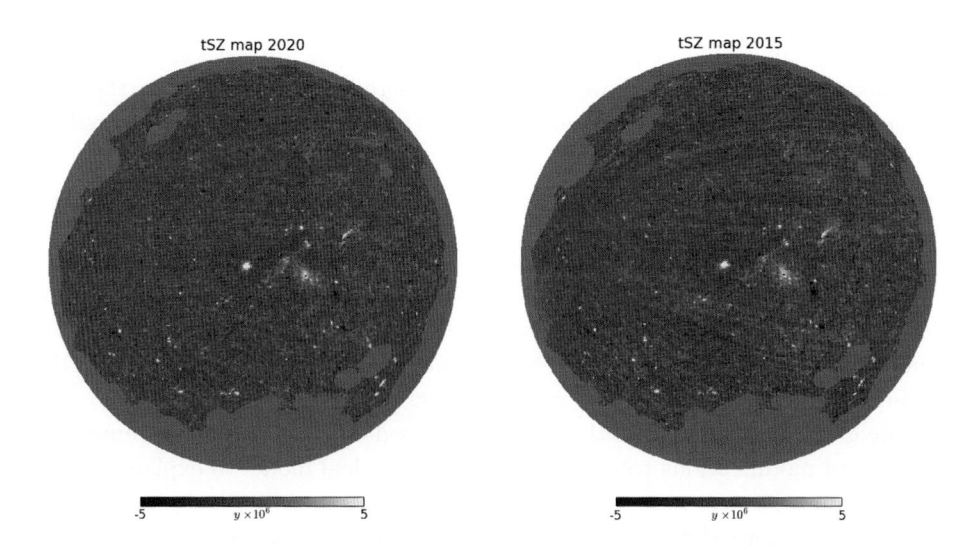

Fig. 1. MILCA all-sky Compton y parameter maps reconstructed in this work (*left*) and 2015[9] (*right*) in orthographic projections. The pixel resolution is changed from Nside = 2048 to Nside = 128 for visualization purposes.

3. Cosmological analysis and result

For our cosmological analyses, we also reconstructed two y-maps from the first and last halves of the data for a cosmological analysis. We considered a cross-angular power spectrum between these y-maps to avoid the bias induced by the noise in the auto-angular power spectrum. This tSZ cross-power spectrum is affected by residual foreground emissions from radio and IR point sources and CIB emission. Thus we fitted our measurement with the cosmology-dependent tSZ model, including the radio and IR point source models[10] and the CIB model[11] (*left* panel in Fig. 2).

The cosmological analysis of the tSZ cross-power spectrum allowed us to set constraints on cosmological parameters, mainly of the S_8 parameter. We obtained $S_8 = 0.764^{+0.015}_{-0.018}$. Our obtained S_8 value is fully consistent with recent weak lensing results from KiDS and DES. It is also consistent with the Planck CMB's result[1] within 2σ, while it is slightly lower by $\sim 1.7\sigma$ (*right* panel in Fig. 2).

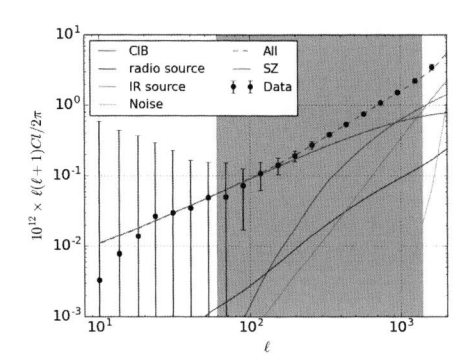

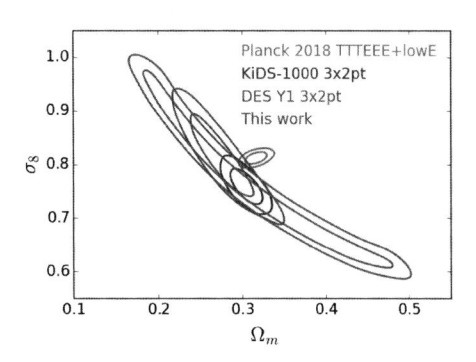

Fig. 2. *Left*: Cross-power spectrum (black) fitted with the tSZ (red), foreground models, and fiducial model of instrumental noise. The considered foregrounds are CIB (green), radio sources (blue), infrared sources (cyan) and noise (yellow). The sum of the tSZ and foreground models is shown in red dashed line. *Right*: Posterior distribution of the cosmological parameters, σ_8 and Ω_m, with 68% and 95% confidence interval contours obtained from our cosmological analysis. It is compared with the Planck CMB's (gray), KiDS-1000 3x2pt (blue), and DES Y1 3x2pt results (green).

4. Systematic effects in the cosmological analysis

Finally, we considered systematic uncertainties in our cosmological analysis introduced by the mass bias and the pressure profile model. First, we consider a systematic uncertainty from the mass bias. To investigate its impact on our cosmological analysis, we replaced our fiducial mass bias (CCCP:[12] $1 - b = 0.780 \pm 0.092$) prior with two other mass bias models from WtG[13] ($1 - b = 0.688 \pm 0.072$) and BIFFI[14] ($1 - b = 0.877 \pm 0.015$). The left panel in Fig. 3 shows their comparison in σ_8 and Ω_m. The result shows that the S_8 value increases as the mass bias increases (or $1 - b$ decrease). This systematic uncertainty may cause a $\sim 1\sigma$ shift in the S_8 parameter from our fiducial value.

In addition, the pressure profile model may affect the cosmological analysis with the tSZ power spectrum. To investigate its impact on our cosmological analysis, we replaced the pressure profile model (P13[15]) with two other models from A10[16] and PACT21[17]. The right panel in Fig. 3 shows their comparison in σ_8 and Ω_m. The PACT21 model reduces the S_8 discrepancy between the Planck CMB and our tSZ results by $\sim 1\sigma$ relative to our fiducial model. It may imply that the discrepancy can be further reconciled or amplified by a better understanding of baryonic physics in galaxy clusters.

In conclusion, we included these systematic uncertainties and obtained $S_8 = 0.764 \,^{+0.015}_{-0.018} (stat) \,^{+0.031}_{-0.016} (sys)$.

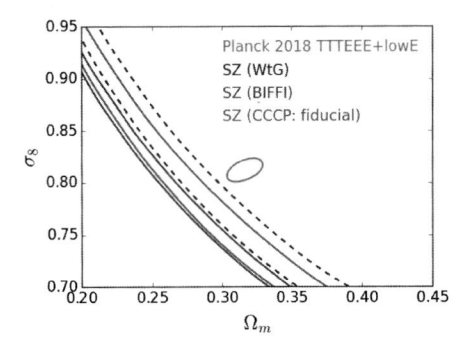

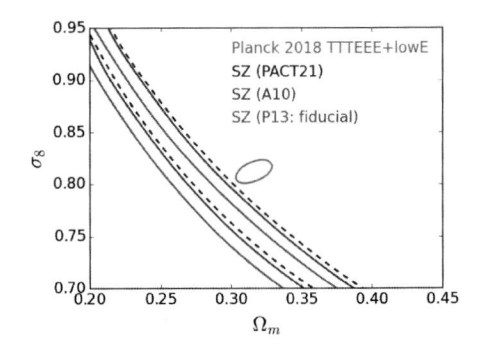

Fig. 3. *Left*: Posterior distribution of the cosmological parameters, σ_8 and Ω_m, with 68% confidence interval contours obtained from the Planck CMB analysis in gray and our tSZ analysis with three different mass bias priors. Our fiducial model of CCCP is shown in red. It is compared with the WtG model in blue and BIFFI model in green. *Right*: Posterior distribution of the cosmological parameters, σ_8 and Ω_m, with 68% confidence interval contours obtained from the Planck CMB analysis in gray and our tSZ analysis with three different pressure profile models. Our fiducial model of PA13 is shown in red. It is compared with the PACT21 model in blue and A10 model in green.

Acknowledgement

This research has been supported by the funding for the ByoPiC project from the European Research Council (ERC) under the European Union's Horizon 2020 research and innovation programme grant agreement ERC-2015-AdG 695561.

References

1. Planck Collaboration, *A&A* **641**, p. A6 (September 2020).
2. Planck Collaboration, *A&A* **571**, p. A20 (November 2014).
3. Planck Collaboration, *A&A* **594**, p. A24 (September 2016).

4. C. Heymans *et al.*, *A&A* **646**, p. A140 (February 2021).
5. Dark Energy Survey Collaboration, *Phys. Rev. D* **98**, p. 043526 (August 2018).
6. DES Collaboration, *arXiv e-prints* , p. arXiv:2105.13549 (May 2021).
7. E. Komatsu and U. Seljak, *MNRAS* **336**, 1256 (November 2002).
8. G. Hurier *et al.*, *A&A* **558**, p. A118 (October 2013).
9. Planck Collaboration, *A&A* **594**, p. A22 (September 2016).
10. J. Delabrouille *et al.*, *A&A* **553**, p. A96 (May 2013).
11. A. Maniyar *et al.*, *A&A* **645**, p. A40 (January 2021).
12. H. Hoekstra *et al.*, *MNRAS* **449**, 685 (May 2015).
13. A. von der Linden *et al.*, *MNRAS* **443**, 1973 (September 2014).
14. V. Biffi *et al.*, *ApJ* **827**, p. 112 (August 2016).
15. Planck Collaboration, *A&A* **550**, p. A131 (February 2013).
16. M. Arnaud *et al.*, *A&A* **517**, p. A92 (July 2010).
17. E. Pointecouteau *et al.*, *arXiv e-prints* , p. arXiv:2105.05607 (May 2021).

The CMB dipole: Eppur si muove

R. M. Sullivan* and D. Scott

*Physics and Astronomy, University of British Columbia,
Vancouver, BC, Canada*
E-mail: rsullivan@phas.ubc.ca
www.ubc.ca

The largest temperature anisotropy in the cosmic microwave background (CMB) is the dipole. The simplest interpretation of the dipole is that it is due to our motion with respect to the rest frame of the CMB. As well as creating the $\ell=1$ mode of the CMB sky, this motion affects all astrophysical observations by modulating and aberrating sources across the sky. It can be seen in galaxy clustering, and in principle its time derivative through a dipole-shaped acceleration pattern in quasar positions. Additionally, the dipole modulates the CMB temperature anisotropies with the same frequency dependence as the thermal Sunyaev-Zeldovich (tSZ) effect and so these modulated CMB anisotropies can be extracted from the tSZ maps produced by *Planck*. Unfortunately this measurement cannot determine if the dipole is due to our motion, but it does provide an independent measure of the dipole and a validation of the y maps. This measurement, and a description of the first-order terms of the CMB dipole, are outlined here.

Keywords: Cosmic Microwave Background; Cosmic Microwave Background dipole; Special relativity; Thermal Sunyaev-Zeldovich effect.

1. The CMB Sky from *Planck*

Planck[a] was a space-based telescope that measured the microwave sky in nine wavebands, allowing it to capture not only the cosmic microwave background (CMB) but also several Galactic and extragalactic foreground components. This is most clearly seen in figure 51 from Ref. 1, which shows the various wavebands of the *Planck* satellite and the frequency spectra of the foreground signals across those bands. One signal of interest to this study is the thermal Sunyaev-Zeldovich (tSZ) effect, which produces so-called y-type distortion signals. This comes from CMB photons being inverse-Compton scattered, mostly through hot galaxy clusters, which makes holes (or lowers the flux) at low frequencies and up-scatters (or makes an excess flux) at high frequencies. This signal allows us to construct a novel and independent measure of the CMB dipole because temperature anisotropies stemming from the CMB dipole contaminate the y maps. It can also be used as a valuable test of the quality of the y maps. We will start in Sec. 2 by setting out relevant notation for

---

[a]*Planck* (http://www.esa.int/Planck) is a project of the European Space Agency (ESA) with instruments provided by two scientific consortia funded by ESA member states and led by Principal Investigators from France and Italy, telescope reflectors provided through a collaboration between ESA and a scientific consortium led and funded by Denmark, and additional contributions from NASA (USA).

the unboosted CMB sky. Next, in Sec. 3 we will boost the CMB sky, and explore the relevant terms that arise from that boost in the subsections. Of particular relevance, in Sec. 3.3 we will discuss our measurement of the dipole modulation terms that mix with the tSZ effect. We will finish in Sec. 4 with a short discussion and conclusion regarding our work.

2. The Unboosted CMB Sky

To derive the connection between the y map and the dipole we will begin by defining some useful terms regarding the unboosted CMB sky:

$$x \equiv \frac{h\nu}{k_\text{B} T}; \tag{1}$$

$$I \equiv \frac{2 k_\text{B}^3 T^3}{h^2 c^2} \frac{x^3}{e^x - 1}; \tag{2}$$

$$f(x) \equiv \frac{x e^x}{e^x - 1}; \tag{3}$$

$$Y(x) \equiv x \frac{e^x + 1}{e^x - 1} - 4. \tag{4}$$

These are the dimensionless frequency, the standard Planck blackbody intensity function, the frequency dependence of the CMB anisotropies and the relative frequency dependence of the tSZ effect or y type distortions, respectively. Thus, to first order the anisotropies of intensity measured by *Planck* can be written as

$$\frac{\delta I(\hat{\mathbf{n}})}{I f(x)} = \frac{\delta T(\hat{\mathbf{n}})}{T_\text{CMB}} + y(\hat{\mathbf{n}}) Y(x), \tag{5}$$

where $\hat{\mathbf{n}}$ is the line of sight direction on the sky and we have only considered the temperature anisotropies and the y signals here.

3. The Boosted CMB Sky

If we apply a boost to Eq. 5, with a dimensionless velocity $\boldsymbol{\beta}$, we find

$$\begin{aligned}\frac{\delta I'(\hat{\mathbf{n}}')}{I f(x)} &= \beta\mu + \frac{\delta T(\hat{\mathbf{n}}')}{T_\text{CMB}}(1 + 3\beta\mu) \\ &\quad + Y(x)\left(y(\hat{\mathbf{n}}')(1 + 3\beta\mu) + \beta\mu \frac{\delta T(\hat{\mathbf{n}}')}{T_\text{CMB}}\right) \\ &\quad + \beta\mu y(\hat{\mathbf{n}}')\left(Y^2(x) - x \frac{dY(x)}{dx}\right) + \mathcal{O}(\beta^2), \end{aligned} \tag{6}$$

where $\mu = \cos(\theta)$, and θ is the angle between the boost $\boldsymbol{\beta}$ and the line of sight $\hat{\mathbf{n}}'$. The first line has the same frequency dependence as thermal fluctuations and so appear in typical CMB temperature anisotropy maps. Crucially for our analysis, the middle line has the same frequency dependence as y-type distortions and thus describes the signals in the y map. The final line has more obscure frequency dependence and is not discussed here. Additionally, the direction of the incoming photons will change from $\hat{n}$ to $\hat{n}'$, where $\hat{n}' = \hat{n} - \nabla(\hat{n} \cdot \beta)$; this deflection of the photons by $\nabla(\hat{n} \cdot \beta)$ is due to aberration, an effect that is not unique to the microwave sky and occurs for all astronomical observations. We will now discuss each of these terms in turn.

3.1. *The CMB dipole:* $\beta\mu$

In the first line of Eq. 6, the term $\beta\mu$ describes the pure CMB dipole, as discussed previously. This mainly (or perhaps entirely) comes from our local motion with respect to the CMB rest frame and it has been previously measured in Refs. 2, 3, and 4, and most recently in Refs. 5, 6, and 7. Taking the large dipole as being solely caused by our motion, the velocity is $v = (369.82 \pm 0.11)\,\mathrm{km\,s^{-1}}$ in the direction $(l, b) = (264°021 \pm 0°011, 48°253 \pm 0°005)^5$ and can be easily seen in the CMB frequency maps, such as in Fig. 1.

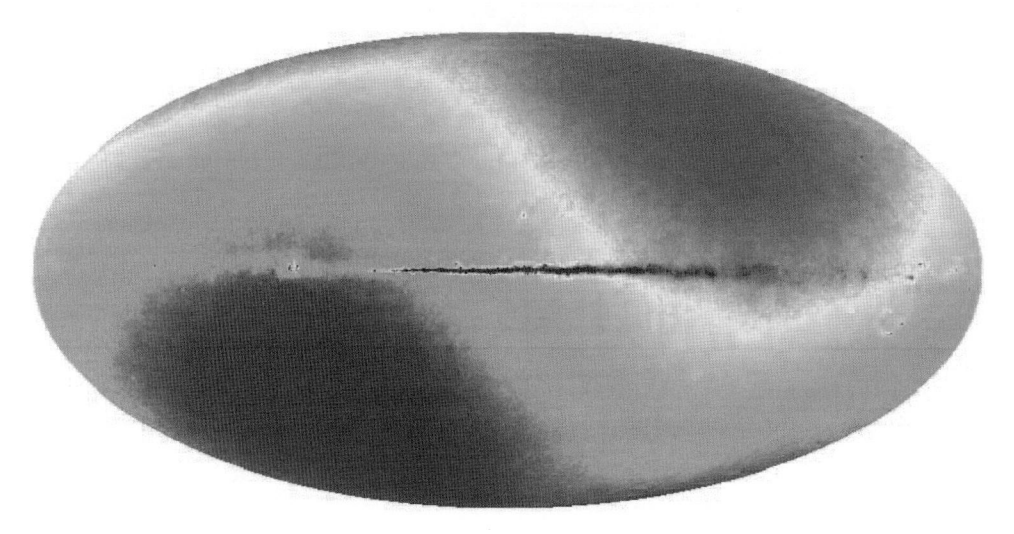

Fig. 1. *Planck* 100-GHz channel map from the NPIPE (PR4) data release,[8] showing the dominant $\ell = 1$ mode or dipole across the sky. The temperature difference across the sky here is 3.36 mK.

3.2. *Aberration and modulation of the CMB anisotropies:* $(1 + 3\beta\mu)\delta T(\hat{n}')/T_{\mathrm{CMB}}$

The second term in the first line of Eq. 6 is the dipole aberration and modulation of the temperature anisotropies of the CMB. The modulation causes the temperature anisotropies to be brighter in the forwards direction, and dimmer in the reverse direction. The aberration causes the anisotropies to be more condensed in the forwards direction, and more stretched out in the reverse direction (effectively the same as $\ell = 1$ lensing). These two effects can be seen in Fig. 2. This effect was first measured in Ref. 9 to about $4\,\sigma$.

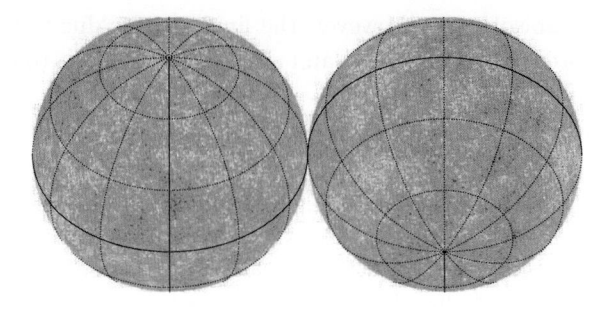

(a) The unboosted CMB sky.

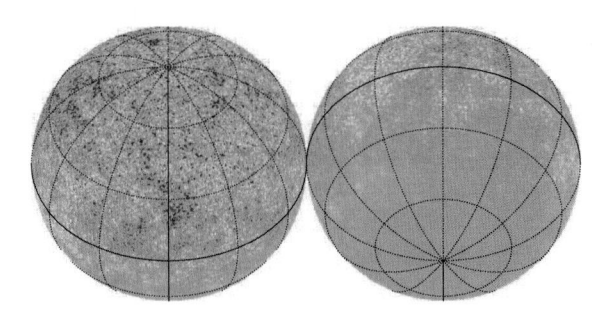

(b) The modulated CMB sky.

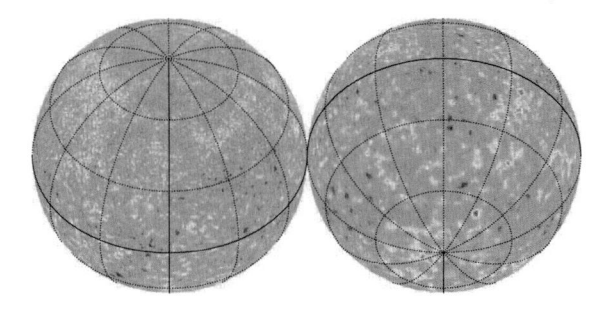

(c) The aberrated CMB sky.

Fig. 2. Here the CMB sky is shown unboosted in (a), with a modulation from a boost of 90 % the speed of light in (b), and with aberration from a boost of 90 % of the speed of light in (c). In the case of modulation, the anisotropies are more intense in the forward direction and less so in the reverse direction, whereas the aberration condenses the anisotropies in the forwards direction and causes them to be more spread out in the reverse direction.

3.3. *Temperature modulation and the tSZ effect:* $Y(x)\beta\mu\delta T(\hat{n}')/T_{\text{CMB}}$

The second line of Eq. 6 shows the dipole-generated signals in the y maps produced by *Planck*. The first half is the same modulation and aberration terms as were seen in the temperature anisotropies; however, the final term is due to the second-order expansion of the intensity about T_{CMB} and adds a contribution to the y maps from the temperature anisotropies.

We can look for this signal by cross-correlating a template map, derived from the CMB temperature data, with a y map. To this end, we use the so-called 2D-ILC CMB temperature map which was produced by the "Constrained ILC" component-separation method designed by Ref. 10 to explicitly null out the contribution from the y-type spectral distortions in the CMB map. We also use the SMICA-NOSZ temperature map, similarly produced with the express intent of removing the y-type spectral distortions, and which was generated for the *Planck* 2018 data release.[11] Likewise, we use the corresponding 2D-ILC y map, and the *Planck* MILCA y map, which explicitly null out the contributions from a (differential) blackbody spectral distribution in the y map.[12,13] If we multiply our CMB map with $\beta\mu$ and cross-correlate that with our tSZ map, then we can directly probe the dipole modulation.

In Ref. 9 a quadratic estimator was used to determine the dipole aberration and modulation, in essence using the auto-correlation of the CMB fluctuation temperature maps. In this work we use the fact that we know the true CMB fluctuations with excellent precision and therefore know the signal that should be present in the y map. Thus, we fully exploit the angular dependence of the modulation signal and remove much of the cosmic variance that would be present in the auto-correlation. In order to implement this idea we define three templates, B_i (with $i = 1, 2, 3$) as

$$B_i(\hat{\mathbf{n}}) = \beta \hat{\mathbf{n}} \cdot \hat{\mathbf{m}}_i \frac{\delta T}{T_0}(\hat{\mathbf{n}}), \tag{7}$$

where $\beta = v/c$[5] is 1.23357×10^{-3} and $\hat{\mathbf{m}}_1, \hat{\mathbf{m}}_2, \hat{\mathbf{m}}_3$ are the CMB dipole direction, an orthogonal direction in the Galactic plane, and the third remaining orthogonal direction (see Fig. 3). Due to the presence of the CMB dipole, the signal B_1 should be present in the y map and so we can directly cross-correlate B_1 with our y map to pull out the signal. Likewise, the cross-correlation of B_2 and B_3 with our y map should give results consistent with noise.

Our y simulations are generated by first computing the power spectra of our data y maps; specifically we apply the MASTER method using the NaMASTER routine[14] to account for the applied mask.[15] Then we generate y maps using this power-spectrum with the HEALPix[16] routine synfast. We finally apply a Gaussian smoothing of $5'$ to model the telescope beam. For each analysis method we estimate the amplitude of the dipole ($\hat{\beta}_i$) in each of the three orthogonal directions. We apply the same analysis procedure on a suite of 1000 y simulations, generated with and without the dipolar modulation term.

We use two methods of cross-correlation: the first is performed directly in map-space; and the second is performed in harmonic space. For both methods we first apply our mask to the templates B_i and the y map.

In the map-space method we then locate all peaks (i.e., local maxima or minima) of the template map B_i and select a patch of radius $2°\!.0$ around each peak. For every

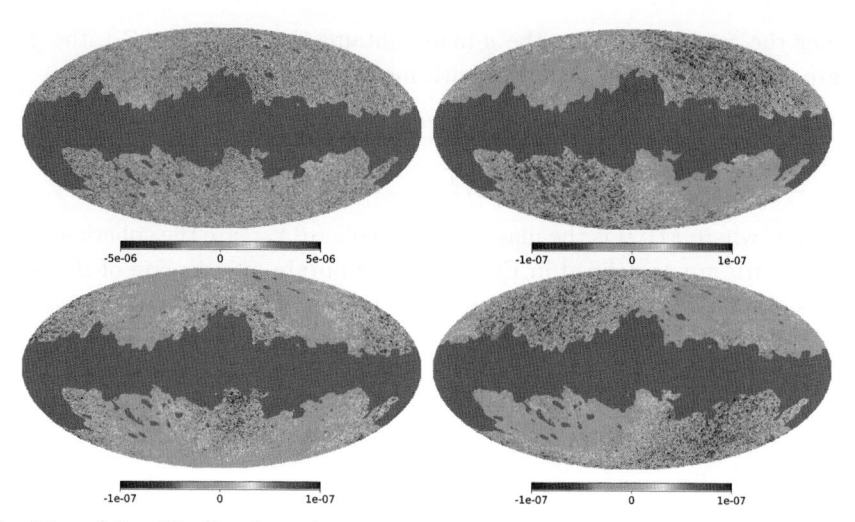

Fig. 3. Map of the tSZ effect from the MILCA component-separation method in y-map units (top left) and the expected modulated CMB signal (top right) generated using the SMICA-NOSZ CMB map in units of T_0. The bottom left and right panels are the CMB anisotropies modulated in orthogonal directions to the CMB dipole. Note that the map of the tSZ effect (top left) has a different scale bar when compared to the other three (i.e., the modulation signal is about 50 times weaker).

peak we obtain an estimate of $\hat{\beta}_i$ through the simple operation

$$\hat{\beta}_{i,p} = \beta \frac{\sum_{k \in D(p)} B_{i,k} y_k}{\sum_{k \in D(p)} B_{i,k}^2}, \qquad (8)$$

where $D(p)$ is the collection of all *unmasked* pixels in a $2°\!.0$ radius centred on pixel p, and p is the position of a peak. Equation 8 is simply a cross-correlation in map space and by itself offers a highly noisy (and largely unbiased) estimate. We then combine all individual peak estimates with a set of weights (w_p) to give our full estimate:

$$\hat{\beta}_i = \frac{\sum_p w_{i,p} \hat{\beta}_{i,p}}{\sum_p w_{i,p}}. \qquad (9)$$

We choose w_p to be proportional to the square of the dipole, and use weights that are proportional to the square of the Laplacian at the peak;[17] this favours sharply defined peaks over shallow ones. Finally we account for the scan strategy of the *Planck* mission by weighting by the 217-GHz hits map,[18] denoted H_p^{217}. The weights are then explicitly

$$w_{i,p} = |\hat{\mathbf{n}} \cdot \hat{\mathbf{m}}_i|_p^2 \left(\nabla^2(B_i) \big|_p \right)^2 H_p^{217}. \qquad (10)$$

We apply the method for each of our simulated y maps, in exactly the same way as for the data.

Under the assumption that the y map contains the template (B_i), the y multipoles are Gaussian random numbers with mean and variance given by

$$s^i_{\ell m} = \int d\Omega\, \beta\, \hat{\mathbf{m}}_i \cdot \hat{\mathbf{n}}\, \frac{\delta T}{T_0} M(\Omega) Y^*_{\ell m}, \qquad (11)$$

$$\sigma^2_\ell = C^y_\ell + N^y_\ell, \qquad (12)$$

respectively, where $M(\Omega)$ is the mask over the sphere, $Y_{\ell m}$ are the spherical harmonics, and the $\hat{\mathbf{m}}_i$ are as defined in Eq. 7. We can obtain an estimate of β_i by taking the cross-correlation with inverse-variance weighting. Our estimator is therefore

$$\hat{\beta}_i = \beta \sum_{i'} \left[\sum_{\ell m}^{\ell_{\max}} s^i_{\ell m}(s^{i'}_{\ell m})^*/\sigma^2_\ell \right]^{-1} \sum_{\ell m}^{\ell_{\max}} s^{i'}_{\ell m}(y_{\ell m})^*/\sigma^2_\ell. \qquad (13)$$

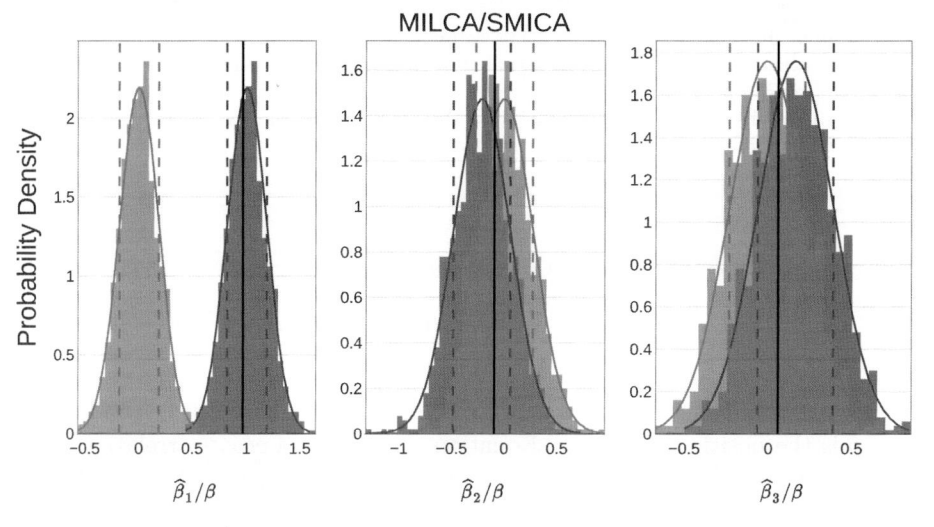

Fig. 4. Histograms of $\hat{\beta}_i/\beta$ values (with 1, 2, and 3 corresponding to the CMB dipole direction, the Galactic plane, and a third orthogonal direction) using the map-space analysis for MILCA y maps, and for CMB template maps SMICA-NOSZ. Blue histograms are simulations with the dipolar modulation term, while orange histograms are simulations without modulation. Black vertical lines denote the values of the real data, demonstrating that they are much more consistent with the existence of the dipolar modulation term than without it. Dashed lines show the 68 % regions for a Gaussian fit to the histograms. To see the full results with all data analysis combinations see Ref. 19.

First we compare the consistency of the data with our two sets of simulations (with and without the dipole term). This comparisons shown in Figs. 4 and 5 have blue histograms being the simulations *with* the dipole term and orange histograms being *without*. The data (black line) for 2D-ILC and MILCA can clearly be seen to be consistent with the simulations with the dipole term. Further details and analysis may be found in Ref. 19.

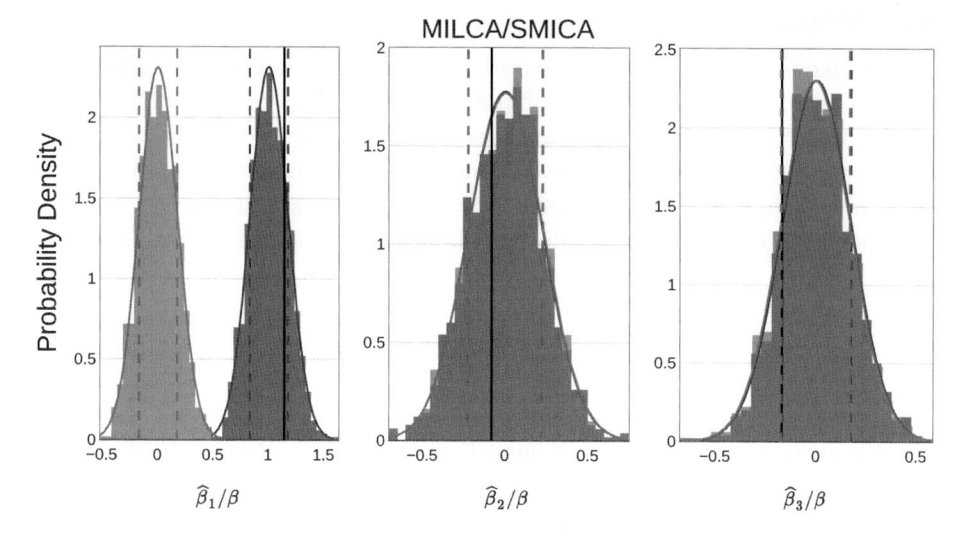

Fig. 5. As in Fig. 4, except now for the harmonic-space analysis.

4. Conclusion: Distinguishing Intrinsic and Extrinsic CMB Dipoles

The frequency-dependent part of the dipolar-modulation signal is agnostic to the source of the large CMB dipole. Therefore, its measurement is an independent determination of the CMB dipole. While it may be tempting to use this signal to distinguish an intrinsic dipole, it has been shown that an intrinsic dipole and a dipole induced by a velocity boost would in fact have the same dipolar-modulation signature on the sky.[20,21]

Due to the existence of the CMB dipole, a tSZ map necessarily contains a contaminating signal that is simply the dipole modulation of the CMB anisotropies. This occurs because CMB experiments do not directly measure temperature anisotropies, but instead measure intensity variations that are conventionally converted to temperature variations. This contamination adds power to the tSZ map in a Y_{20} pattern, with its axis parallel to the dipole direction. We have measured this effect and determined a statistically independent value of the CMB dipole, which is consistent with direct measurements of the dipole. Using a conservative multipole cut on the y map, the significance of the detection of the dipole modulation signal is around 5 or 6 σ, depending on the precise choice of data set and analysis method.

The question as to whether an intrinsic dipole could ever be observationally distinguished from an extrinsic dipole (i.e. a Doppler boost) remains an open question. The terms discussed in Eq. 6 are based on the assumption of a CMB blackbody spectrum and cannot be used to distinguish the two, as they would naturally arise whether the CMB dipole is caused by a boost, or if there is for some other reason a dipole on the sky with the same magnitude and direction.

Acknowledgements

We would like to acknowledge the support of the Natural Sciences and Engineering Research Council of Canada. Some of the results in this paper have been derived using the HEALPix package. Results are based on observations obtained with Planck (http://www.esa.int/Planck), an ESA science mission with instruments and contributions directly funded by ESA Member States, NASA, and Canada. We would also like to thank Dagoberto Contreras for collaboration on topics within this paper.

References

1. Planck Collaboration X, *Planck* 2015 results. X. Diffuse component separation: Foreground maps, *A&A* **594**, p. A10 (2016).
2. A. Kogut, C. Lineweaver, G. F. Smoot, C. L. Bennett, A. Banday, N. W. Boggess, E. S. Cheng, G. de Amici, D. J. Fixsen, G. Hinshaw, P. D. Jackson, M. Janssen, P. Keegstra, K. Loewenstein, P. Lubin, J. C. Mather, L. Tenorio, R. Weiss, D. T. Wilkinson and E. L. Wright, Dipole Anisotropy in the COBE Differential Microwave Radiometers First-Year Sky Maps, *ApJ* **419**, p. 1 (December 1993).
3. D. J. Fixsen, E. S. Cheng, J. M. Gales, J. C. Mather, R. A. Shafer and E. L. Wright, The Cosmic Microwave Background Spectrum from the Full COBE FIRAS Data Set, *ApJ* **473**, p. 576 (December 1996).
4. G. Hinshaw, J. L. Weiland, R. S. Hill, N. Odegard, D. Larson, C. L. Bennett, J. Dunkley, B. Gold, M. R. Greason, N. Jarosik, E. Komatsu, M. R. Nolta, L. Page, D. N. Spergel, E. Wollack, M. Halpern, A. Kogut, M. Limon, S. S. Meyer, G. S. Tucker and E. L. Wright, Five-Year Wilkinson Microwave Anisotropy Probe (WMAP) Observations: Data Processing, Sky Maps, and Basic Results, *ApJS* **180**, 225 (February 2009).
5. Planck Collaboration I, *Planck* 2018 results. I. Overview, and the cosmological legacy of *Planck*, *A&A* **641**, p. A1 (2020).
6. Planck Collaboration II, *Planck* 2018 results. II. Low Frequency Instrument data processing, *A&A, in press* (2019).
7. Planck Collaboration III, *Planck* 2018 results. III. High Frequency Instrument data processing, *A&A, in press* (2019).
8. Planck Collaboration Int. LVII, *Planck* intermediate results. LVII. NPIPE: Joint *Planck* LFI and HFI data processing, *A&A* **643**, p. 42 (2020).
9. Planck Collaboration XXVII, *Planck* 2013 results. XXVII. Doppler boosting of the CMB: Eppur si muove, *A&A* **571**, p. A27 (2014).
10. M. Remazeilles, J. Delabrouille and J.-F. Cardoso, CMB and SZ effect separation with constrained Internal Linear Combinations, *MNRAS* **410**, 2481 (February 2011).
11. Planck Collaboration IV, *Planck* 2018 results. IV. Diffuse component separation, *A&A, in press* (2019).
12. G. Hurier, J. F. Macías-Pérez and S. Hildebrandt, MILCA, a modified internal linear combination algorithm to extract astrophysical emissions from multifrequency sky maps, *A&A* **558**, p. A118 (October 2013).
13. Planck Collaboration XXII, *Planck* 2015 results. XXII. A map of the thermal Sunyaev-Zeldovich effect, *A&A* **594**, p. A22 (2016).
14. D. Alonso, J. Sanchez, A. Slosar and L. D. E. S. Collaboration, A unified pseudo-$C\ell$ framework, *Monthly Notices of the Royal Astronomical Society* **484**, 4127 (01 2019).

15. E. Hivon, K. M. Górski, C. B. Netterfield, B. P. Crill, S. Prunet and F. Hansen, MASTER of the Cosmic Microwave Background Anisotropy Power Spectrum: A Fast Method for Statistical Analysis of Large and Complex Cosmic Microwave Background Data Sets, *ApJ* **567**, 2 (March 2002).
16. K. M. Górski, E. Hivon, A. J. Banday, B. D. Wandelt, F. K. Hansen, M. Reinecke and M. Bartelmann, HEALPix: A Framework for High-Resolution Discretization and Fast Analysis of Data Distributed on the Sphere, *ApJ* **622**, 759 (April 2005).
17. V. Desjacques, Baryon acoustic signature in the clustering of density maxima, *Phys. Rev. D* **78**, p. 103503 (November 2008).
18. Planck Collaboration VIII, *Planck* 2015 results. VIII. High Frequency Instrument data processing: Calibration and maps, *A&A* **594**, p. A8 (2016).
19. Planck Collaboration Int. LVI, *Planck* intermediate results. LVI. Detection of the CMB dipole through modulation of the thermal Sunyaev-Zeldovich effect: Eppur si muove II, *A&A* **644**, p. 100 (2020).
20. A. Challinor and F. van Leeuwen, Peculiar velocity effects in high-resolution microwave background experiments, *Phys. Rev. D* **65**, p. 103001 (May 2002).
21. A. Notari and M. Quartin, CMB all-scale blackbody distortions induced by linearizing temperature, *ArXiv e-prints* (October 2015).

High angular resolution Sunyaev Zel'dovich observations: The case of MISTRAL

E. S. Battistelli[1,*], E. Barbavara[1], P. de Bernardis[1], F. Cacciotti[1], V. Capalbo[1],
E. Carretti[2], F. Columbro[1], A. Coppolecchia[1], A. Cruciani[3], G. D'Alessandro[1], M. De Petris[1],
F. Govoni[4], G. Isopi[1], L. Lamagna[1], P. Marongiu[4], S. Masi[1], L. Mele[1], E. Molinari[4],
M. Murgia[4], A. Navarrini[4], A. Orlati[2], A. Paiella[1], G. Pettinari[5], F. Piacentini[1], T. Pisanu[4],
S. Poppi[4], G. Presta[1] and F. Radiconi[1]

[1] *Dipartimento di Fisica, Sapienza Università di Roma - Piazzale Aldo Moro, 5, I-00185 Rome, Italy*
[2] *INAF - Istituto di Radioastronomia - Via P. Gobetti, 101 - I-40129 Bologna, Italy*
[3] *INFN - Sezione di Roma, Piazzale Aldo Moro 5 - I-00185, Rome, Italy*
[4] *INAF - Osservatorio Astronomico di Cagliari, Via della Scienza 5 - I-09047 Selargius (CA), Italy*
[5] *Istituto di Fotonica e Nanotecnologie - CNR, Via Cineto Romano 42, I-00156 Rome, Italy*
E-mail: elia.battistelli@roma1.infn.it

The MIllimeter Sardinia radio Telescope Receiver based on Array of Lumped elements kids, MISTRAL, is a millimetric ($\simeq 90 GHz$) multipixel camera being built for the Sardinia Radio Telescope. It is going to be a facility instrument and will sample the sky with 12 arcsec angular resolution, 4 arcmin field of view, through 408 Kinetic Inductance Detectors (KIDs). The construction and the beginning of commissioning is planned to be in 2022. MISTRAL will allow the scientific community to propose a wide variety of scientific cases including protoplanetary discs study, star forming regions, galaxies radial profiles, and high angular resolution measurements of the Sunyaev Zel'dovich (SZ) effect with the investigation of the morphology of galaxy cluster and the search for the Cosmic Web.

Keywords: Millimetric astronomy, large radio telescopes, Sunyaev Zel'dovich effect

1. Introduction

High angular resolution millimetric observation are key to understand a wide variety of scientific cases. Among others, the interaction of Cosmic Microwave Background (CMB) photons with the hot electron gas in galaxy clusters and surrounding medium (the Sunyaev Zel'dovich, SZ effect) promises to study galaxy clusters and their deviation from relaxed behaviour. This include high angular resolution measurements of the SZ effect with the investigation of the morphology of galaxy cluster and the search for the Cosmic Web. Also, protoplanetary discs study, star forming regions, and galaxies radial profiles are among the important scientific cases one could achieve with high angular resolution millimetric observation.

Only a handful of instruments are capable of measuring, for instance, galaxy clusters with high enough angular resolution to resolve them. Among them, we mention

MUSTANG2 at the Green Bank Telescope (GBT[a]) and NIKA2 at IRAM telescope[b]. MUSTANG2[1] is a millimetric cryogenic camera installed at the 100m GBT. It is operating in the frequency range between 75GHz and 105GHz and samples 4 arcmin f.o.v. in the sky with 223 microstrip-coupled Transition Edge Sensors (TESs). The resulted diffraction limited angular resolution is of the order of 9 arcsec. A frequency domain multiplexing technique is used to read MUSTANG2 detectors through flux-ramp modulation technique.

Another receiver which addresses similar science goals, although it takes data at higher frequencies, is NIKA2.[2–4] NIKA2 is a 2 channel millimetric camera measuring at 150GHz (one array) and 260GHz (two arrays). It observes from the 30m IRAM telescope with a field of view (f.o.v.) of 6.5 arcmin while the angular resolution is around 18 arcsec at 150GHz and around 10 arcsec at 260GHz. NIKA2 hosts 3 arrays of Kinetic Inductance Detectors (KIDs), each of around 2000 pixels, cooled down at 100mK with a dilution refrigerator. Both MUSTANG2 and NIKA2 are very active in the field of millimetric astronomy especially for the high angular resolution detection of the SZ effect.

A third instrument being prepared for such scientific cases is the MIllimeter Sardinia radio Telescope Receiver based on Array of Lumped elements kids, MISTRAL, to be fielded at the 64m Sardinia Radio Telescope (SRT[c]). MISTRAL will use an array of 408 KIDs with a f.o.v. of 4 arcmin and an angular resolution of around 12 arcsec. It is a cryogenic instrument with detectors cooled down at 270mK and with frequency domain multiplexing, ROACH2 based read-out.

2. Sardinia Radio Telescope and its upgrade

2.1. *Sardinia Radio Telescope*

The Sardinia Radio Telescope (SRT - Lat. 39.4930 N; -Long. 9.2451 E), is a Gregorian configured fully steerable 64m primary mirror radio telescope which can work from 300MHz and 116GHz[5] (see Fig. 1). It is a multipurpose instrument operated in either single dish or Very Long Baseline Interferometer mode and managed by the Italian Astrophysics National Institute (INAF). The telescope manufacturing started in 2003 and was completed in August 2012 when the technical commissioning started. The scientific exploitation of the SRT started on 2016 with an Early Science Program, while regular proposals started in 2018.

SRT has a f/0.33 primary focus and f/2.34 secondary focus allowing to host the low frequency receivers ($\nu < 2GHz$) in the primary focus, and high frequency receivers in the Gregorian room. The 64-m primary mirror (M1) is composed of 1008 electromechanically controlled aluminum elements by actuators. The secondary mirror (M2) is a 7.9m mirror composed of 49 aluminum elements adjustable for focus

---

[a]https://greenbankobservatory.org/science/telescopes/gbt/
[b]https://www.iram-institute.org/EN/30-meter-telescope.php
[c]http://www.srt.inaf.it/

Fig. 1. The 64-m Sardinia Radio Telescope (image credits F. Guidi).

operations. Both M1 and M2 are shaped to minimize spillover and the standing waves between the receiver and the subreflector.[5]

2.2. Observational site

The location of the SRT is in the island of Sardinia, $\simeq$50km north of Cagliari, at 600m a.s.l.. It is a region suited for radio-observations and the telescope was designed to be operating up to 116GHz. Estimation of sky opacity, based on recorded dedicated radiometer data, reports[d] an opacity $\tau < 0.15Np$ (50th percentile) at 93GHz during the winter nights. The average precipitable water vapour (PWV) in the same conditions is mainly 8mm. For comparison, the GBT reports $\tau < 0.125$ (50th percentile) at 86GHz, and an average $PWV < 9mm$ (50th percentile)[e]. The above estimation is confirmed by radiosondes profiles taken at Cagliari airport and scaled for the SRT site. This shown $PWV < 11mm$ (50th precentile) and opacities $< 0.2Np$ (50th percentile) at 100GHz.[6]

2.3. PON upgrade

In 2018, a National Operational Program (PON) grant was assigned to INAF with the aim to exploit to the full the SRT capability to reach mm wavelenghts up to 116GHz.[7] One of the Working Packages includes a metrological system to measure

---

[d]http://hdl.handle.net/20.500.12386/28787
[e]https://www.gb.nrao.edu/mustang/wx.shtml

with high precision deformations of the SRT due to gravitational and thermal effects; by means of the active surface it will be possible to correct the deformations of the main mirror allowing the surface roughness needed for observations up to 116 GHz. Also, the metrological system will allow high precision pointing measuring and correcting the subreflector displacement from the optical axis together with the deformation of the whole structure.

In addition an upgrade of the SRT receiver fleet is foreseen including an extension to higher frequencies up to 116GHz, thus exploiting to the full its optical surface. This grant was divided in 9 working packages which include new receivers like a 19 feeds, double polarization Q-band heterodyne receiver, a triple band (K, Q, W) coherent receiver, a 16 double polarization W-band heterodyne receiver, and a W-band, total power, 408 pixels bolometric[f] receiver: MISTRAL.

3. MISTRAL

3.1. *Introduction*

MISTRAL is a facility instrument to be installed at the SRT in 2022. It operates in an atmospheric window in the frequency range 78-103GHz, namely W-band, that is interesting for a number of scientific reasons, and most importantly it provides low optical depth and allows high efficiency observations. It will be installed in the Gregorian room of the SRT and as such, it needs to meet several requirements and limitations. These include:

- 250kg maximum weight;
- 700mm x 700mm x 2400mm (h) maximum occupation. In addition, the top part should not interfere with the Gregorian room structure;
- adeguate Radio Frequency shielding;
- ability to work from 30° elevation to 80° and the need not to be damaged in the range 0-90° elevation;
- long ($\simeq$100m) long helium lines for the Pulse Tube head-compressor connection;
- remote operations;
- MISTRAL will be installed on the Gregorian room turret (a rotating structure which hosts MISTRAL an all other receivers) and needs to be agile enough to be inserted in the SRT focus or removed through rotation of the turret itself (see Fig. 2).

---

[f] Actually MISTRAL will implement Kinetic Inductance Detectors which are not properly bolometers.

3.2. Cryostat

MISTRAL consists of a cryostat, being constructed by QMC instruments[g], with a Pulse Tube cryocooler, an He-10 sorption refrigerator, custom optics and detectors. We use a Sumitomo[h] RP-182B2S-F100H Pulse Tube (PT) cryocooler. From Sumitomo user manuals, PT heads work properly in vertical position with inclination no larger than $+/-20°$. In order to have the PT heads as close as possible to vertical position during observations, we have positioned the head with an inclination of $57.5°$ with respect to the focal plane. This allows a nominal observation elevation of 37.5-$77.5°$. Nevertheless, we have tested higher inclinations and there is no impact on the cryogenics with inclination of $+/-25°$ (resulting in elevation range of 32.5-$82.5°$) with no degradation of the thermal performance. MISTRAL has a $40K$ shield, a $4.2K$ shield and a sub-Kelvin stage. The PT is used to cool down the $40K$ and $4.2K$ shields and provides a cooling power of $36W$ for the $40K$ shield and $1.5W$ for the $4.2K$ shield.

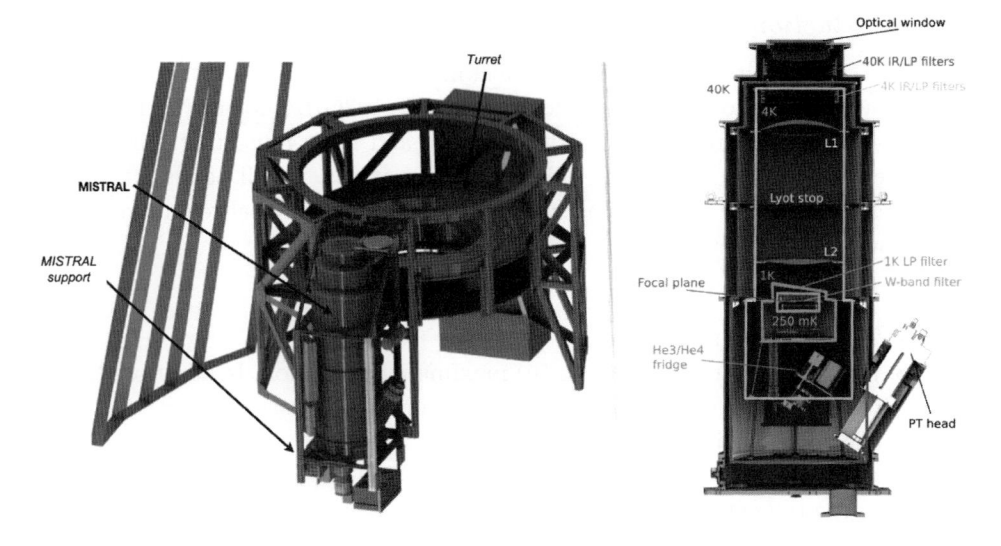

Fig. 2. Left: SRT Turret. with MISTRAL installed. Right: a cut of MISTRAL cryostat highlighting the main parts.

The PT head is controlled by a PT compressor which cannot be inclined with the telescope elevation angle. For this reason, MISTRAL compressor will not be located at the Gregorian room, but rather in a compressor room at the base of the radio telescope, that can rotate with the azimuth angle but does not change inclination with the elevation angle. This requires about 100m of flexible lines for the

---

[g] http://www.terahertz.co.uk/qmc-instruments-ltd
[h] https://www.shicryogenics.com/

compressor-to-PT head connection. Sumitomo (as well as other companies) report 20m maximum length for this operations so on-site tests were performed in order to verify if a PT can keep the $4.2K$ base temperature and with which dissipated power.[8] We made these tests using a Sumitomo RP-082B2S cryocooler, which is similar to the one chosen for MISTRAL but with lower cooling power (i.e. $0.9W$ at $4.2K$). It was shown that this cryocooler was able to hold a base temperature of $4.2K$ with a power load of $0.6W$ with $119m$ of flexible lines. Since the power dissipation requirement for MISTRAL is of the order of $0.6W$, the $1.5W$ PT will be able to satisfy the requirement with some margin. In addition, a vibration dumper, and a remote PT valve, will allow to reduce vibration into the detectors.

Attached to the $40K$ and the $4.2K$ stages, it will be applied radiation shields as well as radiation filters allowing to block thermal input of the sub-K stages of MISTRAL. The sub-K fridge is a Chase[i] He^3/He^4 sorption refrigerator (Twin GL10 sorption fridge) allowing a nominal cooling power as in the following table:

Stage	temperature no load	temperature loaded	Load applied
He^4	$0.840K$	$0.913K$	$150\mu W$
He^3	$0.299K$	$0.332K$	$30\mu W$
Ultra cold He^3	$0.195K$	$0.251K$	$20\mu W$

The total room to be cooled down is of the order of $1.5m^3$ and the total weight of MISTRAL is around $250kg$. The top part of the cryostat has been shaped in such a way it does not interfere with the Gregorian room walls while rotating in and out of the focus position (see Fig. 2).

3.3. Optics and quasi-optics

The optical design of MISTRAL includes a set of radiation quasi-optical filters, anchored at the different thermal stages of the cryostat, an Anti Reflection Coated (ARC) Ultra High Molecular Weight (UHMW) polyetilene window, and two ARC Silicon lenses able to image the Gregorian Focus on the array of detectors. Detectors are coupled to radiation through open space (filled array) so cryogenic cold stop, placed in between the two lenses, is needed.

Quasi-optical filters are a combination of metal mesh filters, thin IR filters, sub-mm low pass filters (LPE), and a final 78-103GHz Band pass filter produced at QMC instruments[j]. The final configuration still needs to be settled down as it depends on cryogenic tests and performance that still need to be carried on. Nevertheless, the filter chain will include:

- $300K$: ARC UHMW window of 190mm outer diameter, plus two blocking thermal filters;

---

[i]https://www.chasecryogenics.com/
[j]http://www.terahertz.co.uk/qmc-instruments-ltd

- $40K$: two additional thermal filters plus a Low Pass Edge filter;
- $4K$: two more thermal filters (IR5 and IR6) and another Low Pass filter;
- $1K$: Low Pass filters;
- $0.350\ K$: Low Pass filters;
- $0.250\ K$: Band Pass Filter centered at 90GHz with a bandwidth either of 30GHz or of 20GHz (to be defined).

Some characteristics of the SRT optical configuration (which were adopted to make the SRT suitable for a wide range of applications) limit the Diffraction Limited Field Of View (DLFOV) usable by the mm camera. As mentioned, we plan to implement a naked Kinetic Inductance Detectors (KIDs) array (a filled array) optically coupled to the antenna by a relay optics. This is the preferred solution for satisfying the following requirements:

- to possibly rescale the Gregorian telescope focal plane;
- to insert a cold aperture stop;
- to provide a gaussian wavelength independent beam telescope configuration;
- to provide a telecentric optics.

The first requirement allow us to tune the size of the KID array preserving the telescope DLFOV. The second condition allows us to introduce an aperture conjugated to the secondary mirror, reduces the spillover contribution due to subreflector and/or primary mirror, ensuring the highest edge taper in a cold aperture. The third condition enables a magnification of the relay optics and the output beam waist location wavelength-independent, at least inside the expected bandwidth, which is a considerable innovation point. The fourth requirement ensures a homogeneous illumination of the array, apart from a possible aberrations impact, suitable for the solution of a naked array maintaining an adequate Strehl Ratio.

Silicon is a suitable material for lens fabrication at millimetri wavelenghts due to its high dielectric constant, low loss tangent, and high thermal conductivities. The two Silicon lenses allow to report 4 arcmin of the SRT focus onto the array of 408 KIDs. They are anti-reflection coated with Rogers RO3003. Their diameter is 290mm and 240mm respectively while the aperture cold stop diameter of 125mm. All the lenses+cold stop system is kept at 4K. The in band average simulations report excellent values with a Strehl Ratio from 0.97 to 0.91 for on-axis and F. O. V. edge positions. Analogously, the FWHM is 12.2 arcsec on axis, and 12.7 arcsec at 45mm off axis.

3.4. *Detectors*

MISTRAL will take advantage of the high sensitivity and the capability of Frequency Domain Multiplexing of KIDs cryogenic detectors. KIDs are superconductive detectors where millimetric radiation with higher energy with respect to the Cooper pair binding energy, can break Cooper pairs producing a change in the population densities and thus in the kinetic inductance. In fact, the inductance L of a thin superconductor is dominated by the kinetic inductance L_k, which depends on the Cooper pair density.

If we integrate this inductance into a resonating RLC circuit, with a well defined resonant frequency, we will see a change in the impedance of the circuit when the inductance is illuminated. This change in impedance can be measured by exciting the circuit with an RF tone at the resonant frequency and monitoring both amplitude and phase of the outcoming tone. The amplitude, and similarly the phase, will change because of the variation in L_k. The general effect is that a decrease in the Cooper pair density increases L_k, thus it lowers the resonant frequency. Furthermore, the increase of the quasi-particle density increases the internal dissipations, thus reducing the quality factor of the resonator. KIDs are intrinsically easy to multiplex in the frequency domain because an array of resonators with different resonant frequencies can be simultaneously readout by sending a comb of Radio Frequency (RF) tones through a single feed-line.

MISTRAL KIDs are Ti-Al bilayer 10 + 30 nm with critical temperature Tc=945mK and are fabricated at CNR-IFN[k].[9,10] They are front-illuminated 3rd order Hilbert crude absorber with backshort on the opposite side of the wafer. The detector array is composed of 408 KIDs detectors. They are 3mm x 3mm each and are arranged on an equilateral triangle every 4.2mm on a 4 inches silicon wafer (see Fig. 3). They sample the focal plane with a FWHM angular spacing of 10.6 arcsec lower the each pixel angular resolution.

As mentioned, KIDs behave as high quality factor, Q, LC resonators. High values of Q allow to multiplex thousands of KIDs, with different frequencies, all coupled to the same feedline. KIDs are in fact intrinsically easy to multiplex in the frequency domain, because an array of resonators with different resonant frequencies can be simultaneously readout by sending a comb of RF tones through a single feed-line. We will use ROACH2 based Frequency Domain Multiplexing which was originally developed for the OLIMPO experiment.[11]

3.5. Magnetic shield

Another important part of MISTRAL is a 1-mm thick Cryoperm 10 μ-metal shield, characterized by an high magnetic permeability ($\mu > 7000$), that acts as a shielding from spurious magnetic fields such as the geomagnetic field. When a KID, usually composed of a thin wire, is exposed to an external magnetic field, a shielding current will be induced. Consequentially, its kinetic inductance changes. The external magnetic field will increase the kinetic inductance of the circuit, thus increasing the total inductance, eventually reducing the quality factor of the resonator. This effect was observed on the MISTRAL detector array[13] and required a magnetic shield to be lower than the earth magnetic shield.

---

[k]https://www.roma.ifn.cnr.it/

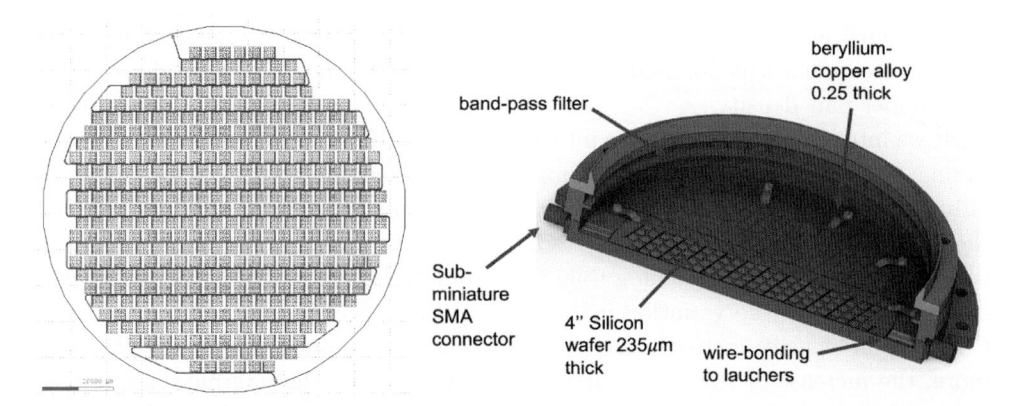

Fig. 3. Left: a design of the focal plane of MISTRAL with its feedline.[12] Right: KIDs holder with the surrounding components.

4. Sensitivity forecast and scanning strategy

4.1. *Noise estimate*

A crucial step to predict the performance on the sky is estimating the expected noise which should affect our detectors. Electrical Noise Equivalent Power (NEP) should be compared with Photon noise NEP due to warm optics and atmosphere emission. The latter, should be considered in its emission part and turbulence part which will act as correlated noise.

Electrical NEP of MISTRAL detectors was measured to be temperature dependent. If we assume a final detectors temperature of 270mK we have average values of our test-bed array of detectors of $NEP_{avg} = 3.5 \times 10^{-16} W/\sqrt{Hz}$ with a maximum and a minimum range of $NEP_{max} = 7.4 \times 10^{-16} W/\sqrt{Hz}$ and $NEP_{min} = 1.6 \times 10^{-16} W/\sqrt{Hz}$ respectively. These numbers need to be compared with estimated photon noise and turbulence noise from atmosphere. The photon noise part was estimated to be, within the 30GHz bandwidth, of $NEP_{ph} = 0.9 \times 10^{-16} W/\sqrt{Hz}$ (which converts into a Noise Equivalent Flux Density of 0.30mJy/beam). To this, in order to estimate the real sensitivity of MISTRAL, we have to add the atmospheric effects due to turbulence. An a-priori calculation of this effect is quite complicated because it also depends on the kind of filtering and on the scanning strategy: the best option would be directly measuring the atmosphere with MISTRAL. This will happen during the commissioning phase, but it is possible to give an early estimate by using experimental data taken at different frequencies. We have SRT data in the K-band (at 22GHz) and we can assume that the ratio between atmospheric fluctuations is equal to the squared ratio of the opacities. In this way, we can infer the atmospheric fluctuation noise at 90GHz using atmospheric modelling softwares such as am^1. This increases the atmospheric noise estimation a factor 10 with respect to

---

[1]https://www.cfa.harvard.edu/~spaine/am/

the photon noise level even in the best 5% percentile resulting in a noise Noise Equivalent Flux Density of $3mJy/beam$. The final result is that MISTRAL detectors will be dominated by atmospheric noise rather than by electric noise, as desired.[14]

4.2. *Scanning strategy*

The final noise level of our maps will depend on the detectors sensitivity, on the atmospheric contamination but also on the scanning strategy and the filtering of the data. We can clearly clean observations very aggressively at the cost of loosing large angular scales on sky. Among the many scientific goals of MISTRAL, the possibility of retrieving large angular scales at the level of its field of view (i.e. 4 arcmin) and even more would be crucial for the study of galaxy clusters and, for instance, for the search for the Cosmic Web in close-by clusters. Scanning strategy drives also the sensitivity as we can more or less efficiently remove atmosphere emission and its fluctuations

At the SRT it is already in use an on-the-fly map scanning strategy which allows orthogonal scans in R.A./Dec or Azimuth/Elevation each composed by parallel subscans. In addition, we are working on the scanning strategy based on Lissajou daisy scanning already in use on different Telescopes such as, for instance, the GBT[m] which has the advantage to reduce to the minimum the overhead due to Telescope inversion and optimize the integration time on the center of an observed field (see Fig. 4). This kind of scanning strategy can easily be analysed with Fourier space filtering of (typically) 0.1Hz (cut-on) and 7.5Hz (cut-off frequency).

5. Science case

MISTRAL will be a facility instrument. Thus, it will be open to the scientific community to decide what kind of scientific output it can achieve and propose the observations to the Time Allocation Committee of the Sardinia Radio Telescope. Nevertheless, we will list in the following a few science cases including those that we think are the most interesting.

Protoplanetary discs millimetric measurements in star forming regions allow to break the degeneracy present in InfraRed (IR) measurements due to the optically thick nature of the hot inner disc. Measuring the SED at mm wavelengths with high angular resolution (i.e. $\simeq$ 10 arcsec) can add information to planetary formation theories.[15] Star formation in molecular clouds with high enough angular resolution allow to distinguish starless cores with respect to those hosting protostars. This is for instance what was attempted with the Large Millimeter Telescope.[n,16] Continuum resolved galaxies observations can give information about morphology and radial

---

[m]https://www.gb.nrao.edu/scienceDocs/GBTog.pdf
[n]http://lmtgtm.org/

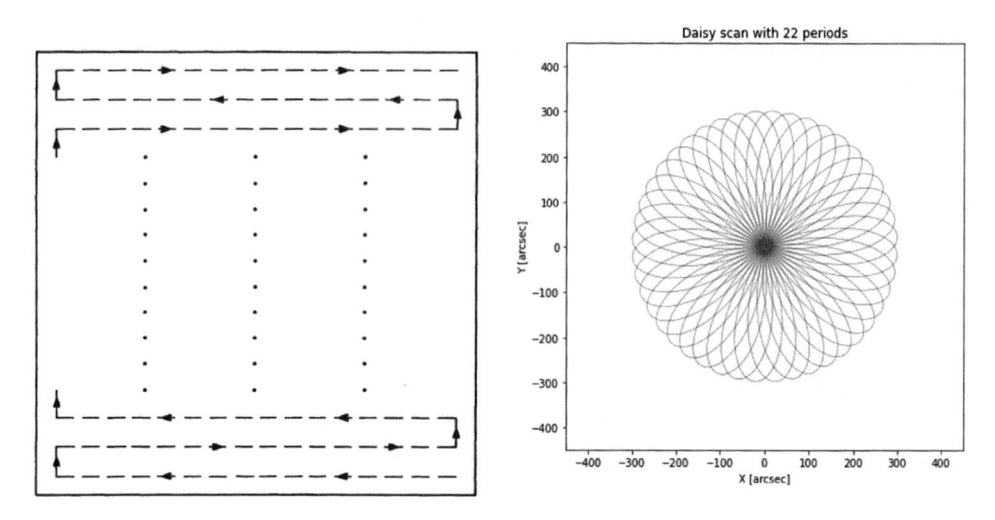

Fig. 4. Left: on-the-fly map scanning strategy already implemented at the SRT. Right: simulation of 22 periods dasy scanning over a 10 arcmin sky area.

profiles (gas column profiles, dust temperature profiles).[17] Spatially resolved high-z radio galaxies can provide info about cold dust re-emission.[18]

When the CMB photons scatter off a hot electron gas, for example in galaxy clusters, they undergo inverse Compton scattering which is visible in the frequency spectrum of the CMB. The resulting distorted spectrum is thus:

$$\frac{\Delta I(x)}{I_0} = y \frac{x^4 e^x}{(e^x - 1)^2} \left(x \coth \frac{x}{2} - 4 \right) = y g(x) \qquad (1)$$

where: $I_0 = \frac{2h}{c^2} \left(\frac{k_b T_{CMB}}{h} \right)^3$, T_{CMB} is the CMB temperature, $x = \frac{h\nu}{k_b T_{CMB}}$ is the adimensional frequency, and $y = \int n_e \sigma_T \frac{k_B T_e}{m_e c^2} $ is the Comptonization parameter, the integral along the line of sight dl of the electron density n_e multiplied by the electron temperature T_e (see Fig. 5). This is the Sunyaev Zel'dovich (SZ) effect[19,20] and can be used to study the physics of Galaxy clusters. In fact, galaxy clusters can experience a wide variety of situation including collisions, merging, and non-relaxed situation. In addition, not only galaxy clusters can host relativistic electrons. Hydrodynamical simulations[21,22] suggested that galaxy clusters occupy the knots of the so called Cosmic Web and Warm to Hot Intergalactic Medium (WHIM) is disposed connecting galaxy cluster forming filaments that could be seen through the SZ effect itself.

What is probably one of the most impacting expected result of MISTRAL is in fact the possibility to observe and resolve the SZ effect through galaxy clusters and surrounding medium. With respect to moderate to low angular resolution observations, high angular resolution ($\simeq 10$ arcsec) detections can investigate non relaxed

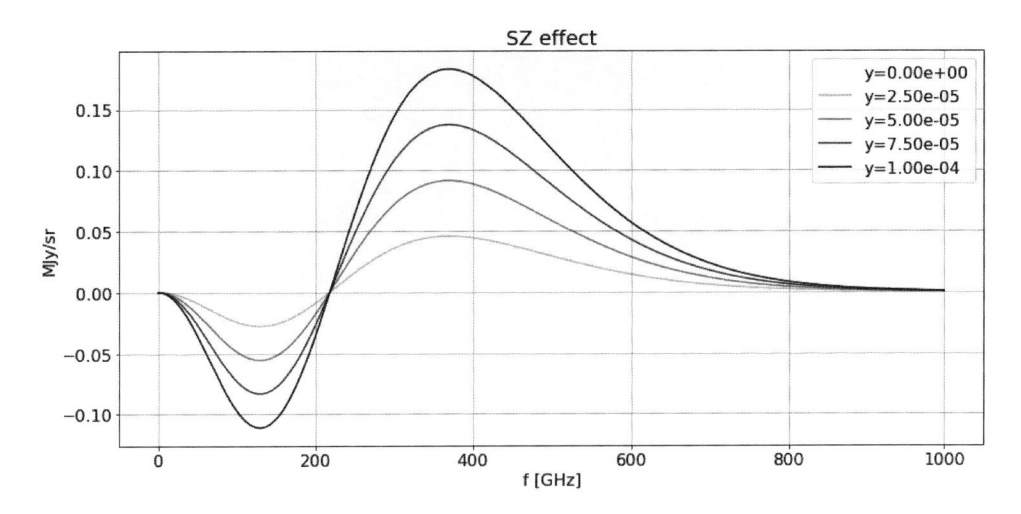

Fig. 5. The SZ effect with different Comptonization parameters.

clusters, study merging clusters, understanding the self similarities of galaxy cluster, study the pressure profiles and understand the AGN feedback expected in some environments.

Understanding the self similarities of galaxy clusters, their identical appearance or scaled properties regardless of their mass or distance is crucial. Self-similarity seems demonstrated but this is not always the case. Galaxy clusters in fact interact, collide, merge. This brings to important degeneracies and deviation from specific models. High angular resolution SZ effect measurements allow to solve the density vs temperature profile degeneracy together with X-ray information especially for high z clusters. In order to understand the physics in different environments, it is very important to study the Intra Cluster Medium (ICM) thermodynamics, including the impact of feedback, bulk and turbulent motions, substructures and cluster asphericity.

Sometimes, clusters are assumed to follow the β profile,[23] the generalized Navarro Frank and Withe (gNFW)[24] profile, or the Universal model.[25] High angular resolution SZ measurements allow to disentangle between models and to identify the most appropriate ones. Even relaxed clusters experience pressure fluctuations and compressions of the ICM. The study of pressure power spectrum allows to separate relaxed vs non-relaxed clusters where larger perturbations increase in the outer shells of the clusters (where SZ is more sensitive with respect to X-ray). Resolved SZ measurements allow to infer cluster masses from integrated Y mass (Y-M) relations. The Y-M relation is sensitive to the cluster astrophysics, radiative cooling, star formation, energy injection from stars and AGN feedback. In general, it allows to study of the pressure profiles and fluctuations of the ICM. This, again, can allow to understanding the self-similarity of galaxy clusters.

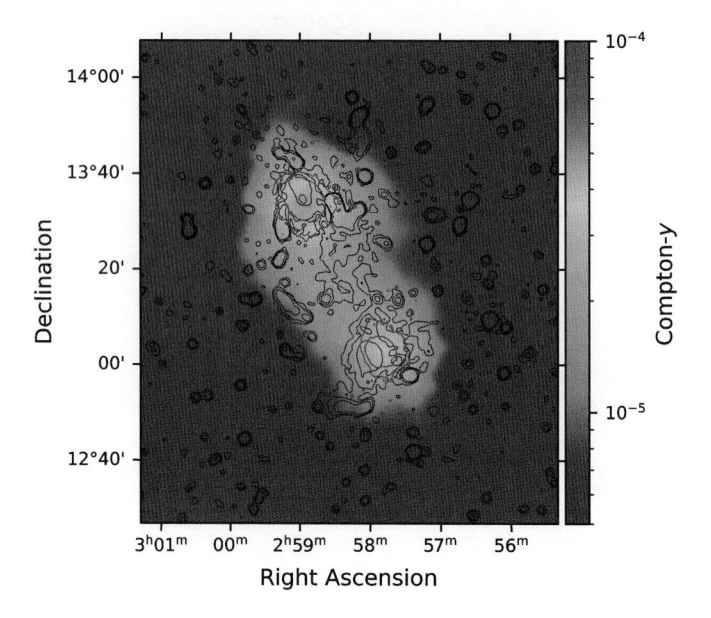

Fig. 6. Planck PR2 MILCA Compton-y map of Abell 401 (north-east) and Abell 399 (south-west). Black contour level are from the LOFAR map[26] at 0.0035, 0.008 and 0.02 Jy. Magenta contour level at 0.00008, 0.0015 and 0.001 Counts/s refer to the XMM-Newton map of the system.[27] The figure shows a good agreement between the radio and SZ signal both in the clusters and in the intracluster region, while the X-ray emission is appreciable only in correspondence with the two clusters.

In addition, point sources can be a contamination and need to be correctly subtracted not to bias the estimate of the y-parameter in a galaxy cluster. This is for instance what was achieved with MUSTANG2 at the GBT.[28]

Galaxy clusters experience hierarchical growth through mergers. Pre-mergers clusters should be connected through the Cosmic Web and simulations endorse this[21,22] (see, e.g. Figure 6). On the other hand, post mergers clusters dissipate an enormous quantity of energy with turbulence and shocks (pressure discontinuity up to mach number 3). The *Bullet* cluster or *El Gordo* are example of this unrelaxed occurrence.

The wide majority of the SZ is in fact localized towards galaxy clusters but the baryons distribution is still an open issue for modern cosmology: half of the baryons are still missing. Magneto-hydrodynamical and hydrodynamical simulations predict that they are structured in the cosmic web, filaments, and voids in the form of Warm Hot Intergalactic Medium (WHIM).[21,22] WHIM are expected to be distributed as over-desities in filamentary structures between galaxy clusters: high angular resolution SZ measurements can detect WHIM better than X-ray under low density circumstances. This is probably the most challenging and most rewarding of the achievements that an experiment like MISTRAL can achieve.

6. Conclusions

High angular resolution millimetric observation are key to understand a wide variety of scientific cases including structure formation and missing baryons issue. MISTRAL is a facility millimetric camera that will study several scientific case and that will be installed and commissioned at the Sardinia Radio Telescope during 2022. MISTRAL is going to be a unique camera: agile cryostat, 408 KIDs, optics allowing 12 arcsec resolution and a 4 arcmin f.o.v. at 90GHz. Sapienza University will do the technical commissioning, will participate to the astronomical commissioning, and will release MISTRAL to the scientific community.

Acknowledgments

The Enhancement of the Sardinia Radio Telescope (SRT) for the study of the Universe at high radio frequencies is financially supported by the National Operative Program (Programma Operativo Nazionale - PON) of the Italian Ministry of University and Research Research and Innovation 2014-2020; Notice D.D. 424 of 28/02/2018 for the granting of funding aimed at strengthening research infrastructures, in implementation of the Action II.1 - Project Proposal PIR01_00010.

References

1. S. R. Dicker, P. A. R. Ade, J. Aguirre et al., MUSTANG2: a large focal plan array for the 100 meter Green Bank Telescope, in *Millimeter, Submillimeter, and Far-Infrared Detectors and Instrumentation for Astronomy VII*, eds. W. S. Holland and J. Zmuidzinas, Society of Photo-Optical Instrumentation Engineers (SPIE) Conference Series, Vol. 9153 July 2014.
2. A. Catalano, R. Adam, P. A. R. Ade, P. André, H. Aussel, A. Beelen, A. Benoît, A. Bideaud, N. Billot, O. Bourrion, et al., The nika2 instrument at 30-m iram telescope: Performance and results, *Journal of Low Temperature Physics* **193**, 916 (Mar 2018).
3. R. Adam et al., The nika2 large-field-of-view millimetre continuum camera for the 30 m iram telescope, *Astronomy and Astrophysics* **609**, p. A115 (January 2018).
4. L. Perotto et al., Calibration and performance of the nika2 camera at the iram 30-m telescope, *Astronomy and Astrophysics* **637**, p. A71 (May 2020).
5. P. Bolli, A. Orlati, L. Stringhetti et al., Sardinia radio telescope: General description, technical commissioning and first light, *Journal of Astronomical Instrumentation* **04**, p. 1550008 (Dec 2015).
6. F. T. Nasir, F. Buffa and G. L. Deiana, Characterization of the atmosphere above a site for millimeter wave astronomy, *Experimental Astronomy* **29**, 207 (Apr 2011).
7. F. Govoni et al., The high-frequency upgrade of the sardinia radio telescope, *2021 XXXIVth General Assembly and Scientific Symposium of the International Union of Radio Science -*, 1 (- 2021).
8. A. Coppolecchia, E. Battistelli, Masi et al., Pulse tube cooler with $>$ 100m flexible lines optimized for operation of cryogenic detector arrays at large radiotelescopes 19th International Workshop on Low Temperature Detectors 2021.
9. A. Paiella et al., Development of lumped element kinetic inductance detectors for the w-band, *Journal of Low Temperature Physics* **184**, 97 (July 2016).

10. A. Coppolecchia *et al.*, W-band lumped element kinetic inductance detector array for large ground-based telescopes, *Journal of Low Temperature Physics* **199**, 130 (April 2020).
11. A. Paiella, E. S. Battistelli, M. G. Castellano *et al.*, Kinetic inductance detectors and readout electronics for the olimpo experiment, *Journal of Physics: Conference Series* **1182**, p. 012005 (Feb 2019).
12. A. Paiella *et al.*, MISTRAL and its KIDs (19th International Workshop on Low Temperature Detectors (LTD19), 2021).
13. A. Paiella, E. S. Battistelli, P. de Bernardis *et al.*, The cryogenic detectors of MISTRAL *14th Workshop On Low Temperature Electronics* April 2021.
14. G. Isopi, The mistral receiver: read-out electronics and observational strategies, *MASTER degree thesis* - (October 2021).
15. M. S. Petersen, R. A. Gutermuth, E. Nagel, G. W. Wilson and J. Lane, Early science with the large millimetre telescope: new mm-wave detections of circumstellar discs in ic 348 from lmt/aztec, *MNRAS* **488**, 1462 (Sep 2019).
16. A. D. Sokol, R. A. Gutermuth, R. Pokhrel *et al.*, Early science with the large millimetre telescope: An lmt/aztec 1.1 mm survey of dense cores in the monoceros r2 giant molecular cloud, *MNRAS* **483**, 407 (Feb 2019).
17. W. F. Wall, I. Puerari, R. Tilanus *et al.*, Continuum observations of m 51 and m 83 at 1.1 mm with aztec, *MNRAS* **459**, 1440 (Jun 2016).
18. A. Humphrey, M. Zeballos, I. Aretxaga *et al.*, Aztec 1.1-mm images of 16 radio galaxies at $0.5 < z < 5.2$ and a quasar at z= 6.3, *MNRAS* **418**, 74 (Nov 2011).
19. R. A. Sunyaev and Y. B. Zeldovich, The observations of relic radiation as a test of the nature of x-ray radiation from the clusters of galaxies, *Comments on Astrophysics and Space Physics* (Nov 1972).
20. M. Birkinshaw, The sunyaev-zel'dovich effect, *Physics Reports* **310**, p. 97–195 (Mar 1999).
21. R. Cen and J. P. Ostriker, Where are the baryons?, *The Astrophysical Journal* **514**, 1 (Mar 1999).
22. T. Tuominen, J. Nevalainen, E. Tempel *et al.*, An eagle view of the missing baryons, *Astronomy & Astrophysics* **646**, p. A156 (Feb 2021).
23. A. Cavaliere and R. Fusco-Femiano, Reprint of 1976A&A....49..137C. X-rays from hot plasma in clusters of galaxies., *aap* **500**, 95 (May 1976).
24. J. F. Navarro, C. S. Frenk and S. D. M. White, The structure of cold dark matter halos, *The Astrophysical Journal* **462**, p. 563 (May 1996).
25. M. Arnaud, The β-model of the intracluster medium. Commentary on: Cavaliere A. and Fusco-Femiano R., 1976, A&A, 49, 137, *aap* **500**, 103 (June 2009).
26. F. Govoni *et al.*, A radio ridge connecting two galaxy clusters in a filament of the cosmic web, *Science* **364**, 981 (June 2019).
27. M. Murgia *et al.*, A double radio halo in the close pair of galaxy clusters abell 399 and abell 401, *Astronomy and Astrophysics* **509**, p. A86 (January 2010).
28. S. R. Dicker, E. S. Battistelli, T. Bhandarkar *et al.*, Observations of compact sources in galaxy clusters using mustang2, *MNRAS on line* - (Sep 2021).

Cosmological and astrophysical results exploiting magnification bias with high-z sub-millimetre galaxies

L. Bonavera[1,2,*], M.M. Cueli[1,2,†] and J. Gonzalez-Nuevo[1,2,‡]

[1] *Physics Department, University of Oviedo,*
Oviedo, 33007, Spain
[2] *Instituto Universitario de Ciencias y Tecnologías Espaciales de Asturias (ICTEA),*
C. Independencia 13, 33004 Oviedo, Spain
*E-mail: * bonaveralaura@uniovi.es, †mcueli@uniovi.es, ‡gnuevo@uniovi.es*

The high-z submillimeter galaxies (SMGs) can be used as background sample for gravitational lensing studies thanks to their magnification bias, which can manifest itself through a non-negligible measurement of the cross-correlation function between a background and a foreground source sample with non-overlapping redshift distributions. In particular, the choice of SMGs as background sample enhances the cross-correlation signal so as to provide an alternative and independent observable for cosmological studies regarding the probing of mass distribution.

In particular the magnification bias can be exploited in order to constrain the free astrophysical parameters of a Halo Occupation Distribution model and some of the main cosmological parameters. Urged by the improvements obtained when adopting a pseudo-tomographic analysis, It has been adopted a tomographic set-up to explore not only a ΛCDM scenario, but also the possible time evolution of the dark energy density in the ω_0CDM and $\omega_0\omega_a$CDM frameworks.

Keywords: Cosmology; Gravitational lensing; Sub-millimeter galaxies.

1. Magnification bias

Magnification bias is due to the gravitational lensing effect and consists in the apparent excess in the number of high redshift sources (the lensed sources) close to the position of low redshift galaxies (the lenses). In fact, the gravitational lensing deflects the light rays of high redshift sources causing the stretching of the apparent sky area in the region affected by the lensing. This also causes a boost in the flux density of the high redshift sources, making them more likely to be detected above a given instrument flux density limit (e.g. Ref. 1). This is sketched in Fig. 1(a). The red objects in the backward plane (source plane) are the sources with flux density limit above the instrument detection limit, and thus detectable while the orange ones are those with a flux density below the instrument detection limit, and thus not detectable unless boosted by the magnification bias. The blue objects in the lens plane are the possible lenses that might cause the magnification bias effect. Finally in the observer plane, the blue objects of the lens plane will be observable together with the red objects of the source plane and some of the orange objects whose flux have been boosted. The peculiarity of such magnified orange objects is that they will be found close to some of the blue objects (their lenses).

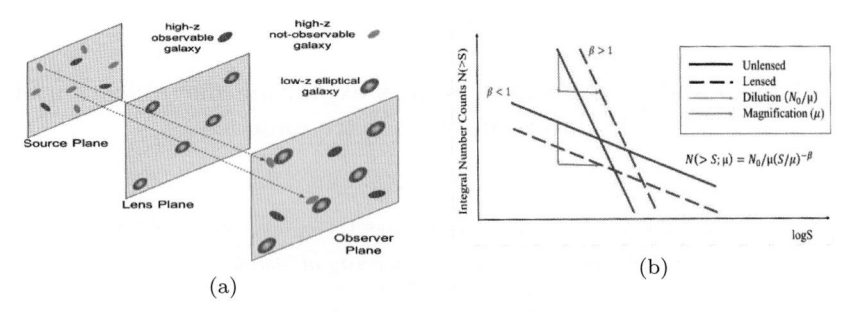

Fig. 1. Scheme of magnification bias (a) and how it affect the integral number counts of the lensed sources (b). See text for details.

On this respect, magnification bias main advantage relies on the steepness of background sources counts and on the fact that it does not require either ellipticity measurements or knowledge on the galaxies' orientation (as shear does). In particular, given that n_0 are the unlensed integrated background source number counts (number of background sources per solid angle and redshift with observed flux density larger than S in the absence of gravitational lensing):

$$n_0(>S,z) \equiv \int_S^\infty \frac{dN}{dSdz\,d\Omega} dS \qquad (1)$$

the background source number counts at an angular position $\vec{\theta}$ within an image are modified by dilution and magnification following Ref. 2:

$$n(>S,z;\vec{\theta}) = \frac{1}{\mu(\vec{\theta})} n_0\left(>\frac{S}{\mu(\vec{\theta})},z\right) \qquad (2)$$

where $\mu(\vec{\theta})$ is the magnification field at angular position $\vec{\theta}$. Assuming a power-law behaviour of the unlensed integrated number counts with β the source number count steepness, i.e. $n_0(>S,z) = AS^{-\beta}$,

$$\frac{n(>S,z;\vec{\theta})}{n_0(>S,z)} = \mu^{\beta-1}(\vec{\theta}) \qquad (3)$$

Depending on the value of β the source counts might increase because of lensing: Fig. 1(b) sketched the increase or decrease of the source number counts for $\beta > 1$ (in red) and $\beta < 1$ (in blue), respectively.

2. Cross-correlation

Magnification bias is usually observed by means of angular cross-correlation function (CCF) measurements between two samples of sources: how many background sources fall 'near' the position of a lens, repeated for each object in the lens sample. Since the samples are at different redshifts, the detection of a non-zero signal would be exclusively due to the gravitational lensing induced by the lenses.

2.1. The estimator

Thus, magnification bias can be measured through the cross-correlation between the low and high redshift objects.

The CCF of two source populations (D_f and D_b) is the fractional excess probability, relative to a random distribution (R_f and R_b), of finding a D_f source separated by an angle θ from a D_b source within an infinitesimal solid angle $d\theta$. The CCF can be computed using a modified version of the Landy & Szalay (Ref. 3) estimator (see Ref. 4):

$$\tilde{w}_{fb}(\theta) = \frac{D_f D_b(\theta) - D_f R_b(\theta) - D_b R_f(\theta) + R_f R_b(\theta)}{R_f R_b(\theta)} \quad (4)$$

In particular, $D_f D_b$, $D_f R_b$, $D_b R_f$ and $R_f R_b$ are the normalized foreground-background, foreground-Poisson, background-Poisson and Poisson-Poisson pair counts for a given angular separation θ. Given two source samples with non-overlapping redshift distributions, the excess signal when computing their cross-correlation with respect to the random case is due to the magnification bias. Being such signal related to lensing and thus to cosmological distances and the galaxy halo characteristics, it can be used to constrain cosmological and astrophysical parameters.

2.2. The halo model

To achieve this, the adopted theoretical description of the cross-correlation is the one by Cooray & Sheth (Ref. 5):

$$w_{fb}(\theta) = 2(\beta - 1)\int_0^\infty \frac{dz}{\chi^2(z)} n_f(z) W^{\text{lens}}(z) \int_0^\infty l \frac{dl}{2\pi} P_{\text{gal-dm}}(l/\chi^2(z), z) J_0(l\theta) \quad (5)$$

$$W^{\text{lens}}(z) = \frac{3}{2}\frac{H_0^2}{c^2}\left[\frac{E(z)}{1+z}\right]^2 \int_z^\infty dz' \frac{\chi(z)\chi(z'-z)}{\chi(z')} n_b(z') \quad (6)$$

where l is the multipole, H_0 is the Hubble constant, $E(z)$ the quantity where the contribution to the energy density are included (see section 2.3 for details), $n_b(z)$ ($n_f(z)$) is the normalized background (foreground) redshift distribution, $\chi(z)$ is the comoving distance, J_0 is the zeroth-order Bessel function of the first kind, $W^{\text{lens}}(z)$ is the lensing kernel and β is the source number count steepness, commonly fixed to 3 for submillimeter galaxies (Ref. 6 and reference therein). Therefore, the cross-correlation signal can be interpreted under the halo model parametrization (Ref. 5) considering that both galaxy samples trace the same dark matter distribution around redshift $z \sim 0.4$. This dark matter distribution is traced directly by the foreground galaxies while, in the case of the background sample, it is traced thanks to the weak lensing effect. According to this model, the galaxy distribution power spectrum is parametrized as the sum of a 2-halo term, related to the correlations between one halo traced by the foreground galaxies and another one traced by the background sources and that therefore dominates at large scales, and a 1-halo term, that describes the correlation between sub-halos (traced by both samples) inside the same halo and therefore more important at small scales. Moreover, the halo model also suggests a simple parametrization of the cross-correlation between the galaxy and dark matter distributions (see Refs. 5,7,8). According to the halo model (Cooray & Sheth, Refs. 5):

$$P_{\text{g-dm}}(k,z) = P^{1h}_{\text{g-dm}}(k,z) + P^{2h}_{\text{g-dm}}(k,z) \qquad (7)$$

$$P^{1h}_{\text{g-dm}}(k,z) = \int_0^\infty dM\, M \frac{n(M,z)}{\bar{\rho}(z)} \frac{\langle N_g \rangle_M}{\bar{n}_g(z)} |u_{\text{dm}}(k,z|M)||u_g(k,z|M)|^{p-1}$$

$$P^{2h}_{\text{g-dm}}(k,z) = P^{\text{lin}}(k,z) \Big[\int_0^\infty dM\, M \frac{n(M,z)}{\bar{\rho}(z)} b_1(M,z) u_{\text{dm}}(k,z|M) \Big] \cdot$$

$$\cdot \Big[\int_0^\infty dM\, n(M,z) b_1(M,z) \frac{\langle N_g \rangle_M}{\bar{n}_g(z)} u_g(k,z|M) \Big]$$

In these equations $\bar{\rho}$ is the background density, $\langle N_g \rangle_M$ the mean number of galaxies within a halo of mass M, $\bar{n}_g(z)$ the mean number density of galaxies at redshift z, p is set to 1 for central galaxies and to 2 for satellites (Ref. 5), k is the wave number, $n(M,z)$ is the Sheth & Tormen halo mass function by Ref. 9, $P^{lin}(k,z)$ is the linear matter power spectrum, $b_1(M,z)$ is the linear large-scale bias (via the peak background split), and $u_g(k,z|M)$ is the normalized Fourier transform of the galaxy density distribution within a halo, which is assumed to equal the dark matter density profile, i.e. $u_g(k,z|M) = u_{dm}(k,z|M)$. Halos are defined as overdense regions whose mean density is 200 times the mean background density of the universe according to the spherical collapse model, and the halo density profiles $\rho(r)$ adopted is the one by Ref. 10, hereafter NFW, with the concentration parameter in Ref. 11.

The halo occupation distribution (HOD) assumed is the one by Zheng et al. in Ref. 12:

$$N_{\text{cen}}(M_h) = \begin{cases} 0 & \text{if } M_h < M_{\min} \\ 1 & \text{otherwise} \end{cases} \qquad (8)$$

$$N_{\text{sat}}(M_h) = N_{\text{cen}}(M_h) \cdot \left(\frac{M_h}{M_1}\right)^\alpha \qquad (9)$$

In this model, the mean number of galaxies is represented by N_{gal} where, the distinction between central and satellite galaxies is made: $N_{gal} = N_{cen} + N_{sat} = 1 + N_{sat}$. All halos above a minimum mass M_{min} host a galaxy at their centre, while any remaining galaxies are classified as satellites and are distributed in proportion to the halo mass profile (see Ref. 12). Halos host satellites when their mass exceeds the M_1 mass, and the number of satellites is a power-law function of halo mass $N_{\text{sat}}(M_h)$. These parameters define the adopted HOD.

2.3. The barotropic index of the dark energy

In the theoretical model, a possible redshift evolution of the dark energy (DE) can be introduced by allowing different values for the dark energy equation of state parameter, ω. For a flat cosmology, a redshift-dependent function $f(z)$ in the quantity

$$E(z) \equiv \sqrt{\Omega_r(1+z)^4 + \Omega_M(1+z)^3 + \Omega_k(1+z)^2 + \Omega_{DE}f(z)} \tag{10}$$

takes into account the possible time evolution of the dark energy density, where Ω_x is the present-day density parameters for radiation r, matter (M), curvature (k) and dark energy DE. In particular, by assuming that the barotropic index of dark energy

$$\omega(z) = \omega_0 + \omega_a \frac{z}{1+z} \tag{11}$$

the dark energy density has a redshift dependence given by $\rho(z) = \rho_0 f(z)$, where

$$f(z) = (1+z)^{3(1+\omega_0+\omega_a)} e^{-3\omega_a \frac{z}{1+z}} \tag{12}$$

being ρ_0 the dark energy density at $z = 0$. As for the dark energy density parameter, it can be written as

$$\Omega_{DE}(z) = \frac{\Omega_{DE}f(z)}{E(z)^2} \tag{13}$$

In this framework, the ΛCDM is recovered when $\omega_0 = -1$ and $\omega_a = 0$.

3. Background and foreground samples

In order to achieve the cross-correlation measurement, a clear separation of the background and foreground sources is needed. For example, in the recent works

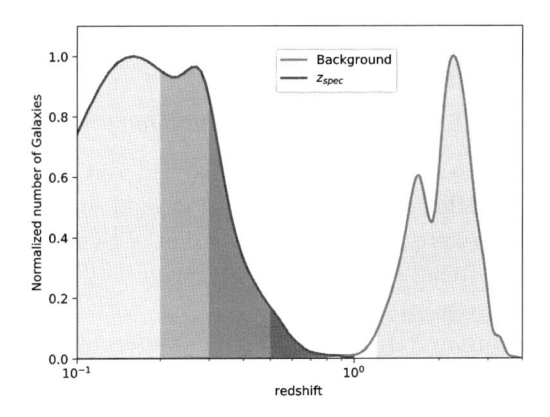

Fig. 2. Redshift distribution of background (orange) and foreground objects (green). The different shades of green indicate the bins of redshift used in Ref. 13. Credit: Bonavera et al., A&A, in press, DOI 10.1051/0004-6361/202141521, 2021, reproduced with permission © ESO.

by Bonavera et al. (Refs. 6, 13), the redshift distribution of the foreground and background galaxies sample is the one in Fig. 2 in green and orange respectively. The different shades of green indicate the bins of redshift used in Ref. 13.

As for the foreground sample, different kind of sources at relatively low redshift can be used. For example, in their recent work (Ref. 14) Bonavera et al. adopt the same sample of quasi-stellar object (QSOs) with $0.2 < z < 1.0$ as in Ref. 15. They are selected from the publicly available Sloan Digital Sky Survey (SDSS-II and SDSS-III) Baryon Oscillation Spectroscopic Survey (BOSS) catalogues. In Refs. 6, 13, 16–18 the galaxies in the Galaxy and Mass Assembly (GAMA, Ref. 19) survey with $0.2 < z < 0.8$ have been used and in Ref. 13 those with $0.1 < z < 0.8$ (see Fig. 2).

Currently the best way to measure the CCF is to choose as background samples the high-z sub-millimetre galaxies (SMGs). In fact they have steep number counts $\beta \sim 3$ (Refs. 20, 21), shown by the Herschel Space Observatory (Herschel; Ref. 22) and the South Pole Telescope (SPT; Ref. 23) observations. Such property enhances their magnification, as explained in Sect. 1. Moreover, the SMGs are faint in the optical avoiding the possibility of being confused with the foreground lens sample, which is on its turn invisible at sub-millimetre (sub-mm) wavelength (Refs. 24, 25). Finally, the redshifts of the SMGs are usually greater than $z > 1 - 1.5$, which guarantees no overlap with the foreground sample. This makes the SMGs the perfect background sample for magnification bias studies by means of CCF measurements and thus allowing the tracing of the mass density (baryonic and dark matter) and its evolution with time.

Moreover, it has been confirmed when, due to their magnification bias, Dunne et al. in Ref. 26 made a serendipitous direct observation of high-redshift SMGs. They were performing a study of gas tracers with Atacama Large Millimeter Array (ALMA) observation of galaxies by targeting a statistically complete sample of twelve galaxies selected at 250μm with z=0.35 and magnified SMGs appears around the position of half of them.

4. Recent results with SMGs magnification bias

The first attempt to measure the CCF was carried out in Ref. 27 with Herschel/SPIRE galaxies and low-z galaxies as background and foreground samples, respectively. Their results were a strong confirmation of this lensing-induced effect.

To study this possible bias, Ref. 28 relied on much better statistics and carried out a more detailed analysis by measuring the CCF with Herschel Astrophysical Terahertz Large Area Survey (H-ATLAS) high-z sources at $z > 1.5$ and two optical samples selected from SDSS (Sloan Digital Sky Survey, Ref. 27) and GAMA (Ref. 19) surveys, with redshifts $0.2 < z < 0.6$. The resulting CCF was measured with high significance, $> 10\sigma$ and using realistic simulations, they concluded that the signal was entirely explained with the magnification bias produced by the weak lensing effect caused by galaxy groups/clusters whose halo masses are in the range of $10^{13.2} - 10^{14.5} M_\odot$ and that are signposted by the brightest galaxies in the optical samples. Later on, Gonazelz-Nuevo et al. in Ref. 16 and Bonavera et al. in Ref. 13 showed furthermore that the SMGs properties make them the perfect background sample for constraining the free parameters of a halo occupation distribution (HOD) model. In particular, the results by Ref. 16 suggest that the lenses are massive galaxies or clusters, with a minimum mass of $M_{min} = 10^{13} M_\odot$. They also carried out tomographic studies on the HOD parameters: they divided the foreground sample in four bins of redshift, $0.1 < z < 0.2$, $0.2 < z < 0.3$, $0.3 < z < 0.5$ and $0.5 < z < 0.8$. They main findings were that while M_1 is almost redshift independent, M_{min} evolves: it increases with redshift, as predicted by theoretical estimations. Bonavera et al. in Ref. 14 study with the magnification bias the mass properties of a sample of QSOs whose position signpost the lenses at $0.2 < z < 1.0$ obtaining $M_{min} = 10^{13.6^{+0.9}_{-0.4}} M_\odot$. This again suggests that the lensing is actually produced by halos of the size of clusters placed close to the QSOs positions.

Furthermore, magnification bias trough CCF measurements can be used to constrain the halo mass function. In particular, Cueli et al. in Ref. 18 successfully test such possibility according to two common parametrisations: the Sheth & Tormen and Tinker fits. They find general agreement with traditional values for the involved parameters, with a slight difference in the Sheth & Tormen fit for intermediate and high masses, where the results suggest a hint at a somewhat higher number of halos.

5. Cosmological studies with magnification bias

Moreover, some of the main cosmological parameters can be also estimated using the magnification bias, as in Ref. 6. They use the CCF measured between a foreground sample of GAMA galaxies with spectroscopic redshifts in the range of $0.2 < z < 0.8$ and a background sample of H-ATLAS galaxies with photometric redshifts $z > 1.2$ (as described in section 3) to constrain the astrophysical parameters (M_{min}, M_1, and α) and the Ω_M, σ_8, and H_0 cosmological ones (the matter density parameter, the present root-mean-square matter fluctuation averaged over a sphere of radius $8h^{-1}$Mpc where h is the dimensionless Hubble constant, and the Hubble density parameters). These parameters are estimated through a Markov chain Monte Carlo analysis, using the Python package emcee (Ref. 29). They study various cases and in particular they perform a run by setting flat priors to those in Table 1.

Table 1. Flat priors for the ΛCDM run in Ref. 6.

$\log M_{min}$	$\mathcal{U}[\,11.6,\,13.6]$	Ω_M	$\mathcal{U}[\,0.1,\,0.8]$
$\log M_1$	$\mathcal{U}[\,13.0,\,14.5]$	σ_8	$\mathcal{U}[\,0.6,\,1.2]$
α	$\mathcal{U}[\,0.5,\,1.37]$	h	$\mathcal{U}[\,0.5,\,1.0]$

Note: The HOD parameters names and flat priors are listed in the first two columns. The cosmological ones in the third and fourth columns.

They obtain a lower limit at 95% confidence level (CL) on $\Omega_M > 0.24$, a slight trend towards $H_0 > 70$ km s^{-1} Mpc^{-1} values and an upper limit at 95% CL of $\sigma_8 < 1$. Such results are summarised in the $\Omega_M - \sigma_8$ plane in Fig. 3 (a) with the dot-dashed blue line.

Given the large number of studies that can be performed with magnification bias through CCF data, a systematic analysis of possible bias that might affect the estimation have been carried out. In particular, in Ref. 17 Gonzalez-Nuevo et al. take into account different biases at cosmological scales in the source samples to carefully measure unbiased CCF. More precisely, their background sample consists of H-ATLAS galaxies with $z > 1.2$ whereas they use two independent foreground samples with $0.2 < z < 0.8$: GAMA galaxies with spectroscopic redshifts and SDSS galaxies with photometric redshifts. These independent samples allowed them to perform a pseudo-tomographic study that yields to constrain $\Omega_M = 0.50^{+0.14}_{-0.20}$ and $\sigma_8 = 0.75^{+0.07}_{-0.10}$. Such analysis also suggests that a tomographic approach might improve the results.

Driven by the conclusions mentioned above, Bonavera et al. in Ref. 13 adopt the unbiased sample by Gonzalez-Nuevo et al. in Ref. 17 dividing the foreground sample into four redshift bins ($0.1 - 0.2$, $0.2 - 0.3$, $0.3 - 0.5$ and $0.5 - 0.8$). The background objects are a sample of H-ATLAS galaxies with photometric redshifts $z > 1.2$. The redshift distribution are shown in Fig. 2 and the redshift bins of the foreground sample are highlighted with different shades of green. They use magnification bias in tomography to jointly constrain the astrophysical HOD parameters (M_{min}, M_1 and α) in each one of the selected redshift bins together with the Ω_M, σ_8, and H_0 cosmological ones. In particular, the analysis is carried out both in the ΛCDM scenario and with the introduction of the dark energy density related w_0 and w_a parameters in the w_0CDM and $w_0 w_a$CDM frameworks. The parameters priors for the three described runs are listed in Table 2.

Table 2. Flat priors for the ΛCDM, w_0CDM and $w_0 w_a$CDM models in Ref. 13.

$\log M_{min} \mathcal{U}[a_i, b_i]$	$\log M_1 \mathcal{U}[c_i, d_i]$		
$[a_1, b_1] = \mathcal{U}[10.0, 13.0]$	$[c_1, d_1] = \mathcal{U}[12.0, 15.5]$	Ω_M	$\mathcal{U}[0.1, 0.8]$
$[a_2, b_2] = \mathcal{U}[11.0, 13.0]$	$[c_2, d_2] = \mathcal{U}[12.0, 15.5]$	σ_8	$\mathcal{U}[0.6, 1.2]$
$[a_3, b_3] = \mathcal{U}[11.5, 13.5]$	$[c_3, d_3] = \mathcal{U}[12.5, 15.5]$	h	$\mathcal{U}[0.5, 1.0]$
$[a_4, b_4] = \mathcal{U}[13.0, 15.5]$	$[c_4, d_4] = \mathcal{U}[13.0, 15.5]$	w_a	$\mathcal{U}[-3.0, 3.0]$
		w_0	$\mathcal{U}[-2.0, 0.0]$

Note: For the four different bins of redshift, the M_{min} flat priors are listed in the first column while the M_1 ones in the second column. The α prior is $\alpha = \mathcal{U}[0.5, 1.37]$ in all bins. The cosmological parameters names and flat priors are in the third and fourth columns.

As for the HOD parameters, M_{min} shows a trend towards higher values at higher redshift confirming the findings in Ref. 16. For the ΛCDM model, they obtain a mean(maximum) posterior value [68% CL] of $\Omega_M = 0.33(0.26)$ [0.17, 0.41]

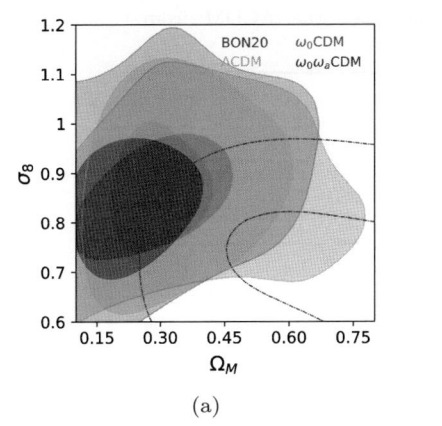

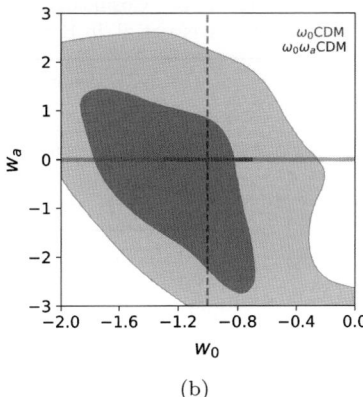

Fig. 3. Contour plot of the 2D posterior distributions with contours set to 0.393 and 0.865. (a) Ω_M and σ_8 for the non-tomographic case in Ref. 6 (dot-dashed blue line) and the tomographic runs in Ref. 13 within ΛCDM (in yellow), ω_0CDM (in green) and $\omega_0\omega_a$CDM (in purple). (b) ω_0 and ω_a for the $\omega_0\omega_a$CDM model. Credit: Bonavera et al., A&A, in press, DOI 10.1051/0004-6361/202141521, 2021, reproduced with permission © ESO.

and of $\sigma_8 = 0.87$ [0.75,1], being H_0 not yet constrained. For the ω_0CDM model, they find similar results on Ω_M and σ_8 and a mean(maximum) posterior value [68% CL] of $\omega_0 = -1(-0.97)$ $[-1.56, -0.47]$. For the $\omega_0\omega_a$CDM model, $\omega_0 = -1.09(-0.92)$ $[-1.72, -0.66]$ and $\omega_a = -0.19(-0.20)$ $[-1.88, 1.48]$. These results are summarised in Tables 3 and 4, where the the mean, peak and $68\%CL$ of the posterior distributions for the estimated cosmological parameters are given. In particular, the first column gives the parameter name, the second and third columns in Table 3 are the results for the ΛCDM model in the non-tomographic and tomographic cases, and in Table 4 are those for the ω_0CDM and $\omega_0\omega_a$CDM models in the tomographic case.

The $\Omega_M - \sigma_8$ plane is shown in Fig. 3(a) for the ΛCDM (in yellow), ω_0CDM (in green) and $\omega_0\omega_a$CDM (in purple) models. The results in the $\omega_0 - \omega_a$ plane are shown in Fig. 3(b). The ω_0 results are shown in Fig. 4 for the ω_0CDM (in green) and $\omega_0\omega_a$CDM (in purple) cases, where they are compared with other results from literature. Moreover, the tomographic analysis presented in Ref. 13 confirms that magnification bias results do not show the degeneracy found with cosmic shear measurements and that, related to dark energy, do show a trend of higher ω_0 values for lower H_0 values.

6. Conclusion

In conclusion, all these works confirm that the SMGs are a perfect background sample for magnification bias studies and serendipitous direct observation of magnified SMGs have been performed with ALMA (i.e. Ref. 26). It has been demonstrated in Ref. 28 and Ref. 16 for astrophysical studies and in Ref. 6 for cosmological ones.

Table 3. Cosmological results for the ΛCDM from Bonavera et al. in Refs. 6, 13.

	ΛCDM nontomo		ΛCDM	
	$\mu(Peak)$	68%CL	$\mu(Peak)$	68%CL
Ω_M	0.54(0.67)	[0.46,0.80]	0.33(0.26)	[0.17,0.41]
σ_8	0.78(0.74)	[0.63,0.85]	0.87(0.87)	[0.75,1.00]
h	0.76(-)	[0.68,1.00]	0.72(0.72)	<0.79

Note: Mean(Peak) and 68%CL of the posterior distributions for the cosmological parameters (listed in the first column) estimated according to the ΛCDM model in the non-tomographic case (second and third columns) and in the tomographic one (fourth and fifth columns) models in the tomographic case. With the exception of the estimated cosmological parameters, the cosmology is fixed to the *Planck* one.

Table 4. Cosmological results for the ω_0CDM and $\omega_0\omega_a$CDM models from Bonavera et al. in Ref. 13.

	ω_0CDM		$\omega_0\omega_a$CDM	
	$\mu(Peak)$	68%CL	$\mu(Peak)$	68%CL
Ω_M	0.38(0.26)	[0.13,0.47]	0.34(0.21)	[0.11,0.41]
σ_8	0.87(0.85)	[0.73,0.98]	0.88(0.84)	[0.72,1.01]
h	0.70(-)	<0.75	0.70(-)	<0.76
ω_0	-1.00(-0.97)	[-1.56,-0.47]	-1.09(-0.92)	[-1.72,-0.66]
ω_a	-	-	-0.19(-0.20)	[-1.88,1.48]

Note: Mean(Peak) and 68%CL of the posterior distributions for the cosmological parameters (listed in the first column) estimated according to the ω_0CDM (second and third columns) and $\omega_0\omega_a$CDM (fourth and fifth columns) models in the tomographic case. With the exception of the estimated cosmological parameters, the cosmology is fixed to the *Planck* one.

In particular magnification bias proves to be useful as an independent and additional cosmological probe for ΛCDM and beyond ΛCDM models, as done in Ref. 13.

In these works, the performance of magnification bias through CCF measurements has been compared in non-tomographic and tomographic analysis. The conclusion is that tomography improves non-tomographic studies despite the worsening in the statistics of the measured CCFs.

Moreover, the CCF can be computed adopting different foreground samples, e.g. galaxies in Ref. 6 or QSOs in Ref. 14 and the measurements are improved by taking into account observational biases correction (i.e. Ref. 17). In addition, variation of the ingredients of the models, as the HMF, might be tested with magnification bias (e.g. Ref. 18).

Up to now, the main conclusions are the fact that astrophysical results are robust for all models (ΛCDM and beyond ΛCDM) and that ΛCDM compatible

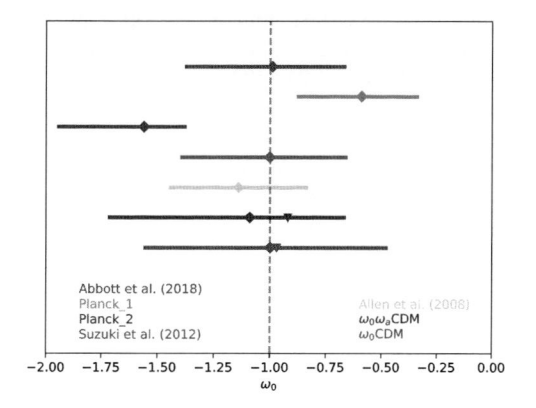

Fig. 4. Results on ω_0 within the ω_0CDM (green) and $\omega_0\omega_a$CDM (purple) models compared with those by DES (blue), Planck1 (basewwaplikHMTTlowllowEBAO, salmon), Planck2 (basewplikHMTTlowllowE, brown), Supernovae (red), x-ray measurements (yellow). Credit: Bonavera et al., A&A, in press, DOI 10.1051/0004-6361/202141521, 2021, reproduced with permission © ESO.

results have been found with tomographic and non-tomographic approaches, i.e. $\Omega_M \sim 0.33$, $\sigma_8 \sim 0.87$, $\omega_0 \sim -1$ and $\omega_a \sim -0.19$.

Acknowledgments

LB, JGN and MMC acknowledge the PGC 2018 project PGC2018-101948-B-I00 (MICINN/FEDER). MMC acknowledges support from PAPI-20-PF-23 (Universidad de Oviedo). LB acknowledges Carlo Burigana forhis help in the clarity of the manuscript.

References

1. P. Schneider, J. Ehlers and E. E. Falco, *Gravitational Lenses* 1992.
2. M. Bartelmann and P. Schneider, Weak gravitational lensing, *Physics Reports* **340**, 291 (2001).
3. S. D. Landy and A. S. Szalay, Bias and Variance of Angular Correlation Functions, *The Astrophysical Journal* **412**, p. 64 (July 1993).
4. D. Herranz, Foreground-Background Galaxy Correlations in the Hubble Deep Fields, in *Cosmological Physics with Gravitational Lensing*, eds. J. Tran Thanh Van, Y. Mellier and M. Moniez January 2001.
5. A. Cooray and R. Sheth, Halo models of large scale structure, *Physics Reports* **372**, 1 (Dec 2002).
6. L. Bonavera, J. González-Nuevo, M. M. Cueli, T. Ronconi, M. Migliaccio, L. Dunne, A. Lapi, S. J. Maddox and M. Negrello, Cosmology with the submillimetre galaxies magnification bias: Proof of concept, *Astronomy & Astrophysics* **639**, p. A128 (July 2020).
7. U. Seljak, Analytic model for galaxy and dark matter clustering, *Monthly Notices of the Royal Astronomical Society* **318**, 203 (October 2000).

8. J. Guzik and U. Seljak, Galaxy-dark matter correlations applied to galaxy-galaxy lensing: predictions from the semi-analytic galaxy formation models, *Monthly Notices of the Royal Astronomical Society* **321**, 439 (March 2001).
9. R. K. Sheth and G. Tormen, Large-scale bias and the peak background split, *Monthly Notices of the Royal Astronomical Society* **308**, 119 (September 1999).
10. J. F. Navarro, C. S. Frenk and S. D. M. White, The Structure of Cold Dark Matter Halos, *The Astrophysical Journal* **462**, p. 563 (May 1996).
11. J. S. Bullock, T. S. Kolatt, Y. Sigad, R. S. Somerville, A. V. Kravtsov, A. A. Klypin, J. R. Primack and A. Dekel, Profiles of dark haloes: evolution, scatter and environment, *Monthly Notices of the Royal Astronomical Society* **321**, 559 (March 2001).
12. Z. Zheng, A. A. Berlind, D. H. Weinberg, A. J. Benson, C. M. Baugh, S. Cole, R. Davé, C. S. Frenk, N. Katz and C. G. Lacey, Theoretical Models of the Halo Occupation Distribution: Separating Central and Satellite Galaxies, *The Astrophysical Journal* **633**, 791 (November 2005).
13. L. Bonavera, M. M. Cueli, J. González-Nuevo, T. Ronconi, M. Migliaccio, A. Lapi, J. M. Casas and D. Crespo, Cosmology with the sub-millimetre galaxies magnification bias: Tomographic Analysis, *arXiv e-prints*, p. arXiv:2109.12413 (September 2021).
14. L. Bonavera, J. Gonz'alez-Nuevo, S. L. Suárez Gómez, A. Lapi, F. Bianchini, M. Negrello, E. Díez Alonso, J. D. Santos and F. J. de Cos Juez, QSOs sigposting cluster size halos as gravitational lenses: halo mass, projected mass density profile and concentration at z~0.7, *Journal of Cosmology and Astroparticle Physics* **2019**, p. 021 (September 2019).
15. F. Bianchini, G. Fabbian, A. Lapi, J. Gonzalez-Nuevo, R. Gilli and C. Baccigalupi, Broadband Spectral Energy Distributions of SDSS-selected Quasars and of Their Host Galaxies: Intense Activity at the Onset of AGN Feedback, *The Astrophysical Journal* **871**, p. 136 (February 2019).
16. J. González-Nuevo, A. Lapi, L. Bonavera, L. Danese, G. de Zotti, M. Negrello, N. Bourne, A. Cooray, L. Dunne, S. Dye, S. Eales, C. Furlanetto, R. J. Ivison, J. Loveday, S. Maddox, M. W. L. Smith and E. Valiante, H-ATLAS/GAMA: magnification bias tomography. Astrophysical constraints above ~1 arcmin, *Journal of Cosmology and Astroparticle Physics* **2017**, p. 024 (October 2017).
17. J. González-Nuevo, M. M. Cueli, L. Bonavera, A. Lapi, M. Migliaccio, F. Argüeso and L. Toffolatti, Cosmological constraints on the magnification bias on sub-millimetre galaxies after large-scale bias corrections, *Astronomy & Astrophysics* **646**, p. A152 (February 2021).
18. M. M. Cueli, L. Bonavera, J. González-Nuevo and A. Lapi, A direct and robust method to observationally constrain the halo mass function via the submillimeter magnification bias: Proof of concept, *Astronomy & Astrophysics* **645**, p. A126 (January 2021).
19. S. P. Driver, D. T. Hill, L. S. Kelvin, A. S. G. Robotham, J. Liske, P. Norberg, I. K. Baldry, S. P. Bamford, A. M. Hopkins, J. Loveday, J. A. Peacock, E. Andrae, J. Bland-Hawthorn, S. Brough, M. J. I. Brown, E. Cameron, J. H. Y. Ching, M. Colless, C. J. Conselice, S. M. Croom, N. J. G. Cross, R. de Propris, S. Dye, M. J. Drinkwater, S. Ellis, A. W. Graham, M. W. Grootes, M. Gunawardhana, D. H. Jones, E. van Kampen, C. Maraston, R. C. Nichol, H. R. Parkinson, S. Phillipps, K. Pimbblet, C. C. Popescu, M. Prescott, I. G. Roseboom, E. M. Sadler, A. E. Sansom, R. G. Sharp, D. J. B. Smith, E. Taylor, D. Thomas, R. J. Tuffs, D. Wijesinghe, L. Dunne, C. S. Frenk, M. J. Jarvis, B. F. Madore, M. J. Meyer, M. Seibert, L. Staveley-Smith, W. J. Sutherland and S. J. Warren, Galaxy and Mass Assembly (GAMA): survey diagnostics and core data release, *Monthly Notices of the Royal Astronomical Society* **413**, 971 (May 2011).

20. A. W. Blain, Galaxy-galaxy gravitational lensing in the millimetre/submillimetre waveband, *Monthly Notices of the Royal Astronomical Society* **283**, 1340 (December 1996).
21. M. Negrello, F. Perrotta, J. González-Nuevo, L. Silva, G. de Zotti, G. L. Granato, C. Baccigalupi and L. Danese, Astrophysical and cosmological information from large-scale submillimetre surveys of extragalactic sources, *Monthly Notices of the Royal Astronomical Society* **377**, 1557 (June 2007).
22. G. L. Pilbratt, J. R. Riedinger, T. Passvogel, G. Crone, D. Doyle, U. Gageur, A. M. Heras, C. Jewell, L. Metcalfe, S. Ott and M. Schmidt, Herschel Space Observatory. An ESA facility for far-infrared and submillimetre astronomy, *Astronomy & Astrophysics* **518**, p. L1 (July 2010).
23. J. E. Carlstrom, P. A. R. Ade, K. A. Aird, B. A. Benson, L. E. Bleem, S. Busetti, C. L. Chang, E. Chauvin, H. M. Cho, T. M. Crawford, A. T. Crites, M. A. Dobbs, N. W. Halverson, S. Heimsath, W. L. Holzapfel, J. D. Hrubes, M. Joy, R. Keisler, T. M. Lanting, A. T. Lee, E. M. Leitch, J. Leong, W. Lu, M. Lueker, D. Luong-Van, J. J. McMahon, J. Mehl, S. S. Meyer, J. J. Mohr, T. E. Montroy, S. Padin, T. Plagge, C. Pryke, J. E. Ruhl, K. K. Schaffer, D. Schwan, E. Shirokoff, H. G. Spieler, Z. Staniszewski, A. A. Stark, C. Tucker, K. Vand erlinde, J. D. Vieira and R. Williamson, The 10 Meter South Pole Telescope, *Publications of the ASP* **123**, p. 568 (May 2011).
24. M. W. Auger, T. Treu, A. S. Bolton, R. Gavazzi, L. V. E. Koopmans, P. J. Marshall, K. Bundy and L. A. Moustakas, The Sloan Lens ACS Survey. IX. Colors, Lensing, and Stellar Masses of Early-Type Galaxies, *The Astrophysical Journal* **705**, 1099 (November 2009).
25. M. Negrello, R. Hopwood, G. De Zotti, A. Cooray, A. Verma, J. Bock, D. T. Frayer, M. A. Gurwell, A. Omont, R. Neri, H. Dannerbauer, L. L. Leeuw, E. Barton, J. Cooke, S. Kim, E. da Cunha, G. Rodighiero, P. Cox, D. G. Bonfield, M. J. Jarvis, S. Serjeant, R. J. Ivison, S. Dye, I. Aretxaga, D. H. Hughes, E. Ibar, F. Bertoldi, I. Valtchanov, S. Eales, L. Dunne, S. P. Driver, R. Auld, S. Buttiglione, A. Cava, C. A. Grady, D. L. Clements, A. Dariush, J. Fritz, D. Hill, J. B. Hornbeck, L. Kelvin, G. Lagache, M. Lopez-Caniego, J. Gonzalez-Nuevo, S. Maddox, E. Pascale, M. Pohlen, E. E. Rigby, A. Robotham, C. Simpson, D. J. B. Smith, P. Temi, M. A. Thompson, B. E. Woodgate, D. G. York, J. E. Aguirre, A. Beelen, A. Blain, A. J. Baker, M. Birkinshaw, R. Blundell, C. M. Bradford, D. Burgarella, L. Danese, J. S. Dunlop, S. Fleuren, J. Glenn, A. I. Harris, J. Kamenetzky, R. E. Lupu, R. J. Maddalena, B. F. Madore, P. R. Maloney, H. Matsuhara, M. J. Michałowski, E. J. Murphy, B. J. Naylor, H. Nguyen, C. Popescu, S. Rawlings, D. Rigopoulou, D. Scott, K. S. Scott, M. Seibert, I. Smail, R. J. Tuffs, J. D. Vieira, P. P. van der Werf and J. Zmuidzinas, The Detection of a Population of Submillimeter-Bright, Strongly Lensed Galaxies, *Science* **330**, p. 800 (November 2010).
26. L. Dunne, L. Bonavera, J. Gonzalez-Nuevo, S. J. Maddox and C. Vlahakis, Overdensity of SMGs in fields containing z ∼ 0.3 galaxies: magnification bias and the implications for studies of galaxy evolution, *Monthly Notices of the Royal Astronomical Society* **498**, 4635 (November 2020).
27. L. Wang, A. Cooray, D. Farrah, A. Amblard, R. Auld, J. Bock, D. Brisbin, D. Burgarella, P. Chanial, D. L. Clements, S. Eales, A. Franceschini, J. Glenn, Y. Gong, M. Griffin, S. Heinis, E. Ibar, R. J. Ivison, A. M. J. Mortier, S. J. Oliver, M. J. Page, A. Papageorgiou, C. P. Pearson, I. Pérez-Fournon, M. Pohlen, J. I. Rawlings, G. Raymond, G. Rodighiero, I. G. Roseboom, M. Rowan-Robinson, D. Scott, P. Serra, N. Seymour, A. J. Smith, M. Symeonidis, K. E. Tugwell, M. Vaccari, J. D. Vieira,

L. Vigroux and G. Wright, HerMES: detection of cosmic magnification of submillimetre galaxies using angular cross-correlation, *Monthly Notices of the Royal Astronomical Society* **414**, 596 (June 2011).
28. J. González-Nuevo, A. Lapi, M. Negrello, L. Danese, G. De Zotti, S. Amber, M. Baes, J. Bland-Hawthorn, N. Bourne, S. Brough, R. S. Bussmann, Z. Y. Cai, A. Cooray, S. P. Driver, L. Dunne, S. Dye, S. Eales, E. Ibar, R. Ivison, J. Liske, J. Loveday, S. Maddox, M. J. Michałowski, A. S. G. Robotham, D. Scott, M. W. L. Smith, E. Valiante and J. Q. Xia, Herschel-ATLAS/GAMA: SDSS cross-correlation induced by weak lensing, *Monthly Notices of the Royal Astronomical Society* **442**, 2680 (August 2014).
29. D. Foreman-Mackey, D. W. Hogg, D. Lang and J. Goodman, emcee: The MCMC Hammer, *Publications of the ASP* **125**, p. 306 (Mar 2013).

The impact of the Lorentz symmetry violation on the CMB polarization

Seddigheh Tizchang

School of Particles and Accelerators, Institute for Research in Fundamental Sciences (IPM) PO BOX19395-5531, Tehran, Iran
E-mail: s.tizchang@ipm.ir

Rohoollah Mohammadi

Iranian National Science and Technology Museum (INMOST), PO BOX: 11369-14611, Tehran, Iran
School of Astronomy, Institute for Research in FundamentalSciences (IPM), PO BOX 19395-5531,Tehran, Iran
E-mail: rmohammadi@ipm.ir

She-Sheng Xue

ICRANet and Department of Physics, Sapienza University of Rome P.le A. Moro 5, 00185 Rome, Italy
E-mail: xue@icra.it

In the standard cosmological scenario, no circular polarization is predicted for Cosmic Microwave Background (CMB) radiation. However, in the frame of moving particle, Lorentz symmetry violation leads to circular polarization for CMB radiation. We estimate the circular polarization power spectrum $C_{Vl}^{(S)}$ in CMB radiation due to Compton scattering in the presence of the Lorentz symmetry violation. We show that the V-mode power spectrum can be obtained in terms of linear polarization power spectrum at the last scattering surface.

Keywords: Circular polarization, CMB, power spectrum

1. Introduction

Numerous valuable information could be obtained from temperature anisotropies and polarization of the CMB. In particular, tempreture anisotropy in CMB radiation could generate polarization for the CMB. The theoretical calculation predicts at the most 10% of linear polarization for the CMB known as E-mode and B-mode which is originated from Compton scattering of photons on the electron plasma at the recombination epoch. The E-mode and B-mode polarization are different polarization pattern arisen from scalar and tensor temperature anisotropy, respectively.[1-3] Besides, the standard model of cosmology peredict no circular polarization for the CMB due to Compton scattering, and circular polarization has not been measured yet. However, most recently the CLASS experiment has established tightest upper bound on angular power spectrum of the CMB at 95% confidence from $0.4\mu K^2$ to $13.5\mu K^2$ on $\ell(\ell+1)C_\ell^{VV}/(2\pi))$ at multipole moments $1 \leq \ell \leq 120$.[4] The circular polarization for the CMB is a rare process so that observation of any level of circular polarization could be a hint for the existence of new physics. In particular, Faraday conversion could be a source of the CMB circular polarization in which linear polarized light propagates through a medium and lead to various indexes of refraction along the two transverse axes. Besides, Compton scattering of CMB from the electron in the presence of a trivial background field such as a magnetic field[5,6] or non-trivial background like Non-Commutative space-time[7,8] and Lorentz symmetry violation[6,9] will rise circular polarization for the CMB. Moreover, scattering of CMB photon from non-standard particles like vector or fermionic dark matter can lead to circular polarization of the CMB[10,11] and cosmic photons.[12]

In this study, we would like to explore the effects of Lorentz symmetry violation (LIV) as a non-trivial background on the angular power spectrum of the CMB. The energy scale for LIV is the Planck scale which is out of reach based on direct experiments. An alternative way to study such effects is the Standard Model Extension (SME) based on effective field theory approach.[13] The Lorentz violation at the SME is induced by spontaneous symmetry breaking and result in new terms including LIV parameters and can behave such as constant backgrounds. The phenomenological aspects of LIV have been widely studied in the literature which total obtained constraints are gathered at Ref.[14].

In this paper, we give a brief overview of the SME in section 2. Then the effect of LIV on the CMB polarization is given in section 3. Finally, in section 4 we give a conclusion and summary.

2. The SME

We assume the CMB photon scatter from cosmic electron while the Lorentz invariance is violated. The LIV effect is appliable by the SME. The minimal version of the SME contains all possible gauge invariant operators, made by all the SM fields and LIV is specified with new couplings.[13] The QED part of SME including charged fermion interaction with photon is defined as follows:

$$\mathcal{L}_{\text{QED}}^{\text{LIV}} = \frac{1}{2} i \bar{\psi}(\gamma^\nu + c^{\mu\nu}\gamma_\mu) \overleftrightarrow{D}_\mu \psi - \bar{\psi} m_e \psi, \tag{1}$$

where ψ is the fermion field, $\mathcal{D}_\mu$ shows the covariant derivative with $u \overleftrightarrow{D}_\mu v \equiv u D_\mu v - v D_\mu u$,[15] the mass of electron is m_e, and γ_μ indicates the Dirac gamma matrices and the coefficient for Lorentz symmetry violation is $c^{\mu\nu}$ in fermion sector. We assume $c^{\mu\nu}$ to be symmetric and traceless tensor. For convenience, the constraint on the SME parameters are expressed in a standard reference frame, *i.e* Sun-centered, celestial equatorial frame (SCCEF) with coordinates $\{T, X, Y, Z\}$, the coordinates of lab frame are denoted by $\{t, x, y, z\}$. Conversion to a lab frame at convenient time t is defined by[16]

$$\begin{pmatrix} \hat{x} \\ \hat{y} \\ \hat{z} \end{pmatrix} = \begin{pmatrix} \cos\chi \cos\Omega t & \cos\chi \sin\Omega t & -\sin\chi \\ -\sin\Omega t & \cos\Omega t & 0 \\ \sin\chi \cos\Omega t & \sin\chi \sin\Omega t & \cos\chi \end{pmatrix} \begin{pmatrix} \hat{X} \\ \hat{Y} \\ \hat{Z} \end{pmatrix}. \tag{2}$$

If we consider the lab frame on the earth Ω would be the earth sidereal rotation frequency equivalent to $2\pi/(23\text{h } 56 \text{ min})$ and $0 \leq \chi \leq \pi$. Some experimental bounds on the components of c parameter in the SCCEF frame is given in Tab 1. Therefore,

$c_{\mu\nu}$	Experimental bounds	system
c_{TT}	2×10^{-15}	Collider physics[17]
c_{YY}	3×10^{-15}	Astrophysics[18]
c_{ZZ}	5×10^{-15}	Astrophysics[18]
$c_{(XY)}$	3×10^{-15}	Astrophysics[18]
$c_{(YZ)}$	1.8×10^{-15}	Astrophysics[18]
$c_{(XZ)}$	3×10^{-15}	Astrophysics[18]
$c_{(TX)}$	-30×10^{-14}	Collider physics[17]
$c_{(TY)}$	-80×10^{-15}	Collider physics[17]
$c_{(TZ)}$	-11×10^{-13}	Collider physics[17]

we also use correlation between components of laboratory frame and SCCEF given in Ref[16] to transfer the result to SCCEF frame.

3. Effect of LIV on the CMB polarization

The theoretical aspect of polarization of the CMB photon is characterized by four Stokes parameters: $[I, Q, U, V]^1$ which can be related to component of density matrix as:

$$\rho = \frac{1}{2}\begin{pmatrix} I+Q & U-iV \\ U+iV & I-Q \end{pmatrix}, \quad (3)$$

where I indicates the total radiation intensity (temperature), Q and U indicates linear polarization and V is circular polarization of the CMB radiation which satisfy the inequality $I^2 \geq Q^2 + U^2 + V^2$. Compton scattering cannot generate circular polarization V, so in the standard model of cosmology circular polarization is not anticipated for the CMB. For an ensemble of photon which are assumed free before as well as after scattering, the time evolution for Stokes parameters will be obtained by solving the following quantum Boltzmann equation, given as[1]

$$(2\pi)^3 \delta^3(0) 2p^0 \frac{d}{dt}\rho_{ij}(0, \mathbf{p}) = i\langle[H_I^0(0), \hat{\mathcal{D}}_{ij}(\mathbf{p})]\rangle \quad (4)$$

$$- \frac{1}{2}\int_{-\infty}^{\infty} dt \langle[H_I^0(t), [H_I(0), \hat{\mathcal{D}}_{ij}(\mathbf{p})]]\rangle,$$

where p^0 represents the energy of photon and the photon number operator is given with $\hat{\mathcal{D}}_{ij}(\mathbf{p}) = \hat{a}_i^\dagger(\mathbf{p})\hat{a}_j(\mathbf{p})$ where $\hat{a}_i^\dagger(\mathbf{p})$ and $\hat{a}_j(\mathbf{p})$ are rising and lowering operators, respectively.

In the Eq. (4), H_I^0 is an interacting Hamiltonian that includes all possible interactions at leading order. First term on the right-hand side of the above equation is known as 'forward scattering' where the incoming particles interact without exchange the momenta and this term is linearly proportional to H_I^0. The second term is called 'Damping term' and quadratically proportional to H_I^0. In the case of Compton scattering, the contribution of first term of Eq. (4) is equal to zero. Moreover, time evolution of the circular polarization is zero ($\dot{V} = 0$) for both terms of right-hand side of Eq. (4). Therefore, contribution of any new physics in polarization of photon in forward scattering would be considerable.

We obtain the Boltzmann equation for circular polarization of CMB radiation in the presence of LIV by using the Eq. (4), and reconstructing the Stokes parameters[6] as follows:

$$\frac{d}{d\eta}\Delta_I^{(S)} + iK\mu\Delta_I^{(S)} + 4[\dot{\psi} - iK\mu\varphi] = C_{e\gamma}^I,$$

$$\frac{d}{d\eta}\Delta_P^{\pm(S)} + iK\mu\Delta_P^{\pm(S)} = C_{e\gamma}^\pm - i\kappa_{LIV}^\pm \Delta_V^{(S)},$$

$$\frac{d}{d\eta}\Delta_V^{(S)} + iK\mu\Delta_V^{(S)} = C_{e\gamma}^V + \frac{i}{2}\left[\kappa_{LIV}^+ \Delta_P^{-(S)} + \kappa_{LIV}^- \Delta_P^{+(S)}\right], \quad (5)$$

where η represents conformal time. Scalar perturbation corresponding to the potential of Newton and spacial curvature perturbation are shown with ψ and ϕ. $\Delta_P^{\pm(S)} = Q^{(S)} \pm iU^{(S)}$ is a linear combination of $Q^{(S)}$ and $U^{(S)}$ polarization. The scalar product of wave vector $\mathbf{K}$ and the CMB propagating direction is given by μ. $C_{e\gamma}^I$, $C_{e\gamma}^\pm$ and $C_{e\gamma}^V$ represents the contribution of the SM Compton scattering in $\Delta_P^{\pm(S)}$ polarization and $\Delta_V^{(S)}$ polarization,[1] respectively. $\kappa_{LIV}^\pm$ indicates the involvement of Compton scattering by considering fermionic part of the SME Lagrangian at Boltzmann equations (Eq. (5)) which are obtained as follows:

$$\kappa_{LIV} = -a(\eta)\frac{3}{4}\frac{\sigma_T}{\alpha}\frac{m_e^2}{p_0}\frac{\bar{n}_e}{m_e}, \quad \kappa_{LIV}^\pm = \kappa_{LIV}\, c_{\{\alpha\beta\}}(\rho_Q^{\{\alpha\beta\}} \pm i\rho_U^{\{\alpha\beta\}}), \quad (6)$$

where $\rho_Q^{\{\alpha\beta\}}$ and $\rho_U^{\{\alpha\beta\}}$ are defined as:

$$\rho_Q^{\{\alpha\beta\}} = -\Big[\epsilon^1 \cdot \hat{c} \cdot \epsilon^2 + \sum_{f=e,p}\frac{m_f v_b^2}{2k_0}(\hat{v}\cdot\epsilon^2\hat{v}\cdot\hat{c}\cdot\epsilon^1 + \hat{v}\cdot\epsilon^1\hat{v}\cdot\hat{c}\cdot\epsilon^2) - \frac{v_b}{2}(\hat{v}\cdot\epsilon^2\hat{k}\cdot\hat{c}\cdot\epsilon^1$$

$$+ \hat{v}\cdot\epsilon^1\hat{k}\cdot\hat{c}\cdot\epsilon^2) + \sum_{f=e,p}\frac{2v_b^4 m_f^2}{k_0^2}(\hat{v}\cdot\hat{c}\cdot\hat{v}\hat{v}\cdot\epsilon^2\hat{v}\cdot\epsilon^1) + 2v_b^2\,\hat{k}\cdot\hat{c}\cdot\hat{k}\,\hat{v}\cdot\epsilon^1\,\hat{v}\cdot\epsilon^2\Big],$$

$$\rho_U^{\{\alpha\beta\}} = \Big[\frac{1}{2}(\epsilon^1\cdot\hat{c}\cdot\epsilon^1 + \epsilon^2\cdot\hat{c}\cdot\epsilon^2) + \sum_{f=e,p}\frac{m_f v_b^2}{2k_0}(\hat{v}\cdot\epsilon^1\hat{v}\cdot\hat{c}\cdot\epsilon^1 - \hat{v}\cdot\epsilon^2\hat{v}\cdot\hat{c}\cdot\epsilon^2)$$

$$+\frac{v_b}{2}(\hat{v}\cdot\epsilon^2\hat{k}\cdot\hat{c}\cdot\epsilon^2 - \hat{v}\cdot\epsilon^1\hat{k}\cdot\hat{c}\cdot\epsilon^1) + \sum_{f=e,p}\frac{v_b^4 m_f^2}{2k_0^2}\hat{v}\cdot\hat{c}\cdot\hat{v}(\hat{v}\cdot\epsilon^1\hat{v}\cdot\epsilon^1$$

$$+ \hat{v}\cdot\epsilon^2\hat{v}\cdot\epsilon^2) + \frac{v_b^2}{2}\,\hat{k}\cdot\hat{c}\cdot\hat{k}\,(\hat{v}\cdot\epsilon^1\,\hat{v}\cdot\epsilon^1 + \hat{v}\cdot\epsilon^2\,\hat{v}\cdot\epsilon^2)\Big], \quad (7)$$

here $\alpha, \beta = 0, i, j$ represent time-like and space-like LIV components of coefficient c. The direction of bulk velocity of electrons is shown by $\hat{v}$. It is convenient, to describe the statistical properties of CMB radiation via spherical harmonic. Then the Stokes parameter could be expanded over suitable multipole moment in spin weighted basis[2,3]

$$\Delta^{(S)}_{I,P,V}(\eta, \mathbf{K}, \mu) = \sum_{l=0}^{\infty} (2l+1)(-i)^l \Delta^l_{I,P,V}(\eta, \mathbf{K}) P_l(\mu), \qquad (8)$$

with $P_l(\mu)$ being the Legendre polynomial of rank l. In particular, the value of $\Delta^{(S)}_{I,P,V}$ at the present time η_0 in direction $\hat{n}$ are achieved by integrating the Boltzmann equations (Eq. (5)) along the line of sight and summation over all Fourier modes $\mathbf{K}$ as follows:

$$\Delta^{\pm(S)}_P(\hat{n}) = \int d^3 \mathbf{K} \xi(\mathbf{K}) e^{\pm 2i\phi_{K,n}} \Delta^{\pm(S)}_P(\mathbf{K}, \mathbf{p}, \eta),$$

$$\Delta^{(S)}_V(\hat{n}) = \int d^3 \mathbf{K} \xi(\mathbf{K}) \Delta^{(S)}_V(\mathbf{K}, \mathbf{p}, \eta), \qquad (9)$$

where $\phi_{K,n}$ are characterized to rotate the $\hat{n}$ and $\hat{\mathbf{K}}$ dependent basis to a fixed frame in the sky. The random variable $\xi(\mathbf{K})$ is used to define the initial amplitude of the mode. Then $\Delta^{(S)}_V$ and $\Delta^{\pm(S)}_P$ are obtained as:

$$\Delta^{(S)}_V(\mathbf{K}, \mu, \eta_0) = \frac{1}{2} \int_0^{\eta_0} d\eta \, \dot{\eta}_{e\gamma} e^{ix\mu - \eta_{e\gamma}} \left[3\mu \Delta^{(S)}_{V1} + i\left(\frac{\kappa^+_{LV}}{\dot{\eta}_{e\gamma}} \Delta^{+(S)}_P + \frac{\kappa^-_{LV}}{\dot{\eta}_{e\gamma}} \Delta^{-(S)}_P\right) \right],$$

$$\approx \frac{1}{2} \int_0^{\eta_0} d\eta \, \dot{\eta}_{e\gamma} e^{ix\mu - \eta_{e\gamma}} \left[3\mu \Delta^{(S)}_{V1} + 2i \rho_Q^{\{\alpha\beta\}} c_{\{\alpha\beta\}} \frac{\kappa_{LV}}{\dot{\eta}_{e\gamma}} \Delta^{(S)}_P + ... \right], \qquad (10)$$

$$\Delta^{\pm(S)}_P(\mathbf{K}, \mu, \eta_0) = \int_0^{\eta_0} d\eta \, \dot{\tau}_{e\gamma} e^{ix\mu - \tau_{e\gamma}} \left[\frac{3}{4}(1-\mu^2) \Pi(K, \eta) - i \frac{\kappa^{\mp}_{LV}}{\dot{\eta}_{e\gamma}} \Delta^{(S)}_V \right], \qquad (11)$$

where $\Pi = \Delta^{(S)}_{T2} + \Delta^{(S)}_{P2} + \Delta^{(S)}_{P0}$, the differential and total optical depth caused by Thomson scattering (σ_T) at the time of η are given by $\dot{\eta}_{e\gamma} = a(\eta) n_e \sigma_T$ and $\eta_{e\gamma} = \int_\eta^{\eta_0} \dot{\eta}_{e\gamma} d\eta$ with n_e being electron number density, and $x = \mathbf{K}(\eta_0 - \eta)$. The $\Delta^{(S)}_P$ is linear polarization defined as

$$\Delta^{(S)}_P(\mathbf{K}, \mu, \eta) = \int_0^{\eta} d\eta \, \dot{\eta}_{e\gamma} e^{ix\mu - \eta_{e\gamma}} \left[\frac{3}{4}(1-\mu^2) \Pi(K, \eta) \right]. \qquad (12)$$

The $\Delta^{(S)}_V$ arised from Compton scattering in presence of LIV (Eq. (10)) can be estimated in terms of linear polarization. The term $\frac{\kappa_{LV}}{\dot{\eta}_{e\gamma}} \rho_Q^{\{\alpha\beta\}} c_{\{\alpha\beta\}}$ represents the strength of LIV contribution at circular polarization. Therefore, we consider the dominant term in $\rho_Q^{\{\alpha\beta\}}$ (Eq. (7)).

The correlation function of circular polarization in the presence of LIV in terms of primordial power spectrum is obtained as:

$$\begin{aligned}C_l^V &= \frac{1}{2l+1}\sum_m \left\langle a_{V,lm}^* a_{V,lm}\right\rangle \\ &\approx \frac{1}{2l+1}\int d^3K P_v(\mathbf{K}) \times \\ &\sum_m \left|\int d\Omega Y_{lm}^* \int_0^{\eta_0} d\eta\, \dot{\eta}_{e\gamma}\, e^{ix\mu-\eta_{e\gamma}}\, 2i\, \rho_Q^{\{\alpha\beta\}} c_{\{\alpha\beta\}} \frac{\kappa_{\mathrm{LIV}}}{\dot{\eta}_{e\gamma}} \Delta_P^{(S)}\right|^2,\end{aligned} \quad (13)$$

and $P_v(K)$ is the velocity power spectrum which can be expressed as a function of primordial scalar spectrum:

$$P_v(\mathbf{K},\tau) \sim P_\phi^{(S)}(\mathbf{K},\tau). \quad (14)$$

Finally, we estimate the circular power spectrum C_l^V regarding to linearly polarized two point function C_l^P as follows:

$$C_l^V \approx (\tilde{\kappa}_{\mathrm{LIV}}^{\mathrm{avg}})^2 C_l^P, \quad (15)$$

where

$$\tilde{\kappa}_{\mathrm{LIV}} = c_{\{\alpha\beta\}}\, \rho_Q^{\{\alpha\beta\}} \frac{\kappa_{\mathrm{LIV}}}{\dot{\tau}_{e\gamma}}, \quad \tilde{\kappa}_{\mathrm{LIV}}^{\mathrm{avg}} = \frac{1}{z_{lss}}\int_0^{z_{lss}} dz\, \tilde{\kappa}_{\mathrm{LIV}}(z) \simeq 10^{-3}. \quad (16)$$

here $\tilde{\kappa}_{\mathrm{LIV}}^{\mathrm{avg}}$ is the mean of $\tilde{\kappa}_{\mathrm{LIV}}(z)$ over redshift from last scattering surface $z_{lss} \simeq 1100$ up to today $z = 1$. Similar to Ref.,[19] we assume $c^{\alpha\beta}$ tensor with symmetric component $\alpha = \beta = T,X,Y,Z$ at the order of 10^{-15} and $\chi = \pi/4$.[14] Current experimental value for linearly polarized power spectrum for the CMB is at the order of $C_l^P \equiv 0.1\mu K^2$ for $l < 250$.[20] Applying the value of linearly polarized power spectrum, we estimate the V-mode power spectrum generated from Compton scattering in the presence of LIV as follows

$$C_l^V \approx 0.8\, (nK)^2 \Big(\frac{c^{\alpha\beta}}{10^{-15}}\Big)^2. \quad (17)$$

As we mentioned before, the tightest experimental bound on the circular polarization is obtained by CLASS experiment which is $0.4\mu K^2$ to $13.5\mu K^2$ for $1 \leq l \leq 120$. By improving the sensitivity of experiments in the future, we expect the obtained constraint in Eq. (17) would be comparable to experimental bounds.

4. Summary

In this work we studied the circular polarization of CMB due to forward scattering with cosmic electron in the presence of LIV and scalar perturbations. We derived the Boltzmann equations describing the time evolution of CMB polarization. We also showed that the circular power spectrum of CMB in the presence of LIV can be expressed as linear power spectrum. Circular polarization of CMB might be originated from different sources so that the possibility to separate the contribution of different sources would be valuable. The dominant term of circular polarization for the CMB due to LIV is linearly proportional to wavelength $\lambda = (1/k_0)$ (Eq. (7)) while the wavelength dependence for other effects could be different. This various dependency to wavelength leads to a different distribution of V-mode power spectrum arising from different models and can help us to compare our result with other bounds on circular polarization.

References

1. A. Kosowsky, Cosmic microwave background polarization, *Annals Phys.* **246**, 49 (1996).
2. U. Seljak and M. Zaldarriaga, A Line of sight integration approach to cosmic microwave background anisotropies, *Astrophys. J.* **469**, 437 (1996).
3. M. Zaldarriaga and U. Seljak, An all sky analysis of polarization in the microwave background, *Phys. Rev. D* **55**, 1830 (1997).
4. I. L. Padilla, J. R. Eimer, Y. Li, G. E. Addison, A. Ali, J. W. Appel, C. L. Bennett, R. Bustos, M. K. Brewer, M. Chan, D. T. Chuss, J. Cleary, J. Couto, S. Dahal, K. Denis, R. Dünner, T. Essinger-Hileman, P. Fluxá, D. Gothe, S. K. Haridas, K. Harrington, J. Iuliano, J. Karakla, T. A. Marriage, N. J. Miller, C. Núñez, L. Parker, M. A. Petroff, R. Reeves, K. Rostem, R. W. Stevens, D. A. N. Valle, D. J. Watts, J. L. Weiland, E. J. Wollack and Z. Xu, Two-year cosmology large angular scale surveyor (CLASS) observations: A measurement of circular polarization at 40 GHz, *The Astrophysical Journal* **889**, p. 105 (jan 2020).
5. A. Cooray, A. Melchiorri and J. Silk, Is the cosmic microwave background circularly polarized?, *Phys. Lett. B* **554**, 1 (2003).
6. E. Bavarsad, M. Haghighat, Z. Rezaei, R. Mohammadi, I. Motie and M. Zarei, Generation of circular polarization of the CMB, *Phys. Rev. D* **81**, p. 084035 (2010).
7. S. Tizchang, S. Batebi, M. Haghighat and R. Mohammadi, The generation of B-mode and circular polarization of cosmic photons due to Non-Commutative space-Time background, *PoS* **ICHEP2018**, p. 142 (2019).
8. S. Tizchang, S. Batebi, M. Haghighat and R. Mohammadi, Cosmic microwave background polarization in non-commutative space-time, *Eur. Phys. J. C* **76**, p. 478 (2016).
9. S. Alexander, E. McDonough, A. Pullen and B. Shapiro, Physics Beyond The Standard Model with Circular Polarization in the CMB and CMB-21cm Cross-Correlation, *JCAP* **01**, p. 032 (2020).
10. S. Modares Vamegh, M. Haghighat, S. Mahmoudi and R. Mohammadi, Impact of the vector dark matter on polarization of the CMB photon, *Phys. Rev. D* **100**, p. 103024 (2019).
11. M. Haghighat, S. Mahmoudi, R. Mohammadi, S. Tizchang and S. S. Xue, Circular polarization of cosmic photons due to their interactions with Sterile neutrino dark matter, *Phys. Rev. D* **101**, p. 123016 (2020).
12. M. Cermeño, C. Degrande and L. Mantani, Circular polarisation of gamma rays as a probe of dark matter interactions with cosmic ray electrons (3 2021).
13. D. Colladay and V. A. Kostelecky, CPT violation and the standard model, *Phys. Rev. D* **55**, 6760 (1997).
14. V. A. Kostelecky and N. Russell, Data Tables for Lorentz and CPT Violation (1 2008).
15. D. Colladay and V. A. Kostelecky, Lorentz violating extension of the standard model, *Phys. Rev. D* **58**, p. 116002 (1998).

16. V. A. Kostelecky and C. D. Lane, Constraints on Lorentz violation from clock comparison experiments, *Phys. Rev. D* **60**, p. 116010 (1999).
17. B. Altschul, Laboratory Bounds on Electron Lorentz Violation, *Phys. Rev. D* **82**, p. 016002 (2010).
18. B. Altschul, Synchrotron and inverse compton constraints on Lorentz violations for electrons, *Phys. Rev. D* **74**, p. 083003 (2006).
19. S. Tizchang, R. Mohammadi and S.-S. Xue, Probing Lorentz violation effects via a laser beam interacting with a high-energy charged lepton beam, *Eur. Phys. J. C* **79**, p. 224 (2019).
20. P. A. R. Ade *et al.*, Planck 2015 results. XX. Constraints on inflation, *Astron. Astrophys.* **594**, p. A20 (2016).

Cosmic backgrounds from the radio to the far-infrared: Recent results and perspectives from cosmological and astrophysical surveys*

Carlo Burigana;[1,2,3,a] Elia Sefano Battistelli;[4,5,b] Laura Bonavera;[6,7,c]
Tirthankar Roy Choudhury;[8,d] Marcos Lopez-Caniego;[9,e] Constantinos Skordis;[10,f]
Raelyn Marguerite Sullivan;[11,g] Hideki Tanimura;[12,h] Seddigheh Tizchang;[13,i]
Matthieu Tristram;[14,j] Amanda Weltman[15,k]

[1] *INAF–IRA, Via Piero Gobetti 101, 40129 Bologna, Italy*†
[2] *Dipartimento di Fisica e Scienze della Terra, Università degli Studi di Ferrara,
Via Giuseppe Saragat 1, I-44122 Ferrara, Italy*
[3] *INFN, Sezione di Bologna, Via Irnerio 46, 40126, Bologna, Italy*
[4] *Dipartimento di Fisica, Università di Roma "La Sapienza",
P.le Aldo Moro 2, 00185, Rome, Italy*
[5] *INAF-IAPS Roma, Via del Fosso del Cavaliere 100, 00133 Roma, Italy*
[6] *Departamento de Física, Universidad de Oviedo,
C. Federico García Lorca 18, 33007 Oviedo, Spain*
[7] *Instituto Universitario de Ciencias y Tecnologías Espaciales de Asturias (ICTEA),
C. Independencia 13, 33004 Oviedo, Spain*
[8] *National Centre for Radio Astrophysics, Tata Institute of Fundamental Research,
Ganeshkhind, Pune 411007, India*
[9] *Aurora Technology B.V. for the European Space Agency,
Villanueva de la Canada, Madrid, 28692, Spain*
[10] *CEICO, FZU - Institute of Physics of the Czech Academy of Sciences,
Na Slovance 1999/2, 182 21, Prague*
[11] *Department of Physics & Astronomy, University of British Columbia,
6224 Agricultural Road, Vancouver, British Columbia, Canada*
[12] *Université Paris-Saclay, CNRS, Institut d'Astrophysique Spatiale,
Bâtiment 121, 91405 Orsay, France*
[13] *School of Particles and Accelerators, Institute for Research in Fundamental Sciences (IPM),
PO BOX19395-5531, Tehran, Iran*
[14] *Université Paris-Saclay, CNRS/IN2P3, IJCLab, 91405 Orsay, France*
[15] *High Energy Physics, Cosmology & Astrophysics Theory Group, University of Cape Town,
Private Bag, Cape Town, South Africa, 7700*

[a] *burigana@ira.inaf.it* — [b] *elia.battistelli@roma1.infn.it* — [c] *bonaveralaura@uniovi.es*
[d] *tirth@ncra.tifr.res.in* — [e] *marcos.lopez.caniego@sciops.esa.int* — [f] *skordis@fzu.cz*
[g] *rsullivan@phas.ubc.ca* — [h] *hideki.tanimura@ias.u-psud.fr* — [i] *s.tizchang@ipm.ir*
[j] *tristram@ijclab.in2p3.fr* — [k] *amanda.weltman@uct.ac.za*

Cosmological and astrophysical surveys in various wavebands, in particular from the radio to the far-infrared, offer a unique view of the universe's properties and the formation and evolution of its structures. After a preamble on the so-called tension problem, which occurs when different types of data are used to determine cosmological parameters, we discuss the role of fast radio bursts in cosmology, in particular for the missing baryon

---

*Based on talks presented at the Sixteenth Marcel Grossmann Meeting on General Relativity, July 2021.
†Istituto Nazionale di Astrofisica – Istituto di Radioastronomia, Via Piero Gobetti 101, 40129 Bologna, Italy

problem, and the perspectives from the analysis of the 21 cm redshifted line from neutral hydrogen. We then describe the *Planck* Legacy Archive, its wealth of scientific information and next developments, and the promising perspectives expected from higher resolution observations, in particular for the analysis of the thermal Sunyaev-Zel'dovich effect. Three cosmological results of the *Planck* mission are presented next: the implications of the map of Comptonization fluctuations, the dipole analysis from cross-correlating cosmic microwave background anisotropy and Comptonization fluctuation maps, and the constraints on the primordial tensor-to-scalar perturbation ratio. Finally, we discuss some future perspectives and alternative scenarios in cosmology, such as the study of the Lorentz invariance violation with the cosmic microwave background polarization, the introduction of new gravitational degrees of freedom to solve the dark matter problem, and the exploitation of the magnification bias with high-redshift sub-millimeter galaxies to constrain cosmological parameters.

Keywords: Cosmology; background radiations; observational cosmology; radio, microwave; submillimeter; infrared emission; large-scale structure of the universe; galaxy clusters; radio sources; IR sources; gravitational lenses and luminous arcs; relativity and gravitation; modified theories of gravity; dark matter; special relativity; radiation mechanisms, polarization.

1. Introduction

Over the last century or so, cosmology has progressed from a field that was essentially philosophy to a precision science. The current standard cosmological model is the Λ cold dark matter (ΛCDM) model, which mainly consists of a cosmological constant (Λ) or dark energy (DE) component and cold dark matter (CDM) component, with general relativity (GR) as the assumed theory of gravity. It makes predictions on the smallest and largest scales, that, despite some open questions, are largely verified by a host of observational cosmology experiments.

Cosmological and astrophysical surveys in various wavebands, in particular from the radio to the far-infrared, are crucial to solve many problems in cosmology and to understand the origin and evolution of the cosmic structures at various scales through cosmic time. The accurate observations of the properties of the cosmic microwave background (CMB) began the era of precision cosmology, furthering our understanding of the early universe and its evolution up to the present time and beyond. Similarly, the information contained in the radio sky is of increasing relevance to unravel the complexity of cosmic evolution and to answer a wide range of open questions, thanks to the spectacular experimental improvement achieved in the past years and expected in the future.

The structure of this paper is as follows. In Sect. 2, we begin with a preamble to the so-called tension problem, which occurs when different data are used to determine cosmological parameters. We then discuss the role of fast radio bursts (FRBs) in cosmology to solve the missing baryons problem, followed by the perspectives represented by the analysis of the 21 cm redshifted line from neutral hydrogen (HI). Sect. 3 describes the wealth of scientific information and tools publicly available at the *Planck* Legacy Archive (PLA), with its current and future developments, and the perspectives expected from higher resolution observations at millimeter (mm) and sub-mm wavelengths, in particular for the analysis of the thermal Sunyaev-Zel'dovich (SZ) effect towards galaxy clusters (GCs), focusing on a forthcoming well-defined facility instrument. In Sect. 4 we discuss three important cosmological results based on the data from the *Planck* mission: the implications of the analysis of the thermal SZ (tSZ) map, the dipole analysis based on the cross-correlation of CMB anisotropy and tSZ maps, and the constraints on the ratio between the primordial tensor and scalar perturbations. Finally, Sect. 5 is dedicated to future perspectives and alternative scenarios in cosmology. We consider three specific examples: the study of Lorentz invariance violation with the analysis of CMB polarization, the solution to the dark matter (DM) problem introducing new gravitational degrees of freedom, and the exploitation of the magnification bias with high-z sub-mm galaxies to constrain a set of cosmological parameters.

2. Cosmology in the radio

2.1. *Cosmology with radio astrophysics and tensions in cosmology*

Amongst the successes of modern cosmology, is the remarkable precision in the estimation of the cosmological parameters that describe the contents, geometry and history of our universe. Herein also lies the current greatest tension in the data. Indeed, in spite of the increasing precision in observational cosmology, it is possible we have lost some accuracy: a number of tensions now appear within our data, tensions that more cosmology experiments do not appear to solve. These tensions may require a change in the underlying theory or they may be resolved with novel observational probes of the large scale picture of the universe. Here we will describe an example of the latter, namely, the FRBs, the novel discovery of our century, as potential instruments for cosmology. Indeed we will highlight more broadly the use of radio astrophysics - encompassing both the use of radio transients and intensity mapping tools, and the potential they hold for groundbreaking cosmology discovery.

The Hubble constant, H_0, is anything but constant across observations at different scales (see Ref. 1 for a recent review of most of the data). A brief summary however, is that historically there were two independent measures for H_0, very far apart in value with measurements of roughly $50\,\mathrm{km\,s^{-1}\,Mpc^{-1}}$ or $100\,\mathrm{km\,s^{-1}\,Mpc^{-1}}$ from the early and late universe respectively. However, the error bars on each measurement was large enough, that each was within errors of the other and it was assumed that with improved observations, the error bars would get smaller and the values would get closer and converge. Indeed, this appeared to be the case early this century, but every new data set over the last several years has the values diverging with ever smaller error bars, that critically no longer allow for a simple convergence in the value of H_0. Measurements from the early universe, such as *Planck*, Dark Energy Survey[2,3] (DES), and baryonic acoustic oscillations (BAO) and Big Bang nucleosynthesis (BBN) observations, all point to a smaller value of around $H_0 \simeq 67\,\mathrm{km\,s^{-1}\,Mpc^{-1}}$ and measurements from the late universe, using Cepheids as distance ladders, or lensing for example, find $H_0 \simeq 73\,\mathrm{km\,s^{-1}\,Mpc^{-1}}$ with each measurement having error bars in the range $\simeq 1\div 4\,\text{km}\,\text{s}^{-1}\,\text{Mpc}^{-1}$. Thus this tension is growing with data rather than resolving.

There are longer standing issues with the standard cosmological model, of course, the lack of direct observational evidence for DM which makes up roughly 25% of the total energy budget of the universe is of particular concern. No less resolved is the issue of DE, here making up $\sim 70\%$ of the energy budget of the universe and yet only observed in indirect cosmological experiments with no direct detection and also no compelling theoretical explanation for why it even exists or why it appears to be dominating the total energy budget of the universe at a cosmological time when we are both possible and here to observe it. Early universe inflation is a key component in the model, solving several open problems such as the flatness and horizon problems and yet we still have no theory of inflation that fits within an ultraviolet complete theory with a natural candidate for the inflaton lacking. One hopes that these three problems are resolved together with a leap in the theory space - yet the obligation remains to continue to search for observational data that may yet play a role.

Other problems have lingered for very long, such as the missing baryon problem, where even the $\sim 5\%$ of the universe that we know exists is not entirely accounted for. Indeed adding up all of the observed contributions to the baryons accounts for only $\sim 70\%$ of the total expected. Roughly 30% are considered missing, and expected to be somewhere in the warm hot intergalactic medium (WHIM). Indeed, we should say were considered missing, as we discuss below how to find these missing baryons using the FRBs.

2.1.1. *Fast radio bursts and their role in cosmology*

As the name suggests, FRBs are very bright ($\sim$ Jy), brief ($\sim\mu$s to $\sim$ ms scale) transients, observed in the broad spectrum of the radio. The first was discovered[4] in 2007 and ever since the search has been on to discover more and their properties, first through searches in archival data and more recently through purpose built radio telescopes and arrays to find thousands if not tens of thousands of bursts every year. Our understanding of the properties of FRBs is still evolving; it appears that many but not all repeat, it is not yet known if any of the repeaters repeat in a periodic fashion, and indeed it is likely that ultimately FRBs will fall in several classes as has happened with transients historically. Their other properties such as polarisation, rotation measures etc are all still unknown as the observations do not all point to a single pattern and it is not always possible to disentangle host galaxy effects from propagation effects from intrinsic properties of the bursts. It does appear certain that they are found in host galaxies, and that they lie at cosmological distances,[5] thus making them excellent candidates for cosmology as their propagation will probe the intergalactic medium (IGM) and thus give us a number of novel ways to constrain cosmological parameters (see, e.g., Refs. 6–8 and references therein). From a theoretical standpoint, the progenitor mechanism driving FRBs is not yet known though there are strong hints that at least some are driven by magnetars through one of many physical possible mechanisms. A full database of theories,[9] once outnumbered the observations, but as the amount of data grows, the possibilities for theoretical explanations shrinks and so it is likely that in a few years we will have only a handful of possible contenders remaining, perhaps matching future classes of FRBs.

There are a number of ways FRBs can be used as cosmological probes. Here we focus on a single application. After emission from the source, the photons from the burst travel to the observer through the IGM, and are slowed down differentially as a function of their wavelength, λ, or frequency, $\nu = c/\lambda$, c being the speed of light. The dispersion measure, $M_D \simeq \int n_e dl$, where n_e is the electron number density and the integral along the line of sight runs from the source to the observer, thus contains cosmological information about the distribution of electrons. Indeed, this simple equation combined with precision cosmology constraints from the early universe allows us to make a prediction for the fraction of baryons in the IGM,[7] which can then be experimentally verified. Indeed, the so-called missing baryon problem is not longer an outstanding problem as the results of Ref. 10 used a handful of well located FRBs with the observed dispersion measures to show that indeed the missing baryons are in the IGM as expected, and are playing the predicted role of dispersing the FRB signal. This longstanding open problem is thus resolved not due to any great technological or theoretical breakthrough, but simply through the use of a few transient observations and an understanding of the contributions to M_D from our own galaxy. This suggests that there is immense and untapped potential for great discovery with FRBs and that the future is very bright for this young field.

2.2. *High-redshift universe with redshifted 21 cm line*

The redshifted 21 cm line of HI is one of the most useful probes of the early universe. Several experiments are ongoing and are being planned to detect the signal at high redshift, z. Detection of the signal will help in understanding the first stars in the universe, the formation and evolution of galaxies and also constraining cosmological parameters. This section summarizes the status of observational efforts and theoretical understanding.

The HI evolution can be used to study the thermal and ionization history of the universe and also the evolution of the galaxies.[11,12] The very first HI atoms formed during the so-called 'recombination' epoch. The hydrogen remains in the neutral form until the first stars form which can then start ionizing the HI in the IGM, a process known as *reionization*. This epoch is believed to end around redshifts $z \sim 5.5$ by when almost all the HI in the IGM gets ionized. In the *post-reionization* era, the only regions where HI can survive are the high-density regions, e.g., the interstellar medium (ISM) of the galaxies.

The evolution of HI can be efficiently tracked by the redshifted 21 cm signal arising from hyperfine transition of the ground state of the atom. The signal is observed, either in emission or absorption, in contrast to the CMB signal using low-frequency radio telescopes. Since the hyperfine transition is forbidden, the signal amplitude turns out to be extremely weak and hence is appreciable only when the HI density is significant. There are broadly three regimes where the detection of the 21 cm radiation is being planned: (i) the *cosmic dawn* when the ultraviolet (UV) and X-ray radiation from the very early galaxies lead to a strong absorption signal around $z \sim 20$; (ii) the *epoch of reionization* when the heated and ionized IGM leads to an emission signal around $z \sim 15 - 6$; and (iii) the *post-reionization* signal when HI in galaxies can be detected either directly or through intensity mapping.

Among the different ways to detect the 21 cm signal, perhaps the one that requires simplest of the instruments is the signal averaged over large regions of the sky, i.e., the *global signal*. This signal is believed to be most prominent during the cosmic dawn corresponding to $\nu \simeq 50 - 100$ MHz. The amplitude of the cosmological signal is weak and is buried under other astrophysical signals few orders of magnitude stronger, which makes it extremely challenging to separate it out.

Recently, there has been a claim of a detection of the 21 cm signal from cosmic dawn at $z \sim 18$ by the Experiment to Detect the Global EoR Signature[26] (EDGES), although the recovered signal seems to be 3–4 times larger than that predicted by standard galaxy formation models. This lead to several theoretical interpretation beyond the standard calculations, e.g., exotic physics in the DM sector[27] or strong

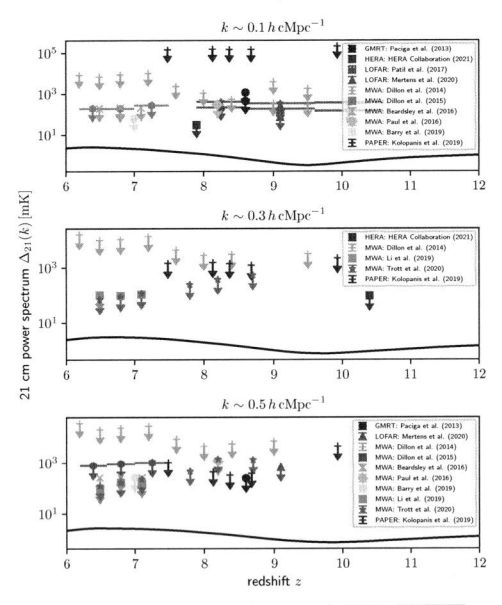

Fig. 1. Observational upper limits to the 21 cm PS, $\sqrt{k^3 P_{21}(k)/2\pi^2}$, for three different comoving wavenumbers k; here $h = H_0/(100 \, \mathrm{km \, s^{-1} \, Mpc^{-1}})$ and cMpc denotes comoving Mpc. Data from different telescopes, namely, the Giant Metrewave Radio Telescope[13] (GMRT), the Low Frequency Array[14,15] (LOFAR), the Murchison Widefield Array[16–22] (MWA), the Precision Array for Probing the Epoch of Reionization[23] (PAPER), the Hydrogen Epoch of Reionization[24] Array (HERA), are shown in comparison with the signal predictions from the Semi-numerical Code for ReIonization with PhoTon-conservation[25] (SCRIPT).

radio background from the first galaxies.[28–30] There have also been concerns regarding the foreground subtraction and other systematics in the data,[31] hence it is important to validate the signal through other low-frequency telescopes.

An alternate way of detecting the 21 cm signal is through the spatial fluctuations. These can, in principle, be useful throughout the cosmic history starting from the cosmic dawn to the post-reionization universe. During the cosmic dawn, the fluctuations arise from those in the galactic radiation, while in the epoch reionization it is the patchiness in the ionization field that drives the 21 cm fluctuation signal. In the post-reionization era, the fluctuations in the 21 cm signal essentially trace the distribution of galaxies and hence the underlying matter fluctuations.

At present, a number of low-frequency interferometers are attempting to detect the 21 cm power spectrum (PS) from the epoch of reionization at scales $\sim 10 h^{-1}$ cMpc. Fig. 1 shows the current upper limits (see Ref. 32 for a complete compilation of available data). These observational attempts are ably complemented by numerical and semi-numerical theoretical models to help interpret the data. The result from the one such semi-numerical simulation SCRIPT[a] is shown in Fig. 1 for a model of reionization consistent with all other available observations.[25] Upcoming facilities like the Square Kilometre Array[b] (SKA) will be able to reach a noise level of ~ 1 mK (~ 0.3 mK) within ~ 100 (1000) hours of observations and hence should constrain reionization models with high statistical significance.

3. Observational results and perspectives in the microwaves

3.1. *The Planck Legacy Archive, present and future*

Planck was an ESA space satellite that measured the microwave sky in nine wavebands, allowing it to not only capture the CMB to incredible precision, but also to accurately study a number of astrophysical diffuse emissions and discrete sources (see fig. 51 in Ref. 33, which shows the various wavebands of the *Planck* satellite, as well as the foregrounds signals and their frequency spectra across those bands).

The PLA hosts and serves over 150 TB of products from *Planck* that are publicly available via the PLA web interface[c] (Fig. 2). This interface provides direct access to the users to a wide variety of products of the *Planck* Collaboration[d] through the Low Frequency Instrument (LFI) Data Processing Centre (DPC) in Trieste, Italy, by the High Frequency Instrument (HFI) DPC in Paris, France, and, more recently, by the US *Planck* Data Center in Pasadena and Berkeley, California, USA. The

---

[a]https://bitbucket.org/rctirthankar/script
[b]https://www.skatelescope.org
[c]https://pla.esac.esa.int
[d]The *Planck* Collaboration acknowledges the support of: ESA; CNES, and CNRS/INSU-IN2P3-INP (France); ASI, CNR, and INAF (Italy); NASA and DoE (USA); STFC and UKSA (UK); CSIC, MINECO, JA, and RES (Spain); Tekes, AoF, and CSC (Finland); DLR and MPG (Germany); CSA (Canada); DTU Space (Denmark); SER/SSO (Switzerland); RCN (Norway); SFI (Ireland); FCT/MCTES (Portugal); ERC and PRACE (EU). A description of the *Planck* Collaboration and a list of its members, indicating which technical or scientific activities they have been involved in, can be found at http://www.cosmos.esa.int/web/planck/planck-collaboration.

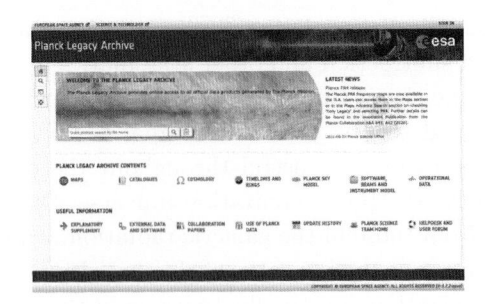

Fig. 2. *Left*: the *Planck* Legacy Archive home page.

PLA is located at the European Space Astronomy Centre (ESAC) near Madrid, Spain, and is maintained by the Data Science and Archives Division personnel.

In the last years, four major releases of *Planck* products have taken place, providing users with the most complete cosmology data set to date.

The *Planck* products can be divided into various categories. *First*, the time-ordered data, that comes in multiple flavors: raw, semi-calibrated and calibrated science ready timelines and compressed timelines (called HPRs). *Second*, the frequency maps produced by the DPCs, in most cases for each detector, detector pair and frequency, and for different combinations of the mission coverage (e.g., yearly maps, nominal mission, half-mission, half-ring, full mission, etc); *third*, the maps of the CMB; and, *fourth*, the so-called astrophysical component maps that contain the diffuse emission from our Galaxy as produced by the dust grains, synchrotron emission from spiraling electrons moving along the magnetic field lines, cosmic infrared background (CIB), etc. See Fig. 3, *left* panel. These CMB and astrophysical maps are derived in the scheme offered by the Hierarchical Equal Area isoLatitude Pixelization of a sphere[34] (`HEALPix`) using different component separation methods, e.g., `Commander`, Spectral Matching Independent Component Analysis (`SMICA`), Spectral Estimation Via Expectation Maximisation (`SEVEM`) and Generalized Needlet Internal Linear Combination (`GNILC`), the four official component separation methods used to extract the CMB maps in the third *Planck* Release (PR3). *Fifth*, source catalogues in various forms, from Galactic and extragalactic compact source catalogues, available in the *Planck* Catalogue of Compact Sources (PCCS), to galactic cold cores, SZ GCs, high-z lensing candidates, etc (Fig. 3, *right* panel). *Sixth*, cosmology products, e.g., the *Planck* likelihood code and associated files, the different flavors of the *Planck* CMB angular PS as a function of the multipole ℓ (e.g., low-ℓ, high-ℓ, temperature-only, temperature and polarization, etc), lensing products and more (Fig. 4, *left* panel).

Advance Search panels are available to extensively query the PLA database, in addition to embedded links to the *Planck* Explanatory Supplement documentation,[e] multiple data download options, and Helpdesk support.

---

[e] https://wiki.cosmos.esa.int/planck-legacy-archive

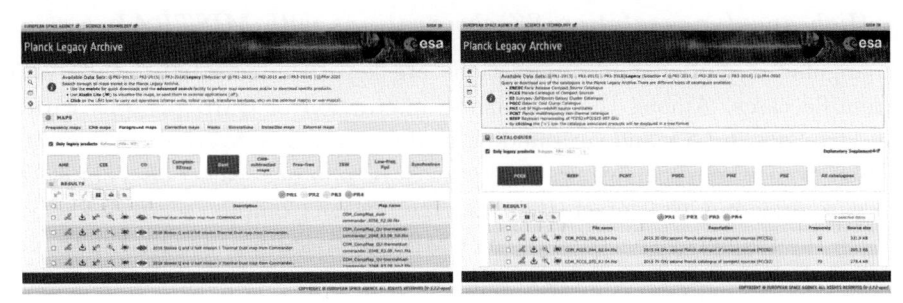

Fig. 3. *Left*: the *Planck* maps area in the PLA, with emphasis to the astrophysical components, and in particular to the Galaxy dust emission. *Right*: the *Planck* source catalogues area in the PLA, with emphasis to the PCCS.

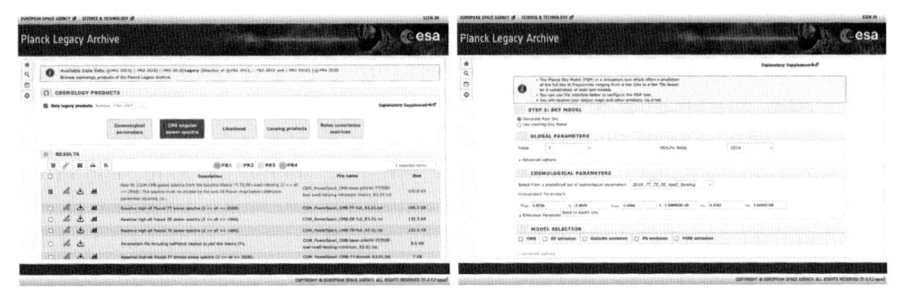

Fig. 4. *Left*: the *Planck* cosmology products area in the PLA, with emphasis to the CMB angular PS. *Right*: the `Planck Sky Model` simulation tool area in the PLA.

Three major releases of *Planck* products took place in 2013, 2015, and 2018 and a selection of products have been tagged as "Legacy" to identify the version of each product most appropriate for general scientific use. In 2021 a new release of products will take place with a joint reprocessing of LFI+HFI time-ordered data that includes additional information not used in previous releases. In addition, EU funded projects reprocessing *Planck* data, or combining it with other experiments, are expected to the deliver to the PLA higher level data products of interest. The PLA also offers specialized tools that facilitate the processing of *Planck* products. These tools are mainly designed to help users who are not familiar with some of the particularities of the *Planck* products, and can be categorized into distinct groups: map operations including component subtraction, unit conversion, colour correction, bandpass transformation, and masking of map-cutouts/full-sky maps; component separation codes, map-making codes and effective beam-averaging. In addition, the PLA includes an interface to the latest version of the `Planck Sky Model` simulation tool (Fig. 4, *right* panel), with a simple user interface that allows users to simulate the microwave/sub-mm sky with *Planck*, as well as future CMB experiments and custom-defined instruments.

In the coming years it is planned to continue releasing data products from improved reprocessing of *Planck* data and combining *Planck* with other experiments.

3.2. *High angular resolution SZ observations with MISTRAL*

High angular resolution mm observations are key to understand a wide variety of scientific cases. Among the others, the interaction of CMB photons with the hot electron gas in GCs and surrounding medium promises to study GCs and their deviation from relaxed behaviour. When the CMB photons scatter off a hot electron gas, for example in GCs, in fact, they undergo inverse Compton scattering which is visible in the frequency spectrum of the CMB. The resulting distorted spectrum is

$$\frac{\Delta I(x)}{I_0} = y\frac{x^4 e^x}{(e^x - 1)^2}\left(x\coth\frac{x}{2} - 4\right) = yg(x), \tag{1}$$

where $I_0 = (2h_P/c^2)(k_B T_{CMB}/h_P)^3$, T_{CMB} is the CMB temperature, $x = h_P\nu/(k_B T_{CMB})$ is the dimensionless frequency, and $y = \int n_e \sigma_T k_B T_e/(m_e c^2) dl$ is the Comptonization parameter, the integral along the line of sight of the electron density n_e multiplied by the electron temperature T_e; σ_T is cross-section of Thomson scattering, k_B and h_P are the Boltzmann and Planck constants. This is the tSZ effect[35,36] and it can be used to study both relaxed and non-relaxed GCs. In fact, GCs can experience a wide variety of situation including collisions, merging, and non-relaxed situation. In addition, not only GCs can host relativistic electrons. Hydrodynamical simulations[37,38] suggested that GCs occupy the knots of the so called cosmic web (CW) and WHIM is disposed connecting GCs forming filaments that could be seen through the SZ effect itself.

An instrument being prepared for such scientific cases is the MIllimeter Sardinia radio Telescope Receiver based on Array of Lumped elements kids[39] (MISTRAL), to be fielded at the 64m Sardinia Radio Telescope[f] (SRT). MISTRAL will use an array of 408 kinetic inductance detectors (KIDs) with a field of view of 4′ and an angular resolution of $\sim 12''$. It is a cryogenic instrument with detectors cooled down at 270 mK and with frequency domain multiplexing (FDM), Reconfigurable Open Architecture Computing Hardware 2 (ROACH2) based read-out.

MISTRAL is a facility instrument to be installed at the SRT in 2022. It operates in an atmospheric window in the frequency range 78÷103 GHz, namely W-band, that is interesting for a number of scientific reasons, and most importantly it provides low optical depth and allows high efficiency observations. It will be installed in the Gregorian room of the SRT (Fig. 5).

MISTRAL consists of a cryostat, being constructed by Queen Mary College (QMC) Instruments,[g] with a Pulse Tube (PT) cryocooler, an He-10 sorption refrigerator, custom optics and detectors. In order to have the PT heads as close as possible to vertical position during observations, we have positioned the head with an inclination of 57.5° with respect to the focal plane. This allows observation elevations in the range of 32.5°÷82.5° with no degradation of the thermal performance.

---

[f]http://www.srt.inaf.it
[g]http://www.terahertz.co.uk/qmc-instruments-ltd

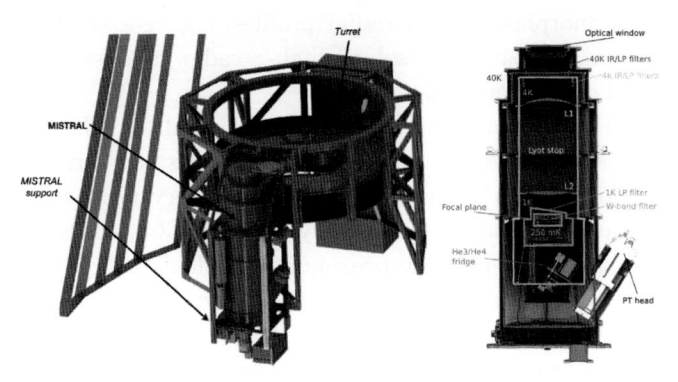

Fig. 5. *Left*: SRT Turret with MISTRAL installed. *Right*: a cut of MISTRAL cryostat highlighting the main parts. Acknowledgement: MISTRAL Collaboration.

The optical design of MISTRAL includes a set of radiation quasi-optical filters, anchored at the different thermal stages of the cryostat, an Anti Reflection Coated (ARC) Ultra High Molecular Weight (UHMW) polyetilene window, and two Silicon lenses able to image the Gregorian Focus on the array of detectors. Detectors are coupled to radiation through open space (filled array) so cryogenic cold stop, placed in between the two lenses, is needed.

MISTRAL will take advantage of the high sensitivity and capability of FDM of KIDs cryogenic detectors. KIDs are superconductive detectors where mm radiation with higher energy with respect to the Cooper pair binding energy, can break Cooper pairs producing a change in the population densities and thus in the kinetic inductance. In fact, the inductance L of a thin superconductor is dominated by the kinetic inductance L_k, which depends on the Cooper pair density. The detector array is composed of 408 KIDs detectors. They are 3 mm × 3 mm each and are arranged on an equilateral triangle every 4.2 mm on a 4 inches silicon wafer. They sample the focal plane with a full width half maximum (FWHM) angular spacing of 10.6″ lower the each pixel angular resolution. The ROACH2 based FDM, originally developed for the Osservatorio nel Lontano Infrarosso Montato su Pallone Orientabile[h] (OLIMPO) experiment,[40,41] will be used.

MISTRAL will be a facility instrument: it will be open to the scientific community to decide what kind of scientific output it can achieve and propose the observations to the Time Allocation Committee of the SRT. Nevertheless, we will list some scientific cases below, including those we find most interesting.

Protoplanetary discs mm measurements in star forming regions allow to break the degeneracy present in infrared (IR) measurements due to the optically thick nature of the hot inner disc.[42] Observations of star formation in molecular clouds with high enough angular resolution allow to distinguish starless cores with respect to those hosting protostars.[43] Continuum resolved galaxies observations can give

---

[h]Far Infrared Observatory Mounted on Orientable Balloon. See http://olimpo.roma1.infn.it.

information about morphology and radial profiles, e.g., gas column profiles, dust temperature profiles.[44] Spatially resolved high-z radio galaxies can provide information about cold dust re-emission.[45]

What is probably the most impacting expected result of MISTRAL is the possibility to observe and resolve the SZ effect through GCs and surrounding medium. With respect to moderate to low angular resolution observations, high ($\simeq 10''$) etections can investigate non relaxed GCs, study merging GCs, understanding the self similarities of GCs, their identical appearance regardless of their mass or distance. Study the pressure profiles and understand the active galactic nuclei (AGN) feedback expected in some environments. Often GCs are assumed to be spherical and isothermal. Nevertheless, they interact, collide and merge, bringing to important degeneracies and deviation from specific models. High angular resolution SZ measurements allow to disentangle between models and to identify the most appropriate ones. Even relaxed GCs experience pressure fluctuations and compressions of the intra cluster medium which would be interesting to study.

GCs experience hierarchical growth through mergers. Pre-mergers GCs should be connected through the CW and simulations endorse this.[37,38] WHIM are expected to be distributed as over-densities in filamentary structures between GCs: high angular resolution SZ measurements can detect WHIM better than X-ray under low density circumstances. This is probably the most challenging and most rewarding of the achievements that an experiment like MISTRAL can achieve.

4. *Planck* cosmological implications

4.1. *New Planck thermal SZ map and its cosmological analysis*

The ΛCDM model provides a wonderful fit to many cosmological data. However, a slight discrepancy was found in the latest data analyses between the CMB anisotropies ($z \sim 1100$) and other cosmological probes at low ($z \sim 0 \div 1$) redshift, z, for the $S_8 (\equiv \sigma_8 (\Omega_M/0.3)^{0.5})$ cosmological parameter representing the amplitude of the structure growth in the universe; here Ω_M and σ_8 are the usual non-relativistic matter density parameter and the density contrast on a scale of 8 $[H_0/(100\,\mathrm{km\,s^{-1}\,Mpc^{-1}})]^{-1}$ Mpc.

For example, the S_8 value was precisely measured to be $S_8 = 0.830 \pm 0.013$ with the *Planck* CMB observation.[46] However, a lower value of $S_8 \sim 0.77 \pm 0.03$ was measured using the population of GCs detected by *Planck* at low-z[47,48] ($z < 0.6$), thus called "S_8 tension". Furthermore, other low-z observations with gravitational lensing by the Kilo-Degree Survey[49] (KiDS) and DES experiments also found lower S_8 values. These results indicate that the cosmic structure growth is slower than the prediction based on the CMB measurement and may demand modifications to the standard cosmological model to explain all these measurements.

One of the most interesting signals extensively studied with *Planck* is the tSZ effect, which produces what are known as y distortions, or y type signals. These primarily come from CMB photons being inverse-Compton scattered through hot

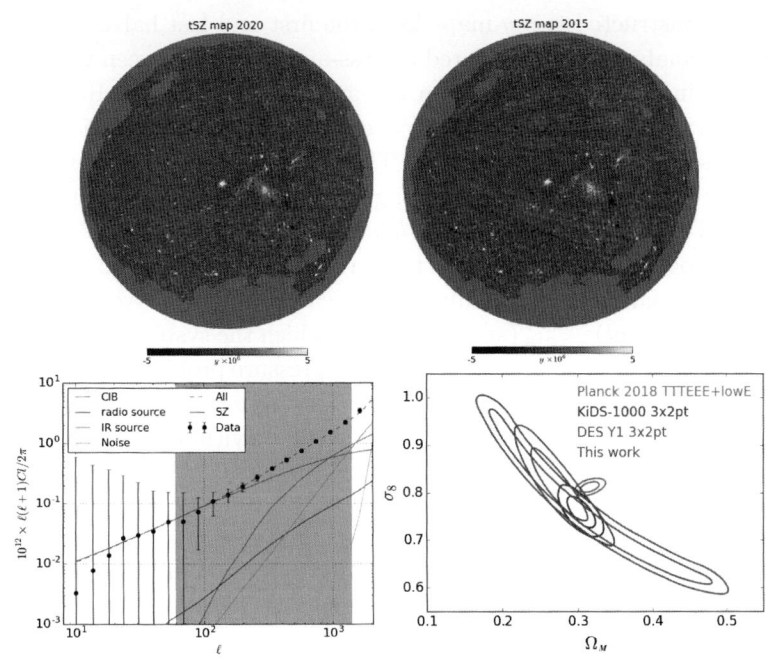

Fig. 6. *Top*: Orthographic projections of the all-sky Compton y parameter maps reconstructed with MILCA (*left*) and in 2015[50] (*right*), with appreciable differences in the striping features. Pixel resolution changed for visualization purposes from $N_{\text{side}} = 2048$ to $N_{\text{side}} = 128$ (i.e. from $\simeq 1.72'$ to $\simeq 27.48'$ pixel size), according to the sky pixelization in Ref. 34. *Bottom*: Cross-PS (black) fitted with the tSZ (red) and foreground models, namely the CIB (green), radio (blue) and IR (cyan) sources, plus noise (yellow), the sum of the tSZ, foreground models and noise being shown in red dashed line (*left*); posterior distribution of the cosmological parameters σ_8 and Ω_M, with 68% and 95% confidence level (CL) interval contours obtained from our cosmological analysis (*right*), compared with the *Planck* CMB's (gray), KiDS-1000 3x2pt (blue), and DES Y1 3x2pt results (green). Acknowledgements: H. Tanimura, M. Douspis, N. Aghanim (CNRS/Univ. Paris-Saclay).

GCs (see Sect. 3.2), which makes holes, or lowers the flux of low frequency photons and up scatters, or makes an excess flux of high frequency photons.

The tSZ signal is subdominant relative to the CMB and other foreground emissions in the *Planck* bands. Thus a tailored component separation algorithm is required to reconstruct the tSZ map. We adopted the Modified Internal Linear Combination Algorithm[51] (MILCA) used for the *Planck* y-map reconstruction in 2015 and applied it to the 100 to 857 GHz frequency channel maps (see Sect. 3.1) from the fourth *Planck* Release (PR4).

The *Planck* PR4 data implemented several improvements from the previous version: the usage of foreground polarization priors during the calibration stage to break scanning-induced degeneracies, the correction of bandpass mismatch at all frequencies, the inclusion of 8% of data collected during repointing maneuvers, etc. With these improvements we produced a new y-map with smaller noises (by $\sim$7%) and reduced strips than the previous version released in 2015 (Fig. 6, *top* panels).

We also reconstructed two y-maps from the first and last halves of the data for a cosmological analysis and considered a cross-angular PS between these y-maps to avoid the bias induced by the noise in the auto-angular PS (see Ref. 52 for more details). This tSZ cross-PS is affected by residual foreground emissions from radio and IR point sources and CIB emission. Thus we fitted our measurement with the cosmology-dependent tSZ model, including the radio and IR point source models,[53] the CIB model[54] and the noise (Fig. 6, *left bottom* panel).

The cosmological analysis of the tSZ cross-PS allowed us to set constraints on cosmological parameters, mainly of the S_8 parameter. We obtained $S_8 = 0.764\,^{+0.015}_{-0.018}$ (*statistical*) $^{+0.031}_{-0.016}$ (*systematic*), in which the systematic uncertainty includes the contributions from the mass bias and pressure profile model. Our obtained S_8 value is fully consistent with recent weak lensing results from KiDS and DES. It is also consistent with the *Planck* CMB's result[46] within 2σ, while it is slightly lower by $\sim 1.7\sigma$ (Fig. 6, *right bottom* panel).

4.2. *The CMB dipole and the thermal SZ effect: Eppur Si Muove*

The largest temperature anisotropy in the CMB is the dipole pattern at $\ell = 1$. The simplest interpretation of the dipole is that it is due to our motion with respect to the rest frame of the CMB (with debate over the possibility of alternative explanations), and is measured to be $\beta = v/c = (1.23357 \pm 0.00036) \times 10^{-3}$ in the direction of the constellation Crater, $(l, b) = (264.021° \pm 0.011°, 48.253° \pm 0.005°)$, see Ref. 55. As well as creating the $\ell=1$ mode of the CMB sky, this motion affects all astrophysical observations by modulating and aberrating sources across the sky, such as the CMB temperature anisotropies. These and other effects will be discussed.

As discussed above, an accurate mapping of the tSZ signal on the sky has been achieved with the *Planck* satellite. This allows us to construct a novel and independent measure of the CMB dipole because the y maps are contaminated by temperature anisotropies stemming from the CMB dipole. This is also valuable as a test of the quality of the y maps.

To derive the connection between the y map and the dipole we will begin by defining some useful terms regarding the unboosted CMB sky,

$$I(x) \equiv \frac{2k_B^3 T_{CMB}^3}{h_P^2 c^2} \frac{x^3}{e^x - 1} \tag{2}$$

$$f(x) \equiv \frac{xe^x}{e^x - 1} \tag{3}$$

$$Y(x) \equiv x\frac{e^x + 1}{e^x - 1} - 4, \tag{4}$$

which are the standard Planck blackbody intensity function, the frequency dependence of CMB anisotropies, and the relative frequency dependence of the tSZ effect or y type distortions, x being the dimensionless frequency (see Sect. 3.2). Thus, to first-order the anisotropies of intensity measured by *Planck* can be written as

$$\frac{\delta I(\hat{\mathbf{n}})}{If(x)} = \frac{\delta T(\hat{\mathbf{n}})}{T_{CMB}} + y(\hat{\mathbf{n}})Y(x), \tag{5}$$

where we have included just the temperature anisotropies and the y signals here.

If we apply a boost to Eq. (5) with a dimensionless velocity $\boldsymbol{\beta}$, it becomes

$$\frac{\delta I'(\hat{\mathbf{n}}')}{If(x)} = \beta\mu + \frac{\delta T(\hat{\mathbf{n}}')}{T_{CMB}}(1 + 3\beta\mu)$$

$$+ Y(x)\left(y(\hat{\mathbf{n}}')(1 + 3\beta\mu) + \beta\mu\frac{\delta T(\hat{\mathbf{n}}')}{T_{CMB}}\right)$$

$$+ \beta\mu y(\hat{\mathbf{n}}')\left(Y^2(x) - x\frac{dY(x)}{dx}\right) + \mathcal{O}(\beta^2); \tag{6}$$

here $\mu = \cos(\theta)$, and θ is the angle from the direction of the boost $\boldsymbol{\beta}$ and the line of sight. Additionally, the aberration effect deflects the direction of the incoming photons from $\hat{\mathbf{n}} \to \hat{\mathbf{n}}'$ where $\hat{\mathbf{n}}' = \hat{\mathbf{n}} - \nabla(\hat{\mathbf{n}} \cdot \boldsymbol{\beta})$. The first line has the same frequency dependence as thermal fluctuations. The term $\beta\mu$ simply describes the pure CMB dipole, as discussed previously. The second term represents the dipole aberration and modulation of the temperature anisotropies of the CMB. This was first measured in Ref. 56 to 5σ. Crucially for our analysis, the middle line has the same frequency dependence as y type distortions, and so encompasses the signals in the y-map. The final line has more obscure frequency dependencies and so will not be discussed here. See Refs. 57, 58 for further details.

The second line of Eq. (6) shows the signals in the y maps produced by *Planck*. The first half is the same boost as was seen in the temperature anisotropies, however, the final term is due to the second-order expansion of the intensity about T_{CMB} and adds a contribution to the y maps from the temperature anisotropies. We measured this signal in Ref. 57 to 6σ by cross-correlating the expected modulated temperature map with the y maps. We confirmed the dipole direction by cross-correlating the temperature maps modulated in two additional perpendicular directions. To test consistency and rule out different systematics, we used the Internal Linear Combination (ILC) in two dimensions, 2D-ILC, and MILCA y-maps, the temperature anisotropies from both 2D-ILC and SMICA, and finally both a harmonic space analysis and a map space analysis.

The question as to whether an intrinsic dipole could be observationally distinguished from an extrinsic dipole remains an open question. The terms discussed in Eq. (6) are based on the assumption of a CMB blackbody spectrum[i] and cannot be used to distinguish the two, as they would naturally arise whether the CMB dipole

---

[i]See instead Ref. 59 for a study exploiting the relaxation of the blackbody assumption and references to other methods.

were caused by a boost, or if there were simply a dipole in the sky with the same magnitude and direction.

4.3. *Planck constraints on the primordial tensor-to-scalar ratio*

Discovering the stochastic field of gravitational waves generated during the early phases of the universe is one of the most ambitious goals of modern cosmology. Various models of inflation predict cosmological perturbations from quantum fluctuations[60–66] in terms of tensor component (gravitational waves) and scalar component (density variations). Inflationary gravitational waves entering the horizon since recombination epoch generate a tensor component contributing to temperature (T), polarization (E and B modes) and cross-correlation TE angular PS, C_ℓ^X where X stands for a given mode[j], of CMB anisotropy,[67–69] in particular at large angular scale (or at low multipoles, $\ell \lesssim 150$, where $\ell \sim 180°/\theta$ approximately relates ℓ to the angular scale θ). C_ℓ^X is typically represented in terms of $D_\ell^X = \ell(\ell+1)C_\ell^X/(2\pi)$, which is nearly flat at low multipoles for $X = T$, although a power suppression at very large scales, first observed by the Cosmic Background Explorer (COBE) an then confirmed by the Wilkinson Microwave Anisotropy Probe (WMAP) and by the *Planck* satellite, is predicted in several inflationary models possibly in connection with universe geometry and topology.

While the E and TE modes contain both scalar and tensor signals mainly coming from the epochs of recombination and reionization, the model does not predict primordial scalar fluctuations in the B-mode. The detection of the primordial B-mode then constitutes a direct way to unravel tensor perturbations from the early universe, and the efforts to measure of the ratio, r, between the amplitudes of primordial tensor and scalar perturbations is the main scientific aim of many ongoing and future CMB projects. When CMB photons pass through gravitational potentials produced by cosmic structures, part of the E-mode power is transformed to B-mode power, the so-called lensing B-mode. This signal, already detected by a number of ground-based observatories and by *Planck*, is particularly important at small angular scale[70] ($\ell \gtrsim 150$), but it may mask the primordial B-mode also at intermediate angular scale and, for low r, even at large angular scale.

Assuming the spectra of scalar and tensor perturbations are described by pure power-laws, $\mathcal{P}_s(k) = A_s(k/k_0)^{n_s-1}$, $\mathcal{P}_t(k) = A_t(k/k_0)^{n_t}$, they are fully defined by the two amplitude parameters A_s, A_t and by the so-called (comoving wavenumber) pivot scale k_0, the definition of $r = A_t/A_s$ being then related to the choice of k_0. Among the various choices adopted in the literature, $k_0 = 0.05\,\text{Mpc}^{-1}$ approximately corresponds to the middle of the logarithmic range of k probed by *Planck*. For historical reasons, a scale-invariant spectrum corresponds to $n_s = 1$ or to $n_t = 0$ for scalar or tensor perturbations, respectively.

---

[j]For simplicity, we use here two letters only for cross modes.

The multipole range $2 \lesssim \ell \lesssim 150$ is the most advantageous to directly extract r from B-mode analyses. According to theoretical predictions, the primordial D_ℓ^B is close to the maximum at $50 \lesssim \ell \lesssim 150$, the region of the so-called recombination bump (i); at large scale, $\ell \lesssim 10$, D_ℓ^B exhibits a pronounced bump generated at late epochs by the reionization process (ii); at $10 \lesssim \ell \lesssim 50$, $\log(D_\ell^B)$ increases almost linearly with $\log(\ell)$ (iii). Exploiting higher ℓ's is of particular relevance for a very accurate treatment (delensing) of lensing B-mode. C_ℓ^B increases almost linearly with r, the reionization bump features depending on r and on the details of the reionization process, which is parametrized to first approximation by the corresponding Thomson optical depth, τ. In general, the detection of primordial B-modes requires exquisite experimental sensitivity and accuracy as well as very precise treatment of the polarized foreground emissions (see, e.g., Ref. 71), particularly for low values of r, which is why a primordial B-mode tensor signal has not yet been detected. On the other hand, recent CMB projects set significant upper limits to r. The great sensitivity achievable by ground-based experiments on selected sky areas has been used to strongly constrain (i), the current tightest B-mode limits on r from these scales coming from the Background Imaging of Cosmic Extragalactic Polarization (BICEP)/Keck measurements[72] (BK15), while the *Planck* all-sky survey allows to constrain (i), (ii) and (iii). In particular, Ref. 73 presents B-mode limits on r from *Planck* data at $\ell \lesssim 30$.

A recent reanalysis of *Planck* data alone and in combination with BK15 (see Ref. 74 for a previous joint analysis) has been performed in Ref. 75 exploiting the whole multipole range $2 \leq \ell \leq 150$. In this study, the *Planck* PR4 data (see Sect. 3.1) were adopted, where the NPIPE[76] processing pipeline was used to create calibrated frequency maps in temperature and polarization from LFI and HFI data, providing several improvements in noise and systematics levels in both frequency and component-separated maps. Various sky masks were considered in order to retain different sky fractions (from 30% to 70%) and to test the impact of data treatment. In polarization, the CMB sky was separated from foregrounds applying the Commander[77] code to a model with three components, namely the CMB, synchrotron, and thermal dust emission, starting from the PLA PR4 maps but downgraded from $N_{\text{side}} = 2048$ to $N_{\text{side}} = 16$ and to $N_{\text{side}} = 1024$ respectively for the analysis at $2 \leq \ell \leq 35$ and at $35 \leq \ell \leq 150$. An updated version of the LOw-ℓ LIkelihood on POlarised Power-spectra (LoLLiPoP) code previously employed by the *Planck* Collaboration in the reionization analysis[78] was used to derive the likelihood from *cross*-power spectra for the CMB maps reprocessed as outlined above. Here, *cross* denotes that the angular PS is extracted analyzing different sets of detectors: indeed, for these *cross*-power spectra the bias is zero when the noise is uncorrelated between maps. Unbiased estimates of the angular PS were derived using an extension of the quadratic maximum likelihood estimator and a classical pseudo-C_ℓ estimator at $2 \leq \ell \leq 35$ and at $35 \leq \ell \leq 150$, respectively. The C_ℓ covariance is deduced from end-to-end simulations and thus includes CMB sample variance, statistical noise, residuals from systematics, uncertainties from foreground subtraction, and correlations generated by masking. These uncertainties are propagated through the likelihood up to the level of cosmological parameters.

Applying this analysis to the B-mode alone, fixing the other cosmological parameters to the fiducial ΛCDM spectrum of *Planck* 2018 results, and considering the cleanest 50% fraction of the sky, the values of r (for $k_0 = 0.05\,\mathrm{Mpc}^{-1}$) retrieved from the posterior distribution analysis at $2 \leq \ell \leq 35$ (that includes the reionization bump) or at $35 \leq \ell \leq 150$ (that includes the recombination bump) are $r_{0.05} = -0.014^{+0.108}_{-0.111}$ or $r_{0.05} = +0.069^{+0.114}_{-0.113}$, respectively. The two multipole windows contribute almost equally to the overall *Planck* sensitivity to r. Combining them gives $r_{0.05} = 0.033 \pm 0.069$, while setting also a positive value of r as a physical prior implies $r_{0.05} < 0.158$ at 95% CL.

A tighter result, $r_{0.05} = -0.031 \pm 0.046$, and a stronger constraint, $r_{0.05} < 0.069$ at 95% CL, slightly improving the BK15 95% CL limit $r_{0.05} < 0.072$, is derived applying the same method but jointly considering the three polarization modes B, E and EB.[k]

These results on r do not depend significantly on the choice of other ΛCDM cosmological parameters. In particular, the constraints on r are unchanged when r is retrieved together with τ: considering all polarization modes $r_{0.05} = -0.015 \pm 0.045$ and $\tau = 0.0577 \pm 0.0056$, while considering only the B-mode $r_{0.05} = 0.025 \pm 0.064$ and τ is undetermined because of the noise.

The *Planck* temperature data are crucial to determine the other ΛCDM parameters and then, when combined with polarization data, to exhaustively verify if the limits on r depend on the other parameters. Furthermore, although *Planck* temperature data, when considered alone, are found to be about two times less sensitive than *Planck* polarization data in constraining r, the tensor contribution to temperature fluctuations allows to further tight the constraints on r derived from polarization data alone. In fact, including also *Planck* temperature data in the analysis using the *Planck* public low-ℓ temperature-only likelihood based on the PR3 CMB map recovered from the `Commander` and the High-ℓ Likelihood on Polarised Power-spectra (`HiLLiPoP`) at $\ell > 30$, and marginalizing over the nuisance and the other ΛCDM cosmological parameters, from the posterior distribution for r the authors[75] derive the currently most stringent upper limit based on *Planck* data alone: $r_{0.05} < 0.056$ at 95% CL.

Finally, in Ref. 75 the *Planck* temperature and polarization data analyzed as summarized above have been combined with the BK15 data, assuming their mutual independence, i.e. simply multiplying their likelihood distributions, as justified given their so different sky coverage, obtaining $r_{0.05} < 0.044$ at 95% CL which currently represents the most stringent upper limit.

---

[k]The primordial EB is expected to be null in the ΛCDM model. On the other hand, special rotation effects of the polarization field (such as birefringence) can produce some EB signal.

5. Future and alternative perspectives

5.1. Lorentz invariance violation and CMB polarization

The standard model of cosmology can explain the CMB radiation from the recombination epoch till today. As discussed above, it predicts the existence of some degrees of linear polarization known as E-modes and B-modes (see also Refs. 79–81). The linear polarization can be induced to the CMB by means of Compton scattering of CMB photons and cosmic electrons in presence of cosmological perturbations. However, the circular polarization for the CMB is a rare process in the standard model of cosmology, so that observation of any level of circular polarization can be a hint for the existence of new physics. The circular polarization for the CMB can be generated through Faraday conversion in which linear polarized light propagates through a medium resulting in different indexes of refraction along the two transverse axes.[82,83] Moreover, the CMB photons scattering from vector or fermionic DM can lead to circular polarization of the CMB.[84,85] Furthermore, circular polarization for the CMB can be induced by electron-photon Compton scattering in presence of a background field such as a magnetic field[82] or non-commutativity in space and time.[83,86]

In this study, we would like to explore the effects of Lorentz invariance violation (LIV) as a new background in the generation of circular polarization (see Ref. 87 for details). To do that we assume the CMB photon and cosmic electron scatter while the particle Lorentz symmetry is violated. To evaluate the LIV effect in the Compton scattering, we focus on an effective field theory approach known as standard model extension (SME). The minimal version of the SME contains every gauge invariant and observer-covariant operator, made by all the standard model (SM) fields which violate Lorentz invariance specified with new couplings.[88] In the SME, LIV is considered in a coordinate that the speed of light is constant c in all frames. The kinetic term in electron sector of electromagnetic quantum electrodynamics (QED) Lagrangian is modified with $c^{\mu\nu}$ tensor as[89]

$$\mathcal{L}_{\text{QED}}^{\text{LIV}} = \frac{1}{2} i \bar{\psi} (\gamma^\nu + c^{\mu\nu} \gamma_\mu) \overleftrightarrow{\mathcal{D}}_\mu \psi - \bar{\psi} m_e \psi, \qquad (7)$$

where $\mathcal{D}_\mu$ represents the covariant derivative with $u \overleftrightarrow{D}^\mu v \equiv u D^\mu v - v D^\mu u$, ψ is the fermion field, γ_μ indicates the Dirac gamma matrices, and the mass of electron is m_e. We assume $c^{\mu\nu}$ to be symmetric and traceless tensor. The $c^{\mu\nu}$ tensor depends on the frame and it is estimated in the standard reference frame, i.e. Sun-centered, celestial equatorial frame (SCCEF).[90] All the available bounds on LIV parameters are given in SCCEF frame to be comparable with each other. Therefore, we also use correlation between components of laboratory frame and SCCEF given in Ref. 90 to transfer the result to SCCEF frame.

The polarization of the scattered CMB photon from cosmic electron in presence of LIV is characterized by four Stokes parameters:[79] $[I, Q, U, V]$. I indicates the overall radiation intensity, Q and U represent linear polarization and V is circular polarization of the CMB radiation satisfying the inequality $I^2 \geq Q^2 + U^2 + V^2$. The time evolution of Stokes parameters, defining the CMB polarization, can be expressed through the quantum Boltzmann equation, schematically as[79]

$$\frac{df}{dt} = C[f], \tag{8}$$

where the left-hand side involves time derivative of Stokes parameters which includes the gravitational effects and space time structure; besides, all possible interactions appear at the right-hand side of Boltzmann equation.

After expanding the intensity and polarization of the CMB radiation in terms of multipole moments in spin-weighted basis, the Boltzmann equations regarding to electron-photon Compton scattering in presence of LIV by considering only scalar perturbation in the metric, are obtained as

$$\frac{d}{d\eta}\Delta_I^{(S)} + iK\mu\Delta_I^{(S)} + 4[\dot{\psi} - iK\mu\varphi] = C_{e\gamma}^I$$

$$\frac{d}{d\eta}\Delta_P^{\pm(S)} + iK\mu\Delta_P^{\pm(S)} = C_{e\gamma}^\pm - i\kappa_{\text{LIV}}^\pm \Delta_V^{(S)}$$

$$\frac{d}{d\eta}\Delta_V^{(S)} + iK\mu\Delta_V^{(S)} = C_{e\gamma}^V + \frac{i}{2}\left[\kappa_{\text{LIV}}^+ \Delta_P^{-(S)} + \kappa_{\text{LIV}}^- \Delta_P^{+(S)}\right]; \tag{9}$$

here η is the conformal time, ψ and ϕ are the scalar perturbation corresponding to the potential of Newton and the spatial curvature perturbation, μ is the scalar product of the wave vector **K** and the CMB photon propagating direction, $\Delta_P^{\pm(S)} = Q^{(S)} \pm iU^{(S)}$ is a linear combination of linear polarizations, $C_{e\gamma}^I$, $C_{e\gamma}^\pm$ and $C_{e\gamma}^V$ indicate the involvement of the SM Compton scattering in $\Delta_P^{\pm(S)}$ and $\Delta_V^{(S)}$ parameters, respectively. In presence of LIV, the terms κ_{LIV} and $\kappa_{\text{LIV}}^\pm$ in Eq. (9) are given by

$$\kappa_{\text{LIV}} = -a(\eta)\frac{3}{4}\frac{\sigma_T}{\alpha}\frac{m_e^2}{k_0}\frac{\bar{n}_e}{m_e}, \quad \kappa_{\text{LIV}}^\pm = \kappa_{\text{LIV}}\, c_{\{\alpha\beta\}}(\rho_Q^{\{\alpha\beta\}} \pm i\rho_U^{\{\alpha\beta\}}); \tag{10}$$

they define the Compton scattering contribution, k_0 being the momentum of the CMB photon. In general, the CMB polarization at the direction $\hat{n}$ and at the present time η_0 is derived by integrating Eq. (9) along the line of sight and summing over all Fourier modes **K**. The circular polarization due to LIV Compton scattering can finally be estimated in terms of linear polarization as follows

$$\Delta_V^{(S)}(\mathbf{K}, \mu, \eta_0) \approx \frac{1}{2}\int_0^{\eta_0} d\eta\, \dot{\eta}_{e\gamma}\, e^{ix\mu - \eta_{e\gamma}} \left[3\mu\Delta_{V1}^{(S)} + 2i\,\rho_Q^{\{\alpha\beta\}} c_{\{\alpha\beta\}} \frac{\kappa_{\text{LIV}}}{\dot{\eta}_{e\gamma}} \Delta_P^{(S)}\right.$$

$$\left. + 2\frac{\kappa_{\text{LIV}}^- \kappa_{\text{LIV}}^+}{\dot{\eta}_{e\gamma}^2}\Delta_V^{(S)}\right], \tag{11}$$

where

$$\Delta_P^{(S)}(\mathbf{K}, \mu, \eta) = \int_0^\eta d\eta\, \dot{\eta}_{e\gamma}\, e^{ix\mu - \eta_{e\gamma}} \left[\frac{3}{4}(1-\mu^2)\Pi(K, \eta)\right], \tag{12}$$

$$\rho_Q^{\{\alpha\beta\}} = -\Big[\epsilon^1 \cdot \hat{c} \cdot \epsilon^2 + \sum_{f=e,p} \frac{m_f v_b^2}{2k_0}(\hat{v} \cdot \epsilon^2 \hat{v} \cdot \hat{c} \cdot \epsilon^1 + \hat{v} \cdot \epsilon^1 \hat{v} \cdot \hat{c} \cdot \epsilon^2)$$
$$-\frac{v_b}{2}(\hat{v} \cdot \epsilon^2 \hat{k} \cdot \hat{c} \cdot \epsilon^1 + \hat{v} \cdot \epsilon^1 \hat{k} \cdot \hat{c} \cdot \epsilon^2)\Big], \qquad (13)$$

$\Pi = \Delta_{T2}^{(S)} + \Delta_{P2}^{(S)} + \Delta_{P0}^{(S)}$ and $\dot{\eta}_{e\gamma} = a(\eta)n_e\sigma_T$ and $\eta_{e\gamma} = \int_\eta^{\eta_0} \dot{\eta}_{e\gamma}(\eta)d\eta$ are the differential optical depth and total optical depth. For a detail calculation of Eqs. (9)-(13) see Ref. 87. The angular PS, C_ℓ^V, arisen from CMB-cosmic electron forward scattering in presence of LIV is obtained as

$$C_\ell^V \approx \frac{1}{2\ell+1} \int d^3K P_v(\mathbf{K}) \times$$
$$\sum_m \Big| \int d\Omega Y_{\ell m}^* \int_0^{\eta_0} d\eta\, \dot{\eta}_{e\gamma}\, e^{ix\mu-\eta_{e\gamma}}\, 2i\, \rho_Q^{\{\alpha\beta\}} c_{\{\alpha\beta\}} \frac{\kappa_{\text{LIV}}}{\dot{\eta}_{e\gamma}} \Delta_P^{(S)} \Big|^2; \qquad (14)$$

here $P_v(\mathbf{K})$ indicates the velocity PS which can be estimated as a function of primordial scalar spectrum $P_v(\mathbf{K},\tau) \sim P_\phi^{(S)}(\mathbf{K},\tau)$. Therefore, we can estimate the C_ℓ^V in terms of linearly polarized angular PS as follows:

$$C_\ell^V \approx (\tilde{\kappa}_{\text{LIV}}^{\text{avg}})^2 C_\ell^P, \qquad (15)$$

with

$$\tilde{\kappa}_{\text{LIV}} = c_{\{\alpha\beta\}}\, \rho_Q^{\{\alpha\beta\}}\, \frac{\kappa_{\text{LIV}}}{\dot{\tau}_{e\gamma}}, \qquad \tilde{\kappa}_{\text{LIV}}^{\text{avg}} = \frac{1}{z_{lss}} \int_0^{z_{lss}} dz\, \tilde{\kappa}_{\text{LIV}}(z) \simeq 10^{-3}, \qquad (16)$$

where $\tilde{\kappa}_{\text{LIV}}^{\text{avg}}$ is average of $\tilde{\kappa}_{\text{LIV}}(z)$ over redshift from last scattering surface, $z_{lss} \simeq 1100$, up to today, $z=0$. Based on recent experimental astrophysics bounds on different components of $c^{\alpha\beta}$ tensor,[91] we assume all component of $c^{\alpha\beta}$ tensor at the order of 10^{-15}. Considering the experimental value for the CMB linearly polarized angular PS of the order of[92] $C_\ell^P \equiv 0.1\mu K^2$ for $\ell < 250$, we can estimate the V-mode angular PS arisen from Compton scattering in presence of LIV as follows:

$$C_\ell^V \approx 0.8\text{ nK}^2 \Big(\frac{c^{\alpha\beta}}{10^{-15}}\Big)^2. \qquad (17)$$

The current experimental bound on the circular polarization coming from the Cosmology Large Angular Scale Surveyor (CLASS) experiment with the 40 GHz polarimeter ranging from $0.4\mu K^2$ to $13.5\mu K^2$ for $1 \leq \ell \leq 120$. We expect that by improving the sensitivity of experiments in future, the constraint obtained in Eq. (17) would be comparable to experimental bounds.

5.2. *New gravitational degrees of freedom and the DM problem*

The nature of DM is the deepest problem of modern cosmology. Assuming GR, DM appears to be a necessary ingredient in theoretical models constructed for explaining astrophysical and cosmological observations on $\sim$ kpc scales or larger. This essentially boils down to a mismatch between the observed dynamics of visible matter and its gravitational influence. Many theories of what is DM have been proposed.[93]

The DM microphysical nature, however, is not crucial to explain many cosmological observations. This leads to a simple description so that the DM dynamics are effectively governed by the collisionless Boltzmann equation, coupled to gravity.

The less explored alternative is that DM is not the cause behind all these observed phenomena, but rather that GR (and also Newtonian gravity) breaks down at ultra-low curvatures and gravitational accelerations and a new description of gravity is necessary. Changing the law of gravity, however, is not as arbitrary as it may seem.[94] Lovelock's theorem[95] tells us that GR is the unique 4-dimensional theory based on a local and diffeomorphism-invariant action where the metric is the only dynamical degree of freedom. If a non-GR gravitational theory is then assumed to explain the DM phenomenon, it is inevitable that one or more of these assumptions must be broken, and this generically leads to new dynamical degrees of freedom, that is, new dynamical fields.

Milgrom proposed[96–98] that DM is only an apparent phenomenon and that one can instead fit galactic rotation curves via a modification of the inertia/dynamics of baryons or of the gravitational law, when accelerations become smaller than $a_0 \sim 1.2 \times 10^{-10}$ m/s^2. Modifying the gravitational law was further explored by Bekenstein & Milgrom[99] who proposed that when the gradients of the potential Φ are smaller than a_0, non-relativistic gravity is effectively governed by

$$\nabla \cdot \left(\frac{|\nabla \Phi|}{a_0} \nabla \Phi \right) = 4\pi G_N \rho, \tag{18}$$

where G_N is the Newtonian gravitational constant, and ρ the matter density. These type of models are referred to as Modified Newtonian Dynamics (MOND).

MOND has enjoyed success in fitting galactic rotation curves and reproducing the baryonic Tully-Fisher relation, while on GC scales it is found that either a_0 must be larger by a factor of 4÷5 or that some DM is still needed at GC cores; see Ref. 100 for a review. As MOND is inherently non-relativistic, it is difficult to test in cosmological settings, since systems such as the CMB require a relativistic treatment. Relativistic theories that yield MOND behavior have been proposed, the most well-known being the Tensor-Vector-Scalar (TeVeS) theory,[101,102] making clear predictions regarding gravitational lensing and cosmology. In cases where the CMB and matter power spectra (MPS) have been computed, no theory has been shown to fit *all* of the cosmological data while preserving MOND phenomenology in galaxies. TeVeS in particular can be compatible with the MPS of large scale structure[103,104] but fails to fit the CMB. Moreover, it leads to a tensor mode gravitational wave (GW) speed different than the speed of light,[105] in contradiction with the Laser Interferometer Gravitational-Wave Observatory (LIGO)/Virgo observations of GW along with an electromagnetic counterpart.

The non-relativistic equation (18) can only be an effective description, due to Lovelock's theorem. To make it into a fully fledged relativistic theory, one can introduce additional fields. Building on TeVeS and later developments,[105,106] Skordis & Zlosnik[107] proposed a simple relativistic theory which in addition to the metric

$g_{\mu\nu}$ has a scalar field ϕ and unit time-like vector field A^μ. Perturbing these fields on a Minkowski background, results in perturbations of ϕ and A_μ which mix with the metric perturbation via gauge transformations, i.e. the metric potentials mix with the perturbations of ϕ and A_μ. Thus, ϕ and A_μ are gravitational fields and not DM fields, because due to this mixing it is impossible to distinguish observationally which of the three is the cause behind the "DM phenomenon", in analogy to the electric/magnetic field mixing resulting in the electromagnetic field.

The theory contains a free function $\mathcal{F}(\mathcal{Y}, \mathcal{Q})$ of two arguments: $\mathcal{Q} = A^\mu \nabla_\mu \phi$ and $\mathcal{Y} = q^{\mu\nu} \nabla_\mu \phi \nabla_\nu \phi$ where $q_{\mu\nu} = g_{\mu\nu} + A_\mu A_\nu$ is the 3-metric orthogonal to A^μ. It must obey certain conditions in order for the theory to serve its purpose and to be observationally viable. To recover MOND on galactic scales, it is necessary that the reduced function $\mathcal{J}(\mathcal{Y}) \equiv \mathcal{F}(\mathcal{Y}, \mathcal{Q}_0)/(2 - \mathcal{K}_B)$ where $\mathcal{Q}_0$ is a non-zero constant, has the limit $\mathcal{J} \to \mathcal{Y}^{3/2}/a_0$ when $\mathcal{Y} \sim |\nabla\varphi|^2$ is small. Imposing that and considering virialized systems in the weak-field approximation, leads to linear equations involving the metric potential Φ and a scalar perturbation φ, sourced by the (baryonic) matter density. These contain an additional term which is not present in MOND, but looks like a mass term for the potential, $\mu^2 \Phi$, where here $\mu^2 = 2\mathcal{K}_2 \mathcal{Q}_0^2/(2 - \mathcal{K}_B)$. It is determined by the other parameters of the theory: $\mathcal{Q}_0$, appearing in as part of the free function, $\mathcal{K}_B$, related to the coupling strength of the vector field and taking values in the range $0 < \mathcal{K}_B < 2$, and $\mathcal{K}_2$, related to the coupling strength of the scalar field. In addition, the resulting equations depend on Milgrom's constant a_0. Thus in the quasistatic weak-field situation, at least two parameter combinations are important: a_0 and μ, although, depending on how the GR limit is attained, there may be further parameters as part of the free function. Due to the presence of the mass term μ, the theory departs from MOND behaviour at ultra-low accelerations determined by μ.

Consider now setups involving the relativistic nature of the theory. The form of the action of the theory ensures that the right amount of gravitational lensing is ensured whenever Φ correctly determines the dynamics and the tensor mode GW speed is equal to the speed of light in all situations. Meanwhile, on Friedmann-Lemaître-Robertson-Walker (FLRW) $\phi = \bar{\phi}(t)$ while A^μ aligns trivially with the time direction so that $\mathcal{Y} \to 0$ and $\mathcal{Q} \to \dot{\phi}$ and the action reduces to that of shift-symmetric K-essence[108] and the low-energy limit of the ghost-condensate theory.[109] Defining then the reduced function $\mathcal{K}(\mathcal{Q}) \equiv -\mathcal{F}(0, \mathcal{Q})/2$, we require that $\mathcal{K} \approx \mathcal{K}_2 (\mathcal{Q} - \mathcal{Q}_0)^2 + \ldots$, with non-zero $\mathcal{Q}_0$ (same constants as what appear above), the energy density of ϕ scales precisely as a^{-3}, $a = 1/(1+z)$ being here the cosmic scale factor, i.e. like pressureless matter, plus small corrections. The equation of state and speed of sound of ϕ also scale as a^{-3} and depend on the constants $\mathcal{K}_2$ and $\mathcal{Q}_0$ of the action. In the late universe limit these tend to zero so that the linear perturbations of ϕ and A_μ can be re-casted by linear transformations into a density contrast δ and velocity divergence θ of pressureless matter. In this limit, the field equations of ϕ and A_μ and their contribution to the Einstein equations, become identical to pressureless-dust equations, i.e. as for CDM. This ensures that the CMB and MPS spectra calculated within this theory, become parametrically close to those from ΛCDM, leading to excellent fits to the CMB angular PS from *Planck* and the MPS obtained from galaxy clustering.

To summarize, the theory is not a MOND extrapolation to cosmology. Rather, it recovers MOND in quasistatic situations on galactic scales, and it tends to ΛCDM behaviour on cosmological scales. It depends on a free function, which is, however, constrained so that these two limits are attained. Doing that, the theory depends on a minimum of 4 parameters, K_B, $\mathcal{Q}_0$, $\mathcal{K}_2$ and a_0, while additional parameters could be part of the free function and be related to the GR limit or the early universe.

5.3. *Exploiting the magnification bias with high-z sub-mm galaxies*

Magnification bias is due to gravitational lensing and consists in the apparent excess in the number of high-z sources (the lenses sources) close to the position of low-z galaxies (the lenses). In fact, the gravitational lensing deflects the light rays of high-z sources causing the stretching of the apparent sky area in the region affected by the lensing. This also causes a boost in the flux density of the high-z sources, making them more likely to be detected above a given instrument flux density limit (see, e.g., Ref. 110). The magnification bias can be measured through the cross-correlation between the low and high-z objects. Given two source samples with non-overlapping redshift distributions, the excess signal when computing their cross-correlation with respect to the random case is due to the magnification bias. Being such signal related to lensing and thus to cosmological distances and the galaxy halo characteristics, it can be used to constrain cosmological parameters.

In order to get the best cross-correlation measurements, at the moment the optimal choice is to use as high-z sources (background samples) the high-z sub-mm galaxies (SMGs) first of all because of their steep number counts, shown with recent observations by the *Herschel* Space Observatory[111] and the South Pole Telescope[112] (SPT) strengthening their magnification. Moreover, the SMGs are faint in the optical which means that they do not get confused with the foreground lens sample, being such sample invisible at sub-mm wavelength. Lastly, the SMGs redshift are usually above $z > 1$ so that their selection as background sample ensures no overlap with the foreground objects. In fact, due to their extreme magnification bias, Dunne et al. (Ref. 113) make a serendipitous direct observation of high-z SMGs. While performing a study of gas tracers with Atacama Large Millimeter/submillimeter Array (ALMA) observation of galaxies targeting a statistically complete sample of twelve galaxies selected at 250 μm with $z = 0.35$, magnified SMGs appears around the position of half of them.

As shown in Refs. 114, 115, these advantages make the SMGs the perfect background sample for tracing the (baryonic and DM) mass density profiles of galaxies and GCs and their time-evolution and for constraining the free parameters of a halo occupation distribution (HOD) model. In the adopted HOD model[116] all halos above a mass M_{min} host a central galaxy and those above a mass M_1 host satellites (galaxies in the halo) whose number is a power-law, $(M/M_1)^\alpha$, of the halo mass M. In particular, the results in Ref. 114 suggests that the lenses are massive galaxies or GCs, with a minimum mass of $10^{13} M_\odot$. Later on, Bonavera et al. (Ref. 115) study with the magnification bias the mass properties of a sample of quasars whose position signpost the lens at $0.2 < z < 1.0$ obtaining a $M_{min} = 10^{13.6^{+0.9}_{-0.4}} M_\odot$. This again suggests that the lensing is actually produced by halos of the size of GCs placed close to the quasar positions.

Moreover, some of the main cosmological parameters can be also estimated using the magnification bias, as in Ref. 117. They use the cross-correlation data measured between a foreground sample of Galaxy And Mass Assembly (GAMA) galaxies with spectroscopic redshifts in the range $0.2 < z < 0.8$ and a background sample of *Herschel* Astrophysical Terahertz Large Area Survey (H-ATLAS) galaxies with photometric redshifts $z > 1.2$ to constrain the HOD astrophysical parameters (M_{min}, M_1, and α) and some of the cosmological ones (Ω_M, σ_8, and H_0). These parameters are estimated through a Markov chain Monte Carlo analysis. They obtain a lower limit at 95% CL on $\Omega_M > 0.24$, a slight trend towards $H_0 > 70$ values and a tentative peak around 0.75 with an upper limit at 95% CL of $\sigma_8 < 1$. Such results are summarized in the $\Omega_M - \sigma_8$ plane in Fig. 7 (*left* panel).

Furthermore, magnification bias trough cross-correlation measurements can be used to constrain the halo mass function. In particular, Ref. 118 successfully tests such possibility according to two common parametrizations, the Sheth & Tormen[119] and the Tinker et al.[120] fits.

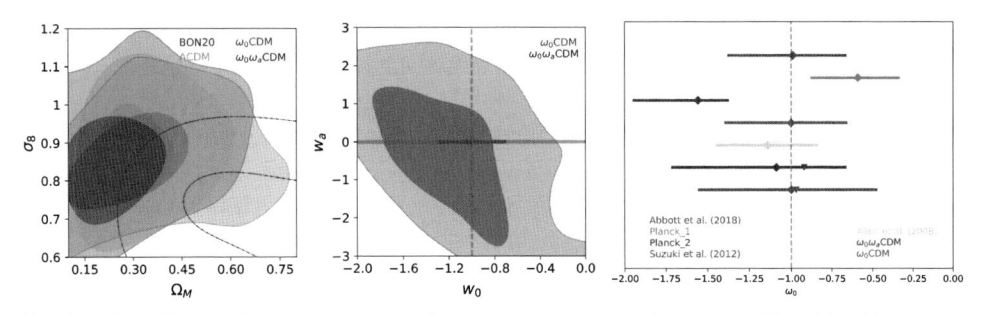

Fig. 7. *Left*: Ω_M and σ_8 contour plot for the non-tomographic case in Ref. 117 (dot-dashed blue line) and the tomographic runs in Ref. 122 for ΛCDM (in yellow), ω_0CDM (in green) and $\omega_0 \omega_a$CDM (in purple) models. *Central*: ω_0 and ω_a contour plot for the $\omega_0 \omega_a$CDM model. In both panels, the contours of the 2-dimensional posterior distributions are set to 0.393 and 0.865. *Right*: ω_0 results for the ω_0CDM (green) and $\omega_0 \omega_a$CDM (purple) models compared with those by DES (blue), *Planck*_1 (base_w_wa_plikHM_TT_lowl_lowE_BAO, salmon), *Planck*_2 (base_w_plikHM_TT_lowl_lowE, brown), Supernovae (red), X-ray measurements (yellow). Adapted from Bonavera et al., A&A, in press, DOI 10.1051/0004-6361/202141521, 2021 (Ref. 122), reproduced with permission from Astronomy & Astrophysics, © ESO.

They find general agreement with traditional values for the involved parameters, with a slight difference in the Sheth & Tormen fit for intermediate and high masses, where the results suggest a hint at a somewhat higher number of halos. Given the large number of studies that can be performed with magnification bias through cross-correlation data, a systematic analysis of possible bias that might affect the estimation is being carried out. In particular, González-Nuevo et al. (Ref. 121) take into account different biases at cosmological scales in the source samples to carefully measure unbiased cross-correlation functions. More precisely, their background sample consists of H-ATLAS galaxies with $z > 1.2$ whereas they use two independent foreground samples with $0.2 < z < 0.8$: GAMA galaxies with spectroscopic redshifts and Sloan Digital Sky Survey (SDSS) galaxies with photometric redshifts. These independent samples allowed them to perform a pseudo-tomographic study that yields to constrain $\Omega_M = 0.50^{+0.14}_{-0.20}$ and $\sigma_8 = 0.75^{+0.07}_{-0.10}$. Such analysis also suggests that a tomographic approach might improve the results.

Driven by the conclusions mentioned above, adopting the unbiased sample by Ref. 121, Bonavera et al.[122] use magnification bias in tomography to jointly constrain the HOD astrophysical parameters in each selected redshift bin together with the Ω_M, σ_8, and H_0 cosmological ones in the ΛCDM scenario and for DE models in the ω_0CDM and $\omega_0\omega_a$CDM frameworks characterized by the ω_0 and ω_a parameters defining the DE barotropic index as $\omega(a) = \omega_0 + \omega_a(1-a)$. The foreground sample has been divided into four redshift bins (0.1–0.2, 0.2–0.3, 0.3–0.5 and 0.5–0.8) and the sample of H-ATLAS galaxies has photometric redshifts $z > 1.2$. As for the HOD parameters, M_{min} shows a trend towards higher values at higher z confirming the findings in Ref. 114. For the ΛCDM model, they obtain a maximum posterior value [68% CL] of $\Omega_M = 0.26$ [0.17,0.41] and of $\sigma_8 = 0.87$ [0.75,1] (implying $S_8 \simeq 0.81$, in good agreement with the result in Sect. 4.1), being H_0 not yet constrained. For the ω_0CDM model, they find similar results on Ω_M and σ_8 and a maximum posterior value [68% CL] of $\omega_0 = -1$ [$-1.56, -0.47$]. For the $\omega_0\omega_a$CDM model, $\omega_0 = -1.09$ [$-1.72, -0.66$] and $\omega_a = -0.19$ [$-1.88, 1.48$]. Fig. 7 shows the results in the $\Omega_M - \sigma_8$ plane for the ΛCDM, ω_0CDM and $\omega_0\omega_a$CDM models (*left* panel) and in the $\omega_0 - \omega_a$ plane (*central* panel). The results on ω_0 for the ω_0CDM and $\omega_0\omega_a$CDM cases are shown in Fig. 7 (*right* panel), together with a comparison with other results from literature. Moreover, the tomographic analysis presented in Ref. 122 confirms that magnification bias results do not show the degeneracy found with cosmic shear measurements and that, related to DE, do show a trend of higher ω_0 values for lower H_0 values (see Ref. 123 for details).

In conclusion, SMGs turn out to be a perfect background sample for magnification bias analyses, useful in astrophysical studies and as a further independent cosmological probe for ΛCDM and beyond ΛCDM models and this can be implemented adopting different foreground samples. Up to now ΛCDM compatible results have been found with tomographic and non-tomographic approaches and serendipitous direct observation of magnified SMGs have been performed with ALMA.

Acknowledgments

CB acknowledges partial support from the INAF PRIN SKA/CTA project FORECaST. LB acknowledges the PGC 2018 project PGC2018-101948-B-I00 (MICINN/FEDER). TRC acknowledges support of the Department of Atomic Energy, Government of India, under project no. 12-R&D-TFR-5.02-0700. CS acknowledges support from the European Research Council under the European Union's Seventh Framework Programme (FP7/2007-2013) / ERC Grant Agreement n. 617656 "Theories and Models of the Dark Sector: Dark Matter, Dark Energy and Gravity" and from the European Structural and Investment Funds and the Czech Ministry of Education, Youth and Sports (MSMT) (Project CoGraDS - CZ.02.1.01/0.0/0.0/15003/0000437). RS acknowledges the support of the Natural Sciences and Engineering Research Council of Canada. HT acknowledges support from the ERC-2015-AdG 695561 (ByoPiC project). AW acknowledges funding from the South African Research Chairs Initiative of the Department of Science and Technology and the National Research Foundation of South Africa. Some of the results in this paper have been derived using the `HEALPix`[34] package. The use of the PLA is acknowledged. It is a pleasure to thank N. Aghanim, D. Contreras, M. M. Cueli, M. Douspis, B. Gaensler, J. Gonzalez-Nuevo, R. Mohammadi, D. Scott, S. S. Xue, the MISTRAL Collaboration and the *Planck* Collaboration for long-standing collaborations on the various topics discussed in this paper.

References

1. E. Di Valentino, O. Mena, S. Pan *et al.*, *Classical and Quantum Gravity* **38**, 153001 (2021).
2. Dark Energy Survey Collaboration, *Phys. Rev. D* **98**, 043526 (2018).
3. DES Collaboration, arXiv:2105.13549 (2021).
4. D. R. Lorimer, M. Bailes, M. A. McLaughlin, D. J. Narkevic and F. Crawford, *Science* **318**, 777 (2007).
5. S. P. Tendulkar, C. G. Bassa, J. M. Cordes *et al.*, *ApJL* **834**, L7 (2017).
6. A. Walters, A. Weltman, B. M. Gaensler, Y.-Z. Ma and A. Witzemann, *ApJ* **856**, 65 (2018).
7. A. Walters, Y.-Z. Ma, J. Sievers and A. Weltman, *Phys. Rev. D* **100**, 103519 (2019).
8. A. Weltman and A. Walters, arXiv:1905.07132 (2019).
9. E. Platts, A. Weltman, A. Walters *et al.*, *Physics Reports* **821**, 1 (2019).
10. J. P. Macquart, J. X. Prochaska, M. McQuinn *et al.*, *Nature* **581**, 391 (2020).
11. R. Barkana and A. Loeb, *Physics Reports* **349**, 125 (2001).
12. T. R. Choudhury, *Current Science* **97**, 841 (2009).
13. G. Paciga, J. G. Albert, K. Bandura *et al.*, *MNRAS* **433**, 639 (2013).
14. A. H. Patil, S. Yatawatta, L. V. E. Koopmans *et al.*, *ApJ* **838**, 65 (2017).
15. F. G. Mertens, M. Mevius, L. V. E. Koopmans *et al.*, *MNRAS* **493**, 1662 (2020).
16. J. S. Dillon, A. Liu, C. L. Williams *et al.*, *Phys. Rev. D* **89**, 023002 (2014).
17. J. S. Dillon, A. R. Neben, J. N. Hewitt *et al.*, *Phys. Rev. D* **91**, 123011 (2015).
18. A. P. Beardsley, B. J. Hazelton, I. S. Sullivan *et al.*, *ApJ* **833**, 102 (2016).
19. S. Paul, S. K. Sethi, M. F. Morales *et al.*, *ApJ* **833**, 213 (2016).

20. N. Barry, M. Wilensky, C. M. Trott et al., ApJ **884**, 1 (2019).
21. W. Li, J. C. Pober, N. Barry et al., ApJ **887**, 141 (2019).
22. C. M. Trott, C. H. Jordan, S. Midgley et al., MNRAS **493**, 4711 (2020).
23. M. Kolopanis, D. C. Jacobs, C. Cheng et al., ApJ **883**, 133 (2019).
24. The HERA Collaboration, arXiv:2108.02263 (2021).
25. T. R. Choudhury and A. Paranjape, MNRAS **481**, 3821 (2018).
26. J. D. Bowman, A. E. E. Rogers, R. A. Monsalve, T. J. Mozdzen and N. Mahesh, Nature **555**, 67 (2018).
27. R. Barkana, Nature **555**, 71 (2018).
28. C. Feng and G. Holder, ApJL **858**, L17 (2018).
29. A. Fialkov and R. Barkana, MNRAS **486**, 1763 (2019).
30. A. Chatterjee, P. Dayal, T. R. Choudhury and R. Schneider, MNRAS **496**, 1445 (2020).
31. R. Hills, G. Kulkarni, P. D. Meerburg and E. Puchwein, Nature **564**, E32 (2018).
32. J. Raste, G. Kulkarni, L. C. Keating et al., MNRAS **507**, 4684 (2021).
33. Planck Collaboration, A&A **594**, A10 (2016).
34. K. M. Górski, E. Hivon, A. J. Banday et al., ApJ **622**, 759 (2005).
35. R. A. Sunyaev and Y. B. Zel'dovich, Comments on Astrophysics and Space Physics **4**, 173 (1972).
36. M. Birkinshaw, Physics Reports **310**, 97 (1999).
37. R. Cen and J. P. Ostriker, ApJ **514**, 1 (1999).
38. T. Tuominen, J. Nevalainen, E. Tempel et al., A&A **646**, A156 (2021).
39. E. S. Battistelli, E. Barbavara and P. de Bernardis et al., in these proceedings.
40. A. Paiella, E. S. Battistelli, M. G. Castellano et al., Journal of Physics: Conference Series **1182**, 012005 (2019).
41. S. Masi, P. de Bernardis, A. Paiella et al., JCAP **07**, 003 (2019).
42. M. S. Petersen, R. A. Gutermuth, E. Nagel, G. W. Wilson and J. Lane, MNRAS **488**, 1462 (2019).
43. A. D. Sokol, R. A. Gutermuth, R. Pokhrel et al., MNRAS **483**, 407 (2019).
44. W. F. Wall, I. Puerari, R. Tilanus et al., MNRAS **459**, 1440 (2016).
45. A. Humphrey, M. Zeballos, I. Aretxaga et al., MNRAS **418**, 74 (2011).
46. Planck Collaboration, A&A **641**, A6 (2020).
47. Planck Collaboration, A&A **571**, A20 (2014).
48. Planck Collaboration, A&A **594**, A24 (2016).
49. C. Heymans et al., A&A **646**, A140 (2021).
50. Planck Collaboration, A&A **594**, A22 (2016).
51. G. Hurier et al., A&A **558**, A118 (2013).
52. H. Tanimura, M. Douspis and N. Aghanim, in these proceedings.
53. J. Delabrouille et al., A&A **553**, A96 (2013).
54. A. Maniyar et al., A&A **645**, A40 (2021).
55. Planck Collaboration, A&A **641**, A1 (2020).
56. Planck Collaboration, A&A **571**, A27 (2014).
57. Planck Collaboration, A&A **644**, 100 (2020).
58. R. M. Sullivan and D. Scott, in these proceedings.
59. T. Trombetti, C. Burigana and F. Chierici, A&A **646**, A75 (2021).
60. V. F. Mukhanov and G. V. Chibisov, Sov. Journal of Exp. and Theor. Phys. Lett. **33**, 532 (1981).
61. V. F. Mukhanov and G. V. Chibisov, Sov. Journal of Exp. and Theor. Phys. **56**, 258 (1982).
62. S. W. Hawking, Physics Letters B **115**, 295 (1982).

63. A. H. Guth and S. Y. Pi, *Phys. Rev. Lett.* **49**, 1110 (1982).
64. A. A. Starobinsky, *Physics Letters B* **117**, 175 (1982).
65. J. M. Bardeen, P. J. Steinhardt and M. S. Turner, *Phys. Rev. D* **28**, 679 (1983).
66. V. F. Mukhanov, *Sov. Journal of Exp. and Theor. Phys. Lett.* **41**, 493 (1985).
67. U. Seljak, *ApJ* **482**, 6 (1997).
68. M. Kamionkowski, A. Kosowsky and A. Stebbins, *Phys. Rev. Lett.* **78**, 2058 (1997).
69. U. Seljak and M. Zaldarriaga, *Phys. Rev. Lett.* **78**, 2054 (1997).
70. M. Zaldarriaga and U. Seljak, *Phys. Rev. D* **58**, 023003 (1998).
71. Planck Collaboration, *A&A* **586**, A133 (2016).
72. BICEP2 Collaboration, Keck Array Collaboration, *Phys. Rev. Lett.* **121**, 221301 (2018).
73. Planck Collaboration, *A&A* **641**, A10 (2020).
74. BICEP2/Keck Collaboration, Planck Collaboration, *Phys. Rev. Lett.* **114**, 101301 (2015).
75. M. Tristram, A. J. Banday, K. M. Górski *et al.*, *A&A* **647**, A128 (2021).
76. Planck Collaboration, *A&A* **643**, A42 (2020).
77. H. K. Eriksen, J. B. Jewell, C. Dickinson *et al.*, *ApJ* **676**, 10 (2008).
78. Planck Collaboration, *A&A* **596**, A108 (2016).
79. A. Kosowsky, *Annals Phys.* **246**, 49 (1996).
80. U. Seljak and M. Zaldarriaga, *ApJ* **469**, 437 (1996).
81. M. Zaldarriaga and U. Seljak, *Phys. Rev. D* **55**, 1830 (1997).
82. A. Cooray, A. Melchiorri and J. Silk, *Phys. Lett. B* **554**, 1 (2003).
83. E. Bavarsad, M. Haghighat, Z. Rezaei *et al.*, *Phys. Rev. D* **81**, 084035 (2010).
84. S. Modares Vamegh, M. Haghighat, S. Mahmoudi and R. Mohammadi, *Phys. Rev. D* **100**, 103024 (2019).
85. M. Haghighat, S. Mahmoudi, R. Mohammadi, S. Tizchang and S. S. Xue, *Phys. Rev. D* **101**, 123016 (2020).
86. S. Tizchang, S. Batebi, M. Haghighat and R. Mohammadi, in *proceedings of The 39th Intern. Conf. on High Energy Physics (ICHEP2018)*, p.142, Proceedings of Science (PoS) (2019).
87. S. Tizchang, R. Mohammadi and S. S. Xue, in *these proceedings*.
88. D. Colladay and V. A. Kostelecky, *Phys. Rev. D* **55**, 6760 (1997).
89. D. Colladay and V. A. Kostelecky, *Phys. Rev. D* **58**, 116002 (1998).
90. V. A. Kostelecky and C. D. Lane, *Phys. Rev. D* **60**, 116010 (1999).
91. V. A. Kostelecky and N. Russell, in *proceedings of the Fourth Meeting on CPT and Lorentz Symmetry*, p. 308, World Scientific (2008).
92. Planck Collaboration, *A&A* **594**, A20 (2016).
93. G. Bertone, D. Hooper and J. Silk, *Physics Reports* **405**, 279 (2005).
94. T. Clifton, P. G. Ferreira, A. Padilla and C. Skordis, *Physics Reports* **513**, 1 (2012).
95. D. Lovelock, *J. Math. Phys.* **12**, 498 (1971).
96. M. Milgrom, *ApJ* **270**, 365 (1983).
97. M. Milgrom, *ApJ* **270**, 371 (1983).
98. M. Milgrom, *ApJ* **270**, 384 (1983).
99. J. Bekenstein and M. Milgrom, *ApJ* **286**, 7 (1984).
100. B. Famaey and S. McGaugh, *Living Reviews in Relativity* **15**, 10 (2012).
101. R. H. Sanders, *ApJ* **480**, 492 (1997).
102. J. D. Bekenstein, *Phys. Rev. D* **70**, 083509 (2004), [Erratum: *Phys. Rev. D* **71**, 069901 (2005)].
103. C. Skordis, D. F. Mota, P. G. Ferreira and C. Boehm, *Phys. Rev. Lett.* **96**, 011301 (2006).

104. S. Dodelson and M. Liguori, *Phys. Rev. Lett.* **97**, 231301 (2006).
105. C. Skordis and T. Zlosnik, *Phys. Rev. D* **100**, 104013 (2019).
106. T. G. Zlosnik, P. G. Ferreira and G. D. Starkman, *Phys. Rev. D* **74**, 044037 (2006).
107. C. Skordis and T. Zlosnik, *Phys. Rev. Lett.* **127**, 161302 (2021).
108. R. J. Scherrer, *Phys. Rev. Lett.* **93**, 011301 (2004).
109. N. Arkani-Hamed, H.-C. Cheng, M. A. Luty and S. Mukohyama, *JHEP* **05**, 074 (2004).
110. P. Schneider, J. Ehlers and E. E. Falco, *Gravitational Lenses*, Springer-Verlag Berlin Heidelberg (1992).
111. G. L. Pilbratt, J. R. Riedinger, T. Passvogel et al., *A&A* **518**, L1 (2010).
112. J. E. Carlstrom, P. A. R. Ade, K. A. Aird et al., *PASP* **123**, 568 (2011).
113. L. Dunne, L. Bonavera, J. Gonzalez-Nuevo, S. J. Maddox and C. Vlahakis, *MNRAS* **498**, 4635 (2020).
114. J. González-Nuevo, A. Lapi, L. Bonavera et al., *JCAP* **10**, 024 (2017).
115. L. Bonavera, J. González-Nuevo, S. L. Suárez Gómez et al., *JCAP* **09**, 021 (2019).
116. Z. Zheng, A. A. Berlind, D. H. Weinberg et al., *ApJ* **633**, 791 (2005).
117. L. Bonavera, J. González-Nuevo, M. M. Cueli et al., *A&A* **639**, A128 (2020).
118. M. M. Cueli, L. Bonavera, J. González-Nuevo and A. Lapi, *A&A* **645**, A126 (2021).
119. R. K. Sheth and G. Tormen, *MNRAS* **308**, 119 (1999).
120. J. Tinker, A. V. Kravtsov, A. Klypin et al., *ApJ* **688**, 709 (2008).
121. J. González-Nuevo, M. M. Cueli, L. Bonavera et al., *A&A* **646**, A152 (2021).
122. L. Bonavera, M. M. M. Cueli M., J. González-Nuevo J. et al., *A&A*, in press, DOI 10.1051/0004-6361/202141521, arXiv:2109.12413 (2021).
123. L. Bonavera, M. M. Cueli and J. González-Nuevo, in *these proceedings*.

CMB μT cross-correlations as a probe of PBH scenarios

Ogan Özsoy

*CEICO, Institute of Physics of the Czech Academy of Sciences,
Prague, Na Slovance 1999/2, 182 21, Czechia
E-mail: ozsoy@fzu.cz*

Gianmassimo Tasinato

*Department of Physics, Swansea University,
Swansea, SA2 8PP, United Kingdom
E-mail: g.tasinato@swansea.ac.uk*

We initiate a new method for probing inflationary models that can produce primordial black hole populations, using only CMB physics at relatively large scales. In these scenarios, profile of the primordial scalar power spectrum exhibit a universal dip feature that is followed by a rapid growth towards small scales, leading to a peak responsible for PBH formation. Focusing on scales around the dip that are well separated from the peak, we first analytically compute expressions for the curvature bispectrum. We then show that the amplitude of the bispectrum is enhanced for the squeezed configuration around the position of the dip, and it acquires a characteristic scale dependence that can be probed by cross correlations between CMB μ-distortions and temperature anisotropies. We quantitatively study the properties of such cross-correlations and how they depend on the underlying model, discussing how they can be tested by the next generation of CMB μ-distortion experiments. This method allows one to experimentally probe inflationary PBH scenarios using well-understood CMB physics, without considering non-linearities associated with PBH formation and evolution.

Keywords: Inflation, Primordial Black Holes, CMB distortions

1. Introduction

Gravitational waves from merging black holes, in conjunction with other probes, can be used for testing our understanding of cosmology. There is the intriguing possibility that part of black holes from merging events have primordial origin, arising from the collapse of overdense regions in the early stages of our universe evolution.[1–3] The existence of such overdense regions might be attributed to the dynamics of inflationary cosmology. In this framework, it is well known that to produce primordial black holes (PBHs) (see *e.g.* reviews[4–7]) with astrophysically relevant masses, the primordial scalar power spectrum should increase by several orders of magnitude with respect to its values at large CMB scales. Within the context of single-field inflation, such an amplification can be realized during a short slow-roll violating non-attractor period during which the would-be decaying mode grows to influence evolution of super-horizon fluctuations. In this set-up, a peak in the curvature perturbation spectrum can be produced, and the non-linear process of PBH production and subsequent evolution depends on the details of the peak, as first explicitly discussed in.[8]

The possible existence of primordial black hole (PBH) populations in our universe demands a detailed understanding of inflationary mechanisms that can give rise to them. Intriguingly, in inflationary scenarios capable of producing PBHs, the profile of the spectrum shows universal features such as the existence of pronounced dip, followed by a rapid growth with a well defined slope[9] towards its peak. The position of the dip is not random, but depends on other global properties of the spectrum, as well as on details of the non-attractor inflationary evolution.[10] It typically occurs at scales much larger than the peak, $k_{\rm dip}/k_{\rm peak} \simeq 10^{-2}$. Since the occurrence of dip seems to be a rather universal feature of power spectrum in single-field models of PBH formation, probing the physics associated with it offers an indirect way of testing these models, independently of the details of non-linear PBH formation and evolution mechanisms.

In this work, we ask whether we can probe the PBH formation mechanism by identifying large scale observables away from the scales associated with the peak of the spectrum.[11] For this purpose, we focus on scales around the dip feature to compute bispectrum of curvature perturbation analytically using the gradient expansion formalism[12,13] and show that it is generically amplified around the dip scale for squeezed configurations, exhibiting a characteristic scale dependence. We then show the influence of such a scale dependent squeezed bispectrum on the properties of cross-correlations between μ distortions and temperature T anisotropies and discuss the prospects of detectability of the $\langle \mu T \rangle$ signal with future spectral distortion experiments.

2. Curvature perturbation at super-horizon scales

Models of primordial black hole (PBH) formation based on single field inflation often include a short phase of non-attractor evolution, characterized by a transient growth of would be the decaying mode which influences the super-horizon evolution of cosmological scalar perturbations[a]. In this section, we review and utilize the *gradient expansion formalism*[b] – first introduced in[12] – to study the statistics of curvature fluctuations in scenarios including a transient non-attractor phase. In this framework, iterative solutions of the comoving curvature perturbation are generated at any desired order in a small-k expansion, in terms of analytic functions controlled by the background evolution. For example, the amplitude of curvature fluctuations at a fiducial late time $\tau = \tau_*$ (e.g. at the reheating surface) is mapped to its value at an initial time around horizon exit $\tau = \tau_k$ in terms of a complex-valued k-dependent

---

[a]Direct enhancement of tensor perturbations on super-horizon scales can be also achieved by devising an analogue non-attractor phase within the generalized scalar-tensor theories of single field inflation.[14,15]

[b]For a detailed account on the spectral profile of the scalar power spectrum that leads to PBH formation and its applications in the context of induced gravitational waves, we refer the reader to[13] where further developments of the gradient expansion formalism is discussed.

coefficient:
$$\mathcal{R}_k(\tau_*) = \alpha_k \mathcal{R}_k(\tau_k) = \left(\alpha_k^R + i\alpha_k^I\right)\mathcal{R}_k(\tau_k), \tag{1}$$

where in the last equality we split the enhancement factor into its real and imaginary parts:
$$\alpha_k \equiv \alpha_k^R + i\alpha_k^I. \tag{2}$$

Once expanded up to second, k^2-order in the gradient expansion, the real and imaginary parts of α_k are given by
$$\alpha_k^R = 1 + D(\tau_k)\, v_\mathcal{R}^R - F(\tau_k)\, k^2, \tag{3}$$
$$\alpha_k^I = D(\tau_k)\, v_\mathcal{R}^I. \tag{4}$$

The quantity $v_\mathcal{R}^R$ and $v_\mathcal{R}^I$ denote the real and imaginary part of the k-dependent fractional velocity of the curvature perturbation, which is defined as
$$v_\mathcal{R}(\tau_k) = \left.\frac{\mathcal{R}_k'}{3\mathcal{H}_k \mathcal{R}_k}\right|_{\tau=\tau_k}. \tag{5}$$

The full k dependence of the expressions (3) and (4) on super-horizon scales is encoded in the quantities $v_\mathcal{R}^R$, $v_\mathcal{R}^I$ and in the functions $D(\tau_k), F(\tau_k)$ (see Appendix A and B), given by the following nested integrals of the pump field appearing in Eq. (15)[12,13]:
$$D(\tau) = 3\mathcal{H}_k \int_\tau^{\tau_*} d\tau' \, \frac{z^2(\tau_k)}{z^2(\tau')}, \tag{6}$$
$$F(\tau) = \int_\tau^{\tau_*} \frac{d\tau'}{z^2(\tau')} \int_{\tau_k}^{\tau'} d\tau'' \, z^2(\tau''). \tag{7}$$

Expressions (6) and (7) indicate that if the pump field increases with time – as in standard slow-roll inflation, where $z \propto a(\tau)$ – the functions D, F rapidly decrease to zero after horizon crossing (*i.e.* $\alpha_k \to 1$). Hence the curvature perturbation in (1) settles to a constant shortly after horizon exit ($\mathcal{R}_k(\tau_*) \simeq \mathcal{R}_k(\tau_k)$). On the contrary, in inflationary models containing phases of non-attractor evolution, $z(\tau)$ transiently decreases and the functions D, F can grow, amplifying the spectrum of curvature perturbation with $|\alpha_k| \gg 1$ at super-horizon scales: see Appendix B.

The curvature perturbation power spectrum. We define the late-time power spectrum evaluated at $\tau = \tau_*$ as
$$\langle \mathcal{R}_k(\tau_*)\mathcal{R}_{k'}(\tau_*)\rangle = (2\pi)^3\, P_\mathcal{R}(\tau_*, k)\, \delta\left(\vec{k}+\vec{k}'\right). \tag{8}$$

Using Eq. (1), we can then relate the power spectrum at late times to the power spectrum evaluated at horizon crossing via
$$\mathcal{P}_\mathcal{R}(\tau_*, k) \equiv \frac{2\pi^2}{k^3} P_\mathcal{R}(\tau_*, k) = \frac{2\pi^2}{k^3}\left[|\alpha_k|^2\, P_\mathcal{R}(\tau_k)\right] \equiv |\alpha_k|^2 \mathcal{P}_\mathcal{R}(\tau_k), \tag{9}$$

where $\mathcal{P}_\mathcal{R}(\tau_k) \equiv k^3 P_\mathcal{R}(\tau_k, k)/2\pi^2$, and $|\alpha_k|^2 = (\alpha_k^R)^2 + (\alpha_k^I)^2$.

A non-linear expression for $\mathcal{R}$. We assume that $\mathcal{R}_k(\tau_k)$ is a Gaussian random variable: nevertheless, the super-horizon evolution typically introduces non-linearities. In fact, we can go beyond the linear theory used for Eq. (1) to compute the bispectrum of the late time curvature perturbation $\mathcal{R}_k(\tau_*)$. For the purpose of deriving an analytic expression for the bispectrum, we will use the following non-linear expression for the curvature perturbation, first derived in[16]

$$\mathcal{R}_k(\tau_*) = \alpha_k \mathcal{R}_k(\tau_k) + \frac{F(\tau_k)}{2}\left\{\int \frac{d^3k'}{(2\pi)^3}\left[4k'^2 - \vec{k}'\cdot(\vec{k}-\vec{k}')\right]\mathcal{R}_{k'}(\tau_{k'})\mathcal{R}_{|\vec{k}-\vec{k}'|}(\tau_{|\vec{k}-\vec{k}'|})\right\}. \quad (10)$$

where the last term represents the non-linear contribution parametrized by the convolution of the Gaussian variable $\mathcal{R}_k(\tau_k)$.

Bispectrum. We define the late-time bispectrum of curvature perturbations as

$$\langle \mathcal{R}_{k_1}(\tau_*)\mathcal{R}_{k_2}(\tau_*)\mathcal{R}_{k_3}(\tau_*)\rangle = (2\pi)^3 B_\mathcal{R}(k_1,k_2,k_3)\,\delta\left(\vec{k}_1+\vec{k}_2+\vec{k}_3\right), \quad (11)$$

and using (10), at leading order in the non-linear term, the bispectrum is given by[16,17]

$$B_\mathcal{R} = \frac{(2\pi^2)^2}{2(k_1 k_2 k_3)^3}\left[\text{Re}[\alpha_{k_1}^*\alpha_{k_2}]F(\tau_{k_3})\left\{5\left(k_1^2+k_2^2\right)-k_3^2\right\}k_3^3\,\mathcal{P}_\mathcal{R}(\tau_{k_1})\mathcal{P}_\mathcal{R}(\tau_{k_2}) \quad (12) \right.$$
$$\left. + \text{ perms}\right],$$

where the permutations are cyclic among the three external momenta $\{\vec{k}_1,\vec{k}_2,\vec{k}_3\}$. Correspondingly, we define the scale-dependent non-linearity parameter f_{NL} as

$$f_{\text{NL}}(k_1,k_2,k_3) = \frac{5}{6}\frac{B_\mathcal{R}(k_1,k_2,k_3)}{[\mathcal{P}_\mathcal{R}(\tau_*,k_1)\mathcal{P}_\mathcal{R}(\tau_*,k_2) + \text{ perms}]}, \quad (13)$$

Using (9) and (12) in (13), we then obtain the scale-dependent f_{NL} as

$$f_{\text{NL}} = \frac{5}{12}\frac{\left(\text{Re}[\alpha_{k_1}^*\alpha_{k_2}]F(\tau_{k_3})\left\{5\left(k_1^2+k_2^2\right)-k_3^2\right\}k_3^3\,\mathcal{P}_\mathcal{R}(\tau_{k_1})\mathcal{P}_\mathcal{R}(\tau_{k_2}) + \text{ perms}\right)}{\left[|\alpha_{k_1}\alpha_{k_2}|^2\,\mathcal{P}_\mathcal{R}(\tau_{k_1})\mathcal{P}_\mathcal{R}(\tau_{k_2})k_3^3 + \text{ perms}\right]}. \quad (14)$$

Eq. (14) inform us that the size and the scale-dependence of the f_{NL} parameter depend on the function $F(\tau_k)$ and the enhancement factor α_k, whose behavior is tightly related with the background dynamics during inflation. We now turn to study the scale dependence of the power spectrum and bispectrum on a representative set-up capable of producing a large PBH population during inflation.

2.1. *Characteristics of the scalar power and bispectrum*

In order to study the spectral shape and enhancement in the power spectrum and bispectrum, we consider a representative scenario that instantly connects at $\tau = \tau_0$

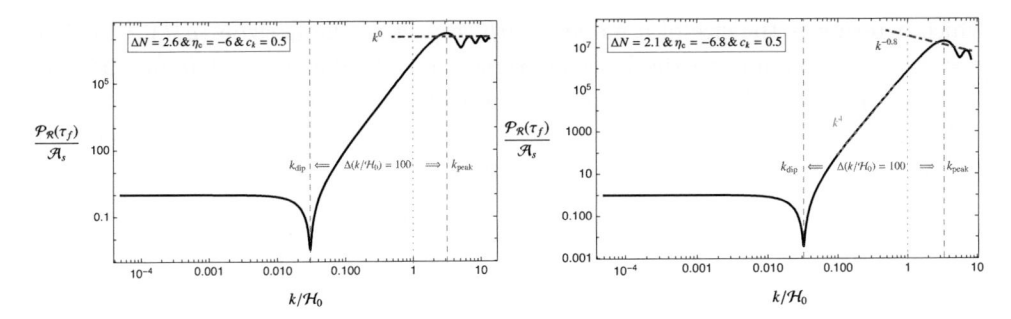

Fig. 1. Scale dependence of the power spectrum for an example ultra slow-roll model ($\eta_c = -6$) (Left) and constant-roll model ($\eta_c = -6.8$)(Right) as function of $k/\mathcal{H}_0$. The vertical gray-dotted lines separate the interval of wave-numbers leaving the horizon during the initial slow-roll era (left side) and the non-attractor era (right side). We define $\mathcal{A}_s = H^2/(8\pi^2 \epsilon_{\rm sr} M_{\rm pl}^2)$.

an initial slow-roll era, with $\eta_{\rm sr} = 0$, to a slow-roll violating, non-attractor phase with constant $\eta_c \leq -6$ lasting until $\tau = \tau_f$. Here η denotes the second slow-roll parameter, $H\eta \equiv d\ln\epsilon/dt$ and the first slow-roll parameter is given by $H\epsilon = -d\ln H/dt$. The pump field $z(\tau)$ appearing in the eqs. (6) and (7) is assumed to have a profile (we take $\tau < 0$):

$$z(\tau) = \begin{cases} z_0 \left(\tau/\tau_0\right)^{-1} & \tau/\tau_0 \geq 1, \\ z_0 \left(\tau/\tau_0\right)^{-(\eta_c+2)/2} & \tau_f/\tau_0 \leq \tau/\tau_0 \leq 1, \end{cases} \qquad (15)$$

describing collectively the initial slow-roll and the slow-roll violating phases, the latter being controlled by the negative $\mathcal{O}(1)$ "slow-roll" parameter η_c. The duration of the non-attractor phase can be parametrized as $\Delta N = \ln(\tau_0/\tau_f)$ in e-fold numbers. We relate the quantity z_0 with a constant slow-roll parameter $\epsilon_{\rm sr}$ via $z_0 = -a(\tau_0)\sqrt{2\epsilon_{\rm sr}} M_{\rm pl}$. For simplicity we parameterize the scale factor as in de Sitter space: $a = -1/(H\tau)$ with a constant Hubble rate H during inflation. We also indicate with $\mathcal{H}_0$ the size of the comoving horizon at the time of the transition to the non-attractor era.

Spectral profile of the power spectrum: We proceed with determining the corresponding growth rate of the power spectrum. For this purpose, we first re-write the dimensionless power spectrum as (see *e.g.* Eq. (9)),

$$\mathcal{P}_\mathcal{R}(\tau_f, k) \equiv |\alpha_k|^2 \mathcal{P}_\mathcal{R}(\tau_k) = \left[(\alpha_k^R)^2 + (\alpha_k^I)^2\right] \mathcal{P}_\mathcal{R}(\tau_k), \qquad (16)$$

and we evaluate this quantity at the end of the non-attractor era $\tau_* = \tau_f$, to characterize the shape of the power spectrum using α_k^R (3), α_k^I (4) and $\mathcal{P}_\mathcal{R}(\tau_k)$ with the help of formulas we derived in Appendix A and B. In this way, we represent our results in Figure 1 for two different sets of parameters associated with the two-phase model of PBH formation characterized by the pump field profile of (15). For understanding the physical implications of our findings within the gradient expansion formalism, it is convenient to introduce a fixed quantity

$$c_k \equiv -k\tau_k \leq 1, \qquad (17)$$

which determines the size of a mode k with respect to the horizon $(aH)^{-1}$ at time $\tau = \tau_k$, corresponding to the horizon crossing epoch. We stress that by virtue of the relation (17) and the super-horizon gradient formalism, all modes we consider in Figure 1 (and in general in this work) are outside the horizon at the initial time τ_k. We then distinguish modes whose momenta lie in the following ranges:

i) modes that become super-horizon during the initial slow-roll era, *i.e.* modes satisfying $\tau_k/\tau_0 > 1$ or equivalently $k/\mathcal{H}_0 < c_k \leq 1$, and

ii) modes that leave the horizon during the non-attractor $\eta_c \leq -6$ phase, $c_k < k/\mathcal{H}_0$.

Focusing on these regimes separately, we discuss below the spectral behavior of $\mathcal{P}_\mathcal{R}$ and some of its global features.

The behaviour of late time $\mathcal{P}_\mathcal{R}$ shown in Figure 1 reflects the accuracy of the gradient expansion formalism in capturing characteristic features of the power spectrum in inflationary backgrounds that transiently violates slow-roll conditions which is required to generate PBHs.[18] In particular, we notice a pronounced dip feature occurring at relatively large scales, associated with modes that still leave the horizon in the initial slow-roll era (*i.e.* $k_{\rm dip} \ll \mathcal{H}_0$) far away from the peak, which occurs at $k_{\rm peak} \simeq 3\mathcal{H}_0$.[19] The presence of such a pronounced dip in the spectrum is a universal feature, being virtually present in all single field models based on non-attractor evolution that are aiming to generate a sizeable peak in the power spectrum for producing PBH, say of order 10^7 (see e.g.[20-29]).

The dip and its properties. It is worth mentioning that such dip feature arise due to competing contributions that appear in the power spectrum that are weighted by opposite signs.[35] The properties of the dip feature turn out to be related with global features of the spectrum profile. As shown in a recent work,[10] the location of the dip position $k_{\rm dip}$ in momentum space can be related with a characteristic pivot scale $k_\star$ associated with the duration of non-attractor evolution by the expression $k_{\rm dip}/k_\star \simeq \mathcal{O}(1) \times (\Delta\mathcal{P}_\mathcal{R}/\mathcal{P}_\mathcal{R})^{-1/4}$. For the scenarios we consider with a pronounced peak in the power spectrum, we expect $k_\star$ to be related with $k_{\rm peak}$, and $(\Delta\mathcal{P}_\mathcal{R}/\mathcal{P}_\mathcal{R})^{-1/4} \simeq (10^7)^{-1/4} \simeq 10^{-2}$. A close examination of Figure 1 confirms these arguments and shows that

$$k_{\rm dip} \simeq 10^{-2}\, k_{\rm peak} \tag{18}$$

is a robust relation, valid in all single field inflationary scenarios that can produce a pronounced peak in the power spectrum. In light of these considerations, we assume (18) for the rest of this work.

Spectral profile of the bispectrum: Let us concentrate on modes that exit during the initial slow-roll era, $k/\mathcal{H}_0 < c_k$, to investigate the scale-dependence of the bispectrum. We expect the bispectrum to have features and be amplified around the scale $k_{\rm dip}$ corresponding to the position of the dip in the power spectrum: in fact, non-linearities are usually enhanced at the location of rapid changes in the

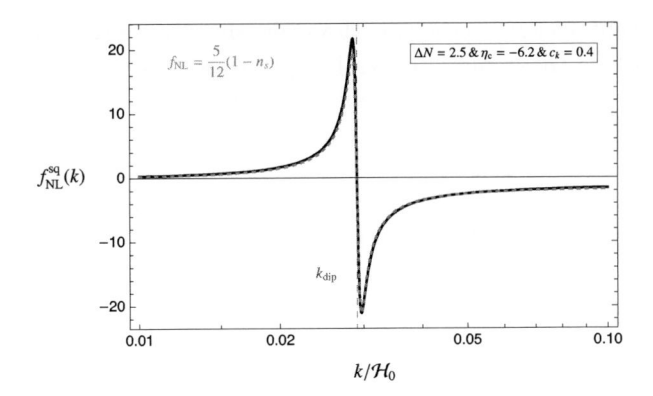

Fig. 2. Scale dependence of the non-linearity parameter $f_{\rm NL}$ around $k_{\rm dip}$ for the squeezed configuration for a transient constant-roll model that can generate a 10^7 enhancement in the power spectrum: $\{\Delta N = 2.5, \eta_c = -6.2, c_k = 0.4\}$. In the right panel, we represent the accuracy of the consistency relation $f_{\rm NL} = 5(1 - n_s)/12$ in capturing the behavior of the $f_{\rm NL}$ in the squeezed limit, using (16) and $n_s - 1 \equiv {\rm d} \ln \mathcal{P}_\mathcal{R}(\tau_f, k)/{\rm d} \ln k$.

power spectrum.[30] In what follows, we confirm this expectation for the system under consideration.

We now analyze the squeezed limit of the scale dependent non-linearity parameter[c]. For scales that exit the horizon during the initial slow-roll era, noting the scale invariance of $\mathcal{P}_\mathcal{R}(\tau_k)$ factors, we take the squeezed limit $\vec{k}_3 \to 0$ ($k_1 \simeq k_2 \equiv q$) of (14) which yields as[11,16]

$$f_{\rm NL}(q, q, k_3 \to 0) \equiv f_{\rm NL}^{\rm sq} = \frac{5}{12}\left(\frac{4\,{\rm Re}[\alpha_q^* \alpha_{k_3}]\, F(\tau_{k_q}) q^2}{|\alpha_q \alpha_{k_3}|^2}\right). \qquad (19)$$

Focusing on a representative choice of parameters that can generate an enhancement of order 10^7 in the power spectrum, in Figure 2 we plot the profile of $f_{\rm NL}$ in the squeezed configuration $k_3 \ll k_1 = k_2$ around the dip scale $k_{\rm dip}$ using (19) and with the help of formulas derived in Appendix B. We observe that the squeezed limit $f_{\rm NL}$ initially grows positive, to then rapidly decrease to negative values around $k_{\rm dip}$, and to finally increase again from negative values, almost in a symmetrical fashion. Intriguingly, as can be seen from the overlap of orange dotted curve with the black solid one in the right panel of Figure 2, the scale dependence of $f_{\rm NL}$ in the squeezed limit agrees very well with the one inferred from Maldacena's consistency condition: $f_{\rm NL} = 5(1 - n_s)/12$. The typical magnitude for the squeezed limit of $|f_{\rm NL}|$ around $k_{\rm dip}$ results of order $\mathcal{O}(10)$, compatible with the large value for the spectral tilt around the dip region.[13]

It is worth stressing that the findings we present here agree well with previous literature[34–36] that numerically studied non-Gaussianity in inflationary setups that

---

[c] A scale-dependent $f_{\rm NL}$ arises in a variety of other inflationary contexts, see e.g. the early works.[31–33]

include a transient non-attractor era. However, the main advantage of our formulas (16) and (19) is the analytic control they provide us to study features in the power and bispectrum in a model independent way without restoring to numerical techniques. In particular, these formulas are flexible enough to ensure an accurate description of the power and bispectrum in various inflationary backgrounds that exhibit a transient, slow-roll violating phase(s) characterized by two essential parameters: the duration ΔN of the non-attractor phase and the value of the slow-roll parameter $\eta_c < 0$ in this phase.

3. μT correlations as a probe of the PBH generation mechanism

In the previous section we studied scale dependence of the squeezed bispectrum around the scales corresponding to the dip scale of the power spectrum. If the dip feature occurs at relatively large scales, say $10\,\mathrm{Mpc}^{-1} \leq k_{\rm dip} \leq 10^4\,\mathrm{Mpc}^{-1}$, the properties of the resulting curvature spectrum can be probed through CMB μ−distortions, using well controlled CMB physics in the linear regime.[37–39] Building on the ideas first introduced by Pajer&Zaldarriaga,[40] this possibility was suggested in our recent work.[11] We stress that the range of scales we identified for $k_{\rm dip}$ above is well motivated for PBH populations with astrophysical masses. For example, given that $k_{\rm dip}/k_{\rm peak} \simeq 10^{-2}$ with a dip scale located around $k_{\rm dip} \simeq 10^3 - 10^4\,\mathrm{Mpc}^{-1}$ corresponds to a peak scale $k_{\rm peak} \simeq 10^5 - 10^6\,\mathrm{Mpc}^{-1}$ that correspond to the formation of PBH in the mass range[6,41] $M_{\rm pbh} \simeq 1 - 100\,M_\odot$.

We now discuss how to use the cross-correlation among CMB spectral μ distortions and temperature anisotropies for probing the statistics of curvature perturbation in inflationary scenarios capable of generating PBHs. The method we propose allows one to indirectly probe the inflationary PBH formation mechanism at relatively large scales, away from the scales where the curvature spectrum grow and has a peak. For a detailed discussion on the formulas we will introduce below, we refer the reader to the works.[11,40,42,43]

We begin by relating the initial curvature perturbation $\mathcal{R}_k$ to the spherical harmonic coefficients of the CMB temperature anisotropies $\Theta(\hat{n}) = \sum_{lm} a^T_{lm} Y_{lm}(\hat{n})$ and μ distortion anisotropies $\mu(\hat{n}) = \sum_{lm} a^\mu_{lm} Y_{lm}(\hat{n})$ which are are given by[40,42]

$$a^T_{lm} = \frac{12\pi}{5}(-i)^l \int \frac{\mathrm{d}^3 k}{(2\pi)^3}\, \mathcal{R}_k\, \Delta_l(k)\, Y^*_{lm}(\hat{k}), \tag{20}$$

$$a^\mu_{lm} \simeq 18.4\pi(-i)^l \int \frac{\mathrm{d}^3 k_1\, \mathrm{d}^3 k_2}{(2\pi)^6} Y^*_{lm}(\hat{k}_+)\, \mathcal{R}_{k_1}\, \mathcal{R}_{k_2}\, W\left(\frac{k_+}{k_s}\right) j_l\,(k_+ \chi_*)$$
$$\times \langle \cos(c_s k_1 \tau) \cos(c_s k_2 \tau)\rangle_p \left[e^{-(k_1^2 + k_2^2)/k_D^2}\right]^{z_i}_{z_f}, \tag{21}$$

where p denotes time averaging over the period acoustic oscillations; $\vec{k}_+ \equiv \vec{k}_1 + \vec{k}_2$; c_s is the sound speed of the radiation perturbations; $\chi_* = \tau_0 - \tau_* \simeq 14\,\mathrm{Gpc}$ is the comoving distance between the last scattering surface and today; and

$\Delta_l(k)$ is the transfer function during radiation domination. Furthermore, in (21), $W(k) = 3k^{-3}[\sin(k) - k\cos(k)]$ is a top-hat filter function in Fourier space that smears the dissipated energy over a volume of radius $k_s^{-1} \gtrsim k_D(z_f)^{-1}$ where k_D denotes the diffusion damping scale during a radiation dominated universe. It depends on redshift as $k_D(z) \simeq [(1+z)/10^5]^{3/2}\, 130\,\mathrm{Mpc}^{-1}$ where the range of redshifts associated with the μ distortions are given by

$$z_f \equiv 5 \times 10^4 < z < 2 \times 10^6 \equiv z_i. \tag{22}$$

We then define angular correlators involving anisotropies labeled by $\{i,j\}$ as

$$\left\langle (a_{lm}^i)^* a_{l'm'}^j \right\rangle = \delta_{ll'}\delta_{mm'} C_l^{ij}, \qquad i = \mu, T. \tag{23}$$

In the following discussion, we make use of the definition (23) to study angular correlations $\langle \mu T \rangle$ and to relate them to scale dependent bispectrum present around the dip scale of the PBH forming inflationary scenarios.

Using the definition (11) of the bispectrum together with (20) and (21), the cross correlations $C_l^{\mu T}$ for a squeezed bispectrum $(\vec{k}_+ = \vec{k}_1 + \vec{k}_2 \to 0)$ can be expressed as,[40,42]

$$C_l^{\mu T} \simeq \frac{27.6}{20\pi^3} \int d\ln k_+ \, \Delta_l(k_+)\, j_l(k_+\chi_*) \tag{24}$$

$$\times \int d\ln q \left[k_+^3 q^3 B_\mathcal{R}(q,q,k_+ \to 0)\right] \left[e^{-2q^2/k_D^2(z)}\right]_{z_f}^{z_i},$$

where we take the filter function $W \to 1$ in the squeezed limit $k_+ \ll k_s \simeq k_D(z_f)$, and relabel $|\vec{k}_1| \simeq |-\vec{k}_2| \equiv q$. Using the general definition (13) of the non-linearity parameter, the squeezed limit bispectrum inside the $d\ln q$ integral in (24) can be expressed as

$$B_\mathcal{R}(q,q,k_+ \to 0) \simeq \frac{12}{5} \underbrace{f_{\rm NL}^{\rm sq}(q)|\alpha_q|^2|\alpha_{k_+}|^2}_{\equiv f_{\rm NL}^{\rm eff}(q)} \mathcal{P}_\mathcal{R}(\tau_q)\mathcal{P}_\mathcal{R}(\tau_{k_+}). \tag{25}$$

In (25), we defined the bispectrum in terms of the two copies of the power spectrum evaluated at around horizon crossing τ_k in the initial slow-roll era. Notice that with this parametrization, (25) represent the scale dependent generalization of the purely local bispectrum through the scale dependent $f_{\rm NL}^{\rm eff}(q)$.

Noticing that $P_\mathcal{R}(\tau_p) = 2\pi^2 \mathcal{P}_\mathcal{R}(\tau_p)/p^3$ and $\mathcal{P}_\mathcal{R}(\tau_p) \simeq 2.1 \times 10^{-9}$ for mode exit during the initial slow-roll era (see e.g. (A.3)), we insert (25) in (24) to express the angular cross correlation as

$$C_l^{\mu T} \simeq 2.7 \times 10^{-17} \frac{2\pi}{l(l+1)} b_{\rm (pbh)}(l), \tag{26}$$

where we define

$$b_{\rm (pbh)}(l) \equiv \frac{6l(l+1)}{\ln\left(\frac{k_D(z_i)}{k_D(z_f)}\right)} \int d\ln k_+ \, \Delta_l(k_+)\, j_l(k_+\chi_*) \int d\ln q \, f_{\rm NL}^{\rm eff}(q) \left[e^{-2q^2/k_D^2(z)}\right]_{z_f}^{z_i}. \tag{27}$$

as the key quantity that determines the multipole dependence and the size of the $\langle \mu T \rangle$ correlator of Eq. (26). Notice that this quantity depends on the transfer function $\Delta_l(k)$ which we decompose as[43]

$$\Delta_l(k) = \rho(l) \Delta_l^{(\text{SW})}(k). \quad (28)$$

$\Delta_l^{(\text{SW})}(k)$ is the transfer function in the large-scale Sachs-Wolfe (SW) limit $l \to 0$,

$$\Delta_l^{(\text{SW})}(k) = \frac{1}{3} j_l(k\chi_*), \quad (29)$$

and

$$\rho(l) \simeq 1.08 \left[1 - 0.022 l - 1.72 \times 10^{-4} l^2 + 2 \times 10^{-6} l^3 - 4.56 \times 10^{-9} l^4 \right], \quad (30)$$

is an analytic fit that includes high-l corrections to the SW approximation.[43] Using (28) and (29), we can then simply take the integral over the long momenta k_+ in (27) and factorize the outcome as

$$b_{(\text{pbh})}(l) = \rho(l) b_{(\text{pbh})}^{(\text{SW})}, \quad (31)$$

with

$$b_{(\text{pbh})}^{(\text{SW})} = \left[\ln \left(\frac{k_D(z_i)}{k_D(z_f)} \right) \right]^{-1} \int d\ln q \, f_{\text{NL}}^{\text{eff}}(q) \left[e^{-2q^2/k_D^2(z)} \right]_{z_f}^{z_i}. \quad (32)$$

Notice that for a purely local spectrum with constant non-linearity parameter, i.e. $f_{\text{NL}}^{\text{eff}}(q) \to f_{\text{NL}}^{(p)}$, we get $b_{(\text{pbh})}^{\text{sw}} = f_{\text{NL}}^{(p)}$ and hence reproduce the standard results derived for $C_l^{\mu T}$ in the SW limit.[40,42] However, $b_{(\text{pbh})}^{\text{sw}}$ can not influence the l dependence of the angular correlator $C_l^{\mu T}$ (26) but it can significantly influence its overall amplitude through a non-trivial scale dependence of $f_{\text{NL}}^{\text{eff}}$. We will concretely see an example of this fact in the PBH forming inflationary scenarios below.

Using the analytic formulas we provide in Appendix A, B, we derive an analytic expression for the scale dependence of the effective non-linearity parameter $f_{\text{NL}}^{\text{eff}}$ (25) in Appendix C. In this way, we compute the expression (32) analytically to obtain

$$\frac{b_{(\text{pbh})}^{(\text{SW})}}{f_{\text{NL}}^{(p)}} = 1 + \frac{1}{\ln \left(\frac{k_D(z_i)}{k_D(z_f)} \right)} \sum_{n=2}^{6} c_{\text{NL}}^{(n)} \frac{\Gamma(n/2)}{2^{(n+2)/2}} \left(\frac{k_D(z)}{\mathcal{H}_0} \right)^n \bigg|_{z_f}^{z_i}, \quad (33)$$

where the dependence of the coefficients $c_{\text{NL}}^{(n)}$ on the background parameters in the non-attractor era, i.e. $\{\eta_c, \Delta N\}$ can be obtained from the formulas we provide in Appendix C, B and A. Armed with (33), we can quantify the extent of which the scale dependence in the bispectrum can influence the μT angular correlator $C_l^{\mu T}$. For this purpose, we use (33) to compute $b_{(\text{pbh})}^{(\text{SW})}$ in terms of the location of the dip in momentum space k_{dip} by noting the relationship $\mathcal{H}_0 \simeq 100 k_{\text{dip}}/3 \simeq 33 \, k_{\text{dip}}$ we derived in Section 2.1. The resulting dependence of $b_{(\text{pbh})}^{(\text{SW})}$ on the location of the dip feature k_{dip} is shown in Figure 3 for two different choices of parameter set that describes an inflationary model including a transient non-attractor era. We observe

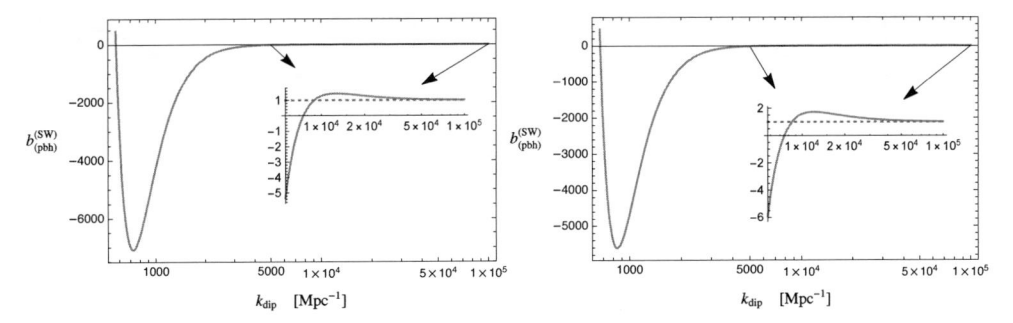

Fig. 3. Parameter $b^{(\text{SW})}_{(\text{pbh})}$ (33) for $f^{(\text{p})}_{\text{NL}} = 1$ as a function of the location of the dip feature $k_{\text{dip}} \simeq 3\mathcal{H}_0/100$ in an inflationary model that contains a transient non-attractor phase parametrized by the parameter sets $\{\Delta N = 2.6, \eta_c = -6, c_k = 0.5\}$ (Left) and $\{\Delta N = 2.5, \eta_c = -6.2, c_k = 0.4\}$ (Right).

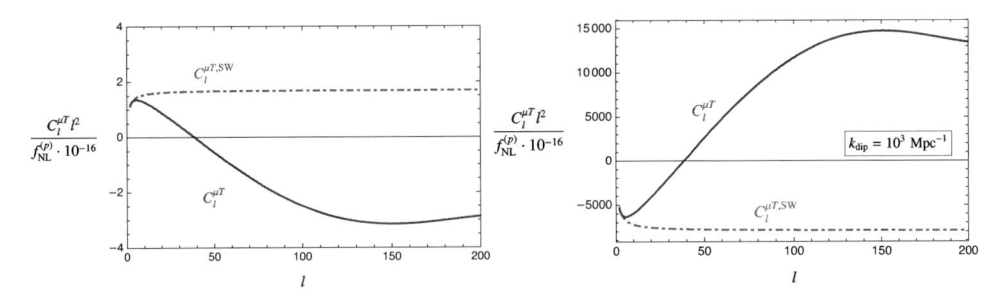

Fig. 4. Multipole dependence of $C^{\mu T}_l$ for a purely local type bispectrum (Left) and for a PBH forming inflationary scenario that contains a transient constant-roll era ($\eta_c = -6.2$) that has a duration of $\Delta N = 2.5$ e-folds and with a dip feature that is located at $k_{\text{dip}} = 10^3 \, \text{Mpc}^{-1}$ (Right).

that for phenomenologically interesting values of k_{dip}, $b^{(\text{SW})}_{(\text{pbh})}$ obtains *large negative* values and hence can alter the *overall amplitude* and *sign* of the $\langle \mu T \rangle$ correlator significantly, in particular compared to a inflationary scenario endowed with a purely local type bispectrum where $b^{(\text{SW})} \to f^{(\text{p})}_{\text{NL}}$.[40]

To further illustrate these points, in Figure 4 we present the multipole dependence of $C^{\mu T}_l$ (26) for a purely local bispectrum and for an inflationary model that contains an intermediate non-attractor phase where we show the resulting angular correlator for both within the Sachs-Wolfe approximation (dot-dashed line), and by taking into account full transfer effects (solid line). We observe that compared to the scale independent local bispectrum case (left panel in Figure 4), the overall amplitude of the angular correlator is enhanced significantly and its behavior from large to small scales is inverted due to the large negative $b^{(\text{SW})}_{(\text{pbh})}$ acquires for the $k_{\text{dip}} = 10^3 \, \text{Mpc}^{-1}$. In other words, for a PBH forming inflationary scenario, μ distortions become anti-correlated with temperature anisotropies at large scales contrary to the case arise for a scale independent local bispectrum. It is worth stressing that this behavior arise because in PBH forming inflationary scenarios,

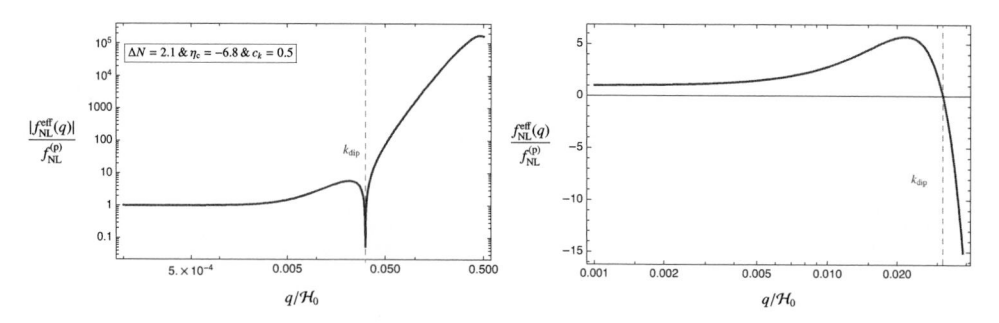

Fig. 5. Scale dependence of the effective non-linearity parameter $f_{\rm NL}^{\rm eff}$ (25) in the squeezed limit $k_3/q \to 0$ for an inflationary model that exhibit an intermediate constant-roll phase $\eta_c = -6.8$ that lasts $\Delta N = 2.1$ e-folds.

the effective scale dependent bispectrum changes sign around the dip feature and grows large in the negative direction as we show in the right panel of Figure 5. This result is interesting on its own as one can in principle distinguish between these scenarios by just looking at the sign of the $C_l^{\mu T}$ at large scales at small l. In summary, our results imply that phases of non-attractor inflation can qualitatively and quantitatively change the properties of the cross-correlations between CMB temperature anisotropies and μ-type distortions.

3.1. *Prospects of detectability for* $\langle \mu T \rangle$

To assess the prospects of detectability for the μT correlator, we now estimate the cumulative signal-to-noise ratio, S/N using[42]

$$\left(\frac{S}{N}\right)^2 = \sum_{l=2}^{l_{\max}} (2l+1) \frac{\left(C_l^{\mu T}\right)^2}{C_l^{TT} C_l^{\mu\mu,N}}, \qquad (34)$$

where C_l^{TT} is the CMB temperature anisotropy power spectrum and $C_l^{\mu\mu,N}$ is the noise level for μ distortions. For an experiment as PIXIE[44] the noise is given by $C_l^{\mu\mu,N} \simeq 4\pi\, \mu_{\min}^2\, e^{l^2/84^2}$ [40] where $\mu_{\min}$ denotes the minimum detectable μ distortion signal. Using (20), we denote the TT correlator in (34) as

$$C_l^{TT} = \frac{36\pi}{25} \int d\ln k\, \mathcal{P}_\mathcal{R}(k) \Delta_l^2(k). \qquad (35)$$

Therefore to estimate the S/N, we require the full knowledge the of the transfer function Δ_l in (35). Taking these effects into account, it was found that the signal to noise ratio can be estimated as 40% of the result that one would obtain by adopting the SW limit,[42,43] adopting $\rho_l \to 1$, $C_l^{TT,\rm SW} = 2\pi \mathcal{P}_\mathcal{R}^{(0)}/(25\,l(l+1))$ [d]. Following the

---

[d]Note that the smallest scales we are interested corresponds to $l_{\max} = 200$, so we can safely assume the scale indepedent part of the power spectrum in (35) although it has non-trivial scale dependence (enhancement) at much smaller scales for inflationary scenarios we are interested in this work.

discussion above, we carry the sum in (34) up to $l_\text{max} = 200$ using (26) and (31) to obtain[11]

$$\left(\frac{S}{N}\right) \simeq 0.35 \times 10^{-3} |f_\text{NL}^{(\text{p})} b_{(\text{pbh})}^{(\text{SW})}| \left(\frac{10^{-8}}{\mu_\text{min}}\right). \tag{36}$$

This result implies that $|f_\text{NL}^{(\text{p})} b_{(\text{pbh})}^{(\text{SW})}| \gtrsim 2892$ should be observable for a PIXIE like experiment. On the other hand, for a spectrometer comparable to PRISM[45] with $\mu_\text{min} = 10^{-9}$, $|f_\text{NL}^{(\text{p})} b_{(\text{pbh})}^{(\text{SW})}| \gtrsim 290$ is required for the detectability. At this point, it is worth mentioning that for a local type $f_\text{NL}^{(\text{p})} \sim 10^{-2}$ at CMB scales as predicted by standard slow-roll backgrounds, such a signal would be challenging to detect.

On the other hand, considering the 2σ limits on the local type bispectrum by Planck[46] at CMB scales: $-11.1 < f_\text{NL}^{(\text{p})} < 9.3$ ($f_\text{NL}^{(\text{p})} = -0.9 \pm 5.1$, 68%CL) and the typical values of $|b_{(\text{pbh})}^{(\text{SW})}| \simeq$ a few $(10^2 - 10^3)$ that can be obtained in inflationary scenarios that can generate PBH populations (See figure 3), we conclude that the impact of the scale dependent non-Gaussianity on the $\langle \mu T \rangle$ correlator should be observable by PIXIE or PRISM for an interesting range of k_dip values relevant for the formation of PBHs within the mass range $M_\text{pbh} \simeq 1 - 100\, M_\odot$.

4. Discussion

We presented a method for probing inflationary scenarios of PBH formation, using only CMB physics at relatively large scales. We based our arguments on the characteristic properties of the spectrum of curvature perturbation in single-field inflationary models that can generate a large population of PBHs. In these models, the curvature perturbation spectrum is characterized by a pronounced dip followed by a rapid growth towards a peak responsible for PBH formation. By making use of the gradient expansion formalism,[12] we analytically computed the properties of the power spectrum and for the first time of the bispectrum around the dip position, which occurs at scales well larger than the peak. Focussing our attention to the squeezed configuration, we found that the bispectrum can be enhanced around the position of the dip; it also acquires a characteristic momentum dependence that is controlled by the underlying inflationary mechanism. Here, we propose to probe such an enhanced squeezed bispectrum through the correlations it induces between CMB μ-distortions and CMB temperature fluctuations. For this purpose, we extended the methods first explored in[40] to include the case of scale-dependent non-Gaussianity from PBH formation mechanisms, finding analytical expression for quantities controlling μT correlations, and discussing how future CMB μ-distortion experiments can test this observable. Interestingly, the method we propose would allow one to experimentally probe inflationary PBH scenarios using well-understood CMB physics at scales much larger than the peak of the spectrum, without considering non-linearities associated with PBH formation and evolution. In particular, owing the relation between relevant scales associated with μ distortions and the features present in the PBH forming inflationary scenarios, our findings are relevant for PBH masses within the $M_{\rm pbh} \sim 1 - 100 M_\odot$. These finding suggest that μT correlations can be used as a useful tool to distinguish between astrophysical vs primordial origin of BHs.

Acknowledgments

The work of OÖ is supported by the European Structural and Investment Funds and the Czech Ministry of Education, Youth and Sports (Project CoGraDS-CZ.02.1.01/0.0/0.0/15003/0000437). GT is partially funded by the STFC grant ST/T000813/1.

Appendix A. The power spectrum $\mathcal{P}_\mathcal{R}(\tau_k)$ and fractional velocity $v_\mathcal{R}$

For the initial slow-roll phase, the solution for the curvature perturbation that reduces to the standard Bunch Davies vacuum can be written as[13]

$$\mathcal{R}_k^{\rm sr} = \frac{iH}{M_{\rm pl}} \frac{e^{-ik\tau}}{\sqrt{4\epsilon_{\rm sr} k^3}} (1 + ik\tau), \qquad \tau_k/\tau_0 > 1, \tag{A.1}$$

where $\epsilon_{\rm sr} \ll 1$ is the slow-roll parameter in the initial slow-roll stage which we assume to be constant. Using the solution (A.1) in the definition, the real and imaginary part of the fractional velocity (evaluated at $\tau = \tau_k$) can be obtained as

$$v_\mathcal{R}^R(c_k) = -\frac{c_k^2}{3(1+c_k^2)}, \quad v_\mathcal{R}^I(c_k) = -\frac{c_k^3}{3(1+c_k^2)}, \qquad \tau_k/\tau_0 > 1, \tag{A.2}$$

where c_k is defined in (17). It is clear from (A.2) that the imaginary part of $v_\mathcal{R}$ includes an extra factor of c_k compared to the real part. We note that unless $c_k = 1$, this translates into an extra suppression for the imaginary part of the fractional velocity.

On the other hand, using (A.1), the power spectrum evaluated at around horizon crossing is given by

$$\mathcal{P}_\mathcal{R}(\tau_k) = \frac{k^3}{2\pi^2} |\mathcal{R}_k(\tau_k)|^2 = \frac{H^2}{8\pi^2 \epsilon_{\rm sr} M_{\rm pl}^2} (1 + c_k^2), \qquad \tau_k/\tau_0 > 1. \tag{A.3}$$

Next, we need to develop an expression for $\mathcal{R}(\tau_k)$ and the fractional velocity continuous through the transition at $\tau = \tau_0$. This was done using a matching procedure for $\mathcal{R}_k$ and its derivative in[11] which gives

$$\mathcal{R}_k = \frac{iH}{M_{\rm pl}} \frac{(\tau/\tau_0)^{n_c/2}}{\sqrt{4\epsilon_{\rm sr} k^3}} (-k\tau)^{3/2} \left[c_1 H_\nu^{(1)}(-k\tau) + c_2 H_\nu^{(2)}(-k\tau) \right], \qquad \tau_k/\tau_0 < 1. \tag{A.4}$$

where $\nu = (3+\eta_c)/2$. The scale dependent coefficients are given by

$$c_1 = y_0^{3/2} e^{iy_0} \frac{y_0 \left(H_\nu^{(2)}(y_0) + iH_{\nu-1}^{(2)}(y_0)\right) - H_{\nu-1}^{(2)}(y_0)}{H_{\nu-1}^{(1)}(y_0)H_\nu^{(2)}(y_0) - H_\nu^{(1)}(y_0)H_{\nu-1}^{(2)}(y_0)}, \qquad (A.5)$$

$$c_2 = y_0^{3/2} e^{iy_0} \frac{(y_0)\left(H_\nu^{(1)}(y_0) + iH_{\nu-1}^{(1)}(y_0)\right) - H_{\nu-1}^{(1)}(y_0)}{H_\nu^{(1)}(y_0)H_{\nu-1}^{(2)}(y_0) - H_\nu^{(2)}(y_0)H_{\nu-1}^{(1)}(y_0)}. \qquad (A.6)$$

where we defined $y \equiv -k\tau$. Then for $\tau_k/\tau_0 < 1$, the real and the imaginary part of the fractional velocity can be obtained as

$$v_{\mathcal{R}}^R(\tau) = -\frac{y}{3}\left[\frac{f_1 f_3 - y_0(f_1 f_4 + f_2 f_3) + y_0^2(f_1 f_3 + f_2 f_4)}{f_3^2 - 2y_0 f_3 f_4 + y_0^2(f_3^2 + f_4^2)}\right], \qquad (A.7)$$

$$v_{\mathcal{R}}^I(\tau) = -\frac{y}{3}\left[\frac{y_0^2(f_1 f_4 - f_2 f_3)}{f_3^2 - 2y_0 f_3 f_4 + y_0^2(f_3^2 + f_4^2)}\right], \qquad (A.8)$$

where we define the functions $f_n = f_n(y, y_0, \nu)$, for $n = 1, 2, 3, 4$ in terms of the Bessel function of the first and second kind as

$$f_1(y, y_0, \nu) = J_{\nu-1}(y_0)Y_{\nu-1}(y) - Y_{\nu-1}(y_0)J_{\nu-1}(y),$$
$$f_2(y, y_0, \nu) = J_\nu(y_0)Y_{\nu-1}(y) - Y_\nu(y_0)J_{\nu-1}(y). \qquad (A.9)$$

Furthermore, we note the following relations $f_4 = f_1(y, y_0, \nu+1)$, $f_3 = -f_2(y_0, y, \nu)$. The continuity of the real and the imaginary part of the fractional velocity can be confirmed explicitly from the eqs in (A.7) and (A.8) as they reduce to their slow-roll counterparts provided in (A.2) at the transition point $\tau_k = \tau_0$. Using the relations we noted earlier, power spectrum evaluated at $\tau = \tau_k$ for modes that leave the horizon during the non-attractor phase ($\tau_k/\tau_0 < 1$) can be obtained as

$$\mathcal{P}_{\mathcal{R}}(\tau_k) = \frac{H^2}{8\pi^2 \epsilon_{\rm sr} M_{\rm pl}^2} \frac{c_k^{2\nu} \pi^2}{4} \left(\frac{k}{\mathcal{H}_0}\right)^{2-2\nu} \left[f_3^2 - 2y_0 f_3 f_4 + y_0^2(f_3^2 + f_4^2)\right]_{\tau=\tau_k}. \qquad (A.10)$$

Similarly, the continuity of the power spectrum can be confirmed explicitly by evaluating (A.10) at the transition point $\tau_k = \tau_0$ at which it reduced to (A.3).

Appendix B. The functions $D(\tau_k)$, $F_k(\tau_k)$

For the two phase background model parametrized by the pump field profile in Eq. (15), scale dependent functions $D(\tau_k)$, $F(\tau_k)$ (see Eqs. (6) and (7)) are calculated in[13] for modes that exit during the initial slow-roll era ($k/\mathcal{H}_0 < c_k$) and in[11] for mode exit during the non-attractor era ($e^{\Delta N} > k/\mathcal{H}_0 > c_k$). Below, we present the explicit formulas for these functions for both stages of inflationary evolution.

$$D(\tau_k) \equiv \mathcal{C}_0^D + \mathcal{C}_3^D \left(\frac{k}{\mathcal{H}_0}\right)^3, \tag{B.1}$$

$$\frac{F(\tau_k)}{\tau_0^2} \equiv \mathcal{C}_{-2}^F \left(\frac{k}{\mathcal{H}_0}\right)^{-2} + \mathcal{C}_0^F + \mathcal{C}_1^F \left(\frac{k}{\mathcal{H}_0}\right), \qquad \frac{k}{\mathcal{H}_0} < c_k,$$

where the coefficients are given by

$$\mathcal{C}_0^D = 1, \qquad \mathcal{C}_3^D \simeq -\frac{3\,e^{-(\eta_c+3)\Delta N}}{(\eta_c+3)c_k^3}, \qquad \mathcal{C}_{-2}^F = \frac{c_k^2}{6},$$

$$\mathcal{C}_0^F \simeq -\frac{\eta_c\, e^{-(\eta_c+3)\Delta N}}{(\eta_c+3)(\eta_c+1)}, \qquad \mathcal{C}_1^F \simeq \frac{e^{-(\eta_c+3)\Delta N}}{c_k(\eta_c+3)} \tag{B.2}$$

where $\tau_f/\tau_0 \equiv x_f = e^{-\Delta N}$ with ΔN denoting the duration of the slow-roll violating ($\eta_c \leq -6$) era. On the other hand, for modes that leave the horizon during the non-attractor era, we have

$$D(\tau_k) \equiv \tilde{\mathcal{C}}_{\eta_c+3}^D \left(\frac{k}{\mathcal{H}_0}\right)^{\eta_c+3} + \tilde{\mathcal{C}}_0^D \tag{B.3}$$

$$\frac{F(\tau_k)}{\tau_0^2} \equiv \tilde{\mathcal{C}}_{\eta_c+1}^F \left(\frac{k}{\mathcal{H}_0}\right)^{\eta_c+1} + \tilde{\mathcal{C}}_{-2}^F \left(\frac{k}{\mathcal{H}_0}\right)^{-2} + \tilde{\mathcal{C}}_0^F, \qquad c_k < \frac{k}{\mathcal{H}_0} < e^{\Delta N}$$

where

$$\tilde{\mathcal{C}}_{\eta_c+3}^D = -\frac{3\,e^{-(\eta_c+3)\Delta N}}{(\eta_c+3)c_k^{\eta_c+3}}, \qquad \tilde{\mathcal{C}}_0^D = -\frac{3}{\eta_c+3}, \qquad \tilde{\mathcal{C}}_0^F = \frac{e^{-2\Delta N}}{2(\eta_c+1)},$$

$$\tilde{\mathcal{C}}_{-2}^F = \frac{c_k^2}{2(\eta_c+3)}, \qquad \tilde{\mathcal{C}}_{\eta_c+1}^F = \frac{e^{-(\eta_c+3)\Delta N}}{(\eta_c+1)(\eta_c+3)c_k^{\eta_c+1}}. \tag{B.4}$$

Appendix C. $f_{\rm NL}^{\rm eff}$ in the squeezed limit

Using the definition (25) with (19), for mode exit during the initial slow-roll era, the squeezed limit effective non-linearity parameter is given by

$$f_{\rm NL}^{\rm eff} = \frac{5}{3}\left({\rm Re}[\alpha_q^* \alpha_{k_3}]\, F(\tau_{k_q}) q^2\right). \tag{C.1}$$

From (C.1), one can show that in the large scale tail of the squeezed limit, i.e. $q > k_+$ as $q \to 0$, $f_{\rm NL}^{\rm eff}$ obtains an "initial" value $f_{\rm NL}^{(0)} = 5 c_{\rm NL}^{(0)}(c_q)/3$ where $c_{\rm NL}^{(0)} \simeq (1 + v_{\mathcal{R}}^R - \mathcal{C}_{-2}^F)^2 \mathcal{C}_{-2}^F$. Since, we send $q \to 0$ to reach this initial value, we do not expect that $f_{\rm NL}^{(0)}$ can reflect an accurate initial value for the squeezed configuration of (C.1). To keep our discussion on the observability of $\langle \mu T \rangle$ (see Section 3.1) as general as possible, we therefore replace this initial value with a fiducial primordial $f_{\rm NL}^{(P)}$ to characterize the effective non-linearity parameter at large scales, i.e. at CMB scales. Using the formulas we derived for the functions $D(\tau_k), F(\tau_k)$ above and the definitions of the enhancement factor α_k in eqs.(3) and (4), at leading order in the $k_+/q \ll 1$ expansion, we can then express $f_{\rm NL}^{\rm eff}$ in terms of simple power law expansion as[11]

$$f_{\rm NL}^{\rm eff} \simeq f_{\rm NL}^{(\rm p)}\left[1 + \sum_{n=2}^{6} c_{\rm NL}^{(n)}(\eta_c, \Delta N, c_q)\left(\frac{q}{\mathcal{H}_0}\right)^n\right] + \mathcal{O}\left(\frac{k_+}{q}\right). \quad (\text{C.2})$$

The coefficients $c_{\rm NL}^{(n)}$ of this expansion can be expressed in terms of the coefficients $\mathcal{C}$ of the F, D functions of Appendix B and the fractional velocities $v_\mathcal{R}^R, v_\mathcal{R}^I$ we defined in (A.2) as

$$c_{\rm NL}^{(0)} \simeq (1 + v_\mathcal{R}^R - \mathcal{C}_{-2}^F)^2 \mathcal{C}_{-2}^F, \quad c_{\rm NL}^{(2)} \simeq \frac{\mathcal{C}_0^F}{\mathcal{C}_{-2}^F}, \quad c_{\rm NL}^{(3)} \simeq \frac{\mathcal{C}_1^F}{\mathcal{C}_{-2}^F} \quad (\text{C.3})$$

$$c_{\rm NL}^{(4)} = -\frac{(\mathcal{C}_0^F)^2}{\mathcal{C}_{-2}^F(1 + v_\mathcal{R}^R - \mathcal{C}_{-2}^F)}, \quad c_{\rm NL}^{(5)} \simeq (1 + v_\mathcal{R}^R - \mathcal{C}_{-2}^F)\left[v_\mathcal{R}^R \mathcal{C}_3^D - 2\mathcal{C}_1^F\right]\mathcal{C}_0^F, \quad (\text{C.4})$$

$$c_{\rm NL}^{(6)} \simeq (1 + v_\mathcal{R}^R - \mathcal{C}_{-2}^F)\left[v_\mathcal{R}^R \mathcal{C}_3^D - \mathcal{C}_1^F\right]\mathcal{C}_1^F, \quad (\text{C.5})$$

where we neglected terms proportional to $v_\mathcal{R}^I$ for $c_k \ll 1$ because in this regime $v_\mathcal{R}^R \gg v_\mathcal{R}^I$ as can be realized from (A.2).

References

1. S. Hawking, Gravitationally collapsed objects of very low mass, *Mon. Not. Roy. Astron. Soc.* **152**, p. 75 (1971).
2. B. J. Carr and S. W. Hawking, Black holes in the early Universe, *Mon. Not. Roy. Astron. Soc.* **168**, 399 (1974).
3. B. J. Carr, The Primordial black hole mass spectrum, *Astrophys. J.* **201**, 1 (1975).
4. B. Carr, F. Kuhnel and M. Sandstad, Primordial Black Holes as Dark Matter, *Phys. Rev.* **D94**, p. 083504 (2016).
5. M. Sasaki, T. Suyama, T. Tanaka and S. Yokoyama, Primordial black holes—perspectives in gravitational wave astronomy, *Class. Quant. Grav.* **35**, p. 063001 (2018).
6. B. Carr and F. Kuhnel, Primordial Black Holes as Dark Matter: Recent Developments, *Ann. Rev. Nucl. Part. Sci.* **70**, 355 (2020).
7. A. M. Green and B. J. Kavanagh, Primordial Black Holes as a dark matter candidate, *J. Phys. G* **48**, p. 4 (2021).
8. C. Germani and I. Musco, Abundance of Primordial Black Holes Depends on the Shape of the Inflationary Power Spectrum, *Phys. Rev. Lett.* **122**, p. 141302 (2019).
9. C. T. Byrnes, P. S. Cole and S. P. Patil, Steepest growth of the power spectrum and primordial black holes, *JCAP* **1906**, p. 028 (2019).
10. G. Tasinato, An analytic approach to non-slow-roll inflation, *Phys. Rev. D* **103**, p. 023535 (2021).
11. O. Özsoy and G. Tasinato, CMB μT cross correlations as a probe of primordial black hole scenarios, *Phys. Rev. D* **104**, p. 043526 (2021).
12. S. M. Leach, M. Sasaki, D. Wands and A. R. Liddle, Enhancement of superhorizon scale inflationary curvature perturbations, *Phys. Rev.* **D64**, p. 023512 (2001).
13. O. Özsoy and G. Tasinato, On the slope of the curvature power spectrum in non-attractor inflation, *JCAP* **04**, p. 048 (2020).

14. M. Mylova, O. Özsoy, S. Parameswaran, G. Tasinato and I. Zavala, A new mechanism to enhance primordial tensor fluctuations in single field inflation, *JCAP* **1812**, p. 024 (2018).
15. O. Ozsoy, M. Mylova, S. Parameswaran, C. Powell, G. Tasinato and I. Zavala, Squeezed tensor non-Gaussianity in non-attractor inflation, *JCAP* **1909**, p. 036 (2019).
16. Y.-i. Takamizu, S. Mukohyama, M. Sasaki and Y. Tanaka, Non-Gaussianity of super-horizon curvature perturbations beyond δ N formalism, *JCAP* **1006**, p. 019 (2010).
17. Y.-i. Takamizu, Application of beyond δN formalism: Varying sound speed, *Phys. Rev. D* **89**, p. 043528 (2014).
18. H. Motohashi and W. Hu, Primordial Black Holes and Slow-Roll Violation, *Phys. Rev.* **D96**, p. 063503 (2017).
19. M. Biagetti, G. Franciolini, A. Kehagias and A. Riotto, Primordial Black Holes from Inflation and Quantum Diffusion, *JCAP* **1807**, p. 032 (2018).
20. J. Garcia-Bellido and E. Ruiz Morales, Primordial black holes from single field models of inflation, *Phys. Dark Univ.* **18**, 47 (2017).
21. J. M. Ezquiaga, J. Garcia-Bellido and E. Ruiz Morales, Primordial Black Hole production in Critical Higgs Inflation, *Phys. Lett.* **B776**, 345 (2018).
22. G. Ballesteros and M. Taoso, Primordial black hole dark matter from single field inflation, *Phys. Rev.* **D97**, p. 023501 (2018).
23. M. P. Hertzberg and M. Yamada, Primordial Black Holes from Polynomial Potentials in Single Field Inflation, *Phys. Rev.* **D97**, p. 083509 (2018).
24. M. Cicoli, V. A. Diaz and F. G. Pedro, Primordial Black Holes from String Inflation, *JCAP* **1806**, p. 034 (2018).
25. O. Ozsoy, S. Parameswaran, G. Tasinato and I. Zavala, Mechanisms for Primordial Black Hole Production in String Theory, *JCAP* **1807**, p. 005 (2018).
26. R. Mahbub, Primordial black hole formation in inflationary α-attractor models, *Phys. Rev. D* **101**, p. 023533 (2020).
27. G. Ballesteros, J. Rey, M. Taoso and A. Urbano, Primordial black holes as dark matter and gravitational waves from single-field polynomial inflation, *JCAP* **07**, p. 025 (2020).
28. J. Liu, Z.-K. Guo and R.-G. Cai, Analytical approximation of the scalar spectrum in the ultraslow-roll inflationary models, *Phys. Rev. D* **101**, p. 083535 (2020).
29. K. Kefala, G. P. Kodaxis, I. D. Stamou and N. Tetradis, Features of the inflaton potential and the power spectrum of cosmological perturbations (10 2020).
30. J. Chluba, J. Hamann and S. P. Patil, Features and New Physical Scales in Primordial Observables: Theory and Observation, *Int. J. Mod. Phys.* **D24**, p. 1530023 (2015).
31. X. Chen, Running non-Gaussianities in DBI inflation, *Phys. Rev.* **D72**, p. 123518 (2005).
32. C. T. Byrnes, S. Nurmi, G. Tasinato and D. Wands, Scale dependence of local fNL, *JCAP* **1002**, p. 034 (2010).
33. C. T. Byrnes, M. Gerstenlauer, S. Nurmi, G. Tasinato and D. Wands, Scale-dependent non-Gaussianity probes inflationary physics, *JCAP* **1010**, p. 004 (2010).
34. V. Atal and C. Germani, The role of non-gaussianities in Primordial Black Hole formation, *Phys. Dark Univ.* **24**, p. 100275 (2019).
35. S. Passaglia, W. Hu and H. Motohashi, Primordial black holes and local non-Gaussianity in canonical inflation, *Phys. Rev. D* **99**, p. 043536 (2019).
36. Q. Gao, Primordial black holes and secondary gravitational waves from chaotic inflation (2 2021).
37. W. Hu, D. Scott and J. Silk, Power spectrum constraints from spectral distortions in the cosmic microwave background, *Astrophys. J. Lett.* **430**, L5 (1994).

38. R. Khatri, R. A. Sunyaev and J. Chluba, Does Bose-Einstein condensation of CMB photons cancel \mu distortions created by dissipation of sound waves in the early Universe?, *Astron. Astrophys.* **540**, p. A124 (2012).
39. J. Chluba and R. A. Sunyaev, The evolution of CMB spectral distortions in the early Universe, *Mon. Not. Roy. Astron. Soc.* **419**, 1294 (2012).
40. E. Pajer and M. Zaldarriaga, A New Window on Primordial non-Gaussianity, *Phys. Rev. Lett.* **109**, p. 021302 (2012).
41. J. García-Bellido, Massive Primordial Black Holes as Dark Matter and their detection with Gravitational Waves, *J. Phys. Conf. Ser.* **840**, p. 012032 (2017).
42. J. Ganc and E. Komatsu, Scale-dependent bias of galaxies and mu-type distortion of the cosmic microwave background spectrum from single-field inflation with a modified initial state, *Phys. Rev. D* **86**, p. 023518 (2012).
43. J. Chluba, E. Dimastrogiovanni, M. A. Amin and M. Kamionkowski, Evolution of CMB spectral distortion anisotropies and tests of primordial non-Gaussianity, *Mon. Not. Roy. Astron. Soc.* **466**, 2390 (2017).
44. A. Kogut *et al.*, The Primordial Inflation Explorer (PIXIE): A Nulling Polarimeter for Cosmic Microwave Background Observations, *JCAP* **07**, p. 025 (2011).
45. P. André *et al.*, PRISM (Polarized Radiation Imaging and Spectroscopy Mission): An Extended White Paper, *JCAP* **02**, p. 006 (2014).
46. Y. Akrami *et al.*, Planck 2018 results. IX. Constraints on primordial non-Gaussianity, *Astron. Astrophys.* **641**, p. A9 (2020).

Theoretical and numerical aspects of CMB spectral distortions from non-thermal energy injections

Sandeep Kumar Acharya

Jodrell Bank Centre for Astrophysics,
School of Physics and Astronomy,
University of Manchester,
Manchester, M13 9PL, United Kingdom
E-mail: sandeep.acharya@manchester.ac.uk

Jens Chluba

Jodrell Bank Centre for Astrophysics,
School of Physics and Astronomy,
University of Manchester,
Manchester, M13 9PL, United Kingdom
E-mail: jens.chluba@manchester.ac.uk

Abir Sarkar

Jodrell Bank Centre for Astrophysics,
School of Physics and Astronomy,
University of Manchester,
Manchester, M13 9PL, United Kingdom
E-mail: abirsarkar.150490@gmail.com

Compton scattering of photons with thermal electrons is one of the most ubiquitous phenomenon in nature. Numerical approaches to solve the evolution of photons in such situations typically assume the energy exchange to be much smaller compared to the temperature of electrons. In this work, we solve the photon evolution in its full generality, without the diffusion approximation, and show the differences between the exact solution and approximate solutions. We point out the importance of solving exact kinematics of Compton scattering for the computation of Cosmic Microwave Background (CMB) spectral distortions at redshifts $(z) \lesssim 3 \times 10^4$.

Keywords: Cosmology; Cosmic Microwave background; CMB spectral distortions.

1. Photon evolution equation

The Boltzmann equation for the evolution of photon spectrum in contact with a thermal electron bath can be written as,[1]

$$\frac{dn_0}{d\tau} = \int P^{\text{th}}(\omega_0 \to \omega) \left[e^{\frac{\omega-\omega_0}{\theta_e}} n(1+n_0) - n_0(1+n) \right] d\omega, \quad (1)$$

where n_0 and n are the photon occupation number at frequency ω_0 and ω respectively, $\theta_e (= \frac{T_e}{m_e})$ is the non-dimensional electron temperature, $d\tau (= cN_e\sigma_T dt)$ is the optical depth of Compton scattering of photons with the electrons. The exact kinematics of Compton scattering is stored in the kernel $P^{\text{th}}(\omega_0 \to \omega)$ which can be computed using CSpack[a].[2] The kernel satisfies the detailed balance relation,

$$P^{\text{th}}(\omega \to \omega_0) = \frac{\omega_0^2}{\omega^2} e^{\frac{\omega-\omega_0}{\theta_e}} P^{\text{th}}(\omega_0 \to \omega), \tag{2}$$

which ensures that the Planck spectrum is the equilibrium solution of photon evolution equation.

In literature, one often uses the diffusion approximation[1] which assumes that the energy exchange between photons and the electrons is much smaller than the electron temperature. Then one can do a Taylor series expansion in $\frac{\omega-\omega_0}{\theta_e}$ in Eq. 1. Further assuming Compton scattering to be non-relativistic, we obtain Kompaneets equation,[3,4]

$$\frac{dn_0}{d\tau} = \frac{\theta_e}{x_0^2} \frac{\partial}{\partial x_0} x_0^4 \left[\frac{\partial}{\partial x_0} n_0 + n_0(1+n_0) \right], \tag{3}$$

where $x_0 (= \frac{\omega_0}{\theta_e})$ is the dimensionless frequency. The photon equilibrium solution is given by,

$$\frac{\partial}{\partial x_0} n_0 + n_0(1+n_0) = 0 \tag{4}$$

We can obtain a relativistically exact equation within diffusion approximation by using the Ansatz (without stimulated scattering terms),[5,6]

$$\frac{dn_0}{d\tau} = \frac{1}{\omega_0^2} \partial_{\omega_0} \left[\mathcal{D}(\omega_0) \partial_{\omega_0} \Delta n_0 + \mathcal{A}(\omega_0) \Delta n_0 \right], \tag{5}$$

where $\mathcal{A}(\omega_0)$ and $\mathcal{D}(\omega_0)$ are tuned to match the relativistically exact first and second moment of photon evolution equation.[5] We call this the improved Fokker-Planck (FP) approximation. Note that the zeroth moment which is the photon number conservation equation is automatically satisfied by Eq. 5. Since the coefficients of Eq. 5 are a function of photon energy ω_0, the equilibrium solution will not be unique and will be a function of photon energy which is unphysical. Therefore, we expect that Eq. 5 can not be a reliable substitute of Eq. 1. We will confirm it with numerical test problems in the next section.

2. Numerical solutions for test problems

As a test problem, we consider monochromatic photon injection at frequency x_{inj}. In Fig. 1, we plot the first and second moment of the evolving photon spectrum as a function of $y = \int \theta_e d\tau$, which can be thought of as a time variable. With time, the photon spectrum spreads out. Therefore, the absolute value of the moments increases until equilibrium is reached at which point there is no more evolution. Since the injected photon energy is higher than the electron temperature ($x = \omega/\theta_e$),

---

[a]CSpack is available at www.chluba.de/CSpack

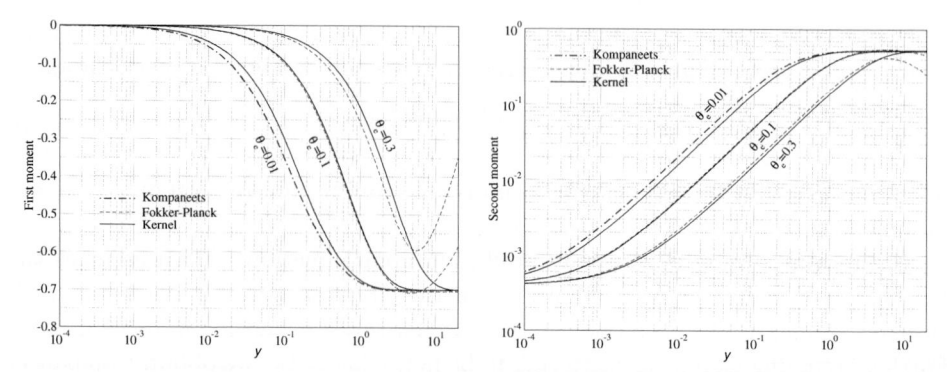

Fig. 1. Evolution of first (left panel) and second (right panel) moments of photon field for injection at $x_{\rm inj} = 10$. Stimulated terms were neglected. The electrons are kept at a constant temperature $\theta_e = 0.1$. We compare the solutions of the Kompaneets equation and the improved FP approach (Eq. 5) with the solution for the exact scattering kernel (Eq. 1). The Kompaneets solutions are independent of the temperature. The temperature dependence is captured well by the improved FP approach at low value of the y parameter. However, this approach fails as expected once equilibrium is reached.

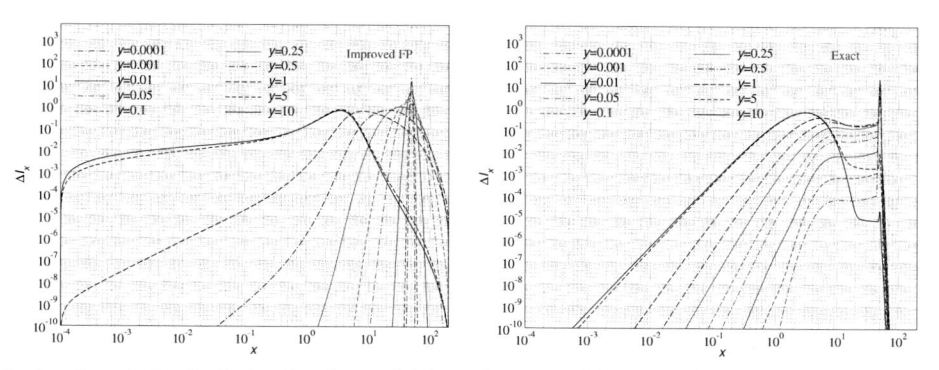

Fig. 2. Snapshots of solution for photon field as a function of frequency for different y parameters and numerical approaches as annotated. On the y-axis, we plot the dimensionless intensity, $I_x = x^3 n$. Photon were injected at $x_{\rm inj} = 50$ at $y = 0$.

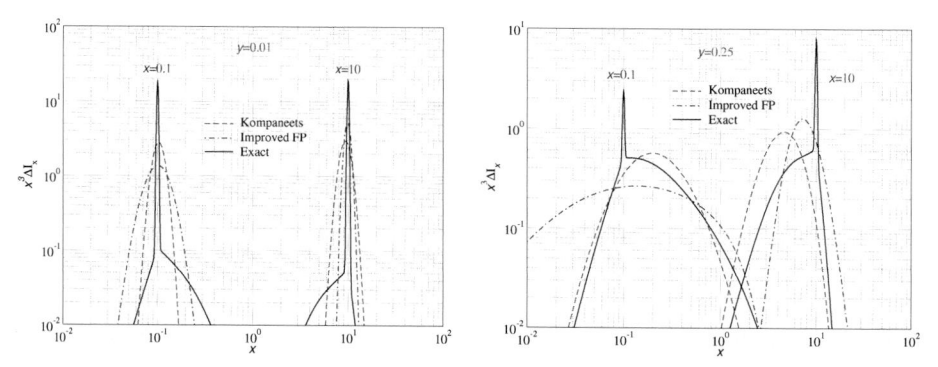

Fig. 3. Comparison of solutions with different approximations and the exact solution with $\theta_e = 0.1$ and various values of injection frequency (x) and y as shown in the figure.

photons lose energy to the electrons on average. This makes the first moment negative for this particular choice of initial photon energy. The second moment which captures the dispersion of the photon spectrum is always positive. The improved FP solution captures the evolution of moments much better than the Kompaneets equation but they do not approach the equilibrium solution for reasons as already explained before.

In Fig. 2, we plot the snapshots of photon evolution and compare the improved FP and the exact solution for a few values of y. The different solutions look significantly different from each other even if the moments of the spectrum are similar. The improved FP solution is much smoother due to the diffusion approximation while in case of the exact solution, we still see a signature of photon injection at $x_{inj} = 50$ at $y \sim 10$. In Fig. 3, we compare Kompaneets, improved FP and the exact solution for few different cases to further illustrate the differences of different approximations.

3. Implications for CMB spectral distortions

The CMB spectrum is accurately described by the Planck spectrum up to a level of 10^{-5}.[7] Injection of non-thermal photons at $z \lesssim 2 \times 10^6$ gives rise to CMB spectral distortions as the CMB can not relax to the Planck spectrum as photon number changing processes become inefficient.[8] As opposed to the test problems considered in the previous section in which electrons were at a constant temperature, in the expanding universe, both the CMB photons and the background electrons evolve together. Therefore, in this scenario, we solve two equations which are the photon evolution equation (Eq. 1) and the temperature of the electrons.[5] We evolve the photon spectrum from the redshift of photon injection up to today when the CMB photons reach us. Here, we consider photon injection at a single redshift.

In Fig. 4, we plot the CMB spectral distortion solutions for photons with energy and redshifts as shown and compare the exact solution with the Kompaneets

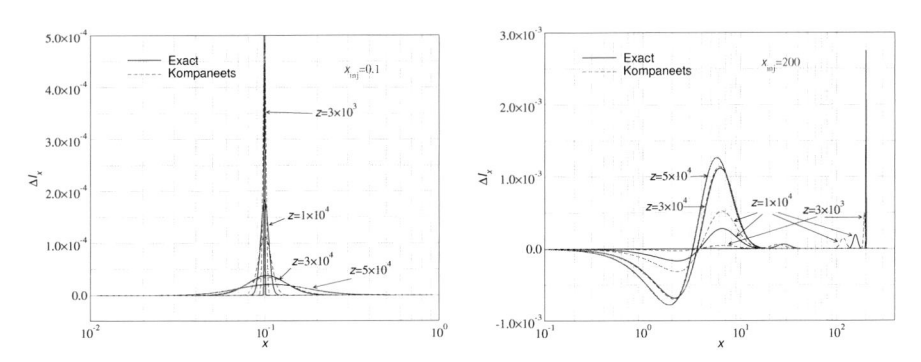

Fig. 4. Spectral distortion solution for energy injection at different redshifts with frequency of injection as denoted. The Kompaneets solution generally overestimates the broadening and mean shifts in the photon distribution. For injection at $x = 200$, the exact solution falls back with respect to the Kompaneets treatment, which overestimates the energy exchange with electrons.

approximation. The electron temperature at these redshifts are of the order of few eV, therefore, relativistic corrections are not important, and the improved FP approximation is identical to Kompaneets approximation. The Kompaneets approximation overestimates the broadening of photon spectrum. At higher frequencies, the Klein-Nishina corrections reduce the energy exchange from the energetic photons to the background electrons which is not captured by the Kompaneets solution. The energy gain by the electrons shows up as y-distortion[4] which, consequently, is not predicted correctly in Kompaneets approximation.

4. Conclusions

In this work, we solve the evolution of photons in contact with a thermal bath of electrons via Compton scattering and compare the exact solutions with various approximations found in literature. We point out and explain the differences between these solutions and show that the various approximations do not capture the physics correctly for the whole photon evolution history. We study CMB spectral distortions from photon injections and show that the exact solution differs significantly from Kompaneets solution and will be important for determining CMB spectral distortion constraints for photon injection scenarios.

References

1. S. Y. Sazonov and R. A. Sunyaev, The Profile of a Narrow Line after Single Scattering by Maxwellian Electrons: Relativistic Corrections to the Kernel of the Integral Kinetic Equation, *ApJ* **543**, 28 (November 2000).
2. A. Sarkar, J. Chluba and E. Lee, Dissecting the Compton scattering kernel I: Isotropic media, *MNRAS* **490**, 3705 (December 2019).
3. A. Kompaneets, The establishment of thermal equilibrium between photons and electrons, *Sov.Phys. JETP* **31**, p. 876 (1956).
4. Y. B. Zeldovich and R. A. Sunyaev, The Interaction of Matter and Radiation in a Hot-Model Universe, *ApSS* **4**, 301 (July 1969).
5. S. K. Acharya, J. Chluba and A. Sarkar, Comparison of numerical methods for computing the repeated Compton scattering of photons in isotropic media, *MNRAS* **507**, 2052 (October 2021).
6. R. Belmont, Numerical computation of isotropic Compton scattering, *A&A* **506**, 589 (November 2009).
7. D. J. Fixsen, E. S. Cheng, J. M. Gales, J. C. Mather, R. A. Shafer and E. L. Wright, The Cosmic Microwave Background Spectrum from the Full COBE FIRAS Data Set, *ApJ* **473**, 576 (December 1996).
8. J. Chluba and R. A. Sunyaev, The evolution of CMB spectral distortions in the early Universe, *MNRAS* **419**, 1294 (January 2012).

BISOU: A balloon project to measure the CMB spectral distortions

B. Maffei[1,*], M. H. Abitbol[2], N. Aghanim[1], J. Aumont[3], E. Battistelli[4], J. Chluba[5], X. Coulon[1],
P. De Bernardis[4], M. Douspis[1], J. Grain[1], S. Gervasoni[1], J. C. Hill[6,7], A. Kogut[8], S. Masi[4],
T. Matsumura[9], C. O'Sullivan[10], L. Pagano[11], G. Pisano[4], M. Remazeilles[5], A. Ritacco[1],
A. Rotti[5], V. Sauvage[1], G. Savini[12], S. L. Stever[13,9], A. Tartari[14], L. Thiele[15], N. Trappe[10]

[1] *Institut d'Astrophysique Spatiale, CNRS-Université Paris-Saclay, Orsay, 91405, France*
E-mail: Bruno.Maffei@universite-paris-saclay.fr

[2] *University of Oxford, Department of Physics, Denys Wilkinson Building, Oxford OX1 4LS, UK*

[3] *IRAP - CNRS, Toulouse, France*

[4] *Dipartimento di Fisica, Università di Roma "La Sapienza", Italy*

[5] *JBCA, School of Physics and Astronomy, The University of Manchester, UK*

[6] *Department of Physics, Columbia University, New York, NY, USA 10027*

[7] *Center for Computational Astrophysics, Flatiron Institute, New York, NY, USA 10010*

[8] *NASA - Goddard Space Flight Center, Greenbelt MD 20771 USA*

[9] *Kavli IPMU (WPI), UTIAS, The University of Tokyo, Kashiwa, Chiba, 277-8583 Japan*

[10] *Department of Experimental Physics, National University of Ireland, Maynooth, Ireland*

[11] *Dipartimento di Fisica e Scienze della Terra - Università degli Studi di Ferrara, Italy*

[12] *Physics and Astronomy Department, University College London, UK*

[13] *Okayama University, Kita-ku, Okayama, 700-8530 Japan*

[14] *Dipartimento di Fisica "E. Fermi" - Università di Pisa - INFN, Pisa, Italy*

[15] *Department of Physics, Princeton University, Princeton, NJ, 08544 USA*

The BISOU (Balloon Interferometer for Spectral Observations of the Universe) project aims to study the viability and prospects of a balloon-borne spectrometer, pathfinder of a future space mission dedicated to the measurements of the CMB spectral distortions. We present here a preliminary concept based on previous space mission proposals, together with some sensitivity calculation results for the observation goals, showing that a 5-σ measurement of the y-distortions is achievable.

Keywords: CMB, Spectral distortions, Balloon project.

1. Introduction

With the success of the ESA Planck mission, the concordance cosmological model is established as the reference framework. However, outstanding questions about this model are still unanswered. In particular the simplest inflationary model proposed as the origin of the initial matter perturbations is favoured by Planck measurement of the spectral index and low non-Gaussianity. Nevertheless, it still needs to be confirmed through the measurement of its smoking gun signature: the relic background of primordial gravitational waves. The latter can only be observed through the Cosmic Microwave Background (CMB) polarisation: namely B-modes. The CMB frequency spectrum is another key observable to probe the cosmological model. Its intensity was precisely measured by COBE/FIRAS almost three decades ago,[1,2] with deviations limited to $\Delta I/I \approx 10^{-5}$. Since then, not much progress has been achieved in measuring its deviation from a true blackbody. However, while the space mission proposals PIXIE[3] and PRISTINE (to ESA F-mission call) have not been successful, following two white papers,[4,5] the ESA Voyage 2050 programme has selected this topic amongst its three themes.

The BISOU (Balloon Interferometer for Spectral Observations of the Universe) project aims to study the viability and prospects of a balloon-borne spectrometer, pathfinder of a future space mission dedicated to the absolute measurement of the CMB spectrum. While PIXIE and PRISTINE were targeting both the measurement of the CMB polarisation, namely a first detection of the CMB B-mode polarisation, and the absolute measurement of the CMB spectral distortions, BISOU's main goal is to perform a first measurement of the later. However, secondary science will also include measurement of the Cosmic Infrared Background (CIB) emission, and potentially the polarisation of the dust up to 2 THz together with Galactic emission lines such as CI, CII, NII and OI.

Taking into account the specificity of a balloon flight in term of requirements and conditions (i.e. residual atmosphere, observation strategy for instance), this CNES Phase 0 study will evaluate if such a spectrometer is sensitive enough to measure at least the Compton y-distortion while consolidating the instrument concept and improving the readiness of some of its key sub-systems.

2. Science goals

While the CMB has a nearly perfect blackbody emission spectrum, deviations from it, referred to as spectral distortions, are expected. These distortions encode information about the full thermal history of the Universe from the early stages (primordial distortions from inflation and cosmological recombination lines) until today (star formation and galaxy clusters). Many of these processes are part of our standard cosmological model and are detailed in several publications.[4,6]

Spectral distortions result from processes that affect the thermal equilibrium between matter and radiation. One of the standard distortions, known as the Compton y-distortion, is created in the regime of inefficient energy transfer (optically thin scattering) between electrons and photons, relevant at redshifts $z < 5 \times 10^4$. Processes creating this type of distortion are dominated by the inverse-Compton scattering of CMB photons off hot electrons during the epoch of reionization and structure formation, also known as the thermal Sunyaev-Zeldovich (tSZ) effect.

Chemical potential or μ-type distortions, on the other hand, are generated by energy release at earlier stages ($z > 5 \times 10^4$), when interactions are still extremely efficient (optically thick scattering) and able to establish kinetic equilibrium between electrons and photons under repeated Compton scattering and photon emission processes.

The COBE-FIRAS limit, $|y| < 1.5 \times 10^{-5}$ (95% C.L.), is roughly one order of magnitude larger than the expected signal,[7] $y \approx 2 \times 10^{-6}$. Signal from μ-type distortions will be even fainter. It is therefore crucial to have reliable models of all the emissions that will be much stronger than these signals in order to properly subtract them.

2.1. *Modeling the signals*

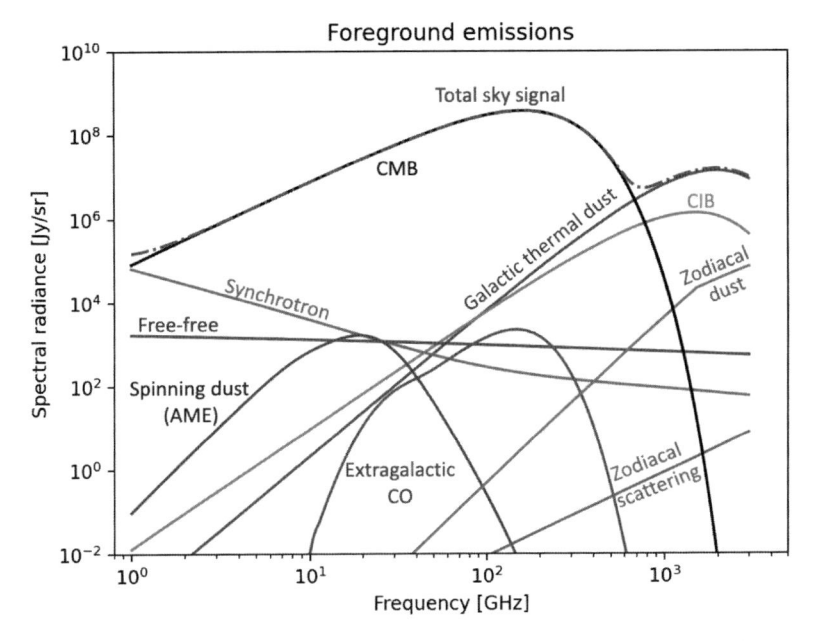

Fig. 1. Foreground emission contributions with respect to the CMB blackbody emission, together with the sum of all astrophysical signals (CMB + foregrounds).

Several astrophysical foregrounds contribute meaningfully to the sky signal at frequencies relevant to CMB spectral distortions. In addition to the ones already modeled[6] from Planck data,[8] additional components from the zodiacal dust have been included. Figure 1 shows the individual contributions together with the sum of all sky signals, including the CMB. At low frequencies (below 70 GHz), the brightest foregrounds are from the synchrotron, the free-free and the so-called anomalous microwave emissions. High frequencies foregrounds (above 100 GHz) are mainly due to the emission of the Galactic thermal dust, the cumulative redshifted emission from thermal dust in distant galaxies, called the cosmic infrared background (CIB), and the zodiacal thermal dust emission. Additional foregrounds contributing to the total sky signal are the cumulative CO emission from distant galaxies at intermediate frequencies and the zodiacal scattering at high frequencies.

2.2. *CMB spectral distortions modeling*

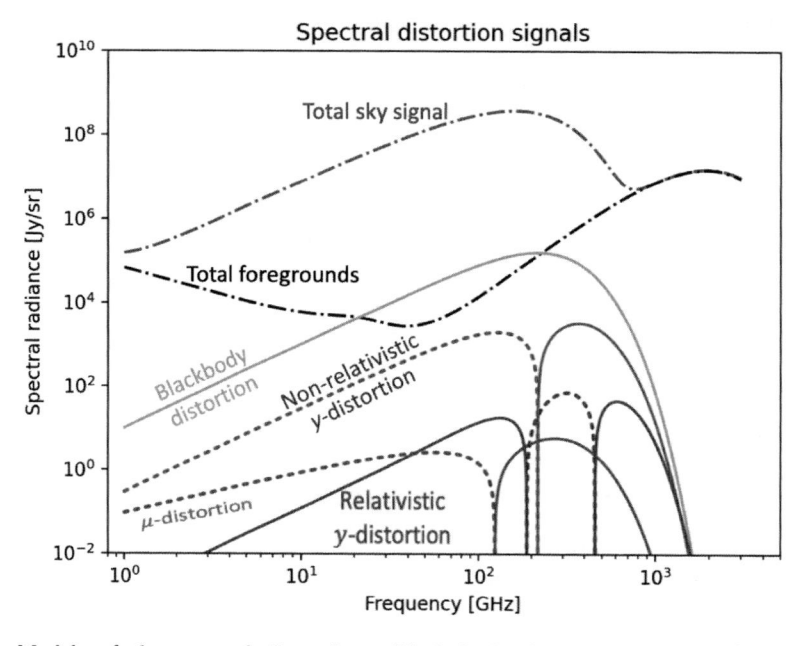

Fig. 2. Models of the spectral distortions: Black body distortion ΔT_{CMB} (orange), non-relativistic y-distortion (blue), relativistic y-distortion (purple) and μ-distortion (green). This is compared to the total foreground signal (dashed black) and the total sky signal - Foregrounds + CMB (dashed red).

Following the same assumptions and processes as the ones presented in Abitbol et al.,[6] figure 2 shows the signals associated with the various distortions of the spectrum, with respect to the total emission of the foregrounds and the total sky signal (including the CMB emission).

Four contributions are considered and modeled. First a blackbody distortion that represents a first order temperature deviation ΔT_{CMB} to the true CMB blackbody spectrum. Then a cumulative thermal SZ y-distortion, including both standard non-relativistic and relativistic contributions (from Hill et al.[7]). The intracluster medium (ICM), the intergalactic medium and reionization contributions are included in the Compton-y signal. A relativistic correction to thermal SZ distortion[7,6] is modeled using the moment-based approach. Finally the chemical potential μ-distortion is generated assuming only signals from acoustic damping and adiabatic cooling. The r-type distortion, sometimes called "residual" distortion, is expected to have a contribution smaller than the μ-type distortion and is not represented in figure 2.

3. Instrument concept

The initial concept is based on a similar one that had been proposed by the PIXIE team[3] (shown in figure 3 left) and also used for the PRISTINE F-class ESA mission proposal. The instrument is a Fourier Transform Spectrometer (FTS) with two inputs and two outputs. Both inputs are going through a separate telescope, both sets of optics being identical in order to minimise the systematics. Because PIXIE has several observation modes, an external calibrator (cooled blackbody) could be located in front of one of the apertures at any one time. In the "spectral distortion" mode, for which the absolute spectrum needs to be measured, one input is directed towards the sky, the second towards a blackbody whose temperature is set to the CMB one, 2.726 K, so that a differential measurement can be achieved. This process can be alternated in order to cancel any asymmetry in both optical systems. After going through a set of polarisers, each of the two outputs is focused on a dual-polarisation multimoded bolometric detector, so that each of the four detectors measures an interference fringe pattern between orthogonal linear polarizations from the two input beams. In order to limit the photon noise, the whole instrument is cooled to about 3 K, the detectors being at sub-K temperature.

3.1. Balloon specificity

The previous studies for the instrument concept were performed on the basis of a space mission. For the case of a balloon project, the conditions, the requirements and therefore the instrument concept will be different. Stratospheric balloon projects might be considered to be in near-space conditions, but there are still many differences, some of these being the potential flight time, access to the sky, thermal environment, etc...

A few will have strong impacts on the payload concept. First the residual atmosphere at an altitude of about 40 km will be of the order of 3 mbar with a temperature of the order of 270 K. This will not only lead to an additional photon noise contribution, but also to the necessity of hosting the overall instrument inside a dewar in order to keep it at a temperature of the order of 3 K under vacuum. Even with a small pressure difference, the dewar will then need to have a window through which the telescope will point towards the sky (see figure 3 right). The

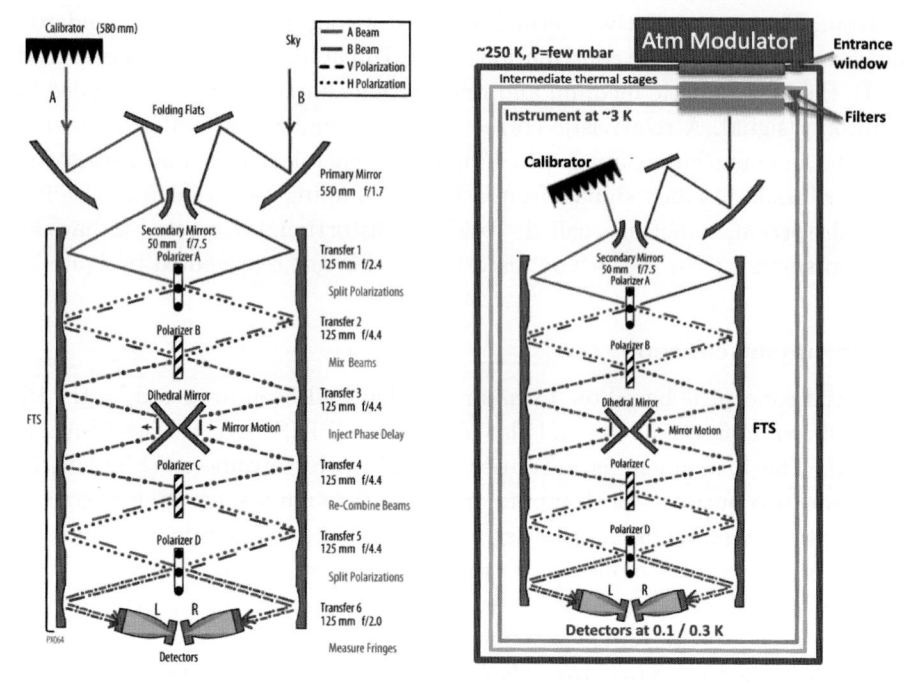

Fig. 3. Left: Original instrument concept from the PIXIE space mission proposal.[3] Right: BISOU instrument scheme.

outside dewar shell being at ambient temperature, intermediate thermal stages will be necessary with thermal filters in order to limit the thermal background load and potential straylight.

This is also preventing the calibrator to be outside the dewar and will then have to be located inside in order to keep it at a very steady temperature of about 3 K.

Due to the mass, power and dimensions constraints of a typical balloon payload, it is unlikely that two sets of optics can be used with a telescope primary diameter of 35 to 40 cm allowing for a multi-moded beam FWHM of about 1.5 deg.

3.2. Gondola, dewar and cooling chain

Assuming that the balloon flight will be provided by CNES, our study is based on the use of the CARMEN gondola[9] design that has been used lately for the PILOT balloon project[10] for instance, allowing for a maximum all-included payload mass of 750 kg (including ballast). While CNES has so far flown these types of payload for a typical 35-hour flight duration, it is planned that a first 5-day test-flight will happen in 2022. We will therefore base our sensitivity calculations on the assumption that this type of flight will be available in the future.

The whole instrument needs to be cooled to about 3 K, where the detectors only will be cooled to a sub-K temperature. A trade-off is being made in order to define the optimum one, but it is highly likely that 300 mK will be low enough (section 4.1) for the focal plane, allowing for the use of a ^{3}He sorption cooler. Due to mass and power limitations, mechanical coolers for balloon platforms are not yet mature enough, even if some developments are being investigated, most notably by NASA. We chose a proven cooling solution using liquid helium to cool the overall instrument, between 4 and 2 K depending on the bath pressure, using the natural low pressure at high altitude. Several intermediate thermal stages and shields cooled with the helium vapour retrieved from the bath will allow for heat load reduction on the 3 K stage. Typical intermediate temperature stages are 150 K, 80 K and 20 K.

3.3. *Atmosphere*

As already mentioned, the residual atmosphere at 40 km altitude will still create a large photon noise contribution with respect to the extremely faint signal that we are trying to observe. For instance, atmospheric effects at ground level and even at balloon altitudes are shown in Masi et al.[11] with respect to spectral distortion signals. The signal level due to the atmosphere is still 2 to 3 orders of magnitude higher that the non-relativistic y-distortion signal depending on the frequency. In theory, assuming a reliable model, this contribution could be removed.

More important, will be the variations of the atmosphere with altitude, observation elevation and time. This cannot be modelled and will therefore need an atmosphere modulation strategy at a high enough frequency to be compatible with the variation timescale. Such a modulator is already used for COSMO,[11] but for BISOU, another modulator, such as a cold internal beam stirrer is also being considered.

For the time being, at that stage of the study, the atmosphere is not yet considered in our sensitivity and systematic effects calculations.

3.4. *The instrument*

Following the conditions of a balloon project (section 3.1), several points had to be adapted and trade-offs have already been made. With emphasis on the spectral distortions, these measurements will always be performed against the calibrator. Due to the fact that we are using only one telescope to save mass (with therefore an unbalanced optical system), the calibrator will be kept fixed in front of one of the FTS inputs for simplicity and risk mitigation.

With the help of an instrument model being developed, and assuming some initial parameters such as telescope diameter, flight duration and observation efficiency, or again spectral resolution, calculations presented in section 4 are showing that the sensitivity is strongly dependant on three key parameters: the temperature and emissivity of the window, and the maximum frequency of observation as the photon noise is increasing with frequency. The implications of these issues will be discussed in the following sections. However, we see straight away that the dewar window, the warmest optical element, needs to have a very low emissivity, a temperature as low as possible and be as thin as possible to minimise the systematics.

In order to use a very thin window, a valve at the entrance of the dewar, opening only when the pressure difference is small (at a certain altitude), could be used. Such a technique was used for the Archeops[12] balloon project for instance.

The emissivity of the window could be reduced by the application of a copper/gold grid as was done on the ArTéMiS[13] ground based camera.

Finally while the dewar will be at a temperature ranging from 300 to 270 K, the window could have a mount thermally isolated from the structure and actively cooled with the vapour coming from the helium bath. Such a development will be studied with a dedicated R&D programme. This should bring the window temperature below 200 K.

4. Preliminary sensitivity estimates

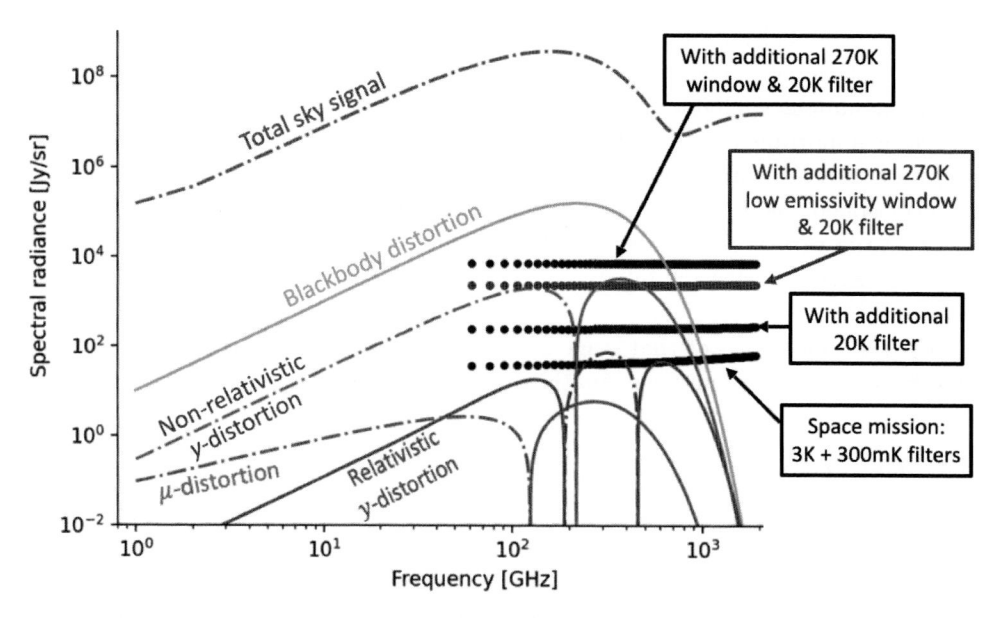

Fig. 4. Estimated instrument sensitivity for different concepts, compared to various spectral distortion signals. All calculations are assuming a 5-day flight. The highest sensitivity assumes a space mission, while the lowest sensitivity is for a balloon flight for which the noise is limited by the emission of the dewar window with pessimistic characteristics.

4.1. Photometric model

A preliminary photometric model has been developed, taking into account only the dewar window and a minimum of two spectral filters on the lowest temperature stages (supposed to be at 20 and 3 K and with a top-hat transmission profile) for the optical input. The emission of all the components in the optical path is modeled as blackbody emission (at the temperature of the component) multiplied by the emissivity of that component at the specified temperature. The load on the detector is estimated by adding the power contributions of the optical components as well as the contribution from the sky, using for each:

$$P(\nu,T) = \int_{\nu_{min}}^{\nu_{max}} eff(\nu) A\Omega(\nu) \epsilon(\nu,T) B(\nu,T) d\nu$$

where $A\Omega$ is the throughput of the multi-moded optics, eff the transmission/efficiency of the optical system, B the blackbody function, and for this first version of our model, the emissivity ϵ is taken as a constant for each component.

We integrate the power received by the detector over the full range of frequencies. In order to assume the worst case scenario for the detector load, when the optical path difference of the Fourier Transform Spectrometer is null, the power is integrated over the full frequency range that we will observe.

The total Noise Equivalent Power (NEP) is then calculated by adding in quadrature the photon NEP from the signal arriving on the detector and the detector NEP which is assumed to be about four times lower than the photon NEP. For the time being, we assume that the other contributions to the total NEP are small in comparison to the photon one. Depending on the assumptions made, for the temperature and emissivity of the optical components for instance, the total NEP is of the order of a few 10^{-16} W Hz$^{-1/2}$ for a space mission to about 10^{-14} W Hz$^{-1/2}$ for a balloon configuration, high enough to allow for the use of detectors at a temperature of about 300 mK.

4.2. Results

Following classic calculations,[3] from the total NEP, the detected noise for a fixed integration time τ is given by:

$$\delta P = \frac{NEP_{total}}{\sqrt{\tau/2}}$$

where τ is taken to be 90 hours, corresponding to a flight duration of 5 days with 75% observation efficiency. From this, the noise at the detector may in turn be referred to the specific intensity, leading to an equivalent instrumental sensitivity that can be compared to spectral emissions. These results are shown on figure 4 for different instrument configurations. For all these configurations, a FTS spectral resolution of 15 GHz, a lowest frequency ν_{min}=60 GHz, and a linear tapered filter to limit the high frequency contribution above 600 GHz have been used.

Figure 4 shows the impact of the window on the sensitivity as it will be the warmest element on the optical chain. Starting from a "space configuration" where the warmest element might be around 3 K (filter at 3 K and 300/100 mK with 0.1% emissivity each), which will be the most sensitive configuration, followed by a configuration with an added filter at T=20 K, then the same configuration with the window at T=270 K added, this with 2 emissivity assumptions for the window, one with ϵ=0.1% like all other filters, and a lower one with $\epsilon = 3 \times 10^{-4}$ (in blue), something that we hope to achieve.

We then conclude that in order to have a first detection of the y-parameter with a decent signal-to-noise ratio, the window will need to be cooled further as previously discussed.

Another parameter which is also crucial, is the maximum observation frequency ν_{max}. All the photon contributions being higher with increasing frequency, the overall sensitivity will drop with increasing ν_{max}. On the other hand, in order to retrieve the "easy" science goals, such as the y-parameter spectral distortions, ΔT_{CMB} and T_{CIB} for the measurement of the Cosmic Infrared Background, measurements have to go to high frequencies. Therefore a trade-off needs to be reached in order to optimise the S/N for each parameter.

This work has started and will be presented in future publications. However, we can already say that, not taking into account the atmosphere, S/N ratios of 5 for the y-distortions, about 30 for ΔT_{CMB} and about 10 for T_{CIB}, can be reached if ν_{max} were to be 1200 GHz.

Obviously a more detailed study will need to take place for a better optimisation, including more sophisticated models and better parameter knowledge.

5. On-going and future work

Aside from more detailed model of the instrument and sensitivity calculations, several points need to be addressed by the end of the Phase 0 study.

The next important hurdle to cross is understanding how to deal with the atmosphere. More accurate models and data for high altitude are being gathered within the consortium but as already stated, a modulator seems inevitable. Concept work and the study of the associated effects of this modulator will be paramount.

Other points to be developed (not exhaustive) can be listed as:

- Observation plan and scanning strategy;
- Calibration strategy, together with the accurate characterisation and control of the calibrator;
- Study on how to increase the sensitivity, by increasing the number of detectors for instance, or having two channels;
- A first cut to the study of the systematic effects, in order to answer at least if the unbalanced optical system between the two inputs will not be a limiting factor;
- Updated science case.

6. Conclusion

So far, assuming that the atmospheric problem can be solved, it seems that according to our preliminary estimates, such a balloon borne instrument will be able to have valid scientific outputs, and not be limited to a technological demonstrator for future space missions. Namely, a measurement of the CIB, a better constraint on ΔT_{CMB}, and more importantly a first 5-σ measurement of the y-distortions if not better.

If these results are confirmed by the end of Phase 0, a proposal to CNES and other funding bodies will be submitted to start a more detailed Phase A study, for a first test-flight on the horizon 2026.

Acknowledgments

The authors acknowledge the support of the French space agency, Centre National d'Etudes Spatiales (CNES).

Kavli IPMU is supported by World Premier International Research Center Initiative (WPI), MEXT, Japan.

References

1. J. C. Mather et al., A Preliminary Measurement of the Cosmic Microwave Background Spectrum by the Cosmic Background Explorer (COBE) Satellite, *ApJL* **354**, p. L37 (May 1990).
2. D. J. Fixsen, E. S. Cheng, J. M. Gales, J. C. Mather, R. A. Shafer and E. L. Wright, The Cosmic Microwave Background Spectrum from the Full COBE FIRAS Data Set, *ApJ* **473**, p. 576 (December 1996).
3. A. Kogut, D. J. Fixsen, D. T. Chuss, J. Dotson, E. Dwek, M. Halpern, G. F. Hinshaw, S. M. Meyer, S. H. Moseley, M. D. Seiffert, D. N. Spergel and E. J. Wollack, The Primordial Inflation Explorer (PIXIE): a nulling polarimeter for cosmic microwave background observations, *JCAP* **2011**, p. 025 (July 2011).
4. J. Chluba, M. H. Abitbol, N. Aghanim et al., New horizons in cosmology with spectral distortions of the cosmic microwave background, *Experimental Astronomy* (May 2021).
5. J. Delabrouille, M. H. Abitbol, N. Aghanim et al., Microwave spectro-polarimetry of matter and radiation across space and time, *Experimental Astronomy* (July 2021).
6. M. H. Abitbol, J. Chluba, J. C. Hill and B. R. Johnson, Prospects for measuring cosmic microwave background spectral distortions in the presence of foregrounds, *MNRAS* **471**, 1126 (October 2017).
7. J. C. Hill, N. Battaglia, J. Chluba, S. Ferraro, E. Schaan and D. N. Spergel, Taking the Universe's Temperature with Spectral Distortions of the Cosmic Microwave Background, *Physical Review Letters* **115**, p. 261301 (December 2015).
8. Planck Collaboration, Planck 2015 results. X. Diffuse component separation: Foreground maps, *A&A* **594**, p. A10 (September 2016).
9. CNES, *CNES Balloons capabilities* https://www.hemera-h2020.eu/facilities-2/cnes-balloons/.
10. A. Mangilli et al., Inflight performance of the PILOT balloon-borne experiment, *Experimental Astronomy* **48**, 265 (December 2019).
11. S. Masi et al., The COSmic Monopole Observer (COSMO), *These proceedings* (2021).

12. A. Benoît *et al.*, Archeops: a high resolution, large sky coverage balloon experiment for mapping cosmic microwave background anisotropies, *Astroparticle Physics* **17**, 101 (May 2002).
13. M. Talvard *et al.*, ArTeMiS: filled bolometer arrays for next generation sub-mm telescopes, in *Society of Photo-Optical Instrumentation Engineers (SPIE) Conference Series*, eds. J. Zmuidzinas, W. S. Holland, S. Withington and W. D. Duncan, Society of Photo-Optical Instrumentation Engineers (SPIE) Conference Series, Vol. 6275 (June 2006).

Cosmic microwave background spectral distortions constraints on decaying dark matter particles and axion-like particles using *COBE/FIRAS* and *EDGES*

Boris Bolliet

Department of Physics, Columbia University, New York, NY 10027, USA
E-mail: boris.bolliet@gmail.com

We present new cosmic microwave background (CMB) spectral distortions constraints on low mass (10^{-10}-10^4 eV) dark matter particles that decay into photons. The constraints are first presented in a model-independent manner and then applied to axions and decaying excited states. For the first time, we place constraints using the full distortion spectra compared to the *COBE/FIRAS* and *EDGES* measurements. This proceeding summarizes results obtained with Jens Chluba and Richard Battye, and published in MNRAS 507 (2021)[a].

Keywords: Cosmology: cosmic microwave background – theory – observations; Dark Matter.

1. Introduction

Spectral distortions are a powerful probe of the thermal history of the universe.[1] They can constrain dark matter candidates with coupling to the electro-magnetic sector, since these typically inject energy into the photon-baryon plasma, generating departure of the CMB spectrum from the black body law. In the past decade, a number of studies have derived constraints on the dark matter cross-section, the mass lifetime and abundance of the decaying or annihilating dark matter particles[e.g.,2-5] Spectral distortions are often characterized by the chemical potential μ and the Compton-y parameter, which are directly proportional to the injected energy and compared with the COBE/FIRAS bounds, $\mu < 9 \times 10^{-5}$ and $y < 1.5 \times 10^{-5}$ (95%CL). However, the μ and y distortions are generally not sufficient to characterize the full distortions. This is the case when the injected photons do not have time to undergo many scatterings, i.e., *comptonize*. For instance, for distortions from decaying particles with a lifetime comparable to the age of the universe, there may be a y distortion but also a peak in intensity located at the rest mass energy of the decaying particle. Here, we present the first constraints that use such features in the distortion spectra.

This is a challenging task: it requires to solve the Boltzmann equation for photons, simultaneously with the time evolution of the electron temperature and the ionisation history. To do so, we use the code `Cosmotherm` as well as packages recently

---
[a]https://arxiv.org/abs/2012.07292

developed at the University of Manchester, namely CSpack for computing energy exchange from Compton scattering[6] and BRpack to compute Bremsstrahlung emission coefficients.[7] We use a standard reionization modeling[8] and a refined treatment of helium and hydrogen recombination initially based on Recfast.[9,10] To run these codes we developed a python package, named specdist[b], so that we could compute in parallel many distortion spectra and the corresponding ionisation histories.

2. Photon injection from decaying particles

We focused on a dark matter particle that decays into two photons, each carrying half of the rest mass energy of the decaying particle. We also considered dark matter excited states where one photon carries the energy difference between the excited and ground state of the decaying particle. The time evolution of the dark matter particle population is described by the exponential decay law with a decay rate Γ that is the inverse of the lifetime. The decay rate determines the time of energy injection and consequently the type of distortion. For short lifetimes we expect a μ-distortion until redshift $z \approx 5 \times 10^4$, and a y-distortion at lower redshift. For photon injection happening after recombination, we expect a more complicated shape due to photons that do not have time to scatter and instead simply redshift as the universe expands.

For the spectrum of the injected photons we used a narrow gaussian that approximates a delta function centered at the rest-mass energy of the decaying particle. The normalization of the spectrum is directly proportional to the abundance of decaying particles which we can write in term of the dark matter fraction $f_{\rm dm}$, that we constrain. To do this, once the distortion is computed we proceed with the exercise of comparing it with CMB frequency spectra measurements such as the measurements from *COBE/FIRAS*[11] and the *EDGES* brightness temperature at 78 MHz.[12]

3. Complementary constraints from ionization histories

We also use complementary constraints from the perturbed ionisation histories that affect the CMB temperature and polarization anisotropy power spectra. The left panel of figure 1 shows several ionisation histories for a particle that decays during the end of recombination, with different masses labelled in dimensionless unit. For some of these we found an interesting time evolution with periodic spikes when we switched on collisional ionisation.

In principle these ionisation histories can be fed to Boltzmann codes such as class[16] or camb[17] to compute the CMB anisotropy power spectra and extract constraints using, e.g., the *Planck* likelihood.[18] A faster method is to use the projection methods developed by Luke Hart and Jens Chluba:[13] the ionisation histories are

---

[b]https://github.com/CMBSPEC/specdist

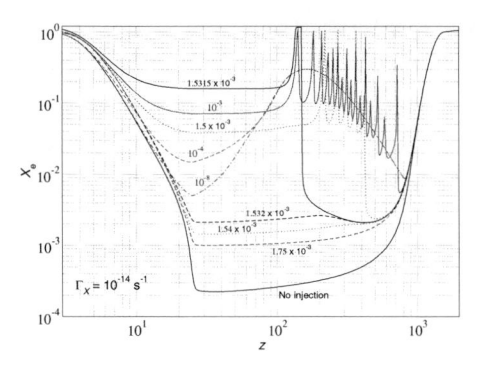

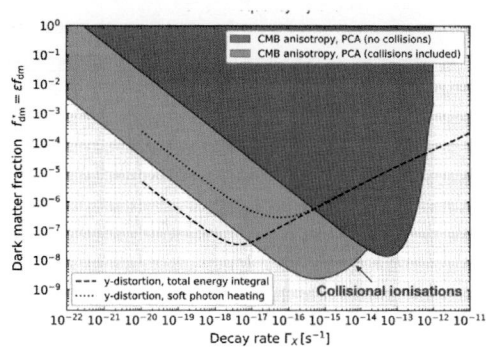

Fig. 1. **Left:** Non-linear responses in the ionization history around critical injection frequencies for $\Gamma = 10^{-14}\,\mathrm{s}^{-1}$ and $\Delta\rho_\gamma/\rho_\gamma = 3 \times 10^{-5}$. For $10^{-3} \lesssim x_{\mathrm{inj},0} = h\nu_{\mathrm{inj},0}/k_\mathrm{B} T_\mathrm{CMB} \lesssim 1.53 \times 10^{-3}$ the free electron fraction shows intermittent bursts due to photon injection, free-free absorption and collisional processes. **Right:** Derived 95% CL dark matter fraction limit, $f^*_{\mathrm{dm}} = \epsilon f_{\mathrm{dm}}$, for a range of lifetimes and $x_{\mathrm{inj},0} \lesssim 10^{-8}$. The CMB anisotropy limits were obtained with the projection method,[13] while the other two are derived assuming $4y \lesssim 6 \times 10^{-5}$ (95% CL) from *COBE/FIRAS*. The dotted curve corresponds to soft photon heating, and the solid dashed line to the total energy integral with the y-era visibility function. For the CMB anisotropy constraints we considered a case where collisional ionisations are not included (blue region) and a case where these are included (red region). As can be seen, atomic collisions are driving post-recombination decay constraints ($\Gamma \lesssim 10^{-14}\,\mathrm{s}^{-1}$). We emphasize that these constraints are for very low mass decaying particles ($m \ll 1\mathrm{eV}$) where all the injected energy in the form of photons is converted into heat, in contrast with scenario where the energy is deposited and leads to direct ionisation.[14,15]

projected onto eigenmodes obtained from a principal component analysis, allowing to derive constraints with a simple root-finding routine.

As shown in the right panel of figure 1, benefiting from the exquisite measurements of *Planck* and *WMAP*, constraints from CMB anisotropy are the strongest for dark matter candidates that decay near recombination, when the CMB is emitted. Nonetheless, *COBE/FIRAS* spectrometer measurements actually beat imager constraints for particles that decay far from recombination, since spectral distortions probe nearly the entire thermal history. Note that the figure illustrates this point with the y-distortion constraints only, while we can now make use of the full distortion spectra.

4. Constraints from the full distortion spectra

In a forthcoming work we will be using machine learning methods in order to build an optimal spectral distortion emulator. For this work, we computed a vast library of distortions so that at any point in the parameter space spanned by the lifetime, mass and abundance of the decaying particle we can interpolate the precomputed spectra and compute the likelihood values given the *COBE/FIRAS* and *EDGES* measurements. A subset of the distortion spectra is shown in figure 2. Our model independent constraints are shown on figure 3. On the left panel, we see the maximally allowed dark matter fraction as a function of the injection energy in eV.

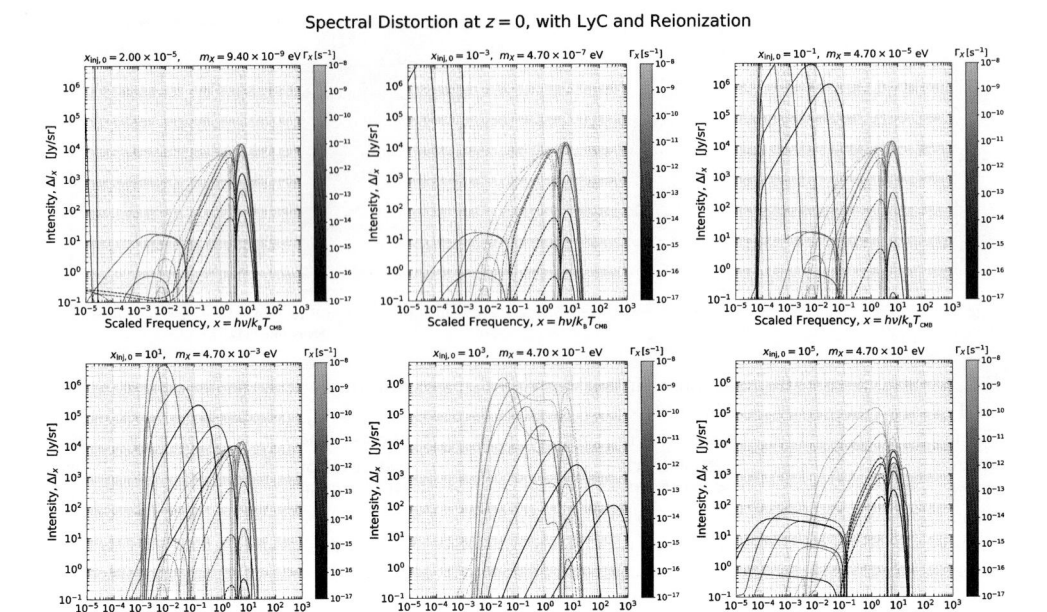

Fig. 2. Solutions for the spectral distortion created by photon injection from decaying particles for several masses, m, and lifetimes, Γ, including simple modelling for reionization in addition to H I, He I and He II photo-ionization (LyC stands for Lyman continuum absorption). All spectra are normalized such that $\Delta\rho/\rho|_{\rm inj} = 3 \times 10^{-5}$. Negative parts of the signal are shown as dashed lines.

The thick line correspond to a a short lifetime, for a particle that decays at early time, towards the end of the μ-era. It is essentially the constraints that one would obtain with a simple μ-estimate calculation by integrating the injected energy over time. There are two differences though: a region near 0.1-10 eV where the chemical potential is actually negative, and a small bump near 1meV associated with photons that have redshifted down to 78MHz where we impose that the CMB brightness temperature should not exceed the *EDGES* measurements. For longer lifetimes, the straight horizontal line constraints corresponding to μ or y estimates is nearly absent: the constraints are driven by the extra redshifted photons that do not scatter efficiently and end up in the *COBE/FIRAS* or *EDGES* frequency range. For decays happening near or after recombination (dotted and dashed-dotted lines respectively), we see strong constraints on the dark matter fraction for energy higher than the ionisation threshold of Hydrogen and Helium (the vertical dashed line on the figure). These constraints are driven by the y-distortion caused by heating from Lyman continuum absorption, and analogous processes for Helium. On the right panel of figure 3, we show the full constraints in the lifetime, injection energy plane with darker colors corresponding to more excluded regions. One piece of modeling that is absent in the constraints of figure 3 are quantum effects associated with the

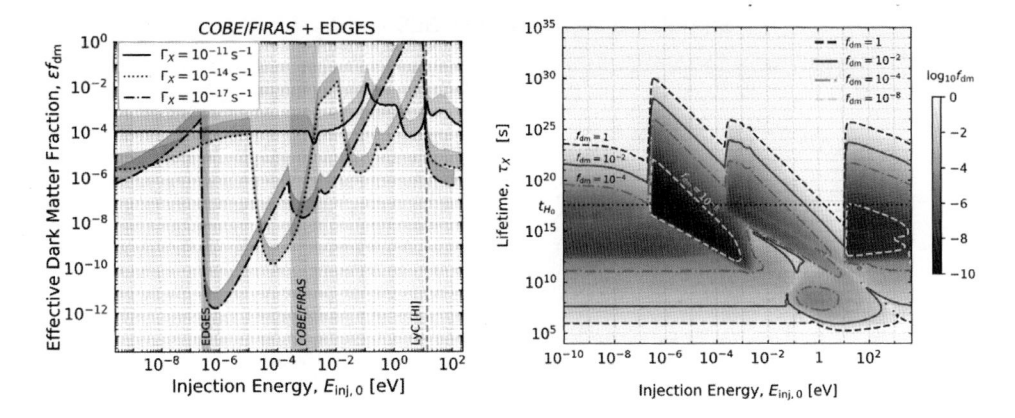

Fig. 3. **Left:** Constraints on the effective DM fraction for decaying particle scenarios (95% CL) for various combinations of data from *COBE/FIRAS*, *EDGES* and *Planck*. The upper panels show the constraints for lifetimes $\Gamma \leq 10^{-11}\,\text{s}^{-1}$ and various combinations of datasets when assuming decay to occur in vacuum. The lower panels show several examples when including stimulated decay. See main text for discussion. **Right:** Constraints (95% CL) on decaying particle models when subsequently including data from *COBE/FIRAS*, *EDGES* and *Planck*. The addition of *EDGES* affects the constraints at $E_{\text{inj}} \simeq 3 \times 10^{-7} - 3 \times 10^{-4}\,\text{eV}$, while the addition of *Planck* has the largest effect at high energies above $E_{\text{inj}} \simeq 13.6\,\text{eV}$.

bosonic or fermionic nature of the decaying particle. We treated the case of bosons, for which the emission is stimulated by the ambient CMB photon bath.[19] The effect of stimulated decay is relatively simple: the decay rate becomes frequency dependent with a term that includes the photon occupation number, evaluated at the injection frequency. One has

$$\Gamma_{\text{stim}} \approx [1 + 2n(x_{\text{inj}})]\,\Gamma \tag{1}$$

where Γ_{stim} is the decay rate in the stimulated case and Γ the would be decay rate without stimulated emission, and where we use the Planck black body law to compute $n(x_{\text{inj}})$ with $x_{\text{inj}} \equiv h\nu_{\text{inj}}/k_B T_{\text{CMB}}$. For large injection frequencies ν_{inj}, both the stimulated decay rate and standard decay rate are equal because $n(x_{\text{inj}}) \approx 0$, but for low injection frequencies the difference between Γ_{stim} and Γ is proportional to $1/\nu_{\text{inj}}$ and is larger at higher redshifts. For instance, for a decay with lifetime roughly the age of the universe today, we expect a small y-distortion and an emission peak centered around the injection frequency. With stimulated decay accounted for, such decaying particle would already have completely decayed a long time ago, in the μ-era, generating a standard μ-distortion. This also implies that with stimulated decay, in the case of low ν_{inj}, one needs much more particles to yield the same amount of energy injection for a fixed lifetime. With this extra piece of modelling we can revisit the constraints of figure 3.

Constraints with stimulated decay accounted for are presented in figure 4 and are the main model independent results of our work. By *model independent*, we mean that at this stage we have not chosen a specific type of particles (other than

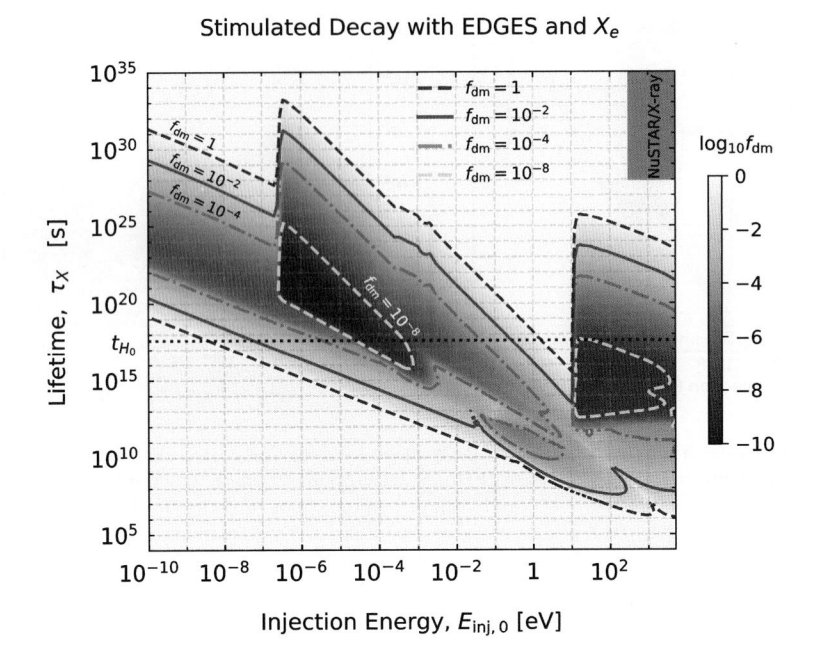

Fig. 4. Same as in figure 3 but with stimulated decay accounted for. The dominant effect of simulated decay is to shift and compress the limits along the τ_X axis for low injection energies/frequencies. We also mark the lifetime corresponding to the age of the Universe ($\tau_X \equiv t_{H_0} \simeq 4.4 \times 10^{17}$ s). For comparison, we have added the current level of constraints of sterile neutrino decay in the X-ray frequency range, namely the lifetime has to be longer than 10^{28} s for masses between 5 − 50keV (green area labeled 'NuSTAR/X-ray'), see Fig 5 of Roach et al.[20]

being bosons). At high injection frequency, namely above 10 eV, the contours are unaffected by the stimulated decay, as expected. But at lower frequency we see an upward tilt of the constraint regions compared to the vacuum decay case of figure 3, towards longer lifetimes, consistent with the discussion above. For comparison, on the top right corner of figure 4 we have added a green exclusion region which comes from the non-detection of X-ray lines expected in radiative decay of sterile neutrinos.[20]

5. Constraints on axion-like particles

We translated our constraints to axion-like particles (ALPs) models. ALPs are pseudo Nambu-Goldston bosons proposed as dark matter candidates and motivated by solutions to the strong CP problem.[21] For these types of particles there is a fundamental relationship between the mass and the decay rate, parameterized the coupling constant $g_{a\gamma\gamma}$.[22] Then, we can replace the x-axis of figure 4 by the ALPs mass, and map the y-axis, which was the lifetime, to the coupling constant. Constraints on ALPs are shown in figure 5. The top right corner of the plot is not constrained

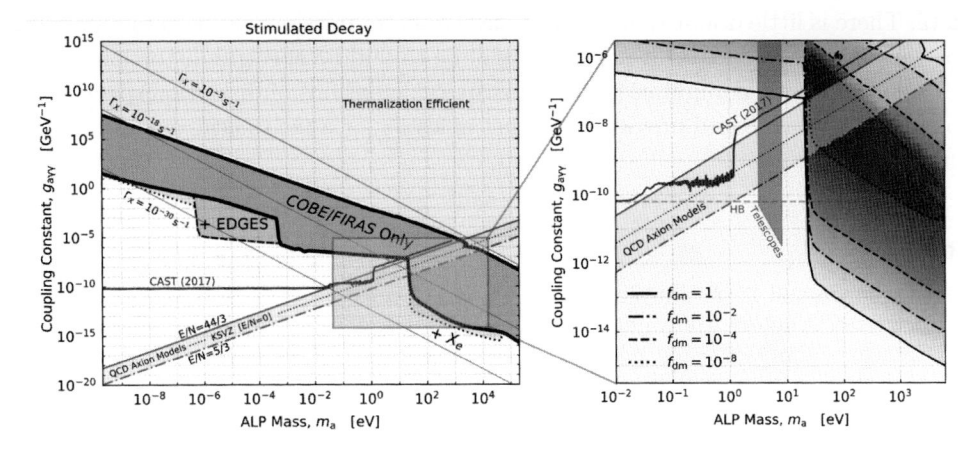

Fig. 5. **Left:** Cumulative *COBE/FIRAS*, *EDGES* and *Planck* constraints (95% CL) on ALPs models and $f_{\rm dm} = 1$. These constraints include blackbody-induced stimulated decay. For reference, we also show that constraint from $CAST$[23] and the physically-motivated region valid for the KSVZ axion model over a range of anomaly coefficients E/N (yellow region). Spectral distortions provide competitive constraints at axion masses of $m_a c^2 \gtrsim 27\,{\rm eV}$. **Right:** Same as left panel but zoomed in on the high-mass end and for various values of $f_{\rm dm}$. Stimulated decay is unimportant in this domain. Axions with masses $m_a c^2 \gtrsim 27{\rm eV}$ are heavily constrained even if they only constitute a small fraction of the DM. For comparison we have added constraints from Horizontal Branch Stars (green dashed line labeled 'HB') and optical telescopes searches focused on Abell clusters (green shaded area).[24, 25] We refer to Fig 91.1 of PDG18[26] for further details on these optical constraints and to Regis et al[27] for the most recent updates.

because it corresponds to very short lifetimes, and all injected energy and photons are thermalized thanks to efficient double Compton and Bremsstrahlung scatterings. The upper part of the pink band is constrained by the μ and y-distortion limits, and the lower part with the peaks correspond to constraints driven by the full spectra. The thick line shows the constraints using *COBE/FIRAS* residuals and the dashed line is the extended constraints when we add the 78 MHz *EDGES* data. The dotted lines are the constraints when we add CMB anisotropy from perturbed recombination. On the right we show a zoomed in region of the plot and we also show the constraints assuming ALPs make up only a fraction of the dark matter. Most of this part of the constraint plot is determined by the y-distortion due to heating from Lyman continuum absorption and it shows that spectral distortion constraints are competitive against other astrophysical constraints on axions, e.g., constraints from *Horizontal Branch* (HB) stars (the green dashed line) and *optical telescopes* (the green area).

6. Conclusion

Here we have presented the first constraints on photon injection processes using the full distortion spectra and ionisation histories. Our work shows that we are still harvesting insights into dark matter from the 30 years old *COBE/FIRAS* spectrometer data. There is little doubt that the next spectrometer mission will be game changing for dark matter models. Our next steps will be to build a spectral distortion emulator to alleviate the computationally expensive calculations of distortion spectra and ionisation histories, and provide a forecast analysis for a next spectrometer mission such as Voyage 2050.[28]

References

1. J. Chluba and R. A. Sunyaev, The evolution of cmb spectral distortions in the early universe, *Monthly Notices of the Royal Astronomical Society* **419**, p. 1294–1314 (Nov 2011).
2. J. Chluba, Green's function of the cosmological thermalization problem – ii. effect of photon injection and constraints, *Monthly Notices of the Royal Astronomical Society* **454**, p. 4182–4196 (Oct 2015).
3. Y. Ali-Haïmoud, J. Chluba and M. Kamionkowski, Constraints on dark matter interactions with standard model particles from cosmic microwave background spectral distortions, *Physical Review Letters* **115** (Aug 2015).
4. V. Poulin, J. Lesgourgues and P. D. Serpico, Cosmological constraints on exotic injection of electromagnetic energy, *Journal of Cosmology and Astroparticle Physics* **2017**, p. 043–043 (Mar 2017).
5. Y. Ali-Haïmoud, Testing dark matter interactions with cmb spectral distortions, *Physical Review D* **103** (Feb 2021).
6. A. Sarkar, J. Chluba and E. Lee, Dissecting the compton scattering kernel i: Isotropic media, *Monthly Notices of the Royal Astronomical Society* **490**, p. 3705–3726 (Oct 2019).
7. J. Chluba, A. Ravenni and B. Bolliet, Improved calculations of electron–ion bremsstrahlung gaunt factors for astrophysical applications, *Monthly Notices of the Royal Astronomical Society* **492**, p. 177–194 (Dec 2019).
8. V. Poulin, P. D. Serpico and J. Lesgourgues, Dark matter annihilations in halos and high-redshift sources of reionization of the universe, *Journal of Cosmology and Astroparticle Physics* **2015**, p. 041–041 (Dec 2015).
9. J. Chluba, Could the cosmological recombination spectrum help us understand annihilating dark matter?, *Monthly Notices of the Royal Astronomical Society* **402**, p. 1195–1207 (Feb 2010).
10. J. Chluba and Y. Ali-Haïmoud, Cosmospec: fast and detailed computation of the cosmological recombination radiation from hydrogen and helium, *Monthly Notices of the Royal Astronomical Society* **456**, p. 3494–3508 (Jan 2016).
11. D. J. Fixsen, E. S. Cheng, J. M. Gales, J. C. Mather, R. A. Shafer and E. L. Wright, The Cosmic Microwave Background Spectrum from the Full COBE FIRAS Data Set, *apj* **473**, p. 576 (December 1996).
12. J. D. Bowman, A. E. E. Rogers, R. A. Monsalve, T. J. Mozdzen and N. Mahesh, An absorption profile centred at 78 megahertz in the sky-averaged spectrum, *Nature* **555**, p. 67–70 (Mar 2018).
13. L. Hart and J. Chluba, Improved model-independent constraints on the recombination era and development of a direct projection method (12 2019).
14. V. Poulin, J. Lesgourgues and P. D. Serpico, Cosmological constraints on exotic injection of electromagnetic energy, *jcap* **2017**, p. 043 (March 2017).
15. M. Lucca, N. Schöneberg, D. C. Hooper, J. Lesgourgues and J. Chluba, The synergy between CMB spectral distortions and anisotropies, *jcap* **2020**, p. 026 (February 2020).

16. D. Blas, J. Lesgourgues and T. Tram, The cosmic linear anisotropy solving system (class). part ii: Approximation schemes, *Journal of Cosmology and Astroparticle Physics* **2011**, p. 034–034 (Jul 2011).
17. A. Lewis, A. Challinor and A. Lasenby, Efficient computation of cosmic microwave background anisotropies in closed friedmann-robertson-walker models, *The Astrophysical Journal* **538**, p. 473–476 (Aug 2000).
18. N. Aghanim, Y. Akrami, M. Ashdown, J. Aumont, C. Baccigalupi, M. Ballardini, A. J. Banday, R. B. Barreiro, N. Bartolo and et al., Planck 2018 results, *Astronomy & Astrophysics* **641**, p. A5 (Sep 2020).
19. A. Caputo, M. Regis, M. Taoso and S. J. Witte, Detecting the stimulated decay of axions at radio frequencies, *Journal of Cosmology and Astroparticle Physics* **2019**, p. 027–027 (Mar 2019).
20. B. M. Roach, K. C. Ng, K. Perez, J. F. Beacom, S. Horiuchi, R. Krivonos and D. R. Wik, Nustar tests of sterile-neutrino dark matter: New galactic bulge observations and combined impact, *Physical Review D* **101** (May 2020).
21. D. J. Marsh, Axion cosmology, *Physics Reports* **643**, p. 1–79 (Jul 2016).
22. G. G. Raffelt, Astrophysical axion bounds, *Axions* , p. 51–71.
23. CAST Collaboration, New CAST Limit on the Axion-Photon Interaction, *Nature Phys.* **13**, 584 (2017).
24. M. A. Bershady, M. T. Ressell and M. S. Turner, Telescope search for a 3-ev to 8-ev axion, *Phys. Rev. Lett.* **66**, 1398 (Mar 1991).
25. D. Grin, G. Covone, J.-P. Kneib, M. Kamionkowski, A. Blain and E. Jullo, Telescope search for decaying relic axions, *Physical Review D* **75** (May 2007).
26. M. Tanabashi and P. D. Group, Review of particle physics, *Phys. Rev. D* **98**, p. 030001 (Aug 2018).
27. M. Regis, M. Taoso, D. Vaz, J. Brinchmann, S. L. Zoutendijk, N. F. Bouché and M. Steinmetz, Searching for light in the darkness: Bounds on alp dark matter with the optical muse-faint survey, *Physics Letters B* **814**, p. 136075 (Mar 2021).
28. J. Chluba, M. H. Abitbol, N. Aghanim, Y. Ali-Haïmoud, M. Alvarez, K. Basu, B. Bolliet, C. Burigana, P. de Bernardis, J. Delabrouille and et al., New horizons in cosmology with spectral distortions of the cosmic microwave background, *Experimental Astronomy* **51**, p. 1515–1554 (May 2021).

The COSmic Monopole Observer (COSMO)

S. Masi*, E. Battistelli, P. de Bernardis, F. Columbro, A. Coppolecchia, G. D'Alessandro,
M. De Petris, L. Lamagna, E. Marchitelli, L. Mele, A. Paiella, F. Piacentini, G. Pisano

Physics Department, Sapienza University of Rome
and INFN Sezione di Roma, P.le A. Moro 2, Rome, 00185, Italy
*E-mail: silvia.masi@roma1.infn.it
https://cosmo.roma1.infn.it

M. Bersanelli, C. Franceschet, E. Manzan, D. Mennella, S. Realini

Physics Department, University of Milan
and INFN Sezione di Milano, Via Celoria 16, 20133 Milan, Italy

S. Cibella, F. Martini, G. Pettinari

IFN-CNR
Via Cineto Romano 42, 00156 Roma, Italy

G. Coppi, M. Gervasi, A. Limonta, M. Zannoni

Physics Department, University of Milan Bicocca
and INFN Sezione di Milano Bicocca, P.zza delle Scienze 1, 20126 Milan, Italy

L. Piccirillo

Department of Physics and Astronomy, University of Manchester
Oxford road, M13 9PL Manchester, UK

C. Tucker

School of Physics and Astronomy, University of Cardiff
The Parade, CF24 3AA Cardiff, UK

The COSmic Monopole Observer (COSMO) is an experiment to measure low-level spectral distortions in the isotropic component of the Cosmic Microwave Background (CMB). Deviations from a pure blackbody spectrum are expected at low level (< 1 ppm) due to several astrophysical and cosmological phenomena, and promise to provide important independent information on the early and late phases of the universe. They have not been detected yet, due to the extreme accuracy required, the best upper limits being still those from the COBE-FIRAS mission. COSMO is based on a cryogenic differential Fourier Transform Spectrometer, measuring the spectral brightness difference between the sky and an accurate cryogenic blackbody. The first implementation of COSMO, funded by the Italian PRIN and PNRA programs, will operate from the Concordia station at Dome-C, in Antarctica, and will take advantage of a fast sky-dip technique to get rid of atmospheric emission and its fluctuations, separating them from the monopole component of the sky brightness. Here we describe the instrument design, its capabilities, the current status. We also discuss its subsequent implementation in a balloon-flight, which has been studied within the COSMOS program of the Italian Space Agency.

Keywords: Cosmic Microwave Background; Spectral Distortions; Fourier Transform Spectrometer.

1. Introduction

Spectral distortions of the CMB represent a research path orthogonal and synergic to CMB polarization studies. Their detection can shed light on cosmic reionization, on the physics of recombination, on dark matter and in general on any energy release in the primeval fireball, and even on the very early universe and cosmic inflation. See[1] and references therein for a comprehensive review. The expected deviations are very small, < 1 ppm, but have characteristic spectral signatures, allowing, in principle, their separation from overwhelming foreground emission and the CMB monopole itself. In figure 1 we compare the largest spectral distortions of the CMB in the mm-wave region to the most important foregrounds.

Current upper limits for spectral distortions are at a level of 0.01% of the peak brightness of the CMB, and were obtained more than 20 years ago by COBE – FIRAS.[2,3] Current technologies promise to achieve much higher sensitivity, the limiting factor remaining the control of instrumental systematic effects and the emission of astrophysical foregrounds. In order to avoid the very large background produced by the earth atmosphere at CMB frequencies, the final measurement must be carried out from space. To this purpose, several proposals for space-based experiments have been submitted, like the PIXIE,[4] CORE[5] and PRISTINE missions. Meanwhile,

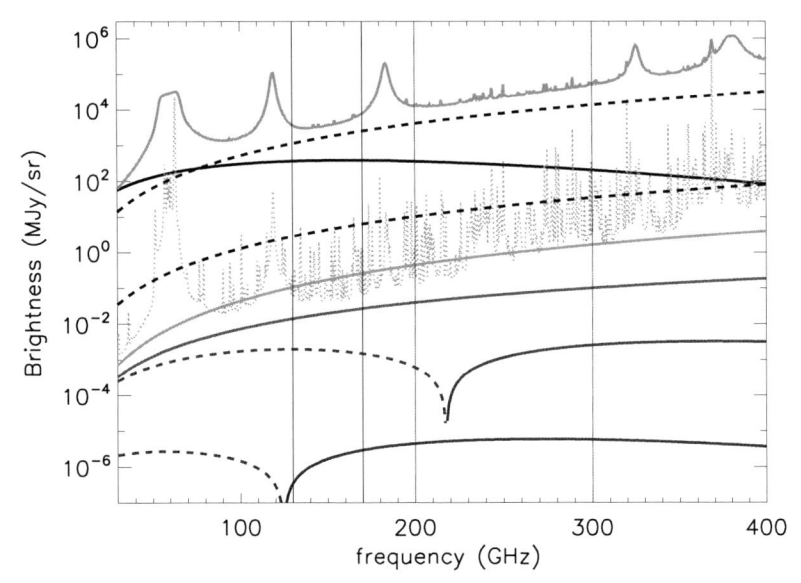

Fig. 1. Plot of isotropic brightness from (top to bottom, continuous lines): Antarctic atmosphere in Dome-C (zenith), CMB, interstellar dust (Galactic average), far infrared background (FIRB) from unresolved galaxies, absolute value of the y-distortion ($y = 1.77 \times 10^{-6}$, negative branch dashed), absolute value of the μ-distortion ($\mu = 2 \times 10^{-8}$, $\beta = 2.19$, negative branch dashed). The two dashed lines represent the emission of the window of the receiver, for the ground based (upper) and the balloon-borne (lower) implementations of COSMO. The dotted line represents atmospheric emission at stratospheric balloon altitude (zenith). The two couples of vertical lines define the observation bands of COSMO in its ground-based implementation.

ground-based and near-space efforts are necessary to test and refine methods, and possibly to detect the largest spectral distortions. Here we focus on the COSMO project, a pathfinder, staged effort to be carried out in Dome-C (Antarctica) first, and then on a stratospheric balloon.

The problem of spectral distortions of the CMB monopole, as evident from figure 1, is that they are very small with respect to other isotropic backgrounds, including instrument emission, atmospheric emission (if present), astrophysical foregrounds from the interstellar medium and the other galaxies along the line of sight, and the CMB monopole itself. Moreover the instrument has to be cryogenic to reduce its own emission, and operate where atmospheric emission is very small and/or can be measured and subtracted. For sure, advanced strategies for components separation are in order (see e.g.[6]).

In the following section we focus on the COSMO experiment, attempting sub-orbital measurements of spectral distortions.

2. The COSMO experiment

2.1. *Measurement method and general design*

COSMO is a cryogenic differential Fourier Transform Spectrometer (FTS) in Martin Puplett Interferometer (MPI) configuration:[7] a two input ports differential instrument comparing the brightness of the sky (port A) to the brightness of an accurate internal blackbody (port B), exactly like in COBE-FIRAS.[8] A simplified instrument model is described by equation 1:

$$I_{sky}(x) = \mathcal{R} \int_0^\infty A\Omega(\sigma)[B_{sky}(\sigma) - B_{ref}(T_{ref},\sigma)]e(\sigma)[1 + \cos(4\pi\sigma x)]d\sigma \quad (1)$$

where $I_{sky}(x)$ is the signal measured by the detector as a function of the optical path difference x between the two arms of the interferometer, which is scanned by means of a moving roof-mirror; σ is the wavenumber, $A\Omega(\sigma)$ is the optical throughput of the detector, $B_{sky}(\sigma)$ is the sky brightness present at input port A, $B_{ref}(T_{ref},\sigma)$ is the brightness of the reference blackbody at temperature T_{ref} present at input port B, $e(\sigma)$ is the spectral efficiency of the instrument, the constant $\mathcal{R}$ is the responsivity of the instrument. During the calibration phase, an external blackbody at a known temperature T_{ext} fills input port A: in these conditions the measured signal is

$$I_{cal}(x) = \mathcal{R} \int_0^\infty A\Omega(\sigma)[B_{ext}(T_{ext},\sigma) - B_{ref}(T_{ref},\sigma)]e(\sigma)[1 + \cos(4\pi\sigma x)]d\sigma. \quad (2)$$

Antitransforming equation 2 one gets the quantity $\mathcal{R}A\Omega(\sigma)e(\sigma)$, which can then be used in the antitransform of equation 1 to estimate $B_{sky}(\sigma)$.

Both B_{ref} and B_{ext} should be at cryogenic temperatures, close to T_{CMB}, in order to avoid saturation or non-linearity effects in the detectors, and extreme requirements on the knowledge of T_{ref}, T_{ext} and the blackbody emissivities.

Since the COSMO instrument operates in environments (Dome-C or the stratosphere) where atmospheric emission is present, special care must be taken to measure the emission from the atmosphere, and the emission of the vacuum window separating the cryogenic instrument from the external environment. Both these emissions are not present in a space-based instrument, while they contribute very significantly to the measured B_{sky} in the case of a suborbital experiment like COSMO. Moreover, the cryogenic external blackbody will necessarily have a vacuum window, adding its emission to B_{ext}.

2.2. Coping with atmospheric emission

In the ground-based implementation, COSMO will operate from the French-Italian Concordia base, in Dome-C (Antarctica). This is likely to be one of the best sites on Earth for mm-wave astronomical observations, being extremely cold and dry. But still atmospheric emission is present. The first defense against atmospheric emission is the selection of the frequency interval. In its ground-based implementation, COSMO uses two frequency channels matching mm-wave atmospheric windows, covering the frequency bands 110-170 GHz and 200-300 GHz. Each frequency channel is detected by an independent focal plane array. In this way radiation from the high frequency band does not overload the low-frequency detectors, so that higher sensitivity can be achieved in the low frequency channel.

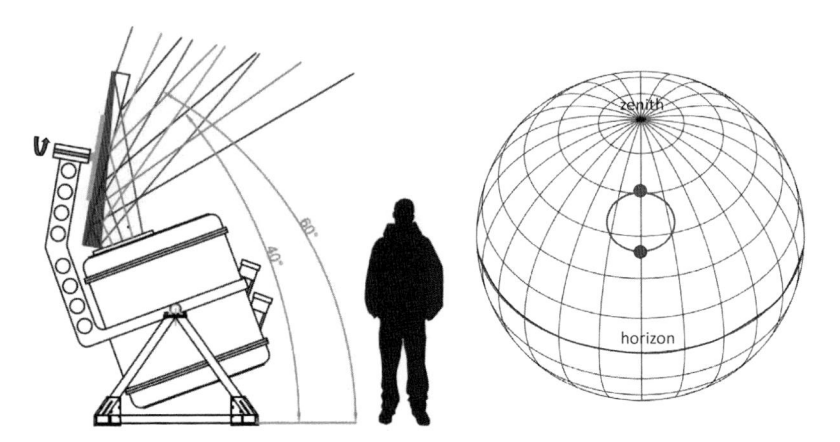

Fig. 2. Geometry of the sky scan for the COSMO experiment. **Left:** The COSMO instrument with the external spinning wedged flat mirror, steering the instrument beam in the sky while spinning. The arrow identifies the spin axis, while the mirror is sketched in two positions (red and blue) corresponding to maximum and minimum elevation of the beams, respectively. The central and marginal beams are also shown in the same colors. **Right:** Resulting scan of the beam (in red) over the celestial sphere. The two spots mark the maximum and minimum elevations explored by the beam. The circular scans, combined with Earth rotation, result in the coverage of several sky patches at different Galactic latitudes.

COSMO uses fast Kinetic Inductance Detectors (KID) and fast elevation scans to separate atmospheric emission and its long-term fluctuations from the monopole of the sky brightness. A fast spinning, wedged flat mirror (>1000 rpm) steers the boresight direction on a circle, $20°$ in diameter, scanning a range of elevations (and the corresponding optical depths of the atmosphere) while the cryogenic interferometer scans the optical path difference (see figure 2).

In this way the recorded interferogram (equation 1) will be the one due to the sky monopole (constant during the sky scan) plus the one due to atmospheric emission, which is modulated by the beam elevation variations during the sky scan. A sample expected interferogram is reported in figure 3 for the low-frequency band of COSMO.

By properly sampling the measured interferograms, the interferograms corresponding to the different elevations e scanned by the instrument can be retrieved. These can be antitrasformed to estimate the measured brightness spectra for the different elevations. For each frequency, a $cosec(e)$ law can be used to estrapolate to zero air-mass, thus estimating the isotropic component of the sky brightness (see figure 4).

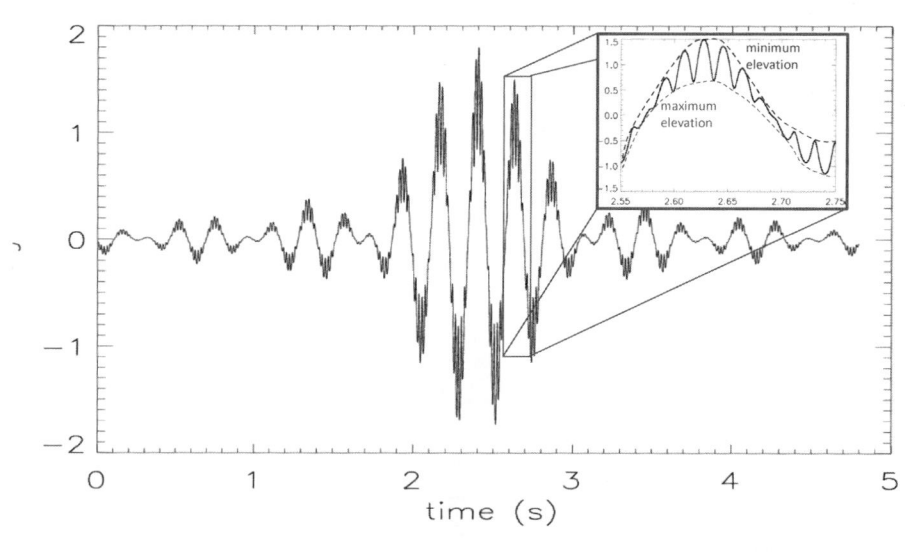

Fig. 3. Example of expected interferogram obtained while the flat wedged mirror is spinning. For each position x of the roof mirror in the MPI (corresponding to a different time on the abscissa), the signal changes due to the fast variation of the observed elevation. Fast (KID) detectors are used to follow these variations. In this example one full scan of the roof mirror is shown (at a mechanical speed of ~ 0.25 cm/s, from -1.27 cm to +1.27 cm of optical path difference). The zoomed inset shows how the interferograms corresponding to the maximum and minimum elevations can be obtained by properly resampling the measured interferogram. Millions of interferograms like this one will be measured during an observation campaign.

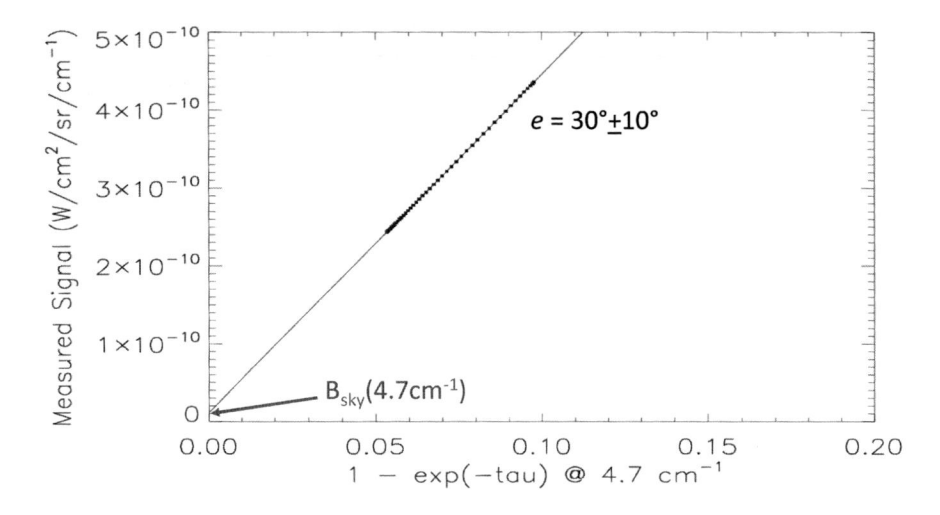

Fig. 4. Extrapolation to zero air-mass to estimate the isotropic component of the sky brightness for each frequency.

Since the instrument measures one interferogram every few seconds, slower atmospheric fluctuations are removed in the process, mitigating the effects of $1/f$ noise, which is characteristic of atmospheric fluctuations.

This measurement method is allowed by the use of fast ($\tau \sim 60\mu s$) KIDs, similar to the ones developed for the OLIMPO experiment.[9] In table 1 we report a possible scanning configuration of the COSMO instrument in its first ground-based implementation.

2.3. Coping with window emission

Both the cryogenic reference blackbody and the FTS of COSMO are enclosed in a vacuum shell, necessary for the cryogenic operations. External radiation enters the vacuum jacket through a vacuum window, made from a transparent material for mm waves. The best solution is to use a slab of polypropylene, which has to be ~ 1 cm thick in the ground based implementation, to withstand atmospheric pressure. This can be significantly thinner at balloon altitude: we assume a 25 μm thick window for that implementation. As visible in figure 1, the emission of the receiver window is very important in both cases. The way we cope with it is to measure spectra keeping the internal reference and the external calibrator at the two input ports and steady, for different, well controlled temperatures of the window. This procedure will produce a calibration of the contribution from window emission in the measured spectra as a function of the temperature of the window. This will be monitored during the sky measurements, so that will be possible to subtract

Table 1. Scanning characteristics of the COSMO instrument[a]

circle radius	5	deg
beam FWHM	0.5	deg
wedged mirror spin	600	rpm
time per beam	200	μs
time for one forward plus one reverse sky dip	0.1	s
maximum wavenumber	20	cm^{-1}
sampling step	125	μm
resolution	5-15	GHz
time to complete one interferogram	25.6	s
sky dips per interferogram element	2	

Note: [a]Example of certainly feasible combination of wedge and roof mirror scans; faster scans are currently under consideration.

window emission using the calibration. The expected accuracy of this process has been investigated: preliminary results show that the residuals after subtraction are subdominant when targeting at the measurement of the y distortion.

3. Implementation of the ground-based COSMO experiment

3.1. *Selection of the site and installation*

Due to the high altitude, extremely low temperatures in the winter, and absence of solar illumination for several months in a row, the Dome-C (Antarctica) site offers unmatched excellent conditions for astronomical observations in the mm-wave atmospheric windows (see e.g.[10,11]). Its latitude (75°S) allows for crosslinked sky scans at constant elevation (which are not possible from the South Pole), similar to those obtained in circumpolar stratospheric balloon flights (see e.g.[12]). The presence of the French-Italian Concordia station provides high quality logistics support (power, communications, resident personnel) for the operations of a modern CMB experiment. The instrument will be hosted in a thermally insulated ISO20 shipping container, with retractable roof, and mounted on a palafitte on top of a hardened snow berm, following a consolidated tradition for medium-size astronomical instruments in Antarctica. The container and the instrument will be oriented so that the elevation movement steers the boresight along the local meridian. As described below (see §4), this simple sky scan strategy allows to observe both high and intermediate Galactic latitudes, totalizing a coverage of $\sim 5\%$ of the sky.

3.2. *The optical system*

3.2.1. *Generalities*

Angular resolution is not the main driver of this experiment, which is aimed at measurements of the *isotropic* monopole component of the CMB brightness. We designed the instrument with and optical aperture of 22 cm in diameter, producing a diffraction limited beam at the longest wavelength (2.4 mm) of $\sim 0.7°$ FWHM. This is the result of a tradeoff between the size of the optical aperture and the need of monitoring the effect of *anisotropic* foregrounds. The telescope and the Fourier Transform Spectrometer are located inside the cryostat to minimize their radiative background. A sketch of the optical setup, based on polyethylene lenses, is shown in the left panel of figure 5, while the main data are reported in table 2.

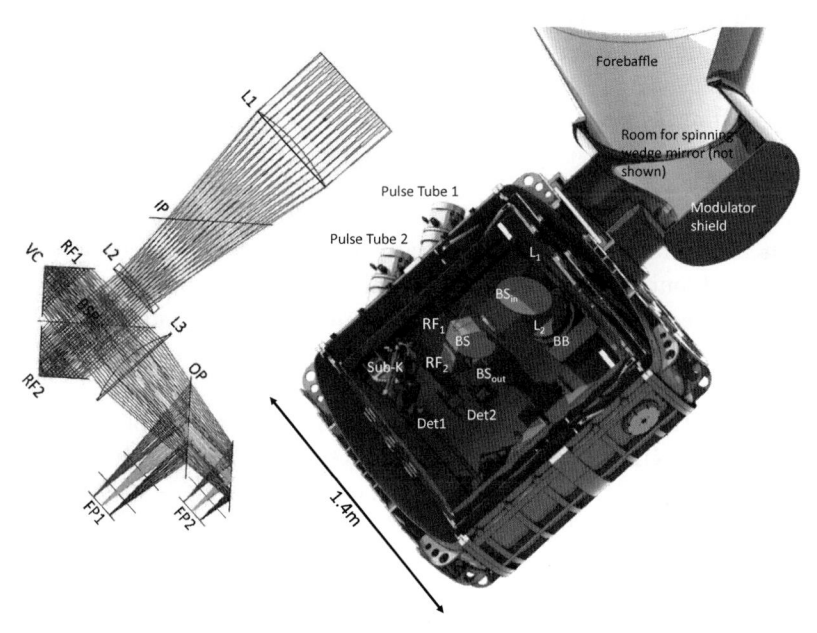

Fig. 5. **Left:** Ray tracing and optical design of COSMO. L1 is the light collector lens, L2 produces a nearly parallel beam for the FTS, L3 focuses radiation of the focal planes FP1 and FP2. The Differential Fourier Transform Spectrometer is costituted by the input polarizer IP, the beam-splitter polarizer BSP, the roof mirrors RF1 and RF2, the output polarizer OP. The input polarizer transmits radiation from the sky and reflects radiation from the cryogenic reference blackbody. **Right:** rendering of the accommodation of the COSMO instrument inside its cryogenic system.

Table 2. Optical parameters of the COSMO instrument.

optical aperture diameter	220	mm
effective focal length	726	mm
multimode pixel antenna aperture diameter	20	mm
focal planes	2	
number of detectors per focal plane	9	
projected pixel to pixel distance (x and y)	0.75	deg
beam FWHM	0.75	deg

3.2.2. *The cryogenic Fourier Transform Spectrometer*

The cryogenic FTS is a MPI, with two delay lines terminated with roof-mirrors. The interferogram is obtained introducing a variable difference in the lengths of the two delay lines. This is obtained with the linear movement of one of the two roof-mirrors (RF1 in figure 5). The maximum optical path difference introduced by the motion of the moving roof mirror is +/- 2 cm, corresponding to a coarse spectral resolution of ~10 GHz. Since the FTS operates at cryogenic temperature, we have to minimize the friction produced by the motion of the roof-mirror. We have designed a cryomechanism based on harmonic steel flexure blades, operating in the elastic regime. The actuator is a coil moving in the radial magnetic field of a strong permanent magnet (figure 6). The position is sensed by a LVDT. Preliminary room-temperature tests confirm the frictionless operation of the device.

3.2.3. *The detectors*

The output beam from the FTS is naturally split in two exit ports by the output polarizer. In each output port we place a focal plane array, consisting of multimode horn antennas feeding multimode lumped elements kinetic inductance detectors (LEKIDs), on a 4 inch Si wafer. The reflected beam serves the high frequency band array, while the transmitted one serves the low frequency band array.

The design of the COSMO LEKIDs was optimized starting from the experience gained with the LEKID arrays realized for the OLIMPO experiment.[25,26] COSMO detectors are 30 nm thick Aluminum LEKIDs, each of which has a front–illuminated V order Hilbert curve absorber/inductor. The large absorber area, ~ 8 mm × 8 mm for both channels, serves to guarantee the efficient absorption of all the modes

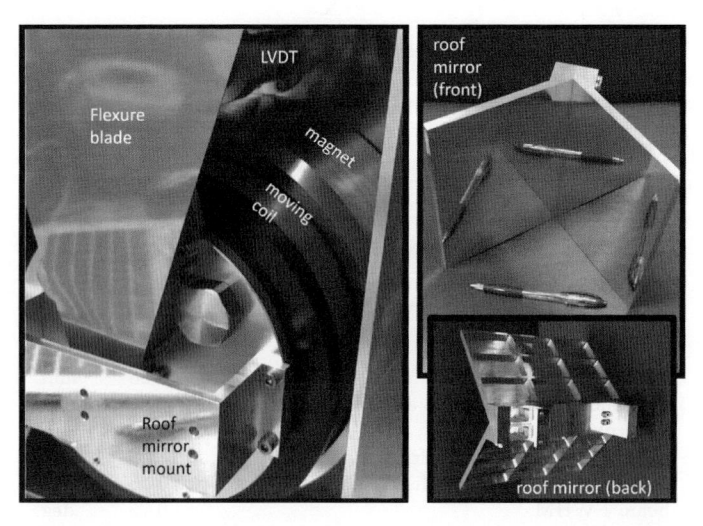

Fig. 6. **Left**: photo of the cryogenic roof-mirror scanner for the MPI FTS. **Right**: the roof mirror. Its projected size is 200 × 200 mm.

Fig. 7. **Left:** photo of the low-frequency array, made of seven antenna plates and a bottom plate with circular waveguides. **Right:** photo of the high-frequency array, which is made as one piece, with a separate bottom plate of circular waveguides.

which propagate through the multimode waveguides. In particular, the size of the waveguide diameter, 4.5 mm for the 150 GHz channel and 4 mm for the 255 GHz channel, allows the propagation of 10 to 19 modes in the 120-180 GHz range and of 23 to 42 modes in the 210-300 GHz range. Because of the size of the focal planes and the horn apertures, each detector array hosts 9 pixels.

The forecast performance for such detectors, in terms of detector noise equivalent power (NEP) is $\mathrm{NEP_{det}} \sim 3.8 \times 10^{-17}$ W/$\sqrt{\mathrm{Hz}}$, with a response time $\tau \sim 60\,\mu\mathrm{s}$, when operated at about 300 mK. These estimations take into account the absorber volume, the superconductor critical temperature, and the simulated absorber efficiency. This performance is more than adequate for the ground-based implementation of COSMO, which is likely to be dominated by atmospheric noise and systematic effects rather than by detector sensitivity.

3.2.4. The detector feedhorns

The radiation coming from the FTS is coupled to the detectors by two arrays of nine multimoded feed-horns working in the 120 − 180 GHz and 210 − 300 GHz range, respectively. Since COSMO will perform only total intensity measurements, we chose a smooth-walled profile which is easier to manufacture than a corrugated one.

The low-frequency array consists of Winston cone antennas while the high-frequency array hosts linear profiled antennas. The antenna design is the result of a trade-off between the multimode requirement on the antenna waveguide, the mechanical constraint on the antenna aperture and the optimization of the antenna directivity within the cryostat aperture window. The forecasted FWHM of the main beam is around 20°, the first side-lobe level is below -15 dB and the far side-lobe level is below -30 dB.

The arrays are machined with CNC milling by Pasquali SRL in Milan, and are obtained by superimposing metal plates through dowel-pins and tightening them with screws, as shown in figure 7. The arrays are cylindrical with a diameter of 101 mm to minimize the mass to be cooled as much as possible; the feed-horns are arranged on a square footprint with a 26 mm center-to-center distance.

Both the arrays are made in ergal (Al7075) to conform to the focal plane and avoid differential thermal contractions during the cryogenic cooling of the experiment. They are mechanically coupled to a band-pass filter on the front (aperture) side and to an interface to the focal plane wafer holder on the back. To this purpose, we used the experience gained with the LSPE-SWIPE experiment[15] to design a flared waveguide interface to directly illuminate the KIDs detectors.

3.2.5. *The reference blackbody*

One of the two inputs of FTS looks at a cryogenic reference blackbody. This is a cavity with the inner surface covered by a microwave absorber. The cavity structure is in copper, to achieve a very uniform temperature. We have optimized the shape of the cavity both through geometrical ray tracing (maximizing the number of internal reflections) and via finite elements electromagnetic simulations (minimizing the S_{11} parameter). The performance in the ray-tracing approximation is assessed assuming a reflectance of the coating as a function of the wavenumber $\bar{\nu}$ as in ref.,[16] $r(\bar{\nu}) = 0.08 + \frac{0.06[cm^{-1}]}{\bar{\nu}}$. The number of internal reflections is always $N > 6$, corresponding to the cavity reflectance $R = r^N < 10^{-6}$ over the band 100-300 GHz. This indirectly provides the cavity emissivity as $(1 - R)$.

Due to the size of the calibrator, much larger than the wavelengths of interest, we used *HFSS* electromagnetic analysis only to simulate the performance of a thin cut section of the cavity. This is a few wavelengths thick, and is representative in terms of the absorbing properties of the cavity. However it is not representative of the direction of the damped outgoing radiation. The simulations have been run for the lowest frequencies of the 150 GHz band, and the corresponding dielectric properties of the absorbing coating (relative permittivity $\epsilon_r = 3.50$ and dielectric loss tangent $tg(\delta) = 0.032$ at 100 GHz at 4 K) have been taken from.[17] The input radiation is set as an *Incident Gaussian Beam*, determined by the lens L1 feeding the blackbody cavity. The reflectance, computed as the ratio of the Poynting vector fluxes of the scattered and incident radiation, is $R(120\,\text{GHz}) = 3.2 \cdot 10^{-6}$. Diffractive effects and reflection coefficients at non-normal incidence, not included in the ray tracing approach, produce discrepancies between the two models.

Finite elements thermal simulations have been performed, considering a perfect thermal contact between the copper external structure and the internal absorbing coating, and including an irradiating internal surface of the cavity to a 4 K background. The external structure temperature was set to 2.725 K, from a starting

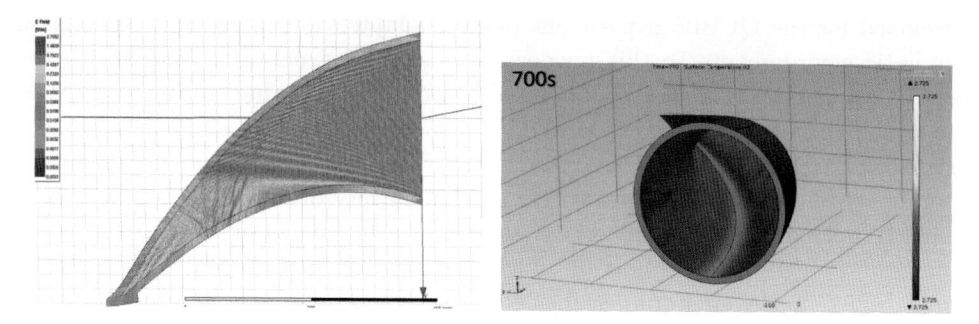

Fig. 8. **Left:** Results of an HFSS simulation of the total electric field propagating within the blackbody cavity, demonstrating its gradual attenuation (colors correspond to a logarithmic scale for field amplitudes. **Right:** Results of a finite elements thermal simulation displaying the temperature at the surface of the internal absorbing coating 700s after cool-down. The temperature gradients are <0.1 mK.

point of 4 K. The thermal properties of the coating are taken from.[18] Preliminary results show a maximum thermal gradient <0.1 mK (see fig.8).

3.2.6. *The atmospheric modulator*

The other input of the FTS looks at the sky through an optical window and a beam-steering mirror, which is used to modulate atmospheric emission and measure it as described in §2.2. The atmospheric scan has to be very fast (up to 2800 rpm) to measure atmospheric emission and subtract it in real time, so that 1/f noise from atmospheric emission is efficiently removed. A light-weighted, all 6061 Aluminum design for the mirror has been optimized to minimize the inertia. The off-axis inertia moments are null using optimized counterweights, allowing us to use simple and reliable electrical motors and shaft bearings.

One of the most dangerous problems in this kind of measurements is the pickup of ground radiation. A custom forebaffle has been designed as the first defense against ground spillover. This forebaffle moves together with the receiver, and will be complemented by much larger steady ground shields. The internal surface will be fully covered with eccosorb absorber. The forebaffle is largely oversized, and has been shaped so that the spillover from its inner surface is not modulated by the spin of the wedge mirror. Heaters and temperature sensors will allow to test any residual spillover contribution to the measured signal by means of custom calibration measurements.

3.3. *The cryogenic system*

A large cryogenic system, based on pulse-tubes and a ^{3}He evaporation cooler is used to cool the optical system and the detector arrays. The system is similar to the one developed for the QUBIC experiment (see[13]), adapted for operation in the harsh Antarctic environment. To this purpose, we used the experience gained with the BRAIN refrigerator, successfully operated in Dome-C more than 10 years ago.[14] In the right panel of figure 5 we show the implementation of the COSMO instrument inside its cryogenic system. Using pulse tube refrigerators, the cryogenic system can operate continuously and does not rely on the delivery of cryogenic liquids, which would be very difficult in dome-C. Of course, continuous power is required, which amounts to about 10 kW, most of which are used for the pulse tube compressors and to warm-up the environment inside the experiment shelter to above 0 Celsius.

3.4. Readout electronics

The arrays of KIDs are read applying a comb of frequencies tuned to the resonances of the different pixels, and reading the S21 parameter for each pixel. A FPGA-based electronic system generates a set of tones corresponding to the KIDs' resonances. The combination of tones is sent to the detectors; the return signal is acquired and analyzed by means of a transceiver which detects the change in amplitude and phase of the tones. The system is based on a commercial architecture (Xilinx Virtex-5 NI7966R). The Virtex5 architecture was selected because it is the most powerful of the family being available as a rad-hard component. This specification not necessary for Antarctica, but is strategic in the perspective of the implementation of COSMO on a stratospheric balloon . We have prepared a state machine which, in the first state, performs a sweep to find the resonance tones of the KIDs. In the second state, a lookup table is generated with the values of the resonances found. With a CORDIC algorithm these tones are generated to compose a comb, which the third state of the machine transmits to the KIDs and acquires in amplitude and phase to measure the variation of the working point of the detectors. We have already tested the functionality of the state machine in the lab by means of Nb kids, fit for a 4 K cryostat. We are currently working to move the entire process of modulation and demodulation on board of the FPGAs, to reach the target rate of acquisition, fit for the operation with the FTS.

4. Performance forecast for the the ground-based COSMO experiment

The performance of the instrument is assessed via ILC[19] (Internal Linear Combination) based simulations. Absolutely-calibrated maps are used as input, containing the superposition of the PySM[20] maps of CMB anisotropies and thermal dust, as the main galactic foreground. The isotropic distortion maps are added as a y-distortion map with $y = 1.77 \cdot 10^{-6}$ and a μ-distortion map with $\mu = 2.0 \cdot 10^{-8}$. The input multi-frequency maps, with a spectral resolution $\Delta \nu = 15\,\text{GHz}$, are smoothed with a FWHM=1°. The noise realization, added as Gaussian noise, is dominated by the photon noise from the cryostat window, whose emission is modeled as a 240 K

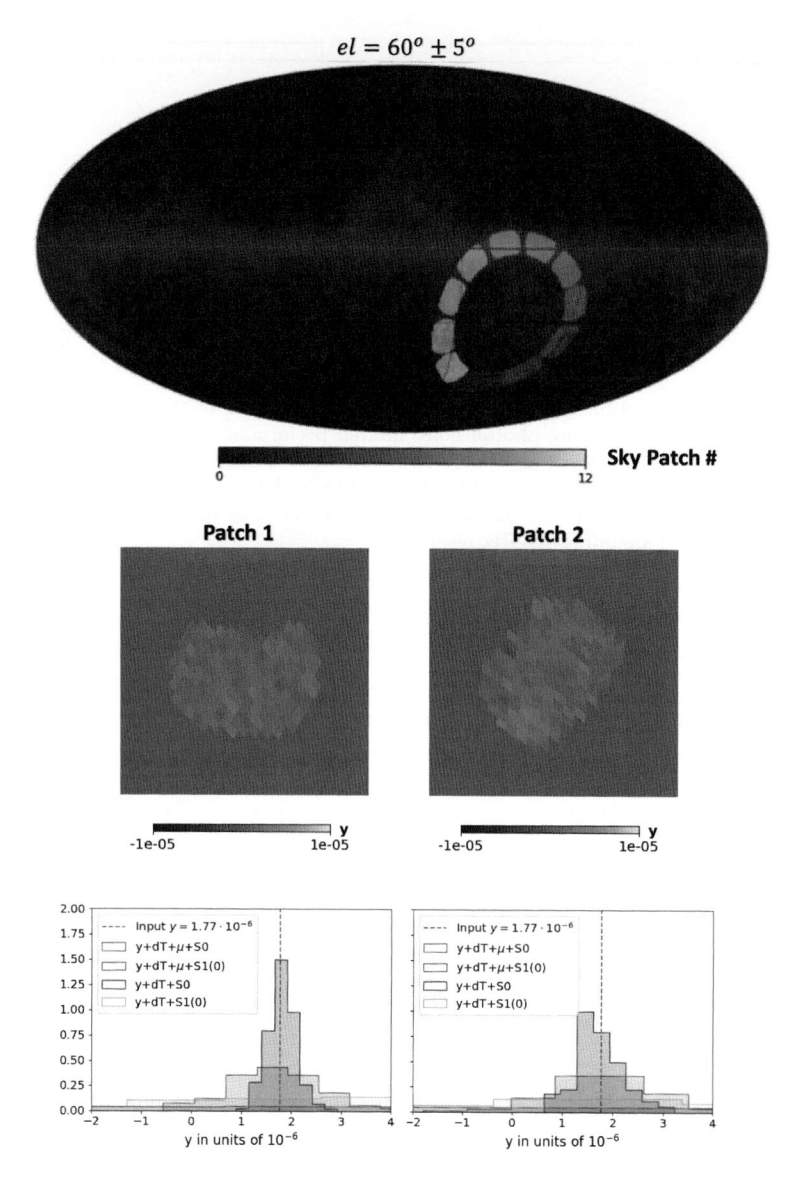

Fig. 9. **Top:** Sky coverage map divided in 11 patches, overlapped to the 270GHz PySM map which includes thermal dust emission and CMB anisotropy. **Middle:** Simulated measured maps for the y distortion sky component, extracted using the ILC method, in two sample sky patches at high Galctic latitude. **Bottom:** Histograms of the simulated estimates for the y values, for the two sky patches above.

grey-body with 1% emissivity, and by the atmospheric emission (modeled based on the *a.m.* software with PWV=0.15mm).

The ILC machinery allows to extract the y-distortion map from the dominant components. Different orders of the thermal dust emission are subtracted from the

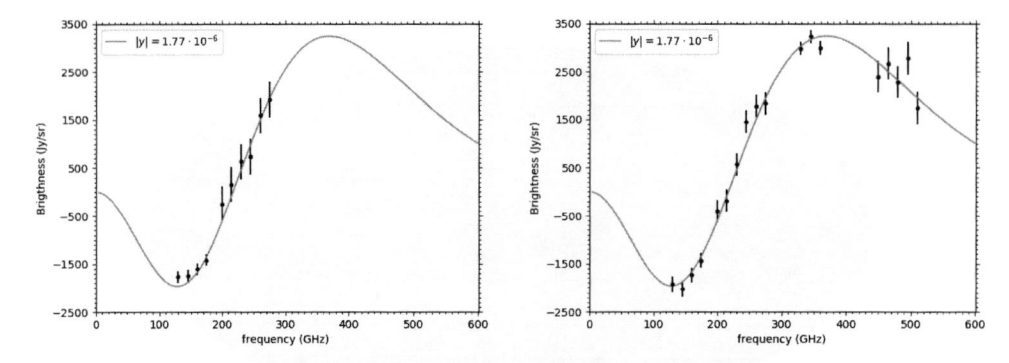

Fig. 10. **Left:** Simulated measurement of the spectral distortion of the CMB after one year of integration in Dome-C, assuming photon noise limited performance dominated by the emissions of the cryostat window and the atmosphere and assuming 15 GHz resolution. **Right:** Simulated measurement of the spectral distortion of the CMB after 15 days of integration on a stratospheric balloon, assuming photon noise limited performance dominated by the CMB, residual atmosphere and warm mirror, and assuming 15 GHz resolution.

solution as in.[21] Histograms of the output Compton-y maps, reported in Fig.9, show that the best ILC solution is provided by subtracting the 0th order of the thermal dust, in combination with the CMB anisotropy.

Assuming a scanning strategy at fixed central elevation, combined with the spinning wedge mirror modulation, 5% of the sky is observed every day, which can be divided for the analysis in 11 sky-patches at different Galactic latitudes (see fig.9). The ILC is independently applied to the patches and the weighted average of the output Compton-y maps provides the estimate of the isotropic y distortion as $y = (1.70 \pm 0.28) \cdot 10^{-6}$.

In figure 10 (left panel) we show the expected spectrum of the spectral distortion we expect to measure after 1 year of integration in Dome-C.

5. Implementation of the balloon-borne COSMO experiment

The spectrum of the CMB at mm wavelengths has been measured from stratospheric balloon platforms in the past (see e.g.[22]). Here we plan to exploit the recent advaces in detector sensitivity and speed, and the atmospheric modulation technique validated with the ground based implementation of COSMO, to take advantage of the very low residual atmospheric emission present at stratospheric altitude (see fig.1). With an atmospheric emission ∼300 times dimmer than in the ground based case, we expect that possible atmospheric residuals, which in the ground based implementation might escape the removal method described in §2.2, will be negligible. In these conditions we expect that the limiting factor will become the emission of the warm components of the instrument, i.e. the room temperature sky scan mirror and the cryostat window. Due to the reduced atmospheric pressure at balloon altitude, the latter can be made very thin (order of 25 μm), implying a factor $\sim$100 reduction of its thermal emission. We have a long-term plan to reuse the LSPE-SWIPE gondola and cryostat ([23]) to fly a modified COSMO instrument in the stratosphere in a time-scale of 4 years. This activity is synergic to the development of the BISOU experiment.[24] Due to the reduced atmospheric load, we can extend our spectral coverage to significantly higher frequencies, in order to easy the separation of spectral distortions from local foreground emission. We rerun our simple simulation (§4) for the case of an observation in a 15-days flight, with photon-noise limited detectors (here the radiative background is dominated by the CMB, the thin window and the sky modulator mirror) obtaining the performance forecast shown in figure 10 (right panel). The S/N ratio for the extraction of the largest spectral distortion is quite high ($>$10).

6. Conclusions

The measurement of spectral distortions in the CMB poses hard experimental challenges, but represents a fundamental cosmology tool, able to test a variety of cosmological phenomena. In particular, this kind of measurement seems to be the best, among very few, to shed light on the pre-recombination evolution of the universe. COSMO represents a pioneering sub-orbital approach to investigate spectral distortions at mm wavelengths. It copes with atmospheric emission and its fluctuations using fast detectors and a fast atmospheric emission modulation technique, able to separate its spectral brightness from the isotropic cosmological component. The instrument is in an advanced stage of development, and promises to detect the largest spectral distortion (the y distortion due to ionized matter in the universe) in 2 years of integration from the French-Italian station of Concordia (Antarctica). A further implementation on a stratospheric balloon platform is under study, and promises significant advantages and a necessary validation step in view of the final space mission devoted to spectral distortions.

Acknowledgments

The COSMO activity is funded in Italy by PNRA (National Program for Antarctic Research) and PRIN (Programs with Relevant National Interest). The balloon-borne implementation is being studied within the COSMOS program of the Italian Space Agency.

References

1. J. Chluba, M.H. Abitbol, N. Aghanim, et al., New horizons in cosmology with spectral distortions of the cosmic microwave background, *Experimental Astronomy*, (2021), https://doi.org/10.1007/s10686-021-09729-5

2. J. Mather, et al., A Preliminary Measurement of the Cosmic Microwave Background Spectrum by the Cosmic Background Explorer (COBE) Satellite, *Ap.J.Letters* **354**, 37 (1990).
3. D. Fixsen, et al., The Cosmic Microwave Background Spectrum from the Full COBE FIRAS Data Set, *Ap.J.* **473**, 576 (1996).
4. A. Kogut, et al., The Primordial Inflation Explorer (PIXIE): a nulling polarimeter for cosmic microwave background observations, *Journal of Cosmology and Astroparticle Physics*, **07**, 025 (2011).
5. P. de Bernardis, et al., Exploring cosmic origins with CORE: The instrument, *Journal of Cosmology and Astroparticle Physics*, **04**, 015 (2018).
6. J. Chluba, et al., Rethinking CMB foregrounds: systematic extension of foreground parametrizations, *MNRAS*, **472**, 1195, (2017).
7. D.H. Martin and E. Puplett, Polarised interferometric spectrometry for the millimetre and submillimetre spectrum, *Infrared Physics*, **10**, 105 (1970)
8. D.J. Fixsen, et al., Calibration of the COBE FIRAS Instrument, *The Astrophysical Journal*, **420**, 457 (1994).
9. S. Masi, et al., Kinetic Inductance Detectors for the OLIMPO experiment: in-flight operation and performance, *Journal of Cosmology and Astroparticle Physics*, **07**, 003 (2019).
10. P. Tremblin, et al., Site testing for submillimetre astronomy at Dome C, Antarctica. *Astronomy and Astrophysics*, **535**, A112, (2011).
11. E. Battistelli, et al., Intensity and polarization of the atmospheric emission at millimetric wavelengths at Dome Concordia, *MNRAS*, **423**, 1293 (2012).
12. S. Masi, et al., Instrument, method, brightness, and polarization maps from the 2003 flight of BOOMERanG, *Astronomy and Astrophysics*, **458**, 687, (2006).
13. S. Masi, et al., QUBIC V: Cryogenic system design and performance, *Journal of Cosmology and Astroparticle Physics*, accepted for publication (arXiv:2008.10659) (2021).
14. G. Polenta, et al., The BRAIN CMB polarization experiment, *New Astronomy Reviews*, **51**, 256 (2007).
15. F. Columbro, et al., SWIPE Multi-mode Pixel Assembly Design and Beam Pattern Measurements at Cryogenic Temperature, *Journal of Low Temperature Physics*, **199**, 312, (2020)
16. J. C. Mather, et al., Calibrator Design for the COBE Far Infrared Absolute Spectrophotometer (FIRAS), *ApJ*, **512**, 511 (1999)
17. J. W. Lamb, Miscellaneous data on materials for millimetre and submillimetre optics, *Int J Infrared Milli Waves*, **17**, 1997–2034 (1996)
18. L. Valenziano et al, Planck-LFI: design and performance of the Kelvin Reference Load Unit, *JINST*, **4**, (2009)
19. M. Remazeilles, et al., Foreground component separation with generalized Internal Linear Combination, *Monthly Notices of the Royal Astronomical Society*, **418**, 467–476 (2011)
20. B. Thorne et al., The Python Sky Model: software for simulating the Galactic microwave sky, *Monthly Notices of the Royal Astronomical Society*, **469**, 2821–2833 (2017)
21. A. Rotti and J. Chluba, Combining ILC and moment expansion techniques for extracting average-sky signals and CMB anisotropies, *Monthly Notices of the Royal Astronomical Society*, **500**, 976–985 (2021)
22. D.P. Woody, P. L. Richards, Near-millimeter spectrum of the microwave background *Astrophysical Journal*, **248**, 18–37 (1981)

23. The LSPE Collaboration, The large scale polarization explorer (LSPE) for CMB measurements: performance forecast, *Journal of Cosmology and Astroparticle Physics*, accepted for publication (arXiv:2008.11049) (2021)
24. B. Maffei, et al., these proceedings.
25. A. Paiella, et al., Kinetic Inductance Detectors for the OLIMPO experiment: design and pre-flight characterization, *Journal of Cosmology and Astroparticle Physics*, **01**, 039 (2019).
26. A. Paiella, et al., Kinetic Inductance Detectors and readout electronics for the OLIMPO experiment, *Journal of Physics: Conference Series*, **1182**, 012005 (2019).

Measuring the Hubble constant H_0 from gravitational lensing

Liliya L.R. Williams

Minnesota Institute for Astrophysics,
University of Minnesota–Twin Cities,
116 Church Street SE, Minneapolis, MN 55454, USA
E-mail: llrw@umn.edu

First proposed in 1964 by Sjur Refsdal, gravitational lensing provides a straightforward and elegant geometrical way of estimating the Hubble constant from cosmologically distant variable sources. The method relies on observationally determined time delays between light arriving through different multiple images, and the mass models of the lens, which are constrained by observed image properties and other information. While the time delays are obtained with increasing precision, the mass models, which are subject to lensing degeneracies, remain the main source of systematic uncertainty. Various modeling groups have adopted different strategies for dealing with degeneracies. In this talk I will describe the basics of extracting H_0 from lensing, the observational successes, modeling challenges, current results, and future prospects.

Keywords: Cosmological parameters – gravitational lensing

1. Introduction

The idea of measuring H_0 from multiple image (i.e., strong) gravitational lensing is due to the Norwegian astronomer, Sjur Refsdal.[1] Because H_0 is the property of global cosmology, with units of inverse time, and because light travel from lensed sources spans cosmological distances, light travel time will depend on H_0. Therefore there should be a way to extract H_0 from gravitational lensing.

Light travel time along null geodesics, from the source, passing the lens and arriving at the observer consists of two contributions: geometrical and gravitational, which are added linearly, since lensing almost always is in the weak field regime of General Relativity:

- **geometrical** – path length, related to the angular location of the image on the sky
- **gravitational** – integrated Newtonian potential along the line of sight, a.k.a. the Shapiro delay

Figure 1 illustrates the basic geometry. The observer on the left sees images at angular locations on the sky, $\vec{\theta}_i, \vec{\theta}_j$. The unlensed source position, $\vec{\beta}$, is also indicated. The light travel time, or the arrival time of the image seen at $\vec{\theta}$ is given by $t(\vec{\theta})$, and consists of the two aforementioned terms. The gravitational time delay is calculated as an integral over the observer sky of the sky-projected normalized (dimensionless) surface mass density in the lens, $\kappa(\vec{\theta})$, with a logarithmic kernel. The prefactor in front of the square brackets is important because it involves cosmological angular diameter distances, each of which scales inversely with H_0. This is where the depence on the Hubble constant comes from in multple image gravitational lensing.

Lensing time delays theory

arrival time not observed: $t(\vec{\theta}) = \frac{(1+z_\ell)D_\ell D_s}{c\,D_{\ell s}}\left[\frac{1}{2}(\vec{\theta}-\vec{\beta})^2 - \frac{1}{\pi}\int d\vec{\theta}'\,\kappa(\vec{\theta}')\ln|\vec{\theta}'-\vec{\theta}|\right]$

angular distances: $D = \frac{c}{H_0}\,fcn(\Omega's,\omega)$

geometrical

gravitational — lens mass model $\tau(\vec{\theta})$

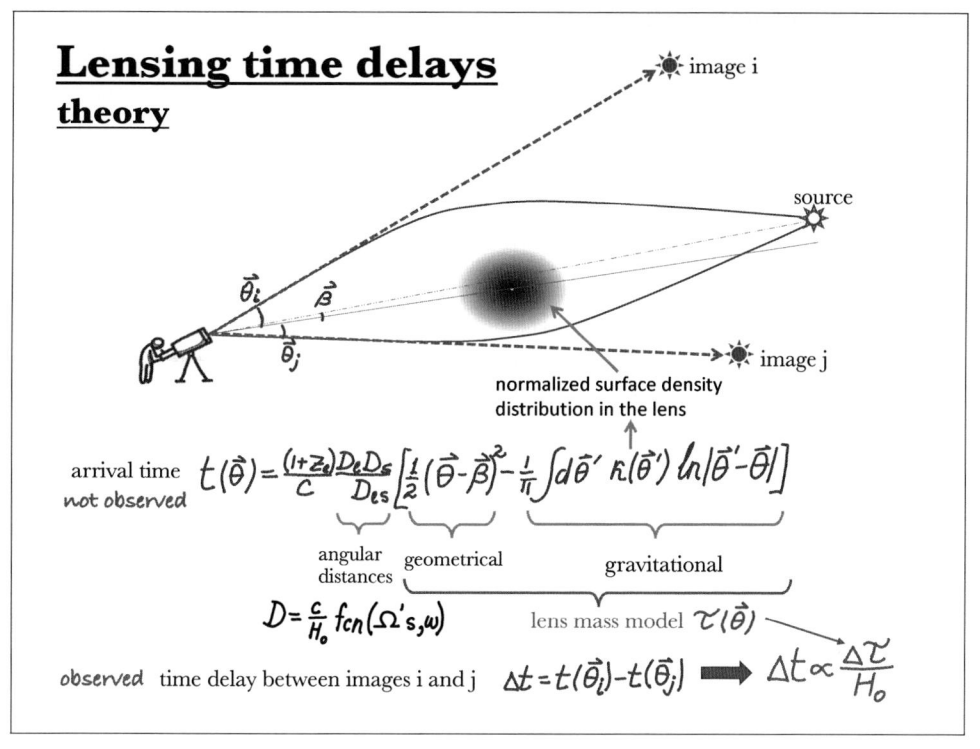

observed time delay between images i and j: $\Delta t = t(\vec{\theta}_i) - t(\vec{\theta}_j) \Rightarrow \Delta t \propto \frac{\Delta \tau}{H_0}$

Fig. 1. A sketch of a multiple image (i.e., strong lensing) geometry. The light rays paths for two images are shown, $\vec{\theta}_{i,j}$, as well as the direction towards the unobservable source, $\vec{\beta}$. Hubble constant, H_0 enters through the angular diameter distance in the equation for the arrival time, $t(\vec{\theta})$. See § 1 for details.

The expression in the square brackets is the model arrival time, $\tau(\vec{\theta})$, because it is calculated from a lens model, which recovers the mass distribution in the lens, $\kappa(\vec{\theta})$, as well as the unobservable $\vec{\beta}$. The total light travel time, sometimes called the arrival time, $t(\vec{\theta})$ is not an observable. What we can observe is the difference between the arrival times of two images, Δt, related to $\Delta \tau$ through H_0:

$$\Delta t \propto \Delta \tau / H_0. \tag{1}$$

This is the essence of the method. Basically, to extract H_0 from lensing, one needs to measure time delays, and to construct a good model of the mass distribution in the lens. Thus, the basic principle of the method is simple, and very appealing because it is a one-step determination of H_0, and works on cosmological distances, bypassing all the rungs of the traditional astronomical distance ladder method, which uses overlaping distance determination methods to reach the Hubble flow. The complications in the lensing measurement of H_0 come from uncertainties in the determination of observational values, as well as lens mass model building.

2. Overview of uncertainties

There are 4 main sources of uncertainties.

- *Line-of-sight (LoS) structures.* The Universe contains not just the source, the lens, and the observer, but also a wide range of other mass structures; in fact, a whole spectrum of mass density fluctuations. The main lens is usually by far the most massive object in the direction of the source, but other, smaller mass clumps also exist. Their influence on the lensing has been recently studied by a number of authors, including Ref. 2, who concluded that the corresponding uncertainty in the determination of H_0 for one lens contributes $\sim 0.6 - 2.4\%$ of scatter, with little bias. If a handful of lenses are used, which is usually the case, the scatter goes down to $\sim 0.5\%$, and at this level it is subdominant to other sources of uncertainty.
- Uncertainties in *cosmological parameters*, like energy densities Ω's, contribute very little to the uncertainties in H_0, typically $< 0.1\%$, if one uses cosmological parameter values that are broadly consistent with the concordance cosmological model ΛCDM.
- *Time delays between images;* see § 3.
- *Mass modeling of the lens;* see § 4.

3. Time delays between lensed images

To measure H_0 one generally uses lens systems that have quasars are sources. Fluxes of most quasars vary in time on scales from seconds to years. The variability is stochastic, its origin being the variations in the conditions of the inner accretion disk around supermassive black holes, residing at the centers of source galaxies. The upper left panel in Figure 2 shows an example of lightcurves (flux vs. time) of images of one particular lens system over about 14 years,[3] and the zoomed in portion below it concentrates on a much narrower time scale, and also resolves time variations of two close images, called A_1 and A_2 (see the sky-plot of the lens on the very left). Observing lightcurves require a lot of effort and dedication. The main group envolved in this is COSMOGRAIL, based at the EPFL in Switzerland.

The lightcurves show features that are common to all images, but displaced in the time direction. (There are also offsets in flux, since images are magnified by different amount by the lens.) These displacements can be measured and are the lensing-induced time delays. There are many algorithms that recover time delays from lightcurves: six examples are shown on the right, for one particular pair of images in this lens system. The two bottom values are two different ways of "averaging" over these individual determinations. In this case, the best estimate is about 36 days,

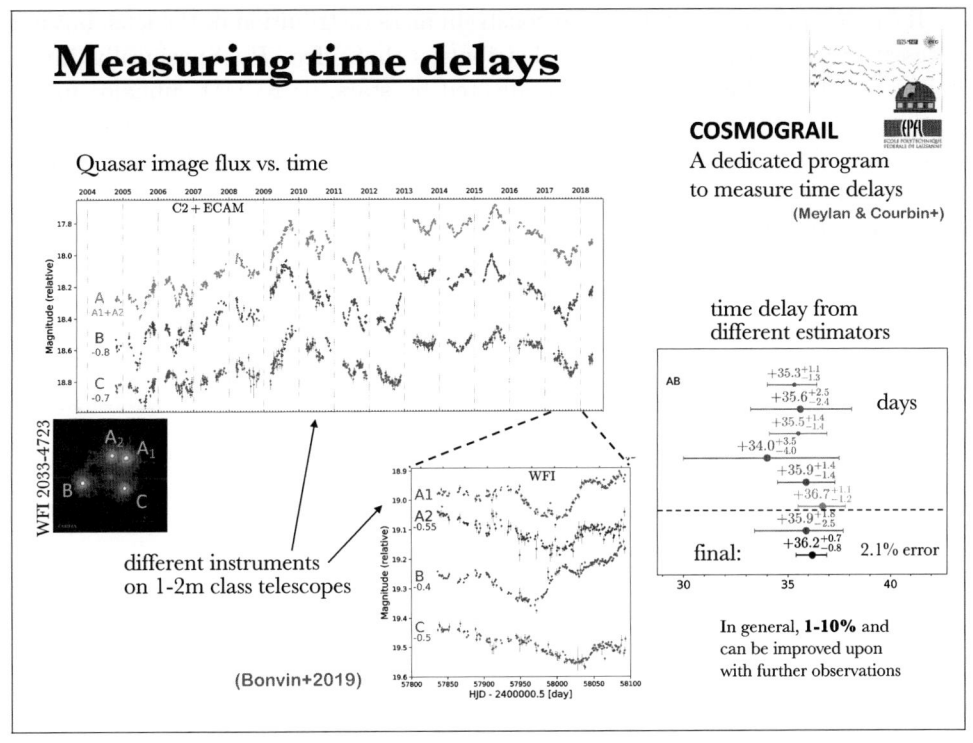

Fig. 2. An example of image lightcurves in one particular quad lens system (left). The results of time delay estimation using different methods are shown in the panel on the right. See § 3 for details.

with an error of 2.1%. In galaxy-scale lens systems, time delays of the order of few days to few weeks are common. Precision ranges from $1-10\%$, and can be improved upon with longer base-line, and possible improvements in the cadence of observations.

4. Mass modeling of lens systems

4.1. *Data constraints*

We start with assembling observational data that will help in constraining the mass distribution in the lensing galaxy. These are

- quasar image positions
- quasar time delays
- quasar image flux ratios
- Einstein ring, formed by the extended and usually merging multiple images of the host galaxy of the source quasar

While the first two are always used in deriving H_0, the last two have caveats.

Ratios of quasar image fluxes do constrain mass distribution in the lens, but not necessarily the aspects of the mass distribution that affect H_0. Specifically, image fluxes, and hence flux ratios can be affected by stars, or ΛCDM subhalos in the lensing galaxy that have relatively little mass, but happen to lie very close to the light path of the images. Interpreting these flux ratios as being due to the mass distribution on galaxy scales will lead to wrong conclusions. Because of this image flux ratios are usually not used.

The extended Einstein rings are spread over many pixels, so in principle can provide a lot of additional information. However, because the *Hubble Space Telescope*'s camera pixels are about a factor of 10 larger in linear dimension than the positional accuracy for quasar point images, the positional information from extended rings is not as constraining. Furthermore, the rings are often faint, with low signal-to-noise ratio. Finally, the shape of the (unlensed) source is unknown.

Modeling constraints

subject to lensing degeneracies
- quasar image positions
- quasar time delays
- quasar image flux ratios — *If due to stars or ΛCDM subhalos, then does not constrain lens models*
- host galaxy's extended Einstein ring — *Often low S/N, low spatial resolution; shape of source unknown*

Mass Sheet Degeneracy

changes steepness of density profile
changes time delays
(Gorenstein+1988
Saha 2000)

$$\Delta t \propto \frac{\Delta \tau}{H_0}$$

MSD has a linear affect on derived H_0

knowing mass density at center will break MSD

→ stellar kinematics
(velocity dispersion measures mass)

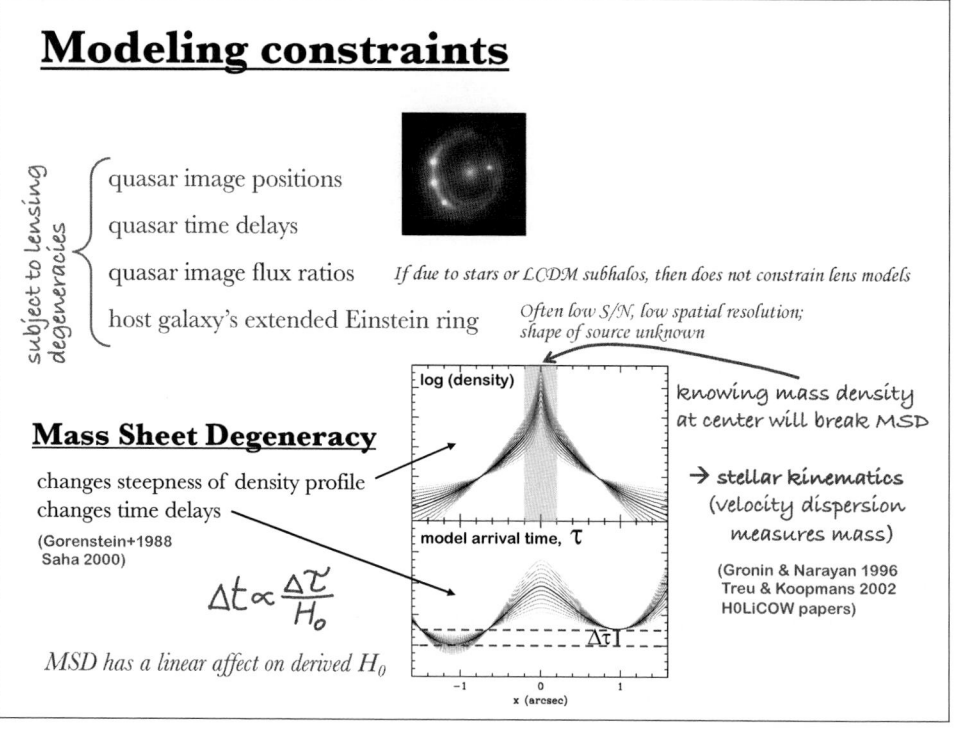

(Gronin & Narayan 1996
Treu & Koopmans 2002
H0LiCOW papers)

Fig. 3. Lens mass modeling constraints (top), and an illustration of models connected by Mass Sheet Degeneracy (MSD, bottom). See §4.2 for details.

4.2. Lensing degeneracies

All the lensing observables are subject to lensing degeneracies. This means that a given set of observables can be reproduced by more than one lens mass distribution. The most famous degeneracy, the Mass Sheet Degeneracy (MSD) is an exact mathematical degeneracy, which was first recognized and described by Ref. 4. The bottom half of Figure 3 illustrates MSD. If the model arrival time surface τ is stretched or shrunk uniformly, i.e., $\tau \to \lambda\tau$, where λ is a constant, then the derived H_0 will be affected similarly, since observed Δt values have to stay the same (see eq. 1). In terms of the lens mass distribution this amounts to (approximately) changing the slope of the density profile, so MSD is sometimes referred to as the steepness degeneracy.[5] Steeper density profiles result in larger derived values of H_0.

The mathematically exact MSD is not the main problem; because of the limited precision of observations, it is actually the approximate version of MSD which we must try to limit in order to obtain good accuracy in derived H_0. This breaking of (approximate) MSD can be achieved if we use an independent method (not lensing) to measure the steepness of the lens density profile. The method usually used is the stellar kinematics: the motion of stars near the center of the lensing galaxy, as measured by the velocity dispersion, depends on the mass distribution.[6,7] The sense of the relation is as follows: If stellar kinematics indicate a lot of mass at the very center, that means the density profile is steep.

However, there are caveats which have been pointed out in the recent papers. Ref. 8 shows that the kinematic priors used in the analysis can have a significant effect on the results. Ref. 9 demonstrate that using kinematics can result in a bias in derived H_0 of a few percent or more. And Ref. 10 conclude that unresolved stellar kinematics—which is what being used today—have limited power to constrain the mass profile. Fortunately, spatially resolved kinematics—which will be possible with the *James Webb Space Telescope*—where stellar velocity dispersion is measured as a function of 2D projected position within the lensing galaxy, will be very helpful in breaking MSD.[11]

Other degeneracies exist as well, most of which affect the shape, or the morphology of the mass distribution in the lens. Known examples are the Source-Position Transformation (SPT), which is a generalization of the MSD,[15] monopole degeneracy,[5,16] and a whole range of other shape degeneracies,[17] which we are yet to classify and fully understand. An example is presented in Figure 4; it shows three different mass models of the same lens system, from Ref. 12 (left panel; parametric with one mass component), 13 (middle panel; parametric with two offset mass components), and 14 (right panel; free-form method). There are many common features in the three mass maps, but the differences in the shape of the mass distributions

Example of shape degeneracies
WFI 2033-4723

Parametric model with 1 mass component — Rusu+2020

Parametric model with 2 offset mass components — Barrera+2021

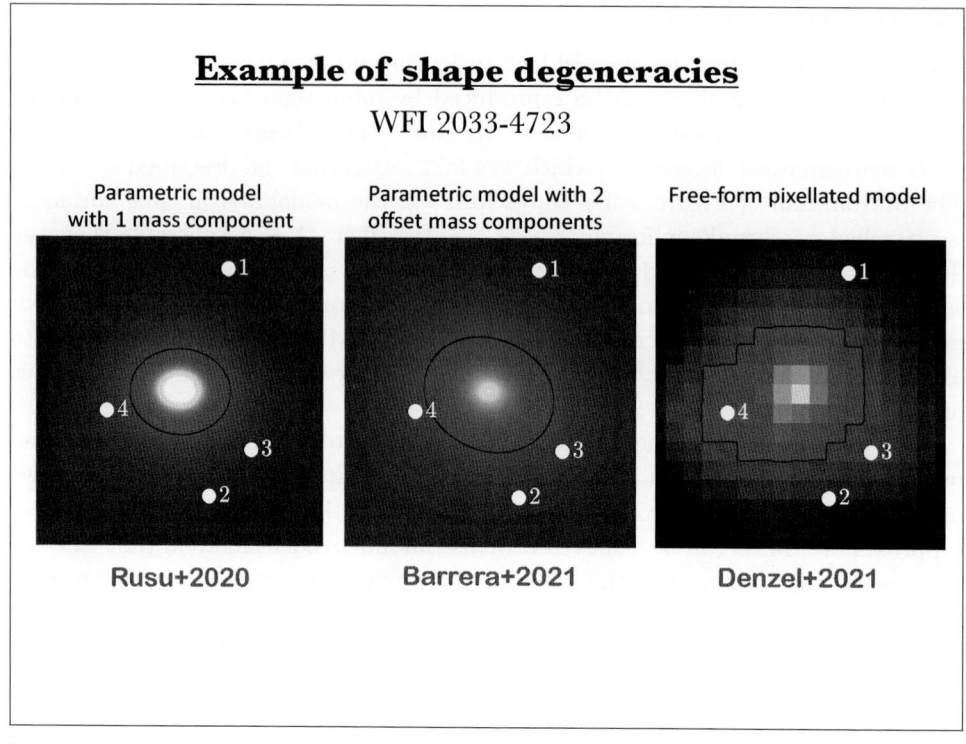

Free-form pixellated model — Denzel+2021

Fig. 4. Three different mass models of the same quad lens system: Ref. 12 (left panel; one mass component), 13 (middle panel; two offset mass components), and 14 (right panel; free-form). These illustrate shape degeneracies in lens mass modeling. See § 4.2 for details.

are also apparent. (Note that the H0LiCOW reconstruction [left panel; Ref. 12)] does not reproduce quasar image positions to even $\sim 5\sigma$, while the the other two [middle & right panels] reproduce these to $\sim 1\sigma$.)

Lensing degeneracies are the largest source of uncertainty in any lensing reconstruction, and hence in the determination of H_0.

4.3. Constructing lens mass models

Because lensing data is limited, and because of the existance of lensing degeneracies, lens mass models are not unique. Therefore, we need to appeal to data to constrain our models, based on our existing knowledge about galaxies. Different modeling groups have varying philosophies as to how much of the prior knowledge to incorporate into their models, and how exactly to parametrize this information.

One way to classify different modeling methods is by the number of models parameters they use. This is the horizontal axis in Figure 5. Please keep in mind that these numbers are approximate. The simplest models represent the lens mass distribution by one mass component, with some density profile slope, ellipticity, position angle, and a tidal term (lensing external shear), which captures the contribution from the external mass. These add up to $\sim 5-6$ parameters. Somewhat more detailed lens mass models use two superimposed mass components, where the two are co-centered, and usually represent baryons (stars), and dark matter, respectively. These result in $\sim 9-15$ parameters. These two types of models are the ones used by the H0LiCOW Collaboration,[18] whose results for H_0 are reported in many papers.

However, there is evidence that these models are not sufficient to describe lenses accurately. For example, as already noted above, one and two co-centered mass component models struggle to reproduce quasar image positions to observational precision.[12] It appears that mass models need more freedom in order to reproduce lens systems more accurately. For example, Ref. 19–22 have shown that offsetting the 2 mass components, which results in deviations from purely elliptical mass distributions, allows better fits for many quad lens systems. The models with the most parameters are the free-form models, which allow each mass pixel in the lens to vary almost independently from others. These models—PixeLens and Glass—have also been used to estimate H_0.[14,17,23] I will present the results in § 5.

Lens mass modeling

Lensing data not sufficient to generate a unique lens model
Need additional assumptions – prior knowledge about galaxies

1 mass component: elliptical power law with fixed or variable slope + tidal term	2 mass components: baryons & DM + tidal term + nearby gals	2 offset mass comp.: baryons & DM + tidal term + nearby gals	pixellated free-form + tidal term
H0LiCOW (Suyu+2014, Chen+2019, Wong+2017, 2019, Birrer+2019, Rusu+2019)		(Nightingale+2018 Gomer & LLRW 2018, 2021 LLRW & Zegeye 2020)	PixeLens / Glass (Saha+2006, Coles 2008, Denzel+2021)
5-6	9-15	14-17	~100 # parameters

more priors
many degeneracies
broken artificially

uncertainties underestimated?
(optimistic)

fewer priors
allow wider range of degenerate models

uncertainties overestimated?
(cautious)

Need different modeling philosophies as cross-checks

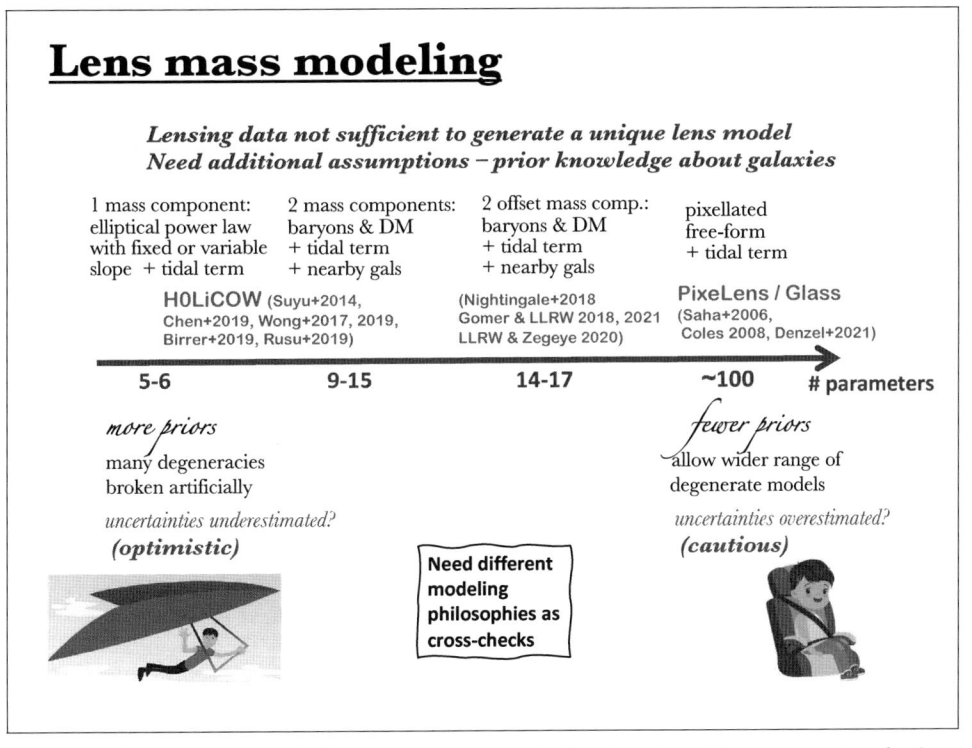

Fig. 5. A few lens mass modeling approaches exist in the literature. One way to classify them is by the number of models parameters they use, represented (approximately) on the horizontal axis. See § 4.3 for details.

Models with fewer parameters and restrictive priors represent a more optimistic view of our knowledge about the galaxies acting as lenses. They suppress lensing degeneracies through the strong assumptions they use, and as a result may underestimate uncertainties in H_0. On the other hand, models with many parameters have fewer priors, and are cautious about how much knowledge we can assume about galaxies. These allow a wider range of degenerate models to be present, and could overestimate the uncertainties. In the face of limited observational data, the best compromise is to have results from different modeling methods act as cross-checks.

Results for H_0

67.4 (5.4%)	
73.3 (7.9%)	TDCOSMO IV (Birrer+2020) 6 quads + 1 double + additional kinematic data
73.3 (2.4%)	TDCOSMO IV (Birrer+2020) + add. kinematic data + self-similar mass profiles
	H0LiCOW (Wong+2019) 5 quads + 1 double

↑ revisit modeling; relax assumptions — **parametric** — Tension with CMB?

71.8 (5%)	Glass (Denzel+2021) 8 quads
71 (10%)	PixeLens (Coles 2008) 3 quads + 8 doubles
72 (13%)	PixeLens (Saha+2006) 3 quads + 7 doubles

↑ more and better data — **free-form** — No tension with CMB

Planck (Planck Collab. 2018)
DES+BAO+BBN (Abbott+2018)

The best check on systematics is to use different modeling philosophies

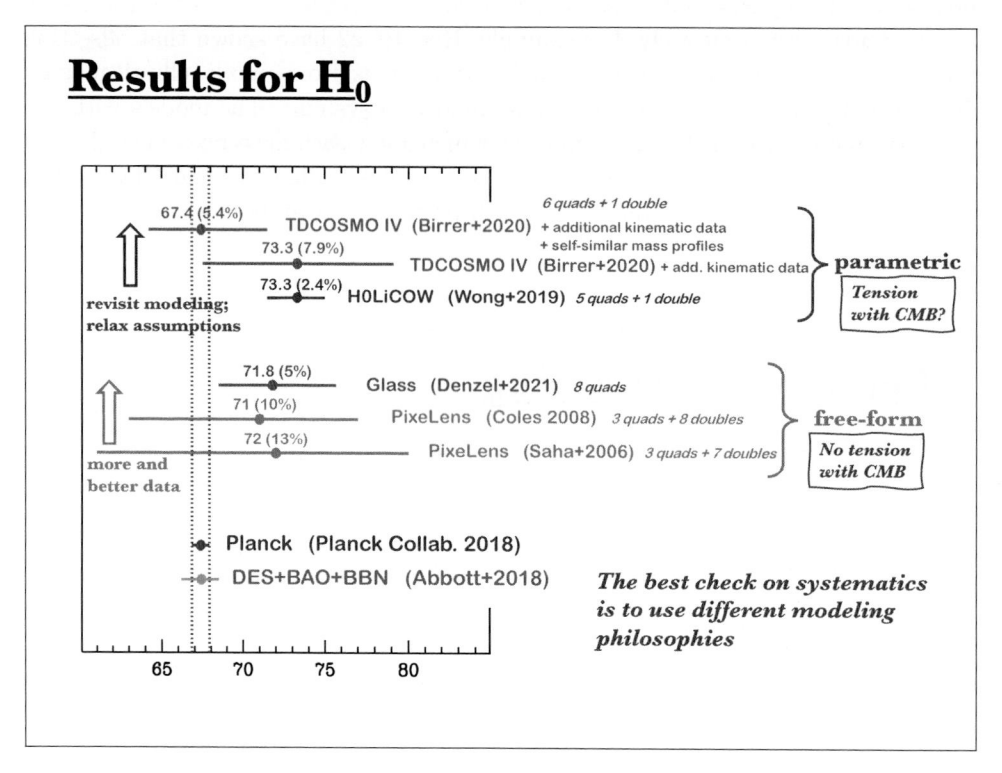

65 70 75 80

Fig. 6. Summary of the current results of H_0 estimation for strong lensing. See § 5 for details.

5. Results

Figure 6 summaries the results for H_0 determination from multiple image lensing from two groups with very different modeling approaches: parameteric models from the H0LiCOW Collaboration,[18,24] and free-form models.[14,25] (I am a part of the latter group.)

The top portion of Figure 6 presents the most recent H0LiCOW results, which used lens models with one and two co-centered mass components (TDCOSMO is a continuation of that group's effort). The H0LiCOW's derived value of $H_0 = 73.3$ km/s/Mpc with 2.4% error[24] is probably the most widely quoted Hubble constant result from gravitational lensing. It is in tension with the Planck result,[26] and the other "early Universe" measurement.[27] About a year ago, the TDCOSMO Collaboration revisited the measurement, relaxing their earlier assumptions.[10] They dropped the assumption on the lens mass density profile, and instead added kinematic data from a larger sample galaxies that do not act as lenses. This recovers the same H_0 value as before, but increases the erorrs to about 7.9%. If one also assumes self-similarity in the galaxy mass distribution, then the central derived value becomes $H_0 = 67.4$, with uncertainty of 5.4%, which is now completely consistent with the early Universe Planck value. (Note that these 3 papers used nearly the same set of lens systems, namely, 5-6 quads and 1 double lens. Quads provide 3 times as many lensing data constrains compared to doubles.)

The middle portion of Figure 6 summarizes the results fro the free-form method. The two earlier papers,[17,23] used 3 quads and 7-8 doubles, and derived H_0 with rather large uncertainties, $10 - 13\%$, which easily encompassed the Planck result. In the past year, the number of quads in the sample was increased to 8, and the uncertainties shunk to 5%. (Most of these quads are in common with those in H0LiCOW and TDCOSMO samples.) The cenral value of H_0 remained nearly the same in all 3 papers. The latest value is $\sim 1.1\sigma$ away from that of the Planck Collaboration. There is no tension between the free-form model results and those from the early Universe probes.

In the estimation of H_0, systematics are the main source of concern. The best way to check on systematics is to use different modeling philosophies and compare their results. The parametric and the free-form methods discussed above have no common modeling assumptions, and yet their most recent results differ by at most $\sim 1\sigma$, and show no significant tension with the Planck early Universe value.

6. Future directions

Many exciting developments in the field of lensing determination of H_0 are just around the corner! In addition to multiply imaged quasars, we will use multiply imaged Supernova Type Ia, Gamma-Ray Bursts, and Fast Radio Bursts.[28-34] Measurements of image time delays from these will be much more precise. Furthermore, since the light from these sources will fade with time (in contrast to that of quasars), it will make it easier to characterize the light from the lensing galaxy, which will help with its mass modeling. Type Ia Superova, whose instrinsic flux is known, will also aide in breaking the mass sheet degeneracy.

In this talk I discussed lensing systems with galaxies as the main lens, but galaxy clusters can also be used,[35,36] especially if the number of lensed images is in the few hundreds. While the mass distribution in galaxy clusters is more complicated than in individual galaxies, clusters lense tens or even hundred(s) of background sources, resulting in 1-few hundred of lensed images, which can constrain the mass distribution suffiently well to yield 1-few percent level accuracy on H_0.[37]

In the next several years, these improvements should be able to deliver $\sim 1\%$ accurary and precision determination of H_0 from gravitational lensing.

References

1. S. Refsdal, On the possibility of determining Hubble's parameter and the masses of galaxies from the gravitational lens effect, *MNRAS* **128**, p. 307 (January 1964).
2. D. Gilman, S. Birrer, A. Nierenberg, T. Treu, X. Du and A. Benson, Warm dark matter chills out: constraints on the halo mass function and the free-streaming length of dark matter with eight quadruple-image strong gravitational lenses, *MNRAS* **491**, 6077 (February 2020).
3. V. Bonvin, M. Millon, J.-H. Chan, F. Courbin, C. Rusu, D. Sluse, S. Suyu, K. Wong, C. Fassnacht, P. Marshall et al., Cosmograil-xviii. time delays of the quadruply lensed quasar wfi2033- 4723, *Astronomy & Astrophysics* **629**, p. A97 (2019).
4. M. V. Gorenstein, E. E. Falco and I. I. Shapiro, Degeneracies in Parameter Estimates for Models of Gravitational Lens Systems, *Astroph. J* **327**, p. 693 (April 1988).
5. P. Saha, Lensing Degeneracies Revisited, *Astron. J.* **120**, 1654 (October 2000).
6. N. A. Grogin and R. Narayan, A New Model of the Gravitational Lens 0957+561 and a Limit on the Hubble Constant, *Astroph. J* **464**, p. 92 (June 1996).
7. T. Treu and L. V. E. Koopmans, The internal structure of the lens PG1115+080: breaking degeneracies in the value of the Hubble constant, *MNRAS* **337**, L6 (December 2002).
8. S. Birrer, A. Amara and A. Refregier, The mass-sheet degeneracy and time-delay cosmography: analysis of the strong lens RXJ1131-1231, *J. Cosmology & Astroparticle Phys.* **2016**, p. 020 (August 2016).
9. M. Gomer and L. L. R. Williams, Galaxy-lens determination of H_0: constraining density slope in the context of the mass sheet degeneracy, *J. Cosmology & Astroparticle Phys.* **2020**, p. 045 (November 2020).
10. S. Birrer, A. J. Shajib, A. Galan, M. Millon, T. Treu, A. Agnello, M. Auger, G. C. F. Chen, L. Christensen, T. Collett, F. Courbin, C. D. Fassnacht, L. V. E. Koopmans, P. J. Marshall, J. W. Park, C. E. Rusu, D. Sluse, C. Spiniello, S. H. Suyu, S. Wagner-Carena, K. C. Wong, M. Barnabè, A. S. Bolton, O. Czoske, X. Ding, J. A. Frieman and L. Van de Vyvere, TDCOSMO. IV. Hierarchical time-delay cosmography – joint inference of the Hubble constant and galaxy density profiles, *Astron. & Astroph.* **643**, p. A165 (November 2020).
11. A. Yıldırım, S. H. Suyu and A. Halkola, Time-delay cosmographic forecasts with strong lensing and JWST stellar kinematics, *MNRAS* **493**, 4783 (April 2020).
12. C. E. Rusu, K. C. Wong, V. Bonvin, D. Sluse, S. H. Suyu, C. D. Fassnacht, J. H. H. Chan, S. Hilbert, M. W. Auger, A. Sonnenfeld, S. Birrer, F. Courbin, T. Treu, G. C. F. Chen, A. Halkola, L. V. E. Koopmans, P. J. Marshall and A. J. Shajib, H0LiCOW XII. Lens mass model of WFI2033-4723 and blind measurement of its time-delay distance and H_0, *MNRAS* **498**, 1440 (October 2020).
13. B. Barrera, L. L. R. Williams, J. P. Coles and P. Denzel, Bridging the Gap Between Simply Parametrized and Free-Form Pixelated Models of Galaxy Lenses: The Case of WFI 2033-4723 Quad, *arXiv e-prints* , p. arXiv:2108.04348 (August 2021).
14. P. Denzel, J. P. Coles, P. Saha and L. L. R. Williams, The Hubble constant from eight time-delay galaxy lenses, *MNRAS* **501**, 784 (February 2021).

15. P. Schneider and D. Sluse, Source-position transformation: an approximate invariance in strong gravitational lensing, *Astron. & Astroph.* **564**, p. A103 (April 2014).
16. J. Liesenborgs and S. De Rijcke, Lensing degeneracies and mass substructure, *MNRAS* **425**, 1772 (September 2012).
17. P. Saha and L. L. R. Williams, Gravitational Lensing Model Degeneracies: Is Steepness All-Important?, *Astroph. J* **653**, 936 (December 2006).
18. S. H. Suyu, V. Bonvin, F. Courbin, C. D. Fassnacht, C. E. Rusu, D. Sluse, T. Treu, K. Wong, M. W. Auger, X. Ding et al., H0licow–i. h 0 lenses in cosmograil's wellspring: program overview, *Monthly Notices of the Royal Astronomical Society* **468**, 2590 (2017).
19. M. R. Gomer and L. L. R. Williams, The impact of ΛCDM substructure and baryon-dark matter transition on the image positions of quad galaxy lenses, *MNRAS* **475**, 1987 (April 2018).
20. J. W. Nightingale, R. J. Massey, D. R. Harvey, A. P. Cooper, A. Etherington, S.-I. Tam and R. G. Hayes, Galaxy structure with strong gravitational lensing: decomposing the internal mass distribution of massive elliptical galaxies, *MNRAS* **489**, 2049 (October 2019).
21. M. R. Gomer and L. L. R. Williams, Galaxy-lens determination of H_0: the effect of the ellipse + shear modelling assumption, *MNRAS* **504**, 1340 (June 2021).
22. L. L. R. Williams and D. Zegeye, Two-component mass models of the lensing galaxy in the quadruply imaged supernova iPTF16geu, *The Open Journal of Astrophysics* **3**, p. 10 (September 2020).
23. J. Coles, A New Estimate of the Hubble Time with Improved Modeling of Gravitational Lenses, *Astroph. J* **679**, 17 (May 2008).
24. K. C. Wong, S. H. Suyu, G. C. F. Chen, C. E. Rusu, M. Millon, D. Sluse, V. Bonvin, C. D. Fassnacht, S. Taubenberger, M. W. Auger, S. Birrer, J. H. H. Chan, F. Courbin, S. Hilbert, O. Tihhonova, T. Treu, A. Agnello, X. Ding, I. Jee, E. Komatsu, A. J. Shajib, A. Sonnenfeld, R. D. Blandford, L. V. E. Koopmans, P. J. Marshall and G. Meylan, H0LiCOW – XIII. A 2.4 per cent measurement of H_0 from lensed quasars: 5.3σ tension between early- and late-Universe probes, *MNRAS* **498**, 1420 (October 2020).
25. P. Saha and L. L. R. Williams, A Portable Modeler of Lensed Quasars, *Astron. J.* **127**, 2604 (May 2004).
26. Planck Collaboration, N. Aghanim, Y. Akrami, M. Ashdown, J. Aumont, C. Baccigalupi, M. Ballardini, A. J. Banday, R. B. Barreiro, N. Bartolo, S. Basak, R. Battye, K. Benabed, J. P. Bernard, M. Bersanelli, P. Bielewicz, J. J. Bock, J. R. Bond, J. Borrill, F. R. Bouchet, F. Boulanger, M. Bucher, C. Burigana, R. C. Butler, E. Calabrese, J. F. Cardoso, J. Carron, A. Challinor, H. C. Chiang, J. Chluba, L. P. L. Colombo, C. Combet, D. Contreras, B. P. Crill, F. Cuttaia, P. de Bernardis, G. de Zotti, J. Delabrouille, J. M. Delouis, E. Di Valentino, J. M. Diego, O. Doré, M. Douspis, A. Ducout, X. Dupac, S. Dusini, G. Efstathiou, F. Elsner, T. A. Enßlin, H. K. Eriksen, Y. Fantaye, M. Farhang, J. Fergusson, R. Fernandez-Cobos, F. Finelli, F. Forastieri, M. Frailis, A. A. Fraisse, E. Franceschi, A. Frolov, S. Galeotta, S. Galli, K. Ganga, R. T. Génova-Santos, M. Gerbino, T. Ghosh, J. González-Nuevo, K. M. Górski, S. Gratton, A. Gruppuso, J. E. Gudmundsson, J. Hamann, W. Handley, F. K. Hansen, D. Herranz, S. R. Hildebrandt, E. Hivon, Z. Huang, A. H. Jaffe, W. C. Jones, A. Karakci, E. Keihänen, R. Keskitalo, K. Kiiveri, J. Kim, T. S. Kisner, L. Knox, N. Krachmalnicoff, M. Kunz, H. Kurki-Suonio, G. Lagache, J. M. Lamarre, A. Lasenby, M. Lattanzi, C. R. Lawrence, M. Le Jeune, P. Lemos, J. Lesgourgues, F. Levrier, A. Lewis, M. Liguori, P. B. Lilje, M. Lilley, V. Lindholm, M. López-Caniego,

P. M. Lubin, Y. Z. Ma, J. F. Macías-Pérez, G. Maggio, D. Maino, N. Mandolesi, A. Mangilli, A. Marcos-Caballero, M. Maris, P. G. Martin, M. Martinelli, E. Martínez-González, S. Matarrese, N. Mauri, J. D. McEwen, P. R. Meinhold, A. Melchiorri, A. Mennella, M. Migliaccio, M. Millea, S. Mitra, M. A. Miville-Deschênes, D. Molinari, L. Montier, G. Morgante, A. Moss, P. Natoli, H. U. Nørgaard-Nielsen, L. Pagano, D. Paoletti, B. Partridge, G. Patanchon, H. V. Peiris, F. Perrotta, V. Pettorino, F. Piacentini, L. Polastri, G. Polenta, J. L. Puget, J. P. Rachen, M. Reinecke, M. Remazeilles, A. Renzi, G. Rocha, C. Rosset, G. Roudier, J. A. Rubiño-Martín, B. Ruiz-Granados, L. Salvati, M. Sandri, M. Savelainen, D. Scott, E. P. S. Shellard, C. Sirignano, G. Sirri, L. D. Spencer, R. Sunyaev, A. S. Suur-Uski, J. A. Tauber, D. Tavagnacco, M. Tenti, L. Toffolatti, M. Tomasi, T. Trombetti, L. Valenziano, J. Valiviita, B. Van Tent, L. Vibert, P. Vielva, F. Villa, N. Vittorio, B. D. Wandelt, I. K. Wehus, M. White, S. D. M. White, A. Zacchei and A. Zonca, Planck 2018 results. VI. Cosmological parameters, *Astron. & Astroph.* **641**, p. A6 (September 2020).

27. T. M. C. Abbott, F. B. Abdalla, J. Annis, K. Bechtol, J. Blazek, B. A. Benson, R. A. Bernstein, G. M. Bernstein, E. Bertin, D. Brooks, D. L. Burke, A. Carnero Rosell, M. Carrasco Kind, J. Carretero, F. J. Castander, C. L. Chang, T. M. Crawford, C. E. Cunha, C. B. D'Andrea, L. N. da Costa, C. Davis, J. DeRose, S. Desai, H. T. Diehl, J. P. Dietrich, P. Doel, A. Drlica-Wagner, A. E. Evrard, E. Fernandez, B. Flaugher, P. Fosalba, J. Frieman, J. García-Bellido, E. Gaztanaga, D. W. Gerdes, T. Giannantonio, D. Gruen, R. A. Gruendl, J. Gschwend, G. Gutierrez, W. G. Hartley, J. W. Henning, K. Honscheid, B. Hoyle, D. Huterer, B. Jain, D. J. James, M. Jarvis, T. Jeltema, M. D. Johnson, M. W. G. Johnson, E. Krause, K. Kuehn, S. Kuhlmann, N. Kuropatkin, O. Lahav, A. R. Liddle, M. Lima, H. Lin, N. MacCrann, M. A. G. Maia, A. Manzotti, M. March, J. L. Marshall, R. Miquel, J. J. Mohr, T. Natoli, P. Nugent, R. L. C. Ogando, Y. Park, A. A. Plazas, C. L. Reichardt, K. Reil, A. Roodman, A. J. Ross, E. Rozo, E. S. Rykoff, E. Sanchez, V. Scarpine, M. Schubnell, D. Scolnic, I. Sevilla-Noarbe, E. Sheldon, M. Smith, R. C. Smith, M. Soares-Santos, F. Sobreira, E. Suchyta, G. Tarle, D. Thomas, M. A. Troxel, A. R. Walker, R. H. Wechsler, J. Weller, W. Wester, W. L. K. Wu, J. Zuntz, Dark Energy Survey Collaboration and South Pole Telescope Collaboration, Dark Energy Survey Year 1 Results: A Precise H_0 Estimate from DES Y1, BAO, and D/H Data, *MNRAS* **480**, 3879 (November 2018).

28. A. Goobar, R. Amanullah, S. R. Kulkarni, P. E. Nugent, J. Johansson, C. Steidel, D. Law, E. Mörtsell, R. Quimby, N. Blagorodnova, A. Brandeker, Y. Cao, A. Cooray, R. Ferretti, C. Fremling, L. Hangard, M. Kasliwal, T. Kupfer, R. Lunnan, F. Masci, A. A. Miller, H. Nayyeri, J. D. Neill, E. O. Ofek, S. Papadogiannakis, T. Petrushevska, V. Ravi, J. Sollerman, M. Sullivan, F. Taddia, R. Walters, D. Wilson, L. Yan and O. Yaron, iPTF16geu: A multiply imaged, gravitationally lensed type Ia supernova, *Science* **356**, 291 (April 2017).

29. S. H. Suyu, T.-C. Chang, F. Courbin and T. Okumura, Cosmological Distance Indicators, *SSRv* **214**, p. 91 (August 2018).

30. S. H. Suyu, S. Huber, R. Cañameras, M. Kromer, S. Schuldt, S. Taubenberger, A. Yıldırım, V. Bonvin, J. H. H. Chan, F. Courbin, U. Nöbauer, S. A. Sim and D. Sluse, HOLISMOKES. I. Highly Optimised Lensing Investigations of Supernovae, Microlensing Objects, and Kinematics of Ellipticals and Spirals, *Astron. & Astroph.* **644**, p. A162 (December 2020).

31. A. Zitrin and D. Eichler, Observing Cosmological Processes in Real Time with Repeating Fast Radio Bursts, *Astroph. J* **866**, p. 101 (October 2018).

32. C. Grillo, P. Rosati, S. H. Suyu, I. Balestra, G. B. Caminha, A. Halkola, P. L. Kelly, M. Lombardi, A. Mercurio, S. A. Rodney and T. Treu, Measuring the Value of the Hubble Constant "à la Refsdal", *Astroph. J* **860**, p. 94 (June 2018).
33. J. Wagner, J. Liesenborgs and D. Eichler, Multiply imaged time-varying sources behind galaxy clusters. Comparing fast radio bursts to QSOs, SNe, and GRBs, *Astron. & Astroph.* **621**, p. A91 (January 2019).
34. X. Ding, T. Treu, S. Birrer, G. C. F. Chen, J. Coles, P. Denzel, M. Frigo, A. Galan, P. J. Marshall, M. Millon, A. More, A. J. Shajib, D. Sluse, H. Tak, D. Xu, M. W. Auger, V. Bonvin, H. Chand, F. Courbin, G. Despali, C. D. Fassnacht, D. Gilman, S. Hilbert, S. R. Kumar, J. Y. Y. Lin, J. W. Park, P. Saha, S. Vegetti, L. Van de Vyvere and L. L. R. Williams, Time delay lens modelling challenge, *MNRAS* **503**, 1096 (May 2021).
35. P. L. Kelly, S. A. Rodney, T. Treu, R. J. Foley, G. Brammer, K. B. Schmidt, A. Zitrin, A. Sonnenfeld, L.-G. Strolger, O. Graur, A. V. Filippenko, S. W. Jha, A. G. Riess, M. Bradac, B. J. Weiner, D. Scolnic, M. A. Malkan, A. von der Linden, M. Trenti, J. Hjorth, R. Gavazzi, A. Fontana, J. C. Merten, C. McCully, T. Jones, M. Postman, A. Dressler, B. Patel, S. B. Cenko, M. L. Graham and B. E. Tucker, Multiple images of a highly magnified supernova formed by an early-type cluster galaxy lens, *Science* **347**, 1123 (March 2015).
36. P. L. Kelly, S. A. Rodney, T. Treu, L. G. Strolger, R. J. Foley, S. W. Jha, J. Selsing, G. Brammer, M. Bradač, S. B. Cenko, O. Graur, A. V. Filippenko, J. Hjorth, C. McCully, A. Molino, M. Nonino, A. G. Riess, K. B. Schmidt, B. Tucker, A. von der Linden, B. J. Weiner and A. Zitrin, Deja Vu All Over Again: The Reappearance of Supernova Refsdal, *ApJLett* **819**, p. L8 (March 2016).
37. A. Ghosh, L. L. R. Williams and J. Liesenborgs, Free-form grale lens inversion of galaxy clusters with up to 1000 multiple images, *MNRAS* **494**, 3998 (May 2020).

Extra components consistency in the Hubble tension and BBN

Osamu Seto

Institute for the Advancement of Higher Education, Hokkaido University,
Sapporo 060-0817, Japan,
Department of Physics, Hokkaido University,
Sapporo 060-0810, Japan
E-mail: seto@particle.sci.hokudai.ac.jp

Yo Toda

Department of Physics, Hokkaido University,
Sapporo 060-0810, Japan
E-mail: y-toda@particle.sci.hokudai.ac.jp

The standard ΛCDM cosmological model now seems to face some puzzles. One of the most serious problems is the so-called Hubble tension; the values of the Hubble constant H_0 obtained by local measurements look inconsistent with that inferred from Cosmic Microwave Background (CMB). Although introducing extra energy components such as the extra radiation or Early Dark Energy appears to be promising, such extra components could alter the abundance of light elements synthesized by Big Bang Nucleosynthesis (BBN). We perform a Monte Carlo simulation to evaluate the effect of those extra component scenarios to solve the Hubble tension on the BBN prediction.

Keywords: Cosmology; Big Bang Nucleosynthesis; Dark energy; Radiation; Hubble constant

1. Introduction

The ΛCDM model has been successful in explaining the evolution of our Universe. However, the tension of the Hubble constant is now apparent between the measurement of the local universe and the distant universe. Assuming ΛCDM model, Planck measurements of Cosmic Microwave Background (CMB) anisotropy infers the Hubble constant $H_0 = 67.4 \pm 0.5$ km/s/Mpc.[1] Other distant observations such as the Atacama Cosmology Telescope,[2] Baryon Acoustic Oscillation(BAO),[3] and the combined analysis of BAO and Big Bang Nucleosynthesis (BBN) (independent of CMB)[4] all infer $H_0 \sim 67$ km/s/Mpc. On the other hand, local measurements of H_0 by the SH0ES collaboration with Cepheids and type Ia supernovae (SNe Ia) in Ref.[5] and Ref.[6] and by the H0LiCOW collaboration with lensed quasars[7] have reported as $H_0 \sim 73$ km/s/Mpc. Another local measurement using the Tip of the Red Giant Branch (TRGB) as distance ladders has obtained a value between Planck and the SH0ES, $H_0 \sim 70$ km/s/Mpc.[8] It appears that the discrepancy is more than 3σ significance.

Several ideas have been proposed to extend ΛCDM model to resolve this tension. Among such ideas, we would like to consider the extra radiation and Early Dark Energy[9–18] solutions to the Hubble tension and the consistency with BBN. These extra components are promising solutions. However, the theoretical abundance of light elements synthesized by BBN should be different from the values of the standard scenario. Through the consideration, we confirm that extra radiation and Early Dark Energy are promising solutions. However, two scenarios are constrained by BBN measurements. Extra radiation is constrained by the helium abundance and Early Dark Energy is constrained by the deuterium abundance.[19]

2. H_0 from CMB

First, we explain how the Hubble constant is derived from the distant observation, especially the CMB anisotropy. The measured anisotropy includes the information of the angular size $\theta_* = r_*/D_{M*}$, where r_* is the comoving sound horizon at the recombination and D_{M*} is the comoving angular diameter distance. Planck team directly and strictly measured $\theta_* = 1.041 \times 10^{-2}$. A simple calculation according to the definition shows that $\theta_* \propto H_0/\sqrt{\rho_{\text{early}}}$, where ρ_{early} is the energy density in the early universe. Therefore, in order for the Hubble constant from CMB to approach the local value, we need to increase ρ in the early universe. Then, we will consider two promising ways to increase ρ; Extra radiation and Early Dark Energy.

3. Modeling

3.1. *Extra radiation*

One simple "solution" to the Hubble tension is increasing the effective number of neutrinos N_{eff}, which is expressed as

$$\Omega_r = \left(1 + \frac{7}{8}\left(\frac{4}{11}\right)^{4/3} N_{\text{eff}}\right) \Omega_\gamma. \tag{1}$$

Here,

$$\Omega_i = \left.\frac{\rho_i}{3M_P^2 H^2}\right|_{t=t_0}, \tag{2}$$

with M_P being the reduced Planck mass, are the present values of density parameters for i spices. γ and r stand for CMB photon and total radiation, respectively.

3.2. *Early Dark Energy*

Another solution to the Hubble tension is introducing Early Dark Energy. In the Early Dark Energy scenario, the dark energy density in the early universe was much larger than today and after the critical point, the energy density decreases faster than the background energy densities do. In our analysis, we consider a model where

[Figure: Energy density evolution of Early Dark Energy, showing ρ_{DE}/ρ_Λ vs scale of the universe, with "Critical Point" and "CMB Photon last scattered" labeled]

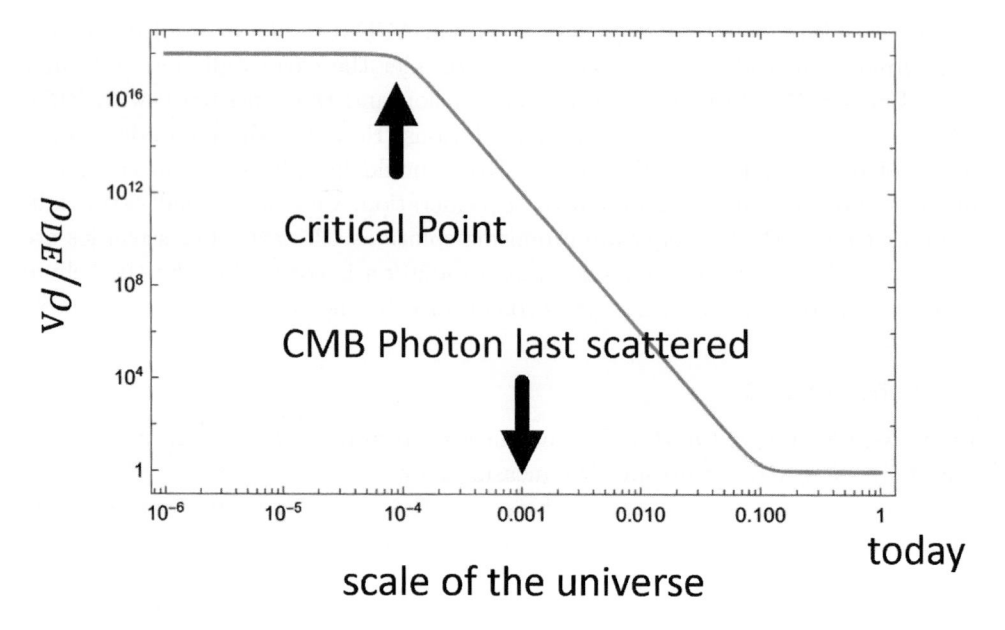

Fig. 1. Energy density evolution of Early Dark Energy

the energy density of Early Dark Energy ρ_{DE} decreases as the kination of scalar field after the critical point at $z = 3000$ around the matter-radiation equality. This setup is according to a preferred parameter set in Ref.[9]. The typical evolution of Dark Energy density $\rho_{DE}(a)$ normalized by ρ_Λ is shown in Fig. 1.

4. Data and Analysis

We perform a Markov-Chain Monte Carlo (MCMC) analysis on a N_{eff} model and the Early Dark Energy model described in the previous section. We use the public MCMC code `CosmoMC-planck2018`[20] with implementing the above Early Dark Energy scenarios by modifying its equation file in `camb`. For estimation of light elements, we have used `PArthENoPE_marcucci`.[21,22]

4.1. Data sets

We analyze models with referring to the following cosmological observation data sets. We include both temperature and polarization likelihoods for high l ($l = 30$ to 2508 in TT and $l = 30$ to 1997 in EE and TE) and low$l$ `Commander` and lowE `SimAll` ($l = 2$ to 29) of Planck (2018) measurement of the CMB temperature anisotropy.[1] We also include Planck lensing.[23] For constraints on low redshift cosmology, we include data of BAO from 6dF,[24] DR7[25] and DR12.[26] We also include Pantheon[27] of the local measurement of light curves and luminosity distance of supernovae as well as SH0ES (R19)[6] of the local measurement of the Hubble constant from the

Hubble Space Telescope observation of Supernovae and Cepheid variables. Finally, we include the data sets of helium mass fraction Y_P measurement[28] and deuterium abundance D/H measurement[29] to impose the constraints from BBN.

5. Result and Discussion

As is well known, an increase of N_{eff} affects the fit with the observation of light elements, because it contributes to the cosmic expansion at BBN epoch and alters the proton to neutron p/n ratio. This leads to increasing both the helium mass fraction Y_P and the deuterium abundance D/H. Thus, larger relativistic degrees are disfavored by the helium mass fraction measurement, while a little favored by deuterium measurement. This can be seen in Fig. 2.

On the other hand, in the Early Dark Energy scenarios, the Early Dark Energy increases the helium mass fraction little because the cosmic expansion rate in the BBN epoch increase little. Therefore, the Early Dark Energy scenario is consistent with the helium fraction measurement. However, increasing $\Omega_b h^2$ to adjust the CMB

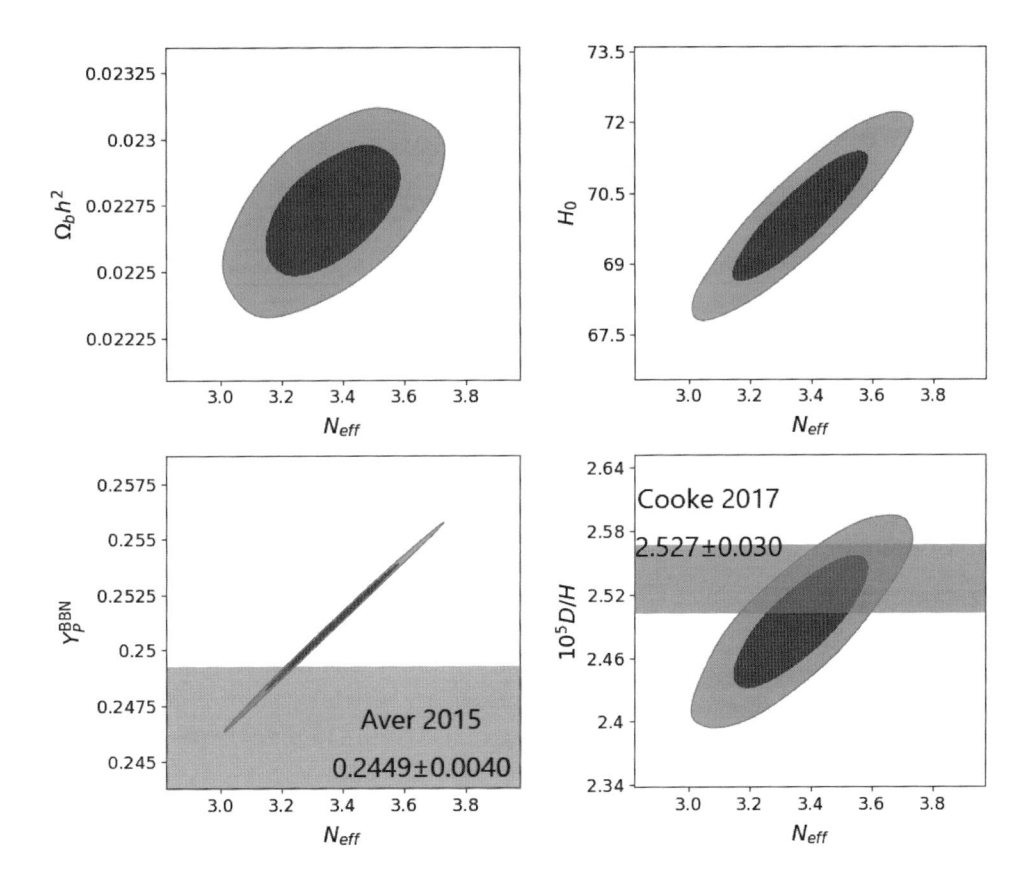

Fig. 2. The posterior and the constraints on the N_{eff} model

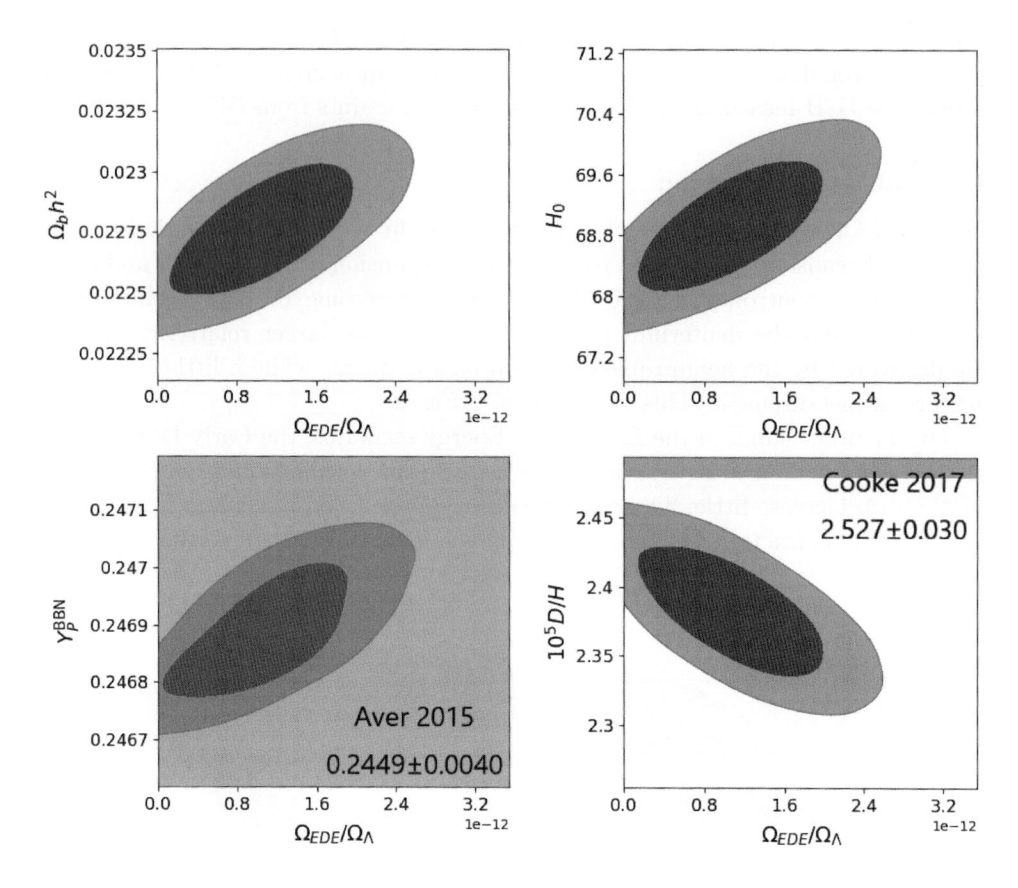

Fig. 3. The posterior and the constraints on the Early Dark Energy model

fit reduces the D/H abundance significantly. Thus, Early Dark Energy is disfavored from the deuterium measurement. This can be seen in Fig. 3.

6. Conclusion

The shorten sound horizon scale at the recombination epoch by introducing extra energy components such as the extra radiation or the Early Dark Energy is a promising solution to the Hubble tension. However, the compatibility with successful BBN would be another concern, because the extra radiation contribute the cosmic expansion or the inferred baryon asymmetry would differ from that in the ΛCDM.

We have performed analyses on the Early Dark Energy models and N_{eff} model with paying attention to the fit to BBN. Not only N_{eff} model but also the Early Dark Energy model is subject to the BBN constraints (as shown in Fig. 4.). Extra radiation is constrained by the helium abundance, while Early Dark Energy is constrained

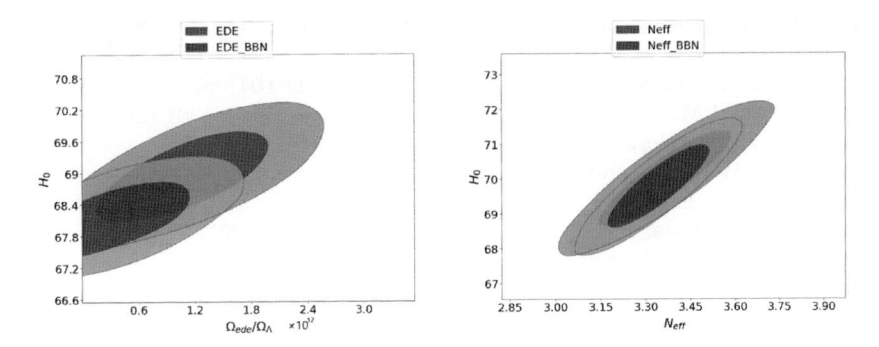

Fig. 4. Comparison of constraints based on data sets with and without BBN for the Early Dark Energy (left) model and the N_{eff} model (right)

by the deuterium abundance. Therefore, when we introduce extra components for the Hubble tension resolution, we should pay attention to the BBN as well.

Acknowledgments

This work of O.S. is supported in part the Japan Society for the Promotion of Science (JSPS) KAKENHI Grants No. 19K03860, No. 19H05091, No. 19K03865, and No. 21H00060.

References

1. N. Aghanim *et al.* [Planck], Astron. Astrophys. **641**, A6 (2020).
2. S. Aiola *et al.* [ACT], JCAP **12**, 047 (2020).
3. G. E. Addison, D. J. Watts, C. L. Bennett, M. Halpern, G. Hinshaw and J. L. Weiland, Astrophys. J. **853**, no. 2, 119 (2018).
4. N. Schöneberg, J. Lesgourgues and D. C. Hooper, JCAP **10**, 029 (2019).
5. A. G. Riess *et al.*, Astrophys. J. **855**, no. 2, 136 (2018).
6. A. G. Riess, S. Casertano, W. Yuan, L. M. Macri and D. Scolnic, Astrophys. J. **876**, no. 1, 85 (2019).
7. K. C. Wong, S. H. Suyu, G. C. F. Chen, C. E. Rusu, M. Millon, D. Sluse, V. Bonvin, C. D. Fassnacht, S. Taubenberger and M. W. Auger, *et al.* Mon. Not. Roy. Astron. Soc. **498**, no. 1, 1420-1439 (2020).
8. W. L. Freedman, B. F. Madore, D. Hatt, T. J. Hoyt, I. S. Jang, R. L. Beaton, C. R. Burns, M. G. Lee, A. J. Monson and J. R. Neeley, *et al.* Astrophys. J. **882**, 34 (2019).
9. V. Poulin, T. L. Smith, T. Karwal and M. Kamionkowski, Phys. Rev. Lett. **122**, no. 22, 221301 (2019).
10. P. Agrawal, F. Y. Cyr-Racine, D. Pinner and L. Randall, [arXiv:1904.01016 [astro-ph.CO]].
11. F. Niedermann and M. S. Sloth, Phys. Rev. D **103**, no. 4, L041303 (2021).
12. V. Poulin, T. L. Smith, D. Grin, T. Karwal and M. Kamionkowski, Phys. Rev. D **98**, no. 8, 083525 (2018) doi:10.1103/PhysRevD.98.083525.
13. S. Alexander and E. McDonough, Phys. Lett. B **797**, 134830 (2019) doi:10.1016/j.physletb.2019.134830.

14. M. X. Lin, G. Benevento, W. Hu and M. Raveri, Phys. Rev. D **100**, no. 6, 063542 (2019).
15. T. L. Smith, V. Poulin and M. A. Amin, Phys. Rev. D **101**, no. 6, 063523 (2020).
16. J. Sakstein and M. Trodden, Phys. Rev. Lett. **124**, no. 16, 161301 (2020).
17. A. Chudaykin, D. Gorbunov and N. Nedelko, JCAP **08**, 013 (2020).
18. M. Braglia, W. T. Emond, F. Finelli, A. E. Gumrukcuoglu and K. Koyama, Phys. Rev. D **102**, no. 8, 083513 (2020).
19. O. Seto and Y. Toda, Phys. Rev. D **103**, no. 12, 123501 (2021).
20. A. Lewis and S. Bridle, Phys. Rev. D **66**, 103511 (2002).
21. O. Pisanti, A. Cirillo, S. Esposito, F. Iocco, G. Mangano, G. Miele and P. D. Serpico, Comput. Phys. Commun. **178**, 956-971 (2008).
22. L. E. Marcucci, G. Mangano, A. Kievsky and M. Viviani, Phys. Rev. Lett. **116**, no. 10, 102501 (2016).
23. N. Aghanim *et al.* [Planck], Astron. Astrophys. **641**, A8 (2020).
24. F. Beutler, C. Blake, M. Colless, D. H. Jones, L. Staveley-Smith, L. Campbell, Q. Parker, W. Saunders and F. Watson, Mon. Not. Roy. Astron. Soc. **416**, 3017-3032 (2011).
25. A. J. Ross, L. Samushia, C. Howlett, W. J. Percival, A. Burden and M. Manera, Mon. Not. Roy. Astron. Soc. **449**, no. 1, 835-847 (2015).
26. S. Alam *et al.* [BOSS], Mon. Not. Roy. Astron. Soc. **470**, no. 3, 2617-2652 (2017).
27. D. M. Scolnic, D. O. Jones, A. Rest, Y. C. Pan, R. Chornock, R. J. Foley, M. E. Huber, R. Kessler, G. Narayan and A. G. Riess, *et al.* Astrophys. J. **859**, no. 2, 101 (2018).
28. E. Aver, K. A. Olive and E. D. Skillman, JCAP **07**, 011 (2015).
29. R. J. Cooke, M. Pettini and C. C. Steidel, Astrophys. J. **855**, no. 2, 102 (2018).

Gravitational anomalies, axions and a string-inspired running vacuum model in Cosmology

Nick E. Mavromatos[*,†]

[*] *Theoretical Particle Physics and Cosmology Group, Physics Department,*
King's College, London,
Strand, London WC2R 2LS, UK,

[†] *Physics Department, School of Applied Mathematical and Physical Sciences,*
National Technical University of Athens,
9, Heroon Polytechneiou Str., Zografou Campus, Athens 157 80, Greece
E-mail: nikolaos.mavromatos@cern.ch

I review a string-inspired cosmological model with gravitational anomalies in its early epochs, which is based on fields from the (bosonic) massless gravitational multiplet of strings, in particular gravitons and Kalb Ramond (KR), string-model independent, axions (the dilaton is assumed constant). I show how condensation of primordial gravitational waves, which are genenared at the very early eras immediately after the big bang, can lead to inflation of the so called running vacuum model (RVM) type, without external inflatons. The role of the slow-roll field is played by the KR axion, but it does not drive inflation. The non-linearities in the anomaly terms do. Chiral fermionic matter excitations appear at the end of this RVM inflation, as a result of the decay of the RVM vacuum, and are held responsible for the cancellation of the primordial gravitational anomalies. Chiral anomalies, however, survive in the post-inflationary epochs, and can lead to the generation of a non perturbative mass for the KR axion, which could thus play the role of dark matter in this Universe. As a result of the condensed gravitational anomaly, there is a Lorentz-invariance violating KR axion background, which remains undiluted during the RVM inflation, and can lead to baryogenesis through leptogenesis in the radiation era, in models with sterile right-handed neutrinos. I also discuss the phenomenology of the model in the modern era, paying particular attention to linking it with a version of RVM, called type II RVM, which arguably can alleviate observed tensions in the current-epoch cosmological data.

Keywords: String Cosmology; Running Vacuum; Inflation, Axions; Dark Matter.

1. Introduction

Although the plethora of the available cosmological data today[1] agree very well with the standard concordance model of Cosmology,[2] also known as ΛCDM, nonetheless there are compelling reasons for seeking alternative models, that go beyond it. Theoretically, given that the ΛCDM model is a global (de Sitter) solution of Einstein's general relativity (GR) theory, with a positive cosmological constant $\Lambda > 0$ added without explanation, one needs to seek microscopic frameworks of quantum gravity, which the GR can be embedded to, that could provide a detailed origin of the observed dark energy component in the current-Universe energy budget.[a] Moreover, one of the most important drawbacks of GR *per se* is that it is a non-renormalizable theory, and as such, it cannot provide by itself a framework for quantising gravity along with the rest of the fundamental interactions in nature (assuming of course that gravity can admit conventional quantization; for alternative views, treating gravity as an entropic force, associated with changes of information pertaining to the positions of material bodies, see Ref. 4). On the observational side, there appear to exist discrepancies ("tensions"[5,6]) between the results of data analyses from Planck Collaboration, based on ΛCDM,[1] and local direct measurements of the Hubble parameter today, the so called H_0 tension,[7–9] but also tensions in the growth-of-galaxies data, the so-called σ_8 tension.[10] Thus, although such tensions could admit more mundane astrophysical explanations,[11–14] or even disappear in future data, being due to statistical uncertainties, nonetheless, several theoretical attempts are currently on the way in order to provide an explanation for them or alleviate them.

One phenomenological framework, which deals successfully with such an alleviation of both the H_0 and the σ_8 tensions, is a mildly modified version of the running vacuum model of cosmology (RVM),[15–20] the so-called type II RVM.[21] In this talk, I will review a microscopic framework for obtaining the RVM, actually a version of RVM somewhat analogous to the aforementioned type II RVM, which pertains to a string-inspired[22] cosmological model with *gravitational anomalies* in the early Universe.[23–28]

The structure of the talk is as follows: in the next section 2, I describe briefly the RVM framework, and then the string-inspired gravitational theory, with gravitational anomalies coupled to *massless* string-model independent (Kalb-Ramond (KR)) axions fields, which can give rise to an RVM inflation, without external inflatons. Only bosonic fields from the massless gravitational string multiplet enter the early-Universe era string-effective action as external fields. Primordial gravitational waves can lead to condensation of the gravitational anomalies, which in turn induces the RVM inflation. In section 3, I describe briefly the post inflationary epochs, placing the emphasis on how a gravitational-anomaly-induced Lorentz-violating (LV) KR axion background, which remans undiluted at the end of the RVM inflationary era, can lead to leptogenesis in models with right-handed sterile neutrinos (RHN) in their spectra. I also explain how the stringy KR axion field can play the rôle of Dark matter, by acquiring a non-perturbative mass during the Quantum Chromo-Dynamics (QCD) epoch of the Universe. In section 4, I speculate on potential links of this stringy RVM effective theory to a modified version of RVM, somewhat analogous (but with crucial differences) to the aforementioned type-II RVM. The crucial

---

[a]See, however, the arguments of Ref. 3 claiming that the "observed" dark energy might be an artefact of supernova data interpretation based on the assumption of homogeneity and isotropy of the universe at large (cosmological) scales, in the context of the Friedman-Lemaitre-Robertson-Walker (FLRW) framework. In our approach here, the large-scale isotropy and homogeneity of the Universe is assumed.

modifications are due to quantum-graviton-mode integration in the respective path integral of the string-inspired theory, and could lead to observable departures from ΛCDM and potential alleviation of tensions in the current-era data. Finally, section 5 contains our conclusions and outlook.

2. Running Vacuum Model (RVM) Framework, its String-Theory Embedding and Inflation from Gravitational Anomalies

I commence the discussion by first summarising briefly the basic features of the RVM framework. This is a phenomenologically successful effective cosmological framework, which leads to observable, in principle, deviations from ΛCDM,[19,20] and alleviation of the current cosmological tensions.[21] It describes a smooth evolution of the Universe from a dynamical inflationary phase till the present era.[18]

2.1. *Features of RVM cosmology*

The basic feature of the RVM cosmology is that the vacuum energy density is a function of even powers of the Hubble parameter at a given era of the Universe, $H(t)$ (with t the cosmic time), due to general covariance. To describe the entire evolution of the Universe from inflation till the present epoch, it is sufficient to truncate this series to quartic powers of $H(t)$, thus writing::[15-18]

$$\rho^\Lambda_{\rm RVM}(H) = \frac{\Lambda(H)}{\kappa^2} = \frac{3}{\kappa^2}\left(c_0 + \nu H^2 + \alpha \frac{H^4}{H_I^2} + \dots \right) > 0, \qquad (1)$$

with κ the four-dimensional gravitational constant $\kappa = \sqrt{8\pi\, G} = M_{\rm Pl}^{-1}$, with $M_{\rm Pl} = 2.43 \times 10^{18}$ GeV (we work in natural units $\hbar = c = 1$ throughout this work), $H_I \sim 10^{-5} M_{\rm Pl}$, the inflationary scale, as inferred from the latest Planck-Collaboration data,[1] and $c_0 \geq 0$, ν and α constants, throughout the Universe evolution. In the conventional RVM, $\nu > 0$ and $\alpha > 0$, while $c_0 > 0$ is the current-epoch cosmological constant.[1,2] The $\dots$ in (1) denote terms of higher orders in $H^2(t)$. In general there is also dependence on $\dot H$ (with the overdot denoting cosmic-time-t derivative), but for a given era of the Universe, one can express $\dot H$ in terms of the cosmic deceleration of that era (assumed approximately constant) and of H^2, hence the expression (1) suffices for our purposes here. The defining feature of the RVM is its de-Sitter type equation of state,[15]

$$p^{\rm vac}_{\rm RVM}(H(t)) = -\rho^{\rm vac}_{\rm RVM}(H(t)) < 0, \qquad (2)$$

despite the fact that the pressure $p^{\rm vac}_{\rm RVM}$ and energy $\rho^{\rm vac}_{\rm RVM}$ densities are time-dependent functions of $H(t)$. We note for completeness that a similar feature characterises the super-critical (Liouville) string cosmologies, where the cosmic time is identified with (the zero mode of) a world-sheet renormalization-group scale.[29]

From the conservation of the total stress tensor of the vacuum plus radiation and matter excitations, the latter being characterised by an equation of state w_m, one can easily arrive at the following evolution equation for the Hubble parameter:[18]

$$\dot{H} + \frac{3}{2}(1+\omega_m) H^2 \left(1 - \nu - \frac{c_0}{H^2} - \alpha \frac{H^2}{H_I^2}\right) = 0 \ . \tag{3}$$

At early stages of the Universe, one may ignore the c_0 term, thus arriving at a solution for $H(a)$ as a function of the scale factor a (in units of the present-era scale factor):[18,19]

$$H(a) = \left(\frac{1-\nu}{\alpha}\right)^{1/2} \frac{H_I}{\sqrt{D\, a^{3(1-\nu)(1+\omega_m)} + 1}}, \tag{4}$$

where $D > 0$ is an integration constant. For the early Universe, one may assume without loss of generality that $D\, a^{3(1-\nu)(1+\omega_m)} \ll 1$, which from (4) leads to an (unstable) dynamical early de Sitter phase, characterised by an approximately constant $H_{\text{de Sitter}} \simeq \left(\frac{1-\nu}{\alpha}\right)^{1/2} H_I$. This inflationary era is due to the non-linear terms H^4 in (1), and is not characterised by external inflaton fields.

After inflation, the RVM evolution (3) is characterised by radiation-dominance ($w_m = 1/3$) and, subsequently, by a matter-dominated ($w_m = 0$) era, both occurring for considerably larger values of the scale factor than the RVM inflation. In such cases, the corresponding quantities $D\, a^{3(1-\nu)(1+\omega_m)} \gg 1$. One can therefore determine the RVM vacuum energy density (1) during radiation as[18,30] $\rho_{\text{RVM}}^{\text{vac radiation era}} \simeq \frac{3H_I^2}{\kappa^2 \alpha} \frac{1}{(1+Da^4)^2}$, and the radiation energy density $\rho_{\text{rad}}(a) \simeq \frac{3H_I^2}{\kappa^2 \alpha} \frac{Da^4}{(1+Da^4)^2}$, thus recovering the familiar a^{-4} scaling for $Da^4 \gg 1$. As the evolution continues, matter starts to dominate ($\omega_m = 0$), and at that point the cosmological constant term c_0 can no longer be ingored, leading eventually to a modern-era scaling of the Hubble parameter $H \ll H_I$ (obtained as the solution of the evolution equation (3) at this era):[18,30] $H_{\text{modern}}^2(a) \simeq \frac{H_0^2}{1-\nu}\left[(1-\Omega_\Lambda^0)a^{-3(1-\nu)} + \Omega_\Lambda^0 - \nu\right]$, with H_0 the present-day Hubble parameter, and $\Omega_\Lambda^0 = \frac{c_0 + H_0^2 \nu}{H_0^2}$. Notice that the presence of the parameter $\nu > 0$ implies observable deviations from the ΛCDM concordance model of cosmology[19,20] (which is recovered in the limit $\nu = 0$, in which case Ω_Λ^0 coincides with the present-era cosmological constant (in units of the current-era critical density)).

We remark at this stage that the non-linearities-induced inflation (4) is different[19,26,30] from Starobinsky's model of inflation,[31] which is also due to conformal-("trace")-anomaly-induced non-linear curvature corrections to Einstein's GR theory. Starobinsky's model does not have in its energy density the crucial H^4 term of the RVM (*cf.* (1)). As discussed in Refs. 19, 26, it is an inflation characterised mainly by $\dot{H} \simeq$ constant rather than $H \simeq$ constant, which is the case of RVM. The crucial for inflation H^4 term of the RVM energy density (1) is also missing in the case of a quantum field theory of a scalar field non-minimally coupled to a gravity background.[32] As we shall discuss below, a direct (geometric in origin) induction of an RVM H^4 term in the corresponding energy density can be achieved through *condensates* of *gravitational anomalies*, induced by primordial gravity waves,[33] in the string-inspired model for cosmology discussed in Refs. 23, 24, 25, 26, 27, 28, which we now come to describe briefly.

2.2. String-inspired RVM, gravitational anomalies and inflation

The basic assumption[24] towards the construction of the string-inspired cosmology model that will lead to RVM, is that at early stages of the Universe, only fields from the bosonic massless gravitational multiplet of strings[22] appear as external fields. Assuming constant dilatons, this assumption implies that the effective action in the four dimensional space time, after string compactification, will consist only of gravitons and antisymmetric tensor fields $B_{\mu\nu} = -B_{\nu\mu}$, $\mu, \nu = 0, \ldots 3$. As a result of an appropriate U(1) gauge symmetry in the closed string sector:[22] $B_{\mu\nu} \to B_{\mu\nu} + \partial_\mu \theta_\nu(X) - \partial_\nu \theta_\mu(X)$, where $\theta_\mu(X)$ are gauge parameters, the field $B_{\mu\nu}$ appears in the effective four space-time dimensional action only through its field strength. Due to the Green-Schwarz anomaly cancellation mechanism,[22] the latter is modified by appropriate gauge and gravitational Chern-Simons terms. In our model, only the latter are present in the early Universe,[24] and as such the modified field strength $\mathcal{H}_{\mu\nu\rho}$ of the field $B_{\mu\nu}$ reads (in differential form language):[22] $\mathcal{H} = \mathbf{dB} + \frac{\alpha'}{8\kappa}\Omega_{3L}$, with $\alpha' = M_s^{-2}$ the Regge slope, M_s the string mass scale, and the gravitational Chern Simons term is defined as $\Omega_{3L} = \omega^a{}_c \wedge \mathbf{d}\omega^c{}_a + \frac{2}{3}\omega^a{}_c \wedge \omega^c{}_d \wedge \omega^d{}_a$, where $\wedge$ denotes the exterior product among forms, $\mathbf{d}$ is the exterior derivative one form. and $\omega^a{}_{\mu\,b}$ is the spin connection, with Latin indices $a, b = 0, \ldots 3$ denoting tangent space indices. The field strength satisfies a Bianchi identity:

$$\varepsilon_{abc}{}^\mu \mathcal{H}^{abc}{}_{;\mu} = \frac{\alpha'}{32\kappa}\sqrt{-g}\, R_{\mu\nu\rho\sigma}\widetilde{R}^{\mu\nu\rho\sigma} \tag{5}$$

where the semicolon denotes covariant derivative with respect to the standard Christoffel connection, $\varepsilon_{\mu\nu\rho\sigma}$ is the gravitationally covariant Levi-Civita tensor density, totally antisymmetric in its indices, and $\widetilde{R}_{\mu\nu\rho\sigma} = \frac{1}{2}\varepsilon_{\mu\nu\lambda\pi}R^{\lambda\pi}{}_{\rho\sigma}$ is the dual Riemann curvature tensor (we follow the conventions of Ref. 24). To lowest (quadratic) order in derivatives, the target-space effective action (for constant dilatons) reads:

$$S_B = \int d^4x \sqrt{-g}\left(\frac{1}{2\kappa^2}[-R - \frac{1}{6}\mathcal{H}_{\lambda\mu\nu}\mathcal{H}^{\lambda\mu\nu} + \ldots\right), \tag{6}$$

with the ... representing higher-derivative terms. We mention at this stage the rôle of $\mathcal{H}_{\mu\nu\rho}$ as a totally antisymmetric component of torsion in string-inspired effective gravitational theories,[22,34] in the sense that the action (6) can be expressed in terms of a generalised curvature scalar with respect to such a torsion. As we shall describe below, the torsion is associated with an axion field.[34]

Indeed, on implementing (5) as a constraint in the respective path-integral of the action (7) by means of a pseudoscalar Lagrange mutl[plier field $b(x)$, and integrating out $\mathcal{H}$, one obtains the effective action[34,35]

$$\begin{aligned}S_B^{\text{eff}} &= \int d^4x \sqrt{-g}\left[-\frac{1}{2\kappa^2}R + \frac{1}{2}\partial_\mu b\, \partial^\mu b + \sqrt{\frac{2}{3}}\frac{\alpha'}{96\,\kappa}b(x)\, R_{\mu\nu\rho\sigma}\widetilde{R}^{\mu\nu\rho\sigma} + \ldots\right] \\ &= \int d^4x \sqrt{-g}\left[-\frac{1}{2\kappa^2}R + \frac{1}{2}\partial_\mu b\, \partial^\mu b - \sqrt{\frac{2}{3}}\frac{\alpha'}{96\,\kappa}\mathcal{K}^\mu(\omega)\, \partial_\mu b(x) + \ldots\right], \end{aligned}\tag{7}$$

where we took into account that the gravitational anomaly is a total derivative $\sqrt{-g}\,R_{\mu\nu\rho\sigma}\widetilde{R}^{\mu\nu\rho\sigma} = \sqrt{-g}\,\mathcal{K}^{\mu}(\omega)_{;\mu} = \partial_{\mu}\left(\sqrt{-g}\,\mathcal{K}^{\mu}(\omega)\right) = -2\,\partial_{\mu}\left[\sqrt{-g}\,\varepsilon^{\mu\nu\alpha\beta}\,\omega_{\nu}^{ab}\left(\partial_{\alpha}\omega_{\beta ab} + \frac{2}{3}\,\omega_{\alpha a}{}^{c}\,\omega_{\beta cb}\right)\right]$. One observes from (7) that the Lagrange multiplier field $b(x)$ became a fully dynamical axion-like field, the so called Kalb-Ramond (KR) or string-model-independent axion.[34,35] Classically, as follows from the saddle-point of the path integral over $\mathcal{H}$, one has the relation:[34] $3\sqrt{2}\,\partial_{\sigma}\bar{b} = -\sqrt{-g}\,\epsilon_{\mu\nu\rho}\,\overline{\mathcal{H}}^{\mu\nu\rho}$, where the bar denotes classical fields. Hence the association of the torsion with the axion field $b(x)$.

The effective action (7) forms the basis of our cosmological model.[24] In a FLRW space-time background the gravitational anomaly terms vanish.[36] This is not true, however, in the presence of primordial gravity waves (GW) perturbations, which violate CP symmetry:

$$ds^2 = dt^2 - a^2(t)\Big[(1 - h_+(t,z))\,dx^2 + (1 + h_+(t,z))\,dy^2 + 2h_\times(t,z)\,dx\,dy + dz^2\Big], \tag{8}$$

using standard notation for the graviton polarizations of the GW. In the metric (8), the gravitational anomaly term is *non zero*.[33] In fact, on assuming an inflationary space time with constant Hubble parameter $H \simeq$ constant, one can compute the anomaly condensate in the presence of GW CP-violating perturbations:[33]

$$\langle R_{\mu\nu\rho\sigma}\widetilde{R}^{\mu\nu\rho\sigma}\rangle \simeq \frac{16}{a^4}\kappa^2 \int^{\mu} \frac{d^3k}{(2\pi)^3}\,\frac{H^2}{2\,k^3}\,k^4\,\Theta = \frac{1}{\pi^2}\left(\frac{H}{M_{\rm Pl}}\right)^2 \mu^4\,\Theta$$
$$= \frac{2}{3\pi^2}\,\frac{1}{96 \times 12}\left(\frac{H}{M_{\rm Pl}}\right)^3 \left(\frac{\mu}{M_{\rm Pl}}\right)^4 M_{\rm Pl} \times \mathcal{K}^0(t), \tag{9}$$

to leading order in the slow-roll parameter

$$\Theta = \sqrt{\frac{2}{3}}\,\frac{\alpha'\,\kappa}{12}\,H\dot{\bar{b}} \ll 1, \tag{10}$$

with the overdot denoting derivative with respect to the cosmic time t. The quantity μ is an UltraViolet (UV) cutoff in the momenta of the graviton modes.

Assuming isotropy and homogeneity in the Universe, the condensate (9) implies the following solution of the Euler-Lagrange equation of the KR axion $b(t)$:[24]

$$\dot{\bar{b}} = \sqrt{\frac{2}{3}}\,\frac{\alpha'}{96\,\kappa}\,\mathcal{K}^0 \simeq \text{constant}, \tag{11}$$

provided $\mu/M_s \simeq 15\,(M_{\rm Pl}/H)^{1/2}$. Combining the slow-roll condition (10), with the transplanckian conjecture, *i.e.* the absence of transplanckian graviton modes ($\mu \le M_{\rm Pl}$), one can show that for the inflationary Hubble parameter $H = H_I = 10^{-5}\,M_{\rm Pl}$, as dictated by data,[1] the string mass scale is restricted to the range:[27,28]

$$2.6 \times 10^{-5}\,M_{\rm Pl} \lesssim M_s \lesssim 10^{-4}\,M_{\rm Pl}. \tag{12}$$

Eq. (11) admits a spontaneous-Lorentz-violating (LV) KR axion background solution, parametrised as:[24,26]

$$b(t) = \bar{b}(0) + \sqrt{2\epsilon} H M_{\text{Pl}} t, \quad H \simeq \text{constant}, \tag{13}$$

with $\bar{b}(0)$ a boundary condition for the field $b(x)$ at the onset of inflation at $t = 0$. For phenomenological reasons[1] we may take[24] $\epsilon = \mathcal{O}(10^{-2})$. Thus, the KR axion is a slow-roll field, but, as we shall discuss next, it does not drive inflation.

To this end, we remark that the condensate (9) implies a condensate of the quantity:[24] $\langle b(t) R_{\mu\nu\rho\sigma} \widetilde{R}^{\mu\nu\rho\sigma} \rangle$, which remains approximately constant during the entire duration of inflation, thus corresponding to a de-Sitter-type (cosmological-constant) contribution to the effective target-space action (7), provided that

$$\frac{|\bar{b}(0)|}{M_{\text{Pl}}} \gg \sqrt{2\epsilon} \mathcal{N} = \mathcal{O}(10), \quad \bar{b}(0) < 0, \tag{14}$$

where the end of inflation[37] has been set to $t_{\text{inf}} H \simeq \mathcal{N}$, with $\mathcal{N}$ the number of e-foldings of the inflationary era, which phenomenologically[1] lies in the range $\mathcal{N} = 60 - 70$.

Expanding the effective action (7) about such de-Sitter background configurations, one can show that the equation of state of the total energy $\rho_{\text{total}} = \rho^b + \rho^{\text{gCS}} + \rho^{\text{condensate}}$ and pressure $p_{\text{total}} = p^b + p^{\text{gCS}} + p^{\text{condensate}}$ densities of this fluid, consisting of contributions from the KR axion (superscript b), fluctuations of the gravitational anomaly (Chern-Simons) term (superscript gCS) and the condensate term (superscript "condensate"), assumes an RVM form:[27]

$$p_{\text{total}} = -\rho_{\text{total}} < 0, \tag{15}$$

with the total energy density being dominated by the H^4 term during the inflationary era

$$0 < \rho_{\text{total}} \simeq 3\kappa^{-4} \left[-1.65 \times 10^{-3} (\kappa H)^2 + \frac{\sqrt{2}}{3} |\bar{b}(0)| \kappa \times 5.86 \times 10^6 (\kappa H)^4 \right] \tag{16}$$

under the condition (14). The reader should notice that the coefficient of the H^2 term is negative, due to the contribution of the anomalous gravitational Chern-Simons terms, and this is a difference from the conventional RVM form (1). We stress that it is the dominance of the condensate term that makes the total energy density (16) positive, and thus leads to a proper RVM fluid. Without the formation of this condensate, the equation of state of the remaining terms curiously acquire the form of an RVM-like (i.e. de Sitter-type) "phantom-matter":[27,38,39]

$$p^b + p^{\text{gCS}} = -(\rho^b + \rho^{\text{gCS}}) > 0, \tag{17}$$

violating the weak energy conditions.[b] Such exotic matter can be used for the stabilisation of traversable wormholes,[40] so in this respect our anomalous gravitational theory, in conditions in which the condensate $\langle b(x)\, R_{\mu\nu\rho\sigma}\, \widetilde{R}^{\mu\nu\rho\sigma}\rangle$ is not formed, might find applications to this problem as well.

The dominance of the non-linear H^4 term in (16) at early eras of this string-inspired Universe, will lead to an RVM type inflation (4), as we discussed in the previous subsection 2.1. It is in this sense that an inflationary phase arises dynamically in a self consistent way in our approach, so our assumption of a constant H in the computation of (9) is justified *a posteriori*.

2.3. *Potential origin of GW: the dynamically-broken supergravity example*

So far, we have assumed the existence of primordial GW perturbations (8), without examining in detail their microscopic origin. In Refs. 26, 27, we have discussed several scenarios which lead to the creation of GW in a pre-RVM-inflationary era of our string-inspired cosmology. One of the most relevant ones to our model, consistent with the basic assumption that only fields from the massless gravitational string multiplet appear as external fields at the very early stages of the Universe, is the scenario considering an underlying superstring theory, whose low energy limit will result in a supergravity model. Although the precise supergravity model depends crucially on the microscopic higher-dimensional string theory considered, for our qualitative purposes here, we may consider a simplified but highly non-trivial example for our (3+1)-dimensional gravitational theory at the very early stages of our cosmology, that of $N=1$ (3+1)-dimensional supergravity.[41]

The model contains massless spin-2 gravitons, $g_{\mu\nu}(x)$, $\mu,\nu = 0,\ldots 3$, and their spin-3/2 supersymmetric partners, the gravitinos, $\psi_\mu(x)$. The supergravity can be broken dynamically in this model as a consequence of gravitino condensation.[42,43] The corresponding effective potential $\widetilde{V}(\sigma)$ of the gravitino-condensate scalar field

---

[b]The computation leading to (17) is based on the fact that the graviton variations of the anomalous gravitational Chern-Simons terms in (7) yield the Cotton tensor $C_{\mu\nu}$:[36]

$$\delta\left[\int d^4x \sqrt{-g}\, b\, R_{\mu\nu\rho\sigma}\, \widetilde{R}^{\mu\nu\rho\sigma}\right] = 4\int d^4x \sqrt{-g}\, \mathcal{C}^{\mu\nu}\, \delta g_{\mu\nu} = -4\int d^4x \sqrt{-g}\, \mathcal{C}_{\mu\nu}\, \delta g^{\mu\nu},$$

where

$$\mathcal{C}^{\mu\nu} \equiv -\frac{1}{2}\left[v_\sigma\left(\varepsilon^{\sigma\mu\alpha\beta} R^\nu_{\ \beta;\alpha} + \varepsilon^{\sigma\nu\alpha\beta} R^\mu_{\ \beta;\alpha}\right) + v_{\sigma\tau}\left(\widetilde{R}^{\tau\mu\sigma\nu} + \widetilde{R}^{\tau\nu\sigma\mu}\right)\right],$$

with $v_\sigma \equiv \partial_\sigma b = b_{;\sigma}$, $v_{\sigma\tau} \equiv v_{\tau;\sigma} = b_{;\tau;\sigma}$. This implies that the Einstein's equations stemming from (7) read: $R^{\mu\nu} - \frac{1}{2} g^{\mu\nu} R - \mathcal{C}^{\mu\nu} = \kappa^2\, T_b^{\mu\nu}$, where $T_b^{\mu\nu}$ is the KR axion stress tensor. Taking into account conservation properties of the Cotton tensor,[36] $\mathcal{C}^{\mu\nu}_{\ \ ;\mu} = \frac{1}{8} v^\nu R^{\alpha\beta\gamma\delta} \widetilde{R}_{\alpha\beta\gamma\delta}$, we observe that there is an exchange of energy between the KR axion and the gravitational anomaly, when $\mathcal{C}_{\mu\nu}$ is non trivial, as is the case of GW perturbations of the metric (*cf.* (8)). We note that classically the Cotton tensor is traceless $g^{\mu\nu}\mathcal{C}_{\mu\nu}=0$. However, the formation of the condensate $\langle b(t) R_{\mu\nu\rho\sigma}\, \widetilde{R}^{\mu\nu\rho\sigma}\rangle$, as a result of (9), introduces in a sense a quantum-gravity-induced trace of $\langle \mathcal{C}^\mu_{\ \mu}\rangle$, which leads to the addition of a de Sitter type cosmological-constant term in the effective action (7).[24]

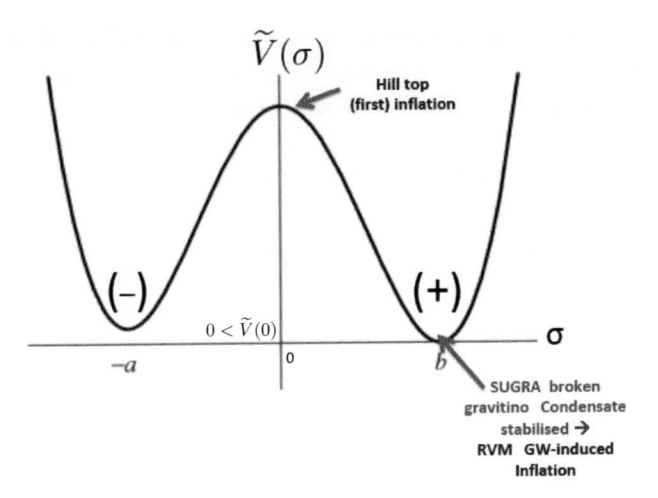

Fig. 1. The biased double-well gravitino potential $\widetilde V(\sigma)$ for dynamical supergravity breaking that could characgterise the early epochs of the string-inspired RTVM Cosmology.[26] The bias between the two ($\pm$) vacua is assumed to be due to percolation effects in the early Universe,[45,46] and leads to the formation of unstable domain walls, whose collapse or collisions lead to GW. There is also a first hill-top inflation near the origin $\sigma = 0$.

$\sigma = \langle \overline{\psi}_\mu \psi^\mu \rangle$, evaluated at one loop in a local de Sitter space-time background,[44] after graviton and gravitino Euclidean path-integration, assumes a double-well shape (see fig. 1), defining two local minima, at each of which the potential takes on non-negative values, compatible with the breaking of global and local supersymmetry. There could be a statistical bias, in the sense of unequal occupation numbers of these two local minima/"vacua", as a result of percolation effects.[45,46] Such a situation leads to the formation of "biased" domain walls in the theory, whose non-spherical collapse or collision, leads to GW. The $N=1$ supergravity model is also characterised by a very early hill-top inflationary phase,[47] which is not necessarily slow roll, and has no observable consequences.

This first inflationary phase is consistent with the study of the theory in a local de Sitter (LDS) background, in the absence of a mass parameter,[44] given the existence of an appropriate general coordinate transformation[48] that maps the LDS space-time without a mass parameter to a cosmological (global) de Sitter one (GDS), and leaves the effective action invariant.[c]

---

[c]The local de Sitter-Schwarzschild metric with a mass parameter M is described by the following invariant element

$$ds^2 = \left(1 - 2\frac{M}{\bar r} - \frac{\Lambda}{3}\bar r^2\right)c^2 dT^2 - \left(1 - 2\frac{M}{\bar r} - \frac{\Lambda}{3}\bar r^2\right)^{-1} d\bar r^2 - \bar r^2(d\bar\theta^2 + \sin^2\bar\theta d\bar\phi^2) \quad (18)$$

in de Sitter-Schwarzschild coordinates. In the case $M = 0$, as required by the isotropy and homogeneity of space, the following transformation[48]

$$x^\mu \equiv \{cT, \bar r, \bar\theta, \bar\phi\} \to x'^\mu \equiv \{ct, r, \bar\theta, \bar\phi\} \text{ (comoving frame)}:$$

$$t = T + \frac{1}{2H}\ln\left(1 - H^2 \bar r^2\right), \quad r = \frac{\bar r}{\sqrt{1 - H^2 \bar r^2}} e^{-HT} = \bar r\, e^{-Ht}, \quad H^2 \equiv \frac{\Lambda}{3} > 0\,. \quad (19)$$

This hill-top inflation is a different phase from our RVM inflation. In fact, it ensures that any spatial inhomogeneities or isotropies are washed out well before entrance into the RVM inflationary phase, so the assumptions and calculations of Refs. 24, 26 are formally justified. The RVM inflation occurs[26] at the phase where the gravitino has settled in its lowest minimum (see fig. 1), is massive and the supergravity is dynamically broken. This phase coincides with the exit phase from the hill-top inflation.[47] This exit phase is characterised by the creation of the biased domain walls and GW, as a consequence of wall collisions. The massive gravitino can be integrated out of the path integral.

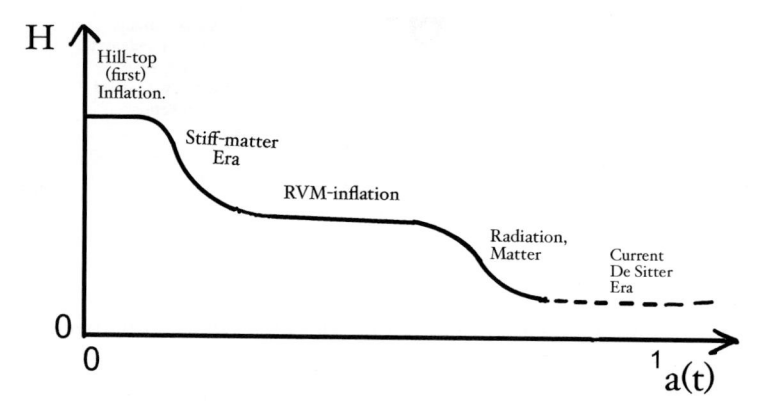

Fig. 2. Schematic evolution of the Hubblle parameter (H) as a function of the scale factor a(t) in the string-inspired RVM universe,[27] from the Big-Bang (a=0) till the current epoch (a=1, in units of today's scale factor).

Embedding this simple supergravity model into our string framework implies[26,28] that the exit from the hill-top inflation may be succeeded by dominance of the KR axion matter,[26] which, due to the lack of a potential, constitutes a stiff matter fluid (with equation of state $w = +1$).[49,50] This era interpolates between the first-hill-top inflation and the GW-induced RVM inflation (see fig. 2). Indeed, the presence of GW as a consequence of domain-wall collapse or collisions, implies the appearance of CP-violating anomalous gravitational Chern Simons terms coupled

---

where t and r denote co-moving frame time and radial space coordinates, respectively, maps the metric (18) to a standard cosmological de Sitter space-time:

$$ds^2 = c^2 dt^2 - a(t)^2 [dr^2 + r^2 d\Omega^2], \quad d\Omega^2 = d\bar{\theta}^2 + \sin^2\bar{\theta} d\bar{\phi}^2 , \qquad (20)$$

where $a(t) = e^{\sqrt{\frac{\Lambda}{3}} t} \equiv e^{Ht}$ (H = constant), is the exponentially expanding scale factor of the de-Sitter/FLRW (inflationary) Universe. The above result is exact, valid for every non-negative value of the cosmological constant $\Lambda \geq 0$. Notice that in this form of the metric there is no preferred origin of space, as appropriate for a space-time generated by a uniform homogeneous and isotropic fluid. The apparent existence of an origin at zero for the radial coordinate in the local form of the pure de-Sitter metric (18) with $M = 0$ is thus an artefact of an inappropriate choice of coordinates, much like the internal observer de Sitter horizon at $\sqrt{\Lambda/3}$.

to the KR axions in the effective action (7). As the cosmic time elapses, conditions for the condensation of GW can develop, leading to the anomaly condensate (9), and the eventual RVM inflationary era, driven by the H^4 term in (16).

Before closing this subsection, we would like to discuss some formal properties of the one-loop corrected effective action of supergravity in the de-Sitter background, which we shall make use of in section 4. As discussed in Ref. 43 (see also Ref. 30), the Euclidean (E) one-loop effective action of the dynamically-broken $N = 1$ supergravity model, in a given gauge, evaluated in a de Sitter background, with (one-loop corrected) cosmological constant $1 \gg \Lambda > 0$ reads:

$$\Gamma^{(\mathrm{E})} \simeq S_{\mathrm{cl}} - \frac{24\pi^2}{\Lambda^2}\left(\alpha_0^F + \alpha_0^B + \left(\alpha_1^F + \alpha_1^B\right)\Lambda + \left(\alpha_2^F + \alpha_2^B\right)\Lambda^2 + \dots\right), \quad (21)$$

where the superscripts $B(F)$ denote terms arising from integration of massless (quantum) gravitons (B) (and gravitinos (F)), f is the scale of supergravity (and global suprsymmetry) breaking, $\sigma_c < f$,[43] is the value of the gravitino condensate field at the minimum of its effective potential (see fig. 1) and S_{cl} denotes the classical supergravity action with tree-level (bare) cosmological constant $\Lambda_0 < 0$

$$\frac{\Lambda_0}{\kappa^2} \equiv \sigma_c^2 - f^2, \quad (22)$$

which is necessarily *negative* for reasons of incompatibility of (unbroken) supergravity with de Sitter vacua.[41–43] The one-loop renormalised cosmological constant Λ, though, is *positive*, due to quantum corrections (*cf.* (25)), compatible with dynamically broken supergravity. Taking into account that the Euclidean de Sitter volume is[44] $24\pi^2/\Lambda^2 \to \int d^4x \sqrt{\widehat{g}_\mathrm{E}}$, we may express the effective action (21) in a generally covariant form (using the notation $\widehat{\dots}$ for quantities evaluated in the background de Sitter space-time):

$$\Gamma^{(\mathrm{E})} \simeq -\frac{1}{2\kappa^2}\int d^4x \sqrt{\widehat{g}_\mathrm{E}}\left[\left(\widehat{R} - 2\Lambda_1\right) + \alpha_1\, \widehat{R} + \alpha_2\, \widehat{R}^2\right], \quad (23)$$

where we have replaced Λ by the curvature scalar,

$$\widehat{R} = 4\Lambda. \quad (24)$$

The various quantities entering (23) are given by[30,43]

$$\Lambda_1 = -\kappa^2\left(-\frac{\Lambda_0}{\kappa^2} + \alpha_0^F + \alpha_0^B\right), \quad (25)$$

where

$$\alpha_0^F = \kappa^4\, \sigma_c^4\left(0.100\, \ln\left(\frac{\kappa^2\, \sigma_c^2}{3\mu^2}\right) + 0.126\right),$$

$$\alpha_0^B = \kappa^4\, (f^2 - \sigma_c^2)^2\left(0.027 - 0.018\ln\left(\frac{3\kappa^2\, (f^2 - \sigma_c^2)}{2\mu^2}\right)\right), \quad (26)$$

and

$$\alpha_1 = \frac{\kappa^2}{2}\left(\alpha_1^F + \alpha_1^B\right), \quad \alpha_2 = \frac{\kappa^2}{8}\left(\alpha_2^F + \alpha_2^B\right), \quad (27)$$

with

$$\alpha_1^F = 0.067\,\kappa^2\sigma_c^2 - 0.021\,\tilde{\kappa}^2\sigma_c^2 \ln\left(\frac{\Lambda}{\mu^2}\right) + 0.073\,\kappa^2\sigma_c^2 \ln\left(\frac{\kappa^2\sigma_c^2}{\mu^2}\right),$$

$$\alpha_2^F = 0.029 + 0.014 \ln\left(\frac{\kappa^2\sigma_c^2}{\mu^2}\right) - 0.029 \ln\left(\frac{\Lambda}{\mu^2}\right),$$

$$\alpha_1^B = -0.083\Lambda_0 + 0.018\,\Lambda_0 \ln\left(\frac{\Lambda}{3\mu^2}\right) + 0.049\,\Lambda_0 \ln\left(-\frac{3\Lambda_0}{\mu^2}\right),$$

$$\alpha_2^B = 0.020 + 0.021 \ln\left(\frac{\Lambda}{3\mu^2}\right) - 0.014 \ln\left(-\frac{6\Lambda_0}{\mu^2}\right), \qquad (28)$$

with the replacement (24) understood in all the above expressions.

The scale μ^2 is a proper-time ultraviolet cutoff, used to regularise UV divergences.[42–44] Supergravity breaks dynamically for μ^2 close to Planck scale.[42] We then set from now on

$$\mu^2 \sim M_{\rm Pl}^2 = \kappa^{-2}. \qquad (29)$$

It can be arranged that the masses of the gravitino condensate and the gravitino become very large compared to the low-energy mass scales. They can be taken to be above the grand-unification scale, even close to Planck scale, for our purposes,[26–28] provided the scale f is chosen appropriately. Since the effective action (23) is evaluated after one-loop integration of (weak) graviton perturbations about the de Sitter background, it is actually a quantum-gravity effective action.

In the broken supergravity RVM phase, where the hypermassive gravitino and gravitino-condensate fields, with masses of order of the Planck mass, are integrated out from the low-energy effective action, leading to Planck-mass suppressed terms, the only leading quantum corrections are those due to massless graviton integration. As can be seen from the expressions (25),(26),(27),(28), such corrections involve $\widehat{R}^n \ln(\kappa^2\widehat{R})$, $n = 1, 2$ terms (cf. coefficients with superscript B). Passing onto a slowly-varying global de Sitter background (via the coordinate transformations[48] (19)), we may approximately replace $\widehat{R} \to 12H^2$, where H is the approximately constant inflationary Hubble parameter.

In the framework of our cosmology, this RVM phase will also involve the KR axion and gravitational anomaly terms, in addition to the aforementioned quantum-gravity corrections of the effective action (23) contributing terms of the form $H^{2n'}\ln(\kappa^2 H^2)$, $n' = 1, 2$. From the pertinent expressions (25),(26),(27),(28), it becomes clear that, on assuming $\kappa^2|\Lambda_0| < 1$, for the scale of the bare cosmological constant (22), and taking into account (14), these quantum-gravity-induced corrections are subdominant compared to the gravitational-anomaly-condensate-induced H^4 term in (16). Thus, our discussion and conclusions on the rôle of anomalies in inducing an RVM inflation are not affected.[27,28]

As we speculated though in Refs. 27, 28, quantum-gravity corrections of the form $H^2\ln(\kappa^2 H^2)$ could lead to observable deviations from the ΛCDM in the modern era (which again is characterised by an approximately de Sitter cosmological space-time background, with $H \simeq H_0$). In particular, they could lead to a modified version of RVM, somewhat analogous to the type-II RVM considered in Ref. 21 for the simultaneous alleviation of the H_0 and σ_8 tensions. We shall briefly discuss these issues in section 4.

3. After RVM Inflation: KR-Axion Dark Matter and Leptogenesis

In this section we review briefly the situation charactrerising the exit from the RVM inflation and post inflationary eras of the model. For details we refer the reader to Refs. 25, 24, 27, 26.

At the exit from RVM inflation, gauge fields and chiral fermionic matter, including massive sterile right-handed neutrinos (RHN) of interest to us here, are assumed to be generated from the decay of the RVM vacuum.[25] Chiral fermions have their own gravitational and chiral anomalies. The former are assumed[24, 26] to cancel the primordial gravitational anomalies due to the Green-Schwarz counterterms. The chiral anomalies, however, remain in the radiation and matter eras:[25]

$$\partial_\mu \Big[\sqrt{-g}\,\Big(\sqrt{\frac{3}{8}}\frac{\alpha'}{\kappa}\,J^{5\mu} - \frac{\alpha'}{\kappa}\sqrt{\frac{2}{3}}\frac{1}{96}\,\mathcal{K}^\mu\Big)\Big]$$
$$= \sqrt{\frac{3}{8}}\frac{\alpha'}{\kappa}\Big(\frac{\alpha_{\rm EM}}{2\pi}\sqrt{-g}\,F^{\mu\nu}\widetilde{F}_{\mu\nu} + \frac{\alpha_s}{8\pi}\sqrt{-g}\,G^a_{\mu\nu}\widetilde{G}^{a\mu\nu}\Big)\,, \tag{30}$$

where $J^{5\mu} = \sum_{i=\text{chiral fermions}} \overline{\psi}_i \gamma^5 \gamma^\mu \psi_i$, $F_{\mu\nu}$ denotes the electromagnetic (EM) Maxwell tensor, $G^a_{\mu\nu}$ is the gluon field strength, with $a = 1, \ldots 8$ an adjoint SU(3) colour index, $\alpha_{\rm EM}$ the electromagnetic fine structure constant, and α_s the strong-interactions fine structure constant. The gluon terms in (30) may lead, through non-perturbative instanton effects in the post-inflationary QCD era, to the generation of a potential and a mass m_b term, for the KR axion, which, due to (12), is within phenomenologically acceptable ranges,[24, 28]

$$1.17 \times 10^{-8} \lesssim m_b/({\rm eV}) \lesssim 1.17 \times 10^{-5}. \tag{31}$$

In this way, the KR axion field can play the rôle of a dominant component of dark matter.[25] In view of the association of the KR axion with torsion, then, one obtains a geometric origin of the dark matter sector of this Universe.

Moreover, the spontaneous-LV KR axion background (13), which remains undiluted at the exit phase from RVM inflation, can trigger the generation of Leptogenesis in models involving RHN, according to the mechanism discussed in Refs. 51, 52. The pertinent lagrangian of the RHN and their interactions with the standard model (SM) sector is:

$$\mathcal{L} = \mathcal{L}_{\rm SM} + i\overline{N}\gamma^\mu \partial_\mu N - \frac{m_N}{2}(\overline{N^c}N + \overline{N}N^c) - \overline{N}\gamma^\mu B_\mu \gamma^5 N - \sum_f y_f \overline{L}_f \tilde{\phi}^d N + {\rm h.c.} \tag{32}$$

where h.c. denotes hermitian conjugate, $\mathcal{L}_{\rm SM}$ denotes the SM Lagrangian, N is the RHN field, of (Majorana) mass m_N, $\tilde{\phi}$ is the SU(2) adjoint of the Higgs field

ϕ ($\tilde\phi_i^d \equiv \varepsilon_{ij}\phi_j$, $i,j = 1,2$, SU(2) indices), L_f is a SM lepton doublet, with f a generation index, $f = e, \mu, \tau$, y_f is a Yukawa coupling of the "Higgs portal" interactions between the SM sector and RHN, which can lead to the generation of SM light neutrino masses, via, e.g., the seesaw mechanism. The quantity B_μ is associated with the KR axion background (13) induced by the anomaly condensates during the RVM inflation:

$$B_\mu = M_{\rm Pl}^{-1} \dot{\bar b}\, \delta_{\mu 0}. \tag{33}$$

As discussed in Ref. 24, during the radiation era, B_μ is slowly varying with the cosmic temperature T ($B_0 \propto T^3$), so the Lagrangian (32) resembles that of a Standard Model Extension (SME) Lagrangian in a LV and CPT Violating (CPTV) (approximately constant) background.[53,54] A lepton asymmetry is then generated due to asymmetric tree-level decays of the RHN N into SM leptons and anti-leptons in the background (33) between the channels I and II:[51,52] Channel $I: N \to l^- h^+$, νh^0, and Channel II: $N \to l^+ h^-$, $\bar\nu h^0$, where $\ell^\pm$ are charged leptons, $h^\pm$ are the charged Higgs fields, which, at the high temperatures, above the electroweak symmetry breaking, at which this leptogenesis takes place,[51,52] do not decouple from the physical spectrum, ν ($\bar\nu$) are the light SM neutrinos (antineutrinos), and h^0 is the neutral Higgs field. The lepton asymmetry reads (assuming that the dominant lepton asymmetry is generated by one sterile neitrino, although extension to more RHN species, as required by the seesaw mechanism, is straightforward):[52]

$$\frac{\Delta L^{TOT}(T=T_D)}{s} \sim q\, \frac{B_0(T_D)\, m_N^2}{T_D^3} \sim q\, 3.5 \times 10^{11} \left(\frac{m_N}{M_{\rm Pl}}\right)^2, \quad q > 0, \tag{34}$$

where $s \propto T^3$ is the entropy density of the Universe, $T_D \simeq m_N$ denotes the freeze-out temperature, and $0 < q = \mathcal{O}(10)$ is a numerical factor expressing theoretical uncertainties in the approximate analytic (Padé) methods used.[52] The lepton asymmetry (34) can then be communicated to the baryon sector via Baryon-minus-Lepton-number $(B - L)$ conserving sphaleron processes in the SM sector.

4. Modern Era Phenomenology: Links of the Stringy RVM to a Modified Type-II RVM and Potential Data Tension Alleviation

In the modern era, the energy density of this stringy Universe also assumes an RVM form,

$$\rho_0 = \frac{3}{\kappa^2}\left(c_0 + \nu_0\, H_0^2\right), \tag{35}$$

where now $\nu_0 > 0$, due to contributions from cosmic electromagnetic background fields[24] (we ignore terms of order H_0^4, as they are negligible in the current era). Comparison with the data[19,20] indicates $\nu_0 = \mathcal{O}(10^{-3})$. The present-day cosmological constant $c_0 > 0$ cannot be uniquely determined in our string-inspired cosmology, given that there might be various contributions to it,[28] some associated with details of the extra dimensional geometry of the underlying microscopic string/brane theory. For comparison with data, we therefore should treat c_0 as a phenomenological parameter at this stage.

What is important to realise is that, as discussed in subsection 2.3, integrating out massless quantum graviton fluctuations in the path integral of the current-era gravitational theory, which is also characterised by a de Sitter background, generates terms in the one-loop effective action of the form (taking into account (29)):

$$\delta \mathcal{L}_{\text{quant. grav.}}^{1-\text{loop}} = \sqrt{-\widehat{g}} \left[\widetilde{\alpha}_0 + \widehat{R}\left(c_1 + c_2 \ln(\frac{1}{12}\kappa^2 \widehat{R})\right) \right] + \dots \qquad (36)$$

From the supergravity example[30,42,43] we have that the constant coefficients $c_i \propto \kappa^2 \mathcal{E}_0$, or $c_i \propto \kappa^2 \mathcal{E}_0 \ln(\kappa^4 |\mathcal{E}_0|)$, $i = 1, 2$, (cf. (28)) with $\mathcal{E}_0$ a bare (constant) vacuum energy density scale (the ellipses ... denote terms of quadratic and higher order in $\widehat{R} = 12H^2$, which are subdominant in the current epoch ($H = H_0$)). The structures (36) appear generic for weak quantum gravity corrections about de Sitter backgrounds,[44] and we may therefore conjecture that they can play a rôle in the current era phenomenology.

From the graviton equations of the one-loop corrected effective Lagrangian, it can be readily seen that the terms (36) will imply corrections to the effective stress-energy tensor in the current era of the form,[28]

$$\delta \rho_0^{\text{vac}} = \frac{1}{2}\widetilde{\alpha}_0 + 3(c_1 - c_2)H_0^2 + 3c_2 H_0^2 \ln(\kappa^2 H_0^2) \ , \qquad (37)$$

which should be added to (35). Moreover, the supergravity prototype[30,42,43] indicates that the one-loop correction (dark-energy-type) term $\frac{1}{2}\widetilde{\alpha}_0$ is constant, independent of $\ln H^2$ terms. This will lead to some crucial differences from the standard type II RVM used in Ref. 21 to alleviate the H_0 and σ_8 tensions, which is characterised only by a mild cosmic-time t dependence of an effective gravitational constant, $\kappa_{\text{eff}}^2(t) = \kappa^2/\varphi(t)$, with $\varphi(t)$ a phenomenological non-dynamical function.

Another issue to be clarified is the sign of the bare cosmological constant $\Lambda_0 \propto \mathcal{E}_0 \kappa^2$ which, as in the supergravity example of subsection 2.3, enters the computation of the effective action about de Sitter backgrounds in generic quantum gravity (QG) models that could describe the current-era. Such a sign depends on the details of the underlying QG theory. In the supergravity example this is negative (22) (Anti de Sitter type (AdS)), due to fundamental reasons of compatibility with supersymmetry.[42,43] One may also use such negative bare cosmological constant scales as formal regulators in the quantization procedure, as, e.g., has been considered in the context of black hole physics[55] motivated by the AdS/conformal-field-theory correspondence.[56] We stress though that the one-loop corrected cosmological constant is always positive in such constructions, compatible with the current phenomenology (and also with the broken supergravity scenario[30,42,43]). We plan to study such issues, and their modern-era phenomenology, in future works.

Before closing the section, we mention that in string theory there might be a mixing of the KR axion with the other, string-model dependent, axions that exist as a result of the compactification procedure.[35] In Ref. 24, we have argued that, depending on details of this mixing, one might obtain KR axion backgrounds that may be characterised by an approximately constant $\dot b$ even in the current era of the string Universe. Such backgrounds can therefore be parametrised by

$$\dot b_0 \sim \sqrt{2\,\epsilon'}\, H_0\, M_{\rm Pl}. \tag{38}$$

Phenomenological considerations, associated with the rôle of the KR axion background as dark matter, imply then that $\epsilon' \sim 10^{-2}$, in order to reproduce a dark matter energy density due to the KR axion in the phenomenologically right ballpark.[1,2] This, in turn, leads to a curious coincidence in the order of magnitude of the slow-roll parameters entering the expressions for $\dot b$ in the RVM-inflationary (13) (ϵ) and modern (38) eras (ϵ'),

$$\epsilon' \sim \epsilon \simeq 10^{-2}\,, \tag{39}$$

which needs to be understood further, in the context of the underlying microscopic string theory models. We do note though[25,28] that the background (38), under the assumption (39), is compatible with the stringent current experimental bounds of LV and CPTV discussed in ref. 54.

5. Conclusions and Outlook

In this talk, I reviewed a string-inspired model of a running vacuum (RVM) cosmology, which seems consistent with the current phenomenology, but also provides a geometrical origin of both, RVM inflation and dark matter. Crucial rôles are played by the gravitational anomalies that characterise the model at early eras, and the KR axion fields from the fundamental massless multiplet of the underlying string theory. The KR axion field is associated with a totally antisymmetric torsion in the underlying string theory. The RVM inflation arises from the non-linear H^4 term in the vacuum energy density (16), which is exclusively due to primordial GW that induce non trivial condensates of the gravitational Chern-Simons terms that are present in the very early stages of this string-inspired cosmology. Such terms do not arise in the context of anomaly-free quantum field theories, or Starobinsky inflation, and, as such, are rather exclusive to our string-inspired RVM. The anomaly condensates also imply LV KR axion backgrounds that induce baryogenesis through leptogenesis. In this sense, we may dare state that our very existence, that is the dominance of matter over antimatter in the Cosmos, is due to cosmic anomalies. *We are anomalously made of star stuff*, to paraphrase the famous quote by Carl Sagan.[23,24]

There are several open issues that we need to understand, and explore further, such as: (i) potential hints in the cosmic-microwave-background data[1] about the LV KR axion backgrounds, (ii) prospects of getting some phenomenological indications in early-Universe data about the negative, anomaly-induced, coefficient of the H^2 term in the RVM-like cosmic energy density (16) during the RVM inflation.

This, however, is a difficult task, in view of the phase transition occurring in our model at the exit from the RVM inflation, (iii) the rich phenomenology of both, the string-model-independent KR axion and the other, string-model dependent, axions, that exist in string theory,[35,57] (iv) the precise rôle of quantum-gravity-induced $H^2 \ln(\kappa^2 H^2)$ corrections in the vacuum energy density of the current era, comparing the model with the type-II RVM,[21] in an attempt to discuss potential alleviation of the observed tensions in the cosmological data, and (v) last but not least: in view of the association of the KR axion with (totally antisymmetric) torsion, the phenomenological comparison of the stringy RVM with other cosmologies with torsion[58,59] (in which the torsion has more components than the totally antisymmetric one characterising our model) or other teleparallel-gravity models[60] (where torsion mimics gravity, in contrast to our case, which contains also graviton fields). We hope to be able to report on these important issues in the near future.

Acknowledgements

NEM thanks A. Gómez-Valent and J. Solà peracaula for the invitation to speak in the *CM3* parallel session: *"Status of the H_0 and σ_8 tensions: theoretical models and model-independent constraints"* of the MG16 Marcel Grossmann virtual Conference, July 5-10 2021. He also acknowledges participation in the COST Association Action CA18108 *"Quantum Gravity Phenomenology in the Multimessenger Approach (QG-MM)"*. This work is funded in part by the UK Science and Technology Facilities research Council (STFC) under the research grant ST/T000759/1.

References

1. N. Aghanim et al. [Planck], Planck 2018 results. VI. Cosmological parameters, Astron. Astrophys. **641**, A6 (2020) doi:10.1051/0004-6361/201833910 [arXiv:1807.06209 [astro-ph.CO]].
2. P. A. Zyla et al. [Particle Data Group], Review of Particle Physics, PTEP **2020**, no. 8, 083C01 (2020) doi:10.1093/ptep/ptaa104.
3. For a recent review see: Mohayaee R., Rameez M. and Sarkar S., Do supernovae indicate an accelerating universe?, Eur. Phys. J. Spec. Top. (2021), doi:10.1140/epjs/s11734-021-00199-6. [arXiv:2106.03119 [astro-ph.CO]].
4. E. P. Verlinde, On the Origin of Gravity and the Laws of Newton, JHEP **04**, 029 (2011) doi:10.1007/JHEP04(2011)029 [arXiv:1001.0785 [hep-th]].
5. L. T. Verde, T. Treu T. and A. G. Riess, Tensions between the Early and the Late Universe, Nature Astron. **3**, 891 (2019) doi:10.1038/s41550-019-0902-0. [arXiv:1907.10625 [astro-ph.CO]].
6. L. Perivolaropoulos L. and F. Skara F. (2021), Challenges for ΛCDM: An update, [arXiv:2105.05208 [astro-ph.CO]].
7. A. G. Riess et al., A 2.4% Determination of the Local Value of the Hubble Constant, Astrophys. J. **826** (2016) no. 1, 56 (2016). doi:10.3847/0004-637X/826/1/56. [arXiv:1604.01424 [astro-ph.CO]].
8. A. G. Riess, et al., New Parallaxes of Galactic Cepheids from Spatially Scanning the Hubble Space Telescope: Implications for the Hubble Constant, Astrophys. J. **855** no. 2, 136 (2018). doi:10.3847/1538-4357/aaadb7. [arXiv:1801.01120 [astro-ph.SR]].

9. A. G. Riess, S. Casertano S., W. Yuan W. J. B. Bowers , L. Macri L., J. C. Zinn and D. Scolnic, Cosmic Distances Calibrated to 1% Precision with Gaia EDR3 Parallaxes and Hubble Space Telescope Photometry of 75 Milky Way Cepheids Confirm Tension with ΛCDM, Astrophys. J. Lett. **908** no. 1, L6 (2021). doi:10.3847/2041-8213/abdbaf. [arXiv:2012.08534 [astro-ph.CO]].
10. E. Di Valentino *et al.*, Cosmology intertwined III: $f\sigma_8$ and S_8, Astropart. Phys. **131**, 102604 (2021). doi:10.1016/j.astropartphys.2021.102604, [arXiv:2008.11285 [astro-ph.CO]] and references therein.
11. G. Efstathiou (2021), To H0 or not to H0?, doi:10.1093/mnras/stab1588. [arXiv:2103.08723 [astro-ph.CO]].
12. E. Mortsell, A. Goobar, J. Johansson and S. Dhawan (2021), The Hubble Tension Bites the Dust: Sensitivity of the Hubble Constant Determination to Cepheid Color Calibration, [arXiv:2105.11461 [astro-ph.CO]].
13. W. L Freedman (2021), Measurements of the Hubble Constant: Tensions in Perspective, [arXiv:2106.15656 [astro-ph.CO]].
14. W. L. Freedman, Cosmology at a Crossroads, Nature Astron. **1**, 0121 (2017). doi:10.1038/s41550-017-0121. [arXiv:1706.02739 [astro-ph.CO]].
15. I. L. Shapiro and J. Sola, On the scaling behavior of the cosmological constant and the possible existence of new forces and new light degrees of freedom, Phys. Lett. B **475**, 236-246 (2000) doi:10.1016/S0370-2693(00)00090-3 [arXiv:hep-ph/9910462 [hep-ph]].
16. I. L. Shapiro and J. Solà, Scaling behavior of the cosmological constant: Interface between quantum field theory and cosmology, JHEP **02**, 006. doi:10.1088/1126-6708/2002/02/006 (2002). [arXiv:hep-th/0012227 [hep-th]].
17. J. Solà, Dark energy: A Quantum fossil from the inflationary Universe?, J. Phys. A **41**, 164066 (2008) doi:10.1088/1751-8113/41/16/164066 [arXiv:0710.4151 [hep-th]], and references therein.
18. S. Basilakos S., J. A. S. Lima and J. Solà, From inflation to dark energy through a dynamical Lambda: An attempt at alleviating fundamental cosmic puzzles, Int. J. Mod. Phys. D **22**, 1342008 (2013). doi:10.1142/S021827181342008X. [arXiv:1307.6251 [astro-ph.CO]].
19. J. Solà and A. Gómez-Valent, The $\bar{\Lambda}$CDM cosmology: From inflation to dark energy through running Λ, Int. J. Mod. Phys. D **24**, 1541003 (2015). doi:10.1142/S0218271815410035 [arXiv:1501.03832 [gr-qc] and references therein.
20. J. Solà, Cosmological constant vis-a-vis dynamical vacuum: bold challenging the ΛCDM, Int. J. Mod. Phys. A **31**, no. 23, 1630035 (2016). doi:10.1142/S0217751X16300350. [arXiv:1612.02449 [astro-ph.CO]].
21. J. Solà Peracaula, A. Gómez-Valent, J. de Cruz Perez and C. Moreno-Pulido, Running vacuum against the H_0 and σ_8 tensions, EPL **134** no. 1, 19001 (2021). doi:10.1209/0295-5075/134/19001. [arXiv:2102.12758 [astro-ph.CO]].
22. J. Polchinski, *String theory. Vol. 1: An introduction to the bosonic string*, and *String theory. Vol. 2: Superstring theory and beyond*, (Cambridge University Press (Cambridge, UK, 2010, 2011), doi:10.1017/CBO9780511816079, doi:10.1017/CBO9780511618123).
23. S. Basilakos, N. E. Mavromatos and J. Solà Peracaula, Do we Come from a Quantum Anomaly?, Int. J. Mod. Phys. D **28**, no. 14, 1944002 (2019) doi:10.1142/S0218271819440024 [arXiv:1905.04685 [hep-th]].
24. S. Basilakos, N. E. Mavromatos and J. Solà Peracaula Gravitational and Chiral Anomalies in the Running Vacuum Universe and Matter-Antimatter Asymmetry, Phys. Rev. D **101** no. 4, 045001 (2020). doi:10.1103/PhysRevD.101.045001. [arXiv:1907.04890 [hep-ph]].

25. S. Basilakos, N. E. Mavromatos and J. Solà Peracaula , Quantum Anomalies in String-Inspired Running Vacuum Universe: Inflation and Axion Dark Matter, Phys. Lett. B **803**, 135342 (2020). doi:10.1016/j.physletb.2020.135342 [arXiv:2001.03465 [gr-qc]].
26. N. E. Mavromatos and J. Solà Peracaula, Stringy-Running-Vacuum-Model Inflation: from primordial Gravitational Waves and stiff Axion Matter to Dynamical Dark Energy, Eur. Phys. J. Spec. Top. (2021), doi:10.1140/epjs/s11734-021-00197-8. [arXiv:2012.07971 [hep-ph]].
27. N. E. Mavromatos and J. Solà Peracaula , Inflationary physics and transplanckian conjecture in the Stringy Running-Vacuum-Model: from the phantom vacuum to the true vacuum [arXiv:2105.02659 [hep-th]] (2021).
28. N. E. Mavromatos (2021), Geometrical origins of the Universe dark sector: string-inspired torsion and anomalies as seeds for inflation and dark matter, [arXiv:2108.02152 [gr-qc]].
29. J. R. Ellis, N. E. Mavromatos and D. V. Nanopoulos, Time dependent vacuum energy induced by D particle recoil, Gen. Rel. Grav. **32**, 943-958 (2000). doi:10.1023/A:1001993226227. [arXiv:gr-qc/9810086 [gr-qc]].
30. S. Basilakos, N. E. Mavromatos and J. Solà, Starobinsky-like inflation and running vacuum in the context of Supergravity, Universe **2**, no. 3, 14 (2016) doi:10.3390/universe2030014 [arXiv:1505.04434 [gr-qc]].
31. A. A. Starobinsky, A New Type of Isotropic Cosmological Models Without Singularity, Phys. Lett. B **91**, 99-102 (1980).
32. C. Moreno-Pulido C. and J. Solà Peracaula J., Running vacuum in quantum field theory in curved spacetime: renormalizing ρ_{vac} without $\sim m^4$ terms, Eur. Phys. J. C **80**, no. 8, 692 (2020). doi:10.1140/epjc/s10052-020-8238-6. [arXiv:2005.03164 [gr-qc]].
33. S. H. S. Alexander, M. E. Peskin and M. M. Sheikh-Jabbari, Leptogenesis from gravity waves in models of inflation, Phys. Rev. Lett. **96**, 081301 (2006). doi:10.1103/PhysRevLett.96.081301 [hep-th/0403069].
34. M. J. Duncan, N. Kaloper N.and K. A. Olive, Axion hair and dynamical torsion from anomalies, Nucl. Phys. B **387**, 215 (1992,).
35. P. Svrcek and E. Witten E., Axions In String Theory, JHEP **06**, 051 doi:10.1088/1126-6708/2006/06/051 (2006). [arXiv:hep-th/0605206 [hep-th]].
36. R. Jackiw R. and S. Y.Pi, Chern-Simons modification of general relativity, Phys. Rev. D **68**, 104012 (2003), doi:10.1103/PhysRevD.68.104012. [gr-qc/0308071].
37. J. Martin, C. Ringeval and V. Vennin, Encyclopædia Inflationaris, Phys. Dark Univ. **5-6**, 75-235 (2014). doi:10.1016/j.dark.2014.01.003 [arXiv:1303.3787 [astro-ph.CO]], and references therein.
38. J. Grande, J. Solà and H. Stefancic, LXCDM: A Cosmon model solution to the cosmological coincidence problem?, JCAP **08**, 011 (2006). doi:10.1088/1475-7516/2006/08/011. [arXiv:gr-qc/0604057 [gr-qc]].
39. J. Grande, A. Pelinson and J. Solà, Dark energy perturbations and cosmic coincidence, Phys. Rev. D **79**, 043006 (2009). doi:10.1103/PhysRevD.79.043006. [arXiv:0809.3462 [astro-ph]]
40. M. S. Morris and K. S. Thorne and U. Yurtsever, Wormholes, Time Machines, and the Weak Energy Condition, Phys. Rev. Lett. **61**, 1446-1449 (1988). doi:10.1103/PhysRevLett.61.1446.
41. P. Van Nieuwenhuizen, Supergravity, Phys. Rept. **68**, 189-398 (1981) doi:10.1016/0370-1573(81)90157-5.
42. J. Alexandre, N. Houston and N. E. Mavromatos, Dynamical Supergravity Breaking via the Super-Higgs Effect Revisited, Phys. Rev. D **88**, 125017 (2013) doi:10.1103/PhysRevD.88.125017 [arXiv:1310.4122 [hep-th]].

43. J. Alexandre, N. Houston and N. E. Mavromatos, Starobinsky-type Inflation in Dynamical Supergravity Breaking Scenarios, Phys. Rev. D **89**, no. 2, 027703 (2014) doi:10.1103/PhysRevD.89.027703 [arXiv:1312.5197 [gr-qc]].
44. E. S. Fradkin and A. A. Tseytlin, One Loop Effective Potential in Gauged O(4) Supergravity, Nucl. Phys. B **234**, 472 (1984) doi:10.1016/0550-3213(84)90074-9.
45. Z. Lalak, S. Lola, B. A. Ovrut and G. G. Ross, Large scale structure from biased nonequilibrium phase transitions: Percolation theory picture, Nucl. Phys. B **434**, 675-696 (1995) doi:10.1016/0550-3213(94)00557-U [arXiv:hep-ph/9404218 [hep-ph]].
46. D. Coulson, Z. Lalak and B. A. Ovrut, Biased domain walls, Phys. Rev. D **53**, 4237-4246 (1996) doi:10.1103/PhysRevD.53.4237.
47. J. Ellis and N. E. Mavromatos, Inflation induced by gravitino condensation in supergravity, Phys. Rev. D **88**, no. 8, 085029 (2013) doi:10.1103/PhysRevD.88.085029 [arXiv:1308.1906 [hep-th]].
48. L. Lanczos, *Bemerkung zur de Sitterschen Welt*, Physikalische Zeitschrift, **23**, 539-543 (1922).
49. Y. B. Zel'dovich 1961 (1962), The equation of state at ultrahigh densities and its relativistic limitations, Zh. Eksp. Teor. Fiz. **41**, 1609-1615 (1961) (Sov.Phys.JETP **14** (1962) 1143-1147). The stiff matter in that model is assumed to be baryons, in contrast to our model, in which the stiff matter consists of potential-free KR axions.
50. P. H. Chavanis, Cosmology with a stiff matter era, Phys. Rev. D **92**, no. 10, 103004 (2015). doi:10.1103/PhysRevD.92.103004. [arXiv:1412.0743 [gr-qc]].
51. M. de Cesare, N. E. Mavromatos and S. Sarkar, On the possibility of tree-level leptogenesis from Kalb–Ramond torsion background, Eur. Phys. J. C **75** no. 10, 514 (2015), doi:10.1140/epjc/s10052-015-3731-z. [arXiv:1412.7077 [hep-ph]].
52. T. Bossingham T., N. E. Mavromatos and S. Sarkar, The role of temperature dependent string-inspired CPT violating backgrounds in leptogenesis and the chiral magnetic effect, Eur. Phys. J. C **79** no. 1, 50 (2019). doi:10.1140/epjc/s10052-019-6564-3. [arXiv:1810.13384 [hep-ph]] and references therein.
53. D. Colladay and V. A. Kostelecky, Lorentz violating extension of the standard model, Phys. Rev. D **58**, 116002 (1998). [hep-ph/9809521].
54. V. A. Kostelecky and N. Russell, , Data Tables for Lorentz and CPT Violation, Rev. Mod. Phys. **83**, 11 (2011). [arXiv:0801.0287 [hep-ph]], and references therein.
55. N. E. Mavromatos and E. Winstanley, Infinitely colored black holes, Class. Quant. Grav. **17**, 1595-1611 (2000) doi:10.1088/0264-9381/17/7/302 [arXiv:hep-th/9909018 [hep-th]].
56. J. M. Maldacena, The Large N limit of superconformal field theories and supergravity, Adv. Theor. Math. Phys. **2**, 231-252 (1998) doi:10.1023/A:1026654312961 [arXiv:hep-th/9711200 [hep-th]].
57. A. Arvanitaki, S. Dimopoulos, S. Dubovsky, N. Kaloper and J. March-Russell, String Axiverse, Phys. Rev. D **81**, 123530 (2010) doi:10.1103/PhysRevD.81.123530 [arXiv:0905.4720 [hep-th]].
58. S. Capozziello, R. Cianci, C. Stornaiolo and S. Vignolo, f(R) cosmology with torsion, Phys. Scripta **78**, 065010 (2008), doi:10.1088/0031-8949/78/06/065010, [arXiv:0810.2549 [gr-qc]] and references therein.
59. J. Magueijo, T. G. Zlosnik and T. W. B. Kibble, Cosmology with a spin, Phys. Rev. D **87**, no. 6, 063504 (2013), doi:10.1103/PhysRevD.87.063504. [arXiv:1212.0585 [astro-ph.CO]].
60. Y. F. Cai, S. Capozziello, M. De Laurentis and E. N. Saridakis, f(T) teleparallel gravity and cosmology, Rept. Prog. Phys. **79** (2016) no. 10, 106901 (2016), doi:10.1088/0034-4885/79/10/106901 [arXiv:1511.07586 [gr-qc]] and references therein.

Early and not so early dark energy. What do cosmological observations tell us about them?

Adrià Gómez-Valent[1,*], Ziyang Zheng[1], Luca Amendola[1], Valeria Pettorino[2]
and Christof Wetterich[1]

[1] *Institut für Theoretische Physik, Ruprecht-Karls-Universität Heidelberg,*
Philosophenweg 16, D-69120 Heidelberg, Germany

[2] *AIM, CEA, CNRS, Université Paris-Saclay, Université Paris Diderot, Sorbonne Paris Cité*
F-91191 Gif-sur-Yvette, France

Cosmological data still allow for the presence of a non-negligible amount of dark energy at very high redshifts, namely during the matter- and radiation-dominated epochs. This is the so-called early dark energy (EDE), which could help to mitigate the tensions that affect the standard model of cosmology since (i) it reduces the sound horizon at the baryon-drag epoch, hence giving room to higher values of H_0 than those found in the ΛCDM; and (ii) it could potentially decrease the number of large-scale structures in the Universe due its negative pressure and its inability to cluster efficiently for large enough values of its sound speed. Here we put constraints on the fraction of EDE using two methods: first, we use a perfect fluid parameterization that produces plateaux in $\Omega_{ede}(z)$ during the relativistic and non-relativistic matter-dominated eras. Second, we apply a tomographic approach to constrain the EDE density in redshift bins, which allows us to reconstruct the evolution of the EDE fraction before and after the decoupling of the Cosmic Microwave Background (CMB) photons. We have employed *Planck* data 2018, the Pantheon compilation of supernovae of Type Ia (SNIa), data on galaxy clustering, the prior on the absolute magnitude of SNIa by SH0ES, and weak lensing data from KiDS+VIKING-450 and DES-Y1. Using our minimal parameterization we find that EDE is not able to loosen the cosmological tensions, and show that the constraints on the EDE fraction weaken considerably when its sound speed takes lower values. Thanks to our binned analysis we are able to put tight constraints on the EDE fraction around the CMB decoupling time, $\lesssim 0.4\%$ at 2σ c.l. We confirm previous results that a significant EDE fraction in the radiation-dominated epoch loosens the H_0 tension, but tends to worsen the tension for σ_8. A subsequent presence of EDE in the matter-dominated era helps to alleviate this problem. When both the SH0ES prior and weak lensing data are considered in the fitting analysis in combination with data from CMB, SNIa and baryon acoustic oscillations, the EDE fractions are constrained to be $\lesssim 2.6\%$ in the radiation-dominated epoch and $\lesssim 1.5\%$ in the redshift range $z \in (100, 1000)$ at 2σ c.l. The two tensions remain with a statistical significance of $\sim 2-3\sigma$ c.l. This contribution to the proceedings of the CM3 parallel session of the MG16 Marcel Grossmann virtual Conference: "Status of the H_0 and σ_8 tensions: theoretical models and model-independent constraints" is based on the paper arXiv:2107.11065,[1] which appeared in the arXiv shortly after my talk of July 6th 2021.

Keywords: Cosmology: observations – Cosmology: theory – cosmological parameters – dark energy – dark matter.

---

*Speaker. E-mail: gomez-valent@thphys.uni-heidelberg.de

1. Introduction

The cosmological constant, Λ, is (together with other assumptions as the Cosmological Principle, the existence of cold dark matter (CDM) and an inflationary period prior to the radiation-dominated era) a key building block of the standard model of Cosmology. By adding this very simple term in Einstein's field equations it is possible to produce the late-time acceleration of the Universe[2,3] and help to explain a large variety of cosmological observations[4–6] without increasing excessively the mathematical complexity of the equations. However, the model is not free from extremely intricate theoretical conundrums, as the famous old cosmological constant[7–9] and coincidence problems, see e.g.[10] The former might be strongly intertwined with the latter, which should not be considered as a "why now" problem,[11] but as a matter of why the energy density associated to Λ, i.e. $\rho_\Lambda = \Lambda/8\pi G$, takes the value $\rho_\Lambda \sim \mathcal{O}(10^{-47})$ GeV^4 in natural units, hence being of the same order of magnitude of the non-relativistic matter energy density $\rho_m(z)$ when $z \lesssim 1$. This is pivotal for the model to exhibit an excellent phenomenological performance. We can soften the coincidence problem if we depart from the ΛCDM by allowing some sort of dynamical dark energy (DE) density instead of considering a rigid ρ_Λ.[12–14] This is a more appealing framework, since it is actually hard to believe in an immutable entity like the cosmological constant. Why should the component in charge of the current acceleration of the Cosmos be insensitive e.g. to the Universe's evolution and energy content? Such dynamics could lead to the presence of a non-negligible fraction of early dark energy (EDE) in the Universe during the radiation-dominated epoch (RDE) and/or the matter-dominated era (MDE). Of particular relevance concerning the coincidence problem are the quintessence models with scaling solutions, as the one with an exponential potential originally proposed by C. Wetterich in the late 80's,[14] in which the EDE fraction follows the dominant component in the Universe in both, the RDE and MDE,[15] making more natural the scenario with $\rho_{de} \sim \mathcal{O}(\rho_m)$ at low redshifts.

Apart from the aforementioned theoretical problems there are also some observational tensions affecting the ΛCDM, making the concordance model less concordant than it was thought to be ten years ago. At least, if these tensions are not induced by systematic errors in the data. The cosmic microwave background (CMB) temperature, polarization and lensing data from *Planck* 2018 leads to a value of the Hubble parameter $H_0 = (67.36 \pm 0.54)$ km/s/Mpc when analyzed under the assumption of the ΛCDM,[4] and a similar result is obtained from measurements of the baryon acoustic oscillations (BAO) and the deuterium abundance, again in the standard model.[16] These values are at odds with the one measured by the SH0ES team, $H_0 = (73.2 \pm 1.3)$ km/s/Mpc,[17] which is obtained with the cosmic distance ladder method and does not rely on the assumption of any cosmological model. There exists a $\sim 4.1\sigma$ tension between them, which has been persistently and consistently increasing in the last years,[18,19] see also the reviews.[20,21] On the other hand, galaxy clustering (through redshift-space distortions, RSD), direct peculiar velocity and weak lensing (WL) measurements suggest that the Universe is less clumpy than preferred by the CMB data under the ΛCDM, see e.g.[22–25] The tension is usually formulated in terms of the root-mean-square (rms) of mass fluctuations at scales of $8h^{-1}$ Mpc, σ_8, and related composite quantities like $S_8 = \sigma_8(\Omega_m^{(0)}/0.3)^{0.5}$, with $\Omega_m^{(0)}$ the current matter energy fraction in the Universe. The first indication of its existence appeared already almost a decade ago[26] and it is still there.[27–29] The tension is in this case less significant from a statistical point of view than the aforesaid one of H_0, of about $2 - 3\sigma$ depending on the data source and the large-scale structure (LSS) estimator employed to quantify the tension. For instance, by combining the KiDS-1000 WL results with BOSS and 2dFLenS data the authors of[25] have shown that it is possible to reduce by a factor ~ 2 the uncertainty on S_8, and also to write the tension only in terms of σ_8, since BOSS puts tight constraints on $\Omega_m^{(0)}$ and the degeneracy in the $\sigma_8 - \Omega_m^{(0)}$ plane can be broken. They find $S_8 = 0.766^{+0.020}_{-0.014}$ and $\sigma_8 = 0.760^{+0.021}_{-0.023}$, which are in 3.1σ and 2.2σ tension with *Planck*, respectively.

Whether the H_0 and S_8/σ_8 tensions are to some degree physical or not is still unclear and under intense debate.[30–32] Hopefully this question will be resolved in the near future. In the meanwhile, theoreticians have worked very hard to find ways of loosening the tensions, taking for granted that they are real, see the reviews[21,33,34] and the complete lists of references therein. It is important to remark, though, that it is very difficult to find models in the literature capable of relieving both tensions at a time in a significant way. There are only some few exceptions that offer better perspectives, as e.g. the running vacuum model of type-II studied in[29] or the Brans-Dicke ΛCDM model explored in.[35,36] The latter, though, might encounter some problems when trying to match the cosmological and local values of the gravitational coupling through an appropriate screening mechanism,[37] and the effect of the *Planck* 2018 CMB polarization data might also hinder its overall fitting performance. Other models are only able to loosen one of the tensions, while worsening the other. This is the case e.g. of the class of new EDE models based on early phase transitions,[38–40] ultra-light axions[41,42] or alike.[43] In practice, all these models fight against the H_0 tension in a very similar way. There is a new component in the energy budget of the Universe that acts as a cosmological constant deep in the RDE and has an associated (constant) density which is of about $5 - 10\%$ the radiation energy density around the matter-radiation equality time, when the EDE fraction reaches its maximum. This excess of energy with respect to the standard model decreases the sound horizon at the baryon-drag epoch, and this forces the Hubble parameter to be larger in order to decrease the angular diameter distance to the last-scattering surface and keep in this way intact the location of the first peak of the temperature CMB anisotropies. The latter is very well constrained by *Planck*. After that moment, the energy density dilutes typically faster than radiation, leaving no imprint in the late-time universe, where a cosmological constant is still assumed to produce the current positive acceleration, as in the standard ΛCDM. Although it is possible to obtain posterior values of the Hubble parameter much closer to the SH0ES measurement[17] in the context of these new EDE models, they require larger values of the current matter energy density in order to compensate the early Sachs-Wolfe effect introduced by EDE in the pre-recombination epoch, and this enhances the LSS formation processes in the late-time Universe, which in turn exacerbates the S_8/σ_8 tension.[44–46]

Here we first explore EDE models with scaling solutions in the MDE and RDE, or just in the MDE. As already discussed above, they can alleviate in some sense the coincidence problem. They could in principle have an impact on the cosmological tensions as well, depending on how strong are the constraints on the EDE fraction imposed by the the cosmological data. In these models, EDE might not be negligible after the recombination era, and this could lead to a softening of the S_8/σ_8 tension. Moreover, the shape of $\Omega_{ede}(z) = \rho_{ede}(z)/\rho_c(z)$, with $\rho_c(z) = 3H^2(z)/8\pi G$ the critical energy density in the Universe, is very different from the one encountered in the new EDE models mentioned in the previous paragraph, since in this case the EDE fraction is constant during the epochs at which the scaling behavior comes into play. Hence, it is clearly worth to study these EDE models and to determine to what extent they can alleviate the tensions, if they do at all. In view of the existing tensions, there is a clear interest of revisiting these models, whose seeds where already present more than thirty years ago.[14] In addition, we also perform a more model-independent analysis, applying a tomographic method to reconstruct the shape of $\Omega_{ede}(z)$ that is preferred by different combinations of cosmological data sets. We will see that this is very useful to extract more general information about how is EDE constrained in the various epochs of the cosmic expansion.

2. Early dark energy

EDE affects observables in several ways. The presence of EDE at decoupling can change the position and height of the peaks in the CMB[47–49] and can also impact it through the early integrated Sachs-Wolfe effect. Furthermore, EDE suppresses the growth of structure:[50–52] a smaller number of clusters can form with respect to the ΛCDM[53] because of the negative pressure of EDE and also because of its large sound speed, which does not allow it to cluster; the lensing potential is also weaker, with an impact on weak lensing and the CMB peaks at large multipoles. Thus, EDE can potentially have a direct impact on the cosmological tensions. In the following we first design a general parameterization able to mimic the background dominant component, and then proceed with a tomographic analysis in different redshift bins.

2.1. Parametric EDE

We build now a simple parameterization of the DE density that allows us to reproduce the behavior of uncoupled quintessence models with scaling solutions. For this reason, we want our parameterization to be able to generate two plateaux in $\Omega_{de}(z)$. The first plateau occurs in the RDE, and the second one in the MDE,

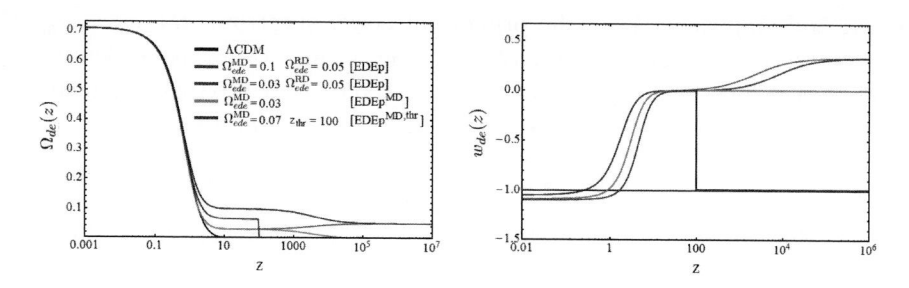

Fig. 1. Functions $\Omega_{de}(z)$ (left plot) and $w_{de}(z) = p_{de}(z)/\rho_{de}(z)$ (right plot) obtained using the parametrizations described in Sec. 2.1, for some illustrative values of the parameters.

and can have different heights in principle. This is what happens for instance in quintessence models with a single exponential potential $V(\phi) = V_0 e^{-\sqrt{8\pi G}\lambda\phi}$, where the fractions of EDE in the RDE and MDE depend only on one parameter, λ.[14,15] By introducing a second exponential potential it is possible to control the height of the two plateaux independently.[54]

With this aim in mind, we generalize the parameterizations proposed earlier in[48,49] and we consider here a DE density with the following form,

$$\rho_{de}(z) = \rho_1(1+z)^4 + \rho_2(1+z)^3 + \rho_3(1+z)^{3(1+w)}, \quad (1)$$

parameterized by the constant energy densities ρ_1, ρ_2 and ρ_3 and by a constant equation of state parameter (EoS) w. We call this parameterization EDEp, where the "p" reminds us of the 'plateaux' that characterise it. The last term of (1) is able to mimic the behavior of a late-time dynamical DE with the wCDM form,[55] whereas the first two terms produce the plateaux in the RDE and MDE. It is useful to write the constants ρ_1 and ρ_2 in terms of dimensionless parameters, as follows

$$\rho_1 = \chi_1 \Omega_{r,*}^{(0)} \rho_c^{(0)}; \qquad \rho_2 = \chi_2 \Omega_{m,*}^{(0)} \rho_c^{(0)}, \quad (2)$$

where $\Omega_{r,*}^{(0)}$ and $\Omega_{m,*}^{(0)}$ are the current density parameters of radiation and matter, respectively, computed considering three massless neutrinos, and $\rho_c^{(0)} = \rho_c(z=0)$. We consider standard General Relativity and a flat Friedmann-Lemaître-Robertson-Walker universe. $\chi_1, \chi_2, \rho_3 > 0$ in order the DE density to be positive during the expansion. Deep in the RDE and MDE the EDE fractions are constant,

$$\Omega_{ede}^{RD} = \frac{\chi_1}{1+\chi_1}; \qquad \Omega_{ede}^{MD} = \frac{\chi_2}{1+\chi_2}. \quad (3)$$

The present dark energy density, $\rho_{de}^{(0)}$, can be directly computed from the Hubble parameter, $H_0 = 100h$ km/s/Mpc, and the reduced CDM and baryon density parameters, $\omega_{cdm} = \Omega_{cdm}^{(0)} h^2$ and $\omega_b = \Omega_b^{(0)} h^2$. Thus, one of the three ρ_i's appearing in (1) can be expressed in terms of the other two, e.g. $\rho_3 = \rho_{de}^{(0)} - \rho_1 - \rho_2$, so in this EDE parametrization we deal with three additional parameters with respect to the ΛCDM. We have nine cosmological parameters in total, namely the spectral index n_s and amplitude A_s of the primordial power spectrum, H_0, ω_b, ω_{cdm}, the optical depth to reionization, τ, together with w, χ_1 and χ_2 (or, equivalently, Ω_{ede}^{RD} and Ω_{ede}^{MD}). We consider a massive neutrino of 0.06 eV and two massless neutrinos.

The DE fluid is covariantly conserved so its associated pressure reads,

$$\dot{\rho}_{de}+3H(\rho_{de}+p_{de})=0 \longrightarrow p_{de}(z) = \frac{\rho_1}{3}(1+z)^4 + w\rho_3(1+z)^{3(1+w)}, \qquad (4)$$

where the dot refers to a derivative with respect to the cosmic time. The corresponding equation of state parameter can be obtained from the ratio of (4) and (1), i.e. $w_{de}(z) = p_{de}(z)/\rho_{de}(z)$. It is clear that $w_{de} = 1/3$ and $w_{de} = 0$ in the RDE and MDE, respectively, and $w_{de} \approx w$ at present for low values of χ_2. For the perturbations, in our main analyses we take the sound speed of the DE fluid to be equal to the speed of light in the DE rest frame,[56] i.e. $\hat{c}_s = 1$, so in our model the DE does not cluster efficiently. We will study also what happens when $\hat{c}_s < 1$.

If we set $\rho_1 = 0$ ($\Omega_{ede}^{RD} = 0$) in (1) EDE is completely negligible during the RDE,

$$\rho_{de}(z) = \rho_2(1+z)^3 + \rho_3(1+z)^{3(1+w)}. \qquad (5)$$

We denote this particular case of EDEp as EDEp^{MD}, to remind us that the plateau is in this case following the matter component. If we turn the first term on in (5) at a particular 'threshold' redshift $z_{\rm thr}$, in the MDE we obtain,

$$\rho_{de}(z) = \rho_2(1+z)^3\theta(z_{\rm thr}-z) + \rho_3(1+z)^{3(1+w)}, \qquad (6)$$

with θ the Heaviside step function. This is what we call EDEp^{MD,thr}. For $z_{\rm thr} \to \infty$ we recover the pure EDEp^{MD} parametrization (5). We show typical shapes of the functions $\Omega_{de}(z)$ and $w_{de}(z)$ obtained with EDEp, EDEp^{MD} and EDEp^{MD,thr} in Fig. 1.

2.2. *Tomographic EDE*

We further consider the possibility of binning the amount of $\Omega_{de}(z)$ in 11 bins to perform a tomographic analysis using the data sets described in Sec. 3. Here, again, $\rho_{de}^{(0)}$ can be directly determined from H_0, ω_b and ω_{cdm}; the other constant densities ρ_i, with $i = A, ..., J$ (see Table 1 in[1] for details), are left free in our Monte Carlo (MC) runs, together with w and the six usual ΛCDM parameters. We keep $\hat{c}_s = 1$. Our main aim is to see how much EDE we can have in each bin, and therefore which shape of $\Omega_{de}(z)$ is preferred by the data, regardless of its complexity. The corresponding fitting results and reconstructed shapes of $\Omega_{de}(z)$ are shown and discussed in Sec. 4.2.

3. Methodology and data

We have implemented the various parametrizations of Sec. 2.1 and also the binned $\rho_{de}(z)$ described in Sec. 2.2 in our own modified version of the Einstein-Boltzmann code CLASS.[57] We have constrained the parameters of our models through a Bayesian exploration of the parameter space, employing the MC sampler `MontePython`.[58] We have used flat priors for the cosmological parameters in common with the ΛCDM model, with widths that fully respect the *Planck* 2018 uncertainties.[4] Regarding the priors on the EDE fractions, previous studies in the literature showed that they are always lower than $\sim 10\%$,[48,49] so we have used $0 < \chi_i < 0.12$ in the MC analyses of the parametrizations of Sec. 2.1, and similar priors for each bin of the tomographic study of Sec. 2.2.

Now we list the various data sets used in this study:

- CMB: We consider the full *Planck* 2018 TTTEEE+lowE and TTTEEE+lowE+lensing likelihoods.[4] We denote these data sets as CMBpol and CMBpolens, respectively.
- Supernovae of Type Ia (SNIa): We use the observed SNIa apparent magnitude and redshifts of the Pantheon compilation.[5] The absolute magnitude of these SNIa, M, is left free in the fitting analysis, and we impose a prior on it. See the next item of the list for details.
- Prior on M: We use in some of our fitting analyses the SH0ES effective calibration prior on the absolute magnitude of the SNIa as provided in,[59] $M_{\rm SH0ES} = -19.2191 \pm 0.0405$. It is obtained from the calibration of nearby SNIa (at $z \lesssim 0.01$) with Cepheids.[60] It is better to use this prior rather than the one on H_0,[17,61] especially when it is combined with data from SNIa compilations that include the same SNIa in the Hubble flow considered by the SH0ES team (as in the Pantheon compilation[5]) because in this way we avoid double-counting issues. In some of our Tables we also provide the best-fit values of M. This allows us to quantify the 'M tension', i.e. the tension between the latter and $M_{\rm SH0ES}$. We show in Sec. 4.2 that the statistical level of the SH0ES-*Planck* tension can be in some cases quite different when formulated in terms of H_0 and M.
- BAO: We have employed the data reported in.[6,22,62–65]
- WL: In some of our fitting analyses we employ the KiDS +VIKING-450+DESY1 prior $S_8 = 0.762^{+0.025}_{-0.024}$.[66] The author of[67] has raised some concerns about the use of σ_8 and derived quantities as S_8. He suggests the use of σ_{12}, defined as the *rms* linear theory variance at the fixed scale of 12 Mpc, and $S_{12} = \sigma_{12}(\omega_m/0.14)^{0.4}$. We provide the values of these parameters in some of our Tables, together with the usual σ_8 and S_8.
- RSD: Data on anisotropic clustering of galaxies in redshift space, and from the direct measurement of peculiar velocities.[6,22,68–75] We call this data set RSD in short because most of these points are obtained from the analysis of redshift-space distortions.

The corresponding fitting results are presented and discussed in Sec. 4. In order to quantify the impact of the SH0ES prior on the fitting results and on the ability of the models to loosen the H_0/M tension we study and compare the constraints on our

Table 1. The mean fit values and 68.3% confidence limits for the ΛCDM, the wCDM, EDEp (1) and EDEp$^{\rm MD}$ (5), using the CMBpol+SNIa and CMBpolens+SNIa+M data sets (cf. Sec. 3). For $\Omega_{ede}^{\rm RD}$ and $\Omega_{ede}^{\rm MD}$ we also show the 2σ limits inside the parentheses. Constraints on τ are provided in.[1] See the comments in Sec. 4.1.

	CMBpol+SNIa			
Parameter	ΛCDM	wCDM	EDEp	EDEp$^{\rm MD}$
ω_b	$0.02239^{+0.00014}_{-0.00015}$	$0.02237^{+0.00016}_{-0.00015}$	$0.02238^{+0.00017}_{-0.00016}$	$0.02234^{+0.00015}_{-0.00016}$
ω_{cdm}	$0.1199^{+0.0014}_{-0.0013}$	0.1204 ± 0.0014	$0.1218^{+0.0016}_{-0.0015}$	$0.1208^{+0.0014}_{-0.0015}$
n_s	0.9659 ± 0.0044	$0.9646^{+0.0044}_{-0.0045}$	$0.9642^{+0.0044}_{-0.0045}$	$0.9642^{+0.0043}_{-0.0046}$
H_0 [km/s/Mpc]	$67.60^{+0.59}_{-0.61}$	$68.55^{+1.12}_{-1.10}$	68.71 ± 1.16	$68.61^{+1.09}_{-1.16}$
σ_8	$0.811^{+0.007}_{-0.008}$	0.823 ± 0.014	$0.817^{+0.014}_{-0.015}$	$0.818^{+0.015}_{-0.014}$
r_d [Mpc]	$147.02^{+0.28}_{-0.32}$	146.92 ± 0.30	$146.18^{+0.66}_{-0.43}$	$146.75^{+0.36}_{-0.30}$
w	-1	$-1.039^{+0.035}_{-0.039}$	$-1.050^{+0.041}_{-0.040}$	$-1.053^{+0.038}_{-0.042}$
$\Omega_{ede}^{\rm RD}$ (%)	0	0	$< 0.91\,(< 2.08)$	0
$\Omega_{ede}^{\rm MD}$ (%)	0	0	$< 0.27\,(< 0.69)$	$< 0.29\,(< 0.69)$
	CMBpolens+SNIa+M			
Parameter	ΛCDM	wCDM	EDEp	EDEp$^{\rm MD}$
ω_b	$0.02257^{+0.00015}_{-0.00014}$	$0.02241^{+0.00014}_{-0.00016}$	$0.02245^{+0.00015}_{-0.00019}$	0.02239 ± 0.00015
ω_{cdm}	0.1179 ± 0.0012	0.1200 ± 0.0015	0.1212 ± 0.0016	0.1206 ± 0.0012
n_s	0.9709 ± 0.0044	$0.9658^{+0.0044}_{-0.0047}$	$0.9659^{+0.0045}_{-0.0044}$	$0.9656^{+0.0041}_{-0.0042}$
H_0 [km/s/Mpc]	$68.56^{+0.56}_{-0.54}$	$70.55^{+0.86}_{-0.88}$	$70.63^{+0.86}_{-0.82}$	$70.20^{+0.52}_{-0.69}$
σ_8	$0.811^{+0.007}_{-0.008}$	0.838 ± 0.014	$0.830^{+0.014}_{-0.013}$	0.835 ± 0.010
r_d [Mpc]	$147.36^{+0.28}_{-0.29}$	$146.98^{+0.33}_{-0.30}$	$146.21^{+0.73}_{-0.44}$	146.79 ± 0.29
w	-1	$-1.098^{+0.035}_{-0.032}$	$-1.099^{+0.034}_{-0.032}$	$-1.099^{+0.030}_{-0.025}$
$\Omega_{ede}^{\rm RD}$ (%)	0	0	$< 1.14\,(2.44)$	0
$\Omega_{ede}^{\rm MD}$ (%)	0	0	$< 0.22\,(0.52)$	$< 0.22\,(0.54)$

EDE models obtained: (i) with a minimal data set composed by CMBpol+SNIa; and (ii) adding on top of the latter the SH0ES prior on M, i.e. using CMBpol+SNIa+M. The SNIa data help to break the strong degeneracies found in the w-H_0 plane when only CMB data are used in the analysis.[76]

The properties and limitations of the EDEp and EDEp$^{\rm MD}$ parametrizations are already grasped with the aforementioned minimal data sets (cf. Table 1). For EDEp$^{{\rm MD},thr}$ we study also the effect of the CMB lensing and BAO+RSD data when combined with CMBpol+SNIa. We provide the corresponding constraints in figures 2 and 3. For the analyses of the binned $\rho_{de}(z)$ described in Sec. 2.2 we report our results in Table 2, where we explicitly test the impact of BAO and the weak lensing data, by considering not only the minimal data sets described in the previous paragraph, but also adding the information on BAO and BAO+WL. In addition, we redo the fitting analyses considering also the CMB lensing in order to quantify its impact. For further explanations on the data we refer the reader to our work[1] and the original data sources.

4. Results and discussion

We present and discuss now the results obtained from the fitting analyses of the EDE parametrizations and the tomographic EDE described in Secs. 2.1 and 2.2, respectively, using the methodology and data sets of the previous section.

4.1. Results for the parametric analysis

The mean fit values and corresponding uncertainties for the various cosmological parameters in the EDEp and EDEp^{MD} parametrizations obtained with the baseline CMBpol+SNIa dataset are reported in Table 1. The constraints on the fraction of early dark energy in the EDEp parametrization in the radiation- and matter-dominated epochs, Ω_{ede}^{RD} and Ω_{ede}^{MD}, are very strong. They lie below $\sim 2\%$ and $\sim 0.7\%$, respectively, at the 2σ c.l. It is interesting to observe that the upper limit of Ω_{ede}^{MD} in the EDEp^{MD} parametrization coincides with the one obtained in the more general EDEp. The constraints on Ω_{ede}^{MD} and Ω_{ede}^{RD} in EDEp are quite independent. Actually, we have checked that the correlation coefficient between these two parameters is pretty small, $\sim 5.6\%$. As already noticed in,[48] the low upper limits on Ω_{ede}^{RD} and Ω_{ede}^{MD} are due to the very tight constraint on the fraction of EDE around the CMB decoupling time. The latter acts as an anchor for Ω_{ede}^{RD} and even more for Ω_{ede}^{MD}, since in the last scattering surface the matter energy density is already ~ 3 times larger than the radiation one.

Another result from Table 1 to remark is that EDEp cannot alleviate significantly the H_0 and σ_8 tensions. The shape of the early dark energy density seems to be too restricted in these parametrization. There is a slight increase of H_0 in EDEp and EDEp^{MD} with respect to the ΛCDM, but it is mainly due to the dynamics of the late-time DE, and this is why the major part of the effect is already found with the wCDM parametrization.[55]

When we include the SH0ES prior in our fitting analysis we increase, of course, the value of the Hubble parameter, see Table 1. The tension with the distance ladder determination is now only of $\sim 1.7\sigma$, but this is again mainly thanks to the lowering of w, which now lies more in the phantom region (3σ away below $w = -1$). The values of w and H_0 are almost identical to those found in the wCDM parametrization, and EDE does not have any important impact on the H_0 tension in the context of the EDEp parametrization. The loosening of the H_0 tension is accompanied by a slight worsening of the σ_8 one due to the positive correlation between H_0 and σ_8. Phantom dark energy leads to lower values of the DE density in the past and this produces, in turn, an increase of the structure formation processes in the Universe. It seems that the EDE density has a too restricted form in the parameterizations under study here. They allow for plateaux and generalize previous

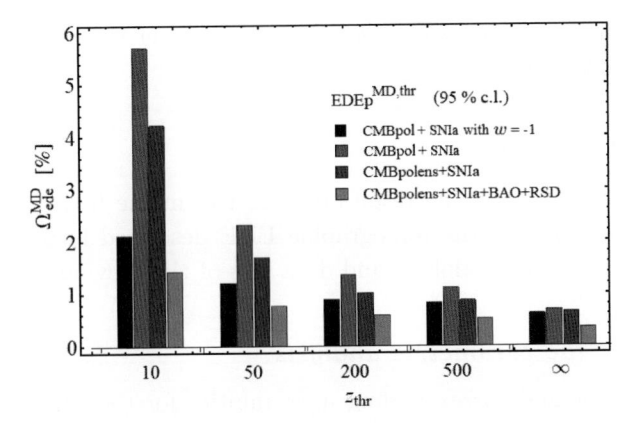

Fig. 2. Constraints on Ω_{ede}^{MD} at 95% c.l. obtained from the fitting analyses of the EDEp^{MD,thr} parametrization (6), and under the data sets shown in the legend.

studies, but still seem to be quite constrained and unable to resolve the tensions. In the next section we then investigate the binned tomographic approach described in Sec. 2.2. Before moving on, however, we discuss briefly two options to weaken the constraints on the fraction of EDE.

Much weaker constraints on the fraction of EDE can be obtained by allowing for values of $\hat{c}_s^2 \ll 1$. The only difference between our EDE and cold dark matter during the MDE is found at the perturbations level. Both are pressureless fluids at the background level, but have different $\hat{c}_s$. The latter is equal to 1 for EDE and 0 for the dark matter. Hence, we expect the constraints on Ω_{ede}^{MD} to loosen if we decrease the value of $\hat{c}_s$ of EDE, and even obtain a full degeneracy between the fraction of EDE and CDM during the MDE in the limit $\hat{c}_s \to 0$. This is actually what happens, as we explicitly show in Fig. 2 of.[1] We have to say, though, that the change in the sound speed does not help to alleviate the cosmological tensions, neither. For instance, under the CMBPol+SNIa data set the Hubble parameter remains close to ~ 67.5 km/s/Mpc, and the 1σ uncertainty is lower than ~ 0.8 km/s/Mpc regardless of the value of $\hat{c}_s$ under consideration when the late-time DE dynamics is switched off.

One can also get weaker constraints on EDE in the MDE by activating EDE at lower redshifts. In order to study this effect we explore the EDEp^{MD,thr} parametrization (6). In Fig. 2 we provide the 2σ c.l. bounds on Ω_{ede}^{MD} obtained with the baseline data set CMBpol+SNIa with and without late-time dark energy dynamics, and also adding the CMB lensing and the BAO+RSD data sets. When $z_{thr} \to \infty$ we recover the constraints obtained in the EDEp^{MD} model, of course, but when we allow for lower values of the threshold redshift (below the CMB decoupling one) we get larger upper bounds on Ω_{ede}^{MD}, which depend on the concrete data set under consideration and also on z_{thr}. We report the results obtained with $z_{thr} = 10, 50, 200, 500, \infty$. The addition of the *Planck* 2018 CMB lensing to the CMBpol+SNIa baseline data set leads to stronger constraints on Ω_{ede}^{MD}. Its value decreases by a $\sim 25\%$ $\forall z_{thr}$. When

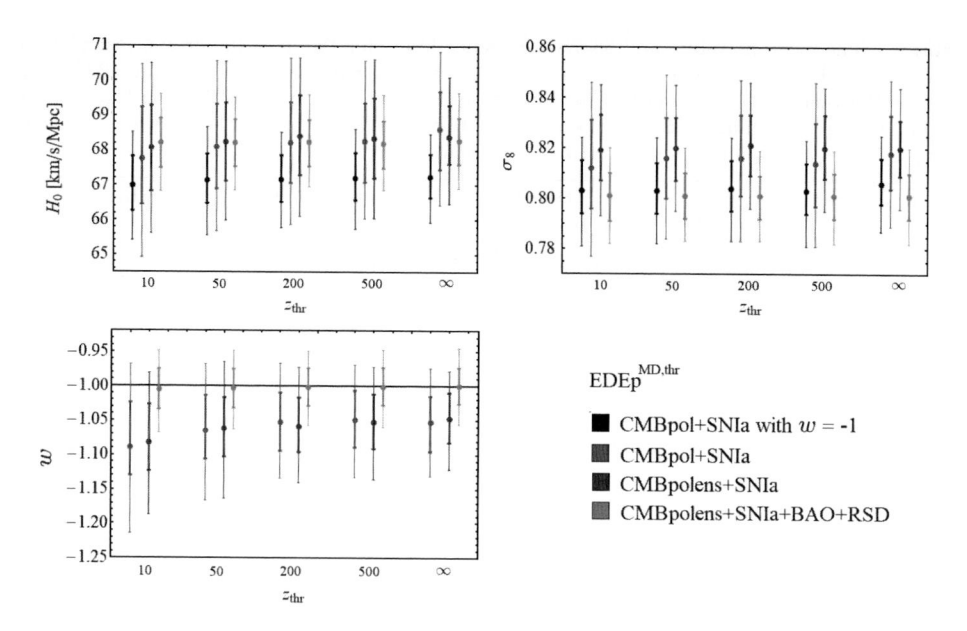

Fig. 3. Constraints for H_0, σ_8 and w at 1σ and 2σ c.l. obtained with the EDEp$^{\text{MD},thr}$ parametrization (6) for different values of the threshold redshift z_{thr} and using the same combined data sets as in Fig. 2.

we also include the BAO+RSD data the decrease is even bigger, $\sim 75\%$. If we turn off the late-time dynamics of DE we also obtain tighter bounds on Ω_{ede}^{MD}, just because in this case we remove the degeneracy between this parameter and w. Our Fig. 2 can be compared with Figs. 6-7 of[48] and Fig. 11 of,[49] which were obviously obtained with older data sets. In[48] the authors employed CMB data from WMAP9 combined with small scale measurements from the South Pole Telescope (SPT), whereas in[49] the authors employed the *Planck* 2015 CMB likelihood and studied the impact of some other background and weak lensing data sets, as described in Sec. 4 in that reference. The results presented in this section constitute a significant update obtained with the *Planck* 2018 likelihood and also other more recent background and LSS data (cf. Sec. 3 for details).

In Fig. 3 we provide the corresponding constraints on H_0, σ_8 and w at 1σ and 2σ c.l. in the EDEp$^{\text{MD},thr}$ parametrization for the same scenarios explored in Fig. 2. They support some of the comments made in the previous paragraphs of this section, e.g. (i) the values of σ_8 and H_0 remain close to those found in the ΛCDM model. In other words, the tensions are not significantly alleviated in this class of scaling early dark energy models; (ii) phantom values of $w < -1$ allow us to decrease the H_0 tension very slightly; and (iii) larger values of w lead to lower values of σ_8 due to the presence of a larger fraction of dark energy at low redshifts. This is why we get $w \sim -1$ when we include the BAO+RSD data set.

The dedicated analysis presented in this section updated and generalized previous constraints on this class of early dark energy models, and motivated the study of

Table 2. The mean fit values and 68.3% confidence limits for the most important cosmological (main+derived) parameters, obtained under different data sets (with and without CMB lensing) for the binned $\rho_{de}(z)$ described in Sec. 2.2. See Fig. 4 for the constraints on $\Omega_{de}(z)$, and Sec. 4.2 for a thorough discussion on these results. Here we have employed the following notation: Base≡CMBpol+SNIa and BaseL≡CMBpolens+SNIa.

Parameter	Base	Base+M	Base+M+BAO	Base+M+BAO+WL
ω_b	$0.02257^{+0.00022}_{-0.00023}$	$0.02277^{+0.00023}_{-0.00025}$	$0.02282^{+0.00024}_{-0.00025}$	0.02259 ± 0.00021
ω_{cdm}	$0.1222^{+0.0020}_{-0.0021}$	0.1221 ± 0.0022	$0.1223^{+0.0020}_{-0.0021}$	$0.1200^{+0.0013}_{-0.0014}$
n_s	$0.9727^{+0.0072}_{-0.0073}$	$0.9752^{+0.0067}_{-0.0069}$	$0.9760^{+0.0070}_{-0.0071}$	$0.9740^{+0.0061}_{-0.0067}$
H_0 [km/s/Mpc]	$68.29^{+1.26}_{-1.36}$	$70.86^{+1.00}_{-1.10}$	$70.38^{+0.84}_{-0.89}$	$69.85^{+0.76}_{-0.77}$
M	-19.405 ± 0.032	$-19.342^{+0.023}_{-0.024}$	$-19.350^{+0.019}_{-0.020}$	$-19.365^{+0.018}_{-0.017}$
σ_8	$0.854^{+0.023}_{-0.025}$	$0.880^{+0.025}_{-0.029}$	$0.877^{+0.026}_{-0.029}$	$0.833^{+0.016}_{-0.017}$
S_8	$0.869^{+0.025}_{-0.029}$	0.863 ± 0.029	$0.866^{+0.026}_{-0.028}$	$0.819^{+0.014}_{-0.016}$
σ_{12}	$0.840^{+0.019}_{-0.022}$	0.843 ± 0.022	$0.843^{+0.020}_{-0.022}$	$0.806^{+0.012}_{-0.013}$
S_{12}	$0.851^{+0.022}_{-0.025}$	$0.854^{+0.024}_{-0.027}$	$0.855^{+0.023}_{-0.026}$	$0.810^{+0.014}_{-0.016}$
r_d [Mpc]	$145.66^{+0.90}_{-0.70}$	$145.22^{+0.95}_{-0.90}$	$145.06^{+0.97}_{-0.89}$	$146.51^{+0.64}_{-0.51}$
w	$-1.037^{+0.043}_{-0.041}$	-1.070 ± 0.038	$-1.048^{+0.037}_{-0.034}$	$-1.037^{+0.032}_{-0.031}$
Parameter	BaseL	BaseL+M	BaseL+M+BAO	BaseL+M+BAO+WL
ω_b	$0.02257^{+0.00021}_{-0.00023}$	$0.02274^{+0.00023}_{-0.00025}$	$0.02277^{+0.00022}_{-0.00024}$	$0.02266^{+0.00021}_{-0.00020}$
ω_{cdm}	0.1215 ± 0.0016	0.1211 ± 0.0017	0.1214 ± 0.0016	$0.1193^{+0.0013}_{-0.0014}$
n_s	$0.9721^{+0.0063}_{-0.0071}$	$0.9748^{+0.0067}_{-0.0071}$	$0.9746^{+0.0068}_{-0.0069}$	$0.9727^{+0.0066}_{-0.0068}$
H_0 [km/s/Mpc]	$68.25^{+1.27}_{-1.26}$	$70.84^{+1.04}_{-1.07}$	$70.21^{+0.80}_{-0.84}$	$70.00^{+0.76}_{-0.73}$
M	$-19.407^{+0.031}_{-0.030}$	$-19.343^{+0.024}_{-0.025}$	-19.355 ± 0.018	-19.362 ± 0.016
σ_8	$0.845^{+0.017}_{-0.020}$	$0.868^{+0.019}_{-0.021}$	$0.864^{+0.019}_{-0.021}$	$0.839^{+0.013}_{-0.015}$
S_8	$0.858^{+0.019}_{-0.021}$	$0.848^{+0.020}_{-0.022}$	$0.853^{+0.019}_{-0.020}$	$0.824^{+0.012}_{-0.013}$
σ_{12}	$0.831^{+0.014}_{-0.015}$	$0.831^{+0.015}_{-0.016}$	$0.833^{+0.015}_{-0.016}$	$0.810^{+0.010}_{-0.011}$
S_{12}	$0.841^{+0.016}_{-0.017}$	$0.840^{+0.017}_{-0.020}$	0.843 ± 0.018	$0.815^{+0.011}_{-0.013}$
r_d [Mpc]	$145.94^{+0.69}_{-0.57}$	$145.65^{+0.82}_{-0.71}$	$145.51^{+0.83}_{-0.71}$	$146.46^{+0.56}_{-0.44}$
w	$-1.035^{+0.040}_{-0.039}$	$-1.067^{+0.037}_{-0.036}$	$-1.050^{+0.034}_{-0.035}$	-1.045 ± 0.032

the next section, in which we will reconstruct the shape of $\Omega_{de}(z)$ without sticking to a restricted family of parametrizations.

4.2. Results for tomographic dark energy

Now we provide the results obtained in the tomographic model described in Sec. 2.2 in order to see whether more general shapes of $\Omega_{de}(z)$ can loosen the cosmological tensions. This is in fact suggested by previous analyses in the literature, see e.g.[38–43,77].

Our results are presented in Table 2 and Fig. 4. They confirm that a significant (and non-constant) fraction of EDE in the RDE can alleviate the H_0 tension if it can be kept below $\sim 0.6\%$ at 2σ c.l. around the CMB decoupling time, i.e. at $z \sim 1000 - 2000$. For instance, from the analysis of the CMBpolens+SNIa and CMBpolens+SNIa+M+BAO data sets we obtain $H_0 = (68.25^{+1.27}_{-1.26})$ km/s/Mpc and $H_0 = (70.21^{+0.80}_{-0.84})$ km/s/Mpc, respectively. They are 2.77σ and 1.95σ below the SH0ES measurement, and the central value is significantly lower when the SH0ES prior is not considered. The authors of[44] reported similar results in the context of the ultra-light axion model. Nevertheless, if we compare the values of M obtained from these data sets with $M_{\rm SH0ES}$ we still obtain a tension of 3.80σ and 3.07σ, respectively. This means that in terms of M, the tension is bigger than when it is formulated in terms of H_0, and the capability of EDE of alleviating the tension is much lower, at least in the EDE framework we are considering here.

We also see that the large fraction of $\Omega_{de}(z)$ required in the RDE to loosen the H_0 tension, which can be of about $\sim 4-5\%$ at 2σ c.l. according to some data sets that include the SH0ES prior on M but no LSS information, leads to higher values of ω_{cdm} and, to a lesser extent, also of n_s, which in turn exacerbates the σ_8/S_8 tension. The former is needed to reduce the early integrated Sachs-Wolfe effect introduced by the EDE. This is aligned with previous works that also consider EDE in the pre-recombination epoch, see e.g.[44–46,78,79] Table 2 shows that the tension decreases $\sim 1\sigma$ when it is analyzed through the LSS estimators σ_{12} and S_{12}.[67] Nevertheless, it does not disappear. Under the CMBpolens+SNIa+M data set the σ_8 tension is of 3.63σ, whereas for the σ_{12} parameter it is of 2.64σ, and a similar decrease is observed when other data combinations are employed in the fitting analysis.

When the SH0ES prior on M is taken into account in absence of LSS data, we get a $\sim 2\sigma$ evidence for the presence of a non-null EDE fraction during the RDE, similar to.[41] Nevertheless, the inclusion of the weak lensing data from KiDS+VIKING-450 and DES-Y1 (cf. Sec. 3) forces the EDE fraction in the RDE to be again compatible at 1σ with 0 in order to allow ω_{cdm} to take values closer to the ΛCDM ones and not to worsen the σ_8/S_8 tension. Notice that, as expected, the upper bound on the fraction of EDE in the MDE that we obtain in our binned analysis is larger than the one found with EDEp and its variants, even when the prior on S_8 is not included (see Table 1 and Fig. 4). Indeed, higher fractions of EDE in the MDE (see again Fig. 4) also allow to keep the amount of LSS more under control. With the CMBpolens+SNIa+M+BAO+WL we obtain $H_0 = (70.00^{+0.76}_{-0.73})$ km/s/Mpc and $M = -19.362 \pm 0.016$. They are in 2.13σ and 3.28σ tension with the SH0ES values, respectively. Again, the tension in M is larger than in H_0 by $\sim 1\sigma$. Regarding the LSS estimators, we obtain $S_8 = 0.824^{+0.012}_{-0.013}$ and $\sigma_{12} = 0.810^{+0.010}_{-0.011}$. The former is in 2.25σ tension with the KiDS+VIKING-450+DESY1 value, whereas the latter is compatible at 1σ with the value obtained in the ΛCDM. The tensions in H_0 and S_8 can be kept at $\sim 2\sigma$ c.l. under this concrete data set, as advocated in.[78]

The effect of the CMB lensing from *Planck* 2018 on the EDE fraction can be appreciated by direct comparison of the plots in the left and right columns of Fig. 4. When the CMB lensing is included, the upper bound on $\Omega_{de}(z)$ is reduced by $\sim 1\%$ for $z \gtrsim 5000$, by a $\sim 0.5\%$ for $3000 \lesssim z \lesssim 5000$ and by a smaller fraction at lower redshifts. Some differences are found, though, depending on the other data sets employed in the fitting analyses. The preferred matter densities decrease, although

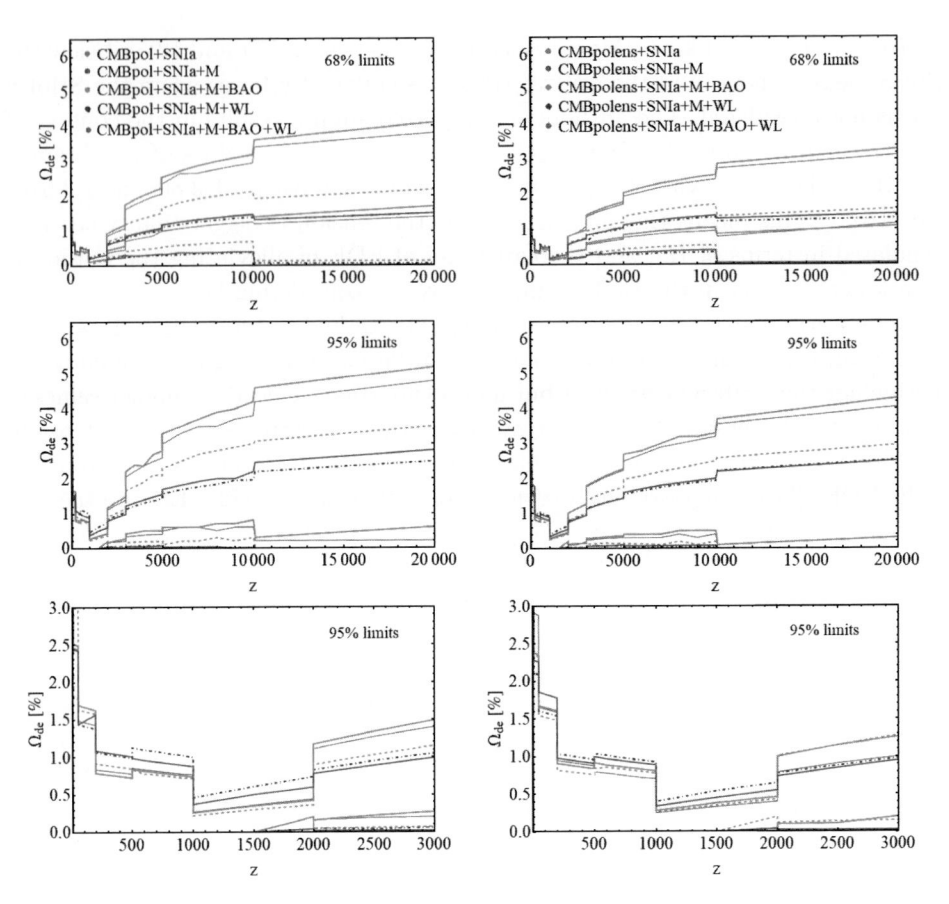

Fig. 4. *Left plots:* Reconstructed shapes of $\Omega_{de}(z)$ obtained from the fitting analyses without the Planck 2018 CMB lensing data (cf. Sec. 3). In the first and second rows we show the constraints in the region $z \in [0, 2 \cdot 10^4]$ at 1σ and 2σ c.l., respectively. In the last row we zoom in the redshift range $z \in [0, 3000]$ to better appreciate the details in the MDE. The tightest upper bound on $\Omega_{de}(z)$ is obtained around the CMB decoupling time, i.e. at $z \sim 1000-2000$, where the data force $\Omega_{de}(z) \lesssim 0.6\%$ at 2σ c.l.; *Right plots:* The same, but including the CMB lensing data. See the comments in Sec. 4.2.

they are still compatible at 1σ with the ones inferred without including the CMB lensing. This leads also to a slight decrease on the LSS estimators when the weak lensing prior is not considered. When the latter is included, the values of σ_{12} and S_{12} (and also σ_8 and S_8) remain stable under the addition of the CMB lensing likelihood.

We would like to remark the very low upper bounds that we obtain for the EDE fraction in the redshift range $z \in (1000, 2000)$, cf. Fig. 4. The exact value for these upper bounds depend on the specific data set, e.g. the constraints are a little bit weaker when the WL prior is used in the fitting analysis, but the EDE fraction when $\hat{c}_s = 1$ is, in any case, very strongly constrained in that epoch and lies always below $\sim 0.6\%$ regardless of the data set under consideration. Under the full data set, the

EDE fractions are constrained to be below 2.6% in the RDE and $\lesssim 1-1.5\%$ in the redshift range $z \in (100, 1000)$ at 2σ c.l. This limits strongly the possible impact of EDE on the value of the Hubble parameter or the present amount of structure.

5. Conclusions

In this work we have studied the phenomenological performance of a family of flexible parametrizations for the dark energy density that are able to mimic the scaling behavior that is encountered in a wide variety of quintessence models. DE has been treated as a perfect fluid with two plateaus in $\Omega_{de}(z)$, one in the matter-dominated epoch and another one in the radiation-dominated era. We have put very tight constraints on the fraction of EDE in the radiation- and matter-dominated epochs in the context of these models. The CMBpol+SNIa data set already forces these two quantities to lie below 2.44% and 0.52% at 2σ c.l., respectively. These strong constraints are necessary to respect the upper bound on the amount of EDE at the last scattering surface, as we have explicitly checked in our tomographic analysis. We have found that this class of scaling EDE models does not lead to a significant alleviation of the H_0 and σ_8 tensions. Larger EDE fractions are allowed by the data if: (i) the sound speed for DE is fixed at values $\hat{c}_s^2 \ll 1$, since in this limit dark energy behaves as dark matter during the matter-dominated epoch at the background and perturbations levels and, hence, there is a huge degeneracy between these two components. If we would assume a vanishing sound speed for dark energy there would be no way to distinguish it from dark matter. We find indeed no bounds on the dark energy fraction in this case. This changes drastically already for a rather small sound speed of EDE of the order 10^{-4}; and (ii) if EDE is switched on at later times, already in the matter-dominated era. Nevertheless, the cosmological tensions remain also in these cases.

EDE can only have a larger impact on the cosmological tensions if $\Omega_{de}(z)$ takes more flexible shapes that allow to respect the very strict constraints found around the CMB decoupling time ($\Omega_{de}(z_{dec}) \lesssim 0.4\%$ at 2σ c.l.), while still leading to a significant EDE fraction in other epochs of the cosmic expansion. The strong bound on EDE for redshift $200 < z < 1000$ ($\Omega_{de}(z) \lesssim 1\%$ at 2σ c.l.) is rather impressive since it is entirely based on the different clustering properties of dark energy and dark matter.

In general, when the SH0ES prior is not included in the fitting analysis there is no significant shift in the value of the Hubble parameter when compared to the ΛCDM, although the uncertainties clearly grow by a factor $2-3$. This allows to decrease the H_0 tension to the 2.66σ c.l. under the minimal CMBpol+SNIa data set. The addition of the CMB lensing has a very mild effect, increasing the tension up to the 2.73σ level.

When the BAO data and the SH0ES prior are also considered, the H_0 tension is reduced to the $\sim 2\sigma$ level by increasing the EDE fraction at the radiation-dominated epoch. A 2σ preference for a non-null EDE density in that epoch is obtained,

$\Omega_{de}(z) \lesssim 4\%$ at 95% c.l. Our reconstructed $\Omega_{de}(z)$ allows for non-peaked shapes, in contrast to what one finds e.g. in models based on ultra-light axions.[41,80] The model needs, though, values of the current dark matter density much larger than the ones typically encountered in the concordance model. This is to lower the early integrated Sachs-Wolfe effect down, which is enhanced by the presence of EDE in the pre-recombination epoch. This automatically leads to an increase of σ_8 and S_8 that worsens the LSS tension, which lies now at the $3-3.5\sigma$ c.l. In terms of σ_{12}, the tension is somewhat lower, but still remains at the $\sim 2.7\sigma$ level, as when the M prior is not used in the analysis. It is also to be noted that the H_0 tension still stays at the 3σ level when formulated in terms of the absolute magnitude of SNIa M.

Finally, when we use the most complete data set, taking also the weak lensing data into account, we find that the model can keep the H_0 and S_8 tensions at the $\sim 2\sigma$ c.l., thanks also to a slight increase of the EDE fraction in the matter-dominated epoch, although, again, the M tension remains at $\gtrsim 3\sigma$.

In view of our results, it seems unlikely that EDE alone can provide a satisfactory resolution of the cosmological tensions. Whether the latter have or not a physical origin, or whether their statistical significance is as high as claimed by some sectors of the cosmological community, is still a matter of discussion and is certainly not a closed subject. Here we conclude that, in any case, if the data sets employed in this study do not suffer from any important systematic errors, uncoupled EDE is not able to relieve completely the tensions. Under our full data set CMBpolens+SNIa+M+BAO+WL they remain at $2-3\sigma$ c.l.

Nothing prevents, though, the solution to the cosmological tensions to be multi-sided, rather than due to a single new physics component. EDE could still play a significant role in this story. Some interesting directions to explore in the future are: (i) a possible coupling of EDE to dark matter, (ii) the impact of more complicated behavior of the EDE sound speed, parameterizing its time dependence, or performing a tomographic analysis similar to the one we have carried out in this work for the EDE density; and (iii) the potential degeneracy between EDE and other cosmological parameters, as the neutrino masses, which could in principle help to soften the S_8 tension while keeping the needed amount of non-relativistic matter at the CMB decoupling time. The latter would be needed, together with a higher EDE fraction in the radiation-dominated epoch, in order to increase the value of the Hubble parameter. We leave these investigations for a future work.

Acknowledgments

The author is very grateful to Prof. Joan Solà Peracaula for his kind invitation to give this talk and co-chair the CM3 session with him. He was funded by the Deutsche Forschungsgemeinschaft (DFG) - Project number 415335479 - during the time at which the MG16 meeting was held and the research of this project carried out.

References

1. A. Gómez-Valent, Z. Zheng, L. Amendola, V. Pettorino and C. Wetterich, Early dark energy in the pre- and post-recombination epochs (7 2021).
2. S. Perlmutter et al., Measurements of Ω and Λ from 42 high redshift supernovae, *Astrophys. J.* **517**, 565 (1999).
3. A. G. Riess et al., Observational evidence from supernovae for an accelerating universe and a cosmological constant, *Astron. J.* **116**, 1009 (1998).
4. N. Aghanim et al., Planck 2018 results. VI. Cosmological parameters, *Astron. Astrophys.* **641**, p. A6 (2020).
5. D. M. Scolnic et al., The Complete Light-curve Sample of Spectroscopically Confirmed SNe Ia from Pan-STARRS1 and Cosmological Constraints from the Combined Pantheon Sample, *Astrophys. J.* **859**, p. 101 (2018).
6. R. Neveux et al., The completed SDSS-IV extended Baryon Oscillation Spectroscopic Survey: BAO and RSD measurements from the anisotropic power spectrum of the quasar sample between redshift 0.8 and 2.2, *Mon. Not. Roy. Astron. Soc.* **499**, 210 (2020).
7. S. Weinberg, The Cosmological Constant Problem, *Rev. Mod. Phys.* **61**, 1 (1989), [,569(1988)].
8. J. Martin, Everything You Always Wanted To Know About The Cosmological Constant Problem (But Were Afraid To Ask), *Comptes Rendus Physique* **13**, 566 (2012).
9. J. Solà Peracaula, Cosmological constant and vacuum energy: Old and new ideas, *J. Phys. Conf. Ser.* **453**, p. 012015 (2013).
10. P. J. E. Peebles and B. Ratra, The Cosmological Constant and Dark Energy, *Rev. Mod. Phys.* **75**, 559 (2003).
11. H. E. S. Velten, R. F. vom Marttens and W. Zimdahl, Aspects of the cosmological "coincidence problem", *Eur. Phys. J. C* **74**, p. 3160 (2014).
12. P. J. E. Peebles and B. Ratra, Cosmology with a Time Variable Cosmological Constant, *Astrophys. J. Lett.* **325**, p. L17 (1988).
13. B. Ratra and P. J. E. Peebles, Cosmological Consequences of a Rolling Homogeneous Scalar Field, *Phys. Rev. D* **37**, p. 3406 (1988).
14. C. Wetterich, Cosmology and the Fate of Dilatation Symmetry, *Nucl. Phys. B* **302**, 668 (1988).
15. E. J. Copeland, A. R. Liddle and D. Wands, Exponential potentials and cosmological scaling solutions, *Phys. Rev. D* **57**, 4686 (1998).
16. G. E. Addison, D. J. Watts, C. L. Bennett, M. Halpern, G. Hinshaw and J. L. Weiland, Elucidating ΛCDM: Impact of Baryon Acoustic Oscillation Measurements on the Hubble Constant Discrepancy, *Astrophys. J.* **853**, p. 119 (2018).
17. A. G. Riess, S. Casertano, W. Yuan, J. B. Bowers, L. Macri, J. C. Zinn and D. Scolnic, Cosmic Distances Calibrated to 1% Precision with Gaia EDR3 Parallaxes and Hubble Space Telescope Photometry of 75 Milky Way Cepheids Confirm Tension with ΛCDM, *Astrophys. J. Lett.* **908**, p. L6 (2021).
18. A. G. Riess et al., A 2.4% Determination of the Local Value of the Hubble Constant, *Astrophys. J.* **826**, p. 56 (2016).
19. A. G. Riess et al., New Parallaxes of Galactic Cepheids from Spatially Scanning the Hubble Space Telescope: Implications for the Hubble Constant, *Astrophys. J.* **855**, p. 136 (2018).
20. L. Verde, T. Treu and A. G. Riess, Tensions between the Early and the Late Universe, *Nature Astron.* **3**, p. 891 (7 2019).
21. E. Di Valentino et al., Snowmass2021 - Letter of interest cosmology intertwined II: The hubble constant tension, *Astropart. Phys.* **131**, p. 102605 (2021).

22. H. Gil-Marín, W. J. Percival, L. Verde, J. R. Brownstein, C.-H. Chuang, F.-S. Kitaura, S. A. Rodríguez-Torres and M. D. Olmstead, The clustering of galaxies in the SDSS-III Baryon Oscillation Spectroscopic Survey: RSD measurement from the power spectrum and bispectrum of the DR12 BOSS galaxies, *Mon. Not. Roy. Astron. Soc.* **465**, 1757 (2017).
23. S. Joudaki *et al.*, KiDS-450 + 2dFLenS: Cosmological parameter constraints from weak gravitational lensing tomography and overlapping redshift-space galaxy clustering, *Mon. Not. Roy. Astron. Soc.* **474**, 4894 (2018).
24. A. H. Wright, H. Hildebrandt, J. L. van den Busch, C. Heymans, B. Joachimi, A. Kannawadi and K. Kuijken, KiDS+VIKING-450: Improved cosmological parameter constraints from redshift calibration with self-organising maps, *Astron. Astrophys.* **640**, p. L14 (2020).
25. C. Heymans *et al.*, KiDS-1000 Cosmology: Multi-probe weak gravitational lensing and spectroscopic galaxy clustering constraints, *Astron. Astrophys.* **646**, p. A140 (2021).
26. E. Macaulay, I. K. Wehus and H. K. Eriksen, Lower Growth Rate from Recent Redshift Space Distortion Measurements than Expected from Planck, *Phys. Rev. Lett.* **111**, p. 161301 (2013).
27. S. Nesseris, G. Pantazis and L. Perivolaropoulos, Tension and constraints on modified gravity parametrizations of $G_{\text{eff}}(z)$ from growth rate and Planck data, *Phys. Rev. D* **96**, p. 023542 (2017).
28. J. Solà Peracaula, J. de Cruz Pérez and A. Gómez-Valent, Possible signals of vacuum dynamics in the Universe, *Mon. Not. Roy. Astron. Soc.* **478**, 4357 (2018).
29. J. Solà Peracaula, A. Gómez-Valent, J. de Cruz Perez and C. Moreno-Pulido, Running vacuum against the H_0 and σ_8 tensions, *EPL* **134**, p. 19001 (2021).
30. G. Efstathiou, A Lockdown Perspective on the Hubble Tension (with comments from the SH0ES team) (7 2020).
31. E. Mortsell, A. Goobar, J. Johansson and S. Dhawan, The Hubble Tension Bites the Dust: Sensitivity of the Hubble Constant Determination to Cepheid Color Calibration (5 2021).
32. W. L. Freedman, Measurements of the Hubble Constant: Tensions in Perspective (6 2021).
33. E. Di Valentino *et al.*, Cosmology intertwined III: $f\sigma_8$ and S_8, *Astropart. Phys.* **131**, p. 102604 (2021).
34. E. Di Valentino, O. Mena, S. Pan, L. Visinelli, W. Yang, A. Melchiorri, D. F. Mota, A. G. Riess and J. Silk, In the realm of the Hubble tension—a review of solutions, *Class. Quant. Grav.* **38**, p. 153001 (2021).
35. J. Solà Peracaula, A. Gómez-Valent, J. de Cruz Pérez and C. Moreno-Pulido, Brans–Dicke Gravity with a Cosmological Constant Smoothes Out ΛCDM Tensions, *Astrophys. J. Lett.* **886**, p. L6 (2019).
36. J. Solà Peracaula, A. Gómez-Valent, J. de Cruz Pérez and C. Moreno-Pulido, Brans–Dicke cosmology with a Λ-term: A possible solution to ΛCDM tensions, *Class. Quant. Grav.* **37**, p. 245003 (2020).
37. A. Gómez-Valent and P. Hassan Puttasiddappa, Difficulties in reconciling non-negligible differences between the local and cosmological values of the gravitational coupling in extended Brans-Dicke theories (5 2021).
38. F. Niedermann and M. S. Sloth, New early dark energy, *Phys. Rev. D* **103**, p. L041303 (2021).
39. A. Gogoi, R. K. Sharma, P. Chanda and S. Das, Early Mass-varying Neutrino Dark Energy: Nugget Formation and Hubble Anomaly, *Astrophys. J.* **915**, p. 132 (2021).

40. F. Niedermann and M. S. Sloth, Resolving the Hubble tension with new early dark energy, *Phys. Rev. D* **102**, p. 063527 (2020).
41. V. Poulin, T. L. Smith, T. Karwal and M. Kamionkowski, Early Dark Energy Can Resolve The Hubble Tension, *Phys. Rev. Lett.* **122**, p. 221301 (2019).
42. T. L. Smith, V. Poulin and M. A. Amin, Oscillating scalar fields and the Hubble tension: a resolution with novel signatures, *Phys. Rev. D* **101**, p. 063523 (2020).
43. P. Agrawal, F.-Y. Cyr-Racine, D. Pinner and L. Randall, Rock 'n' Roll Solutions to the Hubble Tension (4 2019).
44. J. C. Hill, E. McDonough, M. W. Toomey and S. Alexander, Early dark energy does not restore cosmological concordance, *Phys. Rev. D* **102**, p. 043507 (2020).
45. M. M. Ivanov, E. McDonough, J. C. Hill, M. Simonović, M. W. Toomey, S. Alexander and M. Zaldarriaga, Constraining Early Dark Energy with Large-Scale Structure, *Phys. Rev. D* **102**, p. 103502 (2020).
46. G. D'Amico, L. Senatore, P. Zhang and H. Zheng, The Hubble Tension in Light of the Full-Shape Analysis of Large-Scale Structure Data, *JCAP* **05**, p. 072 (2021).
47. M. Doran, M. J. Lilley, J. Schwindt and C. Wetterich, Quintessence and the separation of CMB peaks, *Astrophys. J.* **559**, 501 (2001).
48. V. Pettorino, L. Amendola and C. Wetterich, How early is early dark energy?, *Phys. Rev. D* **87**, p. 083009 (2013).
49. P. A. R. Ade *et al.*, Planck 2015 results. XIV. Dark energy and modified gravity, *Astron. Astrophys.* **594**, p. A14 (2016).
50. P. G. Ferreira and M. Joyce, Structure formation with a selftuning scalar field, *Phys. Rev. Lett.* **79**, 4740 (1997).
51. M. Doran, J.-M. Schwindt and C. Wetterich, Structure formation and the time dependence of quintessence, *Phys. Rev. D* **64**, p. 123520 (2001).
52. R. R. Caldwell, M. Doran, C. M. Mueller, G. Schafer and C. Wetterich, Early quintessence in light of WMAP, *Astrophys. J. Lett.* **591**, L75 (2003).
53. M. Grossi and V. Springel, The impact of early dark energy on non-linear structure formation, *Mon. Not. Roy. Astron. Soc.* **394**, p. 1559–1574 (Apr 2009).
54. T. Barreiro, E. J. Copeland and N. J. Nunes, Quintessence arising from exponential potentials, *Phys. Rev. D* **61**, p. 127301 (2000).
55. M. S. Turner and M. J. White, CDM models with a smooth component, *Phys. Rev. D* **56**, p. R4439 (1997).
56. G. Ballesteros and J. Lesgourgues, Dark energy with non-adiabatic sound speed: initial conditions and detectability, *JCAP* **10**, p. 014 (2010).
57. D. Blas, J. Lesgourgues and T. Tram, The Cosmic Linear Anisotropy Solving System (CLASS) II: Approximation schemes, *JCAP* **07**, p. 034 (2011).
58. B. Audren, J. Lesgourgues, K. Benabed and S. Prunet, Conservative Constraints on Early Cosmology: an illustration of the Monte Python cosmological parameter inference code, *JCAP* **02**, p. 001 (2013).
59. D. Camarena and V. Marra, Local determination of the Hubble constant and the deceleration parameter, *Phys. Rev. Res.* **2**, p. 013028 (2020).
60. A. G. Riess, S. Casertano, W. Yuan, L. M. Macri and D. Scolnic, Large Magellanic Cloud Cepheid Standards Provide a 1% Foundation for the Determination of the Hubble Constant and Stronger Evidence for Physics beyond ΛCDM, *Astrophys. J.* **876**, p. 85 (2019).
61. M. J. Reid, D. W. Pesce and A. G. Riess, An Improved Distance to NGC 4258 and its Implications for the Hubble Constant, *Astrophys. J. Lett.* **886**, p. L27 (2019).

62. P. Carter, F. Beutler, W. J. Percival, C. Blake, J. Koda and A. J. Ross, Low Redshift Baryon Acoustic Oscillation Measurement from the Reconstructed 6-degree Field Galaxy Survey, *Mon. Not. Roy. Astron. Soc.* **481**, 2371 (2018).
63. E. A. Kazin *et al.*, The WiggleZ Dark Energy Survey: improved distance measurements to z = 1 with reconstruction of the baryonic acoustic feature, *Mon. Not. Roy. Astron. Soc.* **441**, 3524 (2014).
64. T. M. C. Abbott *et al.*, Dark Energy Survey Year 1 Results: Measurement of the Baryon Acoustic Oscillation scale in the distribution of galaxies to redshift 1, *Mon. Not. Roy. Astron. Soc.* **483**, 4866 (2019).
65. H. du Mas des Bourboux *et al.*, The Completed SDSS-IV Extended Baryon Oscillation Spectroscopic Survey: Baryon Acoustic Oscillations with Lyα Forests, *Astrophys. J.* **901**, p. 153 (2020).
66. S. Joudaki *et al.*, KiDS+VIKING-450 and DES-Y1 combined: Cosmology with cosmic shear, *Astron. Astrophys.* **638**, p. L1 (2020).
67. A. G. Sanchez, Arguments against using h^{-1}Mpc units in observational cosmology, *Phys. Rev. D* **102**, p. 123511 (2020).
68. K. Said, M. Colless, C. Magoulas, J. R. Lucey and M. J. Hudson, Joint analysis of 6dFGS and SDSS peculiar velocities for the growth rate of cosmic structure and tests of gravity, *Mon. Not. Roy. Astron. Soc.* **497**, 1275 (2020).
69. F. Simpson, C. Blake, J. A. Peacock, I. Baldry, J. Bland-Hawthorn, A. Heavens, C. Heymans, J. Loveday and P. Norberg, Galaxy and mass assembly: Redshift space distortions from the clipped galaxy field, *Phys. Rev. D* **93**, p. 023525 (2016).
70. C. Blake *et al.*, Galaxy And Mass Assembly (GAMA): improved cosmic growth measurements using multiple tracers of large-scale structure, *Mon. Not. Roy. Astron. Soc.* **436**, p. 3089 (2013).
71. C. Blake *et al.*, The WiggleZ Dark Energy Survey: the growth rate of cosmic structure since redshift z=0.9, *Mon. Not. Roy. Astron. Soc.* **415**, p. 2876 (2011).
72. F. G. Mohammad *et al.*, The VIMOS Public Extragalactic Redshift Survey (VIPERS): Unbiased clustering estimate with VIPERS slit assignment, *Astron. Astrophys.* **619**, p. A17 (2018).
73. L. Guzzo *et al.*, A test of the nature of cosmic acceleration using galaxy redshift distortions, *Nature* **451**, 541 (2008).
74. Y.-S. Song and W. J. Percival, Reconstructing the history of structure formation using Redshift Distortions, *JCAP* **10**, p. 004 (2009).
75. T. Okumura *et al.*, The Subaru FMOS galaxy redshift survey (FastSound). IV. New constraint on gravity theory from redshift space distortions at $z \sim 1.4$, *Publ. Astron. Soc. Jap.* **68**, p. 38 (2016).
76. G. Alestas, L. Kazantzidis and L. Perivolaropoulos, H_0 tension, phantom dark energy, and cosmological parameter degeneracies, *Phys. Rev. D* **101**, p. 123516 (2020).
77. A. Chudaykin, D. Gorbunov and N. Nedelko, Combined analysis of Planck and SPTPol data favors the early dark energy models, *JCAP* **08**, p. 013 (2020).
78. R. Murgia, G. F. Abellán and V. Poulin, Early dark energy resolution to the Hubble tension in light of weak lensing surveys and lensing anomalies, *Phys. Rev. D* **103**, p. 063502 (2021).
79. T. L. Smith, V. Poulin, J. L. Bernal, K. K. Boddy, M. Kamionkowski and R. Murgia, Early dark energy is not excluded by current large-scale structure data, *Phys. Rev. D* **103**, p. 123542 (2021).
80. V. Poulin, T. L. Smith, D. Grin, T. Karwal and M. Kamionkowski, Cosmological implications of ultralight axionlike fields, *Phys. Rev. D* **98**, p. 083525 (2018).

Renormalized $\rho_{\rm vac}$ without m^4 terms

Cristian Moreno-Pulido* and Joan Solà Peracaula

Departament de Física Quàntica i Astrofísica, and Institute of Cosmos Sciences, Universitat de Barcelona, Av. Diagonal 647, E-08028 Barcelona, Catalonia, Spain
*E-mails: cristian.moreno@fqa.ub.edu, sola@fqa.ub.edu

The cosmological constant (CC) term, Λ, in Einstein's equations has been for about three decades a fundamental building block of the concordance or standard ΛCDM model of cosmology. Although the latter is not free of fundamental problems, it provides a good phenomenological description of the overall cosmological observations. However, an interesting improvement in such a phenomenological description and also a change in the theoretical status of the Λ-term occurs upon realizing that the vacuum energy is actually a "running quantity" in quantum field theory in curved spacetime. Several works have shown that this option can compete with the ΛCDM with a rigid Λ term. The so-called, "running vacuum models" (RVM) are characterized indeed by a vacuum energy density, $\rho_{\rm vac}$, which is evolving with time as a series of even powers of the Hubble parameter and its time derivatives. This form has been motivated by semi-qualitative renormalization group arguments in previous works. Here we review a recent detailed computation by the authors of the renormalized energy-momentum tensor of a non-minimally coupled scalar field with the help of adiabatic regularization procedure. The final result is noteworthy: $\rho_{\rm vac}(H)$ takes the precise structure of the RVM, namely a constant term plus a dynamical component $\sim H^2$ (which should be detectable in the present universe) including also higher order effects $\mathcal{O}(H^4)$ which can be of interest during the early stages of the cosmological evolution. Besides, it is most remarkable that such renormalized form of the vacuum energy density does not carry dangerous terms proportional to m^4, the quartic powers of the masses of the fields, which are a well-known source of exceedingly large contributions to the vacuum energy density and are directly responsible for extreme fine tuning in the context of the cosmological constant problem.

Keywords: Cosmology, Dark Energy, Quantum Field Theory.

1. Introduction

Since the mid nineties, the cosmological constant (CC) term, Λ, in Einstein's equations has been a crucial ingredient of the 'concordance' or standard ΛCDM model of cosmology.[1] From the phenomenological point of view it was favored only as of the time Λ became a physically measured quantity some twenty years ago.[2] Nowadays, precision cosmology[3] is able to do better measurements of Λ, or more precisely of the associated parameter $\Omega_{\rm vac}^0 = \rho_{\rm vac}^0/\rho_c^0$, established by observations to be $\Omega_{\rm vac}^0 \sim 0.7$. Here, the vacuum energy density (VED) is associated to Λ and defined as $\rho_{\rm vac}^0 = \Lambda/(8\pi G_N)$, where G_N is Newton's constant and $\rho_c^0 = 3H_0^2/(8\pi G_N)$ is the critical density in our times. However, there is a lot of uncertainty with the CC with respect its nature and origin at a fundamental level. For instance it is commonly

---

*Speaker

assumed that Λ may be related with the Zero-Point Energy (ZPE) of the quantum matter fields and with the Higgs potential of the Standard Model (SM). However, if ones compares the observational value $\rho_{\rm vac}$ with the ZPE of a typical SM particle such as the electron we are left with a tiny value of $\rho_{\rm vac}^{\rm obs}/\rho_{\rm ZPE} \sim 10^{-34}$. If compared with the ground state energy of the effective Higgs potential, $V_{\rm eff}$, we find $\rho_{\rm vac}^{\rm obs}/\langle V_{\rm eff}\rangle \sim 10^{-56}$. This issue is generically called the cosmological constant problem[4,5] and affects all forms of dark energy (DE).[6-10] Another aspect of this intriguing topic is the fact that, at the present time, $\rho_{\rm vac}^{\rm obs}$ and $\rho_{\rm CDM}$, the energy density associated to Cold Dark Matter (CDM), are observed to be of the same order of magnitude, despite the fact that $\rho_{\rm CDM}$ is assumed to decrease with the expansion as a^{-3}, being a the scale factor, whereas $\rho_{\rm vac}$ maintains constant.

The astonishing theoretical problems, though, are not the only ones concerning the concordance model. Currently, some important measurements seems to be in tension with the ΛCDM, emphasizing the discrepant values of the Hubble parameter at the present time, H_0, obtained from independent measurements of the early and the local universe.[11] It is still unknown if these tensions are the result of systematic errors, but the chance that a deviation from the ΛCDM model could provide an explanation for such discrepancies[12] is totally open.

As it has been shown in the literature, models mimicking a time-evolving $\rho_{\rm vac}$, which are allowed by the cosmological principle, could help in alleviating the mentioned problems, see e.g.[13-18] and.[19-25] In this work, we review recent work[26] on the possibility of having dynamical vacuum energy density (VED), $\rho_{\rm vac}$, in the context of quantum field theory (QFT) in curved spacetime with a spatially flat Friedmann-Lemaître-Robertson-Walker (FLRW) metric. We want to focus on the dynamics associated to the running vacuum model (RVM);[27-29] for a review, see[30-32] and references therein. Related studies are e.g.[33,34] and,[35,36] but also others extending the subject to the context of supersymmetric theories[37,38] and to supergravity.[39] Recently, some works in the framework of the effective action of string theories[40-45] have been dealt with the topic.

In the calculations reviewed here, the renormalization of the energy-momentum tensor is done using the adiabatic regularization procedure (ARP).[46-49] The renormalization process is a WKB approximation of the field modes in an expanding FLRW background. Once the VED is renormalized, obtained upon inclusion of the renormalized value of ρ_Λ (associated to Λ) at a given scale, it does not include the dangerous contributions depending on the fourth power of the particle masses ($\sim m^4$) and therefore it is free from huge induced corrections to the VED.[26] Additionally, we find a RVM-like form for the VED in the current times, $c_0 + \nu H^2$, with c_0 related to the usual constant term and $|\nu| \ll 1$. This last parameter represents only a small (dynamical) correction to the constant term and, depending on the sign of ν, it can mimic quintessence or phantom DE.

First, in Sec. 2 our framework is defined, consisting of a real scalar field non-minimally coupled to gravity, and we present the classical energy-momentum tensor (EMT). Later on, in Sections 3 and 4, we present the quantum fluctuations in the adiabatic vacuum by means of a WKB expansion of the field modes in the FLRW background and we discuss the adiabatic regularization of the EMT. In Sec. 5 we start with the renormalization of the EMT in the FLRW context through the ARP, which is then needed in Sec. 6 to derive the precise result of ρ_{vac} from the renormalized ZPE up to terms of adiabatic order 4. In our case that means up to $\mathcal{O}(H^4)$. We also demonstrate that the values of the VED at different scales are related by an expression which does not contain quartic powers of the masses. To continue, in Sec. 7, we connect the computed VED in this work with the well-known running vacuum model (RVM), which originally was justified from renormalization group arguments in curved spacetime in previous works. A summary of the conclusions and discussion appear in Sec. 8. At the end, we define our conventions and collect some useful formulas in Appendix.

2. Energy-Momentum Tensor for non-minimally coupled scalar field

Einstein's equations read[a]

$$R_{\mu\nu} - \frac{1}{2}Rg_{\mu\nu} + \Lambda g_{\mu\nu} = 8\pi G_N T_{\mu\nu}^{\text{matter}}, \tag{1}$$

where $T_{\mu\nu}^{\text{matter}}$ is the EMT of matter. They can also be written as

$$\frac{1}{8\pi G_N}G_{\mu\nu} + \rho_\Lambda g_{\mu\nu} = T_{\mu\nu}^{\text{matter}}, \tag{2}$$

where $G_{\mu\nu} \equiv R_{\mu\nu} - \frac{1}{2}Rg_{\mu\nu}$ and $\rho_\Lambda \equiv \Lambda/(8\pi G_N)$ is the VED associated to Λ. The associated contribution of Λ to $T_{\mu\nu}^\Lambda \equiv -\rho_\Lambda g_{\mu\nu}$. But, in general, there are more contributions to the total VED, associated to the quantum fluctuations of the fields, and also to their classical ground state energy. In this work, for practical reasons, we will assume that there is only one (matter) field in the form of a real scalar field, ϕ, and we will denote by $T_{\mu\nu}^\phi$ the piece of the EMT associated to it. Thus $T_{\mu\nu}^{\text{tot}} = T_{\mu\nu}^\Lambda + T_{\mu\nu}^\phi$. We neglect other incoherent matter contributions such as dust and radiation because they can be added without altering the QFT considerations developed here.

A non-minimal coupling between the scalar field and gravity is assumed, without any classical potential for ϕ. The part of the action associated to ϕ is

$$S[\phi] = -\int d^4x\sqrt{-g}\left(\frac{1}{2}g^{\mu\nu}\partial_\nu\phi\partial_\mu\phi + \frac{1}{2}(m^2 + \xi R)\phi^2\right), \tag{3}$$

where ξ is the non-minimal coupling between ϕ and gravity. In the special case $\xi = 1/6$, the massless ($m = 0$) action has conformal symmetry, i.e. symmetric under simultaneous rescalings of the $g_{\mu\nu}$ and ϕ with a local function $\alpha(x)$: $g_{\mu\nu} \to e^{2\alpha(x)}g_{\mu\nu}$ and $\phi \to e^{-\alpha(x)}\phi$. However, we will keep ξ general as it enables a richer phenomenology.

---

[a]Some useful geometrical quantities can be seen in the Appendix.

The Klein-Gordon (KG) equation is satisfied by the field ϕ,
$$(\Box - m^2 - \xi R)\phi = 0. \tag{4}$$
Here $\Box\phi = g^{\mu\nu}\nabla_\mu\nabla_\nu\phi = (-g)^{-1/2}\partial_\mu\left(\sqrt{-g}\,g^{\mu\nu}\partial_\nu\phi\right)$. On the other hand, the EMT takes this form :
$$T_{\mu\nu}(\phi) = -\frac{2}{\sqrt{-g}}\frac{\delta S_\phi}{\delta g^{\mu\nu}} = (1-2\xi)\partial_\mu\phi\partial_\nu\phi + \left(2\xi - \frac{1}{2}\right)g_{\mu\nu}\partial^\sigma\phi\partial_\sigma\phi$$
$$- 2\xi\phi\nabla_\mu\nabla_\nu\phi + 2\xi g_{\mu\nu}\phi\Box\phi + \xi G_{\mu\nu}\phi^2 - \frac{1}{2}m^2 g_{\mu\nu}\phi^2. \tag{5}$$

In this work we consider a spatially flat FLRW metric in the conformal frame. Being η the conformal time we have $ds^2 = a^2(\eta)\eta_{\mu\nu}dx^\mu dx^\nu$, with $\eta_{\mu\nu} = \mathrm{diag}(-1,+1,+1,+1)$ the Minkowski metric. Differentiation with respect the conformal time is denoted by $()' \equiv d()/d\eta$. It is convinient to define $\mathcal{H}(\eta) \equiv a'/a$ and, since $dt = ad\eta$, it is related with the usual Hubble rate $H(t) = \dot{a}/a$ as $\mathcal{H}(\eta) = aH(t)$. Despite the fact we will do intermediate calculations in conformal time, at the end it will be useful to express the VED in terms of the usual Hubble rate $H(t)$, because it is the easiest way to compare with other RVM results in the literature.

3. Quantum fluctuations and WKB ansatz

Now, we can take into account the quantum fluctuations of the field ϕ as an expansion around the background field (or classical mean field), ϕ_b:
$$\phi(\eta, x) = \phi_b(\eta) + \delta\phi(\eta, x). \tag{6}$$
The vacuum expectation value (VEV) of the field is $\langle 0|\phi(\eta,x)|0\rangle = \phi_b(\eta)$, whereas we assume that the VEV of the fluctuations vanishes: $\langle 0|\delta\phi|0\rangle = 0$. The vacuum state to which we are referring to is the so-called adiabatic vacuum, we will make some comments about this below.

The corresponding EMT decomposes itself as $\langle T_{\mu\nu}^\phi \rangle = \langle T_{\mu\nu}^{\phi_b}\rangle + \langle T_{\mu\nu}^{\delta\phi}\rangle$, where $\langle T_{\mu\nu}^{\phi_b}\rangle = T_{\mu\nu}^{\phi_b}$ is the contribution from the background part and $\langle T_{\mu\nu}^{\delta\phi}\rangle$ is related with the quantum fluctuations. In particular, the $\langle T_{00}^{\delta\phi}\rangle$ is associated to the ZPE density of the scalar field in the FLRW background. Thus, the total vacuum contribution to the EMT reads
$$\langle T_{\mu\nu}^{\mathrm{vac}}\rangle = T_{\mu\nu}^\Lambda + \langle T_{\mu\nu}^{\delta\phi}\rangle = -\rho_\Lambda g_{\mu\nu} + \langle T_{\mu\nu}^{\delta\phi}\rangle. \tag{7}$$
This means that the total vacuum EMT receives contributions from the cosmological constant term and from the quantum fluctuations. A renormalized version of this equation will lead us to a renormalized VED, as we will see later.

The KG equation (4) is satisfied independently by the classical field and the quantum part (6). Let us concentrate on the fluctuation $\delta\phi$. Its Fourier decomposition in frequency modes $h_k(\eta)$ is
$$\delta\phi(\eta,\mathbf{x}) = \frac{1}{(2\pi)^{3/2}a}\int d^3k\left[A_\mathbf{k}e^{i\mathbf{k}\cdot\mathbf{x}}h_k(\eta) + A_\mathbf{k}^\dagger e^{-i\mathbf{k}\cdot\mathbf{x}}h_k^*(\eta)\right]. \tag{8}$$

$A_{\mathbf{k}}$ and $A_{\mathbf{k}}^\dagger$ are the (time-independent) annihilation and creation operators, with commutation relations

$$[A_{\mathbf{k}}, A_{\mathbf{k'}}{}^\dagger] = \delta(\mathbf{k} - \mathbf{k'}), \qquad [A_{\mathbf{k}}, A_{\mathbf{k'}}] = 0. \tag{9}$$

Introducing the Fourier expansion (8) in $\left(\Box - m^2 - \xi R\right)\delta\phi = 0$ we find that the frequency modes of the fluctuations satisfy

$$h_k'' + \Omega_k^2 h_k = 0, \qquad \Omega_k^2(\eta) \equiv \omega_k^2(m) + a^2\left(\xi - 1/6\right)R, \tag{10}$$

with $\omega_k^2(m) \equiv k^2 + a^2 m^2$. As we can see, h_k depends uniquely on the modulus $k \equiv |\mathbf{k}|$ of the momentum. Since $\Omega_k(\eta)$ is a nontrivial function of the conformal time, there is no closed form of the solution of (10). Instead of looking to an analytical solution, we will generate an approximate solution from a recursive method based on the phase integral ansatz

$$h_k(\eta) \sim \frac{1}{\sqrt{W_k(\eta)}} \exp\left(i\int^\eta W_k(\tilde{\eta})d\tilde{\eta}\right). \tag{11}$$

Therefore, the function $W_k(\eta)$ satisfies the following differential equation:

$$W_k^2 = \Omega_k^2 - \frac{1}{2}\frac{W_k''}{W_k} + \frac{3}{4}\left(\frac{W_k'}{W_k}\right)^2. \tag{12}$$

This non-linear differential equation can be solved using the WKB approximation. The solution is valid for large k (i.e. for short wave lengths) and the function Ω_k is slowly varying for weak fields. The notion of vacuum we work with it is called the adiabatic vacuum,[50–52] and can be defined as the quantum state annihilated by all the operators A_k of the Fourier expansion of the scalar field, see[46–49] for details. The physical interpretation of the modes (10) with frequencies dependending on time, must be understood in terms of field observables rather than in particle language. Therefore, for a more physical interpretation of the vacuum effects of the expanding background, we must compute the renormalized EMT in the FLRW spacetime, but first we need to regularize it.

4. Adiabatic regularization of the EMT

The adiabatic (slowly varying) Ω_k, is susceptible to be computed using Eq. (12) to generate an (asymptotic) series solution. In this context, the series is obtained through the adiabatic regularization procedure (ARP)[b] and it is organized in what we call adiabatic orders. First, the quantites considered of adiabatic order 0 are: k^2 and a. Of adiabatic order 1 are: a' and $\mathcal{H}$. Then $a'', a'^2, \mathcal{H}'$ and $\mathcal{H}^2$ are quantities

---

[b]This method was introduced for minimally coupled massive scalar fields in.[51,52] In,[50] it is generalized for other couplings. A review can be found in the classic books.[46,47] The ARP has been used in the context of QFT in curved backgrounds[35,36] and also it has been extended to other fields, such as the spin one-half fields in.[53,54]

of adiabatic order 2. We can sum up by saying that each extra derivative in conformal time increases the adiabatic order one unit. As a consequence, the "effective frequency" W_k can be written as an asymptotic expansion:

$$W_k = \omega_k^{(0)} + \omega_k^{(2)} + \omega_k^{(4)} + \ldots, \qquad (13)$$

where each $\omega_k^{(j)}$ is an adiabatic correction of order j. This leads to an expansion of the mode function h_k in even order adiabatic terms. This is justified by arguments of general covariance, since only terms of even adiabatic order (an even number of time derivatives) are allowed in the field equations.

4.1. Introducing the renormalization parameter

We start by defining the 0th order terms

$$\omega_k^{(0)} \equiv \omega_k = \sqrt{k^2 + a^2 M^2}. \qquad (14)$$

In this approach the WKB expansion is performed off-shell, at an arbitrary mass scale M replacing the scalar field mass m in (14). In consequence, ARP can be formulated in such a way that we can relate the adiabatically renormalized theory at two different scales.[36] If $M = m$ we obtain the renormalized theory on-shell. In the computation of the EMT, the parameter $\Delta^2 \equiv m^2 - M^2$ will appear in the correction terms and it has to be considered of adiabatic order 2 since it appears in the WKB expansion together with other terms of the same adiabatic order.[36] If $\Delta = 0$, then $M = m$ and corresponds to the usual on-shell ARP, see.[46,47] With the help of this formalism one can explore the evolution of the VED throughout the cosmological history as it has been done for the first time in.[26] As we shall see, it will be convenient to consider m to be of the order of magnitude as the masses of Grand Unified Theory (GUT) fields in order to explore the dynamics of the VED in the low energy domain $M^2 \ll m^2$ (corresponding to the late universe). For simplicity, we model here all particles in terms of real scalar fields as in.[26] For a generalization to fermion fields, see.[55]

4.2. Regularized ZPE

Our starting point is the initial solution $W_k \approx \omega_k^{(0)}$ indicated in Eq. (14). For $a = 1$, it corresponds to the standard Minkowski space modes. Since $a = a(\eta)$ we have to find a better approximation. We use the initial solution $\omega_k^{(0)}$ in (12) and expand the RHS in powers of ω_k^{-1}, then collect the new terms up to adiabatic order 2 to find $\omega_k^{(2)}$. Now, we repeat the process with $W_k \approx \omega_k^{(0)} + \omega_k^{(2)}$ on the RHS of the same equation, expand again in ω_k^{-1}, collect contributions of adiabatic order 4... After some steps, the expansion seems to be organized in powers of $\omega_k^{-1} \sim 1/k$ (i.e. a short wavelength expansion). The UV divergent terms of the ARP are precisely the first lowest powers of ω_k^{-1}, which are present in the first adiabatic orders of the expansion. Higher adiabatic orders come later in the iteration, and represent finite contributions[50–52] since they decay quickly at large k and the associated integrals are manifestly convergent. In our case, the divergent terms of the EMT are present up to $4th$ adiabatic order so that, at least, we have to compute all the terms up to this order (more detail below in Eq. (16)). After renormalization, we will obtain a finite expression for the EMT and then compute the vacuum energy density. But first, we need to consider the EMT associated to the fluctuations, using Eq. (5) and (6). For the 00-component,

$$\langle T_{00}^{\delta\phi}\rangle = \left\langle \frac{1}{2}(\delta\phi')^2 + \left(\frac{1}{2} - 2\xi\right)\sum_i \partial_i\delta\phi\partial_i\delta\phi \right. $$

$$\left. + 6\xi\mathcal{H}\delta\phi\delta\phi' - 2\xi\delta\phi\nabla^2\delta\phi + 3\xi\mathcal{H}^2\delta\phi^2 + \frac{a^2 m^2}{2}(\delta\phi)^2 \right\rangle, \quad (15)$$

where $\nabla^2 \equiv \sum_{i=1}^{3}\partial_i^2$ and $(\delta\phi')^2 \equiv (\delta\partial_0\phi)^2 = (\partial_0\delta\phi)^2$. We may now substitute the Fourier expansion of $\delta\phi$, as given in (8), into Eq. (15) and apply the commutation relations (9). After symmetrizing the operator field product $\delta\phi\delta\phi'$ with respect to the annihilation and creation operators, we end up with

$$\langle T_{00}^{\delta\phi}\rangle = \frac{1}{8\pi^2 a^2}\int dk k^2 \left[2\omega_k + \frac{a^4 M^4 \mathcal{H}^2}{4\omega_k^5} - \frac{a^4 M^4}{16\omega_k^7}(2\mathcal{H}''\mathcal{H} - \mathcal{H}'^2 + 8\mathcal{H}'\mathcal{H}^2 + 4\mathcal{H}^4)\right.$$

$$+ \frac{7a^6 M^6}{8\omega_k^9}(\mathcal{H}'\mathcal{H}^2 + 2\mathcal{H}^4) - \frac{105 a^8 M^8 \mathcal{H}^4}{64\omega_k^{11}}$$

$$+ \bar\xi\left(-\frac{6\mathcal{H}^2}{\omega_k} - \frac{6a^2 M^2 \mathcal{H}^2}{\omega_k^3} + \frac{a^2 M^2}{2\omega_k^5}(6\mathcal{H}''\mathcal{H} - 3\mathcal{H}'^2 + 12\mathcal{H}'\mathcal{H}^2)\right.$$

$$\left. - \frac{a^4 M^4}{8\omega_k^7}(120\mathcal{H}'\mathcal{H}^2 + 210\mathcal{H}^4) + \frac{105 a^6 M^6 \mathcal{H}^4}{4\omega_k^9}\right)$$

$$\left. + \bar\xi^2\left(-\frac{1}{4\omega_k^3}(72\mathcal{H}''\mathcal{H} - 36\mathcal{H}'^2 - 108\mathcal{H}^4) + \frac{54 a^2 M^2}{\omega_k^5}(\mathcal{H}'\mathcal{H}^2 + \mathcal{H}^4)\right)\right]$$

$$+ \frac{1}{8\pi^2 a^2}\int dk k^2 \left[\frac{a^2 \Delta^2}{\omega_k} - \frac{a^4 \Delta^4}{4\omega_k^3} + \frac{a^4 \mathcal{H}^2 M^2 \Delta^2}{2\omega_k^5} - \frac{5}{8}\frac{a^6 \mathcal{H}^2 M^4 \Delta^2}{\omega_k^7}\right.$$

$$\left. + \bar\xi\left(-\frac{3a^2\Delta^2\mathcal{H}^2}{\omega_k^3} + \frac{9a^4 M^2 \Delta^2 \mathcal{H}^2}{\omega_k^5}\right)\right] + \ldots, \quad (16)$$

where we have defined $\bar\xi \equiv \xi - 1/6$ and we have integrated $\int \frac{d^3 k}{(2\pi)^3}(\ldots)$ over solid angles and expressed the final integration in terms of $k = |\mathbf{k}|$. Let us note the presence of the Δ-dependent terms in the last two rows, which contribute at $2th$ (Δ^2) and $4th$ (Δ^4) adiabatic order.

5. Renormalization of the ZPE in curved spacetime

The ZPE part of the EMT, as given by Eq. (16) can be split into two parts as follows:

$$\langle T_{00}^{\delta\phi}\rangle(M) = \langle T_{00}^{\delta\phi}\rangle_{Div}(M) + \langle T_{00}^{\delta\phi}\rangle_{Non-Div}(M), \quad (17)$$

where

$$\langle T_{00}^{\delta\phi}\rangle_{Div}(M) = \frac{1}{8\pi^2 a^2}\int dk k^2 \left[2\omega_k + \frac{a^2\Delta^2}{\omega_k} - \frac{a^4\Delta^4}{4\omega_k^3}\right.$$
$$\left. - 6\bar{\xi}\mathcal{H}^2\left(\frac{1}{\omega_k} + \frac{a^2 M^2}{\omega_k^3} + \frac{a^2\Delta^2}{2\omega_k^3}\right) - 9\frac{\bar{\xi}^2}{\omega_k^3}(2\mathcal{H}''\mathcal{H} - \mathcal{H}'^2 - 3\mathcal{H}^4)\right], \quad (18)$$

which containts the powers $1/\omega_k^n$ up to $n = 3$, manifestly UV-divergent.

On the other hand, the non-divergent part of (17) involves the integrals with powers of $1/\omega_k$ higher than 3 which are perfectly finite. Computing these convergent integrals (see Eq. (45) in Appendix), the result reads

$$\langle T_{00}^{\delta\phi}\rangle_{Non-Div}(M) = \frac{m^2 \mathcal{H}^2}{96\pi^2} - \frac{1}{960\pi^2 a^2}(2\mathcal{H}''\mathcal{H} - \mathcal{H}'^2 - 2\mathcal{H}^4) + \bar{\xi}\frac{3\Delta^2 \mathcal{H}^2}{8\pi^2}$$
$$+ \frac{1}{16\pi^2 a^2}\bar{\xi}(2\mathcal{H}''\mathcal{H} - \mathcal{H}'^2 - 3\mathcal{H}^4) + \frac{9}{4\pi^2 a^2}\bar{\xi}^2(\mathcal{H}'\mathcal{H}^2 + \mathcal{H}^4) + \ldots \quad (19)$$

where the dots in the last expression correspond to higher adiabatic orders. Let us now focus on the divergent part of the ZPE, Eq. (18). The adiabatic series is an asymptotic series representation of Eq. (15). Thefore, such series is not convergent but it provides an approximation, which is obtained once the series is cut at a particular order.[36] As a consequence there is some arbitrariness in the way of choosing the leading adiabatic order, which we can use in our favour. There is, nonetheless, some previous steps to do before obtaining a meaningful result. First, we are going to set the arbitrary scale at the mass of the scalar field. That is, $M = m$ and hence $\Delta = 0$ (cf. Sec. 4.1). The divergent part (18) is reduced in this case to

$$\langle T_{00}^{\delta\phi}\rangle_{Div}(m) = \frac{1}{8\pi^2 a^2}\int dk k^2 \left[2\omega_k(m) - \bar{\xi}6\mathcal{H}^2\left(\frac{1}{\omega_k(m)} + \frac{a^2 m^2}{\omega_k^3(m)}\right)\right.$$
$$\left. - \bar{\xi}^2 \frac{9}{\omega_k^3(m)}(2\mathcal{H}''\mathcal{H} - \mathcal{H}'^2 - 3\mathcal{H}^4)\right]. \quad (20)$$

What we are going to do next, in order to renormalize the ZPE and the EMT, is to subtract the terms that appear up to 4th adiabatic order at the arbitrary mass scale M. This procedure is enough to cancel the divergent terms through the ARP, as it is discussed in the literature.[46–48]

5.1. Renormalized ZPE for generic M

As said before, our proposal for the renormalized ZPE in curved spacetime at the scale M is[26]:

$$\langle T_{00}^{\delta\phi}\rangle_{\text{Ren}}(M) = \langle T_{00}^{\delta\phi}\rangle(m) - \langle T_{00}^{\delta\phi}\rangle^{(0-4)}(M)$$
$$= \langle T_{00}^{\delta\phi}\rangle_{Div}(m) - \langle T_{00}^{\delta\phi}\rangle_{Div}(M) - \bar{\xi}\frac{3\Delta^2 \mathcal{H}^2}{8\pi^2} + \ldots, \quad (21)$$

here $(0-4)$ means that the expansion is up to fourth adiabatic order and the dots in (21) denote perfectly finite terms of higher adiabatic order. Using now Eq. (20), we arrive to

$$\langle T_{00}^{\delta\phi}\rangle_{\text{Ren}}(M) = \frac{1}{8\pi^2 a^2}\int dk\, k^2 \left[2\omega_k(m) - \frac{a^2\Delta^2}{\omega_k(M)} + \frac{a^4\Delta^4}{4\omega_k^3(M)} - 2\omega_k(M)\right]$$

$$+ \bar{\xi}\frac{6\mathcal{H}^2}{8\pi^2 a^2}\left\{\int dk\, k^2 \left[\frac{1}{\omega_k(M)} + \frac{a^2 M^2}{\omega_k^3(M)} + \frac{a^2\Delta^2}{2\omega_k^3(M)} - \frac{1}{\omega_k(m)} - \frac{a^2 m^2}{\omega_k^3(m)}\right] - \frac{a^2\Delta^2}{2}\right\}$$

$$- \bar{\xi}^2\frac{9\left(2\mathcal{H}''\mathcal{H} - \mathcal{H}'^2 - 3\mathcal{H}^4\right)}{8\pi^2 a^2}\int dk\, k^2 \left[\frac{1}{\omega_k^3(m)} - \frac{1}{\omega_k^3(M)}\right] + \ldots \qquad (22)$$

In this equation we have introduced new notation in order to distinguish between the off-shell energy mode $\omega_k(M) \equiv \sqrt{k^2 + a^2 M^2}$ (formerly denoted just as ω_k) and the on-shell one $\omega_k(m) \equiv \sqrt{k^2 + a^2 m^2}$. The involved computations of these convergent integrals are not so straightforward but, after some algebra and the help of Mathematica,[56] we find

$$\langle T_{00}^{\delta\phi}\rangle_{\text{Ren}}(M) = \frac{a^2}{128\pi^2}\left(-M^4 + 4m^2 M^2 - 3m^4 + 2m^4 \ln\frac{m^2}{M^2}\right)$$

$$- \bar{\xi}\frac{3\mathcal{H}^2}{16\pi^2}\left(m^2 - M^2 - m^2\ln\frac{m^2}{M^2}\right) + \bar{\xi}^2\frac{9\left(2\mathcal{H}''\mathcal{H} - \mathcal{H}'^2 - 3\mathcal{H}^4\right)}{16\pi^2 a^2}\ln\frac{m^2}{M^2} + \ldots \qquad (23)$$

The obtained expression vanishes for $M = m$ as expected from Eq. (21). However, let us remind the reader that this only happens because we have computed the on-shell value $\langle T_{\mu\nu}^{\delta\phi}\rangle_{\text{Ren}}(m)$ up to adiabatic order 4 in Eq. (23). Nevertheless, $\langle T_{\mu\nu}^{\delta\phi}\rangle_{\text{Ren}}(m)$ can be computed up to an arbitrary, but finite, adiabatic order. Beyond 4*th* order one always obtains subleading and perfectly finite corrections. We expect that these effects become suppressed when the physical mass m of the quantum field is large, so that they satisfy the Appelquist-Carazzone decoupling theorem.[57]

So far, we have obtained a renormalized ZPE in curved spacetime (23) which, despite the fact it is finite, it includes the quartic powers of the masses corresponding to undesired contributions to the vacuum energy.

6. Renormalized vacuum energy density

The renormalization in the context of QFT in curved spacetime implies the consideration of the higher derivative (HD) terms in the classical effective action,[46] beyond the usual Einstein-Hilbert (EH) term with a cosmological constant, Λ. In particular, in the FLRW background in four dimensions, the only surviving HD term is $H_{\mu\nu}^{(1)}$, as suggested by the geometric structure of (23). $H_{\mu\nu}^{(1)}$ is obtained by functionally differentiating R^2 with respect the metric (see Appendix). So, the full action contains the EH+HD terms and also the matter part which, in our simplified case, only consists of a scalar field ϕ non-minimally coupled to gravity, Eq. (3).

As usual, the modified Einstein's equations are obtained through the variation of the new action with respect to $g_{\mu\nu}$, extending (2) as follows:

$$\frac{1}{8\pi G_N(M)} G_{\mu\nu} + \rho_\Lambda(M) g_{\mu\nu} + a_1(M) H^{(1)}_{\mu\nu} = T^{\phi_b}_{\mu\nu} + \langle T^{\delta\phi}_{\mu\nu} \rangle_{\text{Ren}}(M), \quad (24)$$

where the dependence in M indicates we are considering renormalized quantities. In particular, the classical part of the matter EMT does not depend on it. Our goal is to relate the theory at different renormalization points[c], and with this purpose in mind let us subtract Einstein's equations as written in (24) at two different scales, M and M_0. We find

$$\langle T^{\delta\phi}_{\mu\nu} \rangle_{\text{Ren}}(M) - \langle T^{\delta\phi}_{\mu\nu} \rangle_{\text{Ren}}(M_0) = f_{G_N^{-1}} G_{\mu\nu} + f_{\rho_\Lambda} g_{\mu\nu} + f_{a_1} H^{(1)}_{\mu\nu}, \quad (25)$$

here $f_X(m, M, M_0) \equiv X(M) - X(M_0)$ for the various couplings involved $X = G_N^{-1}, \rho_\Lambda, a_1$. Since we know the expression of the renormalized EMT within the ARP, namely Eq (23), we can obtain the renormalization shift of the couplings G_N^{-1}, ρ_Λ and a_1 in (25) between the two scales M and M_0. This is possible by taking the value of the components G_{00} and $H^{(1)}_{00}$ (from Appendix) and comparing with (23). Notice that the first term of (23), in the r.h.s, is of 0th adiabatic order and is associated to $f_{\rho_\Lambda}(m, M, M_0)$ and, therefore, to the running of ρ_Λ. By doing this comparision we find that the functions are

$$f_{G_N^{-1}}(m, M, M_0) = \frac{\overline{\xi}}{16\pi^2} \left[M^2 - M_0^2 - m^2 \ln \frac{M^2}{M_0^2} \right],$$

$$f_{\rho_\Lambda}(m, M, M_0) = \frac{1}{128\pi^2} \left(M^4 - M_0^4 - 4m^2(M^2 - M_0^2) + 2m^4 \ln \frac{M^2}{M_0^2} \right), \quad (26)$$

$$f_{a_1}(M, M_0) = -\frac{\overline{\xi}^2}{32\pi^2} \ln \frac{M^2}{M_0^2}.$$

6.1. *Running Vacuum Energy Density. Absence of $\sim m^4$ terms*

At this point we can come back to the definition of vacuum energy (7) which was used in this work. Considering $\langle T^{\text{vac}}_{\mu\nu} \rangle = p_{\text{vac}} g_{\mu\nu} + (p_{\text{vac}} + \rho_{\text{vac}}) u_\mu u_\nu$, with $u_\mu = (a, 0, 0, 0)$, and equating with Eq. (7), and taking the 00-component of the equality (keeping also in mind that $g_{00} = -a^2(\eta)$ in the conformal frame), we obtain

$$\rho_{\text{vac}}(M) = \rho_\Lambda(M) + \frac{\langle T^{\delta\phi}_{00} \rangle_{\text{Ren}}(M)}{a^2}. \quad (27)$$

We write the explicit dependence in the renormalization point M since we are talking about the renormalized quantity at that scale. Equation (27) means that

---

[c]We do not pretend to compute the renormalized couplings from first principles, in particular the VED. Renormalization program allows us to compare the theory at different renormalization points but, at the end, an input from the experiment is needed to predict its value at another scale.

the total VED at an arbitrary scale M is not only receiving contributions from the renormalized cosmological term but also from the quantum fluctuations of fields (i.e. from the renormalized ZPE of the scalar field, in our simplified model). Subtracting the renormalized result at two scales, M and M_0, and using (25), we find:

$$\rho_{\text{vac}}(M) - \rho_{\text{vac}}(M_0) = \rho_\Lambda(M) - \rho_\Lambda(M_0) + \frac{\langle T_{00}^{\delta\phi} \rangle_{\text{Ren}}(M) - \langle T_{00}^{\delta\phi} \rangle_{\text{Ren}}(M_0)}{a^2}$$

$$= f_{\rho_\Lambda}(m, M, M_0) + \frac{f_{G_N^{-1}}(m, M, M_0) G_{00} + f_{\rho_\Lambda}(m, M, M_0) g_{00} + f_{a_1}(M, M_0) H_{00}^{(1)}}{a^2}$$

$$= \frac{f_{G_N^{-1}}(m, M, M_0)}{a^2} G_{00} + \frac{f_{a_1}(M, M_0)}{a^2} H_{00}^{(1)}$$

$$= \frac{3\mathcal{H}^2}{a^2} f_{G_N^{-1}}(m, M, M_0) - \frac{18}{a^4} \left(\mathcal{H}'^2 - 2\mathcal{H}''\mathcal{H} + 3\mathcal{H}^4 \right) f_{a_1}(M, M_0). \quad (28)$$

As we see the term $f_{\rho_\Lambda}(m, M, M_0)$ has disappeared. Finally, from (26) we obtain[26]

$$\rho_{\text{vac}}(M) = \rho_{\text{vac}}(M_0) + \frac{3}{16\pi^2} \bar{\xi} H^2 \left[M^2 - M_0^2 - m^2 \ln \frac{M^2}{M_0^2} \right]$$

$$+ \frac{9}{16\pi^2} \bar{\xi}^2 \left(\dot{H}^2 - 2H\ddot{H} - 6H^2\dot{H} \right) \ln \frac{M^2}{M_0^2}. \quad (29)$$

In addition, we have used Eq. (44) from Appendix to write the final result in terms of the Hubble function in cosmic time ($H = \mathcal{H}/a$). The result (29) is the value of the VED at a particular energy scale M, related with the value of the VED at another renormalization scale M_0, i.e. it expresses the 'running' of the VED. Notice that if $\xi = 1/6$ ($\bar{\xi} = 0$), then the VED is independent of the renormalization scale. However, this is not likely to happen since one also has to consider the contribution from fermions and vector boson fields. It is also important to notice that the running is slow for small H, as it depends as $\mathcal{O}(H^2)$ times a mass scale squared and on $\mathcal{O}(H^4)$ contributions. Finally, we remark that there is no contributions of quartic mass scales.

7. Running vacuum connection

As explained in a footnote in previous sections, the result we were seeking (represented now by Eq. (29)) was not the calculated value of the VED at a given scale, e.g. it says nothing on the actual value of $\rho_{\text{vac}}(M_0)$ and hence it has nothing to do with the cosmological constant problem mentioned in the Introduction. In other words, we have not provided the calculation of the value itself of the vacuum energy at particular point of the cosmic history. This result can nevertheless be useful to study the 'running' of the VED from one scale to another. We can rephrase this by saying that if ρ_{vac} is known at some scale M_0, Eq. (29) can be used to obtain the value of ρ_{vac} at another scale M. Such connection was suggested long ago from renormalization group arguments in curved spacetime[27–29] – see[30,31] and references therein for a review of the running vacuum model (RVM). What is more, it can even set a framework for the possible variation of the so-called fundamental constants of nature[58] with the evolution of the universe. In the next subsection we are going to suggest a possible interpretation of Eq. (29) in the context of the RVM. For this purpose, let us assume that we set one arbitrary scale to the renormalized VED at some Grand Unified Theory (GUT) scale (i.e., set $M_0 = M_X$, where $M_X \sim 10^{16}$ GeV). This value is associated also with the inflationary scale. It is natural to assume that fundamental parameters, such as e.g. $\rho_{\rm vac}$, are defined at that primeval scale, related with the very beginning in the cosmological history. Additionally, a large scale such as the GUT scale insures that all particle masses can be active degrees of freedom to some extent.

7.1. RVM in the currect universe

Equation (29) can, in principle, be used to explore the value of the VED throughout the cosmological history. However, for the study of the very early universe (in particular, inflation) other contributions can appear, which will not be addressed here since in the present work we are just going to study the current universe dynamics in order to compare with the late time RVM phenomenology. For related studies in different contexts, cf.[59–62]. See also[42–45] for a stringy version of the RVM with implications on the mechanism of inflation.

Consider $\rho_{\rm vac}(M_X)$, the value of the VED at $M_0 = M_X$. The value of this energy density is unknown, but our aim is to relate it with the current value of the VED, $\rho_{\rm vac}^0 \equiv \rho_{\rm vac}(H_0)$, by fixing the numerical value of the second scale at $M = H_0$, where H_0 today's value of the Hubble function– it can be considered an estimation for the energy scale associated to the the present FLRW universe. This association is commonly made in the aforementioned references on the RVM.[30] So, (29) applied to the present universe is

$$\rho_{\rm vac}^0 \approx \rho_{\rm vac}(M_X) - \frac{3}{16\pi^2}\bar{\xi}H_0^2\left[M_X^2 + m^2 \ln\frac{H_0^2}{M_X^2}\right]. \qquad (30)$$

Here we ignore all terms of order $\mathcal{O}(H^4)$ (including $\dot{H}^2, H\ddot{H}$ and $H^2\dot{H}$) for the present universe ($H = H_0$). We can use this relation to find the value of $\rho_{\rm vac}(M_X)$, and the result is

$$\rho_{\rm vac}(M_X) = \rho_{\rm vac}^0 - \frac{3\nu_{\rm eff}}{8\pi}H_0^2 M_P^2, \qquad (31)$$

where we have defined $\nu_{\rm eff}$, the 'running parameter' for the VED:

$$\nu_{\rm eff} = -\frac{\bar{\xi}}{2\pi}\frac{M_X^2}{M_P^2}\left(1 + \frac{m^2}{M_X^2}\ln\frac{H_0^2}{M_X^2}\right). \qquad (32)$$

Notice that for $\xi = 1/6$ (or $\bar{\xi} = 0$), it vanishes and there is no running, as mentioned previously. In the case $\xi = 0$ (or $\bar{\xi} = -1/6$) and $m^2/M_X^2 \ll 1$ we obtain $\nu_{\rm eff} \simeq \frac{1}{12\pi}\frac{M_X^2}{M_P^2} \ll 1$. More in general, the structure obtained for $\nu_{\rm eff}$ is very similar to that one obtained previously in other works with the RVM approach, see.[30]

In these contexts, the parameter is related with the one-loop β-function for the renormalization group equation of $\rho_{\rm vac}$. Although, in our case, there is and additional logarithmic contribution $\ln H_0^2/M_X^2$, coming from the direct QFT calculation developed here. At the end of the day it does not make significant differences in practice since $\nu_{\rm eff}$ is a constant parameter which is fitted directly to cosmological data as an effective coefficient. It is natural to expect a small $\nu_{\rm eff}$, i.e. $|\nu_{\rm eff}| \ll 1$, because of the ratio $M_X^2/M_P^2 \sim 10^{-6}$, but notice that $\nu_{\rm eff}$ depends on ξ and also on contributions from other fields (fermions and bosons) and their multiplicities. Heavy fields of the order of the GUT scale can contribute in a significant way $(m \sim M_X)$. As mentioned, $\nu_{\rm eff}$ needs to be fitted the RVM to tbe cosmological data, and this has been done in detail e.g. in,[15,16] the results indicate that $\nu_{\rm eff} \sim 10^{-3}$.

Now, we can us Eq. (29) and (31) to study the late universe. By ignoring $\mathcal{O}(H^4)$, we may estimate the current VED by taking $M = H$ around the present times:

$$\rho_{\rm vac}(H) = \rho_{\rm vac}^0 - \frac{3\nu_{\rm eff}}{8\pi} H_0^2 M_P^2 + \frac{3\nu_{\rm eff}(H)}{8\pi} H^2 M_P^2, \qquad (33)$$

where

$$\nu_{\rm eff}(H) = -\frac{\bar{\xi}}{2\pi} \frac{M_X^2}{M_P^2} \left(1 + \frac{m^2}{M_X^2} \ln \frac{H^2}{M_X^2}\right). \qquad (34)$$

Notice that the last expression is not constant as a difference from (32). However, since the dynamical behaviour of $\nu_{\rm eff}(H)$ is logarithmic, and considering a value of H close to H_0, we can approximate $\nu_{\rm eff}(H)$ by (32). Then, equation (33) may be written as[55]

$$\rho_{\rm vac}(H) \simeq \rho_{\rm vac}^0 + \frac{3\nu_{\rm eff}}{8\pi} (H^2 - H_0^2) M_P^2 = \rho_{\rm vac}^0 + \frac{3\nu_{\rm eff}}{8\pi G_N} (H^2 - H_0^2). \qquad (35)$$

This is exactly the canonical form of the RVM formula.[30] Such approximation holds fine even if we study the CMB epoch, since the difference between $\nu_{\rm eff}(H)$ from $\nu_{\rm eff}$ can be estimated to be less than 8% (for $m \simeq M_X$) or much less when $m \ll M_X$. This is the typical parametrization that has been used in the literature about the RVM.[15,16] As a matter of fact, this parametrization can be promoted to a more general form, by considering also a term proportional to $\dot{H}$ in the running equation for the VED. In the following subsection we are going to give grounds for the appearance of these kind of factors, not yet present in (35).

7.2. *More geometric structures for vacuum in curved spacetime*

Using the definition of the EMT associated to vacuum given in (7) we have derived the expression of the vacuum energy density in equation (27). However, we expect that the definition (7) can be generalized as follows:

$$\langle T_{\mu\nu}^{\rm vac} \rangle = T_{\mu\nu}^{\Lambda} + \langle T_{\mu\nu}^{\delta\phi} \rangle + \alpha_1 R g_{\mu\nu} + \alpha_2 R_{\mu\nu} + \mathcal{O}(R^2). \qquad (36)$$

$\mathcal{O}(R^2)$ represents tensors of adiabatic order 4, that is R^2, $R_{\mu\nu}R^{\mu\nu}$,... and α_i are parameters of dimension +2 in natural units. This new form for the vacuum EMT can be justified from the phenomenological point of view, but we also remind the reader that in a more realistic picture, contributions from other fields (bosons and fermions) are also expected, and general covariance leads to a generic form as represented in (36). Generation of new terms is also possible by considering string-inspired mechanisms as it has been shown recently in.[40–43]

Let us work with the more general form for the vacuum EMT, (36). It is useful to redefine the coefficients of that expression as $\alpha_i(M) \equiv \frac{\lambda_i}{16\pi^2} M^2$. We can check in Appendix the expression of R and R_{00} in flat FLRW spacetime, we obtain after a straightforward calculation:

$$\rho_{\text{vac}}(H) \simeq \rho_{\text{vac}}^0 + \frac{3}{8\pi G_N}\left(\tilde{\nu}_{\text{eff}} H^2 + \bar{\nu}\dot{H}\right), \tag{37}$$

where

$$\tilde{\nu}_{\text{eff}} = \frac{1}{2\pi}\frac{M_X^2}{M_P^2}\left[\left(\frac{1}{6}-\xi\right)\left(1+\frac{m^2}{M_X^2}\ln\frac{H_0^2}{M_X^2}\right) + 4\lambda_1 + \lambda_2\right] \tag{38}$$

and

$$\bar{\nu} = \frac{2\lambda_1 + \lambda_2}{2\pi}\frac{M_X^2}{M_P^2}. \tag{39}$$

As done before, the logarithmic part of $\tilde{\nu}_{\text{eff}}(H)$ can be neglected and we may approximate $\tilde{\nu}_{\text{eff}}(H_0) \simeq \tilde{\nu}_{\text{eff}}$. The parameter $\bar{\nu}$ is treated as constant here, but we can not discard also a possible running of λ_i, acquiring a dependence in M. Although, if this were the case, it is reasonable to expect a logarithmic evolution of the renormalization effects. The above formula is a generalization of Eq. (35) incorporating the additional coefficient $\bar{\nu}$, accompanying $\sim \dot{H}$. Finally, let us comment that several generalized forms of the RVM beyond the usual one containing the H^2 term has been studied before in the literature, see for instance.[13,14]

8. Discussion and conclusions

In this presentation we have investigated the possible dynamics of vacuum in the context of QFT in FLRW spacetime. Specifically, we have revisited the calculation of the renormalized energy-momentum tensor (EMT) of a real quantum scalar field non-minimally coupled to the FLRW background.[26] The approach is based on adiabatic regularization and renormalization of the EMT, starting from the WKB approximation of the field modes in curved spacetime. The renormalized EMT is defined as the difference of its on-shell value and its value at an arbitrary renormalization point M up to 4th adiabatic order. It is sufficient with this subtraction since the divergent terms are present up to 4th adiabatic order. The renormalized EMT is perfectly finite and acquires a dependence on M. We can use this fact to compare the renormalized result at different times of the history of the universe characterized by different energy scales. At this point we can identify the VED from the renormalized EMT. Such VED depends on $\rho_\Lambda(M)$ but also in the ZPE part involving the quantum fluctuations of the scalar field. An interesting implication is that the combination of both quantities is free from terms $\sim m^4$, well-known sources of large contributions to the VED.

This QFT calculation leads us to a renormalized VED which has the usual form of the running vacuum models (RVM's),[30] in which $\rho_{\text{vac}} = \rho_{\text{vac}}(H)$ consists of an additive constant plus a series of powers of H (the Hubble rate) and its time derivatives. In previous works, the RVM was motivated from general renormalization group arguments in QFT in curved spacetime (cf.[30] and references therein). But, in this work, we have reviewed proof that the RVM form of the VED for the current universe emerges also from this calculation of QFT in the FLRW spacetime involving adiabatic regularization. It is found that the powers of H (and its time derivatives) in the EMT carry an even number of time derivatives of the scale factor, which is mandatory if we impose the general covariance of the action. In particular, the lowest order dynamical component of the VED is $\sim \nu H^2$. The dimensionless coefficient ν is expected to be small ($|\nu| \ll 1$). However, at the end, the model has to be fitted with the help of a complet set of cosmological data. This lower order term $\sim H^2$ has the main role in the study of the dynamics of the vacuum in the late universe, whereas the higher order terms may play a major role in the very early universe, for example to describe inflation (despite the fact that we have not exploited this idea in this work). In previous works, the RVM has been succesfully confronted to a large number of cosmological data and the effective parameter ν has been fitted. The encountered results say that ν is positive and around $\sim 10^{-3}$, see[13–16]. To conclude, let us remark that our QFT calculation has some limitations, for instance it has been simplified by the use of just one single field in the form of a real quantum scalar field. For this reason, further investigations have to be done in order to generalize these results for multiple fields involving scalar, fermionic and vectorial degrees of freedom. However, we do not expect major changes beyond computational details and the main results presented here are likely to be maintained.[55]

Acknowledgements

This work is based on the invited talk presented in the CM3 parallel session: "Status of the H_0 and σ_8 Tensions: Theoretical Models and Model-Independent Constraints" of the MG16 Marcel Grossmann virtual Conference, July 5-10 2021. We would like to thank the organizers of MG16 as well as the chairpersons of the session for the excellence of the event and for the invitation.

Work partially funded by projects PID2019-105614GB-C21 and FPA2016-76005-C2-1-P (MINECO, Spain), 2017-SGR-929 (Generalitat de Catalunya) and CEX2019-000918-M (ICCUB). CMP is also partially supported by the fellowship 2019 FI_B 00351 (Generalitat de Catalunya). JSP acknowledges participation in the COST Association Action CA18108 *"Quantum Gravity Phenomenology in the Multimessenger Approach (QG-MM)"*.

Appendix: Conventions, geometrical quantities and useful formulas

Through this work we have used natural units. This means that the gravitational constant is written as $G_N = 1/M_P$, being M_P is the Planck mass and $\hbar = c = 1$.

Conventions regarding the geometrical quantities can be summarized as follows: the metric has the signature $(-,+,+,+)$; the Riemann tensor is $R^\lambda{}_{\mu\nu\sigma} = \partial_\nu \Gamma^\lambda{}_{\mu\sigma} + \Gamma^\rho{}_{\mu\sigma}\Gamma^\lambda{}_{\rho\nu} - (\nu \leftrightarrow \sigma)$; the Ricci tensor is $R_{\mu\nu} = R^\lambda{}_{\mu\lambda\nu}$; and finally, Ricci scalar reads $R = g^{\mu\nu} R_{\mu\nu}$. These elections correspond to $(+,+,+)$ in the Misner-Thorne-Wheeler[63] conventions.

On the other hand, the Einstein tensor is defined as $G_{\mu\nu} = R_{\mu\nu} - \frac{1}{2} R g_{\mu\nu}$ and the field equations are $G_{\mu\nu} + \Lambda g_{\mu\nu} = 8\pi G_N T_{\mu\nu}$. The (non-vanishing) Christoffel symbols, with a line element in terms of the conformal time $ds^2 = a^2(\eta)\eta_{\mu\nu} dx^\mu dx^\nu$ and $\eta_{\mu\nu} = \text{diag}(-1,+1,+1,+1)$, are:

$$\Gamma^0_{00} = \mathcal{H}, \qquad \Gamma^0_{ij} = \mathcal{H}\delta_{ij}, \qquad \Gamma^i_{j0} = \mathcal{H}\delta^i_j. \tag{40}$$

The Ricci scalar and the 00-components of the curvature tensors are:

$$R = 6\frac{a''}{a^3} = \frac{6}{a^2}\left(\mathcal{H}' + \mathcal{H}^2\right) = 6\left(\frac{\dot{a}^2}{a^2} + \frac{\ddot{a}}{a}\right) = 6(2H^2 + \dot{H}) \tag{41}$$

and

$$R_{00} = -3\mathcal{H}' = -3a^2(H^2 + \dot{H}), \qquad G_{00} = 3\mathcal{H}^2 = 3a^2 H^2. \tag{42}$$

Primes are indicating differentiation with respect to conformal time, meanwhile we use dots to represent derivatives with respect cosmic time. The process of renormalization introduces the need for the higher order curvature tensor $H^{(1)}_{\mu\nu}$, obtained by the variation of R^2 with respect the metric in the higher derivative vacuum action:

$$H^{(1)}_{\mu\nu} = \frac{1}{\sqrt{-g}}\frac{\delta}{\delta g^{\mu\nu}}\int d^4x \sqrt{-g} R^2 = -2\nabla_\mu \nabla_\nu R + 2g_{\mu\nu}\Box R - \frac{1}{2}g_{\mu\nu}R^2 + 2RR_{\mu\nu}. \tag{43}$$

In particular, the 00-component is related with the vacuum energy density and in the conformally flat metric is

$$H^{(1)}_{00} = \frac{-18}{a^2}\left(\mathcal{H}'^2 - 2\mathcal{H}''\mathcal{H} + 3\mathcal{H}^4\right) = -18a^2\left(\dot{H}^2 - 2H\ddot{H} - 6H^2\dot{H}\right). \tag{44}$$

Computing integrals with powers of $1/\omega_k$

The following expression is useful to compute all the finite $(n > N)$ and UV-divergent $(n \leq N)$ integrals involved in the EMT computation:

$$I(n,Q) \equiv \int \frac{d^N k}{(2\pi)^N} \frac{1}{(k^2 + Q^2)^{n/2}} = \frac{1}{(4\pi)^{N/2}} \frac{\Gamma\left(\frac{n-N}{2}\right)}{\Gamma\left(\frac{n}{2}\right)} (Q^2)^{\frac{N-n}{2}}, \tag{45}$$

where $k \equiv |\mathbf{k}|$ and Q is an arbitrary scale. We have corrected typos in this formula as compared to that of Appendix B of,[26] with no consequences in the calculation.

References

1. P. J. E. Peebles, Astrophys. J. **284** 439 (1984); *Principles of Physical Cosmology* (Princeton Univ. Press, Princeton, 1993).
2. A. G. Riess *et al.*, Astron. J. **116** 1009 (1998); S. Perlmutter *et al.*, Astrophys. J. **517** 565 (1999).
3. N. Aghanim *et al.* [Planck Collab.], Astron. Astrophys. **641** A6 (2020); P.A.R. Ade *et al.* [Planck Collab.], Astron. Astrophys. **594** A13 (2016).
4. S. Weinberg, Rev. Mod. Phys. **61** 1 (1989).
5. E. Witten, *The Cosmological Constant From The Viewpoint Of String Theory*, Contribution to the 4*th* International Symposium on Sources and Detection of Dark Matter in the Universe (DM 2000), 27-36, hep-ph/0002297.
6. V. Sahni and A. Starobinsky, Int. J. Mod. Phys. D **9** 373 (2000).
7. P. J. E. Peebles and B. Ratra, Rev. Mod. Phys. **75** 559 (2003).
8. T. Padmanabhan, Phys. Rept. **380** 235 (2003).
9. E. J. Copeland, M. Sami and S. Tsujikawa, Int. J. Mod. Phys. D **15** 1753 (2006).
10. L. Amendola and S. Tsujikawa, *Dark Energy*, Cambridge U. Press (2010) & (2015), and references therein.
11. L. Verde, T. Treu and A. G. Riess, Nat. Astron. **3** 891 (2019), and references therein.
12. A. G. Riess, *et al.*, Astrophys. J. **876** 85 (2019).
13. J. Solà, A. Gómez-Valent and J. de Cruz Pérez, Astrophys. J. **811** L14 (2015); Astrophys. J. **836** 43 (2017).
14. S. Basilakos, D. Polarski and J. Solà, Phys. Rev. D **86** 043010 (2012); A. Gómez-Valent, J. Solà and S. Basilakos, JCAP **01** 004 (2015); A. Gómez-Valent and J. Solà, MNRAS **448** 2810 (2015); A. Gómez-Valent, E. Karimkhani and J. Solà, JCAP **1512** 048 (2015).
15. J. Solà, A. Gómez-Valent and J. de Cruz Pérez, Phys. Lett. B **774** 317 (2017).
16. J. Solà Peracaula, J. de Cruz Pérez and A. Gómez-Valent, EPL **121** 39001 (2018); MNRAS **478** 4357 (2018).
17. J. Solà Peracaula, A. Gómez-Valent, J. de Cruz Pérez and C. Moreno-Pulido, Astrophys. J. **886** L6 (2019).
18. M. Rezaei, M. Malekjani and J. Solà Peracaula, Phys. Rev. D **100** 023539 (2019).
19. E. D. Valentino, A. Melchiorri, Olga Mena and S. Vagnozzi, Phys. Rev. D **101** 063502 (2020).
20. E. D. Valentino, A. Melchiorri and O. Mena, Phys. Rev. D **96** 043503 (2017); E.D. Valentino, A. Melchiorri and J. Silk, Phys. Lett. B **761** 242 (2016).
21. J. Ooba, B. Ratra, and N. Sugiyama, Astrophys. Space Sci. **364** 176 (2019).
22. C.-G. Park and B. Ratra, Astrophys. J. **882** 158 (2019); Astrophys. Space Sci. **364** 82 (2019); Astrophys. J. **868** 83 (2018).
23. M. Martinelli, N. B. Hogg, S. Peirone, M. Bruni and D. Wands, MNRAS **488** 3423 (2019) ; V. Salvatelli, N. Said, M. Bruni, A. Melchiorri and D. Wands, Phys. Rev. Lett. **113** 181301 (2014).
24. A. A. Costa, X. D. Xu, B. Wang and E. Abdalla, JCAP **1701** 028 (2017).
25. Y. H. Li, J. F. Zhang and X. Zhang, Phys. Rev. D **93** 023002 (2016); Phys. Rev. D **90** 123007 (2014); Phys. Rev. D **90** 063005 (2014).
26. C. Moreno-Pulido and J. Solà Peracaula, Eur. Phys. J. C **80** 692 (2020).
27. I. L. Shapiro and J. Solà, JHEP **02** 006 (2002); Nucl. Phys. B Proc. Suppl. **127** 71 (2004).
28. J. Solà, J. Phys. A **41** 164066 (2008).
29. I. L. Shapiro and J. Solà, Phys. Lett. B **682** 105 (2009).

30. J. Solà, J. Phys. Conf. Ser. **453** 012015 (2013) [arXiv:1306.1527]; AIP Conf. Proc. **1606** 19 (2015)[arXiv:1402.7049]; J. Phys. Conf. Ser. **283** 012033 (2011) [arXiv:1102.1815].
31. J. Solà and A. Gómez-Valent, Int. J. Mod. Phys. D **24** 1541003 (2015).
32. A. Gómez Valent, *Vacuum energy in Quantum Field Theory and Cosmology* (PhD Thesis), [arXiv:1710.01978]; J. de Cruz Pérez, *Implications of Dynamical Dark Energy in the expansion of the Universe and the Structure Formation* (PhD. Thesis), [arXiv:2105.14800].
33. A. Babic, B. Guberina, R. Horvat and H. Stefancic, Phys. Rev. D **71** 124041 (2005).
34. M. Maggiore, Phys. Rev. D **83** 063514 (2011); M. Maggiore, L. Hollenstein, M. Jaccard and E. Mitsou, Phys. Lett. B **704** 102 (2011); L. Hollenstein, M. Jaccard, M. Maggiore and E. Mitsou, Phys. Rev. D **85** 124031 (2012)
35. K. Kohri and H. Matsui, JCAP **06** 006 (2017).
36. A. Ferreiro and J. Navarro-Salas, Phys. Lett. B **792** 81 (2019).
37. N. Bilic, Phys. Rev. D **83** 105003 (2011); Rom. J. Phys. **57** 793 (2012).
38. N. Bilic, S. Domazet and B. Guberina, Phys. Lett. B **707** 221 (2012).
39. S. Basilakos, N. E. Mavromatos and J. Solà, Universe **2** 14 (2016).
40. S. Basilakos, N. E. Mavromatos and J. Solà Peracaula, Phys. Rev. D **101** 045001 (2020) ; Int. J. Mod. Phys. D **28** 1944002 (2019).
41. S. Basilakos, N. E. Mavromatos and J. Solà Peracaula, Phys. Lett. B **803** 135342 (2020).
42. N. E. Mavromatos and J. Solà Peracaula, Eur. Phys. J. Spec. Top. **230** 2077 (2021).
43. N. E. Mavromatos, *Geometrical origins of the Universe dark sector: string-inspired torsion and anomalies as seeds for inflation and dark matter*, arXiv:2108.02152 (to appear in Phil.Trans.Roy.Soc.Lond.A).
44. N. E. Navromatos and J. Solà Peracaula, *Inflationary physics and transplanckian conjecture in the Stringy Running-Vacuum-Model: from the phantom vacuum to the true vacuum*, arXiv:2105.02659.
45. N. E. Navromatos, *Gravitational anomalies, axions and a string-inspired running vacuum model in Cosmology*, arXiv:2108.03998.
46. N. D. Birrell and P. C. W. Davies, *Quantum Fields in Curved Space*, Cambridge U. Press (1982).
47. L. E. Parker and D. J. Toms *Quantum Field Theory in Curved Spacetime: quantized fields and gravity*, Cambridge U. Press (2009).
48. W. Fulling, *Aspects of Quantum Field Theory in Curved Space-Time*, Cambridge U. Press, (1989).
49. V. F. Mukhanov and S. Winitzki, *Quantum Effects in Gravity*, Cambridge U. Press (2007).
50. T. S. Bunch, J. Phys. A **13** 1297 (1980).
51. L. Parker and S. A. Fulling, Phys. Rev. D **9** 341 (1974); S. A. Fulling and L. Parker, Ann. Phys. **87** 176 (1974); S. A. Fulling, L. Parker and B. L. Hu, Phys. Rev. D **10** 3905 (1974).
52. T. S. Bunch and L. Parker, Phys. Rev. D **20** 2499 (1979).
53. A. Landete, J. Navarro-Salas and F. Torrenti, Phys Rev. D **88** 061501 (2013); Phys. Rev. D **89** 044030 (2014); A. del Rio, J. Navarro-Salas and F. Torrenti, Phys. Rev. D **90** 084017 (2014).
54. J. F. Barbero G., A. Ferreiro, J. Navarro-Salas and E. J. S. Villaseñor, Phys.Rev. D **98** 025016 (2018).
55. J. Solà Peracaula, C. Moreno-Pulido and S. Cheraghchi, in preparation.
56. *Mathematica*, Wolfram Research, Inc.. URL: *https://www.wolfram.com/mathematica*

57. T. Appelquist and J. Carazzone, Phys. Rev. D **11** 2856 (1975).
58. H. Fritzsch and J. Solà, Class. Quant. Grav. **29** 215002 (2012); Mod. Phys. Lett. A **30** 1540034 (2015); Eur. Phys. J. C **77** 193 (2017).
59. S. Basilakos, J. A. S. Lima and J. Solà, MNRAS **431** 923 (2013); E. L. D. Perico, J. A. S. Limta, S. Basilakos and J. Solà, Phys. Rev. D **88** 063531 (2013).
60. J. Solà and A. Gómez-Valent, Int. J. Mod. Phys. D **24** 151003 (2015).
61. J. Solà, Int. J. Mod. Phys. D **24** 1544027 (2015).
62. J. Solà Peracaula and H. Yu, Gen. Rel. Grav. **52** 17 (2020).
63. C. W. Misner, K. S. Thorn and J. A. Wheeler, *Gravitation*, Freeman, San Francisco (1973).

BD-ΛCDM and running vacuum models: Theoretical background and current observational status

Javier de Cruz Pérez[1,*], Joan Solà Peracaula[2], Adrià Gómez-Valent[3] and Cristian Moreno-Pulido[2]

[1] *Department of Physics, Kansas State University, 116 Cardwell Hall, Manhattan, KS 66506, USA*
[2] *Departament de Física Quàntica i Astrofísica, and Institute of Cosmos Sciences, Universitat de Barcelona, Av. Diagonal 647, E-08028 Barcelona, Catalonia, Spain*
[3] *Dipartimento di Fisica, and INFN Sezione di Roma Tor Vergata, via della Ricerca Scientifica 1, 00133 Roma Italy*
E-mail: decruz@fqa.ub.edu, sola@fqa.ub.edu, cristian.moreno@fqa.ub.edu, agvalent@roma2.infn.it

We present an analysis of the Brans-Dicke cosmological model with a cosmological constant and cold dark matter (BD-ΛCDM). We find that the BD-ΛCDM is favored by the overall cosmological data (SNIa+BAO+$H(z)$+LSS+CMB) when it is compared with the standard model of cosmology. The BD-ΛCDM model can be viewed from the GR perspective as a Running Vacuum Model (RVM) with a time evolving vacuum energy density. Due to this fact and also to its time evolving effective gravitational coupling, the model can alleviate the σ_8 and the H_0 tensions at a time. We also present the results for different types of RVM's when they are tested in the light of the cosmological data and we show that a mild dynamics for the vacuum energy density can help to smooth out the aforementioned tensions, thus improving the performance of ΛCDM model.

Keywords: Cosmology, Dark Energy, General Relativity.

1. Introduction

The high quality observations performed during the last two decades, have allowed to demonstrate, with a high confidence range, that the Universe is in expansion and to be more precise in accelerated expansion.[1,2] The standard model of cosmology, the so-called ΛCDM, is based on the assumption that the observed accelerated expansion is due to the existence of a repulsive force, exerted by the Λ term, which counteracts the attractive gravitational force and pushes the clusters of galaxies at a speed that increases with the cosmic expansion. This term, which is called the cosmological constant (CC), is associated with a mysterious form of energy, usually called dark energy (DE) presumably permeating all corners of the Universe as a whole. The cosmological constant is not the only element beyond the conventional matter, namely: baryons, photons and neutrinos, demanded by the observations since it is also essential the presence of large amounts of what is commonly call, cold dark matter (CDM). It is important to remark that the concordance model is

---

*Speaker

defined in the framework of General Relativity (GR), whose field equations were found by Einstein in 1915.[3] The fact that the ΛCDM model, with so few ingredients (encoded in 6 degrees of freedom), has remained robust and unbeaten for a long time turns out to be pretty impressive. It is consistent with a large body of very accurate cosmological data, like the cosmic microwave background (CMB), the baryonic acoustic oscillations (BAO) or the large scale structure (LSS) data.

However, this does not mean at all that we really understand the primary (dynamical) cause for such an acceleration or that we are in position to propose a cosmological model explaining the speeding up of the cosmos at the level of fundamental physics, say quantum field theory (QFT) in curved spacetime, quantum gravity or string theory. For instance, if we try to explain the origin of the cosmological constant in the context of QFT we will immediately realize that we have to face the well-known old cosmological constant problem. This problem was formulated by Zel'dovich[4,5] (see also[6–9]) and basically consists in the tremendous mismatch between the computed value of the vacuum energy density, considering different contributions from QFT, and the experimental measure, being the discrepancy between both values in natural units of at least 55 orders of magnitude.

Thus, in spite of the many virtues of the ΛCDM model, the lack of an explanation for the presence of the CC, leads inevitably to an unsatisfactory theoretical picture which has motivated the search of a wide range of alternatives beyond the standard model. What is more, aside from the theoretical problems some persisting tensions with the cosmological data (being the most important ones, the tension on the local value of the H_0 parameter[10,11] and the one affecting the LSS data[12]) point out that the ΛCDM model might be performing insufficiently at the observational level.

Here we study two alternatives where the aforementioned tension could be alleviated. It has been suggested that it would help to alleviate the tensions if DE would be a dynamical quantity (see for instance the possibility of an early dark energy[13,14]), i.e. slowly evolving with the cosmic expansion. This could be achieved, for example, through scalar field models[15–20] (see[21] for an updated analysis), where the energy density associated to the Λ term is replaced by the energy density of the scalar field, which varies throughout the cosmic history. In this paper, instead of considering a scalar field model we focus on another promising possibility, namely that vacuum energy density $\rho_{vac} = \Lambda/8\pi G_N$ might be a time evolving quantity whose dynamics is triggered by the quantum effects coming from the matter fields. We call these types of models Running Vacuum Models (RVM's). Phenomenologically, these models, have recently been carefully confronted against the wealth of the cosmological data, obtaining a significant success.[22–27]

On the other hand there exists the possibility to consider a completely different approach, where a theoretical framework, different from GR, is assumed. In this regard, Brans & Dicke[28] proposed the first historical attempt to extend Einstein's GR by promoting the Newtonian coupling G_N into a variable one in the cosmic time $G(t)$. Gravity is then not only mediated by the metric but also by an scalar field denoted by ψ. The theory contains an extra *d.o.f.* encoded in ψ and a dimensionless parameter $\omega_{\rm BD}$. In order to recover GR a necessary (though not sufficient) condition is to demand large values of $\omega_{\rm BD}$. We consider the presence of the CC and all the species considered in the standard model, so we call the model studied in the context of Brans-Dicke (BD) gravity, BD-ΛCDM.

In this work we present a summary of the main results recently obtained by confronting the overall cosmological observations with the BD-ΛCDM model and related RVM's and we show how they deal with the aforementioned tensions. See the original references[7,27,29,30] for more details.

2. Background equations for the BD-ΛCDM model

We will consider the original BD-action extended with a cosmological constant density term as it is essential to mimic the conventional ΛCDM model based on GR and reproduce its main successes. We call this the 'BD-ΛCDM model', i.e. the version of the ΛCDM within the BD paradigm. The BD action reads, written in the Jordan frame, as follows [a]:

$$S_{\rm BD} = \int d^4x \sqrt{-g} \left[\frac{1}{16\pi} \left(R\psi - \frac{\omega_{\rm BD}}{\psi} g^{\mu\nu} \partial_\nu \psi \partial_\mu \psi \right) - \rho_{\rm vac}^0 \right] + S_m . \quad (1)$$

For the sake of convenience we denote the constant vacuum energy density as $\rho_{\rm vac}^0$. The (dimensionless) factor in front of the kinetic term of ψ, i.e. $\omega_{\rm BD}$, will be referred to as the BD-parameter and we consider the canonical option, $\omega_{\rm BD} =$const. The last term of (1) stands for the matter action S_m, which is constructed from the Lagrangian density of the matter fields. There is no potential for the BD-field ψ in the original BD-theory, but we admit the presence of a CC term associated to $\rho_{\rm vac}^0$.

The modified field equations (with respect to GR) can be obtained after performing variation of the action (1) with respect to both the metric and the scalar field ψ. While the first variation yields

$$\psi G_{\mu\nu} + \left(\Box\psi + \frac{\omega_{\rm BD}}{2\psi} (\nabla\psi)^2 \right) g_{\mu\nu} - \nabla_\mu \nabla_\nu \psi - \frac{\omega_{\rm BD}}{\psi} \nabla_\mu \psi \nabla_\nu \psi = 8\pi \left(T_{\mu\nu} - g_{\mu\nu} \rho_{\rm vac}^0 \right) , \quad (2)$$

the second variation gives the wave equation for ψ

$$\Box\psi = \frac{8\pi}{2\omega_{\rm BD} + 3} \left(T - 4\rho_{\rm vac}^0 \right) . \quad (3)$$

We have used the definition $(\nabla\psi)^2 \equiv g^{\mu\nu}\nabla_\mu\psi\nabla_\nu\psi$. In the first equation, $G_{\mu\nu} = R_{\mu\nu} - (1/2)Rg_{\mu\nu}$ is the Einstein tensor, and on its *r.h.s.* $T_{\mu\nu} = -(2/\sqrt{-g})\delta S_m/\delta g^{\mu\nu}$ is the energy-momentum tensor of matter, being $T \equiv T_\mu^\mu$ its trace. The total energy-momentum tensor is the sum of the matter and vacuum contributions and it takes

---

[a]We use natural units, $\hbar = c = 1$ and $G_N = 1/m_{\rm Pl}^2$, where $m_{\rm Pl} \simeq 1.22 \times 10^{19}$ GeV is the Planck mass. As for the geometrical quantities, we adopt the $(+,+,+)$ convention of the popular classification by Misner, Thorn and Wheeler.[31]

the perfect fluid form:

$$\tilde{T}_{\mu\nu} = T_{\mu\nu} - \rho^0_{\text{vac}} g_{\mu\nu} = p\, g_{\mu\nu} + (\rho + p) u_\mu u_\nu \,, \qquad (4)$$

with $\rho \equiv \rho_m + \rho_\gamma + \rho_{\text{ncdm}} + \rho^0_{\text{vac}}$ and $p \equiv p_m + p_\gamma + p_{\text{ncdm}} + p^0_{\text{vac}}$. The matter part $\rho_m \equiv \rho_b + \rho_{\text{cdm}}$, contains the pressureless contribution from baryons and cold dark matter and photons are of course relativistic, so $p_\gamma = \rho_\gamma/3$. The functions ρ_{ncdm} and p_{ncdm} ('ncdm' means non-CDM) include the effect of massive and massless neutrinos, and therefore must be computed numerically. As in GR, we have considered a constant vacuum energy density, ρ^0_{vac}, in the BD-action (1), being its equation of state $p^0_{\text{vac}} = -\rho^0_{\text{vac}}$ the usual one.

Let us write down the field equations in the flat (to know more about the nonflat models see the references[32–44]) FLRW metric, $ds^2 = -dt^2 + a^2 \delta_{ij} dx^i dx^j$. Using the previous definitions for the total energy density ρ and pressure p we get the two independent equations:

$$3H^2 + 3H\frac{\dot{\psi}}{\psi} - \frac{\omega_{\text{BD}}}{2}\left(\frac{\dot{\psi}}{\psi}\right)^2 = \frac{8\pi}{\psi}\rho \qquad (5)$$

and

$$2\dot{H} + 3H^2 + \frac{\ddot{\psi}}{\psi} + 2H\frac{\dot{\psi}}{\psi} + \frac{\omega_{\text{BD}}}{2}\left(\frac{\dot{\psi}}{\psi}\right)^2 = -\frac{8\pi}{\psi}p\,, \qquad (6)$$

whereas from (3) we obtain

$$\ddot{\psi} + 3H\dot{\psi} = \frac{8\pi}{2\omega_{\text{BD}} + 3}(\rho - 3p)\,. \qquad (7)$$

Here dots stand for derivatives with respect to the cosmic time and $H = \dot{a}/a$ is the Hubble rate. In the limit $\psi \to 1/G_N$ and $\omega_{\text{BD}} \to \infty$ we recover the standard equations. The connection between GR and the $\omega_{\text{BD}} \to \infty$ limit is sometimes not as straightforward as one might naively think.[45,46]

Matter and the BD-field are not in interaction, as a result, the local conservation law adopts the usual form:

$$\dot{\rho} + 3H(\rho + p) = \sum_N [\dot{\rho}_N + 3H(\rho_N + p_N)] = 0\,, \qquad (8)$$

where the sum is over all components, i.e. baryons, dark matter, neutrinos, photons and vacuum. We assume that all of the components are separately conserved in the main periods of the cosmic evolution. For convenience, we will use a dimensionless BD-field, φ, and the inverse of the BD-parameter, according to :

$$\varphi(t) \equiv G_N \psi(t)\,, \qquad \epsilon_{\text{BD}} \equiv \frac{1}{\omega_{\text{BD}}}\,. \qquad (9)$$

As stated before G_N gives the local value of the gravitational coupling. Note that a nonvanishing value of ϵ_{BD} entails a deviation from GR. Being $\varphi(t)$ a dimensionless quantity, we can recover GR by enforcing the simultaneous limits $\epsilon_{\text{BD}} \to 0$ and $\varphi \to 1$.

Baseline

Parameter	ΛCDM	type I RRVM	type I RRVM$_{\text{thr.}}$	type II RRVM	BD-ΛCDM
H_0(km/s/Mpc)	$68.37^{+0.38}_{-0.41}$	$68.17^{+0.50}_{-0.48}$	$67.63^{+0.42}_{-0.43}$	$69.02^{+1.16}_{-1.21}$	$69.30^{+1.38}_{-1.33}$
ω_b	$0.02230^{+0.00019}_{-0.00018}$	$0.02239^{+0.00023}_{-0.00024}$	$0.02231^{+0.00020}_{-0.00019}$	$0.02245^{+0.00025}_{-0.00027}$	0.02248 ± 0.00025
ω_{cdm}	$0.11725^{+0.00094}_{-0.00084}$	$0.11731^{+0.00092}_{-0.00087}$	$0.12461^{+0.00201}_{-0.00210}$	$0.11653^{+0.00158}_{-0.00160}$	$0.11629^{+0.00148}_{-0.00151}$
ν_{eff}	-	$0.00024^{+0.00039}_{-0.00040}$	$0.02369^{+0.00625}_{-0.00563}$	0.00029 ± 0.00047	-
ϵ_{BD}	-	-	-	-	$-0.00109^{+0.00135}_{-0.00141}$
φ_{ini}	-	-	-	$0.980^{+0.031}_{-0.027}$	$0.972^{+0.030}_{-0.037}$
φ_0	-	-	-	$0.973^{+0.036}_{-0.033}$	$0.963^{+0.036}_{-0.041}$
τ_{reio}	$0.049^{+0.008}_{-0.007}$	$0.051^{+0.008}_{-0.009}$	$0.058^{+0.007}_{-0.009}$	0.051 ± 0.008	0.051 ± 0.008
n_s	$0.9698^{+0.0039}_{-0.0036}$	$0.9716^{+0.0044}_{-0.0047}$	0.9703 ± 0.038	$0.9762^{+0.0081}_{-0.0091}$	
σ_8	0.796 ± 0.007	$0.789^{+0.013}_{-0.014}$	$0.768^{+0.010}_{-0.009}$	$0.791^{+0.013}_{-0.012}$	$0.790^{+0.013}_{-0.012}$
S_8	0.796 ± 0.011	$0.791^{+0.014}_{-0.013}$	$0.797^{+0.012}_{-0.011}$	$0.781^{+0.021}_{-0.020}$	$0.777^{+0.021}_{-0.022}$
r_s (Mpc)	$147.90^{+0.30}_{-0.31}$	$147.99^{+0.35}_{-0.36}$	147.81 ± 0.30	$146.30^{+2.39}_{-2.30}$	$145.72^{+2.44}_{-2.90}$
χ^2_{min}	2290.20	2289.72	2272.44	2288.74	2289.40
ΔDIC	-	-2.70	+13.82	-4.59	-3.53

Note: The mean values and 68.3% confidence limits for the models under study using our Baseline dataset, which is composed by: the full Pantheon likelihood,[47] 13 BAO data points,[48–53] 31 data points on $H(z_i)$, at different redshifts,[54–61] 14 points on the observable $f(z_i)\sigma_8(z_i)$[50, 52, 62–66] and finally the full Planck likelihood for the CMB data.[10] We display the fitting values for the usual parameters, to wit: H_0, the reduced density parameter for baryons ($w_b = \Omega_b^0 h^2$) and also for CDM ($w_{\text{cdm}} = \Omega_{\text{cdm}}^0 h^2$), being $\Omega_i^0 = 8\pi G_N \rho_i^0/3H_0^2$ and h the reduced Hubble constant, the reionization optical depth τ_{reio}, the spectral index n_s and the current matter density rms fluctuations within spheres of radius $8h^{-1}$ Mpc, i.e. σ_8. We include also a couple of derived parameters, namely: the sound horizon at the baryon drag epoch r_s and $S_8 \equiv \sigma_8 \sqrt{\Omega_m^0/0.3}$. For the RRVM's we provide the value of ν_{eff}, and for the type II and BD-ΛCDM[27] we also report the initial and current values of φ, φ_{ini} and φ_0, respectively. The parameter $\epsilon_{\text{BD}} \equiv 1/\omega_{\text{BD}}$ (inverse of the Brans-Dicke parameter[28]) controls the dynamics of the scalar field.[29, 30] We finally provide the corresponding values of χ^2_{min} and ΔDIC.

3. Connection of the BD-ΛCDM model with the Running Vacuum Model

So far, no analytical solutions to the system (5)-(7) have been found, for this reason our actual analysis proceeds numerically. However, it is possible to search for approximate solutions valid in the different epochs of cosmic history, which can provide a qualitative understanding of the numerical results obtained. Actually, a first attempt in this direction trying to show that BD-ΛCDM can mimic the Running Vacuum Model (RVM) was done in,[67, 68] we refer the reader to these references for details. See also.[69, 70] We are interested in looking for solutions in the Matter Dominated Epoch (MDE) in the form of a power-law ansatz in which the BD-field φ evolves very slowly:

$$\varphi(a) = \varphi_0 \, a^{-\epsilon} \qquad (|\epsilon| \ll 1). \tag{10}$$

The ϵ parameter must be a very small parameter in absolute value since $G(a) \equiv G(\varphi(a))$ cannot depart too much from G_N and $\varphi_0 \equiv \varphi(z=0)$. For $\epsilon > 0$, the effective coupling increases with the expansion and hence is asymptotically free since $G(a)$ is smaller in the past, which is the epoch when the Hubble rate (with natural dimension of energy) is bigger. For $\epsilon < 0$, is the other way around and $G(a)$ decreases with the expansion.

Plugging the power-law ansatz into the cosmological equations we end up with the following pair of Friedmann-like equations to $\mathcal{O}(\epsilon)$:[67,68]

$$H^2 = \frac{8\pi G}{3} \left(\rho_m^0 a^{-3+\epsilon} + \rho_{\rm DE}(H) \right) \qquad (11)$$

and for the acceleration equation

$$\frac{\ddot{a}}{a} = -\frac{4\pi G}{3} \left(\rho_m^0 a^{-3+\epsilon} + \rho_{\rm DE}(H) + 3 p_{\rm vac}^0 \right), \qquad (12)$$

with $G = G_N/\varphi_0$. The first of the above equations can be understood as an effective Friedmann's equation with time-evolving cosmological term, in which the DE appears as if it were a dynamical quantity:

$$\rho_{\rm DE}(H) = \rho_{\rm vac}^0 + \frac{3\bar{\nu}_{\rm eff}}{8\pi G} H^2. \qquad (13)$$

Here

$$\bar{\nu}_{\rm eff} \equiv \epsilon \left(1 + \frac{1}{6} \omega_{\rm BD} \epsilon \right) \qquad (14)$$

is the coefficient controlling the dynamical character of the effective dark energy (13). The structure of this dynamical dark energy (DDE) is reminiscent of the Running Vacuum Model (RVM), see[71–73] and references therein. Notice from (11) that, to $\mathcal{O}(\epsilon)$:

$$\Omega_m + \Omega_\Lambda = 1 - \bar{\nu}_{\rm eff}, \qquad (15)$$

so, due to the presence of $\bar{\nu}_{\rm eff}$, we find a slight deviation from the usual sum rule of GR. Only in the case $\epsilon = 0$, we have $\bar{\nu}_{\rm eff} = 0$ and then we recover the usual cosmic sum rule. As stated, the parameter $\bar{\nu}_{\rm eff}$ becomes associated to the dynamics of the dark energy. We shall see more about the most important features of the RVM in the next section. All in all, it turns out that the BD-RVM (we may call it in this way for convenience) can cure the H_0-tension due to the evolution of the effective gravitational $G_{\rm eff}$ and, additionally, by mimicking the RVM it can also alleviate the well-known σ_8-tension thanks to the role played by $\bar{\nu}_{\rm eff}$. Going a little further in this effective picture from (12) we can define the EoS parameter for the effective DDE:

$$w_{\rm eff}(z) = \frac{p_{\rm vac}^0}{\rho_{\rm DE}(H)} \simeq -1 + \frac{3\bar{\nu}_{\rm eff}}{8\pi G \rho_{\rm vac}^0} H^2(z) = -1 + \frac{\bar{\nu}_{\rm eff}}{\Omega_\Lambda} \frac{H^2(z)}{H_0^2}, \qquad (16)$$

where use has been made of (13). As it is clear from the above equation the BD-RVM, unlike the original RVM, does not describe a dark energy of pure vacuum form but a DE whose EoS departs, in a mild way, from the pure vacuum. Actually, for $\epsilon > 0$ ($\epsilon < 0$) we have $\bar{\nu}_{\rm eff} > 0$ ($\bar{\nu}_{\rm eff} < 0$) and the effective DDE behaves quintessence (phantom)-like.

		Baseline + H_0			
Parameter	ΛCDM	type I RRVM	type I RRVM$_{\text{thr.}}$	type II RRVM	BD-ΛCDM
H_0 (km/s/Mpc)	$68.75^{+0.41}_{-0.36}$	$68.77^{+0.49}_{-0.48}$	$68.14^{+0.43}_{-0.41}$	$70.93^{+0.93}_{-0.87}$	$71.23^{+1.01}_{-1.02}$
ω_b	$0.02240^{+0.00019}_{-0.00021}$	$0.02238^{+0.00021}_{-0.00023}$	$0.02243^{+0.00019}_{-0.00018}$	$0.02269^{+0.00025}_{-0.00024}$	$0.02267^{+0.00026}_{-0.00023}$
ω_{cdm}	$0.11658^{+0.00080}_{-0.00083}$	$0.11661^{+0.00084}_{-0.00085}$	$0.12299^{+0.00197}_{-0.00203}$	$0.11602^{+0.00162}_{-0.00163}$	$0.11601^{+0.00161}_{-0.00157}$
ν_{eff}	-	$-0.00005^{+0.00040}_{-0.00038}$	$0.02089^{+0.00553}_{-0.00593}$	$0.00038^{+0.00041}_{-0.00044}$	-
ϵ_{BD}	-	-	-	-	$-0.00130\pm^{+0.00136}_{-0.00140}$
φ_{ini}	-	-	-	$0.938^{+0.018}_{-0.024}$	$0.928^{+0.024}_{-0.026}$
φ_0	-	-	-	$0.930^{+0.022}_{-0.029}$	$0.919^{+0.028}_{-0.033}$
τ_{reio}	$0.050^{+0.008}_{-0.007}$	$0.049^{+0.009}_{-0.008}$	$0.058^{+0.008}_{-0.009}$	0.052 ± 0.008	0.052 ± 0.008
n_s	$0.9718^{+0.0035}_{-0.0038}$	0.9714 ± 0.0046	$0.9723^{+0.0040}_{-0.0039}$	$0.9868^{+0.0072}_{-0.0074}$	$0.9859^{+0.0073}_{-0.0072}$
σ_8	0.794 ± 0.007	0.795 ± 0.013	0.770 ± 0.010	$0.794^{+0.013}_{-0.012}$	$0.792^{+0.013}_{-0.012}$
S_8	$0.788^{+0.010}_{-0.011}$	0.789 ± 0.013	0.789 ± 0.011	$0.761^{+0.018}_{-0.017}$	$0.758^{+0.019}_{-0.018}$
r_s (Mpc)	$147.97^{+0.29}_{-0.31}$	$147.94^{+0.35}_{-0.36}$	$147.88^{+0.33}_{-0.29}$	$143.00^{+1.54}_{-1.96}$	$142.24^{+1.99}_{-2.12}$
$\chi^2_{\min}$	2302.14	2301.90	2288.82	2296.38	2295.36
ΔDIC	-	-2.36	+10.88	+5.52	+6.25

Note: Same as in Table 1, but also considering the prior on $H_0 = (73.5\pm1.4)$ km/s/Mpc from SH0ES.[11]

4. Background equations for the RVM's

In the following we are going to present the theoretical framework where the previously mentioned RVM's are placed[71–73] and references therein. We consider two types of dynamical vacuum energy (DVE) scenarios. In type I scenario the vacuum is in interaction with matter, in contrast, in type II matter is conserved at the expense of an exchange between the vacuum and a slowly evolving gravitational coupling $G(H)$. In both cases, the combined cosmological 'running' of these quantities insures the accomplishment of the Bianchi identity (and the local conservation law). Let us therefore consider a generic cosmological framework described by the spatially flat Friedmann-Lemaître-Robertson-Walker (FLRW) metric. The vacuum energy density in the RVM can be expressed as :[71,72]

$$\rho_{\text{vac}}(H) = \frac{3}{8\pi G_N}\left(c_0 + \nu H^2 + \tilde{\nu}\dot{H}\right) + \mathcal{O}(H^4). \qquad (17)$$

The $\mathcal{O}(H^4)$ terms play no role in the post-inflationary epoch so they can be neglected. The expression (17) can be motivated from the explicit QFT calculations on a FLRW background.[74] The value of the additive constant c_0 is fixed by the boundary condition $\rho_{\text{vac}}(H_0) = \rho^0_{\text{vac}}$. The two dynamical components H^2 and $\dot{H}$ are dimensionally homogeneous and in principle independent. The dimensionless coefficients ν and $\tilde{\nu}$ encode the dynamics of the vacuum at low energy and we naturally expect for both of them $|\nu,\tilde{\nu}|\ll 1$. An estimate of ν in QFT indicates that it is of order 10^{-3} at most.[75] In the calculations performed in[74] these coefficients are expected to be of order $\sim M_X^2/m_{\text{Pl}}^2 \ll 1$, being M_X of order of a typical Grand Unified Theory (GUT) scale. Taking into account the multiplicity of particles in a GUT, the theoretical estimate on ν could be much larger but still subject to a value below 1.

We are interested in a particular form for the vacuum energy density obtained by imposing $\tilde{\nu} = \nu/2$. Consequently

$$\rho_{\text{vac}}(H) = 3/(8\pi G_N) \left[c_0 + \nu \left(H^2 + \frac{1}{2}\dot{H} \right) \right]. \tag{18}$$

We will call this form of the vacuum energy density the 'RRVM' since it realizes the generic RVM density (17) through the Ricci scalar $\mathcal{R} = 12H^2 + 6\dot{H}$, namely

$$\rho_{\text{vac}}(H) = \frac{3}{8\pi G_N} \left(c_0 + \frac{\nu}{12}\mathcal{R} \right) \equiv \rho_{\text{vac}}(\mathcal{R}). \tag{19}$$

Due to the fact that the condition $\mathcal{R}/H^2 \ll 1$ is fulfilled in the early epochs of the cosmological evolution we do not generate any conflict with the BBN nor with any other feature of the modern universe. Of course, early on the RVM has its own mechanism for inflation see[71,72,76,77] for more details.

4.1. Type I RRVM

Taking into account, the dynamical character presented for the vacuum energy density, the Friedmann and the acceleration equations for the different species involved, read

$$3H^2 = 8\pi G_N \left(\rho_m + \rho_{\text{ncdm}} + \rho_\gamma + \rho_{\text{vac}}(H) \right), \tag{20}$$

$$3H^2 + 2\dot{H} = -8\pi G_N \left(p_{\text{ncdm}} + p_\gamma + p_{\text{vac}}(H) \right). \tag{21}$$

As for the BD-model, we define the total nonrelativistic matter density as the sum of the CDM component and the baryonic one: $\rho_m = \rho_{\text{cdm}} + \rho_b$. Therefore the total (relativistic and nonrelativistic) matter density is $\rho_t = \rho_m + \rho_\gamma + \rho_{\text{ncdm}}$. In a similar way, the total matter pressure reads $p_t = p_{\text{ncdm}} + p_\gamma$ (with $p_\gamma = (1/3)\rho_\gamma$). Making use of the functions employed by the system solver CLASS [78] we distinguish between the contributions of the nonrelativistic neutrinos $\rho_h = \rho_{\text{ncdm}} - 3p_{\text{ncdm}}$ and the one from the relativistic neutrinos $\rho_\nu = 3p_{\text{ncdm}}$. This separation allows to compute $\mathcal{R}/12 = H^2 + (1/2)\dot{H}$ appearing in (19) in terms of the energy densities and pressures using (20) and (21):

$$\mathcal{R} = 8\pi G_N \left(\rho_m + 4\rho_{\text{vac}} + \rho_h \right). \tag{22}$$

We can safely neglect the contribution of neutrinos from (22) since it remains well below the contribution of CDM and baryons throughout the whole cosmic history. This fact allows us to solve for the vacuum density as a function of the scale factor a as follows:

$$\rho_{\text{vac}}(a) = \rho_{\text{vac}}^0 + \frac{\nu}{4(1-\nu)} \left(\rho_m(a) - \rho_m^0 \right), \tag{23}$$

where '0' (used as subscript or superscript) always refers to current quantities. For $a = 1$ we confirm the correct normalization: $\rho_{\text{vac}}(a = 1) = \rho_{\text{vac}}^0$. Matter does not follow the standard dilution law, remember that it is in interaction with vacuum, therefore $\rho_m(a)$ is not just $\sim a^{-3}$. The local conservation law for CDM and vacuum can be expressed as follows:

$$\dot{\rho}_{\text{cdm}} + 3H\rho_{\text{cdm}} = -\dot{\rho}_{\text{vac}}. \tag{24}$$

We assume that baryons are self conserved, which implies $\dot{\rho}_b + 3H\rho_b = 0$, and as a consequence the total matter contribution (ρ_m) satisfies the same local conservation law (24) as CDM: $\dot{\rho}_m + 3H\rho_m = -\dot{\rho}_{\text{vac}}$. Using it together with (23) we find

$$\dot{\rho}_m + 3H\xi\rho_m = 0 \tag{25}$$

where, for convenience, we have defined

$$\xi \equiv \frac{1-\nu}{1-\frac{3}{4}\nu}. \tag{26}$$

We encode the deviations with respect to the standard model in terms of the effective parameter $\nu_{\text{eff}} \equiv \nu/4$:

$$\xi = 1 - \nu_{\text{eff}} + \mathcal{O}\left(\nu_{\text{eff}}^2\right). \tag{27}$$

Having reached this point it is straightforward to find the expression for the matter energy densities:

$$\rho_m(a) = \rho_m^0 a^{-3\xi}, \quad \rho_{\text{cdm}}(a) = \rho_m^0 a^{-3\xi} - \rho_b^0 a^{-3}. \tag{28}$$

As expected, by setting $\xi = 1$ ($\nu_{\text{eff}} = 0$) we recover the ΛCDM expressions. The small departure is precisely what gives allowance for a mild dynamical vacuum evolution:

$$\rho_{\text{vac}}(a) = \rho_{\text{vac}}^0 + \left(\frac{1}{\xi} - 1\right)\rho_m^0\left(a^{-3\xi} - 1\right). \tag{29}$$

The vacuum becomes rigid if $\xi = 1$ ($\nu_{\text{eff}} = 0$).

4.2. *Type II RRVM*

Unlike the first kind of models presented, for type II models matter is conserved. However, vacuum can still evolve provided the gravitational coupling also evolves with the expansion: $G = G(H)$. Let us define an auxiliary variable $\varphi = G_N/G$ – in the manner of a Brans-Dicke, without being really so. Notice that $\varphi \neq 1$ in the cosmological domain, but remains very close to it, see Tables 1 and 2. The modified Friedmann's equation for type-II model can be written as

$$3H^2 = \frac{8\pi G_N}{\varphi}\left[\rho_t + C_0 + \frac{3\nu}{16\pi G_N}(2H^2 + \dot{H})\right], \tag{30}$$

with $C_0 = 3c_0/(8\pi G_N)$. The link between the dynamics of φ and that of ρ_{vac} is given by the Bianchi identity:

$$\frac{\dot{\varphi}}{\varphi} = \frac{\dot{\rho}_{\text{vac}}}{\rho_t + \rho_{\text{vac}}}, \tag{31}$$

where ρ_t is as before the total matter energy density and $\rho_{\rm vac}$ adopts exactly the same form as in (19). In the absence of an analytical expression for the vacuum energy density, we can show its approximate behaviour close to the present time by keeping only the terms linear in $\nu_{\rm eff}$ (recall that $|\nu_{\rm eff}| \ll 1$):

$$\rho_{\rm vac}(a) = C_0(1 + 4\nu_{\rm eff}) + \nu_{\rm eff}\rho_m^0 a^{-3} + \mathcal{O}(\nu_{\rm eff}^2). \tag{32}$$

Again, for $\nu_{\rm eff} = 0$ the vacuum energy density is constant, but otherwise it shows a moderate dynamics of $\mathcal{O}(\nu_{\rm eff})$ as in the type I case (29). One can also show that $\rho_{\rm vac}(a) \ll \rho_r(a) = \rho_r^0 a^{-4}$ for $a \ll 1$ and therefore the $\rho_{\rm vac}$ for the type II model does not perturb the normal thermal history (as in the type I model). Regarding the auxiliary variable φ, in the current epoch it exhibits a very mild evolution, almost logarithmic.

4.3. *Threshold redshift scenario for type I models*

One possibility that has been explored in the literature is to consider that vacuum is a dynamical quantity only close to the present time and that remains constant for the rest of the cosmic history (see e.g.[79,80]). So, in this scenario, we keep deactivated the interaction between the vacuum energy density and the CDM until the late universe when dark energy becomes apparent. We denote the threshold value of the scale factor when the activation takes places by a_*. According to this scenario the vacuum energy density was constant prior to $a = a_*$ and it just started to evolve for $a > a_*$. It is important to remark that while $\rho_{\rm vac}$ is a continuous function, its derivative is not. We mimic such situation through a Heaviside step function $\Theta(a - a_*)$. Therefore, we assume that in the range $a < a_*$ (hence for $z > z_*$) we have

$$\rho_{\rm cdm}(a) = \rho_{\rm cdm}(a_*)\left(\frac{a}{a_*}\right)^{-3},$$
$$\rho_{\rm vac}(a) = \rho_{\rm vac}(a_*) = {\rm const.} \qquad (a < a_*), \tag{33}$$

where $\rho_{\rm cdm}(a_*)$ and $\rho_{\rm vac}(a_*)$ are computed from (28) and (29), respectively. In the complementary range, instead, i.e. for $a > a_*$ ($0 < z < z_*$) near our time, the original equations (28) and (29) are the ones considered.

The threshold procedure is only applied within type I models with the main purpose of preserving the standard evolution law for the matter energy density when the redshift is sufficiently high. In fact, the threshold redshift value does not need to be very high and when it is fixed by optimization it turns out to be of order $z_* \simeq 1$. An important consequence of such threshold is that the cosmological physics during the CMB epoch is exactly as in the ΛCDM. On the contrary for type II models there is still some evolution (very mild though) of $\rho_{\rm vac}$ at the CMB epoch, but the matter density follows the same law as in the standard model.

5. Cosmological perturbations

In order to perform a complete analysis of the different models under study we need to consider the evolution of the perturbed cosmological quantities throughout the cosmic history. We refer the reader to the references[23,25,30,81] to know for the details of the perturbation equations since here we just display some basic equations. We consider the perturbed, spatially flat, FLRW metric $ds^2 = a^2(\eta)[-d\eta^2 + (\delta_{ij} + h_{ij})dx^i dx^j]$, in which h_{ij} represents the metric fluctuations which are coupled to the matter density perturbations $\delta_m = \delta\rho_m/\rho_m$ and $d\eta = dt/a$ is the conformal time. In the case of the BD model, at deep subhorizon scales, the differential equation for the matter density contrast is:

$$\delta_m'' + \mathcal{H}\delta_m' - 4\pi G_{\text{eff}}(\bar{\varphi})a^2\bar{\rho}_m\delta_m = 0, \tag{34}$$

where here $()' \equiv d()/d\eta$ and $\mathcal{H} = aH$. In this section when we add a bar over a quantity we indicate that it is a background quantity. We have employed the definition:

$$G_{\text{eff}} = \frac{G_N}{\bar{\varphi}}\left(\frac{4 + 2\omega_{\text{BD}}}{3 + 2\omega_{\text{BD}}}\right), \tag{35}$$

which represents the effective coupling that modifies the Poisson term of the perturbed equation with respect to the standard model.

In the case of the type I RRVM since baryons do not interact with the time evolving vacuum energy density their perturbed conservation equations are not directly affected. On the other hand the equation for the CDM takes the following form:

$$\delta_{\text{cdm}}' + \frac{h'}{2} - \frac{\rho_{\text{vac}}'}{\rho_{\text{cdm}}}\delta_{\text{cdm}} = 0, \tag{36}$$

which is obviously affected by the dynamics of the vacuum in a nontrivial way. We will present the details of the perturbation equations for the type II RRVM elsewhere.

6. Data and methodology

We fit the BD-ΛCDM, the different RVM's together with the standard model to the wealth of the cosmological data compiled from distant type Ia supernovae (SNIa), baryonic acoustic oscillations (BAO), different values of the Hubble function $H(z_i)$, the large scale structure (LSS) formation data embodied in the $f(z_i)\sigma_8(z_i)$ observable and the CMB data from the Planck satellite, see the references in the caption of Table 1. In order to compare the theoretical predictions with the available cosmological data we define the total χ^2 function as:

$$\chi_{\text{tot}}^2 = \chi_{\text{SNIa}}^2 + \chi_{\text{BAO}}^2 + \chi_H^2 + \chi_{f\sigma_8}^2 + \chi_{\text{CMB}}^2. \tag{37}$$

The above terms are defined in the standard way from the data including the corresponding covariance matrices. In particular, the χ_H^2 part may contain or not the

H_0 value measured by[11] depending on the setup indicated in the tables. To obtain the posterior distributions and the corresponding constraints for the dataset described above we have run the Monte Carlo sampler `MontePython`[82] together with the Einstein-Boltzmann system solver `CLASS`.[78] The latter has been properly modified in order to implement the background and the linear perturbation equations for the different models.

7. Discussions and conclusions

The main fitting results of our analysis are displayed in Tables 1 and 2 and in Figure 1. In the tables we compare, for two different datasets denoted as "Baseline" and "Baseline+H_0" (see the corresponding captions for more details), the concordance ΛCDM model with different RRVM's and with the BD-ΛCDM model.

In order to make a fair comparison between models with a different numbers of free parameters we employ the Deviance Information Criterion (DIC):[83] ΔDIC = DIC$_{\Lambda\text{CDM}}$ − DIC$_X$, representing X one of the nonstandard models under study. The DIC is defined as

$$\text{DIC} = \chi^2(\bar{\theta}) + 2p_D. \tag{38}$$

Here $p_D = \overline{\chi^2} − \chi^2(\bar{\theta})$ is the effective number of parameters of the model, and $\overline{\chi^2}$ and $\bar{\theta}$ the mean of the overall χ^2 distribution and the parameters, respectively. As it can be seen from the definition of ΔDIC, if ΔDIC < 0, means that the ΛCDM fits better the cosmological data, whereas for ΔDIC > 0 is the other way around.

Taking a look at the first table, it can be appreciated that a mild dynamics of the vacuum is very much welcome, specially in the case where the time evolution of ρ_{vac} is activated close to the moment when the contribution of this quantity becomes relevant, namely at $z \simeq 1$. It is in this particular scenario where the impact on the description of the cosmological data string SNIa+BAO+$H(z)$+LSS+CMB becomes extraordinary significant on statistical terms, since ΔAIC > +10 which means that a very strong evidence, in favor of this model, is found, when it is compared with the ΛCDM model. At very high redshift the physics of the type I RRVM with a threshold remain basically unaltered with respect to the ΛCDM, however, the activation of the dynamics of the vacuum at $z_* \simeq 1$ allows to suppress an exceedingly amount of structure in the universe, thus leading to a better description of the $f(z)\sigma_8(z)$ data set. On the contrary, non of the other models beyond the standard one is preferred by the cosmological data, and the DIC indicates moderate evidence against them (−5 < DIC < −2). We would like to remark that even if the RRVM's under study are not favoured by the data, in all cases the values of $S_8 \equiv \sigma_8(0)\sqrt{\Omega_m^0/0.3}$ (or the analogous observable $\tilde{S}_8 \equiv S_8/\sqrt{\varphi_0}$ for the type II RRVM and the BD-ΛCDM models) remain compatible with recent weak lensing and galaxy clustering measurements,[84] hence smoothing out the σ_8-tension. Just by including the H_0 prior in

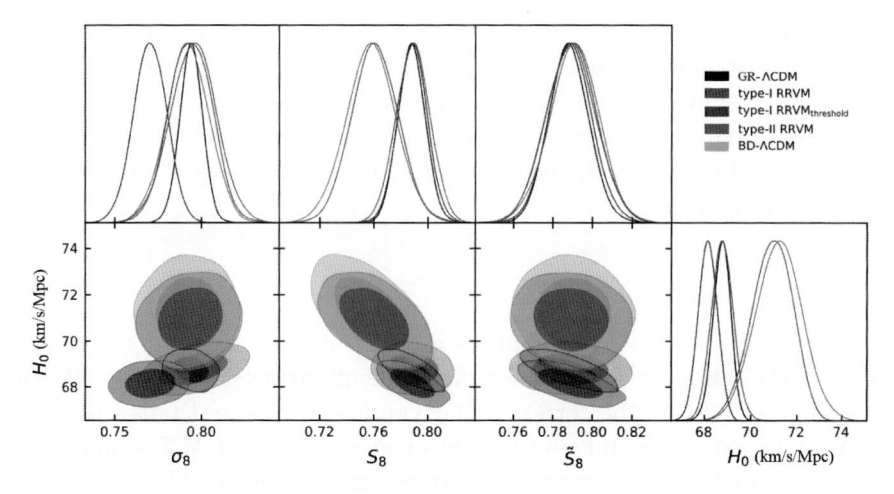

Fig. 1. The contour plots at 1σ and 2σ confidence level in the H_0-$\sigma_8, S_8, \tilde{S}_8$ planes and the corresponding one-dimensional posteriors for the GR- and BD-ΛCDM and the RRVM's obtained from the fitting analyses with our Baseline+H_0 data set. The type II model manifestly alleviates the H_0 tension without spoiling the σ_8 one, whereas the type I model with threshold redshift $z_* \simeq 1$ can fully solve the latter but cannot address the former.

the data set the results change in a very significant way as it can be observed from Table 2. The ΛCDM model, as well as, the two versions of the type I RRVM model are not able to accommodate high values of the H_0 parameter, hence, all of them show their inability to alleviate the H_0-tension. However, the DIC still decides very strongly in the case of the type I RRVM with threshold. On the other hand, the type II RRVM and the BD-ΛCDM model seem to have no problem to fit the H_0 prior since in both cases the fitting value for this parameter is $\simeq 71$km/s/Mpc. To fully appreciate how the cosmological models deal with the H_0 and the σ_8 tensions simultaneously, we have included Figure 1, where we have depicted the contour plots for the different models in the H_0-$\sigma_8, S_8, \tilde{S}_8$ planes of the parameter space. As mentioned before, the RRVM's are able to keep the values of the different parameters related with the structure formation ($\sigma_8, S_8, \tilde{S}_8$) at an intermediate value between Planck measurements[10] and cosmic shear data.[84] Remarkably enough, in the case of the type II RRVM and the BD-ΛCDM models, the contour lines in Figure 1 show a preference for relatively high values of H_0 (the tension is lowered at $\sim 1.6\sigma$) while keeping $\sigma_8 \equiv \sigma_8(0)$ in the low value range (the tension remains at $\sim 0.4\sigma$), thus smoothing out both tensions at a time. We conclude that the models studied in this paper provide very interesting alternatives, either considering a time-evolving vacuum energy density or by extending the paradigm of General Relativity, to alleviate the H_0 and the σ_8 tensions. The better performance of the aforementioned models is reconfirmed by the Deviance Information Criterion, which points out that in some cases a very strong evidence in favor of a nonstandard model is found.

Acknowledgments

I would like to thank J. Solà Peracaula and A. Gómez-Valent for inviting me to speak in the CM3 parallel sesion "Status of the H_0 and σ_8 Tensions: Theoretical Models and Model-Independent Constraints of the MG16 Marcel Grossman Virtual Conference, July 5-10 2021. We also would like to thank the organizers of the MG16 for their great effort organizing such a great event. JdCP is supported by a FPI fellowship associated to the project FPA2016-76005-C2-1-P. JSP and CMP are partially supported by projects FPA2016-76005-C2-1-P (MINECO), 2017-SGR-929 (Generalitat de Catalunya) and MDM-2014-0369 (ICCUB). CMP is partially supported by the fellowship 2019 FI-B 00351. AGV is funded by the INFN – Project number 22425/2020.

References

1. A. G. Riess *et al.*, Observational evidence from supernovae for an accelerating universe and a cosmological constant, *Astron. J.* **116**, 1009 (1998), arXiv:astro-ph/9805201.
2. S. Perlmutter *et al.*, Measurements of Ω and Λ from 42 high redshift supernovae, *Astrophys. J.* **517**, 565 (1999), arXiv:astro-ph/9812133.
3. A. Einstein, The Field Equations of Gravitation, *Sitzungsber. Preuss. Akad. Wiss. Berlin (Math. Phys.)* **1915**, 844 (1915).
4. Y. Zel'dovich, Cosmological constant and elementary particles, *Sov. Phys. JETP. Lett.* **6**, p. 3167 (1967).
5. Y. Zel'dovich, The cosmological constant and the theory of elementary particles, *Sov. Phys. Ups.* **11**, p. 381 (1968).
6. S. Weinberg, The Cosmological Constant Problem, *Rev. Mod. Phys.* **61**, 1 (1989).
7. P. J. E. Peebles and B. Ratra, The Cosmological Constant and Dark Energy, *Rev. Mod. Phys.* **75**, 559 (2003), arXiv:astro-ph/0207347.
8. T. Padmanabhan, Cosmological constant: The Weight of the vacuum, *Phys. Rept.* **380**, 235 (2003), arXiv:hep-th/0212290.
9. E. J. Copeland, M. Sami and S. Tsujikawa, Dynamics of dark energy, *Int. J. Mod. Phys. D* **15**, 1753 (2006), arXiv:hep-th/0603057.
10. N. Aghanim *et al.*, Planck 2018 results. VI. Cosmological parameters, *Astron. Astrophys.* **641**, p. A6 (2020), [Erratum: Astron.Astrophys. 652, C4 (2021)].
11. M. J. Reid, D. W. Pesce and A. G. Riess, An Improved Distance to NGC 4258 and its Implications for the Hubble Constant, *Astrophys. J.* **886**, p. L27 (2019), arXiv:1908.05625.
12. E. Macaulay, I. K. Wehus and H. K. Eriksen, Lower Growth Rate from Recent Redshift Space Distortion Measurements than Expected from Planck, *Phys. Rev. Lett.* **111**, p. 161301 (2013), arXiv:1303.6583.
13. A. Gómez-Valent, Z. Zheng, L. Amendola, V. Pettorino and C. Wetterich, Early dark energy in the pre- and post-recombination epochs (7 2021).
14. G. Benevento, W. Hu and M. Raveri, Can Late Dark Energy Transitions Raise the Hubble constant?, *Phys. Rev. D* **101**, p. 103517 (2020), arXiv:2002.11707.
15. P. J. E. Peebles and B. Ratra, Cosmology with a Time Variable Cosmological Constant, *Astrophys. J.* **325**, p. L17 (1988).
16. B. Ratra and P. J. E. Peebles, Cosmological Consequences of a Rolling Homogeneous Scalar Field, *Phys. Rev.* **D37**, p. 3406 (1988).

17. R. D. Peccei, J. Solà and C. Wetterich, Adjusting the Cosmological Constant Dynamically: Cosmons and a New Force Weaker Than Gravity, *Phys. Lett.* **B195**, 183 (1987).
18. C. Wetterich, Cosmology and the Fate of Dilatation Symmetry, *Nucl. Phys.* **B302**, 668 (1988), arXiv:1711.03844.
19. C. Wetterich, The Cosmon model for an asymptotically vanishing time dependent cosmological 'constant', *Astron. Astrophys.* **301**, 321 (1995), arXiv:hep-th/9408025.
20. L. Amendola, Coupled quintessence, *Phys. Rev.* **D62**, p. 043511 (2000), arXiv:astro-ph/9908023.
21. A. Gómez-Valent, V. Pettorino and L. Amendola, Update on coupled dark energy and the H_0 tension, *Phys. Rev. D* **101**, p. 123513 (2020), arXiv:2004.00610.
22. J. Solà, A. Gómez-Valent and J. de Cruz Pérez, First evidence of running cosmic vacuum: challenging the concordance model, *Astrophys. J.* **836**, p. 43 (2017).
23. J. Solà Peracaula, J. de Cruz Pérez and A. Gómez-Valent, Possible signals of vacuum dynamics in the Universe, *Mon. Not. Roy. Astron. Soc.* **478**, 4357 (2018).
24. J. Solà, A. Gómez-Valent and J. de Cruz Pérez, The H_0 tension in light of vacuum dynamics in the Universe, *Phys. Lett.* **B774**, 317 (2017), arXiv:1705.06723.
25. A. Gómez-Valent and J. Solà Peracaula, Density perturbations for running vacuum: a successful approach to structure formation and to the σ_8-tension, *Mon. Not. Roy. Astron. Soc.* **478**, 126 (2018), arXiv:1801.08501.
26. J. Solà Peracaula, A. Gómez-Valent and J. de Cruz Pérez, Signs of Dynamical Dark Energy in Current Observations, *Phys. Dark Univ.* **25**, p. 100311 (2019), arXiv:1811.03505.
27. J. Solà Peracaula, A. Gómez-Valent, J. de Cruz Pérez and C. Moreno-Pulido, Running vacuum against the H_0 and σ_8 tensions, *EPL* **134**, p. 19001 (2021).
28. C. Brans and R. Dicke, Mach's principle and a relativistic theory of gravitation, *Phys. Rev* **124**, p. 925 (1961).
29. J. Solà Peracaula, A. Gómez-Valent, J. de Cruz Pérez and C. Moreno-Pulido, Brans–Dicke Gravity with a Cosmological Constant Smoothes Out ΛCDM Tensions, *Astrophys. J. Lett.* **886**, p. L6 (2019).
30. J. Solà Peracaula, A. Gómez-Valent, J. de Cruz Pérez and C. Moreno-Pulido, Brans–Dicke cosmology with a Λ-term: a possible solution to ΛCDM tensions, *Class. Quant. Grav.* **37**, p. 245003 (2020).
31. C. W. Misner, K. S. Thorn and J. A. Wheeler, *Gravitation* (Freeman, San Francisco, 1974).
32. J. Ooba, B. Ratra and N. Sugiyama, Planck 2015 Constraints on the Non-flat ΛCDM Inflation Model, *Astrophys. J.* **864**, p. 80 (2018).
33. J. Ooba, B. Ratra and N. Sugiyama, Planck 2015 Constraints on the Nonflat ϕCDM Inflation Model, *Astrophys. J.* **866**, p. 68 (2018).
34. C.-G. Park and B. Ratra, Observational constraints on the tilted flat-XCDM and the untilted nonflat XCDM dynamical dark energy inflation parameterizations, *Astrophys. Space Sci.* **364**, p. 82 (2019).
35. C.-G. Park and B. Ratra, Observational constraints on the tilted spatially-flat and the untilted nonflat ϕCDM dynamical dark energy inflation models, *Astrophys. J.* **868**, p. 83 (2018).
36. C.-G. Park and B. Ratra, Measuring the Hubble constant and spatial curvature from supernova apparent magnitude, baryon acoustic oscillation, and Hubble parameter data, *Astrophys. Space Sci.* **364**, p. 134 (2019).

37. C.-G. Park and B. Ratra, Using SPT polarization, *Planck* 2015, and non-CMB data to constrain tilted spatially-flat and untilted nonflat ΛCDM, XCDM, and ϕCDM dark energy inflation cosmologies, *Phys. Rev. D* **101**, p. 083508 (2020).
38. J. Ryan, Y. Chen and B. Ratra, Baryon acoustic oscillation, Hubble parameter, and angular size measurement constraints on the Hubble constant, dark energy dynamics, and spatial curvature, *Mon. Not. Roy. Astron. Soc.* **488**, 3844 (2019).
39. N. Khadka and B. Ratra, Using quasar X-ray and UV flux measurements to constrain cosmological model parameters, *Mon. Not. Roy. Astron. Soc.* **497**, 263 (2020), arXiv:2004.09979.
40. N. Khadka and B. Ratra, Quasar X-ray and UV flux, baryon acoustic oscillation, and Hubble parameter measurement constraints on cosmological model parameters, *Mon. Not. Roy. Astron. Soc.* **492**, 4456 (2020).
41. S. Cao, J. Ryan, N. Khadka and B. Ratra, Cosmological constraints from higher redshift gamma-ray burst, HII starburst galaxy, and quasar (and other) data, *Mon. Not. Roy. Astron. Soc.* **501**, 1520 (2021).
42. S. Cao, J. Ryan and B. Ratra, Using Pantheon and DES supernova, baryon acoustic oscillation, and Hubble parameter data to constrain the Hubble constant, dark energy dynamics, and spatial curvature, *Mon. Not. Roy. Astron. Soc.* **504**, 300 (2021).
43. N. Khadka and B. Ratra, Do quasar X-ray and UV flux measurements provide a useful test of cosmological models? (7 2021).
44. S. Cao, J. Ryan and B. Ratra, Cosmological constraints from HII starburst galaxy, quasar angular size, and other measurements (9 2021).
45. V. Faraoni, The $\omega \to \infty$ limit of Brans Dicke theory, *Phys. Lett.* **A245**, 26 (1998), arXiv:gr-qc/9805057.
46. V. Faraoni, Illusions of general relativity in Brans-Dicke gravity, *Phys. Rev.* **D59**, p. 084021 (1999), arXiv:gr-qc/9902083.
47. D. M. Scolnic *et al.*, The Complete Light-curve Sample of Spectroscopically Confirmed SNe Ia from Pan-STARRS1 and Cosmological Constraints from the Combined Pantheon Sample, *Astrophys. J.* **859**, p. 101 (2018), arXiv:1710.00845.
48. P. Carter, F. Beutler, W. J. Percival, C. Blake, J. Koda and A. J. Ross, Low Redshift Baryon Acoustic Oscillation Measurement from the Reconstructed 6-degree Field Galaxy Survey, *Mon. Not. Roy. Astron. Soc.* **481**, 2371 (2018), arXiv:1803.01746.
49. E. A. Kazin *et al.*, The WiggleZ Dark Energy Survey: improved distance measurements to z = 1 with reconstruction of the baryonic acoustic feature, *Mon. Not. Roy. Astron. Soc.* **441**, 3524 (2014), arXiv:1401.0358.
50. H. Gil-Marín, W. J. Percival, L. Verde, J. R. Brownstein, C.-H. Chuang, F.-S. Kitaura, S. A. Rodríguez-Torres and M. D. Olmstead, The clustering of galaxies in the SDSS-III Baryon Oscillation Spectroscopic Survey: RSD measurement from the power spectrum and bispectrum of the DR12 BOSS galaxies, *Mon. Not. Roy. Astron. Soc.* **465**, 1757 (2017), arXiv:1606.00439.
51. T. M. C. Abbott *et al.*, Dark Energy Survey Year 1 Results: Measurement of the Baryon Acoustic Oscillation scale in the distribution of galaxies to redshift 1, *Mon. Not. Roy. Astron. Soc.* **483**, 4866 (2019), arXiv:1712.06209.
52. R. Neveux *et al.*, The completed SDSS-IV extended Baryon Oscillation Spectroscopic Survey: BAO and RSD measurements from the anisotropic power spectrum of the quasar sample between redshift 0.8 and 2.2, *Mon. Not. Roy. Astron. Soc.* **499**, 210 (2020).
53. H. du Mas des Bourboux *et al.*, The Completed SDSS-IV Extended Baryon Oscillation Spectroscopic Survey: Baryon Acoustic Oscillations with Lyα Forests, *Astrophys. J.* **901**, p. 153 (2020).

54. R. Jiménez, L. Verde, T. Treu and D. Stern, Constraints on the equation of state of dark energy and the Hubble constant from stellar ages and the CMB, *Astrophys. J.* **593**, 622 (2003), arXiv:astro-ph/0302560.
55. J. Simon, L. Verde and R. Jimenez, Constraints on the redshift dependence of the dark energy potential, *Phys. Rev.* **D71**, p. 123001 (2005), arXiv:astro-ph/0412269.
56. D. Stern, R. Jiménez, L. Verde, M. Kamionkowski and S. A. Stanford, Cosmic Chronometers: Constraining the Equation of State of Dark Energy. I: H(z) Measurements, *JCAP* **1002**, p. 008 (2010), arXiv:0907.3149.
57. M. Moresco et al., Improved constraints on the expansion rate of the Universe up to z 1.1 from the spectroscopic evolution of cosmic chronometers, *JCAP* **1208**, p. 006 (2012), arXiv:1201.3609.
58. C. Zhang, H. Zhang, S. Yuan, T.-J. Zhang and Y.-C. Sun, Four new observational $H(z)$ data from luminous red galaxies in the Sloan Digital Sky Survey data release seven, *Res. Astron. Astrophys.* **14**, 1221 (2014), arXiv:1207.4541.
59. M. Moresco, Raising the bar: new constraints on the Hubble parameter with cosmic chronometers at $z \sim 2$, *Mon. Not. Roy. Astron. Soc.* **450**, L16 (2015), arXiv:1503.01116.
60. M. Moresco, L. Pozzetti, A. Cimatti, R. Jiménez, C. Maraston, L. Verde, D. Thomas, A. Citro, R. Tojeiro and D. Wilkinson, A 6% measurement of the Hubble parameter at $z \sim 0.45$: direct evidence of the epoch of cosmic re-acceleration, *JCAP* **1605**, p. 014 (2016), arXiv:1601.01701.
61. A. L. Ratsimbazafy, S. I. Loubser, S. M. Crawford, C. M. Cress, B. A. Bassett, R. C. Nichol and P. Väisänen, Age-dating Luminous Red Galaxies observed with the Southern African Large Telescope, *Mon. Not. Roy. Astron. Soc.* **467**, 3239 (2017), arXiv:1702.00418.
62. K. Said, M. Colless, C. Magoulas, J. R. Lucey and M. J. Hudson, Joint analysis of 6dFGS and SDSS peculiar velocities for the growth rate of cosmic structure and tests of gravity, *Mon. Not. Roy. Astron. Soc.* **497**, 1275 (2020).
63. F. Simpson, C. Blake, J. A. Peacock, I. Baldry, J. Bland-Hawthorn, A. Heavens, C. Heymans, J. Loveday and P. Norberg, Galaxy and mass assembly: Redshift space distortions from the clipped galaxy field, *Phys. Rev.* **D93**, p. 023525 (2016), arXiv:1505.03865.
64. C. Blake et al., Galaxy And Mass Assembly (GAMA): improved cosmic growth measurements using multiple tracers of large-scale structure, *Mon. Not. Roy. Astron. Soc.* **436**, p. 3089 (2013), arXiv:1309.5556.
65. F. G. Mohammad et al., The VIMOS Public Extragalactic Redshift Survey (VIPERS): Unbiased clustering estimate with VIPERS slit assignment, *Astron. Astrophys.* **619**, p. A17 (2018), arXiv:1807.05999.
66. T. Okumura et al., The Subaru FMOS galaxy redshift survey (FastSound). IV. New constraint on gravity theory from redshift space distortions at $z \sim 1.4$, *Publ. Astron. Soc. Jap.* **68**, p. 38 (2016), arXiv:1511.08083.
67. J. Solà Peracaula, Brans–Dicke gravity: From Higgs physics to (dynamical) dark energy, *Int. J. Mod. Phys.* **D27**, p. 1847029 (2018), arXiv:1805.09810.
68. J. de Cruz Pérez and J. Solà Peracaula, Brans–Dicke cosmology mimicking running vacuum, *Mod. Phys. Lett.* **A33**, p. 1850228 (2018), arXiv:1809.03329.
69. N. Banerjee and D. Pavon, Cosmic acceleration without quintessence, *Phys. Rev. D* **63**, p. 043504 (2001).
70. N. Banerjee and D. Pavon, A Quintessence scalar field in Brans-Dicke theory, *Class. Quant. Grav.* **18**, p. 593 (2001), arXiv:gr-qc/0012098.

71. J. Solà, Cosmological constant and vacuum energy: old and new ideas, *J. Phys. Conf. Ser.* **453**, p. 012015 (2013), arXiv:1306.1527.
72. J. Solà and A. Gómez-Valent, The $\bar{\Lambda}$CDM cosmology: From inflation to dark energy through running Λ, *Int. J. Mod. Phys. D* **24**, p. 1541003 (2015).
73. A. Gómez-Valent, Vacuum energy in Quantum Field Theory and Cosmology, PhD thesis, ICC, Barcelona U.2017. arXiv:1710.01978.
74. C. Moreno-Pulido and J. Solà, Running vacuum in quantum field theory in curved spacetime: renormalizing ρ_{vac} without $\sim m^4$ terms, *Eur. Phys. J. C* **80**, p. 692 (2020), arXiv:2005.03164.
75. J. Solà, Dark energy: A Quantum fossil from the inflationary Universe?, *J. Phys. A* **41**, p. 164066 (2008), arXiv:0710.4151.
76. J. A. S. Lima, S. Basilakos and J. Sola, Expansion History with Decaying Vacuum: A Complete Cosmological Scenario, *Mon. Not. Roy. Astron. Soc.* **431**, 923 (2013).
77. J. Solà, The cosmological constant and entropy problems: mysteries of the present with profound roots in the past, *Int. J. Mod. Phys. D* **24**, p. 1544027 (2015).
78. D. Blas, J. Lesgourgues and T. Tram, The Cosmic Linear Anisotropy Solving System (CLASS) II: Approximation schemes, *JCAP* **1107**, p. 034 (2011), arXiv:1104.2933.
79. V. Salvatelli, N. Said, M. Bruni, A. Melchiorri and D. Wands, Indications of a late-time interaction in the dark sector, *Phys. Rev. Lett.* **113**, p. 181301 (2014), arXiv:1406.7297.
80. M. Martinelli, N. B. Hogg, S. Peirone, M. Bruni and D. Wands, Constraints on the interacting vacuum–geodesic CDM scenario, *Mon. Not. Roy. Astron. Soc.* **488**, 3423 (2019), arXiv:1902.10694.
81. J. Solà Peracaula, J. de Cruz Pérez and A. Gómez-Valent, Dynamical dark energy vs. $\Lambda =$ const in light of observations, *EPL* **121**, p. 39001 (2018).
82. B. Audren, J. Lesgourgues, K. Benabed and S. Prunet, Conservative Constraints on Early Cosmology: an illustration of the Monte Python cosmological parameter inference code, *JCAP* **1302**, p. 001 (2013), arXiv:1210.7183.
83. D. J. Spiegelhalter, N. G. Best, B. P. Carlin and A. van der Linde, Bayesian measures of model complexity and fit, *J. Roy. Stat. Soc.* **64**, p. 583 (2002).
84. C. Heymans *et al.*, KiDS-1000 Cosmology: Multi-probe weak gravitational lensing and spectroscopic galaxy clustering constraints, *Astron. Astrophys.* **646**, p. A140 (2021).

Cosmological tensions: Hints for a new concordance model?

E. Di Valentino

School of Mathematics and Statistics, University of Sheffield,
Hounsfield Road, Sheffield S3 7RH, United Kingdom
E-mail: e.divalentino@sheffield.ac.uk

The Cosmic Microwave Background (CMB) temperature and polarization anisotropy measurements have provided strong confirmation of the ΛCDM model of structure formation. Even if this model can explain incredibly well the observations in a vast range of scales and epochs, with the improvement of the experimental sensitivity, a few interesting tensions between the cosmological probes, and anomalies in the CMB data, have emerged with different statistical significance. While some portion of these discrepancies may be due to systematic errors, their persistence across probes strongly hints at cracks in the standard ΛCDM cosmological scenario. The most statistically significant is the Hubble constant puzzle and I will show a couple of interesting extended cosmological scenarios that can alleviate it.

Keywords: CMB; cosmology; H_0 tension.

1. Introduction

The aphorism "All the models are wrong, but some are useful" it is particularly true for the standard model adopted in cosmology. Actually, the model that has now practically been selected as the "standard" cosmological model is the Lambda Cold Dark Matter (ΛCDM) scenario, where Λ is the cosmological constant, that provides a remarkable fit to the bulk of available cosmological data.

However, despite its incredible success, ΛCDM harbours large areas of phenomenology and ignorance. For example, it still cannot explain key concepts in our understanding of the structure and evolution of the Universe, at the moment based on unknown quantities, that are also its largest components. In addition, their physical evidence comes from cosmological and astrophysical observations only, without strong theoretical motivations. In particular, the ΛCDM models is based on three unknown pillars:

- *Inflation*: an early stage of accelerated expansion which produces the initial, tiny, density perturbations, needed for structure formation,
- *Dark Matter*: a clustering matter component to facilitate structure formation,
- *Dark Energy*: an energy component to explain the current stage of accelerated expansion.

Furthermore, the ΛCDM model is based on the simplest form for these unknown quantities, mostly motivated by the computational simplicity, i.e. the theoretical predictions under CDM for several observables are, in general, easier to compute and include fewer free parameters than most other solutions. These specific solutions for ΛCDM are:

- Inflation is given by a single, minimally coupled, slow-rolling scalar field;
- Dark Matter (DM) is a pressureless fluid made of cold, i.e., with low momentum, and collisionless particles;
- Dark Energy (DE) is a cosmological constant term.

Therefore, the 6 parameter ΛCDM model lacks the deep underpinnings a model requires to approach fundamental physics laws. It can be rightly considered, at best, as an effective theory of an underlying physical theory, yet to be discovered. In this situation, we must be careful not to cling to the model too tightly or to risk missing the appearance of departures from the paradigm. With the improvement of the number and the accuracy of the observations, deviations from ΛCDM may be expected. And, actually, discrepancies among key cosmological parameters of the models have emerged with different statistical significance. While some proportion of these discrepancies may have a systematic origin, their persistence across probes should require multiple and unrelated errors, strongly hinting at cracks in the standard cosmological scenario and the necessity of new physics. These tensions can indicate a failure of the canonical ΛCDM model.

2. The H_0 tension

The most statistically significant, long-lasting and widely persisting tension is the H_0 disagreement between the Planck estimate obtained assuming a "vanilla" ΛCDM cosmological model, i.e. $H_0 = 67.27 \pm 0.60$ km/s/Mpc at 68% CL,[1] and the local measurements obtained by the SH0ES collaboration, the so called R19[2] ($H_0 = 74.03 \pm 1.42$ km/s/Mpc at 68% CL) or R20[3] using the parallax measurements of Gaia EDR3 ($H_0 = 73.2 \pm 1.3$ km/s/Mpc at 68% CL).

However there are other many important measurements of the H_0 parameter. On the same side of Planck, i.e. preferring smaller values of H_0 we have the ground based CMB telescope, South Pole Telescope (SPT-3G)[4] that gives $H_0 = 68.8 \pm 1.5$ km/s/Mpc at 68% CL in ΛCDM, or Atacama Cosmology Telescope (ACT-DR4) + Wilkinson Microwave Anisotropy Probe (WMAP)[5] finding $H_0 = 67.6 \pm 1.1$ km/s/Mpc at 68% CL in ΛCDM. Moreover, there are the Baryon Acoustic Oscillations (BAO) + Big Bang Nucleosynthesis (BBN) from BOSS and eBOSS estimates,[6] that provide $H_0 = 67.35 \pm 0.97$ km/s/Mpc at 68% CL. These estimates are CMB independent but still ΛCDM dependent.

Moreover, we have many other direct late time measurements on the same side of SH0ES, i.e. preferring higher values of H_0 (see for example the compilation in Ref.[7] and references therein). For example, we have the measurements obtained from the Supernovae calibrated with the Cepheids,[3,8–10] or with the Tip of the Red Giant

Branch (TRGB),[8,11–14] where we find the well discussed Freedman et al. 2020 measurement[12] or the more updated Freedman 2021[15] that is completely in the middle between early and late measurements, so it can't really say anything about the tensions. Moreover, this TRGB-SNIa measurement has been reanalysed independently by Ref.[16] and we can see a shift towards higher values, more in agreement with SH0ES. Then we have the measurements obtained from the Supernovae calibrated with MIRAS,[17] variable red giant stars from older stellar populations, or the Megamaser Cosmology Project,[18] that measures H_0 avoiding any distance ladder and by providing the geometric distance directly into the Hubble flow. We have also measurements of the Hubble constant based on the Tully-Fisher Relation,[19,20] that are using as calibrators Cepheids and TRGB, or on the Surface Brightness Fluctuation,[21,22] that are substitutive distance ladder for long range indicator, and can be calibrated by both Cepheids and TRGB giving the same result,[21] or on Type II Supernovae[23] used as standardisable candles and calibrated again with both Cepheids and TRGB. Finally we have the strong lensing results, and, while the previous H0LiCOW[24] and STRIDES[25] results were more in agreement with SH0ES, the latest TDCOSMO+SLAC[26] constraints are shifted towards lower values, but with error bars much more weak, so they are not able to discriminate between SH0ES and Planck. This happens because the previous analyses were assuming a specific form for the mass density profile of the lens, and while this assumption is relaxed in a more agnostic approach, the constraints change significantly. This means that these kinds of measurements, even if cosmological model independent, are instead astrophysical model dependent.

The robustness of the H_0 disagreement can be proven considering several combinations of the late time measurements, as it has been done in Ref.,[7] where it is shown that also removing some of the most precise and strong measurements the discordance ranges between $\sim 3-6\sigma$, making it very difficult to be explained by systematic errors. Actually, we see a high precision and consistency of the data at both ends, the indirect ones preferring a lower value and the direct ones a higher value. Therefore, a possible solution should have enough rigor to explain multiple observations. A recent Review[15] seems to suggest that the situation is improving during the last 4 decades, with the H_0 measurement converging towards the same value. However, while in the past the tension was within the same types of measurements and at the same redshifts and thus pointing directly to systematics, now there are no late universe measurements below the early ones and vice versa, as expected in case of a scatter around the true value. Therefore, since it is hard to believe that a single type of systematic error could effectively resolve the Hubble constant tension, and because the discordance is robust under the removal of the measurements of any single type of object, mode or calibration, it is difficult to believe that unrelated systematic errors could coherently bias the measurements in the same direction and solve the H_0 puzzle.

3. Solutions

An alternative possibility for solving the Hubble tension is instead to change the assumptions about the cosmological model considered to derive the indirect constraints, modifying directly the three unknown pillars on which the standard vanilla ΛCDM is based.

3.1. *First pillar: Dark matter*

For example, we can consider modifications in the dark matter sector.

A classical extension is the effective number of relativistic degrees of freedom N_{eff},[27] i.e. additional relativistic matter at recombination, corresponding to a modification of the expansion history of the universe at early times, before the recombination epoch. The radiation density ρ_r can be recast as a function of the photon density ρ_γ, where we it is assumed the ratio $T_\nu/T_\gamma = (4/11)^{1/3}$ between the background temperatures of neutrinos and photons under the approximation of instantaneous neutrino decoupling:

$$\rho_r = \rho_\gamma \left[1 + \frac{7}{8}\left(\frac{4}{11}\right)^{4/3} N_{\text{eff}}\right]. \tag{1}$$

The expected value is $N_{\text{eff}} = 3.046$,[28–32] if we assume standard electroweak interactions and three active massless neutrinos, but can be larger in presence of extra relativistic particles at recombination, such as, for example, sterile neutrinos[33–37] or thermal axions,[38–45] or decaying dark matter.[46–48] Additional relativistic degrees of freedom other than the three standard model neutrinos will produce more radiation, smearing and shifting of the acoustic peaks in the damping tail of the CMB temperature power spectrum, and delaying the matter to radiation equivalence,[49,50] with a corresponding increase of the early Integrated Sachs-Wolfe (eISW) effect, and therefore of the amplitude of the peak around multipoles $\ell \sim 200$. This parameter was often considered to increase the H_0 estimate because of the strong positive correlation present between these two quantities. However, N_{eff} should be around $N_{\text{eff}} \approx 3.95$ in order to obtain a value of H_0 from Planck 2018 + BAO + Pantheon in perfect agreement with SH0ES,[51] and this value is significantly excluded by the latest Planck 2018 data. In particular, even when N_{eff} can vary freely, the H_0 tension is still above 3.6σ, and therefore this is no longer a suitable solution.

3.2. *Second pillar: Dark energy*

For example, we can consider modifications in the dark energy sector.

A classical extension is a varying dark energy equation of state, that is a modification of the expansion history of the universe at late times, after the recombination epoch. In this case we replace the cosmological constant Λ in the expansion rate of the Universe with a Dark Energy with an equation of state w free to vary. A dark energy component with a time-varying equation of state $w \equiv p_{\rm DE}/\rho_{\rm DE}$ modifies the Hubble rate through the first Friedmann equation:

$$H^2(z) = H_0^2 \left[\Omega_r(1+z)^4 + \Omega_m(1+z)^3 + \Omega_{\rm DE}(1+z)^{3(1+w)} + \Omega_k(1+z)^2\right] \quad (2)$$

where Ω_r, Ω_m, $\Omega_{\rm DE}$ and Ω_k are the density parameters, evaluated at present time, for radiation, matter, dark energy and curvature for, and for the case $w = -1$ the dark energy component acts as a cosmological constant of density parameter $\Omega_{\rm DE}$. Changing the dark energy equation of state w, we are introducing a geometrical degeneracy with the Hubble constant that will be unconstrained using the CMB data only, resulting in agreement with SH0ES within 2σ at the price of a phantom dark energy with $w < -1$. Actually, a likelihood analysis of Planck 2018 gives $w = -1.58^{+0.16}_{-0.35}$ at 68% CL and $H_0 > 69.9 \,\rm km\, s^{-1}\, Mpc^{-1}$ at 95% CL.[1] A phantom Dark energy implies that the energy density of this component increases with time in an expanding universe that will end in a Big Rip.[52] Moreover, it has many theoretical problems, but there exist models that expect an effective energy density with a phantom equation of state that can avoid them.

3.3. *Third pillar: Inflation*

For example, we can consider modifications in the inflationary sector.

Actually, a strong correlation is present between the scalar spectral index n_s of the primordial density fluctuations and the Hubble constant H_0. Therefore it is natural to ask if the simple Harrison-Zel'dovich model is able to solve the Hubble tension, or if there is support for a more complicated perturbation spectrum.

The inflationary theory predicts that the primordial spectrum should be a power law with a value of the spectral index to be nearly one, $n_s \sim 1$, reflecting the constancy of the Hubble horizon during inflation, but at the same time not exactly one, due to the dynamics of the inflaton field. An exact value of $n_s = 1$ is indeed not expected in inflation and would coincide with the phenomenological model proposed by Harrison,[53] Zel'dovich,[54] and Peebles and Yu,[55] known as Harrison - Zel'dovich (HZ) spectrum, proposed well before the formulation of inflation, and corresponding to perfect scale-invariance of the fluctuations. This model has one parameter fewer than standard vanilla ΛCDM model, and it is therefore less complicated (from the point of view of the number of parameters). While it is still possible to have inflationary models with spectral index nearly identical to HZ, a measurement of n_s close to, but different from, one should be considered as a further corroboration of inflation. The presence of the Hubble tension in current cosmological data does not rule out a HZ spectrum at high statistical significance because it predicts a Hubble constant value in agreement with SH0ES.[56] See also Ref.[57] for an updated analysis of the available CMB data in light of the different inflationary scenarios.

3.4. *Examples of formally successful models in solving H_0*

It is possible to classify the formally successful models in solving H_0 looking at the Hubble constant that a model predicts once the Planck 2018 data are analysed (see Table B1 of Ref.[58]). In this case, without any consideration about the goodness of the fit, excellent solutions in solving the H_0 tensions are late time solutions, i.e. mostly Dark Energy and Modified gravity models.

In these class of models we can find for example the Parker Vacuum Metamorphosis (VM),[59–61] which has a phase transition in the nature of the vacuum, is physically motivated by quantum gravitational effects and can mimic a phantom DE behaviour at low redshifts. This model can solve the Hubble tension in an excellent way.[62–64] For this model the expansion rate above and below the phase transition for a flat universe is for $z > z_t$:

$$\frac{H^2}{H_0^2} = \Omega_m(1+z)^3 + \Omega_r(1+z)^4 - M\left\{1 - \left[3\left(\frac{4}{3\Omega_m}\right)^4 M(1-M-\Omega_r)^3\right]^{-1}\right\}, \quad (3)$$

and for $z \leq z_t$:

$$\frac{H^2}{H_0^2} = (1-M)(1+z)^4 + M, \quad (4)$$

where $M = m^2/(12H_0^2)$ and the redshift of the phase transition is

$$z_t = -1 + \frac{3\Omega_m}{4(1-M-\Omega_r)}. \quad (5)$$

Therefore, above the phase transition, the universe behaves as one with matter and radiation plus a constant, and after the phase transition it effectively has a dark radiation component that rapidly redshifts away leaving a de Sitter phase. The original model did not include an explicit high redshift cosmological constant and therefore we have:

$$\Omega_m = \frac{4}{3}\left[3M(1-M-\Omega_r)^3\right]^{1/4}, \quad (6)$$

i.e. the parameter M is fixed and depends on the matter density, and this model has the same number of degrees of freedom as ΛCDM. For this model, the DE equation of state behaviour is phantom today, and more deeply phantom in the past. In the case without the cosmological constant, instead, there is no DE above the phase transition. If we now fit the current cosmological data with this model, we obtain H_0 exactly in agreement with SH0ES even if BAO and Pantheon SnIa data are included.[63] However, this considerably worsened the fit of the full Planck2018+BAO+Pantheon data combination because the model fails to recover the shape of H(z) at low redshifts.

Additionally, we can also consider an extended VM where M is an independent parameter. In this case, the massive scalar field has a vacuum expectation value that manifests as a cosmological constant, and the conditions that the transition happens in the past plus the Ω_{DE} is always positive are assumed:

$$\frac{4}{3}(1 - M - \Omega_r) \leq \Omega_m \leq \frac{4}{3}\left[3M(1 - M - \Omega_r)^3\right]^{1/4}, \qquad (7)$$

This more ad hoc VM model that includes a cosmological constant, i.e. allowing the vacuum criticality parameter M to float, is even better in fitting the CMB cosmological data alone,[63] but still can't recover the shape of H(z) at low redshifts preferred by BAO+Pantheon.

The problem is that BAO+Pantheon measurements constrain the product of H_0 and the sound horizon r_s. Therefore, in order to have a higher H_0 value in agreement with SH0ES, we need r_s near 137 Mpc. However, Planck, by assuming ΛCDM, prefers r_s near 147 Mpc. Therefore, a cosmological solution that can increase H_0 and at the same time can lower the sound horizon inferred from CMB data is promising to put in agreement all the measurements.[65] Therefore, the late time solutions, as wCDM, are disfavored by the full dataset combination because they increase H_0 but leave r_s unaltered. On the contrary, the early time solutions, as N_{eff} or Early Dark Energy,[66–68] move in the right direction both the parameters, but can't solve completely the H_0 tension with SH0ES, as we can see in Fig. 3 of Ref.[69]

At this point, it is possible to classify the formally successful models in solving H_0 looking at the Hubble constant that a model predicts once the Planck 2018 data combined with additional probes are analysed (see Table B2 of Ref.[58]). In this case, again without any consideration about the goodness of the fit, excellent solutions in solving the H_0 tensions are mostly early time solutions.

However, we should be careful in ruling out all the late time solutions because of the disagreement with the BAO data. Let's consider for example an Interacting model IDE, where DM and DE share interactions other than gravitational. Actually, dark matter and dark energy are described as separate fluids not sharing interactions beyond gravitational ones, even if from a microphysical perspective it is hard to imagine how non-gravitational DM-DE interactions can be avoided, if not forbidden by a fundamental symmetry. At the background level, the conservation equations for the pressureless DM and DE components can be decoupled into two separate equations with an inclusion of an arbitrary function, Q, known as the coupling or interacting function:

$$\dot{\rho}_c + 3\mathcal{H}\rho_c = Q, \qquad (8)$$
$$\dot{\rho}_{DE} + 3\mathcal{H}(1+w)\rho_{DE} = -Q. \qquad (9)$$

We assume the phenomenological form for the interaction rate:

$$Q = \mathcal{H}\xi\rho_{DE} \qquad (10)$$

proportional to the dark energy density ρ_{DE} and the conformal Hubble rate $\mathcal{H}$, via a negative dimensionless parameter ξ quantifying the strength of the coupling, to avoid early-time instabilities. In this scenario of IDE the tension on H_0 between the Planck satellite and SH0ES is completely solved. The coupling could affect the value of the present matter energy density Ω_m. Therefore, if within an interacting model Ω_m is smaller (because for negative ξ the dark matter density will decay into the dark energy one), a higher value of H_0 would be required in order to satisfy the peaks structure of CMB observations, which accurately determine the value of $\Omega_m h^2$ (see Table 1 of Ref.[70]). Therefore, we can safely combine the two datasets together, and we obtain a non-zero dark matter-dark energy coupling ξ at more than 5 standard deviations, i.e. $\xi = -0.66^{+0.09}_{-0.13}$ at 68% CL. For this model we have only an upper limit for the matter density Ω_m, however the IDE scenario is still in agreement with the local structures. Actually, within interacting cosmologies the growth of dark matter perturbations is larger than in uncoupled models.[71] This feature is general for models with negative coupling and in which the energy exchange among the dark sectors is proportional to ρ_{DE}, due to a suppression of the friction term and an enhancement of the source term in the differential growth equation.

For this model, the addition of low-redshift measurements, as BAO data, is extremely important, because it breaks the correlation between the parameters that can produce a fake detection for the coupling (see Ref.[72]). And Planck 2018 + BAO still hints at the presence of a coupling, albeit at a lower statistical significance. Also for these datasets the Hubble constant value is larger than that obtained in the case of a pure ΛCDM scenario, enough to bring the H_0 tension at 2.4σ.[73] This residual tension is however of difficult interpretation. In fact, BAO are formed in the early universe, when baryons are strongly coupled to photons, and the gravitational collapse due to the CDM is counterbalanced by the radiation pressure. Sound waves that propagate in the early universe imprint a characteristic scale on the CMB. Since the scale of these oscillations can be measured at recombination, BAO is considered a "standard ruler". These fluctuations have evolved and we can observe BAO at low redshifts in the distribution of galaxies. Since the data reduction process leading to these measurements requires assumptions about the fiducial cosmology, BAO is model dependent, and the model assumed to extrapolate the data is the standard ΛCDM scenario. In other words, the tension between Planck + BAO and SH0ES could be due to a statistical fluctuation in this case because the modified scenario of interacting dark energy could affect the BAO measurements. In fact, the full procedure which leads to the BAO constraints carried out by the different collaborations might be not necessarily valid in extended DE models. For instance, the BOSS collaboration advises caution when using their BAO measurements (both the pre- and post- reconstruction measurements) in more exotic dark energy cosmologies, because their reliability has been assessed only for modifications of the expansion history before recombination, and late modifications that can be parametrized by $w_0 w_a$. Therefore, BAO constraints themselves might need to be revised in a non-trivial manner when applied to constrain extended dark energy cosmologies, such as the IDE model that is showing a coupling different from ΛCDM at more than 5σ.

The IDE model can also solve the M_B tension. It has been pointed out in Ref.[74] that the SH0ES Collaboration, combining together anchors, cepheids and calibrators, produces a constraint on the SN absolute magnitude M_B, that depends on the astrophysical properties of the sources and is independent of cosmology. After that, in order to obtain the H_0 measurement, it uses the Hubble-ow supernovae in the redshift range $0.023 \leq z \leq 0.15$ to probe the luminosity distance-redshift relation, and it adopts a cosmography with $q_0 = 0.55$ and $j_0 = 1$. Therefore, the use of a prior on the Hubble constant could bias the conclusions about hockey-stick dark energy scenarios, i.e. models that have a transition at very-low redshift ($z \leq 0.1$), that can solve the Hubble tension producing a disagreement with M_B at more than 5σ.[75] Therefore, rather than explaining the H_0 tension, one should instead focus on the supernova absolute magnitude tension M_B, because the SH0ES team does not directly measure H_0. The M_B approach allows to skip the cosmography part, and to avoid the double counting of SN in the redshift range $0.023 \leq z \leq 0.15$ when combined with the Pantheon sample. Actually, imposing a H_0 prior, the whole information on the shape of the SN magnitude-redshift relation is lost, as also noticed by Ref.[76] If we consider the M_B parameter, instead, we have that the Planck constraint on the the SN absolute magnitude using the parametric-free inverse distance ladder predicts $M_B = -19.401 \pm 0.027$ mag, while the the SN measurements from SH0ES corresponds to $M_B = -19.244 \pm 0.037$ mag, corresponding to a 3.4σ tension. A classification of the models that can solve the M_B tension has been performed in Ref.,[77] finding that the best model is a closed universe with the electron mass free to vary.[78]

When an IDE model is considered, instead, the M_B tension is always at 2.4σ considering a combination of Pantheon + BAO + BBN, and is completely solved below 1σ when a gaussian prior on M_B is included, with an indication for a coupling different from zero at more than 95% CL.[79] Therefore, an IDE model can alleviate the M_B tension, as well as the H_0 disagreement, and as it is shown in Ref.[79] it is not disfavoured by the Pantheon magnitude-redshift relation.

4. Conclusions

To summarize the state-of-the-arte we have a long-standing Hubble tension that is presenting a serious limitation to precision cosmology. A solution to this problem is mandatory at this point.

On one side early time modifications of the standard models seem most promising for putting in agreement CMB and SH0ES, and agree also with BAO+Pantheon data, but unfortunately they don't completely solve the H_0 tension. On the other hand, late time modifications are instead more powerful in solving the H_0 tension, but are producing a disagreement with the additional BAO+Pantheon data. However, we can have working models, such as the simple IDE scenario, that can relieve the H_0 tension hinting to an interaction different from zero at more than 5σ. However, when BAO data are added in the analysis the Hubble constant tension is restored at about 2.4σ, and this residual tension is difficult to interpret because of the reliability of the BAO data for this model. Alternative solutions can involve the inflationary paradigm, and in this context we saw that a HZ spectrum can solve the H_0 tension without new physics and with fewer parameters free to vary, but is disfavoured by a model comparison with the standard ΛCDM model.

Concluding, more than 300 models have been proposed (see Ref.[58]) to solve the Hubble tension, but at the moment no specific proposal makes a strong case for being highly likely or far better than all others. We therefore need new observations and the investigation of alternative theoretical models and solutions.

Acknowledgment

EDV is supported by a Royal Society Dorothy Hodgkin Research Fellowship.

References

1. N. Aghanim *et al.* [Planck], Astron. Astrophys. **641**, A6 (2020) [erratum: Astron. Astrophys. **652**, C4 (2021)] doi:10.1051/0004-6361/201833910 [arXiv:1807.06209 [astro-ph.CO]].
2. A. G. Riess, S. Casertano, W. Yuan, L. M. Macri and D. Scolnic, Astrophys. J. **876**, no. 1, 85 (2019) doi:10.3847/1538-4357/ab1422 [arXiv:1903.07603 [astro-ph.CO]].
3. A. G. Riess, S. Casertano, W. Yuan, J. B. Bowers, L. Macri, J. C. Zinn and D. Scolnic, Astrophys. J. Lett. **908**, no. 1, L6 (2021) doi:10.3847/2041-8213/abdbaf [arXiv:2012.08534 [astro-ph.CO]].
4. D. Dutcher *et al.* [SPT-3G], Phys. Rev. D **104**, no. 2, 022003 (2021) doi:10.1103/PhysRevD.104.022003 [arXiv:2101.01684 [astro-ph.CO]].
5. S. Aiola *et al.* [ACT], JCAP **12**, 047 (2020) doi:10.1088/1475-7516/2020/12/047 [arXiv:2007.07288 [astro-ph.CO]].
6. S. Alam *et al.* [eBOSS], Phys. Rev. D **103**, no. 8, 083533 (2021) doi:10.1103/PhysRevD.103.083533 [arXiv:2007.08991 [astro-ph.CO]].
7. E. Di Valentino, Mon. Not. Roy. Astron. Soc. **502**, no. 2, 2065-2073 (2021) doi:10.1093/mnras/stab187 [arXiv:2011.00246 [astro-ph.CO]].
8. M. J. Reid, D. W. Pesce and A. G. Riess, Astrophys. J. Lett. **886**, no. 2, L27 (2019) doi:10.3847/2041-8213/ab552d [arXiv:1908.05625 [astro-ph.GA]].
9. L. Breuval, P. Kervella, R. I. Anderson, A. G. Riess, F. Arenou, B. Trahin, A. Mérand, A. Gallenne, W. Gieren and J. Storm, *et al.* Astron. Astrophys. **643**, A115 (2020) doi:10.1051/0004-6361/202038633 [arXiv:2006.08763 [astro-ph.SR]].
10. C. R. Burns *et al.* [CSP], Astrophys. J. **869**, no. 1, 56 (2018) doi:10.3847/1538-4357/aae51c [arXiv:1809.06381 [astro-ph.CO]].
11. J. Soltis, S. Casertano and A. G. Riess, Astrophys. J. Lett. **908**, no. 1, L5 (2021) doi:10.3847/2041-8213/abdbad [arXiv:2012.09196 [astro-ph.GA]].
12. W. L. Freedman, B. F. Madore, T. Hoyt, I. S. Jang, R. Beaton, M. G. Lee, A. Monson, J. Neeley and J. Rich, doi:10.3847/1538-4357/ab7339 [arXiv:2002.01550 [astro-ph.GA]].
13. W. Yuan, A. G. Riess, L. M. Macri, S. Casertano and D. Scolnic, Astrophys. J. **886**, 61 (2019) doi:10.3847/1538-4357/ab4bc9 [arXiv:1908.00993 [astro-ph.GA]].
14. I. S. Jang and M. G. Lee, Astrophys. J. **836**, no. 1, 74 (2017) doi:10.3847/1538-4357/836/1/74 [arXiv:1702.01118 [astro-ph.CO]].

15. W. L. Freedman, Astrophys. J. **919**, no. 1, 16 (2021) doi:10.3847/1538-4357/ac0e95 [arXiv:2106.15656 [astro-ph.CO]].
16. G. S. Anand et al. Astrophys. J., **932**, 1, 15 (2022) e-Print 2108.00007 [astro-ph. CO].
17. C. D. Huang, A. G. Riess, W. Yuan, L. M. Macri, N. L. Zakamska, S. Casertano, P. A. Whitelock, S. L. Hoffmann, A. V. Filippenko and D. Scolnic, doi:10.3847/1538-4357/ab5dbd [arXiv:1908.10883 [astro-ph.CO]].
18. D. W. Pesce, J. A. Braatz, M. J. Reid, A. G. Riess, D. Scolnic, J. J. Condon, F. Gao, C. Henkel, C. M. V. Impellizzeri and C. Y. Kuo, et al. Astrophys. J. Lett. **891**, no. 1, L1 (2020) doi:10.3847/2041-8213/ab75f0 [arXiv:2001.09213 [astro-ph.CO]].
19. E. Kourkchi, R. B. Tully, G. S. Anand, H. M. Courtois, A. Dupuy, J. D. Neill, L. Rizzi and M. Seibert, Astrophys. J. **896**, no. 1, 3 (2020) doi:10.3847/1538-4357/ab901c [arXiv:2004.14499 [astro-ph.GA]].
20. J. Schombert, S. McGaugh and F. Lelli, Astron. J. **160**, no. 2, 71 (2020) doi:10.3847/1538-3881/ab9d88 [arXiv:2006.08615 [astro-ph.CO]].
21. J. P. Blakeslee, J. B. Jensen, C. P. Ma, P. A. Milne and J. E. Greene, Astrophys. J. **911**, no. 1, 65 (2021) doi:10.3847/1538-4357/abe86a [arXiv:2101.02221 [astro-ph.CO]].
22. N. Khetan, L. Izzo, M. Branchesi, R. Wojtak, M. Cantiello, C. Murugeshan, A. Agnello, M. Della Valle, C. Gall and J. Hjorth, et al. Astron. Astrophys. **647**, A72 (2021) doi:10.1051/0004-6361/202039196 [arXiv:2008.07754 [astro-ph.CO]].
23. T. de Jaeger, B. E. Stahl, W. Zheng, A. V. Filippenko, A. G. Riess and L. Galbany, Mon. Not. Roy. Astron. Soc. **496**, no. 3, 3402-3411 (2020) doi:10.1093/mnras/staa1801 [arXiv:2006.03412 [astro-ph.CO]].
24. K. C. Wong, S. H. Suyu, G. C. F. Chen, C. E. Rusu, M. Millon, D. Sluse, V. Bonvin, C. D. Fassnacht, S. Taubenberger and M. W. Auger, et al. Mon. Not. Roy. Astron. Soc. **498**, no. 1, 1420-1439 (2020) doi:10.1093/mnras/stz3094 [arXiv:1907.04869 [astro-ph.CO]].
25. A. J. Shajib et al. [DES], Mon. Not. Roy. Astron. Soc. **494**, no. 4, 6072-6102 (2020) doi:10.1093/mnras/staa828 [arXiv:1910.06306 [astro-ph.CO]].
26. S. Birrer, A. J. Shajib, A. Galan, M. Millon, T. Treu, A. Agnello, M. Auger, G. C. F. Chen, L. Christensen and T. Collett, et al. Astron. Astrophys. **643**, A165 (2020) doi:10.1051/0004-6361/202038861 [arXiv:2007.02941 [astro-ph.CO]].
27. G. Steigman, D. N. Schramm and J. E. Gunn, Phys. Lett. B **66**, 202-204 (1977) doi:10.1016/0370-2693(77)90176-9
28. G. Mangano, G. Miele, S. Pastor, T. Pinto, O. Pisanti and P. D. Serpico, Nucl. Phys. B **729**, 221-234 (2005) doi:10.1016/j.nuclphysb.2005.09.041 [arXiv:hep-ph/0506164 [hep-ph]].
29. P. F. de Salas and S. Pastor, JCAP **07**, 051 (2016) doi:10.1088/1475-7516/2016/07/051 [arXiv:1606.06986 [hep-ph]].
30. K. Akita and M. Yamaguchi, JCAP **08**, 012 (2020) doi:10.1088/1475-7516/2020/08/012 [arXiv:2005.07047 [hep-ph]].
31. J. Froustey, C. Pitrou and M. C. Volpe, JCAP **12**, 015 (2020) doi:10.1088/1475-7516/2020/12/015 [arXiv:2008.01074 [hep-ph]].
32. J. J. Bennett, G. Buldgen, P. F. De Salas, M. Drewes, S. Gariazzo, S. Pastor and Y. Y. Y. Wong, JCAP **04**, 073 (2021) doi:10.1088/1475-7516/2021/04/073 [arXiv:2012.02726 [hep-ph]].
33. A. Melchiorri, O. Mena, S. Palomares-Ruiz, S. Pascoli, A. Slosar and M. Sorel, JCAP **01**, 036 (2009) doi:10.1088/1475-7516/2009/01/036 [arXiv:0810.5133 [hep-ph]].
34. J. Kopp, M. Maltoni and T. Schwetz, Phys. Rev. Lett. **107**, 091801 (2011) doi:10.1103/PhysRevLett.107.091801 [arXiv:1103.4570 [hep-ph]].
35. J. Kopp, P. A. N. Machado, M. Maltoni and T. Schwetz, JHEP **05**, 050 (2013) doi:10.1007/JHEP05(2013)050 [arXiv:1303.3011 [hep-ph]].

36. S. Gariazzo, P. F. de Salas and S. Pastor, JCAP **07**, 014 (2019) doi:10.1088/1475-7516/2019/07/014 [arXiv:1905.11290 [astro-ph.CO]].
37. S. Hagstotz, P. F. de Salas, S. Gariazzo, M. Gerbino, M. Lattanzi, S. Vagnozzi, K. Freese and S. Pastor, [arXiv:2003.02289 [astro-ph.CO]].
38. A. Melchiorri, O. Mena and A. Slosar, Phys. Rev. D **76**, 041303 (2007) doi:10.1103/PhysRevD.76.041303 [arXiv:0705.2695 [astro-ph]].
39. S. Hannestad, A. Mirizzi, G. G. Raffelt and Y. Y. Y. Wong, JCAP **08**, 015 (2007) doi:10.1088/1475-7516/2007/08/015 [arXiv:0706.4198 [astro-ph]].
40. S. Hannestad, A. Mirizzi, G. G. Raffelt and Y. Y. Y. Wong, JCAP **04**, 019 (2008) doi:10.1088/1475-7516/2008/04/019 [arXiv:0803.1585 [astro-ph]].
41. M. Archidiacono, S. Hannestad, A. Mirizzi, G. Raffelt and Y. Y. Y. Wong, JCAP **10**, 020 (2013) doi:10.1088/1475-7516/2013/10/020 [arXiv:1307.0615 [astro-ph.CO]].
42. E. Giusarma, E. Di Valentino, M. Lattanzi, A. Melchiorri and O. Mena, Phys. Rev. D **90**, no. 4, 043507 (2014) doi:10.1103/PhysRevD.90.043507 [arXiv:1403.4852 [astro-ph.CO]].
43. E. Di Valentino, E. Giusarma, M. Lattanzi, O. Mena, A. Melchiorri and J. Silk, Phys. Lett. B **752**, 182-185 (2016) doi:10.1016/j.physletb.2015.11.025 [arXiv:1507.08665 [astro-ph.CO]].
44. W. Giarè, E. Di Valentino, A. Melchiorri and O. Mena, Mon. Not. Roy. Astron. Soc. **505**, no. 2, 2703-2711 (2021) doi:10.1093/mnras/stab1442 [arXiv:2011.14704 [astro-ph.CO]].
45. W. Giarè, F. Renzi, A. Melchiorri, O. Mena and E. Di Valentino, [arXiv:2110.00340 [astro-ph.CO]].
46. Z. Berezhiani, A. D. Dolgov and I. I. Tkachev, Phys. Rev. D **92**, no. 6, 061303 (2015) doi:10.1103/PhysRevD.92.061303 [arXiv:1505.03644 [astro-ph.CO]].
47. K. Vattis, S. M. Koushiappas and A. Loeb, Phys. Rev. D **99**, no. 12, 121302 (2019) doi:10.1103/PhysRevD.99.121302 [arXiv:1903.06220 [astro-ph.CO]].
48. N. Blinov, C. Keith and D. Hooper, JCAP **06**, 005 (2020) doi:10.1088/1475-7516/2020/06/005 [arXiv:2004.06114 [astro-ph.CO]].
49. Z. Hou, R. Keisler, L. Knox, M. Millea and C. Reichardt, Phys. Rev. D **87**, 083008 (2013) doi:10.1103/PhysRevD.87.083008 [arXiv:1104.2333 [astro-ph.CO]].
50. M. Archidiacono, E. Giusarma, S. Hannestad and O. Mena, Adv. High Energy Phys. **2013**, 191047 (2013) doi:10.1155/2013/191047 [arXiv:1307.0637 [astro-ph.CO]].
51. S. Vagnozzi, Phys. Rev. D **102**, no. 2, 023518 (2020) doi:10.1103/PhysRevD.102.023518 [arXiv:1907.07569 [astro-ph.CO]].
52. R. R. Caldwell, M. Kamionkowski and N. N. Weinberg, Phys. Rev. Lett. **91**, 071301 (2003) doi:10.1103/PhysRevLett.91.071301 [arXiv:astro-ph/0302506 [astro-ph]].
53. E. R. Harrison, Phys. Rev. D 1, 2726 (1970).
54. Y. B. Zel'dovich, Mon. Not. Roy. Astron. Soc. 160, (1972).
55. P. J. E. Peebles and J. T. Yu Astrophys. J. 162, 815 (1970).
56. E. Di Valentino, A. Melchiorri, Y. Fantaye and A. Heavens, Phys. Rev. D **98**, no. 6, 063508 (2018) doi:10.1103/PhysRevD.98.063508 [arXiv:1808.09201 [astro-ph.CO]].
57. M. Forconi, W. Giarè, E. Di Valentino and A. Melchiorri, [arXiv:2110.01695 [astro-ph.CO]].
58. E. Di Valentino, O. Mena, S. Pan, L. Visinelli, W. Yang, A. Melchiorri, D. F. Mota, A. G. Riess and J. Silk, Class. Quant. Grav. **38**, no. 15, 153001 (2021) doi:10.1088/1361-6382/ac086d [arXiv:2103.01183 [astro-ph.CO]].
59. L. Parker and D. A. T. Vanzella, Phys. Rev. D **69**, 104009 (2004) doi:10.1103/PhysRevD.69.104009 [arXiv:gr-qc/0312108 [gr-qc]].

60. L. Parker and A. Raval, Phys. Rev. D **62**, 083503 (2000) [erratum: Phys. Rev. D **67**, 029903 (2003)] doi:10.1103/PhysRevD.62.083503 [arXiv:gr-qc/0003103 [gr-qc]].
61. R. R. Caldwell, W. Komp, L. Parker and D. A. T. Vanzella, Phys. Rev. D **73**, 023513 (2006) doi:10.1103/PhysRevD.73.023513 [arXiv:astro-ph/0507622 [astro-ph]].
62. E. Di Valentino, E. V. Linder and A. Melchiorri, Phys. Rev. D **97**, no. 4, 043528 (2018) doi:10.1103/PhysRevD.97.043528 [arXiv:1710.02153 [astro-ph.CO]].
63. E. Di Valentino, E. V. Linder and A. Melchiorri, Phys. Dark Univ. **30**, 100733 (2020) doi:10.1016/j.dark.2020.100733 [arXiv:2006.16291 [astro-ph.CO]].
64. E. Di Valentino, S. Pan, W. Yang and L. A. Anchordoqui, Phys. Rev. D **103**, no. 12, 123527 (2021) doi:10.1103/PhysRevD.103.123527 [arXiv:2102.05641 [astro-ph.CO]].
65. L. Knox and M. Millea, Phys. Rev. D **101**, no. 4, 043533 (2020) doi:10.1103/PhysRevD.101.043533 [arXiv:1908.03663 [astro-ph.CO]].
66. V. Poulin, T. L. Smith, T. Karwal and M. Kamionkowski, Phys. Rev. Lett. **122**, no. 22, 221301 (2019) doi:10.1103/PhysRevLett.122.221301 [arXiv:1811.04083 [astro-ph.CO]].
67. J. C. Hill, E. Calabrese, S. Aiola, N. Battaglia, B. Bolliet, S. K. Choi, M. J. Devlin, A. J. Duivenvoorden, J. Dunkley and S. Ferraro, *et al.* [arXiv:2109.04451 [astro-ph.CO]].
68. V. Poulin, T. L. Smith and A. Bartlett, [arXiv:2109.06229 [astro-ph.CO]].
69. N. Arendse, R. J. Wojtak, A. Agnello, G. C. F. Chen, C. D. Fassnacht, D. Sluse, S. Hilbert, M. Millon, V. Bonvin and K. C. Wong, *et al.* Astron. Astrophys. **639**, A57 (2020) doi:10.1051/0004-6361/201936720 [arXiv:1909.07986 [astro-ph.CO]].
70. E. Di Valentino, A. Melchiorri, O. Mena and S. Vagnozzi, Phys. Dark Univ. **30**, 100666 (2020) doi:10.1016/j.dark.2020.100666 [arXiv:1908.04281 [astro-ph.CO]].
71. G. Caldera-Cabral, R. Maartens and B. M. Schaefer, JCAP **07**, 027 (2009) doi:10.1088/1475-7516/2009/07/027 [arXiv:0905.0492 [astro-ph.CO]].
72. E. Di Valentino and O. Mena, Mon. Not. Roy. Astron. Soc. **500**, no. 1, L22-L26 (2020) doi:10.1093/mnrasl/slaa175 [arXiv:2009.12620 [astro-ph.CO]].
73. E. Di Valentino, A. Melchiorri, O. Mena and S. Vagnozzi, Phys. Rev. D **101**, no. 6, 063502 (2020) doi:10.1103/PhysRevD.101.063502 [arXiv:1910.09853 [astro-ph.CO]].
74. D. Camarena and V. Marra, Phys. Rev. Res. **2**, no. 1, 013028 (2020) doi:10.1103/PhysRevResearch.2.013028 [arXiv:1906.11814 [astro-ph.CO]].
75. D. Camarena and V. Marra, Mon. Not. Roy. Astron. Soc. **504**, 5164-5171 (2021) doi:10.1093/mnras/stab1200 [arXiv:2101.08641 [astro-ph.CO]].
76. G. Efstathiou, Mon. Not. Roy. Astron. Soc. **505**, no. 3, 3866-3872 (2021) doi:10.1093/mnras/stab1588 [arXiv:2103.08723 [astro-ph.CO]].
77. N. Schöneberg, G. Franco Abellán, A. Pérez Sánchez, S. J. Witte, V. Poulin and J. Lesgourgues, [arXiv:2107.10291 [astro-ph.CO]].
78. T. Sekiguchi and T. Takahashi, Phys. Rev. D **103**, no. 8, 083507 (2021) doi:10.1103/PhysRevD.103.083507 [arXiv:2007.03381 [astro-ph.CO]].
79. R. C. Nunes and E. Di Valentino, Phys. Rev. D **104**, no. 6, 063529 (2021) doi:10.1103/PhysRevD.104.063529 [arXiv:2107.09151 [astro-ph.CO]].

Solving both H_0 and σ_8 tensions in $f(T)$ gravity

Emmanuel N. Saridakis

National Observatory of Athens, Lofos Nymfon, 11852 Athens, Greece
E-mail: msaridak@noa.gr

We report how to alleviate both the H_0 and σ_8 tensions simultaneously within $f(T)$ gravity. In particular, we consider the parametrization $f(T) = -T - 2\Lambda/M_P^2 + \alpha T^\beta$, where two out of the three parameters are independent. This model can efficiently fit observations solving the two tensions. To our knowledge, this is the first time where a modified gravity theory can alleviate both H_0 and σ_8 tensions simultaneously, hence, offering an additional argument in favor of gravitational modification.

Keywords: H_0 tension; σ_8 tension; $f(T)$ gravity; MG16 Proceedings.

1. Introduction

It is now well established that the Universe at late times experienced the transition from the matter era to the accelerated expansion phase. Although the simplest explanation would be the consideration of the cosmological constant, the corresponding problem related to the quantum-field-theoretical calculation of its value, as well as the possibility of a dynamical nature, led to two main paths of constructing extended scenarios. The first is to maintain general relativity as the underlying theory of gravity, and consider new, exotic forms of matter that constitute the concept of dark energy.[1,2] The second is to construct extended or modified theories of gravity, that posses general relativity as a low-energy limit, but which in general provide the extra degrees of freedom that can drive the dynamical universe acceleration.[3,4]

With the accumulation of cosmological data, experimental tensions may arise within ΛCDM cosmology. If they were to remain under the increasing precision of experimental observations, they would constitute, in a statistical sense, clear indications of new physics beyond ΛCDM. One recently well-debated tension relates the value of the Hubble parameter at present time H_0 measured from the cosmic microwave background (CMB) temperature and polarization data by the Planck Collaboration[5] to be $H_0 = 67.37 \pm 0.54 \text{ km s}^{-1} \text{ Mpc}^{-1}$, to the one from local measurements of the Hubble Space Telescope[6] yielding $H_0 = 74.03 \pm 1.42 \text{ km s}^{-1} \text{ Mpc}^{-1}$. Recent analyses with the combination of gravitational lensing and time-delay effects data reported a significant deviation[7] at 5.3σ. Another potential tension concerns the measurements of the parameter σ_8, which quantifies the gravitational clustering of matter from the amplitude of the linearly evolved power spectrum at the scale of $8h^{-1}$Mpc. Specifically, a possible deviation was noticed between measurements of CMB and LSS surveys, namely, between Planck[5] and SDSS/BOSS.[8,9] Although these two tensions could in principle arise from unknown systematics, the possibility of physical origin puts the standard lore of cosmology into additional investigations, by pointing to various extensions beyond ΛCDM.

In this work we consider systematically the H_0[10] and σ_8[11] tensions, and report how to alleviate both simultaneously within $f(T)$ gravity, based on the analysis of.[12] We exploit the effective field theory (EFT) of torsional gravity, a formalism that allows for a systematic investigation of the background and perturbations separately. This approach was first developed early for curvature gravity,[13] and recently it was extended to torsional gravity.[14,15] In order to address cosmological tensions, we identify the effects of gravitational modifications within the EFT on the dynamics of the background and of linear perturbation levels. This will allow us to construct specific models of $f(T)$ gravity providing adequate deviation from ΛCDM that can alleviate H_0 and σ_8 tensions.

2. Effective field theory approach

We start our analysis by the question of whether both tensions can be alleviated simultaneously via gravitational modifications in a much general framework. Indeed, the H_0 tension reveals a universe that is expanding faster at late times than that from a cosmological constant preferred by CMB data, while a lower value of σ_8 than the one of CMB most likely ΛCDM would imply that matter clusters either later on or less efficiently. Hence, these two observations seem to indicate that there might be "less gravitational power" at intermediate scales, which phenomenologically advocates a possible modification of gravitation. Accordingly, in this work we address the aforementioned question within the EFT framework for torsional gravity.

For a general curvature-based gravity, the action following the EFT approach in the unitary gauge, invariant by space diffeomorphisms, which expanded around a flat FRW metric $ds^2 = -dt^2 + a^2(t)\,\delta_{ij}dx^i dx^j$, is given by

$$S = \int d^4x \Big\{ \sqrt{-g}\Big[\frac{M_P^2}{2}\Psi(t)R - \Lambda(t) - b(t)g^{00} \\
+ M_2^4(\delta g^{00})^2 - \bar{m}_1^3 \delta g^{00}\delta K - \bar{M}_2^2 \delta K^2 - \bar{M}_3^2 \delta K^\nu_\mu \delta K^\mu_\nu \\
+ m_2^2 h^{\mu\nu}\partial_\mu g^{00}\partial_\nu g^{00} + \lambda_1 \delta R^2 + \lambda_2 \delta R_{\mu\nu}\delta R^{\mu\nu} + \mu_1^2 \delta g^{00}\delta R\Big] \\
+ \gamma_1 C^{\mu\nu\rho\sigma}C_{\mu\nu\rho\sigma} + \gamma_2 \epsilon^{\mu\nu\rho\sigma}C_{\mu\nu}{}^{\kappa\lambda}C_{\rho\sigma\kappa\lambda} \\
+ \sqrt{-g}\Big[\frac{M_3^4}{3}(\delta g^{00})^3 - \bar{m}_2^3(\delta g^{00})^2 \delta K + \cdots\Big]\Big\}, \qquad (1)$$

where $M_P = (8\pi G_N)^{-1/2}$ is the reduced Planck mass with G_N the Newtonian constant. R is the Ricci scalar corresponding to the Levi-Cività connection, $C^{\mu\nu\rho\sigma}$ is the Weyl tensor, δK^ν_μ is the perturbation of the extrinsic curvature, and the functions $\Psi(t)$, $\Lambda(t)$, $b(t)$ are determined by the background evolution.

When the underlying theory also includes torsion,[14] one can generalize the EFT action as[14,15]

$$S = \int d^4x \sqrt{-g}\Big[\frac{M_P^2}{2}\Psi(t)R - \Lambda(t) - b(t)g^{00} + \frac{M_P^2}{2}d(t)T^0\Big] + S^{(2)}. \qquad (2)$$

To compare with the effective action for curvature-based gravity (1), one reads that at background level there is additionally the zeroth part T^0 of the contracted torsion tensor $T^{0\mu}_{\ \ \mu}$, with its time-dependent coefficient $d(t)$. Furthermore, the perturbation part $S^{(2)}$ contains all operators of the perturbation part of (1), plus pure torsion terms including δT^2, $\delta T^0 \delta T^0$, and $\delta T^{\rho\mu\nu}\delta T_{\rho\mu\nu}$, and extra terms that mix curvature and torsion, namely, $\delta T \delta R$, $\delta g^{00}\delta T$, $\delta g^{00}\delta T^0$, and $\delta K \delta T^0$, where $T \equiv \frac{1}{4}T^{\rho\mu\nu}T_{\rho\mu\nu} + \frac{1}{2}T^{\rho\mu\nu}T_{\nu\mu\rho} - T_{\rho\mu}{}^{\rho}T^{\nu\mu}{}_{\nu}$ is the torsion scalar. Adding the matter action S_m to the effective action of torsional-based gravity (2) and then performing variation, one obtains the Friedmann equations to be:[14]

$$H^2 = \frac{1}{3M_P^2}\left(\rho_m + \rho_{DE}^{\text{eff}}\right), \qquad (3)$$

$$\dot{H} = -\frac{1}{2M_P^2}\left(\rho_m + \rho_{DE}^{\text{eff}} + p_m + p_{DE}^{\text{eff}}\right),$$

and where

$$\rho_{DE}^{\text{eff}} = b + \Lambda - 3M_P^2\left[H\dot{\Psi} + \frac{dH}{2} + H^2(\Psi - 1)\right], \qquad (4)$$

$$p_{DE}^{\text{eff}} = b - \Lambda + M_P^2\left[\ddot{\Psi} + 2H\dot{\Psi} + \frac{\dot{d}}{2} + (H^2 + 2\dot{H})(\Psi - 1)\right],$$

are, respectively, the effective DE density and pressure in the general torsional gravity. Moreover, we treat the matter sector as dust that satisfies the conservation equation $\dot{\rho}_m + 3H(\rho_m + p_m) = 0$, which in terms of redshift leads to $\rho_m = 3M_P^2 H_0^2 \Omega_{m0}(1+z)^3$, with Ω_{m0} the value of $\Omega_m \equiv 8\pi G_N \rho_m/(3H^2)$ at present.

3. Model independent analysis

In general, to avoid the H_0 tension one needs a positive correction to the first Friedmann equation at late times that could yield an increase in H_0 compared to the ΛCDM scenario. As for the σ_8 tension, we recall that in any cosmological model, at sub-Hubble scales and through the matter epoch, the equation that governs the evolution of matter perturbations in the linear regime is[16]

$$\ddot{\delta} + 2H\dot{\delta} = 4\pi G_{\text{eff}}\rho_m \delta, \qquad (5)$$

where G_{eff} is the effective gravitational coupling given by a generalized Poisson equation. In general, G_{eff} differs from the Newtonian constant G_N, and thus contains information from gravitational modifications (note that $G_{\text{eff}} = G_N$ in ΛCDM cosmology). Solving for $\delta(a)$ provides the observable quantity $f\sigma_8(a)$, following the definitions $f(a) \equiv d\ln\delta(a)/d\ln a$ and $\sigma(a) = \sigma_8 \delta(1)/\delta(a=1)$. Hence, alleviation of the σ_8 tension may be obtained if G_{eff} becomes smaller than G_N during the growth of matter perturbations and/or if the "friction" term in (5) increases.

To grasp the physical picture, we start with a simple case: $b(t) = 0$ and $\Lambda(t) = \Lambda = const$ [b and Λ are highly degenerate as shown in (4)], while $\Psi(t) = 1$. Hence, from (2), with the above coefficient choices, the only deviation from ΛCDM at the background level comes from the term $d(t)T^0$, and we remind that in FRW geometry $T^0 = H$ when evaluated on the background. In this case, the first Friedmann equation in (3), using for convenience the redshift $z = -1 + a_0/a$ as the dimensionless variable and setting $a_0 = 1$, yields

$$H(z) = -\frac{d(z)}{4} + \sqrt{\frac{d^2(z)}{16} + H_{\Lambda\text{CDM}}^2(z)}, \tag{6}$$

where $H_{\Lambda\text{CDM}}(z) \equiv H_0\sqrt{\Omega_m(1+z)^3 + \Omega_\Lambda}$ is the Hubble rate in ΛCDM, with $\Omega_m = \rho_m/(3M_p^2 H^2)$ the matter density parameter and primes denote derivatives with respect to z. Accordingly, if $d < 0$ and is suitably chosen, one can have $H(z \to z_{\text{CMB}}) \approx H_{\Lambda\text{CDM}}(z \to z_{\text{CMB}})$ but $H(z \to 0) > H_{\Lambda\text{CDM}}(z \to 0)$; i.e., the H_0 tension is solved [one should choose $|d(z)| < H(z)$, and thus, since $H(z)$ decreases for smaller z, the deviation from ΛCDM will be significant only at low redshift]. Additionally, since the friction term in (5) increases, the growth of structure gets damped, and therefore, the σ_8 tension is also solved [note that since we have imposed $\Psi = 1$, then $G_{\text{eff}} = G_N$ as one can verify from (2) and (3); namely, the contributions from T^0 vanish at first order in perturbations].

Furthermore, for typical values that lie well within the 1σ intervals of the $H(z)$ redshift surveys, it is expected that CMB measurements will be sensitive to such a deviation from the ΛCDM scenario for nonvanishing T^0 at early times. Actually, the T^0 operator acts in a similar way as a conventional cosmological constant. Thus, it adds yet another new functional form to parametrize the background and leads to more flexibility in fitting redshift and clustering measurements.

4. $f(T)$ gravity and cosmology

In this section we propose concrete models of torsional modified gravity that can be applied to alleviate the two cosmological tensions based on the torsional EFT dictionary. In particular, we focus on the well-known class of torsional gravity, namely, the $f(T)$ gravity,[17] which is characterized by the action $S = \frac{M_P^2}{2}\int d^4x e f(T)$, with $e = \det(e_\mu^A) = \sqrt{-g}$ and e_μ^A the vierbein, and thus by the Friedmann equations

$$H^2 = \frac{\rho_m}{3M_P^2} + \frac{T}{6} - \frac{f}{6} + \frac{Tf_T}{3}$$

$$\dot{H} = -\frac{1}{2M_P^2}(\rho_m + p_m) + \dot{H}(1 + f_T + 2Tf_{TT}), \tag{7}$$

with $f_T \equiv \partial f/\partial T$, $f_{TT} \equiv \partial^2 f/\partial T^2$, where we have applied $T = 6H^2$ in flat FRW geometry (we follow the convention of[14]). Therefore, $f(T)$ gravity can arise from the general EFT approach to torsional gravity by choosing $\Psi = -f_T$, $\Lambda = \frac{M_P^2}{2}(Tf_T - f)$, $b = 0$, $d = 2\dot{f}_T$,[14] and can restore GR by choosing $f(T) = -T - 2\Lambda/M_P^2$.

The above EFT approach holds for every $f(T)$ gravity by making a suitable identification of the involved time-dependent functions. For instance, we consider the following ansatz: $f(T) = -[T + 6H_0^2(1 - \Omega_{m0}) + F(T)]$, where $F(T)$ describes the deviation from GR [note, however, that in FRW geometry, apart from the regular choice $F = 0$, the ΛCDM scenario can also be obtained for the special case $F(T) = c\,T^{1/2}$ too, with c a constant]. Under these assumptions, the first Friedmann equation becomes

$$T(z) + 2\frac{F'(z)}{T'(z)}T(z) - F(z) = 6H^2_{\Lambda CDM}(z) \ . \tag{8}$$

In order to solve the H_0 tension, we need $T(0) = 6H_0^2 \simeq 6(H_0^{CC})^2$, with $H_0^{CC} = 74.03$ km s^{-1} Mpc^{-1} following the local measurements,[6] while in the early era of $z \gtrsim 1100$ we require the Universe expansion to evolve as in ΛCDM, namely $H(z \gtrsim 1100) \simeq H_{\Lambda CDM}(z \gtrsim 1100)$. This requirement follows from the fact that we are considering modifications kicking in only at late times, and therefore, the results in tension from CMB analysis performed within ΛCDM remain unaffected. This implies $F(z)|_{z \gtrsim 1100} \simeq c T^{1/2}(z)$ (the value $c = 0$ corresponds to standard GR, while for $c \neq 0$ we obtain ΛCDM too). Note that, in this case the effective gravitational coupling is given by[18]

$$G_{\text{eff}} = \frac{G_N}{1 + F_T} \ . \tag{9}$$

Therefore, the perturbation equation at linear order (5) becomes

$$\delta'' + \left[\frac{T'(z)}{2T(z)} - \frac{1}{1+z}\right]\delta' = \frac{9H_0^2\Omega_{m0}(1+z)}{[1 + F'(z)/T'(z)]T(z)}\delta \ , \tag{10}$$

where $\delta \equiv \delta\rho_m/\rho_m$ is the matter overdensity. Since around the last scattering moment $z \gtrsim 1100$ the Universe should be matter-dominated, we impose $\delta'(z)|_{z \gtrsim 1100} \simeq -\frac{1}{1+z}\delta(z)$, while at late times we look for $\delta(z)$ that leads to an $f\sigma_8$ in agreement with redshift survey observations.

By solving (8) and (10) with initial and boundary conditions at $z \sim 0$ and $z \sim 1100$, we can find the functional forms for the free functions of the $f(T)$ gravity that we consider, namely, $T(z)$ and $F(z)$, that can alleviate both H_0 and σ_8 tensions. We find two such forms for $F(T)$. Both models approach the ΛCDM scenario at $z \gtrsim 1100$, with Model-1 approaching $F = 0$ and hence restoring GR, while Model-2 approaches $F \propto T^{1/2}$, and thus it reproduces ΛCDM. In particular, we find that we can well fit the numerical solutions of Model-1 by

$$F(T) \approx 375.47\left(\frac{T}{6H_0^2}\right)^{-1.65} , \tag{11}$$

and of Model-2 by

$$F(T) \approx 375.47\left(\frac{T}{6H_0^2}\right)^{-1.65} + 25T^{1/2} \ . \tag{12}$$

Note that, the first term of Model-2, which coincides with Model-1, provides a small deviation to ΛCDM at late times, while it decreases rapidly to become negligible in the early Universe. In addition, we examine G_{eff} given by (9) for the two models (11) and (12), which are displayed in Fig. 1. As expected, at high redshifts in both models, G_{eff} becomes G_N, recovering the ΛCDM paradigm. At very low redshifts, G_{eff} becomes slightly higher than G_N, increasing slightly the gravitational strength. This gravitational modification is in competition at late times with the accelerating expansion. It turns out that the effect of an increased cosmic acceleration with respect to ΛCDM in our $f(T)$ gravity models dominates over the stronger gravitational strength in the clustering of matter. We check that both models can easily pass the BBN constraints (which demand[19] $|G_{\text{eff}}/G_N - 1| \leq 0.2$), as well as the ones from the Solar System [which demand[20] $|G'_{\text{eff}}(z=0)/G_N| \leq 10^{-3}h^{-1}$ and $|G''_{\text{eff}}(z=0)/G_N| \leq 10^5 h^{-2}$].

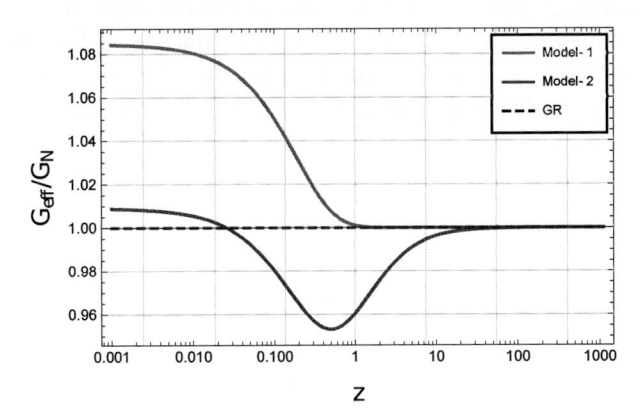

Fig. 1. Redshift evolution of G_{eff}/G_N in Model-1 (brown solid line) and Model-2 (blue solid line) and their comparison to the GR case (black dashed line).

Now we show how Model-1 and Model-2 can alleviate the H_0 and σ_8 tension by solving the background and perturbation equations. In Fig. 2 we present the evolution of $H(z)$, while in Fig. 3 the evolution of $f\sigma_8$, for two $f(T)$ models, and we compare them with ΛCDM. We stress that the H_0 tension can be alleviated as $H(z)$ remains statistically consistent for all CMB and CC measurements at all redshifts. We remind the reader that the two $f(T)$ models differing merely by a term $\propto T^{1/2}$, which does not affect the background as explained before, are degenerate at the background level. However, at the perturbation level, the two models behave differently as their gravitational coupling G_{eff} differs.

We further stress that both models can alleviate the σ_8 tension, and fit efficiently to BAO and LSS measurements. Note that at high redshifts ($z \geq 2$), Model-2 approaches ΛCDM slower than Model-1, but in a way that is statistically indistinguishable for present-day data. Nevertheless, future high-redshift surveys such as eBOSS for quasars and Euclid[24] for galaxies have the potential to discriminate among the predictions of $f(T)$ gravity and the ΛCDM scenario. Moreover, the clusters and CMB measurements on σ_8 are in good agreement in our models, as the CMB preferred values in ΛCDM get further lowered than local ones from rescaling

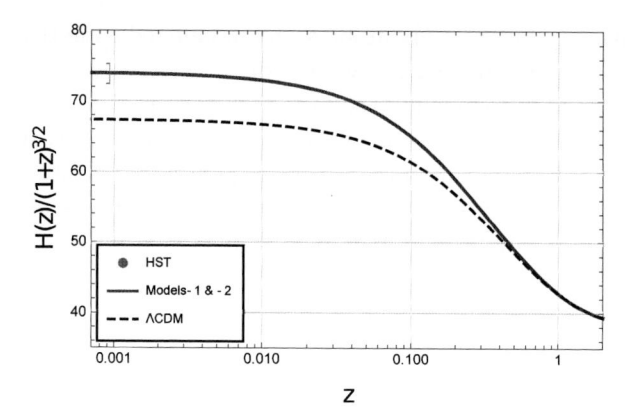

Fig. 2. Evolution of the Hubble parameter $H(z)$ in the two $f(T)$ models (purple solid line) and in ΛCDM cosmology (black dashed line). The red point represents the latest data from extragalactic Cepheid-based local measurement of H_0 provided in.[6]

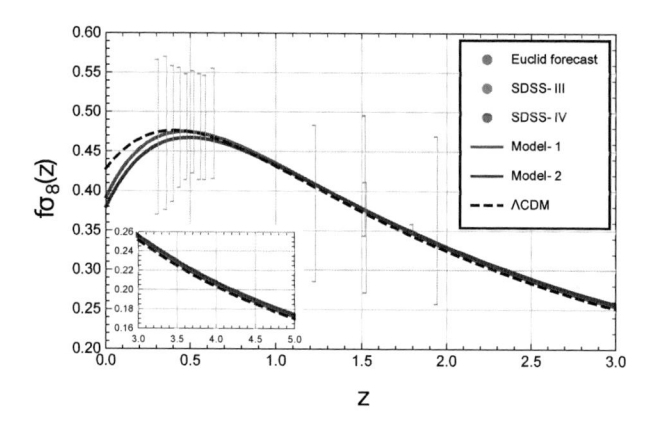

Fig. 3. Evolution of $f\sigma_8$ in Model-1 (brown solid line) and Model-2 (blue solid line) of $f(T)$ gravity and in ΛCDM cosmology (black dashed line). The green data points are from BAO observations in SDSS-III DR12,[21] the gray data points at higher redshift are from SDSS-IV DR14,[22] while the red point around ~ 1.8 is the forecast from Euclid.[23] The subgraph in the left bottom displays $f\sigma_8$ at high redshift $z = 3 \sim 5$, which shows that the curve of Model-2 is above the one of Model-1 and ΛCDM scenario and hence approaches ΛCDM slower than Model-1.

σ_8 by the ratio of the growth factors in $f(T)$ gravity and ΛCDM. More explicitly,

$$\sigma_8^{f(T)}(z=0) = \frac{D^{f(T)}(z=0)}{D^\Lambda(z=0)} \frac{D^\Lambda(z_{\text{eff}})}{D^{f(T)}(z_{\text{eff}})} \sigma_8^\Lambda(z=0), \qquad (13)$$

where $D(z)$ is the growth factor, $f(T)$ and Λ denote our models and ΛCDM respectively, and z_{eff} is the effective redshift of the measurements ($z_{\text{eff}} \sim 0.1$ for clusters experiments and $z_{\text{eff}} \sim 1100$ for CMB temperature fluctuations observations). It turns out that, as at high redshift, $z_{\text{eff}} \sim 1100$, the growth factor is the same in either our $f(T)$-models or in ΛCDM, but at low redshift, $z_{\text{eff}} \sim 0.1$, the growth factor is approximately 1.03 bigger in the later compared to the formers, cluster

σ_8-measurements get bigger by about such an amount reducing the gap with CMB preferred value in this modified gravity scenario.

In short summary, we conclude that the class of $f(T)$ gravity: $f(T) = -T - 2\Lambda/M_P^2 + \alpha T^\beta$, where only two out of the three parameters Λ, α, and β are independent (the third one is eliminated using Ω_{m0}), can alleviate both H_0 and σ_8 tensions with suitable parameter choices. Moreover, such kinds of models in $f(T)$ gravity could also be examined through galaxy-galaxy lensing effects,[25] strong lensing effects around black holes[26] and gravitational wave experiments.[15]

5. Conclusions

In this work we reported how $f(T)$ gravity can alleviate both H_0 and σ_8 tensions simultaneously. Working within the EFT framework, torsional gravity theories can be identified as the EFT operators that allow us to extract the evolution equations of the background and of the perturbations in a model-independent manner. This allows us to address in a systematic way how tensions amongst the observational measurements, such as the ones on H_0 and σ_8, can be relaxed. Following these considerations, we constructed concrete models from specific Lagrangians in $f(T)$ gravity, describing cosmological scenarios where these tensions fade away. Imposing initial conditions at the last scattering that reproduce the ΛCDM scenario, and imposing the late-time values preferred by local measurements, we reconstructed two particular forms of $f(T)$. These models are well described by the parametrization: $f(T) = -T - 2\Lambda/M_P^2 + \alpha T^\beta$. To our knowledge, this is the first time where both H_0 and σ_8 tensions are simultaneously alleviated by a modified gravity theory.

References

1. E. J. Copeland, M. Sami and S. Tsujikawa, *Dynamics of dark energy*, Int. J. Mod. Phys. D **15**, 1753-1936 (2006).
2. Y. F. Cai, E. N. Saridakis, M. R. Setare and J. Q. Xia, *Quintom Cosmology: Theoretical implications and observations*, Phys. Rept. **493**, 1-60 (2010)
3. E. N. Saridakis *et al.* [CANTATA], *Modified Gravity and Cosmology: An Update by the CANTATA Network*, [arXiv:2105.12582 [gr-qc]].
4. S. Capozziello and M. De Laurentis, *Extended Theories of Gravity*, Phys. Rept. **509**, 167-321 (2011).
5. N. Aghanim *et al.* [Planck Collaboration], *Planck 2018 results. VI. Cosmological parameters*, Astron. Astrophys. **641**, A6 (2020) [erratum: Astron. Astrophys. **652**, C4 (2021)].
6. A. G. Riess, S. Casertano, W. Yuan, L. M. Macri and D. Scolnic, *Large Magellanic Cloud Cepheid Standards Provide a 1Determination of the Hubble Constant and Stronger Evidence for Physics beyond ΛCDM*, Astrophys. J. **876**, no. 1, 85 (2019).
7. K. C. Wong *et al.*, *H0LiCOW XIII. A 2.4% measurement of H_0 from lensed quasars: 5.3σ tension between early and late-Universe probes*, Mon. Not. Roy. Astron. Soc. **498**, no.1, 1420-1439 (2020).
8. S. Alam *et al.* [BOSS Collaboration], *The clustering of galaxies in the completed SDSS-III Baryon Oscillation Spectroscopic Survey: cosmological analysis of the DR12 galaxy sample*, Mon. Not. Roy. Astron. Soc. **470**, no. 3, 2617 (2017).

9. M. Ata et al., *The clustering of the SDSS-IV extended Baryon Oscillation Spectroscopic Survey DR14 quasar sample: first measurement of baryon acoustic oscillations between redshift 0.8 and 2.2*, Mon. Not. Roy. Astron. Soc. **473**, no. 4, 4773 (2018).
10. E. Di Valentino, L. A. Anchordoqui, O. Akarsu, Y. Ali-Haimoud, L. Amendola, N. Arendse, M. Asgari, M. Ballardini, S. Basilakos and E. Battistelli, *et al. Snowmass2021 - Letter of interest cosmology intertwined II: The hubble constant tension*, Astropart. Phys. **131**, 102605 (2021).
11. E. Di Valentino, L. A. Anchordoqui, Ö. Akarsu, Y. Ali-Haimoud, L. Amendola, N. Arendse, M. Asgari, M. Ballardini, S. Basilakos and E. Battistelli, *et al. Cosmology intertwined III: $f\sigma_8$ and S_8*, Astropart. Phys. **131**, 102604 (2021).
12. S. F. Yan, P. Zhang, J. W. Chen, X. Z. Zhang, Y. F. Cai and E. N. Saridakis, *Interpreting cosmological tensions from the effective field theory of torsional gravity*, Phys. Rev. D **101**, no.12, 121301 (2020).
13. N. Arkani-Hamed, H. C. Cheng, M. A. Luty and S. Mukohyama, *Ghost condensation and a consistent infrared modification of gravity*, JHEP **0405**, 074 (2004).
14. C. Li, Y. Cai, Y. F. Cai and E. N. Saridakis, *The effective field theory approach of teleparallel gravity, $f(T)$ gravity and beyond*, JCAP **1810**, 001 (2018).
15. Y. F. Cai, C. Li, E. N. Saridakis and L. Xue, *$f(T)$ gravity after GW170817 and GRB170817A*, Phys. Rev. D **97**, no. 10, 103513 (2018).
16. F. K. Anagnostopoulos, S. Basilakos and E. N. Saridakis, *Bayesian analysis of $f(T)$ gravity using $f\sigma_8$ data*, Phys. Rev. D **100**, no. 8, 083517 (2019).
17. Y. F. Cai, S. Capozziello, M. De Laurentis and E. N. Saridakis, *$f(T)$ teleparallel gravity and cosmology*, Rept. Prog. Phys. **79**, no.10, 106901 (2016).
18. S. Nesseris, S. Basilakos, E. N. Saridakis and L. Perivolaropoulos, *Viable $f(T)$ models are practically indistinguishable from ΛCDM*, Phys. Rev. D **88**, 103010 (2013).
19. C. J. Copi, A. N. Davis and L. M. Krauss, *A New nucleosynthesis constraint on the variation of G*, Phys. Rev. Lett. **92**, 171301 (2004).
20. S. Nesseris and L. Perivolaropoulos, *The Limits of Extended Quintessence*, Phys. Rev. D **75**, 023517 (2007).
21. Y. Wang, G. B. Zhao, C. H. Chuang, M. Pellejero-Ibanez, C. Zhao, F. S. Kitaura and S. Rodriguez-Torres, *The clustering of galaxies in the completed SDSS-III Baryon Oscillation Spectroscopic Survey: a tomographic analysis of structure growth and expansion rate from anisotropic galaxy clustering*, Mon. Not. Roy. Astron. Soc. **481**, no. 3, 3160 (2018).
22. H. Gil-Marín et al., *The clustering of the SDSS-IV extended Baryon Oscillation Spectroscopic Survey DR14 quasar sample: structure growth rate measurement from the anisotropic quasar power spectrum in the redshift range $0.8 < z < 2.2$*, Mon. Not. Roy. Astron. Soc. **477**, no. 2, 1604 (2018).
23. L. Taddei, M. Martinelli and L. Amendola, *Model-independent constraints on modified gravity from current data and from the Euclid and SKA future surveys*, JCAP **1612**, 032 (2016).
24. R. Laureijs et al. [EUCLID Collaboration], *Euclid Definition Study Report*, arXiv:1110.3193 [astro-ph.CO].
25. Z. Chen, W. Luo, Y. F. Cai and E. N. Saridakis, *New test on General Relativity using galaxy-galaxy lensing with astronomical surveys*, Phys. Rev. D **102**, no. 10, 104044 (2020).
26. S. Yan, C. Li, L. Xue, X. Ren, Y. F. Cai, D. A. Easson, Y. Yuan and H. Zhao, *Testing the equivalence principle via the shadow of black holes*, Phys. Rev. Res. **2**, no. 2, 023164 (2020).

Precision Cosmology and Hubble tension in the era of LSS surveys

G. Fanizza

*Instituto de Astrofísica e Ciências do Espaço, Faculdade de Ciências
da Universidade de Lisboa, Edifício C8, Campo Grande, P-1740-016, Lisbon, Portugal
and
CERN, Theory Department, CH-1211 Geneva 23, Switzerland
E-mail: gfanizza@fc.ul.pt*

We present a fully relativistic framework to evaluate the impact of stochastic inhomogeneities on the prediction of the Hubble-Lemaître diagram. In this regard, we relate the fluctuations of the luminosity distance-redshift relation in the Cosmic Concordance model to the intrinsic uncertainty associated to the estimation of cosmological parameters from high-redshift surveys (up to z = 4). Within this framework and according to the specific of forthcoming surveys as Euclid Deep Survey and LSST, we show that the cosmic variance associated with the measurement of the Hubble constant will not exceed 0.1 %. Thanks to our results, we infer that deep surveys will provide an estimation of the the Hubble constant H_0 which will be more precise than the one obtained from local sources, at least in regard of the intrinsic uncertainty related to a stochastic distribution of inhomogeneities.

Keywords: Cosmology; Large Scale Structure; Inhomogeneous Universe; Hubble tension

1. Introduction

Along this work, we will summarize the results obtained in Fanizza et al. (2021)[1] and presented at the parallel session *"Status of the H_0 and σ_8 Tensions: Theoretical Models and Model-Independent Constraints"* of the 16th Marcel Grossmann meeting. In particular, we will quantify the cosmic variance concerning the estimation of H_0 from forthcoming high redshift survey with limited sky coverage.

Indeed, the best-fit of the CMB data[2] allows us to infer the value of few cosmological parameters with the highest precision achievable so far in cosmology. Among these parameters, the estimation of H_0, namely the current expansion rate of the Universe, has gained great interest for the cosmologists because of an increasing tension emerging against the value of H_0 itself as estimated from local measurements.[3]

This tension is almost of 5σ, since CMB measurements provide[2] a value for $H_0 = 67.36 \pm 0.54$ km s^{-1} Mpc^{-1}, whereas late time estimations based on local probes, such as Supernovae Ia (SnIa), return[3] $H_0 = 73.2 \pm 1.3$ km s^{-1} Mpc^{-1}.

Given this tension and working within the conservative framework of ΛCDM model, our main interest is to understand whether, in view of the forthcoming Large Scale Structure (LSS) surveys, there could be any theoretical bias increasing the standard deviation in order to alleviate the above-mentioned tension. A first attempt to address this point has been provided in Ben-Dayan et al. (2014),[4] where the effect of velocity dispersion of local SnIa (at redshift lower than 0.1) has been studied and it has been shown that it can introduce a further intrinsic error in the local estimation of H_0 of $\sim 1\%$. This result is in agreement with subsequent analysis,[5] leading to an effect which is large but unfortunately not enough to resolve the tension. Our goal here is to extend the analysis to higher redshifts ($z \leq 3.85$), including then also lensing effects to the analysis, in order to forecast the estimated precision for forthcoming surveys, just like Euclid Deep Survey (EDS) and LSST. To this aim, we will assume that the new generation of standard candles known as Superluminous Supernovae (SLSNe) will provide a suitable dataset, following what has been recently claimed in Inserra et al. (2021).[6]

In Sect. 2 we present the estimator for the cosmic variance in realistic high redshift surveys. In Sect. 3, we recall and discuss the analytic tool, such as the 2-point correlation function of the luminosity distance-redshift relation and its monopole, needed for our estimation. In Sect. 4, we generate a survey according to the specific of forthcoming surveys and forecast the expected cosmic variance. In Sect. 5 our results are summarized and discussed.

2. Local measurements

In order to extend the analysis of Ben-Dayan et al. (2014)[4] to higher redshift, we first need to go beyond the linear relation between luminosity distance and redshift $d_L = z/H_0$. To this aim, we then refer to the luminosity distance-redshift relation $d_L(z)$ in the homogenous and isotropic ΛCDM model

$$d_L(z) = \frac{1+z}{H_0} \int_0^z \frac{dz'}{\sqrt{\Omega_{m0}(1+z')^3 + 1 - \Omega_{m0}}}, \quad (1)$$

where H_0 is indeed the Hubble constant and Ω_{m0} is the energy density of the matter today. Eq. (1) then provides an estimator for H_0 at higher redshifts as

$$H_0 = \frac{1+z}{d_L(z)} \int_0^z \frac{dz'}{\sqrt{\Omega_{0m}(1+z')^3 + 1 - \Omega_{0m}}}. \quad (2)$$

By assuming then *a priori* the value of Ω_{m0} and given that d_L and z can be independently observed, a measurement of H_0 can be directly inferred from the high-redshift surveys thanks to Eq. (2).

Eq. (2) provides also the starting point to estimate the intrinsic uncertainty associated to H_0 given by the presence of inhomogeneities all around our observed Universe. This is the lowest theoretical uncertainty we can reach, according to the sample of sources we have access to and is usually named *cosmic variance*. We hence have that, if we take into account also inhomogeneities in the Universe, the luminosity distance-redshift relation is modified accordingly as

$$\widetilde{d_L}(z,\mathbf{n}) = d_L(z)\left[1 + \delta^{(1)}(z,\mathbf{n}) + \delta^{(2)}(z,\mathbf{n})\right], \quad (3)$$

where $\mathbf{n}$ is the observed direction of the given source and $\delta^{(1)}$ and $\delta^{(2)}$ are linear and second order corrections to the luminosity distance-redshift relation.

At this point, the inhomogeneous value of the Hubble constant $\widetilde{H}_0$ can be evaluated as

$$\widetilde{H}_0 \equiv \frac{1+z}{\widetilde{d_L}(z)} \int_0^z \frac{dz'}{\sqrt{\Omega_{0m}(1+z')^3 + 1 - \Omega_{0m}}}$$

$$= H_0 \left[1 - \delta^{(1)} - \delta^{(2)} + \left(\delta^{(1)}\right)^2\right](z, \mathbf{n}). \quad (4)$$

We notice that $\widetilde{H}_0$ is now a function of z and $\mathbf{n}$. This is in line with the fact that inhomogeneities may render the estimation of H_0 biased by local structures. In principle, these inhomogeneities may affect not only the precision but also the accuracy of H_0 and then shift its averaged value within the sample. Here we neglect this effect since the correction to the Hubble diagram due to the non-linearities has been shown to be small in the regime of redshift of our interest.[7–9]

Because of these fluctuations, it is possibile to define an estimator for the variance associated to the background value of H_0 inferred from a finite survey of N sources observed at positions $(z_i, \mathbf{n}_i)$, where $i = 1, \ldots, N$ runs over the number of the sources. Indeed, the variance associated to the average value of $\widetilde{H}_0$ inferred from a finite survey of N sources will be then

$$\sigma^2_{H_0} = \overline{\left(\sum_{i=1}^N \frac{\widetilde{H}_0(z_i, \mathbf{n}_i)}{N} - H_0\right)\left(\sum_{j=1}^N \frac{\widetilde{H}_0(z_j, \mathbf{n}_j)}{N} - H_0\right)}$$

$$= \frac{1}{N^2} \sum_{i,j=1}^N \overline{\left(\widetilde{H}_0(z_i, \mathbf{n}_i)\widetilde{H}_0(z_j, \mathbf{n}_j) - H_0^2\right)} = \frac{H_0^2}{N^2} \sum_{i,j=1}^N \overline{\delta^{(1)}(z_i, \mathbf{n}_i)\,\delta^{(1)}(z_j, \mathbf{n}_j)}. \quad (5)$$

where $\overline{\cdots}$ represents the *ensemble average* over all the possibile configurations of perturbations. Last equality of Eq. (5) states that our estimator for the cosmic variance of H_0 precisely corresponds to the sum of the 2-point correlation function of the luminosity distance-redshift relation over all the possible pairs of sources in the survey. It then links the details of the surveys, such as angular and redshift distributions of the sources, to the theoretical expressions of the inhomogeneities. We also notice that nonlinear terms in Eq. (5) exactly cancel.

In the next section, these general preliminaries will be applied to the case of linear perturbations of the luminosity distance. This will provide the explicit expression for $\sigma^2_{H_0}$ due to all the linear relativistic corrections.

3. Analytical expressions for leading order effects

Eq. (5) explicitly shows that the cosmic variance $\sigma^2_{H_0}$ is sourced at the leading order only by linear perturbations. It is then enough to take into account the linear relativistic corrections involved in the $\delta^{(1)}$. By restricting our analysis to scalar perturbations as given in the Longitudinal Gauge without anisotropic stress[a], the relativistic effects occurring at linear level are well-known:[12–15] we have lensing of the photon geodesics along the line-of-sight due to cosmic structures, peculiar velocity (also known as Doppler) due to the free falling motion of the sources within local inhomogeneities and then fluctuations of the gravitational potential around the source position and along the photon geodesics, leading to local and integrated Sachs-Wolfe effects and time delay. However, effects due to gravitational potentials are negligible with respect to lensing and peculiar velocity. We then focus the rest of our discussion only to the lensing and peculiar velocity.

The impact of the these effects on $\sigma^2_{H_0}$ is then given by

$$\frac{\sigma^2_{H_0}}{H_0^2} = \frac{1}{N^2} \sum_{i,j} \sum_{E,E'} \int \frac{dk}{k} \mathcal{P}_\psi(k) \mathcal{W}_{Ei,E'j}, \qquad (6)$$

where $i,j = 1, \ldots, N$ and E and E' label the leading relativistic effects such as Lensing ($E, E' = L$) or Peculiar Velocity ($E, E' = PV$). $\mathcal{P}_\psi(k)$ in Eq. (6) is the so-called dimensionless power spectrum of gravitational perturbations in Fourier space

$$\mathcal{P}_\psi(k) \equiv \frac{k^3}{2\pi^2} |\psi_k|^2. \qquad (7)$$

We remark that kernels $\mathcal{W}_{Ei,E'j}$ are functions of the (times) redshifts of the i-th and j-th sources (η_i) z_i and (η_j) z_j and their angular separation $\nu \equiv \mathbf{n}_i \cdot \mathbf{n}_j$. In this way, the only terms involved in our analysis are the auto-correlations of lensing and peculiar velocity

$$\mathcal{W}_{PVi,PVj} = \Xi_i \Xi_j G_i G_j k^2 \left\{ \frac{\Delta\eta_i \Delta\eta_j (1-\nu^2)}{R^2} j_2(kR) \right.$$
$$\left. + \frac{\nu}{3} [j_0(kR) - 2j_2(kR)] \right\} (\eta_i, \eta_j, \nu) \qquad (8)$$

$$\mathcal{W}_{Li,Lj} = \frac{1}{\Delta\eta_i} \frac{1}{\Delta\eta_j} \int_{\eta_i}^{\eta_o} d\eta \frac{\eta - \eta_i}{\eta_o - \eta} \int_{\eta_j}^{\eta_o} d\eta' \frac{\eta' - \eta_j}{\eta_o - \eta'} \frac{g(\eta)g(\eta')}{g^2(\eta_o)} \left[k^4 H^4 j_4(kR) \right.$$
$$\left. - 8k^3 H^2 L\, j_3(kR) + k^2 \left(8L^2 - 6H^2\right) j_2(kR) + 4\,k\,L\, j_1(kR) \right] (\eta, \eta', \nu),$$

and their cross-correlation

$$\mathcal{W}_{PVi,Lj} = \frac{\Xi_i}{\Delta\eta_j} G_i \int_{\eta_j}^{\eta_o} d\eta \frac{\eta - \eta_j}{\eta_o - \eta} \frac{g(\eta)}{g(\eta_o)} \left\{ -k^3 \Delta\eta^2 \frac{(\Delta\eta_i - \nu\Delta\eta)(\Delta\eta - \nu\Delta\eta_i)^2}{R^3} j_3(kR) \right.$$
$$+ k^2 \Delta\eta \left(3\Delta\eta \frac{\Delta\eta_i - \nu\Delta\eta}{R^2} - 2\nu \right) j_2(kR)$$
$$\left. - \frac{k\Delta\eta}{R} \left[k^2 \Delta\eta (\Delta\eta_i - \nu\Delta\eta) - 2\nu \right] j_1(kR) \right\} (\eta_i, \eta, \nu), \qquad (9)$$

[a]This assumption is in line with the fact that we take into account sources located after the decoupling. General expressions in presence of anisotropic stress can be found in Marozzi et al. (2014)[10] for the non-linear luminosity distance-redshift relation and in Fanizza et al. (2018)[11] for the non-linear redshift.

where $j_n(x)$ are the spherical Bessel functions of n-th order and we define

$$R(\eta_x, \eta_y, \nu) = \sqrt{\Delta\eta_x^2 + \Delta\eta_x^2 - 2\Delta\eta_x\Delta\eta_y\nu}$$

$$L(\eta_x, \eta_y, \nu) = \frac{\Delta\eta_x \Delta\eta_y \nu}{R(\eta_x, \eta_y, \nu)}, \quad H(\eta_x, \eta_y, \nu) = \frac{\Delta\eta_x \Delta\eta_y \sqrt{1-\nu^2}}{R(\eta_x, \eta_y, \nu)}$$

$$G_i = \int_{\eta_{in}}^{\eta_i} d\eta \frac{a(\eta)}{a(\eta_i)} \frac{g(\eta)}{g(\eta_o)}, \quad \Xi_i = \left(1 - \frac{1}{\mathcal{H}_i \Delta\eta_i}\right), \qquad (10)$$

with $\Delta\eta_x \equiv \eta_o - \eta_x$. In Eqs. (10), R is the Euclidean distance between two sources and L and H are respectively the normalized scalar and (modulo of the) vector products between the two directions of the sources. Moreover, G_i is the growth factor for the velocity potential of the i-th source, $g(\eta)$ is the growth factor of the gravitational potential, $a(\eta)$ is the scale factor, $\mathcal{H}(\eta) = a'(\eta)/a(\eta)$ and η_o is the value of the conformal time today. The detailed analytic derivation for all the different contributions $\mathcal{W}_{Ei,E'j}$ is reported in Fanizza et al. (2021).[1] We just remark that the kernel $\mathcal{W}_{PVi,PVj}$ is in agreement with the one found in Ben-Dayan et al. (2014).[4]

The values of the 2-point correlation function

$$\xi_{E,E'}(z_i, z_j, \nu) \equiv \int \frac{dk}{k} \mathcal{P}_\psi(k) \mathcal{W}_{Ei,E'j} \qquad (11)$$

for the kernels in Eqs. (8) and (9) are then shown in Fig. 1 for the particular cases of aligned ($\nu = 1$) and anti-aligned ($\nu = -1$) sources. In the regime of interest for us ($0.15 \leq z \leq 3.85$), it is clear from these plots that lensing is always leading with respect to the other terms when the sources are aligned, whereas peculiar velocity turns out to be the leading effect for the anti-aligned sources at redshift smaller than 1.

Another interesting feature emerging from Eqs. (8) and (9) regards the angular average of $\xi_{E,E'}$. It turns out that

$$\int_{-1}^{1} d\nu\, \xi_{E,L}(z_i, z_j, \nu) = 0 \qquad (12)$$

where E may label all the relativistic effects such as lensing itself, peculiar velocity, time delay and (integrated) Sachs-Wolfe effect. This means that, in the limit of full sky coverage surveys and large number of sources[b], lensing does not affects at all the estimation $\sigma_{H_0}^2$. Hence, it follows that in this ideal case the leading contribution to the cosmic variance is entirely addressed to the monopole of $\xi_{PV,PV}$. This can be easily evaluated from the angular integration of the $\mathcal{W}_{PVi,PVj}$ in Eq. (8) and results are shown in Fig. 2. In this ideal case, σ_{H_0} is entirely given by the doppler 2-point correlation function.

---

[b]See Yoo (2020)[16] for a detailed discussion of this ideal case.

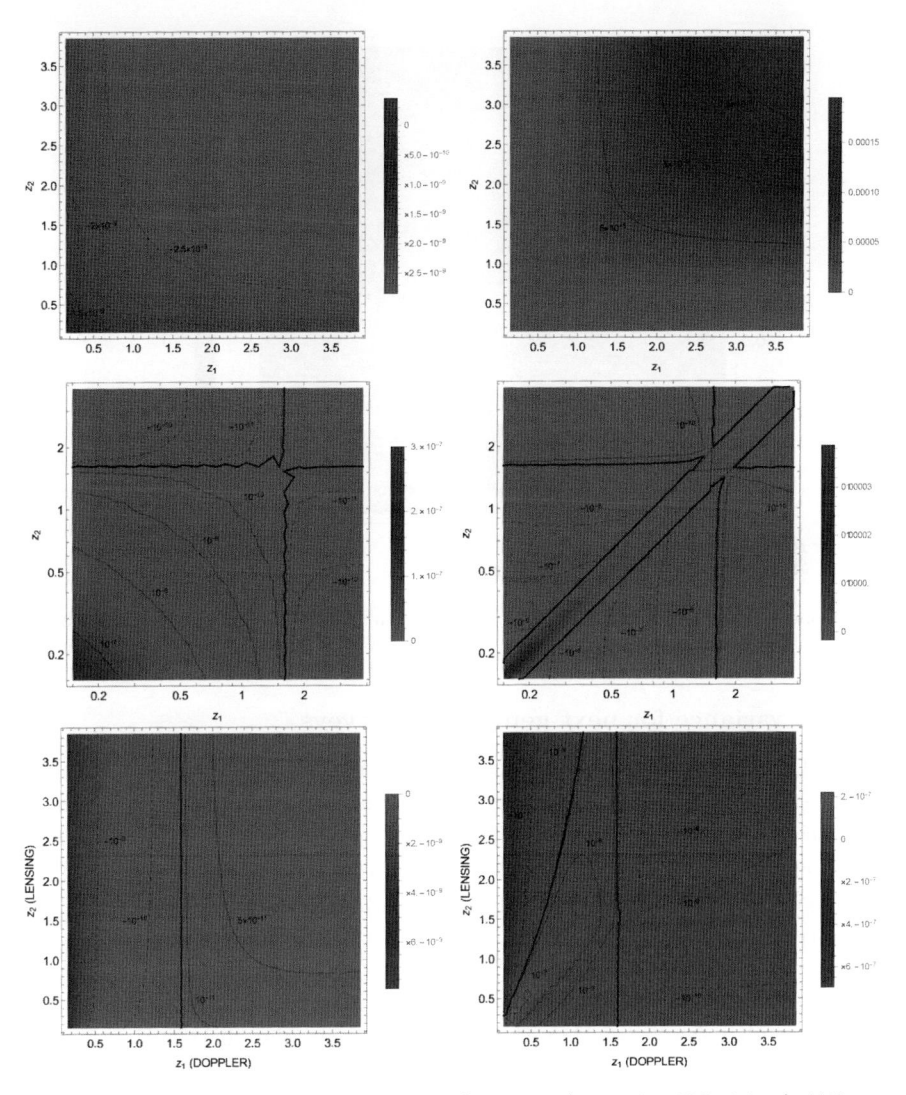

Fig. 1. 2-point correlation functions of Lensing (top panels), Peculiar Velocities (middle panels) and cross-correlation between Lensing and Peculiar Velocity (bottom panels). Left panels refer to anti-aligned sources ($\nu = -1$) wheres right ones consider aligned sources ($\nu = 1$). These plots are obtained by using linear power spectrum for the gravitational potential, following the cosmological parameters provided in Fanizza et al. (2021).[1]

However, realistic surveys deal with finite sky-coverages which can be also very narrow. In this case, monopole of the 2-point correlation functions of $\widetilde{d_L}(z, \mathbf{n})$ is no longer enough and higher multipoles must be taken into account for the evaluation of $\sigma_{H_0}^2$. We redirect the reader interested in the detailed multipoles analysis of $\xi_{E,E'}$ to Fanizza et al. (2021).[1] In the next section, we will apply the numerical results shown in Fig. 1 to the estimator for $\sigma_{H_0}^2$ in Eq. (6).

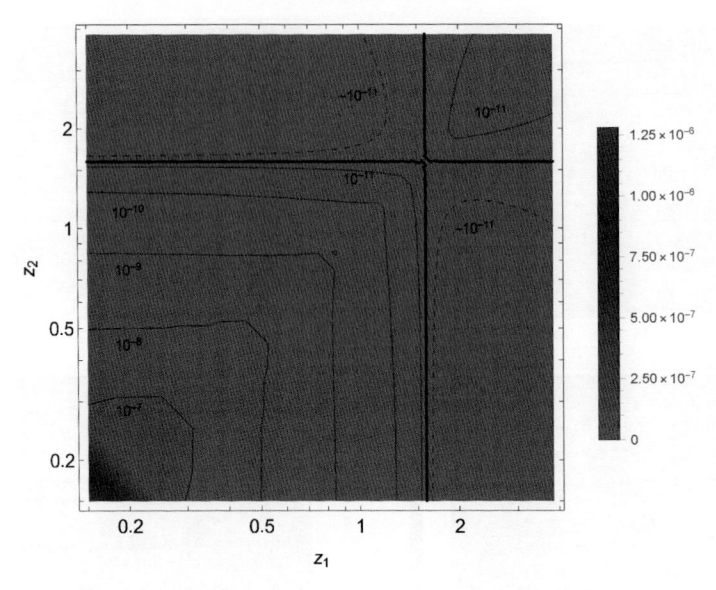

Fig. 2. Monopole of the doppler 2-point correlation function. Thick black lines indicate where function is 0. Dashed lines stand for negative values whereas continues lines refer to positive values.

4. Cosmic variance for next generation surveys

In this section, we apply the analytical and numerical results previously obtained to the case of Superluminous Supernovae (SLSNe). Following the specifics of forthcoming surveys like EDS[17] and LSST,[18] we consider the expected detection rate of SLSNe claimed in Inserra et al. (2021)[6] and reported in our Fig. 3. With these histograms in mind, we have generated two random surveys for the distribution of SLSNe with the following properties

- EDS: 135 sources in 7 redshift bins with $0.5 \leq z \leq 3.5$ and redshift bin width $\Delta z = 0.5$. For this survey, the angular distribution covers two

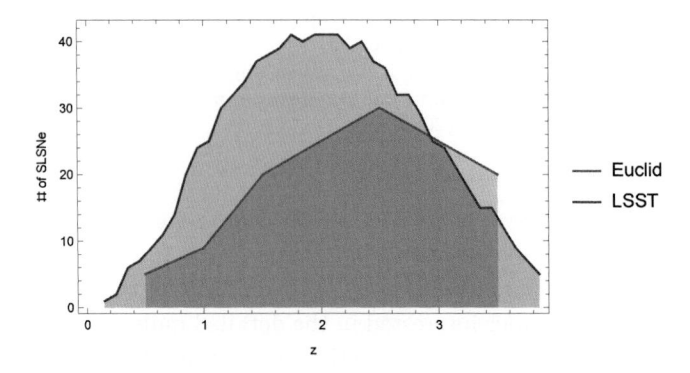

Fig. 3. Simulated SLSNe distributions for Euclid Deep Survey and LSST. From Inserra et al. (2021).[6]

line-of-sights at North and South Poles, with angular opening of 20 deg^2 per line-of-sight,
- LSST: 929 sources in 38 redshift bins with $0.15 \leq z \leq 3.85$ and redshift bin width $\Delta z = 0.1$. For this survey, the angular distribution spans a broad solid angle of 9000 deg^2.

Results are summarized in Table 1. Here we see that the dispersion associated to the measure of H_0, namely $\sigma_{H_0} \equiv \sqrt{\sigma^2_{H_0}}$ is of $\sim 0.2\%$ for EDS but its value drops of almost 1 order of magnitude for LSST, where it contributes with a dispersion of $\sim 0.03\%$. This difference is mainly addressed to the fact that, for larger sky coverage and large number of sources, the total effect due to lensing must tend to 0. The specific of LSST are indeed in line with regime: first of all, the number of sources adopted in our forecast of LSST is almost 1 order of magnitude higher than the one of EDS. Secondly, also the sky coverage is larger.

Table 1. Forecasts for the variance of H_0 in EDS and LSST. In the first line, lensing 2-point correlation function is considered. In the second line, the contributions from 2-point correlation function of peculiar velocities are shown. Values are reported for linear power spectrum truncated at $k_{UV} = 0.1h$ Mpc^{-1} and Non-Linear HaloFit model truncated at $k_{UV} = 10h$ Mpc^{-1}.

$\sigma^2_{H_0}/H_0^2$	EDS (Linear)	LSST (Linear)	EDS (Non-Linear)	LSST (Non-Linear)
Lensing	5.1×10^{-6}	7.6×10^{-8}	1.1×10^{-5}	7.8×10^{-7}
Doppler	2.1×10^{-9}	2.9×10^{-10}	-	-

Another fact that we underline is that doppler effect is always subdominant. Hence we have that the total cosmic variance due to lensing and doppler is

$$\sigma_{H_0} \approx \sigma_{H_0 L} \left[1 + \frac{1}{2} \frac{\sigma^2_{H_0 PV}}{\sigma^2_{H_0 L}} + \mathcal{O}\left(\left(\frac{\sigma^2_{H_0 PV}}{\sigma^2_{H_0 L}}\right)^2\right) \right]. \quad (13)$$

Again from Table 1, we then get that the doppler effect corrects the total cosmic variance associated to H_0 by 0.2% for LSST and by 0.02% for EDS.

This analytical estimation can be naturally extended to $k_{UV} = 10\,h$ Mpc^{-1} where the HaloFit model[19, 20] is taken into account to model the non-linear scales. Results for the lensing are reported again in Table 1 and show that $\sigma^2_{H_0\,NL} = 1.1 \times 10^{-5}\,H_0^2$ for EDS and $\sigma^2_{H_0\,NL} = 7.8 \times 10^{-7}\,H_0^2$ for LSST.

It follows then, for EDS, even if non-linear scales are expected to enhance the lensing correction by almost one order of magnitude, the intrinsic error associated to the measurement of H_0 is almost insensitive to the non-linear scales, since it becomes $\sigma_{H_0\,NL}/H_0 = 0.003$. On the contrary, non-linear scales increase by roughly a factor 3 the dispersion of H_0 within the specific of LSST, raising σ_{H_0} to the value $\sigma_{H_0\,NL}/H_0 = 0.0009$.

Our analysis, provides also a test for the claim done in Ben-Dayan et al. (2014)[4] about small redshift surveys: it has been stated there that the analysis is insensitive to smaller scales fluctuations due to the incoherence of such contributions. According to our investigation, we conclude that this is a reasonable expectation only for EDS. We address this feature to the fact that EDS covers smaller regions in the sky with higher angular density of sources.

5. Summary and conclusions

In this work, we have studied the impact of cosmological inhomogeneities on the estimation of H_0 from the high redshift Hubble diagram. Our analysis considers the possibility, discussed in Inserra et al. (2021),[6] that EDS[17] and LSST[18] will have access to a statistically relevant number of Superluminous Supernovae in the next decade. In this regards, less conservative studies about the Hubble diagram at high redshifts ($z \lesssim 1.5$) have been also investigated by exploiting exact inhomogeneous models in general relativity[21–24] or by considering strongly inhomogeneous dynamical dark energy models.[25] These attempts look interesting especially in light of recent analysis done in Krishnan et al. (2020)[26] and Krishnan et al. (2021)[27] about H0LiCOW[28] and TDCOSMO[29] data and in Dainotti et al. (2021)[30] for the SNe Ia Pantheon sample, suggesting that H_0 could be a decreasing function of redshift already at late time.

However, our approach is more conservative, since it is based on linear perturbations within the Cosmic Concordance model. In this framework, the 2-point correlation function of luminosity distance-redshift relation has been analytically derived and investigated numerically. It turns out that lensing is the leading effect at the considered redshift, as one may expect.

Our first analytical estimations of the cosmic variance for limited-sky-coverage surveys indicate then that forthcoming high-redshift surveys are well-suited to provide a precise determination of cosmological parameters, such as H_0. Moreover, these forecasted errors for LSST and EDS are stable enough to be quite insensitive to the role of non-linearities in the matter power spectrum. Despite our analysis has been performed entirely within the ΛCDM model, from the geometrical structure of the light-cone 2 general features emerge:

- Lensing 2-point correlation function has vanishing monopole, hence in the limit of large sky coverage and huge number of sources, the cosmic variance must be dominated by Doppler effect also on high redshift surveys.
- As a consequence of line-of-sight integration and statistic isotropy, non-linear scales play an important role only when two sources are almost aligned.

However, realistic surveys deal with limited sky coverage and this makes lensing contribution no longer vanishing. In fact, according to the specific of EDS and LSST and to what has been claimed in Inserra et al. (2021),[6] we forecast that the intrinsic error from cosmic variance associated to H_0 is of $\sim 0.03\,\%$ for LSST and $0.3\,\%$ for EDS for the linear power spectrum. Non-linear scales contribute marginally to this estimation within the specific of EDS. For what regard the specific of LSST, the situation is a way worse. Indeed, in this case, we get that non-linear scales enhance our forecast by almost a factor 3. This is a direct consequence of the fact that lensing 2-point correlation function strongly depends on small scales fluctuations for the diagonal entries of the covariance matrix.

Our analysis extends the one performed in Ben-Dayan et al. (2014),[4] where only close Supernovae (up to $z = 0.1$) have been considered. Indeed, we took into account also lensing corrections on top of the peculiar motion of the sources. In fact, the former is the leading relativistic effect expected at those redshifts.[7] Interestingly, our analysis points out that surveys have an intrinsic error for H_0 which tends to decrease when higher redshift sources are considered, whereas low redshift surveys discussed in Ben-Dayan et al. (2014)[4] admits a quite high dispersion for H_0 of $\sim 1\,\%$.

On one hand, our results are not able to alleviate the tension between local and distant measurements of the Hubble constant. However, they indicate that the analysis of fainter sources does not increase the theoretical uncertainty on H_0. The price to pay stands in the fact that the Hubble diagram at higher redshift is no longer model independent.

References

1. G. Fanizza, B. Fiorini and G. Marozzi, Cosmic variance of H0 in light of forthcoming high-redshift surveys, *Phys. Rev. D* **104**, p. 083506 (2021).
2. N. Aghanim *et al.*, Planck 2018 results. VI. Cosmological parameters, *Astron. Astrophys.* **641**, p. A6 (2020).
3. A. G. Riess, S. Casertano, W. Yuan, J. B. Bowers, L. Macri, J. C. Zinn and D. Scolnic, Cosmic Distances Calibrated to 1% Precision with Gaia EDR3 Parallaxes and Hubble Space Telescope Photometry of 75 Milky Way Cepheids Confirm Tension with ΛCDM, *Astrophys. J. Lett.* **908**, p. L6 (2021).
4. I. Ben-Dayan, R. Durrer, G. Marozzi and D. J. Schwarz, The value of H_0 in the inhomogeneous Universe, *Phys. Rev. Lett.* **112**, p. 221301 (2014).
5. D. Camarena and V. Marra, Impact of the cosmic variance on H_0 on cosmological analyses, *Phys. Rev. D* **98**, p. 023537 (2018).
6. C. Inserra *et al.*, The first Hubble diagram and cosmological constraints using superluminous supernovae, *Mon. Not. Roy. Astron. Soc.* **504**, 2535 (2021).
7. I. Ben-Dayan, M. Gasperini, G. Marozzi, F. Nugier and G. Veneziano, Average and dispersion of the luminosity-redshift relation in the concordance model, *JCAP* **1306**, p. 002 (2013).
8. P. Fleury, C. Clarkson and R. Maartens, How does the cosmic large-scale structure bias the Hubble diagram?, *JCAP* **03**, p. 062 (2017).
9. G. Fanizza, M. Gasperini, G. Marozzi and G. Veneziano, Generalized covariant prescriptions for averaging cosmological observables, *JCAP* **02**, p. 017 (2020).
10. G. Marozzi, The luminosity distance–redshift relation up to second order in the Poisson gauge with anisotropic stress, *Class. Quant. Grav.* **32**, p. 045004 (2015), [Erratum: Class.Quant.Grav. 32, 179501 (2015)].
11. G. Fanizza, J. Yoo and S. G. Biern, Non-linear general relativistic effects in the observed redshift, *JCAP* **09**, p. 037 (2018).

12. C. Bonvin, R. Durrer and M. Gasparini, Fluctuations of the luminosity distance, *Phys. Rev. D* **73**, p. 023523 (2006), [Erratum: Phys.Rev.D 85, 029901 (2012)].
13. I. Ben-Dayan, G. Marozzi, F. Nugier and G. Veneziano, The second-order luminosity-redshift relation in a generic inhomogeneous cosmology, *JCAP* **11**, p. 045 (2012).
14. G. Fanizza, M. Gasperini, G. Marozzi and G. Veneziano, A new approach to the propagation of light-like signals in perturbed cosmological backgrounds, *JCAP* **08**, p. 020 (2015).
15. O. Umeh, C. Clarkson and R. Maartens, Nonlinear relativistic corrections to cosmological distances, redshift and gravitational lensing magnification. II - Derivation, *Class. Quant. Grav.* **31**, p. 205001 (2014).
16. J. Yoo, Maximum Cosmological Information from Type-Ia Supernova Observations, *Phys. Rev. D* **101**, p. 043507 (2020).
17. R. Laureijs et al., Euclid Definition Study Report (2011).
18. P. A. Abell et al., LSST Science Book, Version 2.0 (12 2009).
19. R. E. Smith, J. A. Peacock, A. Jenkins, S. D. M. White, C. S. Frenk, F. R. Pearce, P. A. Thomas, G. Efstathiou and H. M. P. Couchman, Stable clustering, the halo model and non-linear cosmological power spectra, *Monthly Notices of the Royal Astronomical Society* **341**, 1311 (Jun 2003).
20. R. Takahashi, M. Sato, T. Nishimichi, A. Taruya and M. Oguri, Revising the halofit model for the nonlinear matter power spectrum, *The Astrophysical Journal* **761**, p. 152 (Dec 2012).
21. L. Cosmai, G. Fanizza, M. Gasperini and L. Tedesco, Discriminating different models of luminosity-redshift distribution, *Class. Quant. Grav.* **30**, p. 095011 (2013).
22. A. E. Romano, Hubble trouble or Hubble bubble?, *Int. J. Mod. Phys. D* **27**, p. 1850102 (2018).
23. L. Cosmai, G. Fanizza, F. Sylos Labini, L. Pietronero and L. Tedesco, Fractal universe and cosmic acceleration in a Lemaître–Tolman–Bondi scenario, *Class. Quant. Grav.* **36**, p. 045007 (2019).
24. S. A. Vallejo-Peña and A. E. Romano, Coordinate independent approach to the calculation of the effects of local structure on the luminosity distance, *JCAP* **03**, p. 023 (2020).
25. R.-G. Cai, Z.-K. Guo, L. Li, S.-J. Wang and W.-W. Yu, Chameleon dark energy can resolve the Hubble tension, *Phys. Rev. D* **103**, p. 121302 (2021).
26. C. Krishnan, E. O. Colgáin, Ruchika, A. A. Sen, M. M. Sheikh-Jabbari and T. Yang, Is there an early Universe solution to Hubble tension?, *Phys. Rev. D* **102**, p. 103525 (2020).
27. C. Krishnan, E. O. Colgáin, M. M. Sheikh-Jabbari and T. Yang, Running Hubble Tension and a H0 Diagnostic, *Phys. Rev. D* **103**, p. 103509 (2021).
28. K. C. Wong et al., H0LiCOW – XIII. A 2.4 per cent measurement of H0 from lensed quasars: 5.3σ tension between early- and late-Universe probes, *Mon. Not. Roy. Astron. Soc.* **498**, 1420 (2020).
29. M. Millon et al., TDCOSMO. I. An exploration of systematic uncertainties in the inference of H_0 from time-delay cosmography, *Astron. Astrophys.* **639**, p. A101 (2020).
30. M. G. Dainotti, B. De Simone, T. Schiavone, G. Montani, E. Rinaldi and G. Lambiase, On the Hubble constant tension in the SNe Ia Pantheon sample, *Astrophys. J.* **912**, p. 150 (2021).

Primordial black holes arise when the inflaton falls

Keisuke Inomata

Kavli Institute for Cosmological Physics, The University of Chicago,
Chicago, IL 60637, USA
E-mail: inomata@uchicago.edu

Primordial black holes (PBHs) can be produced when large density perturbations enter the horizon in the early universe. They can be dark matter (DM) and the black holes detected by the LIGO-Virgo collaborations. In this proceeding, we show that the large enhancement of the perturbations, required for the DM PBHs and LIGO/Virgo PBHs, can be realized in inflation models with a downward step. This enhancement mechanism is related to the particle production associated with the non-adiabatic evolution of the inflaton. This proceeding is based on our original paper.[1]

Keywords: Primordial black holes; inflaton; dark matter.

1. Introduction

Primordial black holes (PBHs) are one of the hottest topics in Cosmology because they are one of the candidates of dark matter (DM) and the black holes (BHs) detected by LIGO-Virgo collaborations.[2–7] PBHs are produced when the large density perturbations enter the horizon during a radiation- or matter-dominated era. The power spectrum of the density perturbations sensitively depends on the inflaton potential.

Throughout this proceeding, we focus on single-field inflation models. In the previous works, the large perturbations for the PBH scenarios are realized by the flat region in the inflaton potential.[8–25] When the inflaton rolls on the flat region, it gets decelerated due to the Hubble friction, which is called the ultra-slow-roll (USR) period. Once the inflaton gets decelerated, the perturbations are enhanced. This can be seen from the form of the power spectrum in the slow-roll approximation, $\mathcal{P}_\mathcal{R} \simeq H^2/(8\pi^2 \epsilon M_{\text{Pl}}^2)$, where H is the Hubble parameter and ϵ is the slow-roll parameter, related to the inflaton velocity through $\epsilon \equiv -\dot H/H^2 = \dot\phi^2/(2H^2 M_{\text{Pl}}^2)$.

On the other hand, in this proceeding, we show that a downward step in the inflaton potential can also realize the large enhancement of the perturbations. Although the perturbation enhancement with the step-like feature is discussed in previous works,[26,27] the $\mathcal{O}(10^7)$ enhancement of $\mathcal{P}_\mathcal{R}$, required for the PBH scenarios, has never been realized. One example of the inflaton potential with the downward step is shown in Fig. 1, whose concrete parameterization will be given in Sec. 3. In the following, we explain why the downward step can enhance the perturbations.

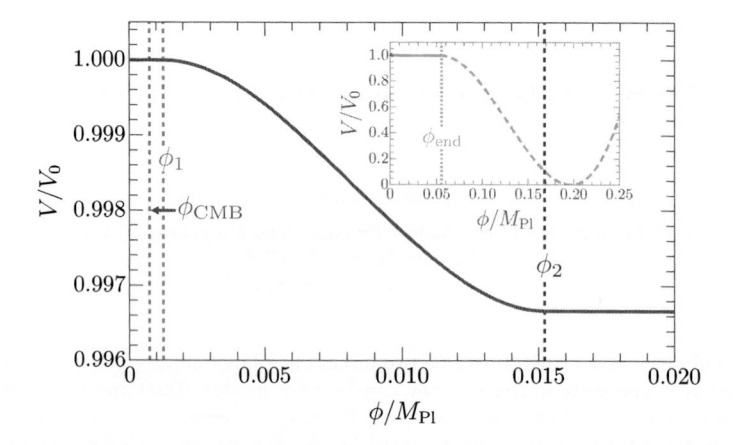

Fig. 1. The inflaton potential of Eq. (10) that realizes the large enhancement of perturbations, with the downward step at $\phi_1 \leq \phi \leq \phi_2$ highlighted and an inset for the full range. The parameters are $n_s = 0.97$, $\epsilon_1 = 7.43 \times 10^{-10}$, $\epsilon_2 = 0.01$, $\epsilon_3 = 10^{-9}$, and $\Delta N_{\text{step}} = 0.5$. ϕ_{end} denotes the end of inflation (red vertical dotted line) and corresponds to 50 e-folds from ϕ_{CMB}. This figure is taken from our original paper.[1]

2. A toy model

In this section, we explain the reason why the downward step causes the large enhancement by using a toy model. In canonical single-field inflation, the curvature perturbation $\mathcal{R}_k$ obeys the following equation:[26, 28, 29]

$$\mathcal{R}_k'' + (2+\eta)\mathcal{H}\mathcal{R}_k' + k^2 \mathcal{R}_k = 0, \qquad (1)$$

where $\eta \equiv \epsilon'/(\mathcal{H}\epsilon)$, $\mathcal{H}$ is the comoving Hubble parameter, and the prime denotes the derivative with respect to the conformal time, $d\tau \equiv dt/a$ with $\tau = 0$ at the end of inflation. We can rewrite this equation as

$$\frac{d^2\mathcal{R}_k}{dx^2} - \frac{2+\eta}{x}\frac{d\mathcal{R}_k}{dx} + \mathcal{R}_k \simeq 0, \qquad (2)$$

where $x \equiv -k\tau$ and we have used the relation $\mathcal{H} \simeq -1/\tau$. Then, we obtain the general solution for the curvature perturbation:

$$\mathcal{R}_k \approx C_1 G_\nu^{(1)}(-k\tau) + C_2 G_\nu^{(2)}(-k\tau), \qquad (3)$$

where $\nu = 3/2 + \eta/2$, C_1 and C_2 are constant in time, and $G_\nu^{(1)}$ and $G_\nu^{(2)}$ are defined with the Hankel functions of the first ($H_\nu^{(1)}$) and the second kind ($H_\nu^{(2)}$) as

$$G_\nu^{(j)}(-k\tau) \equiv (-k\tau)^\nu H_\nu^{(j)}(-k\tau), \qquad (4)$$

with $j \in (1, 2)$.

As a toy model, we consider the case where ϵ changes from $\epsilon_1(\ll 1)$ to $\epsilon_2(> \epsilon_1)$ with constant positive η and, after that, ϵ decreases with $\eta = -6$, which corresponds to a USR phase. Specifically, we parameterize η as

$$\eta = \eta_c \Theta(\tau - \tau_1)\Theta(\tau_2 - \tau) - 6\Theta(\tau - \tau_2). \qquad (5)$$

Once ϵ_1/ϵ_2 is fixed, we have $\tau_2/\tau_1 = (\epsilon_1/\epsilon_2)^{1/\eta_c}$ and $\tau/\tau_2 = (\epsilon(\tau)/\epsilon_2)^{1/6}$ for $\tau > \tau_2$ with $\epsilon(\tau)$ being the value at τ. Substituting this into Eq. (2), we obtain the solution of the curvature perturbation,

$$\mathcal{R}_k = \begin{cases} D_1 G^{(1)}_{3/2}(-k\tau) & (\tau < \tau_1) \\ E_1 G^{(1)}_{\nu_c}(-k\tau) + E_2 G^{(2)}_{\nu_c}(-k\tau) & (\tau_1 \leq \tau \leq \tau_2) \\ F_1 G^{(1)}_{-3/2}(-k\tau) + F_2 G^{(2)}_{-3/2}(-k\tau) & (\tau_2 \leq \tau) \end{cases}$$

where $\nu_c = 3/2 + \eta_c/2$. Imposing the Bunch-Davies vacuum condition as $D_1 = -\sqrt{\pi/2}H/(\sqrt{4k^3\epsilon_1}M_{\rm Pl})$ and the continuity of $\mathcal{R}$ and $\mathcal{R}'$ at τ_1 and τ_2, we determine the other coefficients. Hereafter, as the simplest case, let us consider the large limit of η_c, which corresponds to the step-function like downward step. In this limit, Eq. (1) in $\tau_1 < \tau < \tau_2$ can be approximated as

$$\mathcal{R}_k'' + \frac{\epsilon'}{\epsilon}\mathcal{R}_k' \approx 0. \tag{6}$$

From this relation, we can obtain $\mathcal{R}_k'(\tau_2) = (\epsilon_1/\epsilon_2)\mathcal{R}_k'(\tau_1)$. We can see that $\mathcal{R}_k'$ undergoes a jump down at the transition, by a relative factor of (ϵ_1/ϵ_2), while $\mathcal{R}$ itself is continuous, $\mathcal{R}_k(\tau_1) = \mathcal{R}_k(\tau_2)$, for any finite ϵ. From the relation between the curvature perturbation and the inflaton fluctuation $\delta\phi$ during the inflation, $\mathcal{R} \simeq \delta\phi/(\sqrt{2\epsilon}M_{\rm Pl})$, we can see that, while the curvature perturbations remain constant, the inflaton fluctuations get amplified during the increase of ϵ (the rolling down of the step). This amplification of the inflaton fluctuations can be regarded as the particle production. Note that the amplification of the curvature perturbations occurs after the rolling down phase ($\tau > \tau_2$) because the curvature perturbation evolves as $\mathcal{R}_k \propto 1/\sqrt{\epsilon}$ in $\tau > \tau_2$.

In the limit of $\eta_c \to \infty$, the coefficients F_1 and F_2 approach the following values:

$$F_{1,{\rm lim}} = D_1 \frac{3\epsilon_2 + (2\epsilon_2 + \epsilon_1)(-k\tau_1)^2 + i(\epsilon_2 + \epsilon_1)(-k\tau_1)^3}{2\epsilon_2},$$

$$F_{2,{\rm lim}} = -D_1 e^{-2ik\tau_1}(1 - i(-k\tau_1))\frac{(3\epsilon_2 - 3i\epsilon_2(-k\tau_1) + (\epsilon_1 - \epsilon_2)(-k\tau_1)^2)}{2\epsilon_2}, \tag{7}$$

where note $\tau_1 = \tau_2$ in this limit. Using these expressions, we derive the analytic form of the final power spectrum after the perturbations exit the horizon. Here, we define τ_3 as the time at the end of the USR phase so that $\epsilon_3 = \epsilon(\tau_3)$. After the USR phase, the inflation continues with $\epsilon = \epsilon_3$. In this case, the power spectrum in the large-scale limit, $k \ll 1/|\tau_1|$ becomes

$$\mathcal{P}_\mathcal{R}(k) \simeq \frac{H^2}{8\pi^2 M_{\rm Pl}^2 \epsilon_1}\left[1 - \frac{2}{15}\sqrt{\frac{\epsilon_2}{\epsilon_3}}(-k\tau_1)^2 + \frac{1}{225}\frac{\epsilon_2}{\epsilon_3}(-k\tau_1)^4\right], \tag{8}$$

up to $\mathcal{O}((-k\tau_1)^4)$, and where we have also assumed $\epsilon_3/\epsilon_2 \ll 1$. On the other hand, for modes that were inside the horizon at the transition ($k \gtrsim 1/|\tau_1|$), the power spectrum finally becomes

$$\mathcal{P}_\mathcal{R}(k) \simeq A\frac{1 - \cos(-2k\tau_1)}{2}, \quad A = \frac{H^2}{8\pi^2 M_{\rm Pl}^2 \epsilon_1}\frac{\epsilon_2}{\epsilon_3}, \tag{9}$$

where we have assumed $\epsilon_1/\epsilon_2 \ll 1$. From this expression, we can see that the power spectrum is enhanced by a factor of $\mathcal{O}(\epsilon_2/\epsilon_3)$.

3. A concrete model

Next, we discuss a concrete inflaton potential with a downward step, which realizes the large perturbation enhancement. Specifically, we consider the following potential:

$$V(\phi) = V_b(\phi) F(\phi; \phi_1, \phi_2, h), \tag{10}$$

where V_b is the base potential and F induces the downward step. We take the following form of V_b:

$$V_b(\phi) \simeq V_0 \left(1 - \frac{\beta \phi^2/M_{\rm Pl}^2}{1 + \phi/\phi_{\rm CMB}}\right), \tag{11}$$

where we determine the parameters to make the power spectrum on large scales consistent with CMB observation, $\mathcal{P}_\mathcal{R} \simeq 2 \times 10^{-9}$ and $n_s = 0.97$. Note that the inflaton potential changes from this form around the end of the inflation, which is irrelevant to the enhancement mechanism. The concrete expression of the function F is given by

$$F(\phi; \phi_1, \phi_2, h) \equiv \begin{cases} 1 & (\phi < \phi_1) \\ 1 - hS\left(\frac{\phi - \phi_1}{\phi_2 - \phi_1}\right) & (\phi_1 \leq \phi \leq \phi_2) , \\ 1 - h & (\phi > \phi_2) \end{cases} \tag{12}$$

where $S(x) \equiv x^2(3 - 2x)$ and it changes from 0 to 1 with the change of x from 0 to 1. The parameter h determines the step height, normalized by V_0, and $\phi_2 - \phi_1$ determines the e-folds for the inflaton to pass through the step, which is denoted by $\Delta N_{\rm step}$. With this concrete inflaton potential, we numerically calculate the power spectrum and get the results in Fig. 2. The peak height of the power spectrum in Fig. 2 is $\mathcal{P}_\mathcal{R} \sim \mathcal{O}(10^{-2})$, which is large enough for the scenarios of the DM PBHs and the LIGO-Virgo PBHs.[30] From this figure, we can see that the power spectrum is enhanced by a factor of $\mathcal{O}(\epsilon_3/\epsilon_2)$, which is consistent with the analytical estimate in the previous section. We can also see that the perturbation enhancement does not occur on the very small scales, where Eq. (6) is invalid. This is because Eq. (6) is valid only when the transition timescale, $\tau_2 - \tau_1$, is much smaller than the timescale of the perturbation oscillation, $1/k$.

4. Conclusion

In this proceeding, we have proposed a new type of single-field inflation model for the PBH scenarios. We have shown that a downward step feature in the inflaton potential can enhance the power spectrum by a factor of $\mathcal{O}(10^7)$, required for the PBH scenarios. This perturbation enhancement can be interpreted as the particle production that occurs during the inflaton rolling down of the step.

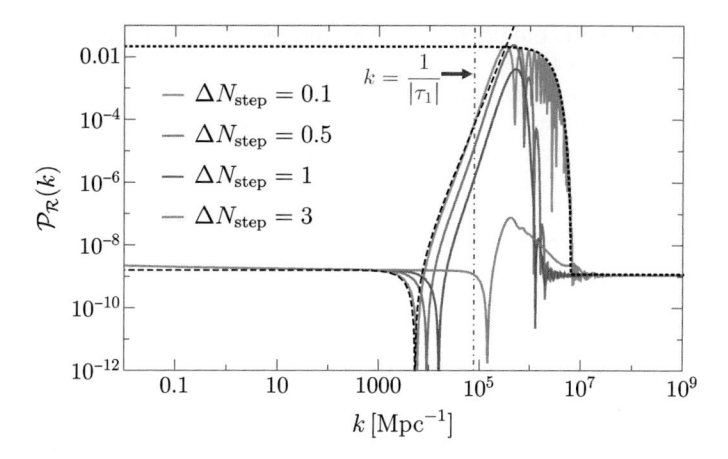

Fig. 2. The power spectrum in the inflaton potential of Eq. (10) with different $\Delta N_{\rm step}$. Except for $\Delta N_{\rm step}$, the parameters are the same as in Fig. 1. The black dotted and dashed lines are the approximate forms of the power spectrum. See our original paper[1] for details. This figure is taken from our original paper.[1]

Acknowledgments

The author was supported by the Kavli Institute for Cosmological Physics at the University of Chicago through an endowment from the Kavli Foundation and its founder Fred Kavli.

References

1. K. Inomata, E. Mcdonough and W. Hu, Primordial Black Holes Arise When The Inflaton Falls (4 2021).
2. S. Bird, I. Cholis, J. B. Muñoz, Y. Ali-Haïmoud, M. Kamionkowski, E. D. Kovetz, A. Raccanelli and A. G. Riess, Did LIGO detect dark matter?, *Phys. Rev. Lett.* **116**, p. 201301 (2016).
3. S. Clesse and J. García-Bellido, The clustering of massive Primordial Black Holes as Dark Matter: measuring their mass distribution with Advanced LIGO, *Phys. Dark Univ.* **15**, 142 (2017).
4. M. Sasaki, T. Suyama, T. Tanaka and S. Yokoyama, Primordial Black Hole Scenario for the Gravitational-Wave Event GW150914, *Phys. Rev. Lett.* **117**, p. 061101 (2016).
5. A. Kashlinsky, LIGO gravitational wave detection, primordial black holes and the near-IR cosmic infrared background anisotropies, *Astrophys. J. Lett.* **823**, p. L25 (2016).
6. A. Kashlinsky, R. G. Arendt, F. Atrio-Barandela, N. Cappelluti, A. Ferrara and G. Hasinger, Looking at cosmic near-infrared background radiation anisotropies, *Rev. Mod. Phys.* **90**, p. 025006 (2018).
7. J. García-Bellido, J. F. Nuño Siles and E. Ruiz Morales, Bayesian analysis of the spin distribution of LIGO/Virgo black holes, *Phys. Dark Univ.* **31**, p. 100791 (2021).
8. P. Ivanov, P. Naselsky and I. Novikov, Inflation and primordial black holes as dark matter, *Phys. Rev. D* **50**, 7173 (1994).

9. S. M. Leach and A. R. Liddle, Inflationary perturbations near horizon crossing, *Phys. Rev. D* **63**, p. 043508 (2001).
10. S. M. Leach, M. Sasaki, D. Wands and A. R. Liddle, Enhancement of superhorizon scale inflationary curvature perturbations, *Phys. Rev. D* **64**, p. 023512 (2001).
11. S. Inoue and J. Yokoyama, Curvature perturbation at the local extremum of the inflaton's potential, *Phys. Lett. B* **524**, 15 (2002).
12. N. C. Tsamis and R. P. Woodard, Improved estimates of cosmological perturbations, *Phys. Rev. D* **69**, p. 084005 (2004).
13. W. H. Kinney, Horizon crossing and inflation with large eta, *Phys. Rev. D* **72**, p. 023515 (2005).
14. J. Garcia-Bellido and E. Ruiz Morales, Primordial black holes from single field models of inflation, *Phys. Dark Univ.* **18**, 47 (2017).
15. J. M. Ezquiaga, J. Garcia-Bellido and E. Ruiz Morales, Primordial Black Hole production in Critical Higgs Inflation, *Phys. Lett. B* **776**, 345 (2018).
16. K. Kannike, L. Marzola, M. Raidal and H. Veermäe, Single Field Double Inflation and Primordial Black Holes, *JCAP* **1709**, p. 020 (2017).
17. C. Germani and T. Prokopec, On primordial black holes from an inflection point, *Phys. Dark Univ.* **18**, 6 (2017).
18. G. Ballesteros and M. Taoso, Primordial black hole dark matter from single field inflation, *Phys. Rev.* **D97**, p. 023501 (2018).
19. M. P. Hertzberg and M. Yamada, Primordial Black Holes from Polynomial Potentials in Single Field Inflation, *Phys. Rev. D* **97**, p. 083509 (2018).
20. S.-L. Cheng, W. Lee and K.-W. Ng, Superhorizon curvature perturbation in ultraslow-roll inflation, *Phys. Rev. D* **99**, p. 063524 (2019).
21. C. T. Byrnes, P. S. Cole and S. P. Patil, Steepest growth of the power spectrum and primordial black holes, *JCAP* **1906**, p. 028 (2019).
22. S. Passaglia, W. Hu and H. Motohashi, Primordial black holes and local non-Gaussianity in canonical inflation, *Phys. Rev. D* **99**, p. 043536 (2019).
23. M. Drees and Y. Xu, Overshooting, Critical Higgs Inflation and Second Order Gravitational Wave Signatures, *Eur. Phys. J. C* **81**, p. 182 (2021).
24. P. Carrilho, K. A. Malik and D. J. Mulryne, Dissecting the growth of the power spectrum for primordial black holes, *Phys. Rev. D* **100**, p. 103529 (2019).
25. K.-W. Ng and Y.-P. Wu, Constant-rate inflation: primordial black holes from conformal weight transitions (2 2021).
26. V. Miranda, W. Hu, C. He and H. Motohashi, Nonlinear Excitations in Inflationary Power Spectra, *Phys. Rev. D* **93**, p. 023504 (2016).
27. K. Kefala, G. P. Kodaxis, I. D. Stamou and N. Tetradis, Features of the inflaton potential and the power spectrum of cosmological perturbations, *Phys. Rev. D* **104**, p. 023506 (2021).
28. M. Sasaki, Large Scale Quantum Fluctuations in the Inflationary Universe, *Prog. Theor. Phys.* **76**, p. 1036 (1986).
29. V. F. Mukhanov, Quantum Theory of Gauge Invariant Cosmological Perturbations, *Sov. Phys. JETP* **67**, 1297 (1988).
30. M. Sasaki, T. Suyama, T. Tanaka and S. Yokoyama, Primordial black holes—perspectives in gravitational wave astronomy, *Class. Quant. Grav.* **35**, p. 063001 (2018).

Effects of the modification of gravity on the production of primordial black holes

Sergio Andrés Vallejo Peña

ICRANet, Piazza della Repubblica 10, I–65122 Pescara, Italy
Instituto de Física, Universidad de Antioquia, A.A.1226, Medellín, Colombia
E-mail: sergio.vallejo@udea.edu.co

The enhancement of the spectrum of primordial comoving curvature perturbation $\mathcal{R}$ can induce the production of primordial black holes (PBH) which could account for part of present day dark matter. As an example of the effects of the modification of gravity on the production of PBHs, we investigate the effects on the spectrum of $\mathcal{R}$ produced by the modification of gravity in the case of G-inflation, deriving the relation between the unitary gauge curvature perturbation ζ and the comoving curvature perturbation $\mathcal{R}$, and identifying a background dependent enhancement function $\mathcal{E}$ which can induce large differences between the two gauge invariant variables.

When ζ is not constant in time it is different from $\mathcal{R}$, for example on sub-horizon scales, or in models exhibiting an anomalous super-horizon growth of ζ, but since this growth cannot last indefinitely, eventually they will coincide. We derive the general condition for super-horizon growth of ζ, showing that slow-roll violation is not necessary. Since the abundance of PBHs depends on the statistics of the peaks of the comoving density contrast, which is related to the spectrum of $\mathcal{R}$, it is important to take into account these effects on the PBHs abundance in modified gravity theories.

Keywords: Modified gravity, primordial curvature perturbations, primordial black holes.

1. Introduction

The study of primordial perturbations is fundamental in any cosmological model, since it allows to make predictions of the conditions which provided the seeds for the anisotropies of the cosmic microwave background (CMB) radiation or for the process of structure formation. Among the different theoretical scenarios proposed to explain the accelerated expansion of the Universe, Horndeski's theory[1] has received a lot of attention, both in the context of inflation and dark energy.

The calculation of the equation for cosmological perturbations for these theories have been so far performed in the so called unitary gauge, also known as uniform field gauge. While the unitary gauge has some computational convenience in general relativity when only a scalar field is present, in general it is not directly related to observations, which depend on the comoving curvature perturbations $\mathcal{R}$. The production of PBHs[2–6] is an example of phenomenon depending on $\mathcal{R}$[7] and not on the unitary gauge curvature perturbations ζ. Another example are the numerical codes developed for the solution of the Boltzman's equations in a perturbed Friedman-Lemaître-Robertson-Walker (FLRW) Universe, which are using equations in the synchronous gauge,[8] which for adiabatic perturbations coincides approximately with the comoving gauge,[9] justifying the use of the comoving slices gauge for early Universe calculations.

The comoving gauge can differ from the unitary gauge in modified gravity theories because the effective energy momentum tensor arising from the modification of gravity can produce some effective entropy terms, which are absent in $K(X)$ theories, but are present in any more complicated Hordenski's theory. In this letter we compute the general relation between $\mathcal{R}$ and ζ in G-Inflation.[10,11] As an application we use this relation to investigate the effects of the modification of gravity on the power spectrum of $\mathcal{R}$, and its implications on the production of PBHs.

2. G-inflation

In G-inflation the scalar field Φ is minimally coupled to gravity according to the action[10,12]

$$S = \int d^4x \sqrt{-g} \left(\frac{M_{Pl}^2}{2} R + L(\Phi, X) \right),$$

where $X = -g^{\mu\nu}\partial_\mu \Phi \partial_\nu \Phi/2$, R is the Ricci scalar and we use a system of units in which $c = \hbar = 1$. The Lagrangian density of the scalar field corresponds to

$$L(\Phi, X) = K(\Phi, X) + G(\Phi, X)\Box\Phi, \tag{1}$$

where K and G are arbitrary functions. The corresponding effective stress-energy-momentum tensor (EST) is given by

$$T_{\mu\nu} = L_{,X}\nabla_\mu \Phi \nabla_\nu \Phi + P_\Phi g_{\mu\nu} + \nabla_\mu \Phi \nabla_\nu G + \nabla_\nu \Phi \nabla_\mu G, \tag{2}$$

where

$$L_{,X} = \partial_X L = K_X(\Phi, X) + G_X(\Phi, X)\Box\Phi, \tag{3}$$
$$P_\Phi = L - \nabla_\mu (G\nabla^\mu \Phi) = K - g^{\mu\nu}\nabla_\mu \Phi \nabla_\nu G. \tag{4}$$

3. The perturbed effective energy-stress-momentum tensor

The most general scalar perturbations with respect to a flat FLRW background can be written as

$$ds^2 = a^2 \Big\{ -(1+2A)d\tau^2 + 2\partial_i B dx^i d\tau + [\delta_{ij}(1-2C) + 2\partial_i \partial_j E] dx^i dx^j \Big\}. \tag{5}$$

For the decomposition of the scalar field and the EST into their background and perturbation parts we use the notation

$$\Phi(x^\mu) = \phi(\tau) + \delta\phi(x^\mu), \tag{6}$$
$$T^\mu{}_\nu = \overline{T}^\mu{}_\nu + \delta T^\mu{}_\nu. \tag{7}$$

The background components of the EST are

$$\overline{T}^0{}_0 = -\overline{\rho} = K(\phi,\chi) + \frac{3\mathcal{H}\phi'^3}{a^4}G_\chi(\phi,\chi) - \frac{\phi'^2}{a^2}\left[K_\chi(\phi,\chi) + G_\phi(\phi,\chi)\right], \quad (8)$$

$$\overline{T}^0{}_i = \overline{T}^i{}_0 = 0, \quad (9)$$

$$\overline{T}^i{}_j = \delta^i{}_j \overline{P},$$

$$\overline{P} = K(\phi,\chi) - \frac{\mathcal{H}\phi'^3}{a^4}G_\chi(\phi,\chi) + \frac{\phi'^2}{a^2}\left[G_\phi(\phi,\chi) + \frac{\phi''}{a^2}G_\chi(\phi,\chi)\right], \quad (10)$$

where the primes stand for derivatives with respect to τ, χ is given by $\chi = \frac{\phi'^2}{2a^2}$, and the subscripts ϕ and χ denote partial derivatives with respect to these quantities, i.e. $G_\phi(\phi,\chi) = \partial_\phi G(\phi,\chi)$ and $G_\chi(\phi,\chi) = \partial_\chi G(\phi,\chi)$. In order to define the comoving slices gauge we need this component of the perturbed EST

$$\delta T^0{}_i = -\left(K_\chi + 2G_\phi - \frac{3\mathcal{H}\phi'}{a^2}G_\chi\right)\frac{\phi'^2}{a^2}\partial_i\delta\phi - \frac{\phi'^2}{a^4}G_\chi \partial_i\left(\delta\phi' - \phi' A\right), \quad (11)$$

where $\mathcal{H} = a'/a$. The remaining components of the perturbed EST are not relevant to the computations done in this letter, and we will give them in a future work. Under a gauge transformation of the form $(\tau, x^i) \to (\tau + \delta\tau, x^i + \delta x^i)$ the perturbations $\delta\phi$, A, B, C, and E transform according to[13]

$$\delta\phi \to \delta\phi - \phi'\delta\tau, \quad (12)$$

$$A \to A - \mathcal{H}\delta\tau - \delta\tau', \quad (13)$$

$$B \to B + \delta\tau - \delta x', \quad (14)$$

$$C \to C + \mathcal{H}\delta\tau, \quad (15)$$

$$E \to E - \delta x. \quad (16)$$

4. Evolution of curvature perturbations in the unitary gauge

In single scalar field models the unitary gauge is defined by the condition $\delta\phi_u = 0$. From the gauge transformation in eq.(12) we can see that the time translation $\delta\tau_u$ necessary to go to the unitary gauge is given by

$$\delta\tau_u = \frac{\delta\phi}{\phi'}. \quad (17)$$

Using eq.(15) we can compute the curvature perturbation in the unitary gauge ζ

$$\zeta \equiv -C_u = -C - \mathcal{H}\delta\tau_u = -C - \mathcal{H}\frac{\delta\phi}{\phi'}. \quad (18)$$

which is by construction gauge invariant. We can also define other gauge invariant quantities such as the unitary gauge lapse function

$$A_u \equiv A - \mathcal{H}\delta\tau_u - \delta\tau'_u = A - \mathcal{H}\frac{\delta\phi}{\phi'} - \left(\frac{\delta\phi}{\phi'}\right)'. \quad (19)$$

The second order action for ζ in Horndeski's theories was computed in[14]

$$S_\zeta^{(2)} = \int dt d^3 x a^3 \left[\mathcal{G}_S \dot\zeta^2 - \frac{\mathcal{F}_S}{a^2} (\partial_i \zeta)^2 \right], \tag{20}$$

where $\mathcal{G}_S$ and $\mathcal{F}_S$ are functions of $K(\phi,\chi)$ and $G(\phi,\chi)$ and their derivatives. The Lagrange equations for this action give the equation of motion of ζ

$$\zeta'' + \left(2\mathcal{H} + \frac{\mathcal{G}_S'}{\mathcal{G}_S} \right) \zeta' - c_s^2 \overset{(3)}{\Delta} \zeta = 0, \tag{21}$$

where $c_s^2(\tau) = \mathcal{F}_S/\mathcal{G}_S$.

For the Fourier transform of the above equation we use the notation

$$\zeta_k'' + \left(2\mathcal{H} + \frac{\mathcal{G}_S'}{\mathcal{G}_S} \right) \zeta_k' + c_s^2 k^2 \zeta_k = 0. \tag{22}$$

5. Comoving slices gauge in G-inflation

The comoving slices gauge is defined by the condition $\delta T^0{}_i = 0$. In G-inflation, combing eqs.(12-13) with eq.(11) we have that under an infinitesimal time translation

$$\delta T^0{}_i \to \delta T^0{}_i + \partial_i \left(\frac{\phi'^2}{a^4} D \delta\tau \right), \tag{23}$$

where

$$D = a^2 (2G_\phi + K_\chi) + G_\chi (-4\mathcal{H}\phi' + \phi''), \tag{24}$$

from which we get the time translation $\delta\tau_c$ required to go to the comoving slices gauge

$$\delta\tau_c = \frac{1}{\phi' D} \left[-\phi' G_\chi (3\mathcal{H}\delta\phi + \phi' A - \delta\phi') + a^2 (2G_\phi + K_\chi) \delta\phi \right]. \tag{25}$$

Note that in the particular case in which G does not depend explicitly on χ, i.e. $G(\phi,\chi) = G(\phi)$ the above transformation reduces to

$$\delta\tau_c = \frac{\delta\phi}{\phi'}, \tag{26}$$

and the comoving gauge coincides with the unitary gauge, since in this case the system is equivalent to a $K(X)$ theory.[15,16]

The comoving curvature perturbation $\mathcal{R}$ is then defined as

$$\mathcal{R} \equiv -C_c = -C - \mathcal{H}\delta\tau_c. \tag{27}$$

Our goal is to derive the relation between ζ and $\mathcal{R}$, and we can achieve this by performing the gauge transformation between the unitary and comoving slices gauge.

Using the general gauge transformation defined in eq.(25), when $\delta\phi = 0$ and $A = A_u$, we get

$$\delta\tau_{uc} = -\frac{\phi' G_\chi}{D} A_u, \tag{28}$$

from which we obtain

$$\mathcal{R} = \zeta + \mathcal{H}\frac{\phi' G_\chi}{D} A_u. \tag{29}$$

The gauge invariant variable A_u can be expressed in terms of ζ using the perturbed Einstein's equation $\delta G^0{}_i = \delta T^0{}_i/M_{Pl}^2$ in the unitary gauge, which using eq.(11) gives

$$-\zeta' + \mathcal{H} A_u = -\frac{\phi'^3 G_\chi}{2 M_{Pl}^2 a^2} A_u. \tag{30}$$

We can then combine eq.(29) and eq.(30) to obtain the relation between $\mathcal{R}$ and ζ only

$$\mathcal{R} = \zeta + \mathcal{H}\frac{\phi' G_\chi}{D}\left(\frac{\phi'^3 G_\chi}{2 M_{Pl}^2 a^2} + \mathcal{H}\right)^{-1}\zeta' = \zeta + \mathcal{E}(\tau)\zeta', \tag{31}$$

where we have defined the enhancement factor $\mathcal{E}(\tau)$, a quantity depending only on the background, which can induce a significant difference between the curvature perturbations on comoving and uniform field slices. The relation between the power spectrum of ζ and $\mathcal{R}$ is then given by

$$P_\mathcal{R} = \frac{k^3}{2\pi^2}|\mathcal{R}_k|^2 = P_\zeta + \frac{k^3}{2\pi^2}\Delta, \tag{32}$$

where

$$\Delta = \left[\mathcal{E}\zeta^*\zeta' + \mathcal{E}^*\zeta'^*(\zeta + \mathcal{E}\zeta')\right]. \tag{33}$$

Note that the above relations are valid on any scale, since they are just based on gauge transformations, without assuming any sub or super horizon limit. This implies that the spectra of $\mathcal{R}$ and ζ could be different due to a change in the evolution of both sub-horizon and super-horizon modes during the time interval when $\mathcal{E}(\eta)$ is large. On sub-horizon scales the effect is always present, since ζ is oscillating and $\zeta' \neq 0$, while for super-horizon scales the effect could be suppressed if $\zeta \approx 0$, but even for models conserving ζ there could be an effect, since the freezing does not happen immediately after horizon crossing. We will discuss later the implication on the production of PBHs.

6. Conservation of $\mathcal{R}$ and ζ

From eq.(31) we can reach the important conclusion that

$$\zeta = const \Rightarrow \zeta = \mathcal{R} = const; \tag{34}$$

however the opposite is not true, i.e.

$$\mathcal{R} = const \nRightarrow \zeta = const, \tag{35}$$

which can have important implications for conservation laws of $\mathcal{R}$ and non-Gaussianity consistency conditions.[17] As explained previously, $\mathcal{R}$ is the quantity related to observations, so it would be inconsistent to infer constraints on ζ from CMB observations for example, since the latter depend on $\mathcal{R}$. From a theoretical point of view the models approximately conserving ζ on super-horizon scales may be incompatible with observations for large enhancement functions $\mathcal{E}(\tau)$, because $\mathcal{R}$ could be not conserved, implying for example a violation of the non-Gaussianity consistency condition or a miss-estimation of PBHs abundance.

Nevertheless it should be noted that the super-horizon growth of perturbations cannot last indefinitely, or the entire perturbative treatment of the problem would breakdown, leading to inhomogeneities much larger than those imprinted in the CMB for example. For this reason it is expected that for any model compatible with observations the super-horizon growth of ζ should be only temporary, and according to eq.(34), at some time after horizon crossing $\zeta \approx \mathcal{R}$. This simplifies the calculation of $\mathcal{R}$, whose evolution can be then traced during and after reheating, too, contrary to ζ.

The only exception to this argument could be very small scales ζ modes which leave the horizon very late, and whose super-horizon growth could continue until horizon re-enter, without affecting the validity of the perturbative treatment of the problem. For these small scale modes the difference between $\mathcal{R}$ and ζ could be important, but it would still be computationally convenient to solve the equation for ζ and then obtain $\mathcal{R}$ using the gauge transformation given in eq.(31).

7. Enhancement of curvature perturbations

As already observed for comoving curvature perturbation $\mathcal{R}$ in general relativity for standard kinetic term single field models,[18] a temporary violation of slow-roll conditions can lead to the anomalous growth of what would normally be a decaying mode. A similar mechanism can induce the growth of ζ, as we will show in this section. We can re-write eq.(22) in the form

$$\frac{\mathrm{d}}{\mathrm{d}a}\left(a^3 \mathcal{H} \mathcal{G}_S \frac{\mathrm{d}\zeta_k}{\mathrm{d}a}\right) + a\mathcal{F}_S \frac{k^2}{\mathcal{H}} \zeta_k = 0, \tag{36}$$

from which it is possible to find a super-horizon scale solution of the form

$$\zeta_k = A + B \int \frac{\mathrm{d}a}{a} f, \quad f = \frac{1}{a^2 \mathcal{H} \mathcal{G}_S}, \tag{37}$$

where A and B are constants. For standard slow-roll models the function f decreases as the scale factor increases, implying that ζ tend to a constant value, i.e. the second term in eq.(37) is a decaying mode. If the function f is a growing function of a then the second term in eq.(37) becomes a growing mode, and there can be a super-horizon growth. It follows that the general condition for super-horizon growth of ζ_k is then

$$\frac{\mathrm{d}f}{\mathrm{d}a} \geq 0, \tag{38}$$

or equivalently
$$\frac{df}{da} = \frac{1}{a'}\frac{df}{d\tau} = \frac{1}{a\mathcal{H}}f' \geq 0. \tag{39}$$

During inflation $a\mathcal{H} > 0$ and this condition reduces to
$$f' \geq 0. \tag{40}$$

In the case of a minimally coupled single scalar field the unitary gauge and the comoving gauge coincide, and the general condition given above takes the form[18]
$$3 - \epsilon + \eta \leq 0, \tag{41}$$

where the slow-roll parameters are defined according to
$$\epsilon \equiv -\frac{a}{\mathcal{H}^2}\left(\frac{\mathcal{H}}{a}\right)' = \frac{a^2(\bar{\rho} + \bar{P})}{2M_{Pl}^2 \mathcal{H}^2} \quad , \quad \eta \equiv \frac{\epsilon'}{\epsilon \mathcal{H}}. \tag{42}$$

In G-Inflation the condition given in eq.(40) implies that
$$f' = \frac{d}{d\tau}\left(\frac{1}{a^2 \mathcal{H} \mathcal{G}_S}\right) = \frac{3 - \epsilon + \mathcal{G}_S'/\mathcal{H}\mathcal{G}_S}{a^2 \mathcal{G}_S} = \frac{\gamma}{\delta} \leq 0, \tag{43}$$

which gives the general condition for super-horizon growth in an expanding Universe. For a contracting Universe the inequality would be inverted.

As can be seen from the above equation the super-horizon growth can be achieved in different cases, corresponding to γ and δ having opposite signs, contrary to what happened for the standard kinetic term single field scenario, in which δ sign is fixed. Note also that contrary to standard kinetic term single field models, the super-horizon growth does not depend only on the slow-roll parameters, implying that it can occur also during slow-roll.

The anomalous super-horizon growth of ζ, and consequently of $\mathcal{R}$, can increase the abundance of PBHs, since it affects the statistics of the density perturbations peaks which can seed the PBHs.

8. Production of primordial black holes

The super-horizon growth of $\mathcal{R}_k$ could produce primordial black holes which could possibly account for part of dark matter[2,4,7,19–26] and produce gravitational waves (GW) detectable with future GW detectors such as LISA.[5,7] In this session we will show how to obtain some approximate estimation of the effetcs of the modification of gravity on the PBH production, without considering any specific model, leaving this to a future work.

The mass M of PBHs produced by the mode $\mathcal{R}_k$ re-entering the horizon during the radiation domination can be approoximated as[7]
$$M = \gamma M_H\Big|_F, \tag{44}$$

where $\gamma \approx 0.2$ is a correction factor, and $M_H\big|_F$ is the horizon mass $M_H \equiv (4\pi/3)\bar{\rho}(a\mathcal{H})^{-3}$ at the time of PBH formation, corresponding to the horizon crossing time

$$k = (a^2\mathcal{H})\big|_F. \qquad (45)$$

Note the above is just a rough estimation, and a more accurate treatment would involve the use of a scaling relation.[27, 28]

The present time fraction f_{PBH} of PBHs of mass M against the total dark matter component can then be approximated as[7]

$$f = 2.7 \times 10^8 \left(\frac{\gamma}{0.2}\right)^{1/2} \left(\frac{g_{*F}}{106.75}\right)^{-1/4} \left(\frac{M}{M_\odot}\right)^{-1/2} \beta,$$

where g_{*F} is the number of relativistic degrees of freedom at formation, the quantity β is the energy density fraction of PBHs at formation time

$$\beta \equiv \frac{\bar{\rho}_{PBH}}{\bar{\rho}}\bigg|_F, \qquad (46)$$

which can be written in terms of the probability of the density contrast $P(\delta)$ as[3, 29]

$$\beta(M) = \gamma \int_{\delta_t}^{1} P(\delta)\mathrm{d}\delta, \qquad (47)$$

where δ_t is the threshold for PBH formation. Assuming the density perturbations follow a Gaussian distribution β is given by

$$\beta(M) \approx \frac{\gamma}{\sqrt{2\pi}\nu(M)} \exp\left[-\frac{\nu(M)^2}{2}\right], \qquad (48)$$

where $\nu(M) \equiv \delta_t/\sigma(M)$, and $\sigma(M)$ is an estimation of the standard deviation of the density contrast on scale R from the variance

$$\sigma^2(M) = \int \mathrm{d}\ln k\, W^2(kR) \mathcal{P}_\delta(k) = \int \mathrm{d}\ln k\, W^2(kR) \left(\frac{16}{81}\right)(kR)^4 \mathcal{P}_\mathcal{R}(k), \qquad (49)$$

where $W(kR)$ is a window function smoothing over the comoving scale $R(M) = (a^2\mathcal{H})^{-1}\big|_F = 2GM/a_F\gamma^{-1}$, and the relation between δ and $\mathcal{R}$ has been used in the second equality. It should be mentioned that eq.(48) can be used as a guideline, but more accurate calculations would involve the use of the results of numerical simulations.[30, 31] The choice of the window function could also affect[32, 33] the results of the calculation.

Our aim here is not make an accurate estimation of the PBHs abundance for a specific model, but to show why in general it can be impacted by the modification of gravity, and the approximations adopted so far are enough to serve this general purpose. According to the equations above, the PBH fraction β is affected by the power spectrum of $\mathcal{R}$ since this can increase the standard deviation of the density field $\sigma(M)$. Note that the above approximations to estimate the PBHs abundance can receive important corrections depending on the shape of power spectrum, on non-gaussianity, and non-linear statistics.[34–36] Due to the importance of all these different effects it is difficult to find a general model independent analytical formula to estimate the PBHs abundance for a generic G-inflation theory, but any enhancement of the power spectrum is expected, according to eq.(32), to affect the probability of production of PBHs. Beside this, numerical relativity simulations of the PBHs formation are based on general relativity, so the effects of the modification of gravity on the process of gravitational collapse are at the moment not fully understood and would require investigations beyond the scope of this paper.[37]

At the end of its anomalous super-horizon growth, ζ will coincide with $\mathcal{R}$, and the consequent enhancement of the spectrum will lead to an increased PBH abundance. Contrary to what happens for standard kinetic term single field models in general relativity,[18] in the case of G-inflation this power spectrum enhancement can be achieved also during slow-roll, as long as the condition in eq.(43) is satisfied, which can be attained by an appropriate choice of the function $\mathcal{G}_S$. We expect a similar behavior for more complex modified gravity theories as well.

9. Conclusions

We have computed the effective energy-stress-tensor for G-inflation theories in the comoving slices gauge and have used it to derive a general relation between the unitary gauge curvature ζ and the comoving curvature perturbation $\mathcal{R}$, involving an enhancement function which depends on the evolution of the background, and which can cause a large difference between the two gauge invariant quantities.

When ζ is not constant in time it differs from $\mathcal{R}$, for example on sub-horizon scales, or in models exhibiting an anomalous super-horizon growth of ζ, but since this growth cannot last indefinitely, eventually they will coincide. We have derived the general condition for super-horizon growth of ζ, showing that slow-roll violation is not necessary, and discussed how the the enhancement of the spectrum of $\mathcal{R}$ can affect the PBH abundance.

We expect similar results to hold for other modified gravity theories such as other Horndeski's theories,[1] since also for these theories there can be effective entropy or anisotropy terms which can modify the evolution of curvature perturbations. In the future it will be interesting to extend this study to other modified gravity theories or to multi-fields systems, and to use observations to constraints the different types of theories. It would also be important to perform numerical simulations of the PBHs formation taking into account the non perturbative effects of the modification of gravity on the process of black hole formation.

References

1. G. W. Horndeski, Second-order scalar-tensor field equations in a four-dimensional space, *Int. J. Theor. Phys.* **10**, 363 (1974).
2. K. M. Belotsky, A. D. Dmitriev, E. A. Esipova, V. A. Gani, A. V. Grobov, M. Yu. Khlopov, A. A. Kirillov, S. G. Rubin and I. V. Svadkovsky, Signatures of primordial black hole dark matter, *Mod. Phys. Lett.* **A29**, p. 1440005 (2014).
3. B. J. Carr, The primordial black hole mass spectrum., *Astrophysical Journal* **201**, 1 (Oct 1975).
4. M. Y. Khlopov, Primordial Black Holes, *Res. Astron. Astrophys.* **10**, 495 (2010).
5. M. Sasaki, T. Suyama, T. Tanaka and S. Yokoyama, Primordial Black Hole Scenario for the Gravitational-Wave Event GW150914, *Phys. Rev. Lett.* **117**, p. 061101 (2016), [erratum: Phys. Rev. Lett.121,no.5,059901(2018)].
6. A. S. Josan, A. M. Green and K. A. Malik, Generalised constraints on the curvature perturbation from primordial black holes, *Phys. Rev.* **D79**, p. 103520 (2009).
7. M. Sasaki, T. Suyama, T. Tanaka and S. Yokoyama, Primordial black holes—perspectives in gravitational wave astronomy, *Class. Quant. Grav.* **35**, p. 063001 (2018).
8. M. Bucher, K. Moodley and N. Turok, The General primordial cosmic perturbation, *Phys. Rev.* **D62**, p. 083508 (2000).
9. A. E. Romano, S. Mooij and M. Sasaki, Adiabaticity and gravity theory independent conservation laws for cosmological perturbations, *Phys. Lett.* **B755**, 464 (2016).
10. T. Kobayashi, M. Yamaguchi and J. Yokoyama, G-inflation: Inflation driven by the Galileon field, *Phys. Rev. Lett.* **105**, p. 231302 (2010).
11. S. Hirano, T. Kobayashi and S. Yokoyama, Ultra slow-roll G-inflation, *Phys. Rev. D* **94**, p. 103515 (2016).
12. C. Deffayet, O. Pujolas, I. Sawicki and A. Vikman, Imperfect Dark Energy from Kinetic Gravity Braiding, *JCAP* **1010**, p. 026 (2010).
13. H. Kodama and M. Sasaki, Cosmological Perturbation Theory, *Prog. Theor. Phys. Suppl.* **78**, 1 (1984).
14. T. Kobayashi, M. Yamaguchi and J. Yokoyama, Generalized G-inflation: Inflation with the most general second-order field equations, *Prog. Theor. Phys.* **126**, 511 (2011).
15. A. E. Romano, General background conditions for K-bounce and adiabaticity, *Eur. Phys. J.* **C77**, p. 147 (2017).
16. J. Garriga and V. F. Mukhanov, Perturbations in k-inflation, *Phys. Lett.* **B458**, 219 (1999).
17. A. E. Romano, S. Mooij and M. Sasaki, Global adiabaticity and non-Gaussianity consistency condition, *Phys. Lett.* **B761**, 119 (2016).
18. R. Saito, J. Yokoyama and R. Nagata, Single-field inflation, anomalous enhancement of superhorizon fluctuations, and non-Gaussianity in primordial black hole formation, *JCAP* **06**, p. 024 (2008).
19. B. J. Carr, K. Kohri, Y. Sendouda and J. Yokoyama, New cosmological constraints on primordial black holes, *Phys. Rev. D* **81**, p. 104019 (2010).
20. B. Carr, K. Kohri, Y. Sendouda and J. Yokoyama, Constraints on Primordial Black Holes (2 2020).
21. J. Yokoyama, Formation of MACHO primordial black holes in inflationary cosmology, *Astron. Astrophys.* **318**, p. 673 (1997).
22. J. Garcia-Bellido and E. Ruiz Morales, Primordial black holes from single field models of inflation, *Phys. Dark Univ.* **18**, 47 (2017).
23. J. Garcia-Bellido, A. D. Linde and D. Wands, Density perturbations and black hole formation in hybrid inflation, *Phys. Rev.* **D54**, 6040 (1996).

24. P. Ivanov, P. Naselsky and I. Novikov, Inflation and primordial black holes as dark matter, *Phys. Rev.* **D50**, 7173 (1994).
25. G. F. Chapline, Cosmological effects of primordial black holes, *Nature* **253**, 251 (Jan 1975).
26. K. M. Belotsky, V. I. Dokuchaev, Y. N. Eroshenko, E. A. Esipova, M. Yu. Khlopov, L. A. Khromykh, A. A. Kirillov, V. V. Nikulin, S. G. Rubin and I. V. Svadkovsky, Clusters of primordial black holes, *Eur. Phys. J.* **C79**, p. 246 (2019).
27. J. Yokoyama, Cosmological constraints on primordial black holes produced in the near critical gravitational collapse, *Phys. Rev. D* **58**, p. 107502 (1998).
28. J. C. Niemeyer and K. Jedamzik, Near-critical gravitational collapse and the initial mass function of primordial black holes, *Phys. Rev. Lett.* **80**, 5481 (1998).
29. A. M. Green, A. R. Liddle, K. A. Malik and M. Sasaki, A New calculation of the mass fraction of primordial black holes, *Phys. Rev.* **D70**, p. 041502 (2004).
30. T. Nakama, T. Harada, A. G. Polnarev and J. Yokoyama, Identifying the most crucial parameters of the initial curvature profile for primordial black hole formation, *JCAP* **01**, p. 037 (2014).
31. M. Shibata and M. Sasaki, Black hole formation in the Friedmann universe: Formulation and computation in numerical relativity, *Phys. Rev. D* **60**, p. 084002 (1999).
32. K. Ando, K. Inomata and M. Kawasaki, Primordial black holes and uncertainties in the choice of the window function, *Phys. Rev. D* **97**, p. 103528 (2018).
33. K. Tokeshi, K. Inomata and J. Yokoyama, Window function dependence of the novel mass function of primordial black holes, *JCAP* **12**, p. 038 (2020).
34. C. Germani and I. Musco, Abundance of Primordial Black Holes Depends on the Shape of the Inflationary Power Spectrum, *Phys. Rev. Lett.* **122**, p. 141302 (2019).
35. V. Atal and C. Germani, The role of non-gaussianities in Primordial Black Hole formation, *Phys. Dark Univ.* **24**, p. 100275 (2019).
36. C. Germani and R. K. Sheth, Nonlinear statistics of primordial black holes from Gaussian curvature perturbations, *Phys. Rev. D* **101**, p. 063520 (2020).
37. C.-Y. Chen, Threshold of primordial black hole formation in modified theories of gravity (2019).

$U(1)$ local strings in generalized hybrid metric-Palatini gravity

Hilberto M. R. da Silva

Instituto de Astrofísica e Ciências do Espaço, Universidade do Porto, CAUP, Rua das Estrelas, PT4150-762 Porto, Portugal and Centro de Astrofísica da Universidade do Porto, Rua das Estrelas, PT4150-762 Porto, Portugal

Tiberiu Harko

Astronomical Observatory, 19 Ciresilor Street, 400487 Cluj-Napoca, Romania
Faculty of Physics, Babes-Bolyai University, 1 Kogalniceanu Street, 400084 Cluj-Napoca, Romania
School of Physics, Sun Yat-Sen University, Xingang Road, 510275 Guangzhou, People's Republic of China

Francisco S. N. Lobo

Instituto de Astrofísica e Ciências do Espaço, Faculdade de Ciências da Universidade de Lisboa, Edifício C8, Campo Grande, P-1749-016 Lisbon, Portugal

João Luís Rosa

Institute of Physics, University of Tartu, W. Ostwaldi 1, 50411 Tartu, Estonia

In this work we will explore $U(1)$ local cosmic string solutions in the context of the generalized hybrid metric-Palatini theory of gravity in its scalar-tensor representation. Using a general static cillindrically symmetric metric to find the dynamical equations for this particular case, we will simplify the equations by imposing boost invariance along t and z directions. The physical and geometrical properties of the cosmic strings are determined by the two scalar fields, as well by an effective field potential, functionally dependent on both scalar fields. While for some forms of the potential, the dynamical equations can be solved exactly, for more general formas of the potential the solutions are found numerically. In this way, we obtain a large class of stable stringlike astrophysical configurations, whose basic parameters (string tension and radius) depend essentially on the effective field potential, and on the boundary conditions.

Keywords: Cosmic Strings, Modified Gravity, hybrid metric-Palatini theory

1. Introduction

The main motivation to investigate hybrid metric-Palatini theories resides on the fact that these theories are able to overcome flaws of both the metric and the Palatini approaches to $f(R)$ gravity. For example, in both the metric and the Palatini formalisms of $f(R)$ gravity, one is able to model the late-time cosmic acceleration period without invoking dark energy sources,[1] but both approaches present unavoidable disadvantages: the metric $f(R)$ was shown to be inconsistent with solar-system constraints unless chameleon mechanisms are considered,[2,3] whereas the Palatini $f(R)$ gravity induces microscopic instabilities, surface singularities in polytropic star models, and is unable to describe the evolution of cosmological perturbations.[4,5] The HMPG successfully unifies the late-time cosmic acceleration period with the weak-field solar system dynamics without the need for chameleon mechanisms,[6] thus being a viable and relevant modification to GR. We refer the reader to Refs.[7–9] for recent reviews on the topic.

Inspired by the success of electroweak theory,[10–12] which unifies the weak and electromagnetic interaction under the gauge group $SU(2)\times U(1)$ at a scale of around $10^2 GeV$, Grand Unified Theories (GUT) propose the unification of electroweak and strong interactions under a more general symmetry that takes place at higher energy scales, around $10^{16} GeV$, the Grand Unification Scale. GUT theories are supported by the observation that the coupling "constants" of the Standard Model for Particle Physics seem to slowly vary with the energy scale, converging to a common value at the Grand Unification Scale.[13]

These symmetries presented at higher energies are spontaneously broken as the system lowers its energy state. In several GUT scenarios proposed, a universal covering group G, which would be effective above the GUT scale, would spontaneously break into the Standard Model $SU(3) \times SU(2) \times U(1)$, where $SU(3)$ is the symmetry group of quantum chromodynamics, describing the strong interaction, and $SU(2) \times U(1)$ is the aforementioned electroweak group.

These phase transitions may have left behind some relics that can help shed some light into earlier times of our Universe.[14] These relics are known as topological defects and are a well known, and studied, phenomena in physics, particularly in the context of condensed matter (namely metal crystallization,[15] liquid crystals,[16] superfluid helium-3 and helium-4,[17] and superconductivity[18]).

The underlying idea behind topological defect formation is the one of Spontaneous symmetry breaking, which is the principle behind the Higgs-Englert mechanism.[19]

Cosmic strings are one of the possible topological defects formed after spontaneous symmetry breaking (SSB) during phase transitions in the history of the Universe.

The type of strings to be considered in this work are local $U(1)$ cosmic strings, which are an extension of the global $U(1)$ strings to include gauge fields. Local strings differ from the global cosmic strings in what concerns the symmetry that is effective above the spontaneous breaking scale; in the case of local strings, the lagrangian remains invariant under local transformations of the type $\phi(x) \longrightarrow e^{i\alpha(x)}\phi(x)$.

The study of the properties and dynamics of cosmic strings in the context of modified theories of gravity is crucial in the advent of powerful observatories, such as LISA, as it may allow us to constrain both Modified Gravity theories and Grand Unified theories.

2. Generalized Hybrid Metric-Palatini Gravity

The generalized HMPG theory is described by an action S of the form

$$S = \frac{1}{2\kappa^2} \int_\Omega \sqrt{-g} f(R,\mathcal{R}) d^4x + \int_\Omega \sqrt{-g}\, \mathcal{L}_m d^4x, \qquad (1)$$

where $\kappa^2 \equiv 8\pi G/c^4$, G is the gravitational constant and c the speed of light, Ω is the spacetime manifold described by a system of coordinates x^a, g is the determinant of the spacetime metric g_{ab}, where Latin indices run from 0 to 3, $R = g^{ab}R_{ab}$ is the Ricci scalar of the metric g_{ab} and where R_{ab} is the Ricci tensor, $\mathcal{R} \equiv \mathcal{R}^{ab}g_{ab}$ is the Palatini Ricci scalar, where the Palatini Ricci tensor $\mathcal{R}_{ab}$ is defined in terms of an independent connection $\hat{\Gamma}^c_{ab}$ in the usual form as $\mathcal{R}_{ab} = \partial_c \hat{\Gamma}^c_{ab} - \partial_b \hat{\Gamma}^c_{ac} + \hat{\Gamma}^c_{cd}\hat{\Gamma}^d_{ab} - \hat{\Gamma}^c_{ad}\hat{\Gamma}^d_{cb}$, where ∂_a denotes partial derivatives with respect to the coordinates x^a, $f(R,\mathcal{R})$ is a well-behaved function of R and $\mathcal{R}$, and $\mathcal{L}_m$ is the matter Lagrangian density considered to be minimally coupled to the metric g_{ab}. Equation (1) depends on two independent variables, namely the metric g_{ab} and the independent connection $\hat{\Gamma}^c_{ab}$, and thus two equations of motion can be obtained.

Taking a variation of Eq. (1) with respect to the metric g_{ab} leads to the modified field equations

$$\frac{\partial f}{\partial R}R_{ab} + \frac{\partial f}{\partial \mathcal{R}}\mathcal{R}_{ab} - \frac{1}{2}g_{ab}f(R,\mathcal{R}) - (\nabla_a \nabla_b - g_{ab}\Box)\frac{\partial f}{\partial R} = \kappa^2 T_{ab}, \qquad (2)$$

where ∇_a denotes covariant derivatives and $\Box = \nabla^a \nabla_a$ the d'Alembert operator, both with respect to g_{ab}, and T_{ab} is the energy-momentum tensor defined as usual:

$$T_{ab} = -\frac{2}{\sqrt{-g}} \frac{\delta(\sqrt{-g}\,\mathcal{L}_m)}{\delta(g^{ab})}. \qquad (3)$$

On the other hand, taking a variation of Eq. (1) with respect to the independent connection $\hat{\Gamma}^c_{ab}$ yields

$$\hat{\nabla}_c \left(\sqrt{-g}\frac{\partial f}{\partial \mathcal{R}}g^{ab}\right) = 0, \qquad (4)$$

where $\hat{\nabla}_a$ is the covariant derivative written in terms of the independent connection $\hat{\Gamma}^c_{ab}$. Since $\sqrt{-g}$ is a scalar density of weight 1, then $\hat{\nabla}_c \sqrt{-g} = 0$ and Eq. (4) can be rewritten in the form $\hat{\nabla}_c \left(\frac{\partial f}{\partial \mathcal{R}}g^{ab}\right) = 0$. This result implies the existence of a new metric, h_{ab}, conformally related to the metric g_{ab} via

$$h_{ab} = g_{ab}\frac{\partial f}{\partial \mathcal{R}}, \qquad (5)$$

in such a way that the independent connection is the Levi-Civita connection of the metric h_{ab}, i.e., $\hat{\Gamma}^c_{ab}$ can be written as

$$\hat{\Gamma}^a_{bc} = \frac{1}{2}h^{ad}\left(\partial_b h_{dc} + \partial_c h_{bd} - \partial_d h_{bc}\right). \qquad (6)$$

2.1. *Scalar-tensor representation of generalized HMPG with matter*

It is sometimes useful to represent the generalized HMPG theory in a dinamically equivalent scalar-tensor representation in which the two extra scalar degrees of freedom of the theory are explicitly carried by two scalar fields. To obtain this representation, we introduce two auxiliary fields α and β into Eq. (1) and rewrite it in the form

$$S = \frac{1}{2\kappa^2} \int_\Omega \sqrt{-g} \left[f(\alpha, \beta) + \frac{\partial f}{\partial \alpha}(R - \alpha) + \frac{\partial f}{\partial \beta}(\mathcal{R} - \beta) \right] d^4x + \int_\Omega \sqrt{-g}\, \mathcal{L}_m d^4x. \tag{7}$$

At this point one verifies that if $\alpha = R$ and $\beta = \mathcal{R}$ one recovers Eq. (1). This equivalence between the two representations is only guaranteed if the determinant of the Hessian matrix of the function $f(\alpha, \beta)$ is non-zero, i.e., if $f_{\alpha\alpha} f_{\beta\beta} - f_{\alpha\beta}^2 \neq 0$, where the subscripts α and β denote partial derivatives with respect to these variables. Defining two scalar fields as $\varphi = \partial f(\alpha,\beta)/\partial \alpha$ and $\psi = -\partial f(\alpha,\beta)/\partial \beta$, where the negative sign in ψ is imposed to avoid the presence of ghosts, Eq. (7) takes the form

$$S = \frac{1}{2\kappa^2} \int_\Omega \sqrt{-g} \left[\varphi R - \psi \mathcal{R} - V(\varphi, \psi) \right] d^4x + \int_\Omega \sqrt{-g}\, \mathcal{L}_m d^4x, \tag{8}$$

where the function $V(\varphi, \psi)$ plays the role of an interaction potential between the two scalar fields and it is defined as

$$V(\varphi, \psi) = -f(\alpha, \beta) + \varphi \alpha - \psi \beta. \tag{9}$$

Recalling the conformal relation between h_{ab} and g_{ab} in Eq. (5), which can now be written in the form $h_{ab} = -\psi g_{ab}$ by taking into consideration the definition of ψ, one can derive a relationship between R and $\mathcal{R}$ as

$$\mathcal{R} = R + \frac{3}{\psi^2} \partial^a \psi \partial_a \psi - \frac{3}{\psi} \Box \psi, \tag{10}$$

which can be used to eliminate $\mathcal{R}$ from Eq. (8) and gives the final form of the action

$$S = \frac{1}{2\kappa^2} \int_\Omega \sqrt{-g} \left[(\varphi - \psi) R - \frac{3}{2\psi} \partial^a \psi \partial_a \psi - V(\varphi, \psi) \right] d^4x + \int_\Omega \sqrt{-g}\, \mathcal{L}_m d^4x. \tag{11}$$

Equation (11) is now a function of three independent variables, namely, the metric g_{ab} and the two scalar fields φ and ψ. Taking a variation of Eq. (11) with respect to the metric g_{ab} yields the modified field equations in the scalar-tensor representation. Varying the action (11) with respect to the metric g_{ab} provides the following gravitational equation

$$(\varphi - \psi) G_{ab} = \kappa^2 T_{ab} + \nabla_a \nabla_b \varphi - \nabla_a \nabla_b \psi + \frac{3}{2\psi} \partial_a \psi \partial_b \psi$$
$$- \left(\Box \varphi - \Box \psi + \frac{1}{2} V + \frac{3}{4\psi} \partial^c \psi \partial_c \psi \right) g_{ab}. \tag{12}$$

Note that Eq. (12) could be obtained directly from Eq. (2) via the introduction of the definitions of φ, ψ and $V(\varphi, \psi)$, which further emphasizes the equivalence between the two representations.

Finally, the equations of motion for the scalar fields φ and ψ can be obtained via a variation of Eq. (11) with respect to these fields, respectively, which after algebraic manipulations can be written in the forms

$$\Box \varphi + \frac{1}{3}(2V - \psi V_\psi - \varphi V_\varphi) = \frac{\kappa^2 T}{3}, \qquad (13)$$

$$\Box \psi - \frac{1}{2\psi} \partial^a \psi \partial_a \psi - \frac{\psi}{3}(V_\varphi + V_\psi) = 0, \qquad (14)$$

respectively.

Notice from Eq.(11) that the coupling between the scalar fields and the Ricci scalar is the combination $\varphi - \psi$. Since φ and ψ are arbitrary functions, it is not guaranteed that this combination preserves the positivity of the coupling. We thus introduce a redefinition of the scalar field φ as $\xi^2 = \varphi - \psi$. With this redefinition, any solution obtained for which ξ is a real function preserves the positivity of the coupling $(\varphi - \psi) R$. Equations (12) to (14) thus become

$$\xi^2 G_{ab} = \kappa^2 T_{ab} + \nabla_a \nabla_b \xi^2 + \frac{3}{2\psi} \partial_a \psi \partial_b \psi - \left(\Box \xi^2 + \frac{1}{2}\bar{V} + \frac{3}{4\psi} \partial^c \psi \partial_c \psi \right) g_{ab}, \qquad (15)$$

$$\Box \xi^2 + \frac{1}{2\psi} \partial^a \psi \partial_a \psi + \frac{1}{6}(4\bar{V} - \xi \bar{V}_\xi) = \frac{\kappa^2 T}{3}, \qquad (16)$$

$$\Box \psi - \frac{1}{2\psi} \partial^a \psi \partial_a \psi - \frac{\psi}{3}\left(\frac{1}{2\xi}\bar{V}_\xi + \bar{V}_\psi \right) = 0, \qquad (17)$$

where $\bar{V}(\xi, \psi)$ is the potential written in terms of the scalar fields ξ and ψ and the subscript ξ denotes a partial derivative with respect to this scalar field. In the next section, we will use the equations of motion (15)–(17) to find cosmic string solutions. Finally, one can also obtain a relationship between the potential $\bar{V}$ and the function $f(R, \mathcal{R})$ from Eq.(9) as

$$\bar{V}(\xi, \psi) = -f(R, \mathcal{R}) + \xi^2 R + \psi(R - \mathcal{R}), \qquad (18)$$

where we have used the fact that the scalar-tensor representation is only defined if $\alpha = R$ and $\beta = \mathcal{R}$. This equation becomes a PDE for $f(R, \mathcal{R})$ by replacing $\psi = f_\mathcal{R}$ and $\xi^2 = f_R + f_\mathcal{R}$.

Hence Eq. (18) becomes

$$V\left(\sqrt{\frac{\partial f(R,\mathcal{R})}{\partial R} + \frac{\partial f(R,\mathcal{R})}{\partial \mathcal{R}}}, \frac{\partial f(R,\mathcal{R})}{\partial \mathcal{R}} \right) = -f(R,\mathcal{R}) + R\frac{\partial f(R,\mathcal{R})}{\partial R} + \mathcal{R}\frac{\partial f(R,\mathcal{R})}{\partial \mathcal{R}}. \qquad (19)$$

3. Dynamical equations of local strings in hybrid metric-palatini using Vilenkin's approximation

In this work, we consider a straight infinite Abelian-Higgs cosmic string, using Vilenkin's approximation[20]

$$T_t^t = T_z^z = -\sigma(r), \tag{20}$$

where σ is the string tension. We further assume cylindrical symmetry with a general metric of the form:

$$ds^2 = -e^{2(K-U)}dt^2 + e^{2(K-U)}dr^2 + e^{-2U}W^2 d\theta^2 + e^{2U}dz^2, \tag{21}$$

where t, r, θ and z denote the time, radial, angular and axial cylindrical coordinates, respectively, and K, U and W are functions of r alone. This metric is invariant under a set of transformations of the type: $x^0 \to x^0 + c_1$, $x^3 \to x^3 + c_2$, $x^0 \to -x^0$ and $x^3 \to -x^3$, where c_1 and c_2 are constants, which renders this metric static and cylindrically symmetric.

Since in this model the matter field couples minimally with curvature, it is possible to show that the energy conservation equation still holds, i.e.,

$$\nabla_a T^a{}_b = 0, \tag{22}$$

which provides $K'\sigma = 0$ and, apart from the trivial vacuum solution $\sigma = 0$, this implies that $K' = 0$, where the prime represents a differentiation w.r.t. r. Thus, we consider from now on that $e^K = 1$.

Note that local gauge strings preserve boost invariance along t and z,[20] so that this requires $U = 0$. Hence the only surviving non-trivial metric tensor component is $g_{\theta\theta} = W^2(r)$. From a geometric point of view $W(r)$ is the radius of the coordinate circles $r = $ constant, $z = $ constant, parameterized by the angle θ. Since in this geometry the perimeter of a circle equals $2\pi W$, in the following we will call the only remaining metric tensor component $W^2(r)$ a *circular radius*. On the other hand $W^2(r)$ also has the geometric meaning of a length that may be counted from any zero point, with its value at $r = 0$ not distinguished geometrically. Hence the metric of the cosmic string reduces to the form

$$ds^2 = -dt^2 + dr^2 + W^2(r)d\theta^2 + dz^2. \tag{23}$$

Applying this symmetry, the gravitational field equations simplify considerably. Equation (15) provides three independent field equations, which are

$$\xi^2 \frac{W''}{W} + 2\xi\xi'\frac{W'}{W} + \frac{3\psi'^2}{4\psi} + 2\left(\xi'^2 + \xi\xi''\right) + \frac{\bar{V}}{2} = -\kappa^2\sigma, \tag{24}$$

$$2\xi\xi'\frac{W'}{W} - \frac{3\psi'^2}{4\psi} + \frac{\bar{V}}{2} = 0, \tag{25}$$

$$2\left(\xi'^2 + \xi\xi''\right) + \frac{3\psi'^2}{4\psi} + \frac{\bar{V}}{2} = \frac{d^2}{dr^2}\xi^2 + \frac{3\psi'^2}{4\psi} + \frac{\bar{V}}{2} = 0, \tag{26}$$

whereas the scalar field equations for ξ and ψ, provided by Eqs. (16) and (17), give

$$2\left(\xi'^2 + \xi\xi''\right) + 2\xi\xi'\frac{W'}{W} + \frac{\psi'^2}{2\psi} + \frac{1}{6}\left(\bar{V} - \xi\bar{V}_\xi\right) = -\frac{2\kappa^2}{3}\sigma, \qquad (27)$$

$$\psi'' + \frac{W'}{W}\psi' - \frac{\psi'^2}{2\psi} - \frac{\psi}{3}\left(\bar{V}_\psi + \frac{1}{2\xi}\bar{V}_\xi\right) = 0. \qquad (28)$$

The system of Eqs. (24)-(28) is a system of five equations from which only four are linearly independent. This statement can be proven by taking a radial derivative of Eq. (25), using Eq. (24) to cancel the factors W''', using Eq. (27) to cancel σ, and finally using Eqs. (26) and (28) to cancel the second-order derivatives of the scalar fields ξ'' and ψ'', respectively. As a result, one recovers Eq. (25), thus proving that the system of equations is linearly dependent. Thus, one only needs to consider four of these equations to completely determine the solution in the sections that follow. Given its complexity, we chose to discard Eq. (24) from the analysis.

Furthermore, an equation for the potential $\bar{V}$ can be obtained by summing the field equations in Eqs. (25) and (26), yielding

$$\bar{V} = -2\left(\xi'^2 + \xi\xi''\right) - 2\xi\xi'\frac{W'}{W}. \qquad (29)$$

This equation is particularly useful to obtain an equation for W' in terms of the scalar fields ξ and ψ and their derivatives after setting an explicit form of the potential $\bar{V}$.

The system of basic equations describing the structure of a cosmic string can thus be reformulated in the form of a first-order dynamical system. By defining $\alpha = \xi^2$, and by introducing two extra dynamical variables as $u = \alpha'$ and $v = \psi'$, the dynamical system takes the form

$$\frac{d\alpha}{dr} = u, \qquad \frac{d\psi}{dr} = v, \qquad (30)$$

$$\frac{dW}{dr} = \frac{1}{u}\left(\frac{3v^2}{4\psi} - \frac{\bar{V}}{2}\right)W, \qquad (31)$$

$$\frac{du}{dr} = -\frac{3v^2}{4\psi} - \frac{\bar{V}}{2}, \qquad (32)$$

$$\frac{dv}{dr} = -\frac{v}{u}\left(\frac{3v^2}{4\psi} - \frac{\bar{V}}{2}\right) + \frac{v^2}{2\psi} + \frac{\psi}{3}\left(\bar{V}_\psi + \frac{1}{2\sqrt{\alpha}}\bar{V}_{\sqrt{\alpha}}\right), \qquad (33)$$

where Eq. (30) is the explicit definition of u and v, and Eqs. (31)–(33) are reformulations of Eqs. (25), (27), and (28), respectively. Once the functional form of the potential $\bar{V}(\xi,\psi)$ is specified, the system of Eqs. (30)-(33) represents a system of ordinary, strongly nonlinear, differential equations for the variables $\left(\alpha = \xi^2, \psi, W, u, v\right)$. To solve this system, one has to impose a set of boundary conditions at some radius $r = r_0$, i.e., $\alpha(r_0) = \alpha_0$, $\psi(r_0) = \psi_0$, $W(r_0) = W_0$, $u(r_0) = u_0$, and $v(r_0) = v_0$, respectively, which specify the boundary values of the variables on, or nearby the string axis. Moreover, we will also impose the condition $u(r_0) \neq v(r_0)$. Once the system is solved, the string tension can be obtained from Eq. (27), and it is given by

$$\frac{2}{3}\kappa^2 \sigma = \bar{V} - \frac{v^2}{2\psi} - \frac{1}{6}\left(\bar{V} - \sqrt{\alpha}\bar{V}_{\sqrt{\alpha}}\right). \tag{34}$$

An important physical characteristic of the string-like objects is their mass per unit length m_s, defined as

$$m_s(R_s) = \int_0^{2\pi} d\theta \int_0^{R_s} \sigma(r)W(r)dr = 2\pi \int_0^{R_s} \sigma(r)W(r)dr, \tag{35}$$

where R_s is the radius of the string, defined as the distance from the center where the string tension vanishes, $\sigma(R_s) = 0$, and $\sigma(r) \equiv 0, \forall r \geq R_s$. Note that, in general, the solutions obtained for σ do not satisfy the property $\sigma(r) \equiv 0, \forall r \geq R_s$, and this condition must be imposed manually by performing a matching between the string spacetime and an exterior cosmological spacetime. This matching must be performed via the use of the junction conditions of the theory, previously used in.[21] However, we do not pursue this analysis here as it is out of the scope of this paper. Using Eqs. (26) and Eq. (24) the mass per unit length of the string can be expressed as

$$\kappa^2 m_s(R_s) = 3\pi \int_0^{R_s} \left[\bar{V} - \frac{v^2}{2\psi} - \frac{1}{6}\left(\bar{V} - \sqrt{\alpha}\bar{V}_{\sqrt{\alpha}}\right)\right] W \, dr. \tag{36}$$

4. Solutions to the dynamical equations with specific potentials

In this section we will investigate the application of the set of equations deduced on the previous section to different potential configurations, for a more complete set of possible potential configurations, we refer the reader to the original article Ref. 22.

4.1. *Constant potential*

We consider the case when the potential V is a constant, so that $V = \Lambda =$ constant. In this case Eq. (19) takes the form

$$-f(R,\mathcal{R}) + R\frac{\partial f(R,\mathcal{R})}{\partial R} + \mathcal{R}\frac{\partial f(R,\mathcal{R})}{\partial \mathcal{R}} = \Lambda, \tag{37}$$

and it has the general solution

$$f(R,\mathcal{R}) = Rg\left(\frac{\mathcal{R}}{R}\right) + \mathcal{R}h\left(\frac{R}{\mathcal{R}}\right) - \Lambda, \tag{38}$$

where g and h are arbitrary functions.

For a constant potential Eq. (28) simplifies to

$$\frac{W'}{W} = -\frac{\psi''}{\psi'} + \frac{1}{2}\frac{\psi'}{\psi}, \tag{39}$$

which allows us to write Eq. (25) in the form
$$\frac{d}{dr}\xi^2 = \frac{3\psi'^2/4\psi - \Lambda/2}{W'/W} = \frac{3\psi'^2/4\psi - \Lambda/2}{-\psi''/\psi' + (1/2)\psi'/\psi}. \tag{40}$$

To facilitate the analysis, we introduce now a new function $h = \psi'^2/\psi$. The radial derivative of this function can be written in terms of ψ and its derivatives as
$$h' = 2h\left(\frac{\psi''}{\psi'} - \frac{1}{2}\frac{\psi'}{\psi}\right). \tag{41}$$

This definition allows us to rewrite Eq. (40) in terms of h as
$$\frac{d}{dr}\xi^2 = -\frac{(3/4)h - \Lambda/2}{h'/2h}, \tag{42}$$

which can then be differentiated with respect to r and inserted into Eq. (26) to cancel the dependency in $d^2\xi^2/dr^2$ and ψ''. As a result, we obtain an equation depending solely in h of the form
$$\frac{(2\Lambda - 3h)\left(3h'^2 - 2hh''\right)}{4h'^2} = 0. \tag{43}$$

This equation is undefined for $h' = 0$, as the denominator vanishes in this case. Thus, in the following we ignore the solution corresponding to $h = 2\Lambda/3 = $ constant, giving $h' = 0$, and $W = $ constant. The general solution of Eq. (43) is given by
$$h(r) = \frac{c_2}{(r + 2c_1)^2}, \tag{44}$$

where c_1 and c_2 are arbitrary integration constants. Recalling that $h' = \psi'^2/\psi$, Eq. (44) becomes a separable ODE for ψ which can be directly integrated and provides the general solution
$$\psi(r) = \left[c_3 \pm \frac{\sqrt{c_2}}{2}\ln(r + 2c_1)\right]^2, \tag{45}$$

where c_3 is an arbitrary integration constant. Inserting Eq. (45) into Eq. (42) and integrating gives for ξ^2 the expression
$$\xi^2(r) = \xi_0^2 + \frac{1}{4}\left[3c_2\ln(r + 2c_1) - \Lambda r(r + 4c_1)\right], \tag{46}$$

where ξ_0^2 is an integration constant. Inserting Eq. (45) into Eq. (39) we obtain the solution for W
$$W(r) = W_0(r + 2c_1), \tag{47}$$

where W_0 is a constant of integration. Hence the cosmic string metric tensor component $W(r)$ is the same in both $V = 0$ and $V = \Lambda$ cases. Finally, the string tension can be computed via Eq. (27), leading to
$$\kappa^2\sigma = \frac{\Lambda}{2} - \frac{3c_2}{4(2c_1 + r)^2}. \tag{48}$$

On the string axis $r = 0$ we obtain for the string tension the value

$$\kappa^2 \sigma_0 = \kappa^2 \sigma(0) = \frac{\Lambda}{2} - \frac{3c_2}{16c_1^2}. \tag{49}$$

The condition of the positivity of the string tension imposes the condition $c_2/c_1^2 < 8\Lambda/3$ on the integration constants.

For $\Lambda = 0$ we reobtain the expression corresponding to the case $V = 0$. However, by an appropriate choice of the integration constants, and by assuming $\Lambda > 0$, the string tension can be made positive in this model for all $r > 0$. Moreover, $\lim_{r \to \infty} \sigma(r) = \Lambda/2\kappa^2$, and hence at infinity the string tension becomes equal to the cosmological constant. However, in this case one can obtain a finite radius string configuration, with the radius R_s determined by the condition $\sigma(R_s) = 0$, and given by

$$R_s = \sqrt{\frac{3}{2}\frac{c_2}{\Lambda}} - 2c_1. \tag{50}$$

For a positive string tension at the origin $r = 0$, the string radius is also positive.

As for the mass of the string we obtain

$$m_s(R_s) = \frac{2\pi W_0}{\kappa^2}\left\{\frac{1}{2}\Lambda\left[R_s + c_1(\Lambda W_0 + 2)\right] - \frac{3c_2 W_0}{8c_1}\right.$$
$$\left. - \frac{6c_1 c_2}{8c_1\left[R_s + c_1(\Lambda W_0 + 2)\right] - 3c_2 W_0}\right\}. \tag{51}$$

By an appropriate choice of the integration constants, giving the boundary conditions of the fields φ and ψ for $r = 0$, one can always satisfy the condition $m_s(R_s) > 0, \forall R_s$. In the limit $R_s \to \infty$, we obtain $m_s(R_s) \approx (\pi W_0 \Lambda/\kappa^2) R_s$, that is, for large distances the mass of the string linearly increases with its radius.

4.2. $\bar{V}(\xi, \psi) = \bar{V}_0 \xi^2 \psi^2$

Next we will consider string type solutions in the Generalized Hybrid Metric Palatini Gravity under the assumption that the potential $\bar{V}$ is given by $\bar{V} = \bar{V}_0 \xi^2 \psi^2 = \bar{V}_0 \alpha \psi^2$, with $\bar{V}_0$ constant. Equation (19) then becomes

$$-f(R, \mathcal{R}) + R\frac{\partial f(R, \mathcal{R})}{\partial R} + \mathcal{R}\frac{\partial f(R, \mathcal{R})}{\partial \mathcal{R}} = \bar{V}_0 \frac{\partial f(R, \mathcal{R})}{\partial \mathcal{R}}\left(\frac{\partial f(R, \mathcal{R})}{\partial \mathcal{R}} + \frac{\partial f(R, \mathcal{R})}{\partial R}\right) \tag{52}$$

and a particular solution for the function $f(R, \mathcal{R})$ is

$$f(R, \mathcal{R}) = \sqrt{\frac{R}{\bar{V}_0}(R - \mathcal{R})}. \tag{53}$$

For this potential the field equations describing the string-like structure take the form

$$\frac{d\alpha}{dr} = u, \quad \frac{d\psi}{dr} = v, \tag{54}$$

$$\frac{dW}{dr} = \frac{1}{2u}\left(\frac{3v^2}{2\psi} - \bar{V}_0\alpha\psi^2\right)W, \tag{55}$$

$$\frac{du}{dr} = -\frac{3v^2}{4\psi} - \frac{\bar{V}_0\alpha\psi^2}{2}, \tag{56}$$

$$\frac{dv}{dr} = -\frac{v}{u}\left(\frac{3v^2}{4\psi} - \frac{\bar{V}_0\alpha}{2}\right) + \frac{v^2}{2\psi} + \frac{2V_0}{3}\psi^2\left(\alpha + \frac{\psi}{2}\right). \tag{57}$$

For this model the string tension is given by

$$\frac{2\kappa^2}{3}\sigma = \frac{7}{6}\bar{V}_0\alpha\psi^2 - \frac{v^2}{2\psi}. \tag{58}$$

The metric function W^2 and the string tension σ are depicted in Fig. 1, for a varying initial condition $\psi'(0) = \psi_0$, while all the other initial conditions are fixed. In this case the radial metric function is an increasing function of the radial coordinate r, and its rate of increase is strongly dependent on the variations in the numerical values of ψ_0. Similarly to the previous cases, the string tension is a monotonically decreasing function of r, and it vanishes at a finite value of r, $r = R_s$, which uniquely defines the string radius. The string radius is weakly dependent on the variation of ψ_0, however, significant variations in σ do appear for small values of r.

The variations of the potential and of the function ψ are represented in Fig. 2. $\bar{V}$ is a slowly decreasing positive function of r, strongly dependent on the initial condition for ψ'. The function ψ takes negative values, and show a strong dependence on ψ_0.

The behavior of the function $\xi^2(r)$ is depicted in Fig. 3. ξ^2 is positive for $r \in [0, R_s]$, and thus the physical nature of the gravitational coupling in the present model is guaranteed. ξ^2 is a monotonically decreasing function of r, and its variation depends significantly on the numerical values of the initial conditions for $\psi'(0)$.

5. Conclusions

In this work we studied the existence and physical properties of local $U(1)$ cosmic strings in the context of the generalized hybrid metric-Palatini gravity. The theory is an extension to General Relativity, combining both metric and Palatini formalism. A main success of the theory is the possibility to generate long-range forces that pass the classical local tests of gravity at the Solar System level, thus avoiding some problematic features of the standard $f(R)$ theories. Another interesting advantage of the theory is that it admits an equivalent scalar-tensor representation, simplifying greatly the dynamical equations. The type of strings studied in this work are local gauge strings, using an approximation to the Vilenkin-prescribed energy-momentum tensor and different potential configurations.

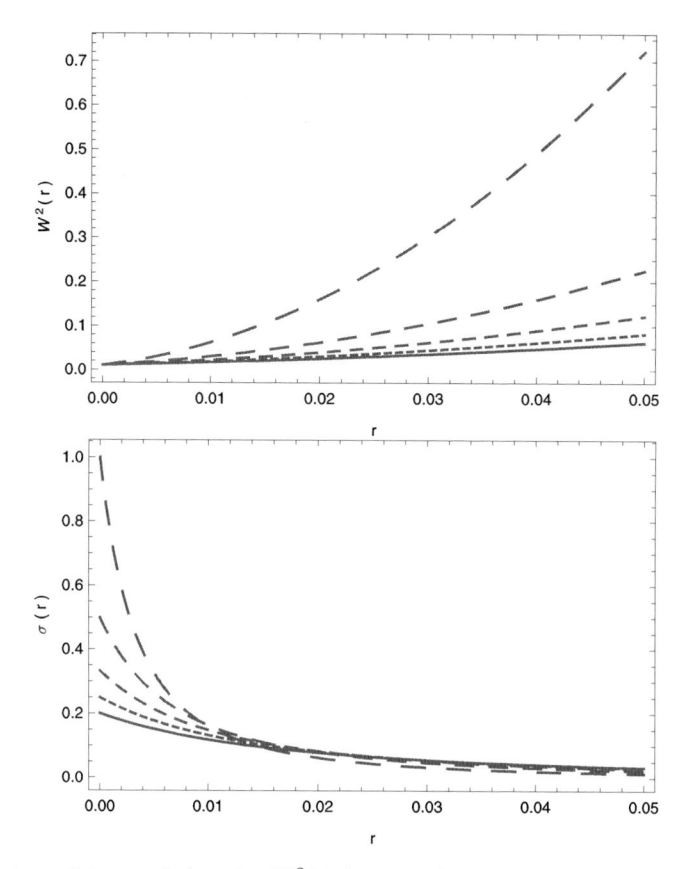

Fig. 1. Variations of the metric function $W^2(r)$ (top panel), and of the string tension $\sigma(r)$ (bottom panel) as a function of r (with all quantities in arbitrary units) for the $\bar{V}(\xi,\psi) = \bar{V}_0\xi^2\psi^2$ potential, for $\psi_0 = -0.025$ (solid curve), $\psi_0 = -0.020$ (dotted curve), $\psi_0 = -0.015$ (short dashed curve), $\psi_0 = -0.01$ (dashed curve), and $\psi_0 = -0.005$ (long dashed curve), respectively. For $\bar{V}_0$ we have adopted the value $\bar{V}_0 = 10$, while the boundary conditions used to numerically integrate the field equations are $u_0 = -0.01$, $\alpha_0 = 0.025$, $W(0) = 0.10$, and $v_0 = 0.10$, respectively.

The field equations determine the string tension σ. These equations must be solved by choosing a functional form for the potential, and by imposing some appropriate boundary conditions at $r = 0$ on the two scalar fields (ξ^2, ψ), on their derivatives, and for $W^2(0)$. Since in the present approach these boundary conditions are arbitrary, and since the second order, strongly nonlinear system of the gravitational field equations is extremely sensitive to the variation of the boundary conditions, many types of cosmic string structures can be obtained by adopting some specific forms of V, and different sets of initial conditions.

The gravitational field equations describing cosmic string structures in generalized HMPG can be solved exactly in the simple cases of the vanishing and constant potentials.

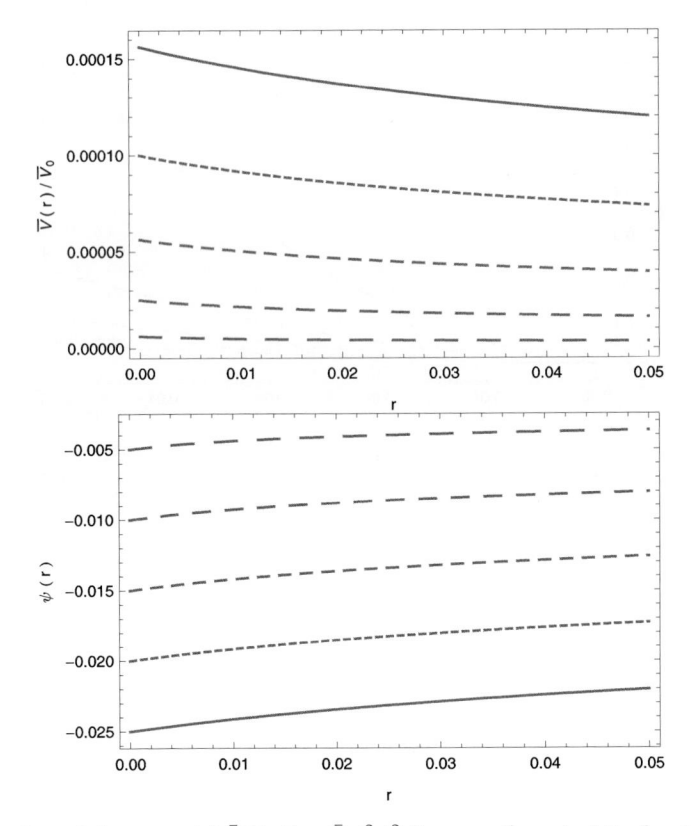

Fig. 2. Variations of the potential $\bar{V}(\xi,\psi) = \bar{V}_0\xi^2\psi^2$ (top panel), and of the function ψ (bottom panel) as a function of r (with all quantities in arbitrary units) for the $\bar{V}(\xi) = \bar{V}_0\xi^2\psi^2$ potential, for $\psi_0 = -0.025$ (solid curve), $\psi_0 = -0.020$ (dotted curve), $\psi_0 = -0.015$ (short dashed curve), $\psi_0 = -0.01$ (dashed curve), and $\psi_0 = -0.005$ (long dashed curve), respectively. For $\bar{V}_0$ we have adopted the value $\bar{V}_0 = 10$, while the boundary conditions used to numerically integrate the field equations are $u_0 = -0.01$, $\alpha_0 = 0.025$, $W(0) = 0.10$, and $v_0 = 0.10$, respectively.

In the case of the constant, nonzero potential, the field equations can be solved exactly, and some simple expressions for the geometrical and physical parameters can be obtained. In this case, the string tension can be made positive by an appropriate choice of the potential. A solution with a constant string tension $\kappa^2\sigma = \Lambda/2$ can also be constructed, as well as a solution having $W(r) = W_0 r$, which can describe the standard general relativistic string if $W_0^2 = 1 - 8\pi G\mu$. The string radius R_s can be uniquely defined, and it is given in terms of the constant potential, as well as two integration constants. Under the assumption that the string tension is positive in $r = 0$, the string radius is also positive.

For other, more complicated forms of the potential it seems very difficult, if not impossible, to obtain exact analytical solutions of the field equations, and hence they must be solved numerically.

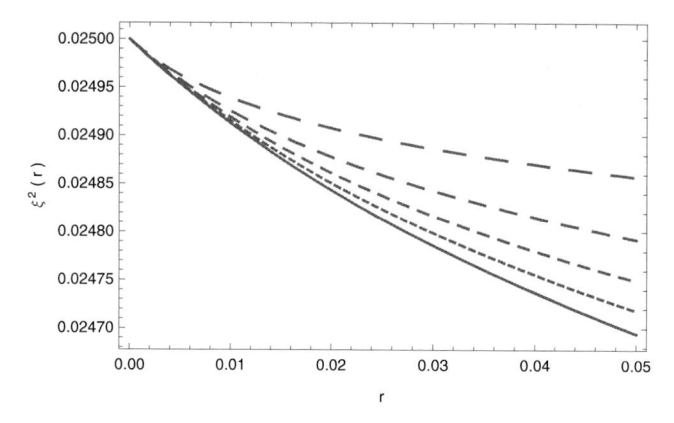

Fig. 3. Variation of ξ^2 as a function of r (with all quantities in arbitrary units) for the $\bar{V}(\xi,\psi) = \bar{V}_0 \xi^2 \psi^2$ potential, for $\psi_0 = -0.025$ (solid curve), $\psi_0 = -0.020$ (dotted curve), $\psi_0 = -0.015$ (short dashed curve), $\psi_0 = -0.01$ (dashed curve), and $\psi_0 = -0.005$ (long dashed curve), respectively. For $\bar{V}_0$ we have adopted the value $\bar{V}_0 = 10$, while the boundary conditions used to numerically integrate the field equations are $u_0 = -0.01$, $\alpha_0 = 0.025$, $W(0) = 0.10$, and $v_0 = 0.10$, respectively.

Since the potentials depend on at least one extra constant parameter, together with the five boundary conditions we obtain a very large boundary parameter space, containing from six to nine arbitrary parameters. The large number of parameters allows the construction of a large number of different numerical cosmic string models. However, we have restricted the set of parameters, as well as the physical nature of the solutions, by imposing three physical constraints, namely, that the string tension is positive inside the string, and it vanishes at the vacuum boundary, that the string must have a well defined and unique radius R_s, obtained from the condition $\sigma(R_s) = 0$, and that $\xi^2 > 0$, $\forall r \in [0, R_s]$. Even after imposing this set of restrictions, a large variety of string models in generalized HMPG theory can be obtained.

In conclusion, in the present work we have considered specific cosmic string models that are solutions of the field equations of the generalized HMPG theory. Modified gravity theories may have profound implications on the formation, properties and structure of cosmic strings, interesting and important topological objects that may have been generated in the early Universe. Hence, the theoretical investigations of strings in modified gravity models may therefore be a worthwhile pathway for future research.

Acknowledgments

FSNL acknowledges support from the Fundação para a Ciência e a Tecnologia (FCT) Scientific Employment Stimulus contract with reference CEECINST/00032/2018, and the research grants No. UID/FIS/04434/2020, No. PTDC/FIS-OUT/29048/2017 and No. CERN/FIS-PAR/0037/2019. JLR was supported by the European Regional Development Fund and the programme Mobilitas Pluss (MOBJD647).

References

1. T. P. Sotiriou and V. Faraoni, Rev. Mod. Phys. **82** (2010), 451-497 doi:10.1103/RevModPhys.82.451 [arXiv:0805.1726 [gr-qc]].
2. J. Khoury and A. Weltman, Phys. Rev. Lett. **93** (2004), 171104 doi:10.1103/PhysRevLett.93.171104 [arXiv:astro-ph/0309300 [astro-ph]].
3. J. Khoury and A. Weltman, Phys. Rev. D **69** (2004), 044026 doi:10.1103/PhysRevD.69.044026 [arXiv:astro-ph/0309411 [astro-ph]].
4. G. J. Olmo, Int. J. Mod. Phys. D **20** (2011), 413-462 doi:10.1142/S0218271811018925 [arXiv:1101.3864 [gr-qc]].
5. D. Sáez-Chillón Gómez, Phys. Lett. B **814** (2021), 136103 doi:10.1016/j.physletb.2021.136103 [arXiv:2011.11568 [gr-qc]].
6. T. Harko, T. S. Koivisto, F. S. N. Lobo and G. J. Olmo, Phys. Rev. D **85** (2012), 084016 doi:10.1103/PhysRevD.85.084016 [arXiv:1110.1049 [gr-qc]].
7. T. Harko and F. S. N. Lobo,
8. S. Capozziello, T. Harko, T. S. Koivisto, F. S. N. Lobo and G. J. Olmo, Universe **1** (2015) no. 2, 199-238 doi:10.3390/universe1020199 [arXiv:1508.04641 [gr-qc]].
9. T. Harko and F. S. N. Lobo, Int. J. Mod. Phys. D **29** (2020) no. 13, 2030008 doi:10.1142/S0218271820300086 [arXiv:2007.15345 [gr-qc]].
10. S. Weinberg, Phys. Rev. Lett. **19** (1967), 1264-1266 doi:10.1103/PhysRevLett.19.1264
11. A. Salam and J. C. Ward, Nuovo Cim. **11** (1959), 568-577 doi:10.1007/BF02726525
12. A. Salam and J. C. Ward, Phys. Lett. **13** (1964), 168-171 doi:10.1016/0031-9163(64)90711-5
13. U. Amaldi, W. de Boer, P. H. Frampton, H. Furstenau and J. T. Liu, Phys. Lett. B **281** (1992), 374-382 doi:10.1016/0370-2693(92)91158-6
14. R. Jeannerot, J. Rocher and M. Sakellariadou, Phys. Rev. D **68** (2003), 103514 doi:10.1103/PhysRevD.68.103514 [arXiv:hep-ph/0308134 [hep-ph]].
15. N. D. Mermin, Rev. Mod. Phys. **51** (1979), 591-648 doi:10.1103/RevModPhys.51.591
16. I. Chuang, B. Yurke, R. Durrer and N. Turok, Science **251** (1991), 1336-1342 doi:10.1126/science.251.4999.1336
17. M. M. Salomaa and G. E. Volovik, Rev. Mod. Phys. **59** (1987), 533-613 [erratum: Rev. Mod. Phys. **60** (1988), 573-573] doi:10.1103/RevModPhys.59.533
18. A. A. Abrikosov, Sov. Phys. JETP **5** (1957), 1174-1182
19. P. W. Higgs, Phys. Rev. Lett. **13** (1964), 508-509 doi:10.1103/PhysRevLett.13.508
20. A. Vilenkin, Phys. Rev. D **23** (1981), 852-857 doi:10.1103/PhysRevD.23.852
21. J. L. Rosa, J. P. S. Lemos and F. S. N. Lobo, Phys. Rev. D **98** (2018) no. 6, 064054 doi:10.1103/PhysRevD.98.064054 [arXiv:1808.08975 [gr-qc]].
22. João Luís Rosa, José P. S. Lemos, Junction conditions for generalized hybrid metric-Palatini gravity with applications, Physical Review D. Volume 104, Issue 12, article id. 124076

New evidence of the azimuthal alignment of quasars spin vector in Large Quasar Groups and cosmic strings

R. J. Slagter

ASFYON, Astronomisch Fysisch Onderzoek Nederland,
former: University of Amsterdam, Dept. Theor. Phys., The Netherlands
E-mail: info@asfyon.com

There has been observational evidence about spin axes of quasars in large quasar groups correlated over hundreds of Mpc. This is seen in the radio spectrum as well as in the optical range. There is not yet a satisfactory explanation of this "spooky" alignment. This alignment cannot be explained by mutual interaction at the time that quasars manifest themselves optically. A cosmological explanation could be possible in the formation of superconducting vortices (cosmic strings) in the early universe, just after the symmetry-breaking phase of the universe. We gathered from the NASA/IPAC and SIMBAD extragalactic databases the right ascension, declination, inclination, position angle and eccentricity of the host galaxies of 3 large quasar groups to obtain the azimuthal and polar angle of the spin vectors. The alignment of the azimuthal angle of the spin vectors of quasars in their host galaxy is confirmed in the large quasar group U1.27 and compared with two other groups in the vicinity, i.e., U1.11 and U1.28, investigated by Clowes (2013). It is well possible that the azimuthal angle alignment fits the predicted azimuthal angle dependency in the theoretical model of the formation of general relativistic superconducting vortices, where the initial axially symmetry is broken just after the symmetry breaking of the scalar-gauge field.

Keywords: Quasar groups; alignment spin vectors; host galaxy; cosmic strings; scalar-gauge field.

1. Introduction

A large quasar group (LQG) is a cluster of quasars that makes the largest astronomical structures in the current universe. Their sizes can be of the order of hundreds of Mpc. Astronomers believe that a quasar is an active galactic nuclei (AGN) with a vibrant eruption of radiation both optical and in radio range originated by a spinning (Kerr-) black hole, surrounded by an accretion disk. A LQG has an internal non-uniform distribution of spin vectors seen in the radio spectrum[1] and the optical spectrum as observed by Hutsemekers et al.[2,3] This coherence is mysterious and cannot be explained by mutual interaction at the time scale of primordial galaxies formation but rather by use of a more advanced method[4–6] In a recent study, Slagter[7] found that the azimuthal angle of the spin vector of quasars in their host galaxies in six quasar groups, show preferred directions. This is demonstrated through an emergent azimuthal angle dependency of the general relativistic Nielsen-Olesen (NO) vortices at the point after the symmetry breaking at grand unified theory (GUT)-scale. This review focuses on three more LQG, studied by

Clowes.[8,9] In section 2 we outline the theoretical model and in section 3 we present a theoretical proof of the breaking of the axial symmetry and in section 4 we present the data analysis.

2. The model

2.1. *The U(1) scalar-gauge field*

Superconductivity can be described by the famous Ginsburg-Landau model.[10] It is a beautiful example of a quantum field model, where a scalar field acts as an order parameter. This construction was made before the introduction of the scalar Higgs field of the Standard Model of particle physics! For the type II superconductivity of the Ginzburg-Landau (GL) theory,[11,12] the electro-magnetic (EM) gauge invariance is broken and the well-known Meissner effect occurs.[14] One says that the phase symmetry is spontaneously broken and the EM field acquires a length scale, which introduces a penetration depth of the gauge field A_μ in the superconductor and a coherence length of Φ. In the relativistic case one says that the photon acquires mass. Because we have three space dimensions, these solutions of the GL theory behave like magnetic flux vortices (or Nielsen-Olesen (NO) strings[13]) extended to tubes and carry a quantized magnetic flux $2\pi n$, with n an integer, the topological charge or winding number of the field. It was discovered by Abrikosov[14] that these vortices can form a lattice. These localized vortices (or solitons) in the GL-theory are observed in experiments. The phenomenon of magnetic flux quantization in the theory of superconductivity is characteristic for so-called ordered media. After the discovery of the electroweak unification, one could formulate the relativistic vortex solution, nicely expressed by Nielsen and Olesen. We write the scalar field and gauge field as

$$\Phi = \eta X(t,r)e^{in\varphi}, \qquad A_\mu = \frac{n}{e}\bigl[P(t,r) - 1\bigr]\nabla_\mu \varphi,. \qquad (1)$$

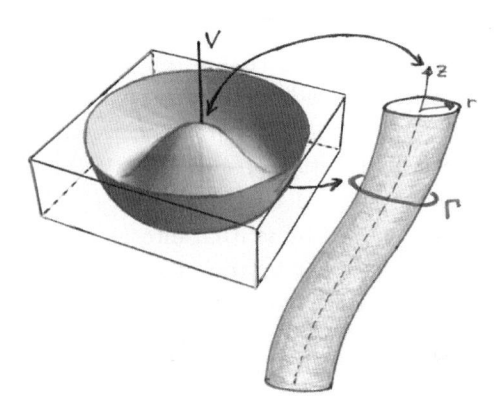

Fig. 1.   Mapping the degenerated minima of the potential to position space.

The model is invariant under the group U(1) of local gauge transformations (of the second kind)

$$\Phi(\mathbf{x}) \to e^{i\chi(x)}\Phi(x), \qquad A_a(\mathbf{x}) \to A_a(x) + \frac{1}{e}\partial_a\chi(\mathbf{x}). \qquad (2)$$

The scalar potential is the well-known "mexican hat" potential (see figure 1) $V(\Phi) = \frac{1}{8}\lambda\left(\Phi\Phi^* - \eta^2\right)^2$ with η the vacuum expectation value. Further, $\frac{m_\Phi}{m_A} = \frac{e^2}{\lambda}$ is the ratio of the scalar to gauge masses. This potential leads to a nonzero η and spontaneously breaking of the U(1) symmetry (note that the parameters are in general temperature dependent[a]. We say that the "false" vacuum for $\Phi = 0$ is broken and the true vacuum is then at the lowest points of the potential. The points of the false vacuum form one or more continuous curves or filaments in space. Such a filament of non-zero Higgs field energy is called a (cosmic-) string (CS) and first proposed by Kibble (1976). The mass and dimensions of the CS are largely determined by the energy scale at which the relevant phase transition occurs. The mass in the GUT scale can be of the order $10^{21} gcm^{-1}$ and there is no restriction for the length. The forces existing between the vortices are the electromagnetic- and scalar force. When the vortices get close together, the problem becomes non-linear and the resulting forces depends on the ratio $\frac{e^2}{\lambda}$. For details, see, for example, the text book of Felsager.[15]

The vortex solution possesses mass, so it will couple to gravity. The resulting self-gravitating cosmic strings (CS) still show all the features of superconductivity, but the stability conditions complicate considerably. The stability of the formed lattices depends critically on the parameters of the model, certainly when gravity comes into play. The force between the gauged vortices depends on the the strength of the self-interaction potential of the Higgs field, the gauge-coupling constant, the energy scale at which the phase transition takes place and the spacetime structure. When the mass of the Higgs field is greater than the mass of the gauge field, vortices will repel each other. So gravity could balance the vortices. The energy of the vortex

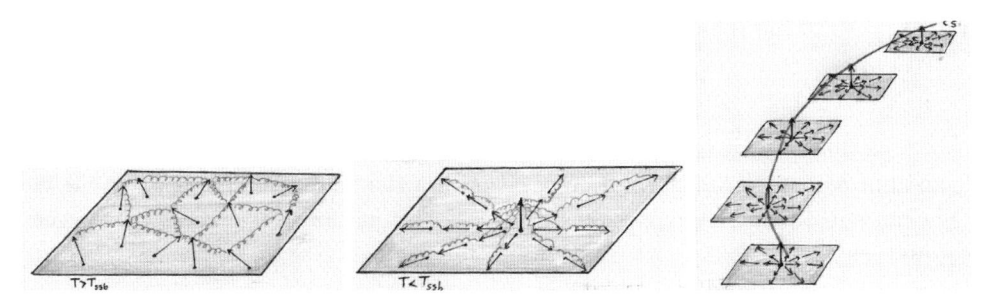

Fig. 2. Formation of the cosmic string. When the temperature drops, not all the "points" in the configuration can follow the dictated new symmetry.

---

[a]The string structure is cylindrical symmetric, so one uses the polar coordinates (t, r, z, φ). This choice is very convenient, when one considers rotating compact objects, such as a Kerr spacetime.

grows by increasing multiplicity n, so configurations with $n > 1$ can be seen as multi-soliton states and it is energetically favourable for these to decay into n well separated $n = 1$ solitons. Vortices with high multiplicity can be formed during the symmetry breaking. The total vortex number n is the sum of multiplicities $n_1, n_2, ..$ of isolated points (zero's of Φ).[12]

2.2. *The high-frequency approximation*

A linear approximation of wavelike solutions of the Einstein equations is not adequate when one is dealing with high curvature (or high energy scale), i.e., close to the horizons of black holes or in the early stage of the universe at the time of mass formation by the Higgs mechanism. There will be a "back-reaction" on the background spacetime. There is a powerful approximation method which can deal with these non linearities: the multiple-scale method. Pioneer work was done by ChoquetBruhat.[16] One expands the relevant fields[17]

$$V_i = \sum_{n=0}^{\infty} \frac{1}{\omega^n} F_i^{(n)}(\mathbf{x}, \xi), \tag{3}$$

where ω represents a dimensionless parameter ("frequency"), which will be large. Further, $\xi = \omega \Theta(\mathbf{x})$, with Θ a scalar (phase) function on the manifold. The small parameter $\frac{1}{\omega}$ can also be the ratio of the characteristic wavelength of the perturbation to the characteristic dimension of the background. On warped spacetimes it could also be the ratio of the extra dimension to the background dimension. In the vacuum case, we expand the metric

$$g_{\mu\nu} = \bar{g}_{\mu\nu} + \frac{1}{\omega} h_{\mu\nu}(\mathbf{x}, \xi) + \frac{1}{\omega^2} k_{\mu\nu}(\mathbf{x}, \xi) + ..., \tag{4}$$

where we defined

$$\frac{dg_{\mu\nu}}{dx^\sigma} = g_{\mu\nu,\sigma} + \omega l_\sigma \dot{g}_{\mu\nu}, \quad g_{\mu\nu,\sigma} = \frac{\partial g_{\mu\nu}}{\partial x^\sigma}, \quad \dot{g}_{\mu\nu} = \frac{\partial g_{\mu\nu}}{\partial \xi}, \tag{5}$$

with $l_\mu = \frac{\partial \Theta}{\partial x^\mu}$. One then says that

$$V_i = \sum_{n=-m}^{\infty} \frac{1}{\omega^n} F_i^{(n)}(\mathbf{x}, \xi) \tag{6}$$

is an approximate wavelike solution of order n of the field equation, if $F_i^{(n)} = 0, \forall n$. One can substitute the expansion into the field equations. The Ricci tensor then expands as

$$R_{\mu\nu} \to \omega R_{\mu\nu}^{(-1)} + \left(\bar{R}_{\mu\nu} + R_{\mu\nu}^{(0)} \right) + \frac{1}{\omega} R_{\mu\nu}^{(1)} + ... \tag{7}$$

By equating the subsequent orders to zero, we obtain

$$R_{\mu\nu}^{(-1)} = 0 = \frac{1}{2} \bar{g}^{\beta\lambda} (l_\lambda l_\mu \ddot{h}_{\beta\nu} + l_\nu l_\beta \ddot{h}_{\mu\lambda} - l_\lambda l_\beta \ddot{h}_{\mu\nu} - l_\nu l_\mu \ddot{h}_{\beta\lambda}), \tag{8}$$

$$R^{(0)}_{\mu\nu} + \bar{R}_{\mu\nu} = 0, \qquad R^{(1)}_{\mu\nu} = 0, \qquad .... \tag{9}$$

Here we used $l_\mu l^\mu = 0$. The rapid variation is observed in the direction of l_μ. In the radiative outgoing Eddington-Finkelstein coordinates, we have $x^1 = u = \Theta(\mathbf{x}) = t - r$ and $l_\mu = (1, 0, 0, 0)$, while the bar stands for the background.

We now expand the scalar and gauge field

$$A_\mu = \bar{A}_\mu(\mathbf{x}) + \frac{1}{\omega} B_\mu(\mathbf{x}, \xi) + \frac{1}{\omega^2} C_\mu(\mathbf{x}, \xi) + ..., \tag{10}$$

$$\Phi = \bar{\Phi}(\mathbf{x}) + \frac{1}{\omega} \Psi(\mathbf{x}, \xi) + \frac{1}{\omega^2} \Xi(\mathbf{x}, \xi) + ..., \tag{11}$$

where we write the subsequent orders of the scalar field as

$$\bar{\Phi} = \eta \bar{X}(t, r) e^{in_1\varphi}, \quad \Psi = Y(t, r, \xi) e^{in_2\varphi}, \quad \Xi = Z(t, r, \xi) e^{in_3\varphi}, \tag{12}$$

with n_i the winding numbers. So we suppose that the winding numbers of the subsequent orders of the scalar field expansion coefficients are different. This can happen by the quantum fluctuations just after the symmetry breaking scale.

2.3. The exitation and decay of the vortices

The energy of the string in flat spacetime is given by

$$E = \frac{1}{2} \frac{n^2}{e^2 r^2} (\partial_r P)^2 + \frac{1}{2} \eta^2 (\partial_r X)^2 + \frac{1}{2} n^2 \eta^2 \frac{P^2 X^2}{r^2} + \frac{1}{8} \beta \eta^4 (X^2 - 1)^2. \tag{13}$$

The energy is proportional with n^2, so there can be no exact ground state for the string carrying multiple flux quanta (the expression changes when gravity comes into play and new features will emerge). So the configuration will dissociate into n well separated $n = 1$ vortices.

It turns out, when one evaluates the field equations, that an imprint will be left over of the azimuthal dependency of the orientation of the clustering of Abrikosov vortices. See figure 3. The azimuthal angle φ does not reach of course, the partial differential equations (PDE) in the unperturbed case. So the axial symmetry is dynamically broken. The azimuthal dependency emerges already to first order in the approximation. For example,

$$^4 T^{(0)}_{\varphi\varphi} = e^{-2\bar{\gamma}} r^2 \dot{Y} (\partial_t \bar{X} - \partial_r \bar{X}) \cos[(n_2 - n_1)\varphi] + e^{2\bar{\psi} - 2\bar{\gamma}} \frac{\dot{B}}{\bar{W}_1^2 \epsilon} (\partial_r \bar{P} - \partial_t \bar{P}). \tag{14}$$

However, in $T^{(1)}_{\varphi\varphi}$ there appears terms like $\cos(n_2 - n_1)\varphi$ and $\cos(n_3 - n_1)\varphi$. The perturbative appearance of a nonzero energy-momentum component $T_{t\varphi}$ can be compared with the phenomenon of bifurcation along the Maclaurin-Jacobi sequence of equilibrium ellipsoids of self-gravitating compact objects, signalling the onset of secular instabilities.[18] This shows a similarity with the Goldstone-boson modes of spontaneously broken symmetries of continuous groups. The recovery of the SO(2) symmetry from the equatorial eccentricity takes place at a time comparable to the

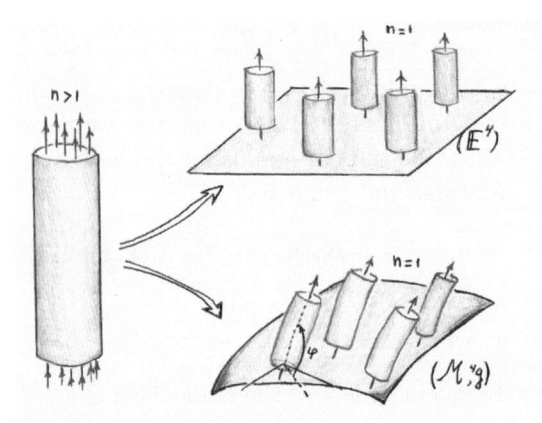

Fig. 3. Excitation and decay of a high multiplicity vortex into correlated vortices of unit flux $n = 1$. Top: the Abrikosov lattice in Euclidean space. Bottom: correlated vortices with preferred azimuthal angle φ in curved spacetime after the symmetry breaking.

emission of gravitational waves. The particular ellipsoid orientation in the frame (r, φ, z) expressed as $\varphi_0 \equiv \varphi(t_0)$, is at $t > t_0$ and determined by the transformation $\varphi \to \varphi_0 - Jt$, where J is the rotation frequency (circulation or "angular momentum") of the coordinate system. The angle φ_0 is fixed arbitrarily at the onset of symmetry breaking.

2.4. *Contribution from the bulk*

It is conjectured that the imprint of the azimuthal dependency will be to faint to contribute to observational evidence, after the expansion of the universe. However, let us consider the warped 5D spacetime

$$ds^2 = \mathcal{W}(t,r,y)^2 \left[e^{2(\gamma(t,r) - \psi(t,r))}(-dt^2 + dr^2) + e^{2\psi(t,r)} dz^2 \right.$$
$$\left. + r^2 e^{-2\psi(t,r)} d\varphi^2 \right] + dy^2, \tag{15}$$

with $\mathcal{W} = W_1(t,r) W_2(y)$ is the warp factor. All standard model fields reside on the brane, while gravity can propagate into the bulk. An extended treatment of the warped five-dimensional spacetime and the effective gravitational equations can be found in Shiromizu et al.[19] and Slagter.[20] The warpfactor can be solved exactly in the case of the spacetime Eq.(15) from the 5D Einstein equations

$$\mathcal{W}^2 = W_2(y)^2 W_1(t,r)^2 = \frac{e^{2\sqrt{-\frac{1}{6}\Lambda_5}(y-y_0)}}{\tau r}$$
$$\cdot \left(d_1 e^{(\sqrt{2\tau})t} - d_2 e^{-(\sqrt{2\tau})t} \right) \left(d_3 e^{(\sqrt{2\tau})r} - d_4 e^{-(\sqrt{2\tau})r} \right), \tag{16}$$

If we inspect, for example, the several orders of the (t, φ) components of the energy momentum tensor

$$^4\bar{T}_{t\varphi} = 0, \qquad ^4\bar{T}_{t\varphi}^{(0)} = \bar{X} \bar{P} \dot{Y} \sin[(n_2 - n_1)\varphi] \tag{17}$$

$$^4T^{(1)}_{t\varphi} = \Big[\partial_t \bar{X} Y(n_1 - n_2 - \bar{P}) + \bar{X}(\bar{P}\partial_t Y + \epsilon B\dot{Y})\Big]\sin[(n_2 - n_1)\varphi]$$
$$+ \bar{X}\bar{P}\dot{Z}\sin[(n_3 - n_1)\varphi] + \frac{e^{2\bar{\psi}-2\bar{\gamma}}}{\bar{W}_1^2}\dot{Y}h_{14}(\partial_t \bar{X} - \partial_r \bar{X})\cos[(n_2 - n_1)\varphi]$$
$$+ \bar{X}^2 \bar{P}\epsilon B_0 - \frac{1}{8}\beta(\bar{X}^2 - \eta^2)^2 h_{14}$$
$$- \frac{e^{2\bar{\psi}-2\bar{\gamma}}}{2\bar{W}_1^2}h_{14}\Big[\frac{e^{2\bar{\psi}}}{r^2\bar{W}_1^2\epsilon^2}(\partial_t \bar{P} - \partial_r \bar{P})^2 + \partial_r \bar{X}^2 - \partial_t \bar{X}^2 + e^{2\bar{\gamma}}\frac{\bar{X}^2 \bar{P}^2}{r^2}\Big], \quad (18)$$

then it is observed that the warpfactor enters in the denominator for some terms. So the φ terms can dominate at late times (see also Eq.(14)). It will evident that an emergent imprint of a preferred azimuthal angle φ_0 is left over on the lattice of vortices when the ground state is reached ($n = 1$). The configuration will become again axially symmetric.

3. A fundamental proof of the breaking of axially symmetry: The pure gravitational wave case

So far, we found that temporarily off-diagonal terms occurred in the perturbative approach of the Einstein scalar gauge field. What remains unclear is if the breaking of the axially symmetry already appears in the vacuum case like in the vicinity of the black hole spacetime. It is conjectured that the formation of primordial (Kerr-) black holes (and so quasars) happened in the early stages of the evolution of the universe before the stars were formed. Therefore, consider the radiative Vaidya spacetime in Eddington-Finkelstein coordinates [b]

$$ds^2 = -\Big(1 - \frac{2M(u)}{r}\Big)du^2 - 2dudr + r^2(d\theta^2 + \sin^2\theta d\varphi^2), \quad (19)$$

which is the Schwarzschild black hole spacetime with $u = t - r - 2M\log(\frac{r}{2M} - 1)$. Here we used $l_\mu l^\mu = 0$. In the radiative coordinates, we have $x^1 = u = \Theta(\mathbf{x})$ and $l_\mu = (1, 0, 0, 0)$. From Eq.(8) we obtain

$$h_{rr} = h_{r\theta} = h_{r\varphi} = 0, \qquad h_{\varphi\varphi} = -\sin^2\theta h_{\theta\theta}. \quad (20)$$

From the zero-order equations Eq.(9) we obtain

$$\ddot{k}_{rr} = 0, \qquad \dot{h}_{\theta\theta} = r\partial_r h_{\theta\theta}, \qquad \dot{h}_{\theta\varphi} = r\partial_r h_{\theta\varphi}. \quad (21)$$

So one writes

$$h_{\theta\theta} = r\alpha(u, \theta, \varphi, \xi), \quad h_{\theta\varphi} = r\beta(u, \theta, \varphi, \xi), \quad h_{\varphi\varphi} = -r\alpha\sin^2\theta. \quad (22)$$

Further, we have

$$\ddot{k}_{r\theta} = \frac{1}{r}\Big(2\dot{\alpha}\cot\theta + \partial_\theta\dot{\alpha} + \frac{1}{\sin^2\theta}\partial_\varphi\dot{\beta}\Big), \quad (23)$$

---

[b]This spacetime is also applied to describe the evaporation of a black hole by hawking radiation in a quantum mechanical way.

$$\ddot{k}_{r\varphi} = \frac{1}{r}\left(\dot{\beta}\cot\theta - \partial_\varphi\dot{\alpha} + \partial_\theta\dot{\beta}\right), \qquad (24)$$

$$\frac{dM}{du} = -\frac{\ddot{k}_{\phi\phi} + \sin^2\theta\,\ddot{k}_{\theta\theta}}{4\sin^2\theta} - \frac{1}{2}r\dot{h}_{uu} - \frac{1}{4}\left(\dot{\alpha}^2 + \frac{\dot{\beta}^2}{\sin^2\theta}\right) + \frac{1}{4}\left(\ddot{\alpha}^2 + \frac{\ddot{\beta}^2}{\sin^2\theta}\right). \qquad (25)$$

Not all the components of $h_{\mu\nu}$ and $k_{\mu\nu}$ are physical, so one needs some extra gauge conditions. Suitable choice of α and β (Choquet-Bruhat uses, for example, $\alpha = 0, \beta = g(u)h(\xi)\sin\theta$), leads to a solution to second order which is in general not axially symmetric. We can integrate these zero order equations with respect to ξ. One obtains then some conditions on the background fields, because terms like $\int \dot{\alpha}\,d\xi$ disappear. From Eq. (25), we obtain

$$\frac{dM}{du} = -\frac{1}{4\tau}\int_0^\tau \left(\dot{\alpha}^2 + \frac{\dot{\beta}^2}{\sin^2\theta}\right)d\xi, \qquad (26)$$

which is the back-reaction of the high-frequency disturbances on the mass M. τ is the period of $\dot{h}_{\mu\nu}$. This expression can be substituted back into Eq.(25). However, in the non-vacuum case, the right-hand side will also contain contributions from the matter fields. In order to obtain propagation equations for $h_{\mu\nu}$ and $k_{\mu\nu}$, one proceeds with the next order equation $R^{(1)}_{\mu\nu} = 0$. First of all, Eq.(23) and (24) are consistent with $R^{(1)}_{r\varphi} = 0$ and $R^{(1)}_{r\theta} = 0$. Further, one obtains propagation equations for α and β and for some second order perturbations, such as $k_{\varphi\varphi}$. Moreover, the (φ,θ)-dependent part of the PDE's for α and β (say $A(\theta,\varphi), B(\theta,\varphi)$) can be separated (for the case $k_{\theta\varphi} \neq 0$):

$$\partial_\varphi B + 2\sin\theta\cos\theta\,A + \sin^2\theta\,\partial_\theta A = 0, \qquad (27)$$

$$\sin^2\theta\,\partial_{\theta\theta}A + 7\sin\theta\cos\theta\,\partial_\theta A + 4\cot\theta\,\partial_\varphi B + 2(5\cos^2\theta - 1)A + 2\partial_{\theta\varphi}B = 0. \qquad (28)$$

A non-trivial simple solution is

$$A = \frac{\cos\theta(\sin\varphi + \cos\varphi)}{\sin^3\theta}, \quad B = \frac{\sin\varphi - \cos\varphi}{\sin^2\theta} + G(\theta), \qquad (29)$$

with $G(\theta)$ arbitrary. So the breaking of the spherically and axially symmetry is evident.

4. Data analysis on quasar groups

In our model it is conjectured that the azimuthal dependency expresses itself in the φ alignment of quasar spin vectors in LQG.[7] From the NASA/IPAC extragalactic database and SIMBAD we extract for the three LQG U1.11, U1.27 and U.28 the right ascension, declination, inclination, position angle and eccentricity of the host galaxies. The 3D orientation of the spin vectors can then be calculated by[21-23] by

$$\cos^2 i = \frac{\epsilon^2 - \epsilon_0^2}{1 - \epsilon_0^2}, \qquad (30)$$

$$\sin\theta = -\cos i\sin\delta \pm \sin i\sin p\cos\delta, \qquad (31)$$

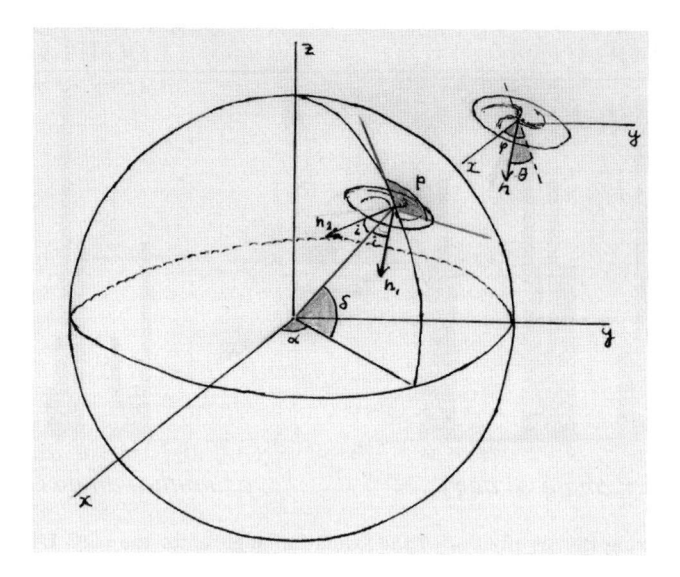

Fig. 4. The two polar coordinates (φ, θ)

azimuthal angle φ (deg)

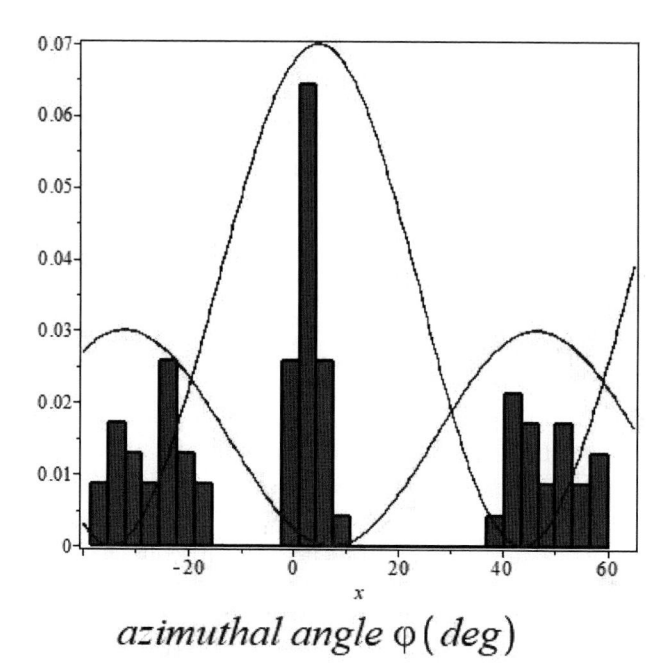

Fig. 5. Plot of the azimuthal angle φ in degrees. This shows the distribution of the azimuthal angle of the spin vectors in the LQG U1.27 (N=71) with a best-fit of two trigonometric functions with a phase shift range of 45°.

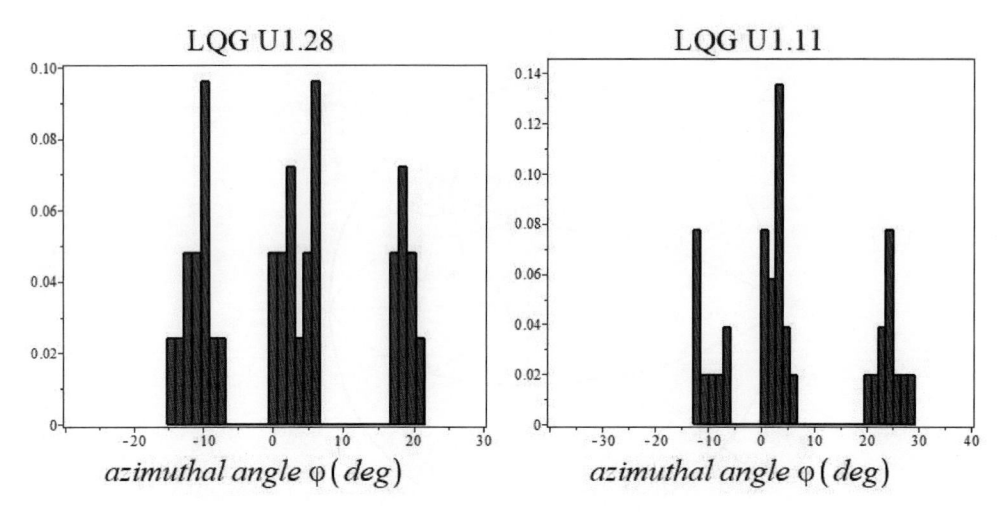

Fig. 6. Plot showing the distribution of the azimuthal angle φ for the LQG U1.28 (N = 34) and U1.11 (N = 38).

$$\sin\varphi = \frac{-\cos i \cos\delta \sin\alpha + \sin i(\mp \sin p \sin\delta \sin\alpha \mp \cos p \cos\alpha)}{\cos\theta}. \tag{32}$$

We used for the intrinsic flatness (ϵ_0) the value 0.2, which is the standard value when we have no information about the morphological types of the analyzed galaxies. In figure 5 and 6 we plotted the azimuthal angle. Without statistical analysis one can conclude that the preferred orientations are evident. In the case of LQG U1.27 (see Table 1 for the data), we fitted two trigonometric functions on the distribution, which can theoretically be explained.

5. Conclusion

We find in a nonlinear approximation, an emergent azimuthal-angle dependency of Nielsen-Olesen vortices just after the symmetry breaking at GUT scale. Using a approximation scheme, the azimuthal-angle dependency appears in the first and second order field equations as trigonometrical functions $\sin(n_i - n_j)\varphi$ and $\sin(n_i - n_j)\varphi (i > j)$, with n_i the multiplicities of subsequent perturbation terms of the scalar field. Vortices with high multiplicity decay into a lattice with entangled Abrikosov vortices. The stability of this lattice of correlated flux $n = 1$ vortices with preferred azimuthal-angle is guaranteed by the contribution from the bulk spacetime by means of the warp factor: the cosmic string becomes super-massive for some time during the evolution. These so-called super-massive cosmic strings arise in a natural way in string theory or M-theory., i.e., brane-world models and are produced when the universe underwent phase transitions at energies much higher than the GUT scale, $G\mu > 1$. The imprint on the effective 4D brane spacetime can be

Table 1. Data for the LQG U1.27 (N=71) from NASA/IPAC and SIMBAD. The successive columns represent: right ascension, declination, redshift, inclination, eccentricity, position angle, azimuthal angle and polar angle. We omitted the other two values $\pi - \theta$ in the last column, belonging to the minus sign of φ.

RA	Dec	z	inc	ecc	PA(deg)	φ(rad)	θ(rad)
160.413150	14.591740	1.221	.830	.69	87	±.298 / ±.427	.575 / 1.083
160.840103	14.600057	1.271	.606	.83	113	.571 / .013	.305 / .796
161.128848	16.045854	1.233	.526	.87	45	.034 / .782	.619 / .102
161.187666	15.317133	1.237	.741	.75	68	.049 / .763	.421 / .925
161.335962	14.290068	1.270	.586	.84	63	.063 / .678	.751 / .275
161.516893	14.044789	1.290	.547	.86	6	.227 / .889	-.155 / .263
161.567993	16.753510	1.282	.772	.73	48	.186 / 1.04	.779 / .294
161.601093	14.502540	1.372	.660	.80	60	.007 / .775	.322 / .792
162.056815	16.480304	1.290	.506	.88	170	.82 / .215	.336 / -.167
162.248981	12.889527	1.368	.677	.79	99	.419 / .156	.434 / .890
162.344193	15.726700	1.263	.772	.73	42	.257 / 1.05	.258 / .699
162.351272	15.698897	1.301	.435	.91	8	.129 / .762	-.190 / .306
162.409269	21.808144	1.235	.526	.87	33	.127 / .849	-.067 / .612
162.423677	15.306867	1.341	.676	.79	3	.379 / 1.00	-.175 / .240
162.449082	16.371282	1.300	.566	.85	142	.745 / .225	.080 / .589
162.505093	15.565017	1.255	.357	.94	17	.038 / .671	-.154 / .357
162.676146	16.015594	1.269	.771	.73	125	.744 / .340	.843 / .359
162.767371	16.316926	1.253	.287	.96	170	.592 / .004	.322 / -.224
162.820881	13.193341	1.337	.483	.89	102	.400 / .175	.700 / .243
162.831696	14.436524	1.315	.659	.80	54	.084 / .812	.743 / .287
162.845783	11.981222	1.309	.437	.91	159	.707 / .132	.344 / -.039
162.857213	12.796204	1.283	.641	.81	139	.779 / .275	.595 / .207
162.884258	14.937553	1.367	.756	.74	94	.354 / .211	1.014 / .494
162.918357	20.655882	1.174	.567	.85	49	.062 / .799	.743 / .082
162.937035	12.974699	1.316	.461	.90	110	.455 / .107	.654 / .207
163.041780	16.928818	1.339	.436	.91	59	.077 / .576	.656 / .083
163.092251	12.515036	1.316	.355	.94	21	.035 / .647	-.082 / .331
163.098712	14.090468	1.256	.622	.82	101	.415 / .127	.365 / .852
163.100377	20.776172	1.203	.504	.88	25	.160 / .827	-.120 / .525
163.190868	13.682636	1.356	.482	.89	60	.057 / .590	.181 / .643
163.238226	10.992647	1.266	.483	.89	89	.285 / .305	.291 / .674
163.242363	20.284854	1.253	.356	.94	41	.026 / .611	-.111 / .569
163.552829	14.959790	1.231	.678	.79	120	.625 / .184	.330 / .812
163.591268	21.358676	1.257	.606	.83	120	.579 / .164	.161 / .862
163.648532	10.304548	1.260	.385	.93	16	.084 / .671	-.064 / .271
163.677979	10.722398	1.335	.725	.76	144	.872 / .393	.247 / .550
163.694730	19.952953	1.220	.566	.85	20	.246 / .889	-.116 / .478
163.845984	13.102997	1.358	.588	.84	11	.295 / .889	.296 / -.085
163.854942	19.298998	1.201	.773	.73	146	.906 / .531	.651 / .133
163.857047	11.617507	1.293	.527	.87	119	.538 / .027	.650 / .260
163.924334	11.298387	1.331	.845	.68	88	.249 / .335	.648 / 1.042
163.984288	18.788475	1.277	.355	.94	87	.262 / .305	.027 / .683
164.046989	17.140997	1.344	.845	.68	72	.012 / .780	.505 / 1.066
164.091276	14.566966	1.243	.207	.98	129	.409 / .138	.412 / -.091
164.156218	15.013202	1.371	.787	.72	109	.541 / .147	.979 / .483
164.158278	10.052025	1.273	.435	.91	128	.544 / .023	.507 / .170
164.230688	14.829509	1.229	.625	.82	133	.696 / .257	.208 / .671
164.308435	18.798158	1.285	.382	.91	152	.614 / .106	-.133 / .484

Table 1. (*Continued*)

RA	Dec	z	inc	ecc	PA(deg)	φ(rad)	θ(rad)
164.521231	20.061417	1.273	.587	.94	72	.095 / .549	.211 / .895
164.633396	17.082247	1.286	.462	.90	17	.175 / .750	-.139 / .398
164.668752	17.904320	1.269	.527	.87	50	.062 / .700	.101 / .684
164.730550	8.230752	1.246	.677	.79	8	.401 / .953	-.025 / .199
164.869078	16.782794	1.300	.623	.82	116	.533 / .122	.272 / .829
165.025092	9.444098	1.252	.567	.85	65	.019 / .556	.348 / .666
165.070384	19.606880	1.240	.832	.69	114	.597 / .372	.423 / 1.040
165.166670	16.952878	1.300	.802	.71	127	.739 / .454	.354 / .851
165.452792	8.368669	1.196	.413	.92	9	.153 / .671	-.071 / .197
165.676652	8.655867	1.240	.411	.92	60	.046 / .481	.205 / .500
166.268588	8.759810	1.241	.566	.85	57	.072 / .606	.322 / .610
166.589189	8.686458	1.244	.548	.86	53	.098 / .618	.286 / .571
166.902560	9.020778	1.228	1.02	.55	87	.161 / .347	.860 / 1.175
166.935900	9.924171	1.225	.383	.93	14	.143 / .613	-.071 / .251
167.532914	10.802888	1.211	.248	.97	129	.374 / .052	.006 / .378
167.539961	7.868564	1.208	.740	.75	10	.508 / .967	.015 / .219
168.567405	10.390996	1.210	.693	.78	151	.803 / .472	.168 / .460
168.938775	8.249943	1.194	.547	.86	106	.349 / .012	.381 / .665
169.508801	10.550690	1.215	.526	.87	134	.548 / .234	.196 / .540
169.596744	9.084715	1.197	.787	.72	98	.303 / .018	.620 / .934
170.081761	8.984773	1.229	.641	.81	56	.193 / .613	.373 / .662
170.246993	10.185907	1.208	.384	.93	77	.085 / .271	.196 / .551
170.290711	7.999635	1.141	.461	.90	93	.195 / .143	.320 / .599
169.508801	10.550690	1.215	.526	.87	134	.548 / .234	.196 / .540
169.596744	9.084715	1.197	.787	.72	98	.303 / .018	.620 / .934
170.081761	8.984773	1.229	.641	.81	56	.193 / .613	.373 / .662
170.246993	10.185907	1.208	.384	.93	77	.085 / .271	.196 / .551
170.290711	7.999635	1.141	.461	.90	93	.195 / .143	.320 / .599

caused by wavelike disturbances triggered by the huge mass of the cosmic strings in the bulk. One conjectures that these disturbances could act as an effective dark energy field. Another possible effect can be the formation of massive KK-modes as the imprint of the 5D gravitational field on the 4D brane. We used the azimuthal-angle correlation for the explanation of the recently observed alignment of polarization axes of quasars in large quasar groups. The detailed behavior of this alignment can be explained with our model. The two different orientations perpendicular to each other in quasars groups of less richness could be a second order effect in our model.

More data of high-redshift quasars will be needed in order to test the second order effect predicted in our model.

6. The Data

The data of LQG U1.27 underlying this article are gathered in Table 1.

References

1. A. R. Taylor, and P. Jagannathan, *Alignments of radio galaxies in deep radio imaging of ELAIS N1*, Mon. Not. Roy. Astr. Soc. **459**, 459 (2016).
2. D. Hutsemekers, R. Cabanac, H. Lamy and D. Sluse, (2005) *New optical polarization measurements of quasi-stellar objects. The data*, Astron. Astrophys. **441**, 915, (2005).
3. D. Hutsemekers, L. Braibant, V. Pelgrims, and D. Sluse, *Alignment of quasar polarizations with large-scale structures*, Astron. Astrophys. **572**, A18 (2014).
4. R. J. Slagter, *Alignment of quasar polarizations on large scales explained by warped cosmic strings*, J. of Mod. Phys. **7, no 6**, 501,k (2016).
5. R. J. Slagter, *Alignment of quasar polarizations on large scales explained by warped cosmic strings PART II: The second order contribution*, J. of Mod. Phys. **8, no 2**, 163 (2017).
6. R. J. Slagter, *Evidence of cosmic strings by the observation of the alignment of quasar polarization axes on Mpc scale*, Int. J. Mod. Phys. D **27**, 185009 (2018).
7. R. J. Slagter and P. G. Miedema, *On the azimuthal alignment of quasars spin vector in large quasar groups and cosmic strings*, MNRAS **501**, 2, 3054 (2021).
8. R. G. Clowes, et al. *A structure in the early universe at $z = 1.3$ that exceeds the homogeneity scale of the R-W concordance cosmology*, Mon. Not. Roy. Astron. Soc., **429**, 2910 (2013).
9. R. G. Clowes, et al., *Two close large quasar groups of size $= 350$ Mpc at $z = 1.2$*, Mon. Not. Roy. Astron. Soc., **419**, 556 (2012)
10. V. Ginzburg, V. L. and L. D. Landau, *On the theory of superconductivity*, Zh. Eksp. Teor. Fiz. **20**, 1064 (1950).
11. A. Jaffa and C. Taubes, *Vortices and monopoles*, 2nd edn. (Birkhauser, Boston, 1981).
12. N. Manton and P. Sutcliffe, *Topological solitons* (Cambridge University press, Cambrigde, 2007).
13. H. B. Nielsen and P. Olesen, *Vortex line models for dual strings* Nucl. Phys. **B61**, 45, (1973).
14. A. A. Abrikosov, *On the Magnetic properties of superconductors of the second group*, Soviet Physics JETP **5**, 1174 (1957).
15. B. Felsager, *Geometry, particles and fields*, (Odense University press, Odense, 1987).
16. Y. Choquet-Bruhat, (1969) Commun. Math. Phys. **12**, 16 (1969).
17. R. J. Slagter, *Gravitational waves from spinning non-Abelian cosmic strings*, Class. and Quantum Grav. **18**, 463 (2001).
18. D. Gondek-Rosinska and E. Gourgoulhon, Jacobi-like bar mode instability of relativistic rotating bodies. Phys. Rev. **D66**, 044021 (2002).
19. T. Shiromizu, K. Maeda and M. Sasaki, *The Einstein equations on the 3-brane world*. Phys. Rev. **D62** 024012 (2000).
20. R. J Slagter and S. Pan, *A New Fate of a Warped 5D FLRW Model with a U(1) Scalar Gauge Field*, Found. of Phys. **46**, 1075 (2016).
21. P. Pajowska, W. Godlowski, Z. Zhu, J. Poliela and E. Panko, *Investigation of the orientation of galaxies in clusters: The importance, methods and results of research*, J. Cosm. Astroparticles **02**, 005 (2019).
22. W. Godlowski, *Galactic orientation within the Local Supercluster*, Mon. Not. R. Astron. Soc. **265**, 874 (1993).
23. W. Godlowski, Acta Phys. Pol. **B42**, 2323 (2011).

Summary parallel session cosmic strings I

Reinoud Jan Slagter

Astronomisch Fysisch Onderzoek Nederland (ASFYON),
University of Amsterdam (on leave)
E-mail: info@asfyon.com

Batool Imtiaz[*]

Department of Astronomy, School of Physical Sciences,
University of Science and Technology of China, Hefei, Anhui 230026, China
CAS Key Laboratory for Researches in Galaxies and Cosmology,
University of Science and Technology of China, Hefei, Anhui 230026, China
*E-mail: batool24@mail.ustc.edu.cn

Keywords: Cosmic strings.

Cosmic strings (CS's) are topological defects formed at the GUT symmetry breaking scale in the Einstein-U(1) scalar- gauge field model. This model shows a surprising resemblance with superconductivity and the relativistic Nielsen-Olesen quantized magnetic flux vortex solution. In the standard model of particle physics this scalar-gauge field is responsible for the spontaneously broken symmetry (Higgs mechanism). So one could say that this quantum field with the Mexican hat potential has lived up to its reputation. In cosmological context, the confined regions of the false vacuum of the scalar field form a locus of trapped energy, i.e., a CS. The mass and dimension of a CS is largely determined by the energy scale at which the phase transition takes place. It is believed that in the FLRW model a scale-invariant cosmic string-network is formed. Observational bounds, however, predict a negligible contribution of CS's to large-scale inhomogeneities such as the angular distribution in the CMB radiation. A renewed interest occurred when it was realized that CS's could be produced within the framework of superstring theory inspired cosmological models, i.e., brane-world models. Supersymmetric GUT's can even demand the existence of CS. These super-massive CS's could be produced when the universe underwent phase transitions at energies much higher than the GUT scale, so their gravitational impact increases. Although evidence of CS are not yet found, new observational windows are opened by these super-massive CS's.

In this CS1 parallel session one could present cosmic string-related subjects, such as observational results on CS, gravitational waves and CS, vortex solutions and GRT, cosmic strings and higher dimensional models.

Silva evaluates the possibility of the existence of gravitationally bound string-like objects in the framework of the general hybrid metric-Palatini gravity theory, in which the gravitational action is represented by functions in terms of the Ricci and Palatini scalars, respectively. This theory recognizes equivalent scalar-tensor representations in two independent scalar fields. Assuming cylindrical symmetry and metric invariance, he obtains a gravitational field equation that theoretically describes the structure of the cosmic string. The physical and geometric properties of the cosmic string are determined by two scalar fields, as well as the effective field potential, which functionally depends on two scalar fields. The field equation can be solved exactly for constant and zero potential, respectively, with the corresponding string tensions taking negative and positive values. In addition, for a more general class of potential, which has an additive algebraic structure and multiplication in two scalar fields, the equations of the gravitational field are solved numerically. For each potential, he investigated the effect of changing the parameters of the potential and boundary conditions on the structure of the cosmic string. Thus, he obtains a large class of stable string configurations, the main parameters of which (string tension and radius) substantially depend on the effective field potential and boundary conditions.

Rosa studied 5-dimensional braneworld scenarios in the scalar-tensor representation of the generalized hybrid metric-Palatini gravitational theory. He starts by considering a model for a brane supported purely by the gravitational scalar fields of the theory and then considers other distinct cases where the models are also supported by an additional matter scalar field. He investigates the stability of the gravity sector and shows that the models are all robust against small fluctuations of the metric. In particular, in the presence of the additional scalar field, he finds that the profile of the gravitational zero mode may be controlled by the parameters of the model, being also capable of developing internal structure.

Slagter tried to explain the observational evidence of the correlation of the spin axes of quasars in large quasar groups over hundreds of Mpc. This is seen in the radio spectrum as well as in the optical range. There is not yet a satisfactory explanation of this "spooky" alignment. This alignment cannot be explained by mutual interaction at the time that quasars manifest themselves optically. A cosmological explanation could be possible in the formation of superconducting vortices (cosmic strings) in the early universe, just after the symmetry-breaking phase of the universe. He gathers from the NASA/IPAC and SIMBAD extragalactic databases the right ascension, declination, inclination, position angle and eccentricity of the host galaxies of 3 large quasar groups to obtain the azimuthal and polar angle of the spin vectors. The alignment of the azimuthal angle of the spin vectors of quasars in their host galaxy is confirmed in the large quasar group U1.27 and compared with two other groups in the vicinity, i.e., U1.11 and U1.28, investigated by Clowes (2013). It is well possible that the azimuthal angle alignment fits the predicted azimuthal angle dependency in the theoretical model of the formation of general relativistic superconducting vortices, where the initial axially symmetry is broken just after the symmetry breaking of the scalar-gauge field.

Blasi presented research in gravitational wave astronomy which could open a new window of exploration in fundamental physics. The recent analysis by the NANOGrav collaboration based on the 12.5-year pulsar-timing data set has shown evidence for a common red process which is compatible with a stochastic background of gravitational waves. He discusses the interpretation of this signal in terms of physics beyond the Standard Model with focus on cosmic strings, highly energetic topological defects arising as a consequence of cosmological phase transitions in the early Universe.

Scaling solutions of wiggly cosmic strings

A. R. R. Almeida

Centro de Astrofísica da Universidade do Porto, and
Instituto de Astrofísica e Ciências do Espaço, Universidade do Porto,
Rua das Estrelas, 4150-762 Porto, Portugal, and
Faculdade de Ciências da Universidade do Porto
Rua do Campo Alegre 687, 4169-007 Porto, Portugal
E-mail: Ana.Almeida@astro.up.pt

C. J. A. P. Martins

Centro de Astrofísica da Universidade do Porto, and
Instituto de Astrofísica e Ciências do Espaço, Universidade do Porto,
Rua das Estrelas, 4150-762 Porto, Portugal
E-mail: Carlos.Martins@astro.up.pt

Cosmic string networks form during cosmological phase transitions as a consequence of the Kibble mechanism. The evolution of the simplest networks is accurately described by the canonical Velocity Dependent One-Scale (VOS) model. However, numerical simulations have demonstrated the existence of significant quantities of short-wavelength propagation modes on the strings, known as wiggles, which motivated the recent development of a wiggly string extension of the VOS. Here we summarize recent progress in the physical interpretation of this model through a systematic study of the allowed asymptotic scaling solutions of the model. The modeling mainly relies on three mechanisms: the universe's expansion rate, energy transfer mechanisms (e.g., the production of loops and wiggles), and the choice of the scale in which wiggles are coarse-grained. We consider the various limits in which each mechanism dominates and compare the scaling solutions for each case, in order to gain insight into the role of each mechanism in the overall behavior of the network. Our results show that there are three scaling regimes for the wiggliness, consisting of the well-known Nambu-Goto solution, and non-trivial regimes where the amount of wiggliness can grow as the network evolves or, for specific expansion rates, become a constant. We also demonstrate that full scaling of the network is more likely in the matter era than in the radiation epoch, in agreement with numerical simulations.

Keywords: Cosmology; Topological Defects; Cosmic Strings; Wiggly Strings.

1. Introduction

Cosmic string networks arise in many theories of unification beyond the standard model. In the context of cosmology, they are predicted to have been formed in the early universe as a consequence of the Kibble mechanism.[1] Due to the non-linearity and non-trivial interactions intrinsic to these networks, a complete quantitative description of their evolution, as well as of their observational consequences, proves to be a difficult task.[2]

An accurate description of cosmic strings is accomplished through two complementary approaches: numerical simulations (Nambu-Goto or Abelian-Higgs) and analytic models. The analytic modeling of string networks relies on the statistical physics of the network so as to derive a description of its thermodynamics. The analytic framework for the simplest Nambu-Goto string networks is the Velocity Dependent One-Scale (VOS) model.[3,4] As the direct comparisons with Nambu-Goto and Abelian-Higgs numerical simulations[5–8] demonstrate, the VOS is able to capture the key large-scales properties of the network extremely well. The VOS is built upon the one-scale assumption embodied in the original model developed by Kibble,[9] which expresses the evolution of the network in terms of a single length scale. This length scale can be the inter-string distance, the correlation length ξ, or the average curvature radius R (note these length scales are expected to be identical in this formalism). Various frameworks attempting to describe the dynamics of string defects have been developed, like the three-scale approach,[10] but it was only with the advent of the VOS that a model capable of making robust predictions in various cosmological epochs emerged. The key difference in the VOS framework lies in an additional macroscopic quantity, a root-mean-square (RMS) velocity, whose evolution is described by an extension of the Newton's Second Law. The equations of the standard Nambu-Goto VOS model are rigorously deduced from the Nambu-Goto effective action.

In spite of the successes of the VOS, the model fails to give an accurate description of realistic networks of strings, whose worldsheets are expected to have additional degrees of freedom. In particular, the aforementioned numerical simulations of cosmic strings in expanding universes have demonstrated the existence of great amounts of short-wavelength propagation modes on the strings, known as wiggles, on scales orders of magnitude below the correlation length. The presence of small-scale structure is simply a byproduct of the energy loss phenomena of the network, and thus, if one aims to have an accurate analytic framework of string networks, it is imperative that these small-scale wiggles are accounted for. This motivated the development of a wiggly extension of the VOS that describes the evolution of both large-scale and small-scale properties of string networks.[11,12]

Here we continue the work recently reported in Ref. 13 studying the properties of wiggly cosmic strings, through an improvement of its physical interpretation and modeling. We carry out a systematic study of the asymptotic scaling solutions of the wiggly generalization of the VOS, so as to explore the allowed scaling regimes, other than the trivial Nambu-Goto solution, where wiggliness grows, disappears, or evolves towards a constant value. One of the open questions in the wiggly model is whether the wiggliness reaches scaling, and if so, under what physical conditions. Numerical studies[6] hint at scaling being reached at least in the matter-dominated era.

Another aim of this mathematical exploration is to determine the role that each mechanism has in the overall behavior of the network, as we know the nature of the scaling solutions is highly dependent on the dominant physical mechanism.[12] We consider the various limits in which each mechanism dominates and compare the scaling solutions for each case. Finally, this study also aims to pave the way for a future calibration of the wiggly model. Having determined the various possible scaling regimes, and particularly the behavior of the small-scale structure, we can plan future field theory and Nambu-Goto simulations that are optimized for this calibration and able to test the consistency relations of the solutions, as well as to make numerical predictions of the wiggliness on the strings.

This paper is organized as follows. Section 2 gives a brief overview of the wiggly extension of the VOS. In Section 3, we discuss the asymptotic scaling solutions without and with cosmological expansion, followed by a discussion of their physical implications. Finally we present some conclusions and an outlook in Section 4.

2. Wiggly Strings Dynamics

A wiggly extension of the VOS is accomplished by noting that, in direct contrast with Nambu-Goto strings, wiggly strings have their local string tension T differ from the energy density in the string's local rest frame U. In particular, we can define a parameter w that ranges from 0 to 1 (unity being the value of a Nambu-Goto string), such that

$$\frac{T}{\mu_o} = w, \quad \frac{U}{\mu_o} = \frac{1}{w}, \tag{1}$$

where μ_o is the string mass per unit length. The total energy of a piece of string is given by

$$E = a \int \epsilon U d\sigma = \mu_o a \int \frac{\epsilon}{w} d\sigma, \tag{2}$$

which can be decomposed into two contributions: one for the bare string segments E_o,

$$E_o = \mu_o a \int \epsilon d\sigma, \tag{3}$$

and another due to the small-scale wiggles E_w:

$$E_w = \mu_o a \int \frac{1-w}{w} \epsilon d\sigma. \tag{4}$$

Wiggly strings can be conceived as containing a mass current that renormalizes the bare energy per unit length.[14] We define the renormalization factor

$$\mu \equiv \frac{E}{E_o} \geq 1, \tag{5}$$

which is a measure of the energy due to the wiggles of the network, known as the renormalized string mass per unit length. μ is a scale-dependent quantity, that is, it depends on the renormalization scale ℓ at which the wiggliness is being measured. Each energy contribution yields a characteristic length scale

$$\rho \equiv \frac{\mu_o}{L^2} \tag{6}$$

$$\rho_o \equiv \frac{\mu_o}{\xi^2}, \qquad (7)$$

which are related by

$$\mu = \left(\frac{\xi}{L}\right)^2. \qquad (8)$$

This procedure makes it clear that a quantitative description of small-scale structure implies that the one-scale assumption implicit to the VOS no longer holds. Instead, we have two distinct length scales L and ξ, which will have different dynamics as it will become apparent in their evolution equations. Thus, an averaged model for wiggly cosmic string evolution implies three evolution equations, instead of two, with this additional equation accounting for the evolution of the network's small-scale structure. We note the assumption of $\xi \sim R$ still holds in the wiggly formalism, but it can be tested numerically.[6] It should also be noted that while ξ measures a physical length, L is the length that a Nambu-Goto string with the same total energy would have, and thus should not be interpreted as a physical length.

The equations for the evolution of the network's dynamical quantities are obtained from averaging the microscopic string equations of motion, and so one needs to define the averaging procedure. There are two natural approaches to this. The first consists of averaging over the total energy, so as to give more weight to string segments with larger mass currents. For a generic quantity Q, this is defined as:

$$\langle Q \rangle = \frac{\int Q \frac{\epsilon}{w} d\sigma}{\int \frac{\epsilon}{w} d\sigma}. \qquad (9)$$

An alternative approach consists of averaging over the bare string energy

$$\langle Q \rangle_0 = \frac{\int Q \epsilon d\sigma}{\int \epsilon d\sigma} \qquad (10)$$

The two procedures are related by:

$$\langle Q \rangle = \frac{\langle QU \rangle_0}{\langle U \rangle_0} = \frac{\langle Q/w \rangle_0}{\mu}. \qquad (11)$$

In the wiggly formalism[11,12] the first averaging method is the one adopted (and is the one we adopt in what follows).

The various interactions by which the network loses energy still need to be discussed and included in the evolution equations. In particular, we need to define the phenomenological terms that account for the energy transfers between the bare string and the wiggles. While in the standard VOS model, long string intercommutings had no effect on the evolution of the network, in wiggly strings, they lead to the formation of kinks that increase the energy due to wiggles, and thus, need to be taken into consideration. The energy transfer from the bare string to the wiggles is modeled by:

$$\left(\frac{1}{\rho_o}\frac{d\rho_o}{dt}\right)_{\text{wiggles}} = -cs(\mu)\frac{v}{\xi},, \qquad (12)$$

in which s approaches 0 in the Nambu-Goto limit. Besides accounting for the gain in small-scale structure, s should also include the effects of kink decay by gravitational radiation.

Another mechanism by which the network loses energy is the production of loops. In the VOS model, this is encoded in a phenomenological parameter c, the loop chopping efficiency. The loop chopping parameters of the wiggly model are defined in analogy with the VOS definition, but now the energy transferred to the loops may come from the bare string or from the wiggles

$$\left(\frac{1}{\rho_o}\frac{d\rho_o}{dt}\right)_{\text{loops}} = -cf_o(\mu)\frac{v}{\xi}, \tag{13}$$

$$\left(\frac{1}{\rho_w}\frac{d\rho_w}{dt}\right)_{\text{loops}} = -cf_1(\mu)\frac{v}{\xi}, \tag{14}$$

such that

$$\left(\frac{1}{\rho}\frac{d\rho}{dt}\right)_{\text{loops}} = \left(\frac{1}{\rho}\frac{d\rho_0}{dt}\right)_{\text{loops}} + \left(\frac{1}{\rho}\frac{d\rho_w}{dt}\right)_{\text{loops}}. \tag{15}$$

For simplicity, one can define an overall energy loss parameter

$$\left(\frac{1}{\rho}\frac{d\rho}{dt}\right)_{\text{loops}} \equiv -cf(\mu)\frac{v}{\xi}, \tag{16}$$

which using equations (13–15) can be shown to yield:

$$f(\mu) = \frac{f_o(\mu)}{\mu} + \left(1 - \frac{1}{\mu}\right)f_1(\mu). \tag{17}$$

Note that f has an explicit dependence on μ so as to account for the fact that loop production is favored in regions of the long string network with more small-scale structure than average.[6,15,16] In what follows we adopt the assumptions introduced in Ref. 12

$$\begin{aligned} f_o(\mu) &= 1 \\ f(\mu) &= 1 + \eta\left(1 - \frac{1}{\sqrt{\mu}}\right) \\ s(\mu) &= D\left(1 - \frac{1}{\mu^2}\right), \end{aligned} \tag{18}$$

where two additional phenomenological parameters η and D were introduced, which should be interpreted as probabilities for small-scale structure loss and gain, respectively.

Finally, we emphasize that the renormalized string mass per unit length is defined at a renormalization scale ℓ that need not be fixed but can be time dependent (e.g., the correlation length). In fact, the choice of scale is equivalent to altering what defines a wiggle, and consequently, must have a direct influence on the energy distribution between the bare string and the wiggles. One accounts for this by introducing the following scale-drift terms

$$\frac{1}{\mu}\frac{\partial \mu}{\partial \ell}\frac{d\ell}{dt} \sim \frac{d_m - 1}{l}\frac{d\ell}{dt}, \qquad (19)$$

$$\frac{\partial v^2}{\partial \ell}\frac{d\ell}{dt} = \frac{1-v^2}{1+\langle w^2 \rangle}\frac{\partial \langle w^2 \rangle}{\partial \ell}\frac{d\ell}{dt}, \qquad (20)$$

where $d_m(\ell)$ is the multifractal dimension of a string segment at scale ℓ. It should be emphasized that while (19) is a mere geometric identity, (20) is a consequence of ensuring energy conservation at all scales. We will also assume the following phenomenological relation

$$d_m(\mu) = 2 - \frac{1}{\mu^b}, \qquad (21)$$

where b is a free parameter that imposes the transition limit between two regimes ($d_m = 2$ for Brownian networks, $d_m = 1$ for small scales).

We are now ready to derive the system of equations that compose the wiggly model[11,12]

$$2\frac{dL}{dt} = HL\left[3 + v^2 - \frac{(1-v^2)}{\mu^2}\right] + \frac{cfv}{\sqrt{\mu}} \qquad (22)$$

$$2\frac{d\xi}{dt} = H\xi\left[2 + \left(1 + \frac{1}{\mu^2}\right)v^2\right] + v\left[k\left(1 - \frac{1}{\mu^2}\right) + c(f_o + s)\right] + [d_m(\ell) - 1]\frac{\xi}{\ell}\frac{d\ell}{dt} \qquad (23)$$

$$\frac{dv}{dt} = (1-v^2)\left[\frac{k}{\xi\mu^2} - Hv\left(1 + \frac{1}{\mu^2}\right) - \frac{1}{1+\mu^2}\frac{[d_m(\ell) - 1]}{v\ell}\frac{d\ell}{dt}\right] \qquad (24)$$

$$\frac{1}{\mu}\frac{d\mu}{dt} = \frac{v}{\xi}\left[k\left(1 - \frac{1}{\mu^2}\right) - c(f - f_o - s)\right] - H\left(1 - \frac{1}{\mu^2}\right) + \frac{[d_m(\ell) - 1]}{\ell}\frac{d\ell}{dt}, \qquad (25)$$

where $H \equiv \dot{a}/a$ is the Hubble parameter (which we will assume to be of the form $a \propto t^\lambda$) and k the momentum parameter already introduced in the VOS formalism. k essentially quantifies the local curvature of strings. It should be noted that equations (22), (23) and (25) are not independent, being related by Eq. (8).

3. Scaling Solutions

We carry out a mathematical exploration of the landscape of scaling solutions of the wiggly model, so as to characterize the behavior of the wiggliness of the network. One important yet unanswered question in the wiggly model is whether the wiggliness is able to scale, i.e, evolve towards a constant value, and if so, what are the underlying physical conditions of the network that lead to this behavior. In spite of current numerical simulations not giving a definitive answer to this question,[6] they hint at scaling being reached in the matter-dominated era ($\lambda = 2/3$), with the behavior in the radiation era being more complex. This may be indicative of an absence of a scaling solution or of a slower scaling regime (since there is less Hubble damping).

As shown by the system of equations (22)–(25), the evolution of the network is driven by three main mechanisms: the universe's expansion, energy loss by intercommutation, and the choice of the scale in which wiggles are coarse-grained. In what follows, we study the effects of each of them on the possible asymptotic scaling solutions by considering the case where each mechanism dominates and by doing a subsequent comparison of the obtained scaling solutions in each case. This allows us to gain insight into the role that each mechanism has on the evolution of the network.

From a physical point of view, we expect three types of scaling solution regimes. Firstly, we evidently expect the Nambu-Goto solution $\mu = 1$, as the wiggly model reduces to the VOS in the appropriate limit. Secondly, we also expect a regime where the wiggliness scales, $\mu = m_o$. Finally, a regime where small-scale structure grows $\mu \propto t^\gamma$ as the network evolves is also expected. In general we will assume

$$L = L_o t^\alpha$$
$$v = v_o t^\beta \qquad (26)$$
$$\mu = m_o t^\gamma,$$

or alternatively, using Eq. (8):

$$\xi = L_o m_o^{1/2} t^{\alpha + \gamma/2}. \qquad (27)$$

It should also be noted that we will discard ultra-relativistic $v = 1$ solutions in our analysis, as well as other branches of solutions that are mathematically allowed but have no physical meaning. This includes solutions in Minkowski space $H = 0$ (expanding universes $H \neq 0$) that hold for non-null values of the momentum parameter $k \neq 0$ (null values of momentum parameter $k = 0$). The reason behind this is we expect the VOS to hold for $k = 0$ in Minkowski space,[6,7,14,17] and in an analogous manner, we expect $k \neq 0$ when $H \neq 0$.[6]

3.1. *Scaling Solutions Without Expansion*

First, we consider the allowed scaling solutions in Minkowski space. We note that linear scaling has been observed in numerical simulations in Minkowski space.[6,18] We also note that a more detailed analysis of some of these solutions has already been published in Ref. 13.

3.1.1. *No dynamical mechanism*

We start by considering the simplest case where no dynamical mechanisms act on the network. In this case we find a trivial solution that depicts a network where all four dynamical quantities remain constant but undetermined

$$\begin{aligned} L &= L_o \\ v &= v_o \\ \mu &= m_o \\ \xi &= \sqrt{m_o} L_o. \end{aligned} \quad (28)$$

The values of these quantities could be determined by measurement in numerical simulations. The physical interpretation of this solution is clear: the network is in equilibrium due to the absence of energy loss mechanisms, and thus its dynamical quantities have no time evolution.

3.1.2. *With running averaging scale*

In this case we assume the fractal dimension introduced in Eq. (21) with the specific choice $b = 2$, as numerical simulations suggest this value is reasonable.[6] We also assume a generic power-law shaped averaging scale

$$l = l_o t^\delta, \quad 0 < \delta \leq 1. \quad (29)$$

In the absence of energy loss mechanisms, we expect that the characteristic length scale of the network remains constant. We find two distinct scaling solutions, the first being the Nambu-Goto limit

$$\begin{aligned} L &= L_o \\ v &= v_o \\ \mu &= 1 \\ \xi &= L_o, \end{aligned} \quad (30)$$

which is analogous to that of Eq. (28), with the difference that μ is no longer arbitrary but restricted to the Nambu-Goto value. This solution gives a clear depiction of how, when there is no small-scale structure, a variation in the coarse-graining scale makes no difference. In other words, this solution exists for any value of δ and has no explicit dependence on its choice.

The second solution yields growing wiggliness

$$\begin{aligned} L &= L_o \\ v &= v_o t^{-\delta} \\ \mu &= m_o t^\delta \\ \xi &= \sqrt{m_o} L_o t^{\delta/2}, \end{aligned} \quad (31)$$

subject to the following constraint:

$$v_o^2 m_o^2 = 1. \quad (32)$$

We note that in the fixed scale limit $\delta \longrightarrow 0$ we recover the scaling exponents of Eq. (29). In addition, note that choosing our renormalization scale to be the correlation length $l \propto \xi$, yields $\delta = \delta/2 = 0$, implying $\gamma = 0$, or in other words, the only possible solution in this case is the Nambu-Goto one. The physical interpretation of this solution is clear. The presence of small-scale structure made this solution explicitly dependent on δ. In particular, we are always able to find small-scale structure for all choices of scale, and a variation in the scale simply modifies the way energy migrates from the bare string to the wiggles, with the total energy of the network staying constant. Moreover, the growth of the wiggliness is compensated by a decrease in the velocity, which suggests that not only is μ scale-dependent, but v also depends on δ. This agrees with the mesoscopic velocity interpretation of the wiggly model, instead of the traditional interpretation of a microscopic RMS one embodied in the VOS.[11,12]

3.1.3. *With energy losses*

We now consider the case where the network is losing energy due the various energy loss mechanisms inherent to the network, as previously described. In particular, we assume the energy loss terms are modeled after Eq. (18). It is clear that the presence of energy losses must lead to a different behavior for the network's characteristic length scales L and ξ, as they are now forced to scale in time. We find two solution regimes. The first solution implies non-trivial wiggliness:

$$\begin{aligned} L &= L_o t \\ v &= v_o \\ \mu &= m_o \\ \xi &= \sqrt{m_o} L_o t, \end{aligned} \tag{33}$$

such that

$$L_o = \frac{c v_o}{2} \frac{(1+\eta) m_o^{1/2} - \eta}{m_o} \tag{34}$$

$$D\left(1 - \frac{1}{m_o^2}\right) = \eta\left(1 - \frac{1}{m_o^{1/2}}\right), \quad \eta \geq D. \tag{35}$$

This allows for a wide range of values of the wiggliness m_o, depending on the values of the small-scale structure parameters D and η. In particular, one retrieves the Nambu-Goto case $m_o = 1$ under the condition $D = \eta$. For realistic values of D and η, Eq. (35) has two real solutions and a pair of complex conjugate solutions. Having in mind that realistic values of the wiggliness imply $m_o \geq 1$, it follows that for values of the parameters such that $D/\eta < 1/4$ the only physically meaningful solution consists of $m_o = 1$, while in the range $D/\eta \in \,]1/4, 1[$, we find solutions with $m_o > 1$. From a physical point of view, this should be interpreted as: if the amount of wiggliness generated by the network is a small fraction of the amount that is lost, as in the case of $D/\eta < 1/4$, then no wiggliness can asymptotically survive on the string network, resulting in the Nambu-Goto solution. On the other hand, if this ratio takes up large enough values, then the small-scale structure of the network is able to survive.

In the second regime, we find a solution where small-scale structure builds-up in the network:

$$\begin{aligned} L &= L_o t^\alpha \\ v &= v_o \\ \mu &= m_o t^{2-2\alpha} \\ \xi &= \sqrt{m_o} L_o t \end{aligned} \qquad (36)$$

with the following constraints and conditions

$$L_o = \frac{cv_o}{2\alpha} \frac{1+\eta}{m_o^{1/2}} \qquad (37)$$

$$\alpha = \frac{1+\eta}{1+D} < 1 \qquad (38)$$

$$\gamma = 2\frac{D-\eta}{1+D}, \quad D > \eta, \qquad (39)$$

which yields Eq. (33) in the limit where the two small-scale structure parameters balance each other $D \longrightarrow \eta$.

The set of solutions (33) (36) allows us to infer the exact physical conditions that dictate the nature of the scaling regime. As seen in Eq. (33), when the amount of small-scale structure removed (e.g., loop production) is greater than its gain (e.g., kink formation upon intercommutation), $\eta > D$, the wiggliness of the network remains constant. On the other hand, as illustrated by Eq. (36), when there is more generation of small-scale structure on the network than loss, $D > \eta$, we find that the long string wiggliness must grow. Moreover, another interesting difference between these two solutions lies in the behavior of μ and L (or equivalently, the total energy density of the network), with ξ scaling linearly ($\xi \propto t$) in both solutions. The fact that ξ maintains its linear scaling independently of the scaling of L just further emphasizes the two scale feature of the wiggly VOS extension.

3.1.4. *With energy losses and a running averaging scale*

If one allows for both energy losses and a varying renormalization scale $\delta \neq 0$, one finds two possible solutions. The first yields constant wiggliness such that:

$$\begin{aligned} L &= \frac{c(1+\eta)v_o}{2} t \\ v &= v_o \\ \mu &= 1 \\ \xi &= L, \end{aligned} \qquad (40)$$

which is analogous to that of Eq.(33) with the caveat that m_o is no longer arbitrary but restricted to the Nambu-Goto case. This solution depicts, yet again, that if the network is devoid of small-scale structure a change in the coarse-graining scale makes no difference.

In the second solution, we find that the small-scale structure of the network grows as the network evolves

$$\begin{aligned} L &= L_o t^\alpha \\ v &= v_o t^{-\gamma} \\ \mu &= m_o t^\gamma \\ \xi &= \sqrt{m_o} L_o t^{\frac{1}{3}+\frac{2}{3}\alpha}, \end{aligned} \quad (41)$$

subject to

$$L_o = \frac{c(1+\eta)v_o}{2\alpha m_o^{1/2}} \quad (42)$$

$$\alpha = \frac{(\frac{2}{3}-\delta)(1+\eta)}{\frac{2}{3}(1+\eta)+2(D-\eta)} < 1, \quad D > \eta \quad (43)$$

$$\gamma = \frac{2}{3} - \frac{2}{3}\alpha = \frac{2(D-\eta)+\delta(1+\eta)}{3(D-\eta)+(1+\eta)} \quad (44)$$

$$\delta = \gamma v_o^2 m_o^2 \in \left]0, \frac{2}{3}\right[\quad (45)$$

Note that if we consider the fixed scale limit $\delta \longrightarrow 0$, we recover Eq. (36) $\gamma \longrightarrow 0$, $\alpha \longrightarrow 1$. We can also take the limit of no energy losses $D, \eta \longrightarrow 0$ on (41) where we partially recover the previous solution of Eq. (31), namely the dynamics for the velocity and wiggliness $\gamma = -\beta = \delta$, but with different behavior of both length scales. Unlike the other solutions so far, δ is restricted because Eq. (45) must always hold. Specifically, the averaging scale is now bounded from above, which can be attributed to the energy losses of the network. In other words, if the scale does not evolve slowly enough, we are unable to find small-scale structure. Furthermore, we note that the total energy of the network, more specifically the exponent α, explicitly depends on δ, hinting at an apparent scale dependence of the total energy of the network. However, one would expect this quantity to be scale-invariant, that is, the way the network loses energy should not depend on the choice of averaging scale choice. Having said this, it is clear that the physics behind this behavior needs to be explored in future studies.

3.2. Scaling Solutions With Expansion

We are now concerned with solutions in expanding universes, where we expect $k \neq 0$.[6]

3.2.1. *No dynamical mechanisms*

We start with the case of no energy losses and a fixed scale. In this case, we find the three expansion regimes. Firstly, we find the canonical Nambu-Goto VOS solution

$$L = \left(\frac{k^2}{4\lambda(1-\lambda)}\right)^{1/2} t$$
$$v = \left(\frac{1-\lambda}{\lambda}\right)^{1/2} \tag{46}$$
$$\mu = 1$$
$$\xi = \left(\frac{k^2}{4\lambda(1-\lambda)}\right)^{1/2} t.$$

The range of expansion rates of this solution depends on the physical interpretation of the velocity. Interpreted as a microscopic velocity, we require $v_o^2 < 1$ and we find that the radiation epoch is the limiting case $\lambda > 1/2$. This implies that scaling can be achieved in the matter-dominated era, but not in the radiation epoch, since in the latter the network does not lose enough energy by Hubble damping. Alternatively, one can also interpret this velocity as an average one, with now the physical constraint being $v_o^2 \leq 1/2$ (corresponding to the average velocity of loops in Minkowski space), leading to the matter era becoming the limiting case $\lambda \geq 2/3$.

Secondly, we find a solution of non-trivial constant wiggliness, only viable in the matter era

$$L = L_o t$$
$$v = v_o$$
$$\mu = m_o \tag{47}$$
$$\xi = \sqrt{m_o} L$$
$$\lambda = \frac{2}{3}$$

$$L_o = \frac{3k}{2(m_o^3 + m_o)^{1/2}}, \quad v_o = \frac{1}{(1+m_o^2)^{1/2}}, \tag{48}$$

which in principle holds for any value of the wiggliness m_o. We note that by choosing $m_o = 1$, we retrieve the previous solution (46). This solution also demonstrates that scaling is more easily reached in the matter era than in the radiation era, in agreement with Nambu-Goto numerical simulations.[6] In addition, the behavior depicted by this solution is analogous to the one previously identified for chiral superconducting strings.[19]

Thirdly, a regime of growing wiggliness is also allowed, which implies decreasing velocities $\beta < 0$, and $\alpha = 3/2\lambda$, as well as the consistency relations $3/2\lambda + \gamma/2 - \beta = 1$, and $\beta + \gamma \geq 0$. This narrows the range of allowed expansion rates to slower rates than the matter era one $\lambda < 2/3$. There are two solution regimes, depending on the value of the expansion rate. For very slow expansion rates we have

$$\begin{aligned} L &= L_o t^{3/2\lambda} \\ v &= v_o t^{-\lambda} \\ \mu &= m_o t^{2-5\lambda} \\ \xi &= \frac{v_o k}{2 - 4\lambda} t^{1-\lambda}, \end{aligned} \tag{49}$$

subject to the following constraints:

$$m_o = \left(\frac{v_o k}{L_o (2 - 4\lambda)}\right)^2 \tag{50}$$

$$\lambda \leq \frac{1}{3}. \tag{51}$$

Conversely, in the intermediate expansion rate regime, we find

$$\begin{aligned} L &= L_o t^{3/2\lambda} \\ v &= v_o t^{-\gamma} \\ \mu &= m_o t^{\gamma} \\ \xi &= \sqrt{m_o} L_o t^{\lambda + \frac{1}{3}} \\ \gamma &= \frac{2}{3} - \lambda, \end{aligned} \tag{52}$$

with the following constraints:

$$v_o = \frac{2}{3} \left(\frac{L_o}{(\frac{4}{3}\lambda - \frac{4}{9})^{1/4} k}\right)^{2/3}, \quad m_o = \left(\frac{k}{(\frac{4}{3}\lambda - \frac{4}{9})^{1/2} L_o}\right)^{2/3} \tag{53}$$

$$\lambda \in \left]\frac{1}{3}, \frac{2}{3}\right[. \tag{54}$$

We note that in the limit $\lambda \longrightarrow 1/3$ this solution matches the scaling solution obtained in the slow regime. In addition, we also recover the full scaling solution (47) in the limit $\lambda \longrightarrow 2/3$, apart from differences in the coefficients for the velocity.

It is instructive to consider the particular case of the radiation epoch ($\lambda = 1/2$), where we find

$$L \propto t^{3/4}, \quad v \propto t^{-1/6} \quad \mu \propto t^{1/6} \quad \xi \propto \sqrt{m_o} L_o t^{5/6}, \tag{55}$$

These relations provide an opportunity for testing with Nambu-Goto simulations where energy loss terms can be switched off on demand.

3.2.2. *With a running averaging scale*

We consider the averaging scale previously introduced in Eq. (29). In this case we still find the Nambu-Goto solution

$$
\begin{aligned}
L &= L_o t \\
v &= v_o \\
\mu &= 1 \\
\xi &= \sqrt{m_o} L_o t \\
\lambda &> \frac{1}{2},
\end{aligned}
\tag{56}
$$

$$
L_o = \left(\frac{k^2}{4\lambda(1-\lambda)}\right)^{1/2}, \quad v = \left(\frac{1-\lambda}{\lambda}\right)^{1/2}. \tag{57}
$$

We observe that the introduction of a running averaging scale neither affected the scaling behavior of the previous obtained solution (46) nor did it impose any restriction on δ.

We also find a full scaling solution

$$
\begin{aligned}
L &= L_o t \\
v &= v_o \\
\mu &= m_o \\
\xi &= \sqrt{m_o} L_o t \\
\lambda &< \frac{2}{3}
\end{aligned}
\tag{58}
$$

$$
v_o = \left(\frac{1 + m_o^2(2\lambda^{-1} - 3)}{1 + m_o^2}\right)^{1/2} \tag{59}
$$

$$
\delta = \left(1 - \frac{3}{2}\lambda\right) m_o^2(1 + m_o^2). \tag{60}
$$

This solution demonstrates how the inclusion of a renormalization scale decreased the value of the expansion rate for which full scaling can occur: this is now achieved for expansion rates lower than the matter era one.

Lastly, we find two possible solutions with growing wiggliness, which entail the same dynamics for the characteristic length scale and velocity as found for the expansion case, namely $\alpha = 3\lambda/2$, $\beta < 0$, $3/2\lambda + \gamma/2 - \beta = 1$, and $\beta + \gamma \geq 0$. For very slow expansion rates we have

$$
\begin{aligned}
L &= L_o t^{3/2\lambda} \\
v &= v_o t^{-\lambda} \\
\mu &= m_o t^{2-5\lambda} \\
\xi &= \sqrt{m_o} L_o t^{1-\lambda} \\
\lambda &\leq \frac{1}{3},
\end{aligned}
\tag{61}
$$

where the scaling coefficients are related by:

$$m_o = \left(\frac{kv_o}{L_o(2-4\lambda+\delta)}\right)^2, \qquad (62)$$

while in the intermediate expansion regime we determine:

$$\begin{aligned} L &= L_o t^{3/2\lambda} \\ v &= v_o t^{-\gamma} \\ \mu &= m_o t^\gamma \\ \xi &= \sqrt{m_o} L_o t^{1/3+\lambda} \\ \frac{1}{3} &< \lambda < \frac{2}{3}, \end{aligned} \qquad (63)$$

such that

$$v_o = \left(\frac{1}{(3\lambda-1)m_o^2}\right)^{1/2}, \quad m_o = \left(\frac{kv_o}{L_o(\frac{2}{3}+\delta)}\right)^2 \qquad (64)$$

$$\gamma = \frac{2}{3} - \lambda. \qquad (65)$$

Note that the two regimes match for an expansion rate $\lambda = \frac{1}{3}$.

3.2.3. *With energy losses*

We finally consider the most realistic case, where the network is losing energy in the context of an expanding universe. Firstly, we recover the canonical VOS Nambu-Goto solution

$$\begin{aligned} L &= L_o t \\ v &= v_o \\ \mu &= 1 \\ \xi &= L_o t, \end{aligned} \qquad (66)$$

$$L_o = \left(\frac{k(k+c)}{4\lambda(1-\lambda)}\right)^{1/2}, \quad v = \left(\frac{k(1-\lambda)}{\lambda(k+c)}\right)^{1/2}. \qquad (67)$$

We note that Eq. (46) is a particular case of Eq. (66) for which $c = 0$, which can be physically interpreted as the network's intrinsic energy losses being unnecessary for the network to reach linear scaling because Hubble damping is enough to ensure this.

Secondly, there is also a non-trivial wiggliness solution

$$\begin{aligned} L &= L_o t \\ v &= v_o \\ \mu &= m_o \\ \xi &= \frac{k}{\lambda v_o(1+m_o^2)} t, \end{aligned} \qquad (68)$$

subject to the following constraints:

$$L_o^2 = \frac{k}{\lambda} \frac{k + c(1+\eta)m_o^2 - c\eta m_o^{3/2}}{m_o(1+m_o^2)(\lambda + (2-3\lambda)m_o^2)} \tag{69}$$

$$v_o^2 = \frac{k}{\lambda} \frac{\lambda + (2-3\lambda)m_o^2}{(1+m_o^2)(k + c(1+\eta)m_o^2 - c\eta m_o^{3/2})} \tag{70}$$

$$\left(\lambda + m_o^2(2-3\lambda)\right)\left((k+cD)\left(1 - \frac{1}{m_o^2}\right) - c\eta\left(1 - \frac{1}{m_o^{1/2}}\right)\right)$$
$$= \lambda\left(1 - \frac{1}{m_o^2}\right)\left(k + (1+\eta - \eta m_o^{-1/2})m_o^2 c\right). \tag{71}$$

We note that the previous solution (47) is recovered by direct substitution of $\lambda = 2/3$, and $c = 0$ on this solution. So as to understand more about its physical implications, we consider the case study of large amounts of wiggliness. Before proceeding to this analysis, we define new parameters

$$k_{eff} \equiv k + c(D - \eta)$$
$$c_{eff} \equiv c(1 + \eta). \tag{72}$$

This is not only convenient, but also makes sense from a physical point of view: it is known that the presence of small-scale structure on the long strings modifies its typical curvature, as well as enhances energy losses.[12] The large wiggliness limit $m_o \gg 1$ yields:

$$L_o = \left(\frac{kc_{eff}}{\lambda m_o^3(2 - 3\lambda)}\right)^{1/2}$$
$$v_o = \left(\frac{k(2 - 3\lambda)}{c\lambda m_o^2(1+\eta)}\right)^{1/2} \tag{73}$$
$$\lambda = \frac{2k_{eff}}{c_{eff} + 3k_{eff}}.$$

This solution clearly illustrates that when there are great amounts of wiggliness on the network, the overall energy density increases while the velocity decreases, as expected. In addition, it is interesting to note that in the radiation era, the effective parameters balance one another

$$k_{eff} = c_{eff}. \tag{74}$$

This relation constitutes an opportunity for testing with Nambu-Goto numerical simulations.

Thirdly, there also exists a growing wiggliness regime. This has the same implications as found for the expanding case, namely a decreasing velocity $\beta < 0$, although $\alpha = 3\lambda/2$ no longer holds, and instead we have $\alpha > 3\lambda/2$. Physically, this makes sense as the energy loss terms enable faster energy loss. We again distinguish two regimes according to their expansion rates. For slow expansion rates,

$$L = L_o t^\alpha$$
$$v = v_o t^{-\lambda}$$
$$\mu = m_o t^\gamma \quad (75)$$
$$\xi = \sqrt{m_o} L_o t^{1-\lambda},$$

$$\alpha = \frac{1}{2} \frac{2c_{eff} + \lambda(3k_{eff} - c_{eff})}{k_{eff} + c_{eff}} \quad (76)$$

$$\gamma = 2(1 - \lambda - \alpha) = \frac{2k_{eff} - \lambda(c_{eff} + 5k_{eff})}{k_{eff} + c_{eff}} \quad (77)$$

$$\gamma \in]0, 2 - 5\lambda[\quad (78)$$

$$\lambda \leq \frac{k_{eff}}{3k_{eff} + c_{eff}}. \quad (79)$$

It is worthy of note that one recovers the previous slow expansion solution (49) in the limit $c \longrightarrow 0$.

As far as the intermediate expansion rate regime is concerned, we find

$$L = L_o t^\alpha$$
$$v = v_o t^{-\gamma}$$
$$\mu = m_o t^\gamma \quad (80)$$
$$\xi = \sqrt{m_o} L_o t^{\frac{1}{3} + \frac{2}{3}\alpha}$$

$$L_o^2 = \frac{kc_{eff}}{(2\alpha - 3\lambda)(\lambda + \frac{2}{3}\alpha - \frac{2}{3})m_o^3} \quad (81)$$

$$v_o^2 = \frac{k(2\alpha - 3\lambda)}{c_{eff}(\lambda + \frac{2}{3}\alpha - \frac{2}{3})m_o^2} \quad (82)$$

$$\alpha = \frac{\frac{2}{3}c_{eff} + \lambda(3k_{eff} + c_{eff})}{\frac{2}{3}c_{eff} + 2k_{eff}} \quad (83)$$

$$\gamma = \frac{2}{3} - \frac{2}{3}\alpha = \frac{2k_{eff} - \lambda(3k_{eff} + c_{eff})}{c_{eff} + 3k_{eff}} \quad (84)$$

$$\lambda \in \left] \frac{k_{eff}}{3k_{eff} + c_{eff}}, \frac{2k_{eff}}{3k_{eff} + c_{eff}} \right[, \quad (85)$$

where one is also able to retrieve the previous solution Eq. (52) in the limit $c \longrightarrow 0$. It should be emphasized that the domain of the expansion rate is now broader, when in comparison to Eq. (52), which is due to the two energy loss mechanisms acting on the network (not just Hubble damping).

Note that the two regimes match for the expansion rate

$$\lambda = \frac{k_{eff}}{3k_{eff} + c_{eff}}, \qquad (86)$$

which is half of the expansion rate of Eq. (73). We also note that in the no energy losses limit $c \longrightarrow 0$, the expansion rate approaches $\lambda = 1/3$.

Finally, it is also instructive to consider a particular case study where the two effective parameter balance each other $k_{eff} = c_{eff}$ which yields in the slow regime

$$\alpha_{slow} = \frac{1+\lambda}{2}, \quad \gamma_{slow} = 1 - 3\lambda, \quad \lambda \leq \frac{1}{4}, \qquad (87)$$

while in the intermediate regime we find:

$$\alpha_{int} = \frac{1}{4} + \frac{3}{2}\lambda, \quad \gamma_{int} = \frac{1}{2} - \lambda, \quad \lambda \in \left]\frac{1}{4}, \frac{1}{2}\right[. \qquad (88)$$

This solution leads to full scaling in the radiation epoch and growing wiggliness regimes for slower expansion rates than the radiation one. The transition between slow and intermediate regimes takes place at $\lambda = 1/4$.

4. Conclusions and Further Work

We have improved the physical interpretation of the wiggly generalization of the VOS model,[11,12] building upon a mathematical exploration of the landscape of possible scaling solutions. Not only did we successfully characterize the behavior of the wiggliness in various regimes, but we also have managed to determine the effect that each dynamical mechanism has on the scaling solutions.

In Minkowski space, we find that the network is in a trivial equilibrium solution in the absence of energy loss mechanisms. Allowing the network to lose energy, we find that the network's correlation length always maintains its linear scaling, while the behavior of the characteristic length scale depends on the dynamics of the wiggliness. If the wiggliness is constant, L scales linearly, while if the wiggliness grows in time, L exhibits slower growth specified by the energy loss parameters. These results agree with linear scaling observed in Minkowski space simulations.[6,18] Moreover, the inclusion of a renormalization scale led to a possible regime where small-scale structure grows in time, but is compensated by a decreasing velocity, with the network's total energy density remaining constant and the domain of the scale remaining unrestricted due to energy conservation. Lastly, when the network is subject to both mechanisms, we determined that the averaging scale becomes bounded from above, as a consequence of the network losing energy.

In power-law expanding universes, we determined that the three scaling regimes were possible, primarily depending on the expansion rate. For slow and intermediate expansion rates one has growing wiggliness solutions, while in fast expansion regimes one has the Nambu-Goto regime. For a specific value of expansion rate, one finds a full scaling solution. In the absence of energy losses, this expansion rate coincides with the matter era one, whereas the inclusion of energy loss mechanisms decreases this value, possibly reaching the radiation era for an appropriate value of the energy losses. Our results also demonstrate that scaling is more easily achieved in the matter era rather than the radiation epoch, in agreement with numerical simulations[6,16,15]. It is also interesting to note that the three scaling behaviors here determined have also been found for the case of chiral superconducting strings[19] and other current-carrying strings.[20] The case where all three mechanisms act on the network was not included in this work for reasons of space. Lastly, one aspect that remains unclear and should be subject to future studies, is the role of the coarse-graining scale, and in particular, the apparent scale dependence of the total energy of the network.

These analytic results pave the way for a future calibration of the wiggly model. While our results show qualitative agreement with previous Nambu-Goto numerical simulations, the current available data does not allow for a detailed comparison. Our work therefore motivates additional, higher resolution simulations that cover a broad range of expansion rates and that are able to extract accurate numerical diagnostics for the wiggliness.

Acknowledgements

This work was financed by FEDER—Fundo Europeu de Desenvolvimento Regional funds through the COM-PETE 2020—Operational Programme for Competitiveness and Internationalisation (POCI), and by Portuguese funds through FCT - Fundação para a Ciência e a Tecnologia in the framework of the project POCI-01-0145-FEDER-028987 and PTDC/FIS-AST/28987/2017.

References

1. T. W. Kibble, Topology of cosmic domains and strings, *Journal of Physics A: Mathematical and General* **9**, p. 1387 (1976).
2. A. Vilenkin and E. P. S. Shellard, *Cosmic Strings and other Topological Defects* (Cambridge University Press, Cambridge, U.K., 1994).
3. C. J. A. P. Martins and E. P. S. Shellard, Quantitative string evolution, *Phys. Rev. D* **54**, 2535 (1996).
4. C. J. A. P. Martins and E. P. S. Shellard, Scale-invariant string evolution with friction, *Phys. Rev. D* **53**, R575 (Jan 1996).
5. J. N. Moore, E. P. S. Shellard and C. J. A. P. Martins, Evolution of abelian-higgs string networks, *Physical Review D* **65**, p. 023503 (2001).
6. C. J. A. P. Martins and E. P. S. Shellard, Fractal properties and small-scale structure of cosmic string networks, *Physical Review D* **73**, p. 043515 (2006).

7. J. R. C. C. C. Correia and C. J. A. P. Martins, Extending and Calibrating the Velocity dependent One-Scale model for Cosmic Strings with One Thousand Field Theory Simulations, *Phys. Rev. D* **100**, p. 103517 (2019).
8. J. R. C. C. C. Correia and C. J. A. P. Martins, Quantifying the effect of cooled initial conditions on cosmic string network evolution, *Phys. Rev. D* **102**, p. 043503 (2020).
9. T. W. B. Kibble, Evolution of a system of cosmic strings, *Nuclear Physics B* **252**, 227 (1985).
10. D. Austin, E. J. Copeland and T. W. B. Kibble, Evolution of cosmic string configurations, *Physical Review D* **48**, p. 5594 (1993).
11. C. J. A. P. Martins, E. P. S. Shellard and J. P. P. Vieira, Models for small-scale structure of cosmic strings: Mathematical formalism, *Phys. Rev. D* **90**, p. 043518 (Aug 2014).
12. J. P. P. Vieira, C. J. A. P. Martins and E. P. S. Shellard, Models for small-scale structure on cosmic strings. II. Scaling and its stability, *Phys. Rev. D* **94**, p. 096005 (2016), [Erratum: Phys.Rev.D 94, 099907 (2016)].
13. A. R. R. Almeida and C. J. A. P. Martins, Scaling solutions of wiggly cosmic strings, *Phys. Rev. D* **104**, p. 043524 (2021).
14. C. J. A. P. Martins, *Defect evolution in cosmology and condensed matter: Quantitative analysis with the velocity-dependent one-scale model* (Springer, 2016).
15. B. Allen and E. P. S. Shellard, Cosmic-string evolution: A numerical simulation, *Physical review letters* **64**, p. 119 (1990).
16. D. P. Bennett and F. R. Bouchet, High-resolution simulations of cosmic-string evolution. i. network evolution, *Physical Review D* **41**, p. 2408 (1990).
17. C. J. A. P. Martins, J. N. Moore and E. P. S. Shellard, Unified model for vortex-string network evolution, *Physical review letters* **92**, p. 251601 (2004).
18. M. Sakellariadou and A. Vilenkin, Cosmic-string evolution in flat spacetime, *Physical Review D* **42**, p. 349 (1990).
19. M. F. Oliveira, A. Avgoustidis and C. J. A. P. Martins, Cosmic string evolution with a conserved charge, *Physical Review D* **85**, p. 083515 (2012).
20. C. J. A. P. Martins, P. Peter, I. Y. Rybak and E. P. S. Shellard, Charge-velocity-dependent one-scale linear model, arXiv:2108.03147 (2021).

High resolution calibration of string network evolution

J. R. C. C. C. Correia

Centro de Astrofísica da Universidade do Porto, and
Instituto de Astrofísica e Ciências do Espaço, Universidade do Porto,
Rua das Estrelas, 4150-762 Porto, Portugal, and
Faculdade de Ciências da Universidade do Porto
Rua do Campo Alegre 687, 4169-007 Porto, Portugal
E-mail: jose.correia@astro.up.pt

C. J. A. P. Martins

Centro de Astrofísica da Universidade do Porto, and
Instituto de Astrofísica e Ciências do Espaço, Universidade do Porto,
Rua das Estrelas, 4150-762 Porto, Portugal
E-mail: Carlos.Martins@astro.up.pt

The canonical velocity-dependent one-scale (VOS) model for cosmic string evolution contains a number of free parameters which cannot be obtained ab initio. Therefore it must be calibrated using high resolution numerical simulations. We exploit our state of the art graphically accelerated implementation of the evolution of local Abelian-Higgs string networks to provide a statistically robust calibration of this model. In order to do so, we will make use of the largest set of high resolution simulations carried out to date, for a variety of cosmological expansion rates, and explore the impact of key numerical choices on model calibration, including the dynamic range, lattice spacing, and the choice of numerical estimators for the mean string velocity. This sensitivity exploration shows that certain numerical choices will indeed have consequences for observationally crucial parameters, such as the loop chopping parameter. To conclude, we will also briefly illustrate how our results impact observational constraints on cosmic strings.

Keywords: Cosmic strings; Velocity-dependent One-Scale model; Abelian-Higgs string simulations; Observational consequences

1. Introduction

Topological defects are expected consequences of phase transitions in the early Universe, formed via means of the Kibble mechanism.[1] Depending on the symmetry broken different defects, with different dimension, can appear. The most studied defects are the filament-like cosmic strings. These are generically predicted in many candidates of Grand Unified Theories[2] and superstring theory,[3] and are cosmologically safe, in the sense that they are not expected to overclose the Universe.

Due to their ubiquitous nature they have become a primary target for observational facilities, both current[4,5] and forthcoming.[6,7] Analytical and observational studies of defect networks (strings included) often rely on a combination of semi-analytical modelling and simulations.

Here we present an up-to-date model calibration using high-resolution simulations, that ran in one of Europe's largest supercomputers, Piz Daint, using up to

4096 GPUs. In order to ensure robustness, we will also explore how sensitive the model calibration is to certain numerical choices. We will also discuss our recently developed visualization strategy and avenues it might open in the study of defects. Some of this work has been published in Ref. 8.

2. Simulation Setup

We begin with a brief description of our simulations. Take a Lagrangian density which, while originally invariant under $U(1)_L$ transformations, is already in the broken symmetry phase,

$$\mathcal{L} = |D_\mu \phi|^2 - \frac{\lambda}{4}(|\phi|^2 - 1)^2 - \frac{1}{4e^2} F^{\mu\nu} F_{\mu\nu}, \tag{1}$$

where ϕ is a complex scalar field, $D_\mu \phi = \partial \phi - ieA_\mu$ are the covariant derivatives, A_μ is a gauge field, $F_{\mu\nu} = \partial_\mu A_\nu - \partial_\nu A_\mu$ is a gauge field strength and the scalar and gauge couplings are λ and e, respectively. The defect network that will form corresponds to homotopically stable solutions of the equations of motion of this Lagrangian. In fact a cosmic a string is the result of a specific solution of the equations of motion, which maps ϕ to the symmetry breaking scale (here set to u; minima of potential) infinitely away from the string, and to zero at its core (maxima of potential). The equations of motion in Friedmann-Lemaitre-Robertson-Walker Universes and under the assumption of the temporal gauge ($A_0 = 0$) are

$$\ddot{\phi} + 2\frac{\dot{a}}{a}\dot{\phi} = D^j D_j \phi - \frac{a^2 \lambda}{2}(|\phi|^2 - 1)\phi \tag{2}$$

$$\dot{F}_{0j} = \partial_j F_{ij} - 2a^2 e^2 Im[\phi^* D_j \phi]. \tag{3}$$

Abelian-Higgs field theory simulations of cosmic strings[9,10] merely use the discretization procedure of lattice gauge theory[8]—which places scalar fields on lattice points distanced by $\Delta = 0.5$, and gauge fields on lattice links—to provide a discretized set of equations to update fields every conformal timestep. Due to the existence of Hubble damping and due to the topological nature of the potential, the initial conditions eventually relax into a configuration with multiple string networks. For simplicity, and to mimic what the fields are post-phase-transition, the initial conditions are set as follows: null on every field, except ϕ which is set to have a random phase and unit magnitude.

We will additionally set scalar and gauge couplings to $\lambda = 2$ and $e = 1$, respectively, which sets the Bogmolnyi ratio to $\frac{\lambda}{2e^2} = 1$ (a usual choice in the literature) and force the gauge and scalar core to have the same width. Given that the string radius varies as $r \propto \frac{1}{\sqrt{\lambda}a}$ and this could cause strings to "slip" through the lattice, we will make each coupling vary as

$$\lambda = \lambda_0 a^{2(1-\beta)} \qquad\qquad e = e_0 e a^{(1-\beta)} \tag{4}$$

where β is set to zero. This unphysical constant comoving width trick was first proposed in Ref. 11 and has been used throughout the literature to avoid resolution problems. We note that while previous work has suggested that $\beta = 0$ and $\beta = 1$ dynamics seem to agree, it is unknown presently if changing the value of β would somehow pose a systematic error source in model calibration. This particular effect will be studied in a future publication and is beyond the scope of the present work.

In order to characterize the defect network that forms and its evolution throughout cosmic time, we also need to characterize the mean comoving distance between strings, ξ, and the mean squared velocity, $\langle v^2 \rangle$. For velocity estimators we will use two different forms, one first proposed in Ref. 12 and the other in Ref. 10. The first one is based on a boosted static string (detailed derivation in Ref. 10) and will be referred to as the scalar field velocity estimator. It has the following form

$$<v^2>_\phi = \frac{2R}{1+R}, \qquad R = \frac{\int |\Pi|^2 \mathcal{W} dx^3}{\int (\sum_i |D_i^+ \phi|^2) \mathcal{W} dx^3}. \tag{5}$$

where $\mathcal{W}$ is weight function, chosen to localize the estimator on strings. We will use the Lagrangian density $\mathcal{L}$ to this end. Additionally, we will use the equation of state based velocity estimator,

$$<v^2>_\omega = \frac{1}{2}\left(1 + 3\frac{\int p\mathcal{W} dx^3}{\int \rho \mathcal{W} dx^3}\right). \tag{6}$$

We remark that the work of Reef. 10 showed the second estimator to perform better in Minkowski space than the scalar based estimator, i.e. it is in better agreement with the analytical expectation for the velocity of an oscillating string in flat space. Such disagreement is lattice space dependent, and indeed an exploration of this feature in the opposite low velocity limit is published in Ref. 13.

One way to characterize the typical distance between strings is by counting the total amount of string in the box, L,

$$\xi_W = \sqrt{\frac{\mathcal{V}}{L}}, \tag{7}$$

where $\mathcal{V}$ is box volume, and L as mentioned the total amount of string. L can be counted in multiple ways, but we will use an integer called winding. To explain it, remember one can think of a string as a magnetic flux tube, where the flux is quantized around the string,

$$\Phi = \oint dx^\mu A_\mu = \frac{2\pi}{e} \tag{8}$$

and the integer n is the winding. If a cell face is pierced by a string, then the lattice version of the winding[14] will be non-zero (1 for the choices of λ and e made above), and therefore we can say that a segment of length Δx pierced the plaquette. Summing all the segments (taking care not to double-count) we then obtain the total length of string in the box, L.

Note that output of cells pierced by windings forms the basis of our visualization strategy. Given that this novel aspect of our simulation has thus far not been described elsewhere, we will now describe the strategy itself and what avenues it opens for the study of defect networks.

2.1. Visualization strategy I — In-situ windings

One of the most stringent and common bottlenecks for many High-Performance Computing simulations is related to Input/Output. Not only does computational throughput grow much faster than the typical read/write speeds of most storage solutions, but also, very often, the amount of data required to do science exceeds the amount of storage available. It is thus no surprise that in recent years there has been a push towards techniques of in-situ visualization, where the output data is heavily reduced beforehand and a smaller subset is used afterwards. There are many literature examples of successful application of such techniques.[15–19] In this section we will detail how this technique is applied in our multiGPU cosmic string simulations[20] and the resulting performance gains.

In order to use an in-situ approach to outputting string positions in the lattice, we use ParaView Catalyst version 5.8.0. There are then two relevant components: the Adaptor code (written in C++) and a Python script which applies three filters to the data and then outputs an Unstructured grid (in *.pvtu format).

In the case of the Adaptor, it begins (if necessary) by creating a vtkMultiBlock-Dataset, where each rank contains then a vtkImageData with the correct information about block extent (in number of points), lattice spacing and origin of each block or sub-domain of the grid. Afterwards a series of vtkFloatArray are either created or updated by copying the contents of 7 different arrays pinned host memory buffers updated by GPUs before-hand. Six of these arrays (one for each cell face) contain only ± 1 in case a string pierces a cell face and 0 otherwise. The last array is merely an OR of the previous six, and will be used to determine which cells are pierced by strings and should therefore be outputted.

This determination is done in the Python script, which applies a Threshold filter to the data, selecting only cells wherein the last array is non-zero. In other words, from this point on we already have a reduced dataset. The Merge Block filter is then applied to collect pieces of strings spread throughout several sub-domain. To finalize the Parallel Unstructured Grid writer is used to output data in the *.pvtu format (alongside multiple block files *.vtu).

Table 1. A summary of typical output sizes for a timestep either with Raw output of all cells (HDF5) or using only the unstructured grid outputs from our in-situ approach.

Lattice size	Output data size (MB)		Time taken (s)	
	HDF5 estimated	In-situ measured	HDF5 estimated	In-situ measured
512^3	5296	[8.7, 25.0]	0.9	[2.6, 3.5]
1024^3	42368	[11.0, 126.0]	0.9	[2.7, 3.2]
2048^3	338944	[33.0, 199.0]	3.0	[2.9, 5.6]
4096^3	2711552	[99.0, 144.0]	23.9	[4.1, 8.2]

Note: Given that the in-situ approach size depends on the number of cells that are part of a string, we indicate the range of sizes obtained over the conformal time ranges where we output.

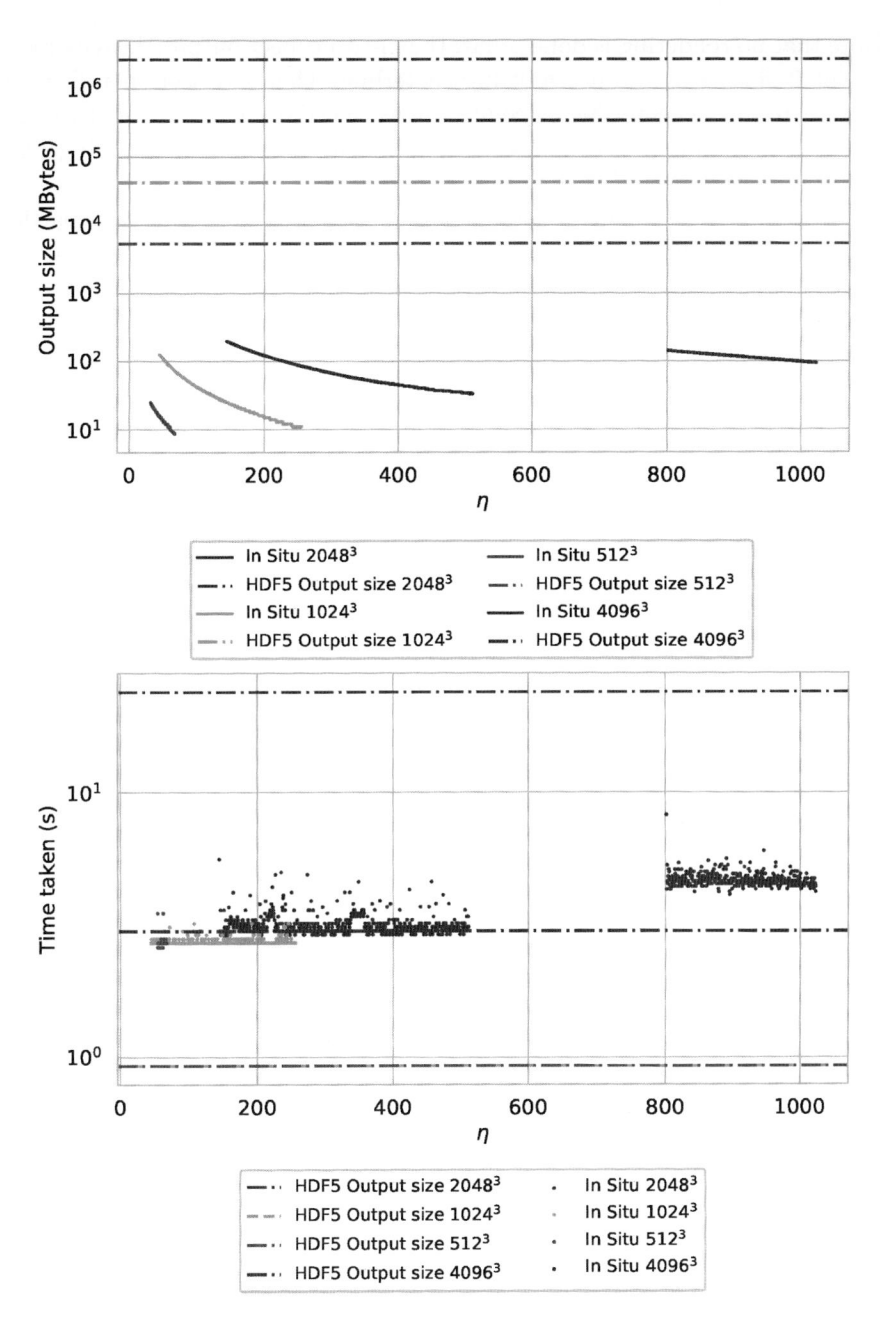

Fig. 1. Top: Size of raw HDF5 data output (windings for six cell faces, dashed lines) and of that for the In-Situ approach, where Unstructured grids are output (full lines), for lattice sizes: 4096^3 (blue), 2048^3 (purple), 1024^3 (orange) and 512^3 (green). Bottom: corresponding output times.

Note that no rendering is done so far: the in-situ aspect outputs heavily reduced data, but it does not produce a string centerline. The next section will describe how to create such a centerline by connecting each cell of each individual string and applying an averaging to string positions, such that the effect of taxicab geometry is greatly reduced.

Before we move on, we must detail the gains obtained from using this particular approach to data output, by comparing to the previous method of output of the simulation, which was to output all cells throughout the domain in HDF5 files (file-per-process approach). All benchmarks were conducted at Piz Daint, the Swiss National Supercomputer, the $4th$ most powerful supercomputer in Europe at the time of writing.[21] This machine features 5704 nodes, each equipped with an Nvidia Tesla P100, together with a *scratch* partition which is a Cray Sonexion 3000 Lustre filesystem with 8.8PB capacity. The system contains 40 object storage targets, and can handle a file per process approach well as long as there are not thousands of files in a single folder (this can be circumvented by grouping files according to rank for instance).

The first, more obvious consequence is how this results in less data being output. The smallest size of single HDF5 file with 7 single precision floating point datasets of dimension $(256, 256, 256)$ is around 662 MB in our test set. In order to determine the total typical output size for the benchmarks we are about to describe, we need to multiply the number by the number of ranks used. Keeping the problem size per process fixed. We will then run the benchmarks for in-situ with the following lattice sizes 512^3, 1024^3, 2048^3 and 4096^3 with domain decomposition of $(2,2,2)$, $(4,4,4)$, $(8,8,8)$ and $(16,16,16)$. In all benchmarks we output data every five timesteps. The obtained total timestep output sizes are shown in Table 1 and in Figure 1. We note that as the networks evolve, and the strings interact, the energy density of strings decreases which has an immediate and obvious effect on the number of cells output: they decrease with conformal time. This is translated in the total timestep size, which decreases with conformal time for every lattice size. The other important conclusion is that there is a vast reduction in total storage space required, at worst two orders of magnitude, at best four. This not only allows us to output data at a larger temporal rate (more timesteps), but also allows the possibility of adding more data to the outputs, if necessary.

We must also ask if there a performance (wall-clock time) speed-up or a performance penalty, or if, even including a costly filter like Merge Blocks, we can output data at similar rates as in the previous case. In order to do so, we will use the maximum measured writing bandwidth of our file per process approach with HDF5 files with 8, 64 and 512 writers for 512^3, 1024^3 and for both 2048^3 and 4096^3. The three maximum bandwidth are, respectively 5712, 45640 and 113300 MB/s. Note that we will use the maximum measured bandwidth of 512 writers for 4096 as it is already very close to the estimated peak bandwidth of the Lustre filesystem on Piz Daint.

Using these maximum bandwidths and the estimated storage needed for each file allows us to calculate a typical time taken. For in-situ we measure the time taken to output each timestep where data is written out. Our results, shown in table 1 and in figure 1, indicate that in-situ is definitely worth it if the file size becomes extremely large and the bandwidth is already saturated (close to the theoretical maximum bandwidth of the filesystem). This is evident when comparing the 2048^3 and 4096^3 cases where the amount of time taken is roughly comparable for 2048^3 but in the 4096^3 the amount of time taken for in-situ is roughly an order of magnitude below.

In conclusion, the technique described herein makes studying small-scale structure of strings possible with large lattices, not only reducing the amount of storage required by the simulation towards feasible amounts, but also permitting a significant speed-up, circumventing the limitation imposed by the maximum bandwidth of the filesystem.

2.2. *Visualization of string networks II — post-processing*

After the simulation runs, we can use the Unstructured grid output to construct string centerlines. The first step is to group neighboring cells via the Connectivity filter, and then use the PassArrays filter to pass all the data arrays to the input of the custom filter. The centerline script loops over each region identified by the connectivity filter and by each cell. The problem of trying to connect cells based on the order of the cellId in the Unstructured grid is that they are ordered by index (i,j,k) and not by the order they should be in a string.

The way to solve this issue is to begin in a cell in the string, ask for the neighbors according to the connectivity filter and then use the information contained in each of the winding arrays to understand if the connectivity established via cell faces is physically valid, i.e. if magnetic flux passes through that cell face. Note that we choose the positive, +1 direction for the magnetic flux but the script would work if working in the opposite direction too. Once a valid neighbor is identified, the vortexBounds for the specific cell and the next one are used to find cell center coordinates. These coordinates used to trace a vtkLine connecting one cell to the next, passing in the middle of a cell face. Cell by cell and segment by segment, the string centerline begins taking shape, as a collection of vtkLines (hence the output is of vtkPolyDataCollection type).

There are however some special cases to be mentioned as they can cause issues in the correct visualization and analysis.These are merely a consequence of the phenomenology of a string network. When two strings meet at one point (forming an X-shaped region), they can exchange ends, i.e. intercommute, and two new strings emerge immediately afterwards. On the other hand, if strings are to either meet in two points or to self-intersect, it is very likely that a closed loop forms. Loops are

Fig. 2. String cells colored by region in two close-up screenshots of 2048^3 radiation era simulation. We show in addition the output of the centerlines custom filter with smoothing via a Hanning window. A Loop (in blue) is shown at the center of the top panel screenshot. An intercomutation event (in red) is shown on the left-hand side of the bottom panel.

extremely important for observational consequences, as they shrink and dissipate energy[a] therefore generating some observational fingerprints.

Intercommutation events (or X-regions) can cause the string centerline to stop at the boundary of the box but not go through all the cells of the entire region. In effect the initial version of the custom filter would draw a single string (corresponding to two legs of the X-region, so to say). This can be avoided by comparing the number of cells used for the creation of the centerline so far and the total number of cells in the region. If one is much smaller, then the centerline drawing must restart at a cell not used previously and create the other two legs. Loops require us to close the path of the centerline, in other words, to connect the last cell and the first. Identifying

---

[a]Here lies a disagreement between two types of cosmic string simulation in the literature: in what type of energy do loops decay? Gravitational waves, massive radiation? This can alter the overall energy loss of the network, subsequent evolution of the network, and observational imprints. The scientific goal of the numerical techniques developed in the present work is to address this issue.

whether a loop is present can be done using the number of points and the number of cells. Should they differ by one, it is necessary to close this path.

After dealing with these two problematic cases we now have the string positions along every stair-case-like segment. This staircase behavior is no more, no less a consequence of the discrete nature of the lattice and of not having complete information about where exactly in each cell face a string lies (one assumes perfectly in the middle but this is not entirely realistic either). There is therefore some small-scale structure on the resulting strings in a scale roughly of the lattice size. Given that this is not a physical effect, we wish to remove it. In Ref. 12 the smoothed string was obtained by averaging string positions along the string path. Here we convolve each string with a window function in order to remove such artificial structure. The specific window function and the window size can be chosen in the filter. Given that numpy and scipy are used for this procedure, possible window functions by default include Hanning, Haming, Bartlett, Blackman. Figure 2 shows a collection of cells in two long strings and one loop either in cells as the resulting output of the Connectivity filter or as string centerlines (in white) smoothed over with the Hanning window function. Qualitatively this is more representative of a natural string. An example of the completed centerlines for a 4096^3 lattice simulation, with $\Delta x = 0.5$ aand $\Delta \eta = 0.1$ in radiation epoch is shown in Fig. 3.

3. Extended Velocity-dependent One-Scale model

The canonical semi-analytic model for string network evolution is the so-called Velocity dependent One-Scale model of Refs. 22, 23. It can be thought of as thermodynamic model in the sense that it describes the time evolution of two network averaged quantities, the mean string separation L, and the root mean squared velocity v. The cosmological history of these quantities is described in terms of relevant physical effects. For instance, the expansion of the Universe tends to act as a friction force on the strings (thereby affecting velocities) and also acts to dilute the network (affecting the mean separation). The model takes the following form, in comoving coordinates,

$$\frac{d\xi}{d\eta} = \frac{m\xi}{(1-m)\eta}v^2 + F(v) \tag{9}$$

$$\frac{dv}{d\eta} = (1-v^2)\left[\frac{k(v)}{\xi} - \frac{2mv}{(1-m)\eta}\right], \tag{10}$$

where $\xi = La$ is the comoving mean string separation, η is the conformal time, related to t by means of $d\eta = adt$, $\mathcal{H}$ is the conformal Hubble parameter, m is an expansion rate such that the scale factor $a \propto t^m$, and $k(v)$ and $F(v)$ are two phenomenological functions, related to the curvature of strings and to energy loss processes, respectively. In the original VOS, $k(v)$ can be analytically determined by comparison with the helicoidal string ansatz. However, for the present work, we will

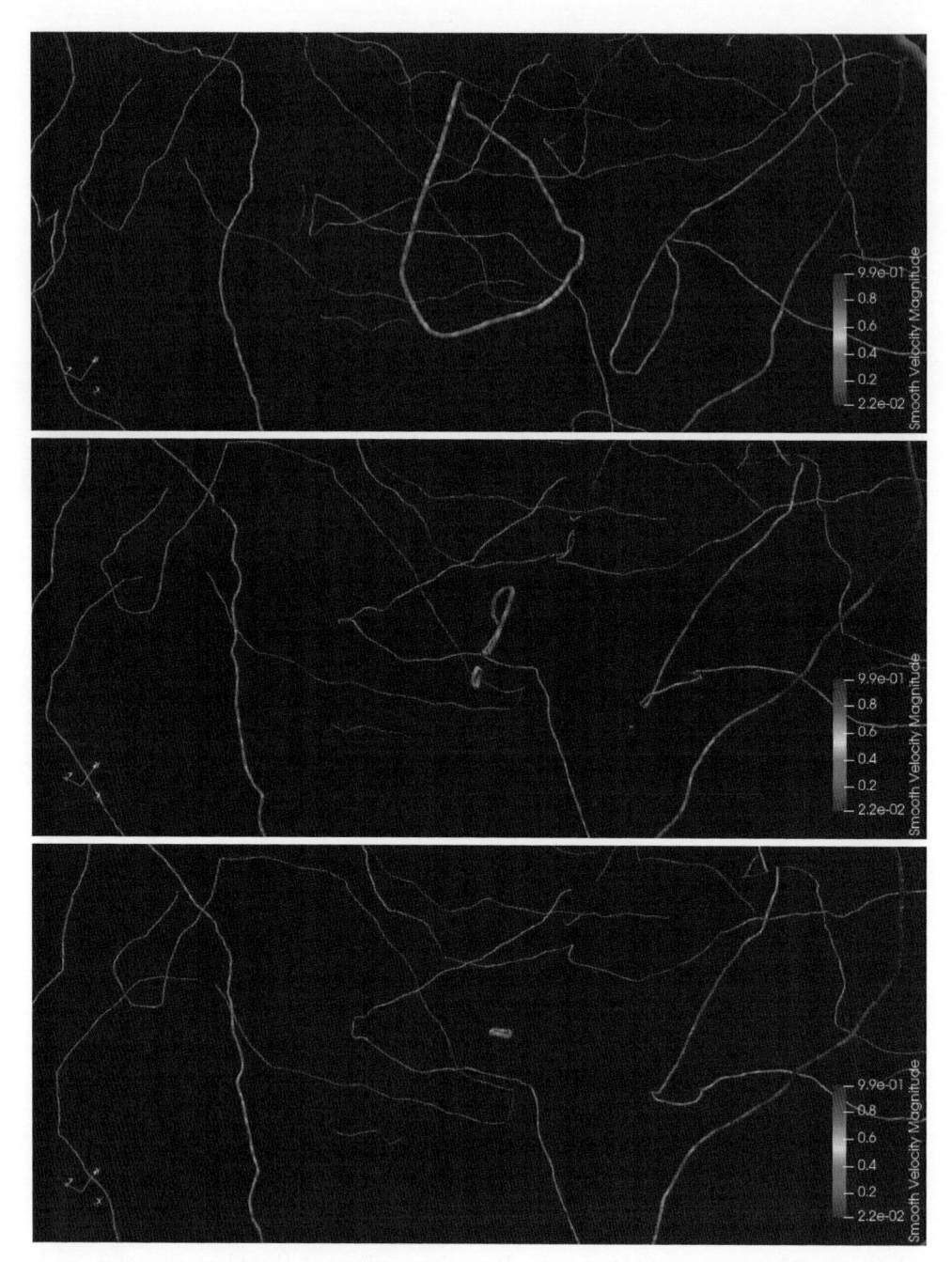

Fig. 3. Comparison of the mean rate of change of correlation length ξ/η (top left) and the mean velocity $\langle v \rangle$ (top right) with the solid lines corresponding to the calibration and the shaded regions to the uncertainty of the measurements of each estimator for three different box sizes. The bottom plots show how these differences impact the momentum parameter $k(v)$ (bottom left) and in the energy loss parameter $F(v)$ (bottom right).

allow a more general form,

$$k(v) = k_0 \frac{1 - (qv^2)^\beta}{1 + (qv^2)^\beta}. \tag{11}$$

where q, k_0 and β are free parameters, which in the case of q and k_0 have a clear physical meaning. The former corresponds to the inverse of the maximum defect velocity squared $q \approx 1/v^2$ and the latter to the maximal value of $k(v)$, obtained in the low velocity limit. Note that the helicoidal ansatz corresponds to setting $q = 2$, $k_0 = \frac{\sqrt{2}\pi}{2}$ and $\beta = 3$. Letting these parameters free allows us to verify if small-scale structure on strings deviates from the Nambu-Goto expectation significantly, as this would be reflected on parameters q, k_0 and β taking different values from the analytical expectation.

The energy loss function $F(v)$ was originally devised to only include a term linearly proportional to the velocity to model energy loss via loop chopping. However, recent work on radiation on Abelian-Higgs strings,[10] then prompted the authors of Ref. 24 to introduce a radiative loss term when studying domain wall evolution. Such a term is described by a power law of curvature,

$$F(v) = cv + d[k_0 - k]^r, \tag{12}$$

where c, d and r are free parameters which express the loop chopping parameter and the energy loss normalization and exponent, respectively. Although the original VOS, with the helicoidal ansatz and no explicit energy loss, had only one parameter, the extended version has 6. This is not a problem per se, as long as one can extract the correct velocity dependencies of each function $k(v)$ and $F(v)$. It is for this reason we will simulate string networks in Universes where with a power law scale factor, $a \propto m$ and with expansion rates m in the range $m \in [0.5, 0.95]$ (i.e. not only matter and radiation epoch are simulated).

We note that since string networks, under any Universe with a power law scale factor ($a \propto t^m \propto \eta^{m/(1-m)}$), are expected to evolve according to the so-called linear scaling regime where,

$$\xi \propto \eta \propto d_H \qquad v = const, \tag{13}$$

we can easily use the measured $\dot{\xi} \sim \frac{\xi}{\eta}$ and v to extract the proper velocity dependencies of $k(v)$ and $F(v)$, and also calibrate model parameters. To this end, we will use the same Markov Chain Monte Carlo pipeline of Ref. 25 to assess posterior distributions on all model parameters, and thus unveil possible correlations, and predict likelihood maxima and uncertainties. All model parameters are sampled from uniform distributions, with the range of these distributions adapted to each dataset as necessary. The logarithm of the likelihood is to be given by the χ^2 statistic. We will use 32 walkers and a minimum of 10000 steps.

4. Dynamic range and lattice size

String simulations have a problem of separation of scales, as it is often necessary to resolve scales all the way from the size of the horizon, down to scales comparable to the radius of the strings. When it comes to better resolving small-scale structure, there are two possible ways to do so, either by decreasing lattice spacing or by increasing lattice size, which in turn increases dynamic range. The latter follows because the lattice size directly determines the final simulation time: half-a-light crossing time or when the horizon size is half the box size. If a larger horizon can be reached by the end of the simulation, then for the same lattice spacing we can better resolve scales of a fraction of the horizon.

We now explore the effects of increasing lattice size, while keeping spacing constant throughout ($\Delta x = 0.5$). To this end, we calibrate the VOS with 1024^3, 2048^3 and 4096^3 lattices, with expansion rates $m \in [0.45, 0.95]$, 10 simulation runs each. For now we will use the equation of state velocity estimator. The resulting calibrations are summarized in table 2 and the corresponding posterior plots are found in figure 3 of Ref. 13, remade in Fig. 4.

Table 2. Calibrated VOS model parameters for our three different lattice sizes, 1024^3, 2048^3 and 4096^3, all with the same lattice spacing $\Delta x = 0.5$, and two different choices of velocity estimators, $\langle v_\omega^2 \rangle$ and $\langle v_\phi^2 \rangle$ (in the top and bottom parts of the table, respectively),

Lattice size	Δx	Velocity estimator	d	r	β	k_0	q	c
1024^3			$0.32^{+0.04}_{-0.04}$	$1.51^{+0.48}_{-0.37}$	$1.82^{+0.34}_{-0.30}$	$1.27^{+0.08}_{-0.06}$	$2.41^{+0.13}_{-0.13}$	$0.15^{+0.05}_{-0.07}$
2048^3	0.5	$\langle v_\omega^2 \rangle$	$0.37^{+0.02}_{-0.02}$	$1.27^{+0.17}_{-0.15}$	$2.33^{+0.21}_{-0.20}$	$1.21^{+0.03}_{-0.03}$	$2.57^{+0.06}_{-0.06}$	$0.03^{+0.02}_{-0.03}$
4096^3			$0.39^{+0.02}_{-0.02}$	$1.36^{+0.15}_{-0.13}$	$2.32^{+0.20}_{-0.18}$	$1.18^{+0.03}_{-0.03}$	$2.59^{+0.05}_{-0.05}$	$0.00^{+0.01}_{-0.01}$
1024^3			$0.35^{+0.23}_{-0.10}$	$2.39^{+1.58}_{-0.94}$	$2.79^{+0.73}_{-0.56}$	$1.06^{+0.05}_{-0.05}$	$2.95^{+0.18}_{-0.19}$	$0.44^{+0.04}_{-0.05}$
2048^3	0.5	$\langle v_\phi^2 \rangle$	$0.33^{+0.05}_{-0.04}$	$1.86^{+0.39}_{-0.32}$	$2.65^{+0.28}_{-0.26}$	$1.05^{+0.03}_{-0.03}$	$2.84^{+0.08}_{-0.08}$	$0.31^{+0.02}_{-0.02}$
4096^3			$0.36^{+0.03}_{-0.03}$	$1.72^{+0.26}_{-0.23}$	$2.50^{+0.21}_{-0.20}$	$1.06^{+0.02}_{-0.02}$	$2.83^{+0.06}_{-0.06}$	$0.23^{+0.01}_{-0.01}$

Note: Displayed values correspond to 16th, 50th, 84th percentiles of the posterior distributions.

We see that most parameters remain relatively unchanged by increasing the lattice size, being subject only to a reduction of uncertainties (smaller contours in Fig. 4). The only exceptions are parameters c and (to a lesser extent) d. We remark as well that these differences are qualitatively larger when comparing 1024^3 with 2048^3, than if comparing 2048^3 to 4096^3, which might hint that there is a minimum lattice size/dynamic range for model calibration. Gradually, c is even reduced to zero at 4096^3 which seems to suggest that as lattice resolution increases, loop-chopping is eventually replaced by radiative losses, bu this is at odds with information from visually seeing the network evolve—as loops are formed at various instants and at various sizes—as can be inferred from Fig. 3.

In Ref.[13] we found, by comparing asymptotic quantities at all expansion rates, that the main culprit for the changes we discussed in the previous paragraph was the behavior of ξ/η. In fact, while the velocities remain mostly unchanged, ξ/η is

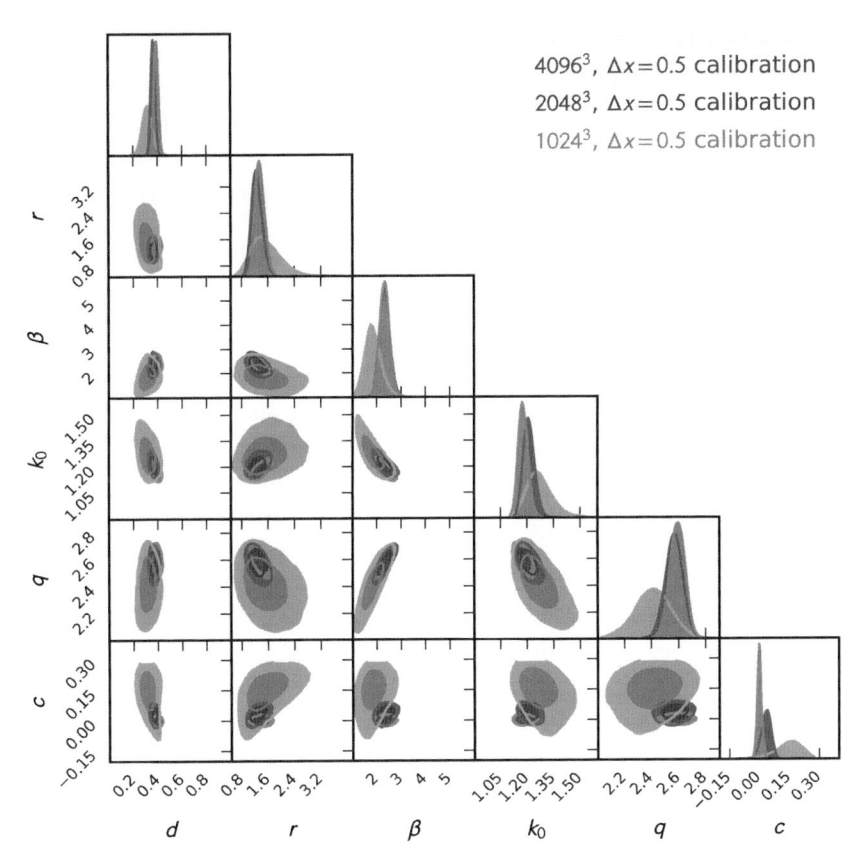

Fig. 4. Corner plots for the MCMC calibration of the VOS model, obtained with the velocity estimator $\langle v_\omega \rangle$, lattice spacing $\Delta x = 0.5$, box sizes 4096^3, 2048^3 and 1024^3. Remake of figure 3 of Ref. 13.

decreases (this is present in the literature too[9,12]) with lattice size, as does it uncertainty. The reduction of the uncertainties is responsible for the narrower posterior distributions, and the lower mean value translates itself in change in a downwards shift of $F(v)$. This is reflected in the parameters that control the normalization of $F(v)$, i.e. in c and (to a lesser extent), via anti-correlation d. Again the differences are larger when going from 1024^3 to 2048^3 than from 2048^3 to 4096^3.

Going back to our previous discussion of c, it appears the calibration suggested the loop-chopping parameter would eventually go to zero, however the visualization strategy showed loops being produced at different sizes and different size. Perhaps, as a cross-check, we should also repeat this analysis using the scalar field velocity estimator. The resulting parameters are summarized in the bottom half of Table 2 and in figure 4 of Ref. 13. This now leads to a surprisingly different calibration, with very different model parameters, namely c is statistically non-zero. This prompts an investigation on the biases of each velocity estimator and on possible solutions.

5. Lattice spacing and velocity estimators

Here we investigate why both velocity estimators give vastly different calibrations and suggest one possible solution. From the point-of-view of the extended VOS, the high expansion rates can be some of the most important (statistically) for two reasons. First, in the low-velocity limit, both velocity functions are reduced to one parameter each,

$$\lim_{v \to 0} F(v) = cv \qquad \lim_{v \to 0} k(v) = k_0 , \qquad (14)$$

and this means that overall the model becomes reduced to only two parameters. Uncertainties on observed asymptotic quantities also decrease with decreasing velocity (increasing expansion rate). Statistically this will mean that the high expansion rate limit will be important in determining c and k_0, which will in turn affect all variables correlated with them, and that the lower uncertainties give a larger statistical weight to higher expansion rates. This leads us to suspect that the high expansion rate behavior of both velocity estimators might be the cause, as the difference between them increases with expansion rate.[10]

If we compare velocity estimators in the range $m \in [0.5, 0.95]$ (see figure 3 of Ref. 26) the difference is maximal at $m = 0.95$, and of about $\sim 10\%$. For even larger expansion rates, in the range $m \in [0.95, 0.997]$ (left panel of figure 5 of Ref. 13), the velocity estimators can disagree up to 60% in the worst case scenario for lattice spacing $\Delta x = 0.5$, In the work of Ref. 10, which explored the differences between the two estimators in Minkowski space (the opposite limit), it was shown that lattice spacing could reduce this disagreement. But even at high expansion rate this remains true: the disagreement is heavily reduced when we halve lattice spacing $\Delta x = 0.25$ as can be seen on the right panel of the aforementioned Figure 5. There is however one interesting difference between two opposite limits of high expansion rate and Minkowski: in the first the equation of state estimator approximates the scalar field, in the latter the opposite occurs. There is no a priori reason as to why both should behave the same way under lattice spacing reductions, therefore this is not in contradiction with previous results.

As expected, the differences and their reduction under lattice spacing, are also reflected in the velocity functions $k(v)$ and $F(v)$. This as can be seen in Figure 6 of Ref. 13, where two conclusions can be drawn. First, the equation of state velocity estimator yields unphysical $F(v)$ at lattice spacing $\Delta x = 0.5$, leading one to question its validity at the low velocity limit. Second, as the lattice is made finer, this brings both estimators in better agreement, namely by approximating $F(v)$ and $k(v)$ obtained via the equation of state estimator to the scalar field estimator. Note that this doesn't solve the problem of unphysical $F(v)$ completely, although for our intents and purposes it brings agreement for expansion rates $m \in [0.93, 0.95]$.

Now we compare the resulting model parameters for the two choices of lattice spacing. The results are summarized in Table 3 and in the corresponding posterior contours of figures Figures 7 and 8 of Ref. 13. We also showcase the contours of the

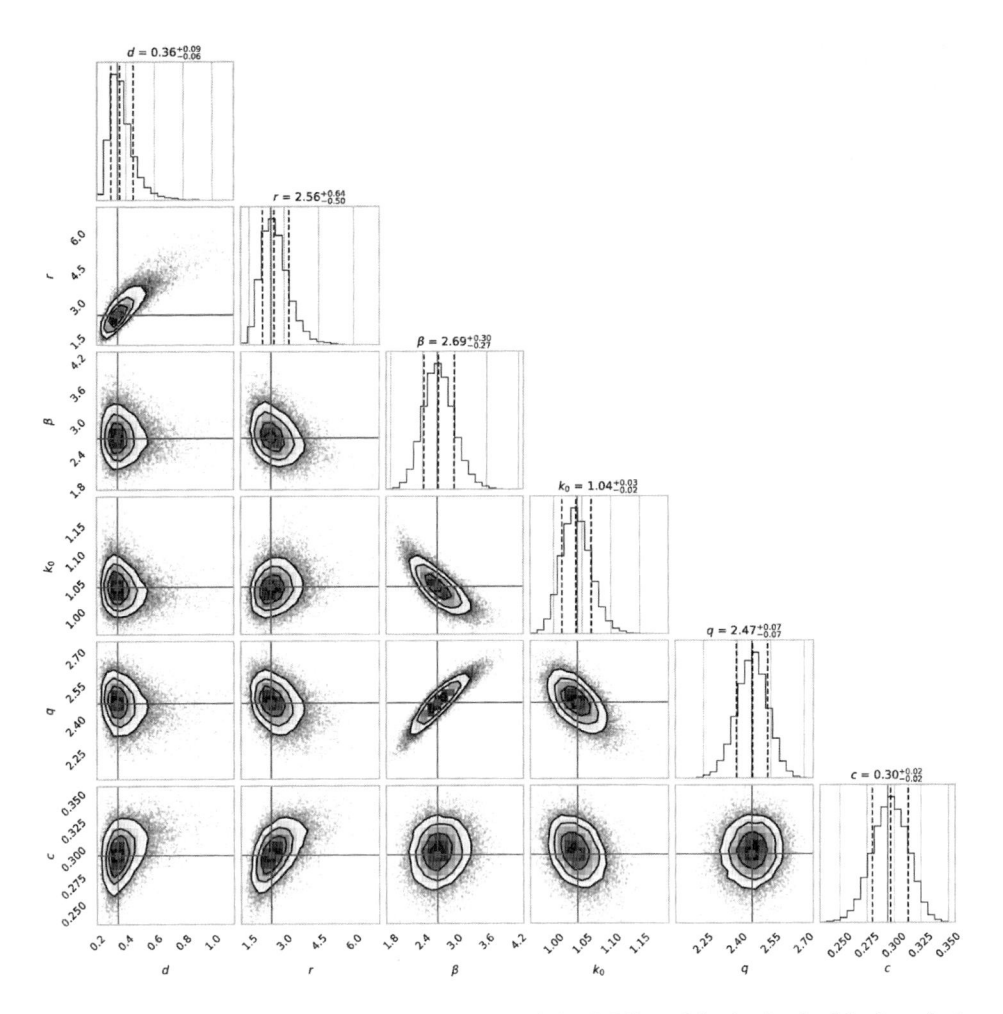

Fig. 5. Corner plots for the MCMC calibration of the VOS model, obtained with the velocity estimator $\langle v_\phi \rangle$, lattice spacing $\Delta x = 0.25$, box size 4096^3.

4096^3, $\Delta x = 0.25$, $\langle v_\phi^2 \rangle$ calibration in Fig. 5. Since the equation of state velocity estimator is highly sensitive to lattice spacing at large expansion rate, it is no surprise that the calibration drastically changes for all model parameters under a reduction of spacing, as can be seen both in the table and in the first aforementioned figure of Ref.[13] With the finer calibration, it is also obvious the value of c is no longer consistent with zero, that indeed loop-chopping is still a viable energy loss mechanism.

The calibrations performed with the scalar field velocity estimator mostly reduce uncertainties (with one exception) as the lattice spacing is reduced, as can be inferred from the lower half of Table 3 and from the contours of Figure 8 from

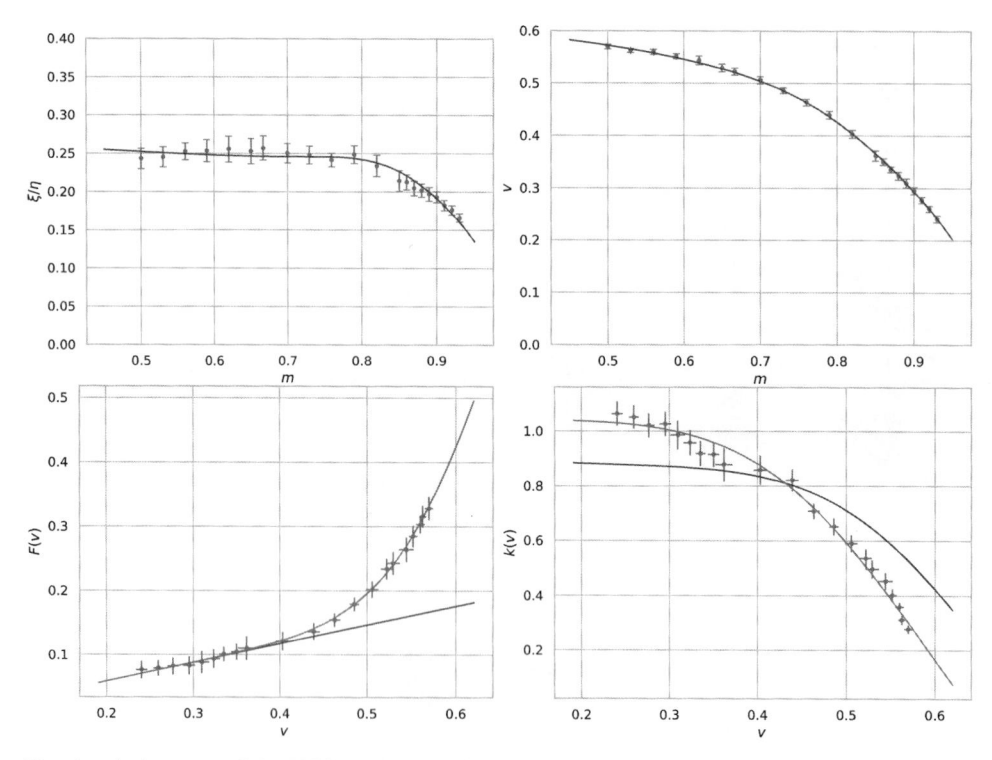

Fig. 6. A showcase of the VOS predictions for the mean rate of change of correlation length ξ/η (top left) and the mean velocity $\langle v \rangle$ (top right) with the solid blue lines corresponding to the calibration and the green points to the measured quantities with statistical $1 - \sigma$ uncertainties. The bottom plots show the functions $F(v)$ and $k(v)$ with green points showing measured values and the blue lines showing the standard VOS prediction with the extended VOS prediction in orange.

Ref. 13. The only exception to this is the parameter q which is again expected, as it is related to the maximal defect velocity and the estimator changes mostly in the high velocity limit.

Thus lowering lattice spacing brings both calibrations, with different velocity estimators, into better agreement with the only different parameter being c. Overall this means one of the most important parameters from an observational point of view, c, is the most sensitive in the model, being somewhat affected by resolution effects and choice of velocity estimator.

To conclude we present the VOS predictions of the best-case scenario calibration, with lattice 4096^3, spacing, $\Delta x = 0.25$ and velocity estimator $\langle v_\phi^2 \rangle$ in Fig. 6. The VOS model predicts reasonably well, for all expansion rates, the values of ξ/η and v. We can see the measured value of $k(v)$ and $F(v)$ seem to be well described by the generalized forms, while the standard forms fail to predict the proper velocity dependency.

Table 3. Calibrated VOS model parameters for our two choices of lattice spacing Δx and corresponding lattice sizes, for the two different choices of velocity estimators, $\langle v_\omega^2 \rangle$ and $\langle v_\phi^2 \rangle$, further described in the main text.

Lattice size	Δx	Velocity estimator	d	r	β	k_0	q	c
2048^3	0.5	$\langle v_\omega^2 \rangle$	$0.37^{+0.02}_{-0.02}$	$1.27^{+0.17}_{-0.15}$	$2.33^{+0.21}_{-0.20}$	$1.21^{+0.03}_{-0.03}$	$2.57^{+0.06}_{-0.06}$	$0.03^{+0.02}_{-0.03}$
4096^3	0.25		$0.34^{+0.07}_{-0.05}$	$2.32^{+0.52}_{-0.40}$	$2.62^{+0.29}_{-0.26}$	$1.06^{+0.03}_{-0.02}$	$2.37^{+0.06}_{-0.07}$	$0.25^{+0.02}_{-0.02}$
2048^3	0.5	$\langle v_\phi^2 \rangle$	$0.33^{+0.05}_{-0.04}$	$1.86^{+0.39}_{-0.32}$	$2.65^{+0.28}_{-0.26}$	$1.05^{+0.03}_{-0.03}$	$2.84^{+0.08}_{-0.08}$	$0.31^{+0.02}_{-0.02}$
4096^3	0.25		$0.36^{+0.09}_{-0.06}$	$2.56^{+0.64}_{-0.50}$	$2.69^{+0.30}_{-0.27}$	$1.04^{+0.03}_{-0.02}$	$2.47^{+0.07}_{-0.07}$	$0.30^{+0.02}_{-0.02}$

Note: Displayed values correspond to 16th, 50th, 84th percentiles of the posterior distributions.

6. Observational Impact

We will now a highlight the impact of different calibrations on observational footprints of cosmic string networks. Note that a detailed study is beyond the scope of this manuscript, and this is merely illustrative of the need for an accurate calibration.[13]

We can use the CMBACT4 code[27,28] to compute the Cosmic Microwave Background anisotropies generated by a string network, assuming different VOS calibrations. This code assumes the Unconnected Segment Model,[27] where ensembles of straight, randomly oriented segments with separations and velocities given by the VOS model are used to compute power spectra.

We cancompare four different calibrations: standard VOS compatible with Nambu-Goto, standard VOS calibrated for Abelian-Higgs and two extended VOS calibrations present in the previous section, a worst (1024^3, $\Delta x = 0.5$, $\langle v_\omega^2 \rangle$) and best ($4096^3$, $\Delta x = 0.25$, $\langle v_\phi^2 \rangle$) case scenario. The resulting TT, TE, EE and BB can be found in figure 9 of Ref. 13, all normalized to a string tension $G\mu = 1.0 \times 10^{-7}$. It is clear that the Abelian-Higgs spectra are in better agreement between each other, than the Nambu-Goto one, which is expected.[29–34]

However, there are still some noticeable differences between Abelian-Higgs calibrations. The most discrepant overall is the 1024^3 calibration—the worst-case scenario. The 4096^3 calibration and the standard VOS one are in better agreement, although it should be noted there still exist some scale-dependent differences. To exemplify, at $l = 10$, the relative difference between the two TT spectra is around 16%, 30% and 11% for scalar, vector, tensor C_l, respectively.

The exact quantifying of how much of these differences are uniquely due to the calibrations or due to the USM requires a more in-depth, detailed study. Nevertheless, this illustrative comparison highlights the need for accurate VOS calibrations.

7. Conclusion

In this work we used our recently developed multiGPU Abelian-Higgs code and high-end computational resources of Piz Daint to obtain a robust calibration of the canonical semi-analytical model of string evolution. Using high-resolution simulations from lattice sizes ranging from 1024^3 to 4096^3 and various choices of expansion rate. We explored the impact of two different numerical choices on the obtained calibrations. This allowed us to not only reduce statistical uncertainties but also to correct for systematic error sources. Since we tested the sensitivity of model parameters to each of these choices we uncovered that the loop-chopping parameter is highly sensitive to both resolution effects and also to choice of velocity estimator. We showed that a minimum dynamic range of about 512.0 conformal time units and a minimum lattice spacing of $\Delta x = 0.25$ are necessary to minimize the impacts of these systematic error sources.

We then illustrated one of the main motivations to pursue an accurate, high-resolution calibration of the VOS: observational consequences. We specifically showed that different calibrations can give rise to scale-dependent differences on the computed CMB anisotropy power spectra. Although one cannot (at least without a more in-depth study) exclude that these differences are caused by the various approximations of the Unconnected Segment Model, it is still clear that precise and accurate calibrations are necessary to for both current and future constraints.

Acknowledgements

This work was financed by FEDER—Fundo Europeu de Desenvolvimento Regional funds through the COM-PETE 2020—Operational Programme for Competitiveness and Internationalisation (POCI), and by Portuguese funds through FCT - Fundação para a Ciência e a Tecnologia in the framework of the project POCI-01-0145-FEDER-028987 and PTDC/FIS-AST/28987/2017. J. R. C. is supported by an FCT fellowship (SFRH/BD/130445/2017). We gratefully acnknowledge the support of NVIDIA corporation with the donation of the Quadro P5000 GPU used in this research. We acknowledge PRACE for awarding us access to Piz Daint at CSCS, Switzerland, through Preparatory Access proposal 2010PA4610, Project Access proposal 2019204986 and Project Access proposal 2020225448. Technical support from Jean Favre at CSCS is gratefully acknowledged.

References

1. T. W. B. Kibble, Topology of Cosmic Domains and Strings, *J. Phys.* **A9**, 1387 (1976).
2. R. Jeannerot, J. Rocher and M. Sakellariadou, How generic is cosmic string formation in SUSY GUTs, *Phys. Rev.* **D68**, p. 103514 (2003).
3. S. Sarangi and S. H. H. Tye, Cosmic string production towards the end of brane inflation, *Phys. Lett.* **B536**, 185 (2002).
4. P. A. R. Ade *et al.*, Planck 2013 results. XXV. Searches for cosmic strings and other topological defects, *Astron. Astrophys.* **571**, p. A25 (2014).

5. B. P. Abbott *et al.*, Constraints on cosmic strings using data from the first Advanced LIGO observing run, *Phys. Rev.* **D97**, p. 102002 (2018).
6. F. Finelli *et al.*, Exploring cosmic origins with CORE: Inflation, *JCAP* **1804**, p. 016 (2018).
7. P. Binetruy, A. Bohe, C. Caprini and J.-F. Dufaux, Cosmological Backgrounds of Gravitational Waves and eLISA/NGO: Phase Transitions, Cosmic Strings and Other Sources, *JCAP* **1206**, p. 027 (2012).
8. K. G. Wilson, Confinement of quarks, *Phys. Rev. D* **10**, 2445 (Oct 1974).
9. N. Bevis, M. Hindmarsh, M. Kunz and J. Urrestilla, CMB power spectrum contribution from cosmic strings using field-evolution simulations of the Abelian Higgs model, *Phys. Rev.* **D75**, p. 065015 (2007).
10. M. Hindmarsh, J. Lizarraga, J. Urrestilla, D. Daverio and M. Kunz, Scaling from gauge and scalar radiation in Abelian Higgs string networks, *Phys. Rev.* **D96**, p. 023525 (2017).
11. W. H. Press, B. S. Ryden and D. N. Spergel, Dynamical Evolution of Domain Walls in an Expanding Universe, *Astrophys. J.* **347**, 590 (1989).
12. M. Hindmarsh, S. Stuckey and N. Bevis, Abelian Higgs Cosmic Strings: Small Scale Structure and Loops, *Phys. Rev. D* **79**, p. 123504 (2009).
13. J. R. C. C. Correia and C. J. A. P. Martins, High resolution calibration of the cosmic strings velocity dependent one-scale model, *Phys. Rev. D* **104**, p. 063511 (2021).
14. K. Kajantie, M. Karjalainen, M. Laine, J. Peisa and A. Rajantie, Thermodynamics of gauge invariant U(1) vortices from lattice Monte Carlo simulations, *Phys. Lett.* **B428**, 334 (1998).
15. J. J. Camata, V. Silva, P. Valduriez, M. Mattoso and A. L. Coutinho, In situ visualization and data analysis for turbidity currents simulation, *Computers & Geosciences* **110**, 23 (2018).
16. M. Rautenhaus, M. Böttinger, S. Siemen, R. Hoffman, R. M. Kirby, M. Mirzargar, N. Röber and R. Westermann, Visualization in meteorology—a survey of techniques and tools for data analysis tasks, *IEEE Transactions on Visualization and Computer Graphics* **24**, 3268 (2018).
17. D. Mu, J. Moran, H. Zhou, Y. Cui, R. Hawkins, M. Tatineni and S. Campbell, In-situ analysis and visualization of earthquake simulation (2019).
18. R. Sohrabi, S. Omlin and S. A. Miller, Geyser: 3d thermo-hydrodynamic reactive transport numerical simulator including porosity and permeability evolution using gpu clusters, *Computational Geosciences* **23**, 1317 (Dec 2019).
19. A. KAGEYAMA, N. SAKAMOTO, H. MIURA and N. OHNO, Interactive exploration of the in-situ visualization of a magnetohydrodynamic simulation, *Plasma and Fusion Research* **15**, 1401065 (2020).
20. J. R. C. C. Correia and C. J. A. P. Martins, Abelian–Higgs cosmic string evolution with multiple GPUs, *Astron. Comput.* **34**, p. 100438 (2021).
21. Top500, Top500 november 2020 list https://top500.org/lists/top500/2020/11/, (2018).
22. C. J. A. P. Martins and E. P. S. Shellard, Quantitative string evolution, *Phys. Rev.* **D54**, 2535 (1996).
23. C. Martins and E. Shellard, Extending the velocity dependent one scale string evolution model, *Phys. Rev. D* **65**, p. 043514 (2002).
24. C. J. A. P. Martins, I. Y. Rybak, A. Avgoustidis and E. P. S. Shellard, Extending the velocity-dependent one-scale model for domain walls, *Phys. Rev.* **D93**, p. 043534 (2016).

25. J. R. C. C. C. Correia and C. J. A. P. Martins, Quantifying the effect of cooled initial conditions on cosmic string network evolution, *Phys. Rev. D* **102**, p. 043503 (2020).
26. J. R. C. C. C. Correia and J. A. P. Martins, Extending and Calibrating the Velocity dependent One-Scale model for Cosmic Strings with One Thousand Field Theory Simulations, *Phys. Rev.* **D100**, p. 103517 (2019).
27. L. Pogosian and T. Vachaspati, Cosmic microwave background anisotropy from wiggly strings, *Phys. Rev. D* **60**, p. 083504 (1999).
28. T. Charnock, A. Avgoustidis, E. J. Copeland and A. Moss, CMB constraints on cosmic strings and superstrings, *Phys. Rev. D* **93**, p. 123503 (2016).
29. B. Allen and E. P. S. Shellard, Cosmic string evolution: A numerical simulation, *Phys. Rev. Lett.* **64**, 119 (1990).
30. K. D. Olum and V. Vanchurin, Cosmic string loops in the expanding universe, *Phys. Rev.* **D75**, p. 063521 (2007).
31. D. P. Bennett and F. R. Bouchet, High resolution simulations of cosmic string evolution. 1. network evolution, *Phys. Rev.* **D41**, p. 2408 (1990).
32. J. J. Blanco-Pillado, K. D. Olum and B. Shlaer, Large parallel cosmic string simulations: New results o n loop production, *Phys. Rev.* **D83**, p. 083514 (2011).
33. A. Lazanu, E. P. S. Shellard and M. Landriau, CMB power spectrum of Nambu-Goto cosmic strings, *Phys. Rev. D* **91**, p. 083519 (2015).
34. A. Lazanu and P. Shellard, Constraints on the Nambu-Goto cosmic string contribution to the CMB power spectrum in light of new temperature and polarisation data, *JCAP* **02**, p. 024 (2015).

Radiation from Global Cosmic Strings using adaptive mesh refinement

Amelia Drew* and E. P. S. Shellard

Centre for Theoretical Cosmology, Department of Applied Mathematics and Theoretical Physics, University of Cambridge, Wilberforce Road, Cambridge CB3 0WA, United Kingdom
*E-mail: a.drew@damtp.cam.ac.uk

We present results from adaptive mesh refinement (AMR) simulations of global cosmic strings. Using the public code, GRChombo, we perform a quantitative investigation of the dynamics of single sinusoidally displaced string configurations. We study a wide range of string energy densities $\mu \propto \ln \lambda$, defined by the string width parameter λ over two orders of magnitude. We investigate the resulting massless (Goldstone boson or axion) and massive (Higgs) radiation signals, using quantitative diagnostic tools to determine the eigenmode decomposition. Given analytic radiation predictions for global Nambu-Goto strings, we compare the oscillating string decay with a backreaction model accounting for radiation energy losses, finding excellent agreement. We establish that backreaction decay is accurately characterised by the inverse square of the amplitude being proportional to the inverse tension μ for $3 \lesssim \lambda \lesssim 100$. The investigation of massive radiation at small to intermediate amplitudes finds evidence that it is suppressed exponentially relative to the preferred massless channel with a $\sqrt{\lambda}$ dependence in the exponent. We conclude that analytic radiation modelling in the thin-string (Nambu-Goto) limit provides the appropriate cosmological limit for global strings.

Keywords: Cosmic strings; adaptive mesh refinement.

1. Introduction

Cosmic strings are a fundamental prediction of many physically motivated field theories with symmetry-breaking phase transitions. They are a potential source of dark matter axions,[1] as well as gravitational waves.[2] However, their complex non-linear evolution means that significant uncertainties in their observational signatures and other properties persist in the literature.

The simplest example of cosmic string defects are 'global strings' formed from the breaking of a $U(1)$ symmetry with a single complex scalar field φ, given by

$$\mathcal{L} = (\partial_\mu \bar\varphi)(\partial^\mu \varphi) - \frac{\lambda}{4}(\bar\varphi\varphi - \eta^2)^2 \,. \tag{1}$$

The symmetry breaking scale with this potential is set by the constant λ, which also determines the width of the string core $\delta \approx (\sqrt{\lambda}\,\eta)^{-1}$, where η is also a constant. Massive ϕ and massless (Goldstone) ϑ radiative modes are generated when these global strings oscillate, which can be analysed respectively using the following diagnostics:

$$\Pi_\phi \equiv \frac{\phi_1\dot{\phi}_1 + \phi_2\dot{\phi}_2}{\phi}, \qquad \mathcal{D}_i\phi \equiv \frac{\phi_1\nabla_i\phi_1 + \phi_2\nabla_i\phi_2}{\phi},$$
$$\Pi_\vartheta \equiv \frac{\phi_1\dot{\phi}_2 - \phi_2\dot{\phi}_1}{\phi}, \qquad \mathcal{D}_i\vartheta \equiv \frac{\phi_1\nabla_i\phi_2 - \phi_2\nabla_i\phi_1}{\phi}. \qquad (2)$$

Despite their apparent simplicity, the study of cosmic strings using large-scale numerical simulations poses a very significant computational challenge. This is due to the vast difference in scale between the typical string width δ and the string curvature scale (set by the Hubble radius $R \lesssim H^{-1}$, where H is the Hubble scale). This is characterised by the ratios $\ln R/\delta \sim 70$ and $\ln R/\delta \sim 100$ for QCD axion and GUT scale strings respectively. This challenge is typically addressed by using the Nambu-Goto action (e.g. Ref. 3), or field theory simulations with a fixed (comoving) core width (e.g. Ref. 4). This work addresses some of the uncertainties introduced by these methods by implementing field theory simulations of individual string configurations using adaptive mesh refinement.

2. Simulations

In this work, we perform adaptive mesh simulations of single, sinusoidally displaced strings with $0.3 \leq \lambda \leq 100$ and spatial periodicity (wavelength) $L = 32$. After an initial period of dissipative damping, strings are subsequently evolved from a desired initial amplitude A_0, with both linear and nonlinear evolution regimes investigated. The oscillation amplitude is measured by calculating the position of the string core i.e. where there is non-zero winding, and the massive and massless diagnostics Π_ϕ and $\mathcal{D}_i\vartheta$ are extracted on a cylinder far from the string core. Our simulations are performed using the adaptive mesh refinement code, GRChombo.[5]

In this study, we measure the string radiation damping rate for a range of $1 \leq \lambda \leq 100$, and investigate the massless radiation spectrum for $\lambda = 1$ and $\lambda = 10$ at linear and nonlinear oscillation amplitudes.[6] We also investigate the massive radiation in detail for strings with $\lambda \leq 2.5$.[7]

3. Results

It has been previously shown[8] that for a sinusoidally displaced string, the massless quadrupole radiation rate can be described using a simple analytic backreaction model, derived from the Kalb-Ramond string action. The effect of radiation energy losses on the string oscillation amplitude A is given by

$$\frac{1}{\varepsilon^2} - \frac{1}{\varepsilon_0^2} = \frac{\beta t}{\bar{\mu}L} \quad \Rightarrow \quad \varepsilon = \varepsilon_0\left(1 + \frac{\beta\varepsilon_0^2 t}{\bar{\mu}L}\right)^{-1/2}. \qquad (3)$$

Here, $\varepsilon = 2\pi A/T$ is the amplitude relative to the oscillation time period T of the string, where ε_0 is measured at time $t = 0$. The normalised energy per unit length

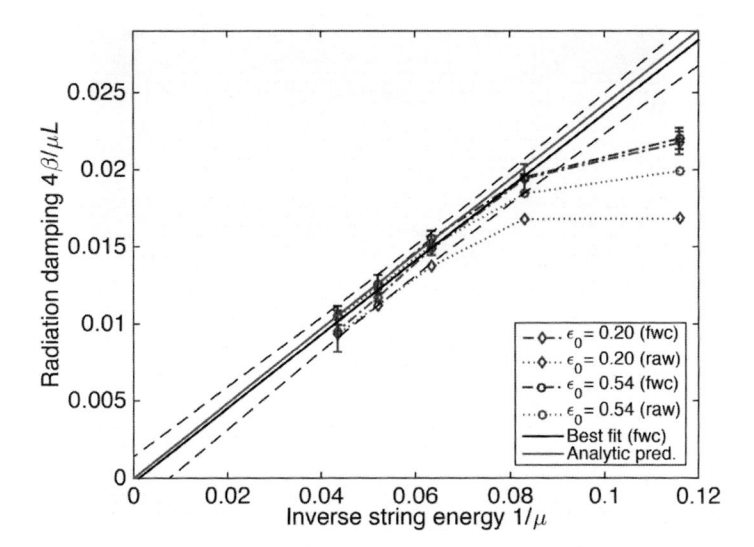

Fig. 1. Radiative damping rate measured using the inverse square model, plotted as a function of inverse string density μ^{-1}. We apply a finite size correction (fwc) to the data and exclude the result at $\lambda = 1$ from the best fit, due to string width effects which limit radiative damping at small λ. The analytic prediction in red uses an effective string radius cutoff $R = 3.5$. The dashed black lines show the error in the extrapolated slope. We observe that the damping rate tends to zero as $\mu \to \infty$ ($\lambda \to \infty$).

$\bar{\mu} = \mu/\eta^2 \approx 2\pi \ln(\sqrt{\lambda} \eta R)$, where the cutoff R is related to the radius of curvature of the string, $\beta = \pi^3/4 \approx 7.75$ is a constant and L is the spatial period of the string.

Figure 1 shows the main result of the work: the damping rate of a string measured using the inverse square model (3) depends linearly on the inverse of the string tension. We find that the model provides a good fit to the decay rate using the parameters $\beta = 7.6 \pm 1.6$ and $\ln R = 1.3 \pm 0.3$ ($R \approx 3.6$) (after applying a modest finite width correction of $\sim 8\%$ to account for internal oscillations within the string core). These values are consistent with the analytic damping coefficient β, and indicate an effective radial cutoff $R \approx L/8$, about half the string radius of curvature $L/4$. Hence, the inverse square radiation model provides an accurate picture of an oscillating and radiating global string, predicting both the correct power law dependence $\varepsilon^{-2} \propto \mu^{-1}$ and magnitude of the radiation damping.

We also investigate the spectrum of the massless eigenmodes emitted by oscillating strings for $\lambda = 1$ and $\lambda = 10$. Figure 2 gives an example of the massless radiation emitted from a $\lambda = 1$ string with intermediate initial amplitude $A_0 = 4$, showing an apparent dominant quadrupole signal. Figure 3 shows the dominant massless radiative modes for a $\lambda = 1$ string with initial amplitude $A_0 = 1$. We observe the $\{mn\} = \{2\,0\}$ quadrupole mode is dominant (where m and n denote the θ and z eigenvalues respectively), with a $\{1\,1\}$ self-field mode present from the start of the simulation and higher modes present at $\lesssim 100\times$ magnitude. We observe similar results for higher initial amplitudes in the nonlinear regime, $A_0 = 4$ and $A_0 = 8$,

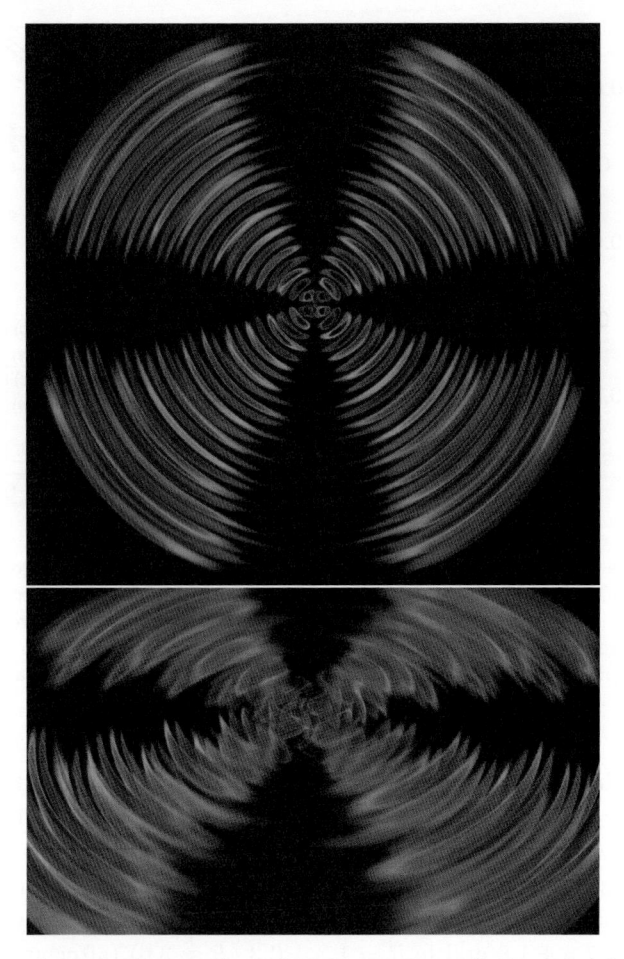

Fig. 2. Volume rendering in 3D space (x, y, z) of the massless radiation $\mathcal{D}\vartheta \cdot \hat{\mathbf{r}}$ from a $\lambda = 1$ string with initial amplitude $A_0 = 4$. The radiation is emitted from a string at the centre of the grid, with the quadrupole mode $\{mn\} = \{2\,0\}$ clearly dominant.

but with higher total magnitude and higher relative amplitude of the subdominant modes as A_0 increases. The amplitudes and spectra are similar for the more massive $\lambda = 10$ with some subtle differences discernible, including a higher initial radiation amplitude and a slightly slower amplitude decay rate. The former arises because, for $\lambda = 1$, finite size effects become important as the string core $\phi < 1$ extends into the radiation zone, causing some suppression of the quadrupole amplitude. The latter is a consequence of the $\lambda = 1$ string being lighter, so there is a larger relative effect from radiation backreaction.

Finally, we briefly present results from an investigation into the massive radiation from light strings with $\lambda \lesssim 3$. Overall, radiation via massive modes is subdominant; even for quasinonlinear intermediate amplitude regimes with $A_0 = 4$ ($\varepsilon \approx 0.7$),

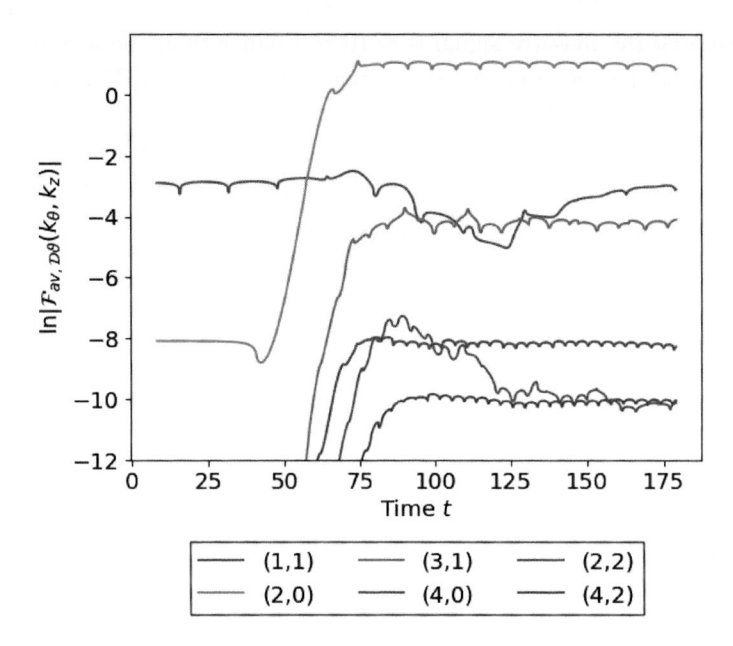

Fig. 3. Dominant 2D Fourier modes of the massless radiation $\mathcal{D}\vartheta \cdot \hat{\mathbf{r}}$ from a $\lambda = 1$ string with an initial amplitude $A_0 = 1$, measured on a cylinder at $R = 64$ and time averaged over approximate half-period $\Delta t = 33/2$.

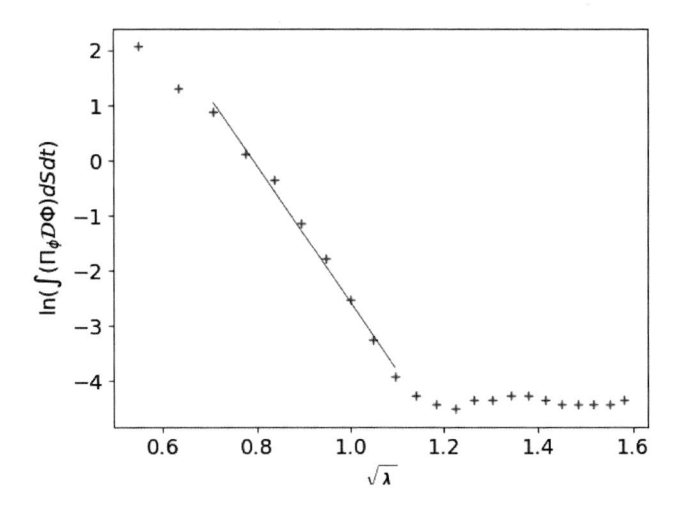

Fig. 4. Log-linear plot of the massive radiation diagnostic $\Pi_\phi \mathcal{D}\phi$ integrated over a diagnostic cylinder S at $R = 64$ from $90 \leq t \leq 228$ for $\varepsilon = 0.5$ and a range of $0.3 \leq \lambda \leq 2.5$. The black line indicates an exponential fit to the data for $0.5 \leq \lambda \leq 1.2$.

the magnitude of the massive signal is $\sim 10^3 \times$ smaller than the massless emission. We propose a simple phenomenological model adapted from Ref. 9 to obtain an expression for the energy loss per period via massive radiation,

$$E(L, A_{\rm rel}, \lambda) = \sqrt{LA_{\rm rel}} \exp\left[-\gamma\sqrt{\lambda}\frac{L}{A_{\rm rel}}\right], \qquad (4)$$

where $A_{\rm rel} = 4A/L$ and γ is a constant to be determined. Figure 4 shows the extracted massive signal $\Pi_\phi \mathcal{D}\phi$ for $A_0 = 4$ ($A_{\rm rel} = 0.5$), integrated over time from $90 \leq t \leq 228$ to give a quantitative estimate for the energy loss through this channel. We observe a clear exponential decay from $0.7 \lesssim \sqrt{\lambda} \lesssim 1.1$ ($0.5 \lesssim \lambda \lesssim 1.2$), consistent with the prediction in (4). We measure

$$\gamma = 0.193 \, (\pm \, 0.007) \qquad (5)$$

and the intercept $\ln \sqrt{LA_{\rm rel}} = 9.80 \, (\pm \, 0.41)$. The first two points are excluded due to finite width effects that appear to suppress radiation, as are $\sqrt{\lambda} \gtrsim 1.1$ ($\lambda \gtrsim 1.3$) where numerical resonance effects become significant. The latter appears to be due to limited grid resolution (despite the use of AMR simulations), but we note that in the small and intermediate amplitude regimes studied the massive radiation always remains subdominant relative to massless modes for all λ.

4. Conclusions

We have presented results from adaptive mesh refinement simulations of global cosmic strings with a range of widths given by $0.3 \leq \lambda \leq 100$. By accurately fitting the oscillation amplitude to an inverse square decay model, we have demonstrated that dual radiation predictions from the Kalb-Ramond action are accurate as we asymptotically approach the small width regime. This lends weight to the Nambu-Goto approach as an accurate method to approximate strings in a cosmological context. We further conclude that the primary radiation channel for sinusoidal string configurations is the massless quadrupole eigenmode $\{mn\} = \{2\,0\}$, strongly dominating other radiation modes even at high amplitude. Finally, we conclude that massive radiation is subdominant in quasilinear regimes and decays exponentially with $\sqrt{\lambda}$ as expected.

Acknowledgements

We thank Josu Aurrekoetxea, Katy Clough, Thomas Helfer, Eugene Lim, Miren Radia and Ulrich Sperhake for useful conversations, as well as Kacper Kornet for invaluable computing support. This work was undertaken primarily on the COSMOS supercomputer at DAMTP, University of Cambridge, funded by BEIS National E-infrastructure capital grants ST/J005673/1 and STFC grants ST/H008586/1, ST/K00333X/1 and ST/P000673/1, as well as the Cambridge CSD3 part of the STFC DiRAC HPC Facility (with STFC grants ST/P002307/1, ST/R002452/1 and ST/R00689X/1). AD is supported by a Junior Research Fellowship from Homerton

College, Cambridge, and previously by an EPSRC iCASE Studentship in partnership with Intel (EP/N509620/1, Voucher 16000206).

References

1. R. L. Davis, Cosmic Axions from Cosmic Strings, *Phys. Lett. B* **180**, 225 (1986).
2. T. Vachaspati and A. Vilenkin, Gravitational Radiation from Cosmic Strings, *Phys. Rev. D* **31**, 3052 (1985).
3. B. Allen and E. P. S. Shellard, Cosmic-String Evolution: A Numerical Simulation, *Phys. Rev. Lett.* **64**, 119 (1990).
4. R. L. Davis and E. P. S. Shellard, Do Axions Need Inflation?, *Nucl. Phys. B* **324**, 167 (1989).
5. K. Clough et al., GRChombo: Numerical Relativity with Adaptive Mesh Refinement, *Class. Quant. Grav.* **32** (2016).
6. A. Drew and E. P. S. Shellard, Radiation from Global Topological Strings using Adaptive Mesh Refinement: Methodology and Massless Modes, *arXiv:1910.01718* (2019).
7. A. Drew and E. P. S. Shellard, Radiation from Global Topological Strings using Adaptive Mesh Refinement: Massive Modes, *in prep.* (2021).
8. R. A. Battye and E. P. S. Shellard, Global String Radiation, *Nucl. Phys. B* **423**, 260 (1994).
9. K. D. Olum and J. J. Blanco-Pillado, Radiation from Cosmic String Standing Waves, *Phys. Rev. Lett.* **84**, 4288 (2000).

Analysing the scaling density of axion strings

A. Lopez-Eiguren

Institute of Cosmology, Department of Physics and Astronomy, Tufts University,
Medford, MA 02155, USA
E-mail: asier.lopez_eiguren@tufts.edu

In the QCD axion dark matter scenario with post-inflationary Peccei-Quinn symmetry breaking, the number density of axions, and hence the dark matter density, depends on the length of string per unit volume at cosmic time t, by convention written ζ/t^2. The expectation has been that the dimensionless parameter ζ tends to a constant ζ_0, a feature of a string network known as scaling. It has recently been claimed that in larger numerical simulations ζ shows a logarithmic increase with time. This case would result in a large enhancement of the string density at the QCD transition, and a substantial revision to the axion mass required for the axion to constitute all of the dark matter. With a set of new simulations of global strings we compare the standard scaling (constant-ζ) model to the logarithmic growth. We also study the approach to scaling, through measuring the root-mean-square velocity v as well as the scaled mean string separation x. We find good evidence for a fixed point in the phase-space analysis in the variables (x, v), providing a strong indication that standard scaling is taking place. We show that the approach to scaling can be well described by a two parameter velocity-one-scale (VOS) model, and show that the values of the parameters are insensitive to the initial state of the network. We conclude that the apparent corrections to ζ are artifacts of the initial conditions, rather than a property of the scaling network.

Keywords: Axionic Dark Matter, Topological Defects, Strings, Field Theory Simulations

1. Introduction

Axions[1,2] were proposed to solve the strong-CP problem, a puzzling question of why QCD does not seem to break Charge Parity (CP) symmetry in strong interactions, but these models also inevitably produce dark matter by releasing their initial potential energy density. However, the analysis of the axions would not only provide us with the information about the dark matter nature or the solution to the strong-CP problem; axion dark matter searches and cosmic microwave background experiments would provide complementary evidences of inflation, a measurement of the axion mass would also immediately determine or constrain the energy scale of cosmic inflation and recent phenomenological analysis has also indicated a possible rich interplay between QCD axions and the electroweak hierarchy problem. Therefore, the analysis of the QCD axions will provide important information about unsolved problems in physics.

The axion particles can be produced in two different scenarios in the non-thermal case. One of these scenarios is described by the so-called misalignment mechanism.[3] In this scenario, the nonperturbative effects at the QCD phase transition generate a mass and the axion field relaxes to its minimum, oscillating around it. The axions created in this process have zero momentum. The other scenario is based on the formation of topological strings after the spontaneous symmetry breaking of the Peccei-Quinn symmetry.[4] These strings show scaling behaviour and therefore emit axion particles in order to reduce their energy. After the QCD phase transition, the network of strings vanishes due to the presence of domain walls. The misalignment mechanism produces a dominant axion contribution when the axions are created before the end of inflation, otherwise axionic string radiation would produce the bulk of the axion population.

As we have mentioned, the axion[1,2] is a particle, the angular excitation of the "Peccei-Quinn" (PQ) field,[5,6] proposed to solve the strong-CP problem. The axion model has one undetermined parameter, the vacuum value of the field, f_a. The mass of the axion, m_a, can be written by using this parameter: $m_a = (\chi(T)/f_a)^{1/2}$. In this expression $\chi(T)$ is the temperature-dependent topological susceptibility of QCD. The value of f_a also determines the amount of axion dark matter that would have been produced in the early Universe, which means that it should be possible to predict the axion mass using the dark matter densities measured by the recent experiments such as Planck.[7] But to do so, we need to understand the efficiency of axion production in cosmology.

Thus, the vacuum value of the axion field, f_a, is an important energy scale to determine the axion mass. However, there is also another important energy scale to analyse the cosmological behaviour of the axion field. This energy scale is the QCD symmetry breaking scale. In the cosmological evolution of the axion field the first important event is the PQ phase transition, which is broken at a high temperature $T \sim f_a > 109$ GeV. In this phase transition a network of axionic strings are formed. These strings decay gradually emitting axion particles. At lower temperatures, temperatures similar to the QCD symmetry breaking, domain walls are formed between strings and the complex hybrid network annihilates into axions in about one Hubble time.

As we have shown the axion production analysis is complicated because topological defect, axionic strings, appear in the axionic field[8] and because the only reliable way to analyse their dynamics is through field simulations. However, numerical simulations cannot cover the whole string evolution and they must be extrapolated. The prediction of the axion density depends on having an accurate description of axion string evolution.

A physical basis is very important for the extrapolation of the simulation results. In the case of strings, the one-scale model[9] and its velocity-dependent improvement[10–12] can give the appropriate basis. These models predict that the system will acquire a scaling regime, where the mean string separation grows in proportion to cosmic time t, and the RMS velocity of the strings is constant. By scaling we mean that at distances much larger than the string width, network length-scales such as the mean string separation are proportional to the cosmic time t.

In the following, we will analyse if the axionic strings follow the standard scaling picture,[13–15] where the dynamical evolution of the network is independent of the string width and tension. Or on the contrary, the system follows the model recently put forward,[16–21] which suggest a logarithmic correction to scaling based on the logarithmic growth in the effective string tension of a global string with their mean separation.

2. Model and Network Parameters

2.1. Field dynamics

The simplest axion model can be constructed using a singlet scalar field with a U(1) symmetry, Φ, with action

$$S = \int d^4x \sqrt{-g}\left(\frac{1}{2}\partial_\mu \Phi \partial^\mu \Phi - \frac{1}{4}\lambda(\Phi^2 - \eta^2)^2\right), \tag{1}$$

where we have written the field as a two-component vector, and the U(1) symmetry is realised as a rotation on the vector.

In a FLRW metric, and when the field is coupled to a thermal bath of weakly-coupled particles, the equations of motion take the form

$$\Phi'' + 2\frac{a'}{a}\Phi' - \nabla^2 \Phi = -a^2\lambda(\Phi^2 - \eta^2(T))\Phi, \tag{2}$$

where a is the scale factor, a prime denotes differentiation with respect to conformal time τ, and in the radiation era $a \propto \tau$. The free energy of the system is minimised at the field magnitude $\eta(T)$, where $\eta^2(T) = d(T_c^2 - T^2)$, $T_c \simeq \eta$ is the critical temperature of the PQ phase transition, and d is a constant computable in perturbation theory. For $T \gg T_c$, it is energetically favourable for the field to fluctuate around $\Phi = 0$. Well below the critical temperature it is energetically favourable for the magnitude of the field to take the value η, with a massless pseudoscalar fluctuation mode (the axion) and a scalar mode of mass $m_{\text{sca}} = \sqrt{2\lambda}\eta$. During the phase transition, the direction in field space is chosen at random in uncorrelated regions of the universe, with the result that the field is forced to stay zero along lines.[22] These lines form the cores of the axion strings.[8] The size of the core is approximately $w_0 = m_{\text{sca}}^{-1}$.

2.2. Network parameters from field averages

The evolution of the network of strings produced after the symmetry breaking can be analysed using the string length ℓ and the RMS velocity v of the strings.

In order to compute the string length we can use a couple of estimators. On the one hand we can use the number of plaquettes pierced by strings. This estimator is known as the winding length ℓ_{w}. The length of the strings is obtained by multiplying the number of plaquettes pierced by strings by the physical lattice spacing $a\delta x$ and then correcting the value by factor of $2/3$ to compensate for the Manhattan effect.[23] The plaquettes pierced by strings are identified by working out the "winding" phase of the field around each plaquette of the lattice.[24] This is an estimate of the length of string measured in the "universe frame", that is, observers comoving with the expansion of the universe.

One can obtain other measures of length taking into account that the energy of a string configuration is proportional to its length. In this case the estimators are constructed using local functions of the fields. Neglecting the expansion of the universe and considering the energy components to be weighted, we can write the rest-frame length ℓ_r and the mean square velocity as

$$\ell_r = \frac{E + f_V L}{\mu(1 - f_V)}, \tag{3}$$

$$v_L^2 = \frac{E + L}{E + f_V L}, \tag{4}$$

where the subscript L denotes the use of the Lagrangian to obtain the estimate. The energy, E, and the lagrangian, L, are defined as:

$$E = E_\pi + E_D + E_V, \tag{5}$$

$$L = E_\pi - E_D - E_V, \tag{6}$$

where E_π is the weighted kinetic energy, E_D is the weighted gradient energy and E_V is the weighted potential energy. Likewise, μ is the weighted mass per unit length of a static string and f_V is the fraction contributed by the potential energy density. In this case their values are $\mu = 0.892\eta^2$ and $f_V = 0.368$. For more information about the weighting procedure and computation of the values of μ and f_V we refer the reader to.[15]

An alternative way of estimating the string velocity comes from the pressure,

$$p\mathcal{V} = E_\pi - \frac{1}{3} E_D - E_V, \tag{7}$$

giving another mean square velocity estimator

$$v_\omega^2 = \frac{1 + 3\omega + 2f_V}{2 + f_V(1 + 3\omega)}, \tag{8}$$

where $\omega = p\mathcal{V}/E$ is the equation of state parameter of the strings. A third estimate for the string velocity can be constructed from the ratio of the kinetic to gradient energies,[25]

$$R_s = \frac{E_\pi}{E_D}, \tag{9}$$

which can be rearranged to give

$$v_s^2 = \frac{2R_s}{1 + R_s}. \tag{10}$$

Following the analysis performed in,[15] the estimators that we are going to use in this paper will be the rest frame length, ℓ_r, and the velocity estimator derived from the kinetic and gradient energies, v_s.

In a cosmological simulations one can express the string length in terms of Hubble lengths per Hubble volume, or

$$\zeta_r = \frac{\ell_r t^2}{\mathcal{V}}. \tag{11}$$

When investigating scaling in string networks, it is more transparent to parametrise the string density by the mean string separation, which is obtained from measures of the string length via

$$\xi_r = \sqrt{\frac{\mathcal{V}}{\ell_r}}. \tag{12}$$

The above estimators were derived for a Minkowski space-time. In an expanding background, one can view the space-time coordinates as representing comoving position and conformal time, from which physical lengths follow by multiplication by the scale factor a.

3. Simulations

In order to perform simulations of axionic string we discretise the equations of motion (2) and evolve them on a cubic lattice with periodic boundary conditions. The system is evolved in conformal time τ. The simulations analysed in this paper are the same set of simulations used in,[14,15] where we analyzed lattices with 1024, 2048 and 4096 sites per dimension with spatial resolution of $\delta x \eta = 0.5$ and conformal time steps of $\delta \tau \eta = 0.1$. We will give a short summary of the procedure and we refer the reader interested in more details to.[14,15]

The field configuration is initiated at conformal time τ_{start} by setting the canonical momentum to zero and the scalar field to be a Gaussian random field with power spectrum $P_\Phi(k) = A\left[1 + (kl_\phi)^2\right]^{-1}$, were A is chosen so that $\langle \Phi^2 \rangle = \eta^2$ and l_ϕ is the field correlation length in comoving coordinates. We use different values of l_ϕ in order to cover a range of string separations in the initial conditions. The values used are $l_\phi = 5, 10, 20, 40$, where $l_\phi = 40$ case have been used only for $s = 1$ case. In order to allow the strings to form, and to remove the energy excess in the field fluctuations around the string configurations, we evolve this configuration with a diffusion equation with unit diffusion constant until conformal time τ_{diff}. We then apply the second-order time evolution equation (2).

Similarly to our previous paper, we extract data from simulations with both fixed comoving string width and fixed physical string width. We promote the scalar self-coupling constant to be a time dependent parameter $\lambda = \lambda_0/a^{2(1-s)}$ following the PRS method.[26] This makes the comoving string width decrease with conformal time as:

$$w(\tau) = \frac{w_0}{a^s(\tau)}. \tag{13}$$

The physical equation of motion, where the physical string width remains constant at $w_0 = 1/\sqrt{2\lambda_0}\eta$, and the comoving width decreases with time, corresponds to $s = 1$. With $s = 0$ the comoving width is constant at w_0 and the physical string width increases in time.

For the $s = 1$ case, it is difficult to avoid the string width being larger than the Hubble length at early times, which also means that the relaxation of the field to its equilibrium value is longer than a Hubble time. In order to speed up the string formation, we arrange the time-dependence of the coupling so that strings are formed and diffused with a constant comoving width, equal to their final comoving width. At the end of the diffusion period, the string width is much smaller than its physical value w_0. The string width is then allowed to grow by setting $s = -1$ until τ_{cg}, which is when the string core has expanded to its correct physical width w_0. After conformal time τ_{cg}, the physical evolution with $s = 1$ starts. We call this procedure core growth. Simulations end at conformal time τ_{end}.

Table 1 contains all simulation parameter choices that have been considered in the procedures described above. Four simulations with different random number seeds were carried out at each parameter choice. The data are analysed in cosmic time $t = (\tau/\tau_{end})^2 \tau_{end}/2$.

Table 1. Run parameters used in simulations. See text for explanation.

Model	$s = 1$	$s = 0$
$l_\phi \eta$	(5,10,20,40)	(5,10,20)
$\tau_{start}\eta$	50	50
$\tau_{diff}\eta$	70	70
s_{cg}	-1	–
$\tau_{cg}\eta$	271.11	–
$\tau_{end}\eta$	1050	1050

4. Results

In Fig. 1 we show the evolution of the mean string separation (12) and the RMS velocities for all the simulations performed with size 4096. In these figures the solid line represents the mean obtained by averaging over realisations and the shaded regions the 1σ standard deviations. In both estimators the uncertainties are worked out by propagating the fluctuations in the weighted energies E_π, E_D and E_V. The color code is as follows: black for $l_\phi \eta = 5$, red for $l_\phi \eta = 10$, blue for $l_\phi \eta = 20$, and green for $l_\phi \eta = 40$. Note that we only have $l_\phi \eta = 40$ simulations in the $s = 1$ case. The end of the core growth period is shown as a vertical green dashed line.

Figure 1 show that, independently of the initial field correlation length, all simulations are compatible, *i.e.* all of them give separation and velocity data which are within 1σ of each other. Moreover, the behaviour of both estimators (ξ and v) qualitatively agrees with the standard scaling, showing a tendency towards linear growth in ξ and a constant RMS velocity.

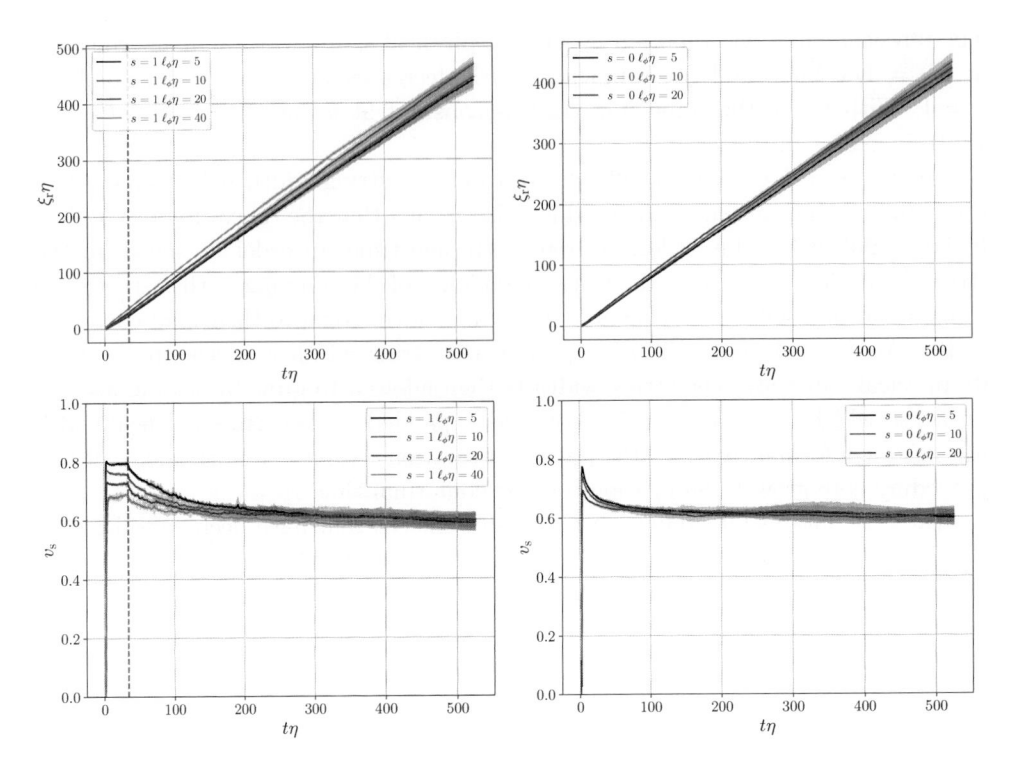

Fig. 1. Mean string separation ξ_r and velocity v_s evolution for $s = 1$ (right) and $s = 0$ (left).

Now we are going to analyse more in detail the scaling behavior of the system. First we will analyse the Length estimator and compare the different behaviors proposed in the literature for the scaling regime. Afterwards using the both length and velocity estimators we will analyse the approach to the scaling phase.

4.1. Length Estimator

As we have previously mentioned after a relatively short period of relaxation, the mean string separation ξ tends to a line that can be well fitted with

$$\xi = 2\beta(t - t_0). \tag{14}$$

where β and t_0 are parameters to be fitted. β is predicted to be a universal parameter, while t_0 is a phenomenological fit parameter to reduce the effect on estimates of β of the initial conditions and evolution of the RMS velocity. This model is known as the standard scaling and in this case the scaling value of the string length in terms of Hubble lengths per Hubble volume, ζ, is $\zeta_0 = 1/4\beta^2$.

We measure the parameters β and t_0 for each one of the individual runs we performed with a linear fit over the ranges in conformal time defined by the boundary times $\tau_b = [6, 10]\tau_s$, and $\tau_s\eta = [25, 50, 100]$ for $N = [1k, 2k, 4k]$. That is, in the $1k$ case the fitting range is $\tau_b = [150, 250]$. The times are chosen in the last half of the conformal time range to minimise the biases coming from the initial conditions.

The values obtained are shown in Fig 2. The color code in this figure is the same as in Fig. 1 and the style of each point represent the size of the simulation box, circles represent $1k$ simulations, triangles pointing downwards represent $2k$ simulations and triangles pointing upwards represent $4k$ simulations. The parameter t_f is taken to be as the end of the fitting period.

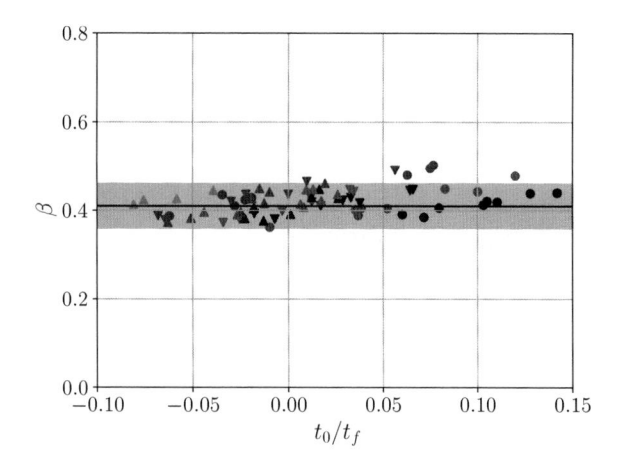

Fig. 2. Parameters β and t_0 for each one of the individual runs.

In Fig. 2 we have also added the mean value for β and its 1σ standard deviation obtained in.[15] As we can see all the points agree with the average value within 2σ and there is no correlation between the value of t_0 and β, showing that the initial conditions are not affecting the value obtained for β.

We now turn to the alternative model recently put forward: logarithmic[16–19,21] correction to scaling

$$\zeta(t) = \zeta_0^* + \alpha^* \log(\eta t) \tag{15}$$

where ζ_0^* and α^* are the fitting parameters. We performed fits over the ranges used previously and we show the values in Fig. 3, where we use the value of t_0 computed previously.

In Fig. 3 we have also added the mean value for β and its 1σ standard deviation obtained in,[15] but in this case translated to ζ_0. One can see that there is a clear correlation between the values of ζ_0^* and α^* with respect to t_0, showing that the initial conditions are affecting the values. Moreover, in the case that $t_0 = 0$ the value of α^* is zero and ζ_0^* agrees with the value obtained in.[15]

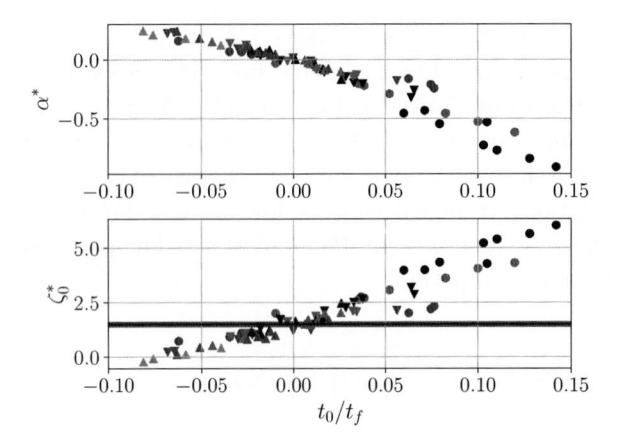

Fig. 3. Parameters ζ_0^* and α^* for each one of the individual runs.

4.2. Length and Velocity Estimators

As we have seen in the previous section, there is a small departure from standard scaling in the earlier phases of the simulations. It is necessary to understand this departure to improve the estimates of the asymptotic behavior of v and ξ, or more precisely the asymptotic values of the *scaled mean string separation*,

$$x = \xi/t. \tag{16}$$

In the previous Section, we have studied scaling using ξ only. Now we will also use the RMS velocity data, which gives extra information about the approach to scaling, and we will avoid the use of t_0. We will see that in doing so we will improve the accuracy of the estimate of β, while remaining consistent with our previous estimate. The analysis of this Section will be performed in simulations with size 4096.

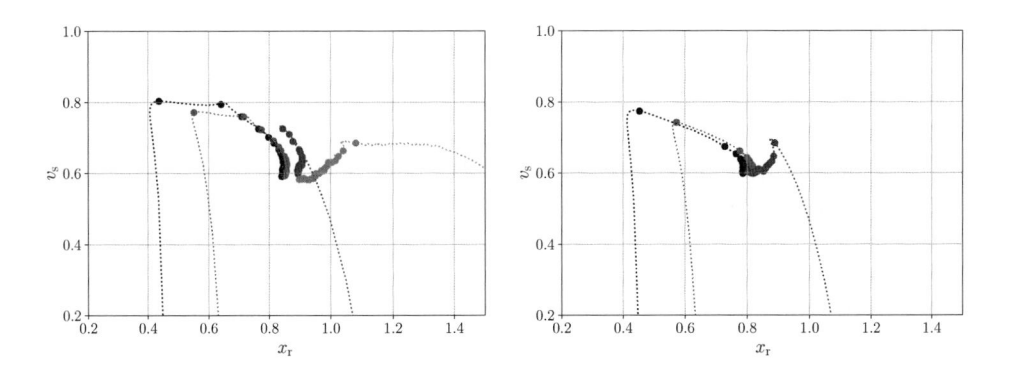

Fig. 4. The evolution of the network in the phase space (x, v).

In Fig. 4 we show the evolution of the network in the phase space (x, v). The phase space representation shows clearly the different regimes in which the network evolves. A rapid increase in the RMS velocity, while the inter-string distance remains nearly constant, happens after the end of the diffusion period, when strings are accelerated under their curvature. In the case of $s = 1$, after the diffusion period we impose a core growth period as part of the preparation of the initial conditions, where the velocities remain approximately constant but the scaled mean string separation changes. This change is different for different initial conditions. For correlation lengths $l_\phi \eta = 5$, 10, the scaled mean string separation grows, whereas for correlation lengths $l_\phi \eta = 20$, 40 it decreases. Finally, when the physical equations of motion (2) are being solved, the system starts to spiral towards an apparent common fixed point for all simulations.

The evolution of the scaled mean string separation and the RMS velocity can be modeled by the velocity-dependent one-scale (VOS) model.[9–12] Assuming that the statistical distribution of string configurations and velocities has a universal form the model parametrised it by the string separation ξ and the RMS velocity v.

The model uses the following equations to describe the dynamical system,

$$\frac{d\xi}{dt} = H\xi(1+v^2) + \frac{1}{2}cv, \tag{17}$$

$$\frac{dv}{dt} = (1-v^2)\left(\frac{k}{\xi} - 2Hv\right), \tag{18}$$

where H is the Hubble parameter. There are two phenomenological parameters, k and c. The parameter c describes the efficiency of the energy loss mechanism, while the parameter k describes the correlation between the string curvature and the velocity.

Using the dimensionless mean string separation variable x (16), and $H = 1/2t$ since we are considering a radiation-dominated universe, we have,

$$t\dot{x} = \frac{1}{2}x\left(v^2 - 1\right) + \frac{c}{2}v \tag{19}$$

$$t\dot{v} = (1 - v^2)\left(\frac{k}{x} - v\right) \tag{20}$$

This dynamical system has a fixed point in the relevant region $0 \leq x$, $0 \leq v < 1$,

$$x_* = \sqrt{k(c+k)} \qquad v_* = \sqrt{\frac{k}{(c+k)}}. \tag{21}$$

The fixed point is a stable spiral. We plot flows in the phase diagram predicted by the VOS model in Fig. 5 for the global best fit (x_*, v_*) (computed from a χ^2 analysis; for more details see[15]), along with the mean values of selected (x, v) from the simulations. The stable spiral form is clearly visible in the streamlines.

To show in a more quantitative way how well the VOS model describe the evolution of the system, we show in Fig. 6 the relative difference between the simulation

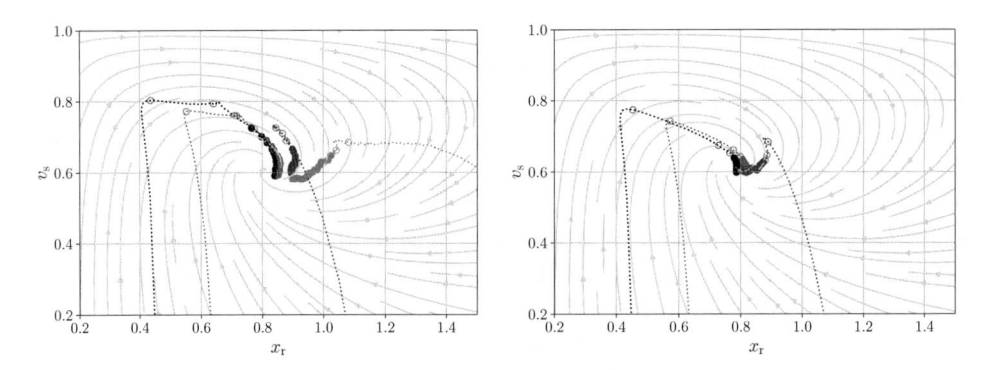

Fig. 5. The evolution of the network in the phase space (x, v) with stream lines.

time series data and the VOS best-fit model for each (s, l_ϕ), where the VOS model is initialized at t_{fit}, which is the same as in the previous Section. Shaded regions correspond to the uncertainties propagated from simulation estimators. It can be observed that the mean relative difference always lies below 5% level of deviation, with zero deviation always within the errors.

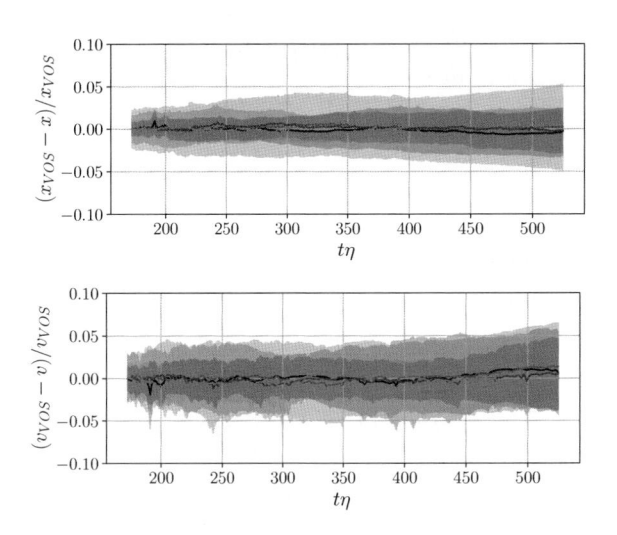

Fig. 6. Relative errors.

To understand better how the network evolves it is fundamental to analyse it in terms of the length density parameter ζ (11). In Fig. 7 we show ζ plottted against the logarithm of time, in order to emphasise the earlier times when the network is further away from scaling. The case that we are showing is this plot is $s = 1$, where we have also added the best-fit VOS models for each correlation length, and their extrapolation to larger values of time. The asymptotic values obtained in[15]

($\zeta_{r,*} = 1.50 \pm 0.11$) is also shown in the figure. The solid line represents the central value and the shaded region represents the 1σ error. In the figure we can see that the simulations approach the asymptotic value of ζ from below and that at the end of the simulations they are still slowly increasing, but within 20% of its asymptotic value. This increase is more visible in the simulations that start very underdense and therefore have much more to evolve until they reach scaling. The extrapolated values of the VOS model show that the system will reach the asymptotic value and become constant.

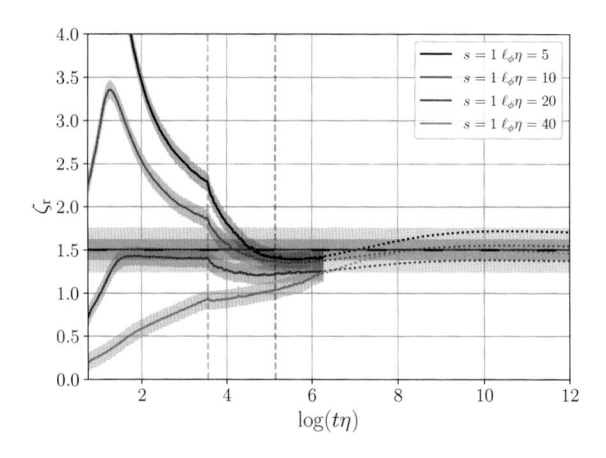

Fig. 7. ζ evolution.

5. Conclusions

In this paper we have analysed the evolution of the mean string separation ξ and the RMS velocity for an axion string network in the radiation era. The axion model has been constructed using a singlet scalar field with a U(1) symmetry, where the field has been considered as a two-component vector and the U(1) symmetry has been realised as a rotation on the vector.

Firstly, we have fitted the mean string separation (12) from the simulations we have performed with two two-parameter models: the standard scaling model with the usual time offset t_0 to account for the initial string evolution and a constant parameter β, and a model with a logarithmically increasing ζ (11). Using linear fits to obtain the values for β we have seen that the value does not depend on the initial conditions, or on the value of t_0. The coefficients of the logarithmically increasing model can be understood in terms of the dependence of ζ on the initial string evolution parameter t_0, and describe a disguised approach to scaling for non-zero values of t_0. We find that the value of the parameter describing the logarithmic increase is consistent with zero when $t_0/t_f \to 0$, where t_f is the final fitting time. In this case the constant term of the model is consistent with the standard scaling values.

Secondly, we have fitted the results of our set of numerical simulations to a two-parameter VOS model (18). We find that the evolution of the network is well described, qualitatively and quantitatively, by the VOS model. Qualitatively, we see that after the effects of the initial conditions are gone the systems turns into a curved approach to the fixed point in the (x, v) plane. A deeper analysis of the spiral behavior of the system showed that the apparent logarithmic growth in ζ is a transient epoch of the system, and that the length of this transient epoch depends on how far the initial conditions are from the fix point. After the transient epoch the system tends to a constant ζ evolution.

Acknowledgments

This work has been performed in collaboration with Mark Hindmarsh, Joanes Lizarraga and Jon Urrestilla. ALE (ORCID ID 0000-0002-1696-3579) is supported by the National Science Foundation grant PHY-1820872. This work has been possible thanks to the computational resources on the STFC DiRAC HPC facility obtained under the dp116 project. Our simulations also made use of facilities at the i2Basque academic network and CSC Finland.

References

1. S. Weinberg, A New Light Boson?, *Phys. Rev. Lett.* **40**, 223 (1978).
2. F. Wilczek, Problem of Strong P and T Invariance in the Presence of Instantons, *Phys. Rev. Lett.* **40**, 279 (1978).
3. J. M. Cline, TASI Lectures on Early Universe Cosmology: Inflation, Baryogenesis and Dark Matter, *PoS* **TASI2018**, p. 001 (2019).
4. R. L. Davis, Cosmic Axions from Cosmic Strings, *Phys. Lett.* B **180**, 225 (1986).
5. R. D. Peccei and H. R. Quinn, CP Conservation in the Presence of Instantons, *Phys. Rev. Lett.* **38**, 1440 (1977).
6. R. D. Peccei and H. R. Quinn, Constraints Imposed by CP Conservation in the Presence of Instantons, *Phys. Rev. D* **16**, 1791 (1977).
7. P. A. R. Ade *et al.*, Planck 2015 results. XIII. Cosmological parameters, *Astron. Astrophys.* **594**, p. A13 (2016).
8. R. L. Davis, Cosmic Axions from Cosmic Strings, *Phys. Lett.* B **180**, 225 (1986).
9. T. W. B. Kibble, Evolution of a system of cosmic strings, *Nucl. Phys.* B **252**, p. 227 (1985), [Erratum: Nucl.Phys.B 261, 750 (1985)].
10. C. J. A. P. Martins and E. P. S. Shellard, Quantitative string evolution, *Phys. Rev. D* **54**, 2535 (1996).
11. C. J. A. P. Martins and E. P. S. Shellard, Extending the velocity dependent one scale string evolution model, *Phys. Rev. D* **65**, p. 043514 (2002).
12. C. J. A. P. Martins, Scaling properties of cosmological axion strings, *Phys. Lett.* B **788**, 147 (2019).
13. A. Lopez-Eiguren, J. Lizarraga, M. Hindmarsh and J. Urrestilla, Cosmic Microwave Background constraints for global strings and global monopoles, *JCAP* **07**, p. 026 (2017).
14. M. Hindmarsh, J. Lizarraga, A. Lopez-Eiguren and J. Urrestilla, Scaling Density of Axion Strings, *Phys. Rev. Lett.* **124**, p. 021301 (2020).

15. M. Hindmarsh, J. Lizarraga, A. Lopez-Eiguren and J. Urrestilla, Approach to scaling in axion string networks, *Phys. Rev. D* **103**, p. 103534 (2021).
16. M. Gorghetto, E. Hardy and G. Villadoro, Axions from Strings: The Attractive Solution, *JHEP* **07**, p. 151 (2018).
17. A. Vaquero, J. Redondo and J. Stadler, Early seeds of axion miniclusters, *JCAP* **04**, p. 012 (2019).
18. M. Kawasaki, T. Sekiguchi, M. Yamaguchi and J. Yokoyama, Long-term dynamics of cosmological axion strings, *PTEP* **2018**, p. 091E01 (2018).
19. M. Buschmann, J. W. Foster and B. R. Safdi, Early-Universe Simulations of the Cosmological Axion, *Phys. Rev. Lett.* **124**, p. 161103 (2020).
20. M. Gorghetto, E. Hardy and G. Villadoro, More axions from strings, *SciPost Phys.* **10**, p. 050 (2021).
21. M. Buschmann, J. W. Foster, A. Hook, A. Peterson, D. E. Willcox, W. Zhang and B. R. Safdi, Dark Matter from Axion Strings with Adaptive Mesh Refinement (8 2021).
22. T. W. B. Kibble, Topology of Cosmic Domains and Strings, *J. Phys. A* **9**, 1387 (1976).
23. L. Fleury and G. D. Moore, Axion dark matter: strings and their cores, *JCAP* **01**, p. 004 (2016).
24. T. Vachaspati and A. Vilenkin, Formation and Evolution of Cosmic Strings, *Phys. Rev. D* **30**, p. 2036 (1984).
25. M. Hindmarsh, J. Lizarraga, J. Urrestilla, D. Daverio and M. Kunz, Scaling from gauge and scalar radiation in Abelian Higgs string networks, *Phys. Rev. D* **96**, p. 023525 (2017).
26. W. H. Press, B. S. Ryden and D. N. Spergel, Dynamical Evolution of Domain Walls in an Expanding Universe, *Astrophys. J.* **347**, 590 (1989).

Electroweak axion string and superconductivity

Yu Hamada

Theory Center, High Energy Accelerator Research Organization (KEK),
Tsukuba 305-0801, Japan
E-mail: yuhamada@post.kek.jp

Yoshihiko Abe and Koichi Yoshioka

Department of Physics, Kyoto University, Kitashirakawa,
Kyoto 606-8502, Japan
E-mail: y.abe@gauge.scphys.kyoto-u.ac.jp
yoshioka@gauge.scphys.kyoto-u.ac.jp

We study axion strings with the electroweak gauge flux in the DFSZ axion model and show that these strings, called electroweak axions, exhibit superconductivity without fermionic zero modes. We also show that the primordial magnetic field in the early universe can induce a large electric current along the string. A pair of the strings carrying such a large current feels a net attractive force between them and can form a Y-shaped junction in the early universe, whose formation probability is roughly estimated to be 1/2.

Keywords: Axion; Cosmic string; Soliton; Higgs

1. Introduction

The strong CP problem is one of the mysteries in the Standard Model (SM) of particle physics. The problem can be naturally solved by the Peccei-Quinn mechanism, in which a global symmetry denoted by $U(1)_{\rm PQ}$ is assumed to be spontaneously broken and provides a (pseudo) Nambu-Goldstone particle, the axion.[1–4] The axion can also play a role of cold dark matter.

The DFSZ model[5,6] is a popular model providing the axion as well as the KSVZ model.[7,8] In the DFSZ model, the scalar sector of the SM is extended to have two Higgs doublets and one SM-singlet complex scalar. The scalar fields and the SM fermions are assumed to be charged under the $U(1)_{\rm PQ}$ symmetry, which is spontaneously broken by a vacuum expectation value (VEV) of the complex scalar. The axion is a linear combination of imaginary components of the doublets and the complex scalar.

It is known that if the $U(1)_{\rm PQ}$ symmetry is broken after the cosmological inflation, the axion strings, which are global cosmic strings, are created by the Kibble-Zurek mechanism.[9,10] To avoid dominating the energy of the universe, the strings should lose their energy by reconnection. When the probability of the reconnection is sufficiently close to unity, the number density of the strings approach $\mathcal{O}(1)$ values per Hubble length, called the scaling regime.

Table 1. Quantum charges of scalar fields.

	H_1	H_2	S
$SU(2)_W$	**2**	**2**	**1**
$U(1)_Y$	1	1	0
$U(1)_{\rm PQ}$	1	-1	1

It has been believed that axion strings almost always reconnect when they collide. This is because the interaction between the strings is thought to be dominated by exchange of the (massless) axion as a long-range force. This is analogous to the case of the magnetic flux tube in the type-II superconductor. However, when there is a strong attractive force between them, they can form a bound state called Y-junction.[11,12] When the Y-junction is formed, the reconnection does not work successfully, making the evolution of the string network non-trivial. Is such an attractive force realized for axion strings?

Sometimes, cosmic strings can be superconducting when $U(1)_{\rm EM}$ is broken inside them. This is called the superconducting string.[13] Electric current flows along the string without dissipation and can induce magnetic attractive interaction between the strings. This enables them to form Y-junctions!

In this work,[14] we show that the axion string in the DFSZ model can become a superconducting string after the breaking of the electroweak (EW) symmetry.[a] This is because the charged fields, the charged Higgs and W bosons, acquire non-zero values inside the string and the $U(1)_{\rm EM}$ symmetry is spontaneously broken there. This is a similar situation to superconductivity of non-Abelian vortices[21,22] and of the $U(1) \times \tilde{U}(1)$ model considered by Witten.[13] Remarkably, the amount of the supercurrent can be of order of the $U(1)_{\rm PQ}$ breaking scale resulting in large magnetic energy. As a consequence, the strings feel a large magnetic interaction, which can overcome the one from the axion exchange. The formation probability of the Y-junctions is roughly estimated to be 1/2.

2. DFSZ axion model

Throughout this article, we concentrate on the bosonic sector of the DFSZ model. The particle contents and the charge assignments under the SM gauge group and the $U(1)_{\rm PQ}$ are shown in Tab. 1. We introduce a SM-singlet complex scalar S and two $SU(2)_W$ doublets, H_1 and H_2, both with the hypercharge $Y = 1$. The Lagrangian which describes the EW and scalar sectors is written as

$$\mathcal{L} = -\frac{1}{4}(Y_{\mu\nu})^2 - \frac{1}{4}(W_{\mu\nu}^a)^2 + \sum_{i=1,2} |D_\mu H_i|^2 + |\partial_\mu S|^2 - V(H_1, H_2, S). \quad (1)$$

---

[a]Our mechanism of superconductivity is different from one using fermionic zeromodes.[15–20] In the DFSZ model, the fermionic zeromodes should be irrelevant for the dynamics of the strings because the mass scale of the SM fermions are much lighter than the $U(1)_{\rm PQ}$ breaking scale.

Here, $Y_{\mu\nu}$ and $W_{\mu\nu}^a$ describe field strength tensors of the hypercharge and weak gauge interactions, respectively, with μ (ν) and a being Lorentz and weak iso-spin indices, respectively. D_μ represents the covariant derivative acting on the Higgs fields, and the index i runs $i = 1, 2$. The scalar potential $V(H_1, H_2, S)$ being invariant under the charge assignments of Tab. 1 is

$$V(H_1, H_2, S) = V_H + V_S + V_{\text{mix}}, \qquad (2)$$

where each part is given by

$$V_H = m_{11}^2 H_1^\dagger H_1 + m_{22}^2 H_2^\dagger H_2 + \frac{\beta_1}{2}\left(H_1^\dagger H_1\right)^2 + \frac{\beta_2}{2}\left(H_2^\dagger H_2\right)^2$$
$$+ \beta_3 \left(H_1^\dagger H_1\right)\left(H_2^\dagger H_2\right) + \beta_4 \left(H_1^\dagger H_2\right)\left(H_2^\dagger H_1\right), \qquad (3)$$

$$V_S = -m_S^2 |S|^2 + \lambda_S |S|^4, \qquad (4)$$

$$V_{\text{mix}} = \left(\kappa S^2 H_1^\dagger H_2 + \text{h.c.}\right) + \kappa_{1S} |S|^2 |H_1|^2 + \kappa_{2S} |S|^2 |H_2|^2, \qquad (5)$$

with $m_S^2 > 0$ which admits S to acquire a non-zero VEV: $\langle S \rangle = v_s$. From astrophysical constraints, v_s is supposed to be $\mathcal{O}(10^{8-12})$ GeV. Without loss of generality, we can suppose that the Higgs fields develop VEVs as $\langle H_1 \rangle = (0, v_1)^{\mathrm{T}}$, $\langle H_2 \rangle = (0, v_2)^{\mathrm{T}}$ with $v_1, v_2 \in \mathbb{R}$. For simplicity, we take $v_1 = v_2 \equiv v$ in this article. Then the electroweak scale, v_{EW} ($\simeq 246$ GeV), can be expressed by these VEVs as $v_{\text{EW}}^2 = 4v^2$.

3. Electroweak axion strings

Similarly to other axion models, the DFSZ axion model provides a vortex string solution known as the axion string corresponding to the breaking of $U(1)_{\text{PQ}}$. On the other hand, after the electroweak phase transition, the axion string can contain flux tubes of the $SU(2)_W \times U(1)_Y$ gauge fields like the Abrikosov-Nielsen-Olesen vortex[23,24] since the two Higgs doublets also acquire the VEVs. We call such vortex strings the EW axion strings.

3.1. *Axion string in DFSZ model*

We first review the conventional axion string in this subsection. Let us consider a case that the $U(1)_{\text{PQ}}$ symmetry is spontaneously broken by $\langle S \rangle \neq 0$ but the EW symmetry remains unbroken, $\langle H_1 \rangle = \langle H_2 \rangle = (0,0)^{\mathrm{T}}$. This situation is realized in the early universe when the temperature of the thermal bath T_{th} satisfies $v_{EW} \ll T_{th} \ll v_s$. In this case, as is well-known, a vortex-string configuration associated with the global $U(1)_{\text{PQ}}$ symmetry exists as a solution to the equation of motion (EOM), which is called the axion string in the literature. The configuration located on the z-axis is described by the following ansatz

$$S = v_s e^{i\theta} \phi(r), \qquad H_1 = H_2 = \begin{pmatrix} 0 \\ 0 \end{pmatrix}, \qquad (6)$$

where r and θ are the distance from the z-axis and the rotational angle, respectively, i.e., $x + iy = re^{i\theta}$. The profile function $\phi(r)$ satisfies the boundary conditions

$$\phi(0) = 0, \quad \phi(\infty) = 1. \tag{7}$$

The detailed form of $\phi(r)$ is determined by solving the EOM. This string has a winding number associated with the $U(1)_{\text{PQ}}$ symmetry, and hence is topologically stable. The $U(1)_{\text{PQ}}$ symmetry is restored at the string core because of $\phi(0) = 0$.

After these axion strings are produced in the early universe, their string network evolves to the scaling regime. This is because the interaction between the strings is dominated by exchange of massless axion particles, resulting in the long-range repulsive force for two parallel axion strings with the same topological charge. The potential of the interaction $V_{\text{st.}}$ is approximately given as $V_{\text{st.}} \sim -v_s^2 \log R$ with R being the distance between the pair.

3.2. *Electroweak axion string with W-flux*

Next, we discuss the EW axion strings. Let us consider a string configuration after the EW phase transition $T_{th} \lesssim v_{\text{EW}}$. The two doublets also acquire the VEVs and can have winding phases.[14] There are three patterns of the winding phases, only one of which (called type-C EW axion string in Ref. 14) is studied in the following.

We consider a configuration that has winding phases in $U(1)_{\text{PQ}}$ and in the $U(1)_{W^1}$ subgroup of the $SU(2)_W$ gauge group. Its asymptotic form is given as

$$S \sim v_s e^{i\theta}, \tag{8}$$

$$H_1 \sim \frac{1}{2} v e^{i\theta} e^{i\theta\sigma_1} \begin{pmatrix} 0 \\ 1 \end{pmatrix}, \quad H_2 \sim \frac{1}{2} v e^{-i\theta} e^{i\theta\sigma_1} \begin{pmatrix} 0 \\ 1 \end{pmatrix}, \tag{9}$$

at $r \to \infty$. The exponential factor with σ_1 means a rotation in the direction of $U(1)_{W^1}$. Since these configuration are singular at $r = 0$, they must be smeared by introducing profile functions as follows:

$$\begin{cases} S = v_s e^{i\theta} \phi(r) \\ H_1 = \frac{1}{2} v_1 e^{i\theta} \begin{pmatrix} f(r)e^{i\theta} - h(r)e^{-i\theta} \\ f(r)e^{i\theta} + h(r)e^{-i\theta} \end{pmatrix} \\ H_2 = \frac{1}{2} v_2 e^{-i\theta} \begin{pmatrix} h(r)e^{i\theta} - f(r)e^{-i\theta} \\ h(r)e^{i\theta} + f(r)e^{-i\theta} \end{pmatrix} \end{cases} \tag{10}$$

The profile functions $f(r), h(r)$ and $\phi(r)$ satisfy the following boundary conditions,

$$f(0) = \phi(0) = 0, \quad \partial_r h|_{r=0} = 0, \quad f(\infty) = h(\infty) = \phi(\infty) = 1. \tag{11}$$

Note that $h(r)$ does not necessarily vanish at the center of the string. Due to the non-zero value of $h(0)$, the EW symmetry is not restored inside the string.

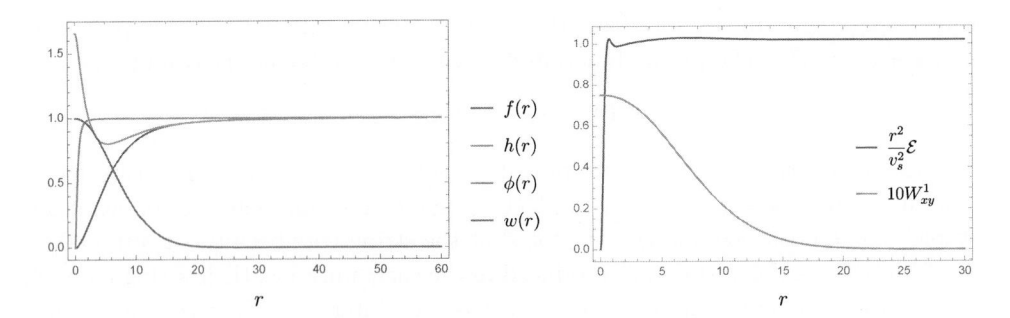

Fig. 1. Numerical solution for the EW axion string. Also we adopt a length unit as $v_s^{-1} = 0.5$. (left): Plots of profile functions. The profile function of the W^1 field, $w(r)$, approaches to zero as $r \to \infty$ starting from unity at $r = 0$. (right): Plots of energy density divided by v_s^2/r^2 and the W^1-flux density multiplied by 10. The tension integrated over $0 \leq r \leq 120\, v_s^{-1}$ is 140.604. The total value of the W^1-flux is calculated to 19.3208, which is consistent with Eq. (14).

To cancel the gradient energy from the windings for $U(1)_{W^1}$ at infinity, the W^1 gauge field is induced as

$$W_i^1 = \frac{-2}{g} \frac{\epsilon_{ij} x_j}{r^2} (1 - w(r)), \tag{12}$$

and $A_i = Z_i = 0$. The profile function $w(r)$ satisfies

$$w(0) = 1, \quad w(\infty) = 0. \tag{13}$$

This string has the confined W^1-flux

$$\Phi_{W^1} = \oint_{r=\infty} dx_i\, W_i^1 = \frac{4\pi}{g}. \tag{14}$$

This feature is similar to the electroweak strings[25,26] in the SM and its extended models. The detailed behavior of the profile functions, ϕ, f, h, and w are obtained by solving the EOMs numerically. The obtained numerical solutions are shown in Fig. 1.

The most important feature of this string is that the $U(1)_{\rm EM}$ symmetry is spontaneously broken inside the string core because the W^1 boson acquires a non-zero value Eqs. (12) and (14). (The charged component of the Higgs doublets also acquires a non-zero value, see Ref. 14). Actually, that is generally inevitable for a configuration with a non-vanishing winding number for charged components,[21,22] i.e., a configuration whose asymptotic form is $\exp[i\hat{T}(\theta)] H_i(\theta = 0)$ with a non-Abelian generator $\hat{T}(\theta)$ satisfying $[\hat{T}(\theta), \hat{Q}] \neq 0$, where $\hat{Q}$ is the generator of $U(1)_{\rm EM}$. ($\hat{T} = \sigma_1 \theta$ in our case.) Due to this breaking of $U(1)_{\rm EM}$, the string is a superconducting string. We discuss its consequence in the next section.

In Ref. 14, other two types of the EW axion strings are studied. Since they do not break $U(1)_{\rm EM}$ inside it and are not superconducting ones, we do not consider them in this article.

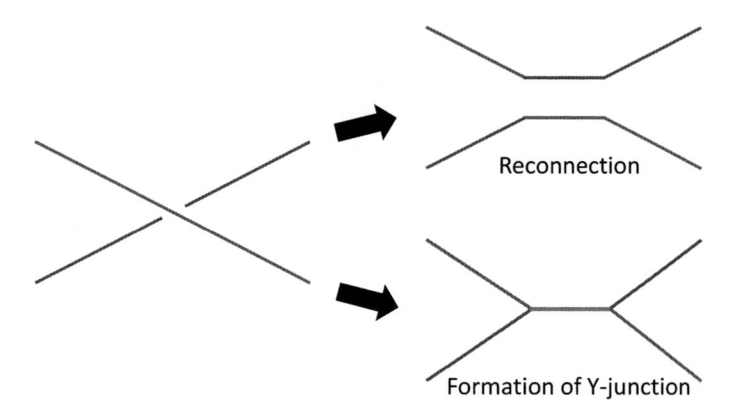

Fig. 2. Reconnection process and formation of a Y-junction.

4. Superconductivity and Y-junction formation

In the EW axion string presented above, the W^1-flux is confined, and the $U(1)_{\rm EM}$ symmetry is broken by the charged Higgs components and the W^1 gauge field, which means that there exists a zero mode (massless excitation) propagating on the string with the speed of light. It can carry an electric current without resistance, resulting in a superconducting current. We will show that such a current changes the interaction between the strings and can lead to formations of the Y-junctions in the early universe.

Firstly, let us assume the presence of a primordial magnetic field (PMF) in the universe after the electroweak phase transition. There are the observational lower and upper bounds on the present strength of intergalactic magnetic fields for a coherent length $\lambda \gtrsim 0.1$ Mpc as 3×10^{-16} G $\lesssim B_0 \lesssim 10^{-11}$ G, given by Refs. 27, 28. For simplicity, we further assume that the power spectrum of PMF is scale invariant and almost coherent over the entire Hubble horizon.

We then show that PMF can induce large superconducting currents on the strings. Such large currents are sufficient to form the Y-junctions. The scale invariant PMF evolves as

$$B(t) \propto a(t)^{-2}, \tag{15}$$

where $B(t)$ and $a(t)$ are the magnetic field strength and the scale factor at the cosmological time t, respectively. It is convenient to define a ratio of the energy density of PMF (ρ_B) to that of photon (ρ_γ),

$$\epsilon \equiv \frac{\rho_B}{\rho_\gamma} \sim B(t)^2 G_N t^2, \tag{16}$$

with G_N being the Newton constant. The ratio ϵ is a constant as the universe expands. If we take the upper limit on B_0, we have $\epsilon \sim 10^{-11}$.

In the early universe, the superconducting strings move with velocity $v_{\rm str}$ ($\sim \mathcal{O}(1)$) in the presence of PMF, and hence feel the electric fields $E \sim B(t) v_{\rm str}$, which

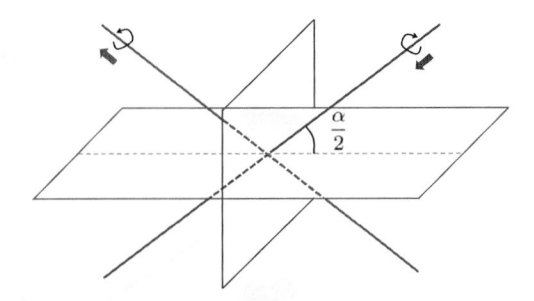

Fig. 3. Two strings (red and blue lines) collide with the crossing angle α. The black arrows indicate the directions of the topological winding number of $U(1)_{\rm PQ}$. The red and blue arrows indicate the directions of the flowing electric currents, which are parallel for $\alpha = 0$. The green and purple planes are orthogonal and include the collision point.

induce the superconducting current,

$$J_{\rm PMF} \sim e^2 B(t) \xi v_{\rm str}, \qquad (17)$$

with ξ being a string typical length. Since there are no superconducting strings before the electroweak phase transition, we can assume that the scaling property $\xi \sim t$ holds at least just after the phase transition, and obtain

$$J_{\rm PMF} \sim 10^{12} \left(\frac{\epsilon}{10^{-11}}\right)^{1/2} {\rm GeV} \sim 10^{12} \left(\frac{B_0}{10^{-11}\,{\rm G}}\right) {\rm GeV}. \qquad (18)$$

Note that this is independent of t. For the upper limit of B_0, yielding $\epsilon \sim 10^{-11}$, the induced current Eq. (18) is $\sim 10^{12}$ GeV. On the other hand, it is shown[14] that the EW axion string can carry an electric current at most $J_{\rm max} \simeq v_s/e$ with e the $U(1)_{\rm EM}$ coupling constant. Thus the current saturates at this value for $v_s \simeq 10^{9-12}$ GeV. In the following argument, we use this maximum current as those the strings carry in the early universe.

Let us discuss the formation of Y-junctions. They can be formed by collisions of two superconducting strings when they feel an attractive force and are trapped in the potential. We suppose that the two strings collide with the crossing angle α and that they are identical and parallel for $\alpha = 0$. The superconducting currents are assumed to flow in the same direction for $\alpha = 0$ (the opposite case will be considered later). The three-dimensional dynamics of the collision event is rather complicated and difficult to analyze. However a qualitative picture can be understood by reducing it on two orthogonal planes including the colliding point[29-31] (see Fig. 3). On one of them (purple plane in Fig. 3), the situation is regarded as a collision (scattering) event of two point-like vortices in two dimensions while, on the other plane (green plane in Fig. 3), as a vortex-antivortex collision resulting in the annihilation in two dimensions. Note that this picture reproduces the reconnection process shown in the upper-right picture in Fig. 2 when the strings have no superconducting current; two scattered vortices on the purple plane and nothing on the green one.

We concentrate on the two-dimensional analysis of the superconducting vortex-vortex collision since the current does not change the annihilation. Unlike the non-superconducting case leading to the 90° scattering, the long-range magnetic interaction plays a crucial role in our case. On the reduced plane, the vortex-vortex pair feel a net interaction potential,

$$V \sim \frac{v_s^2}{e^2} \cos \frac{\alpha}{2} \log r, \tag{19}$$

where r is the distance between the two vortices and we have ignored the axion-mediated repulsive interaction, which should be subleading by a factor e^2 compared to Eq. (19). If the vortices do not have sufficient kinetic energy to escape to infinity, they become trapped by the potential. Thus we obtain a condition to form a bound state,

$$\frac{v_s^2}{e^2} \cos \frac{\alpha}{2} \log \frac{L}{\delta} \geq (\gamma - 1)\mu, \tag{20}$$

where γ and μ are the Lorentz factor and the tension of the colliding vortices. L and δ are the IR and UV cutoff for the potential, which we take as the Hubble radius and the width of the strings, respectively. As considering just after the electroweak phase transition, the logarithmic factor gives $\log(10^{17} \times v_s/v_{\rm EW}) \sim 50$. In addition, we take a mildly relativistic velocity ~ 0.6 for the vortices, yielding $\gamma \sim 1.25$, and thus Eq. (20) gives

$$\cos \frac{\alpha}{2} \geq 10^{-3}, \tag{21}$$

which means that they *almost always* form the bound state except for $\alpha \simeq \pi$.

On the other hand, they cannot form such a bound state in the case that the currents flow in the opposite directions (anti-parallel) on the vortex-vortex plane because they always feel a repulsive force. Therefore, we obtain a rough estimation for the formation probability of the bound state,

$$\begin{cases} \text{Y-junction formed for current in the same directions} \\ \text{not formed for current in the opposite directions} \end{cases}$$
$$\Rightarrow \text{probability} \simeq \frac{1}{2}. \tag{22}$$

Note that this is based on the two-dimensional analysis focusing on the collision point. This picture may break down for the case that the dynamics after colliding is dominated by other parts of the strings than the collision point. Furthermore, the formed Y-junction could be peeled off, depending on the velocities and the crossing angle of the strings. For a more detailed study including these effects, it is necessary to perform a three-dimensional simulation, which is beyond the scope of the present paper.

Finally, we discuss a consequence of the formation of Y-junctions. When a superconducting string intersects with itself, it forms the Y-junction with probability 1/2,

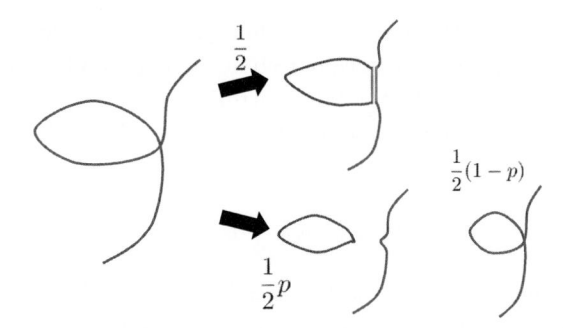

Fig. 4. Self-intersection of a superconducting string. The Y-junction (green doubled line) is formed with probability $\frac{1}{2}$. Otherwise, it reconnects producing a small loop (blue line) or passes through. The reconnection probability is $p \sim 1$.

produces a small loop with probability $p/2$, or passes through with probability $(1-p)/2$ (see Fig. 4), where p is the reconnection probability without the current ($p \sim 1$). If such a Y-junction-connected loop (upper one in Fig. 4) is produced, it is not obvious whether the strings sufficiently loose their energy, and the scaling behavior of the energy density of strings is not ensured. Once the energy density of the universe is dominated by such superconducting strings, it causes large impacts on cosmology, and hence some parameter region in the DFSZ axion model may be constrained.

5. Conclusion

We have studied the axion strings with the electroweak gauge flux, and their superconductivity in the DFSZ model. The superconducting current is induced by PMF in the early universe, and a large electric current can flow along the string. This large current may realize a net attractive force between the axion strings, which could form the so-called Y-junctions in the early universe. By considering the string collision reduced onto two-dimensional planes, the probability of the formation of the Y-junctions is estimated to be $\sim 1/2$.

Once such Y-junctions are formed, they can affect the evolution of the string network and make non-trivial whether the network evolves to the scaling solution. If no obeying the scaling behavior, the string network could dominate the energy density of the the universe and the model is severely constrained. To conclude whether this is true or not, we need detailed numerical simulations on the time evolution of the network taking into account both the axionic and magnetic interactions.

References

1. R. Peccei and H. R. Quinn, *Constraints Imposed by CP Conservation in the Presence of Instantons*, Phys. Rev. D **16** (1977) 1791.
2. R. Peccei and H. R. Quinn, *CP Conservation in the Presence of Instantons*, Phys. Rev. Lett. **38** (1977) 1440.

3. S. Weinberg, *A New Light Boson?*, Phys. Rev. Lett. **40** (1978) 223.
4. F. Wilczek, *Problem of Strong P and T Invariance in the Presence of Instantons*, Phys. Rev. Lett. **40** (1978) 279.
5. A. Zhitnitsky, *On Possible Suppression of the Axion Hadron Interactions. (In Russian)*, Sov. J. Nucl. Phys. **31** (1980) 260.
6. M. Dine, W. Fischler and M. Srednicki, *A Simple Solution to the Strong CP Problem with a Harmless Axion*, Phys. Lett. B **104** (1981) 199.
7. J. E. Kim, *Weak Interaction Singlet and Strong CP Invariance*, Phys. Rev. Lett. **43** (1979) 103.
8. M. A. Shifman, A. Vainshtein and V. I. Zakharov, *Can Confinement Ensure Natural CP Invariance of Strong Interactions?*, Nucl. Phys. B **166** (1980) 493.
9. T. W. B. Kibble, *Some Implications of a Cosmological Phase Transition*, Phys. Rept. **67** (1980) 183.
10. W. H. Zurek, *Cosmological Experiments in Superfluid Helium?*, Nature **317** (1985) 505.
11. L. M. Bettencourt, P. Laguna and R. A. Matzner, *Nonintercommuting cosmic strings*, Phys. Rev. Lett. **78** (1997) 2066 [hep-ph/9612350].
12. L. Bettencourt and T. Kibble, *Nonintercommuting configurations in the collisions of type I U(1) cosmic strings*, Phys. Lett. B **332** (1994) 297 [hep-ph/9405221].
13. E. Witten, *Superconducting Strings*, Nucl. Phys. B **249** (1985) 557.
14. Y. Abe, Y. Hamada and K. Yoshioka, *Electroweak axion string and superconductivity*, JHEP **06** (2021) 172 [2010.02834].
15. G. Lazarides and Q. Shafi, *Superconducting Strings in Axion Models*, Phys. Lett. B **151** (1985) 123.
16. A. Iwazaki, *Spontaneous magnetization of axion domain wall and primordial magnetic field*, Phys. Rev. Lett. **79** (1997) 2927 [hep-ph/9705456].
17. N. Ganoulis and G. Lazarides, *Fermionic Zero Modes for Cosmic Strings*, Nucl. Phys. B **316** (1989) 443.
18. G. Lazarides, C. Panagiotakopoulos and Q. Shafi, *Cosmic Superconducting Strings and Colliders*, Nucl. Phys. B **296** (1988) 657.
19. H. Fukuda, A. V. Manohar, H. Murayama and O. Telem, *Axion strings are superconducting*, 2010.02763.
20. P. Agrawal, A. Hook, J. Huang and G. Marques-Tavares, *Axion string signatures II: A cosmological plasma collider*, 2010.15848.
21. M. G. Alford, K. Benson, S. R. Coleman, J. March-Russell and F. Wilczek, *The Interactions and Excitations of Nonabelian Vortices*, Phys. Rev. Lett. **64** (1990) 1632.
22. M. G. Alford, K. Benson, S. R. Coleman, J. March-Russell and F. Wilczek, *Zero modes of nonabelian vortices*, Nucl. Phys. B **349** (1991) 414.
23. A. A. Abrikosov, *On the Magnetic properties of superconductors of the second group*, Sov. Phys. JETP **5** (1957) 1174.
24. H. B. Nielsen and P. Olesen, *Vortex Line Models for Dual Strings*, Nucl. Phys. **B61** (1973) 45.
25. Y. Nambu, *String-Like Configurations in the Weinberg-Salam Theory*, Nucl. Phys. **B130** (1977) 505.
26. T. Vachaspati, *Vortex solutions in the Weinberg-Salam model*, Phys. Rev. Lett. **68** (1992) 1977.
27. A. Neronov and I. Vovk, *Evidence for strong extragalactic magnetic fields from fermi observations of tev blazars*, Science **328** (2010) 73–75.

28. K. Jedamzik and A. Saveliev, *Stringent limit on primordial magnetic fields from the cosmic microwave background radiation*, Physical Review Letters **123** (2019).
29. E. J. Copeland and N. Turok, *Cosmic String Interactions*.
30. E. P. S. Shellard, *Cosmic String Interactions*, Nucl. Phys. B **283** (1987) 624.
31. E. P. S. Shellard, *Understanding intercommuting*, Proceedings of Yale Workshop: Cosmic Strings: The Current Status (1988).

Hints for the $H_0 - r_d$ tension in uncorrelated Baryon Acoustic Oscillations dataset

Denitsa Staicova

Institute for Nuclear Research and Nuclear Energy,
Bulgarian Academy of Sciences, Sofia, Bulgaria
E-mail: dstaicova@inrne.bas.bg

Baryon Acoustic Oscillations (BAO) datasets use very precise measurements of the spatial distribution of large-scale structures as a distance ladder to help constrain cosmological parameters. In a recent article,[1] we combined 17 uncorrelated BAO measurements in the effective redshift range $0.106 \le z \le 2.36$ with the Cosmic Chronometers data, the Pantheon Type Ia supernova and the Hubble Diagram of Gamma Ray Bursts and Quasars to obtain that the ΛCDM model fit infers for the Hubble constant: $69.85 \pm 1.27 km/sec/Mpc$ and for the sound horizon distance: $146.1 \pm 2.15 Mpc$. Beyond the ΛCDM model we test Ω_kCDM and wCDM and we get $\Omega_k = -0.076 \pm 0.012$, $w = -0.989 \pm 0.049$ accordingly. In this proceeding we present elaborate on our findings and we compare them to other recent results in the literature.

Keywords: Baryon Acoustic Oscillations, Dark Energy, Dark Matter, Large Scale Structure, Hubble Tension

1. Introduction

The $\sim 4\sigma$ tension between the Hubble parameter measured by late universe observations by the SH0ES collaboration[2] and the one measured from the cosmic microwave background (CMB) by the Planck Collaboration[3] is one of the major stumbling block in front of modern cosmology and the theories aiming to explain the evolution of the Universe.[4-22] The default ΛCDM model which uses a combination between cold dark matter and dark energy components has been shown to fit remarkably well current astronomical observations yet it fails to explain not only the beginning of the universe (the inflationary epoch) but also the Hubble tension and the related σ_8 tension.

In a recent article[1] we selected 17 uncorrelated BAO points from the largest collection of BAO data points (333 points). We then combined them with the Cosmic Chronometers data, the Pantheon Type Ia supernova, and the Hubble Diagram of Gamma-Ray Bursts and Quasars. From this combination of datasets, referred in the article sometimes as the *full* dataset, we found: the Hubble constant yields $69.85 \pm 1.27 km/sec/Mpc$, the sound horizon distance is $146.1 \pm 2.15 Mpc$ and the matter energy density – $\Omega_m = 0.271 \pm 0.016$. If one uses the so called *Riess prior* (denoted here as R19) to constrain H_0 by the model-independent local universe measurement,[2] one gets: $H_0 = 71.40 \pm 0.89$, $r_d = 143.5 \pm 2.0$ and $\Omega_m = 0.267 \pm 0.017$. Beyond the ΛCDM model we test Ω_KCDM and wCDM. The spatial curvature is

$\Omega_k = -0.076 \pm 0.012$ and the dark energy equation of states is $w = -0.989 \pm 0.049$. In this proceeding we discuss how our results are situated regarding other published results by emphasizing on the need to consider the H_0-tension in the context of the $H_0 - r_d$ plane or even of the $H_0 - r_d - \Omega_m$ plane.

2. Overview of the used datasets

The Baryon acoustic oscillations (BAO) are fluctuations in the photon-baryonic plasma that froze at recombination at the so called drag sound horizon. Because the sound horizon can be calculated rather simply from basic assumptions of the pre-recombination plasma, they provide a standard ruler which can be seen in the clustering of large scale structures. This provides an independent way to probe cosmological parameters, complimentary to this of the Supernova and the CMB surveys, see.[23–25] The BAO peak can be measured from objects with different nature and using different methods. For example: the BOSS experiment measures the clustering of different galaxies: emission-line galaxies (ELGs), luminous red galaxies (LRGs), and quasars, and also from the correlation function of the Lyman-alpha (Lyα) absorption lines in the spectra of distant quasars etc. The peak can be seen on different redshifts, providing us with a standard ruler evolving with the Universe since the recombination epoch.[26, 27]

The final dataset we use is a set of uncorrelated data points from different **BAO** measurements: the Sloan Digital Sky Survey (SDSS), the WiggleZ Dark Energy Survey, Dark Energy Camera Legacy Survey (DECaLS), the Dark Energy Survey (DES), the 6dF Galaxy Survey (6dFGS).[28–43] To this dataset, we add **cosmic chronometers (CCs)** (30 uncorrelated CC measurements of $H(z)$[44–47]), and **standard candles (SCs)** (the Pantheon Type Ia supernova dataset[48–51]), and quasars[52] and gamma-ray bursts[53] (186 points).

3. Theoretical background

We use the following theoretical setup. If one assumes a Friedmann-Lemaître-Robertson-Walker metric with the scale parameter $a = 1/(1 + z)$, where z is the redshift, one gets for the Friedmann equation for the ΛCDM model:

$$E(z)^2 = \Omega_r(1+z)^4 + \Omega_m(1+z)^3 + \Omega_k(1+z)^2 + \Omega_\Lambda, \qquad (1)$$

where Ω_r, Ω_m, Ω_Λ, and Ω_k are respectively the fractional densities of radiation, matter, dark energy, and the spatial curvature at redshift $z = 0$. Here $E(z) = H(z)/H_0$, and $H(z) = \dot{a}/a$ is the Hubble parameter at z, while H_0 is the Hubble parameter today. The radiation density can be computed as $\Omega_r = 1 - \Omega_m - \Omega_\Lambda - \Omega_k$. For wCDM the Friedmann equation is generalized to $\Omega_\Lambda \to \Omega_{DE}^0 (1+z)^{-3(1+w)}$, while $\Omega_k = 0$ represents a flat universe.

Since in cosmology one deals with the measurements of angles and redshifts, it is needed to connect the different cosmological distances with the observational quantities. The comoving angular diameter distance:[54,55]

$$D_M = \frac{c}{H_0} S_k \left(\int_0^z \frac{dz'}{E(z')} \right), \tag{2}$$

where one accounts for non-zero spatial curvature with:

$$S_k(x) = \begin{cases} \frac{1}{\sqrt{\Omega_k}} \sinh\left(\sqrt{\Omega_k} x\right) & \text{if } \Omega_k > 0 \\ x & \text{if } \Omega_k = 0 \\ \frac{1}{\sqrt{-\Omega_k}} \sin\left(\sqrt{-\Omega_k} x\right) & \text{if } \Omega_k < 0 \end{cases}. \tag{3}$$

The other distances we use are the Hubble distance $D_H(z) = c/H(z)$, the angular diameter distance $D_A = D_M/(1+z)$ and the volume averaged distance:

$$D_V(z) \equiv [zD_H(z)D_M^2(z)]^{1/3}. \tag{4}$$

As said before the BAO use as a standard ruler depends only on the sound horizon r_d at the drag epoch ($z_d \approx 1060$) when photons and baryons decouple:

$$r_d = \int_{z_d}^{\infty} \frac{c_s(z)}{H(z)} dz, \tag{5}$$

where $c_s \approx c \left(3 + 9\rho_b/(4\rho_\gamma)\right)^{-0.5}$ is the speed of sound in the baryon-photon fluid with the baryon $\rho_b(z)$ and the photon $\rho_\gamma(z)$ densities, respectively.[56] One needs to acknowledge that since the actual measured quantities are the projections $\Delta z = r_d H/c$ and $\Delta \theta = r_d/(1+z)D_A(z)$, where Δz and $\Delta \theta$ are the redshift and the angular separation, from BAO one can get information only about the quantity $r_d \times H$. Thus in order to decouple these quantities, one needs some kind of independent measurement of H_0 or an assumption for r_d. Here we take r_d as an independent parameter but use the additional datasets (CC+SC) to decouple the two variables. In a recent paper,[57] we instead use the combination $r_d \times H_0$ as a parameter to break the degeneracy.

4. Numerical methods

To deal with the possible correlations in the BAO dataset, we perform a covariance analysis based on the one proposed in Ref.[58]. We transform the standard covariance matrix for uncorrelated points C_{ii} into C_{ij} as follows:

$$C_{ii} = \sigma_i^2 \quad \longrightarrow \quad C_{ij} = \sigma_i^2 + 0.5\sigma_i\sigma_j \tag{6}$$

by adding randomly certain number of nondiagonal elements while keeping it symmetric. Here $\sigma_i\sigma_j$ are the published 1σ errors of the data points i, j. With this approach we show that the effect of up to 25% random correlations with this magnitude results in less than 10% deviation in the final results, thus it is minimal and the points can be considered uncorrelated.

We use a nested sampler as implemented within the open-source package *Polychord*[59] with the *GetDist* package[60] to present the results. The priors we use to obtain the results and the averaged mean values across the 3 models (ΛCDM, wCDM, Ω_kCDM) can be found in Table A1.

5. Comparison with other results

The complete numerical results for the three models and the three datasets (BAO+R19, BAO+SC+CC, BAO+SC+CC+R19) can be found in Table 3 in.[1] In this article we will focus on comparing our results with other works, by using only the *full* datasets with and without the R19 prior, referred to as BAO+SC+CC+R19 and BAO+SC+CC.

Specifically, on Fig. 1, we use some known measurements in the $H_0 - r_d$ and $H_0 - \Omega_m$ plane. It has been discussed in a number of papers, more notably,[61] that the H_0-tension is actually extended to a tension with respect to the main parameters H_0, r_d and Ω_m, since increasing Ω_m to reduce r_d leads to the opposite to the desired effect on H_0. To demonstrate this, we have plotted the following points: TDCosmo IV,[62] H0LiCOW XIII,[63] LMC Cepheids,[2] Planck 2018,[3] eBOSS SDSS-IV,[64] BAO +BBN+H0LiCOW and BAO +BBN+CC,[65] all listed for convenience in Table A2. Note, some references do not measure r_d, others omit mentioning Ω_m.

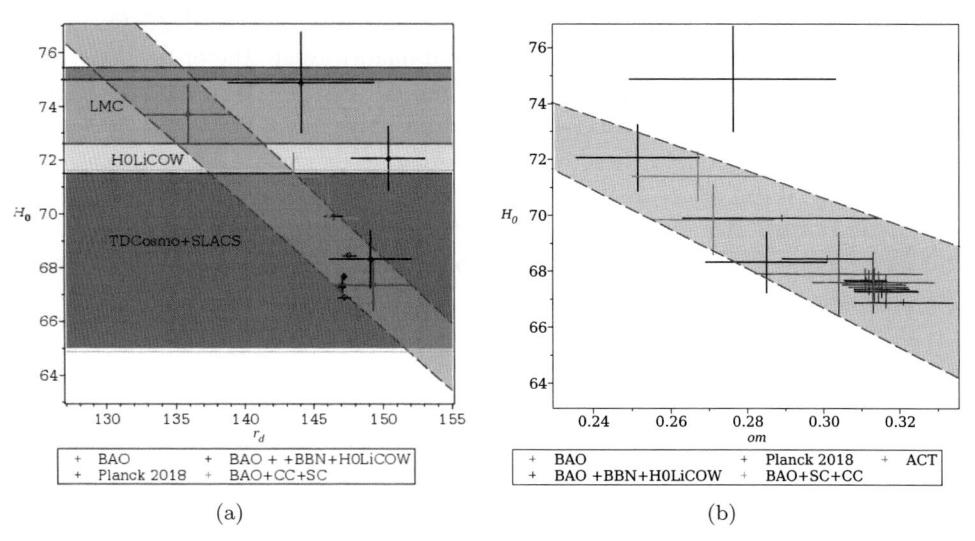

Fig. 1. (a) $H_0 - r_d$ plane comparison of different results. (b) $H_0 - \Omega_m$ plane comparision. Our points are with green, for legend see the text.

On Fig. 1(a) we consider only $H_0 - r_d$ and we see that our results (in green) fit nicely between the results of the pure BAO points by eBOSS (in red) and the Planck 2018 points (in blue).

On this plot, the points we obtain with the R19 prior (top green point) are very close to the local universe measurements (LMC), while the points we obtain with a uniform prior (the lower green point) are close to the early universe (i.e. Planck 2018 with bue). The numbers we obtain are surprisingly close to a measurement of the Tip of the Red Giants Branch $H_0 = 69.8 \pm 1.9 (km/s)/Mpc$[66] — an independent measurement based on the distances to nearby galaxies (in this case based on TRGB stars in the Large Magellanic Cloud, grounded on detached eclipsing binaries).

As for r_d, we see that our points without the R19 prior are again close to the Planck measurement (Planck 2018 $r_d = 147.09 \pm 0.26 Mpc$, ours: $r_d = 146.1 \pm 2.2 Mpc$). The final measurements from the completed SDSS lineage of experiments in large-scale structure provide $r_d = 149.3 \pm 2.8 Mpc$.[67] Using BAO, SNea, the ages of early-type galaxies, and local determinations of the Hubble constant, Ref.[68] reports $r_d = 143.9 \pm 3.1$ Mpc. Thus, one can see clearly the tension between different results from the early and late universe confirming the "tensions in the $r_d - H_0$ plane."[61] The model with the R19 prior gives $r_d = 143.5 \pm 2.0 Mpc$. Importantly, the choice of a prior for r_d has a critical effect on H_0 decreasing or increasing the inferred value to a large extend independently of the prior on H_0.

Another part of the $H_0 - r_d$ puzzle is the effect of the matter energy density Ω_m. A comparison of different results for Ω_m can be seen on Fig. 1(b), where we have plotted the $H_0 - \Omega_m$ plane. Note that the eBOSS points used here are different from the ones used in Table 2, as we use different set of published points (Table 4 in Ref.[64]). Also, we add the points by ACT which can be found in Table 4 in Ref.[69]. Our points are once again in green and as we can see they fit very close to Plancks's results in blue which come with very small error on H_0 but rather large on Ω_m ($\Omega_m^{Planck} = .289, 0 \pm 0.03$). In our case, the matter density is lower than the expected. One can also note that removing the top right point (belonging to BAO +BBN+H0LiCOW, see Table 2) will make the points along with the error bars to lie on approximately one plane, similar to the one in the $H_0 - r_d$ plane and thus hinting at possible degeneracy (in orange and yellow respectively). This has been commented already in[61] and is related to the fact we do not know how exactly the phase space of all parameters looks like. The tension for $H_0 - r_d - \Omega_m$ appears in different measurements (Planck, BAO, ACT etc), some from the early Universe, others from the late one and the independent local measurements. This once again poses the question whether we need to consider the full parameter space when discussing the tension.

Finally, we would like to discuss the results we obtained about the spacial curvature energy density. As already mentioned we get $\Omega_k = -0.076 \pm 0.012$ which excludes flat universe at 68% CL and points to a closed Universe ($k = 1$). Due to the rather small prior used to obtain this number, we now repeat the inference with a larger prior $\Omega_k \in [-0.3, 0.3]$. The results can be seen on Fig. 2. Once again, when calculating for the full dataset with or without the R19 prior, we obtain values excluding flat universe. This has been reported already, for example by the Planck 2018 collaboration[3] for CMB alone which found a preference for a closed universe at 3.4σ. Also,[70] using the CC, Pantheon, and BAO measurements concluded that negative Ω_k also relieves the H_0 tension.

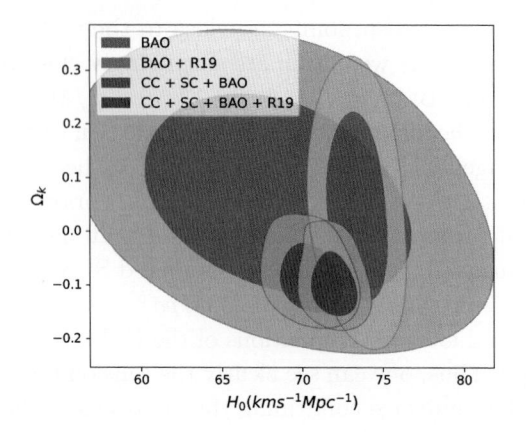

Fig. 2. 2d contour plot of Ω_k vs H_0 for the datasets BAO, BAO + R19, CC+SC+BAO and CC+SC+BAO+R19.

The issue of a possibility for a deviation from a flat Universe is extremely important and has been discussed in a number of works. On Fig. 3, we plot some of the published in the literature results with respect to Ω_k. The reference for the results are accordingly ($N = 1..12$) data from: Planck18Plk, Planck18CamSpec, ACT+WMAP, ACT+Planck, CC+Quasars,CC+SN, BAO+BBN+H0LiCOW, BAO+BBN+CC, taken from[71] to which we add the values we measured with the following dataset: BAO+R19, BAO+CC+SC (same as BAO+CC+SC+R19) and the extended prior points: BAO+CC+SCl, BAO+CC+SC+R19l. One can see that our results seem to add to a mounting evidence that maybe we observe an effect related to a non-flat universe.

The results for the full dataset for the extended prior can be seen in Table A3. We see now that the reported earlier in Ref.[1] lower matter energy density is no longer an issue as we get $\Omega_m \sim 0.326$, also we see that now H_0 is a bit larger, thus pointing to further alleviation of the H_0-tension due to a non-zero spatial curvature. Critically, we see that again $\Omega_k = 0$ is excluded from the 68% CL for both models. Thus we can claim this effect persists with the increase of the prior and it is a feature of the dataset.

On a side note, we mention the result we obtained in Ref.[1] with respect to the wCDM model. For BAO + R19 we get $w < -1$ for ($w = -1.067 \pm 0.065$), while the full datasets seem to tend to $w \geq -1$ ($w = -0.989 \pm 0.049$). Since $w = -1$ is included in the error, the results are essentially consistent with a cosmological constant.

To compare the extended models to ΛCDM we used well known statistical measures, i.e. the Akaike information criteria (AIC)[72–74],[a]. We find that the ΛCDM

---

[a]The definition of AIC we use is $AIC = \chi^2_{min} + 2p$, where p is the number of parameters of the model.

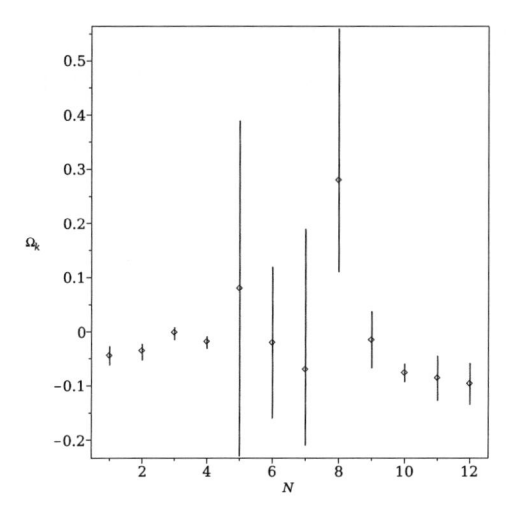

Fig. 3. Comparison of different measurements of Ω_k, see legend in text. Our points are $N = 9-12$, where points with $N = 11, 12$ are with larger prior for Ω_k.

model remains the best fit to the data with difference of 2.3 and 7.6 AIC units for the wCDM and the Ω_kCDM respectively. One can see that wCDM has a little bit more support than Ω_kCDM but also as we mentioned, $w = -1$ enters into the the 68% CL of w for the full dataset which may explain its closeness to ΛCDM in terms of AIC. Our results are consistent with the eBoss collaboration official results.[67] Interestingly, we see that in our case $w \geq -1$ for the full dataset, which differs from the estimations in some of the different cases considered in.[67] Our dataset differs from theirs by the inclusion of the quasars and the GRB data and the exclusion of Planck points, so this may point to a local universe effect.

6. Conclusion

We use a set of 17 uncorrelated BAO points to infer the cosmological parameters for 3 different models: ΛCDM, Ω_kCDM and wCDM. We find that by choosing the sound horizon at drag epoch as an independent parameter and adding additional datasets such as SNe, GRB and quasars, we are able to break the degeneracy between H_0 and r_d and to constrain the cosmological parameters for the different models. The Hubble parameter obtained from the full dataset is very close to the TGRB measurement, while the one with a R19 prior is close to the local universe measurement. We show that we are able to alleviate the H_0-tension to certain degree but not entirely. Another interesting result is the prediction of a non-flat but closed Universe at 68 % CL, which has been confirmed with an increased prior and seems to add to the mounting evidences there may be a deviation from flatness.

Acknowledgments

D.S. is thankful to Bulgarian National Science Fund for support via research grants KP-06-N38/11. We have received partial support from European COST actions CA18108.

References

1. D. Benisty and D. Staicova, Testing late-time cosmic acceleration with uncorrelated baryon acoustic oscillation dataset, *Astron. Astrophys.* **647**, p. A38 (2021).
2. A. G. Riess, S. Casertano, W. Yuan, L. M. Macri and D. Scolnic, Large Magellanic Cloud Cepheid Standards Provide a 1% Foundation for the Determination of the Hubble Constant and Stronger Evidence for Physics beyond ΛCDM, *Astrophys. J.* **876**, p. 85 (2019).
3. N. Aghanim *et al.*, Planck 2018 results. VI. Cosmological parameters, *Astron. Astrophys.* **641**, p. A6 (2020).
4. E. Di Valentino *et al.*, Cosmology Intertwined I: Perspectives for the Next Decade (2020).
5. E. Di Valentino *et al.*, Cosmology Intertwined II: The Hubble Constant Tension (2020).
6. E. Di Valentino *et al.*, Cosmology Intertwined III: $f\sigma_8$ and S_8 (2020).
7. G. Efstathiou, A Lockdown Perspective on the Hubble Tension (with comments from the SH0ES team) (2020).
8. S. Borhanian, A. Dhani, A. Gupta, K. G. Arun and B. S. Sathyaprakash, Dark Sirens to Resolve the Hubble-Lemaître Tension (2020).
9. A. Hryczuk and K. Jodłowski, Self-interacting dark matter from late decays and the H_0 tension, *Phys. Rev.* **D102**, p. 043024 (2020).
10. A. Klypin, V. Poulin, F. Prada, J. Primack, M. Kamionkowski, V. Avila-Reese, A. Rodriguez-Puebla, P. Behroozi, D. Hellinger and T. L. Smith, Clustering and Halo Abundances in Early Dark Energy Cosmological Models (2020).
11. M. M. Ivanov, Y. Ali-Haïmoud and J. Lesgourgues, H0 tension or T0 tension?, *Phys. Rev.* **D102**, p. 063515 (2020).
12. A. Chudaykin, D. Gorbunov and N. Nedelko, Combined analysis of Planck and SPTPol data favors the early dark energy models, *JCAP* **2008**, p. 013 (2020).
13. K.-F. Lyu, E. Stamou and L.-T. Wang, Self-interacting neutrinos: solution to Hubble tension versus experimental constraints (2020).
14. G. Alestas, L. Kazantzidis and L. Perivolaropoulos, H_0 Tension, Phantom Dark Energy and Cosmological Parameter Degeneracies (2020).
15. P. Motloch and W. Hu, Lensinglike tensions in the *Planck* legacy release, *Phys. Rev.* **D101**, p. 083515 (2020).
16. N. Frusciante, S. Peirone, L. Atayde and A. De Felice, Phenomenology of the generalized cubic covariant Galileon model and cosmological bounds, *Phys. Rev.* **D101**, p. 064001 (2020).
17. D. Staicova, Special cases of the Multi-Measure Model – understanding the prolonged inflation (11 2020).
18. D. Staicova and M. Stoilov, Cosmology from multimeasure multifield model, *Int. J. Mod. Phys. A* **34**, p. 1950099 (2019).
19. D. Benisty, E. I. Guendelman, A. van de Venn, D. Vasak, J. Struckmeier and H. Stoecker, The Dark side of the torsion: Dark Energy from kinetic torsion (9 2021).
20. L. Areté Saló, D. Benisty, E. I. Guendelman and J. d. Haro, Quintessential inflation and cosmological seesaw mechanism: reheating and observational constraints, *JCAP* **07**, p. 007 (2021).

21. D. Benisty, Reducing the σ_8 tension with the Redshift Space Distortion data set (2020).
22. S. Bahamonde, K. F. Dialektopoulos, C. Escamilla-Rivera, G. Farrugia, V. Gakis, M. Hendry, M. Hohmann, J. L. Said, J. Mifsud and E. Di Valentino, Teleparallel Gravity: From Theory to Cosmology (6 2021).
23. W. Handley, Curvature tension: evidence for a closed universe (8 2019).
24. E. Di Valentino, A. Melchiorri and J. Silk, Cosmic Discordance: Planck and luminosity distance data exclude LCDM (2020).
25. X. Luo, Z. Huang, Q. Qian and L. Huang, Reaffirming the Cosmic Acceleration without Supernova and CMB (2020).
26. A. Cuceu, J. Farr, P. Lemos and A. Font-Ribera, Baryon Acoustic Oscillations and the Hubble Constant: Past, Present and Future, *JCAP* **10**, p. 044 (2019).
27. W. K. Wu, P. Motloch, W. Hu and M. Raveri, Hubble constant difference between CMB lensing and BAO measurements, *Phys. Rev. D* **102**, p. 023510 (2020).
28. F. Beutler, C. Blake, M. Colless, D. H. Jones, L. Staveley-Smith, L. Campbell, Q. Parker, W. Saunders and F. Watson, The 6dF Galaxy Survey: Baryon Acoustic Oscillations and the Local Hubble Constant, *Mon. Not. Roy. Astron. Soc.* **416**, 3017 (2011).
29. A. J. Ross, L. Samushia, C. Howlett, W. J. Percival, A. Burden and M. Manera, The clustering of the SDSS DR7 main Galaxy sample – I. A 4 per cent distance measure at $z = 0.15$, *Mon. Not. Roy. Astron. Soc.* **449**, 835 (2015).
30. W. J. Percival et al., Baryon Acoustic Oscillations in the Sloan Digital Sky Survey Data Release 7 Galaxy Sample, *Mon. Not. Roy. Astron. Soc.* **401**, 2148 (2010).
31. R. Tojeiro et al., The clustering of galaxies in the SDSS-III Baryon Oscillation Spectroscopic Survey: galaxy clustering measurements in the low redshift sample of Data Release 11, *Mon. Not. Roy. Astron. Soc.* **440**, 2222 (2014).
32. C. Blake et al., The WiggleZ Dark Energy Survey: Joint measurements of the expansion and growth history at z ¡ 1, *Mon. Not. Roy. Astron. Soc.* **425**, 405 (2012).
33. H.-J. Seo et al., Acoustic scale from the angular power spectra of SDSS-III DR8 photometric luminous galaxies, *Astrophys. J.* **761**, p. 13 (2012).
34. L. Anderson et al., The clustering of galaxies in the SDSS-III Baryon Oscillation Spectroscopic Survey: Baryon Acoustic Oscillations in the Data Release 9 Spectroscopic Galaxy Sample, *Mon. Not. Roy. Astron. Soc.* **427**, 3435 (2013).
35. S. Sridhar, Y.-S. Song, A. J. Ross, R. Zhou, J. A. Newman, C.-H. Chuang, F. Prada, R. Blum, E. Gaztañaga and M. Landriau, The clustering of LRGs in the DECaLS DR8 footprint: distance constraints from baryon acoustic oscillations using photometric redshifts (2020).
36. J. E. Bautista et al., The SDSS-IV extended Baryon Oscillation Spectroscopic Survey: Baryon Acoustic Oscillations at redshift of 0.72 with the DR14 Luminous Red Galaxy Sample, *Astrophys. J.* **863**, p. 110 (2018).
37. T. M. C. Abbott et al., Dark Energy Survey Year 1 Results: Measurement of the Baryon Acoustic Oscillation scale in the distribution of galaxies to redshift 1, *Mon. Not. Roy. Astron. Soc.* **483**, 4866 (2019).
38. J. Hou et al., The Completed SDSS-IV extended Baryon Oscillation Spectroscopic Survey: BAO and RSD measurements from anisotropic clustering analysis of the Quasar Sample in configuration space between redshift 0.8 and 2.2 (2020).
39. M. Ata et al., The clustering of the SDSS-IV extended Baryon Oscillation Spectroscopic Survey DR14 quasar sample: first measurement of baryon acoustic oscillations between redshift 0.8 and 2.2, *Mon. Not. Roy. Astron. Soc.* **473**, 4773 (2018).
40. N. G. Busca et al., Baryon Acoustic Oscillations in the Ly-α forest of BOSS quasars, *Astron. Astrophys.* **552**, p. A96 (2013).

41. V. de Sainte Agathe *et al.*, Baryon acoustic oscillations at z = 2.34 from the correlations of Lyα absorption in eBOSS DR14, *Astron. Astrophys.* **629**, p. A85 (2019).
42. P. Carter, F. Beutler, W. J. Percival, C. Blake, J. Koda and A. J. Ross, Low Redshift Baryon Acoustic Oscillation Measurement from the Reconstructed 6-degree Field Galaxy Survey, *Mon. Not. Roy. Astron. Soc.* **481**, 2371 (2018).
43. E. A. Kazin *et al.*, The WiggleZ Dark Energy Survey: improved distance measurements to z = 1 with reconstruction of the baryonic acoustic feature, *Mon. Not. Roy. Astron. Soc.* **441**, 3524 (2014).
44. M. Moresco, L. Verde, L. Pozzetti, R. Jimenez and A. Cimatti, New constraints on cosmological parameters and neutrino properties using the expansion rate of the Universe to z~1.75, *JCAP* **07**, p. 053 (2012).
45. M. Moresco *et al.*, Improved constraints on the expansion rate of the Universe up to z 1.1 from the spectroscopic evolution of cosmic chronometers, *JCAP* **1208**, p. 006 (2012).
46. M. Moresco, Raising the bar: new constraints on the Hubble parameter with cosmic chronometers at $z \sim 2$, *Mon. Not. Roy. Astron. Soc.* **450**, L16 (2015).
47. M. Moresco, L. Pozzetti, A. Cimatti, R. Jimenez, C. Maraston, L. Verde, D. Thomas, A. Citro, R. Tojeiro and D. Wilkinson, A 6% measurement of the Hubble parameter at $z \sim 0.45$: Direct evidence of the epoch of cosmic re-acceleration, *JCAP* **1605**, p. 014 (2016).
48. S. Perlmutter *et al.*, Measurements of Omega and Lambda from 42 high redshift supernovae, *Astrophys. J.* **517**, 565 (1999).
49. A. G. Riess *et al.*, Observational evidence from supernovae for an accelerating universe and a cosmological constant, *Astron. J.* **116**, 1009 (1998).
50. D. Scolnic *et al.*, The Complete Light-curve Sample of Spectroscopically Confirmed SNe Ia from Pan-STARRS1 and Cosmological Constraints from the Combined Pantheon Sample, *Astrophys. J.* **859**, p. 101 (2018).
51. F. K. Anagnostopoulos, S. Basilakos and E. N. Saridakis, Observational constraints on Barrow holographic dark energy, *Eur. Phys. J.* **C80**, p. 826 (2020).
52. C. Roberts, K. Horne, A. O. Hodson and A. D. Leggat, Tests of ΛCDM and Conformal Gravity using GRB and Quasars as Standard Candles out to $z \sim 8$ (2017).
53. M. Demianski, E. Piedipalumbo, D. Sawant and L. Amati, Cosmology with gamma-ray bursts: I. The Hubble diagram through the calibrated $E_{p,i}$ - E_{iso} correlation, *Astron. Astrophys.* **598**, p. A112 (2017).
54. N. B. Hogg, M. Martinelli and S. Nesseris, Constraints on the distance duality relation with standard sirens (2020).
55. M. Martinelli *et al.*, Euclid: Forecast constraints on the cosmic distance duality relation with complementary external probes (2020).
56. E. Aubourg *et al.*, Cosmological implications of baryon acoustic oscillation measurements, *Phys. Rev. D* **92**, p. 123516 (2015).
57. D. Benisty and D. Staicova, A preference for Dynamical Dark Energy? (7 2021).
58. L. Kazantzidis and L. Perivolaropoulos, Evolution of the $f\sigma_8$ tension with the Planck15/ΛCDM determination and implications for modified gravity theories, *Phys. Rev.* **D97**, p. 103503 (2018).
59. W. J. Handley, M. P. Hobson and A. N. Lasenby, PolyChord: Nested sampling for cosmology, *Mon. Not. Roy. Astron. Soc.* **450**, L61 (2015).
60. A. Lewis, GetDist: a Python package for analysing Monte Carlo samples (2019).
61. L. Knox and M. Millea, Hubble constant hunter's guide, *Physical Review D* **101** (Feb 2020).

62. S. Birrer et al., TDCOSMO - IV. Hierarchical time-delay cosmography – joint inference of the Hubble constant and galaxy density profiles, *Astron. Astrophys.* **643**, p. A165 (2020).
63. K. C. Wong et al., H0LiCOW – XIII. A 2.4 per cent measurement of H0 from lensed quasars: 5.3σ tension between early- and late-Universe probes, *Mon. Not. Roy. Astron. Soc.* **498**, 1420 (2020).
64. S. Alam et al., Completed SDSS-IV extended Baryon Oscillation Spectroscopic Survey: Cosmological implications from two decades of spectroscopic surveys at the Apache Point Observatory, *Phys. Rev. D* **103**, p. 083533 (2021).
65. R. C. Nunes and A. Bernui, θ_{BAO} estimates and the H_0 tension (2020).
66. W. L. Freedman, B. F. Madore, T. Hoyt, I. S. Jang, R. Beaton, M. G. Lee, A. Monson, J. Neeley and J. Rich, Calibration of the Tip of the Red Giant Branch (TRGB) (2 2020).
67. S. Alam et al., The Completed SDSS-IV extended Baryon Oscillation Spectroscopic Survey: Cosmological Implications from two Decades of Spectroscopic Surveys at the Apache Point observatory (7 2020).
68. L. Verde, J. L. Bernal, A. F. Heavens and R. Jimenez, The length of the low-redshift standard ruler, *Mon. Not. Roy. Astron. Soc.* **467**, 731 (2017).
69. S. Aiola et al., The Atacama Cosmology Telescope: DR4 Maps and Cosmological Parameters, *JCAP* **12**, p. 047 (2020).
70. E.-K. Li, M. Du and L. Xu, General Cosmography Model with Spatial Curvature, *Mon. Not. Roy. Astron. Soc.* **491**, 4960 (2020).
71. E. Di Valentino et al., Snowmass2021 - Letter of interest cosmology intertwined IV: The age of the universe and its curvature, *Astropart. Phys.* **131**, p. 102607 (2021).
72. K. P. Burnham and D. R. Anderson, Multimodel inference: Understanding aic and bic in model selection, *Sociological Methods & Research* **33**, 261 (2004).
73. A. R. Liddle, Information criteria for astrophysical model selection, *Mon. Not. Roy. Astron. Soc.* **377**, L74 (2007).
74. F. K. Anagnostopoulos, S. Basilakos and E. N. Saridakis, Bayesian analysis of $f(T)$ gravity using $f\sigma_8$ data, *Phys. Rev.* **D100**, p. 083517 (2019).

Appendix A.

Table A1. The priors used to obtain each cosmological parameter.

Parameter	Prior	Average Value [1]	Average Value R19 [2]
Ω_m	$[0.; 1.]$	0.26 ± 0.017	0.26 ± 0.016
Ω_Λ	$[0.; 1 - \Omega_m]$	0.749 ± 0.013	0.751 ± 0.013
H_0	$[50; 100]$	70.19 ± 1.11	-
H_0^{R19}	74.03 ± 1.42	-	71.68 ± 0.9
$r_d/r_{d,fid}$	$[0.9, 1.1]$	0.996 ± 0.019	0.97 ± 0.013
r_d	$[100; 200]$	145.8 ± 2.37	143.3 ± 1.9
w	$[-1.25; -0.75]$	-0.989 ± 0.049	-0.989 ± 0.049
Ω_k	$[-0.1; 0.1]$	-0.076 ± 0.017	-0.076 ± 0.012

Note: [1] average value for the parameter under the flat prior for H_0, [2] average value for the parameter under the Gaussian R19 prior for H_0. H_0 is in $(km/s)/Mpc$, r_d in Mpc.

Table A2. Numbers used to draw Fig 1.

Mission	Reference	H_0 (in km/s/Mpc)	r_d (in Mpc)	Ω_m
TDCosmo IV	62	$74.5^{+5.6}_{-6.1}$	-	-
TDCOSMO+SLACS	62	$67.4^{+4.1}_{-3.2}$	-	-
H0LiCOW XIII	63	$73.3^{+1.7}_{-1.8}$	-	-
LMC DEBs	2	74.22 ± 1.82	-	-
LMC DEBs and NGC 4258 and Milky Way:	2	74.03 ± 1.42	-	-
Planck 2018				
TT+lowE	3	66.88 ± 0.92	147.21 ± 0.48	0.321 ± 0.013
TE+lowE	3	68.44 ± 0.91	147.59 ± 0.49	0.301 ± 0.012
EE+lowE	3	69.9 ± 2.7,	146.46 ± 0.70	$0.289^{+0.026}_{-0.033}$
TT,TE,EE+lowE	3	67.27 ± 0.60	147.05 ± 0.30	0.3166 ± 0.0084
TT,TE,EE+lowE+lensing	3	67.36 ± 0.54	147.09 ± 0.26	0.3153 ± 0.0073
TT,TE,EE+lowE+lensing+BAO	3	67.66 ± 0.42	147.21 ± 0.23	0.3111 ± 0.0056
eBOSS				
BAO+BBN	64	67.35 ± 0.97	149.3 ± 2.8	0.314 ± 0.008
BAO and distance ladder	64	73.7 ± 1.1	135.9 ± 3.2	-
BAO + SDSS (BAO) + BBN	65	$68.32^{+0.98}_{-1.1}$	$151.9^{+3}_{-2.8}$	$0.27^{+0.015}_{-0.016}$
BAO +BBN+H0LiCOW	65	$74.88 \pm 1.95.1$	144.1 ± 5.3	0.2763 ± 0.027
BAO +BBN+CC	65	$72.06^{+1.2}_{-1.3}$	$150.4^{+2.7}_{-3.3}$	0.2515 ± 0.016

Table A3. The results for the Ω_kCDM model with the increased prior on $\Omega_k \in [-0.3, 0.3]$.

Dataset	Parameter	Value
CC+SC+BAO	$H_0 (kms^{-1} Mpc^{-1})$	70.48 ± 1.23
	Ω_k	-0.086 ± 0.042
	Ω_m	0.326 ± 0.027
	Ω_Λ	0.766 ± 0.029
	$r_d (Mpc)$	145.961 ± 2.676
	rat	0.984 ± 0.016
CC+SC+BAO+R19	$H_0 (kms^{-1} Mpc^{-1})$	71.91 ± 0.87
	Ω_k	-0.096 ± 0.039
	Ω_m	0.327 ± 0.026
	Ω_Λ	0.776 ± 0.024
	r_d (Mpc)	143.452 ± 1.948
	rat	0.967 ± 0.013

Observational constraints on nonlinear matter extensions of general relativity

E.-A. Kolonia

Department of Physics, University of Patras,
26504 Patras, Greece

C. J. A. P. Martins

Centro de Astrofísica da Universidade do Porto, and
Instituto de Astrofísica e Ciências do Espaço, Universidade do Porto,
Rua das Estrelas, 4150-762 Porto, Portugal
E-mail: Carlos.Martins@astro.up.pt

We present a phenomenological analysis of current observational constraints on classes of FLRW cosmological models in which the matter side of Einstein's equations includes, in addition to the canonical term, a term proportional to some function of the energy-momentum tensor ($T^2 = T_{\alpha\beta}T^{\alpha\beta} = \rho^2 + 3p^2$), or of its trace ($T = \rho - 3p$). Qualitatively, one may think of these models as extensions of general relativity with a nonlinear matter Lagrangian. As such they are somewhat different from the usual dynamical dark energy or modified gravity models: in the former class of models one adds further dynamical degrees of freedom to the Lagrangian (often in the form of scalar fields), while in the latter the gravitational part of the Lagrangian is changed. We study both of these models under two different scenarios: (1) as phenomenological two-parameter or three-parameter extensions of the standard ΛCDM, in which case the model still has a cosmological constant but the nonlinear matter Lagrangian leads to additional terms in Einstein's equations, which cosmological observations tightly constrain, and (2) as alternatives to ΛCDM, where there is no cosmological constant, and the nonlinear matter term would have to provide the acceleration (which would be somewhat closer in spirit to the usual modified gravity models). A comparative analysis of the observational constraints obtained in the various cases provides some insight on the level of robustness of the Λ model and on the parameter space still available for phenomenological alternatives.

Keywords: Cosmology; Dark energy; Modified gravity; Observational constraints.

1. Introduction

The observational evidence for the acceleration of the universe shows that our canonical theories of cosmology and particle physics are at least incomplete, and possibly incorrect. Mapping the dark side of the universe, in order to ascertain the physical mechanism behind this acceleration, in a compelling observational task for current and future facilities. The CosmoESPRESSO team uses the universe as a laboratory to address, with precision spectroscopy and other observational, computational and theoretical tools, this and other grand-challenge questions. In what follows we highlight recent contributions of the CosmoESPRESSO team to this fundamental quest, pertaining to dark energy phenomenology.

There has been some recent interest in the so-called energy-momentum-squared gravity models,[1] where the matter part of Einstein's equations is modified by the addition of a term proportional to $T^2 \equiv T_{\mu\nu}T^{\mu\nu}$, where $T_{\mu\nu}$ is the energy-momentum tensor. This we later extended[2,3] to the more generic form $(T^2)^n$, dubbed energy-momentum-powered gravity. Reference 4 provided low redshift constraints on these models, using in particular the Pantheon Type Ia supernova compilation[5] and a compilation of 38 Hubble parameter measurements.[6]

In practical terms, we may think of these models as extensions to the canonical ΛCDM, in which case the model still has a cosmological constant but the nonlinear matter Lagrangian leads to additional terms in Einstein's equations, and cosmological observations can constrain these additional model parameters. Typically there are two such additional parameters: the power n of the nonlinear part of the Lagrangian and a further parameter (to be defined below) quantifying the contribution of this term to the energy budget of the universe.

Alternatively, we may ask whether a suitably chosen nonlinear Lagrangian can reproduce the low redshift acceleration of the universe in a model which at low redshift only contains matter (plus a subdominant amount of radiation) but no true cosmological constant. In principle such a scenario is conceivable.[1] It is also somewhat closer in spirit to the usual modified gravity models—with the caveat that, as previously mentioned, in the latter models the modification occurs in the gravitational part of the Lagrangian and not in the matter part.

The analysis of Ref. 4 found that these models do not solve the cosmological constant problem *per se*, but they can phenomenologically lead to a recent accelerating universe without a cosmological constant at the cost of having preferred values of the cosmological parameters that are somewhat different from the standard ΛCDM ones. Here we revisit and update these constraints, and also provide new constraints on models where the new terms depend on the trace of the energy-momentum tensor, $T = \rho - 3p$. As before, we can consider both the scenario with a cosmological constant (in which case the model is an extension of ΛCDM) and the scenario without a cosmological constant (in which case we can check whether such models can accelerate at all). These have been qualitatively studied in the literature,[7,8] and in what follows we provided quantitative constraints on them. We note that in all the analysis that follows the Hubble constant is analytically marginalized as discussed in Ref. 9.

2. Energy-momentum-powered models

The general action for these models is[2]

$$S = \frac{1}{2\kappa} \int \left[R + \eta(T^2)^n - 2\Lambda\right] d^4x + S_{matter}, \tag{1}$$

where $\kappa = 8\pi G$, and η is a constant quantifying the contribution of the T^2-dependent term. In a flat Friedmann-Lemaitre-Robertson-Walker universe and assuming a perfect fluid we have $T^2 = \rho^2 + 3p^2$ and the generalized Friedmann and

Raychaudhuri equations and the corresponding continuity equation can be written

$$3\left(\frac{\dot{a}}{a}\right)^2 = \Lambda + \kappa\rho + \eta(\rho^2 + 3p^2)^{n-1}\left[\left(n - \frac{1}{2}\right)(\rho^2 + 3p^2) + 4np\rho\right] \quad (2)$$

$$6\frac{\ddot{a}}{a} = 2\Lambda - \kappa(\rho + 3p) - \eta(\rho^2 + 3p^2)^{n-1}\left[(n+1)(\rho^2 + 3p^2) + 4np\rho\right] \quad (3)$$

$$\dot{\rho} = -3\frac{\dot{a}}{a}(\rho + p)\frac{\kappa\rho + n\eta\rho(\rho + 3p)(\rho^2 + 3p^2)^{n-1}}{\kappa\rho + 2n\eta(\rho^2 + 3p^2)^{n-1}\left[\left(n - \frac{1}{2}\right)(\rho^2 + 3p^2) + 4np\rho\right]}. \quad (4)$$

As usual, the Bianchi identity implies that only two of these equations are independent.

If we consider the low redshift limit of these models, further assuming that the universe is composed of matter and possibly also a cosmological constant, we can simplify the Einstein equations to

$$3\left(\frac{\dot{a}}{a}\right)^2 = \Lambda + \kappa\rho + \left(n - \frac{1}{2}\right)\eta\rho^{2n} \quad (5)$$

$$6\frac{\ddot{a}}{a} = 2\Lambda - \kappa\rho - (n+1)\eta\rho^{2n} \quad (6)$$

$$\dot{\rho} = -3\frac{\dot{a}}{a}\rho\frac{\kappa + n\eta\rho^{2n-1}}{\kappa + (2n-1)n\eta\rho^{2n-1}}. \quad (7)$$

Broadly speaking, we inspection of the equations leads to the expectation that $n < 1/2$ may be interesting at late times. In general these equations need to be solved numerically. However, there are three particular cases for which analytic solutions can be found (at least approximate, low redshift solutions), corresponding to the values $n = 1$, $n = 1/2$ and $n = 0$ (the latter actually corresponds to the ΛCDM case). These have been studied in the literature, in a general mathematical context,[1,2,10] and also observationally constrained in Ref. 4.

Generically we can treat n as a further model parameter, to be constrained by observations. In order to do this we define a dimensionless cosmological density r, via $\rho = r\rho_0$, where ρ_0 is the present day density, as well as a generic parameter

$$Q = \frac{\eta}{\kappa}\rho_0^{2n-1}. \quad (8)$$

With these assumptions, and keeping for the time being the matter assumption, the continuity equation expressed in terms of redshift has the form

$$\frac{dr}{dz} = \frac{3r}{1+z} \times \frac{1 + nQr^{2n-1}}{1 + (2n-1)nQr^{2n-1}}; \quad (9)$$

$$E^2(z) = \frac{H^2(z)}{H_0^2} = \Omega_\Lambda + \Omega_M r + \left(n - \frac{1}{2}\right)Q\Omega_M r^{2n}, \quad (10)$$

where, since we must have $E(0) = 1$, the model parameters are related by the requirement that $\Omega_\Lambda = 1 - \Omega_M[1 + (n - 1/2)Q]$, and therefore the Friedmann can be recast in the two alternative forms

$$E^2(z) = \Omega_\Lambda + \Omega_M r + (1 - \Omega_M - \Omega_\Lambda)r^{2n} \tag{11}$$

$$E^2(z) = 1 + \Omega_M(r - 1) + \left(n - \frac{1}{2}\right)Q\Omega_M(r^{2n} - 1), \tag{12}$$

the first one is generic, while the second applies only if $\Omega_\Lambda \neq 0$. On the other hand, if $\Omega_\Lambda = 0$ we can also use the flatness assumption to eliminate Q in the continuity equation, writing it as

$$\frac{dr}{dz} = \frac{3r}{1+z} \times \frac{(2n-1)\Omega_M + 2n(1-\Omega_M)r^{2n-1}}{(2n-1)[\Omega_M + 2n(1-\Omega_M)r^{2n-1}]}. \tag{13}$$

This shows that in a phenomenological sense these models could explain the recent acceleration of the universe without invoking a cosmological constant but relying instead on the nonlinearities of the matter Lagrangian in a matter-only universe with $n = 0$. However, we note that even if these models can lead to accelerating universes without a cosmological constant, this is not per se sufficient to solve the 'old' cosmological constant problem of why it should be zero. For n close to but not equal two zero, two things happen: the (formerly) constant term in the Friedmann equation becomes slowly varying, and the continuity equation implies that the matter density does not behave exactly as $r \propto (1+z)^3$. In what follows we discuss the extent to which deviations from the $n = 0$ case are observationally allowed, and also the most general parameter space where a standard cosmological constant is also allowed.

We can also consider a generalization: instead of considering a universe with a matter fluid, we can assume that this fluid has a constant equation of state $w = p/\rho = const.$ (with the matter case corresponding to $w = 0$). In this case the continuity equation becomes

$$\frac{dr}{dz} = \frac{3r}{1+z}(1+w) \times \frac{1 + nQf_1(n,w)r^{2n-1}}{1 + 2nQf_2(n,w)r^{2n-1}}, \tag{14}$$

where for convenience we defined

$$f_1(n,w) = (1+3w)(1+3w^2)^{n-1} \tag{15}$$

$$f_2(n,w) = (1+3w^2)^{n-1}\left[\left(n - \frac{1}{2}\right)(1+3w^2) + 4nw\right]. \tag{16}$$

In this case the Friedmann equation can be written

$$E^2(z) = \Omega_\Lambda + \Omega_M r + f_2(n,w)Q\Omega_M r^{2n}, \tag{17}$$

together with the consistency relation $\Omega_\Lambda = 1 - \Omega_M[1 + f_2 Q]$. It follows that we can also re-write it as

$$E^2(z) = \Omega_\Lambda + \Omega_M r + (1 - \Omega_M - \Omega_\Lambda)r^{2n} \tag{18}$$

$$E^2(z) = 1 + \Omega_M(r - 1) + f_2(n,w)Q\Omega_M(r^{2n} - 1), \tag{19}$$

where again the first is generic—and indeed identical to Eq. (11), although the redshift dependence of r will now be different—while the second holds for $\Omega_\Lambda \neq 0$. Here, if $\Omega_\Lambda = 0$ the continuity equation can also be written in a way that eliminates the parameter Q,

$$\frac{dr}{dz} = \frac{3r}{1+z}(1+w) \times \frac{\Omega_M f_2 + n(1-\Omega_M)f_1 r^{2n-1}}{f_2[\Omega_M + 2n(1-\Omega_M)r^{2n-1}]}. \qquad (20)$$

Table 1. One sigma posterior likelihoods on the power n, the matter density Ω_M and the constant equation of state w (when applicable) for various flat energy-momentum-powered models containing matter, with or without a cosmological constant. The last column lists the reduced chi-square for each best-fit model.

Model assumptions	Ω_M	n	w	χ^2_ν
$\Omega_\Lambda = 0$, $w = 0$	0.39 ± 0.08	0.04 ± 0.04	N/A	0.64
$\Omega_\Lambda \neq 0$, $w = 0$	$0.29^{+0.05}_{-0.03}$	Unconstrained	N/A	0.64
$\Omega_\Lambda = 0$, $w = const.$	$0.28^{+0.12}_{-0.10}$	$-0.08^{+0.06}_{-0.02}$	$-0.11^{+0.07}_{-0.04}$	0.62

Note: The specific assumptions for each case are described in the main text. The constraints come from the combination of the Pantheon supernova data and Hubble parameter measurements.

3. Constraints on energy-momentum-powered models

In what follows we briefly summarize constraints on the generic energy-momentum-powered models, revising and updating the analysis in Ref. 4. We carry out a standard likelihood analysis, using the datasets already mentioned in the introduction, and separately considering three different theoretical scenarios within this class of models. An overview of the results can be found in Table 1.

The constraints for the $\Omega_\Lambda = 0$ matter case are summarized in the top panel pf Fig. 1 and also in the first row of Table 1. As expected given the form of the Friedmann and continuity equations, there is a clear degeneracy between the two parameters. The best-fit values are about one standard deviation away from the canonical values $n = 0$ and $\Omega_M \sim 0.3$, and a non-zero $n \sim 0.04$ and a slightly higher matter density are preferred. However, at the two sigma level the results are consistent with ΛCDM; one should also bear in mind that the $n = 0$ does correspond to the ΛCDM case.

Constraints on the $\Omega_\Lambda \neq 0$ matter case are shown in the bottom panel of Fig. 1 and also in the second row of Table 1. Here there is a strong degeneracy between Q and n, both of which are unconstrained. On the other hand, the matter density is still well constrained (indeed, the constraint is tighter than in the case without a cosmological constant) and fully consistent with the canonical ΛCDM value.

Finally, constraints on the $\Omega_\Lambda = 0$ case while allowing for a constant equation of state, $w = const$ are in Fig. 2 and also in the final row of Table 1. In this case

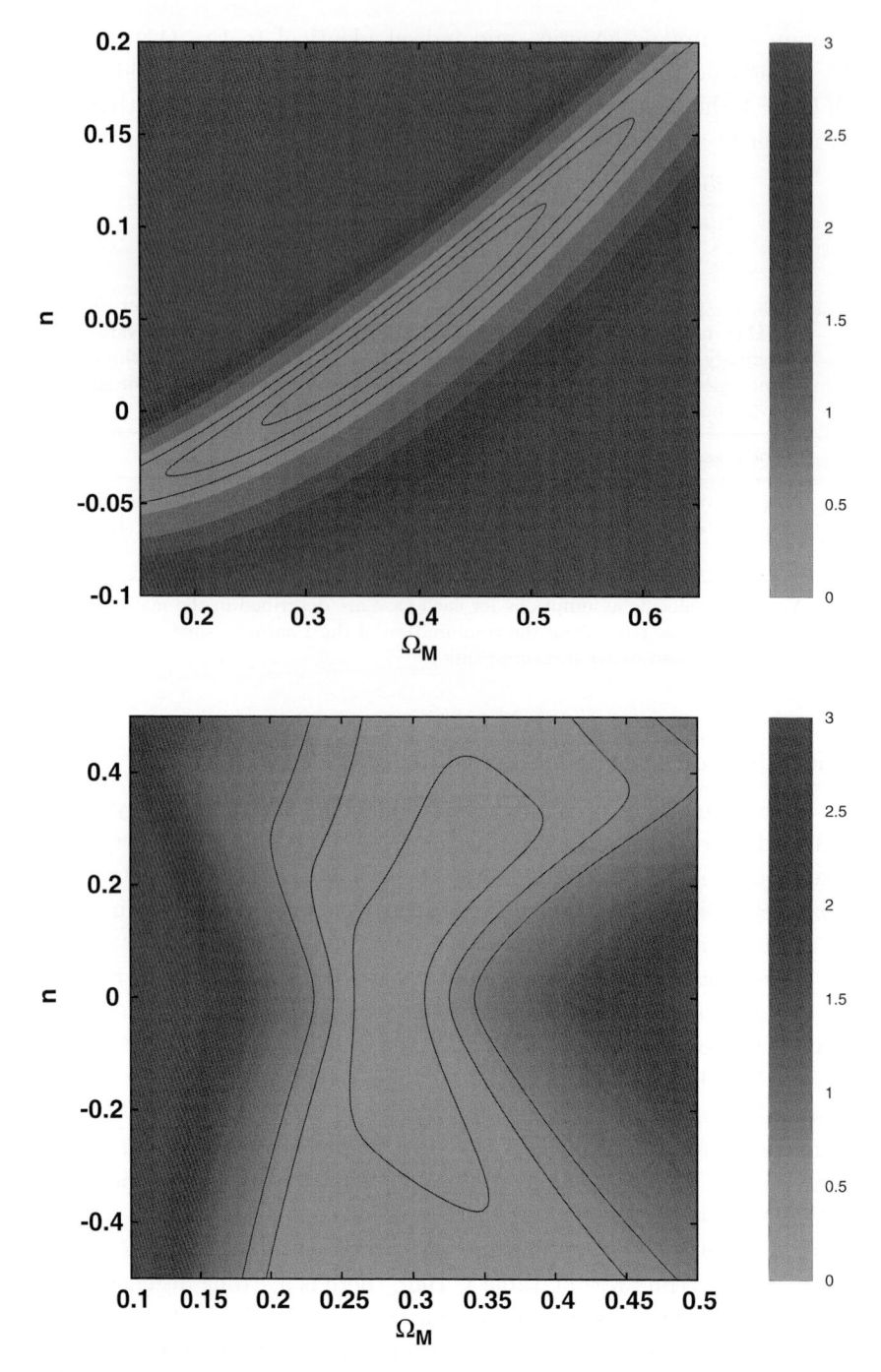

Fig. 1. Constraints on the n–Ω_M parameter space for flat universes with $w = 0$. Top and bottom panels correspond to the $\Omega_\Lambda = 0$ and $\Omega_\Lambda \neq 0$ cases, respectively. The black solid curves show the one, two, and three sigma confidence levels, while the color map depicts the reduced chi-square.

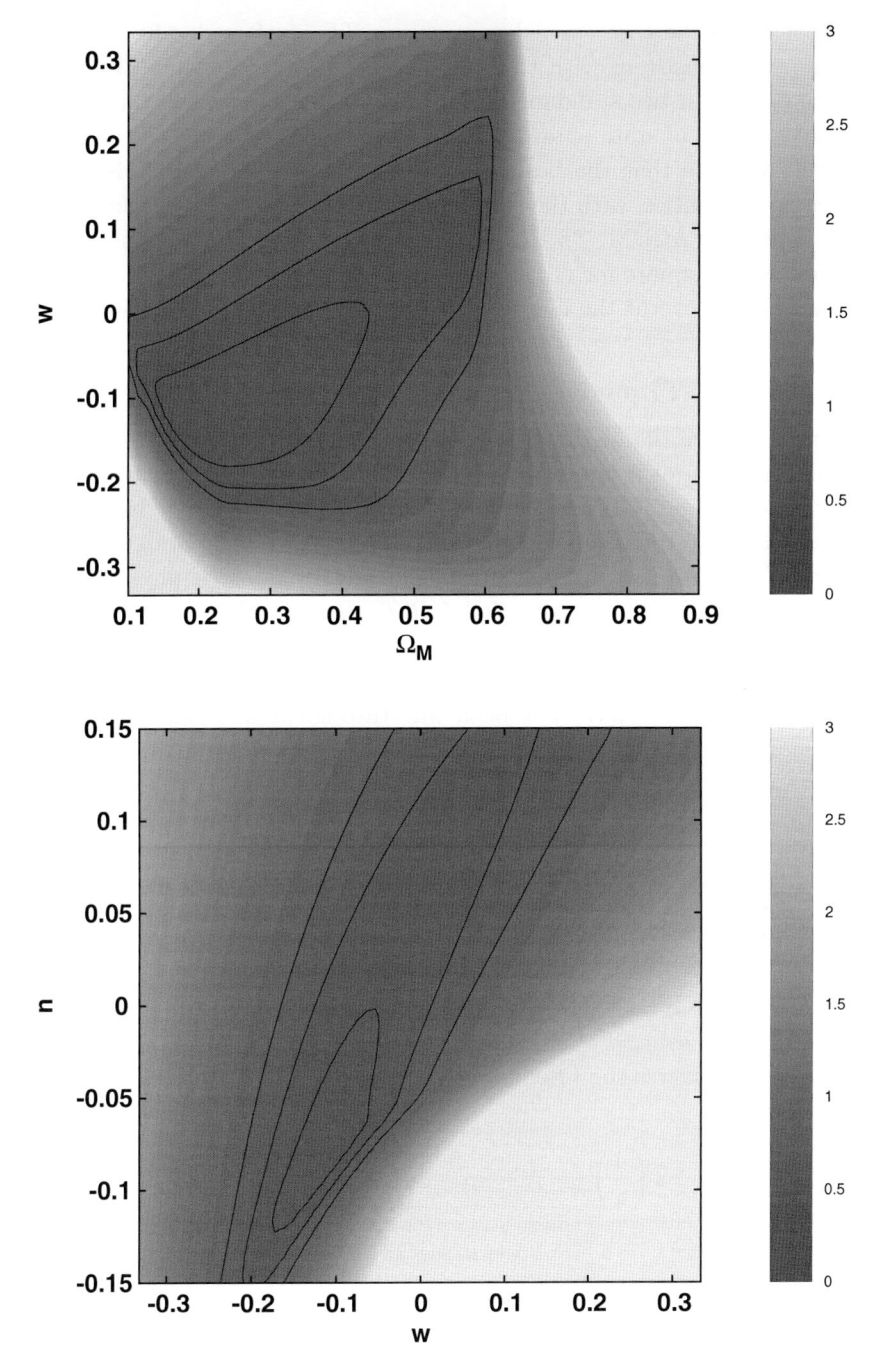

Fig. 2. Constraints on the n–Ω_M–w parameter space for flat universes with $\Omega_\Lambda = 0$. The black solid curves show the one, two, and three sigma confidence levels, while the color maps depict the reduced chi-square.

one can constrain the three model parameters. The preferred value of the matter density is again consistent with the canonical ΛCDM value, while there is a mild preference (less than two standard deviations) for negative values on the exponent n and the equation of state parameter w.

Overall, we note that the best-fit value for the matter density is compatible, within the uncertainties, with the standard one, and there is no significant evidence for deviations from ΛCDM. On the other hand, it is worthy of note that the values of the reduced chi-square for all the best-fit models is significantly below unity, so the models clearly overfit the low redshift data that we are considering.

4. A simple $f(R,T)$ model

We will now explore the modified gravity model recently discussed in Ref. 7. This is actually one case of a larger set of $f(R,T)$ models, to be discussed elsewhere. A class of modified gravity models now dubbed $f(R)$ gravity, R being the scalar curvature, was first considered in Ref. 11, but these models are subject to tight cosmological constraints.[12] A phenomenologically broader (if physically less well motivated) class is that of the so-called $f(R,T)$ models, where T is the trace of the stress energy tensor. A particular subclass of these models has separable function, $f(R,T) = R + f_2(T)$,. These models have been the subject of several mathematical studies but so far they have not been put through a detailed comparison with cosmological observations, with the exception of the recent qualitative analysis of Ref. 8.

Qualitatively, the main difference is that here the new terms depend on the trace of the energy-momentum tensor $T = \rho - 3p$, while in the model considered in the previous sections they depended on $T^2 \equiv T_{\mu\nu}T^{\mu\nu} = \rho^2 + 3p^2$. The procedure for studying the two models should otherwise be similar.

This model,[7] also previously considered in Ref. 8, has the action

$$S = \frac{1}{2\kappa} \int \left[R + \xi\sqrt{T} - 2\Lambda\right] d^4x + S_{matter}. \qquad (21)$$

In a flat FLRW universe the Friedmann and Raychaudhuri equations now have the following form[a]

$$3\left(\frac{\dot{a}}{a}\right)^2 = \Lambda + \kappa\rho + \xi\frac{(\rho-p)}{\sqrt{\rho-3p}} \qquad (22)$$

$$6\frac{\ddot{a}}{a} = 2\Lambda - \kappa(\rho+3p) + \frac{\xi}{2}\frac{(\rho-7p)}{\sqrt{\rho-3p}}. \qquad (23)$$

As a simple comparison, in the $p=0$ case this model leads to a Friedmann equation of the form

$$3H^2 = \Lambda + \kappa\rho + \xi\sqrt{\rho}, \qquad (24)$$

---

[a]We note that there is a minus sign typo in the last term of Eq. (10) in Ref. 7.

while in the energy-momentum-powered model, choosing $n = 1/4$, one has

$$3H^2 = \Lambda + \kappa\rho - \frac{\eta}{4}\sqrt{\rho}. \tag{25}$$

We note that the two Friedmann equations coincide (if one identifies $\xi = -\eta/4$), but the corresponding continuity equations differ in the two cases.

We will again assume constant equations of state ($p = w\rho$), use the standard definitions of Ω_M and Ω_Λ together with $\rho = r\rho_0$ and additionally define

$$\zeta = \frac{\xi}{2\kappa\sqrt{\rho_0}}. \tag{26}$$

We can then rewrite the Friedmann equation as follows

$$E^2(z) = \Omega_\Lambda + \Omega_M r + 2\zeta \frac{(1-w)}{\sqrt{1-3w}} \Omega_M \sqrt{r}. \tag{27}$$

In principle there are therefore 3 free parameters, since the $E(0) = 1$ condition requires that the model parameters are related by $\Omega_\Lambda = 1 - \Omega_M[1 + 2\zeta(1-w)/\sqrt{1-3w}]$. We can also rewrite it as

$$E^2(z) = \Omega_\Lambda + \Omega_M r + (1 - \Omega_M - \Omega_\Lambda)\sqrt{r} \tag{28}$$

$$E^2(z) = 1 + \Omega_M(r-1) + 2\zeta\frac{(1-w)}{\sqrt{1-3w}}\Omega_M(\sqrt{r}-1); \tag{29}$$

the first of these is generic, while the second is only valid if $\Omega_\Lambda \neq 0$. However, note that in general the parameters (ζ, w) still affect the continuity equation, which can be written as

$$\frac{dr}{dz} = \frac{3r}{1+z}(1+w) \times \frac{\sqrt{1-3w} + \zeta/\sqrt{r}}{\sqrt{1-3w} + (1-w)\zeta/\sqrt{r}}. \tag{30}$$

We note that the usual behaviour, $r \propto (1+z)^3$, is recovered for $\zeta = 0$ and that (less trivially) this also occurs for the matter case ($w = 0$) for any value of the parameter ζ. As an illustration of the role of this parameter we can solve the continuity in the $\zeta \to 0$ limit. One finds

$$r(z) = \left[\left(1 + \frac{w\zeta}{\sqrt{1-3w}}\right)(1+z)^{3(1+w)/2} - \frac{w\zeta}{\sqrt{1-3w}}\right]^2, \tag{31}$$

which again has the appropriate limits.

5. Observational constraints on the $\sqrt{T}$ model

The model can now be constrained, and in particular we can again consider both the scenario with a cosmological constant (in which case the model is an extension of ΛCDM) and the scenario without a cosmological constant (in which case we can check whether such models can account for the recent acceleration of the universe at all). An overview of the results can be found in Table 2.

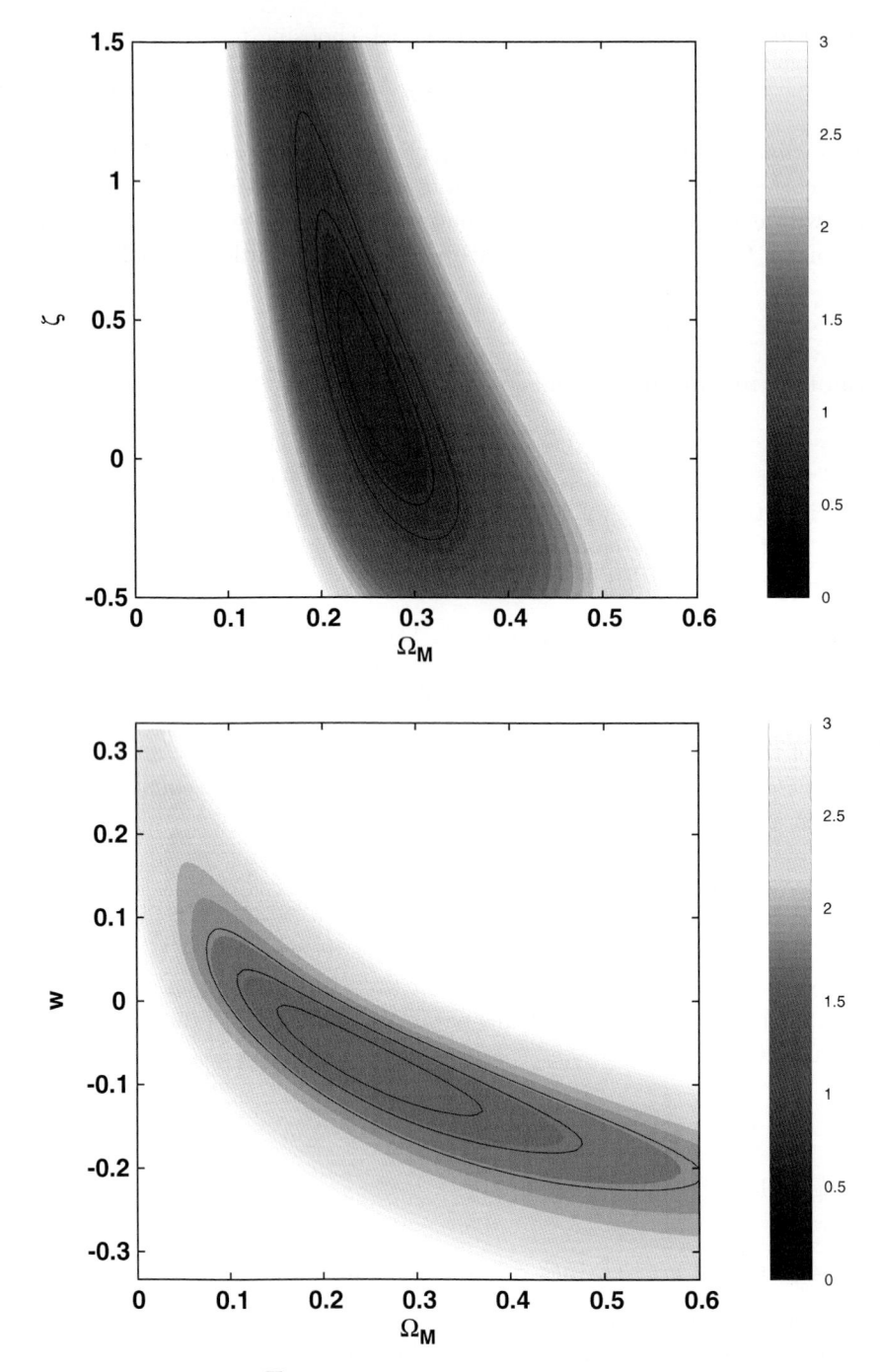

Fig. 3. Constraints on flat $\sqrt{T}$ models. The top panel shows constraints for $\Omega_\Lambda \neq 0$ and $w = 0$, and the bottom panel shows constraints for $\Omega_\Lambda = 0$ and $w = const$. The black solid curves show the one, two, and three sigma confidence levels, and the color maps depict the reduced chi-square.

Table 2. One sigma posterior likelihoods on the matter density Ω_M, the coupling ζ and the constant equation of state w (when applicable) for various flat energy-momentum-powered models containing matter, with or without a cosmological constant. The last column lists the reduced chi-square for each best-fit model.

Model assumptions	Ω_M	ζ	w	χ^2_ν
$\Omega_\Lambda = 0$, $w = 0$	0.15 ± 0.02	2.78 ± 1.72	N/A	1.80
$\Omega_\Lambda \neq 0$, $w = 0$	$0.25^{+0.03}_{-0.02}$	$0.23^{+0.22}_{-0.18}$	N/A	0.63
$\Omega_\Lambda = 0$, $w = const.$	$0.24^{+0.08}_{-0.07}$	Unconstrained	$-0.08^{+0.04}_{-0.05}$	1.80

Note: The specific assumptions for each case are described in the main text. The constraints come from the combination of the Pantheon supernova data and Hubble parameter measurements.

Starting with the case of $\Omega_\Lambda = 0$ and $w = 0$, we effectively have only one independent parameter, since the matter density and coupling parameter are related through $(1 + 2\zeta)\Omega_M = 1$. The obtained constraints are listed in the first row of Table 2. It is clear from the very large value of the reduced chi-square that this model, containing only matter but no cosmological constant, does not fit the data. In other words, this model can not be a true alternative to ΛCDM.

The top panel of Fig. 3 and the second row of Table 2 summarize the constraints for the case of $\Omega_\Lambda \neq 0$ and $w = 0$. In this case we have two independent parameters, and the model is effectively a one parameter extension of ΛCDM. Here, as in the previously discussed case of energy-momentum-powered models, the model slightly overfits the data, and there is no statistically significant preference for a non-zero coupling parameter ζ, The best fit value of the matter density is not significantly changed with respect to its value, for the same datasets, in the ΛCDM model.[13]

Finally, the bottom panel of Fig. 3 and the third row of Table 2 show the constraints for $\Omega_\Lambda = 0$ and $w \neq 0$, where we have three independent parameters. There are now additional degeneracies between the parameters, but the main conclusion remains the same as for the $w = 0$ case: without a cosmological constant this model severely underfits the data, and therefore it is not viable as an alternative to ΛCDM.

6. Outlook

We have discussed observational current low redshift background constraints on classes of FLRW cosmological models in which the matter side of Einstein's equations includes, in addition to the canonical term, either a term proportional to a function of the energy-momentum tensor ($T^2 = \rho^2 + 3p^2$), or of its trace ($T = \rho - 3p$). Both of these can be phenomenologically thought of as extensions of general relativity with a nonlinear matter Lagrangian.

We considered both models under two different scenarios: (1) as phenomenological two-parameter or three-parameter extensions of the standard ΛCDM, in which case the model still has a cosmological constant but the nonlinear matter Lagrangian leads to additional terms in Einstein's equations, which cosmological observations tightly constrain, and (2) as alternatives to ΛCDM, where there is no cosmological constant, and the nonlinear matter term would have to provide the acceleration (which would be somewhat closer in spirit to the usual modified gravity models).

Overall, our analysis suggests that the ΛCDM paradigm is fairly robust or, pragmatically, it is a good phenomenological approximation to a still unknown more fundamental model. In other words, if there is no true cosmological constant, the alternative mechanism must effectively be like one, at least at low redshifts. On the other hand, for parametric extensions of ΛCDM, subdominant (ca. 10% level) contributions are allowed by the low redshift background cosmology data that we have considered. These constraints can of course be tightened by including additional datasets, such as that from cosmic microwave background observations. Our work can be extended to broader classes of $f(R,T)$ models, a discussion of which is left for a subsequent publication.

Acknowledgments

This work was financed by FEDER—Fundo Europeu de Desenvolvimento Regional funds through the COMPETE 2020—Operational Programme for Competitiveness and Internationalisation (POCI), and by Portuguese funds through FCT - Fundação para a Ciência e a Tecnologia in the framework of the project POCI-01-0145-FEDER-028987 and PTDC/FIS-AST/28987/2017. The project that led to this work was started during AstroCamp 2020.

References

1. M. Roshan and F. Shojai, Energy-Momentum Squared Gravity, *Phys. Rev.* **D94**, p. 044002 (2016).
2. C. V. R. Board and J. D. Barrow, Cosmological Models in Energy-Momentum-Squared Gravity, *Phys. Rev.* **D96**, p. 123517 (2017), [Erratum: Phys. Rev. D 98, no. 12, 129902 (2018)].
3. O. Akarsu, N. Katirci and S. Kumar, Cosmic acceleration in a dust only universe via energy-momentum powered gravity, *Phys. Rev.* **D97**, p. 024011 (2018).
4. M. C. F. Faria, C. J. A. P. Martins, F. Chiti and B. S. A. Silva, Low redshift constraints on energy-momentum-powered gravity models, *Astron. Astrophys.* **625**, p. A127 (2019).
5. A. G. Riess et al., Type Ia Supernova Distances at Redshift > 1.5 from the Hubble Space Telescope Multi-cycle Treasury Programs: The Early Expansion Rate, *Astrophys. J.* **853**, p. 126 (2018).
6. O. Farooq, F. R. Madiyar, S. Crandall and B. Ratra, Hubble Parameter Measurement Constraints on the Redshift of the Deceleration–acceleration Transition, Dynamical Dark Energy, and Space Curvature, *Astrophys. J.* **835**, p. 26 (2017).
7. N. Godani and G. C. Samanta, Estimation of cosmological parameters, stability analysis and energy conditions in viable modified gravity, *Chin. J. Phys.* **66**, 787 (2020).
8. H. Velten and T. R. P. Caramês, Cosmological inviability of $f(R,T)$ gravity, *Phys. Rev. D* **95**, p. 123536 (2017).

9. F. K. Anagnostopoulos and S. Basilakos, Constraining the dark energy models with $H(z)$ data: An approach independent of H_0, *Phys. Rev.* **D97**, p. 063503 (2018).
10. N. Katırcı and M. Kavuk, $f(R, T_{\mu\nu}T^{\mu\nu})$ gravity and Cardassian-like expansion as one of its consequences, *Eur. Phys. J. Plus* **129**, p. 163 (2014).
11. H. A. Buchdahl, Non-linear Lagrangians and cosmological theory, *Mon. Not. Roy. Astron. Soc.* **150**, p. 1 (1970).
12. T. Clifton, P. G. Ferreira, A. Padilla and C. Skordis, Modified Gravity and Cosmology, *Phys. Rept.* **513**, 1 (2012).
13. C. B. D. Fernandes, C. J. A. P. Martins and B. A. R. Rocha, Constraining alternatives to a cosmological constant: Generalized couplings and scale invariance, *Phys. Dark Univ.* **31**, p. 100761 (2021).

Constraining the dark energy-dark matter interaction model using low-redshift observations

Archana Sangwan*, Joseph P J[†], and S. Shankaranarayanan[‡]

Department of Physics, Indian Institute of Technology Bombay,
Mumbai 400076, India
* E-mail: arch06san@gmail.com, [†] E-mail: josephpj@iitb.ac.in
[‡] E-mail: shanki@phy.iitb.ac.in

Various observations have shown that dark energy accounts for nearly two-thirds of the energy density of the Universe. The simplest model to explain the nature of dark energy is the cosmological constant (ΛCDM) model. Although Planck observations supports using ΛCDM model as the base cosmological model, there exist some inconsistencies in parameter estimates when compared with independent observations. The most important is the inconsistency in the H_0 estimates from the Planck collaboration which reports $H_0 = 67.5^{+0.5}_{-0.5}\ km\ s^{-1}\ Mpc^{-1}$, a considerably lower value when compared with the direct local distance ladder measurements. This value shows a discrepancy at the level greater than 4σ with the constraints reported by SH0ES collaboration in 2019, $H_0 = 74.3^{+1.42}_{-1.42}\ km\ s^{-1}\ Mpc^{-1}$. These disagreements, called the Hubble tension, point towards a new physics that deviates from the standard ΛCDM model and to resolve this various methods have been proposed. In this work, a quintessence scalar field with an inverse power potential (V(ϕ)~ ϕ^{-n}) is assumed as a description of dark energy and we focus on an interacting dark energy dark matter model where the interacting term is taken to be linear in the field (Φ). We study in detail the evolution of the model and provide constraints on the model parameters using low redshift cosmological observations of Type Ia Supernovae (SN), baryon acoustic oscillations (BAO), direct measurements of Hubble parameter (Hz) and high redshift HII galaxy measurements (HIIG). We find that the model agrees with the existing values of the nonrelativistic matter density parameter, Ω_m and dark energy equation of state parameter, w_0. The analysis shows that the observations prefer a negative value of coupling constant and gives the best fit value of $H_0 = 69.9^{+0.46}_{-1.02}\ km\ s^{-1}\ Mpc^{-1}$ and thereby can be used to alleviates the H_0 tension between Planck measurements and the observations considered.

Keywords: Cosmological parameter, observations, dark energy - dark matter interaction, based on the work [arXiv:2102.12367].[1]

1. Introduction

Many cosmological observations suggest that, at the present epoch, the energy content of the universe is dominated by dark energy, and to explain the observed accelerated expansion of the universe, this dark energy component must have a negative pressure.[2-5] However, the nature of dark energy is still a mystery, and many models are proposed in the literature to explain what dark energy might be. The simplest model is the ΛCDM model, which is also the most consistent model for cosmological observations. The latest results from the Planck mission provide good support to the ΛCDM model as the base cosmological model and also improve upon the uncertainties in parameter estimation.[6,7] With more accurate and precise measurements, the uncertainties from various experiments have been studied and are in disagreement with each other. The most glaring tension is found in the estimation of the Hubble parameter reported by the Planck collaboration and the low redshift cosmological probes.[8–10] In some cases, the tension stands at level greater than 4σ, e.g., Planck 2018 results, which assume standard ΛCDM model as the base cosmological model, report Hubble parameter to be $H_0 = 67.4 \pm 0.5 \; km \; s^{-1} \; Mpc^{-1}$,[7] whereas SH0ES collaboration estimates $H_0 = 73.5 \pm 1.4 \; km \; s^{-1} \; Mpc^{-1}$.[11] Another discrepancy, although not as severe, is found in the estimation of σ_8 reported by Planck 2018 and low redshift observation with stands at a level of 2σ-3σ level.[12–17] The high precision of the data from Planck collaboration and low redshift probes insinuate that the H_0 tension between these experiments cannot result from the systematics and hence, points towards a new physics that deviates from the standard ΛCDM model.

Many models have been proposed and studied to resolve these disagreements in literature. One such proposal is to consider a non-zero interaction between dark energy and dark matter which could alleviate these disagreements.[18–21] In this work, we focus on an interacting dark sector model, which is introduced in.[22] In most cases, this interaction term is introduced in fluid equations by hand, which might not be consistent with the classical field theory action. In the Ref.,[22] instead of putting it by hand, the authors derive the interaction term, which is consistent with both fluid descriptions and classical field theory description. We use this interaction term in our work and study whether the interaction model is consistent with low redshift observations such as direct measurement of Hubble parameter (Hz),[23–28] measurements of HII galaxy (HIIG),[29,30] baryon acoustic oscillations (BAO),[31–36] and type Ia supernovae (SN).[37] We constrain the model parameters, and after analyzing, find that using only the background observations, we cannot distinguish between interacting and noninteracting scenarios. Two see a clear distinction between the two cases; we have to study the evolution of perturbed quantities.

2. Dark Energy Dark Matter Interaction Model

The interacting model is described by the action

$$S = \int d^4x \sqrt{-g} \left(\frac{1}{2\kappa^2} R - \frac{1}{2} g^{\mu\nu} \nabla_\mu \phi \nabla_\nu \phi - U(\phi) - \frac{1}{2} e^{2\alpha(\phi)} g^{\mu\nu} \nabla_\mu \chi \nabla_\nu \chi - e^{4\alpha(\phi)} V(\chi) \right). \tag{1}$$

where dark energy is denoted by the scalar field ϕ, $U(\phi)$ is the scalar field potential, dark matter is represented by the scalar field χ, and $\alpha(\phi)$ denotes the dark energy dark matter interaction (For more details, see[22]).

The Einstein equation in terms of the scalar field (ϕ) and dark matter fluid, specified by four-velocity energy density and pressure, is given by[22]

$$G_{\mu\nu} = 16\pi G \left[\nabla_\mu \phi \nabla_\nu \phi - \frac{1}{2} g_{\mu\nu} \nabla^\sigma \phi \nabla_\sigma \phi - g_{\mu\nu} V(\phi) + p_m g_{\mu\nu} + (\rho_m + p_m) u_\mu u_\nu \right], \tag{2}$$

and the energy-momentum tensor for the dark matter fluid is given by

$$T_\nu^{(m)\mu} = p_m g_{\mu\nu} + (\rho_m + p_m) u_\mu u_\nu \,. \tag{3}$$

The interaction term is described by $\nabla_\mu T_\nu^{(m)\mu} = Q_\nu^{(F)}$, and by demanding that the interaction term Q_ν must have a field theory description, they obtained a unique form of interaction term, given by[22]

$$Q_\nu^{(F)} = T^{(m)} \nabla_\nu \alpha(\phi) \,. \tag{4}$$

We study the evolution of cosmological equations in the presence of the interaction and obtain constraints on the model parameters by assuming a specific form of scalar field potential and the interaction term. In this work, we assume a quintessence scalar field described by the inverse power law potential and an interaction term that is linear in the field (ϕ),

$$U(\phi) \sim \frac{1}{\phi^n}, \qquad n = 1, 2, \tag{5}$$

$$\alpha(\phi) \sim \phi, \qquad \alpha(\phi) = C\phi \tag{6}$$

where C is the interaction strength. The evolution of the scalar field is described by the Klein-Gordon equation given by

$$(\ddot{\phi} + 3H\dot{\phi} + U_{,\phi})\dot{\phi} = Q \,,$$

where $Q = Q_0^{(F)}$. The scalar field potential in terms of dimensionless parameter $\tilde{\phi}$ is

$$U(\tilde{\phi}) = \frac{\kappa}{2} m_{\text{Pl}}^2 \tilde{\phi}^{-n} \tag{7}$$

where κ is a constant and m_{Pl}, is the Planck mass. The evolution of non-relativistic matter density in the presence of interaction is given by

$$\dot{\rho}_m + 3H\rho_m = -Q \,.$$

For interaction term, $Q = -\alpha_{,\phi}\dot{\phi}\rho_m$, on solving the above equation we get, $\rho_m = \rho_{m_0} e^{\alpha(\phi)-\alpha(\phi_0)} a^{-3}$.

We use these equations to study the universe's evolution in the presence of nonzero interaction and establish the consistency of the model with the latest low redshift observations. The observations used in the analysis are: a) the direct measurements of Hubble parameter (Hz) with observations in the redshift range of $0.070 \leq z \leq 1.965$, b) the baryon acoustic oscillations (BAO) data ($0.106 \leq z \leq 2.36$), c) High-redshift HII Galaxy measurements (HIIG) which spans in a range $0.0088 \leq z \leq 2.42935$, and d) type Ia Supernovae (SN) observations with data points between range $0.05 \leq z \leq 1.4$. To obtain the constraints on model parameters, we use the chi-squared minimization technique, which tells about the goodness of the fit by comparing the observed values of an observable with the theoretically expected values for a specific model (dark energy dark matter interaction model in our case).

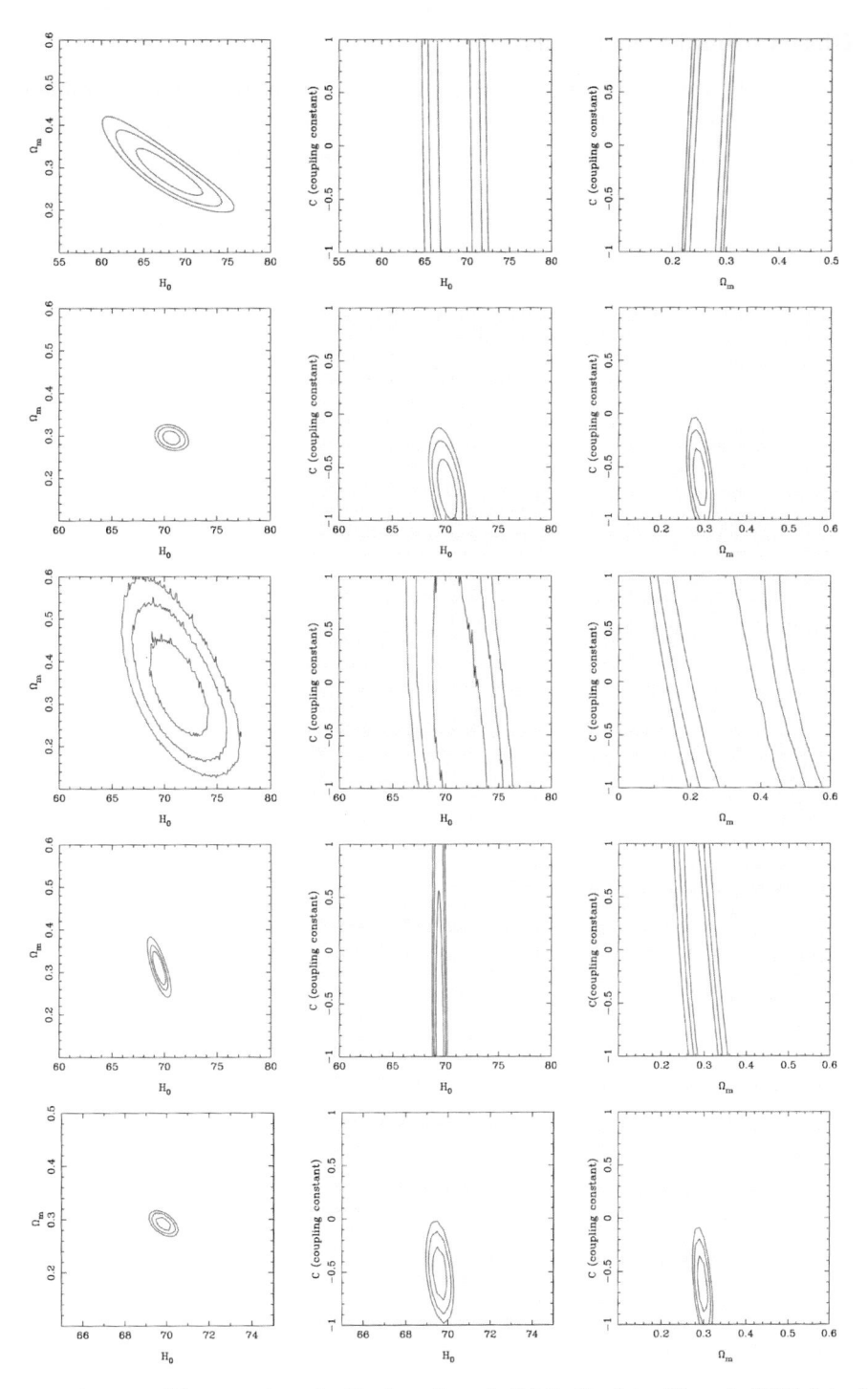

Fig. 1. 1,2,3-σ confidence regions for Hz data (I row), BAO+Hz data (II row), HIIG data (III row), SN+Hz data (IV row) and all four data sets (V row).

3. Observational Constraints

In the analysis, the parameter describing the model are: the Hubble parameter at present (H_0), nonrelativistic matter density parameter (Ω_m), dark energy equation of state parameter at present (w_0), and the interaction strength (C). The priors used in the analysis are given in table below.

Parameter	Lower Limit	Upper Limit
H_0	60.0	80.0
Ω_m	0.1	0.6
w_0	-1.0	1.0
C	-1.0	1.0

We perform the chi-squared minimization technique to obtain the $1, 2, 3 - \sigma$ confidence regions for the four observations we considered in the analysis and provide the results in two-dimensional planes in Fig. 1. We assume $n = 1$ in the analysis and have marginalized over the other parameters to obtain the results in the two-dimensional plane. The results from Hz observation are shown in the first row. The allowed range from Hz data for Ω_m and H_0 parameters are fairly large as compared to the allowed uncertainties obtained from BAO measurements (second row) and SN data (fourth row). On the other hand, the interaction strength parameter C is not constrained by Hz observations, and the entire range is allowed by the observations. BAO+Hz data (second row) provides the tightest constraints on the cosmological parameters, and these observations also obtain the upper limit on interaction strength.

Constraints from HIIG data are presented in the third row (where we have not included the systematic error in the analysis for HIIG data); the HIIG data is unable to constrain the H_0 parameter and provides the largest allowed range for Ω_m among the data sets considered in the analysis. In the fourth row, results from SN+Hz are presented. SN+Hz data also provides narrow constraints on H_0 and Ω_m parameters and gives an upper limit on the interaction strength. Finally, the results from combining the data sets (Hz+BAO+HIIG+SN) are given in row fifth. We find that by performing combined analysis, we get a very narrow range of uncertainties in parameter estimation, and the best fit values of parameters are given by $H_0 = 69.9 \ km \ s^{-1} \ Mpc^{-1}$, $\Omega_m = 0.29$, and $C = -0.47$. From the analysis, we find that all the observations are consistent with negative values of C, and the upper on C is given by SN+Hz and BAO+Hz observations which drive the combined results.

We show the results in $\Omega_m - w_0$ plane obtained from Hz (first row, left), BAO+Hz (first row, right), HIIG (the second row, left), and SN+Hz (second row right) observations in Fig. 2. For all the observations, we find that the model is consistent with the cosmological constant model, and BAO+Hz data provides the narrowest

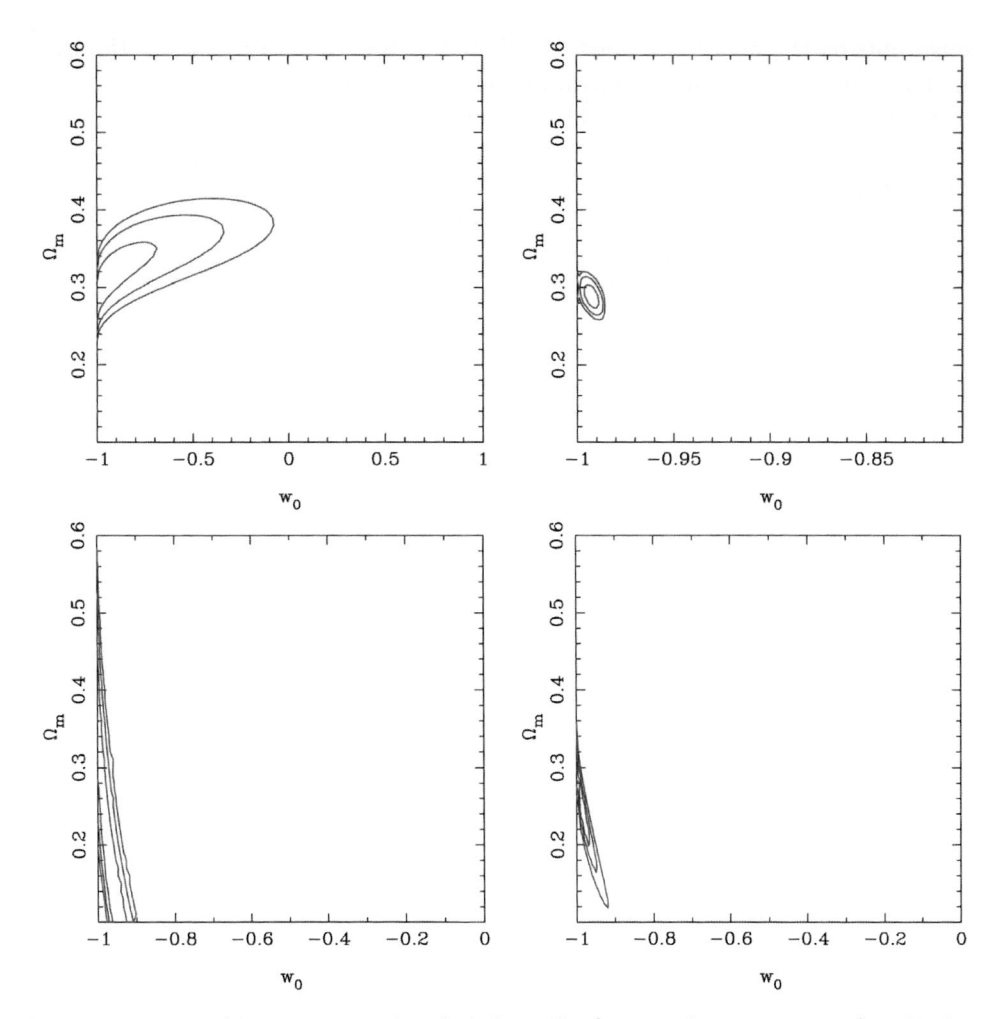

Fig. 2. 1,2,3-σ confidence regions in 'w_0-Ω_m' plane. The first row shows constraints from Hz data (left) and BAO+Hz observations (right). The second row shows constraints from HIIG measurements (left) and SN+Hz observations (right).

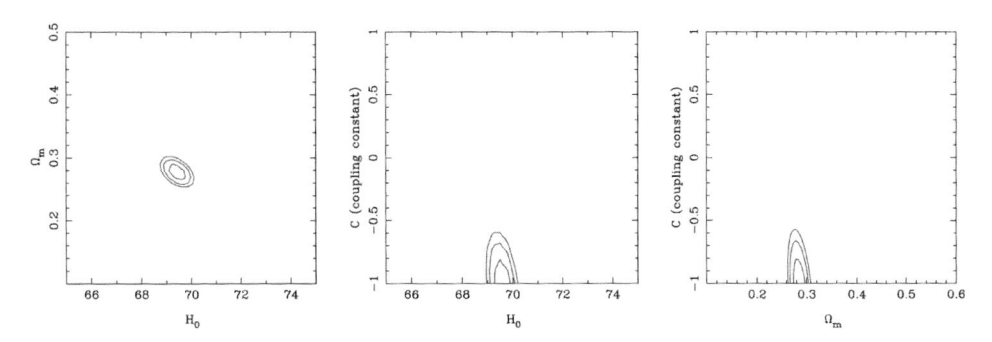

Fig. 3. 1,2,3-σ confidence regions for combined analysis of all four data sets.

constraints on Ω_m and w_0 parameters followed by Sn+Hz measurements. However, Hz data also allows for non-accelerating universe scenarios.

We have also performed the chi-squared analysis for the $n = 2$ case. And we find that the key conclusions from $n = 1$ remain the same that all the observations constrain H_0 to be close to 70 $km\ s^{-1}\ Mpc^{-1}$ and the narrowest constraints are obtained from BAO+Hz and SN+Hz, followed by Hz and HIIG observation. The change in results from individual observations is not significant as we move from $n = 1$ to $n = 2$ case. The only difference worth mentioning is that as n changes from 1 to 2, the contours show a slight shift value of C towards -1, and the model seems to prefer negative values of interaction strength. This preference is more notable in the results from the combined analysis of all the previously mentioned observations. In Fig. 3, we show the 1,2,3-σ confidence regions for combined analysis from all the four data sets considered in the analysis. The effect on Ω_m and H_0 constraints is not significant as we go from $n = 1$ to $n = 2$ case, and the constraints obtained from each dataset are consistent with each other.

Examining the constraints obtained through the evolution of background cosmological equations and using low redshift observations, it is evident that we cannot distinguish between interacting and noninteracting scenarios. Therefore, in the next section, we study the evolution of first-order perturbations in the presence of a nonzero interacting term.

4. Evolution of Perturbations

In this section, we study the evolution of quantities that depends upon the evolution of first-order cosmological perturbations and are related to the observations in current cosmological experiments. The cosmological quantities we discuss are related to structure formation, gravitational lensing and integrated Sachs-Wolfe effect, denoted by δ_m, $\Phi + \Psi$, and $\Phi' + \Psi'$ respectively.

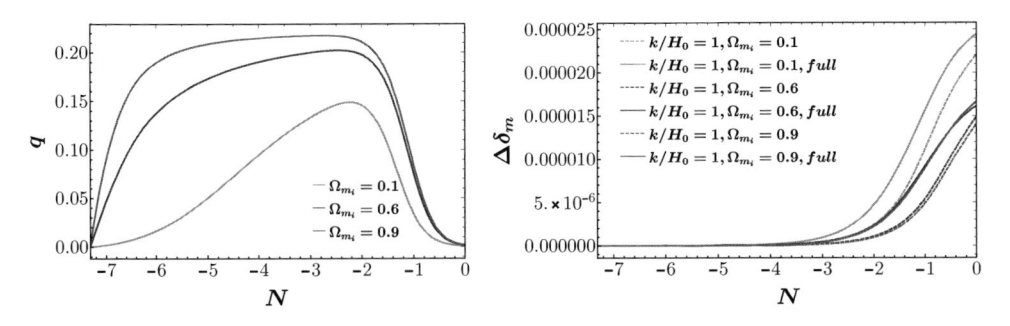

Fig. 4. Evolution of q (left panel) and $\Delta\delta_m$ (right panel) as a function of N with $C = -0.6$.

Structure formation: To study the effect of interaction between dark energy and dark matter on structure formation, we study the evolution of matter density perturbation denoted by δ_m, for various length scales. The parameter δ_m is defined as $\delta_m(t,x,y,z) \equiv \frac{\delta\rho_m(t,x,y,z)}{\overline{\rho_m}(t)}$, where $\overline{\rho_m}(t)$ is the mean matter density at time t.

In Fig. 4, the left plot shows the evolution of the scaled interaction term given by $q = \frac{Q}{H^3 M_{Pl}^2}$ as a function of N for different initial values of matter density parameter Ω_m, where $N = ln(a)$ is the number of e-foldings. We see that for a larger value of initial matter density, the contribution of the interaction term is greater and becomes significant at an earlier time than for smaller initial matter density values. The right plot shows the evolution of $\Delta\delta_m = \delta_{m_i} - \delta_{m_{ni}}$ as a function of N. The plot shows the difference in the evolution of matter density perturbations in the interacting and noninteracting models denoted by parameters δ_{m_i} and $\delta_{m_{ni}}$ respectively. The dotted lines are for the case when the perturbed interaction term is neglected, and the solid line is when we consider the perturbed interaction term. The different colors correspond to the different initial values of the matter density parameter. We see that at around $N \sim 2$, the curves deviate from one another, showing that considering the interaction term changes the evolution of matter perturbations, and the maximum change is observed in smaller Ω_{m_i} case. This demonstrates that its possible to detect the signature of dark energy and dark matter interactions in future large scale structure observations.[38–40]

Weak gravitational lensing: The quantity $\Phi + \Phi$ contributes to the weak gravitational lensing effect that is the result of deviation in photon trajectory because of the mass distribution in space. This section discusses the evolution of Φ as in standard cosmology, $\Phi = \Psi$. The evolution of Φ as a function of N is shown in Fig. 5. The plot on the left is for dark energy dark matter interaction scenario with interaction strength $C = -0.6$, and the right plot is for noninteracting scenarios. The different curves correspond to different length scales represented by different values of k. The curves are obtained by evolving the system of equations with the same initial conditions starting at a redshift of $z_i = 1500$. We find that the effect of interaction is clear on the smallest scale considered in the analysis, i.e., at $k/H_0 = 1$. Therefore, we can use the evolution of scalar perturbations to distinguish between the interacting and noninteracting dark energy dark matter scenarios by the future observations of weak gravitational lensing.[41]

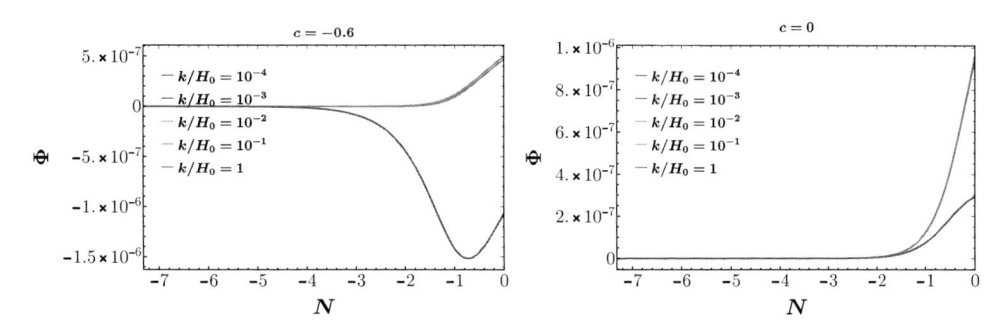

Fig. 5. Evolution of Φ as a function of N. Left: $C = -0.6$, Right: $C = 0$.

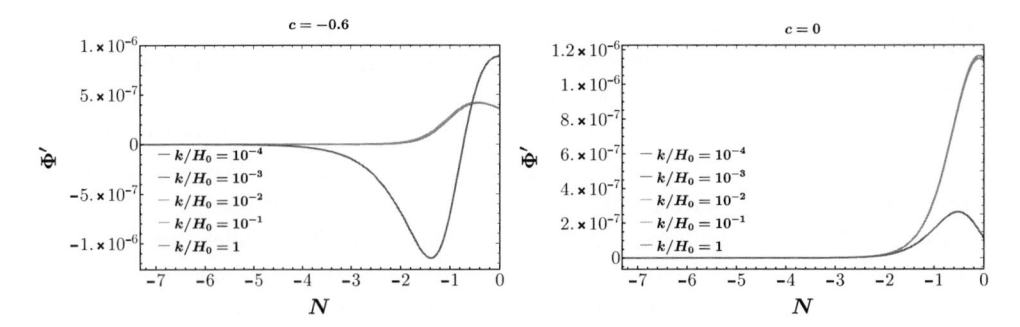

Fig. 6. Evolution of Φ' as a function of N. Left: $C = -0.6$, Right: $C = 0$.

Integrated Sachs-Wolfe effect: This effect manifests in cosmic microwave background radiation anisotropies because of the change in gravitational potential in the path of photons as the photons travel after decoupling from the last scattering surface towards the observer. This effect is given by $\Phi' + \Psi'$, where $'$ denotes the rate of change with respect to conformal time. The change in the evolution of Φ' as a function of N for interacting case with interaction strength $C = -0.6$ (left plot) and noninteracting (right plot) scenarios is given Fig. 6. The different curves correspond to different length scales. The change in the evolution of Φ' because of interaction is observed at $N \sim 3$ where the Φ' is suppressed as compared to the noninteracting scenario. And the maximum change is observed on the smaller scales, and hence, this effect could be observed in the CMB anisotropies. Therefore, using the ISW observations, we can distinguish between interacting and noninteracting scenarios.

5. Conclusion

In this work, we consider a dark energy dark matter interaction model and check the consistency of the model with low redshift observations. In this model, the interaction term is obtained by assuming a one-to-one mapping between the classical field description and the fluid description of the interacting model. We perform the chi-squared minimization technique and obtain the constraints on model parameters. The observations we use in the analysis are direct measurements of Hubble parameter (Hz), baryon acoustic oscillation (BAO) data, measurements of HII galaxies (HIIG), and type Ia supernovae data (SN). We obtain narrow constraints on Hubble parameter H_0, non-relativistic matter density parameter Ω_m, and dark energy equation of state parameter at present w_0. The BAO+Hz and SN+Hz observations provide an upper limit on interaction parameter C. The constraints from these observations are consistent with one another, and the best fit value from all the observations are close to $H_0 \sim 70\ km\ s^{-1}\ Mpc^{-1}$. So there is no tension in the estimated value of H_0 from these observations for the interaction model considered.

The Interaction model is consistent with the abovementioned low redshift observations used in the analysis.

From background analysis, we also observed that it is difficult to distinguish between the interacting and noninteracting models, and therefore we must look at the evolution of perturbations. Therefore, we studied the evolution of first order perturbation quantities such as δ_m, Φ, and Φ' in the interacting and noninteracting case. We find that the evolution of these quantities is modified in the presence of dark energy dark matter interaction terms. Therefore, using the observations of structure formation, weak gravitational lensing, and integrated Sach-Wolfe effect, which depends upon the evolution perturbed quantities mentioned above and carries the signature of the interaction, we can distinguish between the interacting and noninteracting scenarios.

Acknowledgments

The work is partially supported by the ISRO-Respond grant. J.P.J. is supported by CSIR Senior Research Fellowship, India.

References

1. J. P. Johnson, A. Sangwan and S. Shankaranarayanan, Cosmological perturbations in the interacting dark sector: Observational constraints and predictions (2 2021).
2. A. G. Riess *et al.*, Observational evidence from supernovae for an accelerating universe and a cosmological constant, *Astron. J.* **116**, 1009 (1998).
3. S. Perlmutter *et al.*, Measurements of Ω and Λ from 42 high redshift supernovae, *Astrophys. J.* **517**, 565 (1999).
4. D. N. Spergel *et al.*, Wilkinson Microwave Anisotropy Probe (WMAP) three year results: implications for cosmology, *Astrophys. J. Suppl.* **170**, p. 377 (2007).
5. D. M. Scolnic *et al.*, The Complete Light-curve Sample of Spectroscopically Confirmed SNe Ia from Pan-STARRS1 and Cosmological Constraints from the Combined Pantheon Sample, *Astrophys. J.* **859**, p. 101 (2018).
6. N. Aghanim *et al.*, Planck 2018 results. I. Overview and the cosmological legacy of Planck, *Astron. Astrophys.* **641**, p. A1 (2020).
7. N. Aghanim *et al.*, Planck 2018 results. VI. Cosmological parameters, *Astron. Astrophys.* **641**, p. A6 (2020), [Erratum: Astron.Astrophys. 652, C4 (2021)].
8. V. Marra, L. Amendola, I. Sawicki and W. Valkenburg, Cosmic variance and the measurement of the local Hubble parameter, *Phys. Rev. Lett.* **110**, p. 241305 (2013).
9. L. Verde, P. Protopapas and R. Jimenez, Planck and the local Universe: Quantifying the tension, *Phys. Dark Univ.* **2**, 166 (2013).
10. K. C. Wong *et al.*, H0LiCOW – XIII. A 2.4 per cent measurement of H0 from lensed quasars: 5.3σ tension between early- and late-Universe probes, *Mon. Not. Roy. Astron. Soc.* **498**, 1420 (2020).
11. A. G. Riess, S. Casertano, W. Yuan, L. M. Macri and D. Scolnic, Large Magellanic Cloud Cepheid Standards Provide a 1% Foundation for the Determination of the Hubble Constant and Stronger Evidence for Physics beyond ΛCDM, *Astrophys. J.* **876**, p. 85 (2019).

12. P. A. R. Ade *et al.*, Planck 2015 results. XV. Gravitational lensing, *Astron. Astrophys.* **594**, p. A15 (2016).
13. P. A. R. Ade *et al.*, Planck 2015 results. XXVII. The Second Planck Catalogue of Sunyaev-Zeldovich Sources, *Astron. Astrophys.* **594**, p. A27 (2016).
14. K. Kuijken *et al.*, Gravitational Lensing Analysis of the Kilo Degree Survey, *Mon. Not. Roy. Astron. Soc.* **454**, 3500 (2015).
15. S. Joudaki *et al.*, KiDS-450: Testing extensions to the standard cosmological model, *Mon. Not. Roy. Astron. Soc.* **471**, 1259 (2017).
16. S. Joudaki *et al.*, KiDS-450 + 2dFLenS: Cosmological parameter constraints from weak gravitational lensing tomography and overlapping redshift-space galaxy clustering, *Mon. Not. Roy. Astron. Soc.* **474**, 4894 (2018).
17. T. M. C. Abbott *et al.*, Dark Energy Survey year 1 results: Cosmological constraints from galaxy clustering and weak lensing, *Phys. Rev. D* **98**, p. 043526 (2018).
18. E. Di Valentino, A. Melchiorri and O. Mena, Can interacting dark energy solve the H_0 tension?, *Phys. Rev. D* **96**, p. 043503 (2017).
19. W. Yang, A. Mukherjee, E. Di Valentino and S. Pan, Interacting dark energy with time varying equation of state and the H_0 tension, *Phys. Rev. D* **98**, p. 123527 (2018).
20. E. Di Valentino, A. Melchiorri, O. Mena and S. Vagnozzi, Nonminimal dark sector physics and cosmological tensions, *Phys. Rev. D* **101**, p. 063502 (2020).
21. A. Gómez-Valent, V. Pettorino and L. Amendola, Update on coupled dark energy and the H_0 tension, *Phys. Rev. D* **101**, p. 123513 (2020).
22. J. P. Johnson and S. Shankaranarayanan, Cosmological perturbations in the interacting dark sector: Mapping fields and fluids, *Phys. Rev. D* **103**, p. 023510 (2021).
23. J. Simon, L. Verde and R. Jimenez, Constraints on the redshift dependence of the dark energy potential, *Phys. Rev. D* **71**, p. 123001 (2005).
24. D. Stern, R. Jimenez, L. Verde, S. A. Stanford and M. Kamionkowski, Cosmic Chronometers: Constraining the Equation of State of Dark Energy. II. A Spectroscopic Catalog of Red Galaxies in Galaxy Clusters, *he Astrophysical Journal Supplement* **188**, 280 (May 2010).
25. A. L. Ratsimbazafy, S. I. Loubser, S. M. Crawford, C. M. Cress, B. A. Bassett, R. C. Nichol and P. Väisänen, *Mon. Not. Roy. Astron. Soc.* **467**, 3239 (2017).
26. C. Zhang, H. Zhang, S. Yuan, S. Liu, T.-J. Zhang and Y.-C. Sun, Four new observational H(z) data from luminous red galaxies in the Sloan Digital Sky Survey data release seven, *Research in Astronomy and Astrophysics* **14**, 1221 (October 2014).
27. M. Moresco, Raising the bar: new constraints on the Hubble parameter with cosmic chronometers at $z \sim 2$, *Mon. Not. Roy. Astron. Soc.* **450**, L16 (2015).
28. M. Moresco, L. Pozzetti, A. Cimatti, R. Jimenez, C. Maraston, L. Verde, D. Thomas, A. Citro, R. Tojeiro and D. Wilkinson, A 6% measurement of the Hubble parameter at $z \sim 0.45$: direct evidence of the epoch of cosmic re-acceleration, *JCAP* **05**, p. 014 (2016).
29. A. L. González-Morán, R. Chávez, R. Terlevich, E. Terlevich, F. Bresolin, D. Fernández-Arenas, M. Plionis, S. Basilakos, J. Melnick and E. Telles, Independent cosmological constraints from high-z H ii galaxies, *Mon. Not. Roy. Astron. Soc.* **487**, 4669 (2019).
30. R. Terlevich, E. Terlevich, J. Melnick, R. Chávez, M. Plionis, F. Bresolin and S. Basilakos, On the road to precision cosmology with high-redshift H II galaxies, *Mon. Not. Roy. Astron. Soc.* **451**, 3001 (2015).
31. A. Font-Ribera *et al.*, Quasar-Lyman α Forest Cross-Correlation from BOSS DR11 : Baryon Acoustic Oscillations, *JCAP* **05**, p. 027 (2014).

32. J. E. Bautista et al., Measurement of baryon acoustic oscillation correlations at $z = 2.3$ with SDSS DR12 Lyα-Forests, *Astron. Astrophys.* **603**, p. A12 (2017).
33. M. Ata et al., The clustering of the SDSS-IV extended Baryon Oscillation Spectroscopic Survey DR14 quasar sample: first measurement of baryon acoustic oscillations between redshift 0.8 and 2.2, *Mon. Not. Roy. Astron. Soc.* **473**, 4773 (2018).
34. A. J. Ross, L. Samushia, C. Howlett, W. J. Percival, A. Burden and M. Manera, The clustering of the SDSS DR7 main Galaxy sample – I. A 4 per cent distance measure at $z = 0.15$, *Mon. Not. Roy. Astron. Soc.* **449**, 835 (2015).
35. F. Beutler, C. Blake, M. Colless, D. H. Jones, L. Staveley-Smith, L. Campbell, Q. Parker, W. Saunders and F. Watson, The 6dF Galaxy Survey: baryon acoustic oscillations and the local Hubble constant, *Mon. Not. Roy. Astron. Soc.* **416**, 3017 (October 2011).
36. S. Alam et al., The clustering of galaxies in the completed SDSS-III Baryon Oscillation Spectroscopic Survey: cosmological analysis of the DR12 galaxy sample, *Mon. Not. Roy. Astron. Soc.* **470**, 2617 (2017).
37. M. Betoule et al., Improved cosmological constraints from a joint analysis of the SDSS-II and SNLS supernova samples, *Astron. Astrophys.* **568**, p. A22 (2014).
38. L. Amendola et al., Cosmology and fundamental physics with the Euclid satellite, *Living Rev. Rel.* **21**, p. 2 (2018).
39. R. Maartens, F. B. Abdalla, M. Jarvis and M. G. Santos, Overview of Cosmology with the SKA, *PoS* **AASKA14**, p. 016 (2015).
40. M. P. van Haarlem, M. W. Wise, A. W. Gunst, G. Heald, J. P. McKean, J. W. T. Hessels, A. G. de Bruyn, R. Nijboer, J. Swinbank, R. Fallows, M. Brentjens, A. Nelles, R. Beck, H. Falcke, R. Fender, J. Hörandel, L. V. E. Koopmans, G. Mann, G. Miley, H. Röttgering, B. W. Stappers, R. A. M. J. Wijers, S. Zaroubi, M. van den Akker, A. Alexov, J. Anderson, K. Anderson, A. van Ardenne, M. Arts, A. Asgekar, I. M. Avruch, F. Batejat, L. Bähren, M. E. Bell, M. R. Bell, I. van Bemmel, P. Bennema, M. J. Bentum, G. Bernardi, P. Best, L. Bîrzan, A. Bonafede, A. J. Boonstra, R. Braun, J. Bregman, F. Breitling, R. H. van de Brink, J. Broderick, P. C. Broekema, W. N. Brouw, M. Brüggen, H. R. Butcher, W. van Cappellen, B. Ciardi, T. Coenen, J. Conway, A. Coolen, A. Corstanje, S. Damstra, O. Davies, A. T. Deller, R. J. Dettmar, G. van Diepen, K. Dijkstra, P. Donker, A. Doorduin, J. Dromer, M. Drost, A. van Duin, J. Eislöffel, J. van Enst, C. Ferrari, W. Frieswijk, H. Gankema, M. A. Garrett, F. de Gasperin, M. Gerbers, E. de Geus, J. M. Grießmeier, T. Grit, P. Gruppen, J. P. Hamaker, T. Hassall, M. Hoeft, H. A. Holties, A. Horneffer, A. van der Horst, A. van Houwelingen, A. Huijgen, M. Iacobelli, H. Intema, N. Jackson, V. Jelic, A. de Jong, E. Juette, D. Kant, A. Karastergiou, A. Koers, H. Kollen, V. I. Kondratiev, E. Kooistra, Y. Koopman, A. Koster, M. Kuniyoshi, M. Kramer, G. Kuper, P. Lambropoulos, C. Law, J. van Leeuwen, J. Lemaitre, M. Loose, P. Maat, G. Macario, S. Markoff, J. Masters, R. A. McFadden, D. McKay-Bukowski, H. Meijering, H. Meulman, M. Mevius, E. Middelberg, R. Millenaar, J. C. A. Miller-Jones, R. N. Mohan, J. D. Mol, J. Morawietz, R. Morganti, D. D. Mulcahy, E. Mulder, H. Munk, L. Nieuwenhuis, R. van Nieuwpoort, J. E. Noordam, M. Norden, A. Noutsos, A. R. Offringa, H. Olofsson, A. Omar, E. Orrú, R. Overeem, H. Paas, M. Pandey-Pommier, V. N. Pandey, R. Pizzo, A. Polatidis, D. Rafferty, S. Rawlings, W. Reich, J. P. de Reijer, J. Reitsma, G. A. Renting, P. Riemers, E. Rol, J. W. Romein, J. Roosjen, M. Ruiter, A. Scaife, K. van der Schaaf, B. Scheers, P. Schellart, A. Schoenmakers, G. Schoonderbeek, M. Serylak, A. Shulevski, J. Sluman, O. Smirnov, C. Sobey, H. Spreeuw, M. Steinmetz, C. G. M. Sterks, H. J. Stiepel, K. Stuurwold, M. Tagger,

Y. Tang, C. Tasse, I. Thomas, S. Thoudam, M. C. Toribio, B. van der Tol, O. Usov, M. van Veelen, A. J. van der Veen, S. ter Veen, J. P. W. Verbiest, R. Vermeulen, N. Vermaas, C. Vocks, C. Vogt, M. de Vos, E. van der Wal, R. van Weeren, H. Weggemans, P. Weltevrede, S. White, S. J. Wijnholds, T. Wilhelmsson, O. Wucknitz, S. Yatawatta, P. Zarka, A. Zensus and J. van Zwieten, LOFAR: The LOw-Frequency ARray, *Astronomy & Astrophysics* **556**, p. A2 (August 2013).
41. H. Hildebrandt *et al.*, KiDS-450: Cosmological parameter constraints from tomographic weak gravitational lensing, *Mon. Not. Roy. Astron. Soc.* **465**, p. 1454 (2017).

On the evolution of inhomogeneous perturbations in the ΛCDM model and $f(R)$ modified gravity theories

T. Schiavone

Department of Physics "E. Fermi", University of Pisa, Polo Fibonacci,
Largo B. Pontecorvo 3, I-56127, Pisa, Italy
and
INFN, Istituto Nazionale di Fisica Nucleare, Sezione di Pisa, Polo Fibonacci,
Largo B. Pontecorvo 3, I-56127, Pisa, Italy
E-mail: tiziano.schiavone@pi.infn.it

G. Montani

ENEA, Fusion and Nuclear Safety Department, C.R. Frascati,
Via E. Fermi 45, I-00044 Frascati (Rome), Italy
and
Physics Department, "Sapienza" University of Rome,
P.le Aldo Moro 5, I-00185 Rome, Italy

We focus on weak inhomogeneous models of the Universe at low redshifts, described by the Lemaître-Tolman-Bondi (LTB) metric. The principal aim of this work is to compare the evolution of inhomogeneous perturbations in the ΛCDM cosmological model and $f(R)$ modified gravity theories, considering a flat Friedmann-Lemaître-Robertson-Walker (FLRW) metric for the background. More specifically, we adopt the equivalent scalar-tensor formalism in the Jordan frame, in which the extra degree of freedom of the $f(R)$ function is converted into a non-minimally coupled scalar field. We investigate the evolution of local inhomogeneities in time and space separately, following a linear perturbation approach. Then, we obtain spherically symmetric solutions in both cosmological models. Our results allow us to distinguish between the presence of a cosmological constant and modified gravity scenarios, since a peculiar Yukawa-like solution for radial perturbations occurs in the Jordan frame. Furthermore, the radial profile of perturbations does not depend on a particular choice of the $f(R)$ function, hence our results are valid for any $f(R)$ model.

Keywords: Cosmology, Modified gravity, Inhomogeneous Universe, Late Universe, Large Scale Structure

Introduction

The well-known ΛCDM model,[1,2] which includes a cosmological constant Λ and a cold dark matter (CDM) component, is based on General Relativity (GR), and it provides a robust and accurate description of our Universe, supported by cosmological data. Moreover, the Universe appears homogeneous and isotropic at very large scales[3] (cosmological principle), and this kind of geometry is described by the FLRW line element. In this work, based on a paper in preparation,[4] we investigate possible deviations from two pillars of the standard ΛCDM model, focusing on a local inhomogeneous description of the Universe and modified gravity models.

Here, we adopt the LTB metric,[2] a spherically symmetric solution of the Einstein field equations, to account for local deviations of the Universe from the homogeneity. Hence, we regard the weakly inhomogeneous LTB solution as the standard FLRW geometry plus small spherically symmetric perturbations.

Furthermore, in recent years increasing interest raised to provide features able to distinguish between GR and modified gravity approaches. Some open problems in cosmology, such as the Hubble constant tension,[5] may require new physics.[6] The aim of the present work is to compare the evolution of linear inhomogeneous perturbations in the ΛCDM and $f(R)$ modified gravity models.[7,8] More in detail, we used the equivalent formalism in the Jordan frame,[7–9] and we adopt the $f(R)$ Hu-Sawicki model,[10] which is a promising theoretical framework to reproduce the cosmic acceleration in the late Universe via the dynamics of a non-minimally coupled scalar field without a cosmological constant.

Then, we investigate the dynamics of inhomogeneous perturbations in the two cosmological models abovementioned. Moreover, the separable variables method is implemented in the analysis at the first-order of perturbation, and our approach is the same used in Ref. 11. We obtain an analytic expression only for the radial dependence of the linear perturbations, while their time evolution must be numerically evaluated. The most relevant issue, emerging from our analysis, is the different morphology of the radial dependence of the LTB solution in the ΛCDM formulation and Hu-Sawicki dynamics. Indeed, a distinctive Yukawa-like behavior occurs in the Jordan frame gravity regardless of the choice of a specific $f(R)$ model. Hence, we have found a peculiar feature to distinguish a modified gravity model from a cosmological constant scenario.

This work is organized as follows: in Sec. 1 we introduce the framework of the $f(R)$ extended gravity models; in Sec. 2 we adopt the LTB metric; then, in Sec. 3 we implement a perturbation approach to deal with local inhomogeneities. Finally, we summarize our work in Sec. 4. We adopt the metric signature $(-,+,+,+)$, and we set $c = 1$.

1. $f(R)$ models in the Jordan frame

A generalization of the Einstein-Hilbert theory is provided by the so-called $f(R)$ modified gravity models.[7,8] In this context, the gravitational Lagrangian density is expressed as a free function f of the Ricci scalar R, namely an extra degree of freedom compared to GR. The extended field equations in $f(R)$ gravity are fourth-order partial differential equations in the metric tensor components. In particular, if $f(R) = R$, the gravitational field equations end up in the Einstein equations in GR, trivially.

It is often convenient to reformulate $f(R)$ gravity in the scalar-tensor representation in the Jordan frame.[7–9] In doing so, the extra degree of freedom of the $f(R)$ function is converted into a non-minimally coupled scalar field. It can be checked that the following action

$$S_J = \frac{1}{2\chi} \int_\Omega d^4x \sqrt{-g} \left[\phi R - V(\phi)\right] + S_M(g_{\mu\nu}, \psi) \qquad (1)$$

is dynamically equivalent to the action in the $f(R)$ metric formalism, if $f''(R) \neq 0$, where we have defined a scalar field $\phi = f'(R) = df/dR$, and a scalar field potential $V(\phi) = \phi R(\phi) - f(R(\phi))$. In Eq. (1), $\chi \equiv 8\pi G$ is the Einstein constant, G is the Newton constant, g is the determinant of the metric tensor $g_{\mu\nu}$, while S_M is the matter action, and ψ denotes matter fields. The advantage of the Jordan frame is that the corresponding field equations[8] are now second-order differential equations, but one has to deal with the non-minimally coupling.

The increasing attention to these extended gravity models is motivated by the consideration that the actual cosmic acceleration of the Universe might be obtained by geometry rather than a cosmological constant. A geometrical modification, indeed, could be regarded as an effective matter source.

Among several suggested $f(R)$ models,[7,8,12,13] we focus on the Hu-Sawicki proposal,[10] which is largely studied in the late Universe. The deviation $F(R) \equiv f(R) - R$ with respect to the GR scenario for the Hu-Sawicki (HS) model with $n=1$ assumes the following form

$$F(R) = -m^2 \frac{c_1 R/m^2}{c_2 R/m^2 + 1}, \qquad (2)$$

where $m^2 \equiv \frac{\chi \rho_{m0}}{3}$ is related to the present matter density ρ_{m0}, while c_1 and c_2 are dimensionless parameters. It can be checked[10] that an effective cosmological constant is obtained for $R \gg m^2$. Furthermore, c_1 and c_2 can be constrained[10] specifying $F_{R0} \equiv dF/dR \, (z=0)$ at the present cosmic time (redshift $z=0$).

Finally, we write the scalar field potential $V(\phi)$ in the Jordan frame for the HS model with $n=1$:

$$V(\phi) = \frac{m^2}{c_2} \left[c_1 + 1 - \phi - 2\sqrt{c_1(1-\phi)}\right]. \qquad (3)$$

It can be shown[14] that the potential (3) ends in an asymptotically stable de Sitter Universe.

2. Inhomogeneous solutions in GR and in the Jordan frame

An inhomogeneous Universe can be described by using the LTB line element,[2] which is a spherically symmetric solution of the Einstein equations. The Universe in the LTB geometry appears inhomogeneous, but isotropic, from a single preferred point located at the center of the spherical symmetry. For instance, a cosmological dust or a spherical overdensity mass are well described by such a metric.

In the synchronous gauge, the LTB line element may be regarded as a generalization of the FLRW one, and it is given by

$$ds^2 = -dt^2 + e^{2\alpha} dr^2 + e^{2\beta} \left(d\theta^2 + \sin^2\theta \, d\phi^2\right), \qquad (4)$$

where r is the radial distance from the preferred point, while $\alpha = \alpha(t, r)$ and $\beta = \beta(t, r)$ are two metric functions.

Considering a pressure-less dust ($p = 0$) and a cosmological constant Λ in GR, we can write the Einstein equations in the LTB metric. For instance, the 01 component of field equations is written as

$$\frac{\dot{\beta}'}{\beta'} - \dot{\alpha} + \dot{\beta} = 0 \qquad (5)$$

where $(\dot{\,})$ and $(\,)'$ denote derivatives with respect to time t and radial coordinate r, respectively. The other non-zero equations are the 00 and 11 components,[4] while different components vanish due to spherical symmetry.

It is possible to simplify the LTB metric within the framework of GR, using Eq. (5), which allows us to find a relation between the metric functions α and β. Following the approach in Ref. 2, the LTB line element (4) becomes

$$ds^2 = -dt^2 + \frac{[(a\,r)']^2}{1 - r^2 K^2} dr^2 + (a\,r)^2 \left(d\theta^2 + sin^2\theta\, d\phi^2\right), \qquad (6)$$

where $a = a(t, r) = e^{\beta}/r$ is a generalized scale factor in a inhomogeneous geometry, and $K = K(r)$. Note that if $a(t, r)$ and $K(r)$ are independent of r, the metric (6) coincides with the FLRW line element, describing an isotropic and homogeneous geometry. Moreover, the 00 and 11 components of the Einstein equations in the LTB metric provides a generalization of the Friedmann equations in the ΛCDM model.

Concerning the $f(R)$ modified gravity scenario in the equivalent Jordan frame, the 01 component of the gravitational field equations in the LTB metric is written as

$$\frac{\dot{\beta}'}{\beta'} - \dot{\alpha} + \dot{\beta} = -\frac{1}{2\,\phi\,\beta'}\left(\dot{\phi}' - \dot{\alpha}\,\phi'\right). \qquad (7)$$

Furthermore, we can compute[4] also the 00 and 11 of field equations, as well as the scalar field equation in the Jordan frame. Observe that ϕ, ρ, α, and β are all functions of t and r in a inhomogeneous scenario.

Comparing Eq. (7) with the respective equation (5) obtained in GR, an extra term occurs in the Jordan frame due to non-minimal coupling between ϕ and the metric functions α, β. As a consequence, we can not relate α and β to rewrite the LTB metric as in the GR scenario. Moreover, the scalar field potential $V(\phi)$ does not affect Eq. (7), but it is included in the remaining field equations. $V(\phi)$ represents an extra degree of freedom with respect to GR, and the dynamics in the Jordan frame deviates from that of the Einstein theory.

3. Perturbation approach in GR and in the Jordan frame

In this Section, we investigate the different evolution of local inhomogeneities within the framework of GR and modified gravity.[4] Here, we stress one important difference: we can not adopt the LTB metric in the form (6) in the Jordan frame, but we have to refer to the line element in Eq. (4), as motivated in Sec. 2.

Then, we consider the LTB metric to describe local inhomogeneities as small linear perturbations with respect to a flat FLRW metric as background. Hence, we can write all the physical quantities as a background term, denoted with (¯), plus a linear perturbation, which depends on t and r, and it is denoted with δ. For instance, the energy density is written as $\rho(t,r) = \bar{\rho}(t) + \delta\rho(t,r)$. Similarly, we rewrite the scale factor $a(t,r)$ in GR, the scalar field $\phi(t,r)$, the metric functions $\alpha(t,r)$, and $\beta(t,r)$ in the Jordan frame. We also assume that perturbation terms are small corrections if compared with respective background quantities, i.e. $\delta\rho \ll \bar{\rho}$. Furthermore, we consider $K^2(r)$ in the LTB metric (6) as a linear term, since it is related to inhomogeneities. It should be noted that, comparing the LTB line element (4) and a flat FLRW metric, we have to require two constraints: $\bar{\alpha}(t) = \ln(\bar{a}(t))$ and $\bar{\beta}(t,r) = \ln(\bar{a}(t)\,r)$.

Concerning the scalar-tensor formalism in the Jordan frame, we expand the scalar field potential $V(\phi)$ to the first order in $\delta\phi$. It can be easily checked that the zeroth order term $V(\bar{\phi}(t))$ depends only on the background scalar field.[4]

Once we have split background and linear contributions, we focus on the dynamics in the ΛCDM cosmological model and in the Jordan frame gravity. Hence, we rewrite the field equations in GR and in the Jordan frame, separating background and perturbation terms.

3.1. *Comparing background solutions*

To study the time evolution, we define a dimensionless variable $\tau = t/t_0$, where t_0 is the actual time in the synchronous gauge. Note that t_0 is approximately $t_0 \approx 1/H_0$ in terms of the Hubble constant.

In GR, the 00 component of the Einstein equation in the LTB geometry becomes the Friedmann equation in the FLRW metric at background level. We set $\bar{a}_0 = \bar{a}(\tau = 1)$ today, and we neglect relativistic components in the late Universe. Hence, we obtain an analytical solution:[4] the evolution of the background scale factor in terms τ is written as

$$\bar{a}(\tau) = \left(\frac{\Omega_{m0}}{\Omega_{\Lambda 0}}\right)^{1/3} \left\{\sinh\left[\frac{3}{2}\sqrt{\Omega_{\Lambda 0}}\,(\tau - 1) + \operatorname{arcsinh}\left(\sqrt{\frac{\Omega_{\Lambda 0}}{\Omega_{m0}}}\right)\right]\right\}^{2/3}. \quad (8)$$

We used the cosmological density parameters $\Omega_{m0} = \rho_{m0}/\rho_{c0}$, and $\Omega_{\Lambda 0} = \Lambda/(\chi\rho_{c0})$ for matter and cosmological constant components, respectively, where $\rho_{c0} = 3H_0^2/\chi$ is the actual critical energy density of the Universe. We recall also that $\bar{\rho}(\tau) \propto \bar{a}(\tau)^{-3}$ for a matter component.

In Fig. 1 we plot the deceleration parameter $\bar{q}(\tau) \equiv -\ddot{\bar{a}}/(\bar{a}\,\bar{H}^2)$, fixing $\Omega_{m0} = 0.3111$ and $\Omega_{\Lambda 0} = 1 - \Omega_{m0}$ from Ref. 3. Here, the dot denotes the derivative with respect to τ. The scale factor $\bar{a}(\tau)$ increases for growing values of τ, and note that $\bar{q} \to -1$ in the future.

We point out that the solution (8) in the ΛCDM cosmological model is viable only at late times ($\tau \gg 10^{-6}$) in the Universe, otherwise we have to include relativistic components, and solve numerically the Friedmann equation.

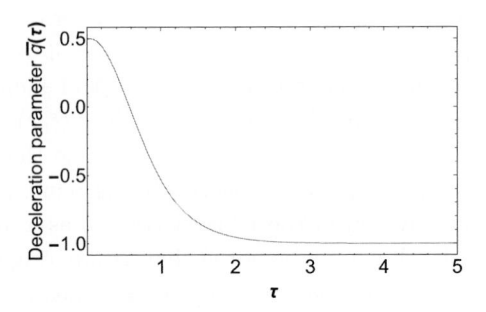

Fig. 1. Background deceleration parameter $\bar{q}(\tau)$ in the FLRW geometry in terms of a dimensionless variable τ. The background scenario in the ΛCDM model are graphically the same comparing it with the one in the $f(R)$ Hu-Sawicki model in the Jordan frame.

Now, we focus on the background field equations in the Jordan frame gravity. Starting from the 01, 00, 11 components of the gravitational field equations in the LTB metric and the scalar field equation, if we do not include local inhomogeneities, we get the respective equation system in the Jordan frame for the background FLRW metric (see the field equations in Ref. 8). We use the Hu-Sawicki model in the Jordan frame, which is characterized by the scalar field potential in Eq. (3).

To solve numerically the equation system, we fix Ω_{m0} at the same value used in the previous study for the ΛCDM model, and we choose[10] $|F_{R0}| = 10^{-7}$ to obtain $c_1 = 2.0 \cdot 10^6$ and $c_2 = 1.5 \cdot 10^5$. We set the free parameters in a way that the Hu-Sawicki model in the Jordan frame is very close to the ΛCDM scenario for the background level. In Fig. 2 note that the scalar field potential (3) exhibits a slow-roll mimicking a cosmological constant.

Finally, we solve numerically the equation system in the Jordan frame,[4] imposing the conditions at $\tau = 1$: $\bar{\phi}(1) = 1 - |F_{R0}|$ and $d\bar{\phi}/d\tau\,(1) = 0$. The resulting plot of the deceleration parameter $\bar{q}(\tau)$ are graphically undistinguishable from the respective ones in the ΛCDM model (see Fig. 1). Concerning the evolution of the scalar field, we plot in Fig. 2 the deviation $|1 - \bar{\phi}(\tau)|$ from the GR limit ($\bar{\phi} = 1$) with a scale 10^{-7}. Note that the dynamics of the Jordan frame is very close to the one in ΛCDM model at the background order for any τ. Now, we can move on to the linearized solutions to highlight the differences between the two cosmological models.

3.2. *Comparing linear solutions*

To examine separately the time and radial evolution of local inhomogeneities, we use the separable variables method at the first-order perturbation theory. So, we

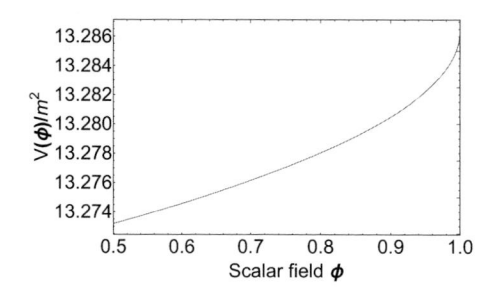

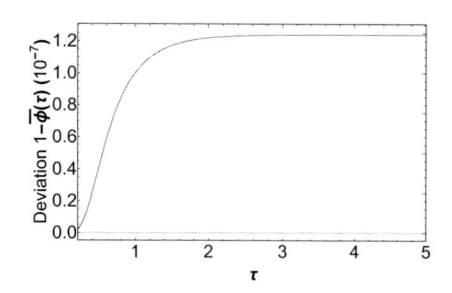

Fig. 2. Plots referred to the Hu-Sawicki model in the Jordan frame, adopting the FLRW metric (background solution). Left panel: scalar field potential of the Hu-Sawicki model in the Jordan frame. Right panel: deviation $|1 - \bar{\phi}(\tau)|$ from the GR scenario.

factorize all the linear perturbations into time and radial functions. More specifically, we rewrite the perturbations of the scale factor $\delta a(\tau, r) \equiv \delta \mathsf{a}(\tau) \delta \mathfrak{a}(r)$, the metric functions $\delta \alpha(\tau, r) \equiv \delta A(\tau) \delta \mathcal{A}(r)$ and $\delta \beta(\tau, r) \equiv \delta B(\tau) \delta \mathcal{B}(r)$, the energy density $\delta \rho(\tau, r) \equiv \delta P(\tau) \delta \varrho(r)$, and the scalar field $\delta \phi(\tau, r) \equiv \delta \Phi(\tau) \delta \varphi(r)$. The factorization is assumed at the linear level to find analytical solutions, but the separation of variables is not a general method, if we also include non-linear terms.

Then, we investigate the effect of inhomogeneities in the dynamics, according to the cosmological model considered. We focus on the linearized equations in the LTB metric within the framework of the ΛCDM cosmological model.

Using the factorization abovementioned, it is easy to show that the 11 component of the linearized Einstein equations in the LTB metric can be separated in two parts.[4] The radial behavior is $\delta \mathfrak{a}(r) = K^2(r)$, while we have an ordinary differential equation in terms of τ for the time evolution:

$$\delta \ddot{\mathsf{a}}(\tau) + \frac{\dot{\bar{a}}(\tau)}{\bar{a}(\tau)} \delta \dot{\mathsf{a}}(\tau) - \delta \mathsf{a}(\tau) \left[\frac{\ddot{\bar{a}}(\tau)}{\bar{a}(\tau)} + \left(\frac{\dot{\bar{a}}(\tau)}{\bar{a}(\tau)} \right)^2 \right] = 0. \tag{9}$$

This equation is solved numerically, once you specify the background solution (8). We impose the following conditions at $\tau = 1$ today: $\delta \mathsf{a}(1) = 10^{-5}$ and $\delta \dot{\mathsf{a}}(1) = 0$. In Fig. 3 we plot the numerical solution, after we have defined the ratio $\eta(\tau)$ between the perturbed scale factor and the background respective quantity, namely $\eta(\tau) \equiv |\delta \mathsf{a}(\tau) / \bar{a}(\tau)|$. Note that the perturbations of the scale factor remain stable, since the background scale factor $\bar{a}(\tau)$ dominates for any τ in the late Universe, i.e. $\eta \ll 1$.

After that, we consider the 00 component of the linearized Einstein equations in the LTB metric, and we combine it with the continuity equation. After long but straightforward calculations,[4] we obtain $\delta \mathfrak{a} \propto 1/r^3$ in GR. According to the cosmological principle, inhomogeneities decay for increasing values of r. Furthermore, we also obtain that the perturbation of the energy density for a matter component follows the same dependence of the respective background quantity in the FLRW metric, namely $\delta P(\tau) \propto 1/\bar{a}^3(\tau)$. However, we can provide $\delta P(\tau) \ll \bar{\rho}(\tau)$ at any times, setting the constant of integration.

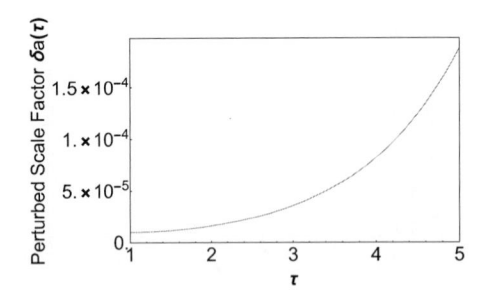

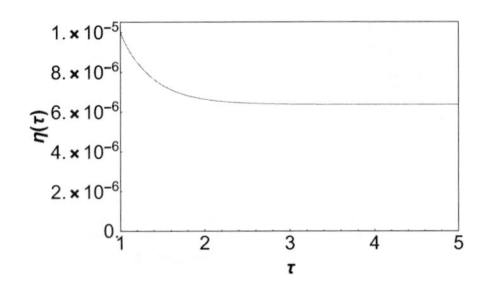

Fig. 3. Left panel: time evolution of the linear perturbation of the scale factor $\delta a(\tau)$. Right panel: the ratio between the linear deviation and background scale factor.

Now, we repeat the same approach in the modified gravity dynamics in the Jordan frame, considering the corresponding linearized field equations in the LTB metric. Expanding the scalar field potential and its derivative around the background scalar field, as mentioned at the beginning of Sec. 3, it can be proved that the potential $V(\phi)$ is involved only in the time evolution of the linearized field equations.[4] As a result, we expect that the radial evolution of local inhomogeneities is completely independent of the choice of a particular $f(R)$ model, since $V(\phi)$ is directly related to $f(R)$.

In what follows, we do not focus on the time evolution of perturbations, but we just mention that we find a numerical solution using again the Hu-Sawicki model (Sec. 1), and we have checked that inhomogeneous perturbations remain smaller than respective background contribution for any time τ.

To obtain an analytical solution for the radial part with the separable variables method, we assume two simplifying conditions: $\delta \dot{A}(\tau) = \delta \dot{B}(\tau)$ and $\delta\varrho(r) \propto \delta\varphi(r)$. After long but straightforward calculations,[4] combining the linearized field equations, we obtain a Yukawa-like solution for the radial part of the linear perturbation of the scalar field

$$\delta\varphi(r) = \frac{C}{r} \exp\left(-\frac{r}{r_c}\right), \tag{10}$$

where C and r_c are constants. We also have a similar behavior for $\delta\mathcal{A}(r)$ and $\delta\mathcal{B}(r)$. It should be emphasized that modified gravity introduces a typical spatial scale, r_c, such that for $r \gg r_c$ the inhomogeneities decay faster than ones in GR. We stress again that this kind of solutions applies to any $f(R)$ model, and the radial evolution is different from the one in GR.

4. Summary and conclusions

We have investigated local inhomogeneities in the LTB metric regarded as small deviations from a flat FLRW background metric. To date, there are no modified gravity models that predict significant deviations from GR, reconciling all possible cosmological data. Hence, to try to discriminate between several cosmological models, it is crucial to test gravity in different regimes or by using other techniques. Here, we have suggested one possible method, studying the different dynamics of inhomogeneous perturbations. Our results have pointed out a distinctive element in the evolution of local inhomogeneities of the Universe from a theoretical point of view, allowing to distinguish between the ΛCDM cosmological model and $f(R)$ modified gravity theories. We have shown that the radial evolution of inhomogeneous perturbations within the framework of the Jordan frame gravity is independent of the scalar field potential $V(\phi)$: the distinctive radial solution is a feature of any $f(R)$ model, and the radial behavior is completely different from the one in GR. This work may be an interesting arena to account for the effects of local inhomogeneities in cosmological observables,[15] when forthcoming missions such as Euclid Deep Survey,[16] will be able to test the large-scale properties of the Universe.

References

1. S. Weinberg, *Cosmology* (Oxford University Press, 2008)
2. P. J. E. Peebles, *Principles of Physical Cosmology* (Princeton University Press, 1993)
3. N. Aghanim, Y. Akrami, M. Ashdown, *et al.*, Planck 2018 results. VI. Cosmological parameters, *A&A* **641**, A6 (2020)
4. T. Schiavone, G. Montani, P. Marcoccia, Signature of $f(R)$ gravity via Lemaître-Tolman-Bondi inhomogeneous perturbations, to be submitted
5. E. Di Valentino, O. Mena, P. Supriya, *et al.*, In the realm of the Hubble tension — A review of solutions, *Class. Quantum Grav.* **38**, 153001 (2021)
6. M. G. Dainotti, B. De Simone, T. Schiavone, G. Montani, E. Rinaldi, and G. Lambiase, On the Hubble Constant Tension in the SNe Ia Pantheon Sample, *ApJ* **912(2)**, 150 (2021)
7. S. Nojiri, and S. D. Odintsov, Introduction to modified gravity and gravitational alternative for dark energy, *IJGMM* **4**, 115 (2007)
8. T. P. Sotiriou, and V. Faraoni, $f(R)$ theories of gravity, *Rev. Mod. Phys.* **82**, 451 (2010)
9. S. Capozziello, and V. Faraoni, *Beyond Einstein gravity* (Springer, 2013)
10. W. Hu, and I. Sawicki, Models of $f(R)$ cosmic acceleration that evade solar system tests, *Phys. Rev. D* **76**, 064004 (2007)
11. P. Marcoccia, and G. Montani, Weakly Inhomogeneous models for the Low-Redshift Universe, arXiv:1808.01489
12. A. A. Starobinsky, Disappearing cosmological constant in $f(R)$ gravity, *JETP Lett.* **86**, 157 (2007)
13. S. Tsujikawa, Observational signatures of $f(R)$ dark energy models that satisfy cosmological and local gravity constraints, *Phys. Rev. D* **77**, 023507 (2008)
14. A. de la Cruz-Dombriz, P. K. S. Dunsby, S. Kandhai, and D. Saez-Gomez, Theoretical and observational constraints of viable $f(R)$ theories of gravity, *Phys. Rev. D* **93**, 084016 (2016)
15. G. Fanizza, B. Fiorini, and G. Marozzi, Cosmic variance of H_0 in light of forthcoming high-redshift surveys, *Phys. Rev. D* **104**, 083506 (2021)
16. L. Amendola, S. Appleby, A. Avgoustidis., *et al.*, Cosmology and fundamental physics with the Euclid satellite, *Living Rev. Relativ.* **21**, 2 (2018)

Soft dark energy and soft dark matter

Emmanuel N. Saridakis

National Observatory of Athens, Lofos Nymfon, 11852 Athens, Greece
E-mail: msaridak@noa.gr

We present "soft cosmology", namely we investigate small deviations from the usual framework due to the effective appearance of soft-matter properties in the Universe sectors. One effect of such a case would be the dark energy to exhibit a different equation-of-state parameter at large scales (which determine the universe expansion) and at intermediate scales (which determine the sub-horizon clustering and the large scale structure formation). Concerning soft dark matter, we show that it can effectively arise due to the dark-energy clustering, even if dark energy is not soft. We propose a novel parametrization introducing the "softness parameters" of the dark sectors. As we see, although the background evolution remains unaffected, due to the extreme sensitivity and significant effects on the global properties even a slightly non-trivial softness parameter can improve the clustering behavior and alleviate e.g. the $f\sigma_8$ tension.

Keywords: Dark energy; Dark matter; Cosmological perturbations; Growth rate; σ_8 tension; MG16 Proceedings.

1. Introduction

Standard cosmology has been proven very efficient, qualitatively and quantitatively, in describing the Universe evolution and properties at early and late times, as well as at large and small scales. Nevertheless, since cosmology has now become an accurate science, with the appearance of a huge amount of data of progressively increasing precision, slight disagreements, deviations and tensions between theory and observations lead to a large variety of extensions and modifications of the concordance paradigm (a procedure that might be assisted by purely theoretical investigation).

Although in the usual ways of extensions one may add various novel fields, fluids, sectors and their mutual interactions,[1,2] or alter the underlying gravitational theory,[3–5] there is a rather strong assumption that is maintained in all of them, namely that the sectors that constitute the Universe are simple, or equivalently that one can apply the physics, the hydrodynamics and thermodynamics of usual, "hard" matter. Nevertheless, in condensed matter physics it is well known that there is a large variety of "soft" matter forms, which are characterized by complexity, simultaneous co-existence of phases, entropy dominance, extreme sensitivity, viscoelasticity, etc, properties that arise effectively at intermediate scales due to scale-dependent effective interactions that are not present at the fundamental scales.[6,7]

In this work, based on,[8] we examine the possibility of "soft cosmology", namely small deviations from the usual framework due to the effective appearance of soft-matter properties in the Universe sectors. We mention that due to the extreme sensitivity and significant effects of softness on the global properties, one does not need to consider a large deviation from standard considerations, since even a very slight departure would be adequate to improve the observed cosmological behavior at the required level. Finally, we stress that new fundamental physics is not directly needed, since the dark energy dynamical evolution and clustering, which is a widely accepted possibility in many scenarios beyond ΛCDM paradigm, is adequate to effectively induce the soft behavior.

2. Standard Cosmology

Let us briefly present the basics of cosmology.[9] The cosmological principle (the universe is homogeneous and isotropic at large scales) allows to consider the Friedmann-Robertson-Walker (FRW) metric $ds^2 = dt^2 - a^2(t)\,\delta_{ij}dx^i dx^j$. Concerning the universe content, one considers the usual baryonic matter and radiation (i.e. all Standard Model particles), the dark matter sector, as well as the dark energy sector. The microphysics of dark matter is unknown, and its source may be most probably some particle(s), however it may arise from black holes, from modified gravity, or even from a combination of the above, i.e. a multi-component dark matter.[10] The microphysics of dark energy is unknown too, and it may arise from new fields or matter forms in the framework of general relativity, or it may have an effective nature of gravitational origin due to modifications of gravity.

The next step is to consider that (at least after a particular stage of the universe evolution) cosmological scales are suitably large in order to allow one to neglect the microphysics of the universe ingredients and describe them effectively through fluid dynamics and continuum flow (at earlier stages one should use the Boltzmann equation). Hence, one can ignore the microscopic Lagrangian of the various sectors, and write their energy momentum tensors as $T^{(i)}_{\mu\nu} = (\rho_i + p_i)u_\mu u_\nu + p_i g_{\mu\nu}$, with ρ_i and p_i the energy density and pressure of the fluid corresponding to the i-th sector, u_μ the 4-velocity vector field and $g_{\mu\nu}$ the metric. Note that one can extend the above expression by including viscosity or/and heat flux.

Under the above considerations, any cosmological scenario will be determined by the two Friedmann equations

$$H^2 = \frac{\kappa^2}{3}(\rho_b + \rho_r + \rho_{dm} + \rho_{de}), \tag{1}$$

$$2\dot{H} + 3H^2 = -\kappa^2(p_b + p_r + p_{dm} + p_{de}), \tag{2}$$

with $\kappa^2 = 8\pi G$, and where $H \equiv \dot{a}/a$ is the Hubble parameter. We mention that the above equations are of general validity, holding for every model of dark matter and dark energy. Additionally, the conservation equation $\nabla^\mu T^{(tot)}_{\mu\nu} = \nabla^\mu \left[\sum_i T^{(i)}_{\mu\nu}\right] = 0$ in the case of FRW geometry and for non-interacting fluids gives rise to the separate conservation equations $\dot{\rho}_i + 3H(\rho_i + p_i) = 0$, while the extension to interacting cosmology can be realized through phenomenological descriptors Q_i of the interaction with $\sum_i Q_i = 0$ and with $\dot{\rho}_i + 3H(\rho_i + p_i) = Q_i$.

In order for the equations to close we need to impose the equation of state for each sector. The usual consideration is to assume barotropic fluids, in which the pressure is a function of the energy density only, with the simplest case being $p_i = w_i \rho_i$ with w_i the equation-of-state parameter. Lastly, note that the above framework provides ΛCDM cosmology for $\rho_{de} = -p_{de} = \Lambda/\kappa^2$, with Λ the cosmological constant.

The above formulation of cosmological evolution allows one to proceed to a more subtle investigation, and study small perturbations around the FRW background. Focusing without loss of generality to the linear theory of scalar isentropic perturbations in the Newtonian gauge, imposing $ds^2 = -(1+2\Psi)dt^2 + a^2(t)(1-2\Phi)\gamma_{ij}dx^i dx^j$, then in a general non-interacting scenario which includes the aforementioned sectors the scalar perturbations are determined by the equations[11,12]

$$\dot{\delta}_i + (1+w_i)\left(\frac{\theta_i}{a} - 3\dot{\Psi}\right) + 3H[c_{\text{eff}}^{(i)2} - w_i]\delta_i = 0, \tag{3}$$

$$\dot{\theta}_i + H\left[1 - 3w_i + \frac{\dot{w}_i}{H(1+w_i)}\right]\theta_i - \frac{k^2 c_{\text{eff}}^{(i)2}\delta_i}{(1+w_i)a} - \frac{k^2 \Psi}{a} = 0, \tag{4}$$

assuming zero anisotropic stress and with k the wavenumber of Fourier modes (in the case of ΛCDM paradigm the corresponding dark-energy perturbation equations are not considered). In the above equations $\delta_i \equiv \delta\rho_i/\rho_i$ are the density perturbations and θ_i is the divergence of the fluid velocity. Furthermore, $c_{\text{eff}}^{(i)2} \equiv \delta p_i/\delta\rho_i$ is the effective sound speed square of the i-th sector (it determines the amount of clustering). Note that the above equations can be simplified through the consideration of the Poisson equation, which at sub-horizon scales can be written as:[11,12]

$$-\frac{k^2}{a^2}\Psi = \frac{3}{2}H^2 \sum_i \left[\left(1 + 3c_{\text{eff}}^{(i)2}\right)\Omega_i \delta_i\right]. \tag{5}$$

Finally, we note here that in general the above formulation can be applied also in the cases where the dark energy sector is an effective one arising from gravitational modifications.

We close this section by mentioning that one can find a big variety and many versions of the above formalism. However, there is a rather strong assumption that is maintained in all of them, namely that the sectors that constitute the Universe are simple, or equivalently that one can apply the physics of usual matter. In particular, the underlying assumption is that the laws that determine the Universe behavior at large scales can be induced by the laws that determine the interactions between its individual constituents. Focusing on the hydrodynamic description, the use of fluid energy densities and pressures arises from the assumption that we can define fundamental "particles" of the corresponding sector, the collective flow of which gives rise to ρ_i and p_i, while all physics below the particle scale has been integrated out.

3. Soft Cosmology

The above formulation of standard cosmology is definitely correct and can provide a quite successful quantitative description of the Universe evolution. However, the question is: could it miss something on the details?

One source of possible information loss is the assumption that the Universe sectors and interactions are simple and more or less scale-independent. For instance, two regions of the dark-matter fluid will mutual interact in the same way in the intermediate- and late-time universe, or the interaction of two big clusters of dark matter can arise by the superposition of all individual interactions of their sub-clusters, etc. In other words, in the concordance cosmological formulation one assumes that the sectors that constitute the Universe behave as usual, "hard" matter.

"Soft" matter is a research field that has attracted a large amount of interest of the condensed matter community,[6,7] since it has very interesting and peculiar properties far different than those of hard matter. The problem is that there is not a definition of what is soft matter. In particular, the best definition we have is that soft matter is the one that has the properties of soft materials. Examples of soft materials are the polymers (plastic, rubber, polystyrene, lubricants etc), the colloids (paints, milk, ice-cream etc), the surfactants, granular materials, liquid crystals, gels, biological matter (proteins, RNA, DNA, viruses, etc), etc. Although these examples of soft matter are very different from each other, they have some common properties and features that distinguish them from usual, hard, matter. Amongst others these include complexity (new qualitative properties arise at intermediate scales due to interactions that are not present at the fundamental scales), co-existence of phases (they have different phase properties depending on the scale at one examines them, e.g at the same time they can be fluid at small scales and solid at large scales), entropy dominance instead of energy dominance, flexibility, extreme sensitivity to reactions, viscoelasticity (they exhibit viscous and elastic properties simultaneously) etc.

In the following we examine the possibility that the dark sectors of the universe may exhibit (intrinsically or effectively) slight soft properties, which could then lead to small corrections to the corcodance model. We mention here that the discussion below holds independently of the underlying gravitational theory, i.e it is valid both in the framework of general relativity as well as in modified gravity, nevertheless in the latter case we have richer possibilities to obtain scale-dependent interactions.

3.1. A. Soft Dark Energy

The nature and underlying physics of dark energy is unknown. The basic framework that has been studied in extensive detail is that the dark energy fluid has the same fluid properties at all scales at a given moment/redshift. However, as we saw, in soft matter the complexity that arises at intermediate scales may lead the material to have a different equation of state (EoS) at different scales simultaneously.

As a simple phenomenological model of soft dark energy we may consider the case where dark energy has the usual EoS at large scales, namely at scales entering the Friedmann equations, but having a different value at intermediate scales, namely at scales entering the perturbation equations. In this case the Universe's expansion history will remain identical to standard cosmology, nevertheless the large-scale structure evolution can deviate from the standard one and can be brought closer to observations. In summary one can obtain richer behavior. We mention that in the following we focus on sub-horizon scales $k \gg aH$ and thus to perturbation modes affected only by the intermediate-scale dark-energy EoS. The full analysis, in which different perturbation modes are affected by different EoS according to their scale, will be presented elsewhere.

A first approach on the subject would be to introduce the effective "softness parameter" s_{de} of the dark energy sector. This implies that while at cosmological, large scales (ls) dark energy has the usual EoS, namely w_{de-ls}, at intermediate scales (is) we have[8]

$$w_{de-is} = s_{de} \cdot w_{de-ls}, \qquad (6)$$

and standard cosmology is recovered for $s_{de} = 1$.

For instance let us assume that the large-scale dark energy EoS w_{de-ls} is a constant one $w_{de-ls} = w_0$ or e.g. the CPL one $w_{de-ls} = w_0 + w_a(1-a)$. According to (6) at intermediate scales the dark energy EoS w_{de-is} is different, either constant $w_{de-is} = w_2$ or time-varying. Hence, the background Universe evolution will remain the same, however since $c_{\text{eff}}^{(de)}$ will change, through the Poisson equation and (3),(4) we will acquire a different evolution for the matter overdensity δ_m. Hence, the resulting $f\sigma_8 \equiv f(a)\sigma(a)$ value, with $f(a) = d\ln\delta_m(a)/d\ln a$ and $\sigma(a) = \sigma_8 \delta_m(a)/\delta_m(1)$, will be different than the corresponding one of standard cosmology with the above dark energy EoS (note that since the background behavior remains unaffected we do not need to worry about incorporating fiducial cosmology.[13] As we observe, we have a straightforward way to alleviate the σ_8 tension since we can suitably adjust w_{de-is} in order to obtain slightly lower $f\sigma_8$. As a specific example in Fig. 1 we depict the $f\sigma_8$ as a function of z. The dashed curve is for ΛCDM. The solid curve is for soft dark energy with $s_{dm} = 1.1$, i.e. with $w_{de-is} = -1.1$, and $c_{\text{eff}}^{(de)} = 0.1$, while dark matter is the standard one (i.e. not soft) with $w_{dm} = 0$. Note that in principle s_{de} can be varying too and one could introduce its parametrization, or one could additionally have more complicated situations in which w_{de-is} and w_{de-ls} have different parametrizations. In this first approach on soft dark energy we consider the simplest case of (6).

Finally, note that soft materials may exhibit different EoS properties not only at different scales, but at different directions too. In this case, one may think of a dark energy sector that has a different EoS at different directions, namely an anisotropic dark energy. However, such an analysis would require to deviate from FRW and consider explicitly anisotropic geometries such as the Bianchi ones. We will study this possibility in a separate work.

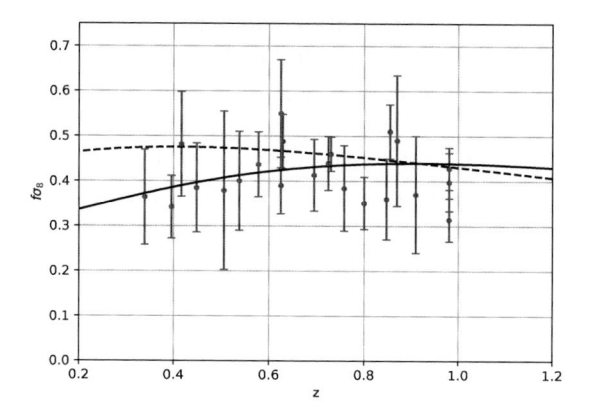

Fig. 1. The $f\sigma_8$ as a function of z. The dashed curve is for ΛCDM. The solid curve is for soft dark energy with $s_{de} = 1.1$, i.e. with $w_{de-ls} = -1$ and $w_{de-is} = -1.1$, and $c_{\text{eff}}^{(de)} = 0.1$, while dark matter is standard (i.e. not soft) with $w_{dm} = 0$.

3.2. B. Soft Dark Matter

In this subsection we examine the possibility that the dark matter sector exhibits soft properties. In the framework of general relativity the gravitational interaction of dark matter with itself or with baryonic matter cannot produce internal complexity (unless the unknown microphysics of dark matter does impose an intrinsic soft structure). However, even if it is not intrinsic, soft behavior in the dark matter sector can still arise in an effective way due to the presence of non-trivial dark energy. Specifically, if the dark energy is clustering then, even if dark energy is not intrinsically soft, it will induce scale-dependent, qualitatively different intermediate structures in the dark matter clustering, at scales similar to the dark energy clusters. In particular, the interaction between two dark-matter clusters below the dark-energy clustering scale (i.e. two dark-matter clusters with sparse dark energy between them) will be different from the interaction between two dark-matter clusters with a dark-energy cluster between them. Hence, one will have the effective appearance of screening effects at intermediate scales, and thus of complexity (this is the standard way that complexity appears in the colloids, namely due to the non-trivial, scale-dependent structure of the bulk between them). In summary, one could have a dark matter sector which at large scales, namely at scales entering the Friedmann equations, behaves in the usual dust way, but which at intermediate scales, namely at scales entering the (sub-horizon) perturbation equations, it could slightly deviate from that.

We can introduce the dark matter softness parameter s_{dm} (standard cosmology is recovered for $s_{dm} = 1$) as:

$$w_{dm-is} + 1 = s_{dm} \cdot (w_{dm-ls} + 1), \tag{7}$$

(mind the difference in the parametrization comparing to soft dark energy, in order to handle the fact that the dark matter EoS at large scales w_{dm-ls} is 0). Similarly to the example of the previous subsection, the background evolution will remain identical with that of standard cosmology, but the perturbation behavior (at subhorizon scales) and the large-scale structure can be improved. In order to provide a specific example, in Fig. 2 we depict the $f\sigma_8$ as a function of z, in the case of soft dark matter with $w_{dm-is} = 0.05$, i.e for dark matter with softness parameter $s_{dm} = 1.05$.

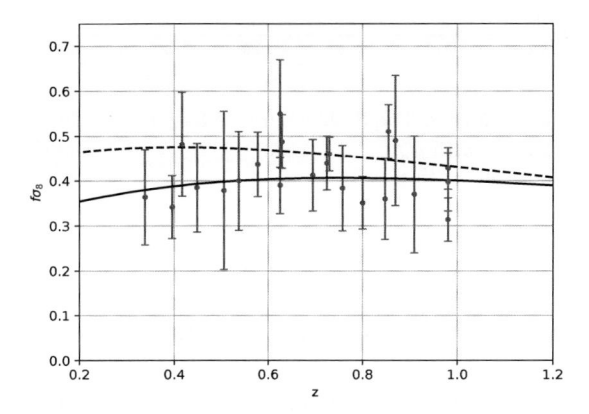

Fig. 2. The $f\sigma_8$ as a function of z. The dashed curve is for ΛCDM. The solid curve is for soft dark matter with softness parameter $s_{dm} = 1.05$, i.e. for dark matter with $w_{dm-ls} = 0$ and $w_{dm-is} = 0.05$ (note that dark energy is not soft).

In the above analysis we did not consider the dark energy sector to be soft. Definitely, proceeding to such a possibility would make the induced soft bahavior for dark matter easier. Moreover, this would be the case if one considers a mutual interaction between dark matter and dark energy too, since a different than usual dark-energy clustering behavior would be transferred to a different than usual dark-matter clustering behavior, due to the interaction. Finally, deviating from general relativity would provide additional possibilities to induce effective soft properties to the dark matter sector, since dark matter will implicitly interact in a scale-dependent way (one would have the additional screening behavior due to the extra (scalar) graviton degrees of freedom that dress the dark matter in a scale-dependent way, altering its self-interaction[16]).

Let us make a comment here on the clustering features. The clustering behavior of soft matter has been extensively studied, and indeed it has been shown that the resulting spectrum, factorial moments, fractal dimension, etc, depend on the specific intermediate-scale features. For instance the fractal dimension has been experimentally found to cover all the range from 1 to 3 according to different materials (e.g. colloids of gold nanoparticle in aqueous media give $d_f = 1.75 \pm 0.05$ for diffusion-limited kinetics and $d_f = 2.01 \pm 0.10$ for reaction-limited kinetics)[17,18]). On the other hand, the large scale structure and the galaxy distribution in the Universe has a fractal dimension $d_f = 1.63 \pm 0.20$.[19,20] The fact that soft matter clustering exhibits naturally non-trivial dynamics due to its intermediate-scale complexity, could be useful in describing the details of the observed large-scale structure. We mention here that the non-trivial clustering of soft matter changes at scales below the intermediate ones, and hence soft dark matter could alleviate the cuspy halo problem,[21] the dwarf galaxy problem,[22] and other clustering-related problems that seem to puzzle the standard collisionless dark matter.

4. Conclusions

We examined the possibility of "soft cosmology", namely small deviations from the usual framework due to the effective appearance of soft properties in the Universe sectors. We started by considering the possibility of soft dark energy due to intermediate-scale features that could arise from its unknown microphysics. One effect of such a case would be the dark energy to exhibit a different EoS at large and intermediate scales. As we saw, although the background evolution remains unaffected, even a slight softness at intermediate scales can improve the clustering behavior and alleviate e.g. the $f\sigma_8$ tension.

We proceeded to the examination of soft dark matter, which can effectively arise just due to the dark-energy clustering even if dark energy is not soft. By considering a slightly different equation of state at large and intermediate scales we were able to improve the clustering behavior. Furthermore, in the additional incorporation of soft dark energy, and/or modified gravity, the effective soft properties of dark matter could be richer, due to the extra screening mechanisms.

We mention that in this work we incorporated softness by phenomenologically introducing a slightly different EoS at different scales. Clearly, in order to incorporate complexity and estimate the scale-dependent behavior of the equation of states from first principles one should revise and extend the cosmological perturbation theory and perform a detailed mesoscopic statistical mechanical analysis. Such a full investigation is necessary and would provide a robust argumentation in favour of soft cosmology.

References

1. E. J. Copeland, M. Sami and S. Tsujikawa, *Dynamics of dark energy*, Int. J. Mod. Phys. D **15**, 1753-1936 (2006).
2. Y. F. Cai, E. N. Saridakis, M. R. Setare and J. Q. Xia, *Quintom Cosmology: Theoretical implications and observations*, Phys. Rept. **493**, 1-60 (2010).
3. E. N. Saridakis *et al.* [CANTATA], *Modified Gravity and Cosmology: An Update by the CANTATA Network*, [arXiv:2105.12582 [gr-qc]].
4. S. Capozziello and M. De Laurentis, *Extended Theories of Gravity*, Phys. Rept. **509**, 167-321 (2011).

5. Y. F. Cai, S. Capozziello, M. De Laurentis and E. N. Saridakis, *f(T) teleparallel gravity and cosmology*, Rept. Prog. Phys. **79**, no.10, 106901 (2016).
6. R. A. L. Jones, *Soft Condensed Matter*, Oxford University Press, Oxford (2002).
7. L. M. C. Sagis, *Dynamic properties of interfaces in soft matter: Experiments and theory*, Rev. Mod. Phys. 83, 1367-1403 (2011).
8. E. N. Saridakis, *Do we need soft cosmology?*, Phys. Lett. B **822**, 136649 (2021).
9. P. J. E. Peebles, *Principles of physical cosmology*, Princeton University Press, Princeton (1993).
10. G. Bertone, D. Hooper and J. Silk, *Particle dark matter: Evidence, candidates and constraints*, Phys. Rept. **405**, 279-390 (2005).
11. V. F. Mukhanov, H. A. Feldman and R. H. Brandenberger, *Theory of cosmological perturbations. Part 1. Classical perturbations. Part 2. Quantum theory of perturbations. Part 3. Extensions*, Phys. Rept. **215**, 203-333 (1992).
12. C. P. Ma and E. Bertschinger, *Cosmological perturbation theory in the synchronous and conformal Newtonian gauges*, Astrophys. J. **455**, 7-25 (1995).
13. N. Aghanim et al. [Planck], *Planck 2018 results. VI. Cosmological parameters*, Astron. Astrophys. **641**, A6 (2020).
14. W. J. Percival and M. White, *Testing cosmological structure formation using redshift-space distortions*, Mon. Not. Roy. Astron. Soc. **393**, 297 (2009).
15. A. P. Deshpande, J. M. Krishnan, S. Kumar, *Rheology of Complex Fluids*, Springer, Heidelberg (2010).
16. A. Joyce, B. Jain, J. Khoury and M. Trodden, *Beyond the Cosmological Standard Model*, Phys. Rept. **568**, 1-98 (2015).
17. D. A. Weitz, J. S. Huang, M. Y. Lin, and J. Sung, *Limits of the Fractal Dimension for Irreversible Kinetic Aggregation of Gold Colloids*, Phys. Rev. Lett. 54 (1985) 1416-1419.
18. S. Lazzari, L. Nicoud, B. Jaquet, M. Lattuada, M. Morbidelli, *Fractal-like structures in colloid science*, Advances in colloid and interface science 235, 1.
19. P. H. Coleman and L. Pietronero, *The fractal structure of the universe*, Phys. Rept. **213**, 311-389 (1992).
20. S. Teles, A. R. Lopes and M. B. Ribeiro, *Fractal Analysis of the UltraVISTA Galaxy Survey*, Phys. Lett. B **813**, 136034 (2021).
21. R. Teyssier, A. Pontzen, Y. Dubois and J. Read, *Cusp-core transformations in dwarf galaxies: observational predictions*, Mon. Not. Roy. Astron. Soc. **429**, 3068 (2013).
22. J. S. Bullock and M. Boylan-Kolchin, *Small-Scale Challenges to the ΛCDM Paradigm*, Ann. Rev. Astron. Astrophys. **55**, 343-387 (2017).
23. M.-a. Watanabe, S. Kanno and J. Soda, *The Nature of Primordial Fluctuations from Anisotropic Inflation*, Prog. Theor. Phys. **123**, 1041-1068 (2010).
24. M. C. Marchetti, J. F. Joanny, S. Ramaswamy, T. B. Liverpool, J. Prost, Madan Rao, and R. Aditi Simha, *Hydrodynamics of soft active matter*, Rev. Mod. Phys. 82 (2013) 1143-1189.

A simple parametrisation for coupled dark energy

Vitor da Fonseca* and Nelson J. Nunes

Instituto de Astrofísica e Ciências do Espaço,
Faculdade de Ciências da Universidade de Lisboa,
Campo Grande, PT1749-016 Lisboa, Portugal
* E-mail: fc52156@alunos.fc.ul.pt

Tiago Barreiro

Instituto de Astrofísica e Ciências do Espaço,
ECEO, Universidade Lusófona de Humanidades e Tecnologias,
Campo Grande, 376, 1749-024 Lisboa, Portugal

We proposes a phenomenological generalisation of the standard model with only one extra degree of freedom that parametrises the evolution of a scalar field responsible for the cosmic acceleration. The model also foresees an additional parameter in the form of a coupling between dark energy and dark matter. This model captures a large diversity of dark energy evolutions at low redshift and could usefully complement common CPL parametrisations widely used. In this context, we have been constraining the parametrisation with data from Planck and KiDS, bringing different results between the early and late universe observations.

Keywords: Quintessence, dark matter, observational cosmology.

1. Introduction

The discovery in 1998 that the Universe is accelerating[1,2] was really stunning at the time. While the source of the cosmic acceleration is yet to be unveiled, the existence of a dark energy component has been postulated to explain it.[3,4] In the standard model, dark energy takes the form of a cosmological constant Λ which by definition possesses a constant energy density and negative pressure that fights the attractive pull of matter.[5] That model is, at the moment, compatible with all observations and it is the simplest one,[6] at least from a parametrisation point of view. One of the outstanding issue in the concordance model is the so-called coincidence problem.[7] Given how the energy densities dilute with the expansion, the fact that the cosmological constant is catching up with matter at the present time necessitates initial conditions at the origin that are dramatically precise. This issue has been paving the way to study varying dark energy[8] in order to reproduce more dynamically the current abundances.

The simplest and model independent approach is phenomenological. It consists in parametrising the dark energy equation of state, being the pressure over the energy density that equals -1 for a cosmological constant. The detection of a time dependence would exclude a cosmological constant. Introducing the fewest possible parameters is ideal to limit degeneracies between them. A simple and popular parametrisation[9] is a Taylor expansion at first order which has a very limited domain of validity. Various improvements have been introduced, like the Chevallier-Polarski-Linder (CPL) parametrisation.[10,11] Also, to account for the possibility of early dark energy, a parametrisation stepwise in redshift[12] has been proposed with a larger number of additional parameters.

Here, we explore an alternative way to parametrise dark energy by proposing to parametrise a scalar field ϕ called quintessence that would be responsible for dark energy both in the early and late Universe.[13] Instead of setting an equation of state parameter evolution, or a scalar potential, this method parametrises the dark energy scalar field itself. We argue that with a single parameter we recover the generic behaviour of the previous parametrisations. We test this approach with data from Planck and KiDS to constrain its specific parameters, identifying contrasting results between the early and late universe observations. This is a comprehensive work going from the analytical solutions to parameter constraints.

2. Scalar field parametrisation

We consider that the cosmological fluid is composed of matter (m), i.e. baryons (b) and cold dark matter (c), as well as the scalar field itself in a flat Friedmann-Lemaitre-Robertson-Walker background. The scalar field is supposed to be canonical and homogeneous at large scale,[14,15] approximated by a perfect fluid. We choose to work with the number of e-folds, $N \equiv \ln a$, as the time variable. In the following, the prime stands for the derivative with respect to the number of e-foldings, and the dot the derivative with respect to cosmic time.

By combining the Friedmann equation,

$$H^2 = \frac{\kappa^2}{3} \left(\rho_b + \rho_c + \rho_\phi \right), \qquad (1)$$

with the continuity equation of the scalar field,

$$\rho'_\phi + 3H^2 \phi'^2 = 0, \qquad (2)$$

and the continuity equation of matter,

$$\rho'_c + 3\rho_c = 0, \qquad (3)$$

one obtains[16] a differential equation for the dark energy density (where we conventionnally set $\kappa = 1$),

$$\frac{\rho'_\phi}{\rho_{m_0}} = -\phi'^2 \left(a^{-3} + \frac{\rho_\phi}{\rho_{m_0}} \right), \qquad (4)$$

whose general solution is our starting point,

$$\frac{\rho_\phi}{\rho_{m_0}} = e^{-\int_0^N dN \phi'^2} \times \left[\frac{\Omega_{\phi_0}}{\Omega_{m_0}} - \int_0^N dN \phi'^2 e^{-3N + \int_0^N dN \phi'^2} \right]. \quad (5)$$

Among possible parametrisations enabling us to solve the former equation analytically,

$$\phi' = \epsilon \phi, \quad (6)$$
$$\phi' = \sigma \phi^{-1}, \quad (7)$$
$$\phi' = \lambda, \quad (8)$$

where ϵ, σ and λ are given constants, we explore the simplest one in Eq. (8).[16]

The advantage of this parametrisation is three folds. Firstly, it is very simple, as we only add one single parameter to extend the standard model. It allows to reconstruct analytically the form of the potential,[16]

$$V(\phi) = A e^{-\frac{3}{\lambda}\phi} + B e^{-\lambda \phi}, \quad (9)$$

with the following mass scales,

$$A = \frac{3}{2} \frac{\lambda^2}{3 - \lambda^2} H_0^2 \, \Omega_{m_0} \, e^{\frac{3}{\lambda}\phi_0}, \quad (10)$$

$$B = \frac{3}{2} \frac{\lambda^2 - 6}{3 - \lambda^2} H_0^2 \left(\frac{\lambda^2}{3} - \Omega_{\phi_0} \right) e^{\lambda \phi_0}, \quad (11)$$

where H_0 is today's Hubble expansion rate and $\Omega_{i_0} = \rho_{i_0}/3H_0^2$ today's abundance parameter of species i. Having a simple form of the potential allows a straightforward implementation of the model within the existing Boltzmann code CLASS[17,18] that can be validated by comparing the numerical results with the expected asymptotic behaviour of the analytic expressions. Given the small number of parameters involved and thanks to its simplicity, our analysis permits to effectively constrain the model parameters with current data as in the next section.

Secondly, this scalar potential, being the sum of two exponential terms, does alleviate the severe fine-tuning of the initial conditions as illustrated in Fig. 1. For small values of the parameter λ, when the first exponential term in the potential is steep enough, the scalar field energy density is attracted and temporarily scales with the background as the universe expands, be it dominated by radiation and then matter. Later, thanks to the second shallow exponential, whose slope is the inverse of the first one, the scalar field energy density eventually freezes, mimicking a cosmological constant. By freezing, dark energy overcomes matter at late time, enabling the acceleration of the universe that we are currently experiencing. This well-known attractor mechanism[19] ensures that one can start from a large domain of initial conditions for the scalar field, to reach unavoidably the tracking solution and end up with the correct order of magnitude both during matter and dark energy domination.

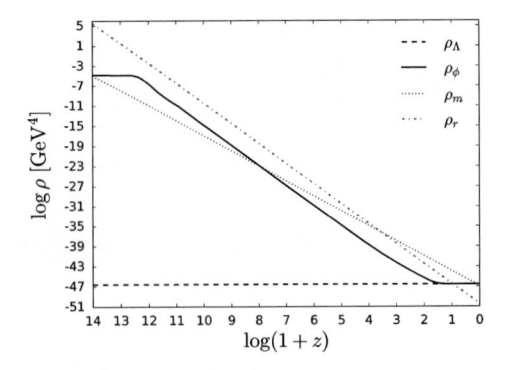

Fig. 1. Energy density dilution of a cosmological constant, as well as quintessence, matter and radiation for the scalar field parametrisation ($\lambda = 0.01$).

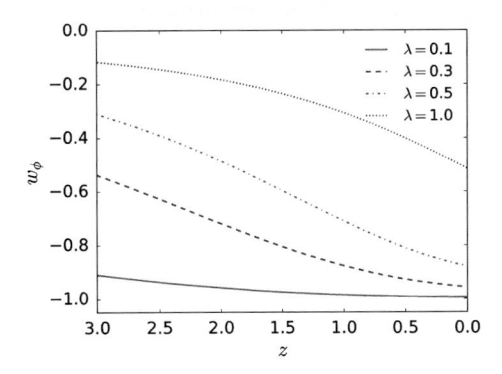

Fig. 2. Dynamics of the dark energy equation of state for given values of the parameter λ.

Last but not least, despite just one extra parameter, the model covers a wide range of possible dark energy evolution at low redshift as displayed in Fig 2. The parametrisation is thus able to capture a large variety of possible dynamics for dark energy. The observational data might even become precise enough in the future for discriminating between these different evolutions.

As a step further, we decide to complement our parametrisation by assuming a non-minimally coupling between dark energy and cold dark matter.[20] Again for the sake of simplicity, we consider a conformal and constant coupling β that parametrises the interaction between dark matter and the scalar field. The stress-energy tensor is jointly conserved within the dark sector in order to ensure the covariance of the theory,

$$\nabla_\mu \left(T^{(\phi)\,\mu}_{\nu} + T^{(c)\,\mu}_{\nu} \right) = 0, \qquad (12)$$

$$\nabla_\mu T^{(\phi)\,\mu}_{\nu} = +\beta \rho_c \nabla_\mu \phi, \qquad (13)$$

$$\nabla_\mu T^{(c)\,\mu}_{\nu} = -\beta \rho_c \nabla_\mu \phi. \qquad (14)$$

Assuming that dark energy does not interact with baryons, the latter are separately conserved contrary to dark matter and quintessence,

$$\rho_b = \rho_{b_0}\, e^{-3N}, \tag{15}$$

$$\rho_c = \rho_{c_0}\, e^{-3N+\beta(\phi-\phi_0)}, \tag{16}$$

$$\rho'_\phi + 3H^2 \phi'^2 = -\beta \phi' \rho_c. \tag{17}$$

The sign of the product $\beta \phi'$, i.e. $\beta \lambda$ in our parametrisation, determines whether energy is being pumped from the scalar field or from dark matter. Similarly to Ref. 16, we use the Friedmann equation (1) with the solution we find for the scalar field energy density,

$$\rho_\phi = \left(\rho_{\phi_0} + \frac{\lambda^2 + \beta\lambda}{\lambda^2 + \beta\lambda - 3} \rho_{c_0} + \frac{\lambda^2}{\lambda^2 - 3} \rho_{b_0} \right) e^{-\lambda^2 N}$$
$$- \frac{\lambda^2 + \beta\lambda}{\lambda^2 + \beta\lambda - 3} \rho_{c_0}\, e^{(\beta\lambda - 3)N} - \frac{\lambda^2}{\lambda^2 - 3} \rho_{b_0}\, e^{-3N}, \tag{18}$$

to reconstruct, for the first time, the corresponding potential with similar properties of the dynamical system as in the minimally coupled case,

$$V(\phi) = A\, e^{\left(-\frac{3}{\lambda}+\beta\right)\phi} + B\, e^{-\lambda\phi} + C\, e^{-\frac{3}{\lambda}\phi}, \tag{19}$$

where the mass scales are now the following,

$$A = \frac{3}{2} \frac{\lambda^2 + 2\beta\lambda}{3 - \lambda^2 - \beta\lambda} H_0^2\, \Omega_{c_0}\, e^{\left(\frac{3}{\lambda}-\beta\right)\phi_0}, \tag{20}$$

$$B = \frac{6 - \lambda^2}{2} H_0^2 \left(1 + \frac{3}{\lambda^2 - 3 + \beta\lambda} \Omega_{c_0} + \frac{3}{\lambda^2 - 3} \Omega_{b_0} \right) e^{\lambda\phi_0}, \tag{21}$$

$$C = \frac{3}{2} \frac{\lambda^2}{3 - \lambda^2} H_0^2\, \Omega_{b_0}\, e^{\frac{3}{\lambda}\phi_0}. \tag{22}$$

We modify the CLASS code to accommodate that potential as well as the coupled equations (16) and (17) to simulate the model with the two additional parameters λ and β. The numerical results plotted in Fig. 3 are in line with the asymptotic solution for the dark energy equation of state during matter domination when baryonic matter is neglected,

$$w_\phi \approx -\frac{\beta}{\lambda + \beta}. \tag{23}$$

One can note that today's equation of state, w_0, does not depend on the coupling, and drops close to -1 during the scalar field dominated epoch for small values of λ,

$$w_0 = -1 + \frac{\lambda^2}{3\Omega_{\phi_0}}. \tag{24}$$

Furthermore, in order to numerically predict observables that we use to constrain the parameters with observational datasets at the perturbative level, we again modify CLASS to implement the coupled evolution of the scalar fluctuations at linear

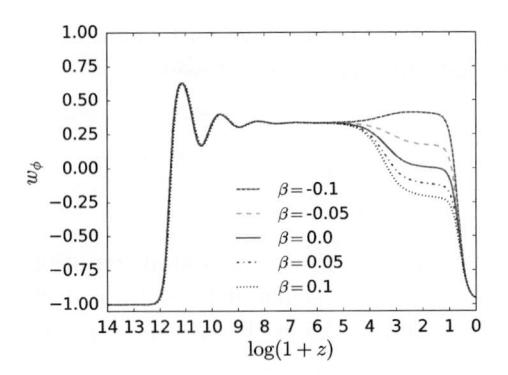

Fig. 3. Dark energy evolution in the coupled parametrisation. Beta negative corresponds to the transfer of energy from the dark matter component to the scalar field.

level in the synchronous gauge adopting usual conventions.[21] We modify the existing perturbed Klein-Gordon equation, as well as the equation of motion for the dark matter density contrast δ_c and velocity perturbations θ_c to account for the coupling, by adding the relevant sources term in the right-hand side,

$$\ddot{\varphi} + 2\mathcal{H}\dot{\varphi} + \left(k^2 + a^2 V_{,\phi\phi}\right)\varphi + \frac{\dot{h}\dot{\phi}}{2} = -\beta a^2 \bar{\rho}_c \delta_c, \qquad (25)$$

$$\dot{\delta}_c + \theta_c + \frac{\dot{h}}{2} = \beta\dot{\varphi}, \qquad (26)$$

$$\dot{\theta}_c + \mathcal{H}\theta_c = \beta\left(k^2\varphi - \dot{\phi}\theta_c\right), \qquad (27)$$

where the overbar denotes the background quantities. Additionally, we adapt the transformation from the synchronous gauge into the comoving gauge to maintain the matter density source function δ_m gauge-invariant,

$$\delta_m^C = \frac{\delta\rho_m}{\bar{\rho}_m} + \left(3 - \frac{\beta\phi'\bar{\rho}_c}{\bar{\rho}_c + \bar{\rho}_b}\right)\frac{\mathcal{H}}{k^2}\theta_m. \qquad (28)$$

In parallel, to provide for the code validation, we derive the analytic equation of motion of the dark matter fluctuations in the Newtonian limit during the domination of matter, precisely when the coupling makes a difference,

$$\delta_c'' + \frac{1}{2}\left(1 + 3\lambda\beta\right)\delta_c' - \frac{3}{2}\left(1 - \frac{\lambda^2}{3} - \frac{\lambda\beta}{3}\right)\left(1 + 2\beta^2\right)\delta_c = 0. \qquad (29)$$

In the left panel of Fig 4, we note that the scalar field slows the growth of perturbations against the standard model, by decreasing the dynamical term in the equation of motion. On the other hand, the existence of the coupling brings competitive effects that further slow the fluctuation or, on the contrary, accelerate them, depending on whether energy is being transferred from the scalar field or into it. We are also able to get an analytic expression of the growth rate $m+$ under the

Newtonian approximation,

$$m_+ = \frac{1}{4}\left[-1 - 3\lambda\beta + \sqrt{24\left(1 - \frac{\lambda^2}{3} - \frac{\lambda\beta}{3}\right)(1 + 2\beta^2) + (1 + 3\lambda\beta)^2}\right]. \quad (30)$$

One can see in the right panel of Fig. 4 that the numerical results in the matter era on a small scale are very much in line with it. The standard growth, which equals 1, is obviously recovered for vanishing values of the parameters λ and β.

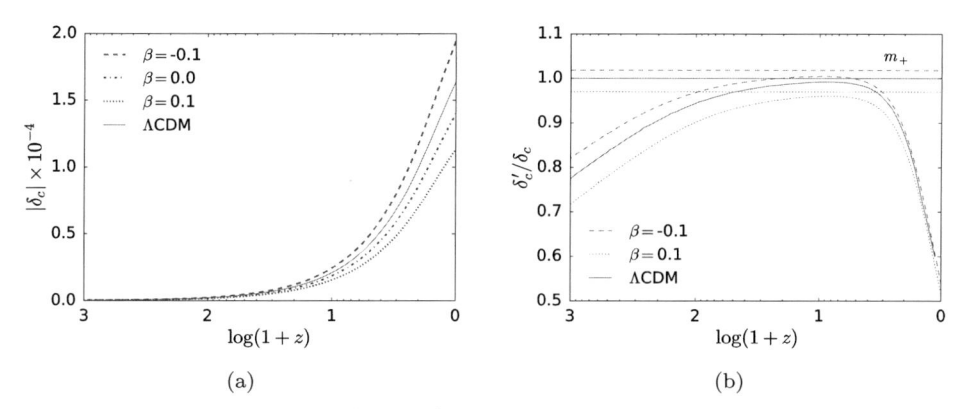

Fig. 4. $\lambda = 0.3$ on scale $k = 0.1\ h/\text{Mpc}$. (a) Dark matter fluctuations. (b) Growth rate function.

3. Observational constraints

We turn now our attention to the observations in order to constrain the value of the posteriors λ and β through Bayesian inference with MontePython[22–27] and GetDist.[28] Given that it affects the growth of dark matter perturbations, our parametrisation leaves observational signatures, both on the CMB anisotropies and matter power spectrum that we can numerically predict with our adapted version of CLASS and compare with observations.

As for the CMB anisotropies, early dark energy as well as the coupling affect the amplitude and position of the acoustic peaks as illustrated on the left panel of Fig. 5. We use the data from the Planck 2018 likelihood[29] on the temperature and polarisation of the CMB in the MCMC analysis. As regards today's linear matter power spectrum, the delay or the acceleration in the growth of dark matter perturbations has consequences too (right panel of Fig. 5). We use the gravitational weak lensing measurements, cosmic shear, from the KiDS-450 survey[30] in the Bayesian fitting.

The probability contours and posterior distribution we obtain in the parameter space are displayed on Fig. 6 for the two specific degrees of freedom of the model. On the one hand, the parameter estimation done with Planck provides an upper bound for the posterior λ which is compatible with a cosmological constant, that

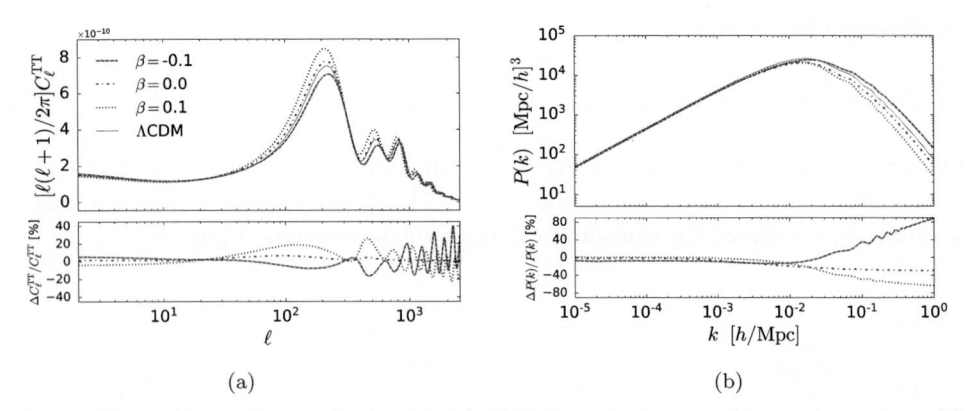

Fig. 5. Observables predictions for $\lambda = 0.3$ (a) CMB dimensionless angular power spectrum. (b) Linear matter power spectrum at redshift $z = 0$.

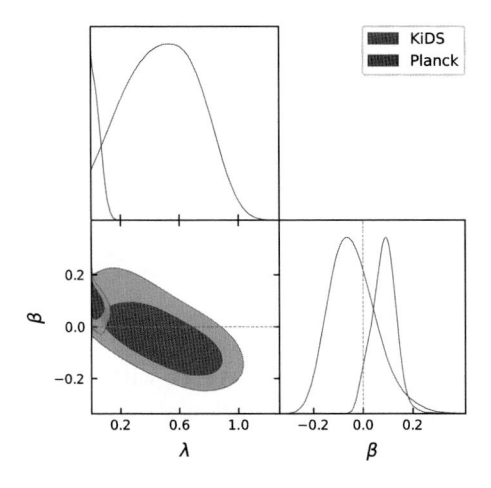

Fig. 6. Constraints on the (λ,β) posterior plane. Contours with 68% and 95% probability.

cannot be discarded. The coupling posterior corresponds to the energy injection from dark energy to dark matter. However, on the other hand, weak lensing data brings a different constraint on the posterior λ, not favouring a vanishing value. It also slightly detects energy transfer from dark matter to dark energy.

We also undertake the same likelihood analysis with the standard model as a benchmark to compare the goodness-of-fit of the parametrisation (Table 1). In light of the reduced chi-square, the two models look more or less equivalent. Nonetheless, according to the Akaike Information Criterion (AIC),[31] since it further penalises model complexity, the favourite cosmology for both probes is ΛCDM, this is particularly true for KiDS.

Table 1. Standard ΛCDM model vs scalar field parametrisation

	Planck		KiDS	
	ΛCDM	ϕ param.	ΛCDM	ϕ param.
χ^2	602.6	599.7	321.5	321.7
$\chi^2_{\rm red}$	1.0	1.0	2.6	2.7
AIC	616.6	617.7	335.5	339.7
ΔAIC	0	1.1	0	4.2

4. Concluding remarks

Despite its simplicity, the parametrisation we propose is able to cover a large span of dark energy evolution with a limited number of parameters. Constraints on more complex parametrisations are usually limited by the degeneracies between the various degrees of freedom. The model preserves the fact that dark matter and dark energy are in comparable ratios today, while relaxing the initial conditions thanks to the existence of tracking solutions. It is thus capable of reproducing the evolution of the background, as well as the CMB anisotropies and the formation of Large Scale Structures. Since the parametrisation has a ΛCDM limit for small λ and vanishing coupling β, it allows a direct test of departures from the standard model. We therefore argue that the parametrisation does help constrain the evolution of the equation of state and the departure from ΛCDM, even though the approach is purely phenomenological. Finally, the MCMC analysis carried out at perturbation level identifies tensions on the posteriors between early and late time probes. Background data is not expected to provide stronger constraints but the upcoming Euclid data will certainly improve the situation.

Acknowledgements

The authors thank Giuseppe Fanizza and Miguel Zumalacarregui for their useful comments. This research was supported by Fundação para a Ciência e a Tecnologia (FCT) through the research grants: UID/FIS/04434/2019, PTDC/FIS-OUT/29048/2017 (DarkRipple), COMPETE 2020:POCI-01-0145-FEDER-028987 & FCT:PTDC/FIS-AST/28987/2017 (CosmoESPRESSO) and IF/00852/2015.

References

1. A. G. Riess *et al.*, Observational evidence from supernovae for an accelerating universe and a cosmological constant, *Astron. J.* **116**, 1009 (1998).
2. S. Perlmutter *et al.*, Measurements of Omega and Lambda from 42 high redshift supernovae, *Astrophys. J.* **517**, 565 (1999).
3. L. Amendola and S. Tsujikawa, *Dark Energy* (Cambridge University Press, 2015).
4. T. Clifton, P. G. Ferreira, A. Padilla and C. Skordis, Modified Gravity and Cosmology, *Phys. Rept.* **513**, 1 (2012).

5. P. J. E. Peebles and B. Ratra, The Cosmological constant and dark energy, *Rev. Mod. Phys.* **75**, 559 (2003) [592(2002)].
6. Planck Collaboration, Planck 2018 results. VI. Cosmological parameters, *arXiv e-prints*, p. arXiv:1807.06209 (Jul 2018).
7. J. Martin, Everything You Always Wanted To Know About The Cosmological Constant Problem (But Were Afraid To Ask), *Comptes Rendus Physique* **13**, 566 (2012).
8. P. J. E. Peebles and B. Ratra, Cosmology with a Time Variable Cosmological Constant, *Astrophys. J.* **325**, p. L17 (1988).
9. J. Weller and A. Albrecht, Future supernovae observations as a probe of dark energy, *Physical Review D* **65** (May 2002).
10. M. Chevallier and D. Polarski, Accelerating Universes with Scaling Dark Matter, *International Journal of Modern Physics D* **10**, 213 (2001), (uses Latex, 12 pages, 6 Figures) Minor corrections, Figures 4, 6 revised. Conclusions unchanged.
11. E. Linder, Exploring the expansion history of the universe, *Physical review letters* **90**, p. 091301 (04 2003).
12. P. S. Corasaniti and E. J. Copeland, Model independent approach to the dark energy equation of state, *Physical Review D* **67** (Mar 2003).
13. C. Wetterich, The Cosmon model for an asymptotically vanishing time dependent cosmological 'constant', *Astron. Astrophys.* **301**, 321 (1995).
14. R. R. Caldwell, R. Dave and P. J. Steinhardt, Cosmological imprint of an energy component with general equation of state, *Physical Review Letters* **80**, p. 1582–1585 (Feb 1998).
15. S. Tsujikawa, Quintessence: A Review, *Class. Quant. Grav.* **30**, p. 214003 (2013).
16. N. J. Nunes and J. E. Lidsey, Reconstructing the dark energy equation of state with varying alpha, *Phys. Rev.* **D69**, p. 123511 (2004).
17. J. Lesgourgues, The cosmic linear anisotropy solving system (class) i: Overview (2011).
18. D. Blas, J. Lesgourgues and T. Tram, The cosmic linear anisotropy solving system (class). part ii: Approximation schemes, *Journal of Cosmology and Astroparticle Physics* **2011**, p. 034–034 (Jul 2011).
19. T. Barreiro, E. J. Copeland and N. J. Nunes, Quintessence arising from exponential potentials, *Phys. Rev.* **D61**, p. 127301 (2000).
20. L. Amendola, Coupled quintessence, *Phys. Rev. D* **62**, p. 043511 (2000).
21. C.-P. Ma and E. Bertschinger, Cosmological perturbation theory in the synchronous and conformal newtonian gauges, *The Astrophysical Journal* **455**, p. 7 (Dec 1995).
22. B. Audren, J. Lesgourgues, K. Benabed and S. Prunet, Conservative Constraints on Early Cosmology: an illustration of the Monte Python cosmological parameter inference code, *JCAP* **1302**, p. 001 (2013).
23. T. Brinckmann and J. Lesgourgues, MontePython 3: boosted MCMC sampler and other features (2018).
24. F. Feroz and M. P. Hobson, Multimodal nested sampling: an efficient and robust alternative to markov chain monte carlo methods for astronomical data analyses, *Monthly Notices of the Royal Astronomical Society* **384**, p. 449–463 (Jan 2008).
25. F. Feroz, M. P. Hobson and M. Bridges, Multinest: An efficient and robust bayesian inference tool for cosmology and particle physics, *Monthly Notices of the Royal Astronomical Society* **398**, p. 1601–1614 (Oct 2009).
26. F. Feroz, M. P. Hobson, E. Cameron and A. N. Pettitt, Importance nested sampling and the multinest algorithm, *The Open Journal of Astrophysics* **2** (Nov 2019).
27. J. Buchner, A. Georgakakis, K. Nandra, L. Hsu, C. Rangel, M. Brightman, A. Merloni, M. Salvato, J. Donley and D. Kocevski, X-ray spectral modelling of the AGN obscuring region in the CDFS: Bayesian model selection and catalogue, *Astron. Astrophys.* **564**, p. A125 (2014).

28. A. Lewis, GetDist: a Python package for analysing Monte Carlo samples (2019).
29. P. Collaboration, Planck 2018 results. v. cmb power spectra and likelihoods (2019).
30. H. Hildebrandt, M. Viola, C. Heymans, S. Joudaki, K. Kuijken, C. Blake, T. Erben, B. Joachimi, D. Klaes, L. Miller and et al., Kids-450: cosmological parameter constraints from tomographic weak gravitational lensing, *Monthly Notices of the Royal Astronomical Society* **465**, p. 1454–1498 (Nov 2016).
31. H. Akaike, A new look at the statistical model identification, *IEEE Transactions on Automatic Control* **19**, 716 (1974).

A tale of two double quasars: Hubble constant tension or biases?

L. J. Goicoechea* and V. N. Shalyapin[†]

GLENDAMA Project Core Team, Universidad de Cantabria,
Avda. de Los Castros 48, E-39005 Santander, Spain
gravlens.unican.es
* E-mail: goicol@unican.es
[†]*Main addresses: O.Ya. Usikov Institute for Radiophysics and Electronics,*
National Academy of Sciences of Ukraine,
12 Acad. Proscury St., UA-61085 Kharkiv, Ukraine
and
Institute of Astronomy of V.N. Karazin Kharkiv National University,
Svobody Sq. 4, UA-61022 Kharkiv, Ukraine

For a flat ΛCDM (standard) cosmology, a small sample of gravitationally lensed quasars with measured time delays has recently provided a value of the Hubble constant H_0 in tension with the *Planck* flat ΛCDM result. Trying to check if this tension is real or not, we used basic observational constraints for two double quasars of the GLENDAMA sample (SBS 0909+532 and SDSS J1339+1310) to discuss the underlying value of H_0 in a standard cosmology. For SBS 0909+532, we were not able to obtain a reliable measurement of H_0. However, the current data of SDSS J1339+1310 are consistent with H_0 around 67.8 km s^{-1} Mpc^{-1} and $\sigma(H_0)/H_0 \sim 10\%$. Although the formal uncertainty is still large and mainly due to the lack of details on the mass density profile of the main lens galaxy, the central value of H_0 coincides with that of the TDCOSMO+SLACS collaboration (using gravitational lens systems) and is within the 1σ interval from *Planck* cosmic microwave background data. After getting these preliminary encouraging results through only one double quasar, we are currently planning to use several GLENDAMA systems to accurately measure the Hubble constant and put constraints on other cosmological parameters.

Keywords: Gravitational lensing: strong; quasars: individual (SBS 0909+532, SDSS J1339+1310); cosmological parameters.

1. Introduction

Optical photometric monitoring of gravitationally lensed quasars (GLQs) brings plenty of astrophysical information.[1] For example, time delays between correlated brightness variations of their multiple images are used to estimate the current expansion rate of the Universe (the so-called Hubble constant H_0), provided lensing mass distributions can be constrained by observational data.[2,3] Throughout this paper, H_0 is expressed in standard units of km s^{-1} Mpc^{-1}, so units only are explicitly given in tables and figures.

Very recently, the H0LiCOW collaboration performed a joint analysis of six GLQs with measured time delays.[4] For a flat ΛCDM standard cosmology, they obtained $H_0 = 73.3^{+1.7}_{-1.8}$, in good agreement with $H_0 = 74.03 \pm 1.42$ from SNe data by the SH0ES collaboration,[5] but in apparent tension with Cosmic Microwave Background (CMB) data.[6] *Planck* observations of the CMB suggested a narrow 1σ interval ranging from 66.9 to 67.9, which is clearly inconsistent with H0LiCOW/SH0ES results. It is also worth noting that Freedman *et al.*[7] obtained an intermediate value of $H_0 = 69.8 \pm 1.9$.

The big question is whether the tension between early and late-Universe probes is due to systematic errors or has a physical origin. Possible systematic errors in some methods may fix this issue, avoiding hasty rejection of the standard cosmological model. Thus, we use two doubly imaged quasars of the Gravitational LENses and DArk MAtter (GLENDAMA) sample[8] to discuss the influence of observational constraints, and hypotheses and priors on the mass model in the estimation of the Hubble constant in a standard cosmology. Section 2 briefly presents the GLENDAMA project and the framework of time-delay cosmography through double quasars, while Sec. 3 and Sec. 4 include preliminary results for the GLQs SBS 0909+532 and SDSS J1339+1310, respectively. A discussion of results and future prospects appear in Sec. 5.

2. GLENDAMA project and H_0 from doubles

The GLENDAMA project[a] is aimed to accurately study a sample of ten GLQs in the Northern Hemisphere over a period of about 25 years, basically covering the first quarter of this century.[8] The sample includes seven double quasars with two images (A and B) each, and three quads having four images (A, B, C and D) each. Figure 1 shows the distribution on the sky of the selected, optically bright GLQs. The Gran Telescopio CANARIAS (GTC) is being used to obtain deep spectroscopy of the lens systems, while the optical variability of quasar images is traced from light curves mainly based on observations with the Liverpool Telescope (LT). These optical light curves are allowing us to measure the time delay Δt_{AB} in doubles, and three independent delays Δt_{AB}, Δt_{AC} and Δt_{AD} in quads (see results in Table 1). Current GLENDAMA delays have been estimated to a typical accuracy of about 5%, with only two exceptions: the relative error in the delay of QSO 0957+561 is well below 5%, and the three delays of the quad HE 1413+117 have larger relative uncertainties.

The time delay between the two images of a double quasar can be expressed in terms of the so-called time-delay distance $D_{\Delta t}$, the speed of light c and a dimensionless factor $\Delta\Phi_{AB}$, so that[3] $\Delta t_{AB} = (D_{\Delta t}/c)\Delta\Phi_{AB}$. Here, $D_{\Delta t}$ depends on the source (quasar) and deflector (main lens galaxy) redshifts, as well as cosmological parameters. Measuring the redshifts, and assuming a flat ΛCDM cosmological model with $\Omega_M = 0.3$ (matter density) and $\Omega_\Lambda = 0.7$ (dark energy density), $D_{\Delta t}/c$ is given as a known constant divided by H_0[b]. Additionally, $\Delta\Phi_{AB}$ depends on the position

---
[a]https://gravlens.unican.es/.
[b]The time-delay distance does not appreciably change when matter and dark energy densities are slightly different to 0.3 and 0.7, respectively.

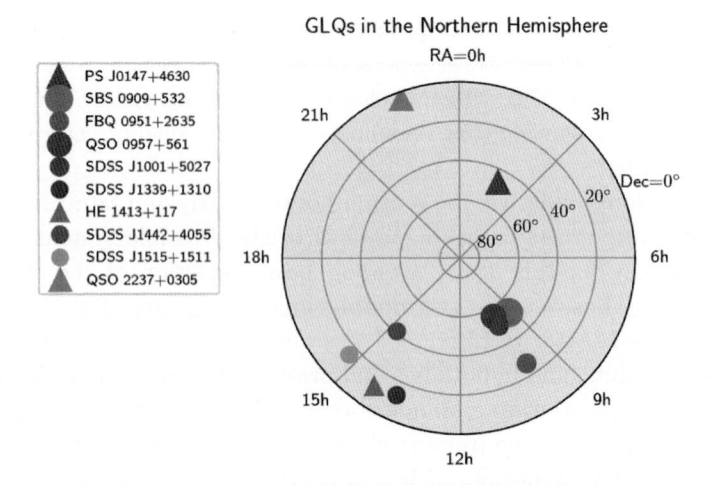

Fig. 1. GLENDAMA GLQs in the Northern Hemisphere. Triangles and circles represent quadruply and doubly imaged quasars, respectively. Larger symbols mean brighter quasars.

Table 1. GLENDAMA time delays from light curves in the SDSS r band.

GLQ	Δt_{AB} (days)	Δt_{AC} (days)	Δt_{AD} (days)	Reference
PS J0147+4630	pm	pm	pm	—
SBS 0909+532	50^{+2}_{-4}	—	—	Ref. 9
FBQ 0951+2635	pm	—	—	—
QSO 0957+561	420.6 ± 1.9	—	—	Ref. 10
SDSS J1339+1310	48 ± 2	—	—	Ref. 11
HE 1413+117	17 ± 3	20 ± 4	23 ± 4	Ref. 12
SDSS J1442+4055	25.0 ± 1.5	—	—	Ref. 13
SDSS J1515+1511	211 ± 5	—	—	Ref. 14

Note: pm = preliminary measure.

of both images and the source, and the lens potential at the image positions.[2,3] Hence, the lensing mass distribution determines the value of the multiplicative factor $\Delta\Phi_{AB}$.

We used a lens model to describe the primary lensing mass in SBS 0909+532 and SDSS J1339+1310. For each of these two double quasars, our lens model consisted of an elliptical surface mass density to account for the main lens galaxy G and an external shear γ due to the gravitational action of other galaxies around the lens system. The surface mass density of G was modeled as a singular power-law distribution since a composite model (treating baryons and dark matter individually) leads to similar results.[15,16] In this preliminar study, instead of using high-resolution imaging to put constraints on the power-law index of G, we focused on an isothermal distribution, i.e., a singular isothermal ellipsoid (SIE). Such distribution is consistent with stellar and gas motions in the Milky Way, as well as observations of many spiral and elliptical galaxies. We also did not use the stellar kinematics of G.[17]

We considered constraints on the time delay, the relative astrometry and the flux ratio between images, along with some observationally-motivated priors on SIE+γ lens model parameters. These constraints/priors and the LENSMODEL software[18] allowed us to simultaneously fit lens model parameters, position and flux of the source quasar, and $H_0^{\rm model}$ with dof = 0, where "dof" means degrees of freedom. In addition to the mass that is explicitly included in the lens model (main deflector plus external shear), we must take the mass along the line of sight to G into account. This additional effect can be approximated as an external convergence in the lens plane $\kappa_{\rm ext}$, which may be positive or negative depending on the mass distribution along the sightline. The true time-delay distance $D_{\Delta t}^{\rm true}$ relates to that derived from the lens model and measured delay $D_{\Delta t}^{\rm model}$ by $D_{\Delta t}^{\rm true} = D_{\Delta t}^{\rm model}/(1 - \kappa_{\rm ext})$ (e.g., see Eq. (4) of Ref. 4), which leads to $H_0^{\rm true} = H_0^{\rm model}(1 - \kappa_{\rm ext})$. Therefore, when accounting for an external convergence, the Hubble constant decreases/increases in a factor $1 - \kappa_{\rm ext}$. The two next sections deal with estimates of $H_0^{\rm model}$ from observations of SBS 0909+532 and SDSS J1339+1310.

3. SBS 0909+532

SBS 0909+532 is a doubly imaged quasar in which the background source (quasar) and the foreground early-type lens galaxy (main deflector) have redshifts $z_{\rm s} = 1.377$ and $z_{\rm d} = 0.830$, respectively.[19–21] Our first set of observational constraints consisted of the SBS 0909+532 time delay in Table 1 taking a symmetric uncertainty (50 ± 3 days)[c], the relative astrometry of B and G (their positions with respect to A at the origin of coordinates) and the flux of B in units such that the flux of A is equal to one. These last astro-photometric constraints were taken from the *HST* near-IR data in Table 3 of Ref. 22. We also considered priors on the ellipticity e and external shear of the SIE+γ lens model described in Sec. 2: $e \leq 0.5$ (see Table 3 of Ref. 23) and $\gamma \leq 0.1$ (see Table 4 of Ref. 22).

Although the data fit yielded a best solution for $H_0^{\rm model}$ of 68.4 (see Table 2), unfortunately, the *HST* relative astrometry of Lehár *et al.*[22] is not so good as would be desirable. For instance, the relative position of the faint lens galaxy G was determined with a large uncertainty of about 100 mas (1 mas = 0."001). The insufficiently accurate astrometric measures were responsible for a broad valley in the χ^2 curve (see the black solid line in Fig. 2), so the 1σ confidence interval for $H_0^{\rm model}$ included values below 55 and above 80. If we were able to improve the Lehár *et al.*'s astrometry, e.g., reducing errors in relative positions of B and G in factors 3 and 10, respectively, the best solution of $H_0^{\rm model}$ would be practically the same, but

---

[c]Despite 49 ± 3 days is fully consistent with the measurement in Table 1, initially we have preferred to keep its central value and divide the error bar into two identical halves.

Table 2. Results for H_0^{model} using a SIE+γ lens model (see main text).

GLQ	Δt_{AB}[a]	Observational constraints					Priors on model parameters			H_0^{model}	
		Δx_{AB}[b]	Δy_{AB}[b]	Δx_{AG}[b]	Δy_{AG}[b]	F_B/F_A[c]	e[d]	θ_e[d]	γ^e	best[f]	1σ[f]
SBS 0909+532	50 ± 3	−0.987 ± 0.003	−0.498 ± 0.003	−0.415 ± 0.100	−0.004 ± 0.100	0.89 ± 0.10	≤ 0.5	—	≤ 0.1	68.4	—
		−0.987 ± 0.001	−0.498 ± 0.001	−0.415 ± 0.010	−0.004 ± 0.010					68.3	68.5 ± 7.5[g]
		−0.9868 ± 0.0006	−0.4973 ± 0.0006	−0.464 ± 0.003	−0.055 ± 0.003	0.88 ± 0.10	0.11 ± 0.08	−48.1 ± 16.9	—	38.1	38.2 ± 3.3[h]
SDSS J1339+1310	47.0 ± 5.5	+1.419 ± 0.001	+0.939 ± 0.001	+0.981 ± 0.010	+0.485 ± 0.010	0.175 ± 0.015	≤ 0.5	—	≤ 0.1	47.5	—
	48 ± 2						0.18 ± 0.05	32 ± 10	—	69.1	69^{+10}_{-8}[i]
										67.6	67.8 ± 4.4

Note:
[a]Time delay between both images in days. Some errors have been made symmetric.
[b]Relative positions of B and G with respect to A at the origin of coordinates. Here, Δx and Δy are given in arc seconds, and their positive directions are defined by west and north, respectively. For SBS 0909+532, some errors have been conveniently approximated.
[c]Flux ratio. For SBS 0909+532, errors are enlarged to 10% to account for moderate microlensing effects.
[d]Ellipticity and position angle of the SIE. The position angle (θ_e) is measured east of north.
[e]External shear strength.
[f]Best solution and 1σ confidence interval for H_0^{model}. We use standard units of km s^{-1} Mpc^{-1}.
[g]Plausible but not real measurement. Astrometric errors have been reduced to "achievable" values (see next row).
[h]Real measurement, but based on a biased astrometry or an inappropriate (strongly affected by microlensing) flux ratio.
[i]Measurement relying on an old, innacurate time delay.

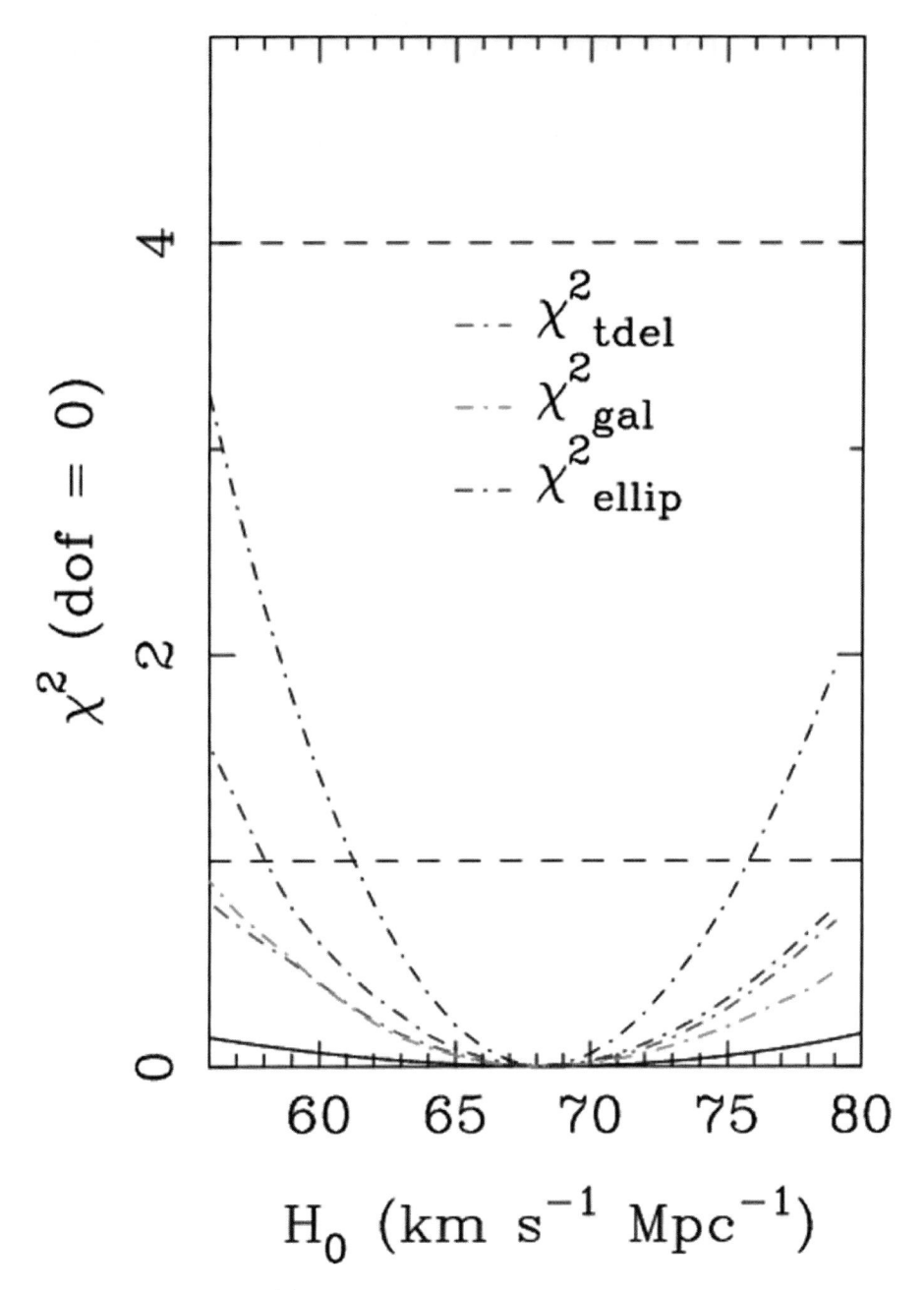

Fig. 2. Estimation of H_0^{model} from the SBS 0909+532 time delay and the astro-photometric constraints of Lehár et al.[22] We also used observationally-motivated priors on the ellipticity of the lens galaxy and the external shear. We show the χ^2 curve (black solid line) along with its 1σ and 2σ maximum thresholds (horizontal dashed lines). The black dashed-dotted line corresponds to an "improved" astrometry (see main text), with blue, green and red dashed-dotted lines describing some contributions to the total χ^2.

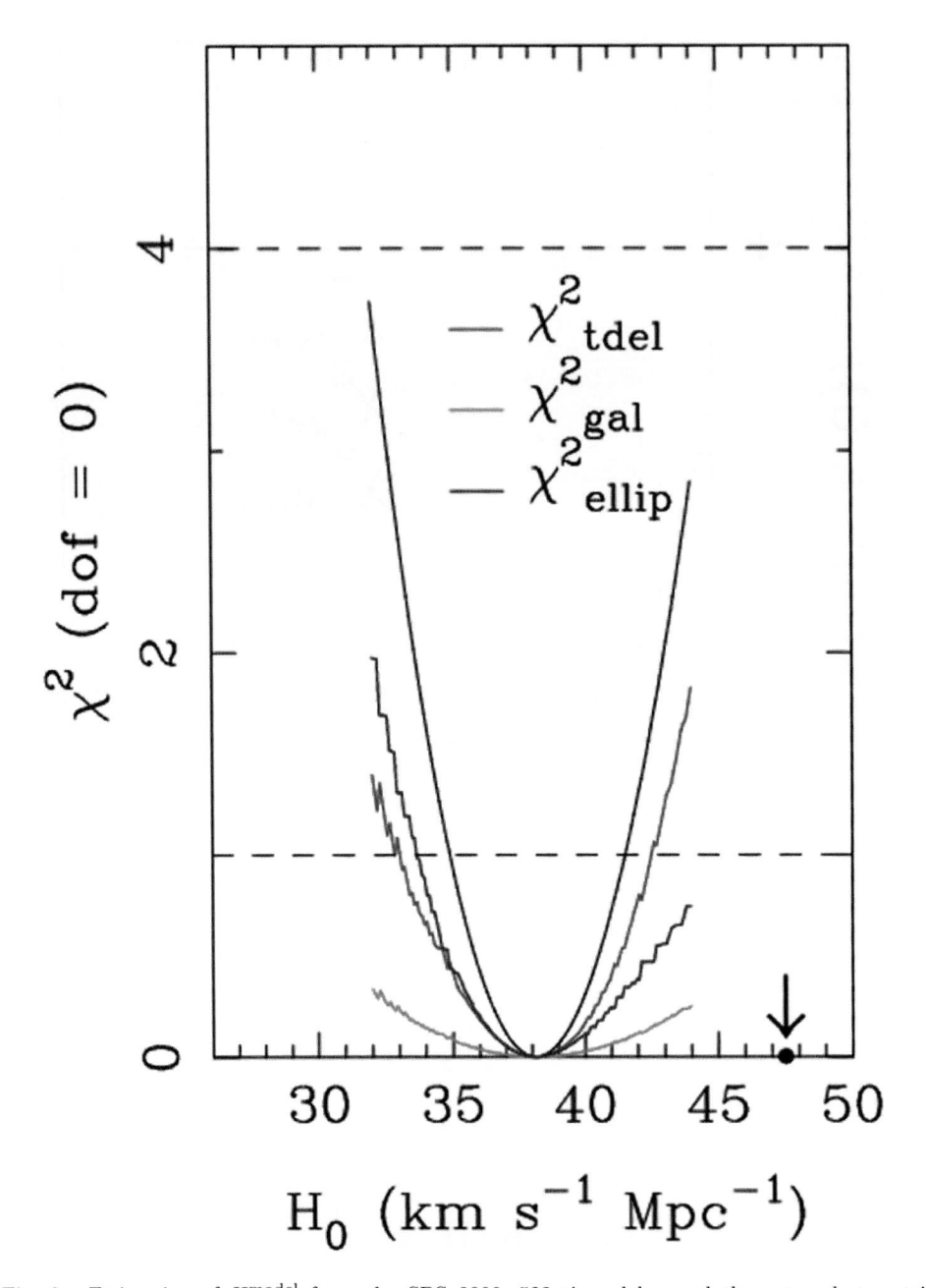

Fig. 3. Estimation of H_0^{model} from the SBS 0909+532 time delay and the astro-photometric constraints of Sluse et al.[23] The solid lines are related to priors on the shape of the lens galaxy (ellipticity and position angle; the black solid line represents the total χ^2), while the black dot and vertical arrow indicate the best solution when using priors on the ellipticity and the external shear.

its uncertainty would be dramatically decreased to about 10%. Using "achievable" uncertainties of 1 mas in B and 10 mas in G, we obtained the black dashed-dotted line in Fig. 2 and $H_0^{\text{model}} = 68.5 \pm 7.5$.

In addition to new observations of the lens system, a reanalysis of the available HST frames of SBS 0909+532 might produce a better astrometry for the system, and thus provide an accurate measure of the Hubble constant. This is a promising task that we and other astronomers are exploring. Sluse et al.[23] have reanalysed the available HST near-IR frames, obtaining a formally improved astrometry and even details on the structure of G. The error in the relative position of G was only 3 mas; about 30–40 times smaller than the uncertainty derived by Lehár et al. We also considered these new constraints to measure H_0^{model}. Using the SBS 0909+532 time delay with symmetric error (see above) and the astro-photometric solutions in Table 4 of Sluse et al., along with the ellipticity and position angle of G in Table 3 of Sluse et al. (priors on the SIE+γ lens model), we found $H_0^{\text{model}} = 38.2 \pm 3.3$ (see Table 2 and the black solid line in Fig. 3). Even the 2σ confidence interval only includes values below 45. Although a moderate increase in the best solution of H_0^{model} is found when taking the previous priors $e \leq 0.5$ and $\gamma \leq 0.1$ (see the black dot and vertical arrow in Fig. 3), the Sluse et al.'s relative astrometry leads to best solutions below 50. Hence, either such astrometry is biased or the near-IR fluxes of the quasar images (optical emission) are strongly affected by microlensing in the lens galaxy.[24]

4. SDSS J1339+1310

The gravitational lens system SDSS J1339+1310 was discovered by Inada et al.[25] It consists of two quasar images (A and B) at $z_s = 2.231$ and an early-type galaxy G at $z_d = 0.607$ acting as main deflector.[26] The first set of observational constraints included the relative astrometry of B and G in the last column of Table 1 of Ref. 27, the macrolens magnification ratio from narrow-line/line-core flux ratios and a standard extinction law (based on emission lines in GTC spectra),[26] and an old time delay from LT light curves.[26] We note that the first time delay we used (47.0 ± 5.5 days) is more inaccurate than the updated delay in Table 1. Additionally, we have taken the ellipticity and position angle of G in the last column of Table 1 of Shalyapin et al.[27] as priors on the SIE+γ lens model. The data fit led to an 1σ confidence interval $H_0^{\text{model}} = 69^{+10}_{-8}$ (accuracy of ~13%; see Table 2 and the black line in Fig. 4). The observational constraint on the time delay is the primary contribution to the χ^2 curve (see the red line in Fig. 4), while other constraints/priors (e.g., the position of G; see the green line in Fig. 4) play a secondary role.

Results in Fig. 4 suggest that a tighter constraint on the time delay would produce a more accurate determination of the Hubble constant. Therefore, in a second approach, we used the updated time delay with a 4% error that appears in Table 1 to more accurate estimate H_0^{model}. The new χ^2 curve in Fig. 5(a) indicates that $H_0^{\text{model}} = 67.8 \pm 4.4$ (see also Table 2). This is a quite robust measurement of

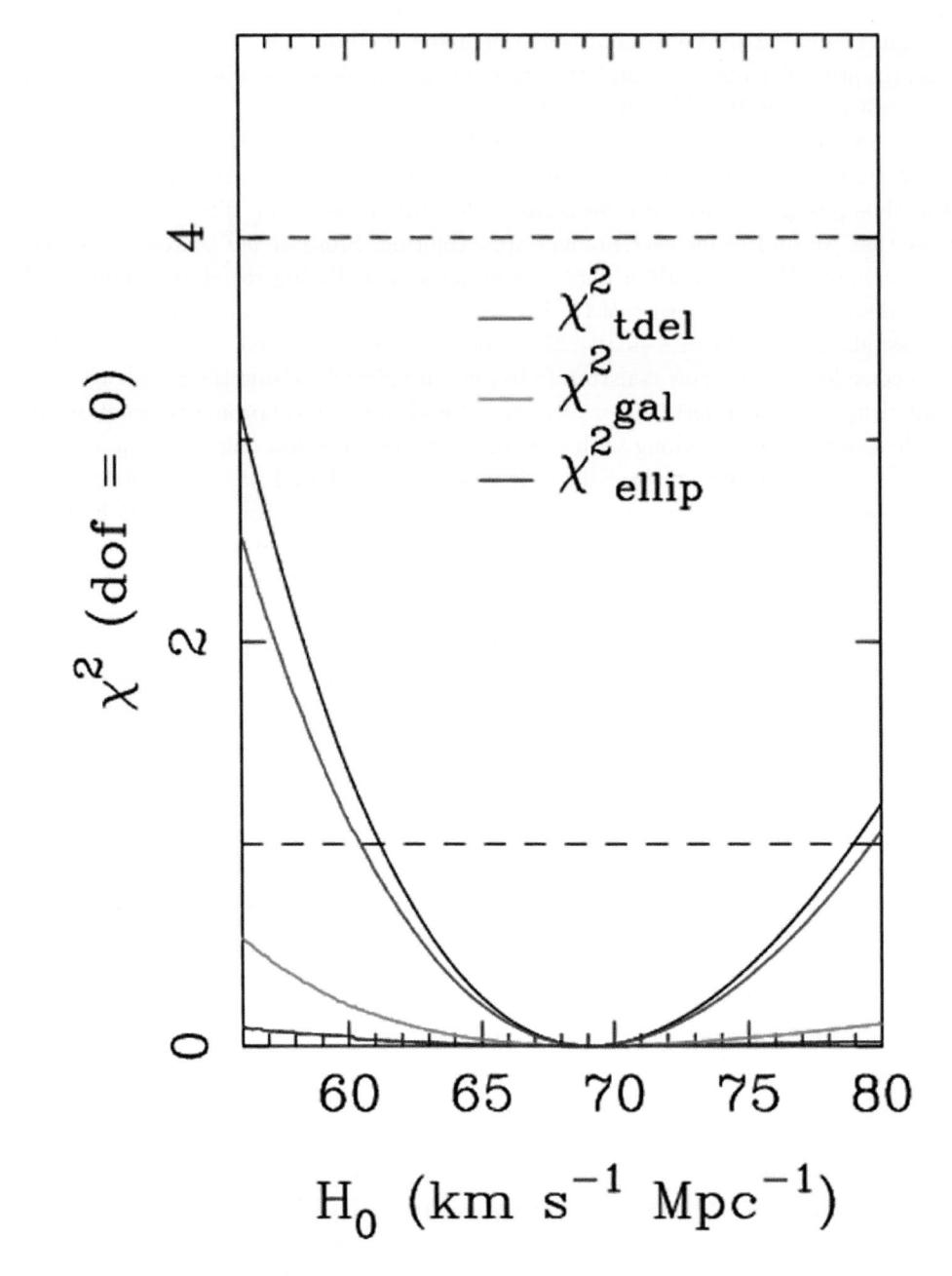

Fig. 4. Estimation of $H_0^{\rm model}$ from an old time delay of SDSS J1339+1310 with an accuracy of ∼12% and constraints/priors from results in Refs. 26 and 27. The black line represents the total χ^2, while the blue, green and red lines describe three different contributions to the total curve. The 1σ and 2σ maximum thresholds are also depicted (horizontal dashed lines).

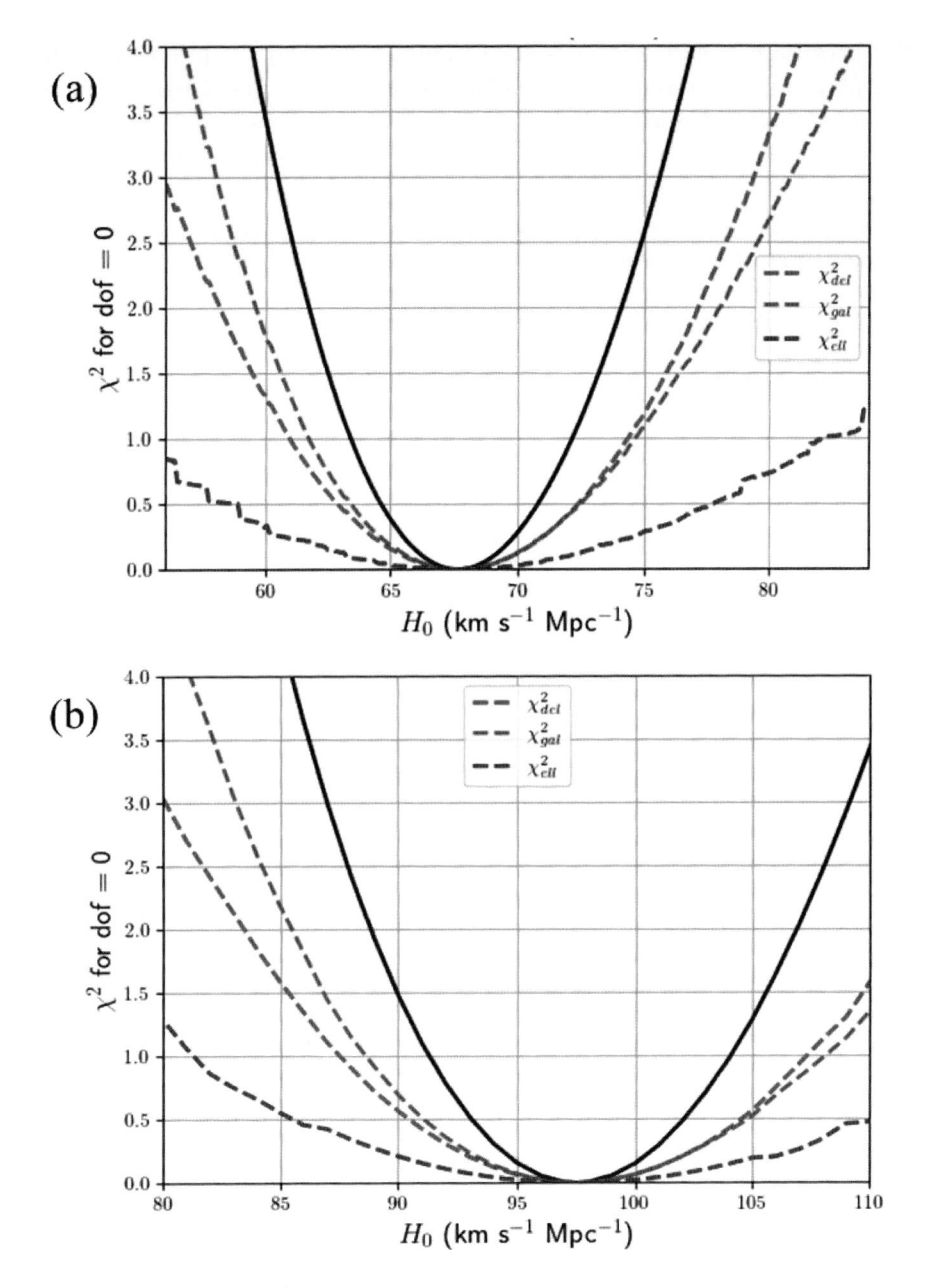

Fig. 5. Estimation of H_0^{model} from the updated time delay of SDSS J1339+1310 with an accuracy of ~4% and constraints/priors from results in Refs. 26 and 27. (a) SIE+γ lens model. (b) DV+γ lens model. To obtain the χ^2 curve in this bottom panel, we have assumed that light traces mass of the main lens galaxy (see main text).

H_0^{model} because its relative error is small (only 6.5%), and the priors on e and θ_e do not play a relevant role (see the blue dashed line in Fig. 5(a)). In addition, the macrolens magnification ratio is not affected by microlensing/extinction effects, and only one major issue must be addressed: the hypothesis about an isothermal mass distribution for G. Using 58 gravitational lens systems from the SLACS Survey, Koopmans et al.[28] concluded that massive early-type galaxies have close to isothermal total density profiles, with a scatter between their logarithmic density slopes below 10%. For a particular lens galaxy, a small deviation from the isothermal power-law index is plausible, and this potential deviation can be taken into account by increasing the error in H_0^{model} (see a more complete discussion in Sec. 5).

It is easy to demonstrate the need for dark matter (e.g., a power-law mass distribution) and the fact that a model in which light traces mass produces biased results. To this end, we again considered the updated time delay in Table 1 and added a new prior, i.e., we worked with three priors instead two. Assuming that light traces mass of G, i.e., a de Vaucouleurs (DV) mass distribution instead a singular isothermal one, in a self-consistent way, the optical structure of G in the last column of Table 1 of Ref. 27 (effective radius, ellipticity and position angle) was used to describe the structure of its mass. This scheme led to a biased H_0^{model} value of about 100 (97.7 ± 6.4; see Fig. 5(b)). Even the 2σ lower limit is above 85.

5. Discussion and future prospects

Using two double quasars of the GLENDAMA sample (see Fig. 1), we focused on the role that some observational constraints and hypotheses/priors on the mass model play in estimating H_0^{model} in a standard cosmology. The main lens galaxies in SBS 0909+532 and SDSS J1339+1310 were modelled with a singular isothermal ellipsoid, in agreement with observations in the Milky Way and SLACS Survey results for massive early-type galaxies acting as gravitational lenses.[28] Adding the external shear γ that is caused by galaxies around a lens system, we initially considered a SIE+γ lens (mass) model.

For SBS 0909+532, there are two different astrometric solutions based on the same *HST* near-IR data. While the Lehár et al.'s solution[22] led to a best value of H_0^{model} equal to 68.4 and a broad 1σ interval for this parameter, the Sluse et al.'s solution[23] provided an 8.6% measurement of H_0^{model} around a central value of 38.2 (we derived biased results making different choices of priors). Assuming that the time delay and flux ratio between quasar images that we used are right, the last astrometry would be biased. However, the observed near-IR fluxes correspond to optical emission from the quasar accretion disk, so they could be strongly affected by microlenses (stars) in the main lens galaxy.[24] Hence, an accurate and reliable astrometric solution along with a detailed analysis of the macrolens magnification ratio (flux ratio free from extinction and microlensing effects) is required before robustly measuring H_0^{model} for a SIE+γ scenario.

Results for SDSS J1339+1310 are really encouraging because its current astrometry, updated time delay and macrolens magnification ratio through GTC spectra allowed us to accurately measure H_0^{model} (67.8 ± 4.4), with priors on the ellipticity and position angle of the SIE not playing a relevant role. It is also noteworthy that our 1σ interval is not in tension with other recent estimates from GLQs[4] and the CMB[6] (see also Ref. 7), and the central value practically coincides with the upper limit of the *Planck* collaboration. Accounting for a potential microlensing effect on the time delay[29] (∼1 day) would only modify H_0^{model} by ∼2%. Additionally, the use of a main galaxy mass model with an unrealistic density profile may have a significant impact on H_0^{model} and be responsible for an error of about 10%.[30–32] At present, we do not know details about the mass density profile of the main deflector in SDSS J1339+1310, and thus we should adopt an uncertainty in H_0^{model} greater than that obtained with a SIE. Very recently, assuming that the deflectors of the H0LiCOW GLQs and the SLACS lenses share the same mass density properties, Birrer *et al.*[33] have obtained $H_0 = 67.4^{+4.1}_{-3.2}$. This new GLQ-based result is in excellent agreement with ours and the CMB-based estimation of H_0, notably reduces tension between early and late-Universe probes, and illustrates the importance of assumptions on mass distributions.

Future time-domain observations of large collections of GLQs will lead to robust constraints on H_0, and the matter and dark energy components of the Universe.[3] The GLENDAMA project includes the first initiative to robotically monitor a small sample of 10 GLQs for about 20 years.[8] This project and the associated robotic monitoring with the LT will end in 2025, after providing accurate time delays for several GLQs and discussing their cosmological implications. In next few years, other ongoing monitoring projects will also measure accurate delays for small/medium samples of GLQs (see the paper by Geoff Chih-Fan Chen in these proceedings), which will contribute to a rich database of tens of measured delays. Despite this optimistic perspective about time-domain results, some issues must be fixed before sheding light on unbiased values of cosmological parameters from such delay database. Deep spectroscopy, high-resolution imaging and other complementary observations will be required. For example, unaccounted mass along GLQ sightlines may produce overestimated/underestimated values of H_0 (see the end of Sec. 2), so accurate H_0 estimates cannot ignore external convergences. Here, although we ignored the external convergence for SDSS J1339+1310, the unaccounted mass is expected to translate to a few percent relative uncertainty in H_0,[33,34] noticeably less than that related to the mass density profile of G (see above).

Acknowledgments

We thank the organizers of Sixteenth Marcel Grossmann Meeting for planning a very interesting event and allowing us to give a talk in the parallel session "Cosmography with Gravitational Lensing". We also thank the chairs of such parallel session for creating a pleasant environment. We acknowledge Claudio Grillo, Mimoza Hafizi and Sherry Suyu for helpful comments that have significantly contributed to prepare the final text of this contribution. Among other things, the Gravitational LENses and DArk MAtter (GLENDAMA) project aims to construct accurate optical light curves of SBS 0909+532 and SDSS J1339+1310, and measure robust time delays for both systems. Although these optical variability studies mainly rely on observations with the Liverpool Telescope (LT), we are particularly grateful to our collaborators working in several institutions, who provide us with complementary data from the Maidanak Astronomical Observatory and the US Naval Observatory, and participate actively in the project development. The LT is operated on the island of La Palma by the Liverpool John Moores University (with financial support from the UK Science and Technology Facilities Council), in the Spanish Observatorio del Roque de los Muchachos of the Instituto de Astrofísica de Canarias. We thank the staff of the telescope for a kind interaction before, during and after the observations. This research has been supported by the grant AYA2017-89815-P funded by MCIN/AEI/10.13039/501100011033 and by "ERDF A way of making Europe", and the grant PID2020-118990GB-I00 funded by MCIN/AEI/10.13039/501100011033.

References

1. P. Schneider, C. S. Kochanek and J. Wambsganss, *Gravitational Lensing: Strong, Weak and Micro* (Springer-Verlag, Berlin, 2006).
2. N. Jackson, The Hubble constant, *Living Rev. Relativ.* **18**, 2 (2015), https://doi.org/10.1007/lrr-2015-2.
3. T. Treu and P. J. Marshall, Time delay cosmography, *Astron. Astrophys. Rev.* **24**, 11 (2016).
4. K. C. Wong, S. H. Suyu, G. C.-F. Chen et al., H0LiCOW XIII. A 2.4% measurement of H_0 from lensed quasars: 5.3σ tension between early and late-Universe probes, *Mon. Notices Royal Astron. Soc.* **498**, 1420 (2020).
5. A. G. Riess, S. Casertano, W. Yuan, L. M. Macri and D. Scolnic, Large Magellanic Cloud cepheid standards provide a 1% foundation for the determination of the Hubble constant and stronger evidence for physics beyond ΛCDM, *Astrophys. J.* **876**, 85 (2019).
6. Planck Collaboration, *Planck* 2018 results. VI. Cosmological parameters, *Astron. Astrophys.* **641**, 6 (2020).
7. W. L. Freedman, B. F. Madore, D. Hatt et al., The Carnegie-Chicago Hubble program. VIII. An independent determination of the Hubble constant based on the tip of the red giant branch, *Astrophys. J.* **882**, 34 (2019).
8. R. Gil-Merino, L. J. Goicoechea, V. N. Shalyapin and A. Oscoz, New database for a sample of optically bright lensed quasars in the northern hemisphere, *Astron. Astrophys.* **616**, 118 (2018).
9. L. J. Hainline, C. W. Morgan, C. L. MacLeod et al., Time delay and accretion disk size measurements in the lensed quasar SBS 0909+532 from multiwavelength microlensing analysis, *Astrophys. J.* **774**, 69 (2013).
10. V. N. Shalyapin, L. J. Goicoechea and R. Gil-Merino, A 5.5-year robotic optical monitoring of Q0957+561: substructure in a non-local cD galaxy, *Astron. Astrophys.* **540**, 132 (2012).

11. V. N. Shalyapin, L. J. Goicoechea, C. W. Morgan, M. A. Cornachione and A. V. Sergeyev, Resolving the inner accretion flow towards the central supermassive black hole in SDSS J1339+1310, *Astron. Astrophys.* **646**, 165 (2021).
12. L. J. Goicoechea and V. N. Shalyapin, Time delays in the gravitationally lensed quasar H1413+117 (Cloverleaf), *Astrophys. J.* **708**, 995 (2010).
13. V. N. Shalyapin and L. J. Goicoechea, Gravitationally lensed quasar SDSS J1442+4055: redshifts of lensing galaxies, time delay, microlensing variability, and intervening metal system at z $\sim$ 2, *Astrophys. J.* **873**, 117 (2019).
14. V. N. Shalyapin and L. J. Goicoechea, Doubly imaged quasar SDSS J1515+1511: Time delay and lensing galaxies, *Astrophys. J.* **836**, 14 (2017).
15. S. H. Suyu, T. Treu, S. Hilbert et al., Cosmology from gravitational lens time delays and *Planck* data, *Astrophys. J.* **788**, L35 (2014).
16. M. Millon, A. Galan, F. Courbin et al., TDCOSMO. I. An exploration of systematic uncertainties in the inference of H0 from time-delay cosmography, *Astron. Astrophys.* **639**, 101 (2020).
17. D. Paraficz and J. Hjorth, Gravitational lenses as cosmic rulers: Ω_m, Ω_Λ from time delays and velocity dispersions, *Astron. Astrophys.* **507**, L49 (2009).
18. C. R. Keeton, Computational methods for gravitational lensing, https://arxiv.org/pdf/astro-ph/0102340.pdf (2001).
19. C. S. Kochanek, E. E. Falco, R. Schild et al., SBS 0909+532: A new double gravitational lens or binary quasar?, *Astrophys. J.* **479**, 678 (1997).
20. A. Oscoz, M. Serra-Ricart, E. Mediavilla, J. Buitrago and L. J. Goicoechea, Support for the gravitational lens interpretation of SBS 0909+532, *Astrophys. J.* **491**, L7 (1997).
21. L. M. Lubin, C. D. Fassnacht, A. C. S. Readhead, R. D. Blandford and T. Kundić, A Keck survey of gravitational lens systems. I. Spectroscopy of SBS 0909+532, HST 1411+5211, and CLASS B2319+051, *Astron. J.* **119**, 451 (2000).
22. J. Lehár, E. E. Falco, C. S. Kochanek et al., *Hubble Space Telescope* observations of 10 two-image gravitational lenses, *Astrophys. J.* **536**, 584 (2000).
23. D. Sluse, V. Chantry, P. Magain, F. Courbin and G. Meylan, COSMOGRAIL: the COSmological MOnitoring of GRAvItational Lenses. X. Modeling based on high-precision astrometry of a sample of 25 lensed quasars: consequences for ellipticity, shear, and astrometric anomalies, *Astron. Astrophys.* **538**, 99 (2012).
24. E. Mediavilla, J. A. Muñoz, C. S. Kochanek et al., The first precise determination of an optical-far-ultraviolet extinction curve beyond the Local Group ($z = 0.83$), *Astrophys. J.* **619**, 749 (2005).
25. N. Inada, M. Oguri, M. Shin et al., Five new high-redshift quasar lenses from the Sloan Digital Sky Survey, *Astron. J.* **137**, 4118 (2009).
26. L. J. Goicoechea and V. N. Shalyapin, Gravitational lens system SDSS J1339+1310: microlensing factory and time delay, *Astron. Astrophys.* **596**, 77 (2016).
27. V. N. Shalyapin and L. J. Goicoechea, Deep optical imaging and spectroscopy of the lens system SDSS J1339+1310, *Astron. Astrophys.* **568**, 116 (2014).
28. L. V. E. Koopmans, A. Bolton, T. Treu et al., The structure and dynamics of massive early-type galaxies: on homology, isothermality, and isotropy inside one effective radius, *Astrophys. J.* **703**, L51 (2009).
29. S. S. Tie and C. S. Kochanek, Microlensing makes lensed quasar time delays significantly time variable, *Mon. Notices Royal Astron. Soc.* **473**, 80 (2018).
30. P. Schneider and D. Sluse, Mass-sheet degeneracy, power-law models and external convergence: Impact on the determination of the Hubble constant from gravitational lensing, *Astron. Astrophys.* **559**, 37 (2013).

31. C. S. Kochanek, Overconstrained gravitational lens models and the Hubble constant, *Mon. Notices Royal Astron. Soc.* **493**, 1725 (2020).
32. H. R. Stacey, C. M. O'Riordan, S. Vegetti *et al.*, The inner density profile of an elliptical galaxy at $z = 1.15$ from gravitational lensing, submitted to *Mon. Notices Royal Astron. Soc.*, https://arxiv.org/pdf/2109.10929.pdf (2021).
33. S. Birrer, A. J. Shajib, A. Galan *et al.*, TDCOSMO IV: Hierarchical time-delay cosmography - joint inference of the Hubble constant and galaxy density profiles, *Astron. Astrophys.* **643**, 165 (2020).
34. C. E. Rusu, C. D. Fassnacht, D. Sluse *et al.*, H0LiCOW – III. Quantifying the effect of mass along the line of sight to the gravitational lens HE 0435−1223 through weighted galaxy counts, *Mon. Notices Royal Astron. Soc.* **467**, 4220 (2017).

Dark energy and dark matter unification from dynamical space time: BBN constraints

D. Benisty

DAMTP, Centre for Mathematical Sciences, University of Cambridge, Wilberforce Road, Cambridge CB3 0WA, United Kingdom
Institute of Astronomy, University of Cambridge, Madingley Road, Cambridge, CB3 0HA, UK
E-mail: benidav@post.bgu.ac.il

A unification of dark matter and dark energy based on a dynamical space time theory is suggested. By introducing a dynamical space time vector field χ_μ as a Lagrange multiplier, a conservation of an energy momentum tensor $T^{\mu\nu}_{(\chi)}$ is implemented. This Lagrangian generalizes the Unified dark energy and dark matter from a scalar field different from quintessence which did not consider a Lagrangian formulation. This generalization allows the solutions which were found previously, but in addition to that also non singular bouncing solutions that rapidly approach to the ΛCDM model. The BBN constraint is also studied.

Keywords: Dark Matter; Dark Energy

1. Introduction

Dark energy and Dark matter constitute most of the observable Universe. Yet the true nature of these two phenomena is still a mystery. One fundamental question with respect to those phenomena is the coincidence problem which is trying to explain the relation between dark energy and dark matter densities. In order to solve this problem, one approach claims that the dark energy is a dynamical entity and hope to exploit solutions of scaling or tracking type to remove dependence on initial conditions. Others left this principle and tried to model the dark energy as a phenomenological fluid which exhibits a particular relation with the scale factor,[1] Hubble constant[2] or even even the cosmic time itself.[3]

Unifications between dark energy and dark matter from an action principle were obtained from K-essence type actions,[4] or by introducing a complex scalar field.[5] Beyond those approaches, a unified description of Dark Energy and Dark Matter using a new measure of integration has been formulated.[6,7] Also a diffusive interacting of dark energy and dark matter models was introduced in[8,9] and it has been found that diffusive interacting dark energy — dark matter models can be formulated in the context of an action principle based on a generalization of those Two Measures Theories in the context of quintessential scalar fields,[10,11] although these models are not equivalent to the previous diffusive interacting dark energy — dark matter models.[8,9]

A model for a unification of dark energy and dark matter from a single scalar field ϕ, was suggested by Gao, Kunz, Liddle and Parkinson.[12] Their model is close to traditional quintessence, and gives dynamical dark energy and dark matter, but introduces a modification of the equations of motion of the scalar field that apparently are impossible to formulate in the framework of an action principle. The basic stress energy tensor which was considered in addition to Einstein equation was:

$$T^{\mu\nu} = -\frac{1}{2}\phi^{,\mu}\phi^{,\nu} + U(\phi)g^{\mu\nu} \qquad (1)$$

where ϕ is a scalar field and $U(\phi)$ is the potential for that scalar. Assuming homogeneous and isotropic behavior the scalar field should be only time dependent $\phi = \phi(t)$. Then the kinetic term $-\frac{1}{2}\phi^{,\mu}\phi^{,\nu}$ is parameterzing the dark matter because it contains only energy density with no pressure and $U(\phi)g^{\mu\nu}$ is parameterzing the dark energy. The basic requirement for this stress energy tensor is it's conservation law $\nabla_\mu T^{\mu\nu} = 0$. By assuming a constant potential $U(\phi) = \mathbf{Const}$ the model provides from the potential the traditional cosmological constant and the kinetic term of the scalar field is shown to provide, from the conservation law of the energy momentum tensor, that the kinetic term dependence has a dust like behavior.

$$-\frac{1}{2}\nabla_\mu(\phi^{,\mu}\phi^{,\nu}) = 0 \quad \Rightarrow \quad \dot{\phi}^2 \sim \frac{1}{a^3} \qquad (2)$$

This simple case refers to the classical ΛCDM model. The special advantage of this model is a unification of dark energy and dark matter from one scalar field and has an interesting possibility for exploring the coincidence problem.

The lack of an action principle for this model brought us to reformulate the unification between dark energy and dark matter idea put forward by Gao, Kunz, Liddle and Parkinson[12] in the framework of a Dynamical Space Time Theory[13,14] which forces a conservation of energy momentum tensor in addition to the covariant conservation of the stress energy momentum tensor that appears in Einstein equation. In the next chapter we explore the equations of motion for these theories. In the third chapter we solve analytically the theory for constant potentials which reproduce the ΛCDM model with a bounce, which gives a possibility to solve the initial big bang singularity. In the last chapter we solve the theory for an exponential potential which gives a good possibility for solving the coincidence problem.

2. Dynamical Space Time Theory

2.1. A basic formulation

One from the basic fatures in the standard approach to theories of gravity is the local conservation of an energy momentum tensor. In the field theory case it's derived as a result rather than a starting point. For example, the conservation of energy can be derived from the time translation invariance principle. The local conservation of an energy momentum tensor can be a starting point rather than a derived result. Let's consider a 4 dimensional case where a conservation of a symmetric energy momentum tensor $T^{\mu\nu}_{(x)}$ is imposed by introducing the term in the action:

$$\mathcal{S}_{(\chi)} = \int d^4x \sqrt{-g}\chi_{\mu;\nu}T^{\mu\nu}_{(x)} \tag{3}$$

where $\chi_{\mu;\nu} = \partial_\nu \chi_\mu - \Gamma^\lambda_{\mu\nu}\chi_\lambda$. The vector field χ_μ called a dynamical space time vector, because of the energy density of $T^{\mu\nu}_{(x)}$ is a canonically conjugated variable to χ_0, which is what we expected from a dynamical time:

$$\pi_{\chi_0} = \frac{\partial \mathcal{L}}{\partial \dot\chi^0} = T^0_0(\chi) \tag{4}$$

If $T^{\mu\nu}_{(x)}$ is being independent of χ_μ and having $\Gamma^\lambda_{\mu\nu}$ being defined as the Christoffel connection coefficients (the second order Formalism), then the variation with respect to χ_μ gives a covariant conservation law:

$$\nabla_\mu T^{\mu\nu}_{(x)} = 0 \tag{5}$$

From the variation of the action with respect to the metric, we get a conserved stress energy tensor $G^{\mu\nu}$ (in appropriate units), which is well known from Einstein equation:

$$G^{\mu\nu} = \frac{2}{\sqrt{-g}} \frac{\delta \sqrt{-g}}{\delta g^{\mu\nu}}[\mathcal{L}_\chi + \mathcal{L}_m], \quad \nabla_\mu G^{\mu\nu} = 0 \tag{6}$$

where $G^{\mu\nu}$ is Einstein tensor, $\mathcal{L}_\chi$ is the Lagrangian in (3) and $\mathcal{L}_m$ is an optional action that involve other contributions.

Some basic symmetries that holds for the dynamical space time theory are two independent shift symmetries:

$$\chi_\mu \to \chi_\mu + k_\mu, \quad T^{\mu\nu}_{(x)} \to T^{\mu\nu}_{(x)} + \Lambda g^{\mu\nu} \tag{7}$$

where Λ is some arbitrary constant and k_μ is a Killing vector of the solution. This transformation will not change the equations of motions, which means also that the process of redefinition of the energy momentum tensor in the action (3) will not change the equations of motion. Of course such type of redefinition of the energy momentum tensor is exactly what is done in the process of normal ordering in Quantum Field Theory for instance.

2.2. A connection to modified measures

A particular case of the stress energy tensor with the form $T^{\mu\nu}_{(x)} = \mathcal{L}_1 g^{\mu\nu}$ corresponds to a modified measure theory. By substituting this stress energy tensor into the action itself, the determinant of the metric is canceled:

$$\sqrt{-g}\chi^\mu_{;\mu}\mathcal{L}_1 = \partial_\mu(\sqrt{-g}\chi^\mu)\mathcal{L}_1 = \Phi\mathcal{L}_1 \tag{8}$$

where $\Phi = \partial_\mu(\sqrt{-g}\chi^\mu)$ is like a "modified measure". A variation with respect to the dynamical time vector field will give a constraint on $\mathcal{L}_1$ to be a constant:

$$\partial_\alpha \mathcal{L}_1 = 0 \quad \Rightarrow \quad \mathcal{L}_1 = M = Const \tag{9}$$

This situation corresponds to the "Two Measures Theory"[15,16] where in addition to the regular measure of integration in the action $\sqrt{-g}$ includes another measure of integration which is also a density and a total derivative. Notable effects that can be obtained in this way are the spontaneous breaking of the scale invariance, the see saw cosmological effects,[15] the resolution of the 5th force problem in quintessential cosmology[17] and a unified picture of both inflation and of slowly accelerated expansion of the present universe.[18,19] As we mentioned before in the introduction Two Measure Theory can serve to build unified models of dark energy and dark matter.

Usually the construction of this measure is from 4 scalar fields φ_a, where $a = 1, 2, 3, 4$.

$$\Phi = \frac{1}{4!}\varepsilon^{\alpha\beta\gamma\delta}\varepsilon_{abcd}\partial_\alpha\varphi^{(a)}\partial_\beta\varphi^{(b)}\partial_\gamma\varphi^{(c)}\partial_\delta\varphi^{(d)} \tag{10}$$

and then we can rewrite an action that uses both of these densities:

$$S = \int d^4x \Phi \mathcal{L}_1 + \int d^4x \sqrt{-g}\mathcal{L}_2. \tag{11}$$

As a consequence of the variation with respect to the scalar fields φ_a, assuming that $\mathcal{L}_1$ and $\mathcal{L}_2$ are independent of the scalar fields φ_a, we obtain that for $\Phi \neq 0$ it implies that $\mathcal{L}_1 = M = const$ as in the dynamical time theory with the case of (9).

3. DE-DM Unified Theory from Dynamical Space-Time

A suggestion of an action which can produce DE-DM unification takes the form:

$$\mathcal{L} = -\frac{1}{2}R + \chi_{\mu;\nu}T^{\mu\nu}_{(x)} - \frac{1}{2}g^{\alpha\beta}\phi_{,\alpha}\phi_{,\beta} - V(\phi) \tag{12}$$

Consisting of an Einstein Hilbert action ($8\pi G = 1$), quintessence and Dynamical space-time action, when the original stress energy tensor $T^{\mu\nu}_{(x)}$ is the same as the stress energy tensor (1) Gao and colleagues used:

$$T^{\mu\nu}_{(x)} = -\frac{1}{2}\phi^{,\mu}\phi^{,\nu} + U(\phi)g^{\mu\nu} \tag{13}$$

The action depends on three different variables: the scalar field ϕ, the dynamical space time vector χ_μ and the metric $g_{\mu\nu}$. Therefore there are 3 sets in for the equation of motions. For the solution we assume homogeneity and isotropy, therefore we solve our theory with a FLRW metric:

$$ds^2 = -dt^2 + a(t)^2\left(\frac{dr^2}{1-Kr^2} + r^2 d\Omega^2\right) \tag{14}$$

According to this ansatz, the scalar field is just a function of time $\phi(t)$ and the dynamical vector field will be taken only with a time component $\chi_\mu = (\chi_0, 0, 0, 0)$, where χ_0 is also just a function of time. A variation with respect to the dynamical space time vector field χ_μ will force a conservation of the original stress energy tensor, which in FRWM gives the relation:

$$\ddot\phi + \frac{3}{2}\mathcal{H}\dot\phi + U'(\phi) = 0 \tag{15}$$

Compared with the equivalent equation which comes from quintessence model, this model gives a different and smaller friction term, as compared to the canonical scalar field. Therefore for increasing redshift, the densities for the scalar field will increase slower than in the standard quintessence.

The second variation with respect to the scalar field ϕ gives a non-conserved current:

$$\chi^{;\lambda}_{;\lambda} U'(\phi) - V'(\phi) = \nabla_\mu j^\mu \tag{16a}$$

$$j^\mu = \frac{1}{2}\phi_{,\nu}(\chi^{\mu;\nu} + \chi^{\nu;\mu}) + \phi^{,\mu} \tag{16b}$$

and the derivatives of the potentials are the source of this current. For constant potentials the source becomes zero, and we get a covariant conservation of this current. In a FLRW metric this equation of motion takes the form:

$$\ddot{\phi}(\dot{\chi}_0 - 1) + \dot{\phi}[\ddot{\chi}_0 + 3\mathcal{H}(\dot{\chi}_0 - 1)] = U'(\phi)(\dot{\chi}_0 + 3\mathcal{H}\chi_0) - V'(\phi) \tag{17}$$

Substituting the term of the potential derivative $U'(\phi)$ from equation (15):

$$[1 - 2\dot{\chi}_0 - 3\mathcal{H}\chi_0]\ddot{\phi} - [\ddot{\chi}_0 - 3\mathcal{H} + \frac{9}{2}\mathcal{H}(\dot{\chi}_0 + \chi_0\mathcal{H})]\dot{\phi} + V'(\phi) = 0 \tag{18}$$

The last variation, with respect to the metric, gives the stress energy tensor that is defined by the value of the Einstein's tensor. For a spatially homogeneous, cosmological case, the energy density and the pressure of the scalar field are:

$$\rho = \dot{\phi}^2(\dot{\chi}_0(1 - \frac{3}{2}\mathcal{H}) - \frac{1}{2}) + V(\phi) - \dot{\phi}\chi_0(U'(\phi) + \ddot{\phi}) \tag{19a}$$

$$p = \frac{1}{2}\dot{\phi}^2(\dot{\chi}_0 - 1) - V(\phi) - \chi_0\dot{\phi}U'(\phi) \tag{19b}$$

Substituting the potential derivative $U'(\phi)$ from Eq. (15) into the energy density term, makes the equation simpler:

$$\rho = (\dot{\chi}_0 - \frac{1}{2})\dot{\phi}^2 + V(\phi) \tag{20}$$

which has no longer dependence on the potential $U(\phi)$ or it's derivatives. Those three variations are sufficient for building a complete solution for the theory. Let's see a few simple cases.

4. The Evolution of the Homogeneous Solutions

4.1. *A bouncing ΛCDM solution*

In order to compute the evolution of the scalar field and to check whether it is compatible with observable universe, we have to specify a form for the potentials. Let's take a simplified case of constant potentials:

$$U(\phi) = C, \quad V(\phi) = \Omega_\Lambda \tag{21}$$

Overall, in the equations of motions only the derivative the potential $U(\phi)$ appears, not the potential itself. Therefore a constant part of the potential $U(\phi)$ does not contribute to the solution. However $V(\phi)$, as we shall see below, gives the cosmological constant. The conservation of the stress energy tensor from equation (15) gives:

$$\dot{\phi}^2 = \frac{2\Omega_m}{a^3} \qquad (22)$$

where Ω_m is an integration constant which appears from the solution. From the second variation, with respect to the scalar field ϕ, a conserved current is obtained, which from equation (18) gives the exact solution of the dynamical time vector field:

$$\dot{\chi}_0 = 1 - \kappa\, a^{-1.5} \qquad (23)$$

where κ is another integration of constant. Eventually, the densities and the pressure for this potentials are given by (20). By substituting the solutions for the scalar $\dot{\phi}$ and the vector $\dot{\chi}_0$ (in units with $\rho_c = \frac{8\pi G}{3H_0^2} = 1$) we get:

$$\rho = \Omega_\Lambda - \frac{\Omega_\kappa}{a^{4.5}} + \frac{\Omega_m}{a^3} \qquad (24a)$$

$$p = -\Omega_\Lambda - \frac{1}{2}\frac{\Omega_\kappa}{a^{4.5}} \qquad (24b)$$

where $\Omega_\kappa = \kappa\Omega_m$. Notice that Ω_m, Ω_κ are integration constants the solution contains and Ω_Λ is parameter from the action of the theory. We can separate the result into three different "dark fluids": dark energy ($\omega = -1$), dark matter ($\omega = 0$) and an exotic part ($\omega = \frac{1}{2}$), which is the responsible for the bounce (for $\kappa > 0$). From Eq. (22) the solution produces a positive Ω_m since it's proportional to $\dot{\phi}^2$. For Ω_Λ the measurements for the late universe forces the choice of this parameter to be positive. However for another solutions (in the context of Anti de-Sitter space, for instance) this parameter could be negative from the beginning.

In addition to those solutions, there is a strong correspondence between the zero component of the dynamical space time vector field and the cosmic time. For ΛCDM there is no bouncing solution $\kappa = 0$ and therefore from equation (23) we get $\chi_0 = t$ that implies that the dynamical time is exactly the cosmic time. For bouncing ΛCDM we obtain a relation between the dynamical and the cosmic time with some delay between the dynamical time and the cosmic time for the early universe (in the bouncing region). For the late universe the dynamical time returns back to run as fast as the cosmic time again. This relation between the dynamical and the cosmic time may have interesting application in the solution to "the problem of time" in quantum cosmology which will discussed elsewhere. Notice that the dynamical time is a field variable while the cosmic time is a coordinate.

In order to constrain our model, we use the Big Bang Nucleosynthesis (BBN) speed-up factor, defined as the ratio of the expansion rate predicted in a given model versus that of the ΛCDM model at the BBN epoch ($z_{BBN} \sim 10^9$). This amounts to the limit[20] with $(\Delta H/H_{\Lambda CDM})^2 < 10\%$, where $H_{\Lambda CDM}$ is the Hubble rate for the ΛCDM model and the ΔH is the difference between the Dynamical Spacetime Hubble rate and the ΛCDM Hubble rate, $\Delta H = H - H_{\Lambda CDM}$. The bounds gives:

$$\Omega_\kappa < 6 \cdot 10^{-10}. \tag{25}$$

With this bound the model is consistent with the cosmological observations.[21]

5. Discussion and Future Work

In this paper the "unified dark energy and dark matter from a scalar field different from quintessence" is formulated through an action principle. Introducing the coupling of a dynamical space time vector field to an energy momentum tensor that appears in the action, determines the equation of motion of the scalar field from the variation of the dynamical space time vector field or effectively from the conservation law of an energy momentum tensor, as in.[12] The energy momentum tensor that is introduced in the action is related but not in general the same as the one that appears in the right hand side of the gravitational equations, as opposed to the non Lagrangian approach of,[12] so our approach and that of[12] are not equivalent. However in many situations the solutions studied in[12] can be also obtained here, but there are other solutions, in special non singular bounce solutions which are not present in.[12]

In those simple solutions, the dynamical time behaves very close to the cosmic time. In particular in solutions which are exactly ΛCDM, the cosmic time and the dynamical time exactly coincide with each other. If there is a bounce, the deviation of the dynamical time with respect to the cosmic time takes place only very close to the bounce region. The use of this dynamical time as the time in the Wheeler de-Witt equation should also a subject of interest.

In principle we can introduce two different scalar potentials: one coupled directly to $\sqrt{-g}$ and the other appearing in the original stress energy tensor $T_{(x)}^{\mu\nu}$. So far, for the purposes of starting the study of the theory, we have only introduced a scalar potential coupled directly to $\sqrt{-g}$ and shown that this already leads to an interacting Dark Energy — Dark Matter model, although the full possibilities of the theory will be revealed when the two independent potentials will be introduced.

Finally, another direction for research has been started by studying models of this type in the context of higher dimensional theories, where they can provide a useful framework to study the "inflation compactication" epoch and an exit from this era to the present LCDM epoch could be further explored.[22]

Acknowledgments

D.B gratefully acknowledge the support the supports of the Blavatnik and the Rothschild fellowships. We have received partial support from European COST actions CA15117 and CA18108.

References

1. V. F. Cardone, A. Troisi and S. Capozziello, Unified dark energy models: A Phenomenological approach, *Phys. Rev. D* **69**, p. 083517 (2004).
2. G. Dvali and M. S. Turner, Dark energy as a modification of the Friedmann equation (1 2003).
3. S. Basilakos, Cosmological implications and structure formation from a time varying vacuum, *Mon. Not. Roy. Astron. Soc.* **395**, p. 2347 (2009).
4. R. J. Scherrer, Purely kinetic k-essence as unified dark matter, *Phys. Rev. Lett.* **93**, p. 011301 (2004).
5. A. Arbey, Dark fluid: A Complex scalar field to unify dark energy and dark matter, *Phys. Rev. D* **74**, p. 043516 (2006).
6. E. Guendelman, E. Nissimov and S. Pacheva, Unified Dark Energy and Dust Dark Matter Dual to Quadratic Purely Kinetic K-Essence, *Eur. Phys. J. C* **76**, p. 90 (2016).
7. E. Guendelman, E. Nissimov and S. Pacheva, Quintessential Inflation, Unified Dark Energy and Dark Matter, and Higgs Mechanism, *Bulg. J. Phys.* **44**, 015 (2017).
8. G. Koutsoumbas, K. Ntrekis, E. Papantonopoulos and E. N. Saridakis, Unification of Dark Matter - Dark Energy in Generalized Galileon Theories, *JCAP* **02**, p. 003 (2018).
9. Z. Haba, A. Stachowski and M. Szydłowski, Dynamics of the diffusive DM-DE interaction – Dynamical system approach, *JCAP* **07**, p. 024 (2016).
10. D. Benisty and E. I. Guendelman, Interacting Diffusive Unified Dark Energy and Dark Matter from Scalar Fields, *Eur. Phys. J. C* **77**, p. 396 (2017).
11. D. Benisty and E. I. Guendelman, Unified DE–DM with diffusive interactions scenario from scalar fields, *Int. J. Mod. Phys. D* **26**, p. 1743021 (2017).
12. C. Gao, M. Kunz, A. R. Liddle and D. Parkinson, Unified dark energy and dark matter from a scalar field different from quintessence, *Phys. Rev. D* **81**, p. 043520 (2010).
13. E. I. Guendelman, Gravitational Theory with a Dynamical Time, *Int. J. Mod. Phys. A* **25**, 4081 (2010).
14. D. Benisty and E. I. Guendelman, Radiation Like Scalar Field and Gauge Fields in Cosmology for a theory with Dynamical Time, *Mod. Phys. Lett. A* **31**, p. 1650188 (2016).
15. E. I. Guendelman, Scale invariance, new inflation and decaying lambda terms, *Mod. Phys. Lett. A* **14**, 1043 (1999).
16. E. I. Guendelman and A. B. Kaganovich, Transition to Zero Cosmological Constant and Phantom Dark Energy as Solutions Involving Change of Orientation of Space-Time Manifold, *Class. Quant. Grav.* **25**, p. 235015 (2008).
17. E. I. Guendelman and A. B. Kaganovich, Absence of the Fifth Force Problem in a Model with Spontaneously Broken Dilatation Symmetry, *Annals Phys.* **323**, 866 (2008).
18. E. I. Guendelman and O. Katz, Inflation and transition to a slowly accelerating phase from SSB of scale invariance, *Class. Quant. Grav.* **20**, 1715 (2003).
19. E. Guendelman, R. Herrera, P. Labrana, E. Nissimov and S. Pacheva, Emergent Cosmology, Inflation and Dark Energy, *Gen. Rel. Grav.* **47**, p. 10 (2015).
20. J.-P. Uzan, Varying Constants, Gravitation and Cosmology, *Living Rev. Rel.* **14**, p. 2 (2011).
21. F. K. Anagnostopoulos, D. Benisty, S. Basilakos and E. I. Guendelman, Dark energy and dark matter unification from dynamical space time: observational constraints and cosmological implications, *JCAP* **06**, p. 003 (2019).
22. D. Benisty and E. I. Guendelman, Inflation compactification from dynamical space-time, *Phys. Rev. D* **98**, p. 043522 (2018).

Entropy and irreversible processes in gravity and cosmology

Llorenç Espinosa-Portalés* and Juan García-Bellido[†]

*Instituto de Física Teórica UAM-CSIC, Universidad Autónoma de Madrid
Cantoblanco, 28049 Madrid, Spain*
* E-mail: llorenc.espinosa@uam.es
[†] *E-mail: juan.garciabellido@uam.es*

General Relativity is *a priori* a theory invariant under time reversal. Its integration with the laws of thermodynamics allows for a formulation of non-equilibrium phenomena in gravity and the introduction of an arrow of time, i.e. the the breaking of such invariance. Even though most of the evolution of the universe takes place in local thermal equilibrium, the effects of irreversible processes on the expansion via entropic forces may be phenomenologically relevant. We review our previous work on the covariant formulation of non-equilibrium thermodynamics in General Relativity and the proposal to explain the recent cosmic acceleration from it.

Keywords: General Relativity, thermodynamics, non-equilibrium phenomena, entropic forces, cosmic acceleration.

1. Introduction

General Relativity is an extremely successful physical theory. More than a century after its formulation, its predictions continue to be valid at all probed scales, albeit an extension at short scales will be required in order to obtain a UV-complete quantum theory of gravity and resolve space-time singularities.

Thermodynamics is an even older discipline. Its fundamental laws seem to resist the pass of time and are still of great relevance today. On the one hand, thermodynamics may help in building the bridge between classical and quantum gravity, as the laws of black hole thermodynamics points towards the existence of a microphysical description of gravity yet to be understood.

On the other hand, the second law of thermodynamics, i.e. the growth of entropy, dictates the sign of the arrow of time. Physical laws are usually invariant under time inversion. The increase in entropy with time in out-of-equilibrium phenomena, however, allows one to distinguish the future-directed from the past directed description of a physical process.

There lacks a consistent and rigorous integration between General Relativity and the laws of thermodynamics. Understanding the very notion of the arrow of time is of particular interest for cosmology. In section 2 we argue for the need of going beyond reversible cosmology. This can be achieved for any space-time metric using variational techniques.[1] We review our main results in this new approach to non-equilibrium thermodynamics in General Relativity and present them in sections 3 to 6.

The growth of entropy associated to the causal horizon in open inflation scenarios may explain the current accelerated expansion of the universe within the general relativistic entropic acceleration (GREA) theory.[2] We briefly describe how this mechanism works in section 7 and finish with our conclusions.

2. Reversible cosmology

Let us begin the study of the problem of reversibility in gravity and cosmology by reviewing a prototypic case of reversible gravitational system: a homogeneous and isotropic universe. It is described by the Friedmann-Lemaître-Robertson-Walker (FLRW) metric

$$ds^2 = -dt^2 + a(t)^2 \left(\frac{dr^2}{1-kr^2} + r^2 d\Omega_2^2 \right), \qquad (1)$$

where $a(t)$ is the scale factor, $k = -1, 0, 1$ is the curvature parameter corresponding to, respectively, an open, flat and closed universe; and $d\Omega_2^2$ is the solid angle element. This space-time is filled with a perfect fluid, described by the stress-energy tensor

$$T_{\mu\nu} = (\rho + p) u_\mu u_\nu + p g_{\mu\nu}, \qquad (2)$$

where ρ and p are, respectively, the density and pressure of the fluid. The Einstein field equations for this metric and matter content deliver the dynamics for the scale factor, the well-known Friedmann equations

$$H^2 + \frac{k}{a^2} = \frac{8\pi G}{3} \rho \qquad \frac{\ddot{a}}{a} = -\frac{4\pi G}{3} (\rho + 3p), \qquad (3)$$

where $H = \dot{a}/a$ is the Hubble parameter. There is a constraint on the stress-energy tensor due to the Einstein field equations and the Bianchi identities, namely its covariant conservation $D_\mu T^{\mu\nu} = 0$. From this constraint one can derive the continuity equation

$$\dot\rho + 3H(\rho + p) = 0. \qquad (4)$$

However, one can also derive this equation from the second law of thermodynamics. Indeed, changes in entropy are related to changes in internal energy and work $TdS = \delta U + \delta W$. If we apply this to a region of fixed comoving volume $a(t)^3$ we get

$$T\frac{dS}{dt} = \frac{d}{dt}\left(\rho a^3\right) + p \frac{d}{dt}\left(a^3\right). \qquad (5)$$

If the expansion of the universe is reversible, we can set the LHS to 0 and recover the continuity equation. However, this is only true in thermodynamical equilibrium and, in general, entropy is a monotonically increasing function of time. Most of the expansion history of the universe is indeed adiabatic. However, it is out-of-equilibrium at certain key points such as (p)reheating, phase transitions or gravitational collapse. Allowing for a time-varying entropy implies the addition of a term in the continuity equation

$$\dot\rho + 3H(\rho + p) = \frac{T\dot S}{a^3}. \qquad (6)$$

Combining this with the first Friedmann equation we obtain a modified, non-equilibrium second Friedmann equation

$$\frac{\ddot{a}}{a} = -\frac{4\pi G}{3}\left(\rho + 3p - \frac{T\dot{S}}{a^3 H}\right). \tag{7}$$

In principle, this evolution equation does not seem to be compatible with the Einstein field equations. In order to achieve that, the laws of thermodynamics need to be rigorously incorporated into the computation of the equations of motion. This can be achieved by applying the variational formalism of non-equilibrium thermodynamics, developed in another context by Gay-Balmaz and Yoshimura,[3,4] to General Relativity.

3. Entropic forces in mechanics and field theory

Entropic forces emerge naturally in any physical system out of equilibrium. They are a consequence of the coarse-graining of physical degrees of freedom and the laws of thermodynamics, which impose entropy to be a monotonically increasing function of time. This breaks time reversibility.

The dynamics of the coarse-grained degrees of freedom is unknown or ignored and so they do not appear in the action of the physical system. It would seem that a variational treatment of an out-of-equilibrium system is not possible. However, both the extremal-action principle and the second law of thermodynamics can be merged consistently by imposing the latter as a constrain on the variational problem defined by the action.[3,4] On the other hand, the first law of thermodynamics is obtained from the symmetries of the problem.

3.1. *Entropic forces in mechanics*

Let us start by reviewing the emergence of entropic forces in a mechanical system. Consider the action

$$\mathcal{S} = \int dt\, L(q, \dot{q}, S), \tag{8}$$

where the Lagrangian depends on the generalized coordinate $q(t)$, its time derivative $\dot{q}(t)$ and the entropy $S(t)$. The variation of the action gives

$$\delta\mathcal{S} = \int dt \left(\frac{\delta L}{\delta q}\delta q + \frac{\partial L}{\partial S}\delta S\right). \tag{9}$$

Setting $\delta\mathcal{S} = 0$ defines the variational problem. In order to enforce the second law of thermodynamics, we need to impose the variational constraint

$$\frac{\partial L}{\partial S}\delta S = f\delta q, \tag{10}$$

which simply states the relationship between variations of the entropy and the generalized coordinate. If we plug this in the variation of the action, then we can readily obtain the equations of motion

$$\frac{\delta L}{\delta q} = \frac{\partial L}{\partial q} - \frac{d}{dt}\left(\frac{\partial L}{\partial \dot{q}}\right) = -f, \tag{11}$$

which is the Euler-Lagrange equation modified by the addition of the entropic force f. In order to know its precise form, we need to impose as well the phenomenological constraint, which is obtained by formally replacing the variations with time derivatives

$$\frac{\partial L}{\partial S}\dot{S} = f\dot{q}. \tag{12}$$

Note that usually temperature can be introduced as

$$T = -\frac{\partial L}{\partial S} > 0 \tag{13}$$

providing a clearer meaning to the variational and phenomenological constraint.

The imposition of the constraints and the emergence of an entropic force break the symmetry under time inversion. First, note that formally the Euler-Lagrange equation is invariant under the $t \to -t$ transformation, even with a non-vanishing entropic force. Next, the positiveness of the temperature and the change of entropy imposes $f\dot{q} < 0$. The entropic force has qualities of a generalized friction, as it opposes the coordinate velocity. Now, if one performs time inversion, this sign constraint becomes $f\dot{q} > 0$, as the temperature remains positive but entropy decreases with time. Before solving the equations of motion, $\dot{q}$ is still a degree of freedom and, thus, one must conclude a flip in the sign of f, which flips the overall sign of the Euler-Lagrange equation. Hence, one concludes that the emergence of an entropic force breaks symmetry under time reversal. The evolution of the system becomes irreversible.

3.2. *Entropic forces in classical field theory*

The extension of the variational formalism of non-equilibrium thermodynamics to the continuum is a bit involved. We present a short-cut derivation that relies on the introduction of an additional constraint. We refer the reader to the appendix of[1] to check its equivalence with the full variational derivation originally presented in.[4]

The action of a scalar field on Minkowski space-time contains now a dependency on a scalar function $s(t,\vec{x})$ that encodes information related to coarse-grained degrees of freedom

$$\mathcal{S} = \int d^4x \mathcal{L}(\phi, \partial_\mu \phi, s). \tag{14}$$

In a similar fashion as before, the extremal-action principle needs to be supplemented by a variational constraint

$$\frac{\partial \mathcal{L}}{\partial s}\delta s = f\delta\phi, \tag{15}$$

so that the equation of motion becomes

$$\frac{\delta \mathcal{L}}{\delta \phi} = \frac{\partial \mathcal{L}}{\partial \phi} - \partial_\mu \frac{\partial \mathcal{L}}{\partial \partial_\mu \phi} = -f, \qquad (16)$$

which is nothing but the Euler-Lagrange equation of a scalar field with a new term of entropic origin. As before, one can usually introduce a temperature as

$$T = -\frac{\partial \mathcal{L}}{\partial s} > 0 \qquad (17)$$

and we would like to interpret s as the entropy density. However, due to spatial fluxes entropy need not necessarily increase locally and, thus, the constraint would not have a fixed sign. Before proceeding, we inspect the corresponding phenomenological constraint

$$\frac{\partial \mathcal{L}}{\partial s} \partial_0 s = f \partial_0 \phi. \qquad (18)$$

Instead, we interpret δs and $\partial_0 s$ as local entropy production and introduce a new function s_{tot} which is the actual entropy density and whose changes δs_{tot} and $\partial_0 s_{\text{tot}}$ are indeed total local changes of the entropy density. Both are related as

$$\partial_0 s = \partial_0 s_{\text{tot}} - \partial_i j_s^i, \qquad (19)$$

where j_s^i is the entropy flux. This latter equation is an additional constraint we impose for the variational formalism to be consistent. Now one can check that $f \partial_0 \phi < 0$ and time reversibility is broken by the same argument used in the mechanics example.

3.3. *Entropic forces in presence of additional symmetries*

The generalization of the above formalism to higher order tensors or to representations of some internal symmetry group is straightforward. Let us consider a field tensor z of contravariant rank r, which is also in some representation of an internal symmetry labelled by an index A. Then one builds the variational constraint as

$$\frac{\partial \mathcal{L}}{\partial s} \delta s = f_{A;\mu_1,\ldots\mu_r} \delta z_A^{\mu_1,\ldots\mu_r}, \qquad (20)$$

which delivers the equation of motion

$$\frac{\delta \mathcal{L}}{\delta z_A^{\mu_1,\ldots\mu_r}} = -f_{A;\mu_1,\ldots\mu_r}. \qquad (21)$$

4. Entropic forces in General Relativity

The previous discussion makes us ready to study entropic forces in General Relativity. However, with the introduction of a dynamical space-time the very notion of time evolution becomes non-trivial. As we will see shortly, it is possible to obtain a modification of entropic origin to Einstein's field equation in the Lagrangian formulation of General Relativity. Its proper interpretation will require, nevertheless, the use of the Hamiltonian formalism.

4.1. Lagrangian formulation

Let us consider the Einstein-Hilbert action plus a matter term

$$S = \frac{1}{2\kappa}\int d^4x\sqrt{-g}R + \int d^4x \mathcal{L}_m(g_{\mu\nu}, s),\qquad(22)$$

where $\kappa = 8\pi G$ is the gravitational coupling and we allow for the dependence of the matter Lagrangian on a function $s(t, \vec{x})$, which will have a similar interpretation to the one presented in the previous section. The extremal-action principle is supplemented by the variational constraint.

$$\frac{\partial \mathcal{L}_m}{\partial s} = \frac{1}{2}\sqrt{-g}f_{\mu\nu}\delta g^{\mu\nu}.\qquad(23)$$

From the extremal-action principle and the variational constraint we obtain the modified Einstein's field equations

$$R_{\mu\nu} - \frac{1}{2}g_{\mu\nu}R = \kappa\left(T_{\mu\nu} - f_{\mu\nu}\right),\qquad(24)$$

where there is an additional term $f_{\mu\nu}$ of entropic origin. In order to obtain an expression for this term and to check the breaking of symmetry under time inversion we need to work in the Hamiltonian formulation of General Relativity.

4.2. Hamiltonian formulation

General Relativity admits a Hamiltonian formulation in the Arnowitt-Deser-Misner (ADM) formalism. Space-time is foliated in constant time hypersurfaces with normal unit vector n^μ, being the its 4-metric split as

$$g_{\mu\nu} = h_{\mu\nu} - n_\mu n_\nu,\qquad(25)$$

where $h_{\mu\nu}$ is the 3-metric induced on the hypersurfaces. Analogously, one can parametrize the 4-metric in terms of the 3-metric h_{ij} and the lapse and shift functions N and N^i

$$ds^2 = -(Ndt)^2 + h_{ij}(dx^i + N^i dt)(dx^j + N^j dt).\qquad(26)$$

Greek indices run from 0 to 3, while Latin ones do from 1 to 3 and are raised and lowered by h_{ij}. The normal vector can be written as

$$n_\mu = (-N, 0, 0, 0).\qquad(27)$$

Note that h_{ij} is the purely spatial part of $h_{\mu\nu}$ and is also the pull-back of $g_{\mu\nu}$ onto the hypersurface.

The Einstein-Hilbert action for this parametrization of the metric is given by the following gravitational Lagrangian:

$$\mathcal{L}_G = \sqrt{-g}R = \frac{1}{2\kappa}N\sqrt{h}\left(^{(3)}R + K_{ij}K^{ij} - K^2\right),\qquad(28)$$

where K_{ij} is the extrinsic curvature of the 3-hypersurface Σ and is given by the Lie derivative along the normal vector n:

$$K_{ij} = \frac{1}{2}\pounds_n h_{ij} = \frac{1}{2N}\left(\partial_0 h_{ij} - \nabla_i N_j - \nabla_j N_i\right) \qquad (29)$$

where ∇ denotes the covariant derivative on Σ with respect to the 3-metric h_{ij}. Its trace and traceless part are:

$$\begin{aligned} K &= h^{ij}K_{ij} = \frac{1}{N}\left(\partial_0 \ln\sqrt{h} - \nabla_i N^i\right) \\ \bar{K}_{ij} &= K_{ij} - \frac{1}{3}K h_{ij}\,. \end{aligned} \qquad (30)$$

Unlike the intrinsic curvature, described by the Riemann tensor $R^\rho_{\mu\nu\lambda}$ and its contractions, the extrinsic curvature is a quantity that depends on the embedding of a surface in a larger manifold.

We are now ready to introduce the Hamiltonian formulation of the theory. Note that the only quantity whose time derivative appears in the gravitational Lagrangian is the 3-spatial metric h_{ij} and, thus, it is the only dynamical or propagating d.o.f. Correspondingly, one defines its conjugate momentum as:

$$\Pi^{ij} = \frac{\partial \mathcal{L}_G}{\partial \dot{h}_{ij}} = \sqrt{h}\left(K^{ij} - K h^{ij}\right)\,. \qquad (31)$$

With this, the gravitational Lagrangian can be rewritten as:

$$\begin{aligned} \mathcal{L}_G &= N\sqrt{h}\,{}^{(3)}R - \frac{N}{\sqrt{h}}\left(\Pi_{ij}\Pi^{ij} - \frac{1}{2}\Pi^2\right) - 2\Pi^{ij}\nabla_i N_j \\ &= \Pi^{ij}\dot{h}_{ij} - N\mathcal{H} - N_i\mathcal{H}^i - 2\nabla_i\left(\Pi^{ij}N_j\right)\,, \end{aligned} \qquad (32)$$

where $\Pi = h_{ij}\Pi^{ij}$ and we introduced the functions:

$$\begin{aligned} \mathcal{H} &= -\sqrt{h}\,{}^{(3)}R + \frac{1}{\sqrt{h}}\left(\Pi_{ij}\Pi^{ij} - \frac{1}{2}\Pi^2\right) \\ \mathcal{H}^i &= -2\nabla_j\left(h^{-1/2}\Pi^{ij}\right)\,. \end{aligned} \qquad (33)$$

Since N and N_i are not dynamical variables, they merely enter the gravitational Lagrangian as Lagrange multipliers. One defines the gravitational Hamiltonian as:

$$\begin{aligned} \mathcal{H}_G &= \Pi^{ij}\dot{h}_{ij} - \mathcal{L}_G \\ &= N\mathcal{H} + N_i\mathcal{H}^i + \nabla_i\left(\Pi^{ij}N_j\right)\,, \end{aligned} \qquad (34)$$

with the Hamiltonian and momentum constraints:

$$\begin{aligned} \frac{\delta \mathcal{H}_G}{\delta N} &= \mathcal{H} = 0 \\ \frac{\delta \mathcal{H}_G}{\delta N_i} &= \mathcal{H}^i = 0\,. \end{aligned} \qquad (35)$$

The Hamiltonian evolution equations are obtained from the variations of the action with respect to the metric and conjugate momentum

$$\delta S = \int d^4x \left[\left(-\dot{\Pi}^{ij} - \frac{\delta \mathcal{H}_G}{\delta h_{ij}} - \kappa N\sqrt{h}\tilde{f}^{ij} + 2\kappa \frac{\partial \mathcal{L}_m}{\partial h_{ij}} \right) \delta h_{ij} + \left(\dot{h}_{ij} - \frac{\delta \mathcal{H}_G}{\delta \Pi^{ij}} \right) \delta \Pi^{ij} \right], \tag{36}$$

where the variational constraint

$$\frac{\partial \mathcal{L}_m}{\partial s} \delta s = -\frac{1}{2} N\sqrt{h}\tilde{f}^{ij} \delta h_{ij} \tag{37}$$

was already implemented. Note that the minus sign arises from

$$\frac{\partial h_{ij}}{\partial h^{kl}} = -\frac{1}{2}\left(h_{ik}h_{jl} + h_{il}h_{jk} \right) \tag{38}$$

and that $\tilde{f}_{ij}$ is the pull-back of $f_{\mu\nu}$ onto the hypersurfaces. By setting the variation to 0 we obtain the two Hamilton equations

$$\begin{aligned}\frac{\delta \mathcal{H}_G}{\delta h_{ij}} &= -\dot{\Pi}^{ij} - \kappa N\sqrt{h}\tilde{f}^{ij} + 2\kappa \frac{\partial \mathcal{L}_m}{\partial h_{ij}} \\ \frac{\delta \mathcal{H}_G}{\delta \Pi^{ij}} &= \dot{h}_{ij}, \end{aligned} \tag{39}$$

which completes the derivation of the entropic modification to the gravitational equations of motion in the Hamiltonian formulation.

The tensor $\tilde{f}_{ij}$ can be obtained from the phenomenological constraint, which can now be stated rigorously. In the ADM formalism, a well-defined notion of time evolution is given by the flow along the normal vector n^μ. Hence, the time derivative is generalized to the Lie derivative along n^μ. Then the phenomenological constraint is given by

$$\frac{\partial \mathcal{L}}{\partial s} \pounds_n s = \frac{1}{2} N\sqrt{h}\tilde{f}_{ij} \pounds_n h^{ij} \tag{40}$$

where growth in entropy by local processes is related to total entropy density growth by

$$\pounds_n s = \pounds_n s^{tot} - \nabla_i j_s^i. \tag{41}$$

Entropy produced locally is expected to grow over time, i.e. with the flow along the hypersurfaces, in compliance with the second law of thermodynamics. This completes the variational formulation of entropic forces in General Relativity.

4.3. *The Raychauduri equation*

Let us explore an immediate dynamical consequence of the inclusion of entropic forces, namely its effect on a congruence of worldlines with tangent vector n^μ. The congruence is then characterized by the tensor:

$$\Theta_{\mu\nu} = D_\nu n_\mu = \frac{1}{3}\Theta h_{\mu\nu} + \sigma_{\mu\nu} + \omega_{\mu\nu} - a_\mu n_\nu \tag{42}$$

where θ is the expansion rate of the congruence, $\sigma_{\mu\nu}$ is its shear or symmetric traceless part and $\omega_{\mu\nu}$ is its vorticity or antisymmetric part. If the worldline is not a geodesic, then the congruence suffers an acceleration given by:

$$a_\mu = n^\nu D_\nu n_\mu \,. \tag{43}$$

One can compute the Lie derivative of the expansion of the congruence along its tangent vector and find the Raychauduri equation:[5]

$$\pounds_n \Theta = -\frac{1}{3}\Theta^2 - \sigma_{\mu\nu}\sigma^{\mu\nu} + \omega_{\mu\nu}\omega^{\mu\nu} - R_{\mu\nu}n^\mu n^\nu + D_\mu a^\mu \,. \tag{44}$$

Let us perform the standard analysis of the sign of this equation. It is clear that $\sigma_{\mu\nu}\sigma^{\mu\nu} > 0$ and $\Theta^2 > 0$. On the other hand, if the congruence is chosen to be orthogonal to the spatial hypersurfaces, as we have been considering, then the vorticity vanishes $\omega_{\mu\nu} = 0$. Lastly, it is left to consider the term $R_{\mu\nu}n^\mu n^\nu$, which we can rewrite with the help of the field equations:

$$R_{\mu\nu}n^\mu n^\nu = 8\pi G\left(T_{\mu\nu}n^\mu n^\nu + \frac{1}{2}T - f_{\mu\nu}n^\mu n^\nu - \frac{1}{2}f\right). \tag{45}$$

If the strong energy condition is satisfied, then:

$$T_{\mu\nu}n^\mu n^\nu \geq -\frac{1}{2}T \tag{46}$$

and, in the absence of intrinsic acceleration, $a_\mu = 0$, we can establish the bound:

$$\pounds_n \Theta + \frac{1}{3}\Theta^2 \leq 8\pi G\left(f_{\mu\nu}n^\mu n^\nu + \frac{1}{2}f\right). \tag{47}$$

For a vanishing entropic force $f_{\mu\nu} = 0$, this means that an expanding congruence cannot indefinitely sustain its divergence and will eventually recollapse. On the contrary, a positive and sufficiently large entropic contribution can avoid such recollapse. This may become relevant for an expanding universe, but also to generic gravitational collapse and the singularity theorems.[6–8]

5. Sources of entropy

A main ingredient in the variational formulation of non-equilibrium thermodynamics in General Relativity is the inclusion of entropy at the Lagrangian level and the derivation of a notion of temperature from it. In this section we present two relevant examples: hydrodynamical matter, which is a prototypical case, and horizons.

5.1. *Entropy from hydrodynamical matter*

A classical fluid is the simplest matter content that can be considered in General Relativity and it is of particular relevance in Cosmology. Without paying attention to microphysical details, the Lagrangian of hydrodynamical matter can be written as

$$\mathcal{L}_m = -\sqrt{-g}\rho(g_{\mu\nu}, s)\,, \tag{48}$$

being then the temperature simply given by

$$T = -\frac{1}{\sqrt{-g}}\frac{\partial \mathcal{L}_m}{\partial s} = \frac{\partial \rho}{\partial s}. \tag{49}$$

This is analogous to the case of a mechanical system, where the Lagrangian is generically given by a kinetic and a potential energy

$$L = E_K(q, \dot{q}) - U(q, S) \tag{50}$$

and temperature can be defined as

$$T = \frac{\partial L}{\partial S} = -\frac{\partial U}{\partial S}. \tag{51}$$

Thus, the energy density of a fluid can be readily interpreted as the thermodynamic internal energy.

5.2. *Entropy from gravity and horizons*

Gravity itself has thermodynamical features. It is known since the discovery of the laws of black hole mechanics and their promotion to laws of black hole thermodynamics, allowed by the introduction of Bekenstein entropy and Hawking temperature. We propose to include the entropy associated with a horizon $\mathcal{H}$ by extending the Einstein-Hilbert actions with surface terms of Gibbons-Hawking-York (GHY) type

$$S_{GHY} = \frac{1}{8\pi G}\int_{\mathcal{H}} d^3 y \sqrt{h} K, \tag{52}$$

where h is the determinant of the induced 3-metric on the horizon and K is the trace of its extrinsic curvature. Definitions are analogous to the ones used in the ADM formalism, but we stress that here the hypersurface of interest is a horizon and not constant-time hypersurfaces.

From the thermodynamic point of view, the GHY term contributes to the internal energy of the system. Hence, it can be rewritten as a function of the temperature and entropy of the horizon

$$S_{GHY} = -\int dt \, N(t) \, TS. \tag{53}$$

We have kept the lapse function $N(t)$, to indicate that the variation of the total action with respect to it will generate a Hamiltonian constraint with an entropy term together with the ordinary matter/energy terms. In order to illustrate this, let us now compute the GHY for the event horizon of a Schwarzschild black hole.

The space-time of a Schwarzschild black hole of mass M is described by the static metric

$$ds^2 = -\left(1 - \frac{2GM}{r}\right)dt^2 + \left(1 - \frac{2GM}{r}\right)^{-1}dr^2 + r^2 d\Omega_2^2. \tag{54}$$

We foliate it with spherical hypersurfaces, i.e. their intersection with constant time hypersurfaces is a 2-sphere around the origin of coordinates. The corresponding normal vector is

$$n = -\sqrt{1 - \frac{2GM}{r}}\partial_r. \tag{55}$$

With this, the trace of the extrinsic curvature for such a sphere scaled by the metric determinant is

$$\sqrt{h}K = (3GM - 2r)\sin\theta. \tag{56}$$

Integrating over the angular coordinates and setting the 2-sphere at the event horizon, i.e. $r = 2GM$, and restoring for a moment $\hbar$ and c, the GHY becomes

$$S_{GHY} = -\frac{1}{2}\int dt M c^2 = -\int dt T_{BH} S_{BH}, \tag{57}$$

where T_{BH} is the Hawking temperature and S_{BH} is the Bekenstein entropy of the Schwarzschild black hole:

$$T_{BH} = \frac{\hbar c^3}{8\pi GM} \quad S_{BH} = \frac{Ac^3}{4G\hbar} = \frac{4\pi GM^2}{\hbar c}. \tag{58}$$

This favors the interpretation of the GHY term of a horizon as a contribution to the internal energy in the thermodynamic sense.

6. Irreversible cosmology

We derived in section 4 a powerful, generic tool to describe non-equilibrium thermodynamic effects in gravity. In the Hamiltonian formulation of General Relativity it is possible to obtain the modified equations of motion and rigorously impose the time-evolution of the entropy as dictated by the second law of thermodynamics.

In section 2 we motivated the study of these phenomena by our interest in understanding the dynamics of irreversible cosmology and justifying its equations of motion. One can obtain them using the Hamilton equations.[1] Here, however, we present a slightly different approach. Due to the symmetries of the FLRW universe, homogeneity and isotropy, there is a preferred slicing and time evolution is well-defined even at the Lagrangian level. Therefore, we can obtain the equations of non-equilibrium cosmology by imposing these symmetries, i.e. making an ansatz for the metric

$$ds^2 = -N(t)^2 dt^2 + a(t)^2\left(\frac{dr^2}{1-kr^2} + r^2 d\Omega_2^2,\right) \tag{59}$$

where the lapse function $N(t)$ accounts for the freedom in choosing the time coordinate, i.e. the symmetry under $t \to f(t)$. The Ricci scalar associated to this metric is

$$R = \frac{6}{a^2}\left(\frac{a\ddot{a}}{N^2} + \frac{\dot{a}^2}{N^2} + k\right). \tag{60}$$

Let us stress that this result is imposed by symmetry, not dynamics. Without loss of generality, we can restrict the action to a region of comoving volume 1 and write it as

$$S = \int dt L = \frac{3}{8\pi G} \int dt N a \left(\frac{a\ddot{a}}{N^2} + \frac{\dot{a}^2}{N^2} + k \right) + \int dt N a^3 \mathcal{L}_m(N, a, S). \quad (61)$$

Effectively, this action describes a mechanical system, for the scale factor $a(t)$ has no spatial dependency and we got rid of the integral over spatial coordinates. The first term can be rewritten using integration by parts in order to get only terms with at most the first derivative of a

$$S = \frac{3}{8\pi G} \int dt N a \left(-\frac{\dot{a}^2}{N^2} + k \right) + \int dt N a^3 \mathcal{L}_m(N, a, S). \quad (62)$$

The variational constraint is here given by the usual expression for a mechanical system

$$\frac{\partial L}{\partial S} \delta S = f \delta a. \quad (63)$$

The Hamiltonian of the system is

$$H = \dot{a} \frac{\partial L}{\partial \dot{a}} - L = \frac{3}{8\pi G} \left(-\frac{\dot{a}^2 a}{N} - kaN \right) - N a^3 \mathcal{L}_m. \quad (64)$$

For an arbitrary lapse function $N(t)$ this can be rewritten as

$$H = N^2 a^3 \frac{\partial \mathcal{L}_m}{\partial N}, \quad (65)$$

which gives the Hamiltonian constraint of the system. On the other hand, the dynamics is obtained from the equation of motion for a

$$\frac{\delta L}{\delta a} = -f. \quad (66)$$

Let us now consider the matter Lagrangian to be that of a perfect fluid, i.e.

$$\mathcal{L}_m = -\rho(a, S). \quad (67)$$

Its stress-energy tensor is given in terms of the density ρ and pressure p by

$$T^{\mu\nu} = (\rho + p) u^\mu u^\nu + p g^{\mu\nu} \quad (68)$$

and $u^m u = (N, 0, 0, 0)$ is the unit vector tangent to a comoving observer. Pressure is then obtained as

$$p = \frac{a^2}{3} T^{ij} \delta_{ij} = -\frac{1}{2a^4} \frac{\partial a^3 \rho}{\partial a}. \quad (69)$$

Using the expressions for ρ and p and rearranging the terms in the Hamiltonian constraint and the equation of motion for $a(t)$ we arrive at the modified Friedmann equations

$$\left(\frac{\dot{a}}{a}\right)^2 + \frac{k}{a^2} = \frac{8\pi G}{3}\rho$$
$$\frac{\ddot{a}}{a} = -\frac{4\pi G}{3}\left(\rho + 3p + \frac{f}{a^2}\right).$$
(70)

The expression for the entropic force F is obtained from the phenomenological constraint

$$\left(\frac{\partial L}{\partial S}\right)\dot{S} = -T\dot{S} = f\dot{a} < 0,$$
(71)

which determines the sign $f < 0$ whenever dealing with an expanding universe $\dot{a} > 0$. We express finally the second Friedmann equation as

$$\frac{\ddot{a}}{a} = -\frac{4\pi G}{3}\left(\rho + 3p - \frac{T\dot{S}}{a^2\dot{a}}\right).$$
(72)

From this equation we can conclude that entropic forces generally drive an acceleration of the expansion of the universe. Whether this can dominate the dynamics of the scale factor will depend on the particular thermodynamic process. Most of the expansion history of the universe takes place in equilibrium. Out of equilibrium processes, such as (p)reheating, phase transitions or gravitational collapse are short-lived. Should their associated entropic force dominate, we still only expect a short period of accelerated expansion.

Symmetry under time inversion is broken by the same arguments presented in section 3. Hence, the Friedmann equations together with the phenomenological constraint, i.e. the second law of thermodynamics, describe cosmic irreversible dynamics.

We currently live in a universe that is undergoing an accelerated expansion. The possibility of explaining this by means of an entropic force is fascinating. In the next section we review our proposal to achieve this by means of the sustained growth of the entropy associated to a causal horizon.

7. Cosmic acceleration as an entropic force

The growth of entropy associated to the cosmic horizon may be responsible for the current observed accelerated expansion of the universe. The choice of horizon is in principle not unique. The only available one which can be defined locally in time is the cosmic apparent horizon, but it fails to significantly affect the expansion.[2]

There is another option in the framework of eternal inflation, according to which we live in an open universe nucleated by quantum tunneling from a false to a true vacuum. After nucleation the bubble universe undergoes its own inflationary era, which renders the local metric almost flat. However, due to the presence of the bubble walls, the true causal horizon is located at a finite distance. It induces an entropic fluid via GHY term with energy density

$$\rho_H a^2 = \frac{T_H S_H}{a} = \frac{x_0}{2G}\sinh(2a_0 H_0 \eta), \quad x_0 \equiv \frac{1-\Omega_0}{\Omega_0} = e^{-2N}\left(\frac{T_{\rm rh}}{T_{\rm eq}}\right)^2 (1+z_{\rm eq}), \tag{73}$$

where η is the conformal time, Ω_0 is the density parameter, $T_{\rm rh}$ is the reheating temperature, $T_{\rm eq}$ and $z_{\rm eq}$ are, respectively, the temperature and redshift at matter-radiation equality. Introducing $\tau = a_0 H_0 \eta$ one can write the second Friedmann equation in conformal time as

$$\left(\frac{a'}{a_0}\right)^2 = \Omega_M \left(\frac{a}{a_0}\right) + \Omega_K \left(\frac{a}{a_0}\right)^2 + \frac{4\pi}{3}\Omega_K \left(\frac{a}{a_0}\right)^2 \sinh(2\tau), \tag{74}$$

where Ω_M is the matter density paremeter and Ω_K is the curvature parameter. We call this the general relatvistic entropic acceleration (GREA) theory.

By solving this equation with cosmological parameters consistent with the CMB values (Planck 2018: $\Omega_M \simeq 0.31$, $\Omega_K \simeq 0.0006$, $h_0 \simeq 0.68$) and initial conditions deep in the matter era, $a_i(\tau) = a_0\, \Omega_M \tau^2/4$, we find generic accelerating behaviour beyond the scale factor $a \sim 1/2$ (i.e. $z \sim 1$), see Fig. 1. This is consistent with the current observed acceleration of the universe and may even resolve the Hubble tension,[9] providing a way to obtain from the CMB a present value of H_0 that is consistent with late-universe observations, see Fig. 2.

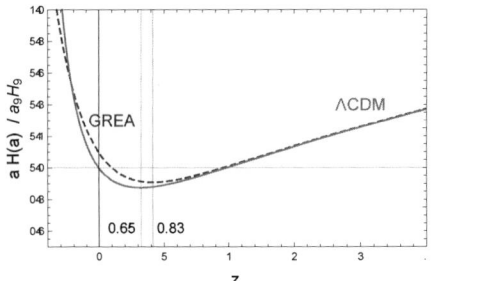

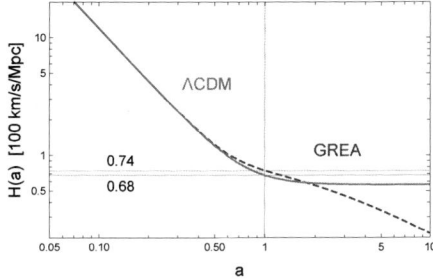

Fig. 1. The left plot shows the evolution of the inverse comoving horizon with the coasting point for each model, at $z \simeq 0.65$ for ΛCDM (in green) and $z \simeq 0.83$ for GREA (in red). The right plot shows the evolution of the rate of expansion. For GREA the present rate of expansion is approximately 74 km/s/Mpc, compared with the value of 68 km/s/Mpc predicted by ΛCDM, in agreement with the asymptotic value at the CMB.

8. Conclusions

The consistent inclusion of non-equilibrium phenomena in General Relativity leads to the modification of the Einstein field equations, as can be checked both in the Lagrangian and Hamiltonian formulations of the theory. This breaks symmetry under time inversion and allows for the introduction of an arrow of time.

In cosmology this implies the appearance of a term of entropic origin in the second Friedmann equation, which tends to accelerate the expansion of the universe as a result of the increase in entropy. Some physical processes such as (p)reheating, phase transitions or gravitational collapse may lead to phenomenologically relevant applications of this formalism. We look forward to further developments.

The sustained entropy growth associated to a causal horizon in the open universe scenario leads to an acceleration consistent with current observations and it may even solve the H_0 tension. Further research will be required to establish the full viability of the GREA theory.

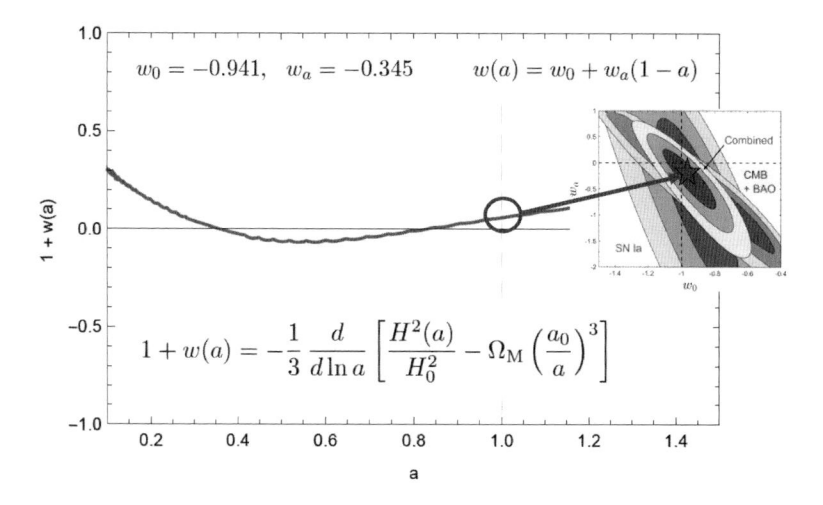

Fig. 2. The effective equation of state of the non-matter component of the GREA theory, as a function of thee sale factor. Note that the predicted effective PCL parameters (w_o, w_a) agree remarkably well with present observations.

Acknowledgments

The authors acknowledge support from the Spanish Research Project PGC2018-094773-B-C32 (MINECO-FEDER) and the Centro de Excelencia Severo Ochoa Program SEV-2016-0597. The work of LEP is funded by a fellowship from "La Caixa" Foundation (ID 100010434) with fellowship code LCF/BQ/IN18/11660041 and the European Union Horizon 2020 research and innovation programme under the Marie Sklodowska-Curie grant agreement No. 713673.

References

1. L. Espinosa-Portales and J. García-Bellido, Covariant formulation of non-equilibrium thermodynamics in General Relativity, *Phys. Dark Univ.* **34**, p. 100893 (2021).
2. J. García-Bellido and L. Espinosa-Portales, Cosmic acceleration from first principles, *Phys. Dark Univ.* **34**, p. 100892 (2021).

3. F. Gay-Balmaz and H. Yoshimura, A lagrangian variational formulation for nonequilibrium thermodynamics. part i: Discrete systems, *Journal of Geometry and Physics* **111**, 169 (2017).
4. F. Gay-Balmaz and H. Yoshimura, A lagrangian variational formulation for nonequilibrium thermodynamics. part ii: Continuum systems, *Journal of Geometry and Physics* **111**, 194 (2017).
5. R. M. Wald, *General Relativity* (Chicago Univ. Pr., Chicago, USA, 1984).
6. R. Penrose, Gravitational collapse and space-time singularities, *Phys. Rev. Lett.* **14**, 57 (1965).
7. R. Penrose, Gravitational collapse: The role of general relativity, *Riv. Nuovo Cim.* **1**, 252 (1969).
8. S. W. Hawking and R. Penrose, The Singularities of gravitational collapse and cosmology, *Proc. Roy. Soc. Lond. A* **314**, 529 (1970).
9. A. G. Riess, The Expansion of the Universe is Faster than Expected, *Nature Rev. Phys.* **2**, 10 (2019).

LHC experiments for long-lived particles of the dark sector

Vasiliki A. Mitsou

Instituto de Física Corpuscular (IFIC), CSIC – Universitat de València,
C/ Catedrático José Beltrán 2, E-46980 Paterna (Valencia), Spain
E-mail: vasiliki.mitsou@ific.uv.es
webific.ific.uv.es/web

Dark matter scenarios are being tested at the LHC in the general-purpose experiments through promptly decaying states. In parallel, new dedicated detectors have been proposed for the LHC to probe dark matter portal theories predicting long-lived particles that decay away from the interaction point: MoEDAL-MAPP, MoEDAL-MALL, FASER, SND@LHC, CODEX-b, MATHUSLA, AL3X, ANUBIS, FACET, milliQan, FORMOSA. In addition, the SHiP beam-dump experiment is planned to operate with the SPS beam to extend the discovery reach for such particles. The detector design and expected physics sensitivity of these experiments is presented with emphasis on scenarios explaining the nature of dark matter.

Keywords: Dark matter; Portal models; Long-lived particles; Displaced vertices; LHC.

1. Introduction

In collider physics, and in particular at the Large Hadron Collider (LHC),[1] there is a growing experimental interest in long-lived particles (LLPs),[2,3] which travel a macroscopic distance before either decaying within the detector or giving rise to anomalous ionisation. In theory, long lifetimes may be due to a symmetry (leading to stable particles), narrow mass splittings, small couplings, or a heavy mediator. In this arena, a class of LLPs called Feebly interacting Particles (FIPs)[4] is characterised by indirect interactions of FIPs with Standard Model (SM) particles through low-dimensional operators. These interactions, commonly referred to as *portals*, may predict dark photons (vector portal), a light dark Higgs boson (scalar portal), axion-like particles (pseudoscalar portal), or heavy neutral leptons (fermion portal).

Scenarios beyond-the-SM (BSM) that introduce a hidden sector in addition to the visible SM sector are required to explain a number of observed phenomena in particle physics, astrophysics and cosmology such as the non-zero neutrino masses, the dark matter (DM), the baryon asymmetry of the Universe and the cosmological inflation. The mystery of DM, in particular, is quite intriguing with around 25% of our Universe invisible (dark) that only interacts through gravity and remains unaccounted for in the SM. This review focuses on the possibility to explore DM with LLPs, as a complementary way to searches performed by the main experiments. ATLAS[5] and CMS[6] look for DM in mono-X final states, in associated production and in resonances via mediators,[7] while LHCb[8] has good prospects for probing DM-portal LLPs after its Phase-I upgrade.[9]

This review is organised as follows. After a brief introduction in Sec. 1, the specially designed LHC experiments to tackle LLPs are concisely presented in Sec. 2. The dark-scalar and dark-vector portals, proposing neutral LLPs that decay in the detector volumes to known particles, are reviewed in Sec. 3 and Sec. 4, respectively. Dark photons at the limit of zero mass, leading to fractionally charged particles, are discussed in Sec. 5. In Sec. 6, other BSM scenarios pertinent to LLPs are highlighted. Finally, possible measurements of new particle properties are outlined in Sec. 7, before summarising and giving an outlook in Sec. 8.

2. Dedicated LLP Experiments at the LHC

There is a constantly growing list of experiments planned for the LHC optimised for the detection of feebly interacting particles. Their projected added value stems mostly from their different operation and geometry parameters: angle w.r.t. the beam axis, the detector volume and distance from IP — probing different ranges of lifetime, couplings to SM and boost (mass) —, their time scale and the detector design.

Besides the detectors highlighted below, there are other, operating or future, non-LHC experiments with sensitivity to DM and other portal models. Such cases include BaBar,[10] existing CERN beam-dump experiments, like the NA48/2,[11] NA62[12] and NA64,[13] the Fermilab SeaQuest[14] and the reactor experiment SoLid.[15] Proposed experiments include the Search for Hidden Particles (SHiP)[16] at the CERN Beam Dump Facility, SHADOWS[17] at the CERN North Area, LUXE-NPOD[18] at DESY, HECATE[19] for the FCC-ee or CEPC, GAZELLE[20] in Bell II at SuperKEKB, SUBMET[21] at J-PARC and FerMINI[22] at Fermilab, among others.

2.1. MAPP – MoEDAL Apparatus for Penetrating Particles

The MoEDAL (Monopole and Exotics Detector at the LHC)[23] experiment is mainly dedicated to searches for manifestations of new physics through highly ionising particles in a manner complementary[24] to ATLAS and CMS. It is the first dedicated *search* LHC experiment. The principal motivation for MoEDAL is the quest for magnetic monopoles[25] and dyons, as well as for any massive, stable or long-lived, slow-moving particle[26] with single or multiple electric charge arising in various extensions of the SM.[27] The MoEDAL detector[28] is deployed around the region at interaction point 8 (IP8) of the LHC in the LHCb[8] vertex locator cavern.

It is a unique and, to a large extend, passive detector based on three different detection techniques: nuclear track detectors (NTDs), magnetic monopole trackers (MMTs) and TimePix pixel devices. MoEDAL has pioneered the quest for magnetic charges, by being the only contender in the high-charge regime[29–32] and by being first in constraining dyons[33] in colliders and in investigating the Schwinger thermal production of monopoles.[34] More analyses, also on electric charges,[35] are ongoing.[36]

The last few years, MoEDAL proposes to deploy MAPP[37,38] in a gallery near IP8 shielded by an overburden of approximately 100 m of limestone from cosmic rays to extent its reach to the *low* ionisation regime. It is envisaged that the first-stage detector, MAPP-1 will be installed during LHC Long Shutdown 2 (LS2) and Run 3.[36] The purpose of the innermost detector, the MAPP-mQP, shown in Fig. 1, is to search for particles with fractional charge as small as 0.001e, the so called *millicharged particles (mCP)*, using plastic scintillation bars. A prototype of the mQP detector (10% of the original system) is already in place since 2017 and the data analysis is ongoing.[39] The Phase-1 MAPP-mQP is going to be deployed in the UA82 gallery in a distance 100 m from IP8.

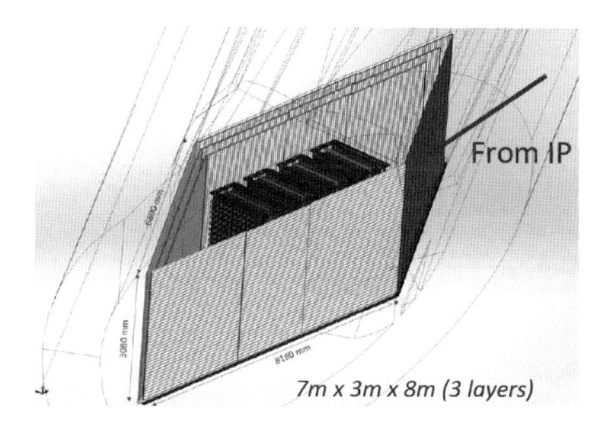

Fig. 1. Diagram of the MAPP-1 detector components: mQP at the centre and three layers of LLP around it.

Another part of the detector, the MAPP-LLP, is deployed as three nested boxes of scintillator hodoscope detectors, in a "Russian doll" configuration, following as far as possible the contours of the cavern as depicted in Fig. 1. It is designed to be sensitive to long-lived neutral particles from new physics scenarios via their interaction or decay in flight in a decay zone of size approximately 5 m (wide) × 10 m (deep) × 3 m (high). The MAPP detector can be deployed in a number of positions in the forward direction, at a distance of $\mathcal{O}(100 \text{ m})$ from IP8. An upgrade plan for the MAPP-1 detector is envisaged for the High-Luminosity LHC (HL-LHC),[40] called MAPP-2, with considerably larger volume than MAPP-1.

Furthermore, the MoEDAL Apparatus for very Long Lived particles (MALL)[37] is intended to push the search for decays of new *electrically charged*, massive and *extremely* long-lived particles, with lifetimes well in excess of a year, by monitoring the exposed MMTs for decay products of trapped BSM particles.[37,38] Quite recently, an independent proposal has been presented to install such absorber volumes near the CMS IP.[41]

2.2. *FASER – ForwArd Search ExpeRiment*

FASER[42] is an approved small and inexpensive experiment designed to search for new particles produced in decays of light mesons copiously present at zero angle at the LHC in Run-3 and beyond. Such particles may be produced in large numbers and travel for hundreds of meters without interacting, and then decay to SM particles. To search for such events, FASER will be located 480 m downstream of the ATLAS[5] IP in the unused service tunnel TI12 (cf. Fig. 12). It is planned to be constructed and installed in LS2 and collect data during Run 3.[43]

An overview of the different detector components is shown in Fig. 2.[44] The magnets are 0.55 T permanent dipole magnets based on the Halbach array design with a radius of 10 cm. There are three scintillator stations for timing, trigger and vetoing incoming charged particles. The electromagnetic calorimeter consists of four spare outer ECAL modules from LHCb. The tracker consists of three tracking stations, each containing three layers instrumented with spare ATLAS semiconductor-tracker barrel modules.

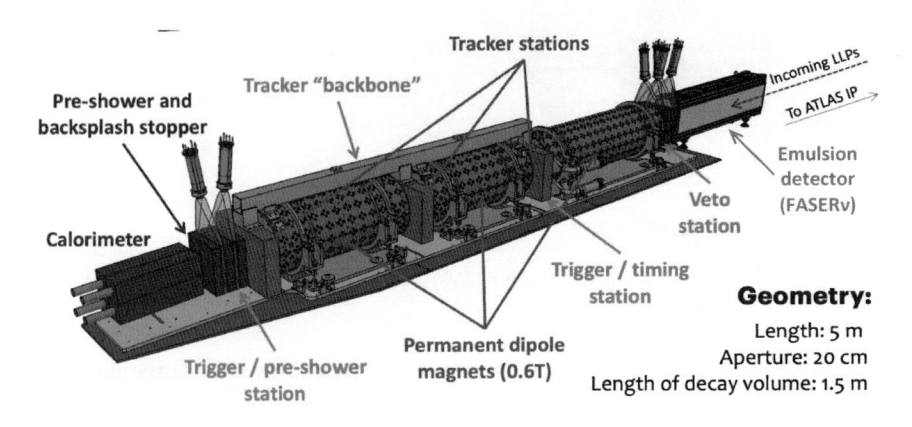

Fig. 2. Annotated schematic view of the FASER detector components.

Moreover, FASERν[45] is designed to directly detect collider neutrinos and study their cross sections at TeV energies. In 2018, a pilot detector employing emulsion films was installed in the far-forward region of ATLAS, also visible in Fig. 2, and collected 12.2 fb^{-1} of pp collision data at a $\sqrt{s}$ = 13 TeV. The first candidate vertices consistent with neutrino interactions at the LHC were observed, an example of which is presented in Fig. 3, with a measured 2.7σ excess of neutrino-like signal above muon-induced backgrounds.[46]

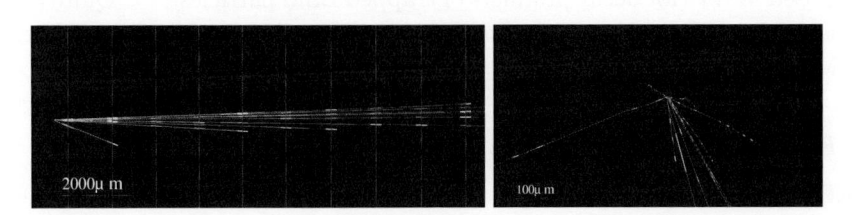

Fig. 3. FASERν event displays of a neutral vertex in the $y - z$ projection longitudinal to the beam direction (left) and in the view transverse to the beam direction (right).[46]

For the HL-LHC, FASER2,[43] a larger successor with roughly $R \sim 1$ m and $L \sim 5$ m is planned to be constructed during LS3 and installed in the LHC Forward Physics Facility (FPF) (cf. Fig. 12). Possible options for FPF locations are an expanded UJ12 cavern or a new cavern ~ 600 m downstream from IP1. Other experiments proposed to be housed in FPF include FASERν2,,[47] a detector with roughly ten times the mass of FASERν, as well as the Forward Liquid Argon Experiment (FLArE),[48] composed of a 10- or 100-tonne-scale liquid argon time projection chamber (LArTPC).

2.3. SND@LHC – Scattering and Neutrino Detector at the LHC

SND@LHC[49] is a recently approved, compact and stand-alone experiment designed to measure neutrinos produced at the LHC and search for FIPs in the unexplored range of $7.2 < \eta < 8.7$, where neutrinos are mostly produced from charm decay. It is a small-scale prototype of the SHiP[50] experiment Scattering and Neutrino Detector (SND). The proposed detector is hybrid, combining the nuclear emulsion technology and electronic detector; a schematic view is provided in Fig. 4. It will be installed in the TI18 tunnel, in a location off-axis with respect to the ATLAS[5] IP1.

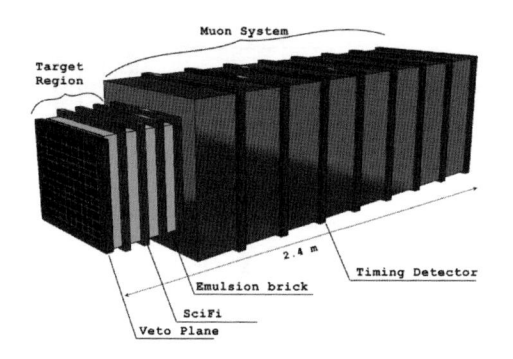

Fig. 4. Annotated schematic view of the SND@LHC detector components.[49]

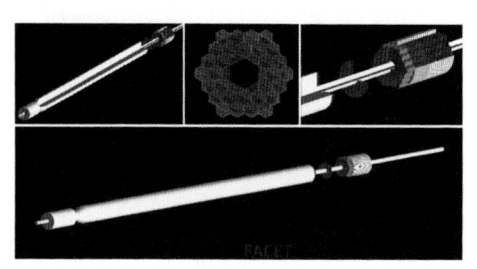

Fig. 5. Diagrams of the detector components of the FACET spectrometer.

2.4. FACET – Forward-Aperture CMS ExTension

FACET[51] is a multi-particle spectrometer to be located at $z \sim +100$ m from the CMS[6] IP5. The detector will have a radius of ~ 50 cm and coverage $6 < \eta < 8$, therefore it will be much closer to the IP and feature much larger decay volume than FASER. It is shielded by about $30 - 50$ m of steel in front of it, which corresponds to $190 - 300$ interaction lengths, λ_{int}. FACET will be fully integrated in CMS and can be used either a forward part of CMS or a standalone detector. Some GEANT4 modelling drawings of the FACET detector components are shown in Fig. 5. If approved, FACET will operate during HL-LHC.

2.5. CODEX-b – COmpact Detector for EXotics at LHCb

CODEX-b[52,53] is proposed as a cubic detector with a nominal fiducial volume of 10 m × 10 m × 10 m to be situated in a transverse location ~ 25 m from the LHCb[8] IP8, as depicted in Fig. 6, corresponding to the pseudorapidity range $0.2 < \eta < 0.6$. It will be composed of six Resistive Plate Chamber (RPC) layers — being fast, precise and cheap for a large-area tracker — at 4 cm intervals on each box face with 1 cm granularity. An additional passive Pb shielding of $25\lambda_{\text{int}}$ with embedded active scintillator veto will reduce IP and secondary backgrounds. It is reminded that IP8 runs at a factor of ~ 10 less luminosity than IP1, IP2 and IP5.

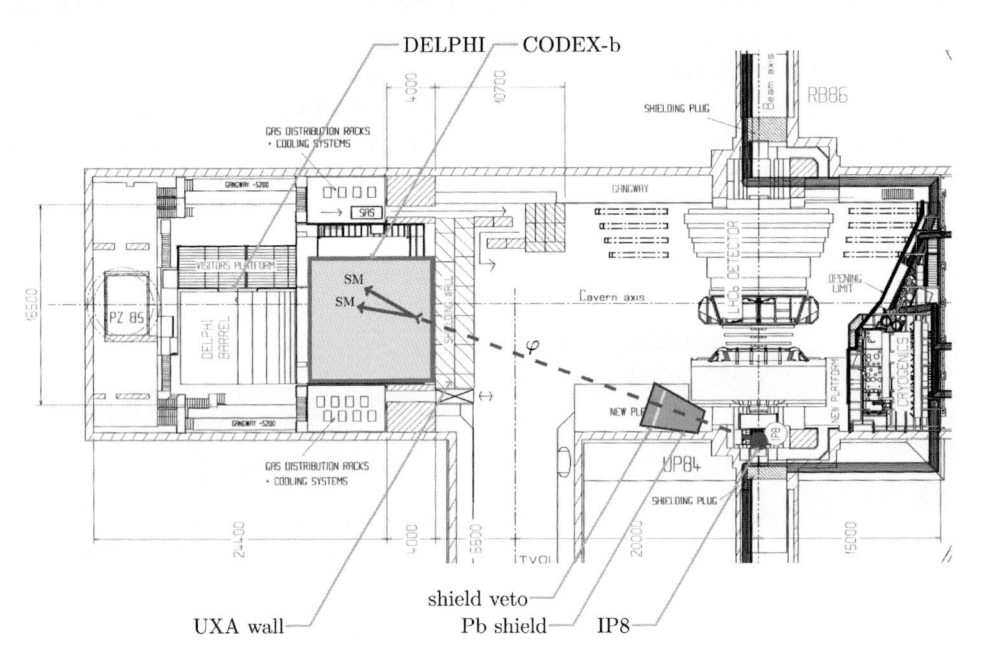

Fig. 6. Layout of the LHCb cavern UX85 at IP8, overlaid with the CODEX-b volume.[53]

CODEX-b will be interfaced with LHCb data acquisition, therefore there will have a unique trigger. Further additions to CODEX-b include calorimetry, which would significantly enhance the physics reach, e.g. photon signatures. Moreover, absorber or pre-shower layers can also perform particle identification, e.g. e/γ separation.

The CODEX-β demonstrator, with a volume of $2 \times 2 \times 2$ m^3, is proposed to be operated during Run 3 to provide proof of concept. Its primary goal is to be integrate with LHCb online, reconstruct K_L^0 and measure background rates. It will provide competitive sensitivity to $b \to s\chi(\to \text{hadrons})$, as well.

2.6. *MATHUSLA – MAsive Timing Hodoscope for Ultra Stable neutraL pArticles*

MATHUSLA[54,55] is a proposed surface detector of a large footprint (area 100 × 100 m^2) and large decay volume (height 25 m) to be located above CMS,[6] as depicted in Fig. 7. The ∼ 90 m of rock between the IP5 and the detector decay volume provides enough shielding for MATHUSLA to work in a clean environment. The air-filled decay volume will be occupied by several detector layers for tracking in a modular way. RPCs and plastic scintillators are proven technologies that meet the specifications. Being a background-free experiment increases the sensitivity to LLPs up to decay lengths of 10^7 m and extends the sensitivity of the main detectors by orders of magnitude.

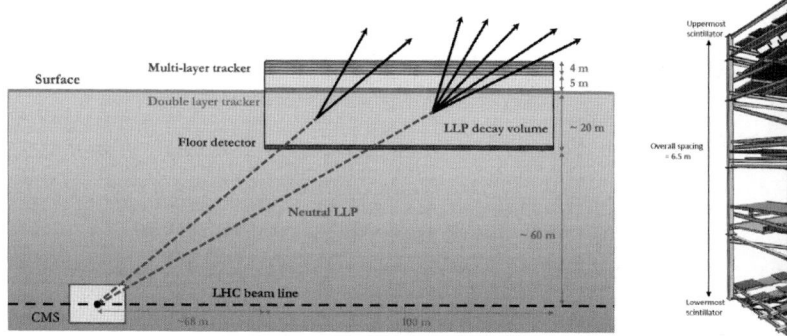

Fig. 7. The MATHUSLA detector layout positioned relative to CMS IP5.[55]

Fig. 8. The MATHUSLA test stand.[56]

A test stand following the concept of the full detector was installed in the surface area above the ATLAS[5] IP, taking data with different beam conditions during 2018.[56] The 2.5 × 2.5 × 6.5 m^3 unit detector is composed of one external layer of scintillators in the upper part and one in the lower part with six layers of RPCs between them, as shown in Fig. 8. The obtained results confirmed the background assumptions in the MATHUSLA proposal.

Moreover, MATHUSLA could act as a cosmic-ray (CR) telescope performing very precise measurements up to the PeV scale.[57,58] By integrating a device with the possibility to measure arrival times and particle densities of extensive air showers, such as an RPC, MATHUSLA can be employed as a CR detector and monitor a big portion of the sky above ($\theta < 80°$), without limitation to inclined events.

2.7. *ANUBIS – AN Underground Belayed In-Shaft*

ANUBIS[59] is an off-axis detector designed for neutral LLPs with $c\tau \gtrsim 5$ m, proposed to occupy the PX14 installation shaft of the ATLAS[5] experiment (cf. Fig. 9(left)), which is not used during regular LHC operation. It will comprise four evenly spaced tracking stations (TS) with a cross-sectional area of 230 m^2 each, shown in Fig. 9(right). The tracking stations will use the same RPC technology as the new ATLAS layers and ATLAS can be used as an active veto of SM activity. The projective decay volume optimises the acceptance for different lifetimes. Two smaller TS prototypes are planned to be installed for Run 3 as a demonstrator.

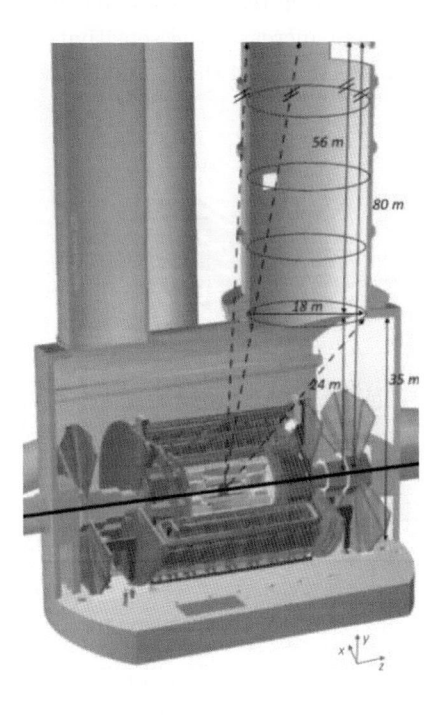

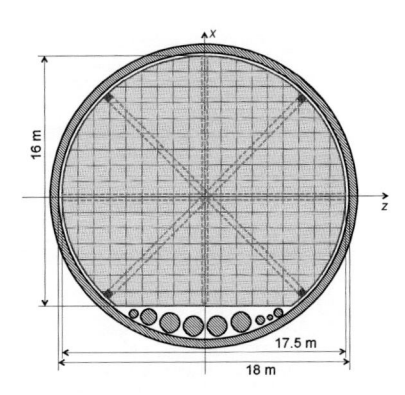

Fig. 9. Left: Location of the ANUBIS detector in the PX14 installation shaft of the ATLAS experiment. Above: One of the four ANUBIS tracking stations in the (x, z) plane. The shaft walls and the ATLAS cavern pipework are shown in gray, the TS in blue and the TS support structure in orange.[59]

2.8. *AL3X – A Laboratory for Long-Lived eXotics*

In the event that ALICE[60] finishes its physics program before the end of HL-LHC, it has been proposed[61] to reuse the L3 magnet at IP2 and the ALICE Time Projection Chamber (TPC) for LLP searches. This proposal requires to move the IP by 11.25 m outside the magnet, as shown in Fig. 10, to allow LLPs to travel before decaying. An additional thick shield and an active veto (D_1 and D_3) will reduce the background. The detector geometry corresponds to a pseudorapidity acceptance $0.9 < \eta < 3.7$. The AL3X configuration is in essence a tracking detector behind a heavy shield, which can be thought of as analogous to a calorimeter that is solely absorber. This permits AL3X to search for much rarer signals in a very low background environment compared to ATLAS and CMS, and in this sense AL3X would be complementary to the existing (and proposed upgraded) multi-purpose detectors.

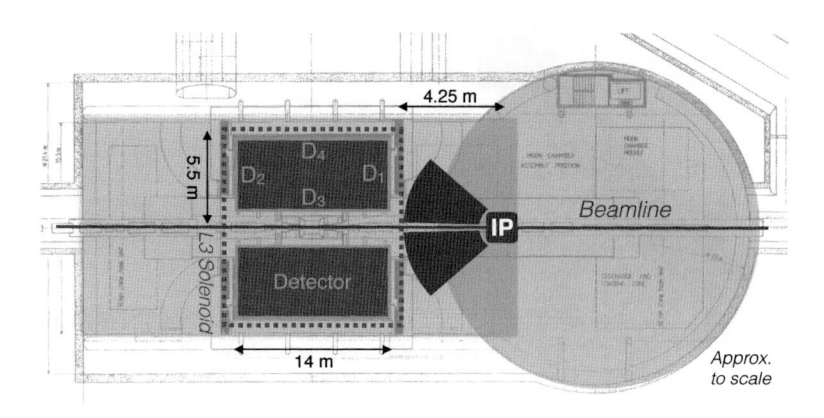

Fig. 10. Schematic view of the AL3X detector layout: the cylindrical TPC (dark green) and the veto and trigger layers D_i (light green). The current L3 magnet is shown (dashed red) for reference.[61]

2.9. milliQan

Just like MAPP-mQP, the milliQan detector,[62,63] to be installed near the CMS[6] IP5, will search for stable *millicharged* particles, unlike the majority of the aforementioned detectors which are sensitive to visible SM particles originating from *neutral* DM decays. The milliQan is located in an underground tunnel at a distance of 33 m from the CMS IP, with 17 m of rock between the IP and the detector that provides shielding from most particles produced in LHC collisions. In order to be sensitive to particles with charges as low as $0.001e$, a large active area of scintillator is required. For Run 3, two detector designs are planned for deployment. The bar detector is made of 0.2 m × 0.2 m × 3 m plastic scintillator bars surrounded by an active μ veto shield. The slab detector will increase the reach for heavier mCPs through 40 cm × 60 cm × 5 cm scintillator slabs.[64]

A small fraction of $\sim 1\%$ of the full detector, the *milliQan demonstrator,* shown in Fig. 11 was installed and operated to measure backgrounds and provide proof of principle. It allowed the first search for millicharged particles at a collider.[65] A data sample of 37.5 fb^{-1} pp collisions at $\sqrt{s} = 13$ TeV has been analysed and no excess over the background prediction observed. The results interpretation in terms dark photons is discussed later in Sec. 5.

2.10. FORMOSA – FORward MicrOcharge SeArch

FORMOSA[66] is also designed to discover millicharged particles, yet in the farforward direction, close to the beam collision axis, where it can benefit from an enhanced mCP production cross section compared to the transverse direction. It is a scintillator-based detector to be hosted in the FPF, shown in Fig. 12. FORMOSA is proposed to start in Run 3 by moving the milliQan demonstrator to UJ12, as a phase called FORMOSA-I, with the full milliQan-type detector, FORMOSA-II, to be deployed at a later stage. The expected physics potential is discussed in Sec. 5.

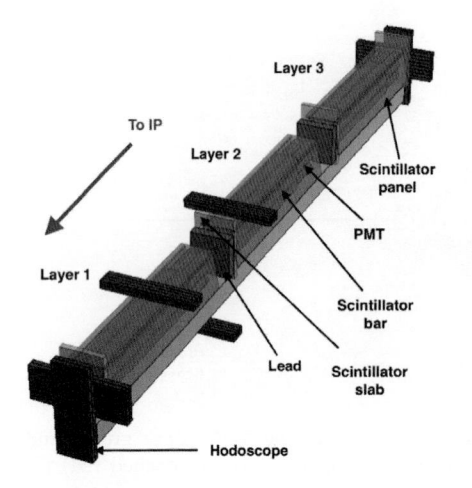

Fig. 11. Diagram of the milliQan demonstrator components.[65]

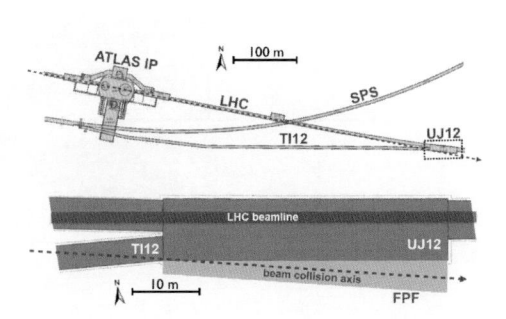

Fig. 12. Location of FORMOSA in the cavern UJ12 or side tunnel TI12 (blue) close to the beam collision axis (red). The FPF extension is shown as a light-blue area.[66]

3. The Higgs Portal

The so-called *scalar portal* involves a new dark scalar S, which mixes slightly with the SM-like Higgs, and provides a simple target for new physics searches.[67] The dark Higgs mixing portal admits exotic inclusive $B \to X\phi$ decays,[a] where ϕ is a light CP-even scalar that mixes with the SM Higgs, with a mixing angle of $\theta \ll 1$. The particle lifetime depends on the degree of mixing. One possible, simple Lagrangian which includes this new dark Higgs mixing is given by[68]

$$\mathcal{L} = \mathcal{L}_{\text{SM}} + \mathcal{L}_{\text{DS}} + \mu_S^2 S^2 - \frac{\lambda_S}{4} S^4 - \epsilon S^2 H^\dagger H, \tag{1}$$

where S is a real scalar field, H is a SM-like Higgs field, ϵ is the portal coupling, and λ_S is a free parameter. The quartic term contains the mixing between the SM Higgs and the new scalar, with the resulting physical fields: the SM Higgs h and the dark Higgs ϕ. Both fields acquire a non-zero VEV and the coupling between these two particles induces new Yukawa-like couplings between the dark Higgs and the SM fermions. In addition, there can appear a non-negligible trilinear interaction term between ϕ and h with the corresponding coupling denoted by λ, i.e. $\propto \lambda h \phi \phi$. Thus, the signal sought after in LLP experiments is two charged lepton tracks originating from dark Higgs decays $\phi \to \ell^+ \ell^-$, in their fiducial volume.

Currently the best experimental limits on dark Higgs production at colliders come from CHARM[69] and LHCb,[70,71] shown in Fig. 13 in the $\sin^2\theta$-versus-m_S plane. If no trilinear coupling is assumed and the background is considered negligible, we derive the exclusion curves for MATHUSLA, SHiP, CODEX-b, MAPP-1

---

[a]D mesons and kaons have much smaller branching ratios into a Higgs-mixed scalar and are neglected.

and MAPP-2 that are shown in the same figure. MAPP-1 during Run 3 (30 fb^{-1}) is expected to provide considerable coverage, when the other experiments will be under construction; from the CODEX-b side, the CODEX-β demonstrator will be in operation. MAPP-2 extents significantly MAPP-1 sensitivity making it competitive with SHiP. As expected, MATHUSLA has better sensitivity in lower mixing angles, thus longer lifetimes, due to its large distance from the IP.

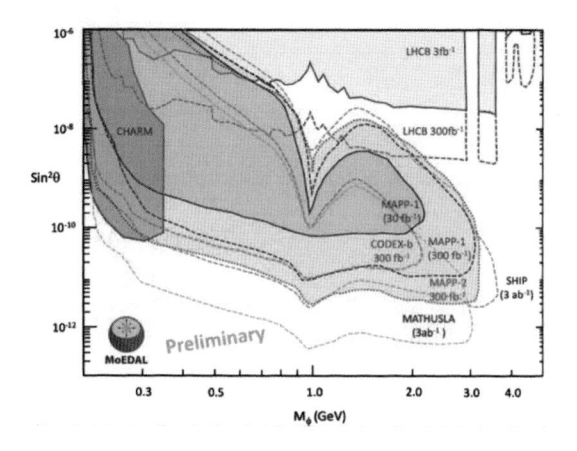

Fig. 13. 95% CL exclusion bounds Projected sensitivity of MoEDAL-MAPP and other experiments for dark Higgs bosons produced in rare B decays at $\sqrt{s} = 14$ TeV. Adopted from Ref. 61.

Assuming now a non-vanishing trilinear coupling λ, the expected sensitivity from the experiments presented in Sec. 2 is shown in Fig. 14. This time, a larger fraction of the parameters space is covered due to the contributions arising from a Higgs in the decay cascade, either virtual, e.g. the $B \to KSS$ mode, or real, e.g. the $h \to SS$. The branching fraction $BR(h \to SS) \sim 10^{-2}$ is considered to remain compatible with the LHC searches for the Higgs to invisible channels. The larger impact is provided by the bigger experiments, MATHUSLA,[72] SHiP,[73] FASER2[68] and CODEX-b,[74] which can explore the region well above the GeV mass scale in a fully uncharted range of couplings.

Dark scalar portals may have cosmological implications, contributing to the observed DM abundance. Dark Higgs bosons may mediate interactions with hidden dark matter that has the correct thermal relic density or resolves small-scale-structure discrepancies. Indeed, there are models with a dark Higgs inflaton strongly favoured by cosmological Planck[75] and BICEP/Keck Array[76] data that constrain the energy scale of inflation. One of these is expected to leave imprints on LHC experiments, such as FASER and MAPP-1.[77]

4. Dark Photons: Neutral Metastable States

A large class of BSM models includes interactions with light new *vector* particles. Such particles can result from additional gauge symmetries of BSM physics. New vector states can mediate interactions between the SM fields and extra dark-sector fields that may eventually play the role of the DM states.

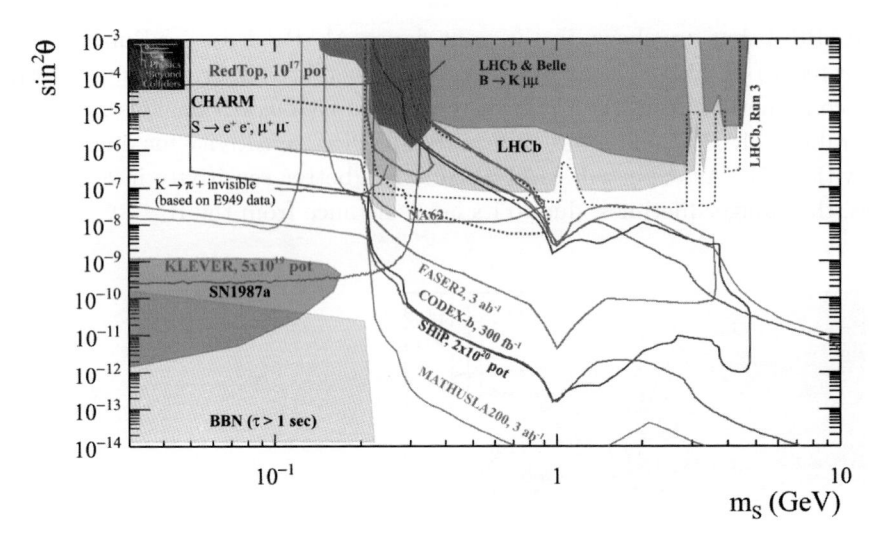

Fig. 14. Prospects on 10-15 year timescale for dark-scalar mixing with Higgs in the $(m_S, \sin^2\theta)$ plane with trilinear coupling $\lambda \neq 0$ and assuming $BR(h \to SS) = 10^{-2}$. The NA62++ and KLEVER curves correspond to $\lambda = 0$, so they are conservative.[74]

The most minimal vector portal interaction can be written as

$$\mathcal{L}_{\text{vector}} = \mathcal{L}_{\text{SM}} + \mathcal{L}_{\text{DS}} - \frac{\epsilon}{2\cos\theta_W} F'_{\mu\nu} B^{\mu\nu}, \qquad (2)$$

where $\mathcal{L}_{\text{SM}}$ is the SM Lagrangian, $B_{\mu\nu}$ and $F'_{\mu\nu}$ are the field stengths of hypercharge and new $U'(1)$ gauge groups, ϵ is the so-called *kinetic mixing* parameter,[78] and $\mathcal{L}_{\text{DS}}$ stands for the dark sector Lagrangian that may include new matter fields χ charged under $U'(1)$,

$$\mathcal{L}_{\text{DS}} = -\frac{1}{4} F'_{\mu\nu} F'^{\mu\nu} + \frac{1}{2} m_{A'}^2 A'_\mu A'^\mu + |(\partial_\mu + ig_D A'_\mu)\chi|^2 + \ldots \qquad (3)$$

If χ is (meta)stable, it may constitute a fraction or entirety of dark matter. At low energy this theory contains a new massive vector particle, a *dark photon* state, coupled to the electromagnetic current with ϵ-proportional strength, $\epsilon A'_\mu J^\mu_{\text{EM}}$.

In the minimal dark photon model, DM is assumed to be either heavy or contained in a different sector. The dark photon, γ_d, decays into SM states (visible decays). The physics potential of the proposed LLP experiments as a function of the dark photon mass $m_{A'}$ and the coupling of dark photon with the SM photon ϵ is shown in Fig. 15, compared with existing bounds from several beam-dump data, e.g. Refs. 79, 80. The sensitivity for dark photons decaying into visible final states is expected to be dominated by SHiP,[73] while FASER2,[68] LDMX[81] and AWAKE[82] will be directly competing with SeaQuest, LHCb, Heavy Photon Search (HPS)[83] experiment, and others. MATHUSLA in this scenario is however not competitive, mostly due to the fact that the dark photon is produced in the forward direction.

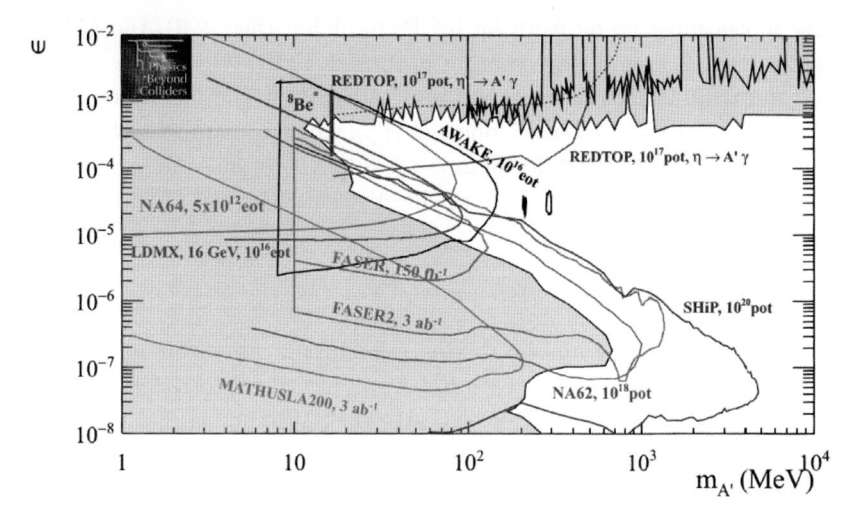

Fig. 15. Future upper limits at 90% CL for a minimal dark-photon model with visible decays in the plane mixing strength ϵ versus mass $m_{A'}$ for various projects on a ~10–15 year timescale.[74]

In a different scenario, light (sub-GeV) DM, χ, may be coupled to a dark photon, constituting a minimally coupled weakly interacting massive particle (WIMP) model. The preferred values of the coupling g_D are such that $A' \to \chi\chi$, with χ potentially scattering further on electrons and nuclei, while $m_{A'}/m_\chi = 3$ is assumed for the masses. Recent studies on DM scattering off electrons[48] and off nuclei[84] in an emulsion detector (FASERν2) and a LArTPC (FLArE) in the FPF showed very interesting sensitivity, probing the thermal-relic region. Neutrino background may be separated from DM signal using energy and angle selection criteria. Such forward detectors open the possibility for performing a direct-detection-type DM search at the LHC.

In inelastic DM, which constitutes a viable and compelling paradigm for light thermal DM, DM couples to the SM only by interacting with a nearly degenerate dark-photon mediator heavier than ~ 10 GeV. For relative mass-splittings larger than $\mathcal{O}(10^{-6})$, DM-nucleon/electron scattering at direct detection experiments is kinematically suppressed. However, at the LHC, where the DM and excited state can be directly produced, for mass-splittings above a few MeV, the excited state can decay back to DM and a pair of SM fermions, often on collider timescales. giving rise to visible displaced vertices. ATLAS, CMS, LHCb, CODEX-b, FASER, and MATHUSLA can detect such DM signals in the cosmologically motivated mass range of ~ 1 − 100 GeV.[85]

5. Dark Photons: Stable Millicharged Particles

Millicharged particles have been discussed in connection with the mechanism of electric charge quantisation and possible non-conservation of electric charge.[86] There are three experiments planned to run at the LHC that are sensitive to the detection of the low ionisation coming from an mCP: milliQan (Sec. 2.9), the MAPP-mQP sub-detector (Sec. 2.1) and, the recently proposed, FORMOSA (Sec. 2.10).

A well-motivated mechanism that predicts mCPs is the introduction of a new massless $U'(1)$ gauge field, the dark photon, $A'_{\mu\nu}$, which is coupled to the SM photon field, $B^{\mu\nu}$. A new massive dark fermion ψ *(dark QED)* of mass M_{mCP}, is predicted, which is charged under the new $U'(1)$ field A' with charge e'. The Lagrangian for the model is given by[62]

$$\mathcal{L} = \mathcal{L}_{\text{SM}} - \frac{1}{4}A'_{\mu\nu}A'^{\mu\nu} + i\bar{\psi}(\slashed{\partial} + ie'\slashed{A}' + iM_{\text{mCP}})\psi - \frac{\kappa}{2}A'_{\mu\nu}B^{\mu\nu}. \quad (4)$$

The last term contains the kinetic mixing, which one can eliminate by expressing the new gauge boson as, $A'_\mu \to A'_\mu + \kappa B_\mu$. Applying this field redefinition reveals a coupling between the charged matter field ψ to the SM hypercharge. The Lagrangian (4) then becomes:

$$\mathcal{L} = \mathcal{L}_{\text{SM}} - \frac{1}{4}A'_{\mu\nu}A'^{\mu\nu} + i\bar{\psi}(\slashed{\partial} + ie'\slashed{A}' - i\kappa e'\slashed{B} + iM_{\text{mCP}})\psi. \quad (5)$$

It is now apparent that the field ψ acts as a field charged under hypercharge with a millicharge $\kappa e'$, which couples to the photon and Z^0 boson with a charge $\kappa e' \cos\theta_W$ and $-\kappa e' \sin\theta_W$, respectively. Expressing the fractional charge in terms of electric charge thus gives $\epsilon = \kappa e' \cos\theta_W / e$.

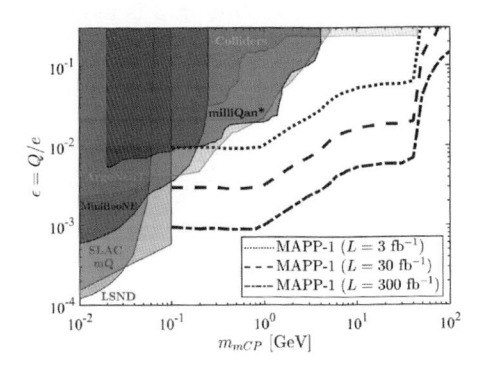

Fig. 16. 95% CL exclusion limits for dark fermion mCPs in the mass vs. charge plane obtained by the milliQan demonstrator[65] compared to previous constraints and to the MAPP-mQP sensitivity for various integrated luminosity assumptions.[87]

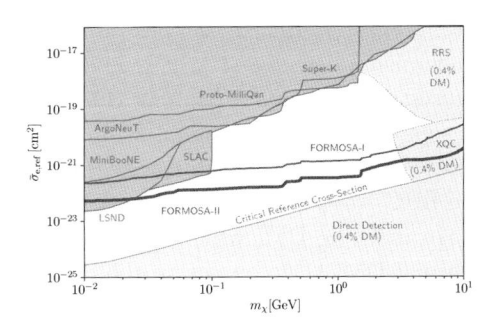

Fig. 17. Sensitivity reaches of FORMOSA in the millicharged SIDM window in terms of the reference cross-section $\bar{\sigma}_{e,\text{ref}}$. In addition to accelerator constraints, constraints from direct-detection experiments (assuming 0.4% DM abundance for the direct-detection experiments) are drawn.[66]

The milliQan 1% scale demonstrator discussed in Sec. 2.9 and shown in Fig. 11 provided the first constraints on mCPs at LHC, as shown in Fig. 16. Pair-production of millicharged particles at 13 TeV is considered through the Drell-Yan process, as well as from Υ, J/ψ, $\psi(2S)$, ϕ, ρ, and ω decays into mCP pairs, and from Dalitz decays of π^0, η, η', and ω. This search excluded mCP masses of $20 - 4700$ MeV for charges varying between $0.006e$ and $0.3e$ depending on mass.[65] MAPP-mQP, on the other hand, can extend these limits especially towards higher masses, while the reach in terms of low charges depends on the integrated luminosity; charges as low as $10^{-3}e$ will need the HL-LHC,[87] as evident from Fig. 16. Similar sensitivity is expected by the full milliQan detector during the HL-LHC run.[64]

When considering DM abundance, mCPs can account for a fraction of it that cannot be detected by direct-detection experiments due to attenuation effects, when the ambient DM has substantial cross section with SM particles making it to lose most of its kinetic energy. For some model parameters,[88,89] the DM particles cannot be detected by ground-based direct detection experiments after interacting with the atmospheric particles and the crust. These DM particles are generally referred to as strongly interacting DM (SIDM). In general, mCP-hunting experiments constrain the larger cross sections, leaving a gap, that can be filled by FORMOSA.[66] This is shown in Fig. 17, where the accessible *reference cross section* versus mCP mass is drawn for accelerator and for direct-detection experiments, together with the FORMOSA expected reach.

In addition to DM, apparent fractionally charged particles may arise as heavy neutrinos with a large enough electric dipole moment (EDM) to yield ionisation in mCP-sensitive detectors. It has been demonstrated that milliQan and MAPP-mQP have very good sensitivity in a scenario where the heavy neutrino is considered to be a member of a fourth generation lepton doublet with the EDM introduced within a dimension-five operator.[90,91]

6. More Portals and Beyond

As highlighted in the introduction in Sec. 1, besides the hidden sectors directly related to DM, namely the dark Higgs and dark photons, there are other portals, such as those predicting heavy neutral leptons and axion-like particles (ALPs). The quest for these objects is of equal interest to Particle Physics open questions, they are often related to dark matter and are similarly relevant to the above mentioned LLP experiments, as those discussed in Secs. 3, 4 and 5. Besides the portal connection to DM, LLPs can probe specific DM models, such as the case of MATHUSLA and dynamical dark matter.[92]

6.1. *Extended neutrino sector*

In the so-called *fermion portal*, new heavy neutral leptons (HNLs) are added to the SM to provide an elegant way to generate non-zero neutrino masses via the seesaw mechanism.[93–95] In type-I seesaw models, one extends the SM by adding neutral right-handed fermions (identified with HNLs) that couple to the SM neutrinos similarly to the coupling between left- and right-handed components of the charged leptons. In a considerable class of these models, the HNLs become long lived and the LLP experiments have good prospects to detect them.[74,96–100]

To highlight an example, in the case of right-handed neutrinos being produced in the decay of an additional Z' boson in the gauged $B-L$ model, which also contains a singlet Higgs that spontaneously breaks the extra $U(1)_{B-L}$ gauge symmetry, MAPP-2 will fill the gap left by CMS, LHCb, MATHUSLA, FASER2 and CODEX-b.[101]

Light sterile neutrinos can account for dark matter,[102–104] while sterile neutrinos with a broad range of masses can account for the baryon asymmetry of the Universe through leptogenesis.[105] Sterile neutrinos may be long-lived in simplified models where the SM is extended with one sterile neutrino[106] or in neutrino-extended SM Effective Field Theories, νSMEFT. Intermediate-mass can be produced in leptonic and semi-leptonic decays of charmed and bottomed mesons, decaying to leptons via neutral and charged weak currents, thus becoming detectable in LHC LLP experiments.[107]

6.2. *Axions & axion-like particles*

Axions, or more generally ALPs, are pseudoscalar pseudo-Nambu-Goldstone bosons arising from approximate Abelian global symmetries beyond the SM which are broken spontaneously at a scale much greater than the electroweak scale. Axions, in particular, were postulated by the Peccei-Quinn theory to resolve the strong CP problem in quantum chromodynamics. ALPs also provide an interesting connection to the puzzle of dark matter, because they can mediate the interactions between the DM particle and SM states and allow for additional annihilation channels relevant for the thermal freeze-out of DM. Prospects for searches for ALPs in LLP experiments are reviewed in Refs. 2, 4, 43, 53, 57, 73, 74, 108.

6.3. *Supersymmetry*

Going even further, supersymmetry (SUSY), a theoretical framework that provides a natural DM candidate, predicts the existence of LLPs. For instance, sleptons, charginos and R-hadrons (namely gluinos, top- or bottom-squarks) with unit electric charge may be detected in the MoEDAL NTDs, in the case they are sufficiently long lived to reach the detector.[109–111]

R-parity violating SUSY also predicts LLPs, such as light long-lived neutralinos $\tilde{\chi}_1^0$ decaying via λ'_{ijk} couplings to charged particles. Benchmark scenarios related to either charm or bottom mesons decaying into $\tilde{\chi}_1^0$ have been considered, in similar fashion as in sterile neutrinos, showing that these experiments can cover various meson production and decay modes and $\tilde{\chi}_1^0$ lifetimes.[53,98,112,113]

7. Post-Discovery Matters

The variety of BSM scenarios predicting LLPs and the sensitivity to those by dedicated LLP experiments — and main detectors equally — begs the question regarding the power to provide qualitative and even quantitative information about the *nature* of these LLPs in the post-discovery phase. The definition of *LLP simplified models*[2] serves as a bridge between specific theoretical models and particular experimental signatures.

The geometry of two-body γ_d/ϕ decays to massless final states can provide information about their velocity and the ability to discriminate between different γ_d/ϕ masses. CODEX-b can reconstruct the γ_d/ϕ velocity to better than 1% using spacial tracking information. If RPC timing information is used in a complementary way to discriminate between slow-moving new states, it is possible to separate between ϕ masses of 0.5 GeV and 2.0 GeV.[52]

If the LLP is pair-produced in Higgs boson decays, it is possible to measure the mass of this particle and determine the dominant decay mode with less than 100 observed events in MATHUSLA. In more general cases, the latter should be able to distinguish the production mode of the LLP and to determine its mass and spin based on the decay products of the long-lived particle.[114]

Moreover, if information from the LLP and the main experiment of the same IP, e.g. MATHUSLA and CMS, is combined, the LLP production mode topology could be determined with as few as ~ 100 observed LLP decays. Underlying theory parameters, like the LLP and parent particle masses, can also be measured with $\lesssim 10\%$ precision.[115]

8. Summary and Outlook

There is an ever increasing interest in long-lived particle searches at the LHC (and not only) to exlore the dark sector besides other unanswered questions in Particle Physics today. Besides the efforts in the main experiments ATLAS, CMS and LHCb, additional complementary experiments have been approved (MoEDAL, FASER, SND@LHC), aiming at data taking in Run 3, or have been proposed (MATHUSLA, CODEX-b, milliQan, ANUBIS, AL3X and others). In addition to these LHC detectors, the SHiP experiment at the SPS is also planned to explore hidden (dark) sectors. Several of these experiments have constructed, operated and analysed the data from small-scale demonstrators that proved the detector concept and provided the first encouraging (physics) results. Others plan to install such prototype for (part of) Run 3, before preparing a complete detector for the HL-LHC operation. The enigma of dark matter is challenged in a different perspective — the lifetime frontier — at the LHC Run 3 and beyond.

Acknowledgements

The author would like to thank the MG16 Meeting organisers for the kind invitation to present this talk. This work was supported in part by the Generalitat Valenciana via a special grant for MoEDAL and via the Project PROMETEO-II/2017/033, and by the Spanish MICIU / AEI and the European Union / FEDER via the grant PGC2018-094856-B-I00.

References

1. L. Evans and P. Bryant, *JINST* **3**, S08001 (2008).
2. J. Alimena *et al.*, *J. Phys. G* **47**, 090501 (2020), arXiv:1903.04497 [hep-ex].
3. L. Lee, C. Ohm, A. Soffer and T.-T. Yu, *Prog. Part. Nucl. Phys.* **106**, 210 (2019), arXiv:1810.12602 [hep-ph].
4. P. Agrawal *et al.* (2 2021), arXiv:2102.12143 [hep-ph].
5. ATLAS Collaboration, G. Aad *et al.*, *JINST* **3**, S08003 (2008).
6. CMS Collaboration, S. Chatrchyan *et al.*, *JINST* **3**, S08004 (2008).
7. V. A. Mitsou, *Int. J. Mod. Phys.* **A28**, 1330052 (2013), arXiv:1310.1072 [hep-ex].
8. LHCb Collaboration, A. A. Alves, Jr. *et al.*, *JINST* **3**, S08005 (2008).
9. M. Borsato *et al.* (5 2021), arXiv:2105.12668 [hep-ph].
10. BaBar Collaboration, J. P. Lees *et al.*, *Phys. Rev. Lett.* **119**, 131804 (2017), arXiv:1702.03327 [hep-ex].
11. NA48/2 Collaboration, J. R. Batley *et al.*, *Phys. Lett. B* **746**, 178 (2015), arXiv:1504.00607 [hep-ex].
12. NA62 Collaboration, E. Cortina Gil *et al.*, *JHEP* **03**, 058 (2021), arXiv:2011.11329 [hep-ex].
13. D. Banerjee *et al.*, *Phys. Rev. Lett.* **123**, 121801 (2019), arXiv:1906.00176 [hep-ex].
14. A. Berlin, S. Gori, P. Schuster and N. Toro, *Phys. Rev. D* **98**, 035011 (2018), arXiv:1804.00661 [hep-ph].
15. SoLid Collaboration, N. Roy, *PoS* **ICHEP2020**, 775 (2021).
16. SHiP Collaboration, M. Anelli *et al.* (4 2015), arXiv:1504.04956 [physics.ins-det].
17. W. Baldini *et al.* (10 2021), arXiv:2110.08025 [hep-ex].
18. Z. Bai *et al.* (7 2021), arXiv:2107.13554 [hep-ph].
19. M. Chrzaszcz, M. Drewes and J. Hajer, *Eur. Phys. J. C* **81**, 546 (2021), arXiv:2011.01005 [hep-ph].
20. S. Dreyer *et al.*, *Physics reach of a long-lived particle detector at Belle II* (5 2021), arXiv:2105.12962 [hep-ph].
21. S. Choi *et al.* (7 2020), arXiv:2007.06329 [physics.ins-det].
22. K. J. Kelly and Y.-D. Tsai, *Phys. Rev. D* **100**, 015043 (2019), arXiv:1812.03998 [hep-ph].
23. MoEDAL Collaboration, J. Pinfold *et al.*, *Technical Design Report of the MoEDAL Experiment*, CERN-LHCC-2009-006 (2009).
24. A. De Roeck, A. Katre, P. Mermod, D. Milstead and T. Sloan, *Eur. Phys. J.* **C72**, 1985 (2012), arXiv:1112.2999 [hep-ph].
25. N. E. Mavromatos and V. A. Mitsou, *Int. J. Mod. Phys. A* **35**, 2030012 (2020), arXiv:2005.05100 [hep-ph].
26. M. Fairbairn, A. C. Kraan, D. A. Milstead, T. Sjostrand, P. Z. Skands and T. Sloan, *Phys. Rept.* **438**, 1 (2007), arXiv:hep-ph/0611040 [hep-ph].
27. MoEDAL Collaboration, B. Acharya *et al.*, *Int. J. Mod. Phys.* **A29**, 1430050 (2014), arXiv:1405.7662 [hep-ph].
28. V. A. Mitsou, *PoS* **CORFU2019**, 009 (2020).
29. MoEDAL Collaboration, B. Acharya *et al.*, *JHEP* **08**, 067 (2016), arXiv:1604.06645 [hep-ex].
30. MoEDAL Collaboration, B. Acharya *et al.*, *Phys. Rev. Lett.* **118**, 061801 (2017), arXiv:1611.06817 [hep-ex].
31. MoEDAL Collaboration, B. Acharya *et al.*, *Phys. Lett.* **B782**, 510 (2018), arXiv:1712.09849 [hep-ex].
32. MoEDAL Collaboration, B. Acharya *et al.*, *Phys. Rev. Lett.* **123**, 021802 (2019), arXiv:1903.08491 [hep-ex].

33. MoEDAL Collaboration, B. Acharya *et al.*, *Phys. Rev. Lett.* **126**, 071801 (2021), arXiv:2002.00861 [hep-ex].
34. MoEDAL Collaboration, B. Acharya *et al.* (6 2021), arXiv:2106.11933 [hep-ex].
35. MoEDAL Collaboration, B. Acharya *et al.*, *Search for highly ionizing particles in pp collisions at the LHC's Run-1 using the prototype MoEDAL detector*, in preparation.
36. V. A. Mitsou, *Results and future plans of the MoEDAL experiment*, in *European Physical Society Conference on High Energy Physics 2021* (2021). arXiv:2111.03468 [hep-ex].
37. J. L. Pinfold, *Phil. Trans. Roy. Soc. Lond.* **A377**, 20190382 (2019).
38. J. L. Pinfold, *Universe* **5**, 47 (2019).
39. M. Staelens, *Recent results and future plans of the MoEDAL experiment*, in *Meeting of the Division of Particles and Fields of the American Physical Society* (10 2019). arXiv:1910.05772 [hep-ex].
40. G. Apollinari, O. Brüning, T. Nakamoto and L. Rossi, *CERN Yellow Rep.*, 1 (2015), arXiv:1705.08830 [physics.acc-ph].
41. J. Kieseler, J. Alimena, J. Simms, T. Aarrestad, M. Pierini and A. Kish (10 2021), arXiv:2110.13837 [hep-ph].
42. J. L. Feng, I. Galon, F. Kling and S. Trojanowski, *Phys. Rev. D* **97**, 035001 (2018), arXiv:1708.09389 [hep-ph].
43. FASER Collaboration, A. Ariga *et al.* (1 2019), arXiv:1901.04468 [hep-ex].
44. FASER Collaboration, M. Queitsch-Maitland, *PoS* **ICHEP2020**, 273 (2021).
45. FASER Collaboration, H. Abreu *et al.*, *Eur. Phys. J. C* **80**, 61 (2020), arXiv:1908.02310 [hep-ex].
46. FASER Collaboration, H. Abreu *et al.* (5 2021), arXiv:2105.06197 [hep-ex].
47. FASER Collaboration, H. Abreu *et al.*, *FASERν2: A forward neutrino experiment at the HL LHC,* https://www.snowmass21.org/docs/files/summaries/NF/SNOWMASS21-NF10_NF6-EF6_EF9-IF0_FASERnu2-006.pdf (7, 2020), Expression of Interest: Snowmass NF10_NF6-EF6_EF9-IF0.
48. B. Batell, J. L. Feng and S. Trojanowski, *Phys. Rev. D* **103**, 075023 (2021), arXiv:2101.10338 [hep-ph].
49. SHiP Collaboration, C. Ahdida *et al.* (2 2020), arXiv:2002.08722 [physics.ins-det].
50. SHiP Collaboration, C. Ahdida *et al.*, *JINST* **14**, P03025 (2019), arXiv:1810.06880 [physics.ins-det].
51. FACET Collaboration, D. Cerci *et al.*, *A Long-Lived Particle and Dark Matter Search at the LHC at z = 80−127 m* https://www.snowmass21.org/docs/files/summaries/EF/SNOWMASS21-EF9_EF8_ALBROW-111.pdf (8, 2020), Expression of Interest: Snowmass EF08+09+10.
52. V. V. Gligorov, S. Knapen, M. Papucci and D. J. Robinson, *Phys. Rev. D* **97**, 015023 (2018), arXiv:1708.09395 [hep-ph].
53. G. Aielli *et al.*, *Eur. Phys. J. C* **80**, 1177 (2020), arXiv:1911.00481 [hep-ex].
54. MATHUSLA Collaboration, H. Lubatti *et al.*, *JINST* **15**, C06026 (2020), arXiv:1901.04040 [hep-ex].
55. MATHUSLA Collaboration, C. Alpigiani *et al.* (9 2020), arXiv:2009.01693 [physics.ins-det].
56. M. Alidra *et al.* (5 2020), arXiv:2005.02018 [physics.ins-det].
57. D. Curtin *et al.*, *Rept. Prog. Phys.* **82**, 116201 (2019), arXiv:1806.07396 [hep-ph].
58. C. Alpigiani, *JINST* **15**, C09048 (2020), arXiv:2006.00788 [physics.ins-det].
59. M. Bauer, O. Brandt, L. Lee and C. Ohm (9 2019), arXiv:1909.13022 [physics.ins-det].
60. ALICE Collaboration, K. Aamodt *et al.*, *JINST* **3**, S08002 (2008).

61. V. V. Gligorov, S. Knapen, B. Nachman, M. Papucci and D. J. Robinson, *Phys. Rev. D* **99**, 015023 (2019), arXiv:1810.03636 [hep-ph].
62. A. Haas, C. S. Hill, E. Izaguirre and I. Yavin, *Phys. Lett. B* **746**, 117 (2015), arXiv:1410.6816 [hep-ph].
63. A. Ball *et al.* (7 2016), arXiv:1607.04669 [physics.ins-det].
64. milliQan Collaboration, A. Ball *et al.*, *Phys. Rev. D* **104**, 032002 (2021), arXiv:2104.07151 [hep-ex].
65. A. Ball *et al.*, *Phys. Rev. D* **102**, 032002 (2020), arXiv:2005.06518 [hep-ex].
66. S. Foroughi-Abari, F. Kling and Y.-D. Tsai, *Phys. Rev. D* **104**, 035014 (2021), arXiv:2010.07941 [hep-ph].
67. B. Patt and F. Wilczek (2006), arXiv:hep-ph/0605188 [hep-ph].
68. FASER Collaboration, A. Ariga *et al.*, *Phys. Rev. D* **99**, 095011 (2019), arXiv:1811.12522 [hep-ph].
69. CHARM Collaboration, F. Bergsma *et al.*, *Phys. Lett. B* **157**, 458 (1985).
70. LHCb Collaboration, R. Aaij *et al.*, *Phys. Rev. Lett.* **115**, 161802 (2015), arXiv:1508.04094 [hep-ex].
71. LHCb Collaboration, R. Aaij *et al.*, *Phys. Rev. D* **95**, 071101 (2017), arXiv:1612.07818 [hep-ex].
72. J. A. Evans, *Phys. Rev. D* **97**, 055046 (2018), arXiv:1708.08503 [hep-ph].
73. S. Alekhin *et al.*, *Rept. Prog. Phys.* **79**, 124201 (2016), arXiv:1504.04855 [hep-ph].
74. J. Beacham *et al.*, *J. Phys. G* **47**, 010501 (2020), arXiv:1901.09966 [hep-ex].
75. Planck Collaboration, Y. Akrami *et al.*, *Astron. Astrophys.* **641**, A10 (2020), arXiv:1807.06211 [astro-ph.CO].
76. BICEP2, Keck Array Collaboration, P. A. R. Ade *et al.*, *Phys. Rev. Lett.* **121**, 221301 (2018), arXiv:1810.05216 [astro-ph.CO].
77. L. A. Popa (10 2021), arXiv:2110.09392 [hep-ph].
78. B. Holdom, *Phys. Lett. B* **166**, 196 (1986).
79. J. Blümlein and J. Brunner, *Phys. Lett. B* **701**, 155 (2011), arXiv:1104.2747 [hep-ex].
80. J. Blümlein and J. Brunner, *Phys. Lett. B* **731**, 320 (2014), arXiv:1311.3870 [hep-ph].
81. A. Berlin, N. Blinov, G. Krnjaic, P. Schuster and N. Toro, *Phys. Rev. D* **99**, 075001 (2019), arXiv:1807.01730 [hep-ph].
82. A. Caldwell *et al.* (12 2018), arXiv:1812.11164 [physics.acc-ph].
83. HPS Collaboration, P. H. Adrian *et al.*, *Phys. Rev. D* **98**, 091101 (2018), arXiv:1807.11530 [hep-ex].
84. B. Batell, J. L. Feng, A. Ismail, F. Kling, R. M. Abraham and S. Trojanowski, *Phys. Rev. D* **104**, 035036 (2021), arXiv:2107.00666 [hep-ph].
85. A. Berlin and F. Kling, *Phys. Rev. D* **99**, 015021 (2019), arXiv:1810.01879 [hep-ph].
86. A. Y. Ignatiev, V. A. Kuzmin and M. E. Shaposhnikov, *Phys. Lett. B* **84**, 315 (1979).
87. M. Staelens, The Search for New Physics at the LHC with the MoEDAL-MAPP Detector and an Investigation of Emergent Magnetic Monopole Like Excitations in an Exotic Condensed Matter System, PhD thesis, Alberta U., (2021).
88. T. Emken, R. Essig, C. Kouvaris and M. Sholapurkar, *JCAP* **09**, 070 (2019), arXiv:1905.06348 [hep-ph].
89. R. Plestid, V. Takhistov, Y.-D. Tsai, T. Bringmann, A. Kusenko and M. Pospelov, *Phys. Rev. D* **102**, 115032 (2020), arXiv:2002.11732 [hep-ph].
90. M. Sher and J. R. Stevens, *Phys. Lett. B* **777**, 246 (2018), arXiv:1710.06894 [hep-ph].
91. M. Frank, M. de Montigny, P.-P. A. Ouimet, J. Pinfold, A. Shaa and M. Staelens, *Phys. Lett.* **B802**, 135204 (2020), arXiv:1909.05216 [hep-ph].
92. D. Curtin, K. R. Dienes and B. Thomas, *Phys. Rev. D* **98**, 115005 (2018), arXiv:1809.11021 [hep-ph].

93. R. N. Mohapatra and G. Senjanovic, *Phys. Rev. Lett.* **44**, 912 (1980).
94. T. Yanagida, *Prog. Theor. Phys.* **64**, 1103 (1980).
95. J. Schechter and J. W. F. Valle, *Phys. Rev. D* **22**, 2227 (1980).
96. F. Kling and S. Trojanowski, *Phys. Rev. D* **97**, 095016 (2018), arXiv:1801.08947 [hep-ph].
97. M. Hirsch and Z. S. Wang, *Phys. Rev. D* **101**, 055034 (2020), arXiv:2001.04750 [hep-ph].
98. D. Dercks, H. K. Dreiner, M. Hirsch and Z. S. Wang, *Phys. Rev.* **D99**, 055020 (2019), arXiv:1811.01995 [hep-ph].
99. C. Arbeláez, J. C. Helo and M. Hirsch, *Phys. Rev. D* **100**, 055001 (2019), arXiv:1906.03030 [hep-ph].
100. G. Cottin, J. C. Helo, M. Hirsch, A. Titov and Z. S. Wang, *JHEP* **09**, 039 (2021), arXiv:2105.13851 [hep-ph].
101. F. Deppisch, S. Kulkarni and W. Liu, *Phys. Rev. D* **100**, 035005 (2019), arXiv:1905.11889 [hep-ph].
102. M. Drewes, *Int. J. Mod. Phys. E* **22**, 1330019 (2013), arXiv:1303.6912 [hep-ph].
103. A. Kusenko, *Phys. Rept.* **481**, 1 (2009), arXiv:0906.2968 [hep-ph].
104. M. Drewes *et al.*, *JCAP* **01**, 025 (2017), arXiv:1602.04816 [hep-ph].
105. F. F. Deppisch, P. S. Bhupal Dev and A. Pilaftsis, *New J. Phys.* **17**, 075019 (2015), arXiv:1502.06541 [hep-ph].
106. G. Cottin, J. C. Helo and M. Hirsch, *Phys. Rev. D* **98**, 035012 (2018), arXiv:1806.05191 [hep-ph].
107. J. De Vries, H. K. Dreiner, J. Y. Günther, Z. S. Wang and G. Zhou, *JHEP* **03**, 148 (2021), arXiv:2010.07305 [hep-ph].
108. J. L. Feng, I. Galon, F. Kling and S. Trojanowski, *Phys. Rev. D* **98**, 055021 (2018), arXiv:1806.02348 [hep-ph].
109. K. Sakurai, D. Felea, J. Mamuzic, N. E. Mavromatos, V. A. Mitsou, J. L. Pinfold, R. Ruiz de Austri, A. Santra and O. Vives, *J. Phys. Conf. Ser.* **1586**, 012018 (2020), arXiv:1903.11022 [hep-ph].
110. D. Felea, J. Mamuzic, R. Masełek, N. E. Mavromatos, V. A. Mitsou, J. L. Pinfold, R. Ruiz de Austri, K. Sakurai, A. Santra and O. Vives, *Eur. Phys. J. C* **80**, 431 (2020), arXiv:2001.05980 [hep-ph].
111. B. S. Acharya, A. De Roeck, J. Ellis, D. K. Ghosh, R. Masełek, G. Panizzo, J. L. Pinfold, K. Sakurai, A. Shaa and A. Wall, *Eur. Phys. J. C* **80**, 572 (2020), arXiv:2004.11305 [hep-ph].
112. D. Dercks, J. De Vries, H. K. Dreiner and Z. S. Wang, *Phys. Rev.* **D99**, 055039 (2019), arXiv:1810.03617 [hep-ph], [arXiv:1810.03617].
113. H. K. Dreiner, J. Y. Günther and Z. S. Wang, *Phys. Rev. D* **103**, 075013 (2021), arXiv:2008.07539 [hep-ph].
114. D. Curtin and M. E. Peskin, *Phys. Rev. D* **97**, 015006 (2018), arXiv:1705.06327 [hep-ph].
115. J. Barron and D. Curtin, *JHEP* **12**, 061 (2020), arXiv:2007.05538 [hep-ph].

Constraining the interactions in the dark sector with cosmological data

Adrià Gómez-Valent[1,*], Valeria Pettorino[2] and Luca Amendola[1]

[1] *Institut für Theoretische Physik, Ruprecht-Karls-Universität Heidelberg,*
Philosophenweg 16, D-69120 Heidelberg, Germany
E-mail: gomez-valent@thphys.uni-heidelberg.de

[2] *AIM, CEA, CNRS, Université Paris-Saclay, Université Paris Diderot, Sorbonne Paris Cité*
F-91191 Gif-sur-Yvette, France

We provide constraints on coupled dark energy (CDE) cosmology with Peebles-Ratra (PR) potential, $V(\phi) = V_0 \phi^{-\alpha}$, and constant coupling strength β. This modified gravity scenario introduces a fifth force between dark matter particles, mediated by a scalar field that plays the role of dark energy. The mass of the dark matter particles does not remain constant, but changes with time as a function of the scalar field. Here we assess the ability of the model to describe updated cosmological data sets that include the *Planck* 2018 cosmic microwave background (CMB) temperature, polarization and lensing, baryon acoustic oscillations, the Pantheon compilation of supernovae of Type Ia, data on $H(z)$ from cosmic chronometers, and redshift-space distortions. We also study the impact of the local measurement of H_0 from SH0ES and the strong-lensing time delay data from the H0LICOW collaboration on β. We find a peak corresponding to a coupling $\beta > 0$ and to a potential parameter $\alpha > 0$, more or less evident depending on the data set combination. We show separately the impact of each data set and remark that it is especially CMB lensing the one data set that shifts the peak the most towards ΛCDM. When a model selection criterion based on the full Bayesian evidence is applied, however, ΛCDM is still preferred in all cases, due to the additional parameters introduced in the CDE model. The model is not able to loosen significantly the H_0 tension. This contribution to the proceedings of the DM1 parallel session of the 16th Marcel Grossmann virtual Conference: "Interacting dark matter" is based on the paper 2004.00610.[1]

Keywords: Cosmology: observations; Cosmology: theory; cosmological parameters; dark energy; dark matter.

1. Introduction

Important observational hints in favor of the positive acceleration of the Universe appeared already more than twenty years ago, thanks to the detection of standardizable high-redshift supernovae of Type Ia (SNIa) and the measurement of their light-curves and redshifts.[2,3] Since then, many other probes have contributed to increase the evidence in favor of the late-time accelerated phase. They range e.g. from the detection of the baryon acoustic peak in the two-point correlation function of matter density fluctuations[4,5] to the very accurate measurement of the cosmic microwave background (CMB) temperature anisotropies by WMAP[6] and *Planck*.[7–9]

---

*Speaker. E-mail: gomez-valent@thphys.uni-heidelberg.de

At the phenomenological level, the easiest explanation for such acceleration is given by the presence of a very tiny cosmological constant in Einstein's field equations, with an associated energy density which is orders of magnitude lower than the quantum field theoretical estimates made for the vacuum energy density. Protecting such low value from radiative corrections is extremely difficult and constitutes the core of the so-called "old" cosmological constant problem, cf. e.g.[10–12] In addition, explaining why the current value of this energy density is of the same order of magnitude as the matter energy density, the so-called "coincidence problem", is considered by part of the cosmological community as another problem that needs to be addressed. The cosmological constant is a pivotal ingredient of the standard cosmological model, also known as ΛCDM or concordance model (cf. e.g. the reviews[13,14]), which can explain most of the cosmological observations with high proficiency. Nevertheless, the aforementioned theoretical conundrums, together with few persistent tensions in some relevant parameters of the model as the Hubble parameter H_0[9,15] and the root-mean-square (*rms*) of mass fluctuations at scales of $8h^{-1}$ Mpc,[16] σ_8 (or $S_8 = \sigma_8 (\Omega_m^{(0)}/0.3)^{0.5}$ [a][17]), with h being the reduced Hubble parameter, motivate theoretical cosmologists to look for alternative scenarios in which these problems can be solved or, at least, alleviated, see[18,19] and references therein. Wherever the solution comes from, i.e. a departure from General Relativity or some sort of new field describing dark energy (DE), it must mimic very well the behavior of a cosmological constant at low redshifts, meaning that the corresponding effective equation of state (EoS) parameter must be very close to -1, and that the new component must not be able to cluster efficiently at low scales.

In this paper we consider a scenario in which dark matter (DM) particles interact via a force mediated by a scalar field, which in turn drives cosmic acceleration. This scenario is referred to as *coupled dark energy* (CDE). It was originally proposed as a means of alleviating the coincidence problem,[20,21] considering not only a potential energy density for quintessence to generate its dynamics, but also allowing an interaction with other sectors of the theory. These interactions extended the original quintessence models.[22–25] They cannot be ruled out *a priori* and, hence, they must be duly constrained by experiments and observations.

Some works already set constraints on this model, but using older cosmological data sets, for instance CMB data from the WMAP satellite and the South Pole Telescope,[26] or considering past (2013, 2015) releases of *Planck* CMB data in combination with other data sets, as e.g. from baryon acoustic oscillations (BAO) and SNIa.[27,28] Intriguingly, these works detected a likelihood peak at a non-vanishing value of the coupling constant. One of our main goals is then to critically revisit and update these results in the light of the recent strengthening of the H_0 tension and of the rich amount of currently available data at our disposal, in particular the *Planck* 2018 CMB temperature, polarization and lensing data, but also other new cosmological data, for instance Refs.[29,30]. For constraints on other models with DM-DE

---

[a]The superscripts (0) will denote from now on quantities evaluated at present, i.e. at $a = 1$.

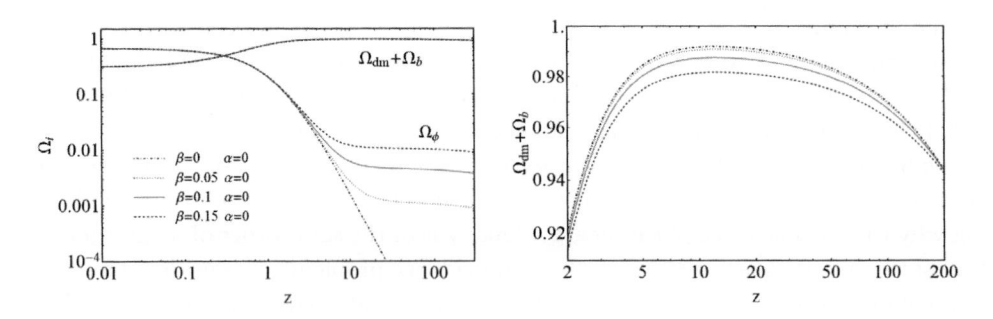

Fig. 1. *Left plot:* Normalized densities $\Omega_{dm}(z) + \Omega_b(z)$ and $\Omega_\phi(z)$ for four alternative values of β and considering a constant potential. The other parameters (including the current energy densities) have been set to the best-fit ΛCDM values from the TTTEEE+lowE *Planck* 2018 analysis.[9] *Right plot:* Here we zoom in the range $z = [2, 200]$ of the $\Omega_{dm} + \Omega_b$ curves in order to better visualize their evolution during the matter-dominated epoch, when the system is near the ϕMDE fixed point. See the text for details.

interactions see e.g.,[31–44] and when the interaction is motivated in the context of the running vacuum models.[40, 41, 45–48]

2. Coupled dark energy

We consider a CDE scenario, as studied in,[21, 49, 50] to which we refer for a detailed description. We here briefly recall the main equations. This CDE model is formulated in the so-called Einstein or observational frame.[51] Apart from the Standard Model of Particle Physics and a potential extension accounting for the origin of the neutrino masses, we consider a dark sector described by the following Lagrangian density:

$$\mathcal{L}_{\text{dark}} = -\partial_\mu \phi \partial^\mu \phi - V(\phi) - m(\phi)\bar{\psi}\psi + \mathcal{L}_{\text{kin}}[\psi], \qquad (1)$$

where ϕ is the scalar field that plays the role of DE, with potential $V(\phi)$, and ψ is the DM field, considered here to be of fermionic nature, just for illustrative purposes. The DM particles interact with the DE due to the ϕ-dependent mass term appearing in (1). Such interaction introduces a fifth force that alters the trajectory in space-time of the DM with respect to the one found in the uncoupled case. As we do not couple ϕ to the standard model sector we avoid the stringent local (Solar System) constraints on the violation of the weak equivalence principle,[52] and also on screened fifth forces that couple ϕ to non-dark matter, e.g. from Casimir experiments,[53] precision measurements of the electron magnetic moment,[54] or measurements of the Eötvös parameter.[55] They have no impact on the CDE model under study.

The variation of the total action with respect to the metric leads as usual to Einstein's equations, and the covariant energy of the joint system DM-DE is conserved. Hence, $\nabla^\mu T^\phi_{\mu\nu} = +Q_\nu$ and $\nabla^\mu T^{dm}_{\mu\nu} = -Q_\nu$, with Q_ν defined as

$$Q_\nu = \beta\kappa T^{dm} \nabla_\nu \phi, \qquad (2)$$

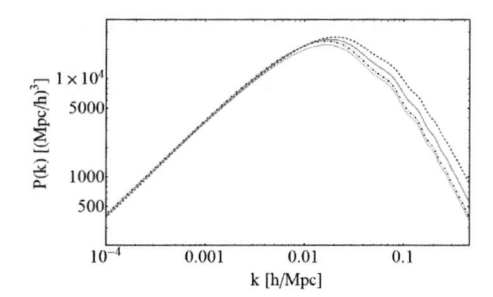

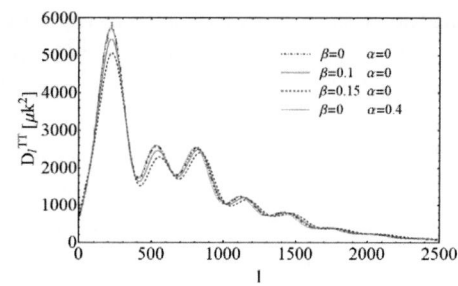

Fig. 2. Theoretical curves of the current matter power spectrum (left plot) and CMB temperature anisotropies (right plot) for the ΛCDM, two CDE models with $\beta = 0.1, 0.15$ and flat potential, and also for the uncoupled Peebles-Ratra model with $\alpha = 0.4$. We set the other parameters as in Fig. 1. In the right plot we also include the observational data from[9] (in red). These figures show: (i) the enhancement of the growth of matter perturbations caused by $\beta > 0$, and the opposite effect produced by $\alpha > 0$; and (ii) the shift to larger multipoles and the amplitude suppression of the acoustic peaks induced by increasing values of β. See the text for further details.

where $\kappa = \sqrt{8\pi G}$, T^{dm} is the trace of the DM energy-momentum tensor, and β controls the strength of the interaction and is in general a function of ϕ. If set to zero, we recover the equations of uncoupled quintessence. In this work we consider β to be a positive constant.

We assume that the Universe is spatially flat, as supported by CMB information from *Planck* 2018 when combined with BAO[9] and/or SNIa,[56] with the curvature parameter $\Omega_K^{(0)}$ constrained to be lower than $\sim 2\%$ at 68% c.l. in ΛCDM. Thus, we can make use of the Friedmann-Lemaître-Robertson-Walker metric, which at the background level reads $ds^2 = a^2(\tau)\left[-d\tau^2 + \delta_{ij}dx^i dx^j\right]$, with a being the scale factor, τ the conformal time, and x^i for $i = 1, 2, 3$ the spatial comoving coordinates. In addition, we treat DM as a pressureless perfect fluid, so the conservation equations for DE and DM can be written, respectively,

$$\beta \kappa a^2 \rho_{dm} = \phi'' + 2\mathcal{H}\phi' + a^2 \frac{\partial V}{\partial \phi}, \tag{3}$$

$$\rho'_{dm} + 3\mathcal{H}\rho_{dm} = -\beta\kappa\rho_{dm}\phi', \tag{4}$$

with ρ_{dm} the DM energy density, $\mathcal{H} = a'/a$, and the primes denoting derivatives w.r.t. the conformal time. All the functions entering these equations are background quantities. If we assume the conservation of the number density of DM particles then their mass evolves as $m(\phi) = m^{(0)} e^{\beta\kappa(\phi^{(0)} - \phi)}$.

A feature of the model is that for $\beta^2 < 3/2$ it has an unstable (saddle) fixed point at $(\Omega_{dm}, \Omega_\phi) = (1 - 2\beta^2/3, 2\beta^2/3)$, where $\Omega_i = \rho_i/\rho_c$, with ρ_c the critical energy density. This fixed point (dubbed ϕMDE in[21]) cannot be reached exactly, since there is also a non-null fraction of baryons, but the system can be quite close to it, since the DM energy density is much larger than the baryonic one (cf. Fig. 1). During this phase the effective EoS parameter, i.e. the ratio of the total pressure and the critical energy density in the Universe, is given by $w_{\text{eff}} = \Omega_\phi$, and hence the deceleration parameter reads $q = \frac{1}{2}(1+3\,w_{\text{eff}}) = \frac{1}{2}+\beta^2$. Thus, the coupling between DM and DE makes the Universe more decelerated with respect to the uncoupled quintessence case during the matter-dominated epoch (MDE). This fact together with the fifth force that enters now as a new source term in the Poisson equation help matter inhomogeneities to grow faster for larger values of β. We also remark that for fixed values of the present energy densities, matter becomes dominant over radiation earlier in time when $\beta > 0$, with respect to the uncoupled case. In the CDE scenario, the equation for the DM density contrast $\delta_{dm} = \delta\rho_{dm}/\rho_{dm}$ at deep subhorizon scales ($k \gg \mathcal{H}$) and when non-linear processes are unimportant, reads,

$$\delta''_{dm} + (\mathcal{H} - \beta\kappa\phi')\delta'_{dm} - 4\pi G a^2[\rho_b\delta_b + \rho_{dm}\delta_{dm}(1 + 2\beta^2)] = 0. \tag{5}$$

If we neglect the contribution of baryons, $\delta_m(a) \sim a^{1+2\beta^2}$. Hence, larger values of β enhance the matter power spectrum (see the left plot of Fig. 2) and leave an imprint on the CMB temperature anisotropies. First, the integrated Sachs-Wolfe effect[57] is enhanced during the MDE earlier than in the uncoupled scenario, in which such effect is only relevant after matter-domination; second, the coupling affects lensing of CMB by large scale structure; the interaction also shifts the position of the acoustic peaks to larger multipoles due to the decrease of the sound horizon at the baryon-drag epoch, which is caused by the increase of the mass of the DM particles. Finally, the amplitude is suppressed, because of the decrease of ρ_b/ρ_{dm} at recombination. These two effects explain why the coupling strength is degenerate with the Hubble parameter today,[27] whose value is related to the position and overall amplitude of the first peak. These and other aspects of the structure formation were already discussed in.[50,58–60] See therein for further details, and also the plots in Fig. 2.

The quintessence potential only rules the dynamics of ϕ in the late-time universe, after the MDE, when the interaction term appearing in the *l.h.s.* of (3) becomes subdominant. It helps to slow down structure formation processes *w.r.t.* the flat-potential scenario (for a fixed value of the current DE density). Hence, it can compensate in lesser or greater extent (depending on its steepness) the enhancement of power generated by the fifth force during the MDE (cf. the left plot of Fig. 2 and its caption).

We employ the Peebles-Ratra (PR) potential,[24,25]

$$V(\phi) = V_0\phi^{-\alpha}, \tag{6}$$

with V_0 and $\alpha > 0$ being constants, and the former having dimensions of mass$^{4+\alpha}$ in natural units, since ϕ has dimensions of mass. We want to update the constraints on the parameters of the CDE model with PR potential that were obtained in some past works using older CMB data, from WMAP and/or past releases of *Planck* (cf.[26–28,61]), so it is natural to stick to (6) here. Also because it has proved to be capable of improving the description of some cosmological data sets with respect to the ΛCDM model in the non-interactive case.[62–64]

The CDE model we are considering (i.e. CDE with PR potential) has three nested models, namely the ΛCDM, the PR model, and the CDE model with flat potential. They are obtained from the full CDE model with (6) in the limits $(\alpha, \beta) \to (0, 0)$, $\beta \to 0$ and $\alpha \to 0$, respectively. For constraints on these scenarios cf. appendix B of Ref.[1].

For recent studies on CDE with an exponential potential, see[31,33,34,43] and appendix C of Ref.[1]. The results are very similar to the ones obtained with the PR potential.

3. Methodology and data

We have implemented the CDE model described in Sec. 2 in our own modified version of the Einstein-Boltzmann system solver `CLASS`.[65] The Bayesian exploration of the parameter space of the model in the light of the various data sets has been carried out with the Monte Carlo sampler `Montepython`.[66] We have also used the `Python` package `GetDist`[67] to process the chains and obtain the mean values and uncertainties of the parameters reported in Table 1, as well as the contours of Figs. 3-4. Finally, we have computed the full Bayesian evidences for all the models and under the various data sets, by processing the corresponding Markov chains with the code `MCEvidence`.[68] This has allowed us to carry out a rigorous model comparison analysis, which we present in Sec. 4.

Our data set is very similar to the one used by the *Planck* collaboration in their 2018 analysis of the ΛCDM and minimal extensions of it.[9] There are some differences, though, e.g. we analyze here the effect of cosmic chronometers and the H0LICOW data, something that was not done there. We refer the reader to Sec. 3 and reference[9] for details.

This is the list of individual data sets that we employ in this work to constrain the CDE model presented in Sec. 2:

- CMB: The main results of this paper are derived making use of the full TTTEEE+lowE CMB likelihood from *Planck* 2018.[9] We also study what is the impact of also including the CMB lensing likelihood.[69]
- BAO: We use the data points reported in[30,70–75]
- SNIa: We consider 6 effective points on the Hubble rate, i.e. $E(z) \equiv H(z)/H_0$, and the associated covariance matrix. They compress the information of 1048 SNIa contained in the Pantheon compilation[76] and the 15 SNIa at $z > 1$ from the Hubble Space Telescope Multi-Cycle Treasury programs.[77]
- Cosmic chronometers (CCH): We have employed the 31 data points on $H(z_i)$ at various redshifts provided in.[78–85] More concretely, we make use of the *processed* sample provided in Table 2 of,[86] which is more conservative, since it introduces corrections accounting for the systematic errors mentioned above.

Table 1. Constraints obtained using the data set combinations described in Sec. 3 on the following parameters of the CDE model: the reduced DM and baryon energy densities, $\Omega_{dm}^{(0)}h^2$ and $\Omega_b^{(0)}h^2$; the reionization optical depth, τ; the Hubble parameter, H_0 (in units of km/s/Mpc); the power of the primordial power spectrum, n_s; the current amplitude of mass fluctuations at $8h^{-1}$ Mpc, σ_8; the coupling strength β; and the power of the PR potential (6). We provide the mean values and 68% confidence intervals for each of them. We also show the differences w.r.t. the ΛCDM of the minimum values of the χ^2-function, and the natural logarithm of the Bayes ratio $B_{\text{CDE},\Lambda}$, as defined in (9)-(10). The (small) negative values of $\chi^2_{min,\text{CDE}} - \chi^2_{min,\Lambda}$ tell us that CDE is able to fit slightly better the data than the ΛCDM; if we use as an alternative estimator the Bayes factor, we find negative values of $\ln(B_{\text{CDE},\Lambda})$, indicating a preference for the ΛCDM model. See Sec. 4 for a thorough discussion.

Parameter/Info. criteria	P18	P18+BSC
$\Omega_{dm}^{(0)}h^2$	$0.1207^{+0.0014}_{-0.0013}$	0.1192 ± 0.0008
$\Omega_b^{(0)}h^2$	0.02237 ± 0.00015	$0.02242^{+0.00010}_{-0.00015}$
τ	0.0538 ± 0.0070	$0.0532^{+0.0075}_{-0.0087}$
H_0	$67.74^{+0.57}_{-0.66}$	68.41 ± 0.38
n_s	$0.9654^{+0.0035}_{-0.0042}$	0.9690 ± 0.0038
σ_8	0.8164 ± 0.0076	0.8104 ± 0.0076
α	< 0.50	0.52 ± 0.17
β	$0.0158^{+0.0067}_{-0.0120}$	$0.0206^{+0.0070}_{-0.0095}$
$\chi^2_{min,\text{CDE}} - \chi^2_{min,\Lambda}$	-0.02	-0.28
$\ln B_{\text{CDE},\Lambda}$	-8.05	-9.95

Parameter	P18+SH0ES+H0LICOW	P18+BSC+RSD
$\Omega_{dm}^{(0)}h^2$	$0.1172^{+0.0012}_{-0.0014}$	0.1187 ± 0.0008
$\Omega_b^{(0)}h^2$	$0.02262^{+0.00016}_{-0.00014}$	$0.02253^{+0.00010}_{-0.00012}$
τ	0.0594 ± 0.0074	0.0501 ± 0.0052
H_0	$69.43^{+0.72}_{-0.53}$	$68.64^{+0.30}_{-0.38}$
n_s	0.9731 ± 0.0042	$0.9701^{+0.0029}_{-0.0033}$
σ_8	$0.8121^{+0.0065}_{-0.0080}$	0.8048 ± 0.0052
α	1.32 ± 0.18	$0.67^{+0.11}_{-0.16}$
β	$0.0294^{+0.0120}_{-0.0076}$	$0.0151^{+0.0073}_{-0.0083}$
$\chi^2_{min,\text{CDE}} - \chi^2_{min,\Lambda}$	-0.58	-1.56
$\ln B_{\text{CDE},\Lambda}$	-7.57	-8.33

Parameter	P18lens+BSC+RSD	P18+BSC+SH0ES+H0LICOW
$\Omega_{dm}^{(0)}h^2$	0.1191 ± 0.0007	0.1185 ± 0.0008
$\Omega_b^{(0)}h^2$	$0.02253^{+0.00013}_{-0.00011}$	$0.02253^{+0.00011}_{-0.00013}$
τ	$0.0525^{+0.0052}_{-0.0064}$	$0.0579^{+0.0069}_{-0.0078}$
H_0	68.45 ± 0.34	$68.79^{+0.35}_{-0.40}$
n_s	0.9685 ± 0.0034	0.9705 ± 0.0034
σ_8	$0.8073^{+0.0048}_{-0.0056}$	0.8120 ± 0.0074
α	$0.25^{+0.09}_{-0.20}$	$0.73^{+0.11}_{-0.27}$
β	$0.0095^{+0.0030}_{-0.0087}$	$0.0206^{+0.0076}_{-0.0100}$
$\chi^2_{min,\text{CDE}} - \chi^2_{min,\Lambda}$	-0.90	-1.34
$\ln B_{\text{CDE},\Lambda}$	-7.83	-7.95

Parameter	P18lens+SH0ES+H0LICOW	-
$\Omega_{dm}^{(0)}h^2$	$0.1182^{+0.0011}_{-0.0010}$	-
$\Omega_b^{(0)}h^2$	$0.02259^{+0.00014}_{-0.00016}$	-
τ	$0.0637^{+0.0065}_{-0.0096}$	-
H_0	68.99 ± 0.51	-
n_s	0.9713 ± 0.0037	-
σ_8	0.8160 ± 0.0068	-
α	$0.33^{+0.19}_{-0.23}$	-
β	$0.0197^{+0.0094}_{-0.0084}$	-
$\chi^2_{min,\text{CDE}} - \chi^2_{min,\Lambda}$	-1.46	-
$\ln B_{\text{CDE},\Lambda}$	-8.75	-

- Redshift-spcae distortions (RSD): We also use large-scale structure measurements from the anisotropic clustering of galaxies in redshift space. Galaxy redshift surveys provide constraints on the product of the growth rate of structure, $f(z) = \frac{d \ln \delta_m(a)}{d \ln a}$, and the *rms* of mass fluctuations at scales of $8h^{-1}$ Mpc, $\sigma_8(z)$. The data points employed in this work are found in Refs.[30,71,87–95]. The internal correlations between the BAO and RSD data from[71] and[30] have been duly taken into account through the corresponding covariance matrices provided in these two references.
- SH0ES: In some of our data set combinations we include the prior on the Hubble parameter, $H_{0,\text{SH0ES}} = (74.03 \pm 1.42)$ km/s/Mpc obtained by the SH0ES Team with the cosmic distance ladder method.[15] This value of the Hubble parameter is in 4.4σ tension with the TTTEEE+lowE+lensing best-fit ΛCDM model of *Planck* 2018,[9] $H_0 = 67.36 \pm 0.54$ km/s/Mpc.
- H0LICOW: In combination with the prior on H_0 from SH0ES we also use the angular diameter distances reported by the H0LICOW collaboration. They analyze six gravitationally lensed quasars of variable luminosity. After measuring the time delay between the deflected light rays and modeling the lenses they are able to measure the so-called time-delay distances $D_{\Delta t}$ (cf.[29] and references therein). We use their reported six time-delay distances (one for each lensed system), and one distance to the deflector B1608+656, which according to the authors of[29] is uncorrelated with the corresponding $D_{\Delta t}$. The relevant information for building the likelihood can be found in Tables 1 and 2 of,[29] and their captions. Assuming the concordance model, these distances lead to a value of $H_0 = (73.3^{+1.7}_{-1.8})$ km/s/Mpc, which is in 3.2σ tension with the one obtained from the TTTEEE+lowE+lensing analysis by *Planck*.[9]

For more detailed information about these data sets see Ref.[1] and the original observational works.

We proceed now to describe the data set combinations under which we have obtained the main results of this work. They are discussed in detail in Sec. 4. We put constraints using the following combinations: (i) TTTEEE+lowE CMB data from *Planck* 2018,[9] in order to see the constraining power of the CMB when used alone, and also to check whether these data lead to a higher value of H_0 than in the ΛCDM. For simplicity, we will refer to this data set as P18 throughout the paper; (ii) P18+BSC, with BSC denoting the background data set BAO+SNIa+CCH; (iii) We add on top of the latter the linear structure formation information contained in the RSD data, P18+BSC+RSD; (iv) We study the impact of the CMB lensing by also adding the corresponding likelihood, P18lens+BSC+RSD; (v) Finally, we analyze the impact of the prior on H_0 from SH0ES[15] and the H0LICOW angular diameter distances[29] by using the data sets P18+SH0ES+H0LICOW, P18lens+SH0ES+H0LICOW and P18+BSC+SH0ES+H0LICOW. The distance ladder and strong-lensing time delay measurements of the Hubble constant are completely independent (see e.g. the reviews[96,97]). When combined, they lead to

$$H_{0,comb} = (73.74 \pm 1.10) \, \text{km/s/Mpc}, \tag{7}$$

in 5.2σ tension with the best-fit ΛCDM value reported by *Planck* 2018.[9] Hence, it is interesting to check what is the response of the CDE model under these concrete data sets, and to compare the results with those obtained using only the CMB likelihood.

4. Results

Our main results are presented in Table 1 and Figs. 3-4. When we only employ the CMB temperature and polarization data from *Planck* 2018[9] (i.e. the P18 data set) to constrain the CDE model, the fitting values obtained for α and β are compatible at 1σ c.l. with 0, i.e. with a cosmological constant and no interaction in the dark sector (cf. the first row, first column in Table 1). The value of H_0 remains low, roughly 4.1σ below the cosmic distance ladder measurement of.[15] Similarly, when we combine *Planck* with BSC background data or with BSC+RSD, we get a value of H_0 which is 3.8σ and 3.7σ away from the SH0ES value, respectively.

As we have explained in Sec. 2, there is a degeneracy between the strength of the fifth force, i.e. the parameter β, and the Hubble parameter. CDE is in principle able to lower the value of the sound horizon at the decoupling time, r_s, and the amplitude of the first peak of the $\mathcal{D}_l^{TT}$'s. The CMB data fix with high precision the angle $\theta_* = r_s/D_A^{(c)}(z_{dec})$, with $D_A^{(c)}(z_{dec})$ the comoving angular diameter distance to the CMB last scattering surface. This means that in order to keep this ratio constant, H_0 will tend to grow for increasing values of the coupling strength, so that $D_A^{(c)}(z_{dec})$ decreases and compensates in this way the lowering of r_s, while keeping the height of the first peak compatible with data. This positive correlation between H_0 and β can be appreciated in the left-most contour plot of Fig. 3. The latter shows 1 and 2σ posterior probabilities for a selection of cosmological parameters. As discussed, we confirm from the first plot a mild degeneracy between H_0 and β. The strength of the fifth force does not seem to be very degenerate with σ_8 nor with the potential parameter α.

The impact of adding background data on top of P18 can be grasped by looking at the one-dimensional posterior distributions of Fig. 3 (in blue), and also at the numbers of the first row/second column of Table 1. Using the P18+BSC combined data set we find that β and α are now ~ 2.5 and $\sim 3.1\sigma$ away from 0, respectively. The values of H_0 and σ_8, are however compatible at 1σ with the ones obtained using only the P18 data set. They are also fully compatible with those obtained with the ΛCDM under the same data set, which read: $H_0 = (68.29 \pm 0.37)$ km/s/Mpc, $\sigma_8 = 0.812^{+0.006}_{-0.008}$. The peaks in β and α may indicate a mild preference of low-redshift data, when combined with the CMB, for a non-null interaction in the dark sector and a running quintessence potential. As noted already in,[28] we remark that this preference does not seem to correspond to a large improvement in the minimum

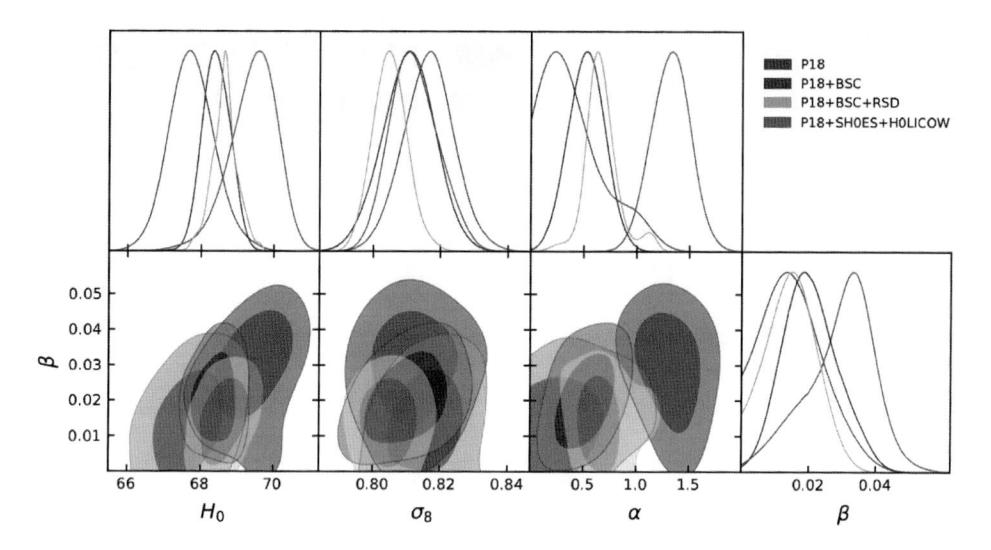

Fig. 3. 1 and 2σ confidence contours obtained using some of the combined data sets described in Sec. 3 in the (H_0, β), (σ_8, β), and (α, β) planes, together with the marginalized one-dimensional posterior distributions for these parameters. See the discussion of these results in Sec. 4.

value of χ^2 with respect to the ΛCDM: under the P18+BSC data set, $\chi^2_{min,\text{CDE}} - \chi^2_{min,\Lambda}$ is negative, but very close to 0, which means that the CDE model only is able to improve the description of the data in a very marginal way.

The addition of the RSD data to the P18+BSC combined data set doesn't change much the result: there is a very small shift in the peak of the one-dimensional posterior distribution for α to larger values and the one for β to lower ones (see the yellow curves in Fig. 3). These two facts reduce a little bit the value of σ_8. The aforesaid peaks are now ~ 5 and $\sim 2\sigma$ away from 0, respectively, with a reduction of χ^2_{min} w.r.t. the ΛCDM of 1.56 units (cf. Table 1, second row/second column), i.e. pointing to a very small preference for CDE. The value of H_0 is almost unchanged.

We find important to highlight the specific impact of CMB lensing data with respect to the P18+BSC+RSD data set. If we include also the CMB lensing information, i.e. if we consider the P18lens+BSC+RSD combined data set, posterior probabilities squeeze, as expected, towards the ΛCDM values. This can be seen in Fig. 4, and also in the third row/first column of Table 1.

In order to further evaluate the level at which the degeneracy observed in the (H_0,β)-plane can alleviate the tension in the Hubble parameter between *Planck* and {SH0ES, H0LICOW} data, we perform a Monte Carlo analysis combining those data within the CDE model: results are shown in the second row/first column in Table 1 and correspond to red contours in Fig. 3. In this case, the best fit corresponds to a value of $\beta = 0.0294^{+0.0120}_{-0.0076}$, i.e. at 3σ from zero coupling, a value of $\alpha = 1.32 \pm 0.18$, with $\alpha > 0$ at $\sim 7\sigma$ c.l., and $H_0 = (69.43^{+0.72}_{-0.53})$ km/s/Mpc. The raise of H_0 is

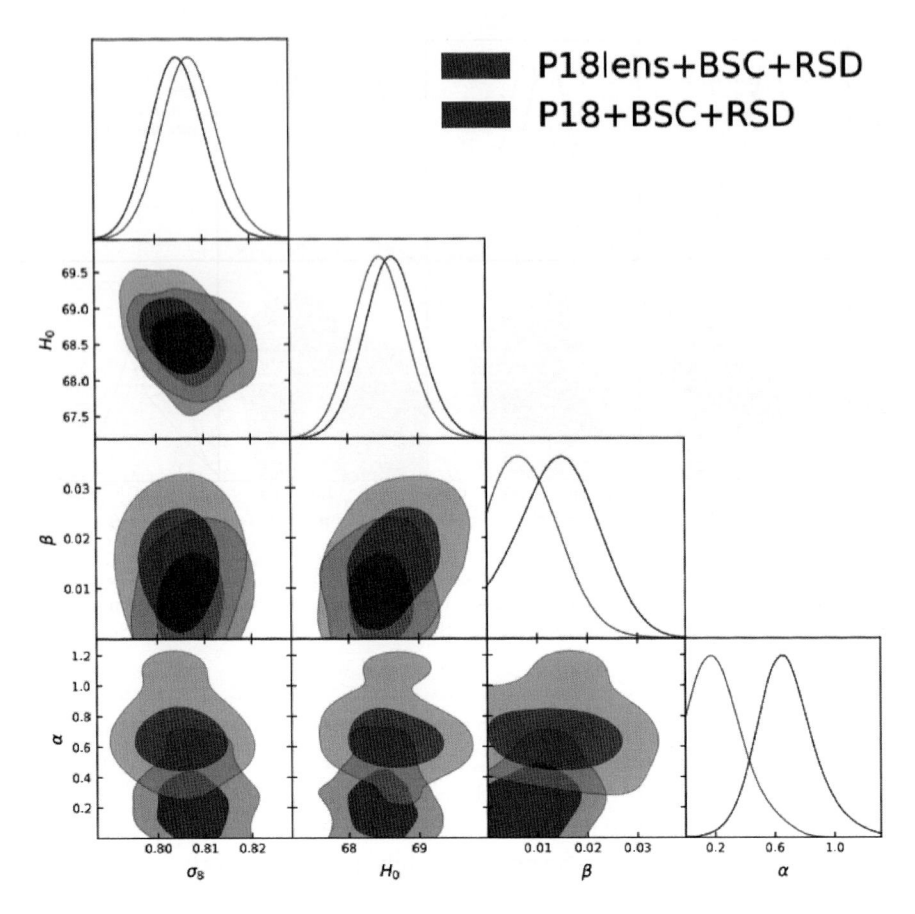

Fig. 4. 1 and 2σ confidence contours obtained with the P18+BSC+RSD and P18lens+BSC+RSD data sets in the most relevant two-dimensional planes of the CDE model parameter space. They allow us to see what is the impact of the CMB lensing on our results. We also show the corresponding marginalized one-dimensional posterior distributions for all the parameters. See the related comments in Sec. 4.

possible thanks to the increase of β, which in turn needs also larger values of α. The tension with the SH0ES+H0LICOW measurement (7) is slightly reduced from 4.8σ (when only P18 is used to constrain the model, cf. the first row/first column of Table 1) to 3.5σ (when also the SH0ES+H0LICOW data are considered). This shifts the H_0 value 1.9σ higher than the best fit using the P18 data set alone, within CDE. Combining also with background data, such as BSC, can partially break degeneracies and leads to $\alpha = 0.73^{+0.11}_{-0.27}$, with $\alpha > 0$ at 3.8σ and $H_0 = (68.79^{+0.35}_{-0.40})$ km/s/Mpc at 4.3σ from the SH0ES+H0LICOW value (7), reducing the chance of CDE to alleviate the tension, as shown in the third row/second column of the table. Finally, the impact of adding CMB lensing is shown in the last row, where now $\beta = 0.0197^{+0.0094}_{-0.0084}$ and $\alpha = 0.33^{+0.19}_{-0.23}$, with $\beta > 0$ and $\alpha > 0$ at 2.2σ and 1.6σ, respectively, i.e. shifting back towards ΛCDM. In this case $H_0 = (68.99 \pm 0.51)$ km/s/Mpc, 3.9σ away from the SH0ES+H0LICOW value (7) and even more had we included also BSC.

Finally, we can further quantify the relative ability of the CDE model to describe the various data sets *w.r.t.* the ΛCDM cosmology using the Bayes ratio, in alternative to the more approximate χ^2 estimate we mentioned so far. Given a data set $\mathcal{D}$, the probability of a certain model M_i to be the best one among a given set of models $\{M\}$ reads,

$$P(M_i|\mathcal{D}) = \frac{P(M_i)\mathcal{E}(\mathcal{D}|M_i)}{P(\mathcal{D})}, \qquad (8)$$

where $P(M_i)$ is the prior probability of the model M_i and $P(\mathcal{D})$ the probability of having the data set $\mathcal{D}$. Obviously, the normalization condition $\sum_{j \in \{M\}} P(M_j) = 1$ must be fulfilled. The quantity $\mathcal{E}(\mathcal{D}|M_i)$ is the so-called marginal likelihood or evidence. If the model M_i has n parameters $p_1^{M_i}, p_2^{M_i}, ..., p_n^{M_i}$, the evidence takes the following form,

$$\mathcal{E}(\mathcal{D}|M_i) = \int \mathcal{L}(\mathcal{D}|\vec{p}^{M_i}, M_i)\pi(\vec{p}^{M_i})d^n p^{M_i}, \qquad (9)$$

with $\mathcal{L}(\mathcal{D}|\vec{p}^{M_i}, M_i)$ being the likelihood and $\pi(\vec{p}^{M_i})$ the prior of the parameters entering the model M_i. The evidence is larger for those models that have more overlapping volume between the likelihood and the prior distributions, but penalizes the use of additional parameters having a non-null impact on the likelihood. Hence, the evidence constitutes a good way of quantifying the performance of the model by implementing in practice the Occam razor principle. If we compare the CDE and ΛCDM models by assuming equal prior probability for both of them, i.e. $P(\text{CDE}) = P(\Lambda\text{CDM})$, then we find that the ratio of their associated probabilities is directly given by the ratio of their corresponding evidences, i.e.

$$\frac{P(\text{CDE}|\mathcal{D})}{P(\Lambda\text{CDM}|\mathcal{D})} = \frac{\mathcal{E}(\mathcal{D}|\text{CDE})}{\mathcal{E}(\mathcal{D}|\Lambda\text{CDM})} \equiv B_{\text{CDE},\Lambda}. \qquad (10)$$

This is known as Bayes ratio and is the quantity we are interested in. For more details we refer the reader to.[18,98,99] Notice that the computation of (10) is not an easy task in general, since we usually work with models with a high number of (mostly nuisance) parameters, so the integrals under consideration becomes quite involved. We have computed the evidences numerically using the Markov chains obtained from the Monte Carlo analyses and with the aid of the numerical code `MCEvidence`,[68] which is publicly available (cf. Sec. 3). We report the values obtained for the natural logarithm of the Bayes ratio (10) in the last row of Table 1. For all the data sets under study we find values of $\ln(B_{\text{CDE},\Lambda}) < -5$, which point to a preference of the ΛCDM over the CDE model according to Jeffreys' scale.[18,98,99] Although the CDE model we are studying here is able to reduce slightly the value of χ^2_{min} w.r.t. the ΛCDM, it has two additional parameters, namely α and β. Moreover, the initial value of the scalar field, ϕ_{ini}, is also left free in the Monte Carlo analysis, cf. Appendix A of Ref.[1] for details[b]. It turns out that the decrease in χ^2_{min} is insufficient to compensate the penalization introduced by the use of these extra parameters. If instead of using the evidences (9) and the Bayes ratio (10) to perform the model comparison we make use of e.g. the Akaike,[100] Bayesian[101] or Deviance[102] information criteria, we reach similar conclusions[c]. We want to note, though, that all these information criteria are approximations of the exact Bayesian approach. Although they allow to skip the demanding computation of the evidence (9), they are only reliable when the posterior distribution is close to a multivariate Gaussian (which is not the case under study), and the Akaike and Bayesian criteria do not take into account the impact of priors nor the existing correlations between the parameters.

Similar results and conclusions are reached using an exponential potential for the scalar field, instead of (6). See appendix C of Ref.[1].

Finally, it is worth to mention that our results are compatible with the ones obtained in the context of the Ricci running vacuum models (RVMs) of type I recently studied in Ref.[48], in which there is also an interaction in the dark sector between dark matter and a dynamical vacuum component with $p_{vac} = -\rho_{vac}$ and $\rho_{vac}(\mathcal{R}) = \frac{3}{8\pi G_N}\left(c_0 + \frac{\nu}{12}\mathcal{R}\right)$, where $\mathcal{R} = 12H^2 + 6\dot{H}$ is the Ricci scalar. These models can be motivated using renormalization group arguments in QFT in curved space-time, see Refs.[12,103] and references therein. In Ref.[48] the authors show that these RVMs are also unable to alleviate the cosmological tensions significantly when the interaction is active around the CMB decoupling time. Allowing for a late-time activation of the interaction around $z \sim 1$, with an energy transfer from the vacuum to the matter sectors, it is possible to mitigate the σ_8 tension due to the increase of the relative amount of vacuum energy with respect to dark matter in the past. Nevertheless, the H_0 tension persists. Other Ricci RVMs (those of Type II) are able to soften both tensions at a time, see[48] for further details.

5. Conclusions

Cosmological observations help to test the dark sector, and in particular interactions between dark matter particles, mediated by a dark energy scalar field, as in CDE cosmologies. Up to a conformal transformation, this is another way of testing gravity at large scales. In this paper we carried out this task in one of the simplest and most studied models, namely, a dark energy-dark matter conformal coupling with a

---

[b]In the computation of the evidence (9) for the CDE model we have employed the following flat priors for the extra parameters: $0 < \beta < 0.1$, $0 < \alpha < 2$, and $0 < \kappa\phi_{ini} < 50$. Slightly broader or tighter priors can be considered, but $\ln(B_{CDE,\Lambda})$ only changes logarithmically, so our conclusions are not very sensitive to them.

[c]For instance, Akaike criterion[100] is given by AIC = $\chi^2_{min} + 2n$, where n is the number of parameters in the model (the degree of correlation between them is not taken into account). Considering that CDE with PR potential has an effective number of parameters between 2 and 3 we find $2.5 < AIC_{CDE} - AIC_\Lambda < 6$ for the scenarios explored in Table 1, which leads to a positive preference for ΛCDM, again using Jeffreys' scale.[18,98,99]

Peebles-Ratra potential. CDE might probe helpful to explain the well-known tension between local and cosmological values of H_0. Any detection of a varying dark energy potential or interaction would clearly constitute a major result and it is therefore important to monitor the constraints that newer data impose. This is particularly true in view of earlier results that detected a non-zero value of the coupling β.[27,28]

We confirm the existence of a peak in the marginalized posterior distribution for β and α, more or less evident depending on the data set combination. While for P18 + SH0ES + H0LICOW $\beta > 0$ at 3σ and $\alpha > 0$ at nearly 7σ, inclusion of background data reduces the evidence to $\beta > 0$ at 2.3σ and $\alpha > 0$ at nearly 3.8σ. Inclusion of CMB lensing shifts both values to be compatible with ΛCDM within 2σ. We find it important to stress that specifically CMB lensing prefers ΛCDM. In all cases, we find that, overall, the peak does not correspond to a better Bayes ratio and ΛCDM remains the favored model when employing Bayesian model comparison, given the extra parameters introduced within the model. With regard to H_0, we find that under the P18+SH0ES+H0LICOW combined data set the simple coupled model with constant coupling investigated in this work leads to a value in 3.5σ tension with (7), or in 4.3σ tension when including further background data. The values of σ_8 are also similar to those found in the ΛCDM (i.e. $\sigma_8 \sim 0.80 - 0.82$), even when RSD data are considered together with CMB and background data. In this case we find $\beta = 0.010^{+0.003}_{-0.009}$ and $\beta = 0.015^{+0.007}_{-0.008}$, with and without CMB lensing, respectively. For the values of the coupling strength preferred by the data we find the typical increase of the mass of the DM particles to be $m(\phi_{ini})/m^{(0)} - 1 \lesssim \mathcal{O}(1)\%$.

The question that naturally arises is then, which modification of CDE can help alleviating the tensions? One can immediately suppose that a varying β can go some way towards this. Or, it could be that a model with both energy- and momentum-couplings (see e.g.[104]), which can introduce a weaker gravity, helps with the tensions. These issues will be investigated in future publications.

Acknowledgments

I want to express my most sincere gratitude to Prof. Mavromatos for his invitation to give my talk at the very interesting DM1 parallel session of the MG16 Meeting. I also want to thank Prof. Luca Amendola and Valeria Pettorino for their collaboration in the work my presentation of July 5th 2021 was based on, namely arXiv:2004.00610.[1]

References

1. A. Gómez-Valent, V. Pettorino and L. Amendola, Update on coupled dark energy and the H_0 tension, *Phys. Rev. D* **101**, p. 123513 (2020).
2. A. G. Riess *et al.*, Observational evidence from supernovae for an accelerating universe and a cosmological constant, *Astron. J.* **116**, 1009 (1998).
3. S. Perlmutter *et al.*, Measurements of Ω and Λ from 42 high redshift supernovae, *Astrophys. J.* **517**, 565 (1999).
4. S. Cole *et al.*, The 2dF Galaxy Redshift Survey: Power-spectrum analysis of the final dataset and cosmological implications, *Mon. Not. Roy. Astron. Soc.* **362**, 505 (2005).

5. D. J. Eisenstein et al., Detection of the Baryon Acoustic Peak in the Large-Scale Correlation Function of SDSS Luminous Red Galaxies, *Astrophys. J.* **633**, 560 (2005).
6. G. Hinshaw et al., Nine-Year Wilkinson Microwave Anisotropy Probe (WMAP) Observations: Cosmological Parameter Results, *Astrophys. J. Suppl.* **208**, p. 19 (2013).
7. P. A. R. Ade et al., Planck 2013 results. I. Overview of products and scientific results, *Astron. Astrophys.* **571**, p. A1 (2014).
8. P. A. R. Ade et al., Planck 2015 results. XIII. Cosmological parameters, *Astron. Astrophys.* **594**, p. A13 (2016).
9. N. Aghanim et al., Planck 2018 results. VI. Cosmological parameters, *Astron. Astrophys.* **641**, p. A6 (2020), [Erratum: Astron.Astrophys. 652, C4 (2021)].
10. S. Weinberg, The Cosmological Constant Problem, *Rev. Mod. Phys.* **61**, 1 (1989), [,569(1988)].
11. J. Martin, Everything You Always Wanted To Know About The Cosmological Constant Problem (But Were Afraid To Ask), *Comptes Rendus Physique* **13**, 566 (2012).
12. J. Solà, Cosmological constant and vacuum energy: old and new ideas, *J. Phys. Conf. Ser.* **453**, p. 012015 (2013).
13. P. J. E. Peebles and B. Ratra, The Cosmological Constant and Dark Energy, *Rev. Mod. Phys.* **75**, 559 (2003).
14. T. Padmanabhan, Cosmological constant: The Weight of the vacuum, *Phys. Rept.* **380**, 235 (2003).
15. A. G. Riess, S. Casertano, W. Yuan, L. M. Macri and D. Scolnic, Large Magellanic Cloud Cepheid Standards Provide a 1% Foundation for the Determination of the Hubble Constant and Stronger Evidence for Physics beyond ΛCDM, *Astrophys. J.* **876**, p. 85 (2019).
16. E. Macaulay, I. K. Wehus and H. K. Eriksen, Lower Growth Rate from Recent Redshift Space Distortion Measurements than Expected from Planck, *Phys. Rev. Lett.* **111**, p. 161301 (2013).
17. H. Hildebrandt et al., KiDS+VIKING-450: Cosmic shear tomography with optical+infrared data, *Astron. Astrophys.* **633**, p. A69 (2020).
18. L. Amendola and S. Tsujikawa, *Dark Energy: Theory and Observations* (Cambridge Univ. Press, Cambridge, 2015).
19. A. Joyce, B. Jain, J. Khoury and M. Trodden, Beyond the Cosmological Standard Model, *Phys. Rept.* **568**, 1 (2015).
20. C. Wetterich, The Cosmon model for an asymptotically vanishing time dependent cosmological 'constant', *Astron. Astrophys.* **301**, 321 (1995).
21. L. Amendola, Coupled quintessence, *Phys. Rev.* **D62**, p. 043511 (2000).
22. R. D. Peccei, J. Solà and C. Wetterich, Adjusting the Cosmological Constant Dynamically: Cosmons and a New Force Weaker Than Gravity, *Phys. Lett.* **B195**, 183 (1987).
23. C. Wetterich, Cosmology and the Fate of Dilatation Symmetry, *Nucl. Phys.* **B302**, 668 (1988).
24. P. J. E. Peebles and B. Ratra, Cosmology with a Time Variable Cosmological Constant, *Astrophys. J.* **325**, p. L17 (1988).
25. B. Ratra and P. J. E. Peebles, Cosmological Consequences of a Rolling Homogeneous Scalar Field, *Phys. Rev.* **D37**, p. 3406 (1988).
26. V. Pettorino, L. Amendola, C. Baccigalupi and C. Quercellini, Constraints on coupled dark energy using CMB data from WMAP and SPT, *Phys. Rev.* **D86**, p. 103507 (2012).
27. V. Pettorino, Testing modified gravity with Planck: the case of coupled dark energy, *Phys. Rev.* **D88**, p. 063519 (2013).

28. P. A. R. Ade *et al.*, Planck 2015 results. XIV. Dark energy and modified gravity, *Astron. Astrophys.* **594**, p. A14 (2016).
29. K. C. Wong *et al.*, H0LiCOW XIII. A 2.4% measurement of H_0 from lensed quasars: 5.3σ tension between early and late-Universe probes (2019).
30. H. Gil-Marín *et al.*, The clustering of the SDSS-IV extended Baryon Oscillation Spectroscopic Survey DR14 quasar sample: structure growth rate measurement from the anisotropic quasar power spectrum in the redshift range $0.8 < z < 2.2$, *Mon. Not. Roy. Astron. Soc.* **477**, 1604 (2018).
31. J.-Q. Xia, New Limits on Coupled Dark Energy from Planck, *JCAP* **1311**, p. 022 (2013).
32. A. Pourtsidou and T. Tram, Reconciling CMB and structure growth measurements with dark energy interactions, *Phys. Rev.* **D94**, p. 043518 (2016).
33. C. van de Bruck, J. Mifsud and J. Morrice, Testing coupled dark energy models with their cosmological background evolution, *Phys. Rev.* **D95**, p. 043513 (2017).
34. C. van de Bruck and J. Mifsud, Searching for dark matter - dark energy interactions: going beyond the conformal case, *Phys. Rev.* **D97**, p. 023506 (2018).
35. Y.-H. Li, J.-F. Zhang and X. Zhang, Exploring the full parameter space for an interacting dark energy model with recent observations including redshift-space distortions: Application of the parametrized post-Friedmann approach, *Phys. Rev.* **D90**, p. 123007 (2014).
36. Y.-H. Li, J.-F. Zhang and X. Zhang, Testing models of vacuum energy interacting with cold dark matter, *Phys. Rev.* **D93**, p. 023002 (2016).
37. E. Di Valentino, A. Melchiorri and O. Mena, Can interacting dark energy solve the H_0 tension?, *Phys. Rev.* **D96**, p. 043503 (2017).
38. E. G. M. Ferreira, J. Quintin, A. A. Costa, E. Abdalla and B. Wang, Evidence for interacting dark energy from BOSS, *Phys. Rev.* **D95**, p. 043520 (2017).
39. A. A. Costa, X.-D. Xu, B. Wang and E. Abdalla, Constraints on interacting dark energy models from Planck 2015 and redshift-space distortion data, *JCAP* **1701**, p. 028 (2017).
40. J. Solà, A. Gómez-Valent and J. de Cruz Pérez, The H_0 tension in light of vacuum dynamics in the Universe, *Phys. Lett.* **B774**, 317 (2017).
41. J. Solà Peracaula, J. de Cruz Pérez and A. Gómez-Valent, Possible signals of vacuum dynamics in the Universe, *Mon. Not. Roy. Astron. Soc.* **478**, 4357 (2018).
42. M. Martinelli, N. B. Hogg, S. Peirone, M. Bruni and D. Wands, Constraints on the interacting vacuum–geodesic CDM scenario, *Mon. Not. Roy. Astron. Soc.* **488**, 3423 (2019).
43. P. Agrawal, G. Obied and C. Vafa, H_0 tension, swampland conjectures, and the epoch of fading dark matter, *Phys. Rev. D* **103**, p. 043523 (2021).
44. S. Pan, G. S. Sharov and W. Yang, Field theoretic interpretations of interacting dark energy scenarios and recent observations, *Phys. Rev. D* **101**, p. 103533 (2020).
45. J. Solà Peracaula, J. de Cruz Pérez and A. Gómez-Valent, Dynamical dark energy vs. $\Lambda =$ const in light of observations, *EPL* **121**, p. 39001 (2018).
46. A. Gómez-Valent and J. Solà Peracaula, Density perturbations for running vacuum: a successful approach to structure formation and to the σ_8-tension, *Mon. Not. Roy. Astron. Soc.* **478**, 126 (2018).
47. P. Tsiapi and S. Basilakos, Testing dynamical vacuum models with CMB power spectrum from Planck, *Mon. Not. Roy. Astron. Soc.* **485**, 2505 (2019).
48. J. Solà Peracaula, A. Gómez-Valent, J. de Cruz Perez and C. Moreno-Pulido, Running vacuum against the H_0 and σ_8 tensions, *EPL* **134**, p. 19001 (2021).

49. L. Amendola, Linear and non-linear perturbations in dark energy models, *Phys. Rev.* **D69**, p. 103524 (2004).
50. V. Pettorino and C. Baccigalupi, Coupled and Extended Quintessence: theoretical differences and structure formation, *Phys. Rev.* **D77**, p. 103003 (2008).
51. L. Amendola and V. Pettorino, Beyond self-acceleration: force- and fluid-acceleration, *Phys. Lett.* **B802**, p. 135214 (2020).
52. C. M. Will, The Confrontation between general relativity and experiment, *Living Rev. Rel.* **9**, p. 3 (2006).
53. B. Elder, V. Vardanyan, Y. Akrami, P. Brax, A.-C. Davis and R. S. Decca, The Classical Symmetron Force in Casimir Experiments, *Phys. Rev.* **D101**, p. 064065 (2020).
54. P. Brax, A.-C. Davis, B. Elder and L. K. Wong, Constraining screened fifth forces with the electron magnetic moment, *Phys. Rev.* **D97**, p. 084050 (2018).
55. J. Bergé, P. Brax, G. Métris, M. Pernot-Borràs, P. Touboul and J.-P. Uzan, MICROSCOPE Mission: First Constraints on the Violation of the Weak Equivalence Principle by a Light Scalar Dilaton, *Phys. Rev. Lett.* **120**, p. 141101 (2018).
56. G. Efstathiou and S. Gratton, The evidence for a spatially flat Universe (2020).
57. R. K. Sachs and A. M. Wolfe, Perturbations of a cosmological model and angular variations of the microwave background, *Astrophys. J.* **147**, 73 (1967), [Gen. Rel. Grav.39,1929(2007)].
58. L. Amendola, V. Pettorino, C. Quercellini and A. Vollmer, Testing coupled dark energy with next-generation large-scale observations, *Phys. Rev.* **D85**, p. 103008 (2012).
59. M. Baldi, V. Pettorino, G. Robbers and V. Springel, Hydrodynamical N-body simulations of coupled dark energy cosmologies, *Mon. Not. Roy. Astron. Soc.* **403**, 1684 (2010).
60. M. Baldi and V. Pettorino, High-z massive clusters as a test for dynamical coupled dark energy, *Mon. Not. Roy. Astron. Soc.* **412**, p. L1 (2011).
61. L. Amendola and C. Quercellini, Tracking and coupled dark energy as seen by WMAP, *Phys. Rev.* **D68**, p. 023514 (2003).
62. J. Solà, A. Gómez-Valent and J. de Cruz Pérez, Dynamical dark energy: scalar fields and running vacuum, *Mod. Phys. Lett.* **A32**, p. 1750054 (2017).
63. J. Ooba, B. Ratra and N. Sugiyama, Planck 2015 constraints on spatially-flat dynamical dark energy models, *Astrophys. Space Sci.* **364**, p. 176 (2019).
64. J. Solà Peracaula, A. Gómez-Valent and J. de Cruz Pérez, Signs of Dynamical Dark Energy in Current Observations, *Phys. Dark Univ.* **25**, p. 100311 (2019).
65. D. Blas, J. Lesgourgues and T. Tram, The Cosmic Linear Anisotropy Solving System (CLASS) II: Approximation schemes, *JCAP* **1107**, p. 034 (2011).
66. B. Audren, J. Lesgourgues, K. Benabed and S. Prunet, Conservative Constraints on Early Cosmology: an illustration of the Monte Python cosmological parameter inference code, *JCAP* **1302**, p. 001 (2013).
67. A. Lewis, GetDist: a Python package for analysing Monte Carlo samples (2019).
68. A. Heavens, Y. Fantaye, A. Mootoovaloo, H. Eggers, Z. Hosenie, S. Kroon and E. Sellentin, Marginal Likelihoods from Monte Carlo Markov Chains (2017).
69. N. Aghanim *et al.*, Planck 2018 results. VIII. Gravitational lensing, *Astron. Astrophys.* **641**, p. A8 (2020).
70. P. Carter, F. Beutler, W. J. Percival, C. Blake, J. Koda and A. J. Ross, Low Redshift Baryon Acoustic Oscillation Measurement from the Reconstructed 6-degree Field Galaxy Survey, *Mon. Not. Roy. Astron. Soc.* **481**, 2371 (2018).

71. H. Gil-Marín, W. J. Percival, L. Verde, J. R. Brownstein, C.-H. Chuang, F.-S. Kitaura, S. A. Rodríguez-Torres and M. D. Olmstead, The clustering of galaxies in the SDSS-III Baryon Oscillation Spectroscopic Survey: RSD measurement from the power spectrum and bispectrum of the DR12 BOSS galaxies, *Mon. Not. Roy. Astron. Soc.* **465**, 1757 (2017).
72. E. A. Kazin *et al.*, The WiggleZ Dark Energy Survey: improved distance measurements to z = 1 with reconstruction of the baryonic acoustic feature, *Mon. Not. Roy. Astron. Soc.* **441**, 3524 (2014).
73. T. M. C. Abbott *et al.*, Dark Energy Survey Year 1 Results: Measurement of the Baryon Acoustic Oscillation scale in the distribution of galaxies to redshift 1, *Mon. Not. Roy. Astron. Soc.* **483**, 4866 (2019).
74. M. Blomqvist *et al.*, Baryon acoustic oscillations from the cross-correlation of Lyα absorption and quasars in eBOSS DR14, *Astron. Astrophys.* **629**, p. A86 (2019).
75. V. de Sainte Agathe *et al.*, Baryon acoustic oscillations at z = 2.34 from the correlations of Lyα absorption in eBOSS DR14, *Astron. Astrophys.* **629**, p. A85 (2019).
76. D. M. Scolnic *et al.*, The Complete Light-curve Sample of Spectroscopically Confirmed SNe Ia from Pan-STARRS1 and Cosmological Constraints from the Combined Pantheon Sample, *Astrophys. J.* **859**, p. 101 (2018).
77. A. G. Riess *et al.*, Type Ia Supernova Distances at Redshift > 1.5 from the Hubble Space Telescope Multi-cycle Treasury Programs: The Early Expansion Rate, *Astrophys. J.* **853**, p. 126 (2018).
78. R. Jiménez, L. Verde, T. Treu and D. Stern, Constraints on the equation of state of dark energy and the Hubble constant from stellar ages and the CMB, *Astrophys. J.* **593**, 622 (2003).
79. J. Simon, L. Verde and R. Jiménez, Constraints on the redshift dependence of the dark energy potential, *Phys. Rev.* **D71**, p. 123001 (2005).
80. D. Stern, R. Jiménez, L. Verde, M. Kamionkowski and S. A. Stanford, Cosmic Chronometers: Constraining the Equation of State of Dark Energy. I: H(z) Measurements, *JCAP* **1002**, p. 008 (2010).
81. M. Moresco *et al.*, Improved constraints on the expansion rate of the Universe up to z 1.1 from the spectroscopic evolution of cosmic chronometers, *JCAP* **1208**, p. 006 (2012).
82. C. Zhang, H. Zhang, S. Yuan, T.-J. Zhang and Y.-C. Sun, Four new observational $H(z)$ data from luminous red galaxies in the Sloan Digital Sky Survey data release seven, *Res. Astron. Astrophys.* **14**, 1221 (2014).
83. M. Moresco, Raising the bar: new constraints on the Hubble parameter with cosmic chronometers at $z \sim 2$, *Mon. Not. Roy. Astron. Soc.* **450**, L16 (2015).
84. M. Moresco, L. Pozzetti, A. Cimatti, R. Jiménez, C. Maraston, L. Verde, D. Thomas, A. Citro, R. Tojeiro and D. Wilkinson, A 6% measurement of the Hubble parameter at $z \sim 0.45$: direct evidence of the epoch of cosmic re-acceleration, *JCAP* **1605**, p. 014 (2016).
85. A. L. Ratsimbazafy, S. I. Loubser, S. M. Crawford, C. M. Cress, B. A. Bassett, R. C. Nichol and P. Väisänen, Age-dating Luminous Red Galaxies observed with the Southern African Large Telescope, *Mon. Not. Roy. Astron. Soc.* **467**, 3239 (2017).
86. A. Gómez-Valent, Quantifying the evidence for the current speed-up of the Universe with low and intermediate-redshift data. A more model-independent approach, *JCAP* **1905**, p. 026 (2019).
87. F. Qin, C. Howlett and L. Staveley-Smith, The redshift-space momentum power spectrum — II. Measuring the growth rate from the combined 2MTF and 6dFGSv surveys, *Mon. Not. Roy. Astron. Soc.* **487**, 5235 (2019).

88. F. Shi et al., Mapping the Real Space Distributions of Galaxies in SDSS DR7: II. Measuring the growth rate, clustering amplitude of matter and biases of galaxies at redshift 0.1, *Astrophys. J.* **861**, p. 137 (2018).
89. F. Simpson, C. Blake, J. A. Peacock, I. Baldry, J. Bland-Hawthorn, A. Heavens, C. Heymans, J. Loveday and P. Norberg, Galaxy and mass assembly: Redshift space distortions from the clipped galaxy field, *Phys. Rev.* **D93**, p. 023525 (2016).
90. C. Blake et al., Galaxy And Mass Assembly (GAMA): improved cosmic growth measurements using multiple tracers of large-scale structure, *Mon. Not. Roy. Astron. Soc.* **436**, p. 3089 (2013).
91. C. Blake et al., The WiggleZ Dark Energy Survey: the growth rate of cosmic structure since redshift z=0.9, *Mon. Not. Roy. Astron. Soc.* **415**, p. 2876 (2011).
92. F. G. Mohammad et al., The VIMOS Public Extragalactic Redshift Survey (VIPERS): Unbiased clustering estimate with VIPERS slit assignment, *Astron. Astrophys.* **619**, p. A17 (2018).
93. L. Guzzo et al., A test of the nature of cosmic acceleration using galaxy redshift distortions, *Nature* **451**, 541 (2008).
94. Y.-S. Song and W. J. Percival, Reconstructing the history of structure formation using Redshift Distortions, *JCAP* **0910**, p. 004 (2009).
95. T. Okumura et al., The Subaru FMOS galaxy redshift survey (FastSound). IV. New constraint on gravity theory from redshift space distortions at $z \sim 1.4$, *Publ. Astron. Soc. Jap.* **68**, p. 38 (2016).
96. L. Verde, T. Treu and A. G. Riess, Tensions between the early and late Universe, *Nature Astronomy* **3**, 891 (2019).
97. A. G. Riess, The Expansion of the Universe is Faster than Expected, *Nature Rev. Phys.* **2**, 10 (2020).
98. R. E. Kass and A. E. Raftery, The WiggleZ Dark Energy Survey: improved distance measurements to z = 1 with reconstruction of the baryonic acoustic feature, *J. Amer. Statist. Assoc.* **90**, 773 (1995).
99. K. P. Burnham and D. R. Anderson, *Model selection and multimodel inference* (Springer, New York, 2002).
100. H. Akaike, A new look at the statistical model identification, *IEEE Trans. Autom. Control* **19**, 716 (1974).
101. G. Schwarz, Estimating the Dimension of a Model, *Ann. Stat.* **6**, 461 (1978).
102. D. J. Spiegelhalter, N. G. Best, B. P. Carlin and A. van der Linde, Bayesian measures of model complexity and fit, *J. Roy. Stat. Soc.* **64**, p. 583 (2002).
103. C. Moreno-Pulido and J. Solà Peracaula, Running vacuum in quantum field theory in curved spacetime: renormalizing ρ_{vac} without $\sim m^4$ terms, *Eur. Phys. J. C* **80**, p. 692 (2020).
104. L. Amendola and S. Tsujikawa, Scaling solutions and weak gravity in dark energy with energy and momentum couplings, *JCAP* **06**, p. 020 (2020).

Running vacuum interacting with dark matter or with running gravitational coupling. Phenomenological implications

Joan Solà Peracaula[a,b]

[a] *Departament de Física Quàntica i Astrofísica,*
and
[b] *Institute of Cosmos Sciences,*
Universitat de Barcelona,
Av. Diagonal 647, E-08028 Barcelona, Catalonia, Spain
E-mail: sola@fqa.ub.edu

The cosmological term, Λ, in Einstein's equations is an essential ingredient of the 'concordance' ΛCDM model of cosmology. In this mini-review presentation, we assess the possibility that Λ can be a dynamical quantity, more specifically a 'running quantity' in quantum field theory in curved spacetime. A great deal of phenomenological works have shown in the last few years that this option (sometimes accompanied with a running gravitational coupling) may cure some of the tensions afflicting the ΛCDM. The 'running vacuum models' (RVM's) are characterized by the vacuum energy density, $\rho_{\rm vac}$, being a series of (even) powers of the Hubble rate and its time derivatives. Here we describe the technical quantum field theoretical origin of the RVM structure in FLRW spacetime, which goes well-beyond the original semi-qualitative renormalization group arguments. In particular, we compute the renormalized energy-momentum tensor using the adiabatic regularization procedure and show that it leads to the RVM form. In other words, we find that the renormalized vacuum energy density, $\rho_{\rm vac}(H)$ evolves as a (constant) additive term plus leading dynamical components $\mathcal{O}(H^2)$. There are also $\mathcal{O}(H^4)$ contributions, which can be relevant for the early universe. Remarkably enough, the renormalized $\rho_{\rm vac}(H)$ does not exhibit dangerous terms proportional to the quartic power of the masses ($\sim m^4$) of the fields. It is well-known that these terms have been the main source of trouble since they are responsible for the extreme fine tuning and ultimately for the cosmological constant problem. In its canonical form, the current $\rho_{\rm vac}(H)$ is dominated by a constant term, as it should be, but it acquires a mild dynamical component $\sim \nu H^2$ ($0 < \nu \ll 1$) which makes the RVM to mimic quintessence.

Keywords: Running Vacuum, Dynamical Dark Energy, Inflation, Dark Matter

1. Introduction

The standard or concordance model of cosmology, the so-called ΛCDM, is a very successful theoretical framework for the description of the Universe.[1] Crucial ingredients of it are left, though, without direct observational evidence and/or a proper theoretical interpretation based on fundamental principles. Such is the situation with dark matter, but also with the cosmological term, Λ, which has been traditionally associated with the vacuum energy density (VED) of the Universe, $\rho_{\rm vac}$. In fact, the notion of VED in cosmology is a most subtle concept, which is challenging theoretical physicists and cosmologists for many decades, specially with the advent of Quantum Theory in general and the more sophisticated machinery of Quantum Field Theory (QFT). The roots of the problem reside in the interpretation of the cosmological constant (CC) term, Λ, in Einstein's equations as a quantity being connected with the VED, which is also a fundamental concept in QFT. The proposed connection is $\rho_{\rm vac} = \Lambda/(8\pi G_N)$, where G_N is Newton's constant. Accurate measurements of $\rho_{\rm vac}$ in the last decades from distant type Ia supernovae (SnIa) and the cosmic microwave background (CMB),[2–4] have put the foundations of the concordance ΛCDM model of cosmology.[1]

The concordance model is formulated in the context of the Friedman-Lemaitre-Robertson-Walker (FLRW) framework and is deeply ingrained in the General Relativity (GR) paradigm. However, one of the most important drawbacks of GR is that it is a non-renormalizable theory. This can be considered a serious theoretical obstruction for GR to be considered a fundamental theory of gravity. This fact adversely impacts on the ΛCDM too. GR cannot properly describe the short distance effects of gravity, i.e. the ultraviolet regime (UV), only the large distance effects (or infrared regime). As a consequence, GR cannot provide by itself a framework for quantizing gravity (the spacetime metric field) along with the rest of the fundamental interactions (assuming of course that gravity is amenable to be quantized on conventional grounds). In this sense, a first (rougher but effective) approach is to treat gravity as a classical (external or background) field and quantize only the matter fields of the fundamental interactions (electroweak and strong interactions). This is the main program of the semiclassical approach, namely the point of view of QFT in curved spacetime, see[5–8] for a review. This will be our pursue here as well. We shall nevertheless still be able to compute the quantum effects from matter and their contribution to the VED. Not only so, it will allow us to renormalize these (originally UV-divergent) quantum effects and obtain a finite quantity that can be better compared with observations. The renormalized VED found in the present framework is free from the traditional $\sim m^4$ effects (proportional to the quartic powers of the masses of the matter fields). This was first shown in the literature in the work[9] and further extended in.[10] It was demonstrated that $\rho_{\rm vac}$ appears (in the current universe) as a constant (dominant) term plus a dynamical component which varies as $\sim \nu H^2 m_{\rm Pl}^2$, with ν a small (dimensionless) and QFT-computable coefficient, $m_{\rm Pl}$ being the usual Planck mass ($m_{\rm Pl} = G_N^{-1/2}$). Quite obviously, such a result is highly compatible with the ΛCDM since it involves only a small departure from the rigid vacuum term enforced in it. Notwithstanding, it makes a significant qualitative (and quantitative) prediction: the quantum vacuum does not remain static throughout the cosmic evolution but is mildly dynamical, and such dynamics can be effectively evaluated from first principles, for ν (as mentioned) can be accounted for using QFT in curved spacetime. As long as the vacuum turns out to be free from the weird $\sim m^4$ effects obtained in simplified renormalization treatments, the finite result which is proposed here appears theoretically distinct and very tantalizing. It suggests to reassess if the Cosmological Constant Problem (CCP)[11–16] is still in force in the current theoretical framework. Remember that the CCP is one of the hardest and longstanding mysteries of theoretical physics, and proves to be a serious impediment to reconcile cosmology with particle physics and quantum field theory in general.[17]

The smoother formulation of the quantum vacuum as put forward here is not only convenient from the theoretical point of view, but also from the observational side. It has long been known that, observationally, there appear to be some discrepancies or "tensions" between the results of data analyses from the Planck Collaboration, based on the ΛCDM,[4] and the local (distance ladder) measurements of the Hubble parameter today, the so called H_0 tension,[18,19] see e.g. the various reviews.[20–23] Not only so, there exist also tensions in the large scale structure (LSS) growth data, the so-called σ_8 tension.[21,22,24] Although such discordances in the arena of the 'concordance' model might admit a variety of more mundane astrophysical explanations,[25–27] or even disappear into thin air when more data will be available in the near future, it has been conceded already that they may well be passing the point of being attributable to a fluke.[19]

As it turns out, the smooth quantum vacuum phenomenological framework described here has the capacity to deal successfully with the H_0 and the σ_8 tensions. Such a framework represents the running vacuum model of cosmology (RVM) – see[17] for a detailed review and references therein. The latter was originally motivated by semi-qualitative renormalization group arguments,[28] which were later on formulated in some cases from an action functional viewpoint[29] – and was finally substantiated from full-fledged QFT calculations in.[9,10] For related studies of vacuum energy in QFT, see e.g.[30–35] In this summarized account I will mainly review the emergence of the RVM from the mentioned QFT calculations in curved spacetime, specifically in the context of the FLRW background as well as the most recent phenomenological applications. It is remarkable that it is also possible to derive a string-inspired version of the RVM cosmological model with gravitational anomalies in the early Universe, see[36] for a detailed exposition and[37–40] for more details and spin-off possibilities.

The structure of our presentation is as follows. In sections 2 and 3 we define our basic QFT framework in curved spacetime and the adiabatic expansion procedure. In section 4 we renormalize the energy-momentum tensor in the FLRW context and make contact with the RVM. In section 5 we apply the RVM to tackle the σ_8 and H_0 tensions. Finally, section 6 contains our conclusions and outlook.

2. Non-minimally coupled scalar field in FLRW background

We consider the semiclassical calculation of the energy density of the vacuum fluctuations of a quantized scalar field in FLRW spacetime. It serves as a representative case of study for the kind of results and difficulties we expect to encounter when dealing with generic quantized fields in a curved background. Such QFT calculation implies to perform renormalization since we meet UV-divergent integrals. Conventional approaches such as e.g. the minimal subtraction scheme lead to quartic dependence on the mass of the field ($\sim m^4$) enforcing a serious fine tuning among the parameters, see e.g.[17] and references therein. Here we avoid using such an unsuccessful method and adopt the adiabatic renormalization procedure (ARP).[5–7] However, we follow the specific approach presented in,[9] which is related to that of.[34] For a full-fledged exposition and calculation details, see.[10]

2.1. Action and classical energy-momentum tensor

We start from the Einstein-Hilbert (EH) action for gravity plus matter[a]:

$$S_{\rm EH} = \frac{1}{16\pi G_N} \int d^4x \sqrt{-g}\, R - \int d^4x \sqrt{-g}\, \rho_\Lambda + S_m. \tag{1}$$

The matter action S_m is generic at this point, but will be specified shortly. The (constant) term ρ_Λ has dimension of energy density. Because it is unrelated to the matter part (fully contained in S_m), ρ_Λ is usually called the vacuum energy density (VED). However, we will not call it that way here since it is not yet the physical VED, $\rho_{\rm vac}$, as we shall see. For us the term ρ_Λ is just a bare parameter of the EH action, as the gravitational coupling G_N itself. The physical values can only be identified after renormalizing the bare theory. The corresponding gravitational field equations emerging from the variation of the action (1) can be put in the convenient form

$$\mathcal{M}_{\rm Pl}^2\, G_{\mu\nu} = -\rho_\Lambda g_{\mu\nu} + T_{\mu\nu}^{\rm m}, \tag{2}$$

where $\mathcal{M}_{\rm Pl} = m_{\rm Pl}/\sqrt{8\pi} = 1/\sqrt{8\pi G_N}$ is the reduced Planck mass, the expression $G_{\mu\nu} = R_{\mu\nu} - (1/2)g_{\mu\nu}R$ is the usual Einstein tensor and $T_{\mu\nu}^{\rm m}$ is the stress-energy-momentum tensor, or just energy-momentum tensor (EMT for short) of matter:

$$T_{\mu\nu}^{\rm m} = -\frac{2}{\sqrt{-g}} \frac{\delta S_{\rm m}}{\delta g^{\mu\nu}}. \tag{3}$$

For simplicity we will assume that there is only one (matter) field contribution to the EMT on the right hand side of (2) in the form of a real scalar field, ϕ. Such contribution will be denoted $T_{\mu\nu}^\phi$. We neglect for the moment the incoherent matter contributions from dust and radiation. They can be added a posteriori without altering the pure QFT aspects on which we wish to focus at this point. We assume that ϕ is non-minimally coupled to gravity. Thus, the part of the action involving ϕ reads

$$S[\phi] = -\int d^4x \sqrt{-g} \left(\frac{1}{2} g^{\mu\nu} \partial_\mu \phi \partial_\nu \phi + \frac{1}{2}(m^2 + \xi R)\phi^2 \right). \tag{4}$$

The non-minimal coupling of ϕ to gravity is ξ. For $\xi = 1/6$, the massless ($m = 0$) action is conformally invariant. We will keep ξ general to explore its influence. We assume also that ϕ does not couple to itself and hence we shall not consider a

---

[a]Our conventions and other useful formulae are those of,[9,10] see the appendices of these references.

possible contribution from a classical potential for ϕ in our analysis. In this study, we wish to target mainly the zero-point energy (ZPE) of ϕ.

The classical EMT can be derived from the action (4) and reads as follows:

$$T_{\mu\nu}^{\phi} = -\frac{2}{\sqrt{-g}}\frac{\delta S[\phi]}{\delta g^{\mu\nu}} = (1-2\xi)\partial_\mu\phi\partial_\nu\phi + \left(2\xi - \frac{1}{2}\right)g_{\mu\nu}\partial^\sigma\phi\partial_\sigma\phi \\ -2\xi\phi\nabla_\mu\nabla_\nu\phi + 2\xi g_{\mu\nu}\phi\Box\phi + \xi G_{\mu\nu}\phi^2 - \frac{1}{2}m^2 g_{\mu\nu}\phi^2. \tag{5}$$

Varying the action (4) with respect to ϕ we find the Klein-Gordon (KG) equation in curved spacetime:

$$(\Box - m^2 - \xi R)\phi = 0, \tag{6}$$

where $\Box\phi = g^{\mu\nu}\nabla_\mu\nabla_\nu\phi = (-g)^{-1/2}\partial_\mu\left(\sqrt{-g}\,g^{\mu\nu}\partial_\nu\phi\right)$. The FLRW line element for spatially flat three-dimensional geometry can be written in conformal coordinates as $ds^2 = a^2(\tau)\eta_{\mu\nu}dx^\mu dx^\nu$, where $\eta_{\mu\nu} = \mathrm{diag}(-1,+1,+1,+1)$ is the Minkowski metric in our conventions. The derivative with respect to the conformal time, τ, will be denoted $' \equiv d/d\tau$ and thus the Hubble rate in conformal time reads $\mathcal{H}(\tau) \equiv a'/a$. Since $dt = a d\tau$, the relation between the Hubble rate in cosmic and conformal times is simply $\mathcal{H}(\tau) = aH(t)$, with $H(t) = \dot{a}/a$ ($\dot{} \equiv d/dt$) the usual Hubble rate.

The KG equation (6) in conformally flat coordinates becomes

$$\phi'' + 2\mathcal{H}\phi' - \nabla^2\phi + a^2(m^2 + \xi R)\phi = 0, \tag{7}$$

where we used the curvature scalar of spacetime: $R = 6a''/a^3$. The separation of variables in these coordinates, namely $\phi(\tau,x) \sim \int d^3k\, A_{\mathbf{k}}\psi_k(\mathbf{x})\phi_k(\tau) + cc$, can be achieved with $\psi_k(\mathbf{x}) = e^{i\mathbf{k}\cdot\mathbf{x}}$. However, in contrast to the Minkowski case we cannot take $\phi_k(\tau) = e^{\pm i\omega_k\tau}$ since the mode frequencies are not constant anymore. The form of the modes $\phi_k(\tau)$ in the curved spacetime case are determined by the KG equation. Starting from the Fourier expansion with separated space and time variables

$$\phi(\tau,\mathbf{x}) = \int\frac{d^3k}{(2\pi)^{3/2}}\left[A_{\mathbf{k}}e^{i\mathbf{k}\cdot\mathbf{x}}\phi_k(\tau) + A_{\mathbf{k}}^* e^{-i\mathbf{k}\cdot\mathbf{x}}\phi_k^*(\tau)\right] \tag{8}$$

(in which $A_{\mathbf{k}}$ and their complex conjugates $A_{\mathbf{k}}^*$ are the classical Fourier coefficients) and substituting it into (7) the mode functions $\phi_k(\tau)$ are determined by solving the nontrivial differential equation

$$\phi_k'' + 2\mathcal{H}\phi_k' + \left(\omega_k^2(m) + a^2\xi R\right)\phi_k = 0, \tag{9}$$

where $\omega_k^2(m) \equiv k^2 + a^2 m^2$. The mode functions depend only on the modulus $k \equiv |\mathbf{k}|$ of the (co-moving) momenta. In the absence of gravitation ($R=0$) the physical frequencies are $\tilde{\omega}_k = \sqrt{\tilde{k}^2 + m^2}$, with $\tilde{k} = k/a$ the physical momenta. However, for $R \neq 0$ and $\xi \neq 0$ the frequencies become a function of the gravitational field as well, which makes the particle interpretation hard. If we perform the change of field mode variable $\phi_k = \varphi_k/a$ the above equation simplifies to $\varphi_k'' + \left(\omega_k^2(m) + a^2\left(\xi - 1/6\right)R\right)\varphi_k = 0$. For conformally invariant matter ($m=0$

and $\xi = 1/6$), such equation boils down to the form $\varphi_k'' + k^2\varphi_k = 0$, whose positive- and negative-energy solutions are just $e^{-ik\tau}$ and $e^{+ik\tau}$, respectively. On the other hand, in the massless case with minimal coupling ($\xi = 0$) the previous equation further simplifies to $\varphi_k'' + (k^2 - a^2 R/6)\varphi_k = 0$. In the radiation epoch ($a \propto \tau$, thus $R = 6a''/a^3 = 0$) we find once more the trivial modes $\varphi_k(\tau) = e^{\pm ik\tau}$. Both in the de Sitter ($a = -1/(H\tau)$, $H =$ const.) and matter-dominated ($a \propto \tau^2$) epochs we have $a^2 R = 12/\tau^2$, which leads to $\varphi_k'' + (k^2 - 2/\tau^2)\varphi_k = 0$. This equation admits an exact (positive-energy) solution in terms of Hankel functions of half integer order, hence in close analytic form. In the de Sitter case ($\tau < 0$) one may impose the Bunch-Davies vacuum limit $\sim e^{-ik|\tau|}$ in the far remote past ($\tau \to -\infty$) and one finds $\varphi(\tau) \propto (1 - i/(k|\tau|))e^{-ik|\tau|}$. The same solution is valid for the matter-dominated era (for which $\tau > 0$). If, however, $m \neq 0$ and/or $\xi \neq 1/6$ no analytic solution of (9) is available, and this leads us to perform a WKB (Wentzel-Kramers-Brillouin) expansion of the solution. But before tackling that method, let us consider the quantization of the scalar field ϕ.

2.2. *Quantum fluctuations*

To account for the quantum fluctuations of the scalar field ϕ we must address the expansion of the field around its background value ϕ_b:

$$\phi(\tau, x) = \phi_b(\tau) + \delta\phi(\tau, x). \tag{10}$$

One starts defining an appropriate vacuum state, called adiabatic vacuum.[41] The vacuum expectation value (VEV) of ϕ is identified with the background value, $\langle 0|\phi(\tau,x)|0\rangle = \phi_b(\tau)$, whereas the VEV of the fluctuation is zero: $\langle\delta\phi\rangle \equiv \langle 0|\delta\phi|0\rangle = 0$. This is not the case for the VEV of the bilinear products of fluctuations, e.g. $\langle\delta\phi^2\rangle \neq 0$. It is convenient to decompose $\langle T_{\mu\nu}^\phi\rangle = \langle T_{\mu\nu}^{\phi_b}\rangle + \langle T_{\mu\nu}^{\delta\phi}\rangle$, where $\langle T_{\mu\nu}^{\phi_b}\rangle = T_{\mu\nu}^{\phi_b}$ is the contribution from the classical background part, whereas $\langle T_{\mu\nu}^{\delta\phi}\rangle \equiv \langle 0|T_{\mu\nu}^{\delta\phi}|0\rangle$ is the genuine vacuum contribution from the field fluctuations. Taking into account that ρ_Λ is also part of the vacuum action (1), the full vacuum contribution is the sum

$$\langle T_{\mu\nu}^{\text{vac}}\rangle = -\rho_\Lambda g_{\mu\nu} + \langle T_{\mu\nu}^{\delta\phi}\rangle. \tag{11}$$

Thus, the total vacuum part receives contributions from both the cosmological term in the action as well as from the quantum fluctuations of the field (the ZPE). However, since these quantities are formally UV-divergent, the physical vacuum can only be identified a posteriori, namely upon suitable regularization and renormalization. For this we adopt the adiabatic method along the lines of.[9,10]

Obviously the classical and quantum parts of the field (10) obey the curved spacetime KG equation (9) separately. Similarly for $\varphi = \varphi_b + \delta\varphi$ (where $\phi = \varphi/a$). Denoting the frequency modes of the fluctuating part $\delta\varphi$ by $h_k(\tau)$, we can write

$$\delta\varphi(\tau, \mathbf{x}) = \int \frac{d^3k}{(2\pi)^{3/2}} \left[A_{\mathbf{k}} e^{i\mathbf{k}\cdot\mathbf{x}} h_k(\tau) + A_{\mathbf{k}}^\dagger e^{-i\mathbf{k}\cdot\mathbf{x}} h_k^*(\tau)\right]. \tag{12}$$

Here $A_\mathbf{k}$ and $A_\mathbf{k}^\dagger$ are now the (time-independent) annihilation and creation operators, which satisfy the commutation relations

$$[A_\mathbf{k}, A_\mathbf{k'}^{'\dagger}] = \delta(\mathbf{k} - \mathbf{k}'), \qquad [A_\mathbf{k}, A_\mathbf{k'}'] = 0. \tag{13}$$

The frequency modes of the fluctuations, $h_k(\tau)$, satisfy the differential equation

$$h_k'' + \Omega_k^2(\tau) h_k = 0 \qquad \Omega_k^2(\tau) \equiv \omega_k^2(m) + a^2(\xi - 1/6)R. \tag{14}$$

Except in the simple cases mentioned above, the solution of that equation requires a recursive self-consistent iteration, the WKB expansion. One start from

$$h_k(\tau) = \frac{1}{\sqrt{2W_k(\tau)}} \exp\left(i \int^\tau W_k(\tilde\tau) d\tilde\tau\right), \tag{15}$$

where the normalization factor $1/\sqrt{2W_k(\tau)}$ insures that the Wronskian condition $h_k' h_k^* - h_k h_k^{*\prime} = i$ is satisfied. It warrants the standard equal-time commutation relations. Functions W_k in the above ansatz obey the (non-linear) equation

$$W_k^2(\tau) = \Omega_k^2(\tau) - \frac{1}{2}\frac{W_k''}{W_k} + \frac{3}{4}\left(\frac{W_k'}{W_k}\right)^2, \tag{16}$$

which is amenable to be solved using the WKB expansion. The latter is applicable only for large k, therefore short wave lengths (as e.g. in geometrical Optics), and weak gravitational fields. The mode functions $h_k(\tau)$ are no longer of the form $\varphi_k(\tau) = e^{\pm i\omega_k \tau}$, hence particles with definite frequencies cannot be strictly defined in a curved background. Notwithstanding, an approximate Fock space interpretation is still feasible if the vacuum is defined as the quantum state which is annihilated by all the operators $A_\mathbf{k}$ of the above Fourier expansion. This defines in a precise way the notion of the adiabatic vacuum.[5–8,41]

2.3. WKB expansion of the mode functions

In the gravitational context, the WKB expansion leads to the adiabatic regularization procedure (ARP). For a review, see e.g. the classic books.[5,6] The regularization involved in the ARP amounts to subtracted integrals which become UV-finite and hence one obtains direct renormalization of the physical quantities. In the two successives works[9,10] the WKB expansion was performed first up to $4th$ and subsequently up to $6th$ adiabatic order. In the latter case the calculational details are rather cumbersome, but are necessary in order to study the on-shell renormalized theory. Here, however, we will limit ourselves to describe the results up to $4th$ order, which is enough to reormalize the theory off-shell. The counting of adiabatic orders in the WKB expansion follows the number of time derivatives. Thus: k^2 and a are of adiabatic order 0; a' and $\mathcal{H}$ of adiabatic order 1; a'', a'^2, $\mathcal{H}'$ and $\mathcal{H}^2$ as well as R are of adiabatic order 2. Each additional derivative increases the adiabatic order by one unit. The expansion collects the different adiabatic orders:

$$W_k = \omega_k^{(0)} + \omega_k^{(2)} + \omega_k^{(4)} + \omega_k^{(6)} \cdots, \tag{17}$$

General covariance precludes the odd adiabatic orders. The $\omega_k^{(j)}$ can be expressed in terms of $\Omega_k(\tau)$ and its time derivatives. Following[9,10] we consider an off-shell procedure in which the frequency ω_k of a given mode is defined not at the mass m of the particle but at an arbitrary mass scale M:

$$\omega_k \equiv \omega_k(\tau, M) \equiv \sqrt{k^2 + a^2(\tau) M^2} \,. \tag{18}$$

At the moment we will use just the notation ω_k to indicate such off-shell value, and when necessary we will distinguish it from the on-shell one using the forms $\omega_k(M)$ and $\omega_k(m)$, both being of course functions of τ (which we will omit to simplify notation). Working out the second and fourth order terms of (17) one finds[9]

$$\begin{aligned}
\omega_k^{(0)} &= \omega_k \,, \\
\omega_k^{(2)} &= \frac{a^2 \Delta^2}{2\omega_k} + \frac{a^2 R}{2\omega_k}(\xi - 1/6) - \frac{\omega_k''}{4\omega_k^2} + \frac{3\omega_k'^2}{8\omega_k^3} \,, \\
\omega_k^{(4)} &= -\frac{1}{2\omega_k}\left(\omega_k^{(2)}\right)^2 + \frac{\omega_k^{(2)} \omega_k''}{4\omega_k^3} - \frac{\omega_k^{(2)\prime\prime}}{4\omega_k^2} - \frac{3\omega_k^{(2)} \omega_k'^2}{4\omega_k^4} + \frac{3\omega_k' \omega_k^{(2)\prime}}{4\omega_k^3} \,.
\end{aligned} \tag{19}$$

The quadratic mass differences $\Delta^2 \equiv m^2 - M^2$ must be counted as being of adiabatic order 2 since they appear in the WKB expansion along with other terms of the same adiabatic order[b]. The on-shell result is recovered for $M = m$, for which $\Delta = 0$ and corresponds to the usual ARP procedure.[5,6] One could extend the expansion up to the next nonvanishing adiabatic order, which is order $6th$, although we refrain from quoting the result here.[10] It is easy to see that the adiabatic expansion becomes an expansion in powers of $\mathcal{H}$ and its time derivatives. For example, the first two derivatives of ω_k read

$$\omega_k' = a^2 \mathcal{H} \frac{M^2}{\omega_k} \,, \quad \omega_k'' = 2a^2 \mathcal{H}^2 \frac{M^2}{\omega_k} + a^2 \mathcal{H}' \frac{M^2}{\omega_k} - a^4 \mathcal{H}^2 \frac{M^4}{\omega_k^3} \,, \tag{20}$$

where we recall that $\mathcal{H}$ is the Hubble function in conformal time. From these elementary differentiations one can then compute the more laborious derivatives appearing in the above expressions, such as $\omega_k^{(2)\prime}, \omega_k^{(2)\prime\prime}$ etc. Therefore, the final result appears as an expansion in powers of $\mathcal{H}$ and multiple derivatives of it.

3. Adiabatic expansion of the ZPE

We have now all the necessary ingredients to compute the zero-point energy (ZPE) associated to the quantum vacuum fluctuations in curved spacetime with FLRW metric. We closely follow the presentation of.[9] Inserting the decomposition (10) of the quantum field ϕ in the EMT as given in Eq. (5) and selecting only the fluctuating

---

[b]In the context of the effective action, it can be justified more formally on replacing m by M in the heat kernel expansion of the propagator, but we shall not take this path here, see[10] for details.

parts $\delta\phi$, the ZPE (which is ssociated to the 00-component) reads

$$\langle T_{00}^{\delta\phi}\rangle = \left\langle \frac{1}{2}(\delta\phi')^2 + \left(\frac{1}{2} - 2\xi\right)(\nabla\delta\phi)^2 + 6\xi\mathcal{H}\delta\phi\delta\phi' \right.$$
$$\left. -2\xi\delta\phi\,\nabla^2\delta\phi + 3\xi\mathcal{H}^2\delta\phi^2 + \frac{a^2m^2}{2}(\delta\phi)^2 \right\rangle. \quad (21)$$

Notice that $\delta\phi'$, the fluctuation of the differentiated field (with respect to conformal time), is given by $\delta\phi' \equiv \delta\partial_0\phi = \partial_0\delta\phi = (\delta\phi)'$. Next we substitute the Fourier expansion of $\delta\phi = \delta\varphi/a$, as given in (12), into Eq. (21) and use the commutation relations (13). At the same time we symmetrize the operator field products $\delta\phi\delta\phi'$ with respect to the creation and annihilation operators. We present the final result in Fourier space, and hence we integrate $\int \frac{d^3k}{(2\pi)^3}(...)$ over solid angles:[9]

$$\langle T_{00}^{\delta\phi(0-4)} \rangle = \frac{1}{8\pi^2 a^2}\int dk\, k^2 \left[2\omega_k + \frac{a^4 M^4 \mathcal{H}^2}{4\omega_k^5} - \frac{a^4 M^4}{16\omega_k^7}(2\mathcal{H}''\mathcal{H} - \mathcal{H}'^2 + 8\mathcal{H}'\mathcal{H}^2 + 4\mathcal{H}^4) \right.$$
$$+ \frac{7a^6 M^6}{8\omega_k^9}(\mathcal{H}'\mathcal{H}^2 + 2\mathcal{H}^4) - \frac{105 a^8 M^8 \mathcal{H}^4}{64\omega_k^{11}}$$
$$+ \left(\xi - \frac{1}{6}\right)\left(-\frac{6\mathcal{H}^2}{\omega_k} - \frac{6a^2 M^2 \mathcal{H}^2}{\omega_k^3} + \frac{a^2 M^2}{2\omega_k^5}(6\mathcal{H}''\mathcal{H} - 3\mathcal{H}'^2 + 12\mathcal{H}'\mathcal{H}^2)\right.$$
$$\left.-\frac{a^4 M^4}{8\omega_k^7}(120\mathcal{H}'\mathcal{H}^2 + 210\mathcal{H}^4) + \frac{105 a^6 M^6 \mathcal{H}^4}{4\omega_k^9}\right)$$
$$\left. + \left(\xi - \frac{1}{6}\right)^2 \left(-\frac{1}{4\omega_k^3}(72\mathcal{H}''\mathcal{H} - 36\mathcal{H}'^2 - 108\mathcal{H}^4) + \frac{54 a^2 M^2}{\omega_k^5}(\mathcal{H}'\mathcal{H}^2 + \mathcal{H}^4)\right) \right]$$
$$+ \frac{1}{8\pi^2 a^2}\int dk\, k^2 \left[\frac{a^2 \Delta^2}{\omega_k} - \frac{a^4 \Delta^4}{4\omega_k^3} + \frac{a^4 \mathcal{H}^2 M^2 \Delta^2}{2\omega_k^5} - \frac{5}{8}\frac{a^6 \mathcal{H}^2 M^4 \Delta^2}{\omega_k^7}\right.$$
$$\left. + \left(\xi - \frac{1}{6}\right)\left(-\frac{3a^2 \Delta^2 \mathcal{H}^2}{\omega_k^3} + \frac{9a^4 M^2 \Delta^2 \mathcal{H}^2}{\omega_k^5}\right)\right]. \quad (22)$$

As expected, only even powers of $\mathcal{H}$ remain in the final result. The Minkowskian spacetime result for the on-shell ZPE ($M = m$) is obtained as a very particular case of the above expression for $a = 1$ ($\mathcal{H} = 0$):

$$\langle T_{00}^{\delta\phi}\rangle\Big|_{\text{Minkowski}} = \frac{1}{4\pi^2}\int dk\, k^2 \omega_k = \int \frac{d^3k}{(2\pi)^3}\left(\frac{1}{2}\hbar\omega_k\right), \quad (23)$$

where $\hbar$ has been restored only in the last expression for better cognizance. The result is quartically UV-divergent. Usual attempts (e.g. through the minimal subtraction scheme) to regularize and renormalize this quantity by e.g. cancelling the corresponding UV-divergence against the bare ρ_Λ term in the action (1) ends up with the well-known fine-tuning problem, which is considered to be the weirdest and toughest aspect of the CCP – see e.g.[17,42] and references therein. We will certainly not proceed in this way here. We seek (and will find) an alternative way.

4. Renormalization of the VED in curved spacetime: the RVM

The vacuum energy density in the expanding universe can be compared with a Casimir device in which the parallel plates slowly move apart ("expand").[17] Although the total VED cannot be measured, the distinctive effect associated to the presence of the plates, and then also to their increasing separation with time, it can. In a similar fashion, in the cosmological spacetime there is a distinctive non-vanishing spacetime curvature R as compared to Minkowskian spacetime that is changing with the expansion. We expect that the measurable VED must be that one which is associated to purely geometric contributions proportional to R, R^2, $R^{\mu\nu}R_{\mu\nu}$ etc., hence to H^2 and $\dot{H}$ (including higher powers of these quantities in the early Universe).

Following,[9,10] a subtraction of the VEV of the EMT is carried out at an arbitrary mass scale M, playing the role of renormalization point. Taking into account that the only adiabatic orders that are divergent in the case of the EMT are the first four ones, the subtraction at the scale M is performed only up to the fourth adiabatic order. The on-shell value of the EMT can be computed of course at any order. The terms beyond the 4th order are finite. The renormalized EMT in this context therefore reads

$$\langle T^{\delta\phi}_{\mu\nu}\rangle_{\rm Ren}(M) = \langle T^{\delta\phi}_{\mu\nu}\rangle(m) - \langle T^{\delta\phi}_{\mu\nu}\rangle^{(0-4)}(M). \qquad (24)$$

Let us apply this procedure to the ZPE part of the EMT, as given by Eq. (22). To ease the presentation of the explicit result, it proves convenient to recover at least in part the more explicit notation (18) so as to distinguish explicitly between the off-shell energy mode $\omega_k(M) = \sqrt{k^2 + a^2 M^2}$ (formerly denoted just as ω_k) and the on-shell one $\omega_k(m) = \sqrt{k^2 + a^2 m^2}$. With this notation, lengthy but straightforward calculations from equations (22) and (24) lead to the following compact result:[9]

$$\langle T^{\delta\phi}_{00}\rangle_{\rm Ren}(M) = \frac{a^2}{128\pi^2}\left(-M^4 + 4m^2 M^2 - 3m^4 + 2m^4 \ln\frac{m^2}{M^2}\right) - \left(\xi - \frac{1}{6}\right)$$
$$\times \frac{3\mathcal{H}^2}{16\pi^2}\left(m^2 - M^2 - m^2 \ln\frac{m^2}{M^2}\right) + \left(\xi - \frac{1}{6}\right)^2 \frac{9\left(2\mathcal{H}''\mathcal{H} - \mathcal{H}'^2 - 3\mathcal{H}^4\right)}{16\pi^2 a^2}\ln\frac{m^2}{M^2} + \ldots$$
$$(25)$$

where dots stand just for higher adiabatic orders. The renormalized expression for the vacuum fluctuations, $\langle T^{\delta\phi}_{\mu\nu}\rangle_{\rm Ren}(M)$, is not yet the final one to extract the renormalized VED. As indicated in (11), the latter is obtained from including the contribution from the ρ_Λ-term in the Einstein-Hilbert action (1). Therefore, the renormalized vacuum EMT at the scale M is given by

$$\langle T^{\rm vac}_{\mu\nu}\rangle_{\rm Ren}(M) = -\rho_\Lambda(M) g_{\mu\nu} + \langle T^{\delta\phi}_{\mu\nu}\rangle_{\rm Ren}(M). \qquad (26)$$

We distinguish between VED and ZPE: the latter is caused by the vacuum fluctuations of the fields, whereas the former combines the ZPE and the parameter ρ_Λ in the action. The renormalized VED is precisely the 00th component of the above

expression:
$$\rho_{\text{vac}}(M) = \frac{\langle T_{00}^{\text{vac}}\rangle_{\text{Ren}}(M)}{a^2} = \rho_\Lambda(M) + \frac{\langle T_{00}^{\delta\phi}\rangle_{\text{Ren}}(M)}{a^2}, \tag{27}$$

where we have used the fact that $g_{00} = -a^2$ in the conformal metric. Explicitly, the VED comes out to be

$$\rho_{\text{vac}}(M) = \rho_\Lambda(M) + \frac{1}{128\pi^2}\left(-M^4 + 4m^2M^2 - 3m^4 + 2m^4\ln\frac{m^2}{M^2}\right)$$
$$-\left(\xi - \frac{1}{6}\right)\frac{3\mathcal{H}^2}{16\pi^2 a^2}\left(m^2 - M^2 - m^2\ln\frac{m^2}{M^2}\right)$$
$$+\left(\xi - \frac{1}{6}\right)^2\frac{9\left(2\mathcal{H}''\mathcal{H} - \mathcal{H}'^2 - 3\mathcal{H}^4\right)}{16\pi^2 a^4}\ln\frac{m^2}{M^2} + \cdots \tag{28}$$

The (very) interesting aspect about this form of renormalized VED is that the first two terms of this expression (i.e. those not depending on $\mathcal{H}$) exactly cancel when we compute the difference of ρ_{vac} values at two scales, say M and M_0:

$$\rho_{\text{vac}}(M) - \rho_{\text{vac}}(M_0) = \left(\xi - \frac{1}{6}\right)\frac{3\mathcal{H}^2}{16\pi^2 a^2}\left(M^2 - M_0^2 - m^2\ln\frac{M^2}{M_0^2}\right)$$
$$+\left(\xi - \frac{1}{6}\right)^2\frac{9}{16\pi^2 a^4}\left(\mathcal{H}'^2 - 2\mathcal{H}''\mathcal{H} + 3\mathcal{H}^4\right)\ln\frac{M^2}{M_0^2}. \tag{29}$$

To verify the cancellation of the mentioned terms, we rewrite Einstein's equations (2) using the renormalized parameters and including the higher derivative tensor $H_{\mu\nu}^{(1)}$, which is necessary for renormalization purposes.[5] We need to write only the vacuum part of the EMT since in doing the mentioned subtraction the background contribution of the field ϕ (and any other contribution, indicated below by ...) will cancel, except the (M-dependent) change of the vacuum EMT at the two scales:

$$\mathcal{M}_{\text{Pl}}^2(M)G_{\mu\nu} + \alpha(M)H_{\mu\nu}^{(1)} = \langle T_{\mu\nu}^{\text{vac}}\rangle_{\text{Ren}}(M) + \ldots \tag{30}$$

On the r.h.s. we have used Eq. (26), which can be made more explicit using Eq. (25). We may now subtract side by side (30) at the scales M and M_0 and project the 00th component. Using the explicit form of G_{00} and $H_{00}^{(1)}$ in the FLRW metric we can perform the identifications on both sides of the subtracted equation. In particular, this renders specific expressions for the shifts $\mathcal{M}_{\text{Pl}}^2(M) - \mathcal{M}_{\text{Pl}}^2(M_0)$ and $\alpha(M) - \alpha(M_0)$, which we need not quote here[9,10]. After performing these identifications, what is left of $\langle T_{\mu\nu}^{\text{vac}}\rangle_{\text{Ren}}(M) - \langle T_{\mu\nu}^{\text{vac}}\rangle_{\text{Ren}}(M_0)$ must be zero. This is how we can prove that $\rho_\Lambda(M) - \rho_\Lambda(M_0)$ exactly cancels against the difference of the second term of (29) at the two scales (see Refs.[9,10] for more details):

$$\rho_\Lambda(M)\big|_{M_0}^M + \frac{1}{128\pi^2}\left(-M^4 + 4m^2M^2 - 3m^4 + 2m^4\ln\frac{m^2}{M^2}\right)\bigg|_{M_0}^M$$
$$= \rho_\Lambda(M) - \rho_\Lambda(M_0) + \frac{1}{128\pi^2}\left(-M^4 + M_0^4 + 4m^2(M^2 - M_0^2) - 2m^4\ln\frac{M^2}{M_0^2}\right) = 0. \tag{31}$$

This important equality, enforced by the renormalized form of Einstein's equations, demonstrates that the renormalized EMT, and in particular the renormalized VED, is free from quartic contributions associated to mass scales. That is why the relation (29) between the VED at the two renormalization points M and M_0 is a smooth function $\sim M^2 \mathcal{H}^2$. With no quartic mass term surviving in this renormalization procedure, there is no need of fine tuning. This is, of course, an extremely welcome feature, which obviously impinges on a possible solution of the CCP. Another appealing (and novel) feature of our renormalization framework is the following: Eq. (30) says that in Minkowski spacetime $\langle T_{00}^{\rm vac}\rangle_{\rm Ren}(M) = 0$, and as a result the renormalized VED in flat spacetime is also zero in this context, $\rho_{\rm vac}^{\rm Mink} = 0$.

Let us now assume that we define the renormalized VED in the context of some Grand Unified Theory (GUT) scale $M_0 = M_X$, where typically $M_X \sim 10^{16}$ GeV is associated with the inflationary scale. We denote by $\rho_{\rm vac}(M_X)$ the value of the VED at M_X. We can relate $\rho_{\rm vac}(M_X)$ with the current value of the VED, $\rho_{\rm vac}^0$, assuming that $\rho_{\rm vac}(M = H_0) = \rho_{\rm vac}^0$, where we choose the second scale at today's value of the Hubble parameter, H_0. This quantity can be used as an estimate for the energy scale of the background gravitational field associated to the FLRW universe at present. We neglect the $\sim H^4$ terms in the current universe. Then, according to Eq. (29), the connection between the two values of the VED is

$$\rho_{\rm vac}^0 = \rho_{\rm vac}(M_X) + \frac{3}{16\pi^2}\left(\frac{1}{6} - \xi\right) H_0^2 \left[M_X^2 + m^2 \ln\frac{H_0^2}{M_X^2}\right], \qquad (32)$$

or swapping terms on both sides:

$$\rho_{\rm vac}(M_X) = \rho_{\rm vac}^0 - \frac{3\nu}{8\pi} H_0^2 \, m_{\rm Pl}^2. \qquad (33)$$

Here we have defined the 'running parameter' for the VED:

$$\nu \equiv \frac{1}{2\pi}\left(\frac{1}{6} - \xi\right) \frac{M_X^2}{m_{\rm Pl}^2}\left(1 + \frac{m^2}{M_X^2} \ln\frac{H_0^2}{M_X^2}\right). \qquad (34)$$

We naturally expect $|\nu| \ll 1$, owing to the ratio $M_X^2/m_{\rm Pl}^2 \ll 1$. The vanishing of ν and hence of the dynamical $\sim H^2$ part of (32) is obtained only for conformal coupling: $\xi = 1/6$. There are, however, fermionic contributions to ν as well. They do not depend on ξ, of course, but shall not be addressed here.[43] The accurate determination of ν can only be obtained by fitting the RVM to the overall cosmological data, as it has been done e.g. in.[44–50] These analyses show that ν is positive and of order 10^{-3}. From (33) and (29) we can approximately estimate the VED near our time by taking M of order of the energy scale defined by the numerical value of H around the current epoch:[9]

$$\rho_{\rm vac}(H) \simeq \rho_{\rm vac}^0 + \frac{3\nu}{8\pi}(H^2 - H_0^2) m_{\rm Pl}^2 = \rho_{\rm vac}^0 + \frac{3\nu}{8\pi G_N}(H^2 - H_0^2). \qquad (35)$$

This expression reproduces the canonical form of the RVM.[17] A generalized form of the RVM is possible in which an additional term proportional to $\dot{H}$ (of order H^2)

can be included on the r-h.s. of (35) with another small coefficient $\tilde{\nu}$, see[9,10] for details. As noted, we have neglected the $\mathcal{O}(H^4)$ terms to derive the previous formulas. These terms can have an impact only for the early universe and produce inflation, but we refer once more the reader to[9,10] for an expanded discussion.

5. Phenomenological applications: H_0 and σ_8 tensions

We are now ready to produce some phenomenological output using the low-energy RVM form (35), or even the generalized one containing the $\sim \dot{H}$ term. In fact, we can use the following extended RVM structure for the VED:[9,10]

$$\rho_{\rm vac}(H) = \frac{3}{8\pi G_N}\left(c_0 + \nu H^2 + \tilde{\nu}\dot{H}\right) + \mathcal{O}(H^4). \tag{36}$$

The additive constant c_0 is fixed by the boundary condition $\rho_{\rm vac}(H_0) = \rho_{\rm vac}^0$. For recent expositions of the RVM and its many phenomenological applications making use of the above form of VED, see[51,52] and references therein[c]. In what follows I will summarize the findings of the recent study,[50] which involves the most complete set of cosmological data. Since the parameters ν and $\tilde{\nu}$ are ultimately to be fitted to observations, we shall simplify our analysis here assuming one single parameter with the choice $\tilde{\nu} = \nu/2$. This does not change anything fundamental. As a result, if we neglect the higher order terms, Eq. (36) takes on the suggestive form

$$\rho_{\rm vac}(H) = \frac{3}{8\pi G_N}\left(c_0 + \frac{\nu}{12}R\right) \equiv \rho_{\rm vac}(R), \tag{37}$$

where $R = 12H^2 + 6\dot{H}$ is the curvature scalar. For this reason we may call this form of the VED the 'RRVM'. Such a RRVM implementation has the double advantage of using one single parameter and provides a safe path to the early epochs of the cosmological evolution since when we approach the radiation dominated era we have $R \simeq 0$, or to be more precise: $R/H^2 \ll 1$. This fact insures that no conflict is generated with the BBN constraints. Early on the RVM has its own mechanism for inflation (as we have already mentioned), but we have no room to address these aspects here, see.[54–57] With one and the same VED given by Eq. (37) we may consider two types of RRVM scenarios, to wit: type I scenario, in which the vacuum interacts with matter; and type II, where matter is conserved at the expense of an exchange between the vacuum and a mildly evolving gravitational coupling $G(H)$. For type I models we assume that the vacuum exchanges energy with cold dark matter (CDM) only, as follows:

$$\dot{\rho}_{dm} + 3H\rho_{dm} = -\dot{\rho}_{\rm vac}. \tag{38}$$

---

[c]It is interesting to mention that at the pure cosmographic/cosmokinetic level (hence in a more model-independent way) the RVM appears also as a favoured model. For example, the form (36) has been used in[53] to study the different types of DE models in the framework of the cosmographic approach. Using the Hubble diagrams for SnIa, quasars, gamma-ray bursts as well as the data on baryonic acoustic oscillations in different combinations, it is found that the RVM fits better the cosmographic data than other DE models, including the concordance ΛCDM.

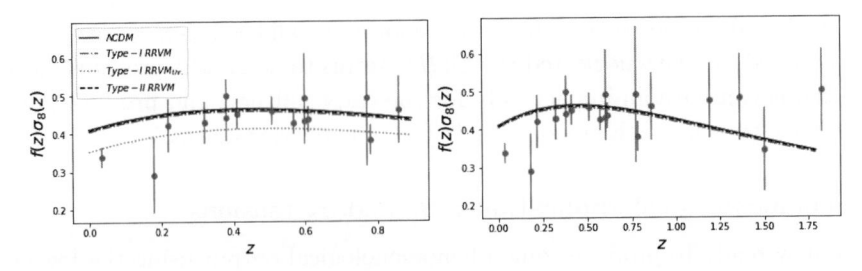

Fig. 1. Theoretically predicted curves of $f(z)\sigma_8(z)$ for the various models (type I and type II), testing the possible existence of a threshold redshift in the case of type I. The data points employed in our analysis are described in.[50] We present the results in two different redshift windows. It can be seen that the type I RRVM with threshold redshift $z_* \simeq 1$ has a most visible and favorable impact on solving the σ_8 tension.

Solving for the matter densities one finds[50]

$$\rho_m(a) = \rho_m^0 a^{-3\xi}, \quad \rho_{dm}(a) = \rho_m^0 a^{-3\xi} - \rho_b^0 a^{-3}, \qquad (39)$$

where $\xi \equiv \frac{1-\nu}{1-\frac{3}{4}\nu}$. They recover the ΛCDM form for $\xi = 1$ ($\nu = 0$). The small departure of ν from zero (or ξ from one) is what permits a mild dynamical vacuum evolution:

$$\rho_{\text{vac}}(a) = \rho_{\text{vac}}^0 + \left(\frac{1}{\xi} - 1\right) \rho_m^0 \left(a^{-3\xi} - 1\right). \qquad (40)$$

For type I models we admit also the possibility that the dynamics of vacuum is relatively recent (see e.g.[58]). For instance, one may assume that the vacuum became dynamical in the form (40) at a threshold redshift $z_* \simeq 1$ (so $\rho_{\text{vac}}(z) = \rho_{\text{vac}}^0$ for $z > z_*$). We shall compare this option with the situation when there is no such threshold. As for type II models, matter is conserved (hence no exchange with vacuum), but the vacuum can still evolve as long as the effective gravitational coupling also evolves (very mildly) with the expansion $G_{\text{eff}} = G_{\text{eff}}(H)$, starting from an initial value (which enters our fit). In this case, we do not consider the effect of the threshold because it proves to be much smaller. One can show that the approximate behavior of the VED in the present time is (recall that $|\nu| \ll 1$):[50]

$$\rho_{\text{vac}}(a) = \frac{3c_0}{8\pi G_N}(1 + 4\nu) + \nu \rho_m^0 a^{-3} + \mathcal{O}(\nu^2). \qquad (41)$$

Once more, for $\nu = 0$ the VED remains constant at the value $\rho_{\text{vac}} = 3c_0/(8\pi G_N) = \Lambda/(8\pi G_N)$, but otherwise it shows a moderate dynamics as in the type I case. One can also show that the effective gravitational coupling evolves approximately as $G_{\text{eff}}(a) \simeq G_N(1 + \epsilon \ln a)$ in the current epoch (with $0 < \epsilon \ll 1$ of order ν), thus confirming the very mild (logarithmic) evolution of G. Since $\epsilon > 0$ the gravitational strength exhibits an asymptotically free behavior (i.e. being smaller in the past).

For an accurate comparison of the theoretical predictions and the observations, the LSS formation data are also of paramount importance, all the more if we take into account that one of the aforementioned ΛCDM tensions (the σ_8 one) stems

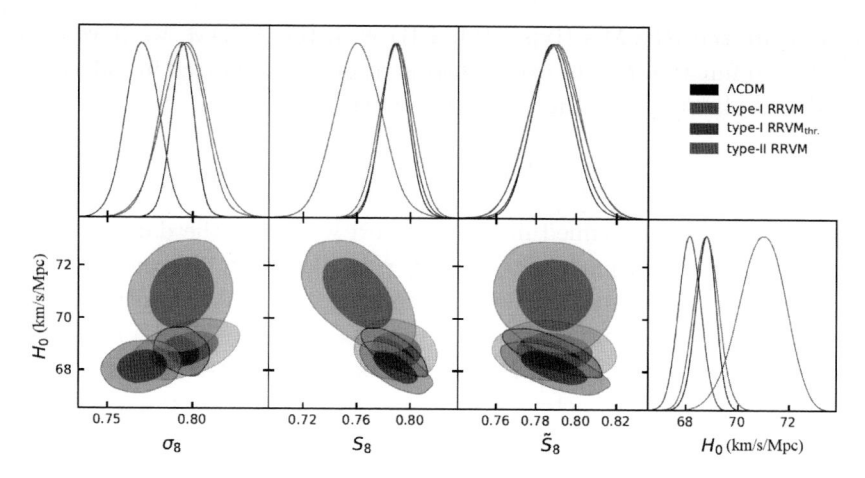

Fig. 2. The 1σ and 2σ c.l. contours in the H_0-$\sigma_8, S_8, \tilde{S}_8$ planes and the corresponding one-dimensional posteriors for the RRVM's obtained from the Baseline+H_0 data set (meaning that the local value of H_0 is included along with the remaining data, see[50]). It is apparent that the type II model alleviates the H_0 tension without spoiling the σ_8 one, whereas the type I model with threshold redshift $z_* \simeq 1$ can fully fix the latter (see also Fig. 1) but cannot reduce the former.

from it. As we shall see, allowing for some evolution of the vacuum can be the clue to alleviate the σ_8 tension since such dynamics affects significantly the cosmological perturbations.[59] We consider the perturbed, spatially flat, FLRW metric $ds^2 = -dt^2 + (\delta_{ij} + h_{ij})dx^i dx^j$, in which h_{ij} stands for the metric fluctuations. These fluctuations are nontrivially coupled to the matter density perturbations $\delta_m = \delta\rho_m/\rho_m$. We have implemented the full perturbations analysis in the context of the Einstein-Boltzmann code CLASS[60] (in the synchronous gauge).[50] Since baryons do not interact with the time-evolving VED the perturbed conservation equations are not directly affected. However, the corresponding equation for CDM is modified in the following way:

$$\dot{\delta}_{dm} + \frac{\dot{h}}{2} - \frac{\dot{\rho}_{\rm vac}}{\rho_{dm}}\delta_{dm} = 0\,, \tag{42}$$

with $h = h_{ii}$ denoting the trace of h_{ij}. We remark that the term $\dot{\rho}_{\rm vac}$ is nonvanishing for these models. Thus, it affects the fluctuations of CDM in a way which produces a departure from the ΛCDM. The above equation is, of course, coupled with the metric fluctuations and the combined system must be solved numerically. The analysis of the linear LSS regime is performed with the help of the weighted linear growth $f(z)\sigma_8(z)$, where $f(z)$ is the growth factor and $\sigma_8(z)$ is the rms mass fluctuation amplitude on scales of $R_8 = 8\,h^{-1}$ Mpc at redshift z. The quantity $\sigma_8(z)$ is directly provided by CLASS. Similarly, we can extract the (observationally measured) linear growth function $f(a)$ directly from the matter power spectrum $P_m(a, \vec{k})$, which is computed numerically by CLASS under adiabatic initial conditions. The results can be seen in Figures 1 and 2 for the various models.

To compare the RRVM's (types I and II) with the ΛCDM, we have defined a joint likelihood function $\mathcal{L}$. The overall fitting results are reported in Tables 1 and 2. The total χ^2 to be minimized in our case is given by

$$\chi^2_{\rm tot} = \chi^2_{\rm SnIa} + \chi^2_{\rm BAO} + \chi^2_H + \chi^2_{f\sigma_8} + \chi^2_{\rm CMB}. \tag{43}$$

The above χ^2 terms are defined in the standard way from the data including the covariance matrices.[16] In particular, the χ^2_H part may contain or not the local H_0 value measured by Riess, see.[50] The local determination of H_0 (which is around 4σ away from the corresponding Planck 2018 value based on the CMB) is the origin of the so-called H_0 tension.[20–23] Taking into account that the RRVM's of type I and II have one and two more parameters, respectively, as compared to the ΛCDM, a fairer model comparison is achieved by computing the numerical differences between the Deviance Information Criterion (DIC) of the ΛCDM model against the RRVM's: ΔDIC = DIC$_{\Lambda\rm CDM}$ − DIC$_{\rm RRVM}$. These differences will be (and in fact are) positive if the RRVM's fit better the overall data than the ΛCDM. The DIC is defined by[61] DIC = $\chi^2(\bar{\theta}) + 2p_D$. Here $p_D = \overline{\chi^2} - \chi^2(\bar{\theta})$ is the effective number of parameters of the model, and $\overline{\chi^2}$ and $\bar{\theta}$ the mean of the overall χ^2 distribution and of the parameters, respectively. The posterior distributions and corresponding constraints for the various dataset combinations have been obtained with Montepython[62] in combination with CLASS.[60]

The DIC value can be obtained from the Markov chains generated with MontePython. If $+5 < \Delta$DIC $< +10$ one should conclude strong evidence favoring the RRVM's over the ΛCDM. For ΔDIC $> +10$ it is said that the evidence is very strong. Such is the case when we use a threshold redshift $z_* \simeq 1$ in type I RRVM. In stark contrast, when the threshold is removed we find only moderate evidence against it (viz. $-3 < \Delta$DIC < -2), although the fitting performance is still slightly better (smaller $\chi^2_{\rm min}$) than the ΛCDM. The effect of the threshold can be very important and suggests that a mild dynamics of the vacuum is welcome, especially if it gets activated at around the epoch when the vacuum dominance appears, namely at $z \simeq 1$. Unfortunately, type I models with fixed $G_{\rm eff} = G_N$ do not help an inch to solve the H_0 tension since the value of H_0 remains stuck around the CMB value.[50] In stark contrast, type II models can alleviate the two tensions at a time. The overall ΔDIC value of the fit is quite significant ($+5.5$), still in the strong evidence region, providing values of H_0 markedly higher as compared to type I models (specifically $H_0 = 70.93^{+0.93}_{-0.87}$ Km/s/Mpc[50]) along with σ_8 and S_8 values in the needed moderate range ($\sigma_8 = 0.794^{+0.013}_{-0.012}$ and $S_8 = 0.761^{+0.018}_{-0.017}$).[50] The values of S_8 in all RRVM's are perfectly compatible with recent weak lensing and galaxy clustering measurements.[63] For type II models a related observable analogous to (but different from) S_8 is $\tilde{S}_8 = S_8\sqrt{G_{\rm eff}(0)/G_N}$. We show the corresponding contours in Fig. 2. The net outcome of this analysis is that the only model capable of alleviating the two tensions (H_0 and σ_8) is RRVM of type II, whereas the type I model can (fully) solve the σ_8 tension but has no bearing on the H_0 one.

6. Conclusions and outlook

In this short review presentation I have described the renormalization of the energy-momentum tensor (EMT) of a real quantum scalar field non-minimally coupled to classical gravity in the cosmological context. The main aim was to show that, out of the very quantum effects of matter, there emerges the running vacuum model (RVM) structure, which is the effective form of the renormalized vacuum energy density (VED). The method is based on an off-shell extension of the adiabatic regularization and renormalization procedure, which we have used in the recent works[9,10] and where for the first time we provided a calculation of the zero point energy (ZPE) of a quantum scalar field that is free from the need of extreme fine tuning. The latter is well-known to be one of the most striking and bizarre aspects of the cosmological constant problem.[11] The absence of need for fine-tuning is related to the non appearance in our framework of the terms which are proportional to the quartic mass of the fields, i.e. $\sim m^4$. In the standard model of particle physics, these terms are usually responsible for the exceedingly large contributions to the VED and requires preposterous fine-tuning with the renormalized vacuum parameter ρ_Λ in the action.[17] The calculational procedure in our approach is based on the WKB expansion of the field modes in the FLRW spacetime and the use of an appropriately renormalized EMT. The latter is obtained by performing a substraction of its on-shell value (i.e. the value defined on the mass shell m of the quantized field) at an arbitrary renormalization point M. The resulting EMT becomes finite because we subtract the first four adiabatic orders (the only ones that can be divergent). Since the off-shell renormalized EMT is a function of the arbitrary renormalization point M, we can compare the renormalized result at different epochs of the cosmic history. The introduction of such 'sliding' scale leads to the renormalization group (RG) flow, which in the case of FLRW cosmology we may associate in a natural way with Hubble's expansion rate H.

While the RG approach was actually the first qualitative idea behind the RVM,[17] with the present QFT calculations in curved spacetime we provide for the first time[9,10] a solid foundation of the RVM, in which the dynamical structure of the VED is seen to emerge from the quantum effects associated with the adiabatic renormalization of the EMT. Let us mention that even though our QFT calculation has been simplified by the use of a single (real) quantum scalar field, further investigations show that the generalization of these results for multiple fields, involving scalar as well as vector and fermionic components, lead as well to the generic RVM structure mentioned here up to (nontrivial) computation details.[43]

At the end of the day, we have been able to show that the genuine form of the VED for the current universe can be achieved from direct calculations of QFT in the FLRW spacetime. In such structure, the powers of H (and its time derivatives) are of even adiabatic order. This means that all of the allowed powers effectively carry an even number of time derivatives of the scale factor, which is essential to preserve the general covariance of the action. Linear terms (cubic, or in general of odd order) in H are incompatible with such a covariance and in fact do not appear in the final result. To be more precise, all terms with an odd number of time derivatives of the scale factor are ruled out. The form of $\rho_{\rm vac}(H)$ predicted by the RVM at low energies is remarkably simple but it certainly goes beyond a rigid cosmological constant term. It consists of an additive constant (to be identified basically with the cosmological term) together with a small dynamical component $\sim \nu H^2$, in which the dimensionless parameter ν can be computed from the underlying QFT framework and is predicted to be small ($|\nu| \ll 1$). Ultimately, its value can only be known upon fitting the RVM to the overall cosmological data. The physical outcome is that today's cosmic vacuum is mildly dynamical. In fact, in previous works the model has been phenomenologically fitted to a large wealth of cosmological data and the running parameter ν has been found to be positive and in the ballpark of $\sim 10^{-3}$ cf.[44–47]

Recent phenomenological analyses involving a large set of updated cosmological data on SnIa+H(z)+BAO+LSS+CMB [50,64] and analyzed with the Boltzmann code CLASS[60] confirm to a large extent the results reported in the aforementioned works, which were carried out within an approximate treatment of the CMB. The basic result is still the same, they point to substantial evidence that a mild dynamics of the cosmic vacuum is helpful to describe the overall cosmological observations as compared to the standard cosmological model with a rigid Λ-term. From our analysis of two variants of the RVM, we have found that for type I models the σ_8 tension can be fully overcome ($\lesssim 0.4\sigma$ c.l.) provided there exists a threshold redshift $z_* \simeq 1$ where the vacuum dynamics is triggered. Solving the H_0 tension, however, proves more demanding as it requires the combination of vacuum dynamics with running G, which is the characteristic of the type II models. Interestingly enough, the two tensions can actually be dealt with at a time, the H_0 remaining at $\sim 1.6\sigma$ and the σ_8 one at $\sim 1.3\sigma$ (or at only $\sim 0.4\sigma$ if stated in terms of S_8).[63] The successful cutback of the two tensions is highly remarkable and is strongly supported by standard information criteria, such as the deviance information criterion (DIC). More work will be needed, of course, to confirm if the RVM can fully solve the σ_8 and H_0 tensions.[64] It will depend also on the upcoming data in the next few years.

Acknowledgements

It is my pleasure to thank N.E. Mavromatos for inviting me to speak in the DM1 parallel session: "Interacting Dark Matter" of the MG16 Marcel Grossmann virtual Conference, July 5-10 2021. Work partially funded by projects PID2019-105614GB-C21 and FPA2016-76005-C2-1-P (MINECO, Spain), 2017-SGR-929 (Generalitat de Catalunya) and CEX2019-000918-M (ICCUB). The author acknowledges participation in the COST Association Action CA18108 "*Quantum Gravity Phenomenology in the Multimessenger Approach (QG-MM)*". This presentation is based in part on works with A. Gómez-Valent, J. de Cruz Pérez and C. Moreno-Pulido. I thank them warmly for the enjoyable collaboration.

References

1. P. J. E. Peebles, Astrophys. J. **284** (1984) 439; L.M. Krauss and M.S. Turner, Gen. Rel. Grav. **27** (1995) 1137; J. P. Ostriker, Paul J. Steinhardt, Nature **377** (1995) 600.
2. A. G. Riess et al., Astron. J. **116** (1998) 1009; S. Perlmutter et al. ApJ **517** (1999) 565.
3. D. M. Scolnic et al., Astrophys. J. **859** (2018) 101.
4. N. Aghanim et al. [Planck Collab.], A & A **641** (2020) A6.
5. N. D. Birrell and P. C. W. Davies, *Quantum Fields in Curved Space*, Cambridge U. Press (1982).
6. L. E. Parker and D. J. Toms *Quantum Field Theory in Curved Spacetime: Quantized fields and gravity*, Cambridge U. Press (2009).
7. W. Fulling, *Aspects of Quantum Field Theory in Curved Space-Time*, Cambridge U. Press, (1989).
8. V. F. Mukhanov and S. Winitzki, *Quantum Effects in Gravity*, Cambridge U. Press (2007).
9. C. Moreno-Pulido. and J. Solà Peracaula, Eur. Phys. J. C**80** (2020) 692.
10. C. Moreno-Pulido and J. Solà Peracaula, *Renormalizing the vacuum energy in cosmological spacetime: Implications for the cosmological constant problem* (in preparation).
11. S. Weinberg, Rev. Mod. Phys. **61** (1989) 1.
12. V. Sahni and A. Starobinsky, Int. J. of Mod. Phys. A**9** (2000) 373.
13. P. J. E. Peebles and B. Ratra, Rev. Mod. Phys. **75** (2003) 559.
14. T. Padmanabhan, Phys. Rept. **380** (2003) 235.
15. E. J. Copeland, M. Sami and S. Tsujikawa, Int. J. Mod. Phys. D **15** (2006) 1753.
16. L. Amendola and S. Tsujikawa, *Dark Energy*, Cambridge U. Press (2010) & (2015).
17. J. Solà, J. Phys. Conf. Ser. **453** (2013) 012015 [arXiv:1306.1527]; AIP Conf. Proc. **1606** (2015) 19 [arXiv:1402.7049]; J. Phys. Conf. Ser. **283** (2011) 012033 [arXiv:1102.1815].
18. A. G. Riess et al., Astrophys. J. **826** (2016) (2016) 56; Astrophys. J. **855** (2018) 136.
19. A. G. Riess et al., Astrophys.J. **876** (2019) 85; Astrophys. J. Lett. **908** (2021) L6.
20. L. T. Verde, T. Treu T. and A. G. Riess, Nature Astron. **3** (2019) 891.
21. L. Perivolaropoulos and F. Skara (2021), *Challenges for ΛCDM: An update*, [arXiv:2105.05208 [astro-ph.CO]].
22. J. Solà Peracaula, Int.J.Mod.Phys.A**33** (2018) 1844009.
23. E. Di Valentino et al., Astropart. Phys. **131** (2021) 102605, Class. Quant. Grav. **38** (2021) 153001.
24. E. Di Valentino et al., Astropart. Phys. **131** (2021) 102604.
25. G. Efstathiou, MNRAS **505** (2021) 3866; W.L. Freedman, Nat. Astron. **1** (2017) 0121.
26. E. Mortsell et al., *The Hubble Tension Revisited: Additional Local Distance Ladder Uncertainties*, arXiv:2106.09400; *The Hubble Tension Bites the Dust: Sensitivity of the Hubble Constant Determination to Cepheid Color Calibration*, arXiv:2105.11461.
27. M. Giovanna Dainotti et al., Astrophys. J. **912** (2021) 150.
28. I. L. Shapiro and J. Solà, JHEP **02** (2002) 006; Phys. Lett. B **682** (2009) 105.
29. J. Solà, J. Phys. A**41** (2008) 164066.
30. A. Babic, B. Guberina, R. Horvat and H. Stefancic, Phys. Rev. D**71** (2005) 124041.
31. M. Maggiore, Phys. Rev. D**83** (2011) 063514; M. Maggiore, L. Hollenstein, M. Jaccard and E. Mitsou, Phys. Lett. B**704** (2011) 102.
32. N. Bilic, Phys. Rev. D**83** (2011) 105003; Rom. J. Phys. **57** (2012) 793.
33. K. Kohri and H. Matsui, JCAP **06** (2017) 006; Phys. Rev. D**98** (2018) 103521.
34. A. Ferreiro and J. Navarro-Salas, Phys. Lett. B **792** (2019) 81; Phys. Rev. D **102** (2020) 045021; A. Ferreiro, S. Nadal-Gisbert, J. Navarro-Salas, Phys. Rev. D **104** (2021) 2, 025003. J. Fernando Barbero et al., Phys. Rev. D **98** (2018) 025016.

35. I. G. Marian et al., *Renormalization of Field-Independent Term in the Cosmological Constant Problem*, arXiv:2107.06069.
36. N. E. Mavromatos and J. Solà Peracaula, Eur. Phys. J. Spec. Top. **230** (2021) 2077.
37. S. Basilakos, N. E. Mavromatos and J. Solà Peracaula, Int. J. Mod. Phys. D **28** (2019) 1944002; Phys. Rev. D **101** (2020) 045001; Phys. Lett. B **803** (2020) 135342.
38. N. E. Mavromatos and J. Solà Peracaula, *Inflationary physics and transplanckian conjecture in the Stringy Running-Vacuum-Model: From the phantom vacuum to the true vacuum*, arXiv:2105.02659.
39. N. E. Mavromatos, *Geometrical origins of the Universe dark sector: String-inspired torsion and anomalies as seeds for inflation and dark matter*, arXiv:2108.02152.
40. N. E. Mavromatos, *Gravitational anomalies, axions and a string-inspired running vacuum model in Cosmology*, arXiv:2108.03998.
41. T. S. Bunch, J. Phys. A**13** (1980) 1297.
42. E.K. Akhmedov, *Vacuum energy and relativistic invariance*, hep-th/0204048.
43. J. Solà Peracaula, C. Moreno-Pulido and S. Cheraghchi (in preparation).
44. J. Solà, A. Gómez-Valent and J. de Cruz Pérez, Astrophys. J. Lett. **811** (2015) L14; Astrophys. J. **836** (2017) 43.
45. A. Gómez-Valent, J. Solà and S. Basilakos, JCAP **01** (2015) 004; A. Gómez-Valent and J. Solà, MNRAS **448** (2015) 2810; A. Gómez-Valent, E. Karimkhani and J. Solà JCAP **12** (2015) 048.
46. J. Solà, A. Gómez-Valent and J. de Cruz Pérez, Phys. Lett. B**774** (2017) 317.
47. J. Solà Peracaula, J. de Cruz Pérez and A. Gómez-Valent, EPL **121** (2018) 39001; MNRAS **478** (2018) 4357.
48. M. Rezaei, M. Malekjani and J. Solà Peracaula, Phys. Rev. D**100** (2019) 023539.
49. J. Solà Peracaula, A. Gómez-Valent, J. de Cruz Pérez and C. Moreno-Pulido, Class. Quant. Grav. **37** (2020) 245003; Astrophys. J. Lett. **886** (2019) L6.
50. J. Solà Peracaula, A. Gómez-Valent, J. de Cruz Pérez and C. Moreno-Pulido, EPL **134** (2021) 19001.
51. A. Gómez-alent, *Vacuum energy in Quantum Field Theory and Cosmology* (PhD. Thesis), arXiv:1710.01978.
52. J. de Cruz Pérez, *Implications of Dynamical Dark Energy in the expansion of the Universe and the Structure Formation* (PhD. Thesis), arXiv:2105.14800.
53. M. Rezaei, J. Solà Peracaula and M. Malekjani, *Cosmographic approach to Running Vacuum dark energy models: New constraints using BAOs and Hubble diagrams at higher redshifts*, arXiv:2108.06255.
54. S. Basilakos, J. A. S. Lima and J. Solà, MNRAS **431** (2013) 923; E. L. D. Perico, J. A. S. Lima, S. Basilakos and J. Solà, Phys. Rev. D **88** (2013) 063531.
55. J. Solà and A. Gómez-Valent, Int. J. Mod. Phys. **D 24** (2015) 1541003.
56. J. Solà, Int. J. Mod. Phys. D**24** (2015) 1544027.
57. J. Solà Peracaula and H. Yu, Gen. Rel. Grav. **52** (2020) 17.
58. M. Martinelli et al., MNRAS **488** (2019) 3423; V. Salvatelli et al., Phys. Rev. Lett. **113** (2014) 181301.
59. A. Gómez-Valent and J. Solà Peracaula, MNRAS **478** (2018) 126; EPL **120** (2017) 39001.
60. D. Blas, J. Lesgourgues and T. Tram, JCAP **1107** (2011) 034.
61. A. R. Liddle, MNRAS **377** (2007) L74.
62. B. Audren, J. Lesgourgues, K. Benabed and S. Prunet, CAP **1302** (2013) 001.
63. C. Heymans et al., A & A **646** (2021) A140.
64. J. Solà Peracaula, A. Gómez-Valent, J. de Cruz Pérez and C. Moreno-Pulido (in preparation).

Dark matter properties from the Fornax globular cluster timing: Dynamical friction and cored profiles

D. Blas

Grup de Física Teòrica, Departament de Física,
Universitat Autònoma de Barcelona, 08193 Bellaterra, Spain, and
Institut de Fisica d'Altes Energies (IFAE),
The Barcelona Institute of Science and Technology, Campus UAB, 08193 Bellaterra , Spain
E-mail: dblas@ifae.es

I summarize our recent results to use the orbits of globular clusters (GCs) in the Fornax dwarf spheroidal (dSph) galaxy to learn more about dark matter (DM) properties. Our focus is on clarifying how dynamical friction (DF) from the DM halo is modified from the different microscopic properties of DM, which may alter *both* the scattering processes responsible of DF and the DM profiles (in particular generating a core), which also modifies DF. We consider: (*i*) fermionic degenerate dark matter (DDM), where Pauli blocking should be taken into account in the dynamical friction computation; (*ii*) self-interacting dark matter (SIDM) and (*iii*) ultralight dark matter (ULDM), for which this problem has been addressed by a variety of methods in recent literature. We derive DF with a Fokker-Planck formalism, reproducing previous results for ULDM and cold DM, while providing new results for DDM. Furthermore, ULDM, DDM and SIDM may generate cores in dSphs, which suppress dynamical friction and prolong GC orbits. We conclude that in all these cases the modifications in the DM modelling does not easily solve the so-called timing 'problem' of Fornax GCs. We finally study this 'problem' in terms of the initial conditions, demonstrating that the observed orbits of Fornax GCs are consistent with this expectation of a cuspy DM profile with a mild 'fine-tuning' at the level of $\sim 25\%$.

Keywords: Dark matter; globular clusters; dynamical friction.

1. Introduction and motivation

The presence of dark matter (DM) in the universe is probed by several different methods. In particular, the rotation curves of *tracers* of the gravitational potential in galaxies has long been considered as one of the most pressing motivations for the existence of a halo of DM extending beyond the volume occupied by visible matter. When tracers move in this *medium*, their dynamics may also be altered by direct momemtum exchange with the DM, which may lead to further dynamical consequences beyond rotation curves, as for instance tidal disruptions, dynamical heating or dynamical friction. The latter is the focus of this contribution, and in particular using it to learn about properties of DM.

Dynamical friction is generated by the relative motion between the tracer (probe) and the DM medium. Indeed, as the probe moves in the DM halo, its gravitational interaction with the latter leaves behind an overdensity of DM particles (wake) that pulls back gravitationally from it. The net result is a friction force, first calculated by Chandrasekhar,[1] and that can be parameterized as (for a probe of mass $m_\star$)[2]

$$\frac{d\mathbf{V}}{dt} = -\frac{4\pi G^2 m_\star \rho}{V^3} C \mathbf{V}, \qquad (1)$$

where $\mathbf{V}$ is the relative velocity, G is Newton's constant, ρ is the energy density of the DM medium and C is a parameter depending on the way momentum is exchanged between the probe and the DM medium. For a classical gas of particles with mass m, and with a cold distribution in velocities v_m given by $f(v_m)$, the later reads

$$C_{\text{class}} = 4\pi \ln \Lambda \int_0^V dv_m v_m^2 f_v(v_m). \qquad (2)$$

In this formula, $\ln \Lambda$ represents the so-called Coulomb logarithm, and is a factor of $O(1)$. We can already understand that different models of DM may alter the previous formula through modifications of the microscopic scattering (for instance if DM is not a simple collection of free classical particles, but has some coherent or quantum properties), different DM energy densities ρ or distribution functions f_v.

The question we want to address is if these features can lead to observable consequences. For this, let us consider a system where DF is supposed to have played a relevant role in current observations: the globular clusters (GCs) of the Milky Way dwarf spheroidal (dSph) satellite galaxies. The latter are believed to be DM dominated 'compact' galaxies.[3,4] One intriguing puzzle about the dSph galaxies related to DF concerns the GCs of the Fornax dSph.[5] Fornax is a very luminous nearby (kpc away) dwarf satellite, with a stellar mass or around $\sim 4 \times 10^7 \, M_\odot$ and of $\sim$ kpc scale. It contains six known GCs,[4,6] with masses around $m_\star \sim 10^5 \, M_\odot$, which we consider as our 'probes' moving in the DM halo. The puzzle arises because 2 of the most innermost GCs should have lost enough momentum due to DF to make them fall to the center of Fornax, while they live relatively far away from this point. In other words, from the expression (1), one can naïvely estimate the typical time scale to fall to center for GCs,

$$\tau \equiv \frac{|\mathbf{V}|}{|d\mathbf{V}/dt|} \sim 1.8 \left(\frac{V}{12 \text{ km/s}}\right)^3 \left(\frac{10^5 \, M_\odot}{m_\star}\right) \frac{2 \times 10^7 \frac{M_\odot}{\text{kpc}^3}}{\rho} \text{ Gpc.} \qquad (3)$$

When applied to the six GCs of Fornax assuming the usual CDM cusp density profile (see, e.g.[7]), this time scale for the six GCs is presented in Table 2[8] (see also[9]). On the other hand, the stellar content of the GCs (and most of the stellar content of Fornax) is old, with life estimates > 10 Gyr[10,11].[12,13] Hence these GCs had enough time to fall to the center since their 'birth'.

This puzzle (in particular the time scales for GC3 and GC4) has been highlighted as a possible tension of the standard DM paradigm that may be solved by changing the properties of DM, see e.g.[9] A first important observation is that the Jeans analysis based on kinematic information of Fornax (the velocity dispersion along the line of sight of ~ 2500 stars as a function of radius) is compatible with the energy density profiles M19 NFW and M19 ISO expected from standard CDM,[7] but also

Table 1. Some details of Fornax GCs: mass, projected radius and CDM instantaneous DF time (Eq. (3)). See Ref.[8] for more details about how these number are obtained and the origin of the discrepancies with previous literature.

	$m_\star \left[10^5 M_\odot\right]$	$r_\perp$ [kpc]	τ_{CDM} [Gyr]
GC1	0.42 ± 0.10	1.73 ± 0.05	119
GC2	1.54 ± 0.28	0.98 ± 0.03	14.7
GC3	4.98 ± 0.84	0.64 ± 0.02	2.63
GC4	0.76 ± 0.15	0.154 ± 0.014	0.91
GC5	1.86 ± 0.24	1.68 ± 0.05	32.2
GC6	~ 0.29	0.254 ± 0.015	5.45

with the presence of a cored distribution arising in different interesting DM models. The latter include fermionic DM of masses where quantum degeneracy may be relevant (DDM) in the dynamics of Fornax,[14–19] ultra-light DM with de Broglie wavelength large enough to affect the dynamics of Fornax[9] or self-interacting DM (SIDM) within the parameter space allowed by other observables, e.g.[20,21] A key motivation for our work is exploring whether DF may distinguish among these options, and hint towards new properties of DM.

2. Derivation of DF for different DM models with a Fokker-Planck approach

In order to include non-trivial properties of the DM microphysics into the expression (1), we followed a Fokker-Planck (FP) approach in,[8] where the probe particle (a GC in our case) correspond to species 1 traveling through a gas of spectator particles (species 2) with a certain distribution f_2 (DM particles in our case). We consider the following elastic scattering process of two particle species,

$$1(p) + 2(k) \to 1(p') + 2(k').$$

The phase space distribution function for the particle species 1 (the GC) evolves according to the Boltzmann equation,

$$\frac{df_1}{dt} = C[f_1]. \tag{4}$$

The collision integral $C[f_1]$ contains information about the elastic scattering processes, and is written as

$$C[f_1] = \frac{(2\pi)^4}{2E_p} \int d\Pi_k d\Pi_{p'} d\Pi_{k'}\, \delta^{(4)}(p+k-p'-k')|\overline{\mathcal{M}}|^2$$
$$\times \Big[f_1(p')f_2(k')(1\pm f_1(p))(1\pm f_2(k)) - f_1(p)f_2(k)(1\pm f_1(p'))(1\pm f_2(k'))\Big], \tag{5}$$

where $|\overline{\mathcal{M}}|^2$ is a squared matrix element averaged over initial and final spins, and $d\Pi_k = \frac{g}{2E_k}\frac{d^3k}{(2\pi)^3}$ is the Lorentz invariant phase element with the number of internal degrees of freedom g. The sign in $1 \pm f_i$ refers to bosons $(+)$ or fermions $(-)$, respectively. The Boltzmann equation can be greatly simplified if the momentum exchange

$$q = p' - p, \qquad (6)$$

is smaller than the typical momentum in the distribution function f_1. This is the adequate limit to compute DF.[2] In such cases, the Boltzmann equation reduces to the nonlinear Fokker-Planck equation,

$$\frac{df_1}{dt} = -\frac{\partial}{\partial p^i}\left[f_1(1 \pm f_1)D_i\right] + \frac{1}{2}\frac{\partial}{\partial p^i}\left[\frac{\partial}{\partial p^j}(D_{ij}f_1) \pm f_1^2\frac{\partial}{\partial p^j}D_{ij}\right], \qquad (7)$$

where the diffusion coefficients are defined in.[2,8] Furthermore, the gravitational scattering of a probe particle of mass $m_\star$ and a particle in the medium with mass m is described by the spin-averaged matrix element

$$\overline{|\mathcal{M}|^2} = \frac{1}{2s+1}\frac{(16\pi G)^2 m^4 m_\star^4}{[(q^0)^2 - \mathbf{q}^2]^2}, \qquad (8)$$

where s is the spin of the particle in the medium, and $(q^0, \mathbf{q})$ is the transferred 4−momentum. In the nonrelativistic limit, we can neglect q^0 and maintain only $\mathbf{q}$ in Eq. (8).

Of particular importance for our analysis is the diffusion coefficient $D_\parallel$, corresponding to the diffusion in momentum parallel to the probe object's instantaneous velocity. Indeed, the DF deceleration on a probe of mass $m_\star$ moving with velocity $\mathbf{V}$ w.r.t. the medium is[2]

$$\frac{d\mathbf{V}}{dt} = \frac{D_\parallel}{m_\star}\hat{\mathbf{V}}. \qquad (9)$$

From (1), we see that the dimensionless coefficient C of the DF reads,

$$C = -\frac{V^2 D_\parallel}{4\pi G^2 m_\star^2 \rho}. \qquad (10)$$

When computed for a gas of classical particles (where f_2 corresponds to a classical distribution), one reproduces the known results of the Chandrasekhar[1] formula, with C given by (2). This limit is also the relevant one for the SIDM case of interest here, since the corresponding cross-sections always correspond to large mean-free paths, where the approximation of the Chandrasekhar calculation holds.

Regarding DDM, when one assumes that f_2 is given by a Fermi-Dirac distribution close to the degeneracy limit[a] one finds

$$C_{\text{DDM}} \to \ln\Lambda \begin{cases} 1 & V \gg v_F \\ \frac{V^3}{v_F^3} & V \ll v_F \end{cases}, \qquad (11)$$

---

[a]Note that it is not known what is the momentum distribution for degenerate fermions interacting only gravitationally. Still, one normally assumes an equilibrium configuration as a first approximation. This assumption may also be used to constrain the mass of fermionic DM from virialized DM objects.[19,22]

where v_F is the Fermi velocity, related to the DM energy density by

$$\rho = \frac{g m_{\text{DM}}^4 v_F^3}{6\pi^2}, \qquad (12)$$

where g represents the number of degrees of freedom of the species (see also[23]). We used m_{DM} for the DM mass. This modification of the DF formula changes the falling time τ, though not parametrically. Furthermore, the DDM case also generates a *core* due to the quantum degeneracy pressure. Both effects are useful to reduce DF and hence prolong τ.

A similar calculation can be done for the bosonic case with large occupation numbers. In this case, the collision term is also modified and allows our formalism to capture the most relevant phenomena for DF in the ULDM case described in.[9,24–26] Indeed, these Bose-enhancement terms in (7) generate large-scale density fluctuations, causing additional velocity drift that can be characterised by an extra term to $C \to C + \Delta C$ as

$$\Delta C = \ln \Lambda \left(\frac{m_{\text{eff}}}{m_\star} \right) \left(\text{erf}(X_{\text{eff}}) - \frac{2 X_{\text{eff}}}{\sqrt{\pi}} e^{-X_{\text{eff}}^2} \right), \qquad (13)$$

where $m_{\text{eff}} = \pi^{3/2} \rho / (m_{\text{DM}} \sigma)^3$ is the ULDM mass enclosed in an effective de Broglie volume and $X_{\text{eff}} \equiv v/\sqrt{2}\sigma_{\text{eff}}$ with $\sigma_{\text{eff}} = \sigma/\sqrt{2}$. Numerically, $m_{\text{eff}} \approx 1.2 \times 10^6 \left(10^{-21} \text{ eV}/m_{\text{DM}} \right)^3 [\rho/(3 \times 10^7 \ M_\odot/\text{kpc}^3)][(10 \text{ km/s})/\sigma]^3 \ M_\odot$. With these numbers and keeping in mind a typical GC mass $m_\star \sim 10^5 \ M_\odot$, the ΔC effect becomes quantitatively important in Fornax for $m \lesssim 3 \times 10^{-20}$ eV. This value starts to be in tension with other constraints of ULDM, see e.g.[27,28] Notice that the previous calculation is correct in the limit $r > \lambda_{\text{db}}$, where λ_{db} is the de Broglie wavelength of DM. In the opposite regime, one can have effects coming from the coherent nature of the DM waves which affect the scattering cross-section,[9] or even resonant processes that our formalism does not capture, see e.g.[26,29]

3. Timing of Fornax GCs for different DM models

From the previous calculation, one can estimate the falling time of the GCs in Fornax once the profile of DM energy density is known. For the latter, one can use a Jeans method consistent with the line-of-sight velocity (LOSV) observed for Fornax.[2] However, as already stressed, the latter is equally well fitted by a M19 NFW, M19 ISO CDM profiles, as long as DDM of mass $m_{\text{DM}} \approx 135$ eV (which should generate a degenerate core of kpc) or a SIDM model with velocity averaged cross section $\langle \sigma v \rangle / m_{\text{DM}} \sim 25$ cm^2 g^{-1} km s^{-1} (also generating a isothermal cored profile of kpc size, this time due the SIDM scatterings[20]). These cases are shown, together with the relevant data of the dispersion in the LOSV, σ_{LOS}, as a function of radius in the left panel of Fig. 1. It should be clear from this panel that this data agrees well with the models just described. The right panel shows the different energy density profiles for these cases also as a function of radius. For completeness we have also shown the energy density of the star content of Fornax, to show explicitly that

DM is needed in this system. Another CDM model (coreNFW) is also shown. This models aims at describing a DM dominated halo where the baryonic feedback is somehow taken into account.

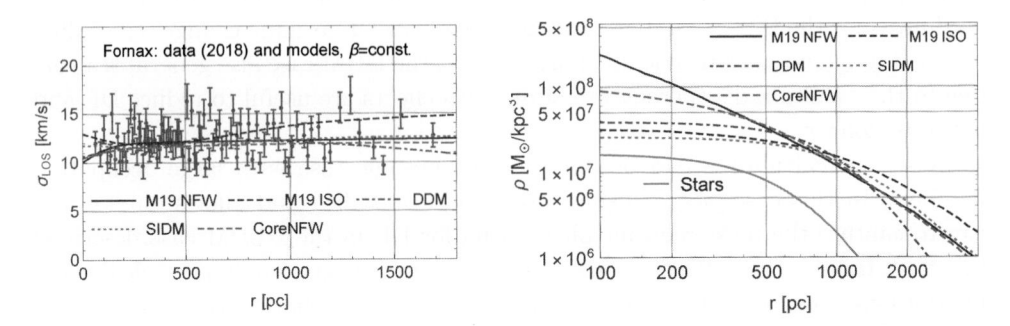

Fig. 1. **Left panel**: LOSVD data and fits for the M19 NFW and M19 ISO of,[7] DDM with mass $m \approx 135\,\text{eV}$ and SIDM models with cores of order kpc. **Right panel**: Density profiles corresponding to these cases. The the energy density of the star content of Fornax is also shown.

Now that we have all the ingredients to compute the DF, we proceed to find the orbital motion of the different GCs of Fornax by solving the equation

$$\frac{d\mathbf{V}}{dt} = -\frac{GM(r)}{r^2}\hat{r} - \frac{4\pi G^2 m_\star \rho}{V^3} C \mathbf{V}, \qquad (14)$$

for the relevant cases. This is a 'semi-analytical' approach that yields good agreement with simulations.[8] The results are only mildly dependent on the Coulomb logarithm $\ln\Lambda$, which we calibrate to numerical work in.[8] As an example, we show in Fig. 2 the evolution of the radius as a function of time, as compared to two profiles studied numerically in.[7]

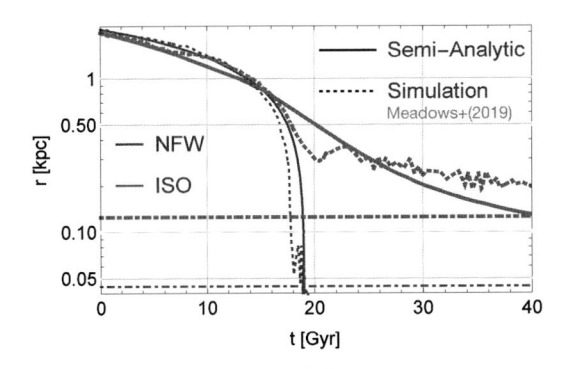

Fig. 2. Radius of an infalling orbit of a GC with mass $m_\star = 3 \times 10^5\,M_\odot$. n dotted blue (thick dotted red) we plot the simulation result in[7] for the NFW (ISO) halo. In solid lines, we plot our semi- analytic integration. Horizontal dot-dashed lines show the radii where the semi-analytic treatment breaks down.

From the previous analysis, we are now in the position to find the time τ that it takes to a GC to fall to the center of Fornax for different DM models. We will address the initial conditions momentarily. For now, let us compare the 'instantaneous' time in the DF formulae for the different GCs in CDM, DDM of mass $m_{\rm DM} \approx 135\,{\rm eV}$ and SIDM generating a kpc core. This is shown in Table 2 and Fig. 3. The conclusion is clear: both models beyond CDM prolong the plunging time of the problematic GCs, and hence alleviate the timing problem.

Table 2. Instantaneous DF times for the GCs of Fornax in the DDM and SIDM models described in the main text.

	$\tau_{\rm CDM}$ [Gyr]	$\tau_{\rm DDM}^{(135)}$ [Gyr]	$\tau_{\rm SIDM}$ [Gyr]
GC1	119	122	79.3
GC2	14.7	7.12	8.82
GC3	2.63	1.48	2.21
GC4	0.91	10.7	14.8
GC5	32.2	30.1	20
GC6	5.45	16.1	22

This conclusion is confirmed by a numerical study of the orbits, where the different DM profiles and dispersion properties are taking into account for the different models. The latter analysis is vital to find the real dynamics of the GCs, since the timescales can vary by $O(1)$ factors. We will skip the details of this study in this short contribution, and the interested reader is invited to check our work[8] for details. Let us simply mention that beyond the numerical integration of Eq. (14), in[8] we also considered different projection effects that alter the radius of the different GCs and their velocities. The main lesson we learned is that the conclusions extracted from the estimates in Table 2 and Fig. 3 are robust against these uncertainties.

The main lesson from Fig. 3 is that cores (including those in coreNFW) increase the time τ, but to make GC4's settling time substantially different, one requires a

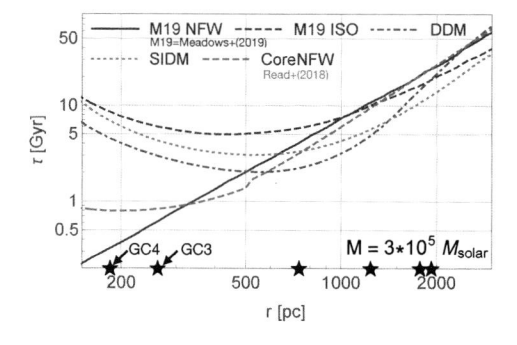

Fig. 3. Instantaneous DF time, evaluated for different DM models for $m_\star = 3 \times 10^5 M_\odot$ as a function of distance to the center of Fornax. The stars represent the positions of the different GCs.

large (kpc-size) core. Note that the microscopic properties in the DF formula are not particularly relevant in our calculations.

Before closing this section, let us notice that in Table 2 and Fig. 3 we have focused on DM models which help prolonging the orbits of GCs in Fornax. However, for the DDM case this requires models with masses already in strong tension with Ly-α observations[30] (and light tension with Jeans analysis of other systems[19]). In fact, regarding the Ly-α constraints, the interesting reader may also find in our work[8] a rather model independent bound from these observations

$$gm_{\rm DM}^4 > 2 \times (1.4 \text{ keV})^4, \tag{15}$$

confirmed in the recent detailed work.[31] On the contrary, the SIDM model we used for the existence of a core at kpc distances can be read from the relation

$$r_c \sim \frac{m_{\rm DM}}{\rho \sigma} = 48 \frac{10^8 M_\odot/\text{kpc}^3}{\rho} \frac{1 \text{ cm}^2/\text{gr}}{\sigma/m_{\rm DM}} \text{kpc}, \tag{16}$$

related to the isothermal profile generated by scattering of DM particles with cross-section σ. The ballpark used in the previous formulae corresponds to viable models of DM,[20, 21] which puts our analysis on a solid phenomenological basis. Indeed, one is tempted to conclude that the Fornax GCs favour the SIDM model.

4. Brief discussion on the late-time distribution of GCs

Our discussion has so far focused on the falling time of the innermost GCs of Fornax. The 'puzzle' we are trying to address relies on this time being smaller than what one would naively expect for arbitrary GCs that have lived in the dSph DM halo for long enough. However, given a collection of GCs, one expects some of them to be form currently at distances that could seem fine tuned for the average GC. Hence, the best-posed question to learn about the DM effects in the dynamics of GCs in Fornax (given that we observe 6 of them) is which is the long-term distribution function of these objects as a function of radius and for different initial conditions. Note first, that the problem of initial conditions has already been identified as a candidate to explain the phenomenology we are discussing.[7, 32] Here we will summaryze the *analytical* treatment developed in.[8] For this, the key analytical tool is the time it takes an object to move from radius r_0 to r_f. In the case of nearly-circular orbits, this time can be estimated as

$$\Delta t(r_i; r_f) = \int_{r_f}^{r_0} \frac{dr}{2r} \left(1 + \frac{d \ln M}{d \ln r}\right) \tau(r, v_{\rm circ}(r)). \tag{17}$$

Quite remarkably, one can show that for objects that today at at small radii $r \ll r_{\rm crit}$, with $r_{\rm crit}$ parametrizing the radius such that any object that *started* its life at $r < r_{\rm crit}$ as already fallen into the center, the conditional distribution function (CDF) of GCs as a function of radius in a NFW profile satisfies

$$F_{\Delta t}(r) \approx A \frac{\tau(r)}{\Delta t}, \tag{18}$$

independently on initial conditions. This prediction is modified in the case of cored profiles. To have a better picture of this effect, we show in Fig. 4 the number of GCs expected to be enclosed at projected radius $r_\perp$, when numerically integrating the orbital motion with our semianalytical model (no need of N-body simulations). The initial conditions we used for these plots are discussed in.[8] They are not very particularly relevant for this discussion since we found that the main features of Fig. 4 are reproduced by all reasonable initial conditions we considered.

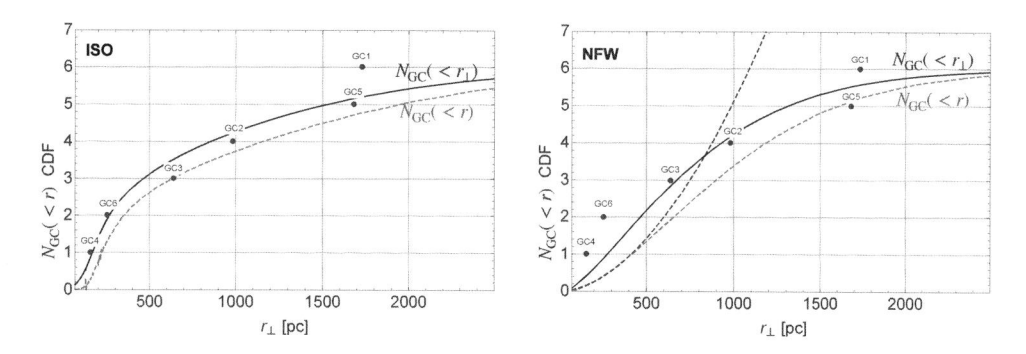

Fig. 4. CDF (number of clusters at $r_\perp$ below the value of the x axes) of projected radii using $\tau(r)$ from Fig. 3. **Left:** Cored ISO halo. **Right:** NFW halo. The solid blue line shows the CDF after projection effects are taken into account. The dashed green line shows the result before projection. For the NFW case, the small-r prediction of Eq. (18) is shown by the red dashed line. Observed Fornax GCs are also shown. The initial radial GC PDFs used to make the plot are explained in.[8]

A visual comparison of the left panel in Fig. 4 (performed with an isothermal cored for the model of SIDM described above) and the right panel (performed with NFW) shows that GC4, GC6 and GC3 tend to align better over the CDF of the second one, in particular after projection effects are taken into account (blue-solid line). As we just mentioned, these figures were produced for one of many possible initial conditions that reproduce reasonably well the distribution of final GCs, and we could not find any other reasonable initial data which could account for the position of GC4 today without destroying the agreement of the rest of GCs. Still, these figures also show that the level of 'fine-tuning' to explain GC4, GC6 and GC3 within the standard NFW profile is not very problematic, which implies that a solid conclusion about the role of DF in the final distribution of GCs requires the observation of (several) other similar systems. Another interesting observation is that any reasonable distribution agreeing with current data should have included several inner GCs which should have fallen to the center of Fornax and generated a nuclear cluster of $\mathcal{O}(10^6\, M_\odot)$. The absence of this nuclear cluster in Fornax may also have something to say about DM properties, though this is a different story.

We are fully aware that the dynamics of GCs is more complex than what we presented in.[8] Still, we believe that our simple analytical model captures some interesting (even intriguing) part of the dynamics, that we hope to study in the future with more realistic methods.

5. Conclusions and outlook

In this presentation, we revisited the timing 'problem' of the GCs in the Fornax dSph, and use it to learn about new properties of DM. The latter are manifested in either a modification of the microscopic origin of dynamical friction (DF) or the halo morphologies, also influencing DF. Some of the 6 GCs of Fornax are placed too close to the center of this galaxy, which may pose a tuning problem in terms of typical time-scales to plunge to the center of this object. Indeed, the last part of the work described in[8] (and briefly reviewed in Sec. 4) was devoted to quantifying this degree of tuning for the standard CDM paradigm yielding NFW profiles. The observations presented in Table 2 can be accounted for as a moderate fluctuation with a Poisson probability of about around 25%.

Still, it is quite interesting that the calculation of DF in different DM models allows us to reduce this tension and find better accuracy with data. This is why a large part of this short presentation has consisted in a succinct explanation of how to derived DF from a Fokker-Planck formalism (which allows the introduction of fermionic and baryonic effects in the collision term). As summarized in Fig. 3, the presence of a small core due to baryonic feedback may slightly alleviate this tension, but not at an interesting level. Once one considers other DM models (as DDM, ULDM and SIDM) a large core (of kpc size) may be formed, which predicts enough reduction of dynamical friction to better reproduce the observed positions of the GCs in Fornax. Still, in these cases, the GC distribution depends strongly on initial conditions. From these models, it seems that SIDM with $\sigma/m_{\rm DM} \approx 1$ cm^2/gr seems favoured, since it does not contradict any other observation, but more data is required to confirm this claim.

The way forward is clear: applying our methods to more extensive data, aiming at enough statistical significance to generate robust conclusions about DM properties. The hint about SIDM we just discussed makes this project particularly exciting, since future data from GCs may finally start closing up on the fundamental nature of DM.

Acknowledgments

It is a please to thank N. Bar, K. Blum and H. Kim for all the hard work they devoted to this work. IFAE is partially funded by the CERCA program of the Generalitat de Catalunya. The research leading to these results has received funding from the Spanish Ministry of Science and Innovation (PID2020-115845GB-I00/AEI/10.13039/501100011033).

References

1. S. Chandrasekhar, Dynamical Friction. I. General Considerations: the Coefficient of Dynamical Friction., *Astrophys. J.* **97**, p. 255 (Mar 1943).
2. J. Binney and S. Tremaine, *Galactic Dynamics: Second Edition* 2008.
3. M. G. Walker, M. Mateo, E. W. Olszewski, J. Penarrubia, N. W. Evans and G. Gilmore, A universal mass profile for dwarf spheroidal galaxies?, *The Astrophysical Journal* **704**, p. 1274 (2009).
4. D. R. Cole, W. Dehnen, J. I. Read and M. I. Wilkinson, The mass distribution of the Fornax dSph: constraints from its globular cluster distribution, *Mon. Not. Roy. Astron. Soc.* **426**, p. 601 (2012).
5. S. Tremaine, The formation of the nuclei of galaxies. ii-the local group, *The Astrophysical Journal* **203**, 345 (1976).
6. M.-Y. Wang, S. Koposov, A. Drlica-Wagner, A. Pieres, T. Li, T. de Boer, K. Bechtol, V. Belokurov, A. Pace, D. Bacon et al., Rediscovery of the sixth star cluster in the fornax dwarf spheroidal galaxy, *The Astrophysical Journal Letters* **875**, p. L13 (2019).
7. N. Meadows, J. F. Navarro, I. Santos-Santos, A. Benítez-Llambay and C. Frenk, Cusp or core? Revisiting the globular cluster timing problem in Fornax, *Mon. Not. Roy. Astron. Soc.* **491**, 3336 (Jan 2020).
8. N. Bar, D. Blas, K. Blum and H. Kim, Assessing the Fornax globular cluster timing problem in different models of dark matter, *Phys. Rev. D* **104**, p. 043021 (2021).
9. L. Hui, J. P. Ostriker, S. Tremaine and E. Witten, Ultralight scalars as cosmological dark matter, *Phys. Rev.* **D95**, p. 043541 (2017).
10. T. de Boer and M. Fraser, Four and one more: The formation history and total mass of globular clusters in the fornax dsph, *Astronomy & Astrophysics* **590**, p. A35 (2016).
11. A. D. Mackey and G. F. Gilmore, Surface brightness profiles and structural parameters for globular clusters in the Fornax and Sagittarius dwarf spheroidal galaxies, *Mon. Not. Roy. Astron. Soc.* **340**, p. 175 (2003).
12. A. del Pino, S. L. Hidalgo, A. Aparicio, C. Gallart, R. Carrera, M. Monelli, R. Buonanno and G. Marconi, Spatial dependence of the star formation history in the central regions of the fornax dwarf spheroidal galaxy, *Monthly Notices of the Royal Astronomical Society* **433**, 1505 (2013).
13. M.-Y. Wang, T. de Boer, A. Pieres, T. Li, A. Drlica-Wagner, S. Koposov, A. Vivas, A. Pace, B. Santiago, A. Walker et al., The morphology and structure of stellar populations in the fornax dwarf spheroidal galaxy from dark energy survey data, *The Astrophysical Journal* **881**, p. 118 (2019).
14. V. Domcke and A. Urbano, Dwarf spheroidal galaxies as degenerate gas of free fermions, *JCAP* **1501**, p. 002 (2015).
15. L. Randall, J. Scholtz and J. Unwin, Cores in dwarf galaxies from fermi repulsion, *Monthly Notices of the Royal Astronomical Society*, p. stx161 (Jan 2017).
16. C. Di Paolo, F. Nesti and F. L. Villante, Phase space mass bound for fermionic dark matter from dwarf spheroidal galaxies, *Mon. Not. Roy. Astron. Soc.* **475**, 5385 (2018).
17. D. Savchenko and A. Rudakovskyi, New mass bound on fermionic dark matter from a combined analysis of classical dSphs, *Mon. Not. Roy. Astron. Soc.* **487**, 5711 (2019).
18. A. Boyarsky, O. Ruchayskiy and D. Iakubovskyi, A Lower bound on the mass of Dark Matter particles, *JCAP* **0903**, p. 005 (2009).
19. J. Alvey, N. Sabti, V. Tiki, D. Blas, K. Bondarenko, A. Boyarsky, M. Escudero, M. Fairbairn, M. Orkney and J. I. Read, New Constraints on the Mass of Fermionic Dark Matter from Dwarf Spheroidal Galaxies (10 2020).

20. M. Kaplinghat, S. Tulin and H.-B. Yu, Dark Matter Halos as Particle Colliders: Unified Solution to Small-Scale Structure Puzzles from Dwarfs to Clusters, *Phys. Rev. Lett.* **116**, p. 041302 (2016).
21. S. Tulin and H.-B. Yu, Dark Matter Self-interactions and Small Scale Structure, *Phys. Rept.* **730**, 1 (2018).
22. S. Tremaine and J. E. Gunn, Dynamical Role of Light Neutral Leptons in Cosmology, *Phys. Rev. Lett.* **42**, 407 (1979), [,66(1979)].
23. P.-H. Chavanis, Landau equation for self-gravitating classical and quantum particles: Application to dark matter, *arXiv e-prints* , p. arXiv:2012.12858 (December 2020).
24. L. Lancaster, C. Giovanetti, P. Mocz, Y. Kahn, M. Lisanti and D. N. Spergel, Dynamical Friction in a Fuzzy Dark Matter Universe, *JCAP* **2001**, p. 001 (2020).
25. B. Bar-Or, J.-B. Fouvry and S. Tremaine, Relaxation in a Fuzzy Dark Matter Halo, *Astrophys. J.* **871**, p. 28 (2019).
26. B. Bar-Or, J.-B. Fouvry and S. Tremaine, Relaxation in a Fuzzy Dark Matter Halo. II. Self-consistent kinetic equations (10 2020).
27. N. Bar, D. Blas, K. Blum and S. Sibiryakov, Galactic rotation curves versus ultralight dark matter: Implications of the soliton-host halo relation, *Phys. Rev.* **D98**, p. 083027 (2018).
28. D. J. Marsh and J. C. Niemeyer, Strong Constraints on Fuzzy Dark Matter from Ultrafaint Dwarf Galaxy Eridanus II, *Phys. Rev. Lett.* **123**, p. 051103 (2019).
29. Y. Wang and R. Easther, Dynamical Friction From Ultralight Dark Matter (10 2021).
30. J. Baur, N. Palanque-Delabrouille, C. Yèche, C. Magneville and M. Viel, Lyman-alpha Forests cool Warm Dark Matter, *JCAP* **08**, p. 012 (2016).
31. M. Carena, N. M. Coyle, Y.-Y. Li, S. D. McDermott and Y. Tsai, Cosmologically Degenerate Fermions (8 2021).
32. S. Shao, M. Cautun, C. S. Frenk, M. Reina-Campos, A. J. Deason, R. A. Crain, J. D. Kruijssen and J. Pfeffer, The survival of globular clusters in a cuspy Fornax (12 2020).

Growth of linear perturbations in a universe with superfluid dark matter

S. Banerjee

Inst. for Quantum Gravity, FAU Erlangen-Nuremberg, Staudtstr. 7, 91058 Erlangen, Germany
E-mail: shreya.banerjee@fau.de

S. Bera

Inter-University Centre for Astronomy and Astrophysics, Post Bag 4, Ganeshkhind, Pune 411007, India
E-mail: sayantani@iucaa.in

D. F. Mota

Institute of Theoretical Astrophysics, University of Oslo, P.O. Box 1029 Blindern, N-0315 Oslo, Norway
E-mail: d.f.mota@astro.uio.no

The Lambda-Cold Dark Matter (ΛCDM) model agrees with most of the cosmological observations, but has some hindrances from observed data at smaller scales such as galaxies. Recently, Berezhiani and Khoury proposed a new theory involving interacting superfluid dark matter with three model parameters in,[1] which explains galactic dynamics with great accuracy. In the present work, we study the cosmological behaviour of this model in the linear regime of cosmological perturbations. In particular, we compute both analytically and numerically the matter linear growth factor and obtain new bounds for the model parameters which are significantly stronger than previously found. These new constraints come from the fact that structures within the superfluid dark matter framework grow quicker than in ΛCDM, and quite rapidly when the DM-baryon interactions are strong.

Keywords: Dark matter, cosmological perturbations

1. Introduction

With the advent of precision cosmology and satellites like Planck and WMAP, we have gained new insights about the evolution of the universe. Till date, Lambda-Cold Dark Matter (ΛCDM) provides the best fit to these available data and has been widely accepted as the standard model of cosmology.[2] The hypothesis of CDM, which are assumed to be collisionless non-relativistic particles, along with baryonic matter explains the CMB temperature anisotropy, matter power spectra, large scale galaxy distributions and lensing data remarkably well. In fact, the abundance of galaxy clusters and observed large scale structure formation history strongly supports the collisionless CDM scenario as opposed to any alternative theories to ΛCDM.[3–5] However, at smaller scales, CDM faces a number of challenges that need to be addressed.[6] For example, the Baryonic Tully-Fisher relation and the corresponding tight correlation between the mass and dispersion velocity at the high-mass end can not satisfactorily be explained by CDM halo which predicts a larger scatter due to feedback processes in the galaxy.[7] Apart from this, there is another issue with the standard CDM picture in the galactic scale, known as the *cusp-core problem*.[8] The simulations of galactic halos with CDM produce a kink (cusp) at the center of the galaxy, whereas observations of various galactic density profile suggest a flat core. With improved observations of the faint dwarf galaxies and substructures within the galaxies like Milky Way and Andromeda, new set of discrepancies arise. While the missing satellite problem in dwarf galaxies[9] has been addressed to some extent, the *Too Big To Fail Problem*, arising from the prediction of satellites that are too massive and too dense by ΛCDM, compared to those observed, still remains unresolved.[10,11]

Due to the above unresolved issues, scientists have looked into other alternative explanations through modifications of General Relativity (GR). Several models have been proposed so far with the aim to explain existing data to the same degree of accuracy as ΛCDM as well as overcome its drawbacks. Many of them have already been ruled out or are highly constrained by the ongoing observations of gravitational waves, but some theories like $f(R)$, $f(T)$, $f(\mathcal{G})$, Scalar-tensor-vector theories of gravity etc. are still consistent with the data, and new observations are required to falsify these theories.[12–18] These theories are relativistic corrections of GR which modify the dynamics of spacetime through the modified field equations. The theory of Modified Newtonian Dynamics (MOND), on the other hand, is a modification to the Newtonian force law that changes the dynamics of interaction between two massive bodies in the non-relativistic limit.[19,20] MOND was first proposed in 1983 by Milgrom to account for the flattened galaxy rotation curves near the edge of the spiral galaxies like Milky Way. There is a universal acceleration scale a_0 in MOND, whose value is obtained as $10^{-8} cm/s^2$. For accelerations much lower than this scale, the Newtonian law is modified, and this explains the flat galaxy rotation curve data for a large number of galaxies.[21] Interestingly, the Baryonic Tully-Fisher relation in galaxies can exactly be derived from MOND where $M \propto v_c^4$. MOND can also explain several other galactic observations like the planar structure of galaxies, low merger rate etc.[22] Thus, we see that MOND, with just one free parameter, is a very well-behaved theory at the galactic scale. However, despite these successes, MOND faces several challenges in extragalactic and cosmological scales. Proper relativistic extension of MOND is not available.[23] Hence it cannot be applied at cosmological scales.

The effectiveness of MOND at small scales and success of ΛCDM at cosmological scales are the main motivations for scientists to look for models which are CDM-MOND hybrids i.e., theories that include usual cold dark matter as collisionless particles at cosmological scales, but give rise to a MOND-like modified force law at galactic scales such that they satisfy both sets of observations. This class of models take into consideration the interacting dark matter-baryon picture where a MOND-like force is mediated through this new interaction term. Based on this idea, many models have been proposed which can reproduce both CDM features as well as MOND in their respective regime of validity.[1,24–27]

In this paper we shall focus on one such model proposed recently by Berezhiani and Khoury,[1] where CDM can form condensates at galactic scales depending upon the surrounding temperature and can behave as superfluid. It has already been shown by the authors that such model can explain a number of galactic scale observations due to their MONDian behaviour, which normal CDM fails to explain.[1,28–30] Although there are recent studies which suggest that the superfluid DM model is disfavoured compared to a spherically symmetric CDM halo at galactic scales as the superfluid DM overestimates the vertical acceleration which has to be counterbalanced to match the observations.[31,32] There are two free parameters in the theory which are assumed to be temperature dependent. It has been argued that at cosmological scales, the theory behaves as usual CDM and thus the background evolution and other cosmic histories remain unchanged as compared to ΛCDM. Here, we study the cosmological evolution of the background as well as the matter perturbations. We check whether the present model remains well-behaved at cosmological scales as has been claimed by the authors and compare our results with ΛCDM.

2. Dark Matter Superfluid-Overview

The central idea of this model is that CDM is made up of particles which undergo phase transition below a particular critical temperature and becomes a superfluid. This requires that the particle CDM needs to be strongly interacting below a particular temperature. The superfluid behaviour depends on the strength of interaction and the mass of the particle. It has been shown in[1] that in order to form a Bose-Einstein Condensate (BEC) the following condition must be satisfied

$$m \lesssim \left(\frac{\rho}{v^3}\right)^{1/4} \tag{1}$$

where m and v corresponds to the mass and velocity of the particle respectively and ρ is the density of the condensate. Assuming virialization of dark matter halo at galactic scales, this gives an upper bound on the mass of the particle forming the halo

$$m \lesssim 2.3(1+z_{vir})^{3/8}\left(\frac{M}{10^{12}h^{-1}M_\odot}\right)^{-1/4} \text{eV} \tag{2}$$

Further assuming thermalization of CDM particles, one obtains the bound on interaction cross section as

$$\frac{\sigma}{m} \gtrsim 52(1+z_{vir})^{-7/2}\left(\frac{m}{eV}\right)^4\left(\frac{M}{10^{12}h^{-1}M_\odot}\right)^{2/3} \text{cm}^2\text{g}^{-1} \tag{3}$$

Using equipartition law, the critical temperature T_c of the CDM condensate can be obtained as

$$T_c = 6.5 \left(\frac{\text{eV}}{m}\right)^{5/3} (1 + z_{vir})^2 \text{mK} \qquad (4)$$

It has been argued in[1] that the temperature of CDM at cosmological scales is much below the critical temperature ($\mathcal{O}(10^{-28})$ for $m \sim$ eV) which implies that the condensate behaves as a $T \approx 0$ superfluid at cosmological scales.

The description of superfluid dark matter is given in terms of a low energy effective theory with the Lagrangian of the form:

$$\mathcal{L} = \frac{2\Lambda(2m)^{3/2}}{3}\left(\dot{\theta} - m\Phi - \frac{(\nabla\theta)^2}{2m}\right)^{3/2} \qquad (5)$$

Let us now understand the motivation of choosing such a Lagrangian. Here, θ is the phase of the wavefunction describing the superfluid phonon modes and Φ is the gravitational potential in which the DM particle sits and is given by the standard Newtonian potential in the usual non-relativistic case. This Lagrangian has a free parameter Λ which defines the strength of the superfluid (i.e. defined by the number of particles in the condensate state). The power of the Lagrangian is defined by the choice of the equation of state (EoS), and a fractional power of 5/2 is indeed obtained in superfluids formed by ultra cold atoms. In the case of CDM superfluid, the choice of the power 3/2 in the Lagrangian is somewhat arbitrary, but motivated by the fact that the superfluid DM should give rise to MOND-like dynamics at galactic scales when baryons are also included. This also corresponds to an equation of state $P \sim \rho^3$ which is suggestive of a dominant three-body interaction process. What kind of particles can lead to such a superfluid with this particular EoS and the physics of its formation has not been discussed earlier and is beyond the scope of this paper. For our purpose, we shall assume the form of this Lagrangian to study the characteristic features of the resultant superfluid DM model.

In the effective field theory formalism, the superfluid is described in terms of interacting phonon modes. The phonon modes can be described by the scalar field θ, which, at a constant chemical potential μ, can be expanded as,

$$\theta = \mu t + \phi$$

where ϕ denotes the excitation of the phonon modes.

The DM superfluid couples to the baryons through the phonon modes via an interaction given by the Lagrangian:

$$\mathcal{L}_{int} = -\alpha \frac{\Lambda}{M_{Pl}} \theta \rho_b \qquad (6)$$

This kind of interaction ensures a MOND force. Here α is a dimensionless free parameter, which sets the interaction strength of the interaction, and ρ_b is the baryonic mass density.

Thus, the complete Lagrangian for an interacting superfluid DM is given by,

$$\mathcal{L} = \frac{2\Lambda(2m)^{3/2}}{3}\left(\dot{\theta} - m\Phi - \frac{(\nabla\theta)^2}{2m}\right)^{3/2} - \alpha\frac{\Lambda}{M_{Pl}}\theta\rho_b \tag{7}$$

It has been shown in[1] that the MONDian acceleration arises as a special case of the dynamics of the above Lagrangian. The validity of this model in solar system and Bullet cluster has also been discussed there.

In the cosmological context, although the authors in[1] discuss some general points regarding the background behaviour and the equation of state of this new superfluid dark matter, they do not shed much light on other important points such as growth of perturbations and structure formation. In the next sections, we solely focus on the cosmological aspects of this new theory.

3. Cosmological Solutions

In this section, we will study this theory in cosmological context. This is of particular interest since the theory also needs to be consistent with the present cosmological data.

3.1. *Background Solutions*

For the background cosmology, we have $\theta = \theta(t)$. In the FLRW background with a scale factor a, the equation of motion for θ can be derived from the action as,

$$\frac{d}{dt}\left[(2m)^{3/2}a^3\dot{\theta}^{1/2}\right] = -\frac{\alpha}{M_{Pl}}a^3\rho_b \tag{8}$$

Assuming the evolution of baryons i.e. $\rho_b \propto 1/a^3$ as in standard ΛCDM, we get,

$$\rho_m = -\frac{\alpha\Lambda}{M_{Pl}}m\rho_b t + \frac{m\Lambda C}{a^3} \tag{9}$$

Here C is an integration constant which has to be determined from the present DM density. The second term (ρ_{dust}) corresponds to the dust like evolution. The form of the density is similar to those obtained in dynamical space-time theories as discussed in.[33–35] For the second term to dominate (such that ρ_m behaves as dust), it can be shown that one needs to satisfy the following constraint:

$$\frac{\alpha\Lambda\rho_b}{M_{Pl}\rho_{dust}}mt_0 \leq 1 \tag{10}$$

where t_0 is the present age of the universe.

Bounds on the model parameters:

- **From the EoS**- Equation of state for the DM superfluid (assuming negligible interaction) is given by,

$$w = \frac{\rho_{dust}^2}{12\Lambda^2 m^6} \quad (11)$$

For DM to behave as dust at the background level, Λ should be bounded from below,

$$\Lambda \gg 0.1 \left(\frac{m}{\text{eV}}\right)^{-3} \text{eV} \quad (12)$$

- **From coupling to baryons**- From (10) and (12), and assuming a constant baryon-to-DM ratio ($\rho_{dust}/\rho_b = 6$), we get,

$$\alpha \ll 2.4 \times 10^{-4} \left(\frac{m}{\text{eV}}\right)^2 \quad (13)$$

These bounds are different from the bounds obtained for galaxies, as discussed in.[1,28]

3.2. *Perturbations*

Study of linear perturbation theory in the context of ΛCDM has been an important step towards understanding the evolution of the universe. CMB spectra carries information about the inhomogeneities present in the early universe. Hence, any cosmological model needs to satisfy the CMB data to a high degree of accuracy. This requires analysing the matter power spectrum resulting from the initial density perturbations. In this section, we examine the growth of cosmological perturbations in DM superfluid model at linear order.

The Lagrangian of the theory in an FLRW matter dominated universe is given as,

$$\mathcal{L} = c_1 \left(\dot{\theta} - \frac{(\nabla\theta)^2}{2m} - m\Phi\right)^{3/2} - c_2 \rho_b \theta \quad (14)$$

where c_1, c_2 are constants expressed as,

$$c_1 = \frac{2\Lambda(2m)^{3/2}}{3}$$
$$c_2 = \alpha \frac{\Lambda}{M_{Pl}} \quad (15)$$

Here, $\theta(x,t) = \bar{\theta}(t) + \delta\theta(x,t)$ is a scalar field which is a fucntion of both space and time.

We can find the Euler-Lagrange equation from the above equation as:

$$\frac{d}{dt}\left(\frac{\partial \mathcal{L}}{\partial \dot{\theta}}\right) - \frac{\partial \mathcal{L}}{\partial \theta} = 0 \quad (16)$$

This gives us the background equation of motion as shown in the previous subsection as well as the first order perturbation equation of the dark matter density. But this single governing equation is inadequate to obtain the complete numerical solution which requires a complete set of differential equations.

In order to get the full set of perturbation equations, we start with the fluid equations that govern the dynamics of the dark matter superfluid. The fluid equations, namely the continuity equation and the Navier-Stokes equation can be derived using the Hamiltonian formalism, as described in.[36] In,[36] the authors work out the fluid equations for an interacting two-component BEC dark matter. Here in this work, we follow the same prescription for a superfluid dark matter which interacts with the baryonic matter. The corresponding Lagrangian is given by (14).

From the Lagrangian, we get the conjugate momentum as,

$$\Pi_\theta = \frac{\partial \mathcal{L}}{\partial \dot{\theta}}$$

$$= \Lambda(2m)^{3/2} \left[\dot{\theta} - m\Phi - \frac{(\nabla\theta)^2}{2m} \right]^{1/2} \quad (17)$$

The Hamiltonian H describing the superfluid can be obtained as,

$$H = \Pi_\theta \dot{\theta} - \mathcal{L} \quad (18)$$

Since, $\dot{\theta} = m\Phi + \frac{(\nabla\theta)^2}{2m} + \frac{\Pi_\theta^2}{\Lambda^2(2m)^3}$ from (17), we get the Hamiltonian H as follows,

$$H = \frac{\Pi_\theta^3}{3\Lambda^2(2m)^3} + \left(m\Phi + \frac{(\nabla\theta)^2}{2m} \right)\Pi_\theta + \frac{\alpha\Lambda}{M_{pl}}\rho_b\theta \quad (19)$$

3.2.1. *Hamilton's equation of motion*

The Hamilton's equations of motion are :

$$\dot{\theta} = \frac{\partial H}{\partial \Pi_\theta} \quad (20)$$

and

$$\dot{\Pi}_\theta = -\frac{\partial H}{\partial \theta} \quad (21)$$

For this model, the two equations become, respectively,

$$\dot{\theta} = \frac{\Pi_\theta^2}{\Lambda^2(2m)^3} + m\Phi + \frac{(\nabla\theta)^2}{2m} \quad (22)$$

and

$$\dot{\Pi}_\theta = \frac{1}{m}\nabla \cdot (\Pi_\theta \nabla\theta) - \frac{\alpha\Lambda}{M_{pl}}\rho_b \quad (23)$$

3.2.2. Fluid equations

In order to get the fluid equations from the above Hamilton's equations of motion, we identify the terms as corresponding hydrodynamical variables. We define the mass density term (as the co-efficient of Φ in the Hamiltonian) and the four-velocity of the fluid, $\vec{u}$ as

$$\rho_m = m\Pi_\theta, \quad \vec{u} = -\frac{\nabla\theta}{m}. \tag{24}$$

Using the above definitions, we get the fluid equations from equation (23) and (22) as follow,

$$\dot{\rho}_m + \nabla \cdot (\rho_m \vec{u}) = -\frac{\alpha\Lambda m}{M_{pl}}\rho_b \tag{25}$$

$$\dot{\vec{u}} + (\vec{u} \cdot \nabla)\vec{u} = -\frac{\rho_m \nabla \rho_m}{4\Lambda^2 m^6} - \nabla\Phi \tag{26}$$

These are the two fluid equations: Continuity equation and Navier-Stokes equation.

Now, the Poisson's equation can be written as

$$\nabla^2 \Phi = 4\pi G(\bar{\rho} + \delta\rho) \tag{27}$$

Integrating twice and substituting the background density using Friedmann equations, we get the potential as:

$$\Phi = -\frac{1}{2}(\dot{H} + H^2)l^2 + \phi \tag{28}$$

where l is the proper distance defined as $\vec{l} = a(t)\vec{x}$ and ϕ is the potential due to inhomogeneities.

Similarly, the four-velocity $\vec{u}$ can be split into two parts, Hubble flow and a peculiar velocity $\vec{v}$ as follows:

$$\vec{u} = H\vec{l} + \vec{v} \tag{29}$$

Expressing everything in comoving co-ordinates $\vec{x}$ and using $\nabla_l = \frac{1}{a(t)}\nabla_x$, we get,

$$\dot{\rho}_m + 3H\rho_m + \frac{1}{a}\nabla \cdot (\rho_m \vec{v}) = -\frac{\alpha\Lambda m}{M_{pl}}\rho_b \tag{30}$$

and

$$\dot{\vec{v}} + H\vec{v} + \frac{1}{a}(\vec{v} \cdot \nabla)\vec{v} = -\frac{\rho_m \nabla \rho_m}{4a\Lambda^2 m^6} - \frac{\nabla\phi}{a} \tag{31}$$

These are the two fluid equations of motion that we shall use for the rest of our calculations.

3.2.3. Evolution of perturbations

The total DM density ρ_m and the baryonic density ρ_b can be split into two parts: background and perturbation:

$$\rho_m = \bar{\rho}_m + \delta\rho_m, \quad \rho_b = \bar{\rho}_b + \delta\rho_b$$

respectively.

We define, the relative density perturbations for these two components as,

$$\delta_m = \frac{\delta\rho_m}{\bar{\rho}_m + \bar{\rho}_b} \quad \text{and} \quad \delta_b = \frac{\delta\rho_b}{\bar{\rho}_m + \bar{\rho}_b}.$$

In the linear perturbation regime, we treat $\delta\rho_m$, $\delta\rho_b$ and $\vec{v}$ to be small, and hence, neglect the higher orders of these terms. Perturbing the two fluid equations in the linear regime gives:

$$\dot{\delta}_m + \frac{\bar{\rho}_m}{a\bar{\rho}}\nabla \cdot \vec{v} = -\frac{\alpha\Lambda m}{M_{pl}}\delta_b \tag{32}$$

and

$$\dot{\vec{v}} + H\vec{v} = -\frac{\bar{\rho}_m \nabla \delta\rho_m}{4a\Lambda^2 m^6} - \frac{1}{a}\nabla\phi \tag{33}$$

By using the above equations along with the Poisson's equation and assuming $\bar{\rho}_m \sim \bar{\rho}$, we get the evolution equation for δ_m as follows:

$$\ddot{\delta}_m + 2H\dot{\delta}_m - \frac{\bar{\rho}_m \delta_m}{2M_{pl}^2} - \frac{\bar{\rho}_m^2 \nabla^2 \delta_m}{4a^2\Lambda^2 m^6} = -\frac{\alpha\Lambda m \dot{\delta}_b}{M_{pl}} - 2H\frac{\alpha\Lambda m \delta_b}{M_{pl}} + \frac{\bar{\rho}_b \delta_b}{2M_{pl}^2} \tag{34}$$

This is a second order differential equation. The coefficient of the spatial derivative ∇^2 gives the square of the sound speed c_s. Thus, we get,

$$c_s^2 = \frac{\bar{\rho}_m^2}{4\Lambda^2 m^6} \tag{35}$$

Below in Fig. 1, we show the plot for c_s^2 vs the redshift z for $m = 1$ eV and $\Lambda = 500$ eV. We take the time evolution of the background density $\bar{\rho}_m$ as

$$\bar{\rho}_m = \frac{0.4(1+z)^3}{(1+1000)^3} \tag{36}$$

where the value of $\bar{\rho}_m$ at equality ($z = 1000$) is set as 0.4 eV^4 ([36]). As evident from the plot, the sound speed is very small (compared to the speed of light $c = 1$).

3.3. Analytical Solution

We now have the perturbation equations (32) and (33) supplemented by the Poisson equation. In the absence of baryons, we recover the usual evolution of CDM as a non-relativistic fluid. This can be seen as follows.

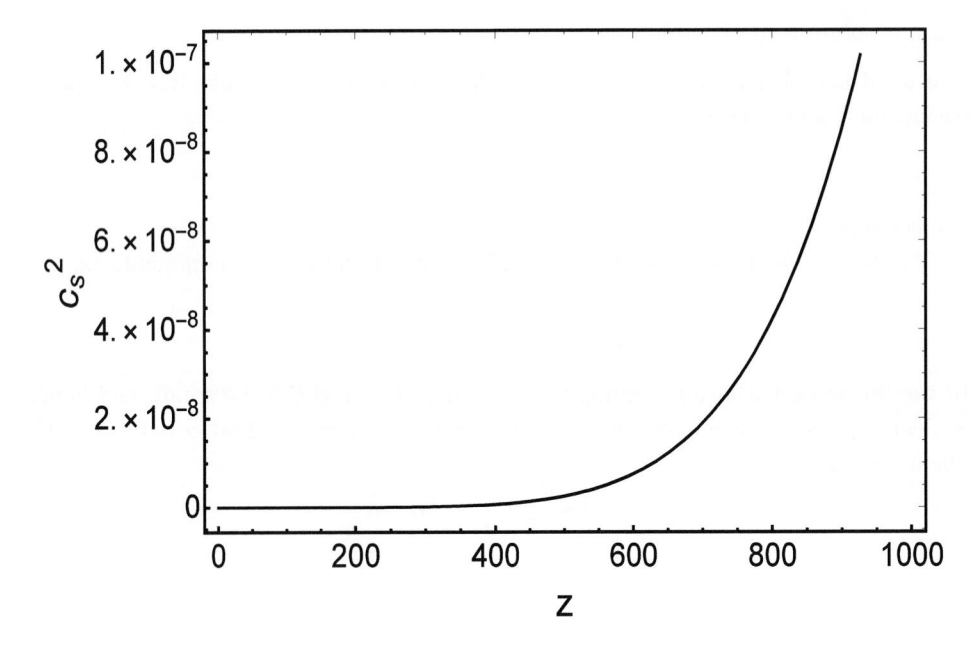

Fig. 1. Plot for c_s^2 vs z. As can be seen, the sound speed is very small compared to the speed of light ($c = 1$ in this case) at all times.

Without baryons:
In the absence of baryons, i.e. by setting $\bar{\rho}_b = 0$ and $\delta\rho_b = 0$ in equations (32) and (33), we obtain a set of equations as follows:

$$\dot{\delta}_m + \frac{1}{a}\nabla \cdot \vec{v} = 0 \tag{37}$$

and

$$\dot{\vec{v}} + H\vec{v} = -\frac{\bar{\rho}_m \nabla \delta\rho_m}{4a\Lambda^2 m^6} - \frac{1}{a}\nabla\phi \tag{38}$$

For $\Lambda \gg 1$, i.e, when the sound speed c_s is taken to be very small, the above set of equations reduce to the usual perturbation evolution equations in a ΛCDM model in the matter-dominated regime.[37] Thus, in the absence of baryons, usual CDM like evolution is recovered at the background level as well as for the perturbations. This can also be seen from the second order differential equation governing the evolution. From equation (34), in the absence of baryons, we obtain,

$$\ddot{\delta}_m + 2H\dot{\delta}_m - \frac{\bar{\rho}_m \delta_m}{2M_{pl}^2} - \frac{\bar{\rho}_m^2 \nabla^2 \delta_m}{4a^2 \Lambda^2 m^6} = 0 \tag{39}$$

As expected, the above equation is the usual evolution equation for CDM in a flat ΛCDM universe, with a small sound speed given by (35). Since the sound speed is very small, for all practical purposes, this term can be neglected and we end up with the following second order differential equation:

$$\ddot{\delta}_m + 2H\dot{\delta}_m - \frac{\bar{\rho}_m \delta_m}{2M_{pl}^2} = 0 \tag{40}$$

This is the evolution equation of non-relativistic CDM in the ΛCDM model.[38] The growing solution of this equation is the usual CDM like evolution, which is $\delta \propto a$ for a matter dominated universe.[37,38] In the absence of baryons, the superfluid dark matter thus behaves exactly like CDM and the growth of perturbations follow the ΛCDM-like evolution.

With baryons:

We now investigate how the perturbations evolve when both baryons and baryonic interactions with superfluid dark matter is present. A complete solution is to be found numerically for different values of the model parameters. This will be pursued in the next section. For now, we try to find the generic nature of the DM perturbations growth with some basic assumptions regarding the baryonic density evolution and the interaction strength between baryons and the superfluid. We assume that the baryon perturbation δ_b follows the same rate of growth as in ΛCDM i.e. at late times $\delta_b \propto a$ as obtained from the observed power spectrum. We now consider equation (34) which is the single second order evolution equation. We are only interested in the temporal behaviour of δ_m. With the assumption that $c_s^2 \ll 1$, equation (34) can be analytically solved for two limiting cases. For the first case when the interaction strength is negligible, one can set $\alpha = 0$. With this condition, the only remaining term in the RHS of (34) is the last term. The resulting equation has a power law solution of the form $\delta \propto t^{2/3} \propto a$ in the matter dominated era. This is the usual CDM-like behaviour as expected when the interaction strength is negligible. The other limiting case solution can be obtained by setting a very strong interaction strength i.e. by taking a large enough α such that the first two terms in the RHS of (34) become dominant. In this case, the solution for the matter dominated universe comes out to be of the form

$$\delta_m \propto t^{5/3} \propto a^{5/2} \tag{41}$$

The time evolution of The DM perturbation growth in the two cases is thus captured by the following form:

$$\delta_m \propto a \quad \text{for no interaction} \tag{42}$$
$$\delta_m \propto a^{5/2} \quad \text{for strong interaction} \tag{43}$$

Important distinct features arise when we look at the time evolution of δ_m for each mode. During the matter dominated era, δ_m grows as a in ΛCDM whereas in this model, it grows as $a^{5/2}$ i.e. at a much faster rate compared to ΛCDM.

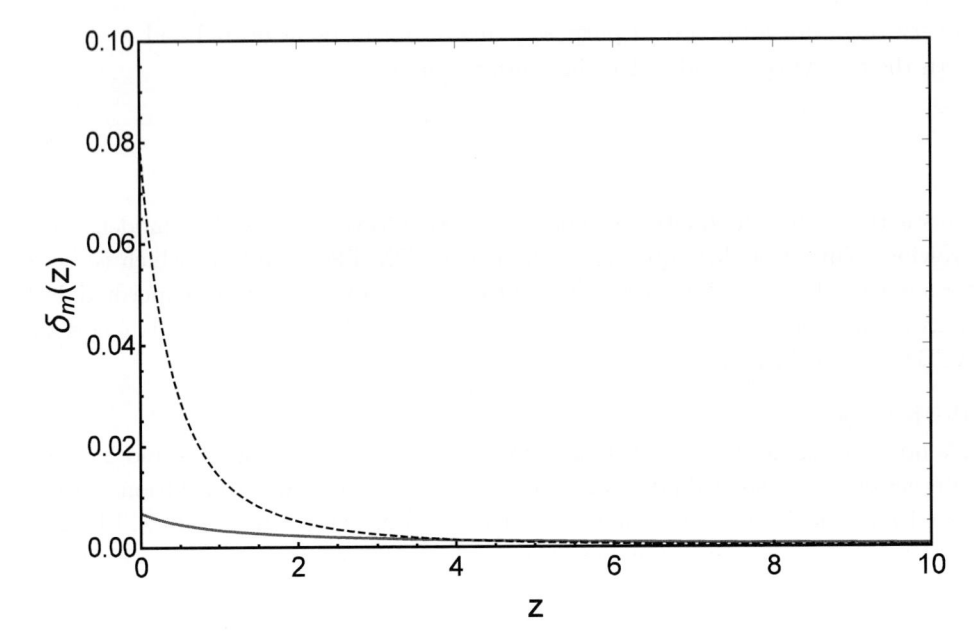

Fig. 2. Growth of δ_m with respect to z. The red solid line represents the growth for ΛCDM and the black dashed line corresponds to the growth for superfluid for $\alpha = 10^{-6}$. The growth in case of superfluid DM is dominated by the term proportional to $a^{5/2}$ and is higher compared to ΛCDM. The higher the value of α, i.e. the stronger the superfluid DM-baryonic interaction, the steeper is the growth rate (as will be discussed in the next section).

For convenience, we write the evolution of δ_m in terms of the redshift:

$$\delta_m \propto \frac{1}{(1+z)^{5/2}} \tag{44}$$

Fig. 2 shows the nature of growth in both the models (red solid curve representing ΛCDM, black dashed curve representing superfluid DM).

A proper way to find the full solution for the perturbed quantities is to solve coupled differential equations using a numerical approach. In the next section we solve the perturbation equations numerically in the linear regime and look for any possible deviations from ΛCDM.

4. Numerical Solution

In order to obtain the solutions for δ_m, we rewrite equations (32) and (33) in the Fourier domain in physical co-ordinate as,

$$\dot{\delta}_m + \frac{\bar{\rho}_m}{\bar{\rho}}(ikv) = -\frac{\alpha \Lambda m}{M_{pl}} \delta_b \tag{45}$$

and
$$ik\dot{v} + ikHv = \frac{k^2 \bar{\rho}_m \bar{\rho} \delta_m}{4\Lambda^2 m^6} + \frac{a^2}{2M_{pl}^2}\left(\delta\rho_m + \delta\rho_b + \frac{3iaH\bar{\rho}v}{k}\right) \quad (46)$$

To solve the above equations, we write them in terms of redshift,
$$-H(1+z)\frac{d\delta_m}{dz} + \frac{\bar{\rho}_m}{\bar{\rho}}(ikv) = -\frac{\alpha\Lambda m}{M_{pl}}\delta_b \quad (47)$$

and
$$-ikH(1+z)\frac{dv}{dz} + ikHv = \frac{k^2 \bar{\rho}_m \bar{\rho}\delta_m}{4\Lambda^2 m^6} + \frac{\bar{\rho}}{2M_{pl}^2(1+z)^2}\left(\delta_m + \delta_b + \frac{3iHv}{k(1+z)}\right) \quad (48)$$

Parameters and initial conditions:

The model parameters involved are m, Λ and α. We take $m = 1$ eV and $\Lambda = 500$ eV while keeping the parameter α as free parameter which is varied to check where the model deviates from flat ΛCDM.

We integrate the perturbation equations using the following initial conditions at the epoch of equality $z = 1000$: We set $\delta_b(z = 1000) = \delta_m(z = 1000) = 10^{-5}$ and $H(z = 1000) = m = 1$ eV.

Since $\bar{\rho}_m \gg \bar{\rho}_b$, we assume $\bar{\rho} = \bar{\rho}_m + \bar{\rho}_b \approx \bar{\rho}_m$ as given in (36).

The initial value of v at $z = 1000$ is chosen to be around 1. For the time evolution of the background density and Hubble parameter, we take the usual ΛCDM evolution of these quantities in matter-dominated era, i.e. $\bar{\rho}_m \propto 1/a^3$ and $H \propto 1/a^{3/2}$. Furthermore, we take $\delta_b \propto a$. We keep the wavenumber k fixed at 0.0001 eV, although the nature remains same for larger values of k.

Figure 3 shows the evolution of the DM density perturbation δ_m with respect to the redshift z for different values of $\alpha = 10^{-8}$, 10^{-7}, 10^{-6}, 10^{-4} and also for ΛCDM corresponding to $\alpha = 0, \Lambda \to \infty$. As expected, the smaller the value of α, the closer the resemblance with ΛCDM-like evolution. As we see in Fig. 3, the plot for $\alpha = 10^{-8}$ coincides with ΛCDM. When α is large enough, the growth is very steep. This is because a large enough α implies large interaction strength between the superfluid phonons and baryons, ensuring that structure formation takes place at an earlier epoch as compared to ΛCDM.

In Figure 4, we plot the relative differences between the perturbation growth in ΛCDM model and superfluid DM model for different values of α in terms of $\delta_{\text{superfluid}}/\delta_{\Lambda\text{CDM}}$. As expected, the ratio is very high at a lower redshift. As we go to higher redshifts, the ratio tends to 1 i.e., they eventually agree with ΛCDM at very high redshifts and matches exactly at $z = 1000$ where we set our initial conditions. The ΛCDM model corresponds to $\alpha = 0$. For $\alpha = 10^{-8}$, the deviation from ΛCDM at low redshift goes up to 0.13% at $z = 0.01$. The larger the value of α, the higher is the ratio, implying a stronger deviation from ΛCDM at low enough redshifts. As α is increased to 10^{-7}, the deviation from ΛCDM becomes much larger ($\sim 62\%$).

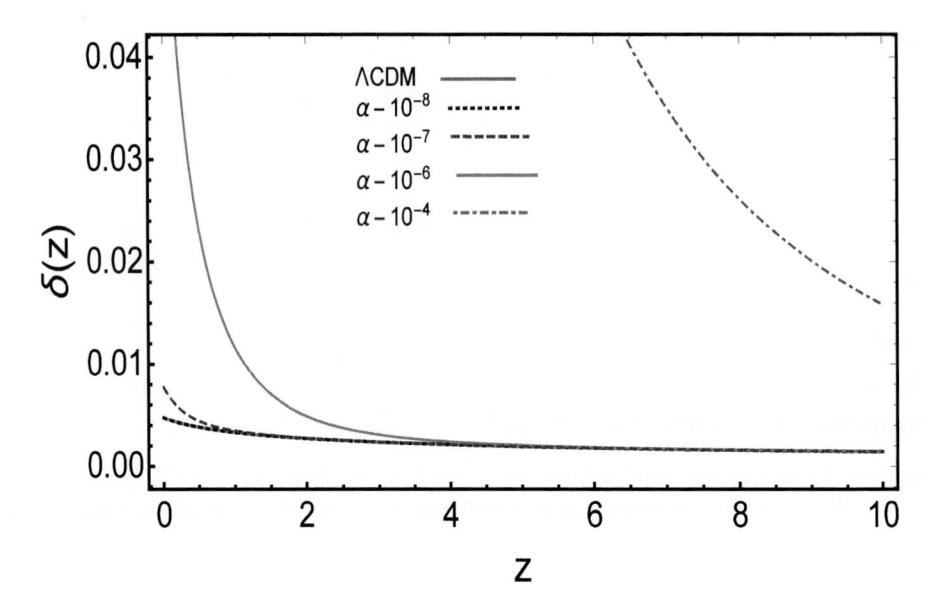

Fig. 3. Plot for δ_m vs z for different values of α as obtained numerically. The different curves correspond to different α as shown in the figure. The curve corresponding to $\alpha = 10^{-8}$ coincides with ΛCDM. For higher values of α, the deviation from ΛCDM increases gradually. The growth rate at a given redshift is maximum for $\alpha = 10^{-4}$ for the cases considered here.

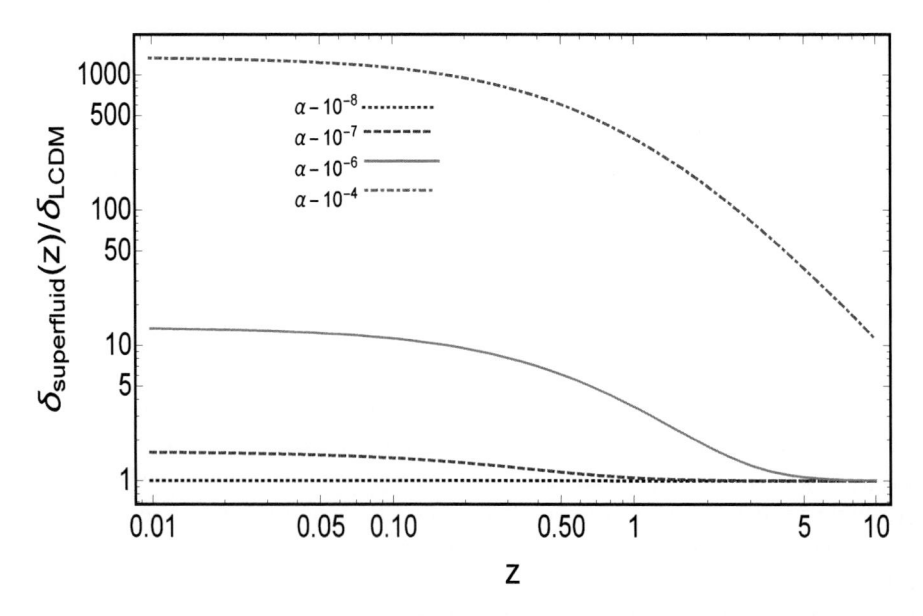

Fig. 4. Plot for $\delta_{\text{superfluid}}/\delta_{\Lambda\text{CDM}}$ vs z for different values of α. For an exact coincidence with ΛCDM, this ratio should be 1. Values > 1 signify larger deviation from ΛCDM. For $\alpha = 10^{-8}$, the ratio is almost nearly 1 showing a deviation only up to 0.13% at $z = 0$. For $\alpha = 10^{-7}$, the deviation increases up to 62% at the same redshift.

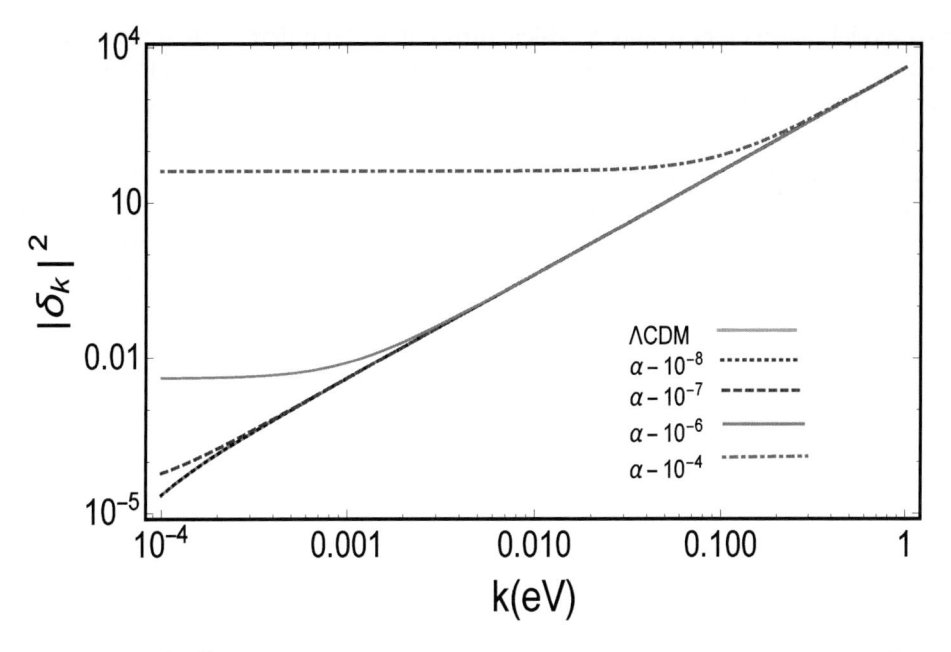

Fig. 5. Plot for $|\delta_k|^2$ vs k at $z = 0$. This is the matter power spectrum up to a constant factor. The plot reaffirms our previous results. In general the power increase approximately linearly with k. However, for large enough α, it becomes relatively flatter.

We can also plot the matter power spectrum $P(k)$ as a function of k at $z = 0$. The matter power spectrum $P(k) \propto |\delta_m(k)|^2$. In Fig. 5, we plot $|\delta_m(k)|^2$ vs. k which shows how the power varies for different values of α. As shown in the figure, the power spectrum for $\alpha = 10^{-8}$ matches with the ΛCDM prediction. As can be seen, the power increases for larger values of α at a given value of k. This is because the perturbation growth is stronger for large α as discussed earlier.

5. Results and Discussions

The superfluid dark matter model is a very promising and newly emerging model of cosmology combining together the rich physics of condensed matter, particle physics and cosmology. In view of its success in explaining a number of observations within the galaxies where ΛCDM fails to provide a satisfactory explanation, this model can be said to offer a greater understanding of the universe. In their earlier works, Khoury and his collaborators have investigated the implications of this model at galactic scales. However, a complete study of cosmological implications have not been performed earlier. In this paper, we have tried to investigate, both analytically and numerically, whether the predicted cosmology of the model tallies well with the observations and how different the predictions are from that of ΛCDM. In the realm of non-relativistic low energy effective theory of superfluid, the background cosmology agrees with the predictions of ΛCDM, and this gives a constraint on the two model parameters α and Λ which turn out to be different than their galactic scale constraints. This result has also been discussed in.[1] At the level of first order perturbation, we find that the above constraints lead to a cosmology which differ significantly from ΛCDM. In particular, our analytical results suggests that the growth of density perturbations of dark matter superfluid roughly goes as $a^{5/2}$, which is much higher compared to the ΛCDM picture ($\delta_m \propto a$). This might be due to the strong interaction between superfluid phonons and baryonic matter. This behaviour has also been verified from the numerical solutions. For the numerical calculations, in particular, we have kept two of the model parameters m and Λ fixed at 1 eV and 500 eV respectively. This gives an upper bound on the third parameter: $\alpha \leq 10^{-8}$ corresponding to just 0.13% deviation from ΛCDM. This is different from the value quoted in.[1] The bound obtained in,[1] for $m = 1$ eV, is $\alpha \leq 10^{-4}$, which, even though predicts the correct background evolution, strongly deviates from ΛCDM in the context of perturbation growth in the present epoch. This can be seen in Figs. 3, 4 and 5. In our analysis, we have assumed the baryonic component to follow standard dust evolution ($\propto \frac{1}{a^3}$). In the absence of baryons, however, this model successfully reproduces the usual non-relativistic CDM evolution as obtained in case of a flat matter dominated ΛCDM universe, both at the background as well as first order perturbation level.

A more complete analysis of the perturbation growth should rely on the proper relativistic extension of the theory, which has not been attempted in this paper. Some relativistic models have been discussed in the original paper,[1] however a rigorous analysis is still lacking. We hope to address the same in a future work. Our work looks into the solution in the linear regime where perturbations are taken to be small. In future, we plan to extend our analysis to the non-linear regime and study the structure formation through spherical collapse. It would also be interesting to see how well this model predicts the CMB or the halo mass function.

Acknowledgments

S. Banerjee would like acknowledge funding from Israel Science Foundation and John and Robert Arnow Chair of Theoretical Astrophysics. S. Bera would like to acknowledge support from Navajbai Ratan Tata Trust and IUCAA research grant. S. Banerjee and S. Bera would also like to thank the hospitality of the Tata Institute of Fundamental Research, India, where part of the work was done. DFM thank the Research Council of Norway for their support. Computations were performed on resources provided by UNINETT Sigma2 – the National Infrastructure for High Performance Computing and Data Storage in Norway.

References

1. L. Berezhiani and J. Khoury, *Theory of dark matter superfluidity*, Phys. Rev. D **92** (2015) 103510.

2. P. A. R. Ade et al. [Planck Collaboration], *XIV. Dark energy and modified gravity*, Astron. Astrophys. **594** (2016) A13.
3. M. Boylan-Kolchin, et al., *Resolving cosmic structure formation with the Millennium-II Simulation*, MNRAS **398** (2009) 1150.
4. F. Iocco, M. Pato and G. Bertone, *Evidence for dark matter in the inner Milky Way*, Nat. Phys. **11** (2015) 245-248.
5. M. Vogelsberger et al., *Introducing the Illustris Project: simulating the coevolution of dark and visible matter in the Universe*, MNRAS **444** (2014) 1518.
6. D. H. Weinberg, et al., *Cold dark matter: Controversies on small scale*, Proc. Nat. Acad. Sci. **112** (2015) 12249.
7. S. McGaugh, *The baryonic Tully-Fisher relation of gas-rich galaxies as a test of CDM and MOND*, Astron. J. **143** (2012) 40.
8. M. G. Walker and J. Penarrubia, *A method for measuring (slopes of) the mass profiles of dwarf spheroidal galaxies*, ApJ **742** (2011) 20.
9. A. A. Klypin, et al., *Where are the Missing Galactic Satellites?*, ApJ **522** (1999) 82-92.
10. M. Boylan-Kolchin, J. S. Bullock and M. Kaplinghat, *Too big to fail? The puzzling darkness of massive Milky Way subhaloes*, MNRAS **415** (2011) L40.
11. M. Boylan-Kolchin, J. S. Bullock and M. Kaplinghat, *The Milky Way's bright satellites as an apparent failure of ΛCDM*, MNRAS **422** (2012) 1203-1218.
12. A. A. Starobinsky, *A new type of isotropic cosmological models without singularity*, Phys. Lett. B **91** (1980) 99.
13. E. V. Linder, *Einstein's Other Gravity and the Acceleration of the Universe*, Phys. Rev. D **81** (2010) 127301.
14. S. M. Carroll, V. Duvvuri, M. Trodden, and M. S. Turner, *Is cosmic speed-up due to new gravitational physics?*, Phys. Rev. D **70** (2004) 043528.
15. G. Cognola, E. Elizalde, S. Nojiri, S. D. Odintsov and S. Zerbini, *Dark energy in modified Gauss-Bonnet gravity: Late-time acceleration and the hierarchy problem*, Phys. Rev. D **73** (2006) 084007.
16. J. P. Uzan, *Varying Constants, Gravitation and Cosmology*, Living Rev. Rel. **14**, (2011) 2.
17. J. R. Brownstein and J. W. Moffat, *Galaxy rotation curves without nonbaryonic dark matter*, ApJ **636** (2006) 721.
18. P. Horava, *Quantum gravity at a Lifshitz point*, Phys. Rev. D **79** (2009) 084008.
19. M. Milgrom, *A modification of the Newtonian dynamics as a possible alternative to the hidden mass hypothesis*, Astrophys. J. **270** (1983) 365.
20. P. Kroupa, M. Pawlowski and M. Milgrom, *The failures of the standard model of cosmology require a new paradigm*, Int. J. Mod. Phys. D **21** (2012) 1230003.
21. W. J. G. de Blok and S. S McGaugh, *Testing modified newtonian dynamics with low surface brightness galaxies: Rotation curve fits*, ApJ **508** (1998) 132.
22. C. Nipoti, P. Londrillo and L. Ciotti, *Galaxy merging in MOND*, MNRAS **381** (2007) 104.
23. C. Skordis, D. F. Mota, P. G. Ferreira and C. Boehm, *Large Scale Structure in Bekenstein's theory of relativistic Modified Newtonian Dynamics*, Phys. Rev. Lett. **96** (2006) 011301.
24. J. P. Bruneton, S. Liberati, L. Sindoni and B. Famaey, *Reconciling MOND and dark matter?*, JCAP **0903** (2009) 021.
25. C. M. Ho, D. Minic and Y. J. Ng, *Cold Dark Matter with MOND Scaling*, Phys. Lett. B **693** (2010) 567.
26. S. Alexander, E. McDonough and D. N. Spergel, *Chiral Gravitational Waves and Baryon Superfluid Dark Matter*, JCAP **1805**, (2018) 003.

27. B. Famaey, J. Khoury and R. Penco, *Emergence of the mass discrepancy-acceleration relation from dark matter-baryon interactions*, JCAP **1803** (2018) 038.
28. L. Berezhiani, B. Famaey and J. Khoury, *Phenomenological consequences of superfluid dark matter with baryon-phonon coupling*, JCAP, **1809** (2018) 021.
29. A. Hodson, H. Zhao, J. Khoury and B. Famaey, *Galaxy Clusters in the Context of Superfluid Dark Matter, Astron. Astrophys.* **607** (2017) A108.
30. J. Khoury, *Another Path for the Emergence of Modified Galactic Dynamics from Dark Matter Superfluidity*, Phys. Rev. D **93** (2016) 103533.
31. M. Lisanti, M. Moschella, N. J. Outmezguine and O. Slone, *The Inconsistency of Superfluid Dark Matter with Milky Way Dynamics*, ArXiv: 1911.12365 (2019).
32. M. Lisanti, M. Moschella, N. J. Outmezguine and O. Slone, *Testing Dark Matter and Modifications to Gravity using Local Milky Way Observables*, Phys. Rev. D **100** (2019) 083009.
33. D. Benisty, E. Guendelman and Z. Haba, *Unification of dark energy and dark matter from diffusive cosmology*, Phys. Rev. D **99** (2019) 123521.
34. D. Benisty and E. Guendelman, *Interacting Diffusive Unified Dark Energy and Dark Matter from Scalar Fields*, Eur. Phys. J.C **77** (2017) 396.
35. S. Banerjee, D. Benisty and E. Guendelman, *Running Vacuum from Dynamical Spacetime Cosmology*, ArXiv: 1910.03933 (2019).
36. E. G. M. Ferreira, G. Franzmann, J. Khoury and R. Brandenberger, *Unified Superfluid Dark Sector*, JCAP **1908** (2019) 027.
37. S. Dodelson, *Modern Cosmology*, Academic Press (2003).
38. R. Brandenberger, *Lectures on the Theory of Cosmological Perturbations*, arXiv:hep-th/0306071 (2003).

Interacting dark sector in the late Universe: Mapping fields and fluids, and observational signatures

Joseph P. J.* and S. Shankaranarayanan[†]

Department of Physics, Indian Institute of Technology Bombay,
Mumbai 400076, India
* E-mail: josephpj@iitb.ac.in
† E-mail: shanki@phy.iitb.ac.in

In this work, we discuss a cosmological model with dark energy – dark matter interaction. Demanding that the interaction strength Q_ν in the dark sector must have a field theory description, a unique form of interaction strength can be obtained. We show the equivalence between the fields and fluids for the $f(R, \chi)$ model where f is an arbitrary, smooth function of R and classical scalar field χ, which represents dark matter. Up to first order in perturbations, there is a one-to-one mapping between the classical field theory description and the phenomenological fluid description of interacting dark energy and dark matter, which exists only for this unique form of interaction. Different formulations of interacting dark energy models in the literature can be classified into two categories based on the field-theoretic description. Then we discuss the quantifying tools to distinguish between the interacting and non-interacting dark sector scenarios. We focus on the variation of the scalar metric perturbed quantities as a function of redshift related to structure formation, weak gravitational lensing, and the integrated Sachs-Wolfe effect and show that the difference in the evolution becomes significant for lower redshifts ($z < 20$), for all length scales.

Keywords: Dark matter - dark energy interaction, based on the work Ref. 1

1. Introduction

Dark matter dominates the galaxy mass, and dark energy forms the majority of our Universe's energy density.[2,3] However, we have little information about the properties of these two components that dominate the energy content of the Universe today.[4] The only information we have about the two components is that (i) Dark energy contributes negative pressure to the energy budget, and (ii) Dark matter has negligible, possibly zero, pressure. The above properties are based on gravitational interactions. More importantly, we do not know how they interact with each other and Baryons/Photons.

It has been shown that the dark matter-dark energy interaction can reconcile the tensions in the Hubble constant H_0.[5,6] In most interacting dark sector models, phenomenologically, the interaction is proposed between the fluid terms in the dark sector (Cf. Ref.[1]). More specifically, individually, dark matter (DM) and dark energy (DE) do not satisfy the conservation equations; however, the combined sector satisfies the energy conservation equation,[7] i. e.,

$$\nabla^\mu T^{(\text{DE,DM})}_{\mu\nu} = Q^{(\text{DE,DM})}_\nu, \quad Q^{(\text{DE})}_\nu + Q^{(\text{DM})}_\nu = 0 \qquad (1)$$

where Q determines the interaction strength between dark matter and dark energy. Since the gravitational effects on dark matter and dark energy are opposite, even a small interaction can impact the cosmological evolution.[8] Since we have little information about the dark sector, in many of these models, the interaction strength Q_ν is put in by hand. However, it is unclear whether these broad classes of phenomenological models can be obtained from a field theory action.

In this work, we show that under conformal transformations, $f(R,\chi)$ is equivalent to a model with two coupled scalar fields. The dark energy - dark matter interaction, represented by the coupling between the classical scalar fields, can also be represented by the evolution equations of the dark energy (represented by a scalar field) and dark matter (represented by a fluid). We show that a one-to-one mapping exists between the field theory and fluid description for a unique interaction term.

To detect the signatures of the interacting dark sector from the observations, one needs to construct theoretical tools to distinguish interacting dark sector models from non-interacting ones. We focus on the three cosmological phenomena: (i) structure formation, (ii) weak gravitational lensing (iii) integrated Sachs Wolfe effect. We study the evolution of the relevant perturbed quantities in the redshift range $0 \leq z \leq 1500$ at different length scales. We see that there is a clear difference in the perturbed evolution in the interacting dark sector model as compared to non-interacting ones. This difference becomes significant for $z < 20$, especially at smaller length scales.

2. Dark sector interaction: Field and fluid description

Consider the following action in Jordan frame:

$$S_J = \int d^4x \sqrt{-\tilde{g}} \left[\frac{1}{2\kappa^2} f(\tilde{R}, \tilde{\chi}) - \frac{1}{2} \tilde{g}^{\mu\nu} \tilde{\nabla}_\mu \tilde{\chi} \tilde{\nabla}_\nu \tilde{\chi} - V(\tilde{\chi}) \right] \tag{2}$$

where $f(\tilde{R}, \tilde{\chi})$ is an arbitrary, smooth function of Ricci scalar, and scalar field $\tilde{\chi}$, and $V(\chi)$ is the self-interaction potential of the scalar field $\tilde{\chi}$. Under the conformal transformation:

$$g_{\mu\nu} = \Omega^2 \tilde{g}_{\mu\nu}, \quad \text{where} \quad \Omega^2 = F(\tilde{R}, \tilde{\chi}) \equiv \frac{\partial f(\tilde{R}, \tilde{\chi})}{\partial \tilde{R}} \tag{3}$$

and a field redefinition, the action in the Einstein frame takes the following form

$$S = \int d^4x \sqrt{-g} \left(\frac{1}{2\kappa^2} R - \frac{1}{2} g^{\mu\nu} \nabla_\mu \phi \nabla_\nu \phi - U(\phi) - \frac{1}{2} e^{2\alpha(\phi)} g^{\mu\nu} \nabla_\mu \chi \nabla_\nu \chi - e^{4\alpha(\phi)} V(\chi) \right). \tag{4}$$

where

$$U = \frac{F\tilde{R} - f}{2\kappa^2 F^2}.$$

and $\alpha(\phi)$ denotes the interaction between dark energy and dark matter.

Defining the dark matter fluid by specifying the four velocity energy density and pressure

$$u_\mu = - \left[-g^{\alpha\beta} \nabla_\alpha \chi \nabla_\beta \chi \right]^{-\frac{1}{2}} \nabla_\mu \chi \tag{5}$$

$$p_m = -\frac{1}{2}e^{2\alpha}\left[g^{\mu\nu}\nabla_\mu\chi\nabla_\nu\chi + e^{2\alpha}V(\chi)\right], \quad \rho_m = -\frac{1}{2}e^{2\alpha}\left[g^{\mu\nu}\nabla_\mu\chi\nabla_\nu\chi - e^{2\alpha}V(\chi)\right]. \tag{6}$$

Then the interaction function in the field theory and fluid descriptions are given by

$$Q_\nu^{(F)} = -e^{2\alpha(\phi)}\alpha_{,\phi}(\phi)\nabla_\nu\phi\left[\nabla^\sigma\chi\nabla_\sigma\chi + 4e^{2\alpha(\phi)}V(\chi)\right] = -\alpha_{,\phi}(\phi)\nabla_\nu\phi(\rho_m - 3p_m) \tag{7}$$

A one-to-one mapping between the field theory description and fluid description of the interacting dark sector described above exist *only* for this form of interaction function. A classification of interacting dark sector models based on the existence of this mapping is given below.[1]

Interacting DE-DM model	DE-DM Interaction $\nabla^\mu T_{\mu\nu}^{(DE,DM)} = Q_\nu^{(DE,DM)}$	Is $Q_\nu \propto Q_\nu^{(F)}$?
Amendola - 1999[9]	$\dot{\rho}_m + 3H\rho_m = -C\rho_m\dot{\phi}$	Yes
Amendola - 1999[10]	$\dot{\rho}_m + 3H\rho_m = -C\rho_m\dot{\phi}$	Yes
Billyard & Coley -1999[11]	$\dot{\phi}(\ddot{\phi} + 3H\dot{\phi} + kV) = \frac{(4-3\gamma)}{2\sqrt{\omega+\frac{3}{2}}}\dot{\phi}\mu$	Yes
Olivares.etal - 2005[12]	$\frac{d\rho_c}{dt} + 3H\rho_c = 3Hc^2(\rho_c + \rho_x)$	No
Amendola.etal - 2006[13]	$\dot{\rho}_{DM} + 3H\rho_{DM} - \delta(a)H\rho_{DM} = 0$	No
Olivares.etal - 2007[14]	$\dot{\rho}_c + 3H\rho_c = 3Hc^2(\rho_x + \rho_c)$	No
Boehmer.etal - 2008[15]	$\dot{\rho}_c + 3H\rho_c = -\sqrt{2/3}\kappa\beta\rho_c\dot{\varphi}$	Yes
	$\dot{\rho}_c + 3H\rho_c = -\alpha H\rho_c$	No
Caldera-Cabral.etal - 2008[16]	$\dot{\rho}_c = -3H\rho_c + 3H(\alpha_x\rho_x + \alpha_c\rho_c)$	No
	$\dot{\rho}_c = -3H\rho_c + 3(\Gamma_x\rho_x + \Gamma_c\rho_c)$	No
He & Wang - 2008[17]	$\dot{\rho}_{DM} + 3H\rho_{DM} - \delta H\rho_{DM} = 0$	No
	$\dot{\rho}_{DM} + 3H\rho_{DM} - \delta H(\rho_{DM} + \rho_{DE}) = 0$	No
Pettorino & Baccigalupi - 2008[18]	$\phi'' + 2\mathcal{H}\phi' + a^2U_{,\phi} = a^2C_c\rho_c$	Yes
Quartin.etal - 2008[19]	$\frac{d\rho_c}{dN} + 3\rho_c = 3\lambda_x\rho_x + \lambda_c\rho_c$	No
Boehmer.etal - 2009[20]	$\dot{\rho}_c = -3H\rho_c - \frac{\alpha}{M_0}\rho_\varphi^2$	No
	$\dot{\rho}_c = -3H\rho_c - \frac{\beta}{M_0}\rho_c^2$	No
	$\dot{\rho}_c = -3H\rho_c - \frac{\gamma}{M_0}\rho_\varphi\rho_c$	No
Beyer.etal - 2010[21]	$\ddot{\varphi} + 3H\dot{\varphi} - \alpha M^3 e^{-\alpha\varphi/M} = \frac{\beta}{M}\rho_\chi$	Yes
Lopez Honorez.etal - 2010[22]	$\dot{\rho}_{dm} + 3H\rho_{dm} = \beta(\phi)\rho_{dm}\dot{\phi}$	Yes
Avelino & Silva - 2012[23]	$\dot{\rho}_m + 3H\rho_m = \alpha H a^\beta \rho_w$	No
Pan.etal - 2012[24]	$\dot{\rho}_m + 3H\rho_m = 3\lambda_m H\rho_m + 3\lambda_d H\rho_d$	No
Salvatelli.etal - 2013[25]	$\dot{\rho}_{dm} + 3\mathcal{H}\rho_{dm} = \xi\mathcal{H}\rho_{de}$	No
Chimento.etal - 2013[26]	$\rho'_m + \gamma_m\rho_m = -\alpha\rho'\rho$	No
Amendola.etal - 2014[27]	$\dot{\rho}_\alpha + 3H\rho_\alpha = -\kappa\sum_i C_{i\alpha}\dot{\phi}_i\rho_\alpha$	Yes
Marra - 2015[28]	$\dot{\rho}_m + 3H\rho_m = \nu\delta_m^n\rho_m\dot{\phi}/M_{Pl}$	No
Bernardi & Landim - 2016[29]	$\dot{\rho}_m + 3H\rho_m = Q(\rho_\phi + \rho_m)\dot{\phi}$	No
	$\dot{\rho}_m + 3H\rho_m = Q\rho_\phi\dot{\phi}$	No
Pan & Sharov - 2016[30]	$\dot{\rho}_{dm} + 3\mathcal{H}\rho_{dm} = 3\lambda_m H\rho_{dm} + 3\lambda_d H\rho_d$	No
Bruck & Mifsud - 2017[31][a]	$\nabla^\mu T_{\mu\nu}^{DM} = Q\nabla_\nu\phi$ $Q = \frac{C_{,\phi}}{2C}T_{DM} + \frac{D_{,\phi}}{2C}T_{DM}^{\mu\nu}\nabla_\mu\phi\nabla_\nu\phi$ $-\nabla_\mu\left[\frac{D}{C}T_{DM}^{\mu\nu}\nabla_\nu\phi\right]$	Yes if $D = 0$
Gonzalez & Trodden - 2018[33]	$\dot{\rho}_\chi + 3H\rho_\chi = \alpha'\dot{\phi}\rho_\chi$	Yes
Barros.etal - 2018[34]	$\dot{\rho}_c + 3H\rho_c = -\kappa\beta\dot{\phi}\rho$	Yes
Landim - 2019[35]	$\ddot{\phi} + 3H\dot{\phi} + V'(\phi) = -Q\rho_m$	Yes

---

[a]Violates causality condition $(D(\phi) > 0)$ for the disformal transformations[32]

3. Cosmological evolution with dark energy – dark matter interaction

Consider the perturbed FRW metric in the Newtonian gauge

$$g_{00} = -(1+2\Phi), \quad g_{0i} = 0, \quad g_{ij} = a^2(1-2\Psi)\delta_{ij}, \tag{8}$$

For the FRW Universe, the background evolution of the scalar fields in the field theory description is given by

$$\ddot{\overline{\chi}} + 3H\dot{\overline{\chi}} + e^{2\alpha}V_{,\chi}(\overline{\chi}) + 2\alpha_{,\phi}(\overline{\phi})\dot{\overline{\phi}}\dot{\overline{\chi}} = 0$$

$$\ddot{\overline{\phi}} + 3H\dot{\overline{\phi}} + U_{,\phi}(\overline{\phi}) + 4e^{4\alpha}\alpha_{,\phi}(\overline{\phi})V(\overline{\chi}) - e^{2\alpha}\alpha_{,\phi}(\overline{\phi})\dot{\overline{\chi}}^2 = 0.$$

In the fluid description, the dark energy scalar field $\overline{\phi}$ and the dark matter fluid energy density $\overline{\rho}_m$ evolve as

$$\ddot{\overline{\phi}}\dot{\overline{\phi}} + 3H\dot{\overline{\phi}}^2 + U_{,\phi}(\overline{\phi})\dot{\overline{\phi}} = \overline{Q}^{(F)}, \quad \dot{\overline{\rho}}_m + 3H(\overline{\rho}_m + \overline{p}_m) = -\overline{Q}^{(F)}$$

where the interaction term $\overline{Q}^{(F)}$ is given by

$$\overline{Q}^{(F)} = -\alpha_{,\phi}(\overline{\phi})\dot{\overline{\phi}}(\overline{\rho}_m - 3\overline{p}_m) = \alpha_{,\phi}(\overline{\phi})\dot{\overline{\phi}}e^{2\alpha(\overline{\phi})}\left[\dot{\overline{\chi}}^2 - 4e^{2\alpha}V(\overline{\chi})\right]. \tag{9}$$

Then the dark matter fluid energy density evolves as

$$\overline{\rho}_m = \overline{\rho}_{m_0}a^{-3(1+\omega_m)}e^{[\alpha(\overline{\phi})-\alpha_0](1-3\omega_m)}, \tag{10}$$

The perturbed evolution in the Newtonian gauge is given by

$$\delta\dot{\rho}_m + 3H(\delta p_m + \delta\rho_m) + (\overline{\rho}_m + \overline{p}_m)\left[\frac{\nabla^2 \delta u^s}{a^2} - 3\dot{\Psi}\right] = -\delta Q \tag{11}$$

$$\dot{\overline{\phi}}\left(\ddot{\delta\phi} - \frac{\nabla^2 \delta\phi}{a^2} - 2\Phi\ddot{\overline{\phi}} + U_{,\phi\phi}(\overline{\phi})\delta\phi\right) + \dot{\delta\phi}\left(\ddot{\overline{\phi}} + 6H\dot{\overline{\phi}} + U_{,\phi}(\overline{\phi})\right)$$

$$-\frac{\dot{\overline{\phi}}^2}{2}\left(3\dot{\Psi} + \dot{\Phi} + 6H\Phi\right) = \delta Q, \tag{12}$$

where

$$\delta Q^{(F)} = -(\delta\rho_m - 3\delta p_m)\alpha_{,\phi}(\overline{\phi})\dot{\overline{\phi}} - (\overline{\rho}_m - 3\overline{p}_m)\left[\alpha_{,\phi\phi}(\overline{\phi})\dot{\overline{\phi}}\delta\phi + \alpha_{,\phi}(\overline{\phi})\dot{\delta\phi}\right] \tag{13}$$

The metric perturbations Φ and Ψ satisfy the equations

$$\Psi - \Phi = 0 \tag{14}$$

$$\dot{\Psi} + H\Phi = \frac{\kappa^2}{2}\left[\dot{\overline{\phi}}\delta\phi - (\overline{\rho}_m + \overline{p}_m)\delta u^s\right] \tag{15}$$

$$3H\dot{\Psi} - \frac{\nabla^2\Psi}{a^2} + 3H^2\Phi = -\frac{\kappa^2}{2}\left(\delta\rho_m + \dot{\delta\phi}\dot{\bar\phi} - \Phi\dot{\bar\phi}^2 + U_{,\phi}(\bar\phi)\delta\phi\right) \tag{16}$$

$$3\ddot{\Psi} + \frac{\nabla^2\Phi}{a^2} + 6\Phi\left(H^2 + \dot{H}\right) + 3H\left(2\dot\Psi + \dot\Phi\right)$$
$$= \frac{\kappa^2}{2}\left(\delta\rho_m + 3\delta p_m + 4\dot{\delta\phi}\dot{\bar\phi} - 4\Phi\dot{\bar\phi}^2 - 2U_{,\phi}(\bar\phi)\delta\phi\right) \tag{17}$$

4. Observable signatures of interacting dark sector

To detect the signatures of dark energy – dark matter interaction in cosmological observation, one needs to study the evolution of perturbed quantities related to cosmological observations. For this purpose, we consider the following cosmological phenomena and the relevant perturbed quantities

(1) Structure formation: $\delta_m(t,x,y,z) \equiv \frac{\delta\rho_m(t,x,y,z)}{\bar\rho_m(t)}$
(2) Weak lensing : $\Phi + \Psi$
(3) Integrated Sachs-Wolfe (ISW) effect: $\Phi' + \Psi'$

where *prime* denoted derivative with respect to $N \equiv \ln a$.

To illustrate the difference between the evolution of perturbations in the interacting and non-interacting scenarios, we consider the following dark energy scalar field potential and interaction function

$$U(\phi) \sim \frac{1}{\phi}, \quad \alpha(\phi) \sim \phi \tag{18}$$

We then study the evolution of the flowing quantities in the redshift range $0 \leq z \leq 1500$ at different length scales

$$\Delta\delta_m = \delta_{m_i} - \delta_{m_{ni}}, \quad \Delta\Phi = \Phi_i - \Phi_{ni}, \quad \Delta\Phi' = \Phi'_i - \Phi'_{ni} \tag{19}$$

Evolution these quantities are given in Figs. 1 and 2.

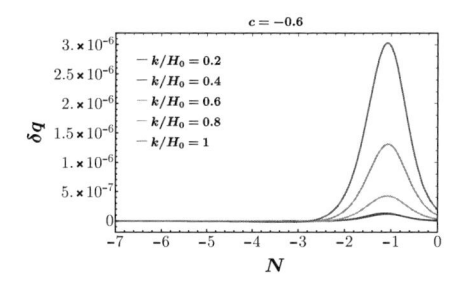

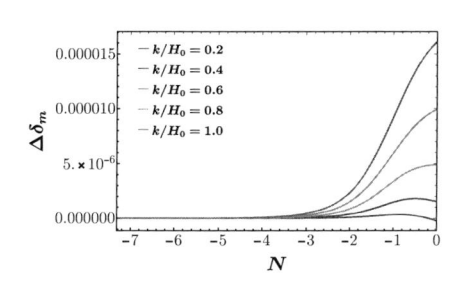

Fig. 1. Evolution of δq(left panel) and $\Delta\delta_m$(right panel) as a function of N for different values of k.

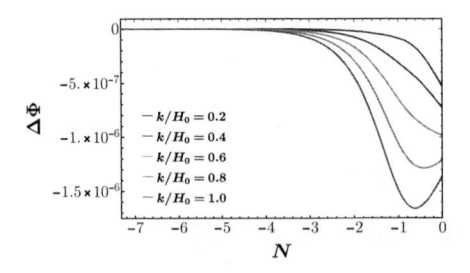

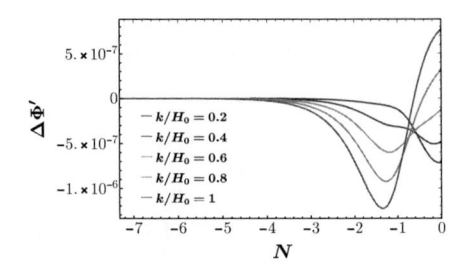

Fig. 2. Evolution of $\Delta\Phi$ (left panel) and $\Delta\Phi'$ (right panel) as a function of N for different values of k.

where δq is the scaled interaction function given by

$$\delta q = \frac{\delta Q}{H^3 M_{Pl}^2}. \qquad (20)$$

Here we see that the evolution of perturbed quantities in the interacting dark sector models shows significant differences for $z < 20$, especially at lower length scale (larger values of k). This trend is consistent with the evolution of scaled interaction function δq.

5. Conclusion

In this work, we consider an interacting dark sector model. We demand that the energy-momentum of individual components of dark sector is conserved, but that of the individual components is not. This model is implemented through a field theory action where dark energy and dark matter are represented by classical scalar fields. This field theory description can be derived from a $f(\tilde{R}, \tilde{chi})$ by means of a conformal transformation and field redefinition. We show that there is a one-to-one mapping between the classical field theory description of the dark energy – dark matter interaction and the fluid description of the interacting dark sector. This mapping exist *only* for a unique interaction term $Q_\nu^{(F)}$. We then classified the popular interacting dark sector models found in literature based on whether or not this mapping is applicable to those models.

We then look at the evolution of first-order scalar perturbations in the interacting dark sector in the redshift range of $0 \leq z \leq 1500$. We consider an inverse power-law dark energy scalar field potential and a linear interaction function. To detect the potential signatures of dark energy - dark matter interaction from cosmological observations, we focus on three cosmological phenomena and related perturbed quantities: (i) structure formation (δ_m) (ii) weak gravitational lensing ($\Phi + \Psi$)(iii) integrated Sachs Wolfe effect ($\Phi' + \Psi'$). We see that the density perturbation δ_m grows at a faster rate in the interacting scenario, especially at the smaller length scales. The effect of the interaction becomes significant for redshift $z < 20$. This is consistent with the evolution of perturbed interaction function δq. We see a similar trend in the case of Φ and Φ', which indicates that the future observations of weak gravitational lensing and integrated Sachs Wolfe effect can be used to distinguish between the interacting and non-interacting models of dark sector.

Acknowledgments

J.P.J. is supported by CSIR Senior Research Fellowship, India. The work is partially supported by the ISRO-Respond grant.

References

1. J. P. Johnson and S. Shankaranarayanan, Cosmological perturbations in the interacting dark sector: Mapping fields and fluids, *Phys. Rev. D* **103**, p. 023510 (2021).
2. A. G. Riess and Others, Observational evidence from supernovae for an accelerating universe and a cosmological constant, *Astron. J.* **116**, 1009 (1998).
3. N. Aghanim *et al.*, Planck 2018 results. vi. cosmological parameters, *Astron. Astrophys.* **641**, p. A6 (2020).
4. E. J. Copeland, M. Sami and S. Tsujikawa, Dynamics of dark energy, *Int. J. Mod. Phys.* **D15**, 1753 (2006).
5. E. Di Valentino, A. Melchiorri and O. Mena, Can interacting dark energy solve the H_0 tension?, *Phys. Rev. D* **96**, p. 043503 (2017).
6. A. Gómez-Valent, V. Pettorino and L. Amendola, Update on coupled dark energy and the h_0 tension, *Phys. Rev. D* **101**, p. 123513 (2020).
7. B. Wang, E. Abdalla, F. Atrio-Barandela and D. Pavon, Dark Matter and Dark Energy Interactions: Theoretical Challenges, Cosmological Implications and Observational Signatures, *Rept. Prog. Phys.* **79**, p. 096901 (2016).
8. Y. L. Bolotin, A. Kostenko, O. Lemets and D. Yerokhin, Cosmological Evolution With Interaction Between Dark Energy And Dark Matter, *Int. J. Mod. Phys. D* **24**, p. 1530007 (2014).
9. L. Amendola, Perturbations in a coupled scalar field cosmology, *Mon. Not. Roy. Astron. Soc.* **312**, p. 521 (2000).
10. L. Amendola, Coupled quintessence, *Phys. Rev. D* **62**, p. 043511 (2000).
11. A. P. Billyard and A. A. Coley, Interactions in scalar field cosmology, *Phys. Rev. D* **61**, p. 083503 (2000).
12. G. Olivares, F. Atrio-Barandela and D. Pavon, Observational constraints on interacting quintessence models, *Phys. Rev. D* **71**, p. 063523 (2005).
13. L. Amendola, G. Camargo Campos and R. Rosenfeld, Consequences of dark matter-dark energy interaction on cosmological parameters derived from SNIa data, *Phys. Rev. D* **75**, p. 083506 (2007).
14. G. Olivares, F. Atrio-Barandela and D. Pavon, Dynamics of Interacting Quintessence Models: Observational Constraints, *Phys. Rev. D* **77**, p. 063513 (2008).
15. C. G. Boehmer, G. Caldera-Cabral, R. Lazkoz and R. Maartens, Dynamics of dark energy with a coupling to dark matter, *Phys. Rev. D* **78**, p. 023505 (2008).
16. G. Caldera-Cabral, R. Maartens and L. Urena-Lopez, Dynamics of interacting dark energy, *Phys. Rev. D* **79**, p. 063518 (2009).
17. J.-H. He and B. Wang, Effects of the interaction between dark energy and dark matter on cosmological parameters, *JCAP* **06**, p. 010 (2008).
18. V. Pettorino and C. Baccigalupi, Coupled and Extended Quintessence: theoretical differences and structure formation, *Phys. Rev. D* **77**, p. 103003 (2008).

19. M. Quartin, M. O. Calvao, S. E. Joras, R. R. Reis and I. Waga, Dark Interactions and Cosmological Fine-Tuning, *JCAP* **05**, p. 007 (2008).
20. C. G. Boehmer, G. Caldera-Cabral, N. Chan, R. Lazkoz and R. Maartens, Quintessence with quadratic coupling to dark matter, *Phys. Rev. D* **81**, p. 083003 (2010).
21. J. Beyer, S. Nurmi and C. Wetterich, Coupled dark energy and dark matter from dilatation anomaly, *Phys. Rev. D* **84**, p. 023010 (2011).
22. L. Lopez Honorez, O. Mena and G. Panotopoulos, Higher-order coupled quintessence, *Phys. Rev. D* **82**, p. 123525 (2010).
23. P. Avelino and H. da Silva, Effective dark energy equation of state in interacting dark energy models, *Phys. Lett. B* **714**, 6 (2012).
24. S. Pan, S. Bhattacharya and S. Chakraborty, An analytic model for interacting dark energy and its observational constraints, *Mon. Not. Roy. Astron. Soc.* **452**, 3038 (2015).
25. V. Salvatelli, A. Marchini, L. Lopez-Honorez and O. Mena, New constraints on Coupled Dark Energy from the Planck satellite experiment, *Phys. Rev. D* **88**, p. 023531 (2013).
26. L. P. Chimento, M. G. Richarte and I. E. Sánchez García, Interacting dark sector with variable vacuum energy, *Phys. Rev. D* **88**, p. 087301 (2013).
27. L. Amendola, T. Barreiro and N. J. Nunes, Multifield coupled quintessence, *Phys. Rev. D* **90**, p. 083508 (2014).
28. V. Marra, Coupling dark energy to dark matter inhomogeneities, *Phys. Dark Univ.* **13**, 25 (2016).
29. F. F. Bernardi and R. G. Landim, Coupled quintessence and the impossibility of an interaction: a dynamical analysis study, *Eur. Phys. J. C* **77**, p. 290 (2017).
30. S. Pan and G. Sharov, A model with interaction of dark components and recent observational data, *Mon. Not. Roy. Astron. Soc.* **472**, 4736 (2017).
31. C. Van De Bruck and J. Mifsud, Searching for dark matter - dark energy interactions: going beyond the conformal case, *Phys. Rev. D* **97**, p. 023506 (2018).
32. J. D. Bekenstein, The Relation between physical and gravitational geometry, *Phys. Rev. D* **48**, 3641 (1993).
33. M. Carrillo González and M. Trodden, Field Theories and Fluids for an Interacting Dark Sector, *Phys. Rev. D* **97**, p. 043508 (2018), [Erratum: Phys. Rev. D 101, 089901 (2020)].
34. B. J. Barros, L. Amendola, T. Barreiro and N. J. Nunes, Coupled quintessence with a ΛCDM background: removing the σ_8 tension, *JCAP* **01**, p. 007 (2019).
35. R. G. Landim, Cosmological perturbations and dynamical analysis for interacting quintessence, *Eur. Phys. J. C* **79**, p. 889 (2019).

The role of self interactions in the cosmological evolution of warm dark matter

R. Yunis[1,2], C. R. Argüelles[1,3], D. López Nacir[4,5], C. Scóccola[3,6], N. Mavromatos[7,8], A. Krut[2]

[1] *International Center for Relativistic Astrophysics Network – ICRANet,*
Piazza della Repubblica 10, 65122 Pescara, Italy
[2] *ICRA, Dipartimento di Fisica, Sapienza Università di Roma,*
Piazzale Aldo Moro 5, 00185 Rome, Italy
[3] *Facultad de Ciencias Astronómicas y Geofísicas, Universidad Nacional de La Plata,*
Paseo del Bosque, B1900FWA La Plata, Argentina
[4] *Departamento de Física Juan José Giambiagi, FCEyN UBA*
[5] *IFIBA CONICET-UBA, Facultad de Ciencias Exactas y Naturales, Ciudad Universitaria,*
Pabellón I, 1428 Buenos Aires, Argentina
[6] *CONICET (Consejo Nacional de Investigaciones Científicas y Técnicas), Argentina*
[7] *Theoretical Particle Physics and Cosmology Group, Physics Department, King's College*
London, Strand, London WC2R 2LS, UK
[8] *Physics Department, School of Applied Mathematical and Physical Sciences,*
National Technical University of Athens, 9, Heroon Polytechneiou Str.,
Zografou Campus, Athens 157 80, Greece

In this work we present a summary of recent studies on the effects of elastic self interactions in the evolution of Warm Dark Matter models (WDM), focusing on structure formation and the evolution of cosmological perturbations. We pay special attention to a particular class of sterile neutrino WDM known as νMSM and provide examples for the case of vector field self interactions. We calculate the effects of assuming self interacting dark matter in X-Ray astrophysical observations, in the formation of fermionic DM halos in (quasi) equilibrium states and in the evolution of DM perturbations in the early universe, assuming particle masses between $\mathcal{O}(1-100)$ keV. In the latter topic, we perform simulations using a modification to the public Boltzmann solver CLASS and compare our results with observations. We find self interactions to be an interesting addition to WDM models, which can alleviate tensions both present in standard CDM cosmology and regarding WDM itself, as well as provide an interesting avenue for DM halo formation.

Keywords: Dark Matter, Self Interactions, Cosmology

1. Introduction

Several observations at large and small scales, such as the distribution of large-scale structure, CMB anisotropies and the internal structure of DM halos has lead to a standard model of cosmology: ΛCDM.[1,2] DM in this model is assumed to be "Cold": a distribution of colissionless, non relativistic particles with negligible velocity dispersion, which forms structure in a "bottom-up" fashion. However, recent observations have challenged this paradigm[3]; namely, the so called missing satellites problem[4–6]; the too big to fail problem[7]; and the core-cusp problem,[3,8,9] among others. While these by no means rule out the standard model, it has sparked interest in the community in other families of DM models.

In one of these families of models, known as Warm Dark Matter (WDM),[10–12] the DM particles are produced while relativistic, but become non relativistic before the energy budget of the universe is dominated by matter. These particles would have a significant amount of velocity dispersion today, which causes a significant reduction of small scale structure population and an alleviation to some of the tensions we mentioned above. While traditionally these models were also expected to aid the *core-cusp* problem, it was shown[13] that the particle mass requirement for this to happen was inconsistent with existing bounds, in what was known as the "catch-22" problem in WDM. However, in recent years it has been shown that WDM halos with a core-halo distribution can exist[14] (and are indeed stable[15]) as end results of the process of violent relaxation, which fit observations from both Milky Way and dwarf galaxies. While these collisionless relaxation processes are thought to result in the formation and thermalization of these halos,[16,17] it has been argued in[18] that the process of Self Interactions can contribute to this end.

A particularly interesting particle candidate that can belong in the family of WDM models can be found in νMSM (Neutrino Minimal Standard model)[12,19] which assumes a light sterile neutrino to be the sole DM component, produced out of equilibrium via neutrino oscillations in the plasma, and requiring only a minimal extension to the Standard Model Lagrangian. Several observations heavily constrain the parameter space of this model, such as X-Ray constraints from astrophysical objects,[20–22] structure formation constraints,[23,24] production bounds[25]), among others. In recent years, Lyman-α observations have been particularly important, almost entirely ruling out the non-thermal production of WDM sterile neutrinos.[24,26] These tight constraints may be alleviated by performing simple extensions to this model: in particular, we focus here on the inclusion of DM Self Interactions, in what we name Self Interacting Warm Dark Matter (SIWDM).[27] As we will summarize in this work, these may not only contribute in the aforementioned challenges, but also allow us to potentially address tensions in ΛCDM previously unaccounted by WDM models alone.

2. Self Interactions and WDM

The addition of DM Self Interactions is a well studied problem, with many realizations mostly based on CDM models.[28,29] Its main assumption is the existence of non gravitational interaction terms between DM particles through a Standard Model or a Dark mediator. Typically, in the realm of structure formation the interactions considered are elastic, and therefore do not change the number or identity of particles. We focus here on interaction channels of these kinds in WDM and characterize their possible effects across cosmological history.

Self Interactions have been invoked in N-body simulations of structure formation, where it has been realized that the inclusion of these interactions can "flatten" the inner cores of dwarf galaxies (as indicated by observations) via a process of thermalization in the inner regions of these halos.[30,31] Thus, a combined model of WDM with the addition of Self Interactions may overcome both structure formation ("missing satellites" and "too big to fail") as well as inner halo dynamics ("core-cusp") challenges at the same time, preserving the benefits of both WDM and Self Interacting models. While there can be many particle physics models that reflect these interactions, we focus here instead on maintaining a certain model independence: some examples of particular model realizations can be found in the literature.[32–35]

Since the first introduction of Self Interactions in WDM,[36] it was realized that a combined model could provide interesting modifications in their dynamics. Indeed, Self Interactions do not only have an effect during structure formation, but also in perturbation evolution[37,38] and DM production.[12,39] This last point was studied in the past in the context of νMSM and, in particular, as mentioned in reference,[40] the phenomenon of mediator decay can significantly relax the parameter space of the model. There it was considered the case of a WDM model with vector field interactions, previously suggested in the literature to provide interesting consequences for DM halos.[41] These studies focus on WDM core-halo distributions,[14] known in the literature as RAR profiles, extended it via a Self Interacting model and calculated its potential effects on νMSM bounds coming from X-Ray observations. Interestingly, although bounds of the same order of magnitude as previous studies (that use N-body simulation-borne DM distributions) were obtained when considering observations of the MW galactic center, it was shown that these core-halo distributions are only compatible with νMSM bounds with the inclusion of additional production channels, such as Self Interactions. We present these results here in figure 1, where we plot the parameter space for νMSM, together with the bounds obtained from X-Ray observations of the MW Galactic Center.

While it was shown in reference[40] that the DM distribution of these halos is not affected by Self Interactions, it is an interesting open question if the formation of these systems may be affected by the inclusion of DM scattering. Indeed, these profiles are constructed assuming (General Relativistic) thermal equilibrium between DM particles. While coarse-grained equilibrium can be achieved by a collisionless fluid, as was shown in previous works,[14,17,42] Self Interactions can thermalize the inner regions of these systems[30] and, potentially, lead to the formation of a fermionic core.

3. SIWDM and Linear Cosmology

Self Interactions have already been found to have significant effects in the evolution of linear cosmological perturbations.[36–38] In particular, the effects of these interactions can be realized in the power spectrum and, in the realm of WDM, it

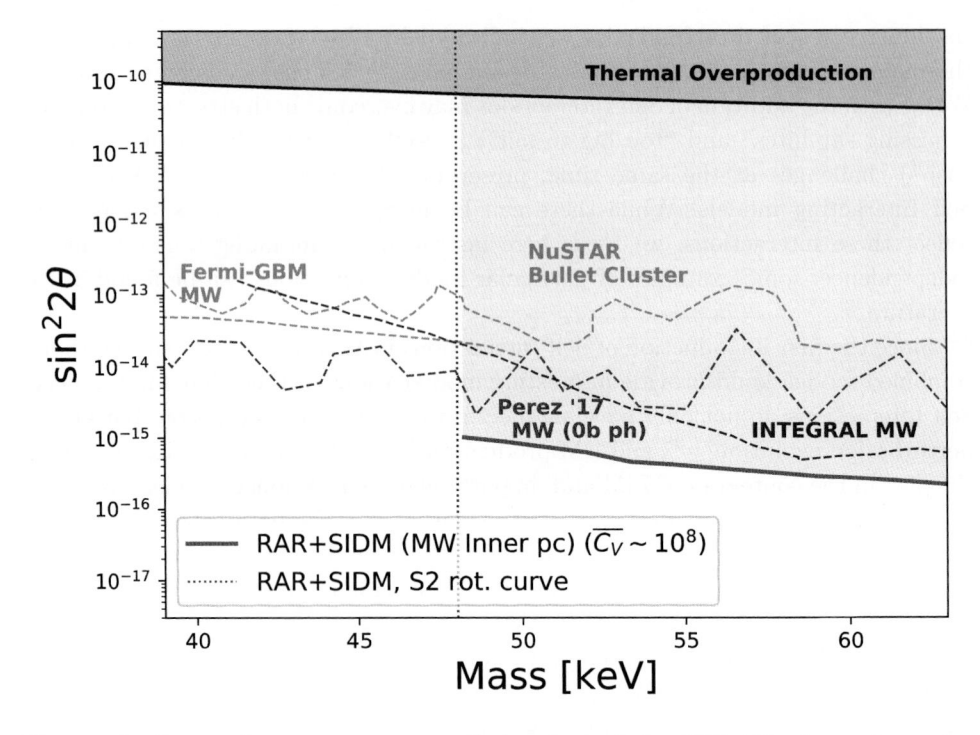

Fig. 1. Sterile neutrino parameter space limits obtained for MW GC observations using RAR+SIDM profiles (continuous red line), when assuming DM production due to self interactions and interaction strength according to Bullet Cluster constraints. The light Red shaded region above the continuous red line corresponds to RAR+SIDM limits given by X-ray bounds (i.e. indirect detection analysis), while the vertical shaded region below 48 keV labels the smallest DM mass compatible with S-cluster stars' rotation curve data that can provide a BH alternative. The upper shaded region corresponds to production mechanism bounds, while other dotted lines refer to several X-ray bounds corresponding to different observations/DM profiles.[20] Reproduced from reference.[40]

can lead to interesting scenarios such as non relativistic self decoupling (a.k.a. late kinetic decoupling). Particularly, the first challenge consists in implementing correctly a collision term in the first order Boltzmann equation for massive species.[43] While many implementations involve performing fluid approximations for the DM component,[44,45] it was realized that this approach is inaccurate in the case of light relics, such as SM interacting neutrinos.[43,46] Based on this realization, some of us obtained a reduced, kernel-based form for the Boltzmann collision term,[27] based on an ansatz for the interaction amplitude that encompasses most tree-level massive mediator models in an exact way. We refer the reader to reference[27] for a full expression of these terms.

The system of equations derived in[27] allows us to study the evolution of DM perturbations under the Relaxation Time Approximation (RTA),[47] shown to be very precise for the case of massive mediator interactions.[46] We can express the Legendre expansion of the first order Boltzmann equation in the synchronous gauge as

$$\dot{F}_0(k, E_q, \tau) \simeq -\frac{qk}{E_q} F_1(k, E_q, \tau) + \frac{\dot{h}}{6} \frac{\partial f_0}{\partial \ln q}$$

$$\dot{F}_1(k, E_q, \tau) \simeq \frac{qk}{3E_q} F_0(k, E_q, \tau) - \frac{2qk}{3E_q} F_2(k, E_q, \tau)$$

$$\dot{F}_2(k, E_q, \tau) \simeq \frac{qk}{5E_q} \left[2F_1(k, E_q, \tau) - 3F_3(k, E_q, \tau) \right] - \frac{\partial f_0}{\partial \ln q} \left[\frac{1}{15} \dot{h} + \frac{2}{5} \dot{\eta} \right] - a\frac{F_2(k, E_q, \tau)}{\tau_{rel}}$$

$$\dot{F}_l(k, E_q, \tau) \simeq \frac{qk}{(2l+1)E_q} \left[lF_{(l-1)}(k, E_q, \tau) - (l+1)F_{(l+1)}(k, E_q, \tau) \right]$$
$$- a\frac{F_l(k, E_q, \tau)}{\tau_{rel}} \quad l \geq 3, \tag{1}$$

where $f(\vec{k}, \vec{q}, \tau) = F(\vec{k}, \vec{q}, \tau) + f_0(q, \tau)$ is the DM distribution, $F(\vec{k}, \vec{q}, \tau)$ is the first order perturbation and we have defined the Legendre moments and the gravitational potentials h, η as in reference.[48] The collision rate $\Gamma(\tau)$ is defined as

$$\tau_{rel}^{-1} = \frac{g_i^3}{32(2\pi)^3} \frac{\int dE_q \, dE_l \, ds \, f_{eq}(E_q, \tau) \, f_{eq}(E_l, \tau) \, \chi(s)}{\int dE_q \, q \, E_q \, f_{eq}(E_q, \tau)}, \tag{2}$$

where this expression is defined according to the notation in references.[18,27] In the same references particular expressions for the collision kernel χ for various interaction models can be found.

These equations involve the background DM distribution f_0. While in the standard approach, this function remains in a relativistic form reminiscent of WDM, a few circumstances can alter this assumption. In particular, if the Self Interactions maintain the DM fluid in kinetic equilibrium all the way until the fluid becomes non relativistic, the background at that moment will switch into a non relativistic form, constituting the scenario known as Non Relativistic Self Decoupling. The consequences of this scenario were explored by some of us in reference.[18] There, it was found that, if one imposes continuity of the limiting expressions for the energy density, the non relativistic distribution function becomes

$$f_0(T < m) \sim 4.534 \mathcal{C}_{\rm NR} \exp\left[-1.075 q^2/T_{0,\rm R}^2\right], \tag{3}$$

where $\mathcal{C}_{\rm NR}, T_{0,\rm R}$ are the normalization and temperature of the species in the relativistic limit.

4. SIWDM Cosmology: Simulations and Observation

In reference[18] some of us developed a numerical implementation of these Self Interacting WDM models using a modified CLASS code, a publicly available Boltzmann solver.[49] This modification is available at the following link github.com/yunis121/siwdm-class. We show there a few examples of the resulting power spectra for the Self Interacting models in figure 2.

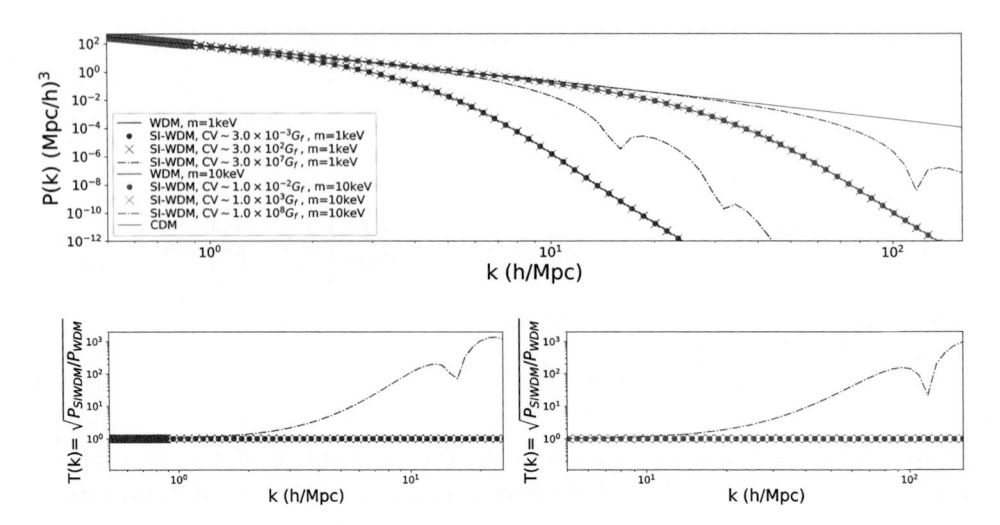

Fig. 2. Power Spectrum (*top panel*) and Transfer Functions with respect to standard WDM (*bottom panels*) for a vector field SI-WDM model, simulated using a modification to CLASS. We assume the relaxation time approximation (1), and consider two values of the DM particle mass: 1 and 10 keV. Also plotted are the power spectra of a CDM model and of WDM models with DM mass of 1 and 10 keV. All WDM and SI-WDM models consider a nonresonant production scenario (Dodelson-Widrow mechanism,[50]) with $T \sim (4/11)^{1/3} T_\gamma$. Reproduced from reference[18]

There, we see some of the particular features of the models. We see that the inclusion of Self Interactions, while modifying slightly the high k behavior of the power spectra, remain small elsewhere in the power spectrum for all models that do not undergo Non Relativistic Self Decoupling. However, for models with Non Relativistic Self Decoupling, the resulting power spectra may differ significantly from its relativistic counterpart. Indeed, we find that in this regime the models are "colder" (i. e. as if they correspond to a higher particle mass), and show even at smaller k values a distinctive oscillatory pattern. This indeed has the effect of increasing the amount of small structure formed for these models.

Most of the tensions inherent to νMSM WDM models come from structure formation, namely MW satellite counts and Lyman-α observations. These are related to the fact that the preferred parameter ranges may underproduce small structure and almost rule out the available parameter space. So, the inclusion of Self Interactions can significantly relax the existing bounds on this family of models.

Reference[18] provides an evaluation of the predictions of these models for the number of MW satellites[23] as well for the observations of the Lyman-α forest. We have found that a maximally interacting model (as allowed by the observations of the Bullet Cluster[41]) can readmit a significant portion of the νMSM parameter space, and we illustrate this in figure 3.

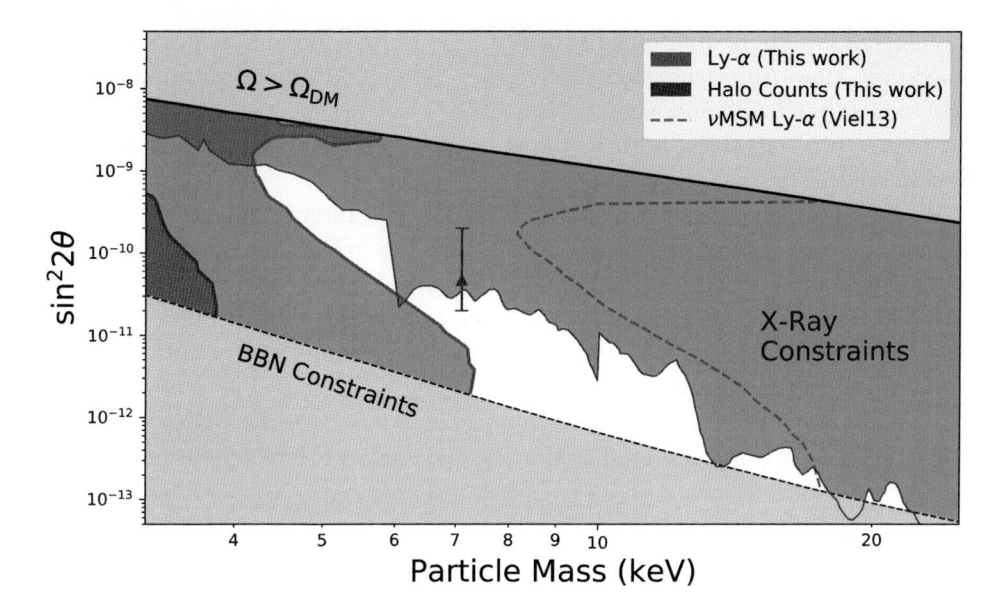

Fig. 3. Parameter space constraints for νMSM, where MW satellite halo counts and Lyman-α forest bounds are analyzed under a self interacting model as outlined above. We consider a self interacting model under a vector field mediator, with its interaction constant given by $\sigma/m \sim 0.144 C_v^2/m^3 = 0.1 \text{cm}^2/\text{g}$, the upper limit given by Bullet Cluster constraints.[41] For comparison, we plot the Lyman-alpha bounds for the non interacting case for a comparable analysis, according to the results in.[26] We also plot other bounds to the νMSM parameter space for informative purposes.[12, 21–23, 25] Also for informative purposes, we plot a model compatible with a tentative 3.5 keV DM signal as a purple triangle[51–53] for informative purposes. Reproduced from reference[18]

5. Conclusions

We have studied in detail the evolution of Warm Dark Matter in the presence of Self Interactions. With the aim of contributing to a detailed study of this subject from both a cosmological and astrophysical perspective we provide here an overview of the results obtained so far.

Reference[40] presents and exploration of the consequences of considering WDM core halo RAR distributions[14] in the parameter space of sterile neutrino WDM. There it is suggested that the inclusion of Self Interactions can at the same time relax the WDM sterile neutrino parameter space via additional production channels, readmit RAR core-halo distributions into these models and assist with relaxation and thermalization of these systems.

Reference[27] provides a theoretical framework for the treatment of cosmological perturbations in WDM that allows to quantify the effects of these extended models in the cosmological perturbations. There, we developed a kernel-based expression for the collision terms based on an ansatz for the interaction amplitude, as well as considered a few approximations to the resulting Boltzmann hierarchies such as the Relaxation Time Approximation. Reference[18] presents a numerical application to these models in CLASS and a comparison of the resulting spectra with MW subhalo and Lyman-α observables, both in the standard decoupling scenario as well as in the non relativistic case.

We have reached conclusions that indicate the Self Interacting models may provide an interesting extension of the sterile neutrino WDM models. In the future, we hope to contribute further in the development of a more accurate treatment of these Self Interactions at a Cosmological level, as well as complementary models for early universe histories and, possibly, a deeper insight into the formation of these core-halo models. While further research is needed if this model is to be considered a viable alternative to standard DM approaches, we believe the work summarized here may be an important stepping stone in the study of these extensions.

Acknowledgments

CRA has been supported by CONICET, Secretary of Science and Technology of FCAG and UNLP (grants G140 and G175), National Agency for the Promotion of Science and Technology (ANPCyT) of Argentina (grant PICT-2018-03743) and ICRANet. CGS is supported by ANPCyT grant PICT-2016-0081; and grants G140, G157 and G175 from UNLP. DLN has been supported by CONICET, ANPCyT and UBA. The work of NEM is supported in part by the UK Science and Technology Facilities research Council (STFC) under the research grant ST/T000759/1. NEM also acknowledges participation in the COST Association Action CA18108 *"Quantum Gravity Phenomenology in the Multimessenger Approach (QG-MM)"*.

References

1. N. A. Bahcall, J. P. Ostriker, S. Perlmutter and P. J. Steinhardt, The Cosmic triangle: Assessing the state of the universe, *Science* **284**, 1481 (1999).
2. P. Collaboration, Planck 2018 results: VI. Cosmological parameters, *Astronomy and Astrophysics* **641**, p. A6 (sep 2020).
3. J. S. Bullock and M. Boylan-Kolchin, Small-Scale Challenges to the ΛcDM Paradigm, *Annual Review of Astronomy and Astrophysics* **55**, 343 (2017).
4. B. F. Griffen, A. P. Ji, G. A. Dooley, F. A. Gómez, M. Vogelsberger, B. W. O'Shea and A. Frebel, The Caterpillar Project: A Large Suite of Milky Way Sized Halos, *The Astrophysical Journal* **818**, p. 10 (2016).
5. W. Janesh, K. L. Rhode, J. J. Salzer, S. Janowiecki, E. A. K. Adams, M. P. Haynes, R. Giovanelli and J. M. Cannon, Five Gas-rich Ultrafaint Dwarf Galaxy Candidates Discovered in WIYN Imaging of ALFALFA Sources, *The Astronomical Journal* **157**, p. 183 (2019).
6. The DES Collaboration, A. Drlica-Wagner, K. Bechtol, E. S. Rykoff, E. Luque, A. Queiroz, Y. Y. Mao, R. H. Wechsler, J. D. Simon, B. Santiago, B. Yanny, E. Balbinot, S. Dodelson, A. F. Neto, D. J. James, T. S. Li, M. A. G. Maia, J. L. Marshall, A. Pieres, K. Stringer, A. R. Walker, T. M. C. Abbott, F. B. Abdalla, S. Allam,

A. Benoit-Levy, G. M. Bernstein, E. Bertin, D. Brooks, E. Buckley-Geer, D. L. Burke, A. C. Rosell, M. C. Kind, J. Carretero, M. Crocce, L. N. da Costa, S. Desai, H. T. Diehl, J. P. Dietrich, P. Doel, T. F. Eifler, A. E. Evrard, D. A. Finley, B. Flaugher, P. Fosalba, J. Frieman, E. Gaztanaga, D. W. Gerdes, D. Gruen, R. A. Gruendl, G. Gutierrez, K. Honscheid, K. Kuehn, N. Kuropatkin, O. Lahav, P. Martini, R. Miquel, B. Nord, R. Ogando, A. A. Plazas, K. Reil, A. Roodman, M. Sako, E. Sanchez, V. Scarpine, M. Schubnell, I. Sevilla-Noarbe, R. C. Smith, M. Soares-Santos, F. Sobreira, E. Suchyta, M. E. C. Swanson, G. Tarle, D. Tucker, V. Vikram, W. Wester, Y. Zhang, J. Zuntz and Others, Eight Ultra-faint Galaxy Candidates Discovered in Year Two of the Dark Energy Survey, *Astrophys. J.* **813**, p. 109 (aug 2015).
7. M. Boylan-Kolchin, J. S. Bullock and M. Kaplinghat, Too big to fail? The puzzling darkness of massive Milky Way subhaloes, *Monthly Notices of the Royal Astronomical Society: Letters* **415**, 1 (feb 2011).
8. S.-H. Oh, D. A. Hunter, E. Brinks, B. G. Elmegreen, A. Schruba, F. Walter, M. P. Rupen, L. M. Young, C. E. Simpson, M. Johnson, K. A. Herrmann, D. Ficut-Vicas, P. Cigan, V. Heesen, T. Ashley and H.-X. Zhang, High-resolution mass models of dwarf galaxies from LITTLE THINGS, *Astronomical Journal* **149** (feb 2015).
9. J. F. Navarro, C. S. Frenk and S. D. M. White, A Universal density profile from hierarchical clustering, *Astrophys.J.* **490**, 493 (1997).
10. P. Bode, J. P. Ostriker and N. Turok, Halo Formation in Warm Dark Matter Models, *The Astrophysical Journal* **556**, 93 (2001).
11. M. R. Lovell, V. Eke, C. S. Frenk, L. Gao, A. Jenkins, T. Theuns, J. Wang, S. D. M. White, A. Boyarsky and O. Ruchayskiy, The haloes of bright satellite galaxies in a warm dark matter universe, *Monthly Notices of the Royal Astronomical Society* **420**, 2318 (2012).
12. A. Boyarsky, M. Drewes, T. Lasserre, S. Mertens and O. Ruchayskiy, Sterile Neutrino Dark Matter, *Prog. Part. Nucl. Phys.* **104**, 1 (2019).
13. A. V. Macciò, S. Paduroiu, D. Anderhalden, A. Schneider and B. Moore, Cores in warm dark matter haloes: a Catch 22 problem, *Monthly Notices of the Royal Astronomical Society* **424**, 1105 (2012).
14. C. Argüelles, A. Krut, J. A. Rueda and R. Ruffini, Novel constraints on fermionic dark matter from galactic observables II: galaxy scaling relations, *Physics of the Dark Universe* **24**, p. 100278 (2019).
15. C. R. Argüelles, M. I. Díaz, A. Krut and R. Yunis, On the formation and stability of fermionic dark matter halos in a cosmological framework, *Monthly Notices of the Royal Astronomical Society* (dec 2020).
16. D. Lynden-Bell, Statistical mechanics of violent relaxation in stellar systems, *Monthly Notices of the Royal Astronomical Society* **136**, p. 101 (1967).
17. P.-H. Chavanis, Statistical mechanics of self-gravitating systems in general relativity: I. The quantum Fermi gas, *Eur. Phys. J. Plus* **135** (aug 2020).
18. R. Yunis, C. R. Argüelles, C. G. Scóccola, D. L. Nacir and G. Giordano, Self-Interacting Dark Matter in Cosmology: accurate numerical implementation and observational constraints (aug 2021).
19. R. Adhikari, M. Agostini, N. Ky, T. Araki, M. Archidiacono, M. Bahr, J. Baur, J. Behrens, F. Bezrukov, P. Bhupal Dev, D. Borah, A. Boyarsky, A. de Gouvea, C. Pires, H. de Vega, A. Dias, P. Di Bari, Z. Djurcic, K. Dolde, H. Dorrer, M. Durero, O. Dragoun, M. Drewes, G. Drexlin, C. Düllmann, K. Eberhardt, S. Eliseev, C. Enss, N. Evans, A. Faessler, P. Filianin, V. Fischer, A. Fleischmann, J. Formaggio, J. Franse,

F. Fraenkle, C. Frenk, G. Fuller, L. Gastaldo, A. Garzilli, C. Giunti, F. Glück, M. Goodman, M. Gonzalez-Garcia, D. Gorbunov, J. Hamann, V. Hannen, S. Hannestad, S. Hansen, C. Hassel, J. Heeck, F. Hofmann, T. Houdy, A. Huber, D. Iakubovskyi, A. Ianni, A. Ibarra, R. Jacobsson, T. Jeltema, J. Jochum, S. Kempf, T. Kieck, M. Korzeczek, V. Kornoukhov, T. Lachenmaier, M. Laine, P. Langacker, T. Lasserre, J. Lesgourgues, D. Lhuillier, Y. Li, W. Liao, A. Long, M. Maltoni, G. Mangano, N. Mavromatos, N. Menci, A. Merle, S. Mertens, A. Mirizzi, B. Monreal, A. Nozik, A. Neronov, V. Niro, Y. Novikov, L. Oberauer, E. Otten, N. Palanque-Delabrouille, M. Pallavicini, V. Pantuev, E. Papastergis, S. Parke, S. Pascoli, S. Pastor, A. Patwardhan, A. Pilaftsis, D. Radford, P.-O. Ranitzsch, O. Rest, D. Robinson, P. Rodrigues da Silva, O. Ruchayskiy, N. Sanchez, M. Sasaki, N. Saviano, A. Schneider, F. Schneider, T. Schwetz, S. Schönert, S. Scholl, F. Shankar, R. Shrock, N. Steinbrink, L. Strigari, F. Suekane, B. Suerfu, R. Takahashi, N. Van, I. Tkachev, M. Totzauer, Y. Tsai, C. Tully, K. Valerius, J. Valle, D. Venos, M. Viel, M. Vivier, M. Wang, C. Weinheimer, K. Wendt, L. Winslow, J. Wolf, M. Wurm, Z. Xing, S. Zhou, K. Zuber and Others, A White Paper on keV Sterile Neutrino Dark Matter, *JCAP* **1701**, p. 25 (2017).
20. K. Perez, K. C. Y. Ng, J. F. Beacom, C. Hersh, S. Horiuchi and R. Krivonos, Almost closing the νMSM sterile neutrino dark matter window with NuSTAR, *Phys. Rev.* **D95**, p. 123002 (2017).
21. J. F. Cherry and S. Horiuchi, Closing in on Resonantly Produced Sterile Neutrino Dark Matter, *Physical Review D* **D95**, p. 83015 (jan 2017).
22. K. C. Y. Ng, B. M. Roach, K. Perez, J. F. Beacom, S. Horiuchi, R. Krivonos and D. R. Wik, New Constraints on Sterile Neutrino Dark Matter from *NuSTAR* M31 Observations, *Physical Review D* **99** (jan 2019).
23. A. Schneider, Astrophysical constraints on resonantly produced sterile neutrino dark matter, *Journal of Cosmology and Astroparticle Physics* **1604**, p. 59 (jan 2016).
24. W. Enzi, R. Murgia, O. Newton, S. Vegetti, C. Frenk, M. Viel, M. Cautun, C. D. Fassnacht, M. Auger, G. Despali, J. McKean, L. V. E. Koopmans and M. Lovell, Joint constraints on thermal relic dark matter from a selection of astrophysical probes, *MNRAS* **000**, 1 (oct 2020).
25. T. Venumadhav, F.-Y. Y. Cyr-Racine, K. N. Abazajian and C. M. Hirata, Sterile neutrino dark matter: Weak interactions in the strong coupling epoch, *Physical Review D* **94**, 1 (2016).
26. M. Viel, G. Becker, J. Bolton and M. Haehnelt, Warm dark matter as a solution to the small scale crisis: New constraints from high redshift Lyman-alpha forest data, *Phys. Rev. D* **88**, p. 43502 (2013).
27. R. Yunis, C. R. Argüelles and D. L. Nacir, Boltzmann hierarchies for self-interacting warm dark matter scenarios, *Journal of Cosmology and Astroparticle Physics* **2020** (feb 2020).
28. M. Vogelsberger, J. Zavala, F.-Y. Y. Cyr-Racine, C. Pfrommer, T. Bringmann and K. Sigurdson, ETHOS - an effective theory of structure formation: dark matter physics as a possible explanation of the small-scale CDM problems, *Mon. Not. Roy. Astron. Soc.* **460**, 1399 (2016).
29. S. Tulin and H.-B. Yu, Dark Matter Self-interactions and Small Scale Structure, *Phys. Rept.* **730**, 1 (2018).
30. J. S. Almeida and I. Trujillo, Numerical simulations of dark matter haloes produce polytropic central cores when reaching thermodynamic equilibrium, *Monthly Notices of the Royal Astronomical Society* **504**, 2832 (apr 2021).
31. S. Balberg, S. L. Shapiro and S. Inagaki, Self-Interacting Dark Matter Halos and the Gravothermal Catastrophe, *The Astrophysical Journal* **568**, 475 (oct 2001).

32. M. Y. Khlopov, Fundamental Particle Structure in the Cosmological Dark Matter, *International Journal of Modern Physics A* **28** (nov 2013).
33. S. Tulin, H.-B. Yu and K. M. Zurek, Resonant Dark Forces and Small Scale Structure, *Physical Review Letters* **110** (oct 2012).
34. L. G. van den Aarssen, T. Bringmann and C. Pfrommer, Is dark matter with long-range interactions a solution to all small-scale problems of Λ CDM cosmology?, *Physical Review Letters* **109** (may 2012).
35. M. A. Buen-Abad, G. Marques-Tavares and M. Schmaltz, Non-Abelian dark matter and dark radiation, *Physical Review D* **92** (2015).
36. S. Hannestad and R. J. Scherrer, Selfinteracting warm dark matter, *Phys. Rev.* **D62**, p. 43522 (2000).
37. R. Huo, Matter Power Spectrum of Light Freeze-in Dark Matter: With or without Self-Interaction, *Physics Letters, Section B: Nuclear, Elementary Particle and High-Energy Physics* **802** (jul 2019).
38. D. Egana-Ugrinovic, R. Essig, D. Gift and M. LoVerde, The Cosmological Evolution of Self-interacting Dark Matter, *Journal of Cosmology and Astroparticle Physics* **2021** (feb 2021).
39. A. De Gouvêa, M. Sen, W. Tangarife and Y. Zhang, Dodelson-Widrow Mechanism in the Presence of Self-Interacting Neutrinos, *Phys. Rev. Lett.* **124**, p. 81802 (2020).
40. R. Yunis, C. R. Argüelles, N. E. Mavromatos, A. Moliné, A. Krut, M. Carinci, J. A. Rueda and R. Ruffini, Galactic Center constraints on self-interacting sterile neutrinos from fermionic dark matter ("ino") models, *Physics of the Dark Universe* **30** (aug 2020).
41. C. R. Argüelles, N. E. Mavromatos, J. A. Rueda and R. Ruffini, The role of self-interacting right-handed neutrinos in galactic structure, *Journal of Cosmology and Astroparticle Physics* **1604**, p. 38 (2016).
42. P.-H. Chavanis, On the 'coarse-grained' evolution of collisionless stellar systems, *Monthly Notices of the Royal Astronomical Society* **300**, 981 (1998).
43. I. M. Oldengott, C. Rampf and Y. Y. Y. Wong, Boltzmann hierarchy for interacting neutrinos I: formalism, *JCAP* **1504**, p. 16 (2015).
44. S. Heimersheim, N. Schöneberg, D. C. Hooper and J. Lesgourgues, Cannibalism hinders growth: Cannibal Dark Matter and the S_8 tension, *Journal of Cosmology and Astroparticle Physics* **2020** (aug 2020).
45. M. Garny, T. Konstandin, L. Sagunski and S. Tulin, Lyman-α forest constraints on interacting dark sectors, *Journal of Cosmology and Astroparticle Physics* **2018** (may 2018).
46. I. M. Oldengott, T. Tram, C. Rampf and Y. Y. Y. Wong, Interacting neutrinos in cosmology: exact description and constraints, *JCAP* **1711**, p. 27 (2017).
47. P. L. Krapivsky, S. Redner and E. Ben-Naim, *A Kinetic View of Statistical Physics* (Cambridge University Press, 2010).
48. C.-P. Ma and E. Bertschinger, Cosmological Perturbation Theory in the Synchronous and Conformal Newtonian Gauges, *The Astrophysical Journal* **455**, p. 7 (jun 1995).
49. J. Lesgourgues and T. Tram, The Cosmic Linear Anisotropy Solving System (CLASS) IV: efficient implementation of non-cold relics, *Journal of Cosmology and Astroparticle Physics* **2011**, p. 32 (apr 2011).
50. S. Dodelson and L. M. Widrow, Sterile Neutrinos as Dark Matter, *Physical Review Letters* **72**, 17 (mar 1993).
51. E. Bulbul, M. Markevitch, A. Foster, R. K. Smith, M. Loewenstein and S. W. Randall, Detection of An Unidentified Emission Line in the Stacked X-ray spectrum of Galaxy Clusters, *Astrophys. J.* **789**, p. 13 (2014).

52. T. E. Jeltema and S. Profumo, Discovery of a 3.5 keV line in the Galactic Centre and a critical look at the origin of the line across astronomical targets, *Mon. Not. Roy. Astron. Soc.* **450**, 2143 (2015).
53. N. Cappelluti, E. Bulbul, A. Foster, P. Natarajan, M. C. Urry, M. W. Bautz, F. Civano, E. Miller and R. K. Smith, Searching for the 3.5 keV Line in the Deep Fields with Chandra : The 10 Ms Observations, *The Astrophysical Journal* **854**, p. 179 (feb 2018).

Interaction energy between a charged medium and its electromagnetic field as a dark matter candidate

Mayeul Arminjon

Lab. 3SR (Grenoble-Alpes University, Grenoble-INP, CNRS),
Grenoble, 38041 cedex 9, France
E-mail: Mayeul.Arminjon@3sr-grenoble.fr
https://www.univ-grenoble-alpes.fr/english/

In the scalar theory of gravitation with a preferred reference frame, a consistent formulation of electrodynamics in the presence of gravitation needs to introduce an additional energy tensor: the interaction energy tensor. This energy is gravitationally active and might contribute to the dark matter, because it has an exotic character and it is not localized inside matter. In order to check if that energy might form representative dark halos, one has to model the interstellar radiation field in a galaxy as a complete electromagnetic field obeying the Maxwell equations. A model has been built for this purpose, based on assuming axial symmetry and on recent results about axisymmetric Maxwell fields. Its predictions for the variation of the spectral energy density inside our Galaxy are relatively close to those of a recent radiation transfer model, except on the symmetry axis of the Galaxy, where the present model predicts extremely high values of the energy density.

Keywords: Dark matter; interstellar radiation field; Maxwell equations; Milky Way.

1. Introduction

Our initial motivation for the present work was independent of the problem of dark matter. It was to develop a consistent electrodynamics in an alternative theory of gravity: "the scalar ether theory", or SET. This is a preferred-frame theory based on a scalar field only,[1,2] that reduces to special relativity (SR) when the gravitational field vanishes. In general relativity (GR), the modification of the equations of electrodynamics in the presence of a gravitational field consists simply in rewriting the equations that are valid in SR, by using the "comma goes to semicolon" rule: $_{,\nu} \to {}_{;\nu}$, i.e.: partial derivatives are replaced by covariant derivatives based on the metric connection. (See Ref. 3 for an interesting discussion.) In particular, the dynamical equation for the energy(-momentum-stress) tensor T that is valid in SR is: $T^{\lambda\nu}_{,\nu} = 0$. Using the rule mentioned above, that equation is modified to: $T^{\lambda\nu}_{;\nu} = 0$, which is indeed the dynamical equation in GR and in many of its extensions or modifications. However, in the general situation, the latter equation is not equivalent to the dynamical equation of SET,[1] hence the foregoing rule cannot be used in SET.

Therefore, in that alternative theory, a different and less obvious path has to be taken for the purpose of adapting classical electrodynamics in the presence of a gravitational field. It turns out that this leads to introduce an exotic form of energy, and that this new form is a possible candidate for dark matter. In this conference paper, we quickly follow that path. We then summarize the Maxwell model of the interstellar radiation field, that we built to prepare the test of this candidate.

2. Necessity of an interaction tensor in SET

In SET, we assume classically that the electromagnetic field tensor $\boldsymbol{F}$ derives from a 4-potential A_μ:

$$F_{\mu\nu} := A_{\nu,\mu} - A_{\mu,\nu} = A_{\nu;\mu} - A_{\mu;\nu}. \tag{1}$$

This is (locally) equivalent to assuming that (i) $\boldsymbol{F}$ is antisymmetric ($F_{\mu\nu} = -F_{\nu\mu}$) and (ii) the first group of the Maxwell equations is satisfied:

$$F_{\lambda\mu,\nu} + F_{\mu\nu,\lambda} + F_{\nu\lambda,\mu} \equiv F_{\lambda\mu;\nu} + F_{\mu\nu;\lambda} + F_{\nu\lambda;\mu} = 0. \tag{2}$$

(The first equality in (2) is indeed an identity due to the antisymmetry of the field tensor and to the symmetry of the metric connection.) Therefore, in SET, the first group of the Maxwell equations is left unchanged. In a first version of electrodynamics in the presence of a gravitational field in SET, the second group of the Maxwell equations was got by applying the dynamical equation of SET to a charged medium in the presence of the Lorentz force, assuming that the following holds for the energy tensors, as is the case in SR and still in GR:

$$\text{(A) Total energy tensor } \boldsymbol{T} = \boldsymbol{T}_{\text{charged medium}} + \boldsymbol{T}_{\text{field}}. \tag{3}$$

(The total energy tensor $\boldsymbol{T}$ is the source of the gravitational field — more precisely, in SET, that source is the component T^{00} in the preferred reference frame of the theory; see Ref. 1 for details.) The additivity (3) leads to a form of Maxwell's second group of equations in SET.[4] But that form of Maxwell's second group in SET predicts charge production/destruction at untenable rates, therefore it has to be *discarded*.[5] The additivity assumption (3) is contingent and may be abandoned. This means introducing an "interaction" energy tensor $\boldsymbol{T}_{\text{inter}}$, such that

$$\boldsymbol{T} = \boldsymbol{T}_{\text{charged medium}} + \boldsymbol{T}_{\text{field}} + \boldsymbol{T}_{\text{inter}}. \tag{4}$$

One then has to constrain the form of $\boldsymbol{T}_{\text{inter}}$ and to derive equations for it.

3. Form of the interaction tensor

In SR, the additivity (3) of the energy tensors does apply, thus $\boldsymbol{T}_{\text{inter}} = \boldsymbol{0}$. In SET we may impose that $\boldsymbol{T}_{\text{inter}}$ should be Lorentz-invariant in the situation of SR, i.e. when the metric γ is Minkowski's metric γ^0 ($\gamma^0_{\mu\nu} = \eta_{\mu\nu}$ in Cartesian coordinates). This is true if and, one can prove,[6] *only if* we have:

$$T_{\text{inter }\mu\nu} = p\,\gamma^0_{\mu\nu} \quad \text{(situation of SR)}, \tag{5}$$

with some scalar field p. This is equivalent to:

$$T^\mu_{\text{inter }\nu} = p\,\delta^\mu_\nu \quad \text{(situation of SR)}. \tag{6}$$

The definition
$$T^{\mu}_{\text{inter }\nu} := p\,\delta^{\mu}_{\nu}, \quad \text{or} \quad (T_{\text{inter}})_{\mu\nu} := p\,\gamma_{\mu\nu}, \tag{7}$$
thus got in a Minkowski spacetime, is in fact generally-covariant. Hence, we adopt (7) for the general case. With a general metric γ, the tensor (7) is still pointwise Lorentz-invariant — in the sense that we have $(T_{\text{inter}})_{\mu\nu}(X) = p(X)\,\eta_{\mu\nu}$ in any coordinates that are Cartesian at a given event X, and this form remains invariant after any coordinate transformation that is Lorentz at X, i.e., such that the matrix $\left(\frac{\partial x'^{\mu}}{\partial x^{\nu}}(X)\right)$ belongs to the Lorentz group.

4. SET electrodynamics with the interaction tensor

With the additivity assumption (3) of the energy tensors, i.e., $\boldsymbol{T}_{\text{inter}} = \boldsymbol{0}$, the system of equations of electrodynamics of SET is closed, but violates charge conservation. With the interaction energy tensor (7) we have just one unknown more: the scalar field p. So we need just one scalar equation more. It turns out to be consistent to add *charge conservation* as the new scalar equation.[7] Then the system of equations of electrodynamics of SET is again closed, and now it satisfies charge conservation.

Based on that closed system, equations were derived that *determine the field p in a given general electromagnetic (EM) field* $(\mathbf{E}, \mathbf{B})$ *and in a given weak gravitational field with Newtonian potential U*:[7] the scalar field p (or more exactly, its first approximation p_1) obeys an advection equation:
$$\partial_T p_1 + u^j \partial_j p_1 = S. \tag{8}$$
That equation has given source S and given characteristic curves, the latter being the integral curves $\mathcal{C}(T_0, \mathbf{x}_0)$ of the spatial vector field $\mathbf{u}$ in Eq. (8). Here, "given" means that the source field S, as also the vector field $\mathbf{u}$ and hence the characteristic curves $\mathcal{C}(T_0, \mathbf{x}_0)$, do not depend on the unknown field p_1. It follows that p_1 can be obtained by integrating the source field S along those curves.[7]

The "medium" defined by the corresponding interaction energy tensor field $\boldsymbol{T}_{\text{inter}} = p\gamma$ can be counted as "dark matter", for

- it is not localized inside (usual) matter: indeed, the equations for the field p_1 show that its source S is, in general, non-zero as soon as there is a general EM field: $\mathbf{E} \neq \mathbf{0}$, $\mathbf{B} \neq \mathbf{0}$, $\mathbf{E}.\mathbf{B} \neq 0$, and a variable gravitational field with $\partial_T U \neq 0$, where the time derivative $\partial_T U$ of the Newtonian potential is taken in the preferred frame;[7]
- it is gravitationally active, since, from its definition (4), it contributes to the source of the gravitational field in SET, that is the component T^{00} in the preferred frame;
- it is "exotic", i.e., it is not usual matter — as shown by the form (7) of its energy tensor, which is very different from the possible energy tensors of any fluid, solid, or EM field. The fact that it is Lorentz-invariant means

that no velocity can be defined for that medium. The energy tensor (7) depends only on one scalar field (p), hence no equation of state is needed.

The foregoing considerations are at the classical level, hence do not tell if the "matter" with the energy tensor (7) is made of quantum particles.

5. Maxwell model of the ISRF

In order to check if the interaction energy E_{inter} might be distributed in the form of dark halos and contribute significantly to the dark matter distribution, we have to compute the field p for a model of a galaxy. This needs that we have a model of the Interstellar Radiation Field in a galaxy (ISRF) that provides that field as a solution of the Maxwell equations. However, the existing models of the ISRF (e.g. Refs. 8–13) focus on the radiation transfer (mainly via absorption, reemission or scattering by dust particles). They follow the paths of light rays or photons. To the best of our knowledge, no previous model of the ISRF did consider the full EM field with its six interacting components subjected to the Maxwell equations. Therefore, we had to build a model entirely from scratch, which involved both theoretical and numerical difficulties.[17]

5.1. *Maxwell model of the ISRF: Main assumptions*

i) *Axial symmetry* is a relevant approximation for many galaxies, and is in fact often used in the existing models of the ISRF (see e.g. Refs. 13–16). We adopt cylindrical coordinates (ρ, ϕ, z) whose the z axis is the symmetry axis.

The primary source of the ISRF is made of the stars or other bright astrophysical objects. We want to describe the ISRF as a smoothed-out field at the galactic scale, not the field in the stars or in their neighborhood. Therefore:

ii) we consider the *source-free* Maxwell equations.

We proved the following result:[18]

Theorem. Any time-harmonic axisymmetric source-free Maxwell field is the sum of two simple fields of that same kind:

- **1)** one deriving from a vector potential $\mathbf{A}$ having just $A_z \ne 0$, with A_z a time-harmonic axisymmetric solution of the scalar wave equation;
- **2)** one deduced from a field of the form (**1**) by EM duality, i.e.

$$\mathbf{E}' = c\mathbf{B}, \quad \mathbf{B}' = -\mathbf{E}/c. \tag{9}$$

5.2. *Maxwell model of the ISRF: Form of the model*

We consider an EM field having a finite set of frequencies (ω_j) $(j = 1, ..., N_\omega)$. That EM field is thus the sum of N_ω time-harmonic EM fields. Using the Theorem above, each of them is generated by potentials A_{jz}, A'_{jz}. The scalar potential A_{jz}, for the field of the form (1) above with frequency ω_j, can be a priori any time-harmonic axisymmetric solution of the scalar wave equation having frequency ω_j.[18] However, in the relevant "totally propagating" case, such a solution can be written explicitly in terms of a spectrum function $S_j = S_j(k)$ $(-K_j \le k \le K_j,\ K_j := \frac{\omega_j}{c})$: $A_{jz} = \psi_{\omega_j\, S_j}$, with[19]

$$\psi_{\omega_j\, S_j}(t,\rho,z) := e^{-\mathrm{i}\omega_j t} \int_{-K_j}^{K_j} J_0\left(\rho\sqrt{K_j^2 - k^2}\right) e^{\mathrm{i}kz} S_j(k)\, \mathrm{d}k, \qquad (10)$$

where J_0 is the Bessel function of the first kind and of order 0. The "dual" potential A'_{jz}, for the field of the form (2) above with frequency ω_j, has just the same form (10), with, in the general case, another spectrum function, say S'_j.

5.3. *Maxwell model of the ISRF: Model of a galaxy*

We model an axisymmetric galaxy as a finite set $\{\mathbf{x}_i\}$ of point-like "stars", the azimuthal distribution of which is uniform. That set of points is obtained by pseudo-random generation of their cylindrical coordinates ρ, ϕ, z with specific probability laws, ensuring that[17]

- the distribution of ρ and z is approximately that valid for the star distribution in the galaxy considered (in the numerical application, we took our Galaxy);
- the set $\{\mathbf{x}_i\}$ is approximately invariant under azimuthal rotations of any angle ϕ.

5.4. *Maxwell model of the ISRF: Determining the potentials*

To determine the potentials A_{jz} and A'_{jz} $(j = 1, ..., N_\omega)$ that generate the model ISRF (Subsect. 5.2), we are fitting to the form (10) a sum of spherical potentials emanating from the "stars" at points $\mathbf{x}_i$, thus determining the unknown spectrum functions S_j and S'_j.[17] For the purpose of this fitting, every point-like "star" is indeed assumed to contribute spherical scalar waves $\psi_{\mathbf{x}_i\, \omega_j}$ having the same frequencies ω_j as has the model ISRF, and whose emission center is the spatial position $\mathbf{x}_i$ of the star:

$$\psi_{\mathbf{x}_i\, \omega_j}(t, \mathbf{x}) := \psi_{\omega_j}(t, \mathbf{x} - \mathbf{x}_i) = \frac{e^{\mathrm{i}(K_j r_i - \omega_j t)}}{K_j r_i}. \qquad (11)$$

Here $r_i := |\mathbf{x} - \mathbf{x}_i|$, $K_j := \frac{\omega_j}{c}$, and the function

$$\psi_{\omega_j}(t, \mathbf{x}) = \frac{e^{\mathrm{i}(K_j r - \omega_j t)}}{K_j r}, \qquad r := |\mathbf{x}| \qquad (12)$$

is (up to an amplitude factor) the unique time-harmonic solution of the scalar wave equation, with frequency ω_j, that has spherical symmetry around $\mathbf{x} = \mathbf{0}$ and that is an outgoing wave. Spherical symmetry is assumed in order to ensure that all of the directions starting from the star are equivalent, of course. Of course also, the uniqueness of the solution (12) means the uniqueness of the solution translated from $\mathbf{x} = \mathbf{0}$ to $\mathbf{x} = \mathbf{x}_i$: the function $\psi_{\mathbf{x}_i\,\omega_j}$ given by Eq. (11). This implies that we cannot define different contributions of the "star" at $\mathbf{x}_i$ to the $A_{j\,z}$ potential and to the "dual" potential $A'_{j\,z}$, other than through multiplying $\psi_{\mathbf{x}_i\,\omega_j}$ by two different amplitude factors — for which there is no apparent reason. Therefore, we actually must assume that $A_{j\,z} = A'_{j\,z}$, thus $S_j = S'_j$, and our fitting problem writes

$$\sum_{i=1}^{i_{\max}} \psi_{\mathbf{x}_i\,\omega_j} \cong \psi_{\omega_j\,S_j} \quad \text{on } G \quad (j = 1, ..., N_\omega). \tag{13}$$

Here the symbol $\cong$ indicates that the equality is in the sense of the least-squares, the two sides being evaluated on some spatio-temporal grid G. The unknown spectrum function S_j is defined (approximately) by its values $S_{nj} := S_j(k_{nj})$ at a regular discretization $k_{nj} = -K_j + n\frac{2K_j}{N}$ ($n = 0, ..., N$) of the integration interval $[-K_j, +K_j]$ for k in the integral (10).[17] With this discretization, (13) becomes the explicit least-squares system

$$\sum_{i=1}^{i_{\max}} \psi_{\mathbf{x}_i\,\omega_j} \cong \sum_{n=0}^{N} f_{nj}\,S_{nj} \quad \text{on } G \quad (j = 1, ..., N_\omega), \tag{14}$$

with $f_{nj}(t, \rho, z) = \exp(-\mathrm{i}\omega_j t)\,g_{nj}(\rho, z)$ a specific time-harmonic function.[20] The complex numbers S_{nj} ($n = 0, ..., N;\ j = 1, ..., N_\omega$) are the solved-for parameters. Note that (14) defines N_ω fitting problems. Previously, a unique "grouped fitting" was done: solving the least-squares system obtained by summing on the frequency index j on both sides of (14).[17] The "separate fitting" (14) is more precise — and also less time-consuming, since actually the common harmonic time dependence can be removed from both sides of (14), thus eliminating the time variable, and hence considering only a spatial grid G' instead of a spatio-temporal grid G.[20] The computer time is indeed an important point to be considered, because a precision better than quadruple must be implemented.[17]

5.5. *Application to the spatial variation of the spectral energy density in the Galaxy*

Because we consider an EM field with a finite frequency spectrum (ω_j) ($j = 1, ..., N_\omega$), each among its six components has the following form:

$$F^{(q)}(t, \mathbf{x}) = \mathcal{R}e\left(\sum_{j=1}^{N_\omega} C_j^{(q)}(\mathbf{x}) e^{-\mathrm{i}\omega_j t}\right) \quad (q = 1, ..., 6). \tag{15}$$

It follows that the time-averaged volumic energy density of the field is given by:[21]

$$\overline{U}(\mathbf{x}) := \overline{\frac{\delta W}{\delta V}}(\mathbf{x}) = \sum_{j=1}^{N_\omega} u_j(\mathbf{x}), \qquad u_j(\mathbf{x}) := \frac{1}{4}\sum_{q=1}^{6} \alpha_q \left|C_j^{(q)}(\mathbf{x})\right|^2, \qquad (16)$$

where $\alpha_q = \epsilon_0$ for an electric field component, whereas $\alpha_q = \epsilon_0 c^2$ for a magnetic field component (here ϵ_0 is the vacuum permittivity, with $\epsilon_0 = 1/(4\pi \times 9 \times 10^9)$ in SI units). Thus, the spectral energy density (SED) has a discrete form.

Specializing to the present axisymmetric model, we thus have $C_j^{(q)} = C_j^{(q)}(\rho, z)$ and $u_j = u_j(\rho, z)$. The potentials $A_{jz} = A'_{jz} = \psi_{\omega_j S_j}$ are determined by the spectrum functions S_j in Eq. (10), which are given in the numerical model by the values $S_{nj} := S_j(k_{nj})$, that are the output of the fitting. These potentials generate the EM field, hence the $C_j^{(q)}(\rho, z)$ coefficients in Eq. (15) are expressed uniquely in terms of the S_{nj}'s.[21] However, in the least-squares problem (14), the scalar radiations emitted by every point-like "star" are taken to be exactly $\psi_{\mathbf{x}_i \omega_j}$. Clearly, we may multiply the l.h.s. of (14) by some number $\xi_j > 0$, thus obtaining now new values $S'_{nj} = \xi_j S_{nj}$ ($n = 0, ..., N$) as the solution of (14). We determine the numbers $\xi_j > 0$ so that the SED measured at our local position $\mathbf{x}_{\text{loc}}$ in the Galaxy coincides with the calculated values $u_j(\mathbf{x}_{\text{loc}})$. This allows us then to make predictions: in particular, ones of the spatial variation of the SED in the Galaxy, which we may compare with the predictions of the existing models of the ISRF. Figures 1–2 show this comparison for the four positions in the Galaxy for which the predicted SED is shown in Ref. 13. The predictions of the two models are quite reasonably close, although the SED predicted by the present model has rather marked oscillations as function of the wavelength. Note that the different wavelengths are fully uncoupled due to the "separate fitting" defined by the N_ω least-square problems (14).

A surprising prediction of this model is that for the values of the maximum of the energy density,

$$u_{j\text{max}} = \text{Max}\{u_j(\rho_m, z_p); \ m = 1, ..., N_\rho, \ p = 1, ..., N_z\}, \qquad (17)$$

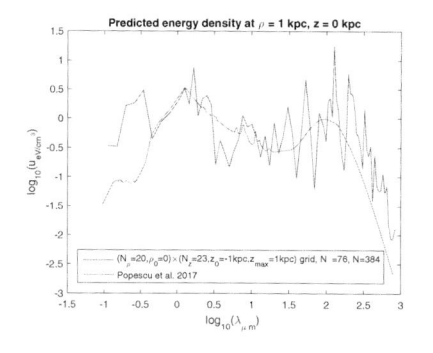

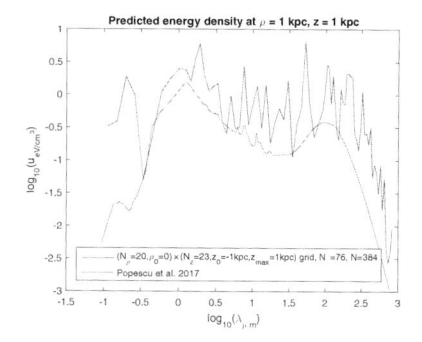

Fig. 1.   SEDs at ($\rho = 1\,\text{kpc}, z = 0$) and at ($\rho = 1\,\text{kpc}, z = 1\,\text{kpc}$).

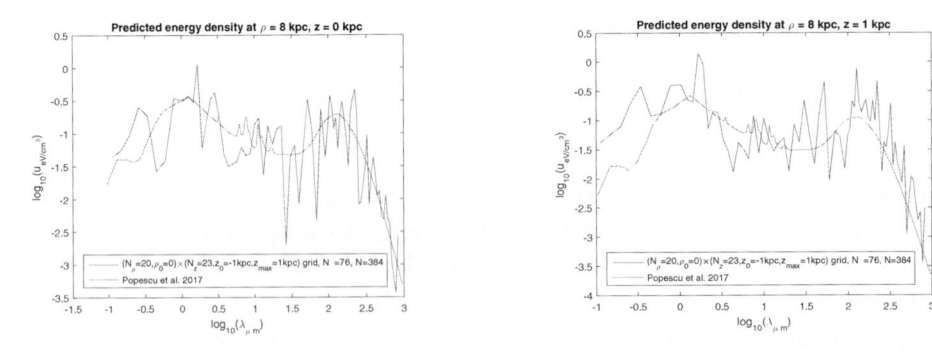

Fig. 2. SEDs at ($\rho = 8\,\text{kpc}$, $z = 0$) and at ($\rho = 8\,\text{kpc}$, $z = 1\,\text{kpc}$).

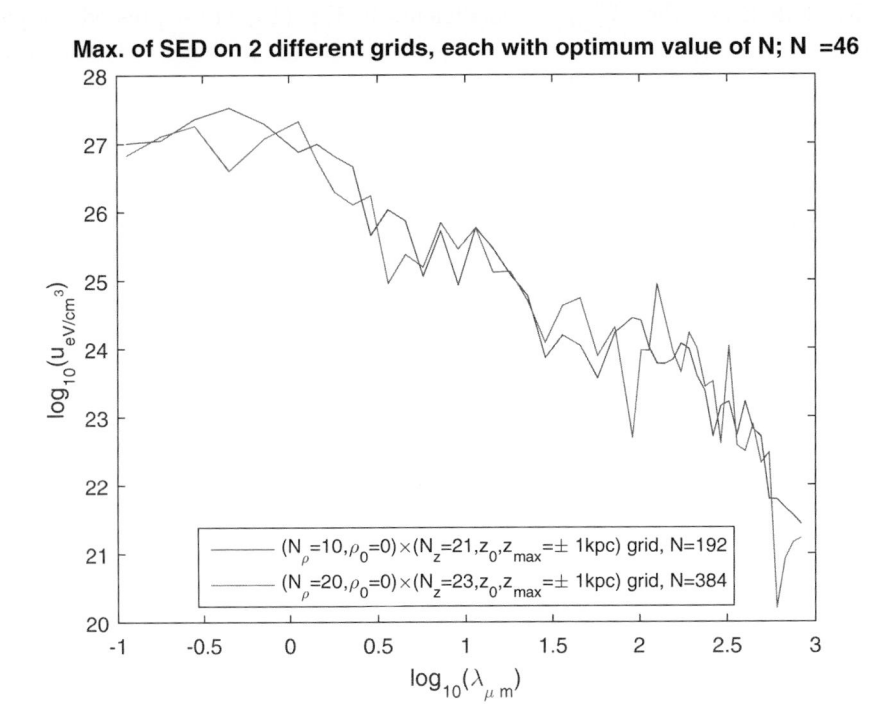

Fig. 3. Maximum of energy density; comparison between two spatial grids.

found for the different spatial grids ($N_\rho \times N_z$) investigated, all having ρ varying regularly from $\rho_0 = 0$ to $\rho_{\max} \simeq 10\,\text{kpc}$ and z varying regularly from $z_0 = 0$ or $z_0 = -z_{\max}$ to $z_{\max} \leq 1\,\text{kpc}$. Figure 3 compares the curves $u_{j\max} = f(\lambda_j)$ found with two spatial grids. It is seen that the two curves are quite close to one another, and both show extremely high levels of $u_{j\max}$, from 10^{27}eV/cm^3 to 10^{21}eV/cm^3. This is confirmed by a rather detailed investigation of the effects of the settings of the calculation (the spatial grid, and also the fineness of the frequency mesh: N_ω, and that of the discretization: N).[20] The values of the maximum of u_j are always found on the axis of the Galaxy ($\rho = 0$), moreover the level of u_j decreases very rapidly when one departs from the axis.[20] This prediction of the model may be described as a kind of self-focusing effect of the ISRF in an axisymmetric galaxy.

6. Conclusion

In the "scalar ether theory" of gravity (SET), a consistent electrodynamics in a gravitational field needs the introduction of an additional energy tensor: $\boldsymbol{T}_{\text{inter}}$, with $T^\mu_{\text{inter } \nu} := p\,\delta^\mu_\nu$. Thus, this energy tensor was not designed to build missing mass. However, it turns out that the corresponding "medium" could contribute to dark matter, for it is not localized inside matter, it is gravitationally active, and it is "exotic". Moreover, the scalar field p, that determines $\boldsymbol{T}_{\text{inter}}$, can be in principle calculated from the data of the EM field and the gravitational field, through explicit equations. This however demands to be able to model the EM field in a galaxy, which is essentially in the form of the interstellar radiation field (ISRF).

Therefore, we built a Maxwell model of the ISRF. This was motivated by the foregoing, but it is also interesting independently of that, as the ISRF is a very important physical characteristic of a galaxy and interacts strongly with the cosmic rays. In any case, this model in itself is totally independent of the theory of gravitation and the assumption about the interaction tensor. It is based on an explicit representation of any time-harmonic axisymmetric source-free Maxwell field through a pair of scalar potentials, and on determining these potentials by fitting contributions emanating from a set of point-like "stars" schematizing a galaxy. The predictions of the model for the variation of the spectral energy distribution in the Galaxy are currently being checked. They are relatively close to the predictions of a recent radiation transfer model — except for the fact that the Maxwell model of the ISRF predicts extremely high values of the energy density on the axis of the Galaxy, that however decrease very rapidly when departing from that axis. We hope to be able in a future work to apply the model to calculate the interaction energy and to check if its distribution resembles a dark halo.

References

1. M. Arminjon, Space isotropy and weak equivalence principle in a scalar theory of gravity, *Braz. J. Phys.* **36**, 177–189 (2006).
2. M. Arminjon and R. W. Winkler, Motion of a test particle according to the scalar ether theory of gravitation and application to its celestial mechanics, *Z. Naturforsch. A* **74**, 305–316 (2019).
3. H. Stephani, *Relativity, An Introduction to Special and General Relativity*, Third edition (Cambridge University Press, Cambridge, 2004), pp. 156–158.
4. M. Arminjon, Continuum dynamics and the electromagnetic field in the scalar ether theory of gravitation, *Open Phys.* **14**, 395–409 (2016).
5. M. Arminjon, Charge conservation in a gravitational field in the scalar ether theory, *Open Phys.* **15**, 877–890 (2017).

6. M. Arminjon, Lorentz-invariant second-order tensors and an irreducible set of matrices, *J. Geom. Symmetry Phys.* **50**, 1–10 (2018).
7. M. Arminjon, On the equations of electrodynamics in a flat or curved spacetime and a possible interaction energy, *Open Phys.* **16**, 488–498 (2018).
8. B. T. Draine, Photoelectric heating of interstellar gas, *Astrophys. J. Suppl. Ser.* **36**, 595–619 (1978).
9. J. S. Mathis, P. G. Mezger and N. Panagia, Interstellar radiation field and dust temperatures in the diffuse interstellar matter and in giant molecular clouds, *Astron. Astrophys.* **128**, 212–229 (1983).
10. X. Chi and A. W. Wolfendale, The interstellar radiation field: a datum for cosmic ray physics, *J. Phys. C: Nucl. Part. Phys.* **17**, 987–998 (1991).
11. K. D. Gordon, K. A. Misselt, A. N. Witt and G. C. Clayton, The DIRTY model. I. Monte Carlo radiative transfer through dust, *Astrophys. J.* **551**, 269–276 (2001).
12. T. P. Robitaille, HYPERION: an open-source parallelized three-dimensional dust continuum radiative transfer code, *Astron. Astrophys.* **536**, A79, 17 pages (2011).
13. C. C. Popescu, R. Yang, R. J. Tuffs, G. Natale, M. Rushton and F. Aharonian, A radiation transfer model for the Milky Way: I. Radiation fields and application to High Energy Astrophysics, *Mon. Not. Roy. Astr. Soc.* **470**, no. 3, 2539–2558 (2017).
14. N. D. Kylafis and J. N. Bahcall, Dust distribution in spiral galaxies, *Astrophys. J.* **317**, 637–645 (1987).
15. T. A. Porter and A. W. Strong, A new estimate of the galactic interstellar radiation field between $0.1\mu m$ and $1000\mu m$, in *Proc. 29th International Cosmic Ray Conference Pune* (Tata Institute of Fundamental Research, Mumbai, 2005), vol. 4, pp. 77–80.
16. C. C. Popescu, R. J. Tuffs, M. A. Dopita, J. Fischera, N. D. Kylafis and B. F. Madore, Modelling the spectral energy distribution of galaxies. V. The dust and PAH emission SEDs of disk galaxies, *Astron. Astrophys.* **527**, A109, 40 pages (2011).
17. M. Arminjon, An analytical model for the Maxwell radiation field in an axially symmetric galaxy, *Open Phys.* **19**, 77–90 (2021).
18. M. Arminjon, An explicit representation for the axisymmetric solutions of the free Maxwell equations, *Open Phys.* **18**, 255–263 (2020).
19. M. Zamboni-Rached, E. Recami and H. E. Hernández-Figueroa, Structure of non-diffracting waves and some interesting applications, in *Localized Waves*, eds. H. E. Hernández-Figueroa, M. Zamboni-Rached, E. Recami (John Wiley & Sons, Hoboken, 2008), pp. 43–77.
20. M. Arminjon, *Interstellar radiation as a Maxwell field: improved numerical scheme and application to the spectral energy density*, Preprint HAL-03341905 (2021).
21. M. Arminjon, Spectral energy density in an axisymmetric galaxy as predicted by an analytical model for the Maxwell field, *Adv. Astron.* **2021**, 5524600, 13 pages (2021).

The maximum mass of dilute axion stars

Pierre-Henri Chavanis

Laboratoire de Physique Théorique, Université de Toulouse, CNRS, UPS, France
E-mail: chavanis@irsamc.ups-tlse.fr

We consider the possibility that dark matter is made of bosons in the form of Bose-Einstein condensates. We establish the mass-radius relation $M(R)$ of nonrelativistic self-gravitating Bose-Einstein condensates with repulsive or attractive self-interaction. If the self-interaction is repulsive there exists an equilibrium state for any value of the mass but if the self-interaction is attractive, as in the case of axions, equilibrium states exist only below a maximum mass $M_{\max}^{\rm NR} = 5.073\, M_P/\sqrt{|\lambda|}$ [P.H. Chavanis, Phys. Rev. D **84**, 043531 (2011)]. This is the maximum mass of dilute axion stars. Above that mass, the star collapses leading to a bosenova, a black hole, a dense axion star or axion drops. We consider how the maximum mass changes with the dimension of space, the presence of a central black hole, a cosmological constant, and relativistic effects. We apply these results to dark matter halos. We establish the general expression of the core mass – halo mass relation $M_c(M_h)$. For a repulsive self-interaction, we show that the core mass M_c is always much below the maximum mass $M_{\max}^{\rm GR}$ set by general relativity so the core cannot collapse towards a black hole. For an attractive self-interaction, we show that the core mass M_c can reach in principle the maximum mass $M_{\max}^{\rm NR}$ in sufficiently large dark matter halos, leading to core collapse, and we discuss if this situation can happen in practice.

Keywords: Self-gravitating Bose-Einstein condensates; axion stars; maximum mass

1. Introduction

The concept of boson stars was introduced by Kaup[1] and Ruffini and Bonazzola[2] in the 1960s. They considered the $T = 0$ limit in which bosons form Bose-Einstein condensates (BECs). In that case, all the bosons are in the same quantum state described by a unique complex wave function $\varphi(x^\mu)$ satisfying the Klein-Gordon-Einstein (KGE) equations. Boson stars can be regarded as macroscopic quantum states that are only prevented from collapsing gravitationally by the Heisenberg uncertainty principle. Kaup[1] and Ruffini and Bonazzola[2] showed that equilibrium states can exist only below a maximum mass $M_{\max}^{\rm GR} = 0.633 M_P^2/m$, where $M_P = (\hbar c/G)^{1/2}$ is the Planck mass, set by general relativity. Above that mass, boson stars are expected to collapse and form a black hole. These results are remarkably similar to those obtained for neutron stars which also display a maximum mass $M_{\max}^{\rm GR} = 0.384\, M_P^3/m^2$ as found by Oppenheimer and Volkoff.[3] However, there also exist crucial differences between boson and fermion stars. In particular, boson stars are stopped from collapsing by the Heisenberg uncertainty principle while gravitational collapse in fermion stars is avoided by the Pauli exclusion principle. This difference is reflected in the scaling with m of the maximum mass of stable configurations. The maximum mass of boson stars scales as $M_{\max}^{\rm GR} \sim M_P^2/m$ instead of $M_{\text{max}}^{\text{GR}} \sim M_P^3/m^2$ for fermions. They differ by a factor $m/M_P \ll 1$. This leads to the concept of "mini-boson stars" or "mini-soliton stars" with extremely high densities.

Colpi et al.[4] considered the case of bosons stars with a repulsive $\frac{\lambda}{4\hbar c}|\varphi|^4$ ($\lambda > 0$) self-interaction and found that the resulting configurations differ markedly from the noninteracting case. In the Thomas-Fermi (TF) limit, the maximum mass set by general relativity is $M_{\text{max}}^{\text{GR}} = 0.06\sqrt{\lambda}M_P^3/m^2$ (see Refs.[4,5]). For $\lambda \sim 1$ it exhibits the same scaling as the maximum mass of fermion stars. This leads to much bigger structures than in the noninteracting case, making them much more astrophysically interesting. They are called "massive boson stars". In a sense, the repulsive self-interaction for bosons plays a role similar to the quantum pressure arising from the Pauli exclusion principle for fermions.

The case of bosons with an attractive $\frac{\lambda}{4\hbar c}|\varphi|^4$ ($\lambda < 0$) self-interaction, like the QCD axion with a mass $m \sim 10^{-4}\,\text{eV}/c^2$ and a negative self-interaction constant $\lambda \sim -7.39 \times 10^{-49}$, was considered by Kolb and Tkachev[6] in a cosmological context. In the early Universe, self-gravity can be neglected. Because of the attractive self-interaction, axions can form miniclusters of mass $M_{\text{axiton}} \sim 10^{-12}\,M_\odot$ and size $R_{\text{axiton}} \sim 10^9$ m called axitons. Tkachev[7] took self-gravity into account and considered the possibility to form axion stars by Jeans instability. However, he assumed a repulsive self-interaction ($\lambda > 0$). When the self-interaction between bosons is attractive, there exists a maximum mass $M_{\text{max}}^{\text{NR}} = 5.073\,M_P/\sqrt{|\lambda|}$ which was first identified by Chavanis.[8] This is the maximum mass of dilute axion stars. This is a purely nonrelativistic result, contrary to the maximum mass of boson and fermion stars discussed above which is due to general relativity. For QCD axion stars, one finds $M_{\text{max}}^{\text{NR}} = 6.46 \times 10^{-14}\,M_\odot$ and a corresponding radius $(R_{99}^*) = 227$ km which are of the order of the mass and size of asteroids. This leads to the notion of "axteroids". For $M > M_{\text{max}}^{\text{NR}}$ there is no equilibrium state and the axion star collapses.[9] This leads to a bosenova[10] or a black hole[11,12] if we take special or general relativity into account, or to the formation of a dense axion star[13] if we take into account higher order terms in the expansion of the self-interaction potential, e.g., a repulsive $|\phi|^6$ self-interaction[14,15] that can stabilize the star against gravitational collapse.[a] The axion star can also fragment into several stable pieces (axion "drops") of mass $M' < M_{\text{max}}$, thereby preventing its complete collapse.[19,20]

If bosons are ultralight,[21] with a mass $m \sim 10^{-22}\,\text{eV}/c^2$, they can form compact objects of galactic size.[b] Therefore, ultralight axions have been invoked in models

---

[a]Visinelli et al.[16] and Eby et al.[17] argue that relativistic effects are crucial on the branch of dense axion stars while self-gravity is negligible. As a result, dense axion stars correspond to "pseudobreathers" or "oscillons" which are described by the sine-Gordon equation. For a real scalar field (SF), these objects are known to be unstable and to decay via emission of relativistic axions on a timescale much shorter than any cosmological timescale. This conclusion is, however, contested by Braaten and Zhang.[18]

[b]More massive bosons with a mass $10^{-22}\,\text{eV}/c^2 \leq m \leq 10^{-3}\,\text{eV}/c^2$ can also form compact objects of galactic size provided that they are self-interacting (with $\lambda \lesssim 10^{-15}$).[22]

of dark matter (DM) halos. Boson stars or BECDM halos can be formed from a dissipationless relaxation process called gravitational cooling[23] or violent relaxation.[24] By this process, large DM halos acquire a "core-halo" structure with a quantum core (soliton) in its ground state surrounded an extended halo which results from the quantum interferences of the excited states. This "core-halo" structure has been evidenced in numerical simulations of the Schrödinger-Poisson equations.[25–33] The quantum core may solve the core-cusp problem of the cold dark matter (CDM) model and the halo (similar to an isothermal of NFW profile) accounts for the flat rotation curves of the galaxies. A general expression of the core mass-halo mass relation $M_c(M_h)$ in BECDM halos with no, repulsive or attractive self-interaction has been obtained in Refs.[22,34–36]. For an attractive self-interaction, and in sufficiently large DM halos, the core mass can overcome the maximum mass $M_{\max}^{\rm NR}$ and collapse. The conditions for this collapse require, however, slightly stronger self-interactions that those commonly allowed by particle physics and cosmology.

In these Proceedings, we review some aspects of our work on self-gravitating BECs. In Sec. 2, we discuss self-gravitating BECs in the nonrelativistic regime described by the Gross-Pitaevskii-Poisson (GPP) equations. In Sec. 3, we discuss the exact mass-radius relation of self-gravitating BECs. In Sec. 4, we obtain an approximation analytical expression of the mass-radius relation of self-gravitating BECs based on a Gaussian ansatz. In Sec. 5, we discuss the maximum mass of dilute axion stars (self-gravitating BECs with attractive self-interaction) and some of its generalizations. In Sec. 6, we apply our results to DM halos and discuss the core mass – halo mass relation and the possibilty or not to have core collapse. In Appendices A and B, we consider general relativistic BECs described by the KGE equations for a complex and a real SF.

2. Self-gravitating BECs

2.1. Gross-Pitaevskii-Poisson equations

We assume that DM is made of bosons (like the axion) in the form of BECs at $T=0$. We use a nonrelativistic approach based on Newtonian gravity. The evolution of the wave function $\psi(\mathbf{r},t)$ of a self-gravitating BEC is governed by the GPP equations[8,37]

$$i\hbar\frac{\partial \psi}{\partial t} = -\frac{\hbar^2}{2m}\Delta\psi + m\Phi\psi + m\frac{dV}{d|\psi|^2}\psi, \qquad (1)$$

$$\Delta\Phi = 4\pi G|\psi|^2, \qquad (2)$$

where m is the mass of the bosons, $\Phi(\mathbf{r},t)$ is the gravitational potential and $\rho(\mathbf{r},t) = |\psi|^2$ is the mass density of the BEC. The first term in Eq. (1) is the kinetic term which accounts for the Heisenberg uncertainty principle. The second term accounts for the self-gravity of the BEC. The third term takes into account the self-interaction of the bosons. We shall consider a standard $|\psi|^4$ potential of the form

$$V(|\psi|^2) = \frac{2\pi a_s \hbar^2}{m^3}|\psi|^4, \qquad (3)$$

where a_s is the scattering length of the bosons. The interaction between the bosons is repulsive when $a_s > 0$ and attractive when $a_s < 0$.

The GPP equations conserve the mass $M = \int |\psi|^2 \, d\mathbf{r}$ and the energy

$$E_{\rm tot} = \frac{\hbar^2}{2m^2} \int |\nabla \psi|^2 \, d\mathbf{r} + \frac{1}{2} \int |\psi|^2 \Phi \, d\mathbf{r} + \int V(|\psi|^2) \, d\mathbf{r}, \qquad (4)$$

which is the sum of the kinetic energy Θ, the gravitational energy W, and the internal energy U (i.e. $E_{\rm tot} = \Theta + W + U$).

2.2. Madelung transformation

Writing the wave function as

$$\psi(\mathbf{r}, t) = \sqrt{\rho(\mathbf{r}, t)} e^{iS(\mathbf{r},t)/\hbar}, \qquad (5)$$

where $\rho(\mathbf{r}, t)$ is the mass density and $S(\mathbf{r}, t)$ is the action, and making the Madelung transformation

$$\rho(\mathbf{r}, t) = |\psi|^2 \quad \text{and} \quad \mathbf{u} = \frac{\nabla S}{m}, \qquad (6)$$

where $\mathbf{u}(\mathbf{r}, t)$ is the velocity field, the GPP equations (1) and (2) can be written under the form of hydrodynamic equations

$$\frac{\partial \rho}{\partial t} + \nabla \cdot (\rho \mathbf{u}) = 0, \qquad (7)$$

$$\frac{\partial S}{\partial t} + \frac{(\nabla S)^2}{2m} + m\Phi + mV'(\rho) + Q = 0, \qquad (8)$$

$$\frac{\partial \mathbf{u}}{\partial t} + (\mathbf{u} \cdot \nabla)\mathbf{u} = -\frac{1}{m}\nabla Q - \frac{1}{\rho}\nabla P - \nabla \Phi, \qquad (9)$$

$$\Delta \Phi = 4\pi G \rho, \qquad (10)$$

where

$$Q = -\frac{\hbar^2}{2m}\frac{\Delta\sqrt{\rho}}{\sqrt{\rho}} = -\frac{\hbar^2}{4m}\left[\frac{\Delta\rho}{\rho} - \frac{1}{2}\frac{(\nabla\rho)^2}{\rho^2}\right] \qquad (11)$$

is the quantum potential taking into account the Heisenberg uncertainty principle, and $P(\rho)$ is the pressure arising from the self-interaction of the bosons given by

$$P(\rho) = \rho V'(\rho) - V(\rho). \qquad (12)$$

For the standard self-interaction potential (3) we get

$$P = \frac{2\pi a_s \hbar^2}{m^3} \rho^2. \qquad (13)$$

This is the equation of state of a polytrope of index $n = 1$. The squared speed of sound is $c_s^2 = P'(\rho) = \rho V''(\rho) = 4\pi a_s \hbar^2 \rho/m^3$. The hydrodynamic equations (7)-(10) are called the quantum Euler-Poisson equations. Equation (7), corresponding to the imaginary part of the GP equation, is the continuity equation. Equation (8), corresponding to the real part of the GP equation, is the quantum Hamilton-Jacobi (or Bernoulli) equation. Equation (9), obtained by taking the gradient of Eq. (8), is the momentum equation. Equation (10) is the Poisson equation. In the TF limit where the quantum potential can be neglected (formally $\hbar \to 0$ with $4\pi a_s \hbar^2/m^3$ finite), they become equivalent to the classical Euler-Poisson equations for a barotropic gas.

The quantum Euler equations conserve the mass $M = \int \rho \, d\mathbf{r}$ and the energy

$$E_{\text{tot}} = \int \rho \frac{\mathbf{u}^2}{2} \, d\mathbf{r} + \frac{1}{m} \int \rho Q \, d\mathbf{r} + \frac{1}{2} \int \rho \Phi \, d\mathbf{r} + \int V(\rho) \, d\mathbf{r}, \qquad (14)$$

which is the sum of the classical kinetic energy Θ_c, the quantum kinetic energy Θ_Q, the gravitational energy W, and the internal energy U.

2.3. *Equilibrium states*

The condition of quantum hydrostatic equilibrium, corresponding to a steady state of the quantum Euler equation (9), writes

$$\frac{\rho}{m} \nabla Q + \nabla P + \rho \nabla \Phi = \mathbf{0}. \qquad (15)$$

Combining Eq. (15) with the Poisson equation (10), and considering a standard BEC described by the potential (3), we obtain the fundamental differential equation of quantum hydrostatic equilibrium[8,37]

$$\frac{\hbar^2}{2m^2} \Delta \left(\frac{\Delta \sqrt{\rho}}{\sqrt{\rho}} \right) - \frac{4\pi a_s \hbar^2}{m^3} \Delta \rho = 4\pi G \rho. \qquad (16)$$

This equation describes the balance between the quantum potential taking into account the Heisenberg uncertainty principle, the pressure due to the self-interaction of the bosons, and the self-gravity. It corresponds to a stationary state of the GPP equations.[8,37] This equation can also be obtained from an energy principle. Indeed, one can show (see Appendix B of Ref.[22]) that an equilibrium state of the GPP equations is an extremum of energy E_{tot} at fixed mass M and that an equilibrium state is dynamically stable if, and only if, it is a minimum of energy at fixed mass.

3. Exact mass-radius relation of self-gravitating BECs

The fundamental equation of hydrostatic equilibrium of self-gravitating BECs, Eq. (16), has been solved numerically (exactly) in Ref.[38] for an arbitrary self-interaction (repulsive or attractive). The nodeless solution describes a compact gravitational quantum object (soliton/BEC) in its ground state. From this solution we have determined the exact mass-radius relation of self-gravitating BECs.

3.1. Noninteracting bosons

For noninteracting bosons ($a_s = 0$), the mass-radius relation is given by[38,39]

$$M = 9.95 \frac{\hbar^2}{Gm^2 R_{99}}, \tag{17}$$

where R_{99} represents the radius containing 99% of the mass (the density profile has not a compact support). The mass decreases as the radius increases. The equilibrium states are all stable.

3.2. Bosons with a repulsive self-interaction

For bosons with a repulsive self-interaction ($a_s > 0$), the exact mass-radius relation is represented in Fig. 1. The mass decreases as the radius increases. In the TF limit $M \gg \hbar/\sqrt{Gma_s}$ where the quantum potential can be neglected, the density profile can be obtained analytically since the system is equivalent to a polytrope of index $n = 1$. We get

$$\rho(r) = \frac{\rho_0 R_{\rm TF}}{\pi r} \sin\left(\frac{\pi r}{R_{\rm TF}}\right). \tag{18}$$

The equilibrium states have a unique radius given by[7,8,40–44]

$$R_{\rm TF} = \pi \left(\frac{a_s \hbar^2}{Gm^3}\right)^{1/2}, \tag{19}$$

which is independent of their mass M. This is the minimum radius of self-gravitating BECs with a repulsive self-interaction. In the noninteracting limit $M \ll \hbar/\sqrt{Gma_s}$ and $R \gg R_{\rm TF}$, we recover Eq. (17).

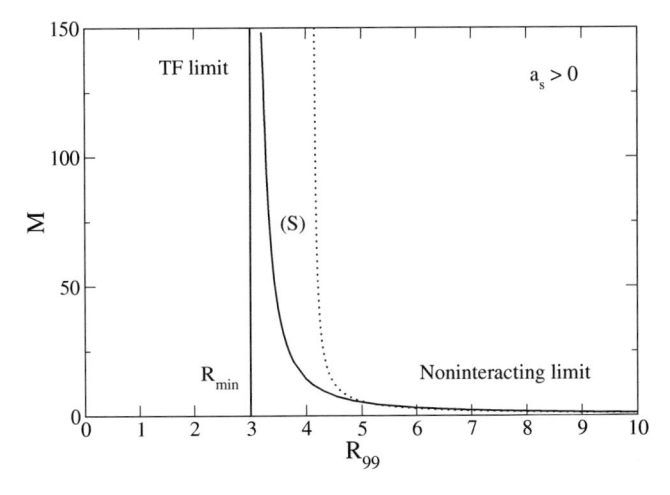

Fig. 1. Mass-radius relation of self-gravitating BECs with $a_s > 0$ (full line: exact;[38] dotted line: Gaussian ansatz[8]). The mass is normalized by $M_a = \hbar/\sqrt{Gma_s}$ and the radius by $R_a = (a_s\hbar^2/Gm^3)^{1/2}$.

3.3. Bosons with an attractive self-interaction

For bosons with an attractive self-interaction ($a_s < 0$), the exact mass-radius relation is represented in Fig. 2. It displays a maximum mass[8,38]

$$M_{\max}^{\rm NR} = 1.012 \frac{\hbar}{\sqrt{Gm|a_s|}} \quad \text{at} \quad R_{99}^* = 5.5 \left(\frac{|a_s|\hbar^2}{Gm^3}\right)^{1/2}. \tag{20}$$

There is no equilibrium state with $M > M_{\max}^{\rm NR}$. In that case, the BEC is expected to collapse.[9] The outcome of the collapse (dense axion star, black hole, bosenova, axion drops...) is discussed in Refs.[9–20]. For $M < M_{\max}$ there are two possible equilibrium states with the same mass. The equilibrium states with $R > R_{99}^*$ are stable and the equilibrium states with $R < R_{99}^*$ are unstable. This can be shown by using the Poincaré criterion, the Wheeler theorem, or by computing the squared pulsation.[8,9,15,38] In the nongravitational limit $M \ll M_{\max}^{\rm NR}$ and $R \ll R_{99}^*$, the mass-radius relation is given by[38]

$$M = 0.275 \frac{mR_{99}}{|a_s|}. \tag{21}$$

These equilibrium states are unstable. In the noninteracting limit $M \ll M_{\max}^{\rm NR}$ and $R \gg R_{99}^*$, we recover Eq. (17). These equilibrium states are stable.

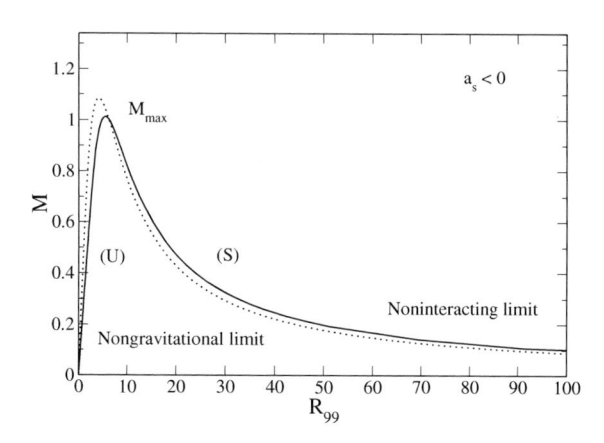

Fig. 2. Mass-radius relation of self-gravitating BECs with $a_s < 0$ (full line: exact;[38] dotted line: Gaussian ansatz[8]). The mass is normalized by $M_a = \hbar/\sqrt{Gm|a_s|}$ and the radius by $R_a = (|a_s|\hbar^2/Gm^3)^{1/2}$.

4. Approximate mass-radius relation of self-gravitating BECs from a Gaussian ansatz

Stable BEC stars correspond to minima of energy $E_{\rm tot}$ at fixed mass M. We can obtain an approximate analytical expression of the mass-radius relation of self-gravitating BECs by making a Gaussian ansatz for the wave function leading to the density profile[c]

$$\rho(\mathbf{r}) = \frac{M}{R^3} \frac{1}{\pi^{3/2}} e^{-r^2/R^2}. \tag{22}$$

The radius containing 99% of the mass is $R_{99} = 2.38167\, R$. With this ansatz the total energy can be written as[8,37]

$$E_{\text{tot}}(R) = \sigma \frac{\hbar^2 M}{m^2 R^2} - \nu \frac{GM^2}{R} + \zeta \frac{2\pi a_s \hbar^2 M^2}{m^3 R^3} \tag{23}$$

with $\sigma = 3/4$, $\nu = 1/\sqrt{2\pi}$ and $\zeta = 1/(2\pi)^{3/2}$. At equilibrium, the condition $E'_{\min}(R) = 0$ (extremum of energy) gives the mass-radius relation[8]

$$M = \frac{\frac{2\sigma}{\nu} \frac{\hbar^2}{Gm^2 R}}{1 - \frac{6\pi\zeta}{\nu} \frac{a_s \hbar^2}{Gm^3 R^2}}. \tag{24}$$

A more general expression of the mass-radius relation is given in Eq. (292) of Ref.[37]. The BEC is stable provided that $E''_{\text{tot}}(R) > 0$ which corresponds to the requirement that the equilibrium state is a minimum of energy at fixed mass or, equivalently, that the squared pulsation is positive ($\omega^2 > 0$).

For noninteracting bosons ($a_s = 0$), the mass-radius relation from Eq. (24) reduces to

$$M = \frac{2\sigma}{\nu} \frac{\hbar^2}{Gm^2 R}. \tag{25}$$

For bosons with a repulsive self-interaction ($a_s > 0$), in the TF limit ($\hbar \to 0$ with fixed $g = 4\pi a_s \hbar^2/m^3$), the mass-radius relation from Eq. (24) reduces to

$$R = \left(\frac{6\pi\zeta}{\nu}\right)^{1/2} \left(\frac{a_s \hbar^2}{Gm^3}\right)^{1/2}. \tag{26}$$

For bosons with an attractive self-interaction ($a_s < 0$), the approximate values of the maximum mass and of the corresponding radius obtained from Eq. (24) are

$$M_{\max} = \left(\frac{\sigma^2}{6\pi\zeta\nu}\right)^{1/2} \frac{\hbar}{\sqrt{Gm|a_s|}}, \qquad R_* = \left(\frac{6\pi\zeta}{\nu}\right)^{1/2} \left(\frac{|a_s|\hbar^2}{Gm^3}\right)^{1/2}. \tag{27}$$

In the nongravitational limit, the mass-radius relation from Eq. (24) reduces to

$$M = \frac{\sigma}{3\pi\zeta} \frac{mR}{|a_s|}. \tag{28}$$

5. Generalizations of the maximum mass of axion stars

In this section, we discuss some generalizations of the maximum mass of axion stars.

---

[c]Here, we restrict ourselves to the equilibrium state, so we just need to make an ansatz for the density profile. See Sec. 8 of Ref.[37] for a more general study.

5.1. Dimension of space

The previous results are valid for spherically symmetric systems in $d = 3$ dimensions. It is possible to generalize them in a space of arbitrary dimension d.[46] For an attractive self-interaction, there is a maximum mass when $2 \leq d \leq 4$.[d] Using a Gaussian ansatz we find that

$$M_{\max} = (4-d)^{\frac{4-d}{2}} (d-2)^{\frac{d-2}{2}} \frac{\sigma}{\nu^{\frac{d-2}{2}} (d\zeta)^{\frac{4-d}{2}}} \frac{\hbar^{d-2}}{(2\pi|a_s|)^{\frac{4-d}{2}} G^{\frac{d-2}{2}} m^{\frac{3d-8}{2}}}, \quad (29)$$

$$R_* = \left(\frac{d-2}{4-d}\right)^{1/2} \left(\frac{d\zeta}{\nu}\right)^{1/2} \left(\frac{2\pi|a_s|\hbar^2}{Gm^3}\right)^{1/2} \quad (30)$$

with $\sigma = d/4$, $\nu = 1/[\Gamma(d/2)2^{d/2}]$ and $\zeta = 1/(2\pi)^{d/2}$. These equations define $M_{\max}(d)$ and $R_*(d)$. In $d = 2$ dimensions, we obtain

$$M_{\max} = \frac{\sigma}{2\pi\zeta} \frac{m}{|a_s|}, \qquad R_* = 0, \quad (31)$$

which corresponds to the nongravitational limit ($G = 0$). The prefactor is equal to $1/2$. This expression can be compared with the exact solution $M_{\max}^{\text{exact}} = 0.465638...\frac{m}{|a_s|}$ associated with the Townes[47] soliton obtained by solving the ordinary GP equation in $d = 2$. In $d = 4$ dimensions, we obtain

$$M_{\max} = \frac{2\sigma}{\nu} \frac{\hbar^2}{Gm^2}, \qquad R_* \to +\infty, \quad (32)$$

which corresponds to the noninteracting limit ($a_s = 0$).

5.2. Central black hole

The effect of a central black hole, creating an external potential $\Phi_{\text{BH}} = -GM_{\text{BH}}/r$, on the value of the maximum mass has been investigated in Ref.[48]. It is found that

$$\frac{M_{\max}}{M_{\max}^{(0)}} = \frac{R_*}{R_*^{(0)}} = -\frac{\mu}{2} + \frac{1}{2}\sqrt{\mu^2 + 4}, \quad (33)$$

where

$$\mu = \frac{\lambda}{\nu} \frac{M_{\text{BH}}}{M_{\max}^{(0)}} \quad (34)$$

is the normalized mass of the black hole. These equations define $M_{\max}(M_{\text{BH}})$ and $R_*(M_{\text{BH}})$. In these expressions, $M_{\max}^{(0)}$ and $R_*^{(0)}$ denote the maximum mass and the corresponding radius in the absence of a central black hole [see Eq. (27)] and $\lambda = 2/\sqrt{\pi}$.

---

[d]When $d < 2$ there is a stable equilibrium state for any mass M. When $d > 4$ there is an equilibrium state for any mass M but it is unstable. When $2 \leq d \leq 4$ there is a maximum mass. The equilibrium states with $R < R_*$ are unstable and the equilibrium states with $R > R_*$ are stable. For a repulsive self-interaction there is a minimum mass when $d \geq 4$ given by an expression similar to Eq. (29). The equilibrium states are stable if $R < R_*$ and unstable if $R > R_*$. Noninteracting bosons stars are unstable when $d \geq 4$. These results show that the dimension $d = 3$ of our universe is very special (see also Ref.[45] for fermion stars).

5.3. Harmonic potential

The effect of an external harmonic potential $\Phi_H = \frac{1}{2}\omega_0^2 r^2$ on the value of the maximum mass has been investigated in Ref.[46]. When $\omega_0^2 > 0$ the potential is confining and can take into account tidal effects from neighboring systems. When $\omega_0^2 < 0$ the potential mimics a solid rotation $\Omega = \sqrt{-\omega_0^2}$ or the effect of the cosmological constant $\Lambda = -3\omega_0^2$ (dark energy). It is found that

$$M_{\max} = \frac{8R_*}{3R_*^2 + 5}, \qquad \omega_0^2 = \frac{2(1 - R_*^2)}{R_*^4(3R_*^2 + 5)}, \tag{35}$$

where $M_{\max}$ is normalized by $M_{\max}^{(0)}$, R_* is normalized by $R_*^{(0)}$, and ω_0 is normalized by the inverse of the dynamical time $t_D = (6\pi\zeta/\nu)(\alpha/\sigma)^{1/2}|a_s|\hbar/(Gm^2)$. These equations define $M_{\max}(\omega_0)$ and $R_*(\omega_0)$ in parametric form. In the nongravitational case ($G = 0$) and $\omega_0^2 > 0$ we find that

$$M_{\max}^{\rm NG} = \frac{4\sigma}{15\pi\zeta}\left(\frac{2\sigma}{5\alpha}\right)^{1/4}\left(\frac{m\hbar}{\omega_0 a_s^2}\right)^{1/2}, \qquad R_*^{\rm NG} = \left(\frac{2\sigma}{5\alpha}\right)^{1/4}\left(\frac{\hbar}{m\omega_0}\right)^{1/2} \tag{36}$$

with $\alpha = 3/2$. The prefactor of the maximum mass is equal to 0.6705.... This result can be compared with the exact solution $M_{\max}^{\rm NG,exact} = 0.573...(m\hbar/\omega_0 a_s^2)^{1/2}$ obtained by numerically solving the ordinary GP equation with a confining harmonic potential.[49]

5.4. Relativistic corrections

For boson stars with an attractive self-interaction ($a_s < 0$), the relativistic corrections to the maximum mass and the corresponding radius are[46]

$$M_{\max} = 1.012 \frac{\hbar}{\sqrt{Gm|a_s|}\left(1 + 2.56\frac{Gm}{|a_s|c^2}\right)}, \tag{37}$$

$$R_* = 5.5\left[\frac{|a_s|\hbar^2\left(1 + 2.56\frac{Gm}{|a_s|c^2}\right)}{Gm^3}\right]^{1/2}. \tag{38}$$

These formulae interpolate between the exact expressions from Eq. (20) when $|a_s| \to +\infty$ and the exact expression of the maximum mass $M_{\max}^{\rm GR} = 0.633\,\hbar c/Gm$ set by general relativity when $a_s = 0$. We see that relativistic corrections tend to reduce the maximum mass and increase the minimum radius of axion stars with respect to the nonrelativistic limit. Relativistic corrections become important when $|a_s| \sim r_S$, where $r_S = Gm/c^2$ is the effective Schwarzschild radius of the bosons. Relativistic corrections are negligible when $|a_s| \gg r_S$. The transition scale $r_S \sim Gm/c^2$ can be obtained by equating $M_{\max}^{\rm NR} \sim \hbar/\sqrt{Gm|a_s|}$ and $M_{\max}^{\rm GR} \sim \hbar c/Gm$.

6. Application to DM halos

We now apply the results of the previous sections to DM halos. DM halos typically have a "core-halo" structure made of a quantum core (soliton) in its ground state surrounded by an approximately isothermal atmosphere arising from quantum interferences of excited states.[34,37] This "core-halo" structure results from a process of gravitational cooling[23] and violent relaxation[24] as evidenced in numerical simulations of the Schrödinger-Poisson equations.[25-33] The results of Secs. 2-5 describe the ground state of a self-gravitating BEC,[8] so they apply to the quantum core of DM halos. The "minimum halo" of mass $(M_h)_{\min}$ (the smallest halo observed in the universe), which is a purely condensed object without atmosphere, corresponds to the condition $M_c = M_h$. For bigger halos of mass $M_h \geq (M_h)_{\min}$, the mass M_c of the quantum core increases with the halo mass M_h. For noninteracting bosons and for bosons with a repulsive self-interaction, we may wonder if the core mass M_c can reach the maximum mass $M_{\max}^{\mathrm{GR}}$ set by general relativity and collapse towards a supermassive black hole (SMBH). For bosons with an attractive self-interaction, we may wonder if the core mass M_c can reach the maximum mass $M_{\max}^{\mathrm{NR}}$ of Ref.[8] and collapse. The outcome of the collapse in that case would be a dense axion "star", a black hole, a bosenova, or axion drops.[9-20]

6.1. *Core mass–halo mass relation*

In Refs.[22,34-36], we have derived the core mass–halo mass relation of DM halos (without or with the presence of a central black hole) from a thermodynamic approach. We have obtained a general relation $M_c(M_h)$ valid for noninteracting bosons as well as for bosons with a repusive or an attractive self-interaction (and for fermions not considered here). To obtain this relation, we have proceeded as follows:

(i) Using some approximations, we have calculated the Lynden-Bell entropy $S(M_c)$ as a function of the core mass M_c. The equilibrium core mass is then obtained by maximizing the Lynden-Bell entropy at fixed total mass and total energy. We have shown[34,35] that this maximization problem is equivalent to the "velocity dispersion tracing" relation according to which the velocity dispersion in the core $v_c^2 \sim GM_c/R_c$ is of the same order as the velocity dispersion in the halo $v_h^2 \sim GM_h/r_h$. This relation can be written as

$$v_c \sim v_h \quad \Rightarrow \quad \frac{M_c}{R_c} \sim \frac{M_h}{r_h}. \tag{39}$$

(ii) To relate the core radius R_c to the core mass M_c, we have used the analytical expression of the mass-radius relation $M_c(R_c)$ of self-gravitating BECs obtained from the Gaussian ansatz [see Eq. (24)] yielding[8]

$$M_c = \frac{3.76 \frac{\hbar^2}{Gm^2 R_c}}{1 - 3\frac{a_s \hbar^2}{Gm^3 R_c^2}} \tag{40}$$

or, equivalently,

$$R_c = 1.87 \frac{\hbar^2}{Gm^2 M_c}\left(1 \pm \sqrt{1 + 0.849 \frac{Gma_s M_c^2}{\hbar^2}}\right). \quad (41)$$

(iii) Assuming that the atmosphere is isothermal, we have shown that the halo mass-radius relation $M_h(r_h)$ is given by[34]

$$M_h = 1.76\, \Sigma_0 r_h^2, \quad (42)$$

where $\Sigma_0 = 141\, M_\odot/\text{pc}^2$ is the universal surface density of DM halos infered from the observations.[e]

Combining Eqs. (39)-(42), we obtain the general expression of the core mass–halo mass relation $M_c(M_h)$ under the form[22, 35]

$$M_c = 2.23 \frac{\hbar \Sigma_0^{1/4} M_h^{1/4}}{G^{1/2} m}\left(1 + 1.06 \frac{a_s}{m} \Sigma_0^{1/2} M_h^{1/2}\right)^{1/2}. \quad (43)$$

Writing $M_c = M_h$ for the minimum halo, we obtain

$$(M_h)_{\min}^{3/2} = 4.99 \frac{\hbar^2 \Sigma_0^{1/2}}{Gm^2}\left(1 + 1.06 \frac{a_s}{m} \Sigma_0^{1/2} (M_h)_{\min}^{1/2}\right). \quad (44)$$

This equation determines the mass $(M_h)_{\min}$ of the minimum halo as a function of m and a_s. Inversely, for given $(M_h)_{\min}$, it determines a consistency relation between m and a_s (see the universal curve plotted in Fig. 19 of Ref.[35]).

6.2. Noninteracting bosons

For noninteracting bosons ($a_s = 0$), the core mass – halo mass relation (43) reduces to[22, 35]

$$M_c = 2.23 \left(\frac{\hbar^4 \Sigma_0 M_h}{G^2 m^4}\right)^{1/4}. \quad (45)$$

On the other hand, according to Eq. (44), the mass of the boson is given by $m = 2.23\,(\hbar^4 \Sigma_0/G^2 (M_h)_{\min}^3)^{1/4} = 2.25 \times 10^{-22}\,\text{eV}/c^2$ [in the numerical applications we assume that $(M_h)_{\min} = 10^8\, M_\odot$]. For a DM halo of mass $M_h = 10^{12}\, M_\odot$ similar to the one that surrounds our Galaxy, we obtain a core mass $M_c = 10^9\, M_\odot$ and a core radius $R_c = 63.5\,\text{pc}$. The quantum core represents a bulge or a nucleus. It cannot mimic a SMBH because it is too much extended ($Rc^2/GM \sim 10^6 \gg 1$).

The maximum mass and the minimum radius of a noninteracting boson star at $T = 0$ set by general relativity are[1, 2]

$$M_{\max}^{\text{GR}} = 0.633 \frac{\hbar c}{Gm}, \qquad R_{\min}^{\text{GR}} = 9.53 \frac{GM_{\max}}{c^2}. \quad (46)$$

---

[e]We note that the halo mass M_h used in our papers[22, 34–36] is related to the virial halo mass M_v used in Ref.[26] by $M_h/M_\odot = 6.01 \times 10^{-6}\, (M_v/M_\odot)^{4/3}$ [see Eq. (146) of Ref.[35]]. As a result, the scalings of the core mass – halo mass relations $M_c(M_h)$ and $M_c(M_v)$ are different.

These scalings can be qualitatively obtained as explained in Appendix B.2 of Ref.[8]. For a boson of mass $m = 2.25 \times 10^{-22}\,\mathrm{eV}/c^2$, we obtain $M_{\max}^{\mathrm{GR}} = 3.76 \times 10^{11}\,M_\odot$ and $R_{\min}^{\mathrm{GR}} = 0.171\,\mathrm{pc}$. The maximum mass is much larger than the typical quantum core mass of a DM halo. According to Eq. (45), the mass of the soliton would be equal to the maximum mass ($M_c = M_{\max}^{\mathrm{GR}}$) in a DM halo of mass $M_h = 6.49 \times 10^{-3} c^4/(G^2 \Sigma_0) = 2.01 \times 10^{22}\,M_\odot$ (remarkably, this expression is independent of the boson mass and is of the order of the mass of the Universe[36]). Such a large halo mass is clearly unrealistic (the biggest DM halos observed in the Universe have a mass $M_h \sim 10^{14}\,M_\odot$). Therefore, the soliton present at the center of a noninteracting BECDM halo can never collapse towards a SMBH. This conclusion was first reached in Appendix C of Ref.[36]. Since $M_c \ll M_{\max}^{\mathrm{GR}}$ in all realistic DM halos, a nonrelativistic approach is justified.

6.3. *Repulsive self-interaction in the TF limit*

For bosons with a repulsive self-interaction in the TF limit, the core mass–halo mass relation (43) reduces to[22, 35]

$$M_c = 2.30 \left(\frac{\hbar^2 \Sigma_0 a_s M_h}{G m^3} \right)^{1/2}. \qquad (47)$$

On the other hand, according to Eq. (44), the ratio a_s/m^3 is given by $a_s/m^3 = 0.189\, G(M_h)_{\min}/\hbar^2 \Sigma_0 = 4.35 \times 10^3\,\mathrm{fm}/(\mathrm{eV}/c^2)^3$. For a DM halo of mass $M_h = 10^{12}\,M_\odot$ similar to the one that surrounds our Galaxy, we obtain a core mass $M_c = 10^{10}\,M_\odot$ and a core radius $R_c = 635\,\mathrm{pc}$. The quantum core represents a bulge or a nucleus. It cannot mimic a SMBH because it is too much extended ($Rc^2/GM \sim 10^6 \gg 1$).

The maximum mass and the minimum radius of a self-interacting boson star at $T = 0$ in the TF limit set by general relativity are[4, 5]

$$M_{\max}^{\mathrm{GR}} = 0.307\, \frac{\hbar c^2 \sqrt{a_s}}{(Gm)^{3/2}}, \qquad R_{\min}^{\mathrm{GR}} = 6.25\, \frac{G M_{\max}}{c^2}. \qquad (48)$$

These scalings can be qualitatively obtained as explained in Appendix B.3 of Ref.[8]. For a ratio $a_s/m^3 = 4.35 \times 10^3\,\mathrm{fm}/(\mathrm{eV}/c^2)^3$, we obtain $M_{\max}^{\mathrm{GR}} = 2.35 \times 10^{15}\,M_\odot$ and $R_{\min}^{\mathrm{GR}} = 703\,\mathrm{pc}$. The maximum mass is much larger than the typical quantum core mass of a DM halo. According to Eq. (48), the mass of the soliton would be equal to the maximum mass ($M_c = M_{\max}^{\mathrm{GR}}$) in a DM halo of mass $M_h = 0.0178 c^4/(G^2 \Sigma_0) = 5.51 \times 10^{22}\,M_\odot$ (remarkably, this expression is independent of the ratio a_s/m^3 and is of the order of the mass of the Universe[36]). Such a large halo mass is clearly unrealistic (the biggest DM halos observed in the Universe have a mass $M_h \sim 10^{14}\,M_\odot$). Therefore, the quantum core present at the center of a BECDM halo with repulsive self-interactions can never collapse towards a SMBH. This conclusion was first reached in Appendix C of Ref.[36]. Since $M_c \ll M_{\max}^{\mathrm{GR}}$ in all realistic DM halos, a nonrelativistic approach is justified.

6.4. Attractive self-interaction

For bosons with an attractive self-interaction, the core mass–halo mass relation (see Fig. 3) presents a maximum when the core mass reaches the critical value [see Eq. (27)]

$$(M_c)_{\max} = 1.085 \frac{\hbar}{\sqrt{Gm|a_s|}} = 10.9 \left(\frac{f^2 \hbar}{c^3 m^2 G} \right)^{1/2} \quad (49)$$

at which it becomes unstable and collapses.[8,9] The collapse of the core, leading to a dense axion "star" (soliton), a black hole, a bosenova or to axion drops,[9–20] occurs in a DM halo of mass[22,35]

$$(M_h)_{\max} = 0.223 \frac{m^2}{a_s^2 \Sigma_0} = 2255 \frac{f^4}{\hbar^2 c^6 \Sigma_0}. \quad (50)$$

We have expressed these results in terms of the decay constant f (see Appendix B) which is related to the mass m and the scattering length a_s by Eq. (B.13). We note that the maximum halo mass $(M_h)_{\max}$ depends only on f while the maximum core mass $(M_c)_{\max}$ depends on f and m.

The maximum mass of a self-gravitating BEC made of ultralight axions with mass $m_{\text{th}} = 2.92 \times 10^{-22} \, \text{eV}/c^2$ and scattering length $(a_s)_{\text{th}} = -3.18 \times 10^{-68} \, \text{fm}$ (corresponding to $f_{\text{th}} = 1.34 \times 10^{17} \, \text{GeV}$ and $\lambda_{\text{th}} = -1.18 \times 10^{-96}$) is $M_{\max} = 5.10 \times 10^{10} \, M_\odot$ and the corresponding radius is $R_{99}^* = 1.09 \, \text{pc}$. The minimum halo $((M_h)_{\min} = 10^8 \, M_\odot, (r_h)_{\min} = 1 \, \text{kpc})$ has a mass much smaller than the maximum mass, so it is stable $((M_h)_{\min} < (M_c)_{\max})$. The halo mass at which the core mass would become unstable $(M_c = (M_c)_{\max})$ and collapse is $(M_h)_{\max} = 1.01 \times 10^{20} \, M_\odot$. Since the largest DM halos observed in the Universe have a much smaller mass, of the order of $M_h \sim 10^{14} \, M_\odot \ll (M_h)_{\max}$, we conclude that the quantum cores of BECDM halos with an attractive self-interaction are always stable $(M_c < (M_c)_{\max})$. Furthermore, since $M_h \ll (M_h)_{\max}$, the attractive self-interaction is negligible. This corroborates our claims[22,35,36] that the attractive self-interaction of the bosons can be neglected for what concerns the structure of DM halos in the nonlinear regime: Everything happens *as if* the bosons were noninteracting.

Remark: We recall that the theoretical value $f_{\text{th}} = 1.34 \times 10^{17} \, \text{GeV}$ of the decay constant used above comes from the constraints from particle physics and cosmology.[21] It may be interesting to relax these constraints and consider arbitrary values of f. In that case, we find that an attractive self-interaction would be important in realistic DM halos of mass $M_h \leq 10^{14} \, M_\odot$, and lead to the collapse of their quantum core when $M_h = (M_h)_{\max}$ [corresponding to $M_c = (M_c)_{\max}$], if $f < 4.22 \times 10^{15} \, \text{GeV}$ [the bound corresponds to $(M_h)_{\max} = 10^{14} \, M_\odot$ in Eq. (50)]. For example, for $f = 1.34 \times 10^{15} \, \text{GeV}$ and $m = 10^{-22} \, \text{eV}/c^2$, we find that the quantum core of a DM halo of mass $(M_h)_{\max} \sim 10^{12} \, M_\odot$ reaches its critical mass $(M_c)_{\max} \sim 10^9 \, M_\odot$ [with $R_*^{99} \sim 300 \, \text{pc}$] and collapses. The collapse of the quantum

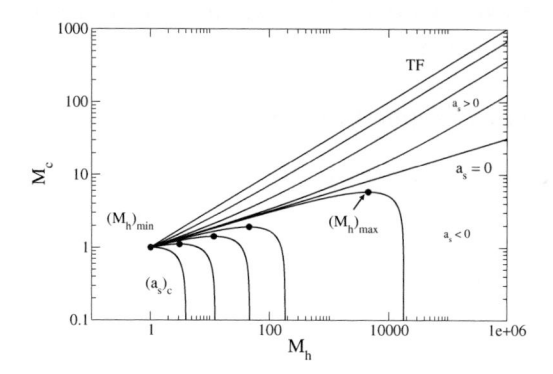

Fig. 3. Core mass M_c as a function of the halo mass M_h for different values of a_s and m such that the minimum halo mass $(M_h)_{\min}$ is fixed [see Eq. (44)]. The mass is normalized by $(M_h)_{\min}$ (typically $(M_h)_{\min} \sim 10^8 \, M_\odot$). We have indicated the position of the minimum halo mass $(M_h)_{\min}$ (common origin) and the position of the maximum halo mass $(M_h)_{\max}$ (bullet) above which the quantum core becomes unstable and collapses (when $a_s < 0$) [see Eqs. (49) and (50)]. We have highlighted the curve corresponding to the noninteracting case $a_s = 0$ [see Eq. (45)] and the curve corresponding to the TF limit $a_s/a'_* \gg 1$ [see Eq. (47)].

core leads to a dense axion "star",[13–15] a bosenova,[10] or axion drops.[19,20f] However, we recall that values of f smaller than 4.22×10^{15} GeV are outside of the range 10^{16} GeV $\leq f \leq 10^{18}$ GeV predicted by particle physics and cosmology (10^{16} GeV is the Grand Unified Theory scale and 10^{18} GeV is the Planck scale),[21] so that, according to these constraints, we do not expect the collapse of the core to occur in realistic DM halos of mass $M_h < 10^{14} \, M_\odot$ (as discussed above and in Refs.[22,35,36]).

7. Conclusion

In these Proceedings, we have emphasized the importance of the maximum mass of dilute axion stars (i.e. nonrelativistic self-gravitating BECs with an attractive self-interaction) first identified in Ref.[8]. Above this maximum mass the star collapses leading to a dense axion "star", a black hole, a bosenova, or axion drops.[9–20] We have discussed some applications of these results in relation to DM halos.[22,35,36] Other applications have been discussed in Refs.[50–55].

Appendix A. Relativistic complex scalar field

In this Appendix, we discuss the main properties of a relativistic complex self-interacting SF, establish its hydrodynamic representation, consider the TF approximation, and determine its equation of state $P(\epsilon)$ for an arbitrary self-interaction

---

[f]It does not lead to a SMBH which would be obtained for much larger values of f (above the reduced Planck mass 10^{18} GeV)[11,12] for which our previous assumptions do not apply.

potential $V(|\varphi|^2)$. For a $|\varphi|^4$ self-interaction, we justify the equation of state introduced by Colpi et al.[4] (see also Refs.[56,57]). We also justify the GPP equations (1) and (2) in the nonrelativistic limit.

Appendix A.1. *Klein-Gordon-Einstein equations*

We consider a relativistic complex SF $\varphi(x^\mu) = \varphi(x, y, z, t)$ which is a continuous function of space and time. It can represent the wavefunction of a relativistic BEC.[56,58] The total action of the system, which is the sum of the Einstein-Hilbert action of general relativity + the action of the SF, can be written as

$$S = \int \left(\frac{c^4}{16\pi G} R + \mathcal{L} \right) \sqrt{-g}\, d^4x, \tag{A.1}$$

where R is the Ricci scalar curvature, $\mathcal{L} = \mathcal{L}(\varphi, \varphi^*, \partial_\mu \varphi, \partial_\mu \varphi^*)$ is the Lagrangian density of the SF, and $g = \det(g_{\mu\nu})$ is the determinant of the metric tensor. We consider a canonical Lagrangian density of the form

$$\mathcal{L} = \frac{1}{2} g^{\mu\nu} \partial_\mu \varphi^* \partial_\nu \varphi - V_{\text{tot}}(|\varphi|^2), \tag{A.2}$$

where the first term is the kinetic energy and the second term is minus the potential energy. The potential energy can be decomposed into a rest-mass energy term and a self-interaction energy term:

$$V_{\text{tot}}(|\varphi|^2) = \frac{m^2 c^2}{2\hbar^2} |\varphi|^2 + V(|\varphi|^2). \tag{A.3}$$

The least action principle $\delta S = 0$ with respect to variations $\delta\phi$ (or $\delta\phi^*$), which is equivalent to the Euler-Lagrange equation

$$D_\mu \left[\frac{\partial \mathcal{L}}{\partial (\partial_\mu \varphi)^*} \right] - \frac{\partial \mathcal{L}}{\partial \varphi^*} = 0, \tag{A.4}$$

yields the KG equation

$$\Box \varphi + 2 \frac{dV_{\text{tot}}}{d|\varphi|^2} \varphi = 0, \tag{A.5}$$

where $\Box = D_\mu \partial^\mu = \frac{1}{\sqrt{-g}} \partial_\mu (\sqrt{-g}\, g^{\mu\nu} \partial_\nu)$ is the d'Alembertian operator. For a free massless SF ($V_{\text{tot}} = 0$), the KG equation reduces to $\Box \varphi = 0$.

The least action principle $\delta S = 0$ with respect to variations $\delta g^{\mu\nu}$ yields the Einstein field equations

$$R_{\mu\nu} - \frac{1}{2} g_{\mu\nu} R = \frac{8\pi G}{c^4} T_{\mu\nu}, \tag{A.6}$$

where $R_{\mu\nu}$ is the Ricci tensor and $T_{\mu\nu}$ is the energy-momentum (stress) tensor of the SF given by

$$T_\mu^\nu = \frac{\partial \mathcal{L}}{\partial (\partial_\nu \varphi)} \partial_\mu \varphi + \frac{\partial \mathcal{L}}{\partial (\partial_\nu \varphi^*)} \partial_\mu \varphi^* - g_\mu^\nu \mathcal{L}. \tag{A.7}$$

For the Lagrangian (A.2), we get

$$T_{\mu\nu} = \frac{1}{2}(\partial_\mu \varphi^* \partial_\nu \varphi + \partial_\nu \varphi^* \partial_\mu \varphi) - g_{\mu\nu} \mathcal{L}. \tag{A.8}$$

Equations (A.5) and (A.6) with Eq. (A.8) form the KGE equations. The conservation of the energy-momentum tensor $D_\mu T^{\mu\nu} = 0$ is automatically included in the Einstein equations through the contracted Bianchi identities.

Appendix A.2. *Hydrodynamic representation*

We can write the KG equation (A.5) under the form of hydrodynamic equations by using the de Broglie transformation (see, e.g., Refs.[56,58]). To that purpose, we write the SF as

$$\varphi = \frac{\hbar}{m}\sqrt{\rho}\, e^{im\theta/\hbar}, \tag{A.9}$$

where ρ is the pseudo rest-mass density[g] and $\theta = S_{\text{tot}}/m$ is the action by unit of mass ($\sim$ phase). They satisfy

$$\rho = |\psi|^2 = \frac{m^2}{\hbar^2}|\varphi|^2 \quad \text{and} \quad \theta = \frac{\hbar}{2mi}\ln\left(\frac{\varphi}{\varphi^*}\right). \tag{A.10}$$

Substituting Eq. (A.9) into the Lagrangian density (A.2), we obtain

$$\mathcal{L} = \frac{1}{2}g^{\mu\nu}\rho\partial_\mu\theta\partial_\nu\theta + \frac{\hbar^2}{8m^2\rho}g^{\mu\nu}\partial_\mu\rho\partial_\nu\rho - V_{\text{tot}}(\rho) \tag{A.11}$$

with

$$V_{\text{tot}}(\rho) = \frac{1}{2}\rho c^2 + V(\rho). \tag{A.12}$$

The Euler-Lagrange equations for θ and ρ, resulting from the least action principle, are

$$D_\mu\left[\frac{\partial \mathcal{L}}{\partial(\partial_\mu \theta)}\right] - \frac{\partial \mathcal{L}}{\partial \theta} = 0, \quad D_\mu\left[\frac{\partial \mathcal{L}}{\partial(\partial_\mu \rho)}\right] - \frac{\partial \mathcal{L}}{\partial \rho} = 0. \tag{A.13}$$

They yield the equations of motion[56,58]

$$D_\mu(\rho\partial^\mu\theta) = 0, \tag{A.14}$$

$$\frac{1}{2}\partial_\mu\theta\partial^\mu\theta - \frac{\hbar^2}{2m^2}\frac{\Box\sqrt{\rho}}{\sqrt{\rho}} - V'_{\text{tot}}(\rho) = 0. \tag{A.15}$$

The same equations are obtained by substituting the de Broglie transformation from Eq. (A.9) into the KG equation (A.5), and separating the real and the imaginary parts. Equation (A.14) can be interpreted as a continuity equation $D_\mu J^\mu = 0$ accounting for the conservation of the charge (or boson number) and Eq. (A.15)

---

[g]We stress that ρ is *not* the rest-mass density. It is only in the nonrelativistic regime $c \to +\infty$ that ρ coincides with the rest-mass density.

can be interpreted as a quantum relativistic Hamilton-Jacobi (or Bernoulli) equation with a relativistic covariant quantum potential

$$Q_{\rm dB} = \frac{\hbar^2}{2m} \frac{\Box\sqrt{\rho}}{\sqrt{\rho}}. \tag{A.16}$$

Appendix A.3. *TF approximation*

In the classical limit or in TF approximation ($\hbar \to 0$), the Lagrangian from Eq. (A.11) reduces to

$$\mathcal{L} = \frac{1}{2} g^{\mu\nu} \rho \partial_\mu \theta \partial_\nu \theta - V_{\rm tot}(\rho). \tag{A.17}$$

The Euler-Lagrange equations (A.13) yield the equations of motion

$$D_\mu \left(\rho \partial^\mu \theta \right) = 0, \tag{A.18}$$

$$\frac{1}{2} \partial_\mu \theta \partial^\mu \theta - V'_{\rm tot}(\rho) = 0. \tag{A.19}$$

The same equations are obtained by making the TF approximation in Eq. (A.15), i.e., by neglecting the quantum potential. Equation (A.18) can be interpreted as a continuity equation and Eq. (A.19) can be interpreted as a classical relativistic Hamilton-Jacobi (or Bernoulli) equation.

Assuming $V'_{\rm tot} > 0$, and using Eq. (A.19), we introduce the fluid quadrivelocity

$$u_\mu = -\frac{\partial_\mu \theta}{\sqrt{2V'_{\rm tot}(\rho)}} c, \tag{A.20}$$

which satisfies the identity $u_\mu u^\mu = c^2$. The energy-momentum tensor is given in the hydrodynamic representation, by

$$T^\nu_\mu = \frac{\partial \mathcal{L}}{\partial(\partial_\nu \theta)} \partial_\mu \theta + \frac{\partial \mathcal{L}}{\partial(\partial_\nu \rho)} \partial_\mu \rho - g^\nu_\mu \mathcal{L}. \tag{A.21}$$

For the Lagrangian (A.17) we get

$$T_{\mu\nu} = \rho \partial_\mu \theta \partial_\nu \theta - g_{\mu\nu} \mathcal{L}. \tag{A.22}$$

This expression can also be obtained from Eq. (A.8) by using the de Broglie representation (A.9) and making the TF approximation. Using Eq. (A.20), we get

$$T_{\mu\nu} = 2\rho V'_{\rm tot}(\rho) \frac{u_\mu u_\nu}{c^2} - g_{\mu\nu} \mathcal{L}. \tag{A.23}$$

The energy-momentum tensor (A.23) can be written under the perfect fluid form

$$T_{\mu\nu} = (\epsilon + P) \frac{u_\mu u_\nu}{c^2} - P g_{\mu\nu}, \tag{A.24}$$

where ϵ is the energy density and P is the pressure, provided that we make the identifications

$$P = \mathcal{L}, \qquad \epsilon + P = 2\rho V'_{\rm tot}(\rho). \tag{A.25}$$

Therefore, the Lagrangian plays the role of the pressure of the fluid. Combining Eq. (A.17) with the Bernoulli equation (A.19), we get

$$\mathcal{L} = \rho V'_{\text{tot}}(\rho) - V_{\text{tot}}(\rho). \tag{A.26}$$

Therefore, according to Eqs. (A.25) and (A.26), the energy density and the pressure derived from the Lagrangian (A.17) are given by[56,59]

$$\epsilon = \rho V'_{\text{tot}}(\rho) + V_{\text{tot}}(\rho) = \rho c^2 + \rho V'(\rho) + V(\rho), \tag{A.27}$$

$$P = \rho V'_{\text{tot}}(\rho) - V_{\text{tot}}(\rho) = \rho V'(\rho) - V(\rho), \tag{A.28}$$

where we have used Eq. (A.12) to get the second equalities. Eliminating ρ between Eqs. (A.27) and (A.28), we obtain the equation of state $P(\epsilon)$. On the other hand, Eq. (A.28) can be integrated into[56]

$$V(\rho) = \rho \int \frac{P(\rho)}{\rho^2}\, d\rho. \tag{A.29}$$

Equation (A.28) determines $P(\rho)$ as a function of $V(\rho)$ while Eq. (A.29) determines $V(\rho)$ as a function of $P(\rho)$.

Appendix A.4. *Nonrelativistic limit*

In the weak-field gravity limit of general relativity $\Phi/c^2 \ll 1$, using the simplest form of the Newtonian gauge, the line element is given by

$$ds^2 = c^2\left(1 + 2\frac{\Phi}{c^2}\right)dt^2 - \left(1 - 2\frac{\Phi}{c^2}\right)\delta_{ij}dx^i dx^j, \tag{A.30}$$

where $\Phi(\mathbf{r}, t)$ is the Newtonian potential. Making the Klein transformation (see, e.g., Ref.[58])

$$\varphi(\mathbf{r}, t) = \frac{\hbar}{m} e^{-imc^2 t/\hbar} \psi(\mathbf{r}, t) \tag{A.31}$$

in the KGE equations (A.5) and (A.6), where ψ is the pseudo wave function satisfying $\rho = |\psi|^2$, we obtain after simplification the general relativistic GP equation[58,60]

$$i\hbar c\, \partial^0 \psi - \frac{\hbar^2}{2m}\Box\psi + \frac{1}{2}mc^2(g^{00} - 1)\psi + i\frac{\hbar c^2}{2}\Box t\, \psi - m\frac{dV}{d|\psi|^2}\psi = 0, \tag{A.32}$$

coupled to the Einstein equations expressed in terms of ψ. We note that $\Box t$ can be written as $\Box t = -\frac{1}{c}g^{\mu\nu}\Gamma^0_{\mu\nu}$, where $\Gamma^\sigma_{\mu\nu}$ are the Christoffel symbols.[58] Taking the nonrelativistic limit $c \to +\infty$ of these equations with the Newtonian gauge (A.30), we obtain the GPP equations (1) and (2) [see Refs.[58,61,62] for the details of the derivation]. For a complex SF, the potential $V(|\psi|^2)$ which occurs in the GP equation (1) coincides with the potential $V(|\varphi|^2)$ which occurs in the KG equation (A.5) with Eq. (A.3) up to the change of function from Eq. (A.31) leading to

$$|\varphi|^2 = \frac{\hbar^2}{m^2}|\psi|^2. \tag{A.33}$$

Appendix A.5. $|\varphi|^4$ *potential*

We consider a $|\varphi|^4$ (quartic) potential of the form

$$V(|\varphi|^2) = \frac{\lambda}{4\hbar c}|\varphi|^4, \tag{A.34}$$

where λ is the dimensionless self-interaction constant. For nonrelativistic BECs, the potential that occurs in the GP equation (1) is usually written as in Eq. (3). Substituting Eq. (A.33) into Eq. (3), we get

$$V(|\varphi|^2) = \frac{2\pi a_s m}{\hbar^2}|\varphi|^4. \tag{A.35}$$

Comparing Eqs. (A.34) and (A.35), we obtain[9]

$$\frac{\lambda}{8\pi} = \frac{a_s m c}{\hbar} = \frac{a_s}{\lambda_C}, \tag{A.36}$$

where $\lambda_C = \hbar/mc$ is the Compton wavelength of the bosons. For the $|\varphi|^4$ model the KG and GP equations can be written as

$$\Box\varphi + \frac{m^2 c^2}{\hbar^2}\varphi + \frac{8\pi a_s m}{\hbar^2}|\varphi|^2\varphi = 0, \tag{A.37}$$

$$i\hbar\frac{\partial\psi}{\partial t} = -\frac{\hbar^2}{2m}\Delta\psi + m\Phi\psi + \frac{4\pi a_s \hbar^2}{m^2}|\psi|^2\psi = 0. \tag{A.38}$$

In terms of the pseudo rest-mass density [see Eqs. (A.9) and (A.10)], the potential (A.35) reads

$$V(\rho) = \frac{2\pi a_s \hbar^2}{m^3}\rho^2. \tag{A.39}$$

Substituting Eq. (A.39) into Eqs. (A.27) and (A.28) we obtain

$$\epsilon = \rho c^2\left(1 + \frac{6\pi a_s \hbar^2}{m^3 c^2}\rho\right), \tag{A.40}$$

$$P = \frac{2\pi a_s \hbar^2}{m^3}\rho^2. \tag{A.41}$$

Eliminating ρ between these two equations, we get

$$P = \frac{m^3 c^4}{72\pi a_s \hbar^2}\left(\sqrt{1 + \frac{24\pi a_s \hbar^2}{m^3 c^4}\epsilon} \mp 1\right)^2. \tag{A.42}$$

This relativistic equation of state $P(\epsilon)$ was introduced by Colpi et al.[4] in the context of boson stars. It was studied in detail by Chavanis and Harko[5] in connection with general relativistic BEC stars and by Li et al.[63] and Suárez and Chavanis[59] in a BECDM cosmological context. This equation of state reduces to that of an $n = 1$ polytrope [see Eq. (A.41) with $\epsilon \sim \rho c^2$] at low densities $\rho \ll m^3 c^2/|a_s|\hbar^2$

(nonrelativistic limit) and to the linear law $P \sim \epsilon/3$ similar to the equation of state of the radiation at high densities (ultrarelativistic limit).

Remark: Sometimes, a $|\varphi|^4$ self-interaction potential is written as

$$V(|\varphi|^2) = \frac{m^2}{2\hbar^4}\lambda_s|\varphi|^4, \tag{A.43}$$

where λ_s is the dimensional self-interaction constant. Comparing Eq. (A.43) with Eqs. (A.34) and (A.35) we get

$$\lambda_s = \frac{4\pi a_s \hbar^2}{m} = \frac{\lambda\hbar^3}{2m^2 c}. \tag{A.44}$$

Appendix B. Relativistic real scalar field

In this Appendix, we discuss the main properties of a relativistic real SF, consider the instantonic potential of axions, take the nonrelativistic limit, and justify the GPP equations (1)-(3) with $a_s < 0$.

Appendix B.1. *Klein-Gordon-Einstein equations*

For a real SF described by a canonical Lagrangian, the KGE equations write

$$\Box\varphi + \frac{m^2 c^2}{\hbar^2}\varphi + \frac{dV}{d\varphi} = 0, \tag{B.1}$$

$$R_{\mu\nu} - \frac{1}{2}g_{\mu\nu}R = \frac{8\pi G}{c^4}T_{\mu\nu}, \tag{B.2}$$

where the energy-momentum tensor is given by

$$T_{\mu\nu} = \partial_\mu\varphi\partial_\nu\varphi - g_{\mu\nu}\left[\frac{1}{2}g^{\rho\sigma}\partial_\rho\varphi\partial_\sigma\varphi - \frac{m^2 c^2}{2\hbar^2}\varphi^2 - V(\varphi)\right]. \tag{B.3}$$

Appendix B.2. *Nonrelativistic limit*

In the nonrelativistic limit $c \to +\infty$ where the SF displays rapid oscillations, the KGE equations can be simplified by averaging over the oscillations. To that purpose, we write

$$\varphi(\mathbf{r},t) = \frac{1}{\sqrt{2}}\frac{\hbar}{m}\left[\psi(\mathbf{r},t)e^{-imc^2 t/\hbar} + \psi^*(\mathbf{r},t)e^{imc^2 t/\hbar}\right], \tag{B.4}$$

where the complex wave function $\psi(\mathbf{r},t)$ is a slowly varying function of time (the fast oscillations $e^{imc^2 t/\hbar}$ of the SF have been factored out). This transformation allows us to separate the fast oscillations of the SF with pulsation $\omega = mc^2/\hbar$ caused by its rest mass from the slow evolution of $\psi(\mathbf{r},t)$. Using the simplest form of the Newtonian gauge [see Eq. (A.30)], substituting Eq. (B.4) into the KGE equations (B.1)-(B.3), averaging over the oscillations and taking the nonrelativistic limit

$c \to +\infty$, we obtain the GPP equations (1) and (2) [see Secs. II and III of Ref.[15] and Appendix A of Ref.[64] for the details of the derivation]. For a real SF, the (effective) potential $V(|\psi|^2)$ that occurs in the GP equation (1) is obtained from the potential $V(\varphi)$ that occurs in the KG equation (B.1) by first substituting Eq. (B.4) into $V(\varphi)$, then averaging over the oscillations. It is different from the potential obtained by directly replacing φ^2 by $(\hbar/m)^2|\psi|^2$ in the potential $V(\varphi)$.

Remark: General relativistic boson stars decribed by a real SF have a naked singularity at the origin and are always unstable.[65,h] It is possible to construct regular solutions which are periodic in time[66,67] when $M < M_{\max}^{\text{GR}} = 0.606\, M_P^2/m$ but, on a long timescale (which can exceed the age of the universe), these "oscillatons" are unstable and disperse to infinity or form a black hole. Their instability is basically due to the fact that the charge (boson number) is not conserved for a real SF. However, in the nonrelativistic limit, particle number conservation is approximately restored and Newtonian boson stars (like axion stars) can be stable (see Sec. 3).

Appendix B.3. *Instantonic potential of axions*

Axions are hypothetical pseudo-Nambu-Goldstone bosons of the Peccei-Quinn phase transition associated with a $U(1)$ symmetry that solves the strong charge parity (CP) problem of quantum chromodynamics (QCD). The axion is a spin-0 particle with a very small mass $m = 10^{-4}\,\text{eV}/c^2$ and an extremely weak self-interaction (with a decay constant $f = 5.82 \times 10^{10}\,\text{GeV}$) arising from nonperturbative effects in QCD. Axions have huge occupation numbers so they can be described by a classical relativistic quantum field theory with a real SF $\varphi(\mathbf{r},t)$ whose evolution is governed by the Klein-Gordon-Einstein (KGE) equations. The instantonic potential of axions is

$$V(\varphi) = \frac{m^2 c f^2}{\hbar^3}\left[1 - \cos\left(\frac{\hbar^{1/2} c^{1/2} \varphi}{f}\right)\right] - \frac{m^2 c^2}{2\hbar^2}\varphi^2, \qquad (B.5)$$

where m is the mass of the axion and f is the axion decay constant. For this potential, the KG equation (B.1) takes the form

$$\Box\varphi + \frac{m^2 c^{3/2} f}{\hbar^{5/2}}\sin\left(\frac{\hbar^{1/2} c^{1/2} \varphi}{f}\right) = 0. \qquad (B.6)$$

This is the general relativistic sine-Gordon equation. Considering the dilute regime $\varphi \ll f/\sqrt{\hbar c}$ (which is valid in particular in the nonrelativistic limit $c \to +\infty$)[i] and expanding the cosine term of Eq. (B.5) in Taylor series, we obtain at leading order the φ^4 potential

$$V(\varphi) = -\frac{m^2 c^3}{24 f^2 \hbar}\varphi^4. \qquad (B.7)$$

---

[h]This result is in agreement with the cosmic censorship conjecture which excludes spacetimes with naked singularities.
[i]According to Eq. (B.10), the axion decay constant f scales as $c^{3/2}$.

In that case, the KG equation (B.1) takes the form

$$\Box\varphi + \frac{m^2c^2}{\hbar^2}\varphi - \frac{m^2c^3}{6f^2\hbar}\varphi^3 = 0. \tag{B.8}$$

In the nonrelativistic limit, the effective potential $V(|\psi|^2)$ appearing in the GP equation (1) is given by[14, 15]

$$V(|\psi|^2) = \frac{m^2cf^2}{\hbar^3}\left[1 - \frac{\hbar^3 c}{2f^2m^2}|\psi|^2 - J_0\left(\sqrt{\frac{2\hbar^3 c|\psi|^2}{f^2m^2}}\right)\right], \tag{B.9}$$

where J_0 is the Bessel function of zeroth order. If we keep only the first term in the expansion of Eq. (B.9), we obtain the $|\psi|^4$ potential

$$V(|\psi|^2) = -\frac{\hbar^3 c^3}{16f^2m^2}|\psi|^4. \tag{B.10}$$

This approximation is valid for dilute axion stars satisfying $|\psi|^2 \ll f^2m^2/\hbar^3 c$. We note that $V(|\psi|^2) \equiv \overline{V(\varphi)}$ is different from the expression that one would have naively obtained by directly substituting $\varphi^2 = (\hbar/m)^2|\psi|^2$ into Eq. (B.5). The difference is already apparent in the first term of the expansion of the potential which involves a coefficient $-1/16$ [see Eq. (B.10)] instead of $-1/24$ [see Eq. (B.7)]. They differ by a factor $2/3$. This is because φ is a real SF. Therefore, substituting φ (exact) from Eq. (B.4) into $V(\varphi)$, *then* averaging over the oscillations, is different from substituting $\varphi^2 = (\hbar/m)^2|\psi|^2$ (already averaged over the oscillations) into $V(\varphi)$.

In general, a quartic potential is written as

$$V(\varphi) = \frac{\lambda}{4\hbar c}\varphi^4, \tag{B.11}$$

where λ is the dimensionless self-interaction constant. Comparing Eqs. (B.7) and (B.11), we find that

$$\lambda = -\frac{m^2c^4}{6f^2}. \tag{B.12}$$

On the other hand, comparing Eq. (B.10) with Eq. (3), we obtain

$$a_s = -\frac{\hbar c^3 m}{32\pi f^2}. \tag{B.13}$$

Equations (B.12) and (B.13) then yield

$$\frac{\lambda}{8\pi} = \frac{2a_s mc}{3\hbar}. \tag{B.14}$$

We note that the relation between λ and a_s is different for a real SF and for a complex SF (see Appendix A). They differ by a factor $2/3$ for the reason indicated previously.

We note that the self-interaction constant λ or the scattering length a_s is negative, so that the φ^4 self-interaction term for axions is *attractive*. This attraction is responsible for the collapse of dilute axion stars above the maximum mass from Eq. (20).[8,9] The next order φ^6 term in the expansion of the potential (B.5) has been considered in Refs.[14,15] and turns out to be repulsive. This repulsion, that occurs at high densities and which has a relativistic origin, may stop the collapse of dilute axion stars and lead to the formation of dense axion stars[13] (see, however, footnote a concerning their possible instability with respect to relativistic decay).

References

1. D.J. Kaup, Phys. Rev. **172**, 1331 (1968).
2. R. Ruffini, S. Bonazzola, Phys. Rev. **187**, 1767 (1969).
3. J.R. Oppenheimer, G.M. Volkoff, Phys. Rev. **55**, 374 (1939).
4. M. Colpi, S.L. Shapiro, I. Wasserman, Phys. Rev. Lett. **57**, 2485 (1986).
5. P.H. Chavanis, T. Harko, Phys. Rev. D **86**, 064011 (2012).
6. E.W. Kolb, I.I. Tkachev, Phys. Rev. D **49**, 5040 (1994).
7. I.I. Tkachev, Sov. Astron. Lett. **12**, 305 (1986).
8. P.H. Chavanis, Phys. Rev. D **84**, 043531 (2011).
9. P.H. Chavanis, Phys. Rev. D **94**, 083007 (2016).
10. D.G. Levkov, A.G. Panin, I.I. Tkachev, Phys. Rev. Lett. **118**, 011301 (2017).
11. T. Helfer *et al.*, JCAP **03**, 055 (2017).
12. F. Michel, I.G. Moss, Phys. Lett. B **785**, 9 (2018).
13. E. Braaten, A. Mohapatra, H. Zhang, Phy. Rev. Lett. **117**, 121801 (2016).
14. J. Eby, M. Leembruggen, P. Suranyi, L.C.R. Wijewardhana, JHEP **12**, 066 (2016).
15. P.H. Chavanis, Phys. Rev. D **98**, 023009 (2018).
16. L. Visinelli, S. Baum, J. Redondo, K. Freese, F. Wilczek, Phys. Lett. B **777**, 64 (2018).
17. J. Eby, M. Leembruggen, L. Street, P. Suranyi, L.C.R. Wijewardhana, Phys. Rev. D **100**, 063002 (2019).
18. E. Braaten, H. Zhang, Rev. Mod. Phys. **91**, 041002 (2019).
19. S. Davidson, T. Schwetz, Phys. Rev. D **93**, 123509 (2016).
20. E. Cotner, Phys. Rev. D **94**, 063503 (2016).
21. L. Hui, J. Ostriker, S. Tremaine, E. Witten, Phys. Rev. D **95**, 043541 (2017).
22. P.H. Chavanis, Phys. Rev. D **103**, 123551 (2021).
23. E. Seidel, W.M. Suen, Phys. Rev. Lett. **72**, 2516 (1994).
24. D. Lynden-Bell, Mon. Not. R. Astron. Soc. **136**, 101 (1967).
25. H.Y. Schive, T. Chiueh, T. Broadhurst, Nature Physics **10**, 496 (2014).
26. H.Y. Schive *et al.*, Phys. Rev. Lett. **113**, 261302 (2014).
27. B. Schwabe, J. Niemeyer, J. Engels, Phys. Rev. D **94**, 043513 (2016).
28. P. Mocz *et al.*, Mon. Not. R. Astron. Soc. **471**, 4559 (2017).
29. P. Mocz, L. Lancaster, A. Fialkov, F. Becerra, P.H. Chavanis, Phys. Rev. D **97**, 083519 (2018).
30. J. Veltmaat, J.C. Niemeyer, B. Schwabe, Phys. Rev. D **98**, 043509 (2018).
31. P. Mocz *et al.*, Phys. Rev. Lett. **123**, 141301 (2019).
32. P. Mocz *et al.*, Mon. Not. R. Astron. Soc. **494**, 2027 (2020).
33. J. Veltmaat, B. Schwabe, J.C. Niemeyer, Phys. Rev. D **101**, 083518 (2020).
34. P.H. Chavanis, Phys. Rev. D **100**, 083022 (2019).
35. P.H. Chavanis, Phys. Rev. D **100**, 123506 (2019).
36. P.H. Chavanis, Phys. Rev. D **101**, 063532 (2020).
37. P.H. Chavanis, Eur. Phys. J. Plus **132**, 248 (2017).
38. P.H. Chavanis, L. Delfini, Phys. Rev. D **84**, 043532 (2011).

39. M. Membrado, A.F. Pacheco, J. Sanudo, Phys. Rev. A **39**, 4207 (1989).
40. M. Membrado, J. Abad, A.F. Pacheco, J. Sañudo, Phys. Rev. D **40**, 2736 (1989).
41. J.W. Lee, I. Koh, Phys. Rev. D **53**, 2236 (1996).
42. J. Goodman, New Astronomy **5**, 103 (2000).
43. A. Arbey, J. Lesgourgues, P. Salati, Phys. Rev. D **68**, 023511 (2003).
44. C.G. Böhmer, T. Harko, J. Cosmol. Astropart. Phys. **06**, 025 (2007).
45. P.H. Chavanis, Phys. Rev. D **76**, 023004 (2007).
46. P.H. Chavanis, preprint.
47. R.Y. Chiao, E. Garmire, C.H. Townes, Phys. Rev. Lett. **13**, 479 (1964).
48. P.H. Chavanis, Eur. Phys. J. Plus **134**, 352 (2019).
49. P.A. Ruprecht, M.J. Holland, K. Burnett, M. Edwards, Phys. Rev. A **51**, 4704 (1995).
50. V. Desjacques, A. Kehagias, A. Riotto, Phys. Rev. D **97**, 023529 (2018).
51. K. Fujikura, M. Hertzberg, E. Schiappacasse, M. Yamaguchi, arXiv:2109.04283.
52. L.E. Padilla, T. Rindler-Daller, P. Shapiro, T. Matos, J.A. Vázquez, Phys. Rev. D **103**, 063012 (2021).
53. J. Chen, X. Du, E. Lentz, D. Marsh, J. Niemeyer, Phys. Rev. D **104**, 083022 (2021).
54. N. Glennon, C. Prescod-Weinstein, Phys. Rev. D **104**, 083532 (2021).
55. J. Eby, S. Shirai, Y.V. Stadnik, V. Takhistov, arXiv:2106.14893.
56. P.H. Chavanis, arXiv:2109.05963.
57. D.R. Karkevandi, S. Shakeri, V. Sagun, O. Ivanytskyi, arXiv:2109.03801.
58. P.H. Chavanis, T. Matos, Eur. Phys. J. Plus **132**, 30 (2017).
59. A. Suárez, P.H. Chavanis, Phys. Rev. D **95**, 063515 (2017).
60. T. Matos, A. Avilez, T. Bernal, P.H. Chavanis, Gen. Rel. Grav. **51**, 159 (2019).
61. A. Suárez, P.H. Chavanis, Phys. Rev. D **92**, 023510 (2015).
62. A. Suárez, P.H. Chavanis, J. Phys.: Conf. Series **654**, 012008 (2015).
63. B. Li, T. Rindler-Daller, P.R. Shapiro, Phys. Rev. D **89**, 083536 (2014).
64. P.H. Chavanis, Phys. Rev. D **102**, 083531 (2020).
65. P. Jetzer, D. Scialom, Phys. Lett. A **169**, 12 (1992).
66. E. Seidel, W.-M. Suen, Phys. Rev. Lett. **66**, 1659 (1991).
67. M. Alcubierre *et al.*, Class. Quantum Grav. **20**, 2883 (2003).

A dark matter solution for the XENON1T electron excess and the galactic center 511 keV line

Yasaman Farzan

School of Physics, Institute for Research in Fundamental Sciences (IPM)
P.O.Box 19395-5531, Tehran, Iran
E-mail: yasaman@theory.ipm.ac.ir
http://physics.ipm.ac.ir/

The excess of the 511 keV line from the Milky Way galactic bulge, confirmed by the INTEGRAL detector, is a longstanding mystery. The morphology of the line appears to be proportional to the square of the dark matter density, hinting towards a dark matter origin. On the other hand, in 2020, XENON1T has reported an excess of electrons with a recoil energy of $2-4$ keV. We present a model based on a dark matter of a few MeV mass that decays into a pair of pico-charged particles with a lifetime much larger than the age of the Universe. The magnetic field of the galaxy accumulates these relativistic pico-charged particles whose scattering on the electrons can explain the signal reported by XENON1T. The annihilation of the pico-charged particles in the galactic bulge leads to e^-e^+ production and therefore to an excess of the 511 keV line. We review the present observational bounds and the strategies to test the model.

Keywords: Dark matter, pico-charged particles, XENON1T electron excess, 511 keV line, galactic bulge

1. Introduction

Various observations such as galactic rotation curves, structure formation, dynamics of the galaxy clusters, collision of bullet clusters and anisotropies of Cosmic Mircowave Background (CMB) point towards existence of a new form of matter all over the universe known as Dark Matter (DM). The constituent particles of DM should be either electrically neutral or their electric charge should be much smaller than the electron electric charge. Otherwise, they will emit photons and will not remain dark. The dark matter lifetime should be much longer than the age of the Universe. The observation of bullet clusters constrain the self-interaction of the dark matter particles indicating that they cannot have strong interactions. Last but not least, at the onset of structure formation, the dark matter should be non-relativistic. None of the Standard Model (SM) elementary particles satisfies these conditions. As a result, the observational hints for dark matter opens a window towards new physics beyond the standard model by introducing a new neutral (meta)stable massive particle that can play the role of dark matter.[a]

---

[a] The primordial blackholes as dark matter candidates have received popularity after observation of gravitational waves by LIGO and VIRGO. We will not however pursue this idea in this letter.

The models for dark matter candidates are quite diverse. Depending on the details of the model, different strategies for dark matter detection have been developed. In a wide class of models known as WIMP, where dark matter has a mass in the wide range of MeV to 100 TeV and it weakly interacts with the Standard Model (SM) particles[b], there are three approaches to dark matter detection: (1) direct dark matter detection, (2) indirect dark matter detection and (3) dark matter production in colliders. No conclusive evidence for dark matter detection has been reported from any of these experiments so far but every now and then, a signal is reported by indirect search experiments which may be interpreted as dark matter. Some of these signals disappear by collecting more data or are eventually proved to be artifacts. There are however signals that pass the test of time but after some period of time simply go out of fashion because the simplistic dark matter models developed to explain them become ruled out by independent observations. However, the dark sector does not need to be simplistic. Indeed, judging from the rich and dazzling structure of the SM, simplicity and minimalism is not the taste of the physics of the elementary particles. Going beyond simplistic dark matter models, it may be possible to resurrect dark matter explanation for the signal.

One example of the signals that has survived the test of time is the 511 keV line observed from galactic center which must come from the positronium (the e^-e^+ atom) decay: $e^- + e^+ \rightarrow \gamma + \gamma$. The intensity of the line indicates an excess of e^+ in the galactic center. Although the excess may come from the SM sources such as pulsars but entertaining a DM origin is too tantalizing to dismiss, especially that the morphology of the intensity of the line follows a ρ_{DM}^2 distribution, further pointing towards DM pair annihilation as the origin of the excess. In Ref.[1], it had been shown that dark matter with mass of a few MeV can explain the excess of the 511 keV line observed from the galactic center by pair annihilation into pairs of electron positron with a cross section of $\langle \sigma(DM + DM \rightarrow e^-e^+)v \rangle \sim O(10^{-38})$ cm^2. This model implies huge energy pump into the plasma at the era of recombination when the DM density is high, through annihilation into e^-e^+. Such entropy pump can distort the CMB fluctuation pattern. The Planck data therefore rules this solution out.[2] Moreover, this model is disfavored by the lack of observation of the 511 keV line from dwarf galaxies.[3]

Ref.[4] proposes a dark matter model for the 511 keV line from the center of the Milky Way (MW) that can avoid the bounds from CMB and explain the lack of the 511 keV line from satellite dwarf galaxies. In this model, dark matter is composed of a scalar particle, X, with a mass of a few MeV which can be identified with the SLIM particle.[5,6] X decays into a pair of pico-charged particle $(C + \bar{C})$ with a lifetime much longer than the age of Universe: $\Gamma(X \rightarrow C + \bar{C})t_0 \ll 1$ in which t_0 is the age of the Universe. The magnetic field of the MW accumulates the C and

---

[b]Here, by weak interactions, we do not necessarily mean nuclear weak interaction, characterized by the SM W and Z gauge boson exchange.

$\bar{C}$ particles. The $C\bar{C}$ pairs eventually annihilate with each other producing e^-e^+ pairs. At the recombination and during the dark ages, the density of $C\bar{C}$ would be too small to pump energy to the plasma so the CMB bound can be avoided. Moreover, the magnetic field in the dwarf galaxies may be too weak to accumulate $C\bar{C}$ so the lack of the 511 keV line from them can be explained.

Ref.[4] predicted a signal at direct dark matter search experiments with low energy threshold. The relativistic C particles wandering around can impart a recoil energy of a few keV via Coulomb interaction to the electrons. In 2020, XENON1T reported an excess of electrons with recoil energy of 2–4 keV.[7] In Ref.[8], we discussed the parameter space where the model can explain both signals. Refs.[9] have also attempted to explain the XENON1T signal via DM.

This paper is organized as follows. In Sect. 2, we describe the model and the bounds that constrain its parameter space. In Sect. 6, we show how the model can explain the 511 keV line from the galactic bulge. In Sect. 4, we describe how the model can explain the XENON1T data. We show that the XENON1T electron recoil spectrum can also set the strongest upper bound on $f = \Gamma(X \to C\bar{C})t_0$. A summary is given in Sect. 5. In Sect. 5, we also discuss how the model can be tested with further collection of the 511 keV data from satellite galaxies and studying the correlation of the intensity with the magnetic field of the host [dwarf] galaxy. We also discuss the signatures in diffuse gamma ray background from the inflight annihilation of positron. We also comment on the positron flux to be detected by Voyager.

2. The model and its constraints

As mentioned in the introduction, the model is based on a scalar dark matter, X with a mass of a few MeV which decays into a pair of pico-charged particles, $C\bar{C}$. The X particle can be identified with the SLIM particle introduced in Ref.[5]. In the SLIM scenario, the DM is thermally produced via interaction with neutrinos and its abundance is set a la freeze-out scenario through lepton number violating annihilation into neutrino or antineutrino pair, $\langle\sigma(X+X \to \nu+\nu)v\rangle = \langle\sigma(X+X \to \bar{\nu}+\bar{\nu})v\rangle \sim pb$. Within the SLIM scenario, the annihilation to neutrino or antineutrino pair takes place via the t-channel exchange of a new Majorana neutrino which has a Yukawa coupling with the SM neutrino and X. A Z_2 symmetry, under which only the new Majorana neutrino and X are odd, guarantees the stability of X which is the lightest among the Z_2 odd particles. The same Z_2 symmetry forbids Yukawa coupling between the leptons, the Higgs and the new Majorana fermions and as a result, neutrinos cannot obtain a Dirac mass at the tree level. The SM neutrinos obtain a Majorana mass at one loop level within the SLIM scenario. The smallness of the neutrino mass is explained, thanks to the loop suppression despite a relatively large Yukawa coupling between, X and neutrinos of order of 10^{-3}. The model is testable by searching for the three body decay of Kaon and pion where along with the charged leptons, these new particles are emitted and appear as missing energy.[10] Ref.[6] shows how the SLIM scenario can be embedded within a UV complete model. Combining the condition $\langle \sigma(X+X)v \rangle \sim pb$ (to obtain the required DM relic abundance via the freeze-out mechanism) with the one-loop contribution to the neutrino mass to be equal to $\sim \sqrt{\Delta m_{atm}^2}$ sets an upper bound of ~ 10 MeV on the dark matter mass. On the other hand, X, being in thermal equilibrium with neutrinos at the time of the neutrino decoupling, cannot be lighter than a few MeV;[11] otherwise, it will lead to too many extra relativistic degrees of freedom. If X is not the SLIM and its production is not thermal, these lower and upper bounds on its mass can be relaxed.

Taking the pico-charged particles C and $\bar{C}$ to be scalars, the decay $X \to C\bar{C}$ can take place via a soft Z_2 symmetry breaking trilinear term of form $AX\bar{C}C$ with a very small A making X metastable. Let us now discuss how C and $\bar{C}$ acquire their minuscule electric charge. For this purpose, we need a new Abelian gauge symmetry such that the C and $\bar{C}$ are charged under the new $U_X(1)$ gauge symmetry. We denote the new gauge boson with A_μ. The kinetic and mass mixings between A_μ and the SM hypercharge gauge boson B_μ lead to a small electric charge for the C and $\bar{C}$ particles. We follow the notation of Ref.[12] and write

$$-\frac{A_{\mu\nu}A^{\mu\nu}}{4} - \frac{B_{\mu\nu}B^{\mu\nu}}{4} - \frac{\delta}{2}A_{\mu\nu}B^{\mu\nu} - \frac{1}{2}(\partial_\mu \sigma + M_1 A_\mu + \epsilon M_1 B_\mu)^2 , \quad (1)$$

where $\delta, \epsilon \ll 1$. In the kinetic and mass basis, the three neutral gauge bosons are the SM γ, Z bosons and a new gauge boson A'_μ which we shall call dark photon. To the first approximation in ϵ and δ, the mass of A' is decoupled from m_Z and is equal to M_1. Up to $O(\epsilon^2, \delta^2)$, the coupling between the SM charged fermions, f and A' can be written as the following:

$$q' \bar{f} \gamma^\mu f A'_\mu \quad \text{where} \quad q' = e \cos\theta_W (\epsilon - \delta) Q_f, \quad (2)$$

in which θ_W is the weak (Weinberg) mixing angle. The coupling of $C\bar{C}$ to A' is given by $g_X J_C^\mu A'_\mu$ where J_C^μ is the current of the C particles. Then, the C particle obtains an electric charge of

$$q_C = -g_X \epsilon \cos\theta_W .$$

From Eq. (2), we observe that in the limit $\epsilon \to \delta$, the SM fermions do not couple to A'. In this limit, if A' is lighter than the $C\bar{C}$ pair with a mass of order of a few keV, it will become metastable with a lifetime much greater than the age of the Universe.[4] This means the A' particles produced in the early universe remain as relics today and contribute as a subdominant DM component. In Ref.[8], we do not however consider this limit and allow for a faster decay of A'. As shown in Ref.[8], the $U_X(1)$ symmetry can be identified with the $L_\mu - L_\tau$ symmetry with a gauge coupling of $g_{\tau-\mu}$ which opens up the possibility of fast decay $A' \to \bar{\nu}_\mu \nu_\mu, \bar{\nu}_\tau \nu_\tau$. The decay can relax the bound from supernova cooling, opening up the window $m_{A'} \sim 100$ keV, $q' \sim 10^{-10} - 10^{-9}$ and $g_{\tau-\mu} \sim 10^{-9}$. Such values of coupling are too small to produce A' with significant abundance in the early universe so the bounds on the extra relativistic degrees of freedom from CMB and BBN can be relaxed. On the other hand, the A' particles produced in the supernova core decay into neutrino and antineutrino pairs in the outer layers of supernova. This process can severely change the supernova evolution. It can even facilitate the shock revival. Thus, in future with better observation of supernovae and more advanced simulations, this part of the parameter range of the model can be tested. For the time being, however, this range of the parameter space is accepted within the uncertainties. The A' particles escaping the core decay into $\nu\bar{\nu}$ pairs so similarly to the standard picture, the binding energy of the star will be emitted in the form of neutrinos to be observed by detectors on the Earth such as Super-Kamiokande.

The C particles produced by the X decay will be relativistic at the production with a velocity far exceeding the escape velocity from the galaxy. They are kept in the galactic disc by the magnetic field. To accumulate the C and $\bar{C}$ particles, their Larmour radius,

$$r_c = (100 \text{ pc}) \frac{3 \times 10^{-11}}{q_C} \frac{m_X}{10 \text{ MeV}} \frac{1 \text{ }\mu\text{Gauss}}{B}$$

should be smaller than the thickness of the galactic disc. This requirement sets a lower bound on q_C: $q_C > 10^{-11}$, see Refs.[4,8]. The strongest upper bound on q_C in this mass range comes from supernova cooling consideration and is $q_C < 10^{-9}$, see Ref.[13].

As shown in Ref.[14], expanding supernova remnants can pump energy to the charged particles, enhancing their Larmor radius and expelling them from the galactic disc with a rate of $(100 \text{ Myr})^{-1}$ unless there is an efficient mechanism for energy loss for the charged particles. As discussed in Ref.[4], in the limit $\delta \to \epsilon$ where A' is (meta)stable, the relic background of A' can behave as a coolant. That is the C and $\bar{C}$ particles can scatter off the background A', losing energy. As discussed in Ref.[8], in general case $\delta \neq \epsilon$ where there is no A' background, another coolant should be introduced. Following Ref.[8], we denote the coolant with Y and take $10 \text{ eV} < m_Y < 10 \text{ keV}$, $n_Y|_{local} = (\rho_{DM}|_{local}/\langle\rho_{DM}\rangle)\langle n_Y\rangle$ with a coupling of g_Y to the C particles leading to the scattering cross section of $\sigma_S \sim g_Y^4/(4\pi E_C^2)$. The energy loss at each collision can be written as $\Delta E_C = m_Y v^2 (E_C/m_C)^2$.

The energy of the C particle at the production from $X \to C\bar{C}$ is equal to $m_X/2$. In the absence of energy pump from supernova, the time scale for the energy loss from $m_X/2$ to $m_C(1+v_f^2/2)$ is

$$\tau_E = \int_{m_C(1+v_f^2/2)}^{m_X/2} \frac{dE_C}{\Delta E_C} \frac{1}{\sigma_S v n_Y} \sim \frac{4\pi m_C^3}{g_Y^4 n_Y m_Y} \left(\frac{1}{v_f} - \frac{1}{v_i}\right). \quad (3)$$

Equating τ_E with the time scale of the energy gain from expanding supernova remnants (i.e., 100 Myr), we find

$$v_f = 0.08 \left(\frac{0.25}{g_Y}\right)^4 \left(\frac{m_C}{3\text{MeV}}\right)^3 \frac{0.1 \times \rho_{DM}|_{local}}{n_Y m_Y}. \quad (4)$$

Let us now discuss the bounds on $\Gamma_X = \Gamma(X \to C\bar{C})$ or equivalently on $f = \Gamma_X t_0$. A rather strong bound comes from the requirement that annihilation $C\bar{C} \to A'A'$ does not deplete the C abundance of the galactic disc: That is $\sigma(C\bar{C} \to A'A')n_C v_f t_0 < 1$ which leads to

$$f < 10^{-2} \frac{m_X}{10 \text{ MeV}} \left(\frac{0.15}{g_X}\right)^4 \left(\frac{m_C}{5 \text{ MeV}}\right)^2 \frac{0.06}{v_f}.$$

A stronger bound comes from the requirement that the process of cooling during the history of the galaxy does not repel all the coolants. We should bear in mind that the coolant is a subdominant DM component which contributes less than 10 % to the whole dark matter content. Ref.[8] shows that this requirement implies

$$f < 10^{-3} \frac{m_X}{10 \text{ MeV}} \frac{m_Y}{10 \text{ keV}} \frac{10\rho_Y}{\rho_{DM}}.$$

As we shall see in Sect. 4, the bound from XENON1T detector on f is much stronger.

In order to produce e^-e^+ from $C\bar{C}$ annihilation yet another interaction is required. We will discuss this coupling in Sect. 6.

3. Explaining the 511 keV line

The 511 keV photon line has been detected from the galactic bulge of the MW for more than 40 years.[21] The INTErnational Gamma-Ray Astrophysics Laboratory (INTEGRAL) is a space telescope launched in 2002. The data from the SPI spectrometer at INTEGRAL over the years has confirmed the 511 keV signal at 56 σ C.L. The narrow photon line peaked at 511 keV, whose energy coincides with the rest mass of electron or positron, should come from the annihilation of the electron positron pairs at rest which form positronium atoms. The source of such large positron abundance in the bulge of MW is subject to debate. An intriguing possibility can be annihilation of DM leading to the e^-e^+ production. Astrophysical sources such as pulsars or X-ray binaries may also contribute to the positron flux but their characteristic spectral shapes do not fit the observations.[15] Moreover, the morphology of the observed 511 keV line is better compatible with the ρ^2_{DM} ditribution than what is predicted from these point sources, hinting further toward a DM annihilation origin.[16]

Ref.[1] proposes DM with mass of few MeV annihilating to e^-e^+ as a solution to the 511 keV line. With an annihilation $\langle\sigma(DM + DM \to e^- + e^+)v\rangle \sim 10^{-2}$ pb, MeVish DM can account for the intensity of the 511 keV line. However, if the annihilation to e^-e^+ is a S-wave process, the reioinzing energy dump at recombination will cause delayed recombination which is in tension with the CMB data.[2] If the annihilation is P-wave, at the freeze-out temperatures, the annihilation cross section will be $\sim$10 pb, washing out the relic density of DM. Thus, we should go beyond this minimal scenario. In the following, we show that the model described in Sect. 2 can provide a reliable explanation.

The X DM particles in the galaxy decay into $C\bar{C}$ with a rate of Γ_X. If these C particles are accumulated close to their production point, their number density after t^0 will be

$$n_C = \frac{\rho_X}{m_X} f \quad \text{with} \quad f = \Gamma_X t^0 \tag{5}$$

in which f is the fraction of X particles that have decayed. According to the INTEGRAL findings,[21] the intensity of 511 keV line from galactic center is $\Phi_{511} = (0.96 \pm 0.07) \times 10^{-3}$ ph cm^{-2} sec^{-1}. If each $C\bar{C}$ annihilation produces N_{pair} pairs of e^-e^+ and subsequently N_{pair} pairs of photons, the flux from the galaxy bulge will be

$$\Phi_{511} \simeq 2 N_{pair} \frac{\int_0^{r_b} (n_X(r))^2 f^2 \langle \sigma_{C\bar{C}} v \rangle 4\pi r^2 dr}{4\pi r_{sol}^2} \tag{6}$$

where $r_{sol} \simeq 8$ kpc is the distance between us and the center of MW, $r_b \simeq 1$ kpc is the galactic bulge radius and $n_X = \rho_X(r)/m_X$. In the minimalistic dark matter scenario in which the dark matter pair annihilates directly into e^-e^+, the flux is given by the formula in Eq. (6), replacing $N_{pair} f^2$ with 1 and $\sigma_{C\bar{C}}$ with $\sigma(\text{DM} + \text{DM} \to e^-e^+)$. In this scenario, the cross section should be of order of $10^{-39} - 10^{-38}$ cm^2 to account for the 511 keV line intensity which implies that in our model:

$$\sigma_{C\bar{C}} \sim 2 \text{ nb} \left(\frac{1.5 \times 10^{-4}}{f}\right)^2 \left(\frac{m_X}{5 \text{ MeV}}\right)^2 \frac{1}{N_{pair}}. \tag{7}$$

Let us now discuss the couplings that leads to the e^-e^+ production from the $C\bar{C}$ annihilation. Taking effective coupling $(\bar{e}e)(\bar{C}C)/\Lambda$, the cross section of 2 nb implies $\Lambda < 100$ GeV which would be within the reach of the LEP collider and other accelerator experiments. We therefore invoke the possibility of intermediate light neutral particles, ϕ, to avoid the bounds from the LEP. Then, the production of e^-e^+ takes place in two steps: First, $C\bar{C} \to \phi\bar{\phi}$ and subsequently $\phi \to e^-e^+$. As a result, $N_{pair} = 2$. The $\phi \to e^-e^+$ decay can take place through

$$g_\phi \phi \bar{e} e. \tag{8}$$

As long as $g_\phi < 10^{-11}$, the ϕ production in the supernova core will be negligible. We need $g_\phi > 10^{-15}$ in order for the ϕ decay length to be shorter than 10 pc. If ϕ travels less than ~ 100 pc in the bulge (i.e., of order of the resolution of the INTEGRAL observatory) before decay, the n_{DM}^2 dependence of the 511 keV line morphology will be maintained, as favored by observation. Thus, $0.3 \times 10^{-15} < g_\phi < 10^{-11}$. ϕ is mainly an electroweak singlet mixed with the SM Higgs via

$$a_\phi \phi |H|^2$$

Then,

$$g_\phi = \sqrt{2} \frac{a_\phi v}{m_h^2} Y_e \tag{9}$$

in which Y_e is the Yukawa coupling of the SM Higgs to the electron. Fortunately, the hierarchy between the H and ϕ masses does not require unnatural fine tuned cancellation at tree level because $a_\phi \lesssim m_\phi$. In the early universe, ϕ can be produced via $e^- e^+ \to \phi \gamma$ with a number density $n_\phi \sim \langle \sigma_\phi v \rangle n_e^2 H^{-1}|_{T=m_\phi}$ where $\sigma_\phi = e^2 g_\phi^2 / 8\pi m_\phi^2$. Thus, during the period between $T = m_\phi$ and Γ_ϕ^{-1}, we can write $n_\phi/n_\gamma = 8 \times 10^{-8} (g_\phi/10^{-11})^2$. As a result, n_ϕ at $T \sim 1$ MeV would be small enough to satisfy the BBN bounds. In the range of g_ϕ in which we are interested, the decay of the ϕ particles takes place long before the recombination. For more details, see Ref.[4].

4. Direct detection of the C particles in the galaxy

The C particles, having a tiny electric charge, can have Coulomb interaction with the electrons and protons. It can also interact with matter fields by the t-channel exchange of dark photon, A'. The velocity of C arriving at the detector is larger than the typical velocity of the DM particles (i.e., velocity of $C \gg 10^{-3}$). As a result, the recoil energy imparted by the C collision can be much larger than that expected from the collision of a DM particle of mass of MeV. This rises the hope to search for C particles by the direct dark matter search experiments, despite C being light. In this section, we shall show how the electron excess with recoil energy of $2-4$ keV at XENON1T can be explained within our model. We will then show that XENON1T sets strongest upper bound on the fraction of the X particle decaying into $C\bar{C}$, f.

According to Eq. (4), the velocity of C particles around us is $v_f \sim 0.08$. The Larmor radius in the Earth magnetic field is 5×10^8 km$(10^{-11}/q_C)(m_C/3$ MeV$)$. Since the Larmor radius is much larger than the Earth radius, the Earth magnetic field cannot accumulate the C particles so their density around the Earth will be similar to anywhere in the solar system (i.e., anywhere in a distance of 8 kpc from the MW galactic center): $(\rho_{DM}|_{local}/m_X)f$ in which $\rho_{DM}|_{local} \sim 0.4$ GeV/cm^3.

Consider a C particle with a velocity of v_f scattering off a non-relativistic particle of mass, m. Up to corrections of $O(v_f^4)$, the maximum recoil energy, which corresponds to the backward scattering, can be written as

$$E_{max} = 2m v_f^2 \frac{m_C^2}{(m+m_C)^2}. \quad (10)$$

For $m_C \sim 1 - 5$ MeV, $v_f = 0.08$ and $m = m_e$, $E_{max} = 3 - 5.5$ keV which is tantalizingly within the range of electron recoil excess observed by XENON1T.[7] Taking m equal to the mass of Xenon or of Argon, E_{max} turns out to be much below the detection energy threshold of the experiments such as XENON1T,[17] DarkSide[18] and even the CRESST detector.[19]

The spectrum of recoiled electrons per detector mass will be

$$\frac{dN}{dE_r} = \frac{Z_{out}}{m_N}\left(2f\frac{\rho_X}{m_X}\right)\int f_C(v)\frac{d\sigma}{dE_r}v dv$$

where m_N is the mass of the nuclei inside the detector; i.e., $m_N = 131$ GeV for the Xenon. Z_{out} denotes the number of the electrons in the outer orbitals of the detector atoms whose binding energies are smaller than E_r. Ref.[20] shows that to a reasonable approximation, the binding energy can be treated with a step function in computing the scattering cross section. For Xenon, $Z_{out} = 44$ which is the number of the electrons in the $n = 3, 4, 5$ orbitals. These outer electrons have velocities smaller than v_f so we neglect their velocity in our analysis. The velocity distributions of the C and $\bar{C}$ particles are given by $f_C(v)$. In our computation, we take $f_C(v) = \delta(v - v_f)$ for simplicity. As far as $|\epsilon|/2m_e E_r \gg |\epsilon - \delta|/(2m_e E_r + m_{A'}^2)$, the t-channel photon exchange gives the dominant contribution to the C particles scattering off the electrons. The differential cross section can be written as[24]

$$\frac{d\sigma}{dE_r} = \frac{e^2 q_C^2}{8\pi m_e v^2} \frac{1}{E_r^2} \left(1 + \frac{2m_e E_r}{2m_e E_r + m_{A'}^2} \frac{\delta - \epsilon}{\epsilon}\right)^2 \quad (11)$$

where $E_r < E_{max} = 2m_e v^2 \left(\frac{m_C}{m_C + m_e}\right)^2$. The first (second) term in the parenthesis comes from the contribution from t channel photon (dark photon, A') exchange.

Analyzing the XENON1T data, we take $v_f = 0.08$, $q_C = 10^{-11}$ and $m_X = 10$ MeV and use the data presented in Fig. 4 of Ref.[7]. Let us define χ^2 as follows

$$\chi^2 = \sum_{bins} \frac{[N_i^{obs} - N_i^{pred}]^2}{\sigma_i^2} \quad (12)$$

where N_i^{obs} is the observed number of events at bin i and N_i^{pred} is the prediction for the sum of the background and the signal from the C scattering in the ith bin. The values of the uncertainty (σ_i), the background and N_i^{obs} are obtained from Fig. 4 of Ref.[7]. We only focus on the first seven bins because the excess appears only at $E_r < 8$ keV. The variation of χ^2 with m_C seems to be only mild.

In Sect. 2, we discussed that for 100 keV $< m_{A'} <$ few MeV, identifying the $U_X(1)$ with the $L_\mu - L_\tau$ gauge symmetry, the bounds on $q' \propto (\delta - \epsilon)$ from supernova cooling can be relaxed because A' can decay into neutrino pairs relatively fast. For $m_{A'} \sim$ few MeV, $2m_e E_r \ll m_{A'}^2$ and we can treat $(\delta - \epsilon)/(\epsilon m_{A'}^2)$ and f as two free parameters to be fitted with the data. Taking $m_C = 5$ MeV, we find that the minimum of χ^2 lies at $f = 10^{-7}$ and $(\delta - \epsilon)/\epsilon = -2 \times 10^3 (m_{A'}/\text{MeV})^2$. For $\epsilon = -q_C/(g_X \cos\theta_W) \sim 10^{-11}/(g_X \cos\theta_W)$, this corresponds to $q' \sim (10^{-8}/g_X)(m_{A'}/\text{MeV})^2$. At this point, $\chi^2 = 4.7$ with $5 = 7 - 2$ degrees of freedom which corresponds to a one-sided goodness of fit of 45 %. The results are shown in Fig. 1 with a red curve. In the first bin, contribution from the dark photon and the SM photon cancel each other. In case of the green curve shown in Fig. 1, we have taken $2m_e E_r(\delta/\epsilon - 1)/m_{A'}^2 \to 0$ so there is no cancellation between dark and SM photons. As seen in the figure, in this case the spectrum diverges for small E_r.

For $m_{A'} \sim 100$ keV, $2m_e E_r$ is comparable to $m_{A'}^2$ and we should use the whole formula to fit the data. Taking $m_C = 5$ MeV and $m_{A'} = 100$ keV ($m_{A'} = 200$ keV),

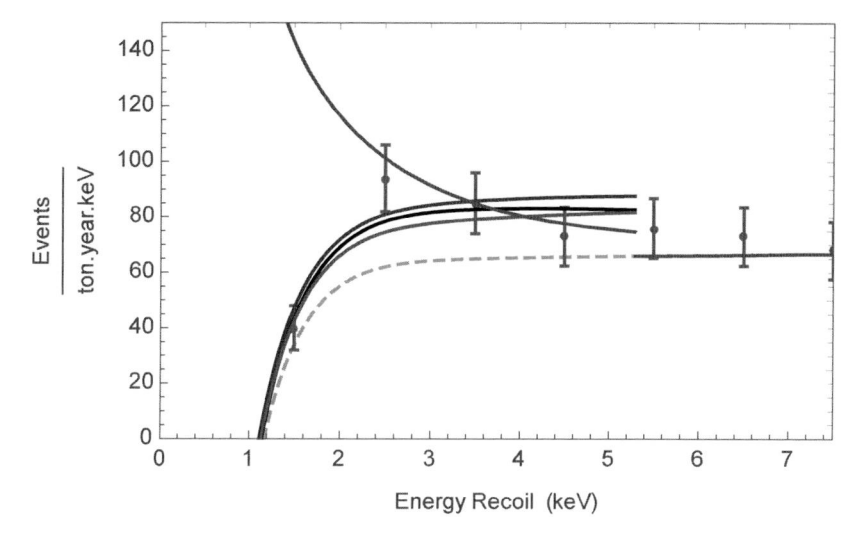

Fig. 1. XENON1T datapoints superimposed on our predictions. We have set $m_C = 5$ MeV corresponding to $E_{max} = 5.3$ keV. The red curve shows the prediction for $m_{A'} > 1$ MeV, $f = 10^{-7}$ and $(\delta-\epsilon)/\epsilon = -2 \times 10^3 (m_{A'}/\text{MeV})^2$. The black curve depicts the prediction for $m_{A'} = 0.1$ MeV, $(\delta - \epsilon)/\epsilon = -13.9$ and $f = 6.6 \times 10^{-7}$. The blue curve illustrates the prediction for $m_{A'} = 0.2$ MeV, $(\delta-\epsilon)/\epsilon = -76$ and $f = 2 \times 10^{-7}$. The green curve shows the SM photon dominant regime with $f = 5 \times 10^{-6}$. The SM background is shown by the cyan dashed curve.

the best fit will correspond to $(\delta-\epsilon)/\epsilon = -13.9$ and $f = 6.6 \times 10^{-7}$ ($(\delta-\epsilon)/\epsilon = -76$ and $f = 2 \times 10^{-7}$) and to the minimum $\chi^2 = 4.11$ ($\chi^2 = 4.5$). From Fig. 1, we observe that both fits result in very close prediction. At this fit, q' is right above the supernova bound ($q' \sim 10^{-10} - 10^{-9}$) which can be ruled in by opening the possibility of decay of A' into neutrino pairs in the outer layers of the supernova as discussed in Sect. 2. The effects of such couplings can be tested by studying the flavor composition, the neutrino energy spectrum and the duration of the neutrino emission. The q' coupling can lead to the production of the A' particles in the early universe, contributing to the extra relativistic degrees of freedom, $\delta N_{eff} < 1$. More accurate δN_{eff} determination by future CMB and BBN studies can test this model with $q' \sim 10^{-10} - 10^{-9}$.

Let us now discuss the bound that can be derived on f from the XENON1T data. To do so, we consider the bins with energy less than 8 keV. Fig. 2 shows χ^2 as a function of f. Since the first bin is close to the detection threshold and it suffers from large uncertainty in the evaluation of the background from ^{214}Pb, we present results both including and excluding the first bin. We have taken $m_C = 4$ MeV, but the results are rather insensitive to the value of m_C. To draw the blue and green lines, we have set $\delta = \epsilon$ which means the dark photon decouples and does not contribute to the scattering. Drawing the orange line, we have chosen the value of $2m_e(\delta - \epsilon)/(m_{A'}^2 \epsilon)$ such that the contributions from SM photon and dark photon cancel each other at $E_r = 1.5$ keV. From the figure we find an upper bound of

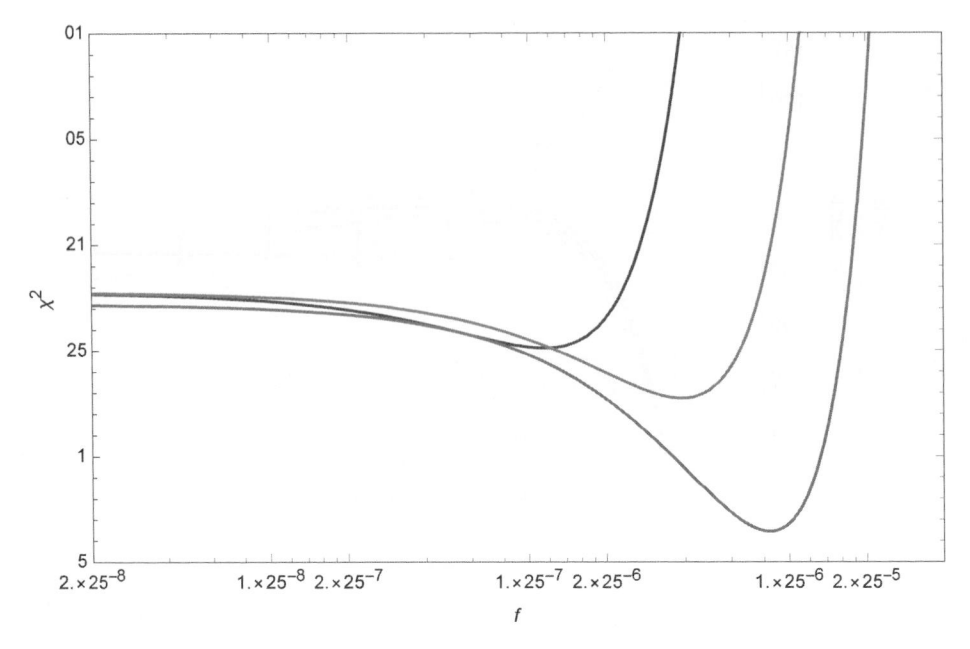

[Figure: χ² vs. f plot]

Fig. 2. χ^2 vs. f. We have taken $v_f = 0.08$, $q_c = 10^{-11}$, $m_X = 10$ MeV and $m_C = 4$ MeV. The blue and orange curves (the green curve) show χ^2 for the seven (six) bins between 1 keV$< E_r <$ 8 keV (2 keV$< E_r <$ 8 keV). To draw the blue and green curves, we have assumed that the photon exchange gives the dominant contribution to the scattering, $(m_e E_r/m_{A'}^2)[(\delta-\epsilon)/\epsilon] \ll 1$. To draw the orange curve we have set $(2m_e/m_{A'}^2)[(\delta-\epsilon)/\epsilon] = -1/(1.5 \text{ keV})$.

1.5×10^{-6} on f at 3 σ, taking all the bins with $E_r < 8$ keV:

$$f < 1.5 \times 10^{-6} \quad \text{at } 3\sigma.$$

Excluding the first energy bin relaxes the bound to 10^{-5}. Notice that these bounds are much stronger than the constraints discussed in Sect. 2. Since $f = \Gamma_X t_0$, the upper bound on f is equivalent to a lower bound on the dark matter lifetime. The lifetime of X should be larger than $10^{15} - 10^{16}$ years.

Let us revisit the explanation for the 511 keV line taking into account this very stringent upper bound on f. To explain the intensity of the 511 keV line from the galactic bulge, the annihilation cross section of $C\bar{C} \to \phi\bar{\phi}$ should be mb$(10^{-7}/f)^2(m_X/5 \text{ MeV})^2$. Taking a quartic coupling between these scalars of form $\lambda_{\phi C}|\phi|^2|C|^2$, we need $\lambda_{\phi C} \sim 0.02$ to obtain an annihilation cross section of mb.

5. Conclusion and discussion

We have presented a dark matter model that can simultaneously explain the 511 keV line from the galactic bulge and the electron excess with recoil energy of 2 − 4 keV reported by XENON1T. The model is based on introducing a dark matter particle with a mass of $O(1-10)$ MeV that decays into a pair of pico-charged particles.

Although the velocities of the C and $\bar{C}$ particles are much larger than the escape velocity from the galaxy, the galactic magnetic field can accumulate them inside the galactic disk. The C particles with velocities of order of $0.08c$ can scatter off the electrons of the direct dark matter search experiments, imparting a recoil energy of a few keV which can explain the electron excess at the low energy bins reported by XENON1T. Moreover, the $C\bar{C}$ accumulated in the galactic bulge can annihilate with each other, giving rise to the excess of the 511 keV line. We have shown that the XENON1T data also sets strong upper bound of 10^{-6} on the fraction of X particles that have decayed into $C\bar{C}$ since early universe until today, $f < 10^{-6}$. The density of $C\bar{C}$ at the time of recombination and during the dark ages would be too low to pump any significant energy and ionize the atoms so the bounds from the CMB on the minimalistic DM explanation for the 511 keV line do not apply here.

The model enjoys a rich phenomenology and can be tested by a myriad of methods. Most obvious test is further data from upcoming direct dark matter search experiments, especially the XENONnT detector which is an upgrade of XENON1T. The XENONnT detector is in the construction phase.

The C particles obtain their electric charge through the mixing of the photon and the dark photon, A' which is the gauge boson of a new $U_X(1)$ symmetry under which C and $\bar{C}$ are charged. Simultaneous explanation for the excess of events with recoil energy between $2-4$ keV and for the absence of an excess at the 1 keV bin requires a cancellation between the contributions from the t-channel exchanges of the photon and A'. Such a cancellation is possible with a light A' with a mass of 100 keV–1 MeV. We have shown that by identifying the $U_X(1)$ symmetry with the $L_\mu - L_\tau$ symmetry and therefore allowing for $A' \to \nu_\mu \bar{\nu}_\mu, \nu_\tau \bar{\nu}_\tau$, it is possible to avoid the present bounds from the supernova cooling consideration. The A' decaying to $\nu\bar{\nu}$ in the outer layers of supernova can however alter the evolution of supernova, leaving its imprint on the duration of neutrino emission, flavor composition, energy spectrum and shock revival. All these signatures provide alternative methods to test the model.

The intensity of the 511 keV line from dwarf galaxies is proportional to the product of the number of C and $\bar{C}$ particles. As a result, there should be a correlation between the magnitude of the magnetic field in dwarf galaxies and the intensity of the 511 keV photon line emitted from them which can be tested in the future.

The positrons from the $C\bar{C}$ annihilation at the production are relativistic. A fraction of these positrons may annihilate in flight giving rise to a continuous γ ray spectrum on which there is a bound, implying that the C particles should be lighter than $6-15$ MeV depending on the models for ionization fraction in the galaxy.[21–23] In future with more data, lighter C can be probed by this consideration. Moreover, there will be an excess cosmic positron at few MeV range. At these energies, the solar wind renders measurements of cosmic positron flux in the MeV range obsolete within the solar system. Fortunately, there are detectors on board the Voyager spacecraft that have set an upper bound on the cosmic positrons outside the solar system. The bound can be interpreted as $m_C < 20$ MeV. Further data from Voyager can test smaller values of m_C or hopefully detect a positron excess which will be a hint in favor of the present model.

Acknowledgments

The article is prepared for the proceedings of the sixteenth Marcel Grossmann meeting (MG16). The author would like to thank the organizers and conveners of this meeting for the kind invitation. She is also grateful for ICRANET whose support made this participation possible.

This project has received funding/support from the European Union's Horizon 2020 research and innovation programme under the Marie Skłodowska–Curie grant agreement No 860881-HIDDeN. The author has also received partial financial support from Saramadan under contract No. ISEF/M/98223, No. ISEF/M/9916 and No. ISEF/M/400188.

References

1. C. Boehm, D. Hooper, J. Silk, M. Casse and J. Paul, Phys. Rev. Lett. **92** (2004) 101301 doi:10.1103/PhysRevLett.92.101301 [astro-ph/0309686].
2. R. J. Wilkinson, A. C. Vincent, C. Boehm and C. McCabe, Phys. Rev. D **94** (2016) no. 10, 103525 doi:10.1103/PhysRevD.94.103525 [arXiv:1602.01114 [astro-ph.CO]].
3. T. Siegert, R. Diehl, A. C. Vincent, F. Guglielmetti, M. G. H. Krause and C. Boehm, Astron. Astrophys. 595 (2016) A25 doi:10.1051/0004-6361/201629136 [arXiv:1608.00393 [astro-ph.HE]].
4. Y. Farzan and M. Rajaee, JHEP **12** (2017), 083 doi:10.1007/JHEP12(2017)083 [arXiv:1708.01137 [hep-ph]].
5. C. Boehm, Y. Farzan, T. Hambye, S. Palomares-Ruiz and S. Pascoli, Phys. Rev. D **77** (2008) 043516 doi:10.1103/PhysRevD.77.043516 [hep-ph/0612228].
6. Y. Farzan, Phys. Rev. D **80** (2009) 073009 doi:10.1103/PhysRevD.80.073009 [arXiv:0908.3729 [hep-ph]].
7. E. Aprile *et al.* [XENON], Phys. Rev. D **102** (2020) no. 7, 072004 doi:10.1103/PhysRevD.102.072004 [arXiv:2006.09721 [hep-ex]].
8. Y. Farzan and M. Rajaee, Phys. Rev. D **102** (2020) no. 10, 103532 doi:10.1103/PhysRevD.102.103532 [arXiv:2007.14421 [hep-ph]].
9. G. Choi, T. T. Yanagida and N. Yokozaki, [arXiv:2007.04278 [hep-ph]]; J. Hisano, A. Ibarra and R. Nagai, [arXiv:2007.03216 [hep-ph]]; D. Aristizabal Sierra, V. De Romeri, L. J. Flores and D. K. Papoulias, [arXiv:2006.12457 [hep-ph]]; G. Choi, T. T. Yanagida and N. Yokozaki, [arXiv:2007.04278 [hep-ph]]; S. Karmakar and S. Pandey, [arXiv:2007.11892 [hep-ph]]; L. A. Anchordoqui, I. Antoniadis, K. Benakli and D. Lust, [arXiv:2007.11697 [hep-th]]; J. Cao, X. Du, Z. Li, F. Wang and Y. Zhang, [arXiv:2007.09981 [hep-ph]]; C. W. Chiang and B. Q. Lu, [arXiv:2007.06401 [hep-ph]]; N. Okada, S. Okada, D. Raut and Q. Shafi, [arXiv:2007.02898 [hep-ph]]; W. DeRocco, P. W. Graham and S. Rajendran, [arXiv:2006.15112 [hep-ph]]; M. Lindner, Y. Mambrini, T. B. d. Melo and F. S. Queiroz, [arXiv:2006.14590 [hep-ph]]; K. Nakayama and Y. Tang, [arXiv:2006.13159 [hep-ph]]; G. Alonso-Álvarez, F. Ertas, J. Jaeckel, F. Kahlhoefer and L. J. Thormaehlen, [arXiv:2006.11243 [hep-ph]]; K. Kannike, M. Raidal, H. Veermäe, A. Strumia and D. Teresi, [arXiv:2006.10735 [hep-ph]];

P. Ko and Y. Tang, [arXiv:2006.15822 [hep-ph]]; L. Delle Rose, G. Hütsi, C. Marzo and L. Marzola, [arXiv:2006.16078 [hep-ph]]; U. K. Dey, T. N. Maity and T. S. Ray, [arXiv:2006.12529 [hep-ph]]; H. Alhazmi, D. Kim, K. Kong, G. Mohlabeng, J. C. Park and S. Shin, [arXiv:2006.16252 [hep-ph]]; P. Ko and Y. Tang, [arXiv:2006.15822 [hep-ph]]; L. Delle Rose, G. Hütsi, C. Marzo and L. Marzola, [arXiv:2006.16078 [hep-ph]]; Y. Jho, J. C. Park, S. C. Park and P. Y. Tseng, [arXiv:2006.13910 [hep-ph]]; B. Fornal, P. Sandick, J. Shu, M. Su and Y. Zhao, [arXiv:2006.11264 [hep-ph]]; Q. H. Cao, R. Ding and Q. F. Xiang, [arXiv:2006.12767 [hep-ph]]; Y. Chen, J. Shu, X. Xue, G. Yuan and Q. Yuan, [arXiv:2006.12447 [hep-ph]]; W. Cho, K. Y. Choi and S. M. Yoo, [arXiv:2007.04555 [hep-ph]]; H. J. He, Y. C. Wang and J. Zheng, [arXiv:2007.04963 [hep-ph]]; H. Davoudiasl, P. B. Denton and J. Gehrlein, [arXiv:2007.04989 [hep-ph]]; H. An and D. Yang, [arXiv:2006.15672 [hep-ph]]; J. Smirnov and J. F. Beacom, [arXiv:2002.04038 [hep-ph]]; N. F. Bell, J. B. Dent, B. Dutta, S. Ghosh, J. Kumar and J. L. Newstead, [arXiv:2006.12461 [hep-ph]]; W. Chao, Y. Gao and M. j. Jin, [arXiv:2006.16145 [hep-ph]]; S. Baek, J. Kim and P. Ko, [arXiv:2006.16876 [hep-ph]]; I. M. Bloch, A. Caputo, R. Essig, D. Redigolo, M. Sholapurkar and T. Volansky, [arXiv:2006.14521 [hep-ph]]; J. Bramante and N. Song, [arXiv:2006.14089 [hep-ph]]; H. M. Lee, [arXiv:2006.13183 [hep-ph]]; M. Baryakhtar, A. Berlin, H. Liu and N. Weiner, [arXiv:2006.13918 [hep-ph]]; D. Choudhury, S. Maharana, D. Sachdeva and V. Sahdev, [arXiv:2007.08205 [hep-ph]]; H. An and D. Yang, [arXiv:2006.15672 [hep-ph]]; Y. Ema, F. Sala and R. Sato, [arXiv:2007.09105 [hep-ph]]; S. Chigusa, M. Endo and K. Kohri, [arXiv:2007.01663 [hep-ph]]; A. Das and M. Sen, [arXiv:2104.00027 [hep-ph]]; S. Vagnozzi, L. Visinelli, P. Brax, A. C. Davis and J. Sakstein, [arXiv:2103.15834 [hep-ph]]; H. J. He, Y. C. Wang and J. Zheng, [arXiv:2012.05891 [hep-ph]]; A. Aboubrahim, M. Klasen and P. Nath, JHEP **02** (2021), 229 doi:10.1007/JHEP02(2021)229 [arXiv:2011.08053 [hep-ph]]; R. Harnik, R. Plestid, M. Pospelov and H. Ramani, Phys. Rev. D **103** (2021) no. 7, 075029 doi:10.1103/PhysRevD.103.075029 [arXiv:2010.11190 [hep-ph]]; B. Salehian, M. A. Gorji, H. Firouzjahi and S. Mukohyama, Phys. Rev. D **103** (2021) no. 6, 063526 doi:10.1103/PhysRevD.103.063526 [arXiv:2010.04491 [hep-ph]]; A. N. Khan, Phys. Lett. B **819** (2021), 136415 doi:10.1016/j.physletb.2021.136415 [arXiv:2008.10279 [hep-ph]]; A. Karozas, S. F. King, G. K. Leontaris and D. K. Papoulias, Phys. Rev. D **103** (2021) no. 3, 035019 doi:10.1103/PhysRevD.103.035019 [arXiv:2008.03295 [hep-ph]]; V. Brdar, A. Greljo, J. Kopp and T. Opferkuch, JCAP **01** (2021), 039 doi:10.1088/1475-7516/2021/01/039 [arXiv:2007.15563 [hep-ph]].

10. Y. Farzan, Mod. Phys. Lett. A **25** (2010), 2111-2120 doi:10.1142/S0217732310034018 [arXiv:1009.1234 [hep-ph]].

11. N. Sabti, J. Alvey, M. Escudero, M. Fairbairn and D. Blas, JCAP **01** (2020), 004 doi:10.1088/1475-7516/2020/01/004 [arXiv:1910.01649 [hep-ph]].

12. D. Feldman, Z. Liu and P. Nath, Phys. Rev. D **75** (2007), 115001 doi:10.1103/PhysRevD.75.115001 [arXiv:hep-ph/0702123 [hep-ph]].

13. S. Davidson, S. Hannestad and G. Raffelt, JHEP **05** (2000), 003 doi:10.1088/1126-6708/2000/05/003 [arXiv:hep-ph/0001179 [hep-ph]].

14. L. Chuzhoy and E. W. Kolb, JCAP **07** (2009), 014 doi:10.1088/1475-7516/2009/07/014 [arXiv:0809.0436 [astro-ph]].

15. R. M. Bandyopadhyay, J. Silk, J. E. Taylor and T. J. Maccarone, Mon. Not. Roy. Astron. Soc. **392** (2009) 1115 doi:10.1111/j.1365-2966.2008.14113.x [arXiv:0810.3674 [astro-ph]].

16. R. Diehl, D. Hartmann, P. Hoppe and N. Prantzos. (2002). Astronomy with Radioactivities, Springer.

17. E. Aprile *et al.* [XENON], Phys. Rev. Lett. **121** (2018) no. 11, 111302 doi:10.1103/PhysRevLett.121.111302 [arXiv:1805.12562 [astro-ph.CO]].
18. P. Agnes te al. (DarkSide-50), Phys. Rev. Lett. 121 (2018) 081307.
19. J. Schieck, G. Angloher, A. Bento, C. Bucci, L. Canonica, X. Defay, A. Erb, F. v. Feilitzsch, N. Ferreiro Iachellini, P. Gorla, A. Gütlein, D. Hauff, J. Jochum, M. Kiefer, H. Kluck, H. Kraus, J. C. Lanfranchi, J. Loebell, M. Mancuso, A. Münster, C. Pagliarone, F. Petricca, W. Potzel, F. Pröbst, R. Puig, F. Reindl, K. Schäffner, S. Schönert, W. Seidel, M. Stahlberg, L. Stodolsky, C. Strandhagen, R. Strauss, A. Tanzke, H. H. T. Thi, C. Türkoglu, M. Uffinger, A. Ulrich, I. Usherov, S. Wawoczny, M. Willers, M. Wüstrich and A. Zöller, PoS **ICHEP2016** (2016), 217 doi:10.22323/1.282.0217 [arXiv:1611.02113 [astro-ph.CO]].
20. C. C. Hsieh, L. Singh, C. P. Wu, J. W. Chen, H. C. Chi, C. P. Liu, M. K. Pandey and H. T. Wong, Phys. Rev. D **100** (2019) no. 7, 073001 doi:10.1103/PhysRevD.100.073001 [arXiv:1903.06085 [hep-ph]].
21. T. Siegert, R. Diehl, G. Khachatryan, M. G. H. Krause, F. Guglielmetti, J. Greiner, A. W. Strong and X. Zhang, Astron. Astrophys. **586** (2016), A84 doi:10.1051/0004-6361/201527510 [arXiv:1512.00325 [astro-ph.HE]].
22. J. F. Beacom and H. Yuksel, Phys. Rev. Lett. **97** (2006), 071102 doi:10.1103/PhysRevLett.97.071102 [arXiv:astro-ph/0512411 [astro-ph]].
23. P. Sizun, M. Casse and S. Schanne, Phys. Rev. D **74** (2006), 063514 doi:10.1103/PhysRevD.74.063514 [arXiv:astro-ph/0607374 [astro-ph]].
24. R. Harnik, Z. Liu and O. Palamara, JHEP **07** (2019), 170 doi:10.1007/JHEP07(2019)170 [arXiv:1902.03246 [hep-ph]].

Preliminary results of rich galaxy clusters' spatial distribution analysis on CfA2 Redshift Survey data: Compact objects or dark matter presence at redshift less 0.032

I. V. Arkhangelskaja

Division of Nuclear Physics and Technologies, National Research Nuclear University MEPhI,
Kashirskoe shosse, 31, Moscow, 115409, Russia
E-mail: IVArkhangelskaya@mephi.ru
https://home.mephi.ru/en/users/1525/public

A. M. Galper

Nuclear Physics and Astrophysics Division, Lebedev Physical Institute, Russian Academy of Sciences, Leninskiy prospekt 53, Moscow, 119991, Russia
Division of Nuclear Physics and Technologies, National Research Nuclear University MEPhI, Kashirskoe shosse, 31, Moscow, 115409, Russia

L. N. Khanh and D. N. Dorosheva

Division of Nuclear Physics and Technologies, National Research Nuclear University MEPhI,
Kashirskoe shosse, 31, Moscow, 115409, Russia

Preliminary results of the investigation of the properties of 13 clusters of galaxies from CfA2 redshift survey are discussed in the presented article. The distributions on absolute magnitude and luminosity represent two areas for clusters ##88, 1101, 1046, 142, 933, 1242, 1652, 107, 150, 316, 317, 961, 977. Redshifts of these clusters are in the region 0.002 – 0.032. The distributions on groups members position, absolute magnitude and luminosity represent two areas for these clusters. Galaxies from these areas are paired accordingly its spectral characteristics and position. Also several anomalies of spatial dynamic of galaxies in these clusters were separated. Such structure could be caused by dark matter presence inside cluster in configuration similar to Zeldovich pancake or gravitational lensing on compact object or dark matter blob located between galaxy cluster and observer. Several peculiarities have found on the spatial distributions of galaxies in clusters ##933, 142, 1046, and 1652. Moreover, these groups reveals associations with high-energy gamma-emission sources on Fermi/LAT 10-Year Point Source Catalog 4FGL DR2 data (4FGLJ1144.9+1937, 4FGLJ0152.2+3714, 4FGLJ1230.8+1223 and 4FGLJ1653.8+3945 correspondingly).These sources are active galaxies 3C 264, B2 0149+37, M87 and MRC 501. Furthermore, 3C 264 and M87 observed in subTeV energy band by VERITAS data. Joint observations of such clusters by orbital gamma-ray observatories with high angular resolution and ground-based Cherenkov air-shower experiments could possibly clarify the type of gravitational lensing and processes of particle acceleration in these objects especially highest energy of emitted gammas. Thus we propose including these and similar clusters in the programs of observations of the planned experiment GAMMA-400 (Gamma Astronomical Multifunctional Modular Apparatus) with angular resolution $\sim 0.01°$ at $E_\gamma = 100\ GeV$ and several TeV upper energy band. Also now it is discussed coordination of multiwavelength observations program of Cherenkov Telescope Array (CTA) and GAMMA-400 objects list for observations.

Keywords: Clusters of galaxies; CfA2 redshift survey.

1. Introduction

Galaxy clusters are the biggest gravitationally bound systems[1,2] reveal an independent approach to the problems related to the distribution of matter at various redshift ranges – particulars given in Ref. 4 and Ref. 5. It possible to use the results of its characteristics investigation to understand processes of formation of such systems and galaxies contained its possibly connecting dark matter halos (DMH) and to constrain cosmological models – see, for example Ref. 6 and Ref. 5. The differences of galaxies were identified by their luminosity, morphology, colour, etc. Moreover, following to Ref. 3 and Ref. 2, it allowed studying the relation between the topology and properties of galaxies at the large-scaling structure and concluding both cosmological parameters and galaxy formation mechanisms. Also the investigation of galaxies clusters relates to the dependence of the characteristics of galaxies on the surrounding medium properties, and the large-scale structure formation. Thus the cluster system dynamic investigation also should estimate possible DM presence due to analysis of several catalogues – for instance, CfA2 Redshift Survey.[8,14,17] Therefore, the large-scale distribution of matter in the Metagalaxy will be described by analysing quantities of galaxies to various limiting magnitudes and the redshift surveys – see, for example Ref. 5 and Ref. 16.

2. The Second CfA Redshift Survey data analysis

Preliminary results of the investigation of the properties of clusters of galaxies from The Second CfA Redshift Survey are discussed in the presented article.

The second CfA redshift survey was started between 1985 and 1995 due measurements of relative distances via redshifts for about 18000 bright galaxies in the northern sky. It contain data of 1971 galaxies groups (totally 6787 members) at galactic latitudes $b \geq 20°$ – see Ref. 17.

Early data from this catalogue were analysed in Ref. 15 and Ref. 14 and it were found several peculiarities for clusters ##933, 1242, 88, 142, 1046, 1101 in distributions of group members on absolute magnitude, angular velocity, etc.

The results of additional analysis of these clusters characteristics are discussed in the presented article. The mean values of it's characteristics are listed in the Table 1 (rows 1 – 5). Several additional peculiarities have found on the distributions of galaxies inside these clusters on magnitude and absolute magnitude on CfA2 data. The examples of such distributions for clusters of galaxies #142 and #88 are presented at figures Fig. 1(a), Fig. 1(b) and Fig. 2(a), Fig. 2(b) correspondingly. Dual structure was separated at distributions of galaxies inside cluster on magnitude and absolute magnitude for these two clusters. Bifurcation points are $m_{142} = 14.5 \pm 0.2$ and $M_{142} = 19.5 \pm 0.2$ for group #142, also $m_{88} = 14.5 \pm 0.2$ and $M_{88} = 19.0 \pm 0.2$ for one #88.

Than we have separate clusters of galaxies contain more than 20 members for subsequent analysis. The mean values of characteristics for other 8 clusters from this subsample are listed in the Table 1 (rows 6 – 13). Fig. 3(a), Fig. 4(a) and

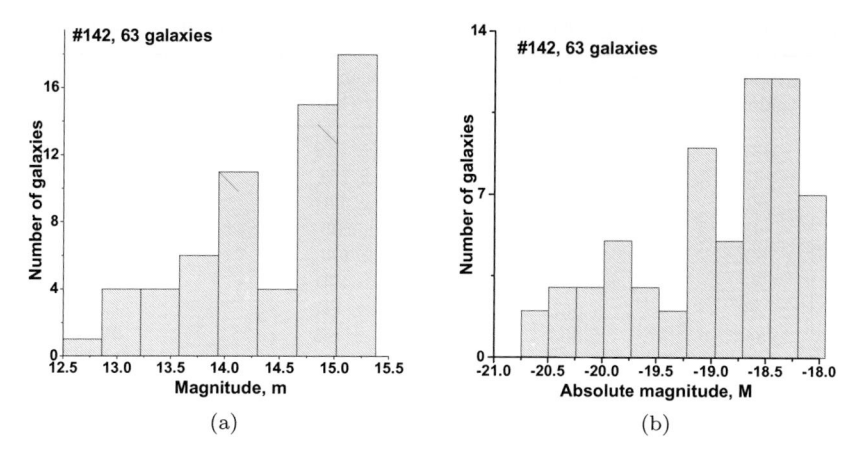

Fig. 1. Several peculiarities on the distributions of galaxies inside cluster #142 on CfA2 data. (a) Graph for distribution of galaxies on magnitude. (b) Graph for distribution of galaxies on absolute magnitude.

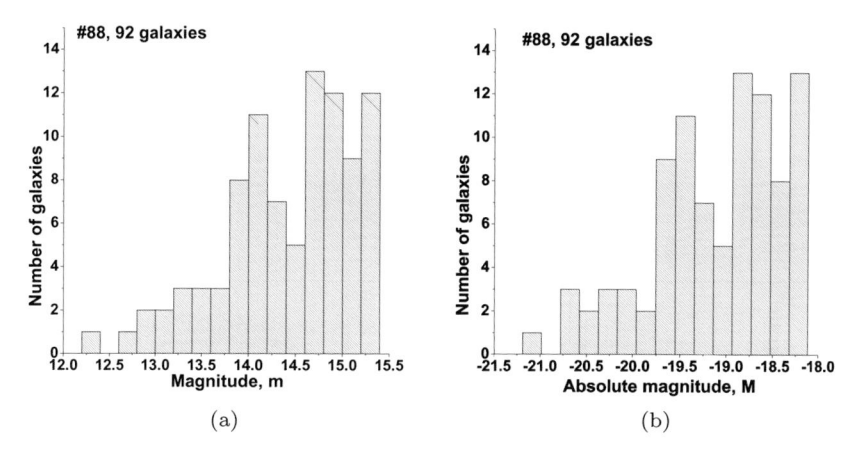

Fig. 2. Several peculiarities on the distributions of galaxies inside cluster #88 on CfA2 data. (a) Graph for distribution of galaxies on magnitude. (b) Graph for distribution of galaxies on absolute magnitude.

Fig. 6(a) shows the other examples of distributions of galaxies inside cluster with members numbers both than 50 and 20 on magnitude for groups #1046, #933 and #1652 correspondingly. Graphs Fig. 3(b), Fig. 4(b) and Fig. 6(b) represents the distributions of galaxies in these clusters on absolute magnitude. Dual structure also was separated at distributions of galaxies inside cluster on magnitude and absolute magnitude for all investigated clusters without any correlation with members numbers. The obtained bifurcation points in the distributions of galaxies in these clusters on magnitude are $m_{1046} = 13.8 \pm 0.2$, $m_{933} = 14.3 \pm 0.2$, $m_{1652} = 14.9 \pm 0.2$ and ones on absolute magnitude are $M_{1046} = -17.9 \pm 0.2$, $M_{933} = -19.8 \pm 0.2$, $M_{1652} = -20.0 \pm 0.2$.

Table 1. The mean values of characteristics for several clusters of galaxies on CfA2 data.

Cluster number	Amount of galaxies	RQF – Relative quantities false (%)	Heliocentric velocity (km/s)	Mean distance of member of group from its centre (Mpc)
1046	337	2.328	1847 ± 519	1.423
1101	118	0.784	7433 ± 751	1.006
88	92	1.426	5040 ± 440	1.357
933	63	0.372	6656 ± 703	0.497
142	63	0.721	4868 ± 496	0.667
1242	26	0.406	2750 ± 190	0.384
1652	28	1.561	9324 ± 427	1.394
107	34	0.303	1530 ± 395	0.354
150	20	1.629	4964 ± 323	0.821
316	21	0.294	6068 ± 269	0.450
317	23	0.504	6152 ± 288	0.564
961	27	2.422	1264 ± 167	0.481
977	20	0.485	6288 ± 402	0.407

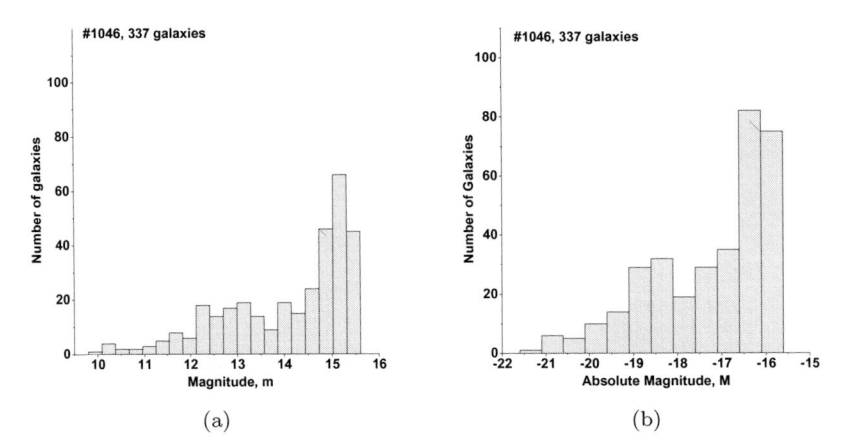

Fig. 3. Several peculiarities on the distributions of galaxies inside cluster #1046 on CfA2 data. (a) Graph for distribution of galaxies on magnitude. (b) Graph for distribution of galaxies on absolute magnitude.

Moreover several peculiarities have found on the distributions on angular velocity and absolute magnitude together with distributions on velocity and distance to cluster centre. Such distributions for clusters of galaxies #142 and #88 are presented at Fig. 7(a), Fig. 7(b) and Fig. 8(a), Fig. 8(b) correspondingly. Dual structure was separated on the distributions of galaxies inside cluster on angular velocity and absolute magnitude for these two clusters with bifurcation points similar to results of analysis of Fig. 1(b) and Fig. 2(b). Also dual structure appear on the distributions on velocity and distance to cluster centre with bifurcation points $Rc_{142} = 0.70 \pm 0.05$ and $Rc_{88} = 1.00 \pm 0.05$ for clusters #142 and #88.

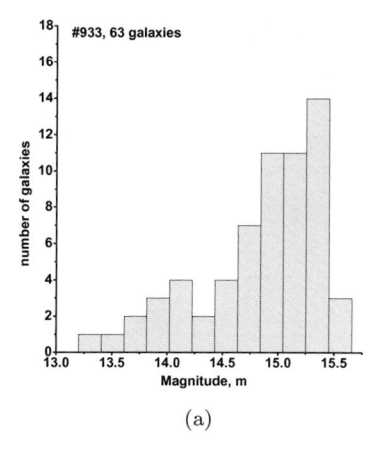

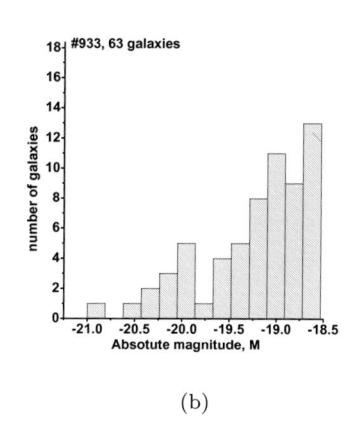

Fig. 4. Several peculiarities on the distributions of galaxies inside cluster #933 on CfA2 data. (a) Graph for distribution of galaxies on magnitude. (b) Graph for distribution of galaxies on absolute magnitude.

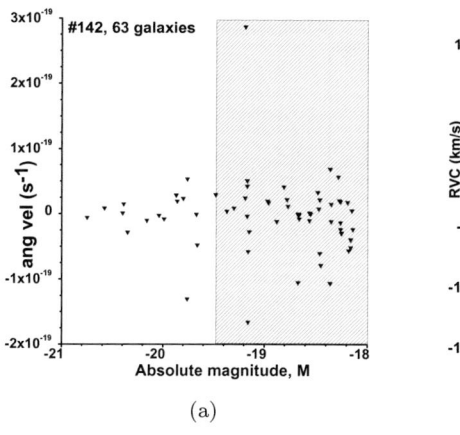

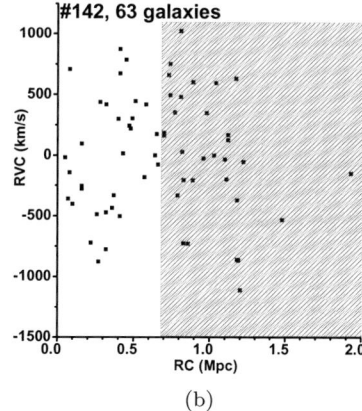

Fig. 5. Several peculiarities on the distributions of galaxies inside cluster #142 on CfA2 data. (a) Graph for distribution of galaxies on angular velocity and absolute magnitude. (b) Graph for distribution of galaxies on velocity and distance to cluster centre.

The distributions on angular velocity and absolute magnitude groups #1046, #933 and #1652 are presented at Fig. 9(a), Fig. 10(a) and Fig. 6(a) correspondingly. Dual structure reveals on these figures with bifurcation points similar to results of analysis of Fig. 3(a), Fig. 4(a) and Fig. 6(a) look like clusters #142 and #88. Moreover dual structure appear on the distributions on velocity and distance to cluster centre with bifurcation points $Rc_{1046} = 1.7 \pm 0.1$, $Rc_{933} = 0.52 \pm 0.05$ and $Rc_{1652} = 1.5 \pm 0.1$ for clusters #1046, #933 and #1652 correspondingly.

The spatial distribution of galaxies in listed in the Table 1 clusters were analysed. Figure 12(a) represents such distribution for cluster #1046. Dual structure

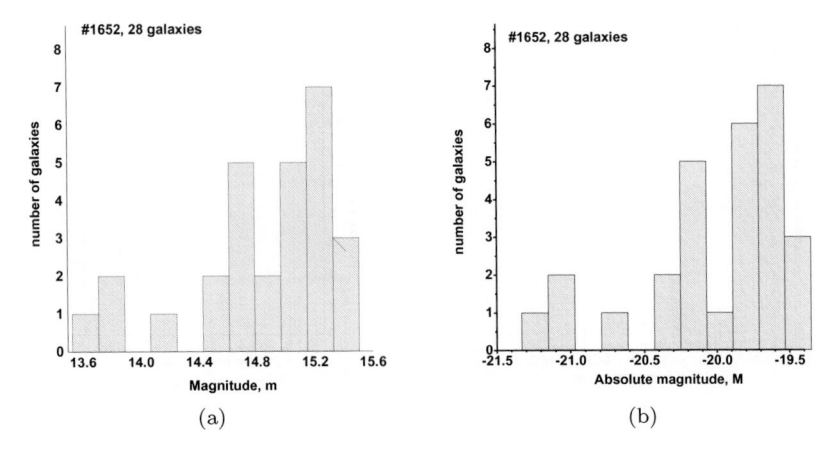

Fig. 6. Several peculiarities on the distributions of galaxies inside cluster #1652 on CfA2 data. (a) Graph for distribution of galaxies on magnitude. (b) Graph for distribution of galaxies on absolute magnitude.

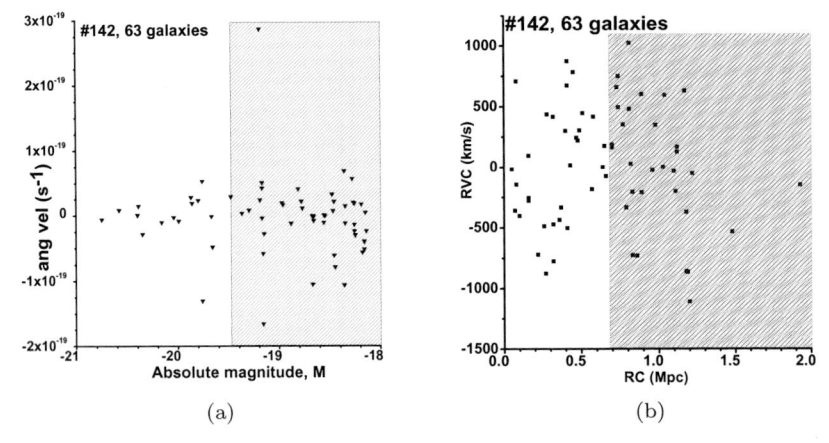

Fig. 7. Several peculiarities on the distributions of galaxies inside cluster #142 on CfA2 data. (a) Graph for distribution of galaxies on angular velocity and absolute magnitude. (b) Graph for distribution of galaxies on velocity and distance to cluster centre. Shaded regions correspond areas from right side of bifurcation points on Fig. 1.

were separated inside this cluster accordingly to preliminary analysis rezults — see Fig. 12(b). Similar peculiarities have found on the spatial distributions for other clusters. The examples are presented at Fig. 13, Fig. 14 and Fig. 15.

The results of preliminary data analysis have shown that the distributions on groups members position, magnitude, absolute magnitude, angular velocity and absolute magnitude also with ones on velocity and distance to cluster centre and represent two areas for clusters ##88, 1101, 1046, 142, 933, 1242, 1652, 107, 150, 316, 317, 961 and 977. Redshifts of these clusters are in the region 0.002 – 0.032.

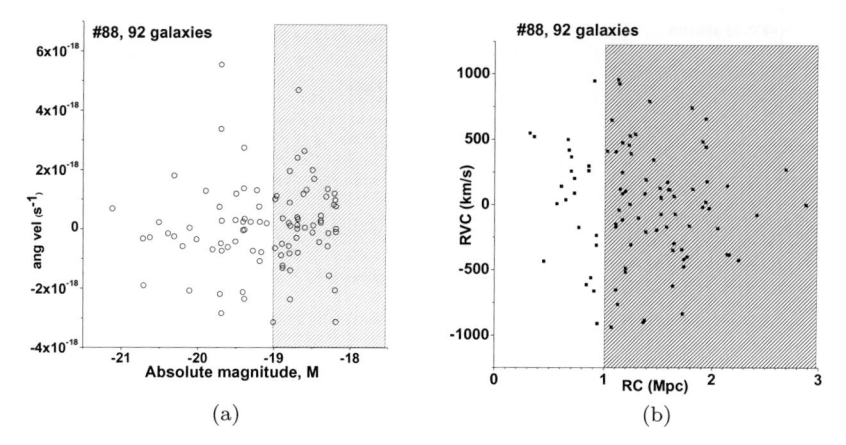

Fig. 8. Several peculiarities on the distributions of galaxies inside cluster #88 on CfA2 data. (a) Graph for distribution of galaxies on angular velocity and absolute magnitude. (b) Graph for distribution of galaxies on velocity and distance to cluster centre. Shaded regions correspond areas from right side of bifurcation points on Fig. 2.

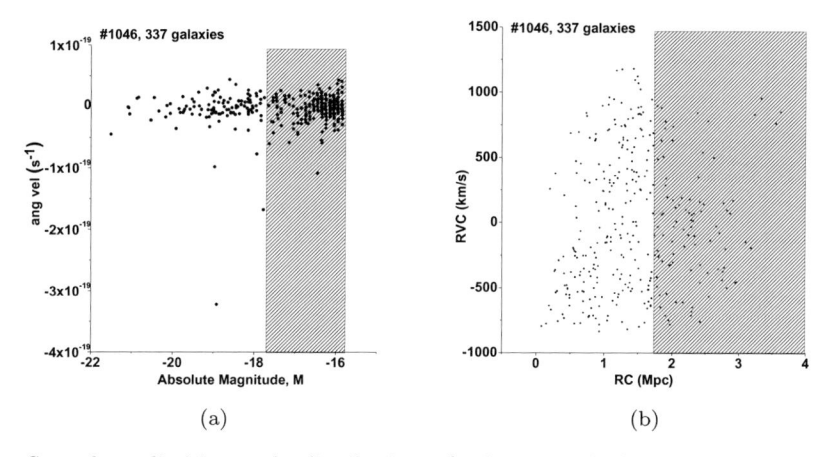

Fig. 9. Several peculiarities on the distributions of galaxies inside cluster #1046 on CfA2 data. (a) Graph for distribution of galaxies on angular velocity and absolute magnitude. (b) Graph for distribution of galaxies on velocity and distance to cluster centre. Shaded regions correspond areas from right side of bifurcation points on Fig. 3.

Galaxies from these areas are paired accordingly its spectral characteristics and position. Unfortunately direct data analysis not allow understanding of reality of such dual structure because it could be caused by several selection effects.

Let's try to investigate dynamic of these systems using Nonlinear Time Series Analysis methods – see, for instance, Ref. 9. Unfortunately real time variables are absent in the analysed systems. But dynamic behavior of cluster's members strongly depend of its velocities and distances to cluster centre.[10] We have construct phase space cluster of galaxies #88 using values of redshift, coordinates, magnitude,

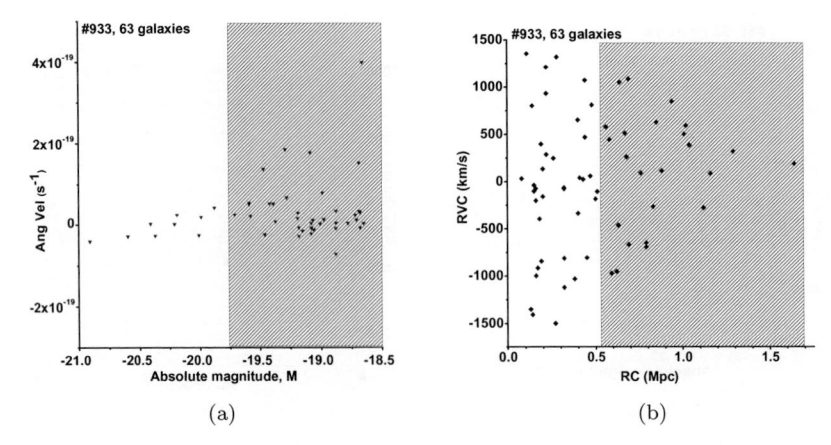

Fig. 10. Several peculiarities on the distributions of galaxies inside cluster #933 on CfA2 data. (a) Graph for distribution of galaxies on angular velocity and absolute magnitude. (b) Graph for distribution of galaxies on velocity and distance to cluster centre. Shaded regions correspond areas from right side of bifurcation points on Fig. 4.

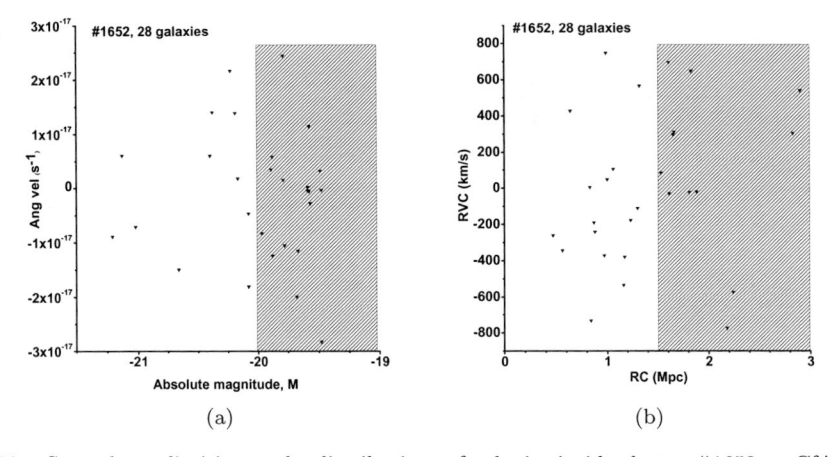

Fig. 11. Several peculiarities on the distributions of galaxies inside cluster #1652 on CfA2 data. (a) Graph for distribution of galaxies on angular velocity and absolute magnitude. (b) Graph for distribution of galaxies on velocity and distance to cluster centre. Shaded regions correspond areas from right side of bifurcation points on Fig. 6.

absolute magnitude and distance to centre. We have use ratio between distance to centre and tangential velocity as time similar variable in the presented article and constructed simple attractors in this phase space for first attempt of investigation of dynamic of system. Let's separate basins of attractors correspondingly to bifurcation points on the analysable distributions. Accordingly to preliminary results of analysis we have obtained two attractors in the phase space of cluster #88 which concludes real dual structure of this system. Figure 16 represents three dimension projection of obtained attractors.

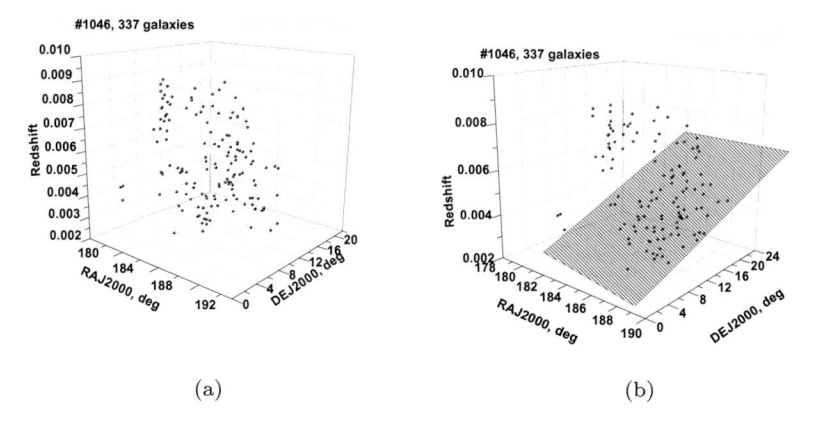

Fig. 12. The spatial distributions of galaxies for cluster #1046 on CfA2 data (a) and dual structure appearance on this distribution (b).

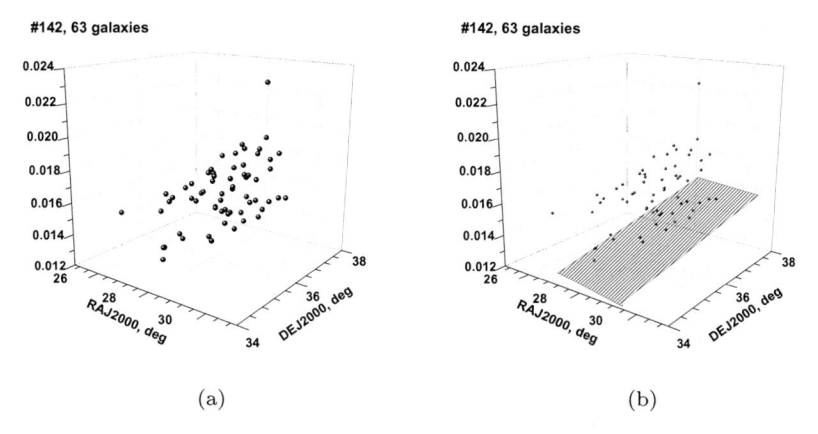

Fig. 13. The spatial distributions of galaxies for cluster #142 on CfA2 data (a) and dual structure appearance on this distribution (b).

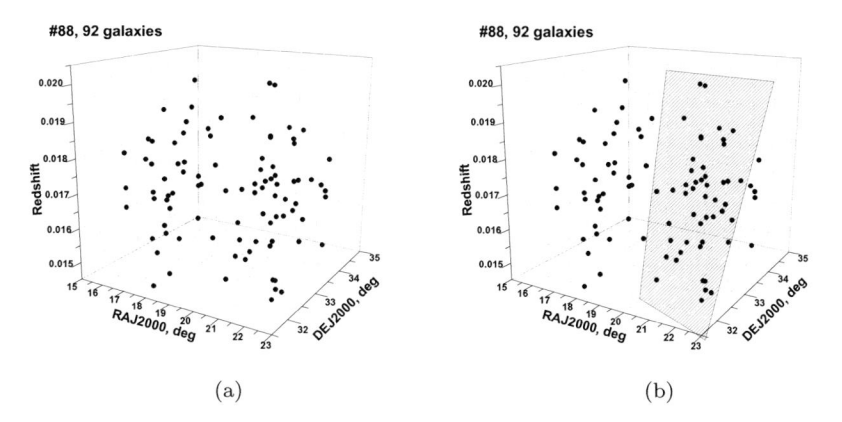

Fig. 14. The spatial distributions of galaxies for cluster #142 on CfA2 data (a) and dual structure appearance on this distribution (b).

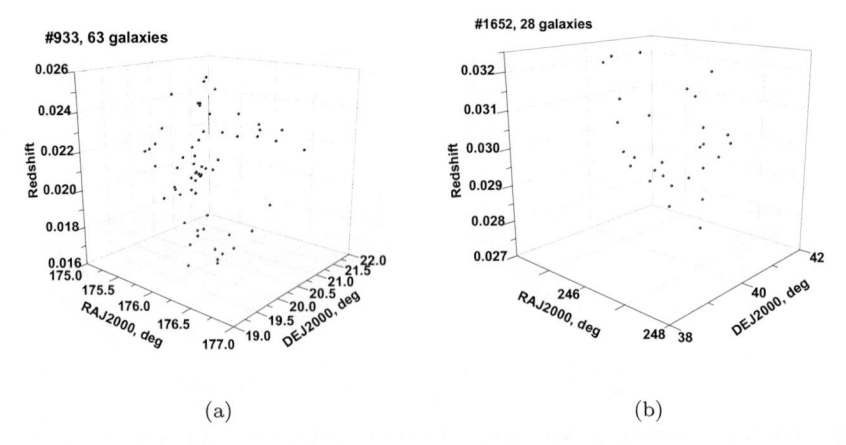

Fig. 15. The spatial distributions of galaxies for several clusters on CfA2 data. (a) Graph for cluster #933. (b) Graph for cluster #1652.

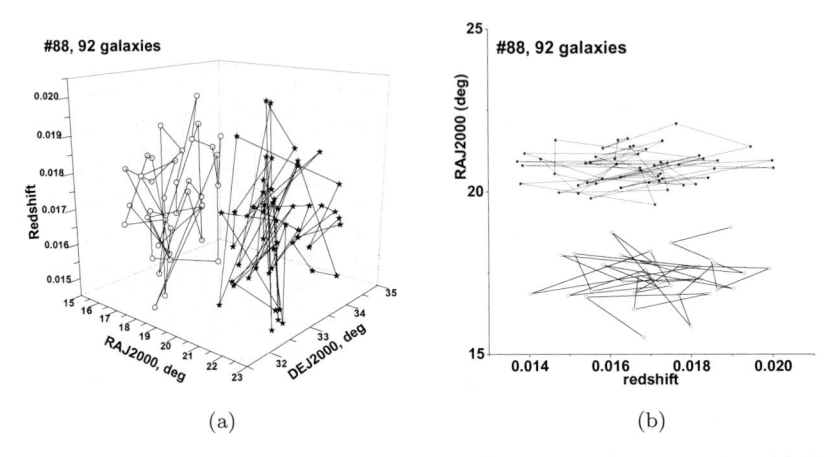

Fig. 16. The projections of six-dimensional system of attractors for cluster #88. (a) Projection in three-dimension space with axes corresponds to coordinates and redshift. (b) Two dimension projection with axes corresponds to RA and redshift.

3. Conclusions

Preliminary results of the properties of 13 clusters of galaxies from CfA2 redshift survey (##88, 1101, 1046, 142, 933, 1242, 1652, 107, 150, 316, 317, 961, 977) are presented. Redshifts of these clusters are in the region 0.002 – 0.032. The distributions on magnitude, absolute magnitude and angular velocity, etc represent two areas for these clusters. Galaxies from these areas are paired accordingly its spectral characteristics and position. Also several anomalies of spatial dynamic of galaxies in these clusters were separated.

The presence of such structure allows conclude two alternatives. In the first one dark matter presence inside cluster in configuration similar to Zeldovich pancake. Second case is gravitational lensing on compact object or dark matter blob located between galaxy cluster and observer.

Also several peculiarities have found on the spatial distributions of galaxies in clusters##933, 142, 1046, and 1652. Moreover, groups ##933, 142, 1046, and 1652 reveals associations with high-energy gamma-emission sources on Fermi/LAT 10–Year Point Source Catalog 4FGL DR2 data (4FGLJ1144.9+1937, 4FGLJ0152.2+3714, 4FGLJ1230.8+1223 and 4FGLJ1653.8+3945 correspondingly).

Furthermore, 4FGLJ1144.9+1937 and 4FGLJ1230.8+1223 observed in subTeV energy band by VERITAS data.

Joint observations of such clusters by orbital gamma-ray observatories with high angular resolution and ground-based Cherenkov air-shower experiments could possibly clarify the type of influence to groups characteristics (gravitational lensing or object inside cluster) and processes of particle acceleration in these objects especially highest energy of emitted gammas. Thus we propose including these and similar clusters in the programs of observations of the planned experiment GAMMA-400 (Gamma Astronomical Multifunctional Modular Apparatus) with angular resolution $\sim 0.01°$ at $E_\gamma = 100\ GeV$ and upper energy band boundary about several TeV. Also now the coordination of multiwavelength observations program of Cherenkov Telescope Array (CTA) and GAMMA-400 is discussed.

Acknowledgments

Authors thank for the support from National Research Nuclear University MEPhI in the framework of the Russian Academic Excellence Project (contract No. 02.a03.21.0005, 27.08.2013).

References

1. F. M. Rieger and A. Levinson, Radio Galaxies at VHE Energies, *Galaxies 6*, **116** (2018).
2. Chervin F. P. Laporte and Simon D. M. White, The re-distribution of matter in the cores of galaxy clusters, *MNRAS 451* **1177–1189** (2015).
3. Y.-Y. Choi, C. Park, J. Kim, J. R. Gott, D. H. Weinberg, M. S. Vogeley, and S. S. Kim (for the SDSS Collaboration), Galaxy clustering topology in the Sloan Digital Sky Survey main galaxy sample: A test for galaxy formation models. Cosmology and Nongalactic Astrophysics, astro-ph.CO.arXiv:1005.0256 (2018).

4. G. O. Abell, Ap. J. Suppl, The Distribution of Rich Clusters of Galaxies, *Astrophysical Journal Supplement, vol. 3* **211** (1958).
5. Z. L.Wen, J. L. Han, and F. Yang, A catalogue of clusters of galaxies identified from all sky surveys of 2MASS, WISE, and SuperCOSMOS, *MNRAS 475* **343** (2018).
6. A. P. Mahtessian and V. G. Movsessian, List of groups of galaxies based on the CfA2 redshift survey, *Astrophys, 53* **70** (2010).
7. John Huchra, (Harvard-Smithsonian Center for Astrophysics) https://www.cfa.harvard.edu/~dfabricant/huchra/ .
8. A. P. Mahtessian, V. H. Movsessian, and V. M. Mahtessian, Relationship of Markarian galaxies with their surroundings, *Astrophys, 40* **285** (1997).
9. H. Kantz and T. Schreiber, Nonlinear Time Series Analysis, *Cambridge University Press, 1st edn.*, (Cambridge, UK, 1997).
10. T. Buzug and G.Pfister, Optimal delay time and embedding dimension for delay-time coordinates by analysis of the glocal static and local dynamic behavior of strange attractors, *Phys. Rev. A 45* **7073–7084** (1992).
11. F. Takens, Detecting strange attractors in fluid turbulence, (In Rand, D. & Young, L. S. eds.) *Dynamical Systems and Turbulence, vol. 898 of Lecture Notes in Mathematics*, **366–381** (Springer-Verlag, Berlin, 1981).
12. J. Ballet and Fermi-LAT Collab, Fermi Large Area Telescope Fourth Source Catalog, *ApJS 247, 33* (2020).
13. R. Mukherjee (for the VERITAS Collab), Observing the Energetic Universe at Very High Energies with the VERITAS Gamma Ray Observatory, *Advances in Space Research* (2018).
14. L. N. Khanh, I.V. Arkhangelskaja, A. M. Galper and D. N. Dorosheva, Rich Galaxy Clusters from CfA2 Redshift Survey: Spatial Dynamic and High-Energy Gamma-Emission, *Physics of Atomic Nuclei Vol. 83, No. 2* **300–306** (2020).
15. I. V. Arkhangelskaja, L. N. Khanh, A. M. Galper and D. N. Dorosheva, The results of analysis of Rich Galaxy Clusters from CfA2 Redshift Survey spatial distribution/I. V. Arkhangelskaja, L. N. Khanh, A. M. Galper and D. N. Dorosheva *J. Phys.: Conf. Ser. vol. 1690* , ID:012025 (2020).
16. T. E. Jeltema, J. Kehayias, and S. Profumo, Gamma Rays from Clusters and Groups of Galaxies: Cosmic Rays versus Dark Matter, *Phys. Rev. D 80, 023005* (2009).
17. A. P. Mahtessian V. H. Movsessian, and V. M. Mahtessian, Relationship of Markarian galaxies with their surroundings, *Astrophys vol. 40* **285** (1997).
18. A. A. Leonov, A. M. Galper, N. P. Topchiev, A. V. Bakaldin, O. D. Dalkarov, E. A. Dzhivelikyan, A. E. Egorov, M. D. Kheymits, V. V. Mikhailov, P. Picozza, R. Sparvoli, S. I. Suchkov, Yu. T. Yurkin, and V. G. Zverev, Multiple Coulomb scattering method to reconstruct low-energy gamma–ray direction in the GAMMA-400 space-based gamma–ray telescope, *Adv. Space Res 63*, **3420-3427** (2019).
19. N. P. Topchiev, A. M. Galper, I. V. Arkhangelskaja, A. I. Arkhangelskiy, A. V. Bakaldin, I. V. Chernysheva, O. D. Dalkarov, A. E. Egorov, Yu. V. Gusakov, M. D. Kheymits, A. A. Leonov, P. Yu. Naumov, N. Yu. Pappe, M. F. Runtso, Yu. I. Stozhkov, S. I. Suchkov, Yu. T. Yurkin and V. G. Zverev, Space-based GAMMA-400 mission for direct gamma- and cosmic-ray observations, *IOP Conf. Series: Journal of Physics: Conf. Series 1181* (2019).

20. I. V. Arkhangelskaja, A. I. Arkhangelskiy, E. N. Chasovikov, A. M. Galper, M. D. Kheymits, A. E. Murchenko and Y. T. Yurkin, The Counting and Triggers Signals Formation System for Gamma-telescope GAMMA-400, *Physics Proce: Conf. Ser. 675, 032015* **212-219** (2016).
21. R. A. Ong and CTA Consortium, *in Proceedings of the 7th Roma International Conference on Astroparticle Physics* (Rome, Italy, 2019), (Ed. by M. De Vincenzi, A. Capone and A. Morselli, EPJ Web Conf. 209, 01038) (2019).

Probing the nature of dark matter with Milky Way subhaloes

M. R. Lovell

Science Institute, University of Iceland,
107 Reykjavík, Iceland
E-mail: lovell@hi.is

The nature of dark matter is one of the most pressing questions in modern physics. Efforts to answer this question have centred on observations that determine its impact on the properties of galaxies plus attempts to detect rare events in which the dark matter indirectly generates photons. In this talk I presented work on using the properties of Milky Way satellite galaxies to constrain models of self-interacting dark matter (SIDM) and warm dark matter (WDM). First I used N-body simulations of an SIDM model with a very large self-interaction at low relative velocities ($\sigma > 100$ cm^{2}gr^{-1}) to demonstrate that subhaloes in such models undergo gravothermal collapse and increase the diversity of satellite matter distributions in line with inferences from observations. Second, I considered the radial distribution of subhaloes in WDM simulations from the point-of-view of stellar stream gap constraints. I showed that the subhalo population within 50 kpc of the host halo centre is comprised of massive satellites that have sunk under dynamical friction. Given that the abundance and structure of massive satellites in WDM is very similar to the fiducial cold dark matter (CDM) model, the differences between the subhalo populations in the two models in the inner halo are much smaller than for the halo as a whole, and therefore the stellar stream gaps statistics, which are only available out to 30 kpc, are not as powerful at discriminating between the models as previously anticipated. I ended with a brief presentation of estimates for the production rate of X-ray photons in dark matter decay, and predicted that the velocity dispersion of X-ray decay lines to be probed in nearby galaxy clusters will have values in the range [500,800] kms^{-1}.

Keywords: Dark matter

1. Introduction

Observations of a wide variety of astrophysical objects have returned evidence for the existence of an invisible substance that constitutes $\sim 82\%$ of the mass of the Universe. These observations include the anisotropies of the cosmic microwave background radiation (CMB)[1] and the rotation curves of galaxies (e.g. Ref 2). All of these observations are consistent with the presence of matter that is dynamically cold, at least on the scales of massive galaxies and larger, and does not interact with light; this material is therefore dubbed cold dark matter (CDM).

The CMB and rotation curves studies probe the properties of dark matter on scales typically larger than 10 kpc. However, on scales of dwarf galaxies, the close match between observations on the one hand and predictions for gwalaxy abundance and structure from CDM N-body simulations start to break down.[3–5] In part, such discrepancies can be explained by astrophysical processes that change the properties of dark matter haloes, through reionisation[6,7] and supernova feedback.[8,9] However, it is not clear that astrophysics alone provides the best match to observations.[10–12] In the context of the non-detection of CDM-type dark matter candidates with either direct detection[13,14] or γ-ray indirect detection experiments,[15,16] it is important to consider dark matter candidates that behave somewhat differently, both in their astrophysical impact on structure formation and in their detection abilities.

In this talk I covered three topics: two in the properties of Milky Way (MW) satellites and a third on the potential for detection of dark matter decay in X-rays. The two MW subhaloes topics concern very different dark matter models: first, an extreme velocity dependent self-interacting dark matter (SIDM) model in the context of MW satellite densities, and second, the effect of the warm dark matter (WDM) model consequences on the spatial distribution of both satellites and non-luminous subhaloes. The dark matter decay results are applicable to any model in which dark matter undergoes two-body decay that does not affect the galaxy kinematics significantly.

These proceedings are organised into three sections. I describe the SIDM work in Section. 2, the WDM work in Section. 3, and the dark matter decay results in Section. 4. The papers from which these three sections were derived are Ref. 17, Ref. 18 and Ref. 19 respectively.

2. Gravothermal collapse in SIDM and the densities of Milky Way satellites

The masses of MW satellites have been a popular probe of dark matter and astrophysics models for at least 10 years. Refs. 5, 20 showed that, at least at a first glance, CDM simulations predicted the existence of satellites more massive and dense than any of the observed MW satellites at the same time that other studies reported evidence for cored dark matter density profiles.[21] A successful dark matter model will have to explain both of these observations simultaneously. Ref. 22 argued that cored SIDM dark matter profiles were insufficiently dense to explain the very high reported masses of the MW's ultrafaint dwarf galaxies, and therefore in order for these models to be viable a fraction of SIDM subhaloes below a given mass scale would need to undergo the process of gravothermal collapse, by which material starts rapidly flowing towards the halo centre and creates a density profile much steeper than in CDM.[23]

For Ref. 22 we had run an extreme model of SIDM that would cause gravothermal collapse to occur in MW satellites within a Hubble time. It featured a strong cross section-velocity dependence: a cross section $\sigma \sim 100$ cm^{2}g^{-1} at interactions velocities < 30 kms^{-1}. This cross-section was chosen in order to induce gravothermal collapse without relying on stripping of the satellite outskirts[24] and to avoid violating published bounds on high velocity interaction cross-sections from cluster mergers;[25] we do not attempt to match the reported measurements of ~ 1 cm^{2}g^{-1} cross-sections at $\sim$1500-2000 kms^{-1} by Refs. 26, 27. Our goal in Ref. 17 was to

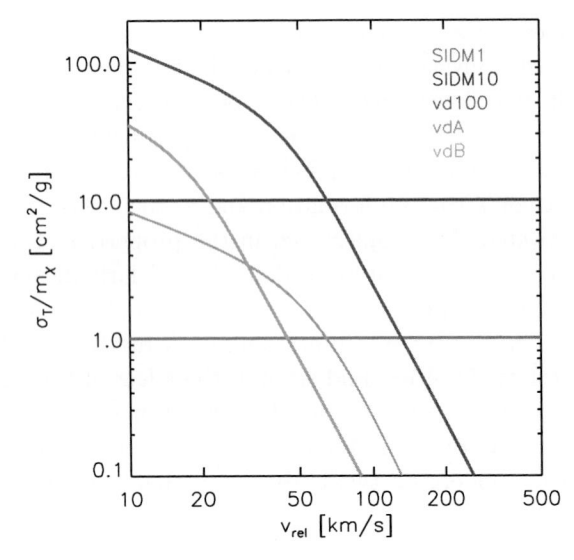

Fig. 1. Self-interaction cross section as a function of particle relative velocity for five SIDM models. The primary model of interest in our study was vd100, which is shown in red. We also show two further velocity-dependent SIDM models, labelled vdA (grey) and vdB (cyan), plus two velocity independent models with cross-sections ~ 1 cm^{2}g^{-1} (SIDM1, green) and ~ 10 cm^{2}g^{-1} (SIDM10, blue). Reproduced from Ref. 17.

investigate the abundance and density of subhaloes in this model, which we dubbed 'vd100'. We present the velocity dependence of the cross section for this model and other SIDM models in Fig. 1.

We explored the properties of the vd100 model using the same simulation that we ran for Ref. 22. This was zoomed resimulation of the Aquarius Aq-A3 MW halo-analogue[28] using the same initial conditions as for the original CDM simulation but with the inclusion of vd100 model self-interactions. The simulation was run with the Arepo code.[29] The host halo virial mass $M_{200} = 1.9 \times 10^{12}$ M$_\odot$, the simulation particle mass was 4.9×10^4 M$_\odot$, and the gravitational softening length $\epsilon = 120.5$ pc. The cosmological parameters were consistent with the WMAP first year results.[30] The same code, simulation parameters and cosmological parameters were used in the other four SIDM simulations.

We looked for evidence of gravothermal collapse through the following methodology. We computed circular velocity curves for subhaloes within each of these simulations that were located within 300 kpc of the centre of the host halo, and parametrised the structure of velocity curves with two numbers: the maximum value of the circular velocity, $V_{\max}$, and the radius $r_{\max}$ at which $V_{\max}$ is attained. $V_{\max}$ is often interpreted as a proxy for the subhalo mass, and $r_{\max}$ as a measure of concentration at fixed $V_{\max}$, with larger $r_{\max}$ corresponding to a less concentrated halo. We present contour plots for the $V_{\max} - r_{\max}$ distributions of haloes in the CDM, SIDM10, vdB, and vd100 simulation subhaloes in Fig. 2.

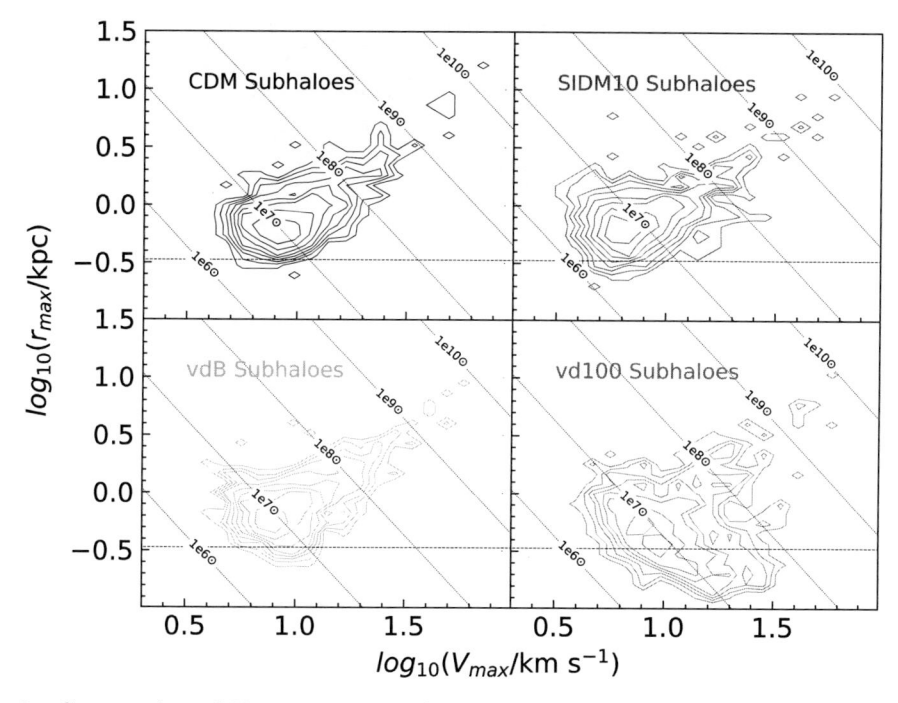

Fig. 2. Contour plots of V_{max} - r_{max} values for subhaloes in four models: CDM (top left panel), SIDM10 (top right), vdB (bottom left) and vd100 (bottom right). Diagonal lines denote parameter space along which the mass enclosed with r_{max} is constant. The horizontal lines denote the radius corresponding to 2.8× the softening length of the simulation and therefore marks the hard resolution limit. Reproduced from Ref. 17.

The vdB subhaloes follow the same relation in V_{max} - r_{max} as their CDM equivalents despite their very high cross-sections at low velocities, > 20 cm^{2}gr^{-1}. By contrast, a large population of vd100 subhaloes have r_{max} well below the CDM relation: the subhaloes are therefore denser than CDM and have undergone gravothermal collapse. We explore this trend further for a sample of subhalo circular velocity curves that have V_{max} values in the range $V_{max} = [25, 35]$ kms^{-1} from the CDM and vd100 runs, which we present in Fig. 3.

The number of vd100 subhaloes with $r_{max} > 1$ kpc is approximately the same as the number of CDM subhaloes in the same V_{max} bin, since the implementation of velocity-dependent SIDM has only a minor impact on the halo mass function[a]. From radii < 2 kpc these vd100 subhaloes' circular velocity profiles decline much faster than their CDM counterparts as a consequence of their cored profiles. However, there also exists a population of approximately twice as many vd100 subhaloes with $r_{max} < 1$ kpc. The accurate values of r_{max} and V_{max} for these subhaloes

---

[a]In models for which the cross-section is large at high velocities, as is common for velocity independent models, interactions between subhaloes and the host can evaporate subhaloes and suppress the mass function.[11,17]

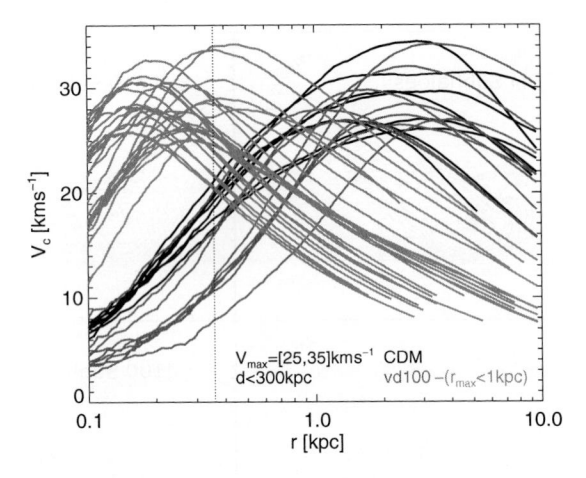

Fig. 3. Circular velocity curves for subhaloes in the CDM and vd100 simulations that have $V_{max} = [25, 35]$ kms^{-1}. CDM subhaloes are shown in black. vd100 subhaloes that have $r_{max} > 1$ kpc are shown in red, and vd100 subhaloes with $r_{max} < 1$ kpc are shown in pink. Reproduced from Ref. 17.

are unknown because the circular velocity curves are still rising at the softening resolution limit; we therefore just state that these haloes have indeed undergone collapse and are concentrated enough to explain the ultrafaint dwarf masses at the same time that the uncollapsed cored haloes can fit the brighter satellites.[22] We also show in Ref. 17 that the density profiles of these objects is a power law of slope -3.

3. The WDM subhalo distribution and implications for gaps in streams studies

For the second part of the talk I switched to MW satellites in the WDM cosmology. The motivation for this model arises from clues that it might, under some circumstances, be a better match to observations than CDM[12] and also that its primary particle physics candidate, the sterile neutrino[31,32] may have been detected in X-ray decay.[33,34] This model suppresses the number of dwarf mass haloes[35] and lowers their concentrations[10] relative to CDM. The WDM model can therefore be constrained by observations that measure the number and concentration of dwarf haloes, especially dark matter haloes so small that they never form stars.

One such method is to attempt to detect gaps in stellar streams. Globular clusters and satellite galaxies experience stripping of their outer layers as they orbit within the gravitational field of their host galaxies, leaving behind a smooth stream of stars. The structure of the stream will be disturbed by interactions with other structures, such as dark matter subhaloes. The effect of dark matter physics on the abundance and density of subhaloes can therefore be inferred from the presence of the gaps in streams.[36–38]

Several studies have claimed strong limits on WDM in particular from the apparent detection of such gaps in streams,[37,38] although the nature of dark matter substructures as a cause is disputed. For the paper from which this talk section was derived, I examined the subhaloes that populate the region where streams can be probed for gaps given current observational constraints, i.e. $\lesssim 30$ kpc from the MW centre, in CDM and in WDM and analysed the difference between these inner-host subhaloes on the one hand and subhaloes at all radii on the other.

For this project, we estimated the subhalo population properties using two N-body simulations, one of CDM and one of a WDM . Our two companion simulations were CDM and WDM variations of the COCO volume;[39,40] a zoomed simulation of a spherical region ~ 28 Mpc in radius with a dark matter simulation particle mass of $\sim 2 \times 10^5$ $M_\odot$. The WDM model was a 3.3 keV thermal relic; this was chosen to be consistent with a set of Lyman-α forest constraints[41] and is also a reasonable approximation to the matter power spectrum of the sterile neutrino that could explain the reported 3.55 keV line.[12] We identified 26 MW-halo analogues: these we selected to be in the mass range $[1.0, 1.5] \times 10^{12}$ $M_\odot$, and also to be isolated in that the distance to any larger halo was > 1 Mpc[b].

We first considered the abundance of subhaloes in two mass bins: $[10^7, 10^8]$ $M_\odot$ and $[10^8, 10^9]$ $M_\odot$. We computed the number of subhaloes in these mass bins for CDM and WDM in two radius bins: < 40 kpc from the halo centre to represent stream gap-generating subhaloes and < 300 kpc for the subhalo population at large. Any changes in these quantities will be driven by two factors: the larger number of haloes generated in CDM plus the additional stripping of subhaloes in WDM due to their lower concentrations. In order to ascertain the contribution of these two factors we therefore performed a 'hybrid' calculation, in which for each CDM subhalo we selected a WDM subhalo with the same infall mass and infall time and assigned this WDM subhalo final time mass to the CDM subhalo. This was equivalent to the mass that the CDM subhalo may have had if it had experienced a WDM stripping rate. Our hybrid calculation therefore factors out the contribution to CDM–WDM differences from the change in infall mass function and retains the differences from stripping.

With these results we compute the ratio of WDM-to-CDM subhalo abundances in the two mass bins plus the ratios of the hybrid measurements and present the results in the left-hand set of panels in Fig. 4. Beginning with the $[10^7, 10^8]$ $M_\odot$ bin, we find strong differences in the relative properties of the models between radius bins. Within the full 300 kpc distance from the host halo centre the number of WDM subhaloes is suppressed to 10% of the CDM value on average, whereas for the 40 kpc bin it is instead 30% in the median, with a much larger scatter. We argue in the paper that this result is due to the inner halo being dominated by the remnants of

---

[b]The MW is located only 750 kpc from the more massive Andromeda galaxy; we expect that this will not affect the results.

massive haloes that have sunk under dynamical friction; the abundance of massive haloes is much more similar between the two models than the mass function down to 10^7 $M_\odot$, therefore the value of this ratio is much closer to 1. A similar result is found for the more massive bin, where the suppression is a median 40% of CDM for the < 300 kpc bin but 60% of CDM.

One possible complication to this picture is the issue of extra stripping in WDM subhaloes as discussed above, and we can tease out the contributions of changes in stripping and changes in the mass function by comparing the hybrid calculation results to the full WDM results: if the hybrid results are the same as the full WDM then the change between WDM and CDM is entirely due to extra stripping, whereas if the hybrid results instead straddle the ratio = 1 line then the change was entirely due to the input mass function. In the lower mass bin the < 300 kpc hybrid ratio is much closer to a ratio of 1 than to 0.1, therefore the change in mass function drives the difference, whereas in the < 40 kpc radius the hybrid suppression ratio is lower than at < 300 kpc as per the switch from unstripped low-infall mass subhaloes to high-mass stripped ones.

The difference in subhalo infall mass at different radii will also have an impact on the concentration–mass relations at these radii, with the subhaloes in the central region more likely to be the dense cores of massive progenitors. The concentration of these objects will also have an effect on the gaps in streams measurements. Obtaining an accurate concentration–mass relation for subhaloes close to the host halo centre with N-body simulations is challenging for a number of reasons, including the possibility that mass from the subhalo is inaccurately ascribed to the host halo and that the mass distribution of the host will be strongly impacted by the presence of the stellar disc, both from the disc itself and from the contraction of the halo. We therefore developed an estimate for the mass and size of subhaloes in the centre using the infall mass / structure plus a measurement of the observed MW mass profile. We used the measured MW mass profile of Ref 42 to calculate the tidal radius of a subhalo at a distance of 20 kpc from the halo centre based on its infall mass and infall density profile, then assumed that the halo layers outside the tidal radius were removed while the mass inside the tidal radius was not affected. We thus calculated a new mass based on the mass interior to the tidal radius, and a new size as the half-mass radius of the remaining (unstripped) material. We computed median mass–radius relations for subhaloes within 50 kpc of the host centre using these estimates of stripped mass and size, and also median relations across the subhalo using the infall mass and infall size. We present these results in the right hand panel of Fig. 4.

Beginning with the whole subhalo population, the CDM and WDM sizes are identical at 6×10^9 $M_\odot$ but quickly diverge towards lower masses, with WDM subhaloes of mass 6×10^7 $M_\odot$ on average 50% larger than CDM subhaloes of the same mass. The subhaloes in the inner halo instead show much smaller sizes, such that

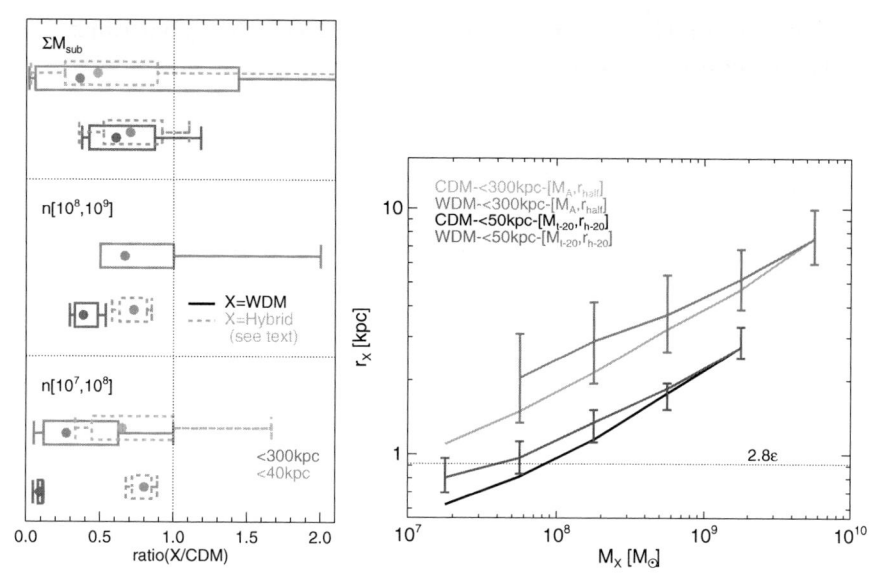

Fig. 4. *Left-hand panels:* ratio of quantities between WDM and CDM versions of the 24 volumes. In the top panel we show the ratio of the mass in WDM and CDM; in the middle panel the fraction of the number of subhaloes in the mass bin $[10^8, 10^9]$ $M_\odot$, and in the bottom panel the ratio of $[10^7, 10^8]$ $M_\odot$ subhalo number. Ratios for subhaloes within 40 kpc of the host centre are shown in orange and within 300 kpc in blue. Filled dots denote median ratios, boxes 68% of the data and error bars 95% of the data. Solid lines are used for the measured WDM subhalo fractions and dashed lines for the hybrid calculation as described in the text; the hybrid calculation is omitted for the mass= $[10^8, 10^9]$ $M_\odot$, distance< 30 kpc bin due to poor statistics. *Right-hand panel:* the mass–radius relation for subhaloes in two radius bins. Data for subhaloes within 300 kpc are shown using infall masses and sizes in grey (CDM) and pink (WDM); data for subhaloes in the < 50 kpc bin are calculated using estimates for the stripping radius at 20 kpc as discussed in the text, and are shown in black (CDM) and red (WDM). Error bars on the WDM relations denote 58% of the data; error bars are omitted for CDM on clarity grounds, and are of the same size as for WDM. Reproduced from Ref. 18.

the WDM subhaloes within 50 kpc are more concentrated the CDM subhalo population. The difference in ratio between the stripped estimates for these inner-host subhaloes is approximately 20% at 10^8 $M_\odot$, and the majority of such WDM subhaloes are less than 2 kpc in size. We therefore argue that the subhaloes likely to generate stream gaps would have to have stream impact parameters less than 2 kpc in order for the difference in concentrations to be imprinted on the gap properties.

In conclusion, I showed in this part of the talk that the properties of the subhaloes that generate gaps are very different to the properties of subhaloes generally, in that they are the stripped, concentrated remnants of massive haloes. Therefore the ability of stream-gap analyses to discern between CDM and WDM is weaker than one would infer from the subhalo population at large.

4. Predictions for the X-ray emission signal from decaying dark matter in galaxy clusters

For the final part of the talk I shifted to indirect detection opportunities for dark matter decay, and presented a prediction for the decay to be measured in nearby galaxy clusters by the XRISM X-ray experiment.

Decay is possible for dark matter particles that have a lifetime much longer than the age of the Universe but are never the less not completely stable. Such particles are typically light and therefore decay in the X-ray band. The prime dark matter particle candidate that has a mass in this range is the resonantly produced sterile neutrino, which in addition to dark matter explains baryogenesis and the oscillations of standard model neutrinos;[31,32,43] it also behaves as WDM,[44,45] and is thus accessible to the constraints from the previous section. The decay of this

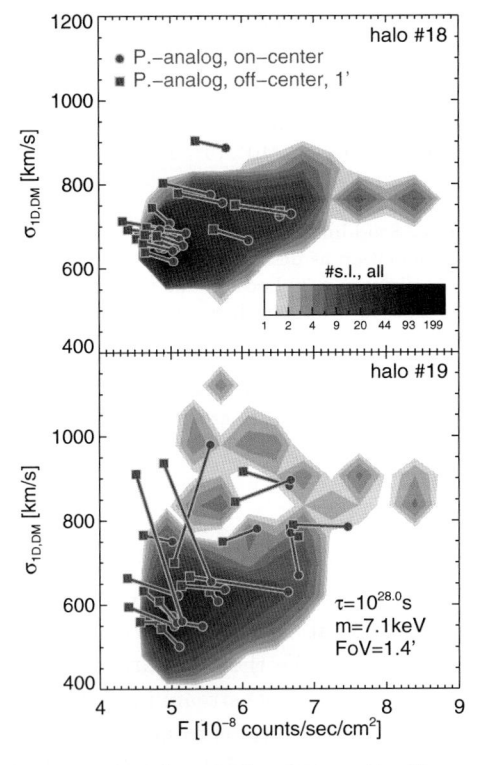

Fig. 5. Predictions for the properties of a putative dark matter X-ray decay line in the Perseus cluster to be measured by the XRISM experiment. We use simulations of two Perseus-mass clusters, and each cluster is represented in one panel and is subject to 500 sightlines. We show contours of the one dimensional velocity dispersion versus the total line flux: the velocity dispersion is independent of the particle physics properties, and the flux assumes $\tau = 10^{28}$ s and $m = 7.1$ keV. The blue circles denote on-centre sightlines for which the velocity dispersion of the cluster member galaxies is the measured velocity dispersion of Perseus cluster members, and the attached blue squares offset 1 arcminute from the centre. Reproduced from Ref. 19.

particle takes the form of a monochromatic X-ray line at an energy half the sterile neutrino rest mass energy. The width of the line is determined by the macroscopic dark matter one dimensional velocity dispersion, and is therefore independent of the particle physics parameters.

The XRISM experiment, to be launched in 2023, will have sufficient spectral resolution to measure the width of the claimed dark matter decay line in nearby clusters of galaxies. I therefore used the C-EAGLE simulations[46,47] of galaxy clusters to perform mock observations with the XRISM field-of-view of dark matter decay lines in Perseus-mass clusters.[19] The flux calculation assumed a particle lifetime $\tau = 10^{28}$ s and mass $m = 7.1$ keV, as inferred from the claimed detections of the 3.55 keV line.[33,34] We identified two of the 30 C-EAGLE clusters as having same mass as Perseus within some tolerance, and computed 500 sightlines through the halo centre from randomized viewing angles. The results are shown in Fig. 5.

The flux of the line can vary by a factor of 50%, with most of the sightlines bunching up towards lower fluxes in the allowed range. The velocity dispersion is concentrated in the [500,800] kms^{-1} range, and exceptionally at [400,1000] kms^{-1}. This velocity dispersion is significantly narrower than the measured velocity dispersion of the member stars, which is typically 1300 kms^{-1}, and is still much broader than astrophysical emission lines (< 200 kms^{-1}). Given that the velocity dispersion is also independent of the particle physics parameters for the sterile neutrino model, the XRISM observatory offers arguably the best opportunity to detect dark matter within the next five years.

5. Conclusions

In this talk I summarised three leads for constraining and identifying the dark matter: the density of the Milky Way (MW) ultrafaint satellites, the properties of subhaloes that carve gaps in stellar streams, and the parameters of X-ray decay lines in galaxy clusters.

First, I investigated how the distribution of ultrafaint satellite densities could be explained by a velocity-dependent self-interacting dark matter model (SIDM) in which the self-interaction cross-section is of order 100 cm^{2}gr^{-1} for relative velocities below 20 kms^{-1}. I showed that this model induces gravothermal collapse in a fraction of the dark matter subhaloes. The density profiles of these collapsed subhaloes exhibit a power law of index -3. The combination of collapsed and cored SIDM subhaloes can potentially explain the diversity of MW satellites masses, in which bright satellites could be hosted in massive, cored satellites whereas ultrafaint dwarfs are hosted in less massive, gravothermally collapsed subhaloes.[17]

For the second part of the talk I switched to comparing the subhaloes that carve gaps in stellar streams between cold dark matter (CDM) and warm dark matter (WDM), for which I extracted subhaloes from the COCO simulations that are located within the same region of configuration space that stream gaps can be detected (< 30 kpc from the host centre). I showed that these central-region subhaloes are the remnants of massive progenitors that have sunk to the halo centre under dynamical friction. I therefore argued that, since the differences between CDM and WDM massive subhaloes are small, the discriminating power of stream gaps as a dark matter probe is weaker than one would infer from comparing all subhaloes associated with each host.[18]

I ended the talk with a brief presentation of work on dark matter indirect detection. I showed calculations for the expected width of putative lines from dark matter decay in a series of nearby galaxy clusters. Given the uncertainty between viewing angles, I showed that the line velocity dispersion would have a value in the range $[500, 800]$ kms^{-1}, which is narrower than the velocity dispersion of the member galaxies but crucially still significantly broader than X-ray emission lines from hot gas.[19] The upcoming XRISM observatory will therefore have an excellent opportunity to determine whether the line detected at 3.55 keV in galaxies and clusters[33,34] is from an astrophysical source or is indeed from dark matter decay.

Acknowledgments

MRL acknowledges support by a Grant of Excellence from the Icelandic Research Fund (grant number 206930). This work used the DiRACDurham facility managed by the Institute for Computational Cosmology on behalf of the STFC DiRAC HPC Facility (www.dirac.ac.uk). The equipment was funded by BEIS capital funding via STFC capital grants ST/K00042X/1, ST/P002293/1 and ST/R002371/1, Durham University and STFC operations grant ST/R000832/1. DiRAC is part of the National e-Infrastructure.

References

1. Planck Collaboration, R. Adam, N. Aghanim, M. Ashdown, J. Aumont, C. Baccigalupi, M. Ballardini, A. J. Banday, R. B. Barreiro, N. Bartolo, S. Basak, R. Battye, K. Benabed, J.-P. Bernard, M. Bersanelli, P. Bielewicz, J. J. Bock, A. Bonaldi, L. Bonavera, J. R. Bond, J. Borrill, F. R. Bouchet, F. Boulanger, M. Bucher, C. Burigana, E. Calabrese, J.-F. Cardoso, J. Carron, H. C. Chiang, L. P. L. Colombo, C. Combet, B. Comis, F. Couchot, A. Coulais, B. P. Crill, A. Curto, F. Cuttaia, R. J. Davis, P. de Bernardis, A. de Rosa, G. de Zotti, J. Delabrouille, E. Di Valentino, C. Dickinson, J. M. Diego, O. Doré, M. Douspis, A. Ducout, X. Dupac, F. Elsner, T. A. Enßlin, H. K. Eriksen, E. Falgarone, Y. Fantaye, F. Finelli, F. Forastieri, M. Frailis, A. A. Fraisse, E. Franceschi, A. Frolov, S. Galeotta, S. Galli, K. Ganga, R. T. Génova-Santos, M. Gerbino, T. Ghosh, J. González-Nuevo, K. M. Górski, A. Gruppuso, J. E. Gudmundsson, F. K. Hansen, G. Helou, S. Henrot-Versillé, D. Herranz, E. Hivon, Z. Huang, S. Ilić, A. H. Jaffe, W. C. Jones, E. Keihänen, R. Keskitalo, T. S. Kisner, L. Knox, N. Krachmalnicoff, M. Kunz, H. Kurki-Suonio, G. Lagache, A. Lähteenmäki, J.-M. Lamarre, M. Langer, A. Lasenby, M. Lattanzi, C. R. Lawrence, M. Le Jeune, F. Levrier, A. Lewis, M. Liguori, P. B. Lilje, M. López-Caniego, Y.-Z. Ma, J. F. Macías-Pérez, G. Maggio, A. Mangilli, M. Maris, P. G. Martin, E. Martínez-González, S. Matarrese, N. Mauri, J. D. McEwen, P. R. Meinhold, A. Melchiorri, A. Mennella, M. Migliaccio, M.-A. Miville-Deschênes, D. Molinari, A. Moneti, L. Montier, G. Morgante, A. Moss,

P. Naselsky, P. Natoli, C. A. Oxborrow, L. Pagano, D. Paoletti, B. Partridge, G. Patanchon, L. Patrizii, O. Perdereau, L. Perotto, V. Pettorino, F. Piacentini, S. Plaszczynski, L. Polastri, G. Polenta, J.-L. Puget, J. P. Rachen, B. Racine, M. Reinecke, M. Remazeilles, A. Renzi, G. Rocha, M. Rossetti, G. Roudier, J. A. Rubiño-Martín, B. Ruiz-Granados, L. Salvati, M. Sandri, M. Savelainen, D. Scott, G. Sirri, R. Sunyaev, A.-S. Suur-Uski, J. A. Tauber, M. Tenti, L. Toffolatti, M. Tomasi, M. Tristram, T. Trombetti, J. Valiviita, F. Van Tent, P. Vielva, F. Villa, N. Vittorio, B. D. Wandelt, I. K. Wehus, M. White, A. Zacchei and A. Zonca, Planck intermediate results. XLVII. Planck constraints on reionization history, *A&A* **596**, p. A108 (December 2016).
2. X. X. Xue, H. W. Rix, G. Zhao, P. Re Fiorentin, T. Naab, M. Steinmetz, F. C. van den Bosch, T. C. Beers, Y. S. Lee, E. F. Bell, C. Rockosi, B. Yanny, H. Newberg, R. Wilhelm, X. Kang, M. C. Smith and D. P. Schneider, The Milky Way's Circular Velocity Curve to 60 kpc and an Estimate of the Dark Matter Halo Mass from the Kinematics of ~2400 SDSS Blue Horizontal-Branch Stars, *ApJ* **684**, 1143 (September 2008).
3. A. Klypin, A. V. Kravtsov, O. Valenzuela and F. Prada, Where Are the Missing Galactic Satellites?, *ApJ* **522**, 82 (September 1999).
4. B. Moore, S. Ghigna, F. Governato, G. Lake, T. Quinn, J. Stadel and P. Tozzi, Dark Matter Substructure within Galactic Halos, *ApJ* **524**, L19 (October 1999).
5. M. Boylan-Kolchin, J. S. Bullock and M. Kaplinghat, Too big to fail? The puzzling darkness of massive Milky Way subhaloes, *MNRAS* **415**, L40 (July 2011).
6. J. S. Bullock, A. V. Kravtsov and D. H. Weinberg, Reionization and the Abundance of Galactic Satellites, *ApJ* **539**, 517 (August 2000).
7. A. J. Benson, C. S. Frenk, C. G. Lacey, C. M. Baugh and S. Cole, The effects of photoionization on galaxy formation - ii. satellite galaxies in the local group, *MNRAS* **333**, 177 (jun 2002).
8. F. Governato, C. Brook, L. Mayer, A. Brooks, G. Rhee, J. Wadsley, P. Jonsson, B. Willman, G. Stinson, T. Quinn and P. Madau, Bulgeless dwarf galaxies and dark matter cores from supernova-driven outflows, *Nature* **463**, 203 (January 2010).
9. T. Sawala, C. S. Frenk, A. Fattahi, J. F. Navarro, T. Theuns, R. G. Bower, R. A. Crain, M. Furlong, A. Jenkins, M. Schaller and J. Schaye, The chosen few: the low-mass haloes that host faint galaxies, *MNRAS* **456**, 85 (February 2016).
10. M. R. Lovell, V. Eke, C. S. Frenk, L. Gao, A. Jenkins, T. Theuns, J. Wang, S. D. M. White, A. Boyarsky and O. Ruchayskiy, The haloes of bright satellite galaxies in a warm dark matter universe, *MNRAS* **420**, 2318 (March 2012).
11. M. Vogelsberger, J. Zavala and A. Loeb, Subhaloes in self-interacting galactic dark matter haloes, *MNRAS* **423**, 3740 (July 2012).
12. M. R. Lovell, V. Gonzalez-Perez, S. Bose, A. Boyarsky, S. Cole, C. S. Frenk and O. Ruchayskiy, Addressing the too big to fail problem with baryon physics and sterile neutrino dark matter, *MNRAS* **468**, 2836 (July 2017).
13. D. S. Akerib, S. Alsum, H. M. Araújo, X. Bai, A. J. Bailey, J. Balajthy, P. Beltrame, E. P. Bernard, A. Bernstein, T. P. Biesiadzinski, E. M. Boulton, R. Bramante, P. Brás, D. Byram, S. B. Cahn, M. C. Carmona-Benitez, C. Chan, A. A. Chiller, C. Chiller, A. Currie, J. E. Cutter, T. J. R. Davison, A. Dobi, J. E. Y. Dobson, E. Druszkiewicz, B. N. Edwards, C. H. Faham, S. Fiorucci, R. J. Gaitskell, V. M. Gehman, C. Ghag, K. R. Gibson, M. G. D. Gilchriese, C. R. Hall, M. Hanhardt, S. J. Haselschwardt, S. A. Hertel, D. P. Hogan, M. Horn, D. Q. Huang, C. M. Ignarra, M. Ihm, R. G. Jacobsen, W. Ji, K. Kamdin, K. Kazkaz, D. Khaitan, R. Knoche, N. A. Larsen, C. Lee, B. G. Lenardo, K. T. Lesko, A. Lindote, M. I. Lopes, A. Manalaysay, R. L. Mannino, M. F. Marzioni, D. N. McKinsey, D. M. Mei, J. Mock, M. Moongweluwan, J. A. Morad,

A. S. J. Murphy, C. Nehrkorn, H. N. Nelson, F. Neves, K. O'Sullivan, K. C. Oliver-Mallory, K. J. Palladino, E. K. Pease, P. Phelps, L. Reichhart, C. Rhyne, S. Shaw, T. A. Shutt, C. Silva, M. Solmaz, V. N. Solovov, P. Sorensen, S. Stephenson, T. J. Sumner, M. Szydagis, D. J. Taylor, W. C. Taylor, B. P. Tennyson, P. A. Terman, D. R. Tiedt, W. H. To, M. Tripathi, L. Tvrznikova, S. Uvarov, J. R. Verbus, R. C. Webb, J. T. White, T. J. Whitis, M. S. Witherell, F. L. H. Wolfs, J. Xu, K. Yazdani, S. K. Young and C. Zhang, Results from a Search for Dark Matter in the Complete LUX Exposure, *Phys. Rev. Lett.* **118**, p. 021303 (January 2017).
14. E. Aprile, J. Aalbers, F. Agostini, M. Alfonsi, L. Althueser, F. D. Amaro, M. Anthony, F. Arneodo, L. Baudis, B. Bauermeister, M. L. Benabderrahmane, T. Berger, P. A. Breur, A. Brown, A. Brown, E. Brown, S. Bruenner, G. Bruno, R. Budnik, C. Capelli, J. M. R. Cardoso, D. Cichon, D. Coderre, A. P. Colijn, J. Conrad, J. P. Cussonneau, M. P. Decowski, P. de Perio, P. Di Gangi, A. Di Giovanni, S. Diglio, A. Elykov, G. Eurin, J. Fei, A. D. Ferella, A. Fieguth, W. Fulgione, A. Gallo Rosso, M. Galloway, F. Gao, M. Garbini, C. Geis, L. Grandi, Z. Greene, H. Qiu, C. Hasterok, E. Hogenbirk, J. Howlett, R. Itay, F. Joerg, B. Kaminsky, S. Kazama, A. Kish, G. Koltman, H. Landsman, R. F. Lang, L. Levinson, Q. Lin, S. Lindemann, M. Lindner, F. Lombardi, J. A. M. Lopes, J. Mahlstedt, A. Manfredini, T. Marrodán Undagoitia, J. Masbou, D. Masson, M. Messina, K. Micheneau, K. Miller, A. Molinario, K. Morå, M. Murra, J. Naganoma, K. Ni, U. Oberlack, B. Pelssers, F. Piastra, J. Pienaar, V. Pizzella, G. Plante, R. Podviianiuk, N. Priel, D. Ramírez García, L. Rauch, S. Reichard, C. Reuter, B. Riedel, A. Rizzo, A. Rocchetti, N. Rupp, J. M. F. dos Santos, G. Sartorelli, M. Scheibelhut, S. Schindler, J. Schreiner, D. Schulte, M. Schumann, L. Scotto Lavina, M. Selvi, P. Shagin, E. Shockley, M. Silva, H. Simgen, D. Thers, F. Toschi, G. Trinchero, C. Tunnell, N. Upole, M. Vargas, O. Wack, H. Wang, Z. Wang, Y. Wei, C. Weinheimer, C. Wittweg, J. Wulf, J. Ye, Y. Zhang and T. Zhu, Dark Matter Search Results from a One Ton-Year Exposure of XENON1T, *Physical Review Letters* **121**, p. 111302 (September 2018).
15. J. M. Gaskins, A review of indirect searches for particle dark matter, *Contemporary Physics* **57**, 496 (October 2016).
16. T. R. Slatyer, TASI Lectures on Indirect Detection of Dark Matter, *ArXiv e-prints* (October 2017).
17. H. C. Turner, M. R. Lovell, J. Zavala and M. Vogelsberger, The onset of gravothermal core collapse in velocity-dependent self-interacting dark matter subhaloes, *MNRAS* **505**, 5327 (August 2021).
18. M. R. Lovell, M. Cautun, C. S. Frenk, W. A. Hellwing and O. Newton, The spatial distribution of Milky Way satellites, gaps in streams, and the nature of dark matter, *MNRAS* **507**, 4826 (November 2021).
19. M. R. Lovell, D. Iakubovskyi, D. Barnes, S. Bose, C. S. Frenk, T. Theuns and W. A. Hellwing, Simulating the Dark Matter Decay Signal from the Perseus Galaxy Cluster, *ApJ* **875**, p. L24 (April 2019).
20. M. Boylan-Kolchin, J. S. Bullock and M. Kaplinghat, The Milky Way's bright satellites as an apparent failure of ΛCDM, *MNRAS* **422**, 1203 (May 2012).
21. M. G. Walker and J. Peñarrubia, A Method for Measuring (Slopes of) the Mass Profiles of Dwarf Spheroidal Galaxies, *ApJ* **742**, p. 20 (November 2011).
22. J. Zavala, M. R. Lovell, M. Vogelsberger and J. D. Burger, Diverse dark matter density at sub-kiloparsec scales in Milky Way satellites: Implications for the nature of dark matter, *Phys. Rev. D* **100**, p. 063007 (Sep 2019).
23. S. Balberg, S. L. Shapiro and S. Inagaki, Self-Interacting Dark Matter Halos and the Gravothermal Catastrophe, *ApJ* **568**, 475 (April 2002).

24. H. Nishikawa, K. K. Boddy and M. Kaplinghat, Accelerated core collapse in tidally stripped self-interacting dark matter halos, *Phys. Rev. D* **101**, p. 063009 (March 2020).
25. A. H. G. Peter, M. Rocha, J. S. Bullock and M. Kaplinghat, Cosmological Simulations with Self-Interacting Dark Matter II: Halo Shapes vs. Observations, *Mon. Not. Roy. Astron. Soc.* **430**, p. 105 (2013).
26. M. J. Jee, H. Hoekstra, A. Mahdavi and A. Babul, Hubble Space Telescope/Advanced Camera for Surveys Confirmation of the Dark Substructure in A520, *ApJ* **783**, p. 78 (March 2014).
27. F. Kahlhoefer, K. Schmidt-Hoberg, J. Kummer and S. Sarkar, On the interpretation of dark matter self-interactions in Abell 3827, *MNRAS* **452**, L54 (September 2015).
28. V. Springel, J. Wang, M. Vogelsberger, A. Ludlow, A. Jenkins, A. Helmi, J. F. Navarro, C. S. Frenk and S. D. M. White, The Aquarius Project: the subhaloes of galactic haloes, *MNRAS* **391**, 1685 (December 2008).
29. V. Springel, E pur si muove: Galilean-invariant cosmological hydrodynamical simulations on a moving mesh, *MNRAS* **401**, 791 (January 2010).
30. D. N. Spergel, L. Verde, H. V. Peiris, E. Komatsu, M. R. Nolta, C. L. Bennett, M. Halpern, G. Hinshaw, N. Jarosik, A. Kogut, M. Limon, S. S. Meyer, L. Page, G. S. Tucker, J. L. Weiland, E. Wollack and E. L. Wright, First-Year Wilkinson Microwave Anisotropy Probe (WMAP) Observations: Determination of Cosmological Parameters, *ApJS* **148**, 175 (September 2003).
31. T. Asaka and M. Shaposhnikov, The @nMSM, dark matter and baryon asymmetry of the universe [rapid communication], *Physics Letters B* **620**, 17 (July 2005).
32. M. Laine and M. Shaposhnikov, Sterile neutrino dark matter as a consequence of νMSM-induced lepton asymmetry, *J. Cosmology Astropart. Phys.* **6**, p. 31 (June 2008).
33. A. Boyarsky, O. Ruchayskiy, D. Iakubovskyi and J. Franse, Unidentified Line in X-Ray Spectra of the Andromeda Galaxy and Perseus Galaxy Cluster, *Physical Review Letters* **113**, p. 251301 (December 2014).
34. E. Bulbul, M. Markevitch, A. Foster, R. K. Smith, M. Loewenstein and S. W. Randall, Detection of an Unidentified Emission Line in the Stacked X-Ray Spectrum of Galaxy Clusters, *ApJ* **789**, p. 13 (July 2014).
35. P. Bode, J. P. Ostriker and N. Turok, Halo Formation in Warm Dark Matter Models, *ApJ* **556**, 93 (July 2001).
36. D. Erkal and V. Belokurov, Properties of dark subhaloes from gaps in tidal streams, *MNRAS* **454**, 3542 (December 2015).
37. N. Banik, J. Bovy, G. Bertone, D. Erkal and T. J. L. de Boer, Novel constraints on the particle nature of dark matter from stellar streams, *arXiv e-prints*, p. arXiv:1911.02663 (Nov 2019).
38. A. Bonaca, D. W. Hogg, A. M. Price-Whelan and C. Conroy, The Spur and the Gap in GD-1: Dynamical Evidence for a Dark Substructure in the Milky Way Halo, *ApJ* **880**, p. 38 (July 2019).
39. W. A. Hellwing, C. S. Frenk, M. Cautun, S. Bose, J. Helly, A. Jenkins, T. Sawala and M. Cytowski, The Copernicus Complexio: a high-resolution view of the small-scale Universe, *MNRAS* **457**, 3492 (April 2016).
40. S. Bose, W. A. Hellwing, C. S. Frenk, A. Jenkins, M. R. Lovell, J. C. Helly and B. Li, The Copernicus Complexio: statistical properties of warm dark matter haloes, *MNRAS* **455**, 318 (January 2016).
41. M. Viel, G. D. Becker, J. S. Bolton and M. G. Haehnelt, Warm dark matter as a solution to the small scale crisis: New constraints from high redshift Lyman-α forest data, *Phys. Rev. D* **88**, p. 043502 (August 2013).

42. M. Cautun, A. Benítez-Llambay, A. J. Deason, C. S. Frenk, A. Fattahi, F. A. Gómez, R. J. J. Grand, K. A. Oman, J. F. Navarro and C. M. Simpson, The milky way total mass profile as inferred from Gaia DR2, *MNRAS* **494**, 4291 (May 2020).
43. A. Boyarsky, O. Ruchayskiy and M. Shaposhnikov, The Role of Sterile Neutrinos in Cosmology and Astrophysics, *Annual Review of Nuclear and Particle Science* **59**, 191 (November 2009).
44. M. Viel, J. Lesgourgues, M. G. Haehnelt, S. Matarrese and A. Riotto, Constraining warm dark matter candidates including sterile neutrinos and light gravitinos with WMAP and the Lyman-α forest, *Phys. Rev. D* **71**, p. 063534 (March 2005).
45. A. Boyarsky, J. Lesgourgues, O. Ruchayskiy and M. Viel, Lyman-α constraints on warm and on warm-plus-cold dark matter models, *J. Cosmology Astropart. Phys.* **5**, p. 12 (May 2009).
46. Y. M. Bahé, D. J. Barnes, C. Dalla Vecchia, S. T. Kay, S. D. M. White, I. G. McCarthy, J. Schaye, R. G. Bower, R. A. Crain, T. Theuns, A. Jenkins, S. L. McGee, M. Schaller, P. A. Thomas and J. W. Trayford, The Hydrangea simulations: galaxy formation in and around massive clusters, *MNRAS* **470**, 4186 (October 2017).
47. D. J. Barnes, S. T. Kay, Y. M. Bahé, C. Dalla Vecchia, I. G. McCarthy, J. Schaye, R. G. Bower, A. Jenkins, P. A. Thomas, M. Schaller, R. A. Crain, T. Theuns and S. D. M. White, The Cluster-EAGLE project: global properties of simulated clusters with resolved galaxies, *MNRAS* **471**, 1088 (October 2017).

Addressing classical cosmological back-reaction with multiple scales

Yonadav Barry Ginat

Faculty of Physics, Technion – Israel Institute of Technology,
Haifa, 3200003, Israel
E-mail: ginat@campus.technion.ac.il

This is a summary of my talk at the 16th Marcel Grossmann conference, given on-line in July 2021. Various aspects of the averaging problem – the problem of finding an effective large-scale cosmological solution of the Einstein field equations, when small-scale perturbations are present — are discussed, and treated with the multiple-scales technique of singular perturbation theory. This allows one to show that a split between a background metric that varies only on large scales, and perturbations to it, is consistent, provided certain conditions are met. I finish by giving an explicit example of the back-reaction of a perturbation consisting of a single small-scale mode, and point at possible future directions.

Keywords: Cosmological perturbation theory; gravity.

1. Introduction

The Universe is usually described, on large scales, by a Friedmann-Lemaître-Robertson-Walker (FLRW) metric[1]

$$ds^2 = a^2(\eta)\left(-d\eta^2 + \gamma_{ij}dx^i dx^j\right), \tag{1}$$

which is a solution of the Einstein equations

$$R_{ab}(g_{ab}) - \Lambda g_{ab} = 8\pi G \rho_{ab} \equiv 8\pi G \left(T_{ab} - \frac{1}{2}T g_{ab}\right), \tag{2}$$

for a homogeneous and isotropic energy-momentum tensor T_{ab}. However, in reality, the matter distribution is inhomogeneous on small scales, and becomes homogeneous and isotropic only on scales of about[2] ~ 100 Mpc so an averaging procedure is required, to find a homogeneous $\overline{\rho}_{ab}$. Such averaging does not, for a general metric, commute with the non-linear operation of computing the Ricci tensor from the metric, so $\overline{R}_{ab} \neq R_{ab}(\overline{g}_{ab})$. Hence, the equation, whose solution is the FLRW metric, does not, strictly speaking, correspond to a realistic universe. An averaged equation should rather be

$$\overline{R}_{ab} - \Lambda \overline{g}_{ab} = 8\pi G \overline{\rho}_{ab}. \tag{3}$$

This discrepancy is a consequence of the averaging, or back-reaction problem.[3–6]

Another instance of the same problem arises in the context of splitting the space-time metric g_{ab} into an FLRW 'background' piece, g_{ab}^{FLRW} and a perturbation, h_{ab}, viz.

$$g_{ab} = g_{ab}^{\text{FLRW}} + h_{ab}, \tag{4}$$

where in standard cosmological perturbation theory, h_{ab} is taken to be small.[1] However, its magnitude depends on scale and, in general, on the co-ordinate system one uses;[7] this calls into question the very validity of such a background-perturbation split, which rests on the consistency of even defining a large-scale background.

Several proposals were put forward in the past to address this problem, including special averaging techniques[8] or special perturbative expansions,[9] and here I wish to describe another proposal, laid down in Ginat (2021),[10] which can address some of the problems with less assumptions than the other techniques.

Below I choose units such that $c = 8\pi G = 1$. The entire discussion here is classical, and quantum aspects of back-reaction are not discussed at all.

2. Multiple-Scales Treatment of the Einstein Equations

2.1. *The Multiple-Scales Method*

The multiple-scales technique consists in treating small scales and large scales as separate variables, interacting via the non-linearity in the dynamical equations that one wishes to study.[11] If ε denotes a certain small parameter involved in the equations, and x denotes the independent variable, then one defines $X = x/\varepsilon$, and changes

$$\frac{\partial}{\partial x^a} \mapsto \frac{\partial}{\partial x^a} + \frac{1}{\varepsilon}\frac{\partial}{\partial X^a} \tag{5}$$

in the dynamical equations; then, one treats x and X as independent variables. This split is done in conjunction with an asymptotic expansion of the dependent variable, the metric $g_{ab}(x, X, \varepsilon)$, in our case, in ε, as $g_{ab}(x, X) \sim g^0_{ab} + \varepsilon g^1_{ab} + \ldots$, and a similar one for the energy-momentum tensor (with the convention that any X-independent terms enter into ρ^0_{ab}). This expansion is consistent, of course, only if the condition $\varepsilon^n |g^n_{ab}| \gg \varepsilon^{n+1} |g^{n+1}_{ab}|$ is satisfied.

The addition of an independent variable, without changing the dynamics, implies that there aren't enough equations to determine the solution fully, leaving certain integration constants, or solutions of homogeneous equations, free. However, in the general case, small-scale resonances yield diverging large-scale behaviour, which potentially violates the above-mentioned consistency requirement. To ensure that it is not, one imposes additional consistency conditions, which determine the undetermined functions or integration constants, in precisely such a manner as to remove the resonances, and ensure the asymptoticity of the expansion. This adds exactly enough equations to fix the solution fully.

2.2. *Application to The Einstein Equations*

Working in harmonic co-ordinates renders the Einstein equations hyperbolic,[12] *viz.*

$$R_{ab} \equiv R^{(h)}_{ab} = -\frac{1}{2} g^{cd} \partial^2_{cd} g_{ab} + P^{cdefgh}_{ab}(g) \partial_c g_{ef} \partial_d g_{gh}, \tag{6}$$

where $P_{ab}^{cdefgh}(g)$ is some function of the metric g, and not of its derivatives. Let us now set x as the cosmological scale and X as some small scale, e.g. a galactic scale; then ε is the ratio between these two scales, and indeed $\varepsilon \ll 1$.

The Einstein equations are second order, so, upon expanding them in ε, the leading order is ε^{-2}, i.e., in harmonic co-ordinates,

$$-\frac{1}{2}g_0^{cd}\partial^2_{X^c X^d}g_{ab}^0 + P_{ab}^{cdefgh}(g_0)\partial_{X^c}g_{ef}^0\partial_{X^d}g_{gh}^0 = \rho_{ab}^{-2}. \quad (7)$$

Here we can already address the question of the existence of a consistent background-perturbation split for the metric: if $\rho_{ab}^{-2} \neq 0$, i.e. if there are small-scale, relativistic sources, like black holes, then necessarily g_{ab}^0 is X dependent, and therefore any good definition of a large-scale background is impossible. On the other hand, if one only considers small-scale, 'Newtonian' sources, for which the gravitational potential is $\ll 1$, then ρ_{ab}^{-2} does vanish, and the solution to equation (7) is an X-independent g_{ab}^0, a true background.

2.3. Consistency Conditions

To establish the background-perturbation split, all that's left to do is to establish the consistency condition for εg_{ab}^1, that is, to show that it remains small relative to g_{ab}^0. The order ε^{-1} equation is

$$\rho_{\text{rel},ab}^{-1} + \rho_{\text{nr},ab}^{-1} = -\frac{1}{2}g_0^{cd}\partial^2_{X^c X^d}g_{ab}^1, \quad (8)$$

where the subscript 'rel' ('nr') is there, to remind one that this is a relativistic (Newtonian) contribution to the energy-momentum tensor, one which arises, upon Fourier transforming in X, from matter modes which have a relativistic (non-relativistic) dispersion relation. In fact, because $\partial_X g^0 = 0$, in-so-far-as the X-co-ordinates are concerned, the space-time over which g_{ab}^1 is defined *qua* a tensor-valued function, is flat: equation (8) is a wave equation for g_{ab}^1, with an X-independent metric $g_{ab}^0 dX^a dX^b$, so its solutions are waves in flat space-time, parameterised by the large-scale co-ordinate x. This also means that a Fourier transform in X is unambiguous.

Since $\rho_{\text{rel},ab}^{-1}$ is in resonance with the wave-equation operator, the consistency of the asymptotic expansion requires that, in fact, it vanish. If it does, then εg_{ab}^1 remains smaller than g_{ab}^0.[10] So far there have been two non-trivial consistency conditions, which limit the applicability to Newtonian sources. Relativistic ones are allowed, though, at all orders, from ε^0 and above. One can generalise this to conclude that whenever $\rho_{\text{rel},ab}^n \neq 0$, one needs an X-dependent g_{ab}^{n-1}, that will precisely cancel the resonances that arise. For example, at $n = 2$, this is the case, and after a few manipulations, one finds, for $k^2 = 0$ (where k is the Fourier conjugate of X)

the following consistency condition:

$$-k^c\partial_{x^c}\hat{g}^1_{\text{hom},ab}(x,k) + P^{cdefgh}_{ab}(g_0)\left(k_c\hat{g}^1_{\text{hom},ef}(x,k)\partial_{x^d}g^0_{gh} + k_d\hat{g}^1_{\text{hom},gh}(x,k)\partial_{x^c}g^0_{ef}\right)$$
$$-\mathrm{i}\int \mathrm{d}^4X e^{ik\cdot X}\left\{P_{ab}(g_0)\partial_X g_1\partial_X g_1 - \frac{1}{2}g^{cd}_1\partial^2_{X^cX^d}g^1_{ab}\right\}_{\text{osc}} = -8\pi\mathrm{i}G\hat{\rho}^0_{ab}(x,k), \quad (9)$$

where a circumflex denotes a Fourier transform in X, a subscript 'osc' means that one removes the X average of the term in the curly brackets from it, and $g^1_{\text{hom},ab}$ is the homogeneous part of the solution of equation (8).

This is the key element of the multiple-scales expansion: the additional degrees of freedom, that are created by treating x and X separately, are fixed by requiring the asymptoticity of the expansion in ε – by removing resonances order-by-order. Indeed, as there is an un-fixed homogeneous part in g^1_{ab}, relativistic sources in ρ^0_{ab} are not a problem.

The X-independent part of the Einstein equation at order ε^0 also gives an effective Einstein equation, governing the large-scale dependence of g^0_{ab}:[10]

$$-\frac{1}{2}g^{cd}_0\partial^2_{x^cx^d}g^0_{ab} + P_{ab}(g_0)\partial_x g_0\partial_x g_0 - \Lambda g^0_{ab} - B_{ab} = 8\pi G\langle\rho^0_{ab}\rangle_X. \quad (10)$$

When computed in a co-ordinate system of a freely-falling observer in the x-spacetime, the back-reaction tensor B_{ab} corresponds, roughly, to the X-averaged Newtonian gravitational potential energy of the sources in $\rho^{-1}_{\text{nr},ab}$. The averaged equation agrees with the one derived by Green & Wald (2011)[9] under different assumptions.

2.4. Single Short Mode

Let me also give a simple example of a situation where $B_{ab} \neq 0$. Consider a cosmological setting, where, in addition to the uniform matter density $\mu_0(\eta)$, the matter distribution has a component $\delta\mu(\eta,\mathbf{x}) = 2\varepsilon\mu_0(\eta)\rho_0\cos(\mathbf{k}\cdot\mathbf{x}/\varepsilon)$, where $\mathbf{k}$ is a constant of order one, and $\rho_0\mu_0$ is much smaller than the critical density of the Universe.[a] Here, η, $\mathbf{x}$ are conformal, co-moving co-ordinates. The back-reaction tensor, in this case, is given by[10]

$$B^{ij} = \frac{\mu^2_0\rho^2_0}{2a^2k^4}\left(k^ik^j + k^2\delta_{ij}\right), \quad (11)$$

with all other components equal to zero, to leading order in ρ_0. This back-reaction, albeit small, introduces, unsurprisingly, anisotropic stress perturbations.

3. Conclusions

In conclusion, the multiple-scales technique enables one to show that there is a well-defined background metric that depends only on the large-scale, as well as to derive an effective Einstein equation where small-scale gravitational potential

---

[a]This latter assumption is not strictly necessary, but simplifies matters considerably, in that it allows one to expand in $\rho_0\mu_0/\rho_{\text{crit}}$, which is an expansion in large-scale cosmological perturbations, and then proceed as one would do for standard cosmological perturbation theory.

energy acts as a source of gravity on the large scale. Additionally, one can determine the consistency conditions under which these conclusions obtain, and, in particular, that they do obtain when small-scale over-densities are chiefly due to non-relativistic matter, to leading order in ε.

In the future it would be worthwhile to try to expand this technique from asymptoticity to a convergence property, e.g. two-scale convergence,[13] and also, perhaps more importantly for practical applications, to attempt to include small-scale relativistic objects, such as neutron stars or black holes, perhaps by utilising some extension of Birkhoff's theorem.[14] It is plausible that this theorem would allow one to include isolated black holes in the multiple-scales framework, by relaxing the requirement $\varepsilon \left| g^1_{ab} \right| \ll \left| g^0_{ab} \right|$, and allowing g^1_{ab} to take extremely large values in some very restricted areas of space-time. This should enable one to conclude from Birkhoff's theorem or something similar that an observer far from any isolated black holes will not observe any more back-reaction than if these black holes were normal stars with the same masses.

References

1. S. Weinberg, *Cosmology* (Oxford University Press, Oxford, 2008).
2. A. A. Coley and G. F. R. Ellis, Theoretical cosmology, *Classical and Quantum Gravity* **37**, p. 013001 (January 2020).
3. T. Futamase, Averaging of a locally inhomogeneous realistic universe, *Phys. Rev. D* **53**, 681 (Jan 1996).
4. R. M. Zalaletdinov, Averaging problem in general relativity, macroscopic gravity and using Einstein's equations in cosmology, *Bull. Astron. Soc. India* **25**, 401 (1997).
5. C. Clarkson, G. Ellis, J. Larena and O. Umeh, Does the growth of structure affect our dynamical models of the universe? The averaging, backreaction and fitting problems in cosmology, *Rept. Prog. Phys.* **74**, p. 112901 (2011).
6. T. Buchert and S. Räsänen, Backreaction in Late-Time Cosmology, *Annual Review of Nuclear and Particle Science* **62**, 57 (Nov 2012).
7. J. Adamek, C. Clarkson, D. Daverio, R. Durrer and M. Kunz, Safely smoothing spacetime: backreaction in relativistic cosmological simulations, *Classical and Quantum Gravity* **36**, p. 014001 (dec 2018).
8. T. Buchert, On Average Properties of Inhomogeneous Fluids in General Relativity: Dust Cosmologies, *General Relativity and Gravitation* **32**, 105 (Jan 2000).
9. S. R. Green and R. M. Wald, New framework for analyzing the effects of small scale inhomogeneities in cosmology, *Phys. Rev. D* **83**, p. 084020 (Apr 2011).
10. Y. B. Ginat, Multiple-scales approach to the averaging problem in cosmology, *JCAP* **2021**, p. 049 (February 2021).
11. G. A. Pavliotis and A. M. Stuart, *Multiscale methods*, Texts in Applied Mathematics, Vol. 53 (Springer, New York, 2008), Averaging and homogenization.
12. Y. Choquet-Bruhat, *General relativity and the Einstein equations*Oxford Mathematical Monographs, Oxford Mathematical Monographs (Oxford University Press, Oxford, 2009).
13. G. Allaire, Homogenization and two-scale convergence, *SIAM J. Math. Anal.* **23**, 1482 (1992).
14. A. Einstein and E. G. Straus, The Influence of the Expansion of Space on the Gravitation Fields Surrounding the Individual Stars, *Reviews of Modern Physics* **17**, 120 (April 1945).

Imaging formation process for DM profiles

Omar de J. Cabrera-Rosas* and Tonatiuh Matos

*Departamento de Física, Centro de Investigación y de Estudios Avanzados del IPN,
México Distrito Federal, A.P. 14-740, 07000, México*
E-mail: omar.cabrera@cinvestav.mx

The imaging formation process in halos for some dark matter profiles is studied. Approaching these models on a small scale, we analyze the images generated on the lens plane by obtaining the analytical surface mass densities $\Sigma(x)$ and their corresponding deflection angles $\alpha(x)$. We identify the presence of Einstein rings, by mapping fringes that represent possible sources (such as other galaxies), placed on the source plane. We approach the simplest case, where lines parallel to the x axis are mapped onto the lens plane, to find out how are the solutions of the **X** vector field, which is in this case, the geometrical equivalent to the usual lens mapping.

Keywords: Dark Matter, Gravitational Lensing

1. Introduction

The dynamics of galaxies is a topic of great interest in cosmology. In recent years, this dynamic has been studied with the observation and analysis of the rotation curves of several samples of galaxies. From these observations an acceleration has been measured, and the presence of Dark Matter (DM) is necessary to explain their dynamics.[1,2]

The restrictions belonging to the central surface density of the halo, determine the value of the quantity μ_{DM} which is always a constant, that it seems to be an universal invariant, and there are evidences of this restriction in spiral, dwarf irregulars and ellipticals galaxies to name some types.[3–6] It is important to observe that μ_{DM} is constructed as the product of the characteristic length r_s and the central density value ρ_s of each galaxy, and this is related with the *soliton* region (the core of the galaxy). This is an important zone, because the extra galactic components do not alter this region and the invariant objects present there, are very helpful to understand the complete behavior of the galaxy.[7] In fact, certain models for Scalar Field Dark Matter (SFDM) have predicted that the total mass of these systems is $M_{DM}(300\text{pc}) \sim 10^7 M_\odot$ with a characteristic size $r_s = 300\text{pc}$; that is, the soliton region is perfectly delimited for its analysis, and it is very important for eventual tests that improves the physics interpretation of the data. Therefore, to study the dynamical process for translating this information to the imaging information, this soliton zone must be analyzed, with the corresponding considerations for that region.

In fact, the universal DM profile (the Navarro-Frenk-White profile NFW) has been exhaustively studied, because it fits properly with observational data[8,9];

however, it presents problems on a small scale, which implicates that there must be another models, that explain the core zone.

For the above reasons, a complete optical analysis of this region is in order, using the proper data that comprehends all the physical information encoded in each model, but at the same time with a simplification of the studied equations. Hence, we use the usual gravitational lensing formalism,[10] that contains all the mathematical restrictions to fully understand such optical processes. Hence, we compute the images on the lens plane, as functions of the positions of the sources, the source plane and the redshift, which is encoded into the critical surface mass density Σ_{cr}, that appears in the volumetric density $\rho(r)$ (and thus, into the deflection angle $\alpha(r)$ generated in each physical situation). Therefore, the principal goal for using this approach, is to describe the images generated for recent models of DM, and test which of them behave like the observed data. In this stage of the work, we only study the images generated by objects (fringes) very near to the observation axis, by finding the roots of the equation that represents the mapping in that zone (see Eq. 13 below). This eventually means to translate the optical information obtained from the corresponding images, and link it with the information of the galactic dynamics.

This work is organized as follows. In section 2 we set the basic equations for gravitational lensing, and we obtain the surface mass density and the deflection angle analytically for each profile. In section 3, we establish the **X** vector field that describes the ray tracing of the optical process; later we use the method provided in,[11] to study the images that will appear on the lens plane. Finally in section 4, we present the conclusions of this work.

2. Basics equations for gravitational lensing

The configuration for gravitational lensing is as usual[10], where the source plane, the lens plane and the observer are shown. D_s, D_l and D_{ls} are the distances between observer and source, observer and lens and between lens and source planes, respectively.[10] Now, assume that the DM density profile is given in the form $\rho(x) = \rho_s f(x)$, with ρ_s, r_s and $x = r/r_s$ are the characteristic density, the characteristic radius and the scale radius, respectively; $f(x)$ is any given function of its argument.[2] Hence, it is necessary to find the deflection angle in each case, and because the systems considered here are axially symmetric, the surface mass density and the deflection angle are given by[10]

$$\Sigma(\xi) = \int_{-\infty}^{\infty} \rho(\xi, z) dz,$$

$$\alpha(x) = \frac{m(x)}{x},$$

(1)

Name (1)	$f(x)$ (2)	$\Sigma(x)$ (3)	$\alpha(x) = m(x)/x$ (4)
Burkert	$\dfrac{1}{(1+x)(1+x^2)}$	$\beta_B F(x)_B$	$\dfrac{\sigma_B}{x} g(x)_B$
M-SFDM	$\dfrac{\sin^2 x}{x^2}$	$\beta_{MsT} F(x)_{MSt}$	$\sigma_{MsT}\left[J_1(2x) + \dfrac{x^3}{3}\right]$
PI	$\dfrac{1}{1+x^2}$	$\dfrac{\beta_{PI}}{\sqrt{1+x^2}}$	$\dfrac{\sigma_{PI}}{x}(\sqrt{x^2+1}-1)$
Spano	$\dfrac{1}{(1+x^2)^{3/2}}$	$\dfrac{\beta_{Sp}}{1+x^2}$	$\dfrac{\sigma_{Sp}}{x}\ln(1+x^2)$
Wave DM	$\dfrac{1}{(1+x^2)^8}$	$\dfrac{\beta_W}{(x^2+1)^{15/2}}$	$\dfrac{\sigma_W}{x}\left(1 - \dfrac{1}{(x^2+1)^{13/2}}\right)$
NFW	$\dfrac{1}{x(1+x)^2}$	$\dfrac{2\mu_{DM}}{x^2-1}F(x)_{NFW}$	$\dfrac{4\kappa_s}{x}\left(\ln\dfrac{x}{2} + \dfrac{2}{\sqrt{1-x^2}}\operatorname{arctanh}\sqrt{\dfrac{1-x}{1+x}}\right)$

where the radial coordinate r is related to cylindrical polar coordinates by $r = \sqrt{\xi^2 + z^2}$ and $m(x)$ is the dimensionless mass defined by

$$m(x) = 2\int_0^x \kappa(\xi)\xi d\xi. \qquad (2)$$

The shear of the system is

$$\kappa(x) = \Sigma(x)/\Sigma_{cr} \qquad (3)$$

and $\Sigma_{cr} = c^2 D_s/(4\pi G D_l D_{ls})$ is the critical surface mass density.

Using Eqs. (1) and (2), it is obtained the above table, by using the Burkert, Multistate-SFDM, PI, Spano, Wave DM and NFW dark matter profiles given in,[2,7] where β and σ are constants that determine the scaling of such core, and they depend on the values of μ_{DM} and κ_s.

For the Burkert profile the $F(x)_B$ function for the surface mass density is given by

$$F(x)_B = \dfrac{1}{\sqrt{1+x^2}}\left[\dfrac{\pi}{2} + \operatorname{arctanh}\left(\dfrac{1}{\sqrt{1+x^2}}\right)\right]$$

$$-2\begin{cases} \dfrac{1}{\sqrt{1-x^2}}\operatorname{arctanh}\sqrt{\dfrac{1-x}{1+x}} & (x<1), \\ \dfrac{1}{\sqrt{x^2-1}}\arctan\sqrt{\dfrac{x-1}{x+1}} & (x>1), \end{cases} \qquad (4)$$

$$= \dfrac{1}{\sqrt{2}}\left[\dfrac{\pi}{2} + \operatorname{arctanh}\left(\dfrac{1}{\sqrt{2}}\right)\right] - 1 \quad (x=1),$$

and the $g_B(x)$ function for the deflection angle is

$$g(x)_B = \frac{1}{2}\left[x^2\left(\frac{\pi}{2} + \operatorname{arctanh}\left(\frac{1}{\sqrt{1+x^2}}\right)\right)\right.$$
$$\left. + \sqrt{1+x^2}\right] + \ln x$$
$$+ 2\begin{cases} \sqrt{1-x^2}\operatorname{arctanh}\sqrt{\dfrac{1-x}{1+x}} & (x<1), \\ -\sqrt{x^2-1}\arctan\sqrt{\dfrac{x-1}{x+1}} & (x>1), \end{cases} \quad (5)$$
$$= \frac{\pi}{4} + \frac{1}{\sqrt{2}} + \frac{1}{2}\operatorname{arctanh}\frac{1}{\sqrt{2}} \quad (x=1).$$

For the Multi-State profile, the F_{MSt} function for the surface mass density is given by

$$F(x)_{MSt} = J_0(2x) + \frac{\pi}{2}[J_1(2x)\mathbf{H}_0(2x) - J_0(2x)\mathbf{H}_1(2x)], \quad (6)$$

where J_ν are the Bessel functions of the first kind of ν-th order and $\mathbf{H}_\mu$ the Struve functions of μ-th order[12,13]; the F_{NFW} function and the corresponding deflection angle for the NFW profile are given in.[8,9]

3. Imaging formation

Knowing the deflection angle for each case, it is possible to develop the imaging formation process. It will be helpful to express the quantities for describing the optical process, in a cylindrical coordinate basis $\{\hat{\varrho}, \hat{\phi}, \hat{z}\}$. From this information, the imaging mapping is given by the vector field

$$\mathbf{X} = \mathbf{r} + l\hat{\mathbf{R}}_G, \quad (7)$$

where $\hat{\mathbf{R}}_G$ is the gravitational refraction ray given by[11]

$$\hat{\mathbf{R}}_G = \cos\alpha\,\hat{z} - \sin\alpha\,\hat{\varrho}, \quad (8)$$

and l is the length from the lens plane $z=0$, to a point on a given deflected light ray.

Using Eq. (7) the deflected light rays are

$$\mathbf{X} = (\varrho - l\sin\alpha)\hat{\varrho} + l\cos\alpha\,\hat{z}. \quad (9)$$

Consider now a family of one dimensional sources in the region $z>0$, locally described by[11]

$$\mathbf{X} = \mathbf{X}(\eta, n), \quad (10)$$

where n denotes the source and η labels the points on that source. From Eqs. (9) and (10), the images that the observer sees on the lens plane $z=0$, given by all the

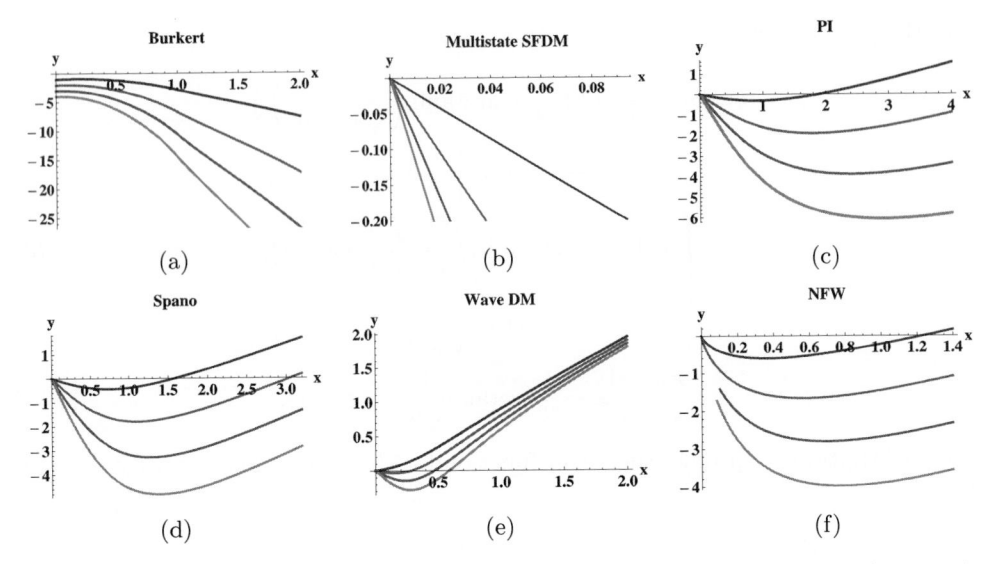

Fig. 1. Plots of the mapping $y = x - z_0\alpha$ for $z_0 = 1, 2, 3, 4$ and $n = 0$. The solutions for $x = 0$ in each profile denote the possible Einstein rings produced in each case. Notice that because in the Burkert and the multistate profiles, the curves does not intersect the horizontal axis, these profiles don't have Einstein rings.

points $(x\cos\phi, x\sin\phi, 0)$, where x and ϕ are solutions to[11]

$$X_s(\eta, n) = [x - Z_s(\eta, n)\alpha(x)]\cos\phi,$$
$$Y_s(\eta, n) = [x - Z_s(\eta, n)\alpha(x)]\sin\phi. \quad (11)$$

Taking the simplest case for line sources that coincide with the x axis, the equations for obtaining the image for each fringe is determined by all the points in the lens plane such that[11]

$$X_s = [x - z_0\alpha(x)]\cos\phi, \quad (12)$$
$$n = [x - z_0\alpha(x)]\sin\phi, \quad (13)$$

with $-L \leq X_s \leq L$.

Now, Eq. (7) encodes the information related with the imaging formation process of the optical system, because describes how is the mapping of points from the lens plane to the source plane; the **X** is related with the usual lens mapping.

Because of the axial symmetry of the optical system, the caustic generated by the vector field (7), has a central branch (along the observation axis z). If this branch has contact with the source plane, the observed image is a ring; these are the *Einstein rings*.

In fact, for $n = 0$ (a source aligned exactly with the observation axis), these rings correspond to the roots of Eq. (13), and this is illustrated in Figs. 1. For example,

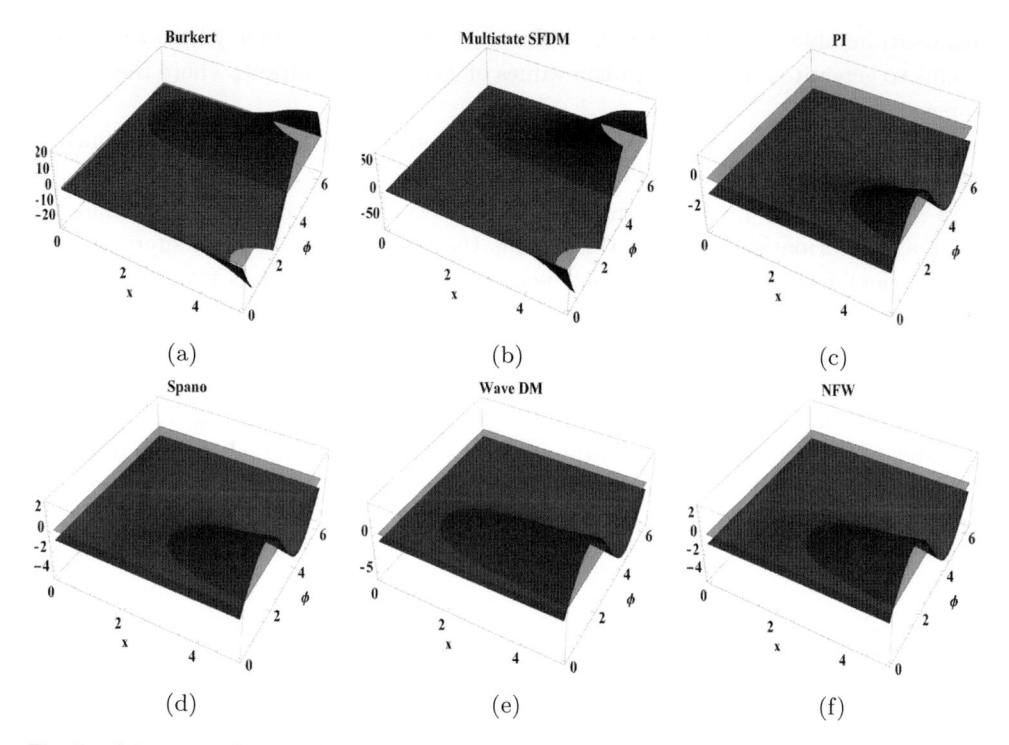

Fig. 2. Schematic of the surfaces representing the solutions of Eq. (13) for each profile on $z_0 = 1$ and $n = 1$. The pink plane intersecting each surface is the $P = 0$ plane. Observe that although the profiles present similar behaviour, the imaging formation process does not begin in the same values of x (neither the values of ϕ are the same).

observe that for the Burkert and Multistate profiles, this function have no roots, hence, they have no presence of Einstein rings for that positions of the source plane.

However, it is important to notice that these rings, are not the only images that could appear in this process. There is another branch of the caustic: a surface of revolution wrapped along the observation axis,[11] that also contributes to the images present on the lens plane, because a change to the source position does not lead to the change of the number of images unless a source moves along a caustic branch,[10] and this situation will appear, if the source and the lens plane are close enough, or in a position where this branch has contact with the source.

In this stage, we are only studying the simplest case, where we are not assuming that the source and the lens are close.

On the other hand, for $n \neq 0$, notice that in general, the deflection angle α is not an invertible function, therefore, it is necessary to find the solutions of Eq. (13) numerically. The above means to analyze Eq. (13) as a family of surfaces labeled by the n index, that are functions of x and ϕ (see Figs. 2).

By analyzing the intersections of these surfaces with the $P = 0$ plane, the image multiplicity according to the deflection angle α (see Fig. 2) can be found. The above means to be able of identifying the differences on the values of x where the profile begins to generate images, or for the values of ϕ on each quadrant, where the images appear.

An important observation is that it has been shown that the DM central surface density μ_{DM} for all these profiles, is a constant (its values lie in the range $\mu_{DM} = (575 - 648) M_\odot \text{pc}^{-2}$)[2,7] and this fact will be very useful for eventual calculations on imaging formation, because this means that the r_s and ρ_s parameters are not independent from each other, and hence by fixing the conditions for one of them, we can establish the correct values for the β and σ parameters.

In fact, because the Navarro-Frenk-White (NFW) profile has been studied in several works,[8,9] it will be important to compare it with the other profiles, and these results must fit with the description of the physical behaviour in DM halos, for later comparing such information with that obtained in the NFW case based on experimental data, but only in the moment where all the profiles can be expressed in a comparable scale.

4. Conclusions

In this work, the analysis for the imaging formation process for dark matter halos has been performed. The goal is to understand if the optical information provided by the lens mapping, gives information about the physical processes that lies in the core of some types of galaxies.

The motivation behind this analysis, was to obtain the analytic equation for the optical mapping from the source plane to the lens plane, and translate directly such information into the images generated on the lens plane.

So far, we have find out that the formation of Einstein rings, depend on the solutions of Eq. (13), that is a projection of the $\mathbf{X}$ vector field (the equivalent of the usual lens mapping) on the lens plane. These calculations are helpful to differentiate the behavior of each profile, and this was carried out by obtaining the deflection angle, encoded in the $\mathbf{X}$ mapping, and later by analyzing the behavior of this function.

This was achieved by plotting the n surfaces that represent the solutions of Eq. (13) to identify the values that correspond to the zones where the imaging formation process begin.

An important observation is that, the ultimate goal for studying such process is to eventually address the problems of the ΛCDM on a small scale, because the NFW profile has problems in this region, and alternative models must be tested there. This means to have at hand an observational tool for testing the possible wave nature of the DM or the species diversity, basing the calculations in the soliton region, because it seems to be that this zone is established by means of an universal invariant μ_{DM} (with the correct values of r_s and ρ_s, that in turn determine our β and σ constants).

Finally, as a future goal based in this work, we consider that we will be able to "draw" the corresponding images mapped from sources (in this case lines) on the lens plane, that represent galaxies or other kind of cosmological objects, by making use of the **X** field. In fact, we already have used this process in the description of a Schwarzschild lens, and the plots allowed us to explicitly identify the positions of the images on the lens plane,[11] that is, by generating images to later compare them with visual data. We believe that the above, can be used as an efficient geometrical way to identify optical configurations, for later interpret the physical data encoded in such images in a nimbly way.

References

1. S. S. McGaugh, F. Lelli and J. M. Schombert, *Radial acceleration relation in rotationally supported galxies*, Phys. Rev. Lett., **117**, 201101 (2016).
2. L. A. Ureña-López, V. H. Robles and T. Matos, *Mass discrepancy-acceleration relation: A universal maximum dark matter acceleration and implications for the ultralight scalar dark matter model*, Phys. Rev. D. **96**, 043005 (2017).
3. M. Spano, M. Marcelin, P. Amram, C. Carignam, B. Epinat and O. Hernández, *GHASP: An H_α kinematic survey of spiral and irregular galaxies — V. Dark matter distribution in 36 nearby spiral galaxies*, MNRAS, 383, 297-316 (2008).
4. F. Donato, G. Gentile, P. Salucci et al,*A constant dark matter halo surface density in galxies* , MNRAS, 397, 1169-1176 (2009).
5. P. Salucci and A. Burkert, *Dark Matter scaling relations*, ApJ **537**, L9 (2000).
6. A. Burkert, *The structure and dark halo core properties of dwarf spheroidal galaxies*, ApJ **808** 158 (2015).
7. L. E. Padilla, J. Solís-López, T. Matos and A. A. Aviléz-López, *Consequences for the Scalar Field Dark Matter Model from the McGaugh Observed-baryon Acceleration Correlation*, The Astrophysical Journal, 909: 162 (16pp), (2021).
8. M. Meneghetti, M. Bartelmann and L. Moscardini, *Cluster cross-sections for strong lensing: analytic and numerical lens models*, Mon. Not. R. Astron. Soc., **340**, 105-114 (2003).
9. G. Golse and J. P. Kneib, *Pseudo elliptical lensing mass model: Application to the NFW mass distribution*, A&A **390**, 821-827 (2002).
10. P. Schneider, C. Kochanek and J. Wambsganss, *Gravitational lensing: strong, weak and micro*, Springer (2006).
11. N. Bretón, O. de J. Cabrera-Rosas, E. Espíndola-Ramos, S. A. Juárez-Reyes, I. Julián-Macías, A. Montiel, P. Ortega-Vidals, E. Román-Hernández, G. Silva-Ortigoza, C. T. Sosa-Sánchez and R. Suárez-Xique, *Towards the Ronchi test for gravitational lenses: the gravitoronchigram*, J. Opt. **19** (2017) 065602 (19pp).
12. I. Gradshteyn and I. Ryzhik, *Table of integrals, series and products*, Academic Press, 7th. Ed. (2007).
13. M. Abramowitz and I. A. Stegun, *Handbook of mathematical functions with formulas, graphs and mathematical tables*, 9th printing (1970).

The self-gravitating Fermi gas in Newtonian gravity and general relativity

Pierre-Henri Chavanis

Laboratoire de Physique Théorique, Université de Toulouse, CNRS, UPS, France
E-mail: chavanis@irsamc.ups-tlse.fr

We review the history of the self-gravitating Fermi gas in Newtonian gravity and general relativity. We mention applications to white dwarfs, neutron stars and dark matter halos. We describe the nature of instabilities and phase transitions in the self-gravitating Fermi gas as energy (microcanonical ensemble) or temperature (canonical ensemble) is reduced. When $N < N_{\rm OV}$, where $N_{\rm OV}$ is the Oppenheimer-Volkoff critical particle number, the self-gravitating Fermi gas experiences a gravothermal catastrophe at E_c stopped by quantum mechanics (Pauli's exclusion principle). The equilibrium state has a core-halo structure made of a quantum core (degenerate fermion ball) surrounded by a classical isothermal halo. When $N > N_{\rm OV}$, a new turning point appears at an energy E_c'' below which the system experiences a gravitational collapse towards a black hole [P.H. Chavanis, G. Alberti, Phys. Lett. B **801**, 135155 (2020)]. When $N_{\rm OV} < N < N_*'$, the self-gravitating Fermi gas experiences a gravothermal catastrophe at E_c leading to a fermion ball, then a gravitational collapse at E_c'' leading to a black hole. When $N > N_*'$, the condensed branch disappears and the instability at E_c directly leads to a black hole. We discuss implications of these results for dark matter halos made of massive neutrinos.

Keywords: Fermi-Dirac statistics; White dwarfs; Neutron stars; Dark matter halos; Black holes

1. Introduction

The self-gravitating Fermi gas can have applications in different astrophysical systems ranging from white dwarfs and neutron stars to dark matter halos, where the fermions are electrons, neutrons and massive neutrinos respectively. The study of the self-gravitating Fermi gas is also of fundamental conceptual importance as it combines quantum mechanics and general relativity. Initially, fermionic models were developed at zero temperature ($T = 0$) but they have been later generalized at nonzero temperature, especially in the case of dark matter halos. In these Proceedings, we provide a brief history of the self-gravitating Fermi gas. A more detailed historical account of the statistical mechanics and thermodynamics of self-gravitating systems (classical and quantum) in Newtonian gravity and general relativity can be found in Refs.[1–4].

The statistical equilibrium state of a system of self-gravitating fermions can be determined from a maximum entropy principle. For systems with long-range interactions the mean field approximation becomes exact in an appropriate thermodynamic limit.[3,5] The most probable distribution of an isolated system of self-gravitating fermions at statistical equilibrium is obtained by maximizing the Fermi-Dirac entropy S at fixed mass-energy $\mathcal{E} = Mc^2$ and particle number N:

$$\max\{S \mid \mathcal{E} = Mc^2, \quad N \quad \text{fixed}\}. \tag{1}$$

The variational problem for the first variations reads

$$\delta S/k_B - \beta_\infty \delta\mathcal{E} + \alpha \delta N = 0, \tag{2}$$

where $\beta_\infty = 1/k_B T_\infty$ and $\alpha = \mu_\infty/k_B T_\infty$ are Lagrange multipliers associated with the conservation of mass-energy and particle number. Here, T_∞ and μ_∞ represent the temperature and the chemical potential measured by an observer at infinity. The maximization problem (1) is associated with the microcanonical ensemble. If the system is in contact with a thermal bath fixing the temperature T_∞ the statistical equilibrium state is obtained by minimizing the free energy $F = \mathcal{E} - T_\infty S$ at fixed particle number N:

$$\min\{F = \mathcal{E} - T_\infty S \mid N \quad \text{fixed}\}. \tag{3}$$

This minimization problem is associated with the canonical ensemble. At $T = 0$ the equilibrium state is obtained by minimizing the mass-energy $\mathcal{E} = Mc^2$ at fixed particle number N. The equilibrium states in the microcanonical and canonical ensembles are the same. They are determined by the variational principle (2). However, their stability may differ in the two ensembles. This is the notion of ensemble inequivalence for systems with long-range interactions.[3,5] Microcanonical stability implies canonical stability but the converse is wrong.

The equilibrium state of a gas of self-gravitating fermions results from the balance between the repulsion due to the quantum pressure (Pauli's exclusion principle) and the gravitational attraction. The variational principle (2) yields all the equations that we need to determine the equilibrium state of the self-gravitating Fermi gas: (i) the Fermi-Dirac distribution function; (ii) the ideal equation of state of fermions; (iii) the Oppenheimer-Volkoff equations determining the condition of hydrostatic equilibrium in general relativity; (iv) the Tolman-Klein relations expressing how the local temperature $T(r)$ and the local chemical potential $\mu(r)$ are affected by the metric. We can solve these equations numerically and plot the caloric curve $T_\infty(\mathcal{E})$ relating the temperature to the energy. When $T > 0$ we need to enclose the system within a spherical box of radius R in order to prevent its evaporation and have equilibrium states with a finite mass. In the general case, the caloric curve depends on N and R. For convenience, instead of $T_\infty(\mathcal{E})$, we shall plot $\beta_\infty(-E)$ where $E = (M - Nm)c^2$ is the binding energy which reduces to the usual energy $E = K + W$ (kinetic + potential) in the nonrelativistic limit $c \to +\infty$. At $T = 0$, the system is self-confined (without the need of a box) and we shall plot the mass-radius relation $M(R)$ where R denotes here the radius where the density vanishes. The maximum entropy formalism for classical and quantum self-gravitating systems in Newtonian gravity and general relativity is reviewed in Refs.[3,4] where all the equations are derived and an exhaustive list of references is given.

2. Self-gravitating fermions at $T = 0$

The study of a self-gravitating gas of fermions started in the context of white dwarf stars when Fowler[6] first realized that these compact objects owe their stability to the quantum pressure of the degenerate electron gas. Indeed, the quantum pressure arising from the Pauli exclusion principle is able to counteract the gravitational attraction and explain the very high densities of white dwarf stars. Early studies were devoted to determining the ground state ($T = 0$) of the system. Nonrelativistic white dwarf stars are equivalent to a polytropic gas of index $n = 3/2$. Their density profile can be obtained by solving the Lane-Emden equation numerically. The density profile of white dwarf stars at $T = 0$ has a compact support, i.e., the density vanishes at a finite radius. The mass-radius relation of nonrelativistic white dwarf stars was first obtained by Stoner,[7] Milne[8] and Chandrasekhar.[9a] They showed that the radius of the star decreases as the mass increases according to the law $M = 91.9\,\hbar^6/(G^3 m^8 R^3)$ (see Fig. 1-a).[11] All the configurations of the series of equilibria are stable.

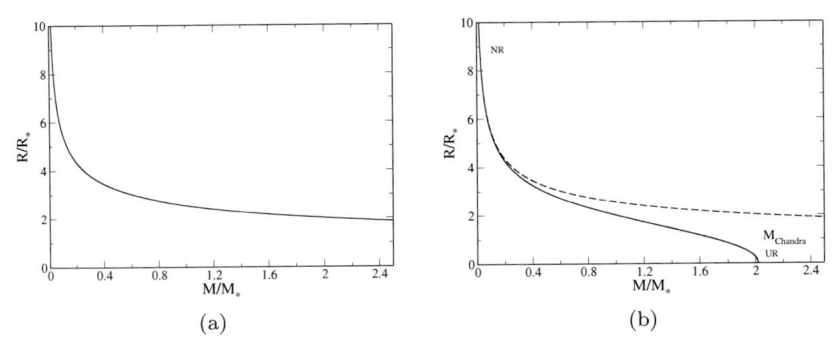

Fig. 1. Mass-radius relation of self-gravitating fermions at $T = 0$ in Newtonian gravity (the mass is normalized by $M_* = (3\pi/4)^{1/2}\hbar^{3/2}c^{3/2}/(G^{3/2}m^2)$ and the radius by $R_* = (3\pi/4)^{1/2}\hbar^{3/2}/(c^{1/2}G^{1/2}m^2)$). (a) Nonrelativistic white dwarf stars. (b) Special relativistic white dwarf stars.

The fact that relativistic effects become important in white dwarf stars whose mass is of the order of the solar mass was first reported by Frenkel[12] in a not well-known paper. However, he did not consider the implications of this result. Special relativistic effects in white dwarf stars were studied in detail by Anderson,[13] Stoner,[14] Chandrasekhar,[15] and Landau.[16] They found that no equilibrium state is possible above a maximum mass, now known as the Chandrasekhar limit.[b] These authors considered the equation of state of a relativistic Fermi gas at $T = 0$ and

---

[a]Stoner[7] developed an analytical approach based on a uniform density approximation for the star while Milne[8] and Chandrasekhar[9] developed a numerical approach based on the Lane-Emden theory of polytropes.[10]
[b]See the introduction of Ref.[17] for a short history of the discovery of the maximum mass of white dwarf stars.

used Newtonian gravity appropriate to white dwarf stars.[c] An ultrarelativistic Fermi gas at $T = 0$ is equivalent to a polytrope of index $n = 3$. Its density profile is obtained by solving the corresponding Lane-Emden equation and it has a compact support. For a polytrope $n = 3$, the mass-radius relation degenerates and indicates that different configurations with an arbitrary radius can exist at the same mass $M_{\text{Chandra}} = 3.1 \, M_P^3/m^2 = 1.5 \, M_\odot$, where $M_P = (\hbar c/G)^{1/2}$ is the Planck mass and m is the proton mass. This argument immediately implies the existence of a critical mass.[15] In a more detailed study, Chandrasekhar[22] considered partially relativistic configurations and numerically obtained the complete mass-radius relation of white dwarf stars, valid for arbitrary densities, joining the nonrelativistic limit to the ultrarelativistic one (see Fig. 1-b).[d] As M approaches M_{Chandra} the radius of the star tends to zero while its density tends to infinity, leading to a Dirac peak. This study unambiguously shows the absence of equilibrium state above a maximum mass. Therefore, the quantum pressure arising from the Pauli exclusion principle cannot balance the gravitational attraction anymore when the star becomes sufficiently relativistic (or when its mass is too large). This is a striking effect of relativity combined with quantum mechanics and gravity. However, the result of Chandrasekhar[22] was severely criticized by Eddington[23] who argued that the absence of equilibrium states above a maximum mass leads to a *reductio ad absurdum* of the formula of relativistic degeneracy. Although the arguments of Eddington were entirely unfounded, his enormous prestige led to an early rejection of Chandrasekhar's work by many in the astronomical community. This pushed Chandrasekhar to abandon the subject, and delayed the discovery of the phenomenon of gravitational collapse and the concept of black hole.

In the following years, similar results were found by Oppenheimer and Volkoff[24] in connection to neutron stars. They solved the equations of general relativity with the relativistic equation of state for fermions at $T = 0$ and found that the mass-radius relation of neutron stars presents a turning point of mass (see Fig. 2).[e] As a result, no equilibrium state exists above a maximum mass $M_{\text{OV}} = 0.384 \, M_P^3/m^2 = 0.710 \, M_\odot$, where m is the neutron mass, called the Oppenheimer-Volkoff limit (note that the density profile with the maximum mass M_{OV} is *not* singular contrary to the Newtonian density profile at the maximum mass M_{Chandra}). They argued that, above that mass, the star undergoes gravitational collapse. This problem was specifically studied by Oppenheimer and Snyder[25] who obtained an analytical solution of the Einstein equations describing the collapse of a pressureless gas up to its

---

[c]In principle, general relativistic effects become important close to the Chandrasekhar maximum mass[18,19] but other phenomena like Coulomb corrections to the electron pressure and the formation of neutrons by inverse beta decay destabilize the star before general relativistic effects come into play.[20,21]

[d]A similar mass-radius relation was obtained earlier by Stoner[14] from an approximate analytical model based on uniform density stars.

[e]It was shown later that the mass-radius relation of neutron stars forms a spiral and that a mode of stability is lost at each turning point of mass.[21]

Schwarzschild radius. Strangely enough, these important results did not receive much attention until the 1960's. At that epoch, detailed models of compact objects with more realistic equations of state taking into account the repulsive effect of nuclear forces and connecting white dwarfs to neutron stars were constructed and the fundamental discoveries of Chandrasekhar, Landau and Oppenheimer and Volkoff were confirmed (unfortunately, the early contributions of Anderson and Stoner were forgotten).[21] Pulsars were discovered by Hewish et al.[26] in 1968. The same year, Gold[27,28] proposed that pulsars are rotating neutron stars, and this is generally accepted today. It is also at that moment that the name "black hole" was used by Wheeler[29] to designate the object resulting from gravitational collapse, and became popular.

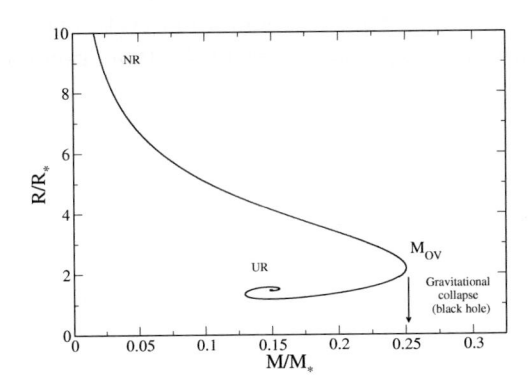

Fig. 2. Mass-radius relation of self-gravitating fermions at $T = 0$ in general relativity (neutron stars).

3. Nonrelativistic classical particles at $T > 0$ and self-gravitating radiation

The thermodynamics of self-gravitating systems is a fascinating subject.[30–32] Its study started with the pioneering work of Antonov[33] who considered an isolated system of nonrelativistic classical particles in gravitational interaction. He used a microcanonical ensemble description in which the mass and the energy are conserved. This situation applies approximately to stellar systems like globular clusters. Their equilibrium state (most probable state) can be obtained by maximizing the Boltzmann entropy S at fixed mass M and energy E.[34] This leads to the mean field Boltzmann distribution which is self-consistently coupled to the Poisson equation. The Boltzmann-Poisson equation was previously introduced and studied in the context of isothermal stars.[10,11] It can be reduced to the Emden equation that has to be solved numerically. Antonov[33] observed that no maximum entropy state exists in an infinite domain (the solution of the Emden equation has an infinite mass), so he proposed to confine the particles within a spherical box of radius R.

This artifice prevents the evaporation of the system and leads to a well-defined mathematical problem. By computing the second variations of entropy, Antonov[33] showed that equilibrium states with a density contrast $\mathcal{R} = \rho_0/\rho(R) < 709$, where ρ_0 is the central density and $\rho(R)$ the density on the edge of the box, are thermodynamically stable (entropy maxima) while equilibrium states with a density contrast $\mathcal{R} > 709$ are thermodynamically unstable (saddle points of entropy). Lynden-Bell and Wood[35] rediscussed the results of Antonov[33] in more physical terms. They plotted the series of equilibria $E(\mathcal{R})$ and showed that it displays damped oscillations. As a result, there is no equilibrium state with an energy $E < E_c = -0.335\,GM^2/R$, where E_c corresponds to the first turning point of energy (with a density contrast $\mathcal{R}_c = 709$). Invoking the Poincaré turning point criterion,[36] they concluded that the series of equilibria becomes unstable at the minimum energy E_c. In this manner, they recovered the critical density contrast $\mathcal{R}_c = 709$ found by Antonov.[33] They also interpreted the Antonov instability in terms of a "gravothermal catastrophe" caused by the negative specific heat of the system in its densest parts. When this instability occurs, the system undergoes core collapse. This ultimately leads to a binary star surrounded by a hot halo. Lynden-Bell and Wood[35] considered other statistical ensembles, notably the canonical ensemble in which the temperature and the mass are fixed. In that case, the equilibrium state is obtained by minimizing the Boltzmann free energy $F = E - TS$ at fixed mass M. The series of equilibria $T(\mathcal{R})$ displays damped oscillations. No equilibrium state exists with a temperature $T < T_c = 0.397\,GMm/(k_B R)$, where T_c corresponds to the first turning point of temperature (with a density contrast $\mathcal{R}'_c = 32.1$).[f] Using the Poincaré turning point criterion,[36] they concluded that equilibrium states with a density contrast $\mathcal{R} < 32.1$ are thermodynamically stable (free energy minima) while equilibrium states with a density contrast $\mathcal{R} > 32.1$ are thermodynamically unstable (saddle points of free energy). Below T_c the system undergoes an "isothermal collapse" leading to a Dirac peak containing all the particles. Since the stability limits in the microcanonical and canonical ensembles differ, Lynden-Bell and Wood[35] encountered for the first time in statistical mechanics a situation of ensemble inequivalence. This is a peculiarity of systems with long-range interactions.[5] In the present context, it is related to the fact that negative specific heats are allowed in the microcanonical ensemble while they are forbidden in the canonical ensemble.[35] Similar results were obtained independently by Thirring.[37] Katz[38] plotted the caloric curve $\beta(E)$ of isothermal self-gravitating spheres and exhibited its spiral behavior (see Fig. 3-a).[g] He also extended the Poincaré theory on linear series of equilibria[36] to the case where there are several turning points and developed a general method to determine the thermodynamical stability of the equilibrium states from the topology of the caloric

---

[f] These results were first found by Emden.[10]
[g] This spiral behavior was previously observed for self-gravitating isothermal stars in other representations.[11,39–44] In the present case, it is associated with the damped oscillations of energy and temperature as a function of the density contrast.

curve $\beta(E)$. A change of stability can only occur at a turning point of energy in the microcanonical ensemble or at a turning point of temperature in the canonical ensemble. A mode of stability is lost if the curve $\beta(-E)$ turns clockwise and gained if it turns anticlockwise. In this manner, one can determine the thermodynamical stability of the system by simply plotting the caloric curve (series of equilibria). The seminal works of Antonov,[33] Lynden-Bell and Wood,[35] and Katz[38] were followed by many other studies (see, e.g., Refs.[45–52]).

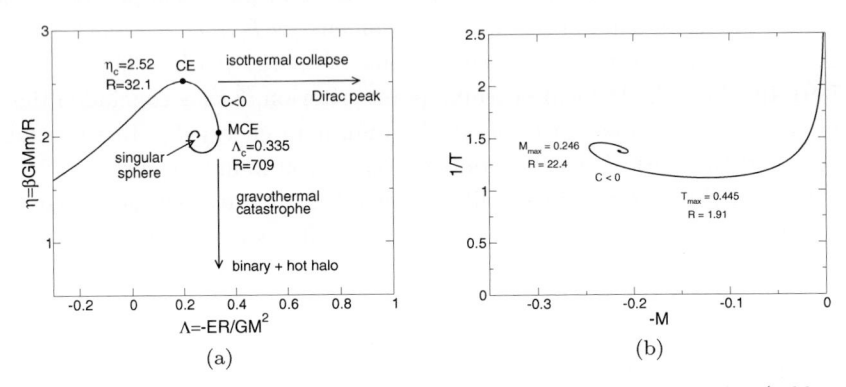

Fig. 3. (a) Caloric curve of nonrelativistic classical self-gravitating particles (cold spiral).[32] We have plotted the normalized inverse temperature $\eta = \beta GMm/R$ as a function of minus the normalized binding energy $\Lambda = -ER/GM^2$. (b) Caloric curve of the self-gravitating radiation in general relativity (hot spiral).[54] We have plotted the normalized inverse temperature $\hbar^{3/4}c^{7/4}/(k_B T_\infty G^{1/4} R^{1/2})$ as a function of minus the normalized energy $-GM/Rc^2$.

The statistical mechanics of the self-gravitating black-body radiation (photon star) confined within a cavity in general relativity was investigated by Sorkin *et al.*[53] and, more recently, by Chavanis.[54] They showed that the caloric curve $\beta_\infty(\mathcal{E})$ forms a spiral (see Fig. 3-b). There is no equilibrium state above a maximum mass-energy $M_{\max}c^2 = 0.246\, Rc^4/G$ (corresponding to a density contrast 22.4) or above a maximum temperature $(T_\infty)_{\max} = 0.445\, \hbar^{3/4}c^{7/4}/(k_B G^{1/4} R^{1/2})$ (corresponding to a density contrast 1.91). In that case, the system is expected to collapse towards a black hole. We note that the "hot spiral" (see Fig. 3-b) of the self-gravitating radiation in general relativity (ultrarelativistic limit) is inverted with respect to the "cold spiral" of the nonrelativistic classical self-gravitating gas (see Fig. 3-a).

4. Classical particles at $T > 0$ in general relativity

The statistical mechanis of classical particles in general relativity has been considered by Roupas[55] and, independently, by Alberti and Chavanis.[1] The caloric curve depends on one parameter, the particle number N (more precisely N/R). Generically, the caloric curve $\beta_\infty(E)$ has the form of a double spiral (see Fig. 4) which combines the aspects of the "cold spiral" corresponding to a nonrelativistic gas and the aspects of the "hot spiral" corresponding to an ultrarelativistic gas discussed in Sec. 3.[h] There is no equilibrium state below a minimum energy (resp. minimum temperature) and above a maximum energy (resp. maximum temperature) in the microcanonical (resp. canonical) ensemble. When the number of particles N increases, the two spirals approach each other, merge, form a loop, and finally disappear (by reducing to a point) at $N_{\max} = 0.1764\, Rc^2/Gm$. For $N > N_{\max}$, there is no equilibrium state whatever the value of mass-energy and temperature.

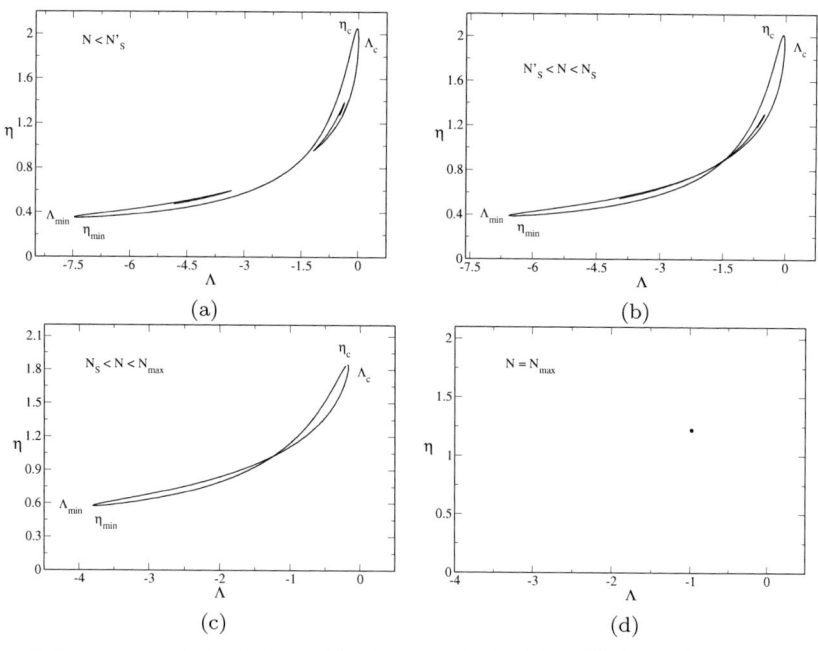

Fig. 4. Caloric curve of classical particles in general relativity. We have plotted the normalized inverse temperature $\eta = \beta_\infty GNm^2/R$ as a function of minus the normalized binding energy $\Lambda = -ER/GN^2m^2$ for different values of the normalized particle number $\nu = GNm/Rc^2$. (a) Double spiral (b) Merging (c) Loop (d) Point.[1]

5. Nonrelativistic fermions at $T > 0$

The statistical mechanics of self-gravitating fermions at nonzero temperature was first studied by Hertel and Thirring[56,57] as a simple (nonrelativistic) model of neutron stars. In that case, the density profile decreases with the distance as r^{-2} and we need to confine the system within a box in order to have an equilibrium state with a finite mass. Hertel and Thirring[56] rigorously proved that the mean field approximation (which amounts to neglecting correlations among the particles) and the Thomas-Fermi approximation (which amounts to neglecting the quantum potential)

---

[h]The hot spiral of ultrarelativistic classical particles in general relativity is similar, but not identical, to the hot spiral of the self-gravitating radiation.[1,3,54]

become exact in a proper thermodynamic limit where $N \to +\infty$. This leads to the Fermi-Dirac-Poisson equations, also known as the temperature-dependent Thomas-Fermi equations. Hertel and Thirring[57] solved these equations numerically and plotted the caloric curve. The caloric curve depends on one parameter, the box radius R (more precisely NR^3). They found that, for sufficiently large systems ($R > R_{\text{CCP}} = 12.8\,\hbar^2/(N^{1/3}Gm^3)$), a negative specific heat region occurs in the microcanonical ensemble (see Fig. 5). Since negative specific heats are forbidden in the canonical ensemble, this implies that the statistical ensembles are inequivalent. The region of negative specific heats which is allowed in the microcanonical ensemble is replaced by a first order phase transition in the canonical ensemble. This phase transition is expected to take place at a transition temperature T_t connecting the gaseous phase to the condensed phase through a horizontal Maxwell plateau in the caloric curve $T(E)$. This is accompanied by a discontinuity of energy. There is also a lower critical temperature T_c (spinodal point) at which the metastable gaseous phase disappears and the system collapses (zeroth order phase transition). This collapse is associated with the isothermal collapse of classical self-gravitating systems.[10,49] However, for self-gravitating fermions, the collapse stops when quantum degeneracy comes into play. In that case, the system achieves a "core-halo" configuration made of a quantum core (fermion ball) containing almost all the mass surrounded by a tenuous isothermal atmosphere. There is also a higher critical temperature T_* (spinodal point) at which the metastable condensed phase disappears and the system explodes. These results were exported by Bilic and Viollier[58] to the context of dark matter.

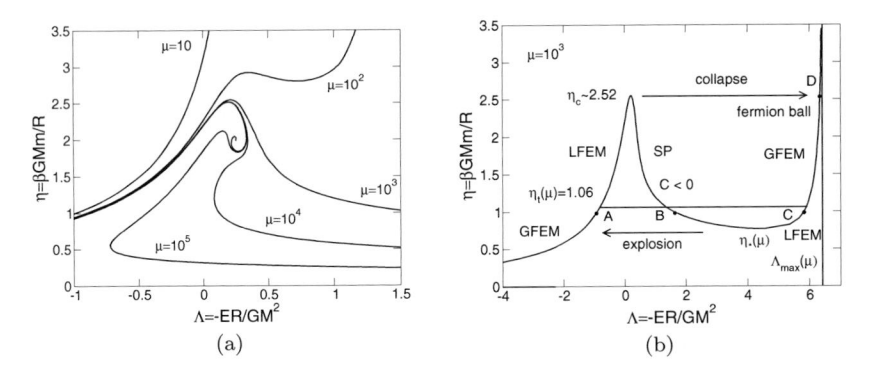

Fig. 5. Caloric curve of nonrelativistic self-gravitating fermions.[32] We have plotted the normalized inverse temperature $\eta = \beta GMm/R$ as a function of minus the normalized energy $\Lambda = -ER/GM^2$ for different values of the normalized radius, or degeneracy parameter $\mu = \eta_0\sqrt{512\pi^4 G^3 M R^3}$, where $\eta_0 = 2m^4/h^3$ is the maximum possible value of the distribution function fixed by the Pauli exclusion principle. (a) Dependence of the series of equilibria on the size of the system. (b) For small systems, the caloric curve has an N-shape structure.

An exhaustive study of phase transitions in the self-gravitating Fermi gas was made by Chavanis[32,59] in both canonical and microcanonical ensembles.

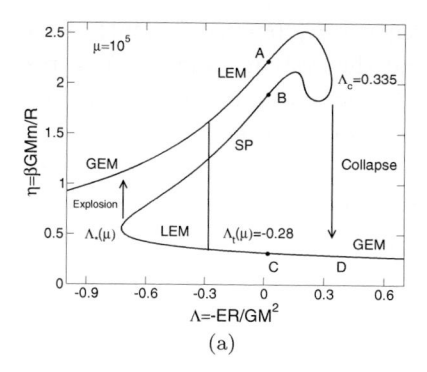

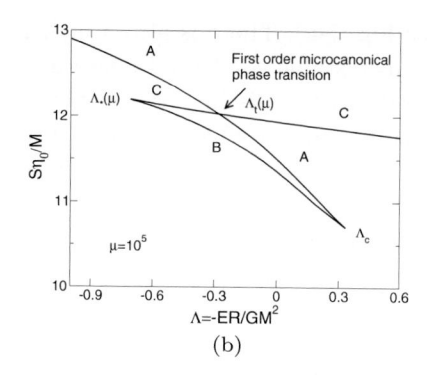

Fig. 6. Caloric curve of nonrelativistic self-gravitating fermions.[32] (a) For large systems, the caloric curve has a Z-shape structure resembling a dinosaur's neck. (b) Illustration of the microcanonical first order phase transition on the $S(E)$ curve.

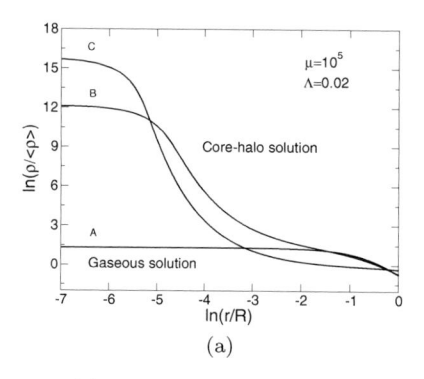

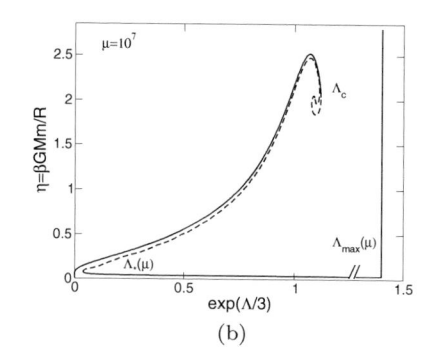

Fig. 7. (a) Density profiles corresponding to the gaseous and core-halo solutions.[32] (b) The classical limit $\mu \to +\infty$ (very large systems).[32] According to the Poincaré-Katz criterion,[36,38] the equilibrium states are unstable in the microcanonical (resp. canonical) ensemble between the first and the last turning points of energy (resp. temperature).

He confirmed the phase transition in the canonical ensemble previously found by Hertel and Thirring[57] and evidenced, for sufficiently large systems ($R > R_{\mathrm{MCP}} = 130\,\hbar^2/(N^{1/3}Gm^3)$), a first order phase transition in the microcanonical ensemble (see Fig. 6). This phase transition is expected to take place at a transition energy E_t connecting the gaseous phase to the condensed phase through a vertical Maxwell plateau in the caloric curve $T(E)$. This is accompanied by a discontinuity of temperature. There is also a lower critical energy E_c (spinodal point) at which the metastable gaseous phase disappears and the system collapses (zeroth order phase transition). This collapse is associated with the gravothermal catastrophe of classical self-gravitating systems.[33,35] However, for self-gravitating fermions, the collapse stops when quantum degeneracy comes into play. In that case, the system achieves a core-halo configuration[60] made of a quantum core (fermion ball) containing a moderate fraction of the total mass surrounded by a massive isothermal atmosphere (see Fig. 7-a). There is also a higher critical energy E_* (spinodal point) at which the metastable condensed phase disappears and the system explodes. As a result, there exist two distinct critical points in the self-gravitating Fermi gas, one in each ensemble, above which phase transitions occur. For small systems ($R < R_{\rm CCP}$), there is no phase transition, for intermediate size systems ($R_{\rm CCP} < R < R_{\rm MCP}$) a phase transition takes place in the canonical ensemble but not in the microcanoncal ensemble, and for large systems ($R > R_{\rm MCP}$) a phase transition takes place in both ensembles. When $R \to +\infty$, the series of equilibria rotates several times before unwinding (see Fig. 7-b) and we recover the classical spiral from Fig. 3-a. Chavanis[32] determined the phase diagram of the nonrelativistic self-gravitating Fermi gas. He also argued that the lifetime of metastable states is extremely long, scaling as e^N where N is the number of particles, so that the first order phase transitions do not take place in practice.[61] Only zeroth order phase transitions associated with the spinodal points are physically meaningful.

6. General relativistic fermions at $T > 0$

The statistical mechanics of self-gravitating fermions at nonzero temperature in general relativity was first considered by Bilic and Viollier.[62] As before, the system has to be confined within a spherical box of radius R in order to prevent its evaporation. The caloric curve depends on two parameters, the box radius R and the particle number N. Bilic and Viollier[62] studied the case where R is relatively small and $N < N_{\rm OV}$. In that case, the results are qualitatively similar to those obtained for nonrelativistic fermions (see Sec. 5). There is a first order phase transition in the canonical ensemble which replaces the region of negative specific heat present in the microcanonical ensemble. An equilibrium state, which is either "gaseous" (corresponding to the classical isothermal sphere) or "condensed" (made of a fermion ball surrounded by a classical isothermal envelope), exists for any value of temperature T_∞ and binding energy E. General relativistic effects only introduce a small correction to the Newtonian results.

A more general study was performed by Alberti, Chavanis and Roupas[2,63,64] who considered arbitrary values of R and N. When $N > N_{\rm OV}$, they identified the existence of a new turning point of temperature in the canonical ensemble and a new turning point of binding energy in the microcanonical ensemble below which the system collapses and forms a black hole of mass $M_{\rm OV}$ (see Fig. 8). This is the finite temperature generalization of the result originally found by Oppenheimer and Volkoff[24] at $T = 0$. These results lead to the following scenario (we restrict ourselves to the microcanonical ensemble which is the most relevant). At high energies, the system is in the gaseous phase. Below a critical energy E_c it becomes thermodynamically unstable and experiences a gravothermal catastrophe. However, core collapse stops when quantum mechanics (Pauli's exclusion principle) comes into play. This leads to the formation of a fermion ball surrounded by a hot halo. Below E_c'', the condensed phase becomes thermodynamically and dynamically unstable

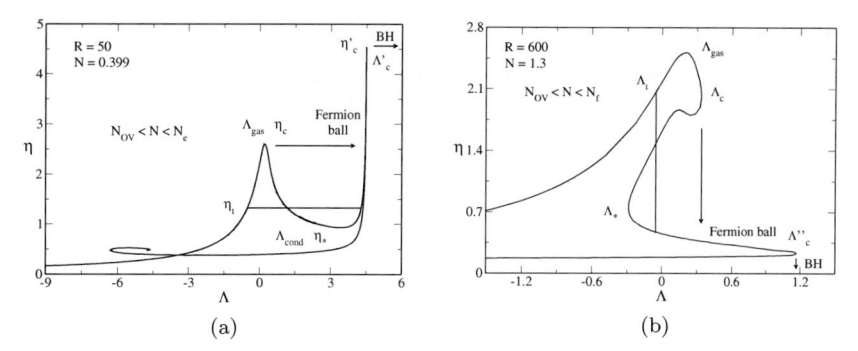

Fig. 8. Caloric curve of self-gravitating fermions in general relativity when $N > N_{\rm OV}$.[2] We have plotted the normalized inverse temperature $\eta = \beta_\infty GNm^2/R$ as a function of minus the normalized binding energy $\Lambda = -ER/GN^2m^2$ for different values of the normalized radius $R/R_{\rm OV}$ and normalized particle number $N/N_{\rm OV}$. (a) Small systems: As T decreases the system experiences an isothermal collapse at T_c leading to a fermion ball, then a gravitational collapse at T'_c leading to a black hole. (b) Large systems: As E decreases the system experiences a gravothermal catastrophe at E_c leading to a fermion ball surrounded by a hot halo, then a gravitational collapse at E''_c leading to a black hole.

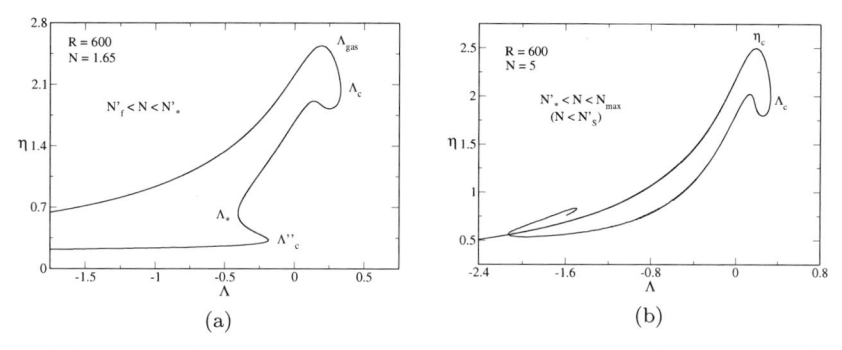

Fig. 9. Caloric curve of self-gravitating fermions in general relativity.[2] When $N > N'_*$ the condensed branch disappears completely so that only the collapse at E_c towards a black hole is possible.

(in a general relativistic sense) and collapses towards a black hole. Alberti and Chavanis[2] also evidenced a critical particle number N'_* above which the condensed phase completely disappears (see Fig. 9). In that case, there is no possibility to form a fermion ball. The gravothermal catastrophe at E_c directly leads to a black hole. In conclusion, for $N < N_{\rm OV}$ the system forms a fermion ball; for $N_{\rm OV} < N < N'_*$ the system generically forms a fermion ball, then (possibly) a black hole; for $N > N'_*$ the system directly forms a black hole. Alberti and Chavanis[2] emphasized the core-halo structure of the equilibrium states in the microcanonical ensemble and mentioned the relation to red-giants (leading to white dwarfs) and supernovae (leading to neutron stars and black holes) suggested in Refs.[64–67]. They also provided the complete phase diagram of the general relativistic Fermi gas.

7. Truncated models

The study of phase transitions in the self-gravitating Fermi gas can be extended to the fermionic King model described by the distribution function

$$f = A \frac{e^{-\beta(\epsilon-\epsilon_m)} - 1}{1 + \frac{A}{\eta_0} e^{-\beta(\epsilon-\epsilon_m)}} \qquad (\epsilon \leq \epsilon_m). \tag{4}$$

The fermionic King model was introduced heuristically by Ruffini and Stella[68] as a generalization of the classical King model[69]

$$f = A \left[e^{-\beta(\epsilon-\epsilon_m)} - 1 \right] \qquad (\epsilon \leq \epsilon_m). \tag{5}$$

The fermionic King model was also introduced independently by Chavanis[70] who derived it from a kinetic theory based on the fermionic Landau equation. The fermionic King model is more realistic than the usual fermionic model because it avoids the need of an artificial box to confine the system. The nonrelativistic fermionic King model was studied by Chavanis et al.[71,72] who showed that the density profiles generically have a core-halo structure with a quantum core (fermion ball) and a tidally truncated isothermal halo leading to flat rotation curves.[i] They also studied the caloric curves, the thermodynamical stability of the equilibrium states, and the phase transitions between gaseous and condensed states (see Figs. 10 and 11). They showed that the phenomenology of phase transitions in the fermionic King model is the same as in the case of box-confined systems obtained in Refs.[32,59]. The results of Chavanis et al.[72] have been generalized by Argüelles et al.[73] to the fermionic King model in general relativity. They also found that the phenomenology of phase transitions in the general relativistic fermionic King model is the same as in the case of box-confined systems obtained in Refs.[2,63,64].

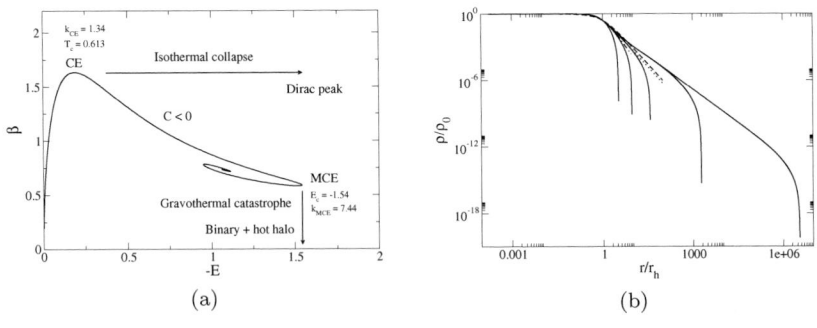

Fig. 10. (a) Caloric curve of the nonrelativistic classical King model.[71] (b) Density profiles along the series of equilibria.[71] The marginal (critical) King profile at the point of gravothermal instability is relatively close to the Burkert[74] profile (dashed line) which provides a good fit of the density profile of dark matter halos.

---

[i]The name "fermionic King model" was introduced in Ref.[72].

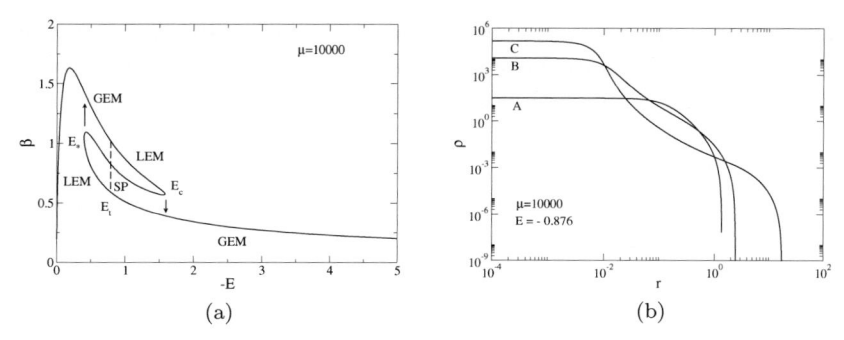

Fig. 11. (a) Caloric curve of the nonrelativistic fermionic King model for large systems.[72] (b) Density profiles corresponding to the stable gaseous phase (A), the stable condensed phase (C), and the unstable intermediate solution (B).[72]

8. Application to dark matter halos

In addition to white dwarfs and neutron stars,[75] the self-gravitating Fermi gas model has been applied in the context of dark matter halos made of massive neutrinos. The suggestion that dark matter is made of massive neutrinos was originally proposed by Markov[76] and Cowsik and McClelland.[77,78] This suggestion has been developed by numerous authors (see the introduction of Ref.[3] for an exhaustive list of references). The first models decribed dark matter halos at $T = 0$ using the equation of state of a completely degenerate fermion gas either in the nonrelativistic limit or in general relativity. Subsequent models considered dark matter halos at nonzero temperature showing that they have a core-halo structure consisting of a dense core (fermion ball) solving the core-cusp problem of classical cold dark matter surrounded by a dilute isothermal atmosphere leading to flat rotation curves. Most models were based on the ordinary Fermi-Dirac distribution in Newtonian gravity or general relativity. Some models were based on the more realistic fermionic King model (describing tidally truncated fermionic dark matter halos). The self-gravitating Fermi gas was also studied in relation to the violent relaxation of collisionless self-gravitating systems described by the Lynden-Bell[79] distribution which is formally similar to the Fermi-Dirac distribution. As argued in Refs.[71,72], the theory of violent relaxation may justify how a collisionless gas of self-gravitating fermions, such as a dark matter halo, can reach a statistical equilibrium state described by the Fermi-Dirac distribution on a timescale smaller than the age of the universe.[j]

The detailed study of the motion of S-stars near the Galactic center has revealed the presence of a very massive central object, Sagittarius A* (Sgr A*). This central object is usually associated with a supermassive black hole (SMBH) of mass

---

[j]The relaxation time due to close gravitational encounters exceeds the age of the universe by many orders of magnitude. The collisional relaxation time may be shorter if the fermions are self-interacting.[80]

$M = 4.2 \times 10^6 \, M_\odot$ and Schwarzschild radius $R_S = 4.02 \times 10^{-7}\,\mathrm{pc}$. Whatever the object may be, its radius must be smaller than $R_P = 6 \times 10^{-4}\,\mathrm{pc}$ ($R_P = 1492\,R_S$), the S2 star pericenter. Similar objects are expected to reside at the center of most spiral and elliptical galaxies, in active galactic nuclei (AGN). Although it is commonly believed that these objects are SMBHs, this is not yet established on a firm observational basis in all cases. Some authors have proposed that such objects could be fermion balls or boson stars that could mimic a SMBH. Let us consider this possibility in the framework of the fermionic dark matter model. More precisely, let us investigate if a fermion ball can mimic a SMBH at the center of the Galaxy.

Bilic et al.[81] developed a general relativistic model of fermionic dark matter halos at nonzero temperature with a fermion mass $m = 15\,\mathrm{keV}/c^2$ that describes both the center and the halo of the Milky Way in a unified manner. The density profile has a core-halo structure made of a quantum core (fermion ball) surrounded by a classical isothermal atmosphere. The core and the halo are separated by an extended plateau. By using the usual Fermi-Dirac distribution and choosing parameters so as to fit observational data at large distances, they found a fermion ball of mass $M_c = 2.27 \times 10^6 \, M_\odot$ and radius $R_c = 18\,\mathrm{mpc}$ and argued that this fermion ball can mimic a SMBH like Sgr A*. Unfortunately, its radius is larger by a factor 100 than the bound $R_P = 6 \times 10^{-4}\,\mathrm{pc}$ set by later observations. This is why Bilic and coworkers abandoned this fermion ball scenario (R. Viollier, private communication). The same problem was encountered later by Ruffini et al.[82] who developed a similar model with a fermion mass $m \sim 10\,\mathrm{keV}/c^2$.

More recently, Argüelles et al.[83] considered the general relativistic fermionic King model accounting for a tidal confinement. They applied this model to the Milky Way and determined the parameters by fitting the core-halo profile to the observations. For a fermion mass $m = 48\,\mathrm{keV}/c^2$ they obtained a fermion ball of mass $M_c = 4.2 \times 10^6 \, M_\odot$ and radius $R_c = R_P = 6 \times 10^{-4}\,\mathrm{pc}$ which, this time, is consistent with the observational constraints of Sgr A*. Therefore, in order to obtain accurate results, it is important to use the fermionic King model[72,83] instead of the usual fermionic model.[32,81,82] Argüelles et al.[83] managed to fit the entire density profile and the entire rotation curve of the Milky Way with the fermionic King distribution and argued that a fermion ball can mimic the effect of a SMBH like Sgr A*. This scenario is very attractive because it can explain the whole structure of the galaxy, the supermassive central object and the isothermal halo, by a single distribution (the fermionic King model[68,70]).

Developing the theory of phase transitions in the self-gravitating Fermi gas, Chavanis et al.[72] argued that the core-halo solution considered by Bilic et al.,[81] Ruffini et al.,[82] and Argüelles et al.[83] with a small fermion ball mimicking a SMBH surrounded by a classical isothermal atmosphere, which was claimed to reproduce the structure of the Milky Way, is thermodynamically unstable because it lies in the intermediate branch of the caloric curve between the first and the last turning points of energy (see Fig. 7-b). As a result, it is a saddle point of entropy, not an entropy maximum. Therefore, Chavanis et al.[72] concluded that this type of solution is not likely to result from a natural evolution and, consequently, they questioned the possibility that a fermion ball could mimic a central SMBH.

Following this study,[72] Argüelles et al.[73] computed the caloric curve of the fermionic King model in general relativity (see Fig. 12). They showed that the core-halo solution of Ref.[83] which provides a good agreement with the structure of the Milky Way lies just *after* the turning point (b) of energy (see the inset of Fig. 12), so that it is thermodynamically stable in the microcanonical ensemble which is the correct ensemble to consider.[k] This is a very interesting result because it shows that this core-halo structure *may* arise from a natural evolution in the sense of Lynden-Bell. This gives further support to the scenario according to which a fermion ball could mimic a SMBH at the center of the galaxies.

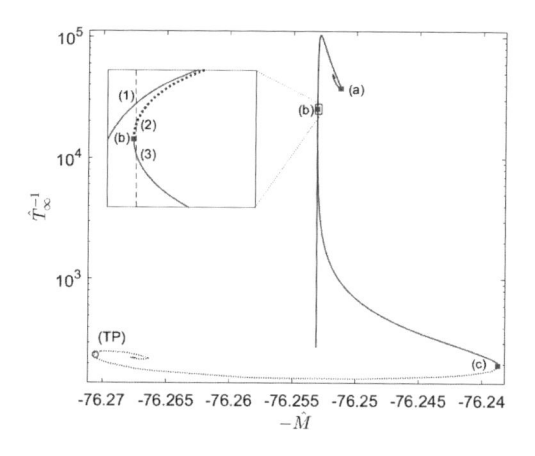

Fig. 12. Caloric curve of the general relativistic fermionic King model (from Ref.[73]).

However, it does not prove that this core-halo structure with a very high central density will necessarily arise from a natural evolution. The reason is that violent relaxation is in general incomplete.[79] The fluctuations of the gravitational potential that are the engine of the collisionless relaxation can die out before the system has reached statistical equilibrium. Therefore, it is not clear if violent relaxation can produce this type of structures.[l] In order to vindicate this scenario, the next step would be to perform direct numerical simulations of collisionless fermionic matter to

---

[k]Chavanis et al.[72] did not focus on the stable branch of condensed states located after point (b) because they argued that these solutions are not astrophysically relevant. Indeed, by considering particular solutions of the condensed branch, they observed that these solutions have a too extended envelope that is not consistent with the structure of dark matter halos (see solution C in Fig. 11-b and Figs. 38-45 of Ref.[72]). Although this claim is correct for most of the solutions on the condensed branch, it turns out that the solutions located just after point (b) *are* astrophysically relevant and correspond to the core-halo solutions studied by Argüelles et al.[83]

[l]It may be easier to form core-halo configurations with a very high central density if the fermions are self-interacting and if the Fermi-Dirac equilibrium state results from a collisional relaxation of nongravitational origin instead of a collisionless relaxation as suggested in Ref.[80].

see if they spontaneously generate fermion balls with the characteristics of SMBHs. A purely gaseous solution without quantum core, which is also a maximum entropy state, may be easier to reach through a violent relaxation process and is consistent with the observations. However, it does not account for a massive central object at the center of the galaxies. In that case, we either have to introduce a primordial SMBH "by hand" or advocate a scenario of gravitational collapse such as the one described below.[80]

For a fermion mass $m = 48\,\text{keV}/c^2$, the mass $M_h = 10^{11}\,M_\odot$ of the Milky Way is larger than the OV mass $M_{\text{OV}} = 2.71 \times 10^8\,M_\odot$, so we have to take into account general relativity in the caloric curve. As first shown by Alberti and Chavanis[2,64] for box-confined fermionic systems, and recovered by Argüelles et al.[73] for tidally truncated models, relativistic effects create a new turning point of energy in the caloric curve at which the condensed branch terminates (see Figs. 8, 9 and point (c) in Fig. 12). Below E''_c the system collapses towards a black hole.

Suppose that violent relaxation selects the gaseous solution. On a secular timescale, because of collisions, the system follows the upper branch of the series of equilibria (gaseous states) up to the point of minimum energy E_c. At that point, it becomes thermodynamically unstable and undergoes a gravothermal catastrophe. However, core collapse is stopped by quantum mechanics, leading to the formation of a fermion ball. Then, if the energy keeps decreasing, the system follows the lower branch of the series of equilibria up to the point of minimum energy E''_c where it becomes thermodynamically and dynamically unstable (in a general relativistic sense) and collapses towards a SMBH of mass M_{OV}. A similar outcome arises if violent relaxation selects the core-halo solution where the fermion ball mimics a SMBH. On a secular timescale, the system follows the lower branch of the series of equilibria up to the point of minimum energy E''_c at which it collapses towards a SMBH. In the two cases, the ultimate fate of the system is to form a SMBH of mass M_{OV} surrounded by an envelope. However, the formation of a SMBH may take time (more than the age of the universe) so that the two objects (fermion ball or SMBH) are possible in practice.

For a fermion mass $m = 48\,\text{keV}/c^2$, the OV mass $M_{\text{OV}} = 2.71 \times 10^8\,M_\odot$ is too large to account for the mass of a SMBH like Sgr A* at the center of the Milky Way. This suggests that the object at the center of the Galaxy (Sgr A*) is a fermion ball instead of a SMBH as argued by Argüelles et al.[73] However, for very large halos ($N > N'_*$), it is shown by Alberti and Chavanis[2] that the condensed branch disappears (see panel (b) of Fig. 9). In that case, there is no stable solution with a fermion ball and the system necessarily collapses towards a SMBH. Therefore, medium size galaxies like the Milky Way should harbor a fermion ball of mass $M_c = 4.2 \times 10^6\,M_\odot$ while very large galaxies like ellipticals should harbor a SMBH of mass $M_{\text{OV}} = 2.71 \times 10^8\,M_\odot$ that could even grow by accretion. This scenario[80] could account for the mass of SMBHs in AGNs like the one recently photographed in M87 ($M_h \sim 10^{13}\,M_\odot$ and $M_{\text{BH}} \sim 10^{10}\,M_\odot$).

On the other hand, for a much larger fermion mass $m = 386 \, \text{keV}/c^2$, the OV mass $M_{\text{OV}} = 4.2 \times 10^6 \, M_\odot$ is comparable to the mass of Sgr A*. Furthermore, when applied to the Milky Way, the caloric curve corresponding to $m = 386 \, \text{keV}/c^2$ is similar to the one reported in panel (b) of Fig. 9 so there is no possibility to form a fermion ball. In that case, the Milky Way could have undergone a gravitational collapse at E_c leading to a SMBH of mass $M_{\text{OV}} = 4.2 \times 10^6 \, M_\odot$.[80] In this process, the halo surrounding the SMBH is left undisturbed and could correspond to a marginal classical King profile, which is known[71,72] to give a good agreement with the empirical Burkert[74] profile of observed dark matter halos (see Fig. 10-b).

Different scenarios are possible depending on the value of the fermion mass m. Argüelles et al.[73,83] determined the mass of the fermionic dark matter particle in such a way that the fermion ball that would be at the center of a large fermionic dark matter halo, like the one that surrounds the Milky Way, mimics the effect of a SMBH of mass $M_c = 4.2 \times 10^6 \, M_\odot$ and radius $R_c = 6 \times 10^{-4}$ pc like Sgr A*. This leads to a fermion mass $m = 48 \, \text{keV}/c^2$.[m] Alternatively, Chavanis[80,86] determined the mass of the fermionic dark matter particle by arguing that the smallest halos observed in the universe (dSphs like Fornax) with a typical mass $M \sim 10^8 \, M_\odot$ and a typical radius $R \sim 1$ kpc represent the ground state of the self-gravitating Fermi gas at $T = 0$. This yields a much smaller fermion mass $m = 165 \, \text{eV}/c^2$. When this model is applied to the Milky Way,[80] it leads to a large fermion ball of mass $M_c = 9.45 \times 10^9 \, M_\odot$ and radius $R_c = 240$ pc. Therefore, it predicts the existence of a large dark matter bulge at the center of the Galaxy instead of a compact fermion ball mimicking a SMBH.[n] A large dark matter bulge is not inconsistent with the observations and may even solve some issues. For example, De Martino et al.[87] have argued that the presence of a bosonic dark matter bulge (soliton) of mass $M_c \simeq 10^9 \, M_\odot$ and radius $R_c \simeq 100$ pc at the center of the Galaxy may account for the dispersion velocity peak observed in the Milky Way. A large dark matter bulge made of fermions should have the same effect.[80]

Finally, we mention potential difficulties or, alternatively, potentially important predictions associated with the model of Argüelles et al.[73,83] If the fermion mass is $m = 48 \, \text{keV}/c^2$, dark matter halos of mass $M_h = 10^8 \, M_\odot$ such as dSphs like Fornax should have a very pronounced core-halo structure since they do not correspond to the ground state of the self-gravitating Fermi gas (unlike the model of Ref.[80] with $m = 165 \, \text{eV}/c^2$). More precisely, the fermionic dark matter model with a fermion mass $m = 48 \, \text{keV}/c^2$ predicts that dSphs of mass $M_h = 10^8 \, M_\odot$ should contain a fermion ball of mass $M_c = 1.57 \times 10^4 \, M_\odot$ and radius $R_c = 5.42$ mpc possibly

---

[m]In very recent works, Becerra-Vergara et al.[84,85] showed that the gravitational potential of a fermion ball (with a particle mass $m = 56 \, \text{keV}/c^2$) leads to a better fit of the orbits of all the 17 best resolved S-stars orbiting Sgr A* (including the S2 and G3 objects) with respect to the one obtained by the central SMBH model.

[n]In that case, a primordial SMBH has to be introduced "by hand" at the center of the Galaxy in order to account for the presence of Sgr A*.

mimicking an intermediate mass black hole.[80] This result is consistent with the detailed work of Argüelles et al.[88] who obtained dense cores of mass between $M_c = 10^3\,M_\odot$ and $M_c = 10^6\,M_\odot$ depending on the central effective temperature of the fermions. This is either a very important prediction (if confirmed by observations) or the evidence that this model is incorrect (if invalidated by observations). It would be extremely important to clarify this issue by confronting the model of Argüelles et al.[73,83] to ultracompact halos in order to determine which of the two models (the model of Argüelles et al.[73,83] with $m = 48\,\text{keV}/c^2$ or the one developed by Chavanis[80] with $m = 165\,\text{eV}/c^2$ or $m \sim 1\,\text{keV}/c^2$) is the most relevant for dark matter halos.

9. Conclusion

In these Proceedings, we have provided a brief history of the self-gravitating Fermi gas in Newtonian gravity and general relativity. We have focused exclusively on papers that discuss the caloric curves and the mass-radius relations of the self-gravitating Fermi gas. We have shown how these curves become more and more complex, displaying various types of phase transitions and instabilities, when gravity effects, thermal effects, quantum effects, relativity effects and tidal effects are progressively taken into account. Of course, there are many more interesting papers on self-gravitating fermions that are not reviewed here. A detailed bibliography on the subject can be found in Refs.[3,80] and in standard textbooks of astrophysics.

We have applied the self-gravitating Fermi gas model to dark matter halos. The Fermi-Dirac distribution may be justified either from the theory of collisionless violent relaxation[72,79] or from a collisional relaxation of nongravitational origin if the fermions are self-interacting.[80] If the fermions have a small mass ($m \lesssim 1\,\text{keV}/c^2$), the caloric curve applied to the Milky Way has an N-shape structure (see Fig. 5-b) and the equilibrium states display a large quantum bulge of mass $M_c \sim 10^{10}\,M_\odot$ and radius $R_c \sim 100$ pc surrounded by an isothermal atmosphere similar to the Burkert profile.[80] If the fermions have a large mass ($m \sim 50\,\text{keV}/c^2$), the caloric curve has a Z-shape structure (see Fig. 6-a). It displays a nonrelativistic turning point of energy at E_c triggering the gravothermal catastrophe. For nonrelativistic fermions, the gravothermal catastrophe is stopped by quantum degeneracy (Pauli's exclusion principle).[60] This may lead to a compact fermion ball of mass $M_c \sim 4.2 \times 10^6\,M_\odot$ and radius $R_c \sim 6 \times 10^{-4}$ pc mimicking a SMBH surrounded by an isothermal atmosphere.[73] When $N > N_{\text{OV}}$, which is the case for the Milky Way, a new turning point of energy appears at E_c'' due to general relativity (see Figs. 8-b and 12). It triggers a gravitational collapse towards a SMBH. This new turning point of energy was first evidenced in Refs.[2,63,64] for box-confined fermions and confirmed in Ref.[73] for the fermionic King model. The possibility to form either a fermion ball or a SMBH at the center of the galaxies depends on the size of the galaxy. In medium size galaxies like the Milky Way (when $N < N_*'$) we expect to form a fermion ball of mass $M_c \sim 4.2 \times 10^6\,M_\odot$ but in large galaxies (when $N > N_*'$) the condensed branch

Fig. 13. Dinosaur (artistic view) similar to Fig. 6-a.

disappears (see Fig. 9-b) and the gravothermal catastrophe necessarily results in the formation of a SMBH of mass $M_{\rm OV} \sim 10^8\, M_\odot$.

It is interesting to study the effect of the dimension of space d on phase transitions in the self-gravitating Fermi gas. This is done in Refs.[17,89–91]. In particular, it is shown that fermion stars are unstable in a universe with $d \geq 4$ dimensions. In that case, quantum mechanics cannot stabilize matter against gravitational collapse even in the nonrelativistic regime.[17,89,90] This is similar to a result found by Ehrenfest[92] who considered the effect of the dimension of space on the laws of physics and showed that planetary motion and the Bohr atom would not be stable in a space of dimension $d \geq 4$. Therefore, the dimension $d = 3$ of our Universe is very particular with possible implications regarding the Anthropic Principle.

Finally, it is interesting to compare the results obtained for fermion stars with those obtained for boson stars and self-gravitating Bose-Einstein condensates (BECs) (see our contribution[93] in these Proceedings). Similarly to fermionic dark matter halos, BEC dark matter halos also have a core-halo structure in which the "fermion ball" is replaced by a "soliton". The analogy between fermionic and bosonic dark matter halos is discussed in Refs.[80,86,94].

References

1. G. Alberti, P.H. Chavanis, Phys. Rev. E **101**, 052105 (2020).
2. G. Alberti, P.H. Chavanis, Eur. Phys. J. B **93**, 208 (2020).
3. P.H. Chavanis, Eur. Phys. J. Plus **135**, 290 (2020).
4. P.H. Chavanis, Eur. Phys. J. Plus **135**, 310 (2020).
5. A. Campa, T. Dauxois, D. Fanelli, S. Ruffo, *Physics of Long-Range Interacting Systems* (Oxford University Press, 2014).
6. R.H. Fowler, Mon. Not. R. Astron. Soc. **87**, 114 (1926).
7. E.C. Stoner, Phil. Mag. **7**, 63 (1929).
8. E.A. Milne, Mon. Not. R. Astron. Soc. **91**, 4 (1930).
9. S. Chandrasekhar, Phil. Mag. **11**, 592 (1931).
10. R. Emden, *Gaskugeln* (Leipzig, 1907).

11. S. Chandrasekhar, *An Introduction to the Theory of Stellar Structure* (University of Chicago Press, 1939).
12. J. Frenkel, Z. Phys. **50**, 234 (1928).
13. W. Anderson, Zeit. f. Phys. **56**, 851 (1929).
14. E.C. Stoner, Phil. Mag. **9**, 944 (1930).
15. S. Chandrasekhar, Astrophys. J. **74**, 81 (1931).
16. L.D. Landau, Phys. Zeit. Sow. **1**, 285 (1932).
17. P.H. Chavanis, Phys. Rev. D **76**, 023004 (2007).
18. S.A. Kaplan, Naukovy Zapiski (Sci. Notes Univ. Lwow) **15**, 109 (1949).
19. S. Chandrasekhar, R.F. Tooper, Astrophys. J. **139**, 1396 (1964).
20. T. Hamada, E.E. Salpeter, Astrophys. J. **134**, 683 (1961).
21. B.K. Harrison, K.S. Thorne, M. Wakano, J.A. Wheeler, *Gravitation Theory and Gravitational Collapse*, (Chicago University Press, Chicago, 1965).
22. S. Chandrasekhar, Mon. Not. R. Astron. Soc. **95**, 207 (1935).
23. A.S. Eddington, Mon. Not. R. Astron. Soc. **95**, 194 (1935).
24. J.R. Oppenheimer, G.M. Volkoff, Phys. Rev. **55**, 374 (1939).
25. J.R. Oppenheimer, H. Snyder, Phys. Rev. **56**, 455 (1939).
26. A. Hewish, S.J. Bell, J.D.H. Pilkington, P.F. Scott, R.A. Collins, Nature **217**, 709 (1968).
27. T. Gold, Nature **218**, 731 (1968).
28. T. Gold, Nature **221**, 25 (1969).
29. J.A. Wheeler, American Scientist **56**, 1 (1968).
30. T. Padmanabhan, Phys. Rep. **188**, 285 (1990).
31. J. Katz, Found. Phys. **33**, 223 (2003).
32. P.H. Chavanis, Int. J. Mod. Phys. B **20**, 3113 (2006).
33. V.A. Antonov, Vest. Leningr. Gos. Univ. **7**, 135 (1962).
34. K.F. Ogorodnikov, *Dynamics of Stellar Systems* (Pergamon, 1965).
35. D. Lynden-Bell, R. Wood, Mon. Not. R. Astron. Soc. **138**, 495 (1968).
36. H. Poincaré, Acta Math. **7**, 259 (1885).
37. W. Thirring, Z. Physik **235**, 339 (1970).
38. J. Katz, Mon. Not. R. Astron. Soc. **183**, 765 (1978).
39. S. Chandrasekhar, Astrophys. J. **87**, 535 (1938).
40. L.R. Henrich, S. Chandrasekhar, Astrophys. J. **94**, 525 (1941).
41. M. Schönberg, S. Chandrasekhar, Astrophys. J. **96**, 161 (1942).
42. R. Ebert, Z. Astrophys. **37**, 217 (1955).
43. W.B. Bonnor, Mon. Not. R. Astron. Soc. **116**, 351 (1956).
44. W.H. McCrea, Mon. Not. R. Astron. Soc. **117**, 562 (1957).
45. T. Padmanabhan, Astrophys. J. Supp. **71**, 651 (1989).
46. H.J. de Vega, N. Sanchez, F. Combes, Phys. Rev. D **54**, 6008 (1996).
47. H.J. de Vega, N. Sanchez, Nucl. Phys. B **625**, 409 (2002).
48. H.J. de Vega, N. Sanchez, Nucl. Phys. B **625**, 460 (2002).
49. P.H. Chavanis, Astron. Astrophys. **381**, 340 (2002).
50. P.H. Chavanis, Astron. Astrophys. **401**, 15 (2003).
51. J. Katz, I. Okamoto, Mon. Not. R. Astron. Soc. **317**, 163 (2000).
52. P.H. Chavanis, Astron. Astrophys. **432**, 117 (2005).
53. R.D. Sorkin, R.M. Wald, Z.Z. Jiu, Gen. Relat. Grav. **13**, 1127 (1981).
54. P.H. Chavanis, Astron. Astrophys. **483**, 673 (2008).
55. Z. Roupas, Class. Quantum Grav. **32**, 135023 (2015).
56. P. Hertel and W. Thirring, Commun. Math. Phys. **24**, 22 (1971).

57. P. Hertel and W. Thirring, Thermodynamic Instability of a System of Gravitating Fermions. In: H.P. Dürr (Ed.): *Quanten und Felder* (Brauschweig: Vieweg 1971).
58. N. Bilic, R.D. Viollier, Phys. Lett. B **408**, 75 (1997).
59. P.H. Chavanis, Phys. Rev. E **65**, 056123 (2002).
60. P.H. Chavanis, J. Sommeria, Mon. Not. R. Astron. Soc. **296**, 569 (1998).
61. P.H. Chavanis, Astron. Astrophys. **432**, 117 (2005).
62. N. Bilic, R.D. Viollier, Eur. Phys. J. C **11**, 173 (1999).
63. Z. Roupas, P.H. Chavanis, Class. Quant. Grav. **36**, 065001 (2019).
64. P.H. Chavanis, G. Alberti, Phys. Lett. B **801**, 135155 (2020).
65. Y. Pomeau, M. Le Berre, P.H. Chavanis and B. Denet, Eur. Phys. J. E **37**, 26 (2014).
66. P.H. Chavanis, B. Denet, M. Le Berre and Y. Pomeau, Eur. Phys. J. B **92**, 271 (2019).
67. P.H. Chavanis, B. Denet, M. Le Berre and Y. Pomeau, Eur. Phys. Lett. **129**, 30003 (2020).
68. R. Ruffini, L. Stella, Astron. Astrophys. **119**, 35 (1983).
69. I.R. King, Astron. J. **70**, 376 (1965).
70. P.H. Chavanis, Mon. Not. R. Astron. Soc. **300**, 981 (1998).
71. P.H. Chavanis, M. Lemou, F. Méhats, Phys. Rev. D **91**, 063531 (2015).
72. P.H. Chavanis, M. Lemou, F. Méhats, Phys. Rev. D **92**, 123527 (2015).
73. C.R. Argüelles, M.I. Díaz, A. Krut, R. Yunis, Mon. Not. R. astr. Soc. **502**, 4227 (2021).
74. A. Burkert, Astrophys. J. **447**, L25 (1995).
75. S.L. Shapiro, S.A. Teukolsky *Black Holes, White Dwarfs, and Neutron Stars* (Wiley Interscience, 1983).
76. M.A. Markov, Phys. Lett. **10**, 122 (1964).
77. R. Cowsik and J. McClelland, Phys. Rev. Lett. **29**, 669 (1972).
78. R. Cowsik and J. McClelland, Astrophys. J. **180**, 7 (1973).
79. D. Lynden-Bell, Mon. Not. Roy. Astr. Soc. **136**, 101 (1967).
80. P.H. Chavanis, *Predictive model of fermionic dark matter halos with a quantum core and an isothermal atmosphere*, preprint
81. N. Bilic, G.B. Tupper, R.D. Viollier, Lect. Notes Phys. **616**, 24 (2003).
82. R. Ruffini, C.R. Argüelles, J.A. Rueda, Mon. Not. R. Astron. Soc. **451**, 622 (2015).
83. C.R. Argüelles, A. Krut, J.A. Rueda, R. Ruffini, Phys. Dark Univ. **21**, 82 (2018).
84. E.A. Becerra-Vergara, C.R. Argüelles, A. Krut, J.A. Rueda, R. Ruffini, Astron. Astrophys. **641**, A34 (2020).
85. E.A. Becerra-Vergara, C.R. Argüelles, A. Krut, J.A. Rueda, R. Ruffini, Mon. Not. Roy. Astr. Soc. **505**, L64 (2021).
86. P.H. Chavanis, Phys. Rev. D **100**, 123506 (2019).
87. I. De Martino, T. Broadhurst, S.H. Henry Tye, T. Chiueh, H.Y. Schive, Phys. Dark Univ. **28**, 100503 (2020).
88. C.R. Argüelles, A. Krut, J.A. Rueda, R. Ruffini, Phys. Dark Univ. **24**, 100278 (2019).
89. P.H. Chavanis, Phys. Rev. E **69**, 066126 (2004).
90. P.H. Chavanis, C. R. Physique **7**, 331 (2006).
91. M. Kirejczyk, G. Müller, P.H. Chavanis, arXiv:2110.01044
92. P. Ehrenfest, Proc. Amst. Acad. **20**, 200 (1917).
93. P.H. Chavanis, *The maximum mass of dilute axion stars*, preprint
94. P.H. Chavanis, Phys. Rev. D **100**, 083022 (2019).

The dark matter: DAMA/LIBRA and its perspectives

R. Bernabei, P. Belli*, V. Caracciolo, R. Cerulli and V. Merlo

Dip. Fisica, Università di Roma "Tor Vergata",
00133 Rome, Italy
INFN sezione di Roma "Tor Vergata", 00133 Rome, Italy
* E-mail: pierluigi.belli@roma2.infn.it

F. Cappella, A. d'Angelo and A. Incicchitti

Dip. Fisica, Università di Roma "La Sapienza",
00185 Rome, Italy
INFN sezione di Roma, 00185 Rome, Italy

C.J. Dai, X.H. Ma and X.D. Sheng

Key Laboratory of Particle Astrophysics, Institute of High Energy Physics,
Chinese Academy of Sciences, 100049 Beijing, PR China

F. Montecchia

INFN sezione di Roma "Tor Vergata", 00133 Rome, Italy
Dip. Ingegneria Civile e Ingegneria Informatica, Università di Roma "Tor Vergata",
00133 Rome, Italy

Z.P. Ye

Key Laboratory of Particle Astrophysics, Institute of High Energy Physics,
Chinese Academy of Sciences, 100049 Beijing, PR China
University of Jinggangshan, Ji'an, Jiangxi, PR China

Experimental observations and theoretical arguments point out that Dark Matter (DM) particles are one of the most prominent component of the Universe. This motivated the pioneer DAMA experiment to investigate the presence of these particles in the galactic halo, by exploiting the model independent signature of the DM annual modulation of the rate and very highly radio-pure apparatus in underground site. In this paper the results obtained by other two annual cycles of DAMA/LIBRA–phase2 are presented and the long-standing model-independent annual modulation effect measured by DAMA deep underground at the Gran Sasso National Laboratory (LNGS) of the I.N.F.N. with different experimental configurations is summarized. In particular, the DAMA/LIBRA–phase2 apparatus, $\simeq$ 250 kg highly radio-pure NaI(Tl), profits from a second generation high quantum efficiency photomultipliers and of new electronics with respect to DAMA/LIBRA–phase1. The improved experimental configuration has also allowed to lower the software energy threshold. Including the results of these other two annual cycles presented here, the total exposure of DAMA/LIBRA–phase2 over 8 annual cycles is 1.53 ton × yr. DAMA/LIBRA–phase2 confirms the evidence of a signal that meets all the requirements of the model independent Dark Matter annual modulation signature, at 11.8 σ C.L. in the energy region (1–6) keV. In the energy region between 2 and 6 keV, where data are also available from DAMA/NaI and DAMA/LIBRA–phase1 (14 additional annual cycles), the achieved C.L. for the full exposure (2.86 ton × yr) is 13.7 σ; the modulation amplitude of the *single-hit* scintillation events is: (0.01014±0.00074) cpd/kg/keV, the measured phase is (142.4 ± 4.2) days and the measured period is (0.99834 ± 0.00067) yr, all these values are well in agreement with those expected for DM particles. No systematics or side reaction able to mimic the exploited DM signature (i.e. to account for the whole measured modulation amplitude and to simultaneously satisfy all the requirements of the signature), has been found or suggested by anyone throughout some decades thus far.

Keywords: Scintillation detectors; elementary particle processes; Dark Matter; annual modulation.

1. Introduction

The DAMA/LIBRA[1–23] experiment, as the pioneer DAMA/NaI,[24–51] has the main aim to investigate the presence of DM particles in the galactic halo by exploiting the DM annual modulation signature (originally suggested in Ref.[52,53]). In addition, the developed highly radio-pure NaI(Tl) target-detectors[1,6,9,54] ensure sensitivity to a wide range of DM candidates, interaction types and astrophysical scenarios (see e.g. Refs.[2,14,16–18,25–32,35–42], and in literature).

The origin of the DM annual modulation signature and of its peculiar features is due to the Earth motion with respect to the DM particles constituting the Galactic Dark Halo. In fact, as a consequence of the Earth's revolution around the Sun, which is moving in the Galaxy with respect to the Local Standard of Rest towards the star Vega near the constellation of Hercules, the Earth should be crossed by a larger flux of DM particles around $\simeq$ 2 June and by a smaller one around $\simeq$ 2 December. In the former case the Earth orbital velocity is summed to that of the solar system with respect to the Galaxy, while in the latter the two velocities are subtracted. The DM annual modulation signature is very distinctive since the effect induced by DM particles must simultaneously satisfy all the following requirements: the rate must contain a component modulated according to a cosine function (1) with one year period (2) and a phase that peaks roughly $\simeq$ 2 June (3); this modulation must only be found in a well-defined low energy range, where DM particle induced events can be present (4); it must apply only to those events in which just one detector of many actually "fires" (*single-hit* events), since the DM particle multi-interaction probability is negligible (5); the modulation amplitude in the region of maximal sensitivity must be $\lesssim$ 7% of the constant part of the signal for usually adopted halo distributions (6), but it can be larger in case of some proposed scenarios such as e.g. those in Ref.[55–59] (even up to $\simeq$ 30%). Thus this signature has many peculiarities and, in addition, it allows to test a wide range of parameters in many possible astrophysical, nuclear and particle physics scenarios.

This DM signature might be mimicked only by systematic effects or side reactions able to account for the whole observed modulation amplitude and to simultaneously satisfy all the requirements given above.

The full description of the DAMA/LIBRA set-up and the adopted procedures during the phase1 and phase2 and other related arguments have been discussed in details e.g. in Refs.[1–6,19–21,23].

At the end of 2010 all the photomultipliers (PMTs) were replaced by a second generation PMTs Hamamatsu R6233MOD, with higher quantum efficiency (Q.E.) and with lower background with respect to those used in phase1; they were produced after a dedicated R&D in the company, and tests and selections.[6,54] The new PMTs have Q.E. in the range 33-39% at 420 nm, wavelength of NaI(Tl) emission, and in the range 36-44% at peak. The commissioning of the DAMA/LIBRA–phase2 experiment was successfully performed in 2011, allowing the achievement of the software energy threshold at 1 keV, and the improvement of some detector's features such as energy resolution and acceptance efficiency near software energy threshold.[6]

The adopted procedure for noise rejection near software energy threshold and the acceptance windows are the same unchanged along all the DAMA/LIBRA–phase2 data taking, throughout the months and the annual cycles. The typical behaviour of the overall efficiency for *single-hit* events as a function of the energy is also shown in Ref.[6]; the percentage variations of the efficiency follow a gaussian distribution with $\sigma = 0.3\%$ and do not show any modulation with period and phase as expected for the DM signal (for a partial data release see Ref.[21]).

At the end of 2012 new preamplifiers and special developed trigger modules were installed and the apparatus was equipped with more compact electronic modules.[60] Here we just remind that the sensitive part of DAMA/LIBRA–phase2 set-up is made of 25 highly radio-pure NaI(Tl) crystal scintillators (5-rows by 5-columns matrix) having 9.70 kg mass each one; quantitative analyses of residual contaminants are given in Ref.[1]. In each detector two 10 cm long UV light guides (made of Suprasil B quartz) act also as optical windows on the two end faces of the crystal, and are coupled to two low background PMTs working in coincidence at single photoelectron level. The detectors are housed in a sealed low-radioactive copper box installed in the center of a low-radioactive Cu/Pb/Cd-foils/polyethylene/paraffin shield; moreover, about 1 m concrete (made from the Gran Sasso rock material) almost fully surrounds (mostly outside the barrack) this passive shield, acting as a further neutron moderator. The shield is decoupled from the ground by a metallic structure mounted above a concrete basement; a neoprene layer separates the concrete basement and the floor of the laboratory. The space between this basement and the metallic structure is filled by paraffin for several tens cm in height.

A threefold-level sealing system prevents the detectors from contact with the environmental air of the underground laboratory and continuously maintains them in HP (high-purity) Nitrogen atmosphere. The whole installation is under air conditioning to ensure a suitable and stable working temperature. The huge heat capacity of the multi-tons passive shield ($\approx 10^6$ cal/°C) guarantees further relevant stability of the detectors' operating temperature. In particular, two independent systems of air conditioning are available for redundancy: one cooled by water refrigerated by a dedicated chiller and the other operating with cooling gas. A hardware/software monitoring system provides data on the operating conditions. In particular, several probes are read out and the results are stored with the production data.

Moreover, self-controlled computer based processes automatically monitor several parameters, including those from DAQ, and manage the alarms system. All these procedures, already experienced during DAMA/LIBRA–phase1,[1-5] allow us to control and to maintain the running conditions stable at a level better than 1% also in DAMA/LIBRA–phase2 (see e.g. Ref.[21,23]).

The light response of the detectors during phase2 typically ranges from 6 to 10 photoelectrons/keV, depending on the detector. Energy calibration with X-rays/γ sources are regularly carried out in the same running condition down to few keV (for details see e.g. Ref.[1]; in particular, double coincidences due to internal X-rays from ^{40}K (which is at ppt levels in the crystals) provide (when summing the data over long periods) a calibration point at 3.2 keV close to the software energy threshold. The DAQ system records both *single-hit* events (where just one of the detectors fires) and *multiple-hit* events (where more than one detector fires) up to the MeV region despite the optimization is performed for the lowest energy.

The radio-purity and details are discussed e.g. in Refs.[1-5,54] and references therein. The adopted procedures provide sensitivity to large and low mass DM candidates inducing nuclear recoils and/or electromagnetic signals.

The data of the former DAMA/NaI setup and, later, those of the DAMA/LIBRA-phase1 have already given (with high confidence level) positive evidence for the presence of a signal that satisfies all the requirements of the exploited DM annual modulation signature.[2-5,35,36]

In this paper the model independent result of eight annual cycles of DAMA/LIBRA–phase2 is presented. The total exposure of DAMA/LIBRA–phase2 is: 1.53 ton × yr with an energy threshold at 1 keV; when including also that of the first generation DAMA/NaI experiment and DAMA/LIBRA–phase1 the cumulative exposure is 2.86 ton × yr, corresponding to twenty-two independent annual cycles.

2. The DAMA/LIBRA–phase2 annual cycles

The details of the annual cycles of DAMA/LIBRA–phase2 are reported in Table 1. The first annual cycle was dedicated to the commissioning and to the optimizations towards the achievement of the 1 keV software energy threshold.[6] This period has: i) no data before/near Dec. 2, 2010 (the expected minimum of the DM signal); ii) data sets with some set-up modifications; iii) $(\alpha - \beta^2) = 0.355$ well different from 0.5 (i.e. the detectors were not being operational evenly throughout the year). Thus, this period cannot be used for the annual modulation studies; however, it has been used for other purposes.[6,13] Therefore, as shown in Table 1 the considered annual cycles of DAMA/LIBRA–phase2 are eight (exposure of 1.53 ton×yr). The cumulative exposure, also considering the former DAMA/NaI and DAMA/LIBRA–phase1, is 2.86 ton×yr.

The total number of events collected for the energy calibrations during the eight annual cycles of DAMA/LIBRA–phase2 is about 1.6×10^8, while about

Table 1. Details about the annual cycles of DAMA/LIBRA–phase2. The mean value of the squared cosine is $\alpha = \langle cos^2\omega(t-t_0)\rangle$ and the mean value of the cosine is $\beta = \langle cos\omega(t-t_0)\rangle$ (the averages are taken over the live time of the data taking and $t_0 = 152.5$ day, i.e. June 2nd); thus, the variance of the cosine, $(\alpha - \beta^2)$, is $\simeq 0.5$ for a detector being operational evenly throughout the year.

DAMA/LIBRA–phase2 annual cycle	Period	Mass (kg)	Exposure (kg×day)	$(\alpha - \beta^2)$
1	Dec. 23, 2010 – Sept. 9, 2011	commissioning of phase2		
2	Nov. 2, 2011 – Sept. 11, 2012	242.5	62917	0.519
3	Oct. 8, 2012 – Sept. 2, 2013	242.5	60586	0.534
4	Sept. 8, 2013 – Sept. 1, 2014	242.5	73792	0.479
5	Sept. 1, 2014 – Sept. 9, 2015	242.5	71180	0.486
6	Sept. 10, 2015 – Aug. 24, 2016	242.5	67527	0.522
7	Sept. 7, 2016 – Sept. 25, 2017	242.5	75135	0.480
8	Sept. 25, 2017 – Aug. 20, 2018	242.5	68759	0.557
9	Aug. 24, 2018 – Oct. 3, 2019	242.5	77213	0.446
DAMA/LIBRA–phase2	Nov. 2, 2011 – Oct. 3, 2019		557109 kg×day $\simeq$ 1.53 ton×yr	0.501
DAMA/NaI + DAMA/LIBRA–phase1 + DAMA/LIBRA–phase2:			2.86 ton×yr	

1.7×10^5 events/keV have been collected for the evaluation of the acceptance window efficiency for noise rejection near the software energy threshold.[1,6]

As it can be inferred from Table 1, the duty cycle of the experiment is high, ranging between 76% and 86%. The routine calibrations and, in particular, the data collection for the acceptance windows efficiency mainly affect it.

3. The annual modulation of the residual rate

Fig. 1 shows the time behaviour of the experimental residual rates of the *single-hit* scintillation events in the (1–3), and (1–6) keV energy intervals for DAMA/LIBRA–phase2. The residual rates are calculated from the measured rate of the *single-hit* events after subtracting the constant part, as described in Refs.[2–5,35,36]. The null modulation hypothesis is rejected at very high C.L. by χ^2 test: $\chi^2 = 176$ and 202, respectively, over 69 d.o.f.. The P-values are P = 2.6×10^{-11}, and P = 5.6×10^{-15}, respectively. The residuals of the DAMA/NaI data (0.29 ton × yr) are given in Ref.[2,5,35,36], while those of the DAMA/LIBRA–phase1 (1.04 ton × yr) in Ref.[2–5].

The former DAMA/LIBRA–phase1 and the new DAMA/LIBRA–phase2 residual rates of the *single-hit* scintillation events are reported in Fig. 2. The energy interval is from 2 keV, the software energy threshold of DAMA/LIBRA–phase1, up to 6 keV. The null modulation hypothesis is rejected at very high C.L. by χ^2 test: $\chi^2/d.o.f. = 240/119$, corresponding to P-value = 3.5×10^{-10}.

The *single-hit* residual rates of the DAMA/LIBRA–phase2 (Fig. 1) have been fitted with the function: $A\cos\omega(t-t_0)$, considering a period $T = \frac{2\pi}{\omega} = 1$ yr and a phase $t_0 = 152.5$ day (June 2nd) as expected by the DM annual modulation signature; this can be repeated for the only case of (2-6) keV energy interval also including the former DAMA/NaI and DAMA/LIBRA–phase1 data. The goodness of the fits

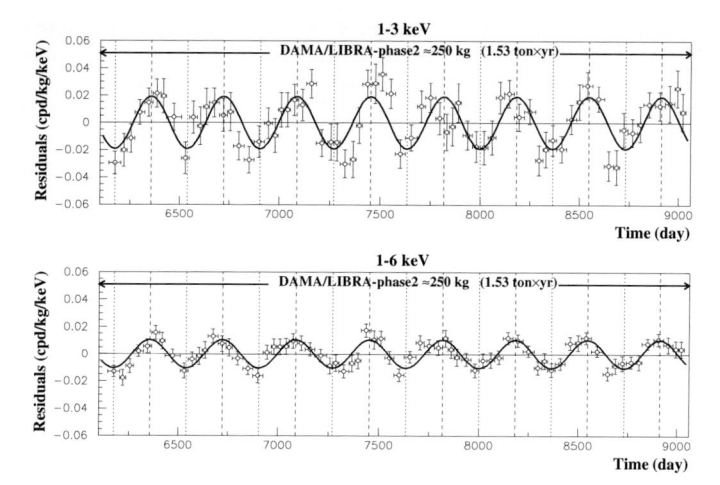

Fig. 1. Experimental residual rate of the *single-hit* scintillation events measured by DAMA/LIBRA–phase2 over eight annual cycles in the (1–3), and (1–6) keV energy intervals as a function of the time. The time scale is maintained the same of the previous DAMA papers for consistency. The data points present the experimental errors as vertical bars and the associated time bin width as horizontal bars. The superimposed curves are the cosinusoidal functional forms $A\cos\omega(t-t_0)$ with a period $T = \frac{2\pi}{\omega} = 1$ yr, a phase $t_0 = 152.5$ day (June 2nd) and modulation amplitudes, A, equal to the central values obtained by best fit on the data points of the entire DAMA/LIBRA–phase2. The dashed vertical lines correspond to the maximum expected for the DM signal (June 2nd), while the dotted vertical lines correspond to the minimum.

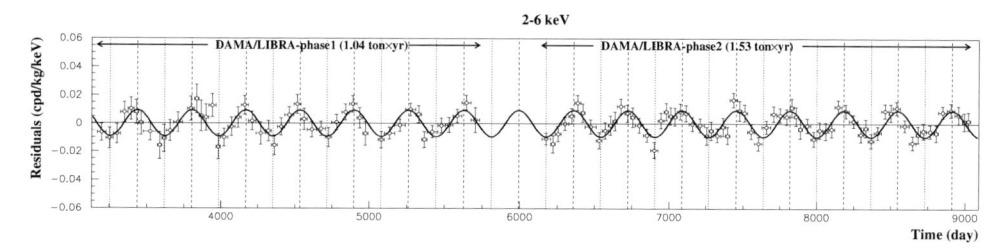

Fig. 2. Experimental residual rate of the *single-hit* scintillation events measured by DAMA/LIBRA–phase1 and DAMA/LIBRA–phase2 in the (2–6) keV energy intervals as a function of the time. The superimposed curve is the cosinusoidal functional forms $A\cos\omega(t-t_0)$ with a period $T = \frac{2\pi}{\omega} = 1$ yr, a phase $t_0 = 152.5$ day (June 2nd) and modulation amplitude, A, equal to the central value obtained by best fit on the data points of DAMA/LIBRA–phase1 and DAMA/LIBRA–phase2. For details see Fig. 1.

is well supported by the χ^2 test; for example, $\chi^2/d.o.f. = 81.6/68, 66.2/68, 130/155$ are obtained for the (1–3) keV and (1–6) keV cases of DAMA/LIBRA–phase2, and for the (2–6) keV case of DAMA/NaI, DAMA/LIBRA–phase1 and DAMA/LIBRA–phase2, respectively. The results of the best fits in the different cases are summarized in Table 2. Table 2 also reports the cases when the period and the phase are kept free in the fitting procedure. The period and the phase are well compatible with expectations for a DM annual modulation signal. In particular, the phase is consistent with

Table 2. Modulation amplitude, A, obtained by fitting the *single-hit* residual rate of DAMA/LIBRA–phase2, as reported in Fig. 1, and also including the residual rates of the former DAMA/NaI and DAMA/LIBRA–phase1. It was obtained by fitting the data with the formula: $A\cos\omega(t-t_0)$. The period $T=\frac{2\pi}{\omega}$ and the phase t_0 are kept fixed at 1 yr and at 152.5 day (June 2nd), respectively, as expected by the DM annual modulation signature, and alternatively kept free. The results are well compatible with expectations for a signal in the DM annual modulation signature.

	A (cpd/kg/keV)	$T=\frac{2\pi}{\omega}$ (yr)	t_0 (days)	C.L.
DAMA/LIBRA–phase2:				
1-3 keV	(0.0191±0.0020)	1.0	152.5	9.7 σ
1-6 keV	(0.01048±0.00090)	1.0	152.5	11.6 σ
2-6 keV	(0.00933±0.00094)	1.0	152.5	9.9 σ
1-3 keV	(0.0191±0.0020)	(0.99952±0.00080)	149.6±5.9	9.6 σ
1-6 keV	(0.01058±0.00090)	(0.99882±0.00065)	144.5±5.1	11.8 σ
2-6 keV	(0.00954±0.00076)	(0.99836±0.00075)	141.1±5.9	12.6 σ
DAMA/LIBRA–phase1 + phase2:				
2-6 keV	(0.00941±0.00076)	1.0	152.5	12.4 σ
2-6 keV	(0.00959±0.00076)	(0.99835±0.00069)	142.0±4.5	12.6 σ
DAMA/NaI + DAMA/LIBRA–phase1 + phase2:				
2-6 keV	(0.00996±0.00074)	1.0	152.5	13.4 σ
2-6 keV	(0.01014±0.00074)	(0.99834±0.00067)	142.4±4.2	13.7 σ

about June 2nd and is fully consistent with the value independently determined by Maximum Likelihood analysis (see later). For completeness, we recall that a slight energy dependence of the phase could be expected (see e.g. Refs.[38,58,59,61–63]), providing intriguing information on the nature of Dark Matter candidate and related aspects.

4. Absence of modulation of the background

As done in previous data releases, absence of any significant background modulation in the energy spectrum has also been verified in the present data taking for energy regions not of interest for DM. In fact, the background in the lowest energy region is essentially due to "Compton" electrons, X-rays and/or Auger electrons, muon induced events, etc., which are strictly correlated with the events in the higher energy region of the spectrum. Thus, if a modulation detected in the lowest energy region were due to a modulation of the background (rather than to a signal), an equal or larger modulation in the higher energy regions should be present.

For example, the measured rate integrated above 90 keV, R_{90}, as a function of the time has been analysed. Fig. 3 shows the distribution of the percentage variations of R_{90} with respect to the mean values for all the detectors in DAMA/LIBRA–phase2. It shows a cumulative gaussian behaviour with $\sigma \simeq 1\%$, well accounted for by the statistical spread expected from the used sampling time.

Moreover, fitting the time behaviour of R_{90} including a term with phase and period as for DM particles, a modulation amplitude $A_{R_{90}}$ compatible with zero has

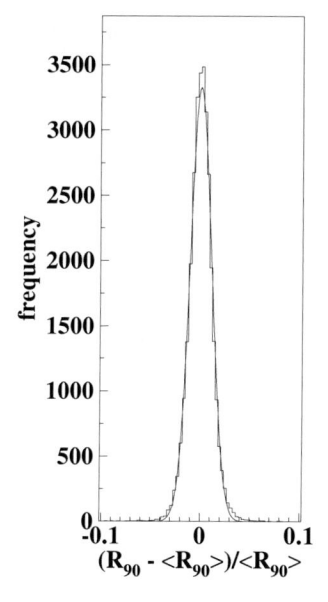

Fig. 3. Distribution of the percentage variations of R_{90} with respect to the mean values for all the detectors in the DAMA/LIBRA–phase2 (histogram); the superimposed curve is a gaussian fit.

been found for all the annual cycles (see Table 3). This also excludes the presence of any background modulation in the whole energy spectrum at a level much lower than the effect found in the lowest energy region for the *single-hit* scintillation events. In fact, otherwise – considering the R_{90} mean values – a modulation amplitude of order of tens cpd/kg would be present for each annual cycle, that is $\simeq 100\ \sigma$ far away from the measured values.

Table 3. Modulation amplitudes, $A_{R_{90}}$, obtained by fitting the time behaviour of R_{90} in DAMA/LIBRA–phase2, including a term with a cosine function having phase and period as expected for a DM signal. The obtained amplitudes are compatible with zero, and incompatible ($\simeq 100\ \sigma$) with modulation amplitudes of tens cpd/kg. Modulation amplitudes, $A_{(6-14)}$, obtained by fitting the time behaviour of the residual rates of the *single-hit* scintillation events in the (6–14) keV energy interval. In the fit the phase and the period are at the values expected for a DM signal. The obtained amplitudes are compatible with zero.

DAMA/LIBRA–phase2 annual cycle	$A_{R_{90}}$ (cpd/kg)	$A_{(6-14)}$ (cpd/kg/keV)
2	(0.12±0.14)	(0.0032±0.0017)
3	-(0.08±0.14)	(0.0016±0.0017)
4	(0.07±0.15)	(0.0024±0.0015)
5	-(0.05±0.14)	-(0.0004±0.0015)
6	(0.03±0.13)	(0.0001±0.0015)
7	-(0.09±0.14)	(0.0015±0.0014)
8	-(0.18±0.13)	-(0.0005±0.0013)
9	(0.08±0.14)	-(0.0003±0.0014)

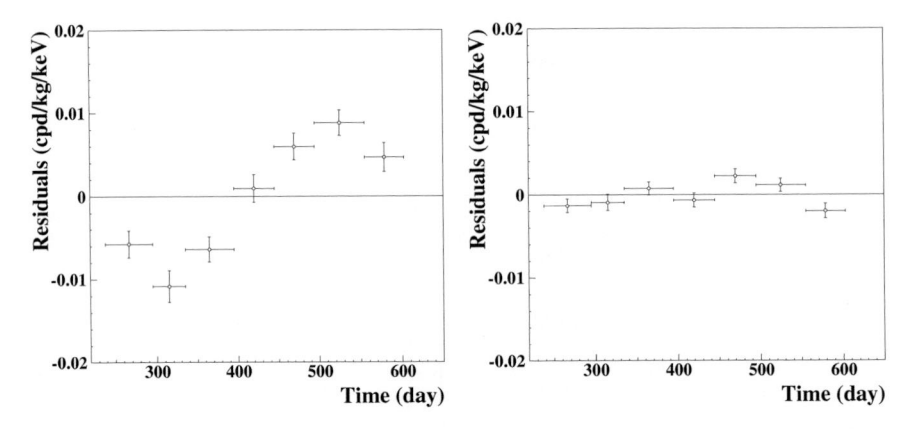

Fig. 4. Experimental *single-hit* residuals in the (1–6) keV and in the (10–20) keV energy regions for DAMA/LIBRA–phase2 as if they were collected in a single annual cycle (i.e. binning in the variable time from the January 1st of each annual cycle). The data points present the experimental errors as vertical bars and the associated time bin width as horizontal bars. The initial time of the figures is taken at August 7th. A clear modulation satisfying all the peculiarities of the DM annual modulation signature is present in the lowest energy interval with A=(0.00956 ± 0.00090) cpd/kg/keV, while it is absent just above: A=(0.0007 ± 0.0005) cpd/kg/keV.

Similar results are obtained when comparing the *single-hit* residuals in the (1–6) keV with those in other energy intervals; for example Fig. 4 shows the *single-hit* residuals in the (1–6) keV and in the (10–20) keV energy regions for DAMA/LIBRA–phase2 as if they were collected in a single annual cycle (i.e. binning in the variable time from the January 1st of each annual cycle).

Moreover, Table 3 shows the modulation amplitudes obtained by fitting the time behaviour of the residual rates of the *single-hit* scintillation events in the (6–14) keV energy interval for the DAMA/LIBRA–phase2 annual cycles. In the fit the phase and the period are at the values expected for a DM signal. The obtained amplitudes are compatible with zero.

A further relevant investigation on DAMA/LIBRA–phase2 data has been performed by applying the same hardware and software procedures, used to acquire and to analyse the *single-hit* residual rate, to the *multiple-hit* one. Since the probability that a DM particle interacts in more than one detector is negligible, a DM signal can be present just in the *single-hit* residual rate. Thus, the comparison of the results of the *single-hit* events with those of the *multiple-hit* ones corresponds to compare the cases of DM particles beam-on and beam-off. This procedure also allows an additional test of the background behaviour in the same energy interval where the positive effect is observed.

In particular, in Fig. 5 the residual rates of the *single-hit* scintillation events collected during DAMA/LIBRA–phase2 are reported, as collected in a single cycle, together with the residual rates of the *multiple-hit* events, in the considered energy intervals. While, as already observed, a clear modulation, satisfying all the

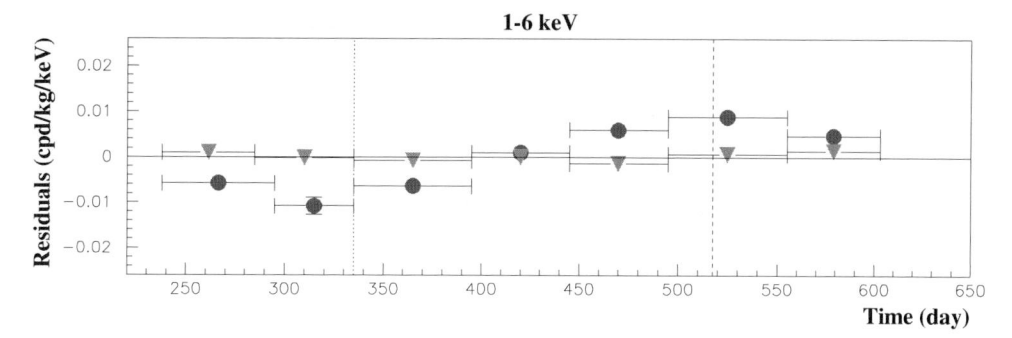

Fig. 5. Experimental residual rates of DAMA/LIBRA–phase2 *single-hit* events (filled red on-line circles), class of events to which DM events belong, and for *multiple-hit* events (filled green on-line triangles), class of events to which DM events do not belong. They have been obtained by considering for each class of events the data as collected in a single annual cycle and by using in both cases the same identical hardware and the same identical software procedures. The initial time of the figure is taken on August 7th. The experimental points present the errors as vertical bars and the associated time bin width as horizontal bars. Analogous results were obtained for DAMA/NaI (two last annual cycles) and DAMA/LIBRA–phase1.[2–5, 36]

peculiarities of the DM annual modulation signature, is present in the *single-hit* events, the fitted modulation amplitude for the *multiple-hit* residual rate is well compatible with zero: (0.00030 ± 0.00032) cpd/kg/keV in the (1–6) keV energy region. Thus, again evidence of annual modulation with proper features as required by the DM annual modulation signature is present in the *single-hit* residuals (events class to which the DM particle induced events belong), while it is absent in the *multiple-hit* residual rate (event class to which only background events belong). Similar results were also obtained for the two last annual cycles of DAMA/NaI[36] and for DAMA/LIBRA–phase1.[2–5] Since the same identical hardware and the same identical software procedures have been used to analyse the two classes of events, the obtained result offers an additional strong support for the presence of a DM particle component in the galactic halo.

In conclusion, no background process able to mimic the DM annual modulation signature (that is, able to simultaneously satisfy all the peculiarities of the signature and to account for the measured modulation amplitude) has been found or suggested by anyone throughout some decades thus far (see also discussions e.g. in Ref.[1–5, 7, 8, 19–21, 23, 34–36]).

5. The analysis in frequency

To perform the Fourier analysis of the DAMA/LIBRA–phase1 and phase2 data in a wider region of considered frequency, the *single-hit* events have been grouped in 1 day bins. Due to the low statistics in each time bin, a procedure detailed in Ref.[64] has been followed. The whole power spectra up to the Nyquist frequency and the zoomed ones are reported in Fig. 6. A clear peak corresponding to a period of

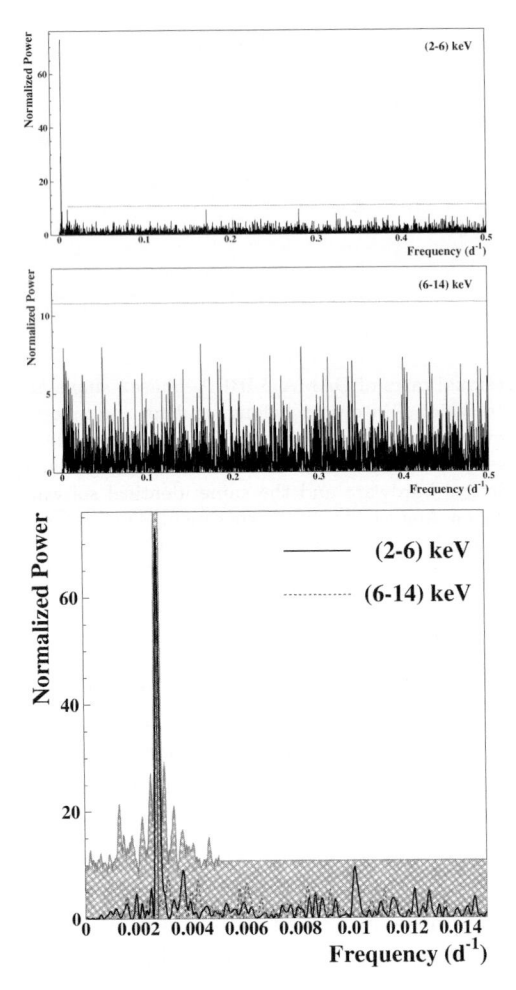

Fig. 6. Power spectra of the time sequence of the measured *single-hit* events for DAMA/LIBRA–phase1 and DAMA/LIBRA–phase2 grouped in 1 day bins. From top to bottom: spectra up to the Nyquist frequency for (2–6) keV and (6–14) keV energy intervals and their zoom around the 1 y^{-1} peak, for (2–6) keV (solid line) and (6–14) keV (dotted line) energy intervals. The main mode present at the lowest energy interval corresponds to a frequency of 2.74×10^{-3} d^{-1} (vertical line, purple on-line). It corresponds to a period of $\simeq$ 1 year. A similar peak is not present in the (6–14) keV energy interval. The shaded (green on-line) area in the bottom figure – calculated by Monte Carlo procedure – represents the 90% C.L. region where all the peaks are expected to fall for the (2–6) keV energy interval. In the frequency range far from the signal for the (2–6) keV energy region and for the whole (6–14) keV spectrum, the upper limit of the shaded region (90% C.L.) can be calculated to be 10.8 (continuous lines, green on-line).

1 year is evident for the lowest energy interval; the same analysis in the (6–14) keV energy region shows only aliasing peaks instead. Neither other structure at different frequencies has been observed.

As to the significance of the peaks present in the periodogram, we remind that the periodogram ordinate, z, at each frequency follows a simple exponential distribution e^{-z} in the case of the null hypothesis or white noise.[65] Therefore, if M independent frequencies are scanned, the probability to obtain values larger than z is: $P(>z) = 1 - (1 - e^{-z})^M$.

In general M depends on the number of sampled frequencies, the number of data points N, and their detailed spacing. It turns out that M is very nearly equal to N when the data points are approximately equally spaced, and when the sampled frequencies cover the frequency range from 0 to the Nyquist frequency.[66,67]

The number of data points used to obtain the spectra in Fig. 6 is $N = 5047$ (days measured over the 5479 days of the 15 DAMA/LIBRA–phase1 and phase2 annual cycles) and the full frequencies region up to Nyquist frequency has been scanned. Therefore, assuming $M = N$, the significance levels $P = 0.10, 0.05$ and 0.01, correspond to peaks with heights larger than $z = 10.8, 11.5$ and 13.1, respectively, in the spectra of Fig 6.

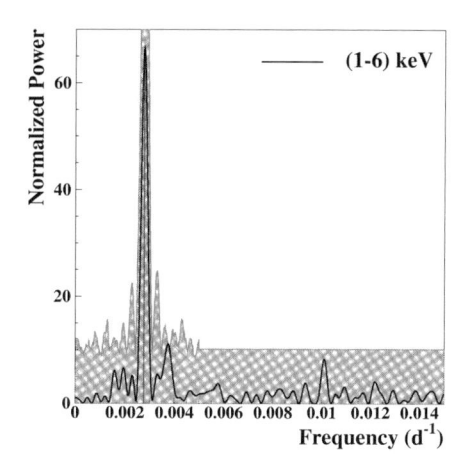

Fig. 7. Power spectrum of the time sequence of the measured *single-hit* events in the (1–6) keV energy interval for DAMA/LIBRA–phase2 grouped in 1 day bin. The main mode present at the lowest energy interval corresponds to a frequency of 2.77×10^{-3} d^{-1} (vertical line, purple on-line). It corresponds to a period of $\simeq 1$ year. The shaded (green on-line) area – calculated by Monte Carlo procedure – represents the 90% C.L. region where all the peaks are expected to fall for the (1–6) keV energy interval.

In the case below 6 keV, a signal is present; thus, to properly evaluate the C.L. the signal must be included. This has been done by a dedicated Monte Carlo procedure where a large number of similar experiments has been simulated. The 90% C.L. region (shaded, green on-line) where all the peaks are expected to fall for the (2–6) keV energy interval is reported in Fig 6. Several peaks, satellite of the one year period frequency, are present.

In conclusion, apart from the peak corresponding to a 1 year period, no other peak is statistically significant either in the low and high energy regions.

Moreover, for each annual cycle of DAMA/LIBRA–phase1 and phase2, the annual baseline counting rates have been calculated for the (2–6) keV energy interval. Their power spectrum in the frequency range 0.00013 − 0.0019 d^{-1} (corresponding to a period range 1.4–21.1 year) has been calculated according to Ref.[5]. No statistically-significant peak is present at frequencies lower than 1 y^{-1}. This implies that no evidence for a long term modulation in the counting rate is present.

Finally, the case of the (1–6) keV energy interval of the DAMA/LIBRA–phase2 data is reported in Fig. 7. As previously the only significant peak is the one corresponding to one year period. No other peak is statistically significant being below the shaded (green on-line) area obtained by Monte Carlo procedure.

6. The modulation amplitudes by the maximum likelihood approach

The annual modulation present at low energy can also be pointed out by depicting the energy dependence of the modulation amplitude, $S_m(E)$, obtained by maximum likelihood method considering fixed period and phase: $T = 1$ yr and $t_0 = 152.5$ day. For such purpose the likelihood function of the *single-hit* experimental data in the k–th energy bin is defined as: $\mathbf{L_k} = \mathbf{\Pi}_{ij} e^{-\mu_{ijk}} \frac{\mu_{ijk}^{N_{ijk}}}{N_{ijk}!}$, where N_{ijk} is the number of events collected in the i-th time interval (hereafter 1 day), by the j-th detector and in the k-th energy bin. N_{ijk} follows a Poisson's distribution with expectation value $\mu_{ijk} = [b_{jk} + S_i(E_k)] M_j \Delta t_i \Delta E \epsilon_{jk}$. The b_{jk} are the background contributions, M_j is the mass of the j-th detector, Δt_i is the detector running time during the i-th time interval, ΔE is the chosen energy bin, ϵ_{jk} is the overall efficiency. The signal can be written as:

$$S_i(E) = S_0(E) + S_m(E) \cdot \cos\omega(t_i - t_0),$$

where $S_0(E)$ is the constant part of the signal and $S_m(E)$ is the modulation amplitude. The usual procedure is to minimize the function $y_k = -2ln(\mathbf{L_k}) - const$ for each energy bin; the free parameters of the fit are the $(b_{jk} + S_0)$ contributions and the S_m parameter.

The modulation amplitudes for the whole data sets: DAMA/NaI, DAMA/LIBRA–phase1 and DAMA/LIBRA–phase2 (total exposure 2.86 ton×yr) are plotted in Fig. 8; the data below 2 keV refer only to the DAMA/LIBRA-phase2 exposure (1.53 ton×yr). It can be inferred that positive signal is present in the (1–6) keV energy interval, while S_m values compatible with zero are present just above. All this confirms the previous analyses. The test of the hypothesis that the S_m values in the (6–14) keV energy interval have random fluctuations around zero yields $\chi^2/d.o.f.$ equal to 20.3/16 (P-value = 21%).

For the case of (6–20) keV energy interval $\chi^2/d.o.f. = 42.2/28$ (P-value = 4%). The obtained χ^2 value is rather large due mainly to two data points, whose centroids are at 16.75 and 18.25 keV, far away from the (1–6) keV energy interval. The P-values obtained by excluding only the first and either the points are 14% and 23%.

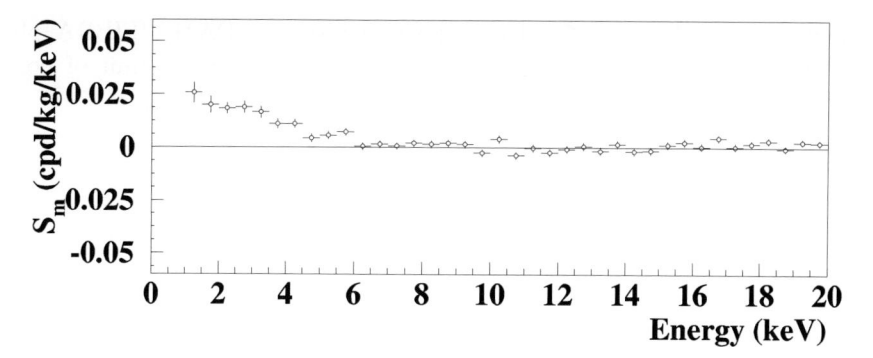

Fig. 8. Modulation amplitudes, S_m, for the whole data sets: DAMA/NaI, DAMA/LIBRA–phase1 and DAMA/LIBRA–phase2 (total exposure 2.86 ton×yr) above 2 keV; below 2 keV only the DAMA/LIBRA-phase2 exposure (1.53 ton × yr) is available and used. The energy bin ΔE is 0.5 keV. A clear modulation is present in the lowest energy region, while S_m values compatible with zero are present just above. In fact, the S_m values in the (6–20) keV energy interval have random fluctuations around zero with $\chi^2/d.o.f.$ equal to 42.2/28 (P-value is 4%).

6.1. The S_m distributions

The method also allows the extraction of the S_m values for each detector. In particular, the modulation amplitudes S_m integrated in the range (2–6) keV for each of the 25 detectors for the DAMA/LIBRA–phase1 and DAMA/LIBRA–phase2 periods can be produced. They have random fluctuations around the weighted averaged value confirmed by the χ^2 analysis. Thus, the hypothesis that the signal is well distributed over all the 25 detectors is accepted.

As previously done for the other data releases,[2–5, 19–21, 23] the S_m values for each detector for each annual cycle and for each energy bin have been obtained. The S_m are expected to follow a normal distribution in absence of any systematic effects. Therefore, the variable $x = \frac{S_m - \langle S_m \rangle}{\sigma}$ has been considered to verify that the S_m are statistically well distributed in the 16 energy bins ($\Delta E = 0.25$ keV) in the (2–6) keV energy interval of the seven DAMA/LIBRA–phase1 annual cycles and in the 20 energy bins in the (1–6) keV energy interval of the eight DAMA/LIBRA–phase2 annual cycles and in each detector. Here, σ are the errors associated to S_m and $\langle S_m \rangle$ are the mean values of the S_m averaged over the detectors and the annual cycles for each considered energy bin.

Defining $\chi^2 = \Sigma x^2$, where the sum is extended over all the 272 (192 for the 16th detector[4]) x values, $\chi^2/d.o.f.$ values ranging from 0.8 to 2.0 are obtained, depending on the detector.

The mean value of the 25 $\chi^2/d.o.f.$ is 1.092, slightly larger than 1. Although this can be still ascribed to statistical fluctuations, let us ascribe it to a possible systematics. In this case, one would derive an additional error to the modulation amplitude measured below 6 keV: $\leq 2.4 \times 10^{-4}$ cpd/kg/keV, if combining quadratically the errors, or $\leq 3.6 \times 10^{-5}$ cpd/kg/keV, if linearly combining them. This possible additional error: $\leq 2.4\%$ or $\leq 0.4\%$, respectively, on the DAMA/LIBRA–phase1 and DAMA/LIBRA–phase2 modulation amplitudes is an upper limit of possible systematic effects coming from the detector to detector differences.

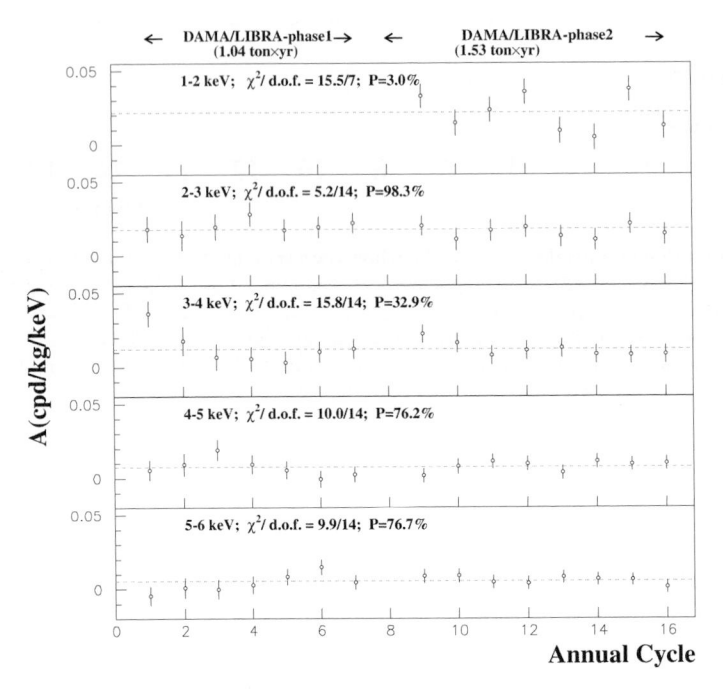

Fig. 9. Modulation amplitudes of each single annual cycle of DAMA/LIBRA–phase1 and DAMA/LIBRA–phase2. The error bars are the 1σ errors. The dashed horizontal lines show the central values obtained by best fit over the whole data set. The χ^2 test and the *run test* accept the hypothesis at 95% C.L. that the modulation amplitudes are normally fluctuating around the best fit values.

Among further additional tests, the analysis of the modulation amplitudes as a function of the energy separately for the nine inner detectors and the remaining external ones has been carried out for DAMA/LIBRA–phase1 and DAMA/LIBRA–phase2, as already done for the other data sets.[2–5,19–21,23] The obtained values are fully in agreement; in fact, the hypothesis that the two sets of modulation amplitudes belong to same distribution has been verified by χ^2 test, obtaining e.g.: $\chi^2/d.o.f.$ = 1.9/6 and 36.1/38 for the energy intervals (1–4) and (1–20) keV, respectively (ΔE = 0.5 keV). This shows that the effect is also well shared between inner and outer detectors.

Fig. 9 shows the modulation amplitudes singularly calculated for each annual cycle of DAMA/LIBRA–phase1 and DAMA/LIBRA–phase2. To test the hypothesis that the amplitudes are compatible and normally fluctuating around their mean values, the χ^2 test has been performed. The $\chi^2/d.o.f.$ values and the P-values are also shown in Fig. 9. In addition to the χ^2 test, another independent statistical test has been applied: the *run test* (see e.g. Ref.[69]); it verifies the hypothesis that the positive (above the mean value) and negative (under the mean value) data points are randomly distributed. The lower (upper) tail probabilities obtained by the *run test* are: 89(37)%, 87(30)%, 17(94)%, 17(94)% and 30(85)%, respectively. This analysis confirms that the data collected in all the annual cycles with DAMA/LIBRA–phase1 and phase2 are statistically compatible and can be considered together.

7. Investigation of the annual modulation phase

Let us, finally, release the assumption of the phase $t_0 = 152.5$ day in the procedure to evaluate the modulation amplitudes. In this case the signal can be alternatively written as:

$$S_i(E) = S_0(E) + S_m(E)\cos\omega(t_i - t_0) + Z_m(E)\sin\omega(t_i - t_0) \qquad (1)$$
$$= S_0(E) + Y_m(E)\cos\omega(t_i - t^*).$$

For signals induced by DM particles one should expect: i) $Z_m \sim 0$ (because of the orthogonality between the cosine and the sine functions); ii) $S_m \simeq Y_m$; iii) $t^* \simeq t_0 = 152.5$ day. In fact, these conditions hold for most of the dark halo models; however, as mentioned above, slight differences can be expected in case of possible contributions from non-thermalized DM components (see e.g. Refs.[38,58,59,61–63]).

Considering cumulatively the data of DAMA/NaI, DAMA/LIBRA–phase1 and DAMA/LIBRA–phase2 the obtained 2σ contours in the plane (S_m, Z_m) for the (2–6) keV and (6–14) keV energy intervals are shown in Fig. 10–*left* while in Fig. 10–*right* the obtained 2σ contours in the plane (Y_m, t^*) are depicted. Moreover, Fig. 10 also shows only for DAMA/LIBRA–phase2 the 2σ contours in the (1–6) keV energy interval.

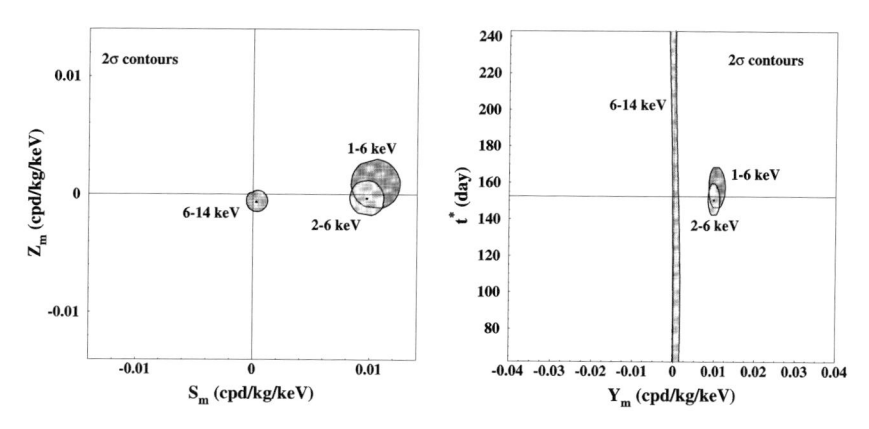

Fig. 10. 2σ contours in the plane (S_m, Z_m) (*left*) and in the plane (Y_m, t^*) (*right*) for: i) DAMA/NaI, DAMA/LIBRA–phase1 and DAMA/LIBRA–phase2 in the (2–6) keV and (6–14) keV energy intervals (light areas, green on-line); ii) only DAMA/LIBRA–phase2 in the (1–6) keV energy interval (dark areas, blue on-line). The contours have been obtained by the maximum likelihood method. A modulation amplitude is present in the lower energy intervals and the phase agrees with that expected for DM induced signals.

The best fit values in the considered cases (1σ errors) for S_m versus Z_m and Y_m versus t^* are reported in Table 4.

Table 4. Best fit values (1σ errors) for S_m versus Z_m and Y_m versus t^*, considering: i) DAMA/NaI, DAMA/LIBRA–phase1 and DAMA/LIBRA–phase2 in the (2–6) keV and (6–14) keV energy intervals; ii) only DAMA/LIBRA–phase2 in the (1–6) keV energy interval. See also Fig. 10.

E (keV)	S_m (cpd/kg/keV)	Z_m (cpd/kg/keV)	Y_m (cpd/kg/keV)	t^* (day)
DAMA/NaI+DAMA/LIBRA–phase1+DAMA/LIBRA–phase2:				
2–6	(0.0097 ± 0.0007)	-(0.0003 ± 0.0007)	(0.0097 ± 0.0007)	(150.5 ± 4.0)
6–14	(0.0003 ± 0.0005)	-(0.0006 ± 0.0005)	(0.0007 ± 0.0010)	undefined
DAMA/LIBRA–phase2:				
1–6	(0.0104 ± 0.0007)	(0.0002 ± 0.0007)	(0.0104 ± 0.0007)	(153.5 ± 4.0)

Finally, setting S_m in eq. (1) to zero, the Z_m values as function of the energy have also been determined by using the same procedure. The Z_m values as a function of the energy for DAMA/NaI, DAMA/LIBRA–phase1, and DAMA/LIBRA–phase2 data sets are expected to be zero. The χ^2 test applied to the data supports the hypothesis that the Z_m values are simply fluctuating around zero; in fact, in the (1–20) keV energy region the $\chi^2/d.o.f.$ is equal to 40.6/38 corresponding to a P-value = 36%.

The energy behaviors of the Y_m and of the phase t^* are produced for the cumulative exposure of DAMA/NaI, DAMA/LIBRA–phase1, and DAMA/LIBRA–phase2. As in the previous analyses, an annual modulation effect is present in the lower energy intervals and the phase agrees with that expected for DM induced signals. No modulation is present above 6 keV and the phase is undetermined.

8. Perspectives

To further increase the experimental sensitivity of DAMA/LIBRA and to disentangle some of the many possible astrophysical, nuclear and particle physics scenarios in the investigation on the DM candidate particle(s), an increase of the exposure in the lowest energy bin and a further decreasing of the software energy threshold are needed. This is pursued by running DAMA/LIBRA–phase2 and upgrading the experimental set-up to lower the software energy threshold below 1 keV with high acceptance efficiency.

Firstly, particular efforts for lowering the software energy threshold have been done in the already-acquired data of DAMA/LIBRA–phase2 by using the same technique as before with dedicated studies on the efficiency. As consequence, a new data point has been added in the modulation amplitude as function of energy down to 0.75 keV, see Fig. 11. A modulation is also present below 1 keV, from 0.75 keV.

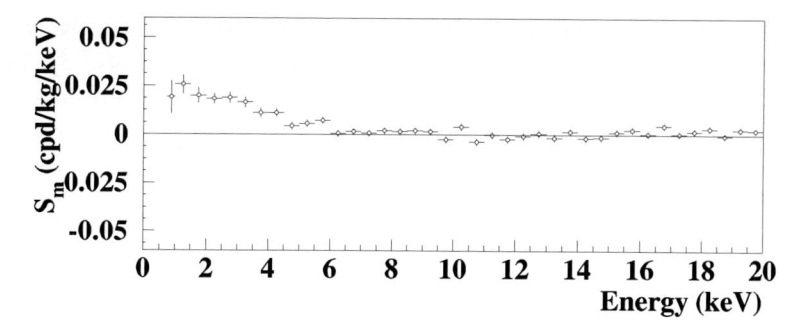

Fig. 11. As Fig. 8; the new data point below 1 keV, with software energy threshold at 0.75 keV, shows that an annual modulation is also present below 1 keV. This preliminary result confirms the necessity to lower the software energy threshold by a hardware upgrade and to improve the experimental error on the first energy bin.

This preliminary result confirms the necessity to lower the software energy threshold by a hardware upgrade and an improved statistics in the first energy bin.

This dedicated hardware upgrade of DAMA/LIBRA–phase2 is underway. It consists in equipping all the PMTs with miniaturized low background new concept preamplifier and HV divider mounted on the same socket, and related improvements of the electronic chain, mainly the use of higher vertical resolution 14-bit digitizers.

9. Conclusions

DAMA/LIBRA–phase2 confirms a peculiar annual modulation of the *single-hit* scintillation events in the (1–6) keV energy region satisfying all the many requirements of the DM annual modulation signature; the cumulative exposure by the former DAMA/NaI, DAMA/LIBRA–phase1 and DAMA/LIBRA–phase2 is 2.86 ton × yr.

As required by the exploited DM annual modulation signature: 1) the *single-hit* events show a clear cosine-like modulation as expected for the DM signal; 2) the measured period is well compatible with the 1 yr period as expected for the DM signal; 3) the measured phase is compatible with the roughly $\simeq 152.5$ days expected for the DM signal; 4) the modulation is present only in the low energy (1–6) keV interval and not in other higher energy regions, consistently with expectation for the DM signal; 5) the modulation is present only in the *single-hit* events, while it is absent in the *multiple-hit* ones as expected for the DM signal; 6) the measured modulation amplitude in NaI(Tl) target of the *single-hit* scintillation events in the (2–6) keV energy interval, for which data are also available by DAMA/NaI and DAMA/LIBRA–phase1, is: (0.01014 ± 0.00074) cpd/kg/keV (13.7 σ C.L.). No systematic or side processes able to mimic the signature, i.e. able to simultaneously satisfy all the many peculiarities of the signature and to account for the whole measured modulation amplitude, has been found or suggested by anyone throughout some decades thus far. In particular, arguments related to any possible role of some natural periodical phenomena have been discussed and quantitatively demonstrated to be unable to mimic the signature (see references; e.g. Refs.[7,8]). Thus, on the basis of the exploited signature, the model independent DAMA results give evidence at 13.7σ C.L. (over 22 independent annual cycles and in various experimental configurations) for the presence of DM particles in the galactic halo.

The new data, released in this Conference, determine the modulation parameters with increasing precision and allow us to disentangle with larger C.L. among different DM candidates, DM models and astrophysical, nuclear and particle physics scenarios.

The DAMA model independent evidence is compatible with a wide set of astrophysical, nuclear and particle physics scenarios for high and low mass candidates inducing nuclear recoil and/or electromagnetic radiation, as also shown in various literature. Moreover, both the negative results and all the possible positive hints, achieved so-far in the field, can be compatible with the DAMA model independent DM annual modulation results in many scenarios considering also the existing experimental and theoretical uncertainties; the same holds for indirect approaches. For a discussion see e.g. Ref.[5] and references therein.

Finally, we stress that to efficiently disentangle among at least some of the many possible candidates and scenarios an increase of exposure in the new lowest energy bin and the decrease of the software energy threshold below the present 1 keV is important. The experiment is collecting data and the hardware efforts towards the lowering of the software energy threshold is in progress.

References

1. R. Bernabei et al., *Nucl. Instr. and Meth. A* **592**, 297 (2008).
2. R. Bernabei et al., *Eur. Phys. J. C* **56**, 333 (2008).
3. R. Bernabei et al., *Eur. Phys. J. C* **67**, 39 (2010).
4. R. Bernabei et al., *Eur. Phys. J. C* **73**, 2648 (2013).
5. R. Bernabei et al., *Int. J. of Mod. Phys. A* **28**, 1330022 (2013).
6. R. Bernabei et al., *J. of Instr.* **7**, P03009 (2012).
7. R. Bernabei et al., *Eur. Phys. J. C* **72**, 2064 (2012).
8. R. Bernabei et al., *Eur. Phys. J. C* **74**, 3196 (2014).
9. DAMA coll., issue dedicated to DAMA, *Int. J. of Mod. Phys. A* **31** (2016) and refs therein.
10. R. Bernabei et al., *Eur. Phys. J. C* **74**, 2827 (2014).
11. R. Bernabei et al., *Eur. Phys. J. C* **62**, 327 (2009).
12. R. Bernabei et al., *Eur. Phys. J. C* **72**, 1920 (2012).
13. R. Bernabei et al., *Eur. Phys. J. A* **49**, 64 (2013).
14. R. Bernabei et al., *Eur. Phys. J. C* **75**, 239 (2015).
15. P. Belli et al., *Phys. Rev. D* **84**, 055014 (2011).
16. A. Addazi et al., *Eur. Phys. J. C* **75**, 400 (2015).
17. R. Bernabei et al., *Int. J. of Mod. Phys. A* **31**, 1642009 (2016).
18. R. Cerulli et al., *Eur. Phys. J. C* **77**, 83 (2017).
19. R. Bernabei et al., *Universe* **4**, 116 (2018).
20. R. Bernabei et al., *Nucl. Phys. At. Energy* **19**, 307 (2018).
21. R. Bernabei, *Bled Workshops in Physics* **19** n. 2, 27 (2018).

22. R. Bernabei et al., *Nucl. Phys. At. Energy* **20(4)**, 317 (2019).
23. R. Bernabei et al., *Prog. Part. Nucl. Phys.* **114**, 103810 (2020).
24. P. Belli, R. Bernabei, C. Bacci, A. Incicchitti, R. Marcovaldi, D. Prosperi, DAMA proposal to INFN Scientific Committee II, April 24th 1990.
25. R. Bernabei et al., *Phys. Lett. B* **389**, 757 (1996).
26. R. Bernabei et al., *Phys. Lett. B* **424**, 195 (1998).
27. R. Bernabei et al., *Phys. Lett. B* **450**, 448 (1999).
28. P. Belli et al., *Phys. Rev. D* **61**, 023512 (2000).
29. R. Bernabei et al., *Phys. Lett. B* **480**, 23 (2000).
30. R. Bernabei et al., *Phys. Lett. B* **509**, 197 (2001).
31. R. Bernabei et al., *Eur. Phys. J. C* **23**, 61 (2002).
32. P. Belli et al., *Phys. Rev. D* **66**, 043503 (2002)
33. R. Bernabei et al., *Il Nuovo Cim. A* **112**, 545 (1999).
34. R. Bernabei et al., *Eur. Phys. J. C* **18**, 283 (2000).
35. R. Bernabei el al., *La Rivista del Nuovo Cimento* **26** n.1, 1-73 (2003), and refs. therein.
36. R. Bernabei et al., *Int. J. Mod. Phys. D* **13**, 2127 (2004) and refs. therein.
37. R. Bernabei et al., *Int. J. Mod. Phys. A* **21**, 1445 (2006).
38. R. Bernabei et al., *Eur. Phys. J. C* **47**, 263 (2006).
39. R. Bernabei et al., *Int. J. Mod. Phys. A* **22**, 3155 (2007).
40. R. Bernabei et al., *Eur. Phys. J. C* **53**, 205 (2008).
41. R. Bernabei et al., *Phys. Rev. D* **77**, 023506 (2008).
42. R. Bernabei et al., *Mod. Phys. Lett. A* **23**, 2125 (2008).
43. R. Bernabei et al., *Phys. Lett. B* **408**, 439 (1997).
44. P. Belli et al., *Phys. Lett. B* **460**, 236 (1999).
45. R. Bernabei et al., *Phys. Rev. Lett.* **83**, 4918 (1999).
46. P. Belli et al., *Phys. Rev. C* **60**, 065501 (1999).
47. R. Bernabei et al., *Il Nuovo Cimento A* **112**, 1541 (1999).
48. R. Bernabei et al., *Phys. Lett. B* **515**, 6 (2001).
49. F. Cappella et al., *Eur. Phys. J.-direct C* **14**, 1 (2002).
50. R. Bernabei et al., *Eur. Phys. J. A* **23**, 7 (2005).
51. R. Bernabei et al., *Eur. Phys. J. A* **24**, 51 (2005).
52. K.A. Drukier et al., *Phys. Rev. D* **33**, 3495 (1986).
53. K. Freese et al., *Phys. Rev. D* **37**, 3388 (1988).
54. R. Bernabei and A. Incicchitti, *Int. J. Mod. Phys. A* **32**, 1743007 (2017).
55. D. Smith and N. Weiner, *Phys. Rev. D* **64**, 043502 (2001).
56. D. Tucker-Smith and N. Weiner, *Phys. Rev. D* **72**, 063509 (2005).
57. D. P. Finkbeiner et al, *Phys. Rev. D* **80**, 115008 (2009).
58. K. Freese et al., *Phys. Rev. D* **71**, 043516 (2005).
59. K. Freese et al., *Phys. Rev. Lett.* **92**, 111301 (2004).
60. P. Belli et al., *Int. J. of Mod. Phys. A* **31**, 1642005 (2016).
61. P. Gondolo et al., *New Astron. Rev.* **49**, 193 (2005).
62. G. Gelmini and P. Gondolo, *Phys. Rev. D* **64**, 023504 (2001).
63. F.S. Ling, P. Sikivie and S. Wick, *Phys. Rev. D* **70**, 123503 (2004).
64. G. Ranucci and M. Rovere, *Phys. Rev. D* **75**, 013010 (2007).
65. J.D. Scargle, *Astrophys. J.* **263**, 835 (1982).
66. W.H. Press et al., *Numerical recipes in Fortran 77: the art of scientific computing*, Cambridge University Press, Cambridge, England 1992, section 13.8.
67. J.H. Horne and S.L. Baliunas, *Astrophys. J.* **302**, 757 (1986).
68. R. Bernabei et al., *Bled Workshop in Physics* **15**, no. 2, 19 (2014).
69. W.T. Eadie et al., *Statistical methods in experimental physics*, ed. American Elsevier Pub. (1971).

Dark matter directionality approach

R. Bernabei, P. Belli, V. Caracciolo*, R. Cerulli, V. Merlo

Dip. di Fisica, Università di Roma "Tor Vergata", Rome, Italy
INFN, sez. di Roma "Tor Vergata", Rome, Italy
* E-mail: vincenzo.caracciolo@roma2.infn.it

F. Cappella, A. Incicchitti

Dip. di Fisica, Università di Roma "La Sapienza", Rome, Italy
INFN, sez. di Roma, Rome, Italy

N. Cherubini, E. Piccinelli

ENEA, Italian National Agency for New Technologies,
Energy and Sustainable Economic Development, C.R: Casaccia, Roma 00123, Italy

F. A. Danevich, D. V. Kasperovych, O. G. Polischuk, V. I. Tretyak

Institute for Nuclear Research of NASU, 03028 Kyiv, Ukraine

Dark Matter candidate particles able to induce nuclear recoils can also be studied using the so-called directionality approach. In this case the correlation between the nuclear recoils direction and the Earth motion in the galactic frame is studied. Several experimental techniques to explore the directionality approach have been proposed. In this talk, a review of such experimental techniques will be addressed.

Keywords: Dark Matter; Directionality; Nuclear Recoil.

1. Introduction

Astrophysical observations have pointed out the presence of Dark Matter (DM) on all astrophysical scales and many arguments have been suggested that a large fraction of it should be in form of relic DM particles.

Currently, several approaches are exploited to investigate DM particles in the galactic halo; here, we will focus our attention on a particular direct strategy: the directionality approach.

In direct detection experiments, a model-independent signature is a powerful tool to provide a DM signal identification with respect to the background. In fact, as originally pointed out in Refs. 1, 2 and discussed in Refs. 3, 4, independently of the considered DM scenario, the events induced by a physical reaction in a target detector depend on the product between the cross-section of the process and the relative velocity between the incident DM particle (DMp) and the target. Such a product is expected to have a characteristic time behaviour in case of DM annual modulation: annual variation of the interaction rate due to Earth motion around the Sun which is moving in the Galaxy, successfully exploited by DAMA collaboration.[5–9]

Besides this main one, other possible signatures are expected: a diurnal modulation, due to the Earth revolution around its axis;[10] a daily variation of the interaction rate due to the different Earth depth crossed by the DMp[11] and the directionality signature, due to the correlation of DM impinging direction with Earth's galactic motion, in case of DMp able to induce nuclear recoils.[12] In fact, the dynamics of the rotation of the Milky Way galactic disc through the halo of DM causes the Earth to experience a wind of DM particles seemingly flowing along a direction opposite to that of the solar motion relative to the DM halo.

Therefore, the observation of an anisotropy in the distribution of nuclear recoil directions could give further evidence and information for such DM candidate particles and the related astrophysics scenario. Thus, a direction-sensitive detector is needed.

2. Dark matter signal in case of elastic DMp–nucleus scattering

Direct detection experiments, using the directionality approach, look for the signal of DMp via their elastic scattering interactions with detector nuclei. Therefore, due to kinematic consideration, the recoil nucleus direction is correlated with the direction of the impinging DMp (see Fig. 1). Assuming an elastic DMp–nucleus scattering (see Fig. 1), the nucleus kinetic energy after the interaction with the impinging DM particle is:

$$E_R = \frac{4 M_A M_{DM}}{(M_{DM} + M_A)^2} \cos^2(\theta) \, E_{DM} \tag{1}$$

where, M_A is the mass of target nucleus, M_{DM} and E_{DM} are the incoming DMp mass and kinetic energy (laboratory system), respectively, E_R is the recoil nucleus kinetic energy (laboratory frame) and θ is the scattering angle of the recoil nucleus in the lab frame. According to the equation (1), depending on the value of $M_A \sim 1-200$ GeV, considering a very simple isothermal halo model with $v \sim 300$ km/s $\cong 10^{-3} c$, thus with $E_{DM} \sim 0.5 \times 10^{-6} M_{DM}$, the maximum E_R can be $\ll 200$ keV up to ~ 200 keV (without considering the quenching effect in the direct detection of

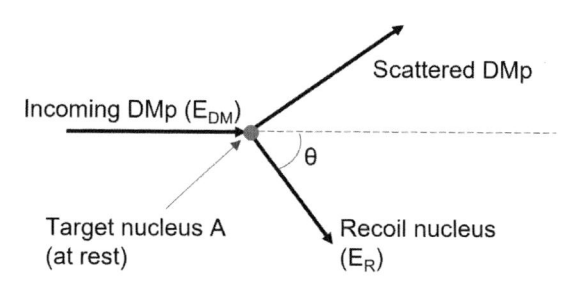

Fig. 1. DMp–nucleus elastic scattering diagrams for the laboratory coordinate systems.

the nuclear recoiling energy). Considering this information, the maximum range of nuclear recoiling is of the order of mm in low pressure gas medium, μm in liquid and less in solid medium.[13–15]

Thus, Low-Pressure Time Projection Chamber looks advantaged, but some drawbacks are present and will be discussed later.

To evaluate the direction of DMp in the laboratory frame, we can determine the detector velocity in the galactic rest frame, $\vec{v_d}(t)$, which varies with time. To study $\vec{v_d}(t)$ it is possible to consider various coordinate frames; in particular, following the formalism in,[12] we consider the horizontal coordinate frame located at the North pole, described by the "polar–zenith", $\Theta_z(t)$, and by the "polar–azimuth", $\phi_a(t)$. In this frame the area described in the sky by the direction of $\vec{v_d}(t)$ is shown in Fig. 2 (green band). Considering an experiment performed at a latitude similar to, e.g., the latitude of the Gran Sasso National Laboratory (LNGS) of I.N.F.N. (42°27′12″ N latitude and 13°34′26″ E longitude), we can assume that Θ_z is always near 40°. In fact, at a certain time of the day ($\approx$ 21:00 h LST) the DMp come mainly from the top, while 12 h later they come near the horizon and from North (see Fig. 2). Thus, assuming $\vec{v}$ to be the velocity of the DMp in the laboratory frame, the DMp velocity in the galactic rest frame is $\vec{v} + \vec{v_d}(t)$; finally we can indicate with $f(\vec{v} + \vec{v_d}(t))$ the DM velocity distribution in the galactic rest frame (having assumed a specific DM halo model) and $\frac{\xi \rho_0}{M_{DM}} v f(\vec{v} + \vec{v_d}(t))$ is the flux of the considered DMp candidate, where ξ is the fraction of the local DM halo density (ρ_0) of the considered candidate; M_{DM} is the mass of the DM candidate particle.

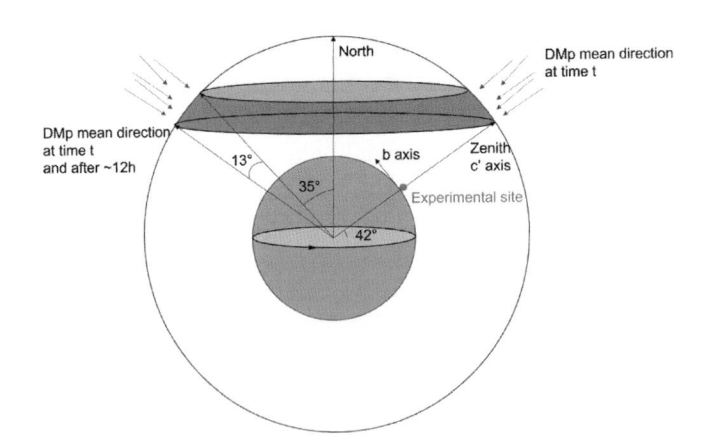

Fig. 2. Schematic representation of the experimental approach mentioned in the text. The detector is considered as placed at the Gran Sasso National Laboratory (LNGS) with the axis in the vertical direction and another axis is pointing to the North. The area in the sky from which the DM particles are preferentially expected is highlighted.

The expected counting rate of the signal, in the window (E_1, E_2) of the detected energy spectrum, as a function of the time t is:

$$R(E_1, E_2, t) = \int d^3 \vec{v} \int d\Omega_{cm} \frac{\xi \rho_0 N_A}{M_{DM}} v f(\vec{v} + \vec{v_d}(t)) \frac{d\sigma_A}{d\Omega_{cm}}$$
$$+ \frac{1}{2} erf\left(\frac{q_A(\Omega_{out})E_R - E_1}{\sqrt{2}\Delta}\right) - \frac{1}{2} erf\left(\frac{q_A(\Omega_{out})E_R - E_2}{\sqrt{2}\Delta}\right)$$

where N_A is the number of target–nuclei of the A–th species per mass unit; Ω_{cm} is the nuclear recoil direction in the center of mass (c.m.) frame; $\frac{d\sigma_A}{d\Omega_{cm}}$ is the differential cross section in the c.m. frame, which is assumed to be isotropic; $q_A(\Omega_{out})$ is the quenching factor (Q.F.) which can depend on the direction of the nuclear recoil in the laboratory frame; and Δ is the detector energy resolution.

3. Detectors attempts

Current directional detectors are at the research and development stage. The experimental strategies are classifiable in two main groups: tracking detectors and detectors using anisotropic features. The first one bases the detection principle on the possibility of evaluating the direction of the nuclear recoils; the second one, instead, uses an anisotropic response of the detector with respect to the direction of the nuclear recoil strongly correlated with the impinging direction of the DMp.

Experiments based on Low-Pressure TPC aims to develop a TPC for directional DM searches and solar neutrino spectroscopy. Some of big drawbacks are the energy threshold, angular and spatial resolutions. Moreover, the total mass is often modest (in the literature are present liquid TPCs very big as ICARUS, DUNE, etc., but they are not applicable to DM sector). Another of the most critical issues is the low angular resolution at very low energy. Other important drawbacks are: low background techniques are not mature; some systematic effects with respect to the direction of the electric field are present in case of high charge gain; the data analysis is based on a strong software gamma rejection, introducing systematics.

The NEWSdm collaboration uses a nuclear emulsion-based detector acting both as a target and as a solid tracking device,[16] declaring a spatial threshold of (120 ± 5) nm. The radioactive contaminants of nuclear emulsion are mainly dominated by contamination of ^{14}C and U/Th chains. The main drawback is to reach enough spatial and angle resolution to be sensible to a range of nuclear recoiling, that at maximum is a few 100 nm, without compromising the emulsion path and minimizing the systematics during the data analysis and with a reasonable duty cycle.

We also mention two other ideas. A proposed method consists in identifying the direction of an incident DMp using the spectroscopy of quantum defects in macroscopic solid-state crystals as diamonds.[17] Instead, in Ref. 18 an odd type of DM detector made of DNA (or RNA) is proposed.

The second main group of detectors is based on the anisotropic response, showing a signal that varies with the direction of impinging particles. In particular, in literature, there are attempts to use (i) carbon nanotubes, (ii) columnar recombination in a TPC dual-phase, (iii) a realistic and very promising technique using anisotropic crystal scintillators.

The first one is an idea based on the use of a large number of carbon nanotubes vertically aligned (VA-CNT). There are weak indications that an electron is extracted from this VA-CNT forrest with a higher probability if the impinging direction of a particle is parallel to the VA-CNT, as compared to the impinging direction perpendicular to the VA-CNT. This possible effect could be implemented to develop an anisotropic sensor.[19]

The second case exploits a dual-phase time projection chamber (TPC) is filled with a liquid noble gas. In those devices, the scintillation light (S1) in the liquid phase and the ionization charge signals (generated in the liquid phase), which is drifted to the gas phase and there converted into a proportional scintillation signal (S2), are measured. Along the drift path, the electrons, due to several reasons, are partially recombined with the medium. It is expected that in case the initial electrons are generated along a direction perpendicular to the electric field (due to the direction of the nuclear recoil scattered from the impinging DMp), the columnar recombination could be less than in case the electrons are generated along the direction of the electron field. If detectable, the S2 signal, in the first case, is expected higher than in the second case as supposed in Ref. 20. The only study, using a very small LAr-TPC (SCENE detector), is published in Ref. 21, with a very poor indication of this phenomenon (see Fig. 21 of Ref. 21). For more information, a synoptic survey on liquid noble gases for DM searches is reported in Ref. 22, where the very low energy application of double phase noble gas detectors is analysed and compared; the main technical aspects of the existing experimental applications have been discussed and some implications have been outlined.

All these practical limitations and problems about these ideas can be overcome using the third approach, i.e. anisotropic scintillation detectors in a suitable low background experimental set-up located deep underground.

4. Anisotropic crystal scintillator

In anisotropic scintillators, the detector response to heavy particles depends on their impinging direction with respect to crystal axes. Therefore, in the case of nuclear recoils induced by DMp, the measured energy spectrum at low energy is expected to change its shape during the sidereal day as a consequence of the changing orientation of the crystal axes with respect to the DM wind. This effect can be pointed out as a peculiar variation of the counting rate measured in a given low energy window and offers the possibility to highlight the DM signal with respect to the electromagnetic background (for details, see, e.g., in Refs. 3, 4, 12).

The use of anisotropic scintillators to study the directionality signature was proposed for the first time in Ref. 3 and revisited in Ref. 4, where the case of anthracene detector was preliminarily analysed and several practical difficulties in the feasibility of such an experiment were underlined. Nevertheless, the authors suggested that competitive sensitivities could be reached with new devoted R&D's of anisotropic scintillators having significantly larger size, higher light response, better stiffness, higher atomic weights and anisotropic features similar as – or even better than – those of the anthracene scintillator.

4.1. $ZnWO_4$ anisotropic scintillator

The potential offered by the anisotropic properties of $ZnWO_4$ crystal scintillator in the search for DM with the directionality approach was indicated for the first time in Ref. 23. Recent measurements and R&D show that the $ZnWO_4$ detector can offer suitable features for the purpose.[12,24–27] In the light of this, the Anisotropic detectors for DArk Matter Observation (ADAMO) project[12,28] was considered and R&Ds have been progressed.

In particular, in the last years various $ZnWO_4$ detectors have been developed in the framework of the collaboration between the DAMA group of INFN (Istituto Nazionale di Fisica Nucleare) and the INR-Kyiv group.[26–36] Formerly, some crystals were produced by the Institute for Scintillation Materials (ISMA, Kharkiv, Ukraine) and, later on, a collaboration with the Nikolaev Institute of Inorganic Chemistry (Novosibirsk, Russia) has started and an R&D to produce ultra-radiopure $ZnWO_4$ by using the low-thermal gradient Czochralski technique in a platinum crucible is ongoing.[37] The produced crystals have been put in measurement in the DAMA/R&D underground facility at the Gran Sasso laboratory (LNGS) of INFN.[26,27,35,36] Measurements and R&D works have shown the competitiveness of $ZnWO_4$ scintillators for a DM experiment based on the directionality. In fact, the light output and the time profile of the scintillation pulse for heavy particles (p, α, nuclear recoils) depends on the direction of such particles with respect to the crystal axes while no difference is observed for γ/β radiation.[23] The shape of the scintillation pulse is also different for $\gamma(\beta)$ radiation and heavy particles (α). This pulse shape discrimination capability can potentially be of interest not only for a DM experiment but also for double beta decay searches. The $ZnWO_4$ also offers a high atomic weight and the possibility to realize single crystals with masses of a few kg.[37] Moreover, the presence of three target nuclei with very different masses (Zn, W and O) makes these scintillators sensitive to both small and large mass DM candidates, as also the NaI(Tl) is. The recently developed $ZnWO_4$ scintillators have a very high level of radiopurity. The upper limits for ^{228}Th are < 0.17 μBq/kg – < 1.3 μBq/kg, for ^{40}K are < 20 μBq/kg and for ^{226}Ra are < 2 μBq/kg.[24,26] A further radio-purification of $ZnWO_4$ crystal scintillators is feasible. The R&D is still ongoing[25,38,39] and very good results have also been obtained in improving the light transmission. The next step will be to suitably increase the size of crystals.

As confirmed by the measurements performed at LNGS, the crystals have relatively high light output at room temperature, being about 20% of the NaI(Tl) scintillator. It appears feasible to further improve the light output of the crystal considering that it can increase when working at low temperature.[40] To study this feature a small cryostat is currently under test at LNGS to realize and optimize the cooling system; this system will allow to reach a stable working temperature around -50°C.

In order to employ the ZnWO$_4$ for DM investigation with the directionality approach it is crucial to measure and quantify the anisotropy of the scintillator for nuclear recoils. For this purpose a campaign of measurements was performed by using a 7.99 g mass ZnWO$_4$ crystal scintillator of (10 × 10 × 10.4) mm^3, in the framework of the ADAMO project. The crystal has been obtained by a second crystallization procedure using the low-thermal gradient Czochralski technique from zinc tungstate crystals made from tungsten oxide additionally purified by double sublimation of tungsten chlorides.[41] The crystallographic axes were identified by the producer and experimentally verified.

Before measuring the response of the ZnWO$_4$ crystal with a monochromatic neutron source at ENEA-CASACCIA, the crystal was irradiated with α particles at LNGS. In the following the obtained results are briefly reported.

4.2. *Measurements with α particles*

The small ZnWO$_4$ crystal was coupled to a HAMAMATSU H11934-200 PMT (Ultra Bialkali photocathode with an effective area of (23 × 23) mm^2 and quantum efficiency $\simeq$ 43% at 400 nm and $\simeq$ 25% at 500 nm). The scintillation pulses coming from the detector were recorded by a LeCroy WaveSurf24X-sA oscilloscope (4 chn, 2.5 GSamples/s, 200 MHz) in a time window of 100 μs. The measurements were performed by using an ^{241}Am source and various sets of thin mylar films as absorbers to decrease the α energy. The beam of α particles was collimated before reaching the crystal face. The energies of α particles were measured with a CANBERRA Alpha Spectrometer (model 7401VR). The energy scale of the crystal for each measurement was calibrated by using ^{137}Cs and ^{22}Na γ sources.

The typical energy distributions of the α particles impinging along the three axes of the crystal are shown in Fig. 3-left. The ZnWO$_4$ crystal was irradiated in the directions perpendicular to the (100), (001) and (010) crystal planes: hereafter crystal axes I (blue on-line), II (green on-line) and III (red on-line), respectively in Fig. 3.

In the Fig. 3-right the dependence of the α/β ratio as a function of the energy for the three different directions of the α beam relatively to the crystal axes is shown. In particular, the quenching factor for α particles measured along the crystal axis III is about 1.2 times larger than that measured along the crystal axes I and II. Instead, the quenching factors measured along the crystal axes I and II are quite similar. The error bars are mainly due to the uncertainty of the alpha energy which is slightly degraded in air.

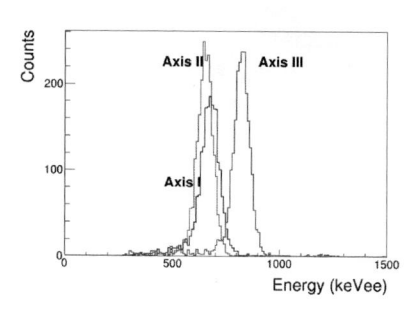

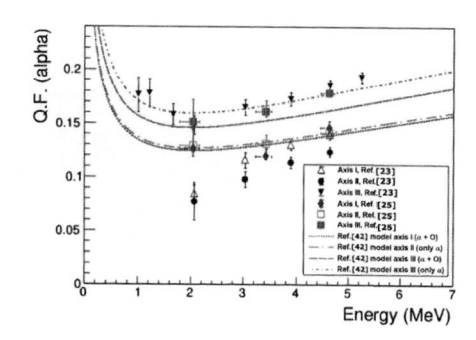

Fig. 3. Left: energy spectra of 4.63 MeV α particles impinging along the three axes of the crystal. Right: dependence of the α/β ratio on the energy of the α particles measured with a ZnWO$_4$ scintillator in Ref. 23 (black points) compared with those reported in Ref. 25 (colored points). The anisotropic behavior of the crystal is evident. The models for each crystal axis, obtained as global fits on all the data (from α's and from recoils; see also later) of Ref. 25 following the prescription of Ref. 42, is also reported.

The quenching factors and the anisotropic effect reported in Ref. 25 are in reasonable agreement with those of Ref. 23, as shown in Fig. 3-right; in the figure the behavior of the α/β ratio as expected for each crystal axis in the model of Ref. 42 are also reported.

Therefore, the data confirm the anisotropic features of ZnWO$_4$ crystal scintillator in case of α particles.

4.3. *Measurements with neutrons*

Monochromatic neutrons were generated by the Thermo Scientific portable generator MP 320. Neutrons are produced in the $d(t,\alpha)n$ reaction with energy around 14.7 MeV by accelerating deuterons toward a tritium target in electric potential. For the requirements of the experiment a configuration with beam acceleration voltage of 60 kV and a beam current of 40 μA was adopted in order to optimize the neutron yield and the stability of the beam operation; the production rate was around 10^7 n/s. In the experimental setup, neutrons leaving the target at 90 degrees to the forward direction were used; at this angle, simple kinematics predicts a value $E_n = 14.05$ MeV for a beam acceleration voltage of 60 kV.

The scattered neutron in the crystal is detected by two neutron detectors placed at a given scattering angle. In such a configuration the energy and the direction of the recoiling nucleus are fixed and, by measuring the energy released in the ZnWO$_4$ detector – in keV electron equivalent (keVee) – it is possible to determine the quenching factor. By changing the crystal axes orientation the quenching factor for the different axes can be measured.

A scheme of the set-up is shown in Fig. 4. The ZnWO$_4$ detector is placed in front of the neutron channel on a revolving platform around a vertical axis (O axis), which allows us to fix the direction of the crystal axis with respect to the impinging neutrons: the α angle as depicted in Fig. 4. The ZnWO$_4$ crystal is centered on

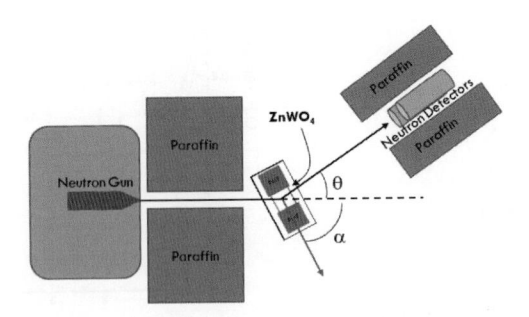

Fig. 4. Schematic view from the top of the experimental set-up. The two neutron detectors are one above the other.

the O axis and is optically coupled to two HAMAMATSU H11934-200 PMTs on opposite faces. In the set-up, the PMTs are on the faces perpendicular to the crystal axis III; thus, α identifies the angle between the crystal axis III and the impinging neutrons direction. The crystal axis I is also on the horizontal plane, while the axis II is vertical. The neutrons scattered off the ZnWO$_4$ crystal are tagged by two neutron detectors by Scionix employing EJ-309 liquid scintillator. The EJ-309 scintillator has a very high capability to discriminate neutrons interactions from the gamma background by Pulse Shape Discrimination (PSD). The neutron detectors are placed 82 cm far from O axis, one above the other to maintain the same neutron scattering angle θ (see Fig. 4) and to improve the solid angle acceptance. They are held by an arm and free to rotate around the O axis.

The signals from the two PMTs coupled to the ZnWO$_4$ detector are summed and recorded by a CAEN DT5720 transient digitizer with 250 MSamples/s. The trigger is obtained by the coincidence between a signal in the ZnWO$_4$ detector and in the EJ-309 detectors within ± 500 ns.

The energy detected in the ZnWO$_4$ detector is evaluated from the digitized pulse area. ^{133}Ba and ^{137}Cs sources were used to calibrate the detector energy scale. The typical energy resolution was $\sigma/E = 4.4\%$ at the 662 keV γ peak of ^{137}Cs. The energy calibration was performed before and after the neutrons irradiation.

Neutron events in the EJ-309 detectors were selected by a PSD data analysis based on: i) head/tail analysis; ii) analysis of the mean time, τ, of the time profile of the pulse. A typical example of the separation between gamma and neutrons exploiting the two techniques is reported in Fig. 5-left and in Fig. 5-right, respectively.

To select the nuclear recoils induced by the elastic scattering of neutrons over the background an important quantity is the TOF between the ZnWO$_4$ detector and the neutron detectors EJ-309. The expectation value of TOF due to the typical velocity of the scattered neutrons is around 15 ns. It can be defined the variable $\Delta t = t_0^{EJ} - t_0^{ZWO}$, where t_0^{EJ} (t_0^{ZWO}) is the starting time of the EJ-309 (ZnWO$_4$) pulse. The transit time of the neutron detectors PMT is ≈ 40 ns while it is ≈ 6 ns for the HAMAMATSU H11934-200. The Δt variable is shifted with respect to TOF

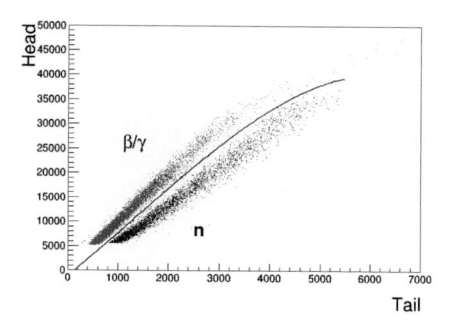

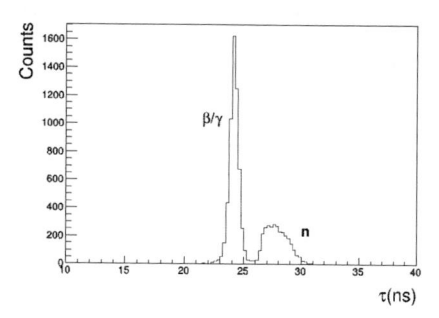

Fig. 5. Example of gamma/neutron separation by PSD in EJ-309 liquid scintillator. Left: head/tail analysis. Right: distribution of the mean time, τ, variable.

and it has been calibrated considering the coincidences between high energy events in the ZnWO$_4$ detector and gamma events in the neutron detectors. A $\Delta t \approx 34$ ns has been obtained from the data in agreement with the expectation. This TOF calibration has been taken into account in the analysis.

For a fixed scattering angle θ and crystal axis, the event pattern searched for was represented by a scintillation pulse in the ZnWO$_4$ detector in coincidence with a neutron in the EJ-309 detectors.

In Fig. 6-left the TOF distribution is depicted for the case of $\theta = 70°$ and crystal axis I, while in Fig. 6-right the bi-dimensional plot TOF vs ZnWO$_4$ energy is presented (E_{ZWO} is in keVee). These plots show a continuum due to random coincidences, a clear excess of events with energy around 80 keVee and TOF in agreement with the expectation for scattered neutrons on target nuclei. The peak in the TOF variable shows a tail on the left due to the first photoelectron delay in ZnWO$_4$ (effective average scintillation decay time ≈ 24 μs[23]). The observed excess can be ascribed to the O recoils in the ZnWO$_4$ detector and its position provides the quenching factor of this nucleus for the used scattering angle and crystal axis. The Zn and W recoils are expected to be well below the energy threshold that has been used in the present experimental conditions.

The behavior of the TOF distribution can be explained by considering that events belong to the sum of two main contributions: 1) a peak due to the coincidences caused by the elastic scatterings of neutrons off the ZnWO$_4$ nuclei, and 2) the random flat coincidences (f_{rnd}). To build a model for the TOF behavior some assumptions can be considered: i) the signal of the neutron detectors is "prompt" (that is the time delay between the neutron interaction and the starting time of the EJ-309 pulse is mostly equal to the PMT transit time); ii) the ZnWO$_4$ time delay between the neutron interaction and the starting time of the pulse is given by the PMT transit time plus the delay of the first photoelectron in ZnWO$_4$ detector; iii) the probability to have the first photoelectron in ZnWO$_4$ at the time t is $\frac{1}{\tau}e^{-t/\tau}$, where τ is the characteristic time decay of the process; iv) the fluctuations of the

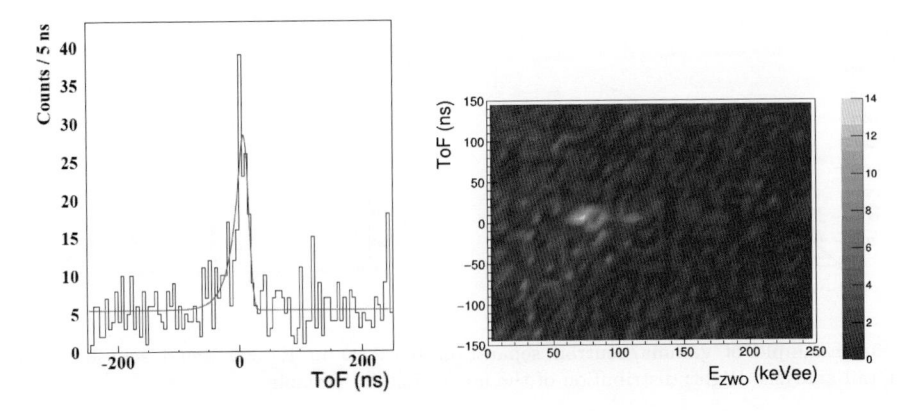

Fig. 6. TOF distribution and bi-dimensional plot TOF vs ZnWO$_4$ energy for coincidences obtained after selecting neutrons in the neutron detectors, for the case of scattering angle $\theta = 70°$ and axis I. Left: The TOF distribution shows a continuum due to random coincidences and a clear peak, that is in agreement with the expected TOF for neutrons after elastic scattering off the nuclei of ZnWO$_4$ detector. The peak shows a tail on the left part due to the first photoelectron delay in ZnWO$_4$. The fit with the function of eq. 3 is superimposed (See text). Right: A clear peak is present at the proper value of TOF and at the given energy. The peak position in the E_{ZWO} distribution provides the quenching factor of the O nucleus for the used scattering angle and crystal axis.

transit times of the PMTs of the ZnWO$_4$ and of the EJ-309 detectors, and the time resolution of the used digitizer (2 ns bin size for the neutron detectors and 4 ns for the ZnWO$_4$ detector) are taken into account by making a convolution of the time distribution with a Gaussian function having a characteristic spread σ. Thus, the model function of TOF can be written as:

$$f(TOF|f_{rnd}, A, \tau, \sigma, TOF_0) = f_{rnd} + A \int_0^\infty e^{-x/\tau} e^{-\frac{(x+TOF-TOF_0)^2}{2\sigma^2}} dx \quad (2)$$

where TOF_0 represents the expectation value of the neutrons time of flight and A is a normalization factor. By solving the integral one gets:

$$f(TOF) = f_{rnd} + Be^{-\frac{TOF_0-TOF}{\tau}} \left[1 - erf\left(-\frac{TOF_0 - TOF}{\sqrt{2}\sigma} + \frac{\sigma}{\sqrt{2}\tau}\right)\right] \quad (3)$$

where B includes only constant factors: $B = A\sqrt{\frac{\pi}{2}}\sigma e^{\frac{\sigma^2}{2\tau^2}}$. The result of the fit of the TOF distribution with the function given in eq. 3 is plotted in Fig. 6-left; it gives: $f_{rnd} \approx 5.5$ counts/ 5 ns, $B \approx 21.6$ counts/ 5 ns, $\tau \approx 16.9$ ns, $\sigma \approx 5.8$ ns and $TOF_0 \approx 15.4$ ns. The model reproduce well the experimental data and is in a good agreement with the expectations. A Monte Carlo simulation gives similar results.

For the estimation of the quenching factors three scattering angles were considered. Since the responses of the crystal axes I and II are rather similar, only the

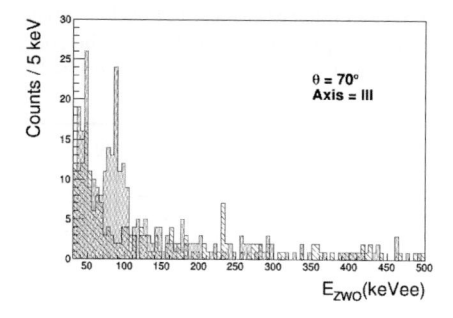

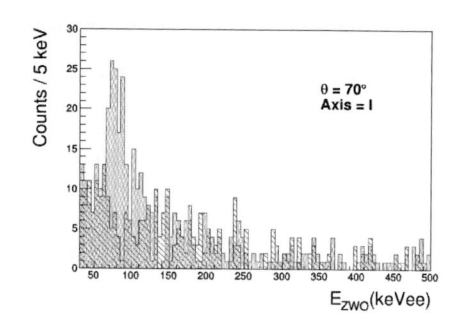

Fig. 7. Energy distributions of the detected energy, E_{ZWO}, in the ZnWO$_4$ detector, measured in keV electron equivalent (keVee) for the case of $\theta = 70°$ and axes III and I. Only events identified as recoils due to neutrons scattering, with subsequent registration of the scattered neutron in the neutrons detectors, are selected. Light (red on-line) histogram: events selected in the proper window of the TOF variable (-20 ns $< TOF < 30$ ns). Dashed (blue on-line) histogram: events selected in the off-window (60 ns $< TOF < 110$ ns).

case of axis I was considered. Figure 7 shows an example of the energy distributions of the detected energy, E_{ZWO}, in the ZnWO$_4$ detector, measured in keV electron equivalent ($\theta = 70°$ and axes III and I). Two distributions are reported for each plot: one is obtained by selecting events in the time window expected for the TOF of neutrons elastically scattered off the nuclei of ZnWO$_4$ detector, -20 ns $< TOF < 30$ ns (light red histogram); the other is presented by selecting off-window events (random coincidences), 60 ns $< TOF < 110$ ns (blue histogram). The off-window events are related to random coincidences and, therefore, their distribution is the background distribution in the histogram of the in-window events. The peaks are evident and can be ascribed to the oxygen nuclear recoils. The positions of the peaks are obtained by fitting them with a Gaussian curve plus an exponential function that simulates the background of the random coincidences. The energy resolutions, σ, of the peaks are between 8 and 12 keVee; the values are well in agreement with the energy dependence: $\sigma \propto \sqrt{E}$.

In Table 1 the summary of the peak positions measured for the three considered angles is reported. The expected recoil energies for the oxygen nucleus, $E_{R,O}$, are also given. The obtained quenching factors are calculated as the ratio $E_{ZWO}/E_{R,O}$ and the last column reports the degree of anisotropy for each scattering-angle/recoil energy.

In Fig. 8 the obtained values for the quenching factors are plotted together with the models for the considered crystal axes derived from Ref. 42 for a single kB parameter. This parameter has been estimated, for each axis, taking into account both the response of ZnWO$_4$ to α particles and to oxygen recoils ($kB = 12.06$ mg MeV^{-1} cm^{-2} for axis I, $kB = 11.80$ mg MeV^{-1} cm^{-2} for axis II – only α data are considered – and $kB = 9.98$ mg MeV^{-1} cm^{-2} for axis III, respectively).

Table 1. Summary table of the peak position due to oxygen nuclear recoils. For each scattering angle, θ, and for the different axes of the ZnWO$_4$ crystal, the peak position, E_{ZWO}, the energy resolution, σ, the expected recoil energies for the oxygen nucleus, $E_{R,O}$, the quenching factors, Q, and the anisotropy, Q_{III}/Q_I ratio, are reported.

Scattering angle, θ	Crystal axis	E_{ZWO} (keVee)	σ (keVee)	$E_{R,O}$ (keV)	Quenching factor, Q	Q_{III}/Q_I
80°	III	99.3 ± 2.5	9	1402	0.0708 ± 0.0018	1.174 ± 0.051
	I	84.5 ± 2.9	12		0.0603 ± 0.0021	
70°	III	86.5 ± 2.0	7	1128	0.0767 ± 0.0018	1.121 ± 0.038
	I	77.2 ± 1.9	10		0.0684 ± 0.0017	
60°	III	75.4 ± 1.8	9	866	0.0871 ± 0.0021	1.166 ± 0.059
	I	64.7 ± 2.9	10		0.0747 ± 0.0033	

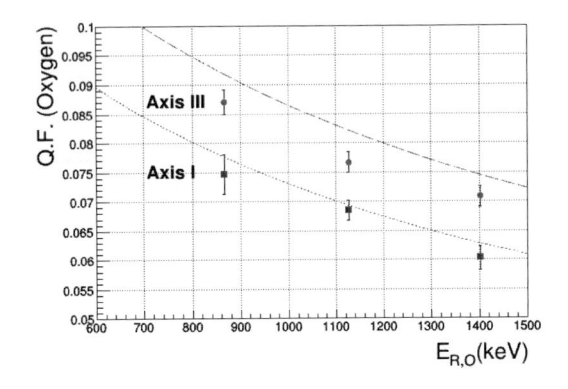

Fig. 8. Quenching factors for oxygen nuclear recoils in ZnWO$_4$ for the crystal axes I and III as function of the expected recoil energies $E_{R,O}$. In the plot the expected behavior of quenching factor for the considered crystal axes is also shown; it has been obtained by the global fits on the α and oxygen recoil data, following the prescription of Ref. 42 (for more details see Ref. 25).

5. Conclusion

The directionality investigates the correlation between the direction of the nuclear recoils induced by DMp and the motion of the Earth in the galactic rest frame. In fact, due to the solar motion in the DM halo, a wind of DMp is expected on the Earth with an seemingly opposite direction with respect to the Earth velocity in the galactic rest frame. As a consequence of the Earth's rotation, an observer on the Earth's surface experiences a change in the DM average arrival direction during a sidereal day. The induced nuclear recoils' directions are expected to be strongly correlated with that of the DM particles. Thus, the study of the nuclear recoils directions can also be pursued to investigate the class of DM candidate particles interacting via elastic-scattering on target nuclei.

A brief review of the R&Ds present in the literature has been addressed. In particular, we have briefly discussed the case of Low-Pressure TPC, the emulsion-based detector, columnar recombination, and some other ideas like the use of DNA based detector, diamonds or VA-CNT. However, such techniques suffer of several big problems, such as the short range of nuclear recoil, high radioactivity level, stability during the running condition, mass limitation etc., making this measurement really difficult. On the other hand, the anisotropic crystal scintillators offer a unique possibility of overcoming all these problems and giving a realistic technique to exploit the directionality approach (see Refs. 12, 25 for details). In fact, the results confirm the anisotropic response of the $ZnWO_4$ crystal scintillator to α particles and to oxygen nuclear recoils. The presence of a good anisotropic response also in the lower energy region is supported by the trend of the measured quenching factors at lower energy. In particular, for nuclear recoils induced by neutrons, the anisotropic response of the $ZnWO_4$ crystal scintillator has been determined at 5.4 standard deviations. This opens a possibility to realize a pioneer experiment to investigate the mentioned DM candidates by means of the directionality with the help of $ZnWO_4$ anisotropic scintillators. The features and the potentiality of these detectors can achieve – in some of the many possible scenarios and for some DM candidates able to induce a nuclear recoil – sensitivities not far from that of the DAMA/LIBRA positive result:[5–7,43] a low background pioneer experiment named ADAMO (Anisotropic detectors for DArk Matter Observation) located deep underground.[12,28]

For the near future, the DAMA, INR–Kyiv and ENEA/Casaccia collaboration plans to further investigate the light response of $ZnWO_4$ concerning the operation temperature (to increase the light-yield eventually), the light response at very low energy in case of the electromagnetic excitation and the Q.F. for nuclear recoils of W and Zn and other scattered angles of oxygen nucleus.

References

1. A.K. Drukier, K. Freese, D.N. Spergel. *Detecting cold dark-matter candidates. Phys. Rev. D* **33**, 3495 (1986).
2. K. Freese, J.A. Frieman, A. Gould. *Signal modulation in cold-dark-matter detection. Phys. Rev. D* **37**, 3388 (1988).
3. P. Belli et al. *Identifying a "dark matter" signal by nonisotropic scintillation detector. Il Nuovo Cimento C* **15**, 473–479 (1992).
4. R. Bernabei et al. *Anisotropic scintillators for WIMP direct detection: revisited. Eur. Phys. J. C* **28**, 203-209 (2003).
5. R. Bernabei et al. *The DAMA project: Achievements, implications and perspectives. Prog. Particle Nucl. Phys.* **114**, 103810 (2020).
6. R. Bernabei et al. *DAMA/LIBRA–phase2 results and implications on several dark matter scenarios. Int. J. Mod. Phys. A* **35(36)**, 2044023 (2020).
7. R. Bernabei et al. *New model-dependent analyses including DAMA/LIBRA-phase2. Nuovo Cim. C* **43(2-3)**, 23 (2020).
8. R. Bernabei et al. *The Future Role of Inorganic Crystal Scintillators in Dark Matter Investigations. Instruments* **5(2)**, 16 (2021).

9. R. Belli et al. *The dark matter: DAMA/LIBRA and its perspectives*. To appear on the proceedings of Sixteenth Marcel Grossmann Meeting - MG16 (2021).
10. R. Bernabei et al. *Model independent result on possible diurnal effect in DAMA/LIBRA-phase1*. Eur. Phys. J. C **74**(3), 2827 (2014).
11. R. Bernabei, et al. *Investigating Earth shadowing effect with DAMA/LIBRA-phase1*. Eur. Phys. J. C **75**(5), 239 (2015).
12. F. Cappella et al. *On the potentiality of the $ZnWO_4$ anisotropic detectors to measure the directionality of Dark Matter*. Eur. Phys. J. C **73**, 2276 (2013).
13. B.G. Harvey. *Recoil techniques in nuclear reaction and fission studies*. Ann. Rev. Nucl. Part. Sci. **10**, 235-258 (1960).
14. M. Ismail. *Measurement of excitation functions and mean projected recoil ranges of nuclei in α-induced reactions on F, Al, V, Co and Re nuclei*. Pramana - J. Phys. **40**, 227 (1993).
15. L. Bryde et al. *Ranges of recoil ions from alpha-reactions*. Mat. Fys. Medd. Dan. Vid. Selsk. **33**, no. 8 (1962).
16. N. D'Ambrosio et al. *Directional detection of Dark Matter with nuclear emulsion based detector*. PoS EPS-HEP2017 059 (2017).
17. S. Rajendran et al. *A method for directional detection of dark matter using spectroscopy of crystal defects*. Phys. Rev. D **96**, 035009 (2017).
18. A. Drukier et al. *New Dark Matter Detectors using DNA or RNA for Nanometer Tracking*. MCTP-12-14. arXiv: 1206.6809 (2012).
19. G. Cavoto et al. *Carbon nanotubes as anisotropic target for dark matter*. J. Phys.: Conf. Ser. **1468**, 012232 (2020).
20. D. R. Nygren. *Columnar recombination: a tool for nuclear recoil directional sensitivity in a xenon-based direct detection WIMP search*. J. Phys.: Conf. Ser. **460**, 012006 (2013).
21. H. Cao et al. *Measurement of scintillation and ionization yield and scintillation pulse shape from nuclear recoils in liquid argon*. Phys. Rev. D **91**, 092007 (2015).
22. R. Bernabei et al. *Liquid noble gases for dark matter searches: An updated survey*. Int. J. Mod. Phys. A **30**(26), 1530053 (2015).
23. F.A. Danevich et al. *$ZnWO_4$ crystals as detectors for 2β decay and dark matter experiments*. Nucl. Instrum. Meth. A **544**, 553–564 (2005).
24. P. Belli et al. *New development of radiopure $ZnWO_4$ crystal scintillators*. Nucl. Instrum. Meth. A **935**, 89–94 (2019).
25. P. Belli et al. *Measurements of $ZnWO_4$ anisotropic response to nuclear recoils for the ADAMO project*. Eur. Phys. J. A **56**, 83 (2020).
26. P. Belli et al. *Radioactive contamination of $ZnWO_4$ crystal scintillators*. Nucl. Instrum. Meth. A **626-627**, 31 (2011).
27. P. Belli et al. *Final results of experiment to search for 2β processes in zinc and tungsten with the help of radiopure $ZnWO_4$ crystal scintillators*. J. Phys. G: Nucl. Part. Phys. **38**, 115107 (2011).
28. V. Caracciolo et al. *The ADAMO Project and developments*. J. Phys.: Conf. Ser. **718**, 042011 (2016).
29. R. Cerulli for DAMA/INR-Kyiv coll., talk at IPRD 2019, October 14-17 2019, Siena, Italy (http://people.roma2.infn.it/dama/pdf/cerulli_IPRD2019.pdf).
30. A. Di Marco for DAMA/INR-Kyiv coll., talk at CYGNUS 2019 workshop on directional DM detection, July 10-12 2019, Rome, Italy (http://people.roma2.infn.it/~dama/pdf/cygnus_2019.pdf).
31. V. Caracciolo for DAMA/INR-Kyiv coll., talk at Particle Physics at the Silver Jubilee of Lomonosov Conferences, 464 (2019).

32. R. Bernabei et al. $ZnWO_4$ anisotropic scintillator for Dark Matter investigation with the directionality technique. EPJ Web of Conferences **136**, 05002 (2017).
33. V. Caracciolo for DAMA/INR-Kyiv coll., talk at CYGNUS-TPC kick-off meeting: a mini-workshop on directional Dark Matter searches and coherent neutrino scattering, LNF, April 7 2016, Italy.
34. R. Bernabei et al. Crystal scintillators for low background measurements. AIP Conference Proceedings **1549**, 189 (2013).
35. P. Belli et al. Search for 2β processes in ^{64}Zn with the help of $ZnWO_4$ crystal scintillator. Phys. Lett. B **658**, 193 (2008).
36. P. Belli et al. Search for double beta decay of zinc and tungsten with low background $ZnWO_4$ crystal scintillators. Nucl. Phys. A **826**, 256 (2009).
37. E.N. Galashov et al. Growing of $ZnWO_4$ single crystals from melt by the low thermal gradient Czochralski technique. Functional Materials **16**, 65 (2009).
38. A.S. Barabash et al. Low background scintillators to investigate rare processes. JINST **15** 07, C07037 (2020).
39. P.Belli et al. Developments and improvements of radiopure $ZnWO_4$ anisotropic scintillators. JINST **15** 05, C05055 (2020).
40. L.L. Nagornaya et al. Tungstate and molybdate scintillators to search for dark matter and double beta decay. IEEE Trans. Nucl. Sci. **56**, 2513 (2009).
41. V.N. Shlegel et al. Recent progress in oxide scintillation crystals development by low-thermal gradient Czochralski technique for particle physics experiments. JINST **12**, C08011 (2017).
42. V.I. Tretyak, Semi-empirical calculation of quenching factors for ions in scintillators. Astropart. Phys. **33**, 40 (2010).
43. R. Bernabei et al. First results from DAMA/LIBRA and the combined results with DAMA/NaI. Eur. Phys. J. C **67**, 39–49 (2010).

Collapse models under test by high sensitivity γ-ray and X-ray measurements

Catalina Curceanu[1,2], Kristian Piscicchia[3,1], Massimiliano Bazzi[1], Mario Bragadireanu[2,1], Michael Cargnelli[4,1], Alberto Clozza[1], Luca De Paolis[1], Raffaele Del Grande[5,1], Carlo Guaraldo[1], Mihail Iliescu[1], Matthias Laubenstein[6], Johann Marton[4,1], Marco Miliucci[1], Fabrizio Napolitano[1], Alessio Porcelli[4,1], Alessandro Scordo[1], Francesco Sgarmella[1], Hexi Shi[4], Diana Laura Sirghi[1,2], Florin Sirghi[1,2], Oton Vazquez Doce[1] and Johann Zmeskal[4,1]

[1] *Laboratori Nazionali di Frascati, INFN, Italy*
[2] *IFIN-HH, Institutul National pentru Fizica si Inginerie Nucleara Horia Hulubei, Romania*
[3] *Centro Ricerche Enrico Fermi – Museo Storico della Fisica e Centro Studi e Ricerche "Enrico Fermi", Italy*
[4] *Stefan-Meyer-Institute for subatomic physics, Austrian Academy of Science, Austria*
[5] *Excellence Cluster Universe, Technische Universität München, Germany*
[6] *Laboratori Nazionali del Gran Sasso, INFN, Italy*

The article reviews our recent experimental results on the Continuous Spontaneous Localization (CSL) model and on the gravity related collapse model developed by Diósi and Penrose (DP). These models of dynamical reduction of the wave function consist in non-linear and stochastic modifications of the Schröedinger equation, which lead to a progressive breakdown of the superposition principle, as the size of the system increases. We performed a high sensitivity survey of the spontaneous radiation phenomenon, predicted by the collapse models, in a dedicated experiment operated in the extremely low background of the Gran Sasso underground National Laboratory of INFN in Italy. Our studies set the strongest bounds on the CSL parameters, in a broad region of the parameters space, and rule out the DP in its present formulation.

Keywords: Collapse Models; Spontaneous Radiation; Germanium Detectors.

1. Dynamical collapse models and spontaneous radiation

Quantum Theory (QT) is the basis of our understanding of the physical world. Since its inception QT successfully described plenty of puzzling experimental phenomena, it explained the spectrum of the black body radiation and the atomic structure, it was the cornerstone of the development of modern chemistry, of nuclear physics and of quantum field theory, just to give some examples, and presently fuels the growth of vanguard technologies. Despite its success and the outstanding precision of the experimental validations, QT still contains a conundrum in its grounding pillars. Why the superposition principle, characterizing the evolution of microscopic systems, does not carry over to macroscopic objects? Why in the act of measuring the deterministic dynamics is replaced by a probabilistic behaviour governed by the Born rule?

Models of dynamical reduction of the wave function represent phenomenological, and testable, concrete solutions to the problem (see e.g.,[1-8] for a review and references see also[9]). They consist in non-linear and stochastic modifications of the

Schröedinger equation, which preserve the QT predictions in the microscopic regime, and go over to classical mechanics in the macroscopic limit, by breaking down the quantum linear evolution proportionally to the growing size of the system.

Besides interferometric experiments (see e.g.[10-14]), which aim to measure the interference pattern of the spatial superposition which is created in an interferometer, collapse models can be also probed with indirect tests (see e.g.[15-27]). Common denominator of this second class of experiments is to exploit the random motion associated to the collapse mechanism, which allows to test the effect of the models predictions on macroscopic objects. Clear advantage is the magnification effect, which leads to the stronger constraints on the collapse models, this is the case of micrometer cantilever,[16] gravitational wave detectors[28,29] and X/γ-ray measurements,[25-27] the latter being the subject of this paper.

We will review in this paper our latest experimental results on the Continuous Spontaneous Localization (CSL) and on the Diósi-Penrose (DP) models. In the CSL model[4-6] the non-linear and stochastic terms are characterized by the interaction with a continuous set of independent noises, with zero average, Gaussian correlation in space and, in the simplest version, white correlation in time. The model is defined in terms of two phenomenological parameters, denoted by λ and r_C. λ has the dimensions of a rate and sets the strength of the collapse. r_C is a correlation length which determines the spatial resolution of the collapse, the collapse is weak if the superposition size is much smaller than r_C, while becomes effective for delocalizations which are much larger than r_C. Different theoretical considerations lead to alternative choices for the parameters: Ghirardi, Rimini and Weber[3] proposed $\lambda = 10^{-17} \text{s}^{-1}$ and $r_C = 10^{-7}$m, Adler[30] proposed $\lambda = 10^{-8\pm 2} \text{s}^{-1}$ for $r_C = 10^{-7}$m, and $\lambda = 10^{-6\pm 2} \text{s}^{-1}$ for $r_C = 10^{-6}$m.

Roger Penrose argued[7,8] that when a system is found in a spatial quantum superposition, a corresponding superposition of two different space-times is generated. The superposition is unstable and decays in time. The more massive the system in the superposition, the larger the difference in the two space-times and the faster the wave-function collapse. The average collapse time τ would then be given by the expression $\tau \approx \hbar/E_g$, where $\hbar$ is the reduced Planck's constant and E_g is the gravitational self-energy of the difference between two (stationary) mass distributions of the superposition. Lajos Diósi developed a dynamical theory of gravity-related wave function collapse[1,2] which predicts the same form for the collapse time. Considered that the gravitational self-interaction energy diverges for point-like constituents, Diósi introduced[31] a minimum length R_0, which limits the spatial resolution of the mass density. E_g is then a function of R_0, the smaller R_0 the faster the collapse.

An unavoidable consequence of the dynamics of both the CSL and the gravity related collapse developed by Diósi, is that the non-linear interaction with the noise-filed induces a Brownian-like diffusion motion for the particles which, if charged, emits radiation. This phenomenon, which is not predicted in the context of QT, is usually called *spontaneous radiation*, and represents the observable which was investigated in our experimental surveys. The spontaneous radiation rate, due to the emission of protons in the atomic nuclei, was calculated in Refs.[26,27] and is given by:

$$\left.\frac{d\Gamma}{dE}\right|_t = N_{atoms} \cdot N_A^2 \cdot \frac{\hbar e^2}{4\pi^2 \epsilon_0 c^3 m_0^2} \cdot \frac{\lambda}{r_C^2} \frac{1}{E}, \quad (1)$$

for the CSL model, and by:

$$\left.\frac{d\Gamma}{dE}\right|_t = N_{atoms} \cdot N_A^2 \cdot \frac{2}{3} \frac{G e^2}{\pi^{3/2} \epsilon_0 c^3} \cdot \frac{1}{R_0^3 E}, \quad (2)$$

for the DP model. N_{atoms} is the number of atoms in the system with atomic number N_A, c is the speed of light, ϵ_0 is the vacuum permittivity, m_0 is the nucleon mass, G is the universal gravitational constant, E and t are the energy and the time. Electrons are relativistic in the energy range which was considered in our analyses, hence their contribution to the spontaneous radiation emission can not be considered.

The paper is organized as follows: in Section 2 the experimental apparatus is described, in Section 3 is given a brief description of the statistical analysis and the constraints on the characteristic parameters of the CSL and DP models are summarized, while concluding remarks and the future developments of our studies are outlined in Section 4.

2. The experimental setup

The experimental apparatus was based on a coaxial p-type High Purity Germanium detector (HPEGe) surrounded by multiple shielding layers: the inner shielding consisting of 5cm thick electrolytic copper, the external part of lead (30 cm from the bottom and 25 cm from the sides). Both the shielding and the cryogenic system were enclosed in an air tight steel housing, flushed with boil-off nitrogen, in order to suppress radon contamination (see Fig. 2 in Ref.[26] for a schematic representation of the setup, further details on the setup structure can be found in Ref.[26] and therein references). The experiment was operated in the extremely low background environment of the Gran Sasso underground National Laboratory of INFN in Italy.

The goal of the measurement was to disentangle a faint contribution of the spontaneous radiation emission process, to the measured spectrum, from environmental background. To this aim an accurate characterization of the whole apparatus was performed with a validated Monte Carlo (MC) code[32] based on the GEANT4 software library.[33]

The measured spectrum (corresponding to an exposure of 124 kg · day) is shown in black in Fig. 1, in the range $\Delta E = (1000 \div 3800)$keV (this is a reproduction of the original Fig. 1 in Ref.[27]). The energy range fulfills the theoretical requirements for the validity of the calculated rates (Eqs. (1) and (2)). In ΔE the main contribution to the background was found to be originated by residual radionuclides, present

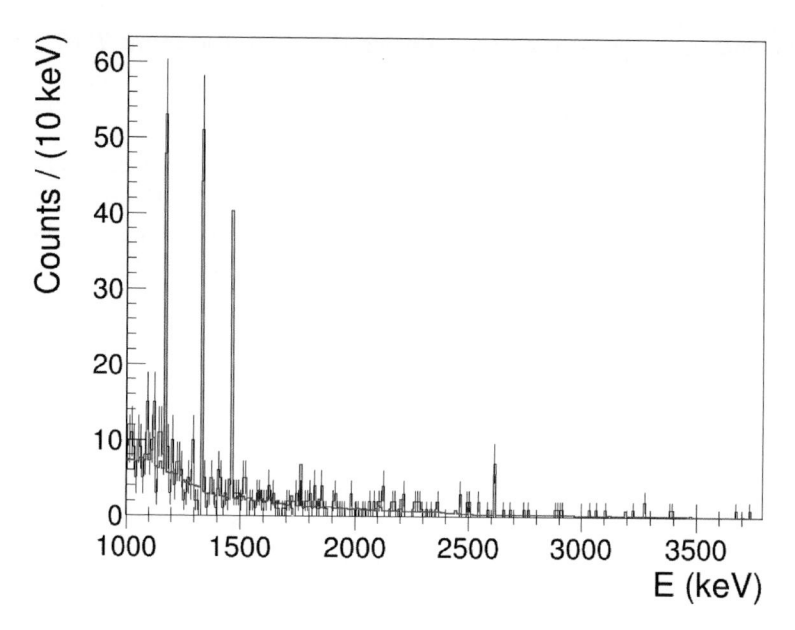

Fig. 1. The measured X-ray spectrum is shown in black in the selected energy range $\Delta E = (1000 - 3800)$ keV. The simulated background distribution is also shown in magenta.

in the materials of the setup, whose measured activities represented the inputs of the MC simulations. The magenta distribution in Fig. 1 represents the simulated background, 88% of the measured spectrum can be described in terms of known emission processes.

The simulation also allowed to compute the efficiencies, as a function of the energy, for the detection of spontaneously emitted photons in each component of the setup. To this end 10^8 photons, with uniform spatial distribution, were generated in each material in steps of 200 keV (i.e. 15 points in the ΔE). The efficiency functions $\epsilon_i(E)$ (i labelling the material of the detector) were then estimated by means of polynomial fits of the corresponding distributions, for each component of the detector which gives an appreciable contribution. The results of this analysis are summarized in Fig. 2 and Table 1 of Ref.[27].

3. Summary of the data analyses and results

The strategy of the Bayesian statistical analysis was to perform a comparison of the theoretically predicted spontaneous emission rate, generated by each component of the apparatus and weighted by the experimental efficiency and acceptance, with the measured distribution, accounting for the estimated background.

Given the calculated efficiency functions, and the theoretical rate (Eqs. (1) and (2)), the expected number of measured events, due to the spontaneous emission by protons belonging to the i-th material, during the acquisition time T is:

$$\int_{\Delta E} \left.\frac{d\Gamma}{dE}\right|_t T \epsilon_i(E)\, dE. \tag{3}$$

Summation over i yields the total expected signal contribution, which is a function of the phenomenological parameters (λ, r_C) or R_0, depending on the selected collapse model. The measured counts were assumed to fluctuate according to a Poissonian distribution and the probability density functions for the expected number of counts were derived, from which the following constraints on the models parameters were calculated, corresponding to a probability of 0.95:

$$\frac{\lambda}{r_C^2} < 52\,\mathrm{s}^{-1}\mathrm{m}^{-2}\,; \qquad R_0 > 0.54 \cdot 10^{-10}\mathrm{m}\,, \tag{4}$$

see Refs.[26,27] for more details concerning the data analysis.

The first limit in Eq. (4) represents the stronger existing bound on the CSL model for values of the correlation length $r_C \leq 10^{-6}$m. The limit on R_0 (right side in Eq. (4)) is about three orders of magnitude stronger than previous bounds in the literature.[29] If R_0 is chosen as the size of the nucleus's wave function (as suggested by Penrose), our result is to be compared with the square-root of the mean square displacement of a nucleus in the lattice. For the Germanium crystal, cooled down at the liquid Nitrogen temperature, this would amount to an R_0 value of about $0.05 \cdot 10^{-10}$m, which is more than one order of magnitude less than the lower limit set by our experiment.

4. Conclusions and perspectives

We summarized the results of a dedicated measurement, performed at the Gran Sasso underground National Laboratory of INFN. The study was devoted to the search of spontaneous radiation emission, predicted by the CSL and the DP models of wave function collapse. We set the strongest bounds on the CSL phenomenological parameters in the region $r_C \leq 10^{-6}$m. Penrose's proposal for a gravity-related collapse of the wave function, in the present formulation, is ruled out. Our result indicates that the idea of gravity-related wave function collapse, which remains very appealing, will probably require a new approach. Indeed new theoretical developments are seeking for non-Markovian and/or dissipative versions of the collapse models, predicting a lower rate of spontanoeus radiation depending on the photon frequency. Both Penrose and Diósi are also pursuing the idea of a radiation free gravity-related collapse.

This pushes our efforts through further refinements our experimental techniques and data analyses methods. We are presently expanding our sensitive energy region from the MeV to few keV, with experimental setups based on Broad Energy Germanium detectors and ultra-radio pure targets. We are investigating the application of Machine Learning algorithms to identify the faint signal of the dynamical collapse, towards a deeper understanding of the foundations of Quantum Mechanics.

Acknowledgments

This publication was made possible through the support of Grant 62099 from the John Templeton Foundation. The opinions expressed in this publication are those of the authors and do not necessarily reflect the views of the John Templeton Foundation. We acknowledge support from the Foundational Questions Institute and Fetzer Franklin Fund, a donor advised fund of Silicon Valley Community Foundation (Grants No. FQXi-RFP-CPW-2008 and FQXi-MGB-2011), and from the H2020 FET TEQ (Grant No. 766900) and INFN (VIP). We thank the Austrian Science Foundation (FWF) which supports the VIP2 project with the grants P25529-N20, project P 30635-N36 and W1252-N27 (doctoral college particles and interactions). K. P. acknowledges support from the Centro Ricerche Enrico Fermi - Museo Storico della Fisica e Centro Studi e Ricerche "Enrico Fermi" (Open Problems in Quantum Mechanics project).

References

1. L. Diosi, A universal master equation for the gravitational violation of quantum mechanics, *Physics letters A* **120**, 377 (1987).
2. L. Diósi, Models for universal reduction of macroscopic quantum fluctuations, *Physical Review A* **40**, p. 1165 (1989).
3. G. C. Ghirardi, A. Rimini and T. Weber, Unified dynamics for microscopic and macroscopic systems, *Physical review D* **34**, p. 470 (1986).
4. P. Pearle, Combining stochastic dynamical state-vector reduction with spontaneous localization, *Physical Review A* **39**, p. 2277 (1989).
5. G. C. Ghirardi, P. Pearle and A. Rimini, Markov processes in hilbert space and continuous spontaneous localization of systems of identical particles, *Physical Review A* **42**, p. 78 (1990).
6. P. Pearle and E. Squires, Bound state excitation, nucleon decay experiments and models of wave function collapse, *Physical Review Letters* **73**, p. 1 (1994).
7. R. Penrose, On gravity's role in quantum state reduction, *Gen. Rel. Grav. 28: 581-600* (1996).
8. R. Penrose, On the gravitization of quantum mechanics 1: Quantum state reduction, *Foundations of Physics 44, 557-575* (2014).
9. A. Bassi and G. Ghirardi, Dynamical reduction models, *Physics Reports* **379**, 257 (2003).
10. T. Kovachy, P. Asenbaum, C. Overstreet, C. Donnelly, S. Dickerson, A. Sugarbaker, J. Hogan and M. Kasevich, Quantum superposition at the half-metre scale, *Nature* **528**, 530 (2015).
11. S. Eibenberger, S. Gerlich, M. Arndt, M. Mayor and J. Tüxen, Matter–wave interference of particles selected from a molecular library with masses exceeding 10000 amu, *Physical Chemistry Chemical Physics* **15**, 14696 (2013).
12. M. Toroš and A. Bassi, Bounds on quantum collapse models from matter-wave interferometry: calculational details, *Journal of Physics A: Mathematical and Theoretical* **51**, p. 115302 (2018).
13. K. C. Lee, M. R. Sprague, B. J. Sussman, J. Nunn, N. K. Langford, X.-M. Jin, T. Champion, P. Michelberger, K. F. Reim, D. England *et al.*, Entangling macroscopic diamonds at room temperature, *Science* **334**, 1253 (2011).

14. S. Belli, R. Bonsignori, G. D'Auria, L. Fant, M. Martini, S. Peirone, S. Donadi and A. Bassi, Entangling macroscopic diamonds at room temperature: Bounds on the continuous-spontaneous-localization parameters, *Physical Review A* **94**, p. 012108 (2016).
15. T. Kovachy, J. M. Hogan, A. Sugarbaker, S. M. Dickerson, C. A. Donnelly, C. Overstreet and M. A. Kasevich, Matter wave lensing to picokelvin temperatures, *Physical review letters* **114**, p. 143004 (2015).
16. A. Vinante, R. Mezzena, P. Falferi, M. Carlesso and A. Bassi, Improved noninterferometric test of collapse models using ultracold cantilevers, *Physical review letters* **119**, p. 110401 (2017).
17. O. Usenko, A. Vinante, G. Wijts and T. Oosterkamp, A superconducting quantum interference device based read-out of a subattonewton force sensor operating at millikelvin temperatures, *Applied Physics Letters* **98**, p. 133105 (2011).
18. A. Vinante, A. Collaboration *et al.*, Present performance and future upgrades of the auriga capacitive readout, *Classical and Quantum Gravity* **23**, p. S103 (2006).
19. B. P. Abbott, R. Abbott, T. Abbott, M. Abernathy, F. Acernese, K. Ackley, C. Adams, T. Adams, P. Addesso, R. Adhikari *et al.*, Gw150914: The advanced ligo detectors in the era of first discoveries, *Physical review letters* **116**, p. 131103 (2016).
20. B. P. Abbott, R. Abbott, T. Abbott, M. Abernathy, F. Acernese, K. Ackley, C. Adams, T. Adams, P. Addesso, R. Adhikari *et al.*, Observation of gravitational waves from a binary black hole merger, *Physical review letters* **116**, p. 061102 (2016).
21. M. Armano, H. Audley, G. Auger, J. Baird, M. Bassan, P. Binetruy, M. Born, D. Bortoluzzi, N. Brandt, M. Caleno *et al.*, Sub-femto-g free fall for space-based gravitational wave observatories: Lisa pathfinder results, *Physical review letters* **116**, p. 231101 (2016).
22. M. Armano, H. Audley, J. Baird, P. Binetruy, M. Born, D. Bortoluzzi, E. Castelli, A. Cavalleri, A. Cesarini, A. Cruise *et al.*, Beyond the required lisa free-fall performance: New lisa pathfinder results down to 20 μ hz, *Physical review letters* **120**, p. 061101 (2018).
23. S. L. Adler and A. Vinante, Bulk heating effects as tests for collapse models, *Physical Review A* **97**, p. 052119 (2018).
24. M. Bahrami, Testing collapse models by a thermometer, *Physical Review A* **97**, p. 052118 (2018).
25. K. Piscicchia, A. Bassi, C. Curceanu, R. D. Grande, S. Donadi, B. C. Hiesmayr and A. Pichler, CSL collapse model mapped with the spontaneous radiation, *Entropy* **19**, p. 319 (2017).
26. S. Donadi, K. Piscicchia, C. Curceanu, L. Diósi, M. Laubenstein and A. Bassi, Underground test of gravity-related wave function collapse, *Nature Physics* **17**, 74 (2021).
27. S. Donadi, K. Piscicchia, R. Del Grande, C. Curceanu, M. Laubenstein and A. Bassi, Novel CSL bounds from the noise-induced radiation emission from atoms, *The European Physical Journal C* **81**, 1 (2021).
28. M. Carlesso, A. Bassi, P. Falferi and A. Vinante, Experimental bounds on collapse models from gravitational wave detectors, *Physical Review D* **94**, p. 124036 (2016).
29. B. Helou, B. Slagmolen, D. E. McClelland and Y. Chen, Lisa pathfinder appreciably constrains collapse models, *Physical Review D* **95**, p. 084054 (2017).
30. S. L. Adler, Lower and upper bounds on csl parameters from latent image formation and IGM heating, *Journal of Physics A: Mathematical and Theoretical* **40**, p. 2935 (2007).
31. L. Diósi, Notes on certain newton gravity mechanisms of wave function localization and decoherence, *J. Phys. A* **40**, *2989-2995* (2007).

32. M. Boswell, Y.-D. Chan, J. A. Detwiler, P. Finnerty, R. Henning, V. M. Gehman, R. A. Johnson, D. V. Jordan, K. Kazkaz, M. Knapp *et al.*, MaGe-a Geant4-based Monte Carlo application framework for low-background germanium experiments, *IEEE Transactions on Nuclear Science* **58**, 1212 (2011).
33. S. Agostinelli, J. Allison, K. a. Amako, J. Apostolakis, H. Araujo, P. Arce, M. Asai, D. Axen, S. Banerjee, G. Barrand *et al.*, Geant4—A simulation toolkit, *Nuclear instruments and methods in physics research section A: Accelerators, Spectrometers, Detectors and Associated Equipment* **506**, 250 (2003).

Leptophilic dark matter at linear colliders

P. S. Bhupal Dev

Department of Physics and McDonnell Center for the Space Sciences, Washington University,
St. Louis, MO 63130, USA
E-mail: bdev@wustl.edu

Leptophilic dark matter (LDM) could naturally arise in many beyond the Standard Model scenarios and could address certain experimental anomalies. We discuss some model-independent collider constraints on the LDM effective couplings with the Standard Model sector, considering its production at a future electron-positron linear collider (with polarized and unpolarized beam options) in both mono-photon and mono-Z channels.[1]

Keywords: Dark Matter, Effective Field Theory, Lepton Collider

1. Introduction

Many of the existing experimental constraints on dark matter (DM) crucially rely on the DM interactions with nucleons, and therefore, can be largely weakened if the DM predominantly interacts with the Standard Model (SM) leptons, but not quarks at tree-level. Such *leptophilic* DM (LDM) could arise naturally in many beyond the Standard Model (BSM) scenarios,[2–23] some of which could even explain various experimental anomalies, such as the muon anomalous magnetic moment,[24] DAMA/LIBRA annual modulation,[25] anomalous cosmic ray positron excess,[26–29] the galactic center gamma-ray excess,[30] and XENON1T electron excess.[31] Dedicated searches for LDM in direct detection[32–34] and beam dump[35,36] experiments have also been discussed.

In this proceedings based on Ref.[1], we focus on the LDM searches at lepton colliders, which are complementary to the direct and indirect detection searches. We adopt an effective field theory (EFT) approach, which has been widely used in the context of collider searches for DM following the early works of Refs.[37–45] The same interactions responsible for DM pair-annihilation in the early universe leading to their thermal freeze-out guarantee their direct production at colliders, as long as kinematically allowed. This will give a characteristic mono-X signature, where the large missing transverse momentum carried away by the DM pair is balanced by a visible sector particle X (which can be either a photon, jet, W, Z, or Higgs, depending on the model) emitted from an initial, intermediate or final state (see Refs.[46,47] for reviews). Specifically, the mono-jet signature has become emblematic for LHC DM searches.[48–51] However, for an LDM with loop-suppressed interactions to the SM quarks, the hadron colliders like the LHC are not expected to provide a better limit than the existing constraints from indirect searches, such as from AMS-02,[52,53] at least within the EFT framework with contact interactions.

On the other hand, lepton colliders provide an ideal testing ground for the direct production of LDM and its subsequent detection via either mono-photon[42,45,54–63] or mono-Z[64–67] signatures. We go beyond the existing literature and perform a comprehensive and comparative study of both mono-photon and mono-Z signatures of LDM at future e^+e^- colliders in a model-independent, EFT approach.[1] Our analysis is generically applicable to all future e^+e^- colliders, such as the ILC,[68] CLIC,[69] CEPC[70] and FCC-ee,[71] but for concreteness, we have taken the $\sqrt{s} = 1$ TeV ILC as our case study for numerical simulations. We also assume the DM to be fermionic and limit ourselves to the dimension-6 operators, but taking into consideration all possible dimension-6 operators of scalar-pseudoscalar (S-P), vector-axialvector (V-A) and tensor-axialtensor (T-AT) type as applicable for the most general DM-electron coupling. Within the minimal EFT approach, the only relevant degrees of freedom in our analysis are the DM mass and an effective cut-off scale Λ which determines the strength of the four-Fermi operators. This enables us to derive model-independent ILC sensitivities on LDM in the (m_χ, Λ) plane in both mono-photon and mono-Z (leptonic and hadronic) channels, after taking into account all relevant backgrounds and systematic uncertainties. We consider both unpolarized and polarized beam options,[68,72] and find that with the proper choice of polarizations for the e^- and e^+ beams (which depends on the operator type), the DM sensitivities could be significantly enhanced.

2. Effective operators

Our primary assumptions are (i) the DM particle χ couples directly only to the SM leptons but not to the quarks (hence leptophilic), and (ii) the energy scale of the associated new physics is large compared to the collider energies under consideration, thus allowing us to integrate out the heavy mediators and parametrize the DM-SM interactions using effective higher-dimensional operators. For concreteness, we assume that the DM particles are Dirac fermions, and therefore, the leading order DM-SM interactions are the dimension-six four-Fermi interactions, with the most-general effective Lagrangian given by[37]

$$\mathcal{L}_{\text{eff}} = \frac{1}{\Lambda^2} \sum_j \left(\overline{\chi}\Gamma_\chi^j \chi\right) \left(\overline{\ell}\Gamma_\ell^j \ell\right), \qquad (1)$$

where Λ is the cut-off scale for the EFT description and the index j corresponds to different Lorentz structures, as shown below. Since our main focus is on e^+e^- colliders, we will just set $\ell = e$ in Eq. (1) and assume this to be the only leading-order coupling, but our discussion below could be easily extended to other cases, e.g. future muon colliders[73] by setting $\ell = \mu$.

A complete set of Lorentz-invariant operators consists of scalar (S), pseudo-scalar (P), vector (V), axial-vector (A), tensor (T) and axial-tensor (AT) currents.

We classify them as follows:

$$\begin{aligned}
\text{S-P type}: \quad & \Gamma_\chi = c_S^\chi + i c_P^\chi \gamma_5\,, & \Gamma_e &= c_S^e + i c_P^e \gamma_5\,, \\
\text{V-A type}: \quad & \Gamma_\chi^\mu = (c_V^\chi + c_A^\chi \gamma_5)\,\gamma^\mu\,, & \Gamma_{e\mu} &= (c_V^e + c_A^e \gamma_5)\,\gamma_\mu\,, \\
\text{T-AT type}: \quad & \Gamma_\chi^{\mu\nu} = (c_T^\chi + i c_{AT}^\chi \gamma_5)\,\sigma^{\mu\nu}\,, & \Gamma_{e\mu\nu} &= \sigma_{\mu\nu}\,,
\end{aligned} \qquad (2)$$

where $\sigma^{\mu\nu} = \frac{i}{2}[\gamma^\mu, \gamma^\nu]$ is the spin tensor and $c_j^{\chi,e}$ are dimensionless, real couplings. For simplicity, in Eq. (1) we have used a common cut-off scale Λ for all Lorentz structures. Furthermore, in our subsequent numerical analysis, we will consider one type of operator at a time, by setting the corresponding couplings $c_j^{\chi,e} = 1$ without loss of generality and all other couplings equal to zero, unless otherwise specified. For instance, setting $c_S^\chi = c_P^\chi = c_S^e = c_P^e = 1$ and all other couplings equal to zero gives us the (S+P)-type operator, which we will simply refer to as the **SP**-type in the following discussion. Similarly, we will denote the $c_V^\chi = c_A^\chi = c_V^e = c_A^e = 1$ case simply as the **VA**-type, and $c_T^\chi = c_{AT}^\chi = 1$ as the **TAT**-type for presenting our numerical results in the (m_χ, Λ) plane. For other choices of the couplings, our results for the sensitivity on Λ can be easily scaled accordingly.

We will impose a theoretical limit of $\Lambda > \sqrt{s}$ for the EFT validity. For relatively larger DM mass, we must also have $\Lambda > 2m_\chi$ in order to describe DM pair annihilation by the EFT. In fact, using $\Lambda = 2m_\chi$ induces 100% error in the EFT prediction for s-channel UV completions. Therefore, we will use $\Lambda > \max\{\sqrt{s}, 3m_\chi\}$ as a conservative lower bound[74] to ensure the validity of our EFT approach.

3. Mono-photon channel

For the mono-photon signal $e^+e^- \to \chi\bar{\chi}\gamma$, the χ's will contribute to the missing transverse energy at the detector. The dominant irreducible SM background to this process comes from neutrino pair production with an associated ISR photon, i.e. $e^+e^- \to \nu\bar{\nu}\gamma$. Since neutrinos are practically indistinguishable from DMs on an event-by-event basis, the majority of this background survives the event selection cuts. However, as we will show later, this background is highly polarization-dependent, and therefore, can be significantly reduced by the proper choice of polarized beams, without affecting the signal much.

Apart from the neutrino background, any SM process with a single photon in the final state can contribute to the total background if all other visible particles escape detected. The SM processes containing either jets or charged particles are relatively easy to distinguish from a DM event, so their contribution to the total background is negligible.[58] The only exception is the *Bhabha scattering* process associated with an extra photon (either from initial or final state radiation), i.e., $e^+e^- \to e^+e^-\gamma$, which has a large cross section, is polarization-independent, and can significantly contribute to the total background whenever the final-state electrons and positrons go undetected, e.g. along beam pipes. In our following analysis, we consider both neutrino and radiative Bhabha backgrounds.

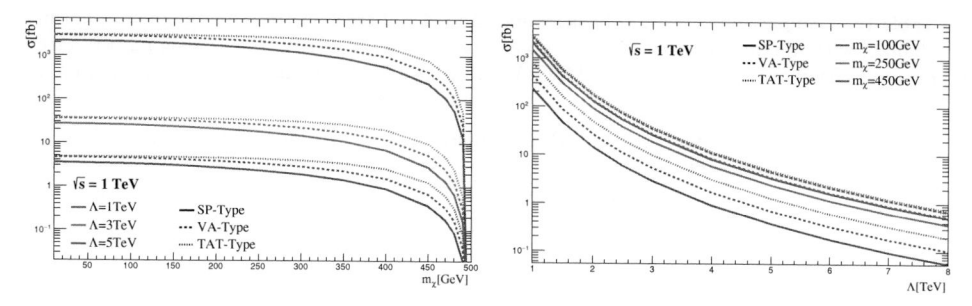

Fig. 1. Variation of mono-photon signal cross-section with the DM mass (left) and the cut-off scale (right) at $\sqrt{s} = 1$ TeV ILC. The solid, dashed and dotted lines are for the SP, VA and TAT-type operators respectively. In the left panel, the red, green and blue curves respectively correspond to different values of the cut-off scale $\Lambda = 1$ TeV, 3 TeV and 5 TeV, while in the right panel, they correspond to different values of the DM mass $m_\chi = 100$ GeV, 250 GeV and 450 GeV.

3.1. *Cross-sections*

The cross-sections for the mono-photon signal $e^+e^- \to \chi\bar{\chi}\gamma$ and the radiative neutrino background $e^+e^- \to \nu\bar{\nu}\gamma$ at $\sqrt{s} = 1$ TeV ILC are estimated using `CalcHEP`[75] with proper implementation of ISR and beamsstrahlung effects, which significantly affect the width and position of the neutrino Z-resonance. For this purpose, the EFT Lagrangian (1) is implemented in `FeynRules`[76] to generate the CHO library required for `CalcHEP`. To avoid collinear and infrared divergences, we limit the phase space in the event generation with the following cuts on the outgoing photon energy E_γ and its polar angle θ_γ:

$$8 \text{ GeV} < E_\gamma < 500 \text{ GeV}, \quad |\cos\theta_\gamma| \leq 0.995. \tag{3}$$

The *radiative* Bhabha scattering events are generated using `WHIZARD`[77] (to better handle the singularities) with the same set of cuts as in Eq. (3) to the matrix element photon (i.e., excluding the ISR and beamsstrahlung photons). Also, some additional cuts are implemented for the Bhabha process to take care of the soft and collinear divergences:

$$M_{e^\pm_{in}, e^\pm_{out}} < 2m_e, \quad M_{e^\pm_{out}, e^\pm_{out}} < 5 \text{ GeV}, \quad P_T^\gamma > 1 \text{ GeV}, \quad \Delta R_{e^\pm, \gamma} > 0.2, \quad \Delta R_{e^\pm, e^\pm} > 0.4. \tag{4}$$

After generating the signal and background events, we perform a fast detector simulation of the `SiD` detector of ILC[78] using `Delphes3`[79] with the configuration card validated in Ref.[80]. The variations of the unpolarized signal cross section as a function of the DM mass and the cut-off scale are shown in Figure 1 left and right panels respectively for all three operator types, namely, SP (solid), VA (dashed) and TAT (dotted)-type. We find that the cross-section is the smallest (largest) for the SP (TAT)-type operator at any given DM mass. In the left panel, the sudden drop in the cross-section as m_χ approaches $\sqrt{s}/2$ is due to phase-space suppression. Otherwise, for smaller DM masses, the cross-section for a given operator type and

Table 1. Comparison of the SM backgrounds and signal cross sections for the mono-photon channel with different choices of beam polarization at $\sqrt{s} = 1$ TeV. For the signal, we have chosen benchmark values of $m_\chi = 100$ GeV and $\Lambda = 3$ TeV. The numbers in bold highlight the optimal polarization choice for a given operator type.

Process type	Unpolarized cross-section (fb)	Polarization $P(e^-, e^+)$	Polarized cross-section (fb)			
			$(+,+)$	$(+,-)$	$(-,+)$	$(-,-)$
$\nu\bar{\nu}\gamma$	4782	(80, 0)	1106	1106	8506	8506
		(80, 20)	1268	963	10160	6793
		(80, 30)	1393	860	10993	5931
$e^-e^+\gamma$	68439	(80, 0)	67920	67920	68867	68867
		(80, 20)	67909	68386	69285	68297
		(80, 30)	67809	68566	69502	68181
SP-type	25.5	(80, 0)	25.5	25.5	25.5	25.5
		(80, 20)	29.6	21.4	21.4	29.6
		(80, 30)	**31.6**	19.4	19.4	31.6
VA-type	34.3	(80, 0)	61.7	61.7	6.9	6.9
		(80, 20)	49.4	74.1	5.5	8.2
		(80, 30)	43.2	**80.3**	4.8	8.9
TAT-type	36.5	(80, 0)	36.5	36.5	36.5	36.5
		(80, 20)	42.3	30.6	30.6	42.3
		(80, 30)	**45.2**	27.7	27.7	45.2

a given cut-off scale is almost independent of the DM mass. In the right panel, we see that for a given DM mass the cross-section drops as Λ^{-4}, as expected.

As for the background, we find that the neutrino background cross section at $\sqrt{s} = 1$ TeV is 4.8 pb, while the radiative Bhabha background is 68.4 pb (though it is substantially reduced after the baseline selection). On the other hand, the DM signal cross section is found to be much smaller, as shown in Table 1 for a benchmark DM mass of $m_\chi = 100$ GeV and the cut-off scale $\Lambda = 3$ TeV.

3.2. Effect of polarization

One important advantage of lepton colliders is that the incoming beams can be polarized. This helps to reduce the neutrino background considerably, as shown in Table 1. To utilize the full advantage of the beam polarization, we investigate the effect of different choices of polarization on the signal and background. At the ILC, the baseline design foresees at least 80% electron beam polarization at the interaction point, whereas the positron beam can be polarized up to 30% for the undulator positron source (up to 60% may be possible with the addition of a photon collimator).[68] For comparison, we show our results for three different nominal absolute values of polarization: $|P(e^-, e^+)| = (80, 0), (80, 20)$ and $(80, 30)$. In each case, we can also have four different polarization configurations, namely, $\text{sign}(P(e^-), P(e^+)) = (+, +), (+, -), (-, +)$ and $(-, -)$, where $+$ and $-$ denote the right- and left-handed helicities respectively.

In Table 1, we show the effect of different schemes of polarizations and helicity orientations on the mono-photon signal and background cross-sections. It is clear that the radiative Bhabha background remains almost unchanged. On the other hand, electron beam polarization is very effective in reducing the neutrino background, as a 80% *right-handed* electron beam can reduce the neutrino background to 23% of the unpolarized case, even without any polarization on the positron beam. The effect is further enhanced by a *left-handed* positron beam. We see that for 20% and 30% left-handed positron beam polarization, the neutrino background is reduced to 20% and 18% of its unpolarized value, respectively.

The signals are also affected to some extent by beam polarization and the optimal helicity configuration depends on the operator type. For SP- and TAT-type operators we see no effect of electron-beam polarization, but a 20% (30%) *right-handed* positron beam can enhance the signal by 16% (24%). The VA-type signal, on the other hand, prefers the $(+,-)$ helicity configuration – the same choice for which the neutrino background is minimized. With the $(+80\%, -30\%)$ configuration, the VA-type signal is enhanced by a factor of 2.3, whereas the $(+80\%, +30\%)$ configuration enhances it by a modest 26%.

Overall, although the $(+80\%, -30\%)$ configuration minimizes the background the most, looking at the different signal to background ratio, we find that the $(+80\%, +30\%)$ configuration is the best for the SP- and TAT-type operators. For direct comparison between the results for different operators, we choose to work with the $(+80\%, +30\%)$ configuration democratically for all the operator types, unless otherwise specified.

3.3. *Cut-based analysis*

Now we analyze various kinematic distributions and perform a cut-based analysis to optimize the signal-to-background ratio. This of course depends on the DM mass, so in Table 2, we list three benchmark points (BPs) with $m_\chi = 100$ GeV, 250 GeV and 350 GeV respectively, and present the corresponding selection cuts optimized for each case. Here we fix $\Lambda = 3$ TeV for illustration, but in the next subsection, we will vary both m_χ and Λ to obtain the 3σ sensitivity limits. As for the choice of the DM mass values, since it was seen from Figure 1 that the signal cross-sections are barely sensitive to the DM mass up to around 100 GeV, our BP1 essentially captures the light DM scenario. Similarly, our BP3 is chosen moderately close to the kinematic limit of $\sqrt{s}/2$ (going too close to $\sqrt{s}/2$ will result in cross-section values too low too low to give sizable event counts after all the selection cuts). The BP2 is chosen for an intermediate mass DM in between BP1 and BP2.

We define our mono-photon signals by those events that pass through the baseline selection criteria as defined below, in addition to the cuts given in Eq. (3):

$$E_\gamma > 10 \text{ GeV}, \quad |\eta_\gamma| < 2.45 \quad \text{and} \quad P_T^{\text{miss}} > 10 \text{ GeV}, \tag{5}$$

where the hardest photon in an event is considered as the signal photon. For the radiative Bhabha background, we define the selection criteria for electrons as $P_{T,e} > 10$ GeV, $|\eta_e| < 2.5$, and have kept only those events which contain no electrons (and positrons) passing these criteria, which means they have escaped detection.

Table 2. Mono-photon selection cuts for different BPs across all operator types.

	BP1	BP2	BP3
Definition	$m_\chi = 100$ GeV, $\Lambda = 3$ TeV	$m_\chi = 250$ GeV, $\Lambda = 3$ TeV	$m_\chi = 350$ GeV, $\Lambda = 3$ TeV
Baseline selection	$E_\gamma > 10$ GeV, $|\eta_\gamma| < 2.45$, $P_T^{\text{miss}} > 10$ GeV		
SP-type			
Cut-1	$E_\gamma < 450$ GeV	$E_\gamma < 340$ GeV	$E_\gamma < 250$ GeV
Cut-2	$|\eta_\gamma| < 1.6$		
Cut-3	$P_T^{\text{miss}} < 450$ GeV	$P_T^{\text{miss}} < 340$ GeV	$P_T^{\text{miss}} < 240$ GeV
Cut-4	$P_T^{\text{frac}} < 1.3$		
Cut-5	$1.1 < \Delta R_{\gamma,\text{MET}} < 4.5$		
VA-type			
Cut-1	$E_\gamma < 440$ GeV	$E_\gamma < 350$ GeV	$E_\gamma < 250$ GeV
Cut-2	$|\eta_\gamma| < 1.7$		
Cut-3	$P_T^{\text{miss}} < 400$ GeV	$P_T^{\text{miss}} < 340$ GeV	$P_T^{\text{miss}} < 250$ GeV
Cut-4	$P_T^{\text{frac}} < 1.2$		
Cut-5	$1.1 < \Delta R_{\gamma,\text{MET}} < 4.5$		
TAT-type			
Cut-1	$E_\gamma < 460$ GeV	$E_\gamma < 360$ GeV	$E_\gamma < 230$ GeV
Cut-2	$|\eta_\gamma| < 1.7$		
Cut-3	$P_T^{\text{miss}} < 450$ GeV	$P_T^{\text{miss}} < 350$ GeV	$P_T^{\text{miss}} < 230$ GeV
Cut-4	$P_T^{\text{frac}} < 1.2$		
Cut-5	$1.1 < \Delta R_{\gamma,\text{MET}} < 4.4$		

After implementing these baseline selection cuts, we find that the signal and the neutrino background are reduced to about 60% of their original values in Table 1. Similarly, the actual Bhabha-induced background relevant for our signal is found to be only about 13% of its original value quoted in Table 1 after the baseline selection cuts, taking into account only the missed electron events. To further enhance our signal-to-background ratio, we then examine the signal versus background distributions of some relevant kinematic variables and devise further cuts, which are dynamic with respect to different BPs, as summarized in Table 2. See Ref.[1] for details.

Even after implementing the baseline and analysis cuts 1 through 5, the neutrino background can only be reduced to about 40% of its original value in Table 1. Similarly, the radiative Bhabha background, although substantially reduced to about 4% of its original value in Table 1 after the baseline selection and analysis cuts, still remains sizable and comparable to the neutrino background. However, an electromagnetic calorimeter in the very forward direction of the beamline (BeamCal)[81] can further suppress the Bhabha background to the per mille level. To properly incorporate the effect of BeamCal, we have used the selection efficiencies obtained from a full detector simulation performed in Ref.[61] by modeling the complete instrumented region in a realistic way. According to this analysis, the selection efficiency of the Bhabha background after the BeamCal veto only is 2.7%, while that of the neutrino background is between 98% and 99.6%. As for the DM signal, we expect it to be

Table 3. Signal significance in the mono-photon channel for the three BPs at $\sqrt{s} = 1$ TeV with $\mathcal{L}_{\text{int}} = 1000$ fb^{-1} integrated luminosity. The values in the parenthesis denote the significances with a 1% background systematic uncertainty.

Operator type	Signal significance for $\mathcal{L}_{\text{int}} = 1000\,\text{fb}^{-1}$					
	Unpolarized beams			Polarized beams		
	BP-1	BP-2	BP-3	BP-1	BP-2	BP-3
SP-type	8.1 (0.6)	5.8 (0.4)	3.5 (0.3)	18.1 (2.4)	13.0 (1.7)	7.8 (1.0)
VA-type	10.9 (0.8)	8.5 (0.6)	5.6 (0.4)	24.9 (3.2)	19.4 (2.5)	12.9 (1.7)
TAT-type	11.8 (0.8)	10.8 (0.8)	8.5 (0.6)	26.2 (3.5)	24.1 (3.2)	19.2 (2.6)

basically unaffected (just like the neutrino background) by the BeamCal veto, as it does not contain highly energetic charged particles in the longitudinal direction.

For the polarized case, after the baseline selection cuts, the Bhabha background remains almost same as in the unpolarized case. The neutrino background, on the other hand, is significantly reduced in the polarized case to about 28% of its unpolarized value. The other cut efficiencies are also slightly better for the neutrino background in the polarized case.

As for the signals, from Table 1, we see that the TAT-type operator has the largest cross section to start with, both for the unpolarized as well as for the $(+80\%, +30\%)$ polarized cases. Even after the baseline selection and the specialized cuts discussed above, the TAT-type signal retains the largest efficiency among the three types. This will be reflected in our signal significance results below.

3.4. *Signal significance*

After implementing all the cuts mentioned above, we calculate the final signal significance for our benchmark scenarios using the definition

$$\text{Sig} = \frac{S}{\sqrt{S + B + (\epsilon B)^2}}, \tag{6}$$

where S and B are the number of signal and total background events respectively for a given integrated luminosity, and ϵ is the background systematic uncertainty. Our results are given in Table 3 for the three BPs. We show the numbers for an ideal case with zero systematics and also for a more realistic case with 1% systematics, i.e. with $\epsilon = 0.01$ (in parentheses). The results are significantly weakened in the latter case because of the relatively large background compared to the signal.

From Table 3, we see that the significance enhances as we go to lower DM mass regions, as expected because of kinematic reasons. Operator-wise we see that TAT and VA-type operators perform better than the SP-type. We also find substantial (around 50%) increase in significance on application of optimal beam polarization.

Going beyond the three BPs, we now vary the DM mass and calculate the signal significance following the same cut-based analysis procedure outlined above. Our results for the 3σ sensitivity contours in the (m_χ, Λ) plane are shown in Figure 2 for all the operator types. The solid (dashed) contours are for the unpolarized (optimally

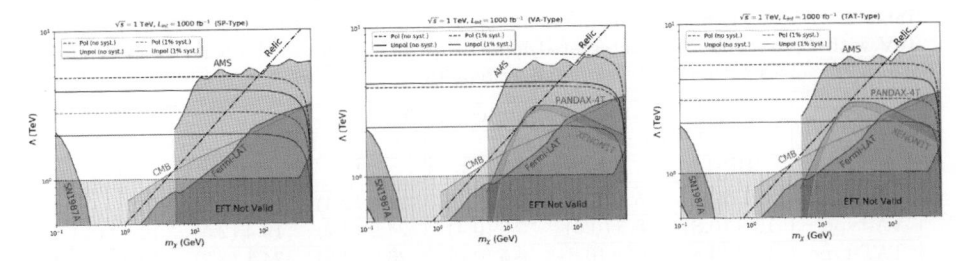

Fig. 2. 3σ sensitivity contours in the mono-photon channel for the SP (left), VA (middle) and TAT (right)-type operators with *unpolarized* (solid lines) and *polarized* (dashed lines) e^+e^- beams at $\sqrt{s} = 1$ TeV center-of-mass energy and with $\mathcal{L}_{\text{int}} = 1000$ fb^{-1} integrated luminosity. The blue (green) contours are assuming zero (1%) background systematics. The various shaded regions are excluded by direct detection (XENON1T, PANDAX-4T), indirect detection (Fermi-LAT, AMS), astrophysics (SN1987A) and cosmology (CMB) constraints. In the shaded region below $\Lambda = \max\{\sqrt{s}/2, 3m_\chi\}$, our EFT framework is not valid. Along the dot-dashed line, the observed DM relic density is reproduced for a thermal DM assuming only DM-electron effective coupling.

polarized) case, and the blue (green) contours are assuming zero (1%) background systematics. The shaded regions are excluded by various constraints. First of all, for $\Lambda < \max\{\sqrt{s}/2, 3m_\chi\}$, our EFT framework is not valid (cf. Section 2). This is shown by the navy blue-shaded regions in Figure 2. For $\sqrt{s} = 1$ TeV as considered here, this EFT validity limit supersedes the previous LEP limit.[42]

The same effective operator given in Eq. (1) also gives rise to DM scattering with electrons $\chi e^- \to \chi e^-$. The exact analytic expressions for these cross sections in our EFT framework can be found in Appendix C of Ref.[82] for all the operator types. Comparing these with the experimental upper limits on $\sigma_{\chi e}$ from dedicated direct detection experiments,[32,33] we can derive a *lower* limit on the cut-off scale Λ as a function of the DM mass m_χ. However, the current best limit on $\sigma_{\chi e}$ from XENON1T is at the level of $\mathcal{O}(10^{-39})$ cm^2,[33] which translates into a very weak bound on Λ and is not relevant for our study. Even the future ambitious proposals like DARKSPHERE can only reach up to $\mathcal{O}(10^{-42})$cm^2,[83] still 5 orders of magnitude weaker than that needed to probe a TeV-scale Λ value.

However, more stringent limits can be derived from DM-nucleon scattering searches. Even for an LDM as in our case, DM-nucleon couplings are necessarily induced at loop level from photon exchange between virtual leptons and the quarks. In fact, as shown in Ref.[37], the loop-induced DM-nucleon scattering almost always dominates over the DM-electron scattering. The analytic expressions for the one and two-loop DM-nucleon scattering cross sections can be found in Ref.[37]. We have translated the experimental upper limits from XENON1T[84] and PANDAX-4T[85] onto the (m_χ, Λ) plane, as shown by the yellow and grey-shaded regions respectively in Figure 2. Note that these limits are only applicable for the vector and tensor lepton currents, i.e. $\Gamma_\ell = \gamma_\mu$, $\sigma_{\mu\nu}$ in Eq. (1). For the scalar lepton current, $\Gamma_\ell = 1$, the one-loop DM-nucleon coupling vanishes, and one has to go to two loops which is suppressed by α_{em}^2 for the S-S type coupling and $\alpha_{em}^2 v^2$ (where $v \sim 10^{-3}$ is the DM velocity) for the P-S type coupling. In contrast, for pseudo-scalar and axial-vector lepton currents, i.e. $\Gamma_\ell = \gamma_5, \gamma_\mu \gamma_5$, the DM-nucleon coupling vanishes to all orders. Therefore, we have not shown the XENON1T and PANDAX-4T limits for the SP-type operator on the top left panel of Figure 2.

The same effective operator given in Eq. (1) also enables DM annihilation into electrons $\chi\bar{\chi} \to e^+ e^-$. The exact analytic expressions for these cross sections in our EFT framework can be found in Appendix C of Ref.[82] for all the operator types. Using these, we calculate the thermal-averaged cross section times relative velocity $\langle \sigma v \rangle$ which goes as m_χ^2/Λ^4 and compare it with the existing indirect detection upper limits on $\langle \sigma v \rangle$ in the $e^+ e^-$ channel to put a lower bound on Λ as a function of the DM mass. This is shown in Figure 2 by the red and brown-shaded regions respectively for the Fermi-LAT[86] and AMS-02[53] constraints on $\langle \sigma v \rangle$. Similar constraints on $\langle \sigma v \rangle$ can be derived using CMB anisotropies,[86] which is shown by the cyan-shaded region in Figure 2, assuming an s-wave annihilation (for p-wave annihilation, the CMB bound will be much weaker).

Along the dot-dashed line in Figure 2, the observed relic density can be reproduced for a DM. In principle, the region to the left and above of this line is disfavored for a thermal DM, because in this region $\langle \sigma v \rangle$ is smaller than the observed value of $\sim (2-5) \times 10^{-26} \text{cm}^3 \text{sec}^{-1}$ (depending on the DM mass[87]), which leads to an overabundance of DM, since $\Omega_\chi h^2 \propto 1/\langle \sigma v \rangle$. However, this problem can be circumvented by either opening up additional leptonic annihilation channels (like $\mu^+ \mu^-$, $\tau^+ \tau^-$ and $\nu \bar{\nu}$) or even going beyond the DM paradigm and invoking e.g., the freeze-in mechanism.[88] This will not affect our main results, since the collider phenomenology discussed here only depends on the DM coupling to electrons.

Also shown in Figure 2 is the supernova constraint, which excludes the magenta-shaded region from consideration of energy-loss and optical depth criteria from the observation of SN1987A.[82] Here we have used an average supernova core temperature of 30 MeV. Note that the supernova bound is only applicable for DM mass below ~ 200 MeV or so, and for a certain range of Λ values, above which the DM particles cannot be efficiently produced in the supernova core, and below which they will no longer free-stream.

From Figure 2, we find that in spite of a large irreducible background, the accessible range of the cut-off scale Λ at $\sqrt{s} = 1$ TeV ILC looks quite promising in the mono-photon channel, especially for low mass DM, where the collider sensitivity is almost flat, whereas the existing direct and indirect detection constraints are much weaker. This complementarity makes the collider searches for DM very promising. With unpolarized beams, the 3σ-reach for the SP-type operator can be up to 3.9 TeV, while for the VA and TAT-type operators, it can be up to 4.2 TeV. With optimally polarized beams, i.e. with $(+80\%, +30\%)$ for the SP and TAT-types and $(+80\%, -30\%)$ for the VA type, the sensitivity reaches can be extended to 4.8 TeV (SP), 6.5 TeV (VA) and 5.3 TeV (TAT), as shown in Figure 2.

4. Mono-Z channel

In addition to the mono-photon channel discussed in the previous section, another useful channel for LDM search at lepton colliders is the mono-Z channel, where the Z-boson is emitted from one of the initial states. Depending on the subsequent decay of the Z-boson to either leptonic or hadronic final states, we perform a dedicated cut-based signal and background analysis, as discussed below.

4.1. *Leptonic mode*

For the leptonic decay of the Z-boson, we examine the process $e^+e^- \to \chi\bar{\chi}Z(\to \ell^-\ell^+)$. We will only consider $\ell = e, \mu$ for simplicity and use the lepton pair as the visible particles for tagging. The main SM background for this channel is $e^+e^- \to \nu\bar{\nu}\,\ell^+\ell^-$, and it is polarization-dependent.

4.1.1. *Unpolarized and polarized cross-sections*

For the signal and background simulation, we generated the UFO library for our EFT framework using `FeynRules`[76] and then generated events for both signal and background using `MadGraph 5`[89] with the following basic baseline cuts:

$$P_T(\ell) > 10 \text{ GeV}, \quad |\eta_\ell| \leq 2.5, \quad \Delta R_{\ell\ell} \geq 0.4. \tag{7}$$

For the signal, the Z-bosons are decayed into the charged lepton pairs via the `MadSpin`[90,91] package which is implemented in `MadGraph 5`, to take care of the spin-correlation effects of the lepton pairs. A fast detector simulation to these events is done using `Delphes 3`[79] with the same configuration card[80] as in Section 3.1.

With unpolarized beams, we find that the neutrino background cross section at $\sqrt{s} = 1$ TeV is 420.5 fb, whereas the DM signal cross section is much smaller, as shown in Table 4 for a benchmark DM mass of $m_\chi = 100$ GeV and the cut-off scale $\Lambda = 3$ TeV. Similar to the mono-photon case, we also examine the effect of polarization on the signal and background cross-sections, as shown in Table 4. The neutrino background can be reduced to 28% of its original value by making the electron beam $+80\%$ polarized, and further reduced to 21% of its original value by additionally making the positron beam -30% polarized. The $(+80\%, -30\%)$ polarization configuration also enhances the VA-type signal by a factor of 2.4. However, the $(+80\%, +30\%)$ configuration is better for the SP and TAT-type signals. For ease of comparison between different operator types, we choose to work with the $(+80\%, +30\%)$ configuration democratically for all operator types, as well as for the background, unless otherwise specified.

4.1.2. *Cut-based analysis*

We define our signals by those events that pass through the baseline selection criteria as defined below: $P_{T,\ell} > 20$ GeV, $|\eta_\ell| < 2.45$, where the Z-boson is reconstructed

Table 4. Comparison of the leptonic mono-Z background and signal cross-sections for different choices of beam polarization for $m_\chi = 100$ GeV and $\Lambda = 3$ TeV at $\sqrt{s} = 1$ TeV ILC. The numbers in bold highlight the optimal polarization choice for a given operator type.

Process type	Unpolarized cross-section (fb)	Polarization $P(e^-,e^+)$	Polarized cross-section (fb)			
			(+,+)	(+,−)	(−,+)	(−,−)
$\nu\bar{\nu}\ell^-\ell^+$	420	(80, 0)	116	116	723	723
		(80, 20)	135	98	856	590
		(80, 30)	145	88	926	523
SP-Type	0.28	(80, 0)	0.26	0.26	0.25	0.25
		(80, 20)	0.29	0.22	0.21	0.29
		(80, 30)	**0.32**	0.19	0.19	0.32
VA-Type	0.08	(80, 0)	0.15	0.15	0.02	0.02
		(80, 20)	0.12	0.18	0.01	0.02
		(80, 30)	0.11	**0.19**	0.01	0.02
TAT-Type	0.68	(80, 0)	0.62	0.62	0.62	0.62
		(80, 20)	0.72	0.52	0.52	0.72
		(80, 30)	**0.77**	0.47	0.47	0.77

by the condition that all final state lepton-pairs are oppositely charged and of same flavor (OSSF). Other selection criteria are dynamic with respect to different BPs. We have taken the same three BPs as in the mono-photon case to probe different regions of the parameter space, namely, BP1 essentially represents all light DM region, BP3 represents the region close to the kinematic limit of $\sqrt{s}/2 - m_Z$, whereas BP2 captures the intermediate DM mass region.

After implementing the baseline selection cuts, we find that the background is reduced to about 40% of its original value in Table 4 for the unpolarized (polarized) case, whereas the signals are reduced to about 60%-70% of their original values. We then consider various kinematic distributions for the signal and background, and devise some specialized selection cuts.[1] We find that after applying all these cuts, we can still retain about 35%-45% of the signal, whereas the background is reduced to below percent level of the original values given in Table 4.

4.1.3. Results

After implementing all these cuts, we calculate the final signal significance for the three BPs using Eq. (6). Our results are given in Table 5 for an integrated luminosity of $\mathcal{L}_{\text{int}} = 1000$ fb^{-1}. We see that as we go higher up in the DM mass the signal significance drops. We also find that the best-performing operator type is the TAT-type, for which more than 97% of the background events are removed after all the selection cuts. For the signal we retain 58% − 61% of the events, although for BP3 only 48% remains. The SP-type operator also gives good results, where we retain 50% − 66% of the signal across BPs and polarization choices, while removing more than 96% of the background events. Even for VA-type we retain more than 50% of the signal events and are able to cut down the background event yields to 11%. We also notice the positive effect of the beam polarization by which we achieve an enhancement of signal significance by more than 2 times compared to the ones with

Table 5. Signal significance in the mono-Z leptonic channel at $\sqrt{s} = 1$ TeV and $\mathcal{L}_{\text{int}} = 1000\,\text{fb}^{-1}$. The values in the parenthesis correspond to 1% background systematic uncertainty.

Operator type	Signal significance for $\mathcal{L}_{\text{int}} = 1000\,\text{fb}^{-1}$					
	Unpolarized beams			Polarized beams		
	BP-1	BP-2	BP-3	BP-1	BP-2	BP-3
SP-type	1.7 (1.3)	0.7 (0.5)	0.1 (0.1)	3.8 (3.6)	1.7 (1.5)	0.3 (0.3)
VA-type	0.2 (0.1)	0.1 (0.1)	0.1 (0.1)	0.5 (0.4)	0.4 (0.3)	0.2 (0.2)
TAT-type	4.5 (3.9)	2.4 (1.9)	0.6 (0.5)	9.4 (9.1)	5.4 (5.1)	1.3 (1.3)

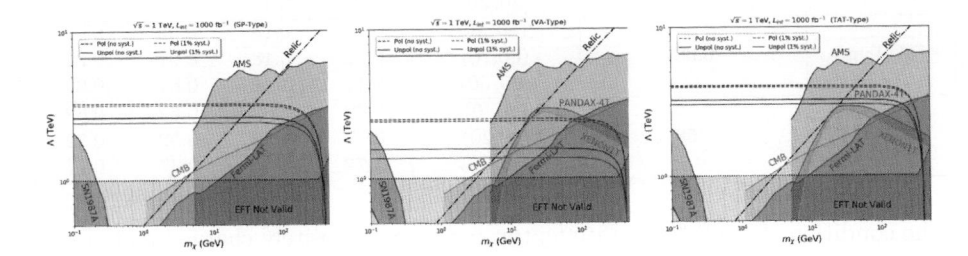

Fig. 3. 3σ sensitivity contours in the mono-Z leptonic channel. Labels are same as in Figure 2.

unpolarized beams. For VA-type though the significance can be further increased for the polarized beam case by choosing the left-handed positron beams as is evident from Table 4.

Going beyond the three BPs, we now vary the DM mass and present the 3σ sensitivity reach for this channel in Figure 3 for all the operators. The labels and shaded regions are the same as in the mono-photon case (cf. Figure 2). We see that the accessible range of the cut-off scale Λ for the unpolarized beams can reach up to 3.2 TeV for the TAT-type operator, whereas for the SP and VA-type, it can reach up to 2.6 TeV and 1.6 TeV respectively. But with the application of optimally polarized beams as discussed earlier, we see an increase by about 25% of the 3σ reach on the Λ scale, up to 3.2 TeV, 2.5 TeV and 4 TeV for the for SP, VA and TAT-type operators, respectively.

4.2. Hadronic mode

Next we study $e^+e^- \to \chi\bar{\chi}Z(\to jj)$, where $j \equiv u, d, c, s, b$ quarks. The relevant SM background processes for this channel are $e^+e^- \to \nu\bar{\nu}jj$ and $e^+e^- \to jj\ell\nu$ (with one charged lepton escaping the detector) where the jets and leptons in the final state can come from any possible source (not necessarily from an on-shell Z).

4.2.1. Unpolarized and polarized cross-sections

We use the same UFO library as before which is implemented using `FeynRules`[76] and simulate the events for the signal and backgrounds via `MadGraph 5`[89] with the

Table 6. Comparison of the hadronic mono-Z background and signal cross-sections for different choices of beam polarization with $m_\chi = 100$ GeV and $\Lambda = 3$ TeV at $\sqrt{s} = 1$ TeV ILC. The numbers in bold highlight the optimal polarization choice for a given operator type.

Process type	Unpolarized cross-section (fb)	Pol. $P(e^-, e^+)$	Polarized cross-section (fb)			
			$(+,+)$	$(+,-)$	$(-,+)$	$(-,-)$
$\nu\bar{\nu}jj$	798	(80, 0)	178	178	1415	1415
		(80, 20)	206	151	1689	1134
		(80, 30)	219	136	1833	989
$jj\ell\nu$	1186	(80, 0)	302	302	2061	2061
		(80, 20)	359	246	2446	1685
		(80, 30)	386	216	2635	1492
SP-Type	2.78	(80, 0)	2.57	2.57	2.58	2.58
		(80, 20)	2.98	2.15	2.15	2.97
		(80, 30)	**3.17**	1.95	1.95	3.17
VA-Type	0.83	(80, 0)	1.35	1.35	0.15	0.15
		(80, 20)	1.07	1.61	0.12	0.18
		(80, 30)	0.94	**1.76**	0.10	0.19
TAT-Type	6.77	(80, 0)	6.22	6.22	6.21	6.21
		(80, 20)	7.23	5.23	5.24	7.21
		(80, 30)	**7.72**	4.73	4.73	7.69

following basic cuts to the parameter space:

$$P_T(j, \ell) > 10 \text{ GeV}, \quad |\eta_j| \leq 3.0, \quad |\eta_\ell| \leq 2.5, \quad \Delta R_{jj,\ell j} \geq 0.4. \qquad (8)$$

For the signals, as in the leptonic case, the on-shell Z-bosons are decayed into the pairs of jets using the MadSpin package,[90,91] implemented in MadGraph 5. Both the signal and background samples are hadronized using Pythia8.2[92] and then the final state jets are reconstructed with with anti-kT[93] clustering algorithm with a minimum P_T of 10 GeV and a cone radius (R) of 0.4 using the FastJet[94] package. The fast detector simulation to these events are done using Delphes 3[79] with the same configuration card[80] as discussed in Section 3.1.

With unpolarized beams, we find the neutrino-pair background is 798 fb, whereas the $jj\ell\nu$ background is 1186 fb. On the other hand, the DM signal is only at a few fb level, as shown in Table 6 for a benchmark DM mass of $m_\chi = 100$ GeV and the cut-off scale $\Lambda = 3$ TeV. We then examine different choices of beam-polarization on both the event samples for this channel, as shown in Table 6. We find that both backgrounds are polarization-dependent and fall off significantly for right-handed electron beam and with increasing degree of polarization. We choose the polarization configuration $P(e^-, e^+) = (+80\%, +30\%)$ democratically over all the operator types.

4.2.2. Cut-based analysis

After obtaining the signal and background cross-sections as reported in Table 6, we proceed with our cut-based analysis to optimize the signal significance. We select the events that contain at least two jets with the following transverse momentum and pseudorapidity requirements: $P_{T,j} > 20$ GeV, $|\eta_j| < 2.45$. The hardest two jets

Table 7. Signal significances of the mono-Z hadronic channel at $\sqrt{s} = 1$ TeV and $\mathcal{L}_{\text{int}} = 1000$ fb^{-1}. The values in the parenthesis denote the significance with a 1% background systematic uncertainty.

Operator types	Signal significance for $\mathcal{L}_{\text{int}} = 1000\,\text{fb}^{-1}$					
	Unpolarized beams			Polarized Beam		
	BP-1	BP-2	BP-3	BP-1	BP-2	BP-3
SP-type	4.7 (3.3)	1.5 (1.0)	0.3 (0.2)	10.3 (9.1)	3.6 (3.1)	0.8 (0.6)
VA-type	0.4 (0.2)	0.3 (0.1)	0.1 (0.1)	0.2 (0.1)	0.1 (0.1)	0.1 (0.04)
TAT-type	14.2 (10.4)	5.8 (3.7)	1.2 (0.7)	27.7 (25.6)	12.9 (11.1)	2.8 (2.3)

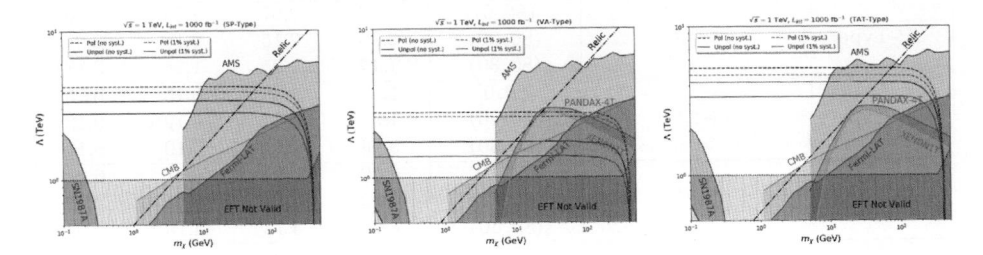

Fig. 4. 3σ sensitivity contours in the mono-Z hadronic channel. Labels are same as in Figure 2.

are required to reconstruct the Z-boson. Further selection cuts are applied some of which depend on the DM mass. So, as in the leptonic channel, we have taken the same three BPs with varying DM mass and impose dynamic cuts.[1]

4.2.3. *Results*

The signal significances calculated using Eq. (6) are tabulated in Table 7. We see similar behavior for the different BPs as in the previously discussed channels, i.e. enhanced signal significance with decreasing mass of the DM. The selection cuts are most efficient for SP- and TAT-type operators. For BP-1 we remove more than 98% of the background events while keeping at least 21% of the signal events for the two operator types, yielding a large signal significance especially for the TAT-type operator with polarized beams.

Varying the DM mass, we display the 3σ sensitivity contours for all three operators in Figure 4. It is clear that the TAT-type operator has the best sensitivity, which reaches up to 4.2 TeV with unpolarized beams and 5.2 TeV with optimally polarized beams. The SP-type operator also has a sensitivity comparable to the mono-photon channel, and can reach up to 3.4 (4.2) TeV with unpolarized (polarized) beams. The VA-type operator has a modest sensitivity in this channel, only up to 1.7 (2.7) TeV with unpolarized (polarized) beams.

5. Conclusion

We have explored the physics potential of the future e^+e^- colliders in probing such *leptophilic* DM in a model-independent way. As a case study, we have taken the

Table 8. Summary of our results for the 3σ sensitivity reach of the cut-off scale Λ in the three different channels discussed in the text. Here we have fixed the DM mass at 1 GeV. The numbers in parentheses are with 1% background systematics. The numbers in bold show the highest Λ value that can be probed for a given operator.

Process type	Beam configuration	3σ sensitivity reach of Λ (TeV)		
		SP	VA	TAT
Mono-γ	Unpolarized	3.91 (1.99)	4.19 (2.14)	4.25 (2.17)
	Polarized	**4.84** (2.81)	**6.49** (**3.94**)	**5.28** (3.08)
Mono-Z leptonic	Unpolarized	2.62 (2.42)	1.57 (1.36)	3.22 (3.00)
	Polarized	3.24 (3.16)	2.47 (2.39)	4.02 (3.93)
Mono-Z hadronic	Unpolarized	3.38 (2.79)	1.74 (1.39)	4.22 (3.38)
	Polarized	4.21 (**3.87**)	2.75 (2.57)	5.25 (**4.71**)

$\sqrt{s} = 1$ TeV ILC with an integrated luminosity of 1000 fb^{-1} and have analyzed the pair-production of fermionic DM using leptophilic dimension-6 operators of all possible bilinear structures, namely, scalar-pseudoscalar, vector-axialvector and tensor-axialtensor. We have performed a detailed cut-based analysis for each of these operators in three different channels based on the tagged particle, namely, mono-photon, mono-Z leptonic and hadronic.

We have taken into account one of the most important and powerful features of lepton colliders, i.e., the possibility of beam-polarization with different degrees of polarization and helicity orientations. We find that the sign$(P(e^-), P(e^+)) = (+, +)$ beam configuration is optimal for the SP and TAT-type operators, while the $(+, -)$ configuration is better for probing the VA-type operators. The maximum value of the cut-off scale Λ that can be probed in each channel at 3σ is given in Table 8. We find that without any systematics, the mono-photon channel provides the best sensitivity across all operator types, while in presence of background systematic effects, the mono-Z hadronic channel provides better sensitivity for the SP and TAT-type operators.

We also demonstrate the complementarity of our lepton collider study with other existing direct and indirect detection searches for LDM (cf. Figures 2, 3 and 4). In particular, we show that lepton colliders will be able to provide the best-ever sensitivity in the still unexplored light DM regime.

Acknowledgments

The work of BD is supported in part by the US Department of Energy under Grant No. DE-SC0017987 and by a Fermilab Intensity Frontier Fellowship.

References

1. S. Kundu, A. Guha, P. K. Das and P. S. B. Dev, A model-independent analysis of leptophilic dark matter at future electron-positron colliders in the mono-photon and mono-Z channels (10 2021).
2. L. M. Krauss, S. Nasri and M. Trodden, A Model for neutrino masses and dark matter, *Phys. Rev. D* **67**, p. 085002 (2003).

3. E. A. Baltz and L. Bergstrom, Detection of leptonic dark matter, *Phys. Rev. D* **67**, p. 043516 (2003).
4. E. Ma, Verifiable radiative seesaw mechanism of neutrino mass and dark matter, *Phys. Rev. D* **73**, p. 077301 (2006).
5. T. Hambye, K. Kannike, E. Ma and M. Raidal, Emanations of Dark Matter: Muon Anomalous Magnetic Moment, Radiative Neutrino Mass, and Novel Leptogenesis at the TeV Scale, *Phys. Rev. D* **75**, p. 095003 (2007).
6. R. Bernabei et al., Investigating electron interacting dark matter, *Phys. Rev. D* **77**, p. 023506 (2008).
7. M. Cirelli, M. Kadastik, M. Raidal and A. Strumia, Model-independent implications of the e+-, anti-proton cosmic ray spectra on properties of Dark Matter, *Nucl. Phys. B* **813**, 1 (2009), [Addendum: Nucl.Phys.B 873, 530–533 (2013)].
8. C.-R. Chen and F. Takahashi, Cosmic rays from Leptonic Dark Matter, *JCAP* **02**, p. 004 (2009).
9. X.-J. Bi, P.-H. Gu, T. Li and X. Zhang, ATIC and PAMELA Results on Cosmic e+- Excesses and Neutrino Masses, *JHEP* **04**, p. 103 (2009).
10. A. Ibarra, A. Ringwald, D. Tran and C. Weniger, Cosmic Rays from Leptophilic Dark Matter Decay via Kinetic Mixing, *JCAP* **08**, p. 017 (2009).
11. P. S. B. Dev, D. K. Ghosh, N. Okada and I. Saha, Neutrino Mass and Dark Matter in light of recent AMS-02 results, *Phys. Rev. D* **89**, p. 095001 (2014).
12. S. Chang, R. Edezhath, J. Hutchinson and M. Luty, Leptophilic Effective WIMPs, *Phys. Rev. D* **90**, p. 015011 (2014).
13. P. Agrawal, Z. Chacko and C. B. Verhaaren, Leptophilic Dark Matter and the Anomalous Magnetic Moment of the Muon, *JHEP* **08**, p. 147 (2014).
14. N. F. Bell, Y. Cai, R. K. Leane and A. D. Medina, Leptophilic dark matter with Z' interactions, *Phys. Rev. D* **90**, p. 035027 (2014).
15. A. Freitas and S. Westhoff, Leptophilic Dark Matter in Lepton Interactions at LEP and ILC, *JHEP* **10**, p. 116 (2014).
16. Q.-H. Cao, C.-R. Chen and T. Gong, Leptophilic dark matter confronts AMS-02 cosmic-ray positron flux, *Chin. J. Phys.* **55**, 10 (2017).
17. B.-Q. Lu and H.-S. Zong, Leptophilic dark matter in Galactic Center excess, *Phys. Rev. D* **93**, p. 083504 (2016), [Addendum: Phys.Rev.D 93, 089910 (2016)].
18. G. H. Duan, L. Feng, F. Wang, L. Wu, J. M. Yang and R. Zheng, Simplified TeV leptophilic dark matter in light of DAMPE data, *JHEP* **02**, p. 107 (2018).
19. E. Madge and P. Schwaller, Leptophilic dark matter from gauged lepton number: Phenomenology and gravitational wave signatures, *JHEP* **02**, p. 048 (2019).
20. S. Junius, L. Lopez-Honorez and A. Mariotti, A feeble window on leptophilic dark matter, *JHEP* **07**, p. 136 (2019).
21. S. Ghosh, A. Dutta Banik, E. J. Chun and D. Majumdar, Leptophilic-portal Dark Matter in the Light of AMS-02 positron excess (3 2020).
22. S. Chakraborti and R. Islam, Implications of dark sector mixing on leptophilic scalar dark matter, *JHEP* **03**, p. 032 (2021).
23. S.-I. Horigome, T. Katayose, S. Matsumoto and I. Saha, Leptophilic fermion WIMP: Role of future lepton colliders, *Phys. Rev. D* **104**, p. 055001 (2021).
24. B. Abi et al., Measurement of the Positive Muon Anomalous Magnetic Moment to 0.46 ppm, *Phys. Rev. Lett.* **126**, p. 141801 (2021).
25. R. Bernabei et al., The DAMA project: Achievements, implications and perspectives, *Prog. Part. Nucl. Phys.* **114**, p. 103810 (2020).
26. S. Abdollahi et al., Cosmic-ray electron-positron spectrum from 7 GeV to 2 TeV with the Fermi Large Area Telescope, *Phys. Rev. D* **95**, p. 082007 (2017).

27. G. Ambrosi et al., Direct detection of a break in the teraelectronvolt cosmic-ray spectrum of electrons and positrons, *Nature* **552**, 63 (2017).
28. O. Adriani et al., Extended Measurement of the Cosmic-Ray Electron and Positron Spectrum from 11 GeV to 4.8 TeV with the Calorimetric Electron Telescope on the International Space Station, *Phys. Rev. Lett.* **120**, p. 261102 (2018).
29. M. Aguilar et al., The Alpha Magnetic Spectrometer (AMS) on the international space station: Part II — Results from the first seven years, *Phys. Rept.* **894**, 1 (2021).
30. M. Ajello et al., Fermi-LAT Observations of High-Energy γ-Ray Emission Toward the Galactic Center, *Astrophys. J.* **819**, p. 44 (2016).
31. E. Aprile et al., Excess electronic recoil events in XENON1T, *Phys. Rev. D* **102**, p. 072004 (2020).
32. E. Aprile et al., Exclusion of Leptophilic Dark Matter Models using XENON100 Electronic Recoil Data, *Science* **349**, 851 (2015).
33. E. Aprile et al., Light Dark Matter Search with Ionization Signals in XENON1T, *Phys. Rev. Lett.* **123**, p. 251801 (2019).
34. D. S. Akerib et al., Projected sensitivities of the LUX-ZEPLIN (LZ) experiment to new physics via low-energy electron recoils (2 2021).
35. C.-Y. Chen, J. Kozaczuk and Y.-M. Zhong, Exploring leptophilic dark matter with NA64-μ, *JHEP* **10**, p. 154 (2018).
36. L. Marsicano, M. Battaglieri, A. Celentano, R. De Vita and Y.-M. Zhong, Probing Leptophilic Dark Sectors at Electron Beam-Dump Facilities, *Phys. Rev. D* **98**, p. 115022 (2018).
37. J. Kopp, V. Niro, T. Schwetz and J. Zupan, DAMA/LIBRA and leptonically interacting Dark Matter, *Phys. Rev. D* **80**, p. 083502 (2009).
38. M. Beltran, D. Hooper, E. W. Kolb, Z. A. C. Krusberg and T. M. P. Tait, Maverick dark matter at colliders, *JHEP* **09**, p. 037 (2010).
39. J. Goodman, M. Ibe, A. Rajaraman, W. Shepherd, T. M. P. Tait and H.-B. Yu, Constraints on Light Majorana dark Matter from Colliders, *Phys. Lett. B* **695**, 185 (2011).
40. Y. Bai, P. J. Fox and R. Harnik, The Tevatron at the Frontier of Dark Matter Direct Detection, *JHEP* **12**, p. 048 (2010).
41. J. Goodman, M. Ibe, A. Rajaraman, W. Shepherd, T. M. P. Tait and H.-B. Yu, Constraints on Dark Matter from Colliders, *Phys. Rev. D* **82**, p. 116010 (2010).
42. P. J. Fox, R. Harnik, J. Kopp and Y. Tsai, LEP Shines Light on Dark Matter, *Phys. Rev. D* **84**, p. 014028 (2011).
43. P. J. Fox, R. Harnik, J. Kopp and Y. Tsai, Missing Energy Signatures of Dark Matter at the LHC, *Phys. Rev. D* **85**, p. 056011 (2012).
44. A. Rajaraman, W. Shepherd, T. M. P. Tait and A. M. Wijangco, LHC Bounds on Interactions of Dark Matter, *Phys. Rev. D* **84**, p. 095013 (2011).
45. Y. J. Chae and M. Perelstein, Dark Matter Search at a Linear Collider: Effective Operator Approach, *JHEP* **05**, p. 138 (2013).
46. F. Kahlhoefer, Review of LHC Dark Matter Searches, *Int. J. Mod. Phys. A* **32**, p. 1730006 (2017).
47. B. Penning, The pursuit of dark matter at colliders—an overview, *J. Phys. G* **45**, p. 063001 (2018).
48. V. Khachatryan et al., Search for dark matter, extra dimensions, and unparticles in monojet events in proton–proton collisions at $\sqrt{s} = 8$ TeV, *Eur. Phys. J. C* **75**, p. 235 (2015).
49. G. Aad et al., Search for new phenomena in final states with an energetic jet and large missing transverse momentum in pp collisions at $\sqrt{s} =8$ TeV with the ATLAS detector, *Eur. Phys. J. C* **75**, p. 299 (2015), [Erratum: Eur. Phys. J. C 75, 408 (2015)].

50. A. M. Sirunyan *et al.*, Search for new physics in final states with an energetic jet or a hadronically decaying W or Z boson and transverse momentum imbalance at $\sqrt{s}$ = 13 TeV, *Phys. Rev. D* **97**, p. 092005 (2018).
51. G. Aad *et al.*, Search for new phenomena in events with an energetic jet and missing transverse momentum in pp collisions at $\sqrt{s}$ =13 TeV with the ATLAS detector, *Phys. Rev. D* **103**, p. 112006 (2021).
52. L. A. Cavasonza, H. Gast, M. Krämer, M. Pellen and S. Schael, Constraints on leptophilic dark matter from the AMS-02 experiment, *Astrophys. J.* **839**, p. 36 (2017), [Erratum: Astrophys.J. 869, 89 (2018)].
53. I. John and T. Linden, Cosmic-Ray Positrons Strongly Constrain Leptophilic Dark Matter (7 2021).
54. J. Abdallah *et al.*, Photon events with missing energy in e+ e- collisions at s**(1/2) = 130-GeV to 209-GeV, *Eur. Phys. J. C* **38**, 395 (2005).
55. A. Birkedal, K. Matchev and M. Perelstein, Dark matter at colliders: A Model independent approach, *Phys. Rev. D* **70**, p. 077701 (2004).
56. P. J. Fox and E. Poppitz, Leptophilic Dark Matter, *Phys. Rev. D* **79**, p. 083528 (2009).
57. P. Konar, K. Kong, K. T. Matchev and M. Perelstein, Shedding Light on the Dark Sector with Direct WIMP Production, *New J. Phys.* **11**, p. 105004 (2009).
58. C. Bartels, M. Berggren and J. List, Characterising WIMPs at a future e^+e^- Linear Collider, *Eur. Phys. J. C* **72**, p. 2213 (2012).
59. H. Dreiner, M. Huck, M. Krämer, D. Schmeier and J. Tattersall, Illuminating Dark Matter at the ILC, *Phys. Rev. D* **87**, p. 075015 (2013).
60. Z. Liu, Y.-H. Xu and Y. Zhang, Probing dark matter particles at CEPC, *JHEP* **06**, p. 009 (2019).
61. M. Habermehl, M. Berggren and J. List, WIMP Dark Matter at the International Linear Collider, *Phys. Rev. D* **101**, p. 075053 (2020).
62. J. Kalinowski, W. Kotlarski, K. Mekala, P. Sopicki and A. F. Zarnecki, Sensitivity of future e^+e^- colliders to processes of dark matter production with light mediator exchange (7 2021).
63. B. Barman, S. Bhattacharya, S. Girmohanta and S. Jahedi, Catch 'em all: Effective Leptophilic WIMPs at the e^+e^- Collider (9 2021).
64. N. Wan, M. Song, G. Li, W.-G. Ma, R.-Y. Zhang and J.-Y. Guo, Searching for dark matter via mono-Z boson production at the ILC, *Eur. Phys. J. C* **74**, p. 3219 (2014).
65. Z.-H. Yu, X.-J. Bi, Q.-S. Yan and P.-F. Yin, Dark matter searches in the mono-Z channel at high energy e^+e^- colliders, *Phys. Rev. D* **90**, p. 055010 (2014).
66. S. Dutta, D. Sachdeva and B. Rawat, Signals of Leptophilic Dark Matter at the ILC, *Eur. Phys. J. C* **77**, p. 639 (2017).
67. B. Grzadkowski, M. Iglicki, K. Mekala and A. F. Zarnecki, Dark-matter-spin effects at future e^+e^- colliders, *JHEP* **08**, p. 052 (2020).
68. P. Bambade *et al.*, The International Linear Collider: A Global Project (3 2019).
69. M. J. Boland *et al.*, Updated baseline for a staged Compact Linear Collider (8 2016).
70. M. Dong *et al.*, CEPC Conceptual Design Report: Volume 2 - Physics & Detector (11 2018).
71. A. Abada *et al.*, FCC-ee: The Lepton Collider: Future Circular Collider Conceptual Design Report Volume 2, *Eur. Phys. J. ST* **228**, 261 (2019).
72. T. Barklow, J. Brau, K. Fujii, J. Gao, J. List, N. Walker and K. Yokoya, ILC Operating Scenarios (6 2015).
73. J. P. Delahaye, M. Diemoz, K. Long, B. Mansoulié, N. Pastrone, L. Rivkin, D. Schulte, A. Skrinsky and A. Wulzer, Muon Colliders (1 2019).

74. S. Matsumoto, S. Mukhopadhyay and Y.-L. S. Tsai, Effective Theory of WIMP Dark Matter supplemented by Simplified Models: Singlet-like Majorana fermion case, *Phys. Rev. D* **94**, p. 065034 (2016).
75. A. Belyaev, N. D. Christensen and A. Pukhov, CalcHEP 3.4 for collider physics within and beyond the Standard Model, *Comput. Phys. Commun.* **184**, 1729 (2013).
76. A. Alloul, N. D. Christensen, C. Degrande, C. Duhr and B. Fuks, FeynRules 2.0 - A complete toolbox for tree-level phenomenology, *Comput. Phys. Commun.* **185**, 2250 (2014).
77. W. Kilian, T. Ohl and J. Reuter, WHIZARD: Simulating Multi-Particle Processes at LHC and ILC, *Eur. Phys. J. C* **71**, p. 1742 (2011).
78. H. Abramowicz *et al.*, The International Linear Collider Technical Design Report - Volume 4: Detectors (6 2013).
79. J. de Favereau, C. Delaere, P. Demin, A. Giammanco, V. Lemaître, A. Mertens and M. Selvaggi, DELPHES 3, A modular framework for fast simulation of a generic collider experiment, *JHEP* **02**, p. 057 (2014).
80. C. T. Potter, DSiD: a Delphes Detector for ILC Physics Studies (2 2016).
81. H. Abramowicz *et al.*, Forward Instrumentation for ILC Detectors, *JINST* **5**, p. P12002 (2010).
82. A. Guha, P. S. B. Dev and P. K. Das, Model-independent Astrophysical Constraints on Leptophilic Dark Matter in the Framework of Tsallis Statistics, *JCAP* **02**, p. 032 (2019).
83. L. Hamaide and C. McCabe, Fuelling the search for light dark matter-electron scattering (10 2021).
84. E. Aprile *et al.*, Dark Matter Search Results from a One Ton-Year Exposure of XENON1T, *Phys. Rev. Lett.* **121**, p. 111302 (2018).
85. Y. Meng *et al.*, Dark Matter Search Results from the PandaX-4T Commissioning Run (7 2021).
86. R. K. Leane, T. R. Slatyer, J. F. Beacom and K. C. Y. Ng, GeV-scale thermal WIMPs: Not even slightly ruled out, *Phys. Rev. D* **98**, p. 023016 (2018).
87. G. Steigman, B. Dasgupta and J. F. Beacom, Precise Relic WIMP Abundance and its Impact on Searches for Dark Matter Annihilation, *Phys. Rev. D* **86**, p. 023506 (2012).
88. L. J. Hall, K. Jedamzik, J. March-Russell and S. M. West, Freeze-In Production of FIMP Dark Matter, *JHEP* **03**, p. 080 (2010).
89. J. Alwall, R. Frederix, S. Frixione, V. Hirschi, F. Maltoni, O. Mattelaer, H. S. Shao, T. Stelzer, P. Torrielli and M. Zaro, The automated computation of tree-level and next-to-leading order differential cross sections, and their matching to parton shower simulations, *JHEP* **07**, p. 079 (2014).
90. S. Frixione, E. Laenen, P. Motylinski and B. R. Webber, Angular correlations of lepton pairs from vector boson and top quark decays in Monte Carlo simulations, *JHEP* **04**, p. 081 (2007).
91. P. Artoisenet, R. Frederix, O. Mattelaer and R. Rietkerk, Automatic spin-entangled decays of heavy resonances in Monte Carlo simulations, *JHEP* **03**, p. 015 (2013).
92. T. Sjöstrand, S. Ask, J. R. Christiansen, R. Corke, N. Desai, P. Ilten, S. Mrenna, S. Prestel, C. O. Rasmussen and P. Z. Skands, An introduction to PYTHIA 8.2, *Comput. Phys. Commun.* **191**, 159 (2015).
93. M. Cacciari, G. P. Salam and G. Soyez, The anti-k_t jet clustering algorithm, *JHEP* **04**, p. 063 (2008).
94. M. Cacciari, G. P. Salam and G. Soyez, FastJet User Manual, *Eur. Phys. J. C* **72**, p. 1896 (2012).

DM6 session: Dark matter and rare processes
– Short summary –

Conveners: R. Bernabei[a] and Z. Berezhiani[b]

[a] Dipartimento di Fisica, Universitá di Roma Tor Vergata, 00133 Rome, Italy
INFN sezione di Roma Tor Vergata, 00133 Rome, Italy
E-mail: rita.bernabei@roma2.infn.it

[b] Dipartimento di Fisica e Chimica, Universitá di L'Aquila, 67100 Coppito, AQ, Italy
INFN, Laboratori Nazionali del Gran Sasso, 67010 Assergi, AQ, Italy
E-mail: zurab.berezhiani@lngs.infn.it

Keywords: Dark matter; direct detection; rare processes.

This session has been dedicated to several topics of Dark Matter (DM) and Rare Processes (RP) field. Some talks have review character while others present some specific experimental results and developments. Mainly the contributions refer to Dark Matter (DM) topics while the last contribution discusses a specific rare process.

The first talk presented by M. Ricci (INFN-LNF) discusses the indirect signatures of DM from Space Satellite missions. Among the indirect searches for DM (complementary to the direct ones), the speaker has reviewed the possibilities of observing the DM signatures in the Cosmic Rays and in the gamma-ray sector, considering space missions like PAMELA, AMS, FERMI, DAMPE and the planned projects like GAPS (on stratospheric balloon) and HERD. An exhaustive overview on the current status and on the perspective of this field has been given.

The second talk presented by P. Belli (INFN-Roma Tor Vergata) is instead related to a direct detection on DM present at galactic scale. In fact, P. Belli has presented a detailed overview of the results of DAMA/LIBRA experiment and new results of two additional annual cycles, which further confirm the evidence of a signal that meets all the requirements of the model-independent DM annual modulation signature, at very high C.L.

A. Messina (INFN-Roma La Sapienza) in his talk discussed in details the known impact of the Migdal effect on the DM detection, mainly for candidates with GeV range masses, and pointed to some new ideas how one could measure such an effect with detectors based on Time Projection Chamber exposed to high neutron flux.

Talk by V. Caracciolo, (INFN-Roma Tor Vergata) was focused on the directionality approach which holds for DM candidates inducing just nuclear recoils. This approach is based on the study of the correlation between the nuclear recoils direction and the Earth motion in the galactic rest frame. Several experimental techniques to explore the directionality approach have been proposed. In this talk, a review of such experimental approaches have been addressed with particular regard to the ADAMO project based on the use of anisotropic scintillators.

Talk of A. D'Angelo (INFN-Roma Tor Vergata) described the Heavy Photon Search (HPS) experiment which searches for an electro-produced dark photon using an electron beam provided by the CEBAF accelerator at the Thomas Jefferson National Accelerator Facility. It has been shown in some details that HPS looks for dark photons through two distinct methods, a resonance search in the e+e- invariant mass distribution above the large QED background (large dark photon-SM particles coupling region) and a displaced vertex search for long-lived dark photons (small coupling region). HPS employs a compact spectrometer, matched to the forward kinematic characteristics of A' electro- production. Three data taking periods took place in 2015, 2016 and 2019, while a fourth run has been scheduled in summer 2021. Results from the available data have been presented together with future projects.

The talk by A. Addazi (Sichuan University) has been focused in some details on the investigation in the laboratory and in the sky of the Mirror Dark Matter candidates. In particular, he discussed prospectives of laboratory search of the neutron to mirror neutron oscillations and its astrophysical implications, in particular for the neutron stars.

A. Zhitnitsky (University of British Columbia) discussed the Axion Quark Nugget Dark Matter Model, suggesting possible explanation of Telescope Array anomaly and for the positive dark matter signal of DAMA/LIBRA via the neutrons produced by quark nuggets in the rock. P. Belli has commented that already existing results disfavour such a hypothesis. It seems that other efforts will be pursued on that model.

B. Dev (Washington University in St. Louis) presented a detailed discussion on the possibilities to detect Leptophillic Dark Matter (LDM) at Linear Colliders. Such candidates could naturally arise in many beyond the Standard Model scenarios and might address certain experimental anomalies. Thus, some collider constraints on the LDM effective couplings with the Standard Model sector, considering its production at a future electron-positron linear collider (with polarized and unpolarized beam options) in the mono-photon and mono-Z channels.

Finally, C Curceanu (INFN-LNF) discussed experiment testing quantum mechanics in the Gran Sasso National Laboratories (LNGS): collapse models and spin-statistics. She has reported that they are experimentally investigating possible departures from the standard quantum mechanics' predictions, and - in particular - with radiation detectors they are searching signals predicted by the collapse models (spontaneous emission of radiation) which were proposed to solve the "measurement problem" in quantum physics and signals coming from a possible violation of the Pauli Exclusion Principle. Recent results published in Nature Physics under the title "Underground test of gravity-related wave function collapse", where they ruled out the parameter-free version of the gravity-related collapse model. More generic results on testing Continuous Spontaneous Localization collapse models have been mentioned and future perspectives discussed. Finally, the VIP experiment looking for possible violations of the Pauli Exclusion Principle by searching for forbidden atomic transitions has been discussed.

This session was held in two subsequent afternoons and in both days the talks have been very interesting, the discussions were constructive and proceeded in exciting and serene atmosphere. The merit goes to the speakers and listeners and we give an account here. Finally, we remind that all the presentations are available on Youtube and that in most cases they refer to previously existing publications. Only some of the participants have sent the written contribution; we thank them.

Primordial black holes as dark matter candidates in the Galactic halo

Lindita Hamolli*, Mimoza Hafizi,

*Department of Physics, University of Tirana,
Tirana, 1016, Albania*
E-mail: lindita.hamolli@fshn.edu.al

Francesco De Paolis, Achille A. Nucita

*Department of Mathematics and Physics "Ennio De Giorgi", University of Salento,
Via Arnesano, 73100 Lecce, Italy*

INFN, Sezione di Lecce, Via Arnesano, 73100 Lecce, Italy

Gravitational microlensing is a powerful method to constrain the abundance of massive dark objects in the Milky Way halo. We calculate the optical depth and the microlensing rate for events caused by Primordial Black Holes (PBHs) eventually distributed in the Milky Way halo, towards some selected directions of observation, as the Galactic bulge, the Large and the Small Magellanic Clouds and the M31 galaxy. The capability of the Euclid space telescope to constraint the abundance of PBHs with mass $\geq 10^{-7}$ $M_\odot$ in observation towards the Galactic bulge is also discussed.

Keywords: Primordial black holes; Gravitational microlensing; Galactic halo.

1. Introduction

Primordial black holes (PBHs) are a hypothetical type of black holes that formed soon after the Big Bang. Their existence was proposed in 1966 by Zel'dovich and Novikov[1] and by Stephen Hawking[2] in 1971 who studied in depth their origins. In the early universe, high densities and heterogeneous conditions could have led sufficiently dense regions to undergo gravitational collapse, forming black holes. There are several mechanisms able to produce such inhomogeneities. For all of these, the increased cosmological energy density at early times plays a major role, yielding a rough connection between the PBH mass and the formation time t (see Ref. 3):

$$M_{PBH} \simeq \frac{c^3 t}{G} \simeq 10^{15}\left(\frac{t}{10^{-23}\,s}\right)\,g \simeq 10^5 \left(\frac{t}{1\,s}\right) M_\odot. \tag{1}$$

Hence PBHs could span an enormous mass range: those formed at the Planck time ($10^{-43} s$) would have the Planck mass 10^{-5} g, whereas those formed at $1\,s$ would be as large as 10^5 $M_\odot$, comparable to the mass of the holes thought to reside in galactic nuclei. By contrast, black holes forming at the present epoch (e.g. in the final stages of stellar evolution) could never be smaller than about $1 M_\odot$.

Then, depending on the PBH formation epoch, black holes of different masses can form in the early universe.

However, primordial black holes originally having mass below about $10^{-18}\ M_\odot$ would not have survived to the present due to Hawking radiation, which causes complete evaporation in a time shorter than the age of the Universe.[3] Hawking thought that PBHs would have formed before the electroweak phase transition, which occurred at $t \simeq 10^{-12}$ s. In this case one finds $M_{PHB} \lesssim 10^{-7}\,M_\odot$. However, there is no reason in principle which forbids the formation of PBHs later on. In this case, the PBH mass can rise of orders of magnitude, even up to $\sim 10^5\,M_\odot$ or so. Certainly, only observations might be able to settle this open issue.

PBHs might lead to various interesting astrophysical consequences, such as providing seeds for supermassive black holes in galactic nuclei,[4,5] influence the generation of large-scale structure through Poisson fluctuations[6] and cause important effects on the thermal and ionization history of the Universe.[7] But, perhaps, the most exciting possibility is that they could provide a non-negligible fraction of the dark matter, which is known to constitute about 25% of the critical density of the Universe.[8]

There are some observational conundra that may be explained by PBHs. They are associated with lensing,[9] accretion,[10] dynamical[11] and gravitational wave (GW) effects.[12] Various constraints on their abundance allowed to conclude that PBHs in three ranges of masses could provide the dark matter:[13] the asteroid mass range ($10^{-17} - 10^{-16}\,M_\odot$), the sublunar mass range ($10^{-13} - 10^{-9}\,M_\odot$) and what is sometimes called the intermediate-mass black hole (IMBH) range ($10 - 10^3\,M_\odot$). In general, constraints from these observables have been computed under the assumption that all PBHs have the same mass, assuming a single Dirac delta function. However, an extended (non-monochromatic) mass function, which will correctly combine constraints across all masses, is necessary.

Concerning the mass-fraction f of PBHs in the Galactic halo, the currently available limits are summarized in Fig. 1 of Carr & Kuhnel.[14] The main constraints are derived from PBH evaporation, different gravitational-lensing experiments, numerous dynamical effects and PBH accretion. Even if many different methods have been proposed in the literature for detecting and constraining PBHs (see, e.g. Refs. [8, 15] and references therein)[a], gravitational microlensing offers the most powerful and robust method of constraining PBHs. By the Kepler microlensing observations of Galactic sources[17] a limit in the planetary mass range: $f < 0.3$ for $2 \times 10^{-9} M_\odot < M < 10^{-7} M_\odot$ was found, while the MACHO project established that $f \sim 0.1$ in the $[0.1, 1] M_\odot$ mass range.[18]

Recently, Niikura et al.,[9] using the largest sample of microlensing events for stars in the Galactic bulge (2622 microlensing data) obtained from the 5-years OGLE observation, provided that PBHs constitute about 1% of the DM in the MW. Moreover, from a seven hour lasting observation with the Subaru Hyper Suprime-Cam (HSC) towards the $M31$ galaxy, a single candidate event was identified, which

---

[a]In addition to the methods discussed in that paper we also mention that lensing by fast radio bursts (FRBs) can allow constraining PBHs with mass larger than about $2\,M_\odot$.[16]

translates into a rather stringent upper bounds on the abundance of PBHs in the mass range[19] $[10^{-11} \div 10^{-6}]$ $M_\odot$.

Gravitational microlensing is the best method to detect objects that do not emit light since this phenomenon may occur when a compact object (lens) passes close enough to the line of sight toward a source star.

In the simplest case, when both the lens and the source are considered as the point-object[b], individual images cannot be resolved (the image separation is the order of $\mu arcsec$), but the total brightness of the images increases with respect to that of the unlensed source, leading to a specific time-dependent amplification of the source star brightness, that is

$$A = \frac{2 + u^2}{u\sqrt{4 + u^2}}. \qquad (2)$$

Here, $u(t)$ is the distance, in units of the Einstein radius, between the source star and the lens at an observation epoch t, and is given by

$$u(t) = \sqrt{u_0^2 + \left(\frac{t - t_0}{t_E}\right)^2}, \qquad (3)$$

where t_0 is the peak time of the event (at the time of closest approach) and u_0 is the impact parameter, whereas $t_E = R_E/v_T$ is the Einstein timescale, which is defined as the time required for the lens to transit the Einstein radius. The Einstein radius is the radius of the ring image formed when the observer, lens and source are perfectly aligned. It is given by, $R_E = \sqrt{\frac{4GMD_S}{c^2}x(1-x)}$, where M is the mass of the lens and $x = D_L/D_S$ is the normalized lens distance, whereas D_S and D_L are the source-observer and lens-observer distances, respectively. We also note that v_T is the relative transverse velocity between the lens and the source. During a microlensing event, when the source position projected in the lens plane encounters the Einstein ring, the projected separation is $u_T = 1$ and the source threshold amplification is $A_T = 1.34$ (a microlensing event occurs when the source trajectory crosses the Einstein ring). The event amplification takes the maximum value for the smallest separation between the source and lens, $u = u_0$. By photometric measurements of the event lightcurve, three parameters can be defined: t_0, t_E and u_0. However, among these parameters, only t_E contains information about the lens and this gives rise to the so-called parameter degeneracy problem, which does not allow to infer the lens parameters uniquely. To break this degeneracy, second-order effects, as the finite source effects[21] and the parallax effect,[22] can be considered. Also, it is well known that a gravitational microlensing event gives rise to an astrometric shift of the source,[23] which may be extremely useful to break, at least partially, the parameter degeneracy problem in microlensing observations.[24]

---

[b]In our analysis we also assume that the relative motion among the observer, lens, and source is uniform (with constant velocity) and linear (on a straight line). See the discussion on this issue in Ref. 20 and references therein.

The goal of this work is to trace the PBHs in Galactic halo (if PBHs contribute to the Galactic halo DM) via microlensing observations. For this purpose we selected four directions (Galactic bulge, LMC, SMC and $M31$) and calculate the optical depth and microlensing rate towards them considering a wide range of possible masses for the PBHs. Moreover, we forecast the number of events caused by PBHs and observable by the Euclid telescope. It is a Medium Class mission of the ESA (European Space Agency), scheduled to be launched in 2022 at the L2 Lagrangian point. For it an additional survey is planned towards Galactic bulge, although not definitely approved as yet.[25] The photometric error of Euclid is expected to be less then[26] $\sim 0.1\%$, so the threshold amplification turns out to be $A_T \simeq 1.001$ and from Eq. (2) one can find $u_T \simeq 6.54$.

Until now, several microlensing surveys have been undertaken towards the Galactic bulge (in particular MOA and $OGLE$), $M31$ ($MEGA$,[27] $AGAPE$,[28] $WeCAPP$,[29] $PLAN$[30]) and the Large and the Small Magellanic Clouds (in particular $MACHO$, $EROS$,[31] $SuperMACHO$[32]). However, due to the way these surveys were designed, they were not able to give reliable constraints on PBHs with mass $\lesssim 10^{-6} \ M_\odot$ in the Galactic halo.

The plan of the paper is as follows: in Section 2, we review the models used in our analysis, for PBHs in Galactic halo and for the source stars in the MW bulge, LMC, SMC and M31. In Section 3 we give some basics for microlensing quantities. In Section 4 we present and discuss the results obtained for the optical depth and microlening rate towards four selected targets and Euclid field of view. Finally, our conclusions are drawn in Section 5.

2. MODEL

The microlensing quantities, the optical depth, the microlensing rate and Einstein timescale depend on the underlying astrophysical model. Below we provide some details for the mass density of the halo dark matter in our Galaxy[c] and the distribution of the stellar components in some favorable directions as the MW bulge, LMC, SMC and the $M31$ galaxy.

2.1. *Distribution of dark matter in Galactic halo*

For the DM in the MW halo region we assume the standard halo model (S), which consists of a cored isothermal sphere with dark matter density given by:

$$\rho_{DM}(r) = \rho_0 \frac{r_c^2 + r_0^2}{r_c^2 + r^2}, \qquad (4)$$

---

[c]Since we are interested in microlensing observations with sources in our Galaxy we neglect[30] the presence of dark matter associated to the targets. In the case of the M31 galaxy this choice, of course, will results in a lower limit of the optical depth, microlensing rate and expected number of events.

where r is the galactocentric radius, $\rho_0 \simeq 0.0079\, M_\odot\, pc^{-3}$ is the local dark matter density, $r_c \simeq 5.6$ kpc is the halo dark matter core radius and $r_0 \simeq 8.5$ kpc is the galactocentric distance of the Sun.[33] Considering a scenario in which PBHs constitute some mass-fraction f of the DM, the PBH mass density distribution is $\rho_{PHB}(r) = f\rho_{DM}(r)$.

2.2. Source star distributions

To trace the microlensing events caused by PBHs in Galactic halo we selected some favorable directions for such observations, as the MW bulge, LMC, SMC and the $M31$ galaxy.

2.2.1. Sources in Galactic bulge

For the mass density distribution of the stellar population in the Galactic bulge we use the triaxial bulge model given by

$$\rho_b = \frac{M_b}{8\pi abc} exp\left(-\frac{s^2}{2}\right). \quad (5)$$

Here $s^4 = (x^2/a^2 + y^2/b^2)^2 + z^4/c^4$, the scale length values are $a = 1.49$ kpc, $b = 0.58$ kpc and $c = 0.40$ kpc (we remind that the coordinates x and y span the galactic disk plane, whereas z is perpendicular to it) and the bulge mass is $M_b \approx 2 \times 10^{10}\, M_\odot$.[34]

2.2.2. Sources in the LMC

The source star distribution in the LMC is generally described as a luminous disk and a bar.[35] The distance between the center of the LMC and the observer is $D_{LMC} \simeq 50$ kpc and the stellar disk is modeled with a double exponential profile:

$$\rho_{disk} = \frac{M_d}{4\pi z_d R_d^2} \exp(-R/R_d - |z|/z_d), \quad (6)$$

where $R = \sqrt{x^2 + y^2}$. $R_d \simeq 1.6$ kpc is the radial scale length, $z_d \simeq 0.3$ kpc is the vertical scale height and $M_d = [2.4, 4.8] \times 10^9\, M_\odot$ is the LMC disk mass. The galactic coordinates for the center of the LMC disk are $l = 297.7°$, $b = -33.5°$. The LMC disk is inclined by an angle $i = 30°$ with respect to our line of sight and its position angle is $\phi = 170°$. In addition to the disk, the LMC possess a stellar bar described by a triaxial Gaussian density profile:

$$\rho_{bar} = \frac{M_{bar}}{(2\pi)^{3/2} x_b y_b z_b} \exp\left(-\frac{1}{2}\left[\left(\frac{x}{x_b}\right)^2 + \left(\frac{y}{y_b}\right)^2 + \left(\frac{z}{z_b}\right)^2\right]\right), \quad (7)$$

where x, y, z are coordinates along the principal axes of the bar. Here, $x_b = 1.0$ kpc, $y_b = 0.3$ kpc, $z_b = 0.3$ kpc are the scale lengths along the three axes and $M_{bar} = [0.6, 1.2] \times 10^9 M_\odot$ is the total mass of the bar. The bar is inclined by an angle $i = 30°$ and has a position angle $\phi = 120°$. The galactic coordinates for the center of the LMC stellar bar are $l = 280.5°, b = -32.8°$.

2.2.3. Sources in the SMC

Accordingly to the star formation history of the SMC, two stellar components can be distinguished: an old star (OS) and a young star (YS) population (see Ref. 36). For the YS mass distribution, we adopt a spheroidal model with a fully Gaussian profile:

$$\rho_{SMC}^{(YS)} = \rho_0^{(YS)} \exp\left(-\frac{1}{2}\left[\left(\frac{\xi}{\xi_{YS}}\right)^2 + \left(\frac{\eta}{\eta_{YS}}\right)^2 + \left(\frac{\zeta}{\zeta_{YS}}\right)^2\right]\right). \quad (8)$$

As far as the OS mass distribution is concerned, we keep the Gaussian profile along the line of sight, and a smoother exponential profile in the orthogonal plane:

$$\rho_{SMC}^{(OS)} = \rho_0^{(OS)} \exp\left[-\sqrt{\left(\frac{\Xi}{\Xi_{OS}}\right)^2 + \left(\frac{\Upsilon}{\Upsilon_{OS}}\right)^2}\right] \exp\left[-\frac{1}{2}\left(\frac{Z}{Z_{OS}}\right)^2\right]. \quad (9)$$

The central density values for the YS and OS population are $\rho_0^{(YS)} = 8.5 \times 10^6 \, M_\odot \, kpc^{-3}$ and $\rho_0^{(OS)} = 3.9 \times 10^7 \, M_\odot \, kpc^{-3}$, respectively. The value of the position angle, with respect to the north direction, is fixed at $\phi_{YS} = 66°$ and $\phi_{OS} = 83°$ for the YS and OS populations, respectively. The reference frames (ξ, η, ζ) and (Ξ, Υ, Z) are directed along the principal axes of the YS and OS spheroid, respectively. For the YS population, we fix $(\xi_{YS}, \eta_{YS}, \zeta_{YS}) = (0.8, 3.5, 1.8)$ kpc and for the OS population, $Z_{OS} = 2.1$ kpc, $(\Xi_{OS}, \Upsilon_{OS}) = (0.8, 2.1)$ kpc. The galactic coordinates for the SMC are $l = 307°, b = -46°$. The YS population is inclined by the angle $i = 74°$, while the OS population is not inclined. The OS and YS populations have a relative distance shift between them, since the centre of the YS population is at a distance of about 2 kpc behind that of the OS component, which is at a distance of $\simeq 63.5$ kpc from the Earth.

2.2.4. Sources in the M31 galaxy

The morphology of M31 is similar to that of the Milky Way, with a central bulge and a disc. The distance between the center of the M31 and the observer is $D_{M31} \simeq 778$ kpc. The M31 bulge is parameterized by a flattened power law of the form

$$\rho_B(R, z) = \rho_B(0) \left[1 + \left(\frac{R}{a}\right)^2 + q^{-2}\left(\frac{z}{a}\right)^2\right]^{-s/2}, \quad (10)$$

where the coordinates x and y span the M31 disk plane (z is perpendicular to it), $\rho_B(0) \simeq 4.5 \times 10^9 M_\odot kpc^{-3}$, $q \simeq 0.6$ is the ratio of the minor to major axes, $a \simeq 1.0$ kpc is the core radius and $s = 3.8$ is the power-law index.[37] The mass density of the M31 disk stars adopting the parameters of the Reference model in Ref. 38 is described by a sech-squared profile as follows:

$$\rho_D(R, z) = \rho_D(0) \exp(-R/h) \operatorname{sech}^2(z/H), \quad (11)$$

where R is the distance to the center of the M31 disk, $H \simeq 0.3$ kpc and $h \simeq 6.4$ kpc are, respectively, the scale height and scale lengths of the disk and $\rho_D(0) \simeq 3.5 \times 10^8 \, M_\odot kpc^{-3}$ is the central mass density. The M31 disk is inclined by the angle $i = 77°$ to our line of sight and has position angle $\phi = 38.6°$.

3. Microlensing events by PBHs

The microlensing events are unpredictable phenomena, and to quantify their rarity we present the optical depth and the microlensing rate.

3.1. *The optical depth*

The microlensing optical depth τ is the probability that any given star is being significantly lensed at any given time by a foreground compact object. For a star and a given model of the lens density distribution one can calculate τ through the equation

$$\tau = \int_0^{D_S} n(D_l) \pi u_T^2 R_E^2 dD_l \tag{12}$$

which is just the probability that a lens object is inside the microlensing tube (see, e.g., Refs. 39 and 40). Here, $n = \rho/M$ is the number density of the lenses (ρ is their mass density) and M is the lens mass. Since $R_E^2 \propto M$, it turns out that the optical depth is simply a geometrical quantity and does not depend on the lens mass.

The sources are not all at the same distance D_S, but are distributed along the line of sight, so we define the average optical depth as:[41]

$$<\tau> = \left[\int_{D_{S,min}}^{D_{S,max}} dD_S n(D_S) D_S^2 \right]^{-1} \int_{D_{S,min}}^{D_{S,max}} dD_S n(D_S) D_S^2 \tau(D_S) \tag{13}$$

where $D_{S,min}$ and $D_{S,max}$ are the minimum and maximum distances (up to the boundary of the observation region) from the observer's position and $n(D_S)$ is the number density distribution of source stars. Considering the above mentioned scenario, that PBHs constitutes some mass fraction f of the halo DM in the MW halo region, where $f = \frac{\Omega_{PHB}}{\Omega_{DM}} = \frac{\rho_{PHB}}{\rho_{DM}}$, the optical depth due to the PBHs can be written in the form $<\tau>_{PBH} = f <\tau>_{DM}$.

3.2. *The microlensing rate*

The event rate is the rate at which a given background star undergoes a microlensing event due to a foreground lensing object. The microlensing event rate for any given source is extremely small, but it can be maximized toward regions with a high surface density of sources, as the Galactic bulge, LMC, SMC and the $M31$ galaxy.

In order to define the microlensing rate, we consider the geometry and variables defined in Fig. 4 of Griest,[39] which gives the differential event rate $(d\Gamma)$ of a lensing object entering a volume element along the line-of-sight, where the lens causes a microlensing with magnification above a certain threshold value. Integrating it along the line of sight to the source, the microlensing rate per background star is defined as

$$\Gamma = \int d\Gamma = \int \frac{n(D_l)f(\vec{v})d^3x d^3v}{dt}, \qquad (14)$$

where $n(D_l)$ is the number density of the lenses, $f(\vec{v})$ is the lens velocity distribution, $d^3x = v_\perp cos(\theta)dt R_E u_T d\alpha d(D_l)$ is the volume element and $d^3v = d^2v_\perp dv_\parallel$ the velocity element (see the Ref. 35 for details). The perpendicular component of the velocity element in cylindrical coordinates can be then written as $d^2v_\perp = v_\perp dv_\perp d\theta$. Therefore, Eq. (14) can be rewritten as:

$$d\Gamma = \frac{\rho}{M} u_T R_E dD_l f(v_\perp, v_\parallel) d^2v_\perp dv_\perp d\theta \cos(\theta) d\alpha dv_\parallel. \qquad (15)$$

We note that the parameters $\theta, \alpha, v_\perp$ in the equation above vary in the range $[-\pi/2, \pi/2]$, $[0, 2\pi]$ and $[0, \infty)$, respectively. Considering the velocity distribution of the lenses and source to be a Maxwellian distribution with dispersion velocity σ_l and σ_s and including the transverse velocity of the microlensing tube $v_{t\perp}$ one gets

$$\Gamma(D_S) = \frac{2u_T D_S}{M} \int_0^1 dx \rho(x) R_E(x) \times \int_0^\infty \frac{v_{s\perp}}{\pi \sigma_s^2} exp(-\frac{v_{s\perp}^2}{\sigma_s^2}) dv_{s\perp}$$
$$\times \int_0^\infty \frac{v_\perp^2}{\pi \sigma_l^2} exp(-\frac{v_\perp^2 + v_{t\perp}^2}{\sigma_l^2}) dv_{l\perp} \times \int_0^{2\pi} exp(-\frac{2v_\perp v_{t\perp} cos\beta}{\sigma_l^2}) d\beta \times \int_0^{2\pi} d\phi. \qquad (16)$$

Using the variables $y = v_{l\perp}/\sigma_l$, $\eta = v_{t\perp}/\sigma_l$ and $z = v_{s\perp}/\sigma_s$, the microlensing rate is

$$\Gamma(D_S) = 4u_T D_S \sqrt{\frac{4GMD_s}{c^2}} \frac{\sigma_l}{\pi M} \int_0^1 dx \rho(x) \sqrt{x(1-x)} \times \int_0^\infty z exp(-z^2) dz$$
$$\times \int_0^\infty y^2 exp(-y^2 - \eta^2) dy \times \int_0^{2\pi} exp(-2y\eta cos\beta) d\beta. \qquad (17)$$

Finally, the average microlensing rate per star can be rewritten as (see, e.g.,[41] for further details)

$$<\Gamma> = \left[\int_{D_{S,min}}^{D_{S,min}} dD_S n(D_S) D_S^2\right]^{-1} \int_{D_{S,min}}^{D_{S,min}} dD_S n(D_S) D_S^2 \Gamma(D_S), \qquad (18)$$

In the same way, the microlensing rate due to the PBHs can be written in the form $<\Gamma>_{PBH} = f <\Gamma>_{DM}$.

The median microlensing timescale is related to the optical depth and the microlensing rate[40] through the relation

$$t_E = \frac{2}{\pi} \frac{\tau}{\Gamma}. \qquad (19)$$

Since τ does not depend on the lens mass and Γ scales with the PBH mass as $M^{-1/2}$, the microlensing timescale t_E turns out to be proportional to the square root of the PBHs mass.

4. Model results

Let us now consider that a mass-fraction f of the Galactic halo DM is in the form of PBHs, assumed to have a mass density distribution exactly as that of the halo DM.

First, we consider a monochromatic mass distribution for the PBHs, so we assume that all PBHs have the same mass. We calculate the optical depth and the microlensing rate for this model, varying masses in the range $10^{-14} M_\odot \leq M \leq 10^2 M_\odot$ (see, e.g. Ref. 42 and references therein). Using the Galactic celestial coordinate variables (l, b), an object at the distance d from the observer (Sun's position) is at a distance $r = \sqrt{r_0^2 - 2r_0 d \cos l \cos b + d^2}$ from the Galactic center, where $r_0 \simeq 8.5$ kpc is the distance between the Sun and Galactic center, $d = \sqrt{x'^2 + y'^2 + z'^2}$ and $x' = d \cos b \cos l$, $y' = d \cos b \sin l$, $z' = d \sin b$. In the Cartesian coordinate system (x', y', z'), the observer is at the coordinate origin. Since we are interested in estimating the optical depth and microlensing rate due to the PBHs in the Galactic halo towards three nearby galaxies, i.e. LMC, SMC and $M31$, we introduce the coordinate system (x_0, y_0, z_0), which has the origin in the center of these galaxies at (l_0, b_0, D_0) and has the $z_0 - axis$ directed toward the observer: the $x_0 - axis$ is assumed to be anti parallel to the galactic longitude axis and the $y_0 - axis$ parallel to the galactic latitude axis. For an object at distance D from the observer, a point with galactic coordinates (l, b) can be defined through the coordinates (x_0, y_0, z_0) as:

$$x_0 = -D \cos b \sin(l - l_0)$$
$$y_0 = D \sin b \cos b_0 - D \cos b \sin b_0 \cos(l - l_0) \quad (20)$$
$$z_0 = D_0 - D \cos b \cos b_0 \cos(l - l_0) - D \sin b \sin b_0$$

Therefore, in order to find the coordinates (x, y, z) according to the selected systems, in the case of LMC and M31 they are obtained by rotating around $z_0 - axis$ with position angle ϕ counterclockwise and around the new $x - axis$ with the inclination angle i clockwise. In the case of SMC, the coordinates (Ξ, Υ, Z) for the OS population and (ξ, η, ζ) for the YS population are obtained by rotating around $z_0 - axis$ with the position angle ϕ counterclockwise and around the new $x - axis$ with the inclination angle i counterclockwise.

In particular, the optical depth depends uniquely on the lens (and source) population spatial density, whereas the microlensing rate depends also on the lens mass function and the lens–source relative velocity.

4.1. Optical depth

Based on Eq. (13) we estimate the average optical depth due to the PBHs towards the Galactic bulge, LMC, SMC and the M31 galaxy. In Table 1 are given the values of the optical depth towards the Galactic bulge, LMC, SMC and M31 galaxy. The galactic coordinate are: $(l_0, b_0) = (0°, 0°)$ for the Galactic bulge, $(l_0, b_0) = (280.5°, -32.8°)$ for LMC, $(l_0, b_0) = (307°, -46°)$ for SMC and $(l_0, b_0) = (121.17°, -21.57°)$ for M31. For definiteness, the values are given for $f_{PBH} = 1$ and $u_T = 1$. In case of other values, the rescaling is obviously a multiplication by f_{PBH} and by u_T^2.

As one can see from Table 1, the largest values of the optical depth are found towards M31 ($\tau \sim 10^{-6}$), with a factor about 20 times larger than those towards the Galactic bulge. This can be certainly attributed to the enormous volume and large mass content between the Earth and M31.

Table 1. The average optical depth, microlensing rate (per source per year) and the Einstein timescale due to PBHs in Galactic halo. From top to bottom, the values are given towards the MW bulge, LMC disk and bar, SMC young and old stellar populations and M31 bulge and disk. For the microlening rate and microlensing timescale t_E are selected two values of the PBH mass M, i.e. $M = 10^{-14} M_\odot$ and $M = 10^2 M_\odot$.

	$<\tau>$ ($\times 10^{-7}$)	$<\Gamma> (10^{-14} M_\odot)$	$<\Gamma> (10^2 M_\odot)$ ($\times 10^{-8}$)	$t_E (10^{-14} M_\odot)$ (s)	$t_E (10^2 M_\odot)$ (year)
MW_{bulge}	1.30	8.14	8.14	0.32	1.02
LMC_{disk}	4.84	9.96	9.96	0.98	3.10
LMC_{bar}	4.84	9.97	9.97	0.98	3.09
SMC_{YS}	7.26	15.7	15.7	0.93	2.95
SMC_{OS}	7.11	16.4	16.4	0.87	2.76
$M31_{bulge}$	14.25	20.64	20.64	1.39	4.40
$M31_{disk}$	14.25	20.35	20.35	1.41	4.46

One can also remark that the optical depth towards SMC is significantly larger than that towards LMC. This has to be attributed mainly to the larger value of the SMC center longitude with respect to the corresponding value of LMC, but also to its larger distance. The ratio of the optical depth towards SMC and LMC turns out to be $<\tau>_{SMC} \simeq 1.4 <\tau>_{LMC}$, consistent with the results to Ref. 43. The LMC optical depth is about 5×10^{-7}, in agreement to the result in Ref. 39, in which the adopted values of the model parameters are slightly different.

We also remark that the optical depth towards the Galactic bulge is compatible with the results obtained in Ref. 9 (see e.g., Table I).

Concerning SMC, there is a more visible difference between the role of the two star populations, mainly due to the fact that their centers are shifted by about 2 kpc one with respect to the other.

4.2. Microlensing rate

Based on Eq. (18), we estimate the average microlensing rate varying the PBH masses in the range $10^{-14} M_\odot \leq M \leq 10^2 M_\odot$ considering the same conditions as in the previous section. Concerning the transverse velocity dispersion, we keep the value $\sigma_l = 210$ km/s as it is considered for the lenses in the MW halo.[35] For the source star populations in the MW bulge, the velocity dispersion is assumed to be $\sigma = 156$ km/s, whereas in the case of the M31 galaxy, we consider[37] $\sigma_{bulge} = 100$ km/s and $\sigma_{disk} = 30$ km/s. For LMC, we have $\sigma_{disk} = 20.2$ km/s and $\sigma_{bar} = 24.7$ km/s, while for SMC,[44] $\sigma_{YS} = 20$ km/s and $\sigma_{OS} = 30$ km/s.

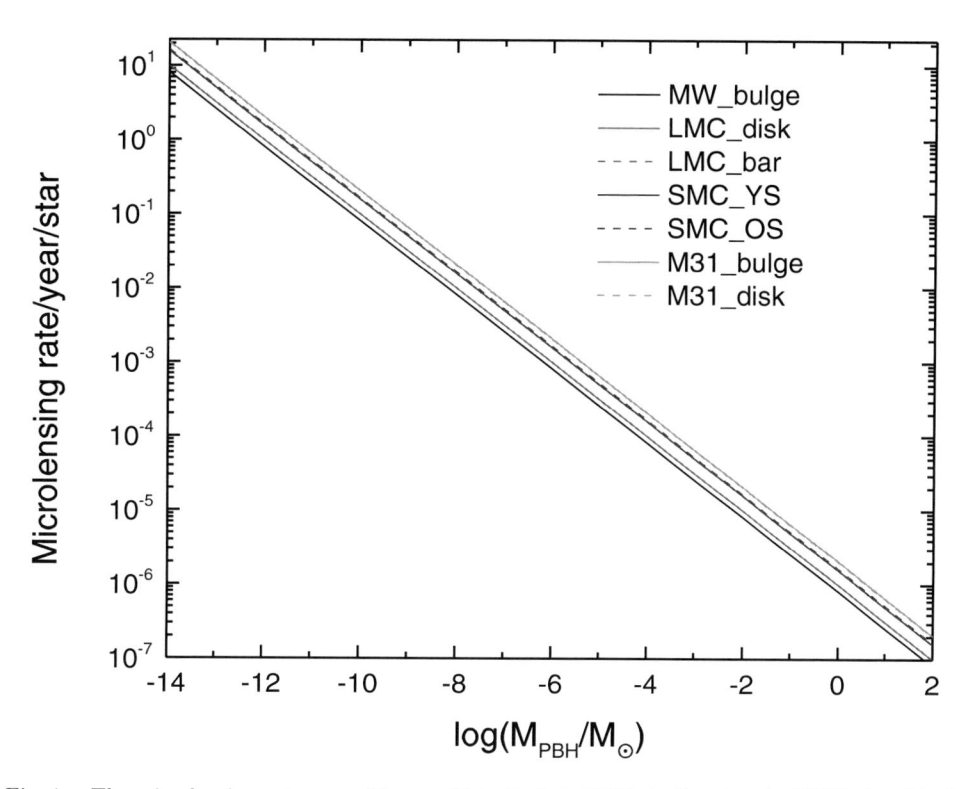

Fig. 1. The microlensing rate caused by our Galactic halo PBHs to the stars in MW bulge (black line), LMC (red line), SMC (blue line), and M31 (green line) is plotted as a function of the PBH mass.

In Fig. 1 we plot the PBH microlensing rate per star per year towards the MW bulge, LMC, SMC and M31 as a function of the PBH mass. We also remind that the plots are given for $f_{PBH} = 1$ and $u_T = 1$. In case of other values, the rescaling is obviously obtained with a multiplication by f_{PBH} and u_T. As one can see, the value of the microlensing rate vary from 10^{-7} for $M \simeq 10^2 M_\odot$ up to

10^1 for $M \simeq 10^{-14}\,M_\odot$. The highest value of the microlensing rate is obtained in the case of observations towards the M31 galaxy, this has to be attributed to the dark matter distribution function as a cored isothermal sphere. Indeed, microlensing observations towards M31 are able to allow a full map of the Galactic halo, whereas the other considered targets are immersed within the Galactic halo.

Based on the Eq. (19) we define the microlensing timescale of the events caused by the PBHs in Galactic halo towards four selected targets. In Table 1 we present the Einstein timescale for events caused by PBHs towards the center of the MW bulge, LMC, SMC and M31 for two extremal cases of $M = 10^{-14}\,M_\odot$ and $M = 10^2\,M_\odot$ of the PBH mass. As expected, due to the wide mass interval in consideration, the t_E values vary by several orders of magnitude, from a fraction of a second up to several years. For that reason, since a sufficiently high image sampling is requested in order to recognize a microlensing event (let's say at least 5-10 images within t_E are necessary for that aim), different observing strategies and facilities are needed in order to probe the full PBH mass range.

4.3. *PBHs by Euclid*

Since an additional survey of the Euclid telescope, although not definitely approved as yet, is to observe for a few months the Galactic bulge, we devote a special attention to its survey towards the Galactic bulge.[25] Based on the galactic coordinates of the line of sight $(l, b) = (1.1°, -1.7°)$ and the distributions of the PBHs and bulge stars we find the optical depth to be $<\tau> \simeq 1.30 \times 10^{-7}$ and the microlensing rate per stars per year to be $<\Gamma> = 8.12 \times 10^{-7}$ for the PBH mass, $M = 1\,M_\odot$. Based on the magnitude limit of the Euclid telescope, which is foreseen to be $m = 24$, the mass-luminosity relation $\frac{L}{L_\odot} = (\frac{M}{M_\odot})^{3.5}$ and considering the middle point 8.5 kpc away from us, we find the lowest value $M_{min} = 0.31 M_\odot$ of the star's mass to be detected by this telescope. Using a Salpeter mass function $\frac{dN}{dM} \propto M^{-2.4}$, for stars in the Galactic bulge, we calculate their mean mass value $<M> = 0.97\,M_\odot$. Considering the distance of the bulge stars to be within the range [7, 10] kpc with mass density distribution given by Eq. (5) and since the Euclid's field of view is 0.54 square degree we obtain that the number N_{ED} of detectable source stars in the Euclid microlensing observations is $N_{ED} = 6.45 \times 10^7$. By multiplying $<\Gamma> N_{ED} t_{obs}$, where t_{obs} is the observation timescale in years, we find about 340 microlensing events per year (for $f_{PBH} = 1$ and $u_T = 6.54$), with a microlensing timescale $t_E \sim 8$ months in the case of a PBH mass of $1\,M_\odot$. In Fig. 2 we plot the PBH microlensing rate and microlensing timescale towards the Euclid field of view as a function of the PHB mass. We remind that the plot of the microlensing rate is given for $f_{PBH} = 1$, $u_T = 6.54$ and the microlensing timescale for $u_T = 6.54$, the last one is independent of f_{PBH}.

Considering a cadence of 20 minutes[25] and no less than 5 points within t_E, we find that Euclid could detect PBHs down to $M = 10^{-7} M_\odot$.

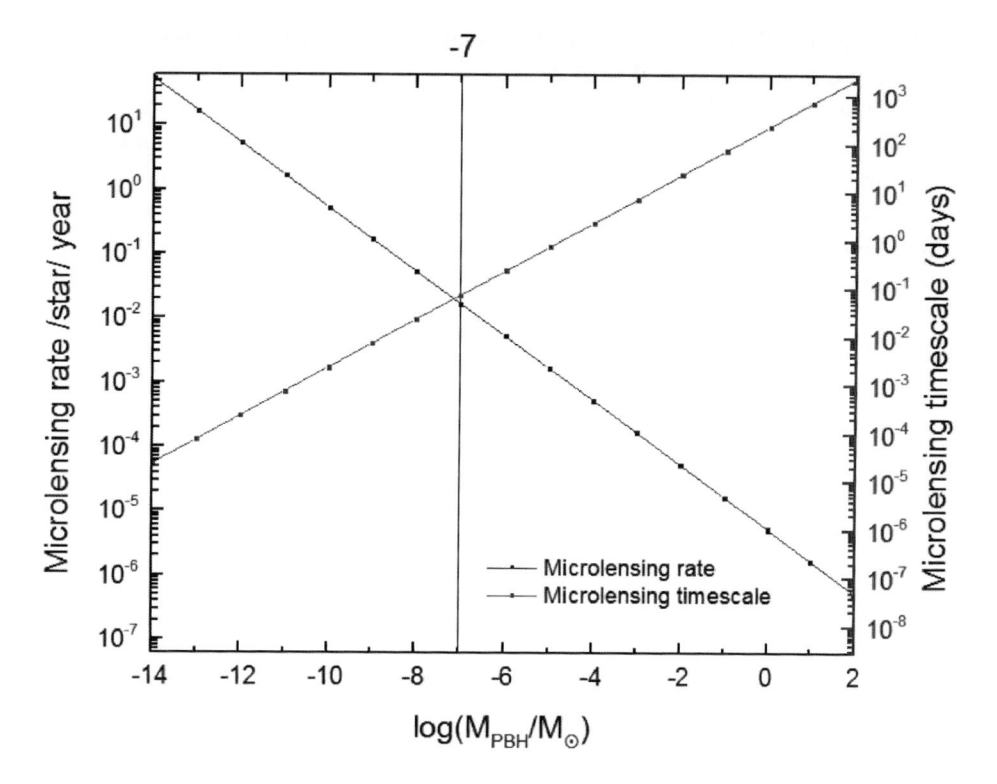

Fig. 2. The microlensing rate (black line) and the microlensing timescale (blue line) caused by our Galactic halo PBHs to the stars in Euclid field view as a function of the PBH mass. The vertical line at $M_{PBH} = 10^{-7}\ M_\odot$ represents the lower mass limit for observations towards the Galactic bulge by the Euclid telescope.

5. Conclusions

To obtain valuable information about the mass function and the spatial distribution of PBHs, if they contribute to a high enough fraction of the Galactic halo dark matter, the gravitational microlensing is the best method. We use this method to investigate the traces of MW halo's PBHs towards four selected targets: the MW bulge, Large and Small Magellanic Clouds and the M31 galaxy.

We estimate the optical depth and the microlensing rate towards these targets, assuming for PBHs a standard halo model and for the target sources, their mass density distributions. The largest values of both the optical depth and the microlensing rate are found for observations towards the M31 galaxy, due to its larger distance.

We calculate and discuss the microlensing timescale, which changes by many orders of magnitude, for the reason of the high mass range $[10^{-14}, 10^2]M_\odot$ of PBHs, taken into consideration. It varies from less than 1 seconds up to about 4.5 years. Therefore, completely different observation strategies are necessary in order to detect PBHs in different bins of masses. We also mention that the present paper is a summary of a more detailed work.[45]

As far as the Euclid observations towards the Galactic bulge is concerned, and based on its features, we define that it will observe and will detect about 340 microlensing events per year (for mass-fraction $f_{PBH} = 1$ and $u_T = 6.54$), with a microlensing timescale $t_E \sim 8$ months in the case of a PBH mass of $1\,M_\odot$. Also, we find that it could detect PBHs with mass down to $M = 10^{-7} M_\odot$. Below this mass limit, the expected number of points in the lightcurve is insufficient to perform a reliable analysis. For PBH masses around this value we estimated a number of about 10^6 events per year, since the microlensing rate varies as $1/\sqrt{M}$.

Since a confusing element in the observed stars is the stellar intrisic variability, it needs a special attention. In fact, this can be avoided by carefully looking at different bands: gravitational microlensing is an achromatic effect, while stellar variability appears different in different spectral bands.

Acknowledgements

FDP and AAN acknowledge the support by the INFN projects TAsP and Euclid.

References

1. Y. B. Zel'dovich and I. Novikov, The hypothesis of cores retarded during expansion and the hot cosmological model, *Astronomicheskii Zhurnal* **43**, p. 758 (1966).
2. S. Hawking, Gravitationally collapsed objects of very low mass, *Monthly Notices of the Royal Astronomical Society* **152**, 75 (1971).
3. B. J. Carr and S. W. Hawking, Black holes in the early universe, *Monthly Notices of the Royal Astronomical Society* **168**, 399 (1974).
4. R. Bean and J. Magueijo, Could supermassive black holes be quintessential primordial black holes?, *Physical Review D* **66**, p. 063505 (2002).
5. J. García-Bellido, Massive primordial black holes as dark matter and their detection with gravitational waves, in *Journal of Physics: Conference Series*, (1)2017.
6. N. Afshordi, P. McDonald and D. Spergel, Primordial black holes as dark matter: the power spectrum and evaporation of early structures, *The Astrophysical Journal Letters* **594**, p. L71 (2003).
7. M. Ricotti, J. P. Ostriker and K. J. Mack, Effect of primordial black holes on the cosmic microwave background and cosmological parameter estimates, *The Astrophysical Journal* **680**, p. 829 (2008).
8. B. Carr, F. Kühnel and M. Sandstad, Primordial black holes as dark matter, *Physical Review D* **94**, p. 083504 (2016).
9. H. Niikura, M. Takada, S. Yokoyama, T. Sumi and S. Masaki, Constraints on earth-mass primordial black holes from ogle 5-year microlensing events, *Physical Review D* **99**, p. 083503 (2019).
10. N. Cappelluti, A. Kashlinsky, R. Arendt, A. Comastri, G. Fazio, A. Finoguenov, G. Hasinger, J. Mather, T. Miyaji and S. Moseley, Cross-correlating cosmic infrared and x-ray background fluctuations: Evidence of significant black hole populations among the cib sources, *The Astrophysical Journal* **769**, p. 68 (2013).

11. S. Clesse, J. García-Bellido and S. Orani, Detecting the stochastic gravitational wave background from primordial black hole formation, *arXiv preprint arXiv:1812.11011* (2018).
12. B. Abbott, S. Jawahar, N. Lockerbie and K. Tokmakov, Ligo scientific collaboration and virgo collaboration (2016) directly comparing gw150914 with numerical solutions of einstein's equations for binary black hole coalescence. physical review d, 94 (6). issn 1550-2368, http://dx.doi.org/10.1103/physrevd.94.064035, *PHYSICAL REVIEW D Phys Rev D* **94**, p. 064035 (2016).
13. A. Barrau, D. Blais, G. Boudoul and D. Polarski, Peculiar relics from primordial black holes in the inflationary paradigm, *Annalen der Physik* **13**, 115 (2004).
14. B. Carr and F. Kühnel, Primordial black holes as dark matter: recent developments, *Annual Review of Nuclear and Particle Science* **70**, 355 (2020).
15. A. M. Green and B. J. Kavanagh, Primordial black holes as a dark matter candidate, *Journal of Physics G: Nuclear and Particle Physics* **48**, p. 043001 (2021).
16. R. Laha, Lensing of fast radio bursts: Future constraints on primordial black hole density with an extended mass function and a new probe of exotic compact fermion and boson stars, *Physical Review D* **102**, p. 023016 (2020).
17. K. Griest, A. M. Cieplak and M. J. Lehner, Experimental limits on primordial black hole dark matter from the first 2 yr of kepler data, *The Astrophysical Journal* **786**, p. 158 (2014).
18. C. Alcock, R. Allsman, D. R. Alves, T. Axelrod, A. C. Becker, D. Bennett, K. H. Cook, N. Dalal, A. J. Drake, K. Freeman et al., The macho project: microlensing results from 5.7 years of large magellanic cloud observations, *The Astrophysical Journal* **542**, p. 281 (2000).
19. H. Niikura, M. Takada, N. Yasuda, R. H. Lupton, T. Sumi, S. More, T. Kurita, S. Sugiyama, A. More, M. Oguri et al., Microlensing constraints on primordial black holes with subaru/hsc andromeda observations, *Nature Astronomy* **3**, 524 (2019).
20. A. Gould, A natural formalism for microlensing, *The Astrophysical Journal* **542**, p. 785 (2000).
21. L. Hamolli, M. Hafizi, F. De Paolis and A. A. Nucita, Estimating finite source effects in microlensing events due to free-floating planets with the euclid survey, *Advances in Astronomy* **2015** (2015).
22. L. Hamolli, F. De Paolis, M. Hafizi and A. Nucita, Predictions on the detection of the free-floating planet population with k2 and spitzer microlensing campaigns, *Astrophysical Bulletin* **72**, 73 (2017).
23. L. Hamolli, M. Hafizi, F. De Paolis and A. A. Nucita, The astrometric signal of microlensing events caused by free floating planets, *Astrophysics and Space Science* **363**, 1 (2018).
24. L. Hamolli, M. Hafizi, F. De Paolis and A. Nucita, Free-floating planets in the milky way, *Arabian Journal of Mathematics* **8**, 305 (2019).
25. R. Laureijs, J. Amiaux, S. Arduini, J.-L. Augueres, J. Brinchmann, R. Cole, M. Cropper, C. Dabin, L. Duvet, A. Ealet et al., Euclid definition study report, *arXiv preprint arXiv:1110.3193* (2011).
26. N. Regnault, Photometric calibration of wide field imagers, PhD thesis, Université Pierre et Marie Curie-Paris VI2013.
27. G. Ingrosso, S. C. Novati, F. De Paolis, P. Jetzer, A. Nucita, G. Scarpetta and F. Strafella, A new analysis of the mega m 31 microlensing events, *Astronomy & Astrophysics* **462**, 895 (2007).
28. V. Belokurov, J. An, N. Evans, P. Hewett, P. Baillon, S. C. Novati, B. Carr, M. Crézé, Y. Giraud-Héraud, A. Gould et al., The point-agape survey—ii. an unrestricted search

for microlensing events towards m31, *Monthly Notices of the Royal Astronomical Society* **357**, 17 (2005).
29. A. Riffeser, S. Seitz and R. Bender, The m31 microlensing event wecapp-gl1/point-agape-s3: evidence for a macho component in the dark halo of m31?, *The Astrophysical Journal* **684**, p. 1093 (2008).
30. S. C. Novati, V. Bozza, I. Bruni, M. Dall'Ora, F. De Paolis, M. Dominik, R. Gualandi, G. Ingrosso, P. Jetzer, L. Mancini *et al.*, The m31 pixel lensing plan campaign: Macho lensing and self-lensing signals, *The Astrophysical Journal* **783**, p. 86 (2014).
31. P. Tisserand, L. Le Guillou, C. Afonso, J. Albert, J. Andersen, R. Ansari, É. Aubourg, P. Bareyre, J. Beaulieu, X. Charlot *et al.*, Limits on the macho content of the galactic halo from the eros-2 survey of the magellanic clouds, *Astronomy & Astrophysics* **469**, 387 (2007).
32. A. Rest, C. Stubbs, A. C. Becker, G. Miknaitis, A. Miceli, R. Covarrubias, S. Hawley, R. C. Smith, N. B. Suntzeff, K. Olsen *et al.*, Testing lmc microlensing scenarios: The discrimination power of the supermacho microlensing survey, *The Astrophysical Journal* **634**, p. 1103 (2005).
33. A. M. Green, Astrophysical uncertainties on stellar microlensing constraints on multi-solar mass primordial black hole dark matter, *Physical Review D* **96**, p. 043020 (2017).
34. M. Hafizi, F. De Paolis, G. Ingrosso and A. A. Nucita, Microlensing signature of a white dwarf population in the galactic halo, *International Journal of Modern Physics D* **13**, 1831 (2004).
35. P. Jetzer, L. Mancini and G. Scarpetta, Microlensing towards the large magellanic cloud, *Astronomy & Astrophysics* **393**, 129 (2002).
36. S. Calchi Novati, S. Mirzoyan, P. Jetzer and G. Scarpetta, Microlensing towards the smc: a new analysis of ogle and eros results, *Monthly Notices of the Royal Astronomical Society* **435**, 1582 (2013).
37. F. De Paolis, G. Ingrosso, A. Nucita and A. Zakharov, Influence of magnification threshold on pixel lensing optical depth, event rate and time scale distributions towards m 31, *Astronomy & Astrophysics* **432**, 501 (2005).
38. E. Kerins, M. Darnley, J. Duke, A. Gould, C. Han, Y.-B. Jeon, A. Newsam, B.-G. Park and (A. Collaboration), The angstrom project: a microlensing survey of the structure and composition of the bulge of the andromeda galaxy, *Monthly Notices of the Royal Astronomical Society* **365**, 1099 (2006).
39. K. Griest, Galactic microlensing as a method of detecting massive compact halo objects, *The astrophysical journal* **366**, 412 (1991).
40. B. S. Gaudi, Microlensing surveys for exoplanets, *Annual Review of Astronomy and Astrophysics* **50**, 411 (2012).
41. M. Kiraga and B. Paczynski, Gravitational microlensing of the galactic bulge stars, *The Astrophysical Journal* **430**, L101 (1994).
42. J. Sureda, J. Magaña, I. J. Araya and N. D. Padilla, Press–schechter primordial black hole mass functions and their observational constraints, *Monthly Notices of the Royal Astronomical Society* **507**, 4804 (2021).
43. C. Afonso, J. Albert, J. Andersen, R. Ansari, É. Aubourg, P. Bareyre, J. Beaulieu, G. Blanc, X. Charlot, F. Couchot *et al.*, Limits on galactic dark matter with 5 years of eros smc data, *Astronomy & Astrophysics* **400**, 951 (2003).
44. S. C. Novati, F. De Luca, P. Jetzer and G. Scarpetta, Microlensing towards the large magellanic cloud: a study of the lmc halo contribution, *Astronomy & Astrophysics* **459**, 407 (2006).
45. L. Hamolli, M. Hafizi, F. De Paolis and A. A. Nucita, Gravitational microlensing constraints on primordial black holes by euclid, *Astrophysics and Space Science* **366**, 1 (2021).

Giant cosmic ray halos around M31 and the Milky Way

S. Recchia

Dipartimento di Fisica, Universitá di Torino,
via P. Giuria 1, 10125 Torino, Italy
E-mail: sarah.recchia@unito.it

Istituto Nazionale di Fisica Nucleare, Sezione di Torino,
Via P. Giuria 1, 10125 Torino, Italy

S. Gabici

Université de Paris, CNRS, Astroparticule et Cosmologie,
F-75006 Paris, France

F. A. Aharonian

Dublin Institute for Advanced Studies,
31 Fitzwilliam Place, Dublin 2, Ireland

Max-Planck-Institut für Kernphysik,
Postfach 103980, D-69029 Heidelberg, Germany

V. Niro

Université de Paris, CNRS, Astroparticule et Cosmologie,
F-75006 Paris, France

Recently, a diffuse γ-rays emission in the energy range 1-100 GeV has been detected around M31, that extends up to 120-200 kpc from its center. Such extended emission is difficult to be explained in the typical scenario of cosmic rays produced in the galactic disk or in the galactic center (GC) and diffusing in the galactic halo. We show that a cosmic ray origin, either hadronic or leptonic, of the emission is viable if non-standard cosmic ray transport scenarios are considered, or if particles are accelerated directly in the galactic halo (*in situ* acceleration). The cosmic ray halo can be powered by the accretion of intergalactic gas or by the activity of galaxy's central black hole. If giant cosmic ray halos are common around galaxies, the interactions of cosmic ray protons and nuclei with the circumgalactic gas surrounding Milky Way could explain the isotropic diffuse flux of neutrinos observed by Icecube.

Keywords: Galaxies: halos; cosmic rays; gamma rays; neutrinos.

1. Introduction

The Andromeda Galaxy (M31) and the Milky Way (MW) present many similarities. Both have a bulge, a disk, an extended gaseous halo, a central supermassive black hole and a dark matter halo with a radial extension of 200 − 300 kpc and a total mass of $\sim 10^{12} M_\odot$.[1] The integrated γ−ray luminosity of the Andromeda galaxy, as reported by *Fermi*-LAT,[2,3] above 100 MeV is of $\sim 6.6 \times 10^{41}$ erg s^{-1}, less than a factor ~ 2 that of the MW.[2] Fermi Bubbles-like structure emanating from the central region of M31 may also exist, as recently reported.[4] However, while in the MW the $\gamma-$ray emission correlates spatially with the gaseous disk, in M31 it appears to be concentrated within the inner ~ 5 kpc region.[3]

Recently the *Fermi*-LAT data have been analyzed in detail in Ref. 1, from a region that corresponds to a projected radius of ~ 200 kpc from the center of M31 and found an excess that extends up to $\sim 120 - 200$ kpc. The analysis was performed with an accurate modeling of the MW foreground emission and considering a spherically symmetric template, centered on M31 and including three regions:

- the inner galaxy (IG)
  a ~ 5.5 kpc radius region that contains the emission from the inner galaxy[3]

- the spherical halo (SH)
  a ring of $\sim 5.5 - 120$ kpc

- the outer halo (OH)
  a ring of $\sim 120 - 200$ kpc.

For each region the authors provide the $\gamma-$ray spectra. Moreover, given the contamination from the MW disk emission, especially relevant for the northern part of the OH, the spectra for the southern and northern part of the SH and OH are also reported. The north/south regions' spectra are quite similar for the SH, while they exhibit relevant differences for the OH, where the spectrum of the northern part shows a bumpy profile likely associated to a contamination from the MW. Thus, the authors concluded that, while the excess from the SH region is likely associated to the halo of M31, the origin of the emission from the OH is much less clear and may be rather related to the MW, or to something else. Here we focus on the SH region.

Two possible spectral fits for the SH region are reported by Ref. 1, one with a power-law plus exponential cut-off parametrization given by

$$I_{SH} \approx 9.8 \times 10^{-11} E_{\text{GeV}}^{-1.9} e^{-E_{\text{GeV}}/11.6} \text{MeV}^{-1} \text{cm}^{-2} \text{s}^{-1} \text{sr}^{-1} \quad (1)$$

and one with pure power-law, as shown in Fig. 1. Here E_{GeV} is the photon energy in GeV. The total $\gamma-$ray luminosity (northern plus southern part) of SH is:

$$L_\gamma \approx 1.7 - 1.9 \times 10^{39} \text{erg/s} \ . \quad (2)$$

where the lower(upper) value corresponds to the power law plus cutoff(pure power law) fit to data. Based on the large extension of $\gamma-$ray halo, on the intensity and spectrum of the various components, the authors of Ref. 1 suggest a dark matter interpretation for such emission[5] and, based on typical CR propagation scenarios, conclude that it is unlikely that a major fraction of the emission is due to cosmic rays (CR) in the halo of M31.

Instead, we illustrate that the $\sim 100 - 200$ kpc extended emission from Andromeda could be naturally explained as the result of CR interactions in the halo provided that: *i)* a non-standard mechanism of CR transport into galactic halos, by means of buoyant bubbles, is considered; *ii)* particles are directly accelerated in the galaxy's halo. In what follows we summarize our results reported in Ref. 6 and we refer the reader to that paper for more details.

Interestingly, if the MW is surrounded by a halo similar to that reported for M31, it could be possible to explain the diffuse Icecube neutrino flux, as previously proposed by Ref. 7. Moreover, such large halo around M31 was previously proposed by Ref. 8, which showed that it could contribute to the isotropic gamma-ray background.

2. Hadronic and leptonic origin of the M31 γ-ray halo: Energetics

2.1. *Leptonic scenario*

In this scenario the γ-ray emission from the SH is the result of inverse Compton scattering (ICS) of relativistic electrons off the interstellar radiation field (IRF). At the distances from the disk of the SH region, the IRF is dominated by CMB photons and the galactic magnetic field is likely below $\sim 1\,\mu$G, so that synchrotron losses are probably negligible compared to ICS losses. Thus, γ-rays in the range $\sim 1 - 100$ GeV would be produced by electrons of energy $\sim 0.6 - 6$ TeV, and the cutoff at $E_\gamma = 11.6$ GeV would correspond to electrons of energy $E_{max,e} \approx 1.9$ TeV. The lepton energy loss time in the CMB field is given by (see Ref. 6 and references therein)

$$\tau_{CMB} \sim 1.3 \times 10^6 E_{\text{TeV}}^{-1} \text{ yr}, \qquad (3)$$

where E_{TeV} is the particle energy in TeV.

Such short timescale implies that, for any realistic interstellar CR diffusion, electrons coming from the disk/GC would lose all their energy before reaching traveling a few kpc in the halo. Thus, if the SH emission of M31 is produced by electrons they have to be directly accelerated in that region. The minimal energy requirement is obtained in the assumption that the γ-ray production takes place in a calorimetric regime (namely the ICS timescale is shorter than any other relevant dynamical scale). In this regime the observed γ-ray luminosity (Eq. 2) equals the electron luminosity:

$$L_e = L_\gamma \approx 1.7 - 1.9 \times 10^{39} \text{erg/s}. \qquad (4)$$

Notice that this luminosity refers only to electrons in the energy band $\approx 0.6 - 6$ TeV, and is of the same order than the total estimated power of CR electrons in the disk of the MW.[9]

2.2. Hadronic scenario

In this scenario γ−rays are produced in proton-proton interactions between CRs and the ambient gas, where photons of energy E_γ are generated by CR protons of $E_p \approx 10\, E_\gamma$. In order to account for the observed γ-ray luminosity L_γ, the required CR proton luminosity reads:[6,7]

$$L_p = 3\, L_\gamma/f, \quad f = 1 - e^{-\tau_{res}/\tau_{pp}}, \tag{5}$$

where τ_{res} is the residence time of CRs in the halo and τ_{pp} is the timescale for pp interactions. The latter depends on the density of the ambient medium and is given by

$$\tau_{pp} \sim 7.1 \times 10^{10} n_{H,-3}^{-1}\, \text{yr} \tag{6}$$

where $n_{H,-3}$ is the halo hydrogen density in units of 10^{-3} cm^{-3}. At a distance of ~ 100 kpc from the Galactic disk, the gas density of the MW halo is probably of the order $\sim 10^{-4} - 10^{-3}$ cm^{-3} (see Ref. 6 and references therein), for which the loss time is larger than the age of the Universe. Given the similarities with M31, we may expect that a similar gaseous halo is also present around Andromeda. Taking a reference value of $\tau_{res} = 10^9 \tau_{res,9}$ yr for the CR residence time, the CR proton luminosity reads:

$$L_p \approx 1.8 \times 10^{41}\, \tau_{res,9}^{-1}\, n_{H,-3}^{-1} \text{erg/s}\,. \tag{7}$$

Notice that for $\tau_{res,9} \gtrsim 1$ and $n_{H,-3} \sim 1$, such luminosity is of the same order of that invoked to explain the population of CR protons observed in the disk of the MW.[9]

3. Origin of the radiating particles

The most popular hypothesis for the origin of Galactic CRs is that particles are accelerated in sources located in the disk (e.g. supernova remnants, pulsars, stellar winds, the GC) and escape form the Galaxy undergoing a diffusive-advective transport, the former due to the scattering of CRs on magnetic inhomogeneities and the latter to the possible presence of a galactic wind.[9] A similar situation is likely present also in M31 and one may wonder whether the emission from the SH results from the transport of particles from the disk/GC of Andromeda. However this hypothesis is very problematic. Indeed, for typical values of the interstellar CR diffusion coefficient, TeV electrons would lose energy due to ICS and sychrotron emission before reaching distances of few kpc from the disk. As for protons, typical models of diffusive-advective propagation from the disk/GC predict a substantial decrease of the CR density with the distance from the disk. Moreover, also the halo gas density decreases moving away from the disk, with a density of ≈ 1 cm^{-3} in the disk and $\approx 10^{-4} - 10^{-3}$ cm^{-3} at a distance of ~ 100 kpc. This imply that, in order to fit the γ-ray flux observed from the SH, the CR proton intensity in the disk of M31 should be large, which would result in a bright γ-ray emission from the disk, which is not observed. In particular, the observed ratio between the average γ-ray emissivity of the IG and SH regions is

$$\frac{\langle\epsilon_{SH}\rangle}{\langle\epsilon_{IG}\rangle} \sim 10^{-3}. \tag{8}$$

while in standard CR propagation scenarios would be (see Ref. 6 for a detailed discussion)

$$\frac{\langle\epsilon_{SH}\rangle}{\langle\epsilon_{IG}\rangle} \lesssim 10^{-5}\frac{n_{SH,-3}}{n_{IG,0}}, \tag{9}$$

where we assumed a typical gas density of $n_{IG} \sim 1\,\mathrm{cm}^{-3}$ and $n_{SH} \sim 10^{-3}\,\mathrm{cm}^{-3}$ for the IG and SH region respectively.

3.1. *Cosmic ray transport by means of buoyant bubbles*

The Fermi Bubbles[10] in the MW are probably the result of past nuclear activity of the GC, and similar structures are possibly present also in the M31.[4] Motivated by these observations, we envisage a scenario in which CR protons produced in periodic episodes of nuclear activity are transported into the SH within buoyant bubbles.

Buoyant bubbles are often observed in the central regions of galaxy clusters,[11,12] but also in galaxies.[13] Such bubbles are generally found to rise at a speed of the order of a fraction of the sound speed (≈ 100 km/s in the hot diffuse circumgalactic gas[14]), before being disrupted due to plasma instabilities. Their lifetime could reach order of $\sim 10^9$ yrs if the possible stabilizing action of a magnetic field (see Ref. 14 and references therein).

Let us assume that bubbles are generated at a rate of $\nu_B = 10^{-2}\nu_{B,-2}\mathrm{Myr}^{-1}$. The effective rate at which CR protons may be injected into the halo is $L_p = \eta E_B \nu_B \sim 3.2 \times 10^{41} \eta E_{B,57} \nu_{B,-2} \mathrm{erg/s}$, where $E_{B,57} = E_B/10^{57}\,\mathrm{erg}^{15,16}$ and η is a CR conversion efficiency that also accounts for possible adiabatic energy losses due to the bubble expansion during its rise in the halo. Comparing this expression with the energy requirement in Eq. 7 one finds

$$\eta \approx 0.56\, \tau_{res,9}^{-1} n_{H,-3}^{-1} E_{B,57}^{-1} \nu_{B,-2}^{-1}. \tag{10}$$

CRs can be transported into the galactic halo within such bubbles before the bubble is disrupted. When the bubble is disrupted CRs are released in the SH and spread diffusively to fill a region of ≈ 100 kpc radius. If the contributions of several bubbles overlap in the SH, a quasi-stationary CR population can be established in this region, while in the IG, an intermittent Fermi Bubble like structure could be observed. In this way, it is possible to populate the SH with CRs without having a large CR density in the IG and in the disk, contrary to the case in which CRs diffuse/advect directly from the galactic disk or the GC.

If the CR diffusion coefficient in the SH increases with the particle energy, similarly to what happens in the near-disk region of the MW, a quasi-stationary CR population can be maintained in the SH for energies such that the diffusion time $\tau_{res} \sim R_{SH}^2/(6\,D)$ over a region of size $R_{SH} \sim 100$ kpc is shorter than the typical time between episodes of nuclear activity $1/\nu_B$. At large enough energy, this condition is no longer valid and protons will populate the halo intermittently, which would result in a spectral cut-off at the particle energy, E_c, such that $D(E_c) = 5 \times 10^{30}\, R_{100}^2 \nu_{B,-2}$ cm^2/s. This would explain the power law plus cut-off fit to γ–ray data (black points in Fig. 1), provided that $E_c \approx 100$ GeV (see Ref. 6 and references therein).

Instead, the pure power law fit to the data (see Fig. 1) could be explained in the case in which the diffusion coefficient is rather flat in energy, and/or if CRs injected during the entire lifetime of M31 are confined in the SH remain confined in the SH.

3.2. *In situ acceleration*

In the case of a leptonic origin, the acceleration of CRs have to take place directly in the SH. Thus, let us assume that a giant spherical shock of radius R_s (whose possible origin is discussed below) is present in the SH. The maximum energy $E_{max,e}$ of accelerated electrons can be estimated: *i*) by assuming that the energy losses due to ICS are the most relevant limitation to the acceleration; *ii*) the particle acceleration at shocks is accompanied by an amplification of the magnetic field. Under such assumptions, he maximum energy reads (see Ref. 6 for the details)

$$E_{max,e} \approx 24\, u_{s,3}^3 n_{0,-4}^{1/4} \left(\frac{\xi_B}{0.035}\right)^{1/4} \text{TeV}, \tag{11}$$

where $n_0 = 10^{-4} n_{0,-4}$ cm^{-3} is the number density of the intergalactic gas, $u_s = 10^3 u_{s,3}$ km/s is the velocity at which matter flows into the shock, $\xi_B \approx 3.5\%$ of the shock ram pressure is converted into magnetic field energy.

Given that the observed γ-ray spectrum extends up to at least a photon energy $E_\gamma \approx 10$ GeV, the electron spectrum should extend at least up to an energy $E_{max,e} \approx 2$ TeV, which requires a shock speed

$$u_{s,3} \gtrsim 0.43\, n_{0,-4}^{-1/12} \left(\frac{\xi_B}{0.035}\right)^{-1/12}. \tag{12}$$

The possible origin of such a shock can be envisaged by noticing that the radius of the SH, $R_{SH} = 100 R_{SH,2}$ kpc, is of the same order of the virial radius of the galaxy. Moreover, the shock velocity inferred above is close to the free fall velocity at the edge of the SH $v_{ff} \sim 0.29 \times 10^3 M_{12}^{1/2} R_{SH,2}^{-1/2}$ km/s, where $M = 10^{12} M_{12} M_\odot$ is the total mass of M31. Thus, it is possible to speculate that particles are accelerated at a spherical accretion shock. However it is important to remark that the existence of accretion shocks around galaxies is matter of debate.[6] The energy flow across the shock would be approximately:

$$L_s \approx (4\pi R_{SH}^2) \frac{\varrho_0 v_{ff}^3}{2} \sim 3.4 \times 10^{42} R_{SH}^{1/2} n_{0,-4} M_{12}^{3/2} \text{erg/s} \tag{13}$$

which could accommodate the energy requirement given by Eq. 4.

A giant spherical shock may also be formed as a result of the GC nuclear activity. In this case an estimate of the shock velocity v_s for a shock radius $R_s \sim R_{SH}$ and a overall duration of the nuclear activity of $\tau_{GC} = 10^9 \tau_{GC,9}$ is given by (see Ref. 6 and references therein)

$$u_s \approx 0.2 \times 10^3 \, L_{GC,43}^{1/5} n_{0,-4}^{-1/5} \tau_{GC,9}^{-2/5} \text{km/s}, \qquad (14)$$

where $L_{GC} = 10^{43} L_{GC,43}$ erg/s is the time averaged rate of energy injection due to galactic nuclear activity. Interestingly, a typical value of 10^{43} erg/s for the energy injection rate is much smaller than the Eddington luminosity of the central supermassive black hole of mass M_{BH}, $L_{Edd} \sim 1.3 \times 10^{46} \left(\frac{M_{BH}}{10^8 \, M_\odot}\right)$ erg/s.

In both scenarios for the origin of the shock, the CR electron luminosity needed to explain observations (Eq. 4) can be explained with an acceleration efficiency of the order of $\eta \approx 10^{-4}$.

From the study of Galactic CRs[9] it emerges that interstellar shocks, together with electrons, also accelerate protons, likely with a much larger efficiency. In this case, the maximum energy $E_{max,p}$ is most likely limited either by the age of the system, $\tau_s = 10^9 \tau_{s,9}$ yr, since in the dilute medium that form the SH the proton-proton loss time is typically larger than the age of the Universe (see Eq. 6), either by the particle confinement time in the accelerator, namely the diffusion length at energy $E_{max,p}$ should be smaller than the size of the accelerator ($\sim R_{SH}$). The two conditions provides similar values of $E_{max,p}$, so we consider here the former, which gives $E_{max,p} \approx 4.6 \times 10^2 \, u_{s,3}^3 \tau_{s,9} n_{0,-4}^{1/2} \left(\frac{\xi_B}{0.035}\right)^{1/2}$ PeV. Thus, the acceleration of CR protons can proceed well beyond the $\sim$ 10-100 TeV needed to explain the γ-ray observations. The latter can be accounted for by an acceleration efficiency at the level of $\approx 1\%$.

4. A giant CR halo around the MW and the origin of Icecube neutrinos

The possible existence of a $\sim 100 - 200$ kpc CR halo surrounding the MW was proposed by Ref. 7 for explaining the diffuse flux of multi-TeV neutrinos detected by Icecube. The differential isotropic flux of astrophysical neutrinos (all flavors, neutrinos plus antineutrinos) measured at Earth can be fitted with a power law[17]

$$\Phi_\nu^{IC}(E_\nu) \sim 6.37 \times 10^{-18} \left(\frac{E_\nu}{100 \text{ TeV}}\right)^{-2.87} \text{GeV}^{-1}\text{cm}^{-2}\text{s}^{-1}\text{sr}^{-1}. \qquad (15)$$

The integrated isotropic flux is

$$F_\nu(> 100 \text{ TeV}) \sim 1.2 \times 10^{-10} \text{ erg/cm}^2/\text{s/sr}. \qquad (16)$$

Let us assume that such neutrino flux is produced in the MW halo due proton-proton interactions at a typical distance of $R_H = 10^2 R_{H,2}$ kpc. The corresponding

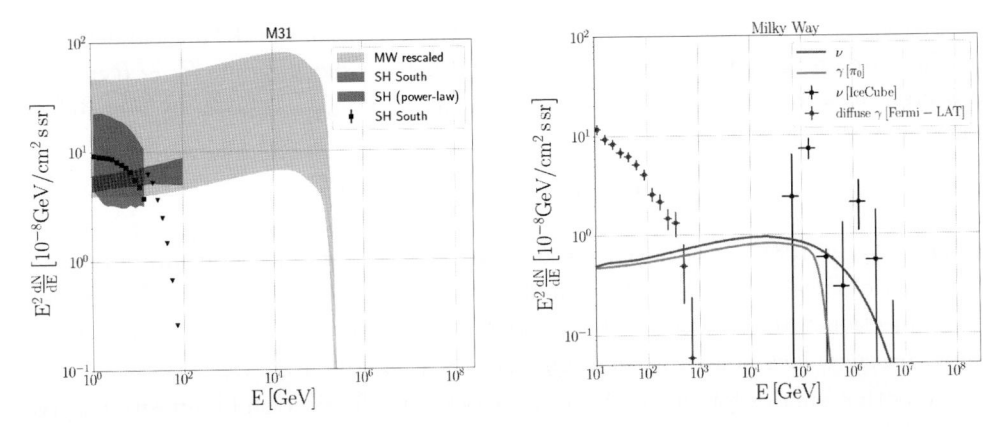

Fig. 1. *left:* Expected γ-ray emission from M31 (shaded cyan region) obtained re-scaling the predictions for the halo of the Milky Way. The black data points and the shaded gray region show *Fermi*-LAT observations of M31[1] *right:* Isotropic diffuse neutrino and γ-ray emission observed by Icecube[17] (black) and *Fermi*-LAT[18] (blue data points). Solid lines are predictions for the neutrino (green) and γ-ray (pink) resulting from the interactions of CR protons with ambient gas in a ∼ 100 kpc halo surrounding the MW.

differential neutrino emissivity from the entire MW would be

$$Q_\nu^{MW}(E_\nu) = (4\pi)^2 \Phi_\nu^{IC}(E_\nu) R_H^2. \tag{17}$$

Then, a neutrino luminosity $L_\nu^{MW}(> 100 \text{ TeV}) \approx 1.8 \times 10^{39} R_{H,2}^2 \text{erg/s}$ is expected, together with an isotropic diffuse γ-ray emission above ∼ 100 TeV with a similar luminosity.

The isotropic diffuse fluxes of γ-rays and neutrinos measured by *Fermi*-LAT[18] and Icecube,[17] respectively, are shown in Fig. 1, together with the predictions from the γ-ray and neutrino emission from CR proton-proton interactions in the MW halo, estimated assuming a proton spectrum $\propto E_p^{-2} \exp(-E_p/20 \text{ PeV})$ normalized in such a way to contain a total energy equal to $W_p \sim 4.6 \times 10^{57} R_{H,2}^2 n_{H,-3}^{-1}$ erg. A cutoff in the γ-ray spectrum appears due to the absorption of very high energy photons by pair production in the CMB.

Since the MW and M31 are quite similar galaxies, and the gas density in their halos are inferred from observations to be comparable (see e.g. Refs. 19, 20), it appears natural to compare the MW halo origin proposed for the Icecube neutrino flux and the M31 γ-ray SH emission. In the proposed scenarios the CR proton density in the halo would scale linearly with the central SMBH mass (if CR protons are powered by the galactic nuclear activity) or with the total mass of the galaxy to the power 3/2 (if CRs are accelerated at an accretion shock). The ratio between the mass of M31 and of the MW is ∼ 2, while the ratio between the SMBH masses is ∼ 33 (see Ref. 6 and references therein), which means that, if the CR confinement time in the halo is similar for the two galaxies (order of Gyr), one may suppose that the γ-ray and neutrino luminosities of M31 are a factor of ≈ 2.8 − 33 than those of the MW. In Fig. 1 we show the rescaled MW neutrino flux together with the $\gamma-$ray spectrum of M31 observed by *Fermi*-LAT for a power law plus exponential cutoff modeling of data (black points and shaded gray region) and for a power law model (blue line and shaded region).[1]

Remarkably, in the absence of a cutoff/steepening in the γ-ray spectrum of M31, we find a good agreement of our predictions and *Fermi*-LAT data, that suggests a possible common origin of the GeV γ-ray emission from the halo of M31 and the neutrino emission from the halo of the MW.

5. Conclusions

Recently, *Fermi*-LAT discovered a giant γ-ray halo of size $\sim$ 100-200 kpc around M31. We investigated a possible CR origin of the emission and we concluded that it could be explained by CR protons interacting with the circumgalactic gas. Particles can be accelerated directly in the SH of M31, or may be produced in the GC of M31 and then transported into the halo by means of buoyant bubbles. The morphology of the emission is expected to be spherically symmetric in the former case and similar to that of Fermi Bubbles, but much more extended, in the latter case. If CR protons can be confined for long times in the SH of M31 (order of gigayears), the emission measured by *Fermi*-LAT could be explained with a time averaged luminosity of CRs injected in the halo of the order of $\gtrsim 10^{40} - 10^{41}$ erg/s, comparable to the estimated luminosity of CR sources in the Galactic disk. Such luminosity can be accounted for by the galaxy nuclear activity or by an accretion shock.

Moreover, if a similar giant CR halo is present also around the MW, which appears plausible given the similarities between the MW and M31 and the observational evidence of similar extended gaseous halos around both galaxies, also the isotropic diffuse neutrino emission observed by Icecube could be explained as originating from the halo of our own Galaxy (as proposed by Ref. 7).

If gaseous halos are a common feature of MW and M31-like galaxies they might all emit both γ-rays and neutrinos, which however are beyond the capabilities of current instruments for distances significantly larger than M31 (see Ref. 6 for a discussion).

Alternatively, the M31 $\gamma-$ray emission could be of leptonic origin, namely the result of ICS of electrons on the CMB. In this case the particles have to be accelerated directly in the SH and no neutrinos would be expected from M31.

References

1. C. M. Karwin, S. Murgia, S. Campbell and I. V. Moskalenko, Fermi-LAT Observations of γ-Ray Emission toward the Outer Halo of M31, *ApJ* **880**, p. 95 (August 2019).
2. A. A. Abdo *et al.*, Fermi Large Area Telescope observations of Local Group galaxies: detection of M 31 and search for M 33, *A&A* **523**, p. L2 (November 2010).
3. M. Ackermann *et al.*, Observations of M31 and M33 with the Fermi Large Area Telescope: A Galactic Center Excess in Andromeda?, *ApJ* **836**, p. 208 (February 2017).

4. M. S. Pshirkov, V. V. Vasiliev and K. A. Postnov, Evidence of Fermi bubbles around M31, *MNRAS* **459**, L76 (June 2016).
5. C. Karwin, S. Murgia, I. Moskalenko, S. Fillingham, A.-K. Burns and M. Fieg, Dark Matter Interpretation of the Fermi-LAT Observations Toward the Outer Halo of M31, *arXiv e-prints*, p. arXiv:2010.08563 (October 2020).
6. S. Recchia, S. Gabici, F. A. Aharonian and V. Niro, Giant Cosmic-Ray Halos around M31 and the Milky Way, *ApJ* **914**, p. 135 (June 2021).
7. A. M. Taylor, S. Gabici and F. Aharonian, Galactic halo origin of the neutrinos detected by IceCube, *Phys. Rev. D* **89**, p. 103003 (May 2014).
8. R. Feldmann, D. Hooper and N. Y. Gnedin, Circum-galactic Gas and the Isotropic Gamma-Ray Background, *ApJ* **763**, p. 21 (January 2013).
9. S. Gabici, C. Evoli, D. Gaggero, P. Lipari, P. Mertsch, E. Orlando, A. Strong and A. Vittino, The origin of Galactic cosmic rays: Challenges to the standard paradigm, *International Journal of Modern Physics D* **28**, 1930022 (January 2019).
10. M. Ackermann et al., The Spectrum and Morphology of the Fermi Bubbles, *ApJ* **793**, p. 64 (September 2014).
11. T. W. Jones and D. S. De Young, Magnetohydrodynamic simulations of relic radio bubbles in clusters, *The Astrophysical Journal* **624**, p. 586–605 (May 2005).
12. E. Churazov, M. Brüggen, C. R. Kaiser, H. Böhringer and W. Forman, Evolution of Buoyant Bubbles in M87, *ApJ* **554**, 261 (June 2001).
13. A. Finoguenov, M. Ruszkowski, C. Jones, M. Brüggen, A. Vikhlinin and E. Mandel, In-Depth Chandra Study of the AGN Feedback in Virgo Elliptical Galaxy M84, *ApJ* **686**, 911 (October 2008).
14. C. Zhang, E. Churazov and A. A. Schekochihin, Generation of internal waves by buoyant bubbles in galaxy clusters and heating of intracluster medium, *Monthly Notices of the Royal Astronomical Society* **478**, 4785 (05 2018).
15. F. Guo and W. G. Mathews, Thefermibubbles. i. possible evidence for recent agn jet activity in the galaxy, *The Astrophysical Journal* **756**, p. 181 (Aug 2012).
16. H. Y. K. Yang, M. Ruszkowski, P. M. Ricker, E. Zweibel and D. Lee, The Fermi Bubbles: Supersonic Active Galactic Nucleus Jets with Anisotropic Cosmic-Ray Diffusion, *ApJ* **761**, p. 185 (December 2012).
17. R. Abbasi et al., The IceCube high-energy starting event sample: Description and flux characterization with 7.5 years of data, *arXiv e-prints*, p. arXiv:2011.03545 (November 2020).
18. M. Ackermann, M. Ajello, A. Albert, W. B. Atwood, L. Baldini, J. Ballet, G. Barbiellini, D. Bastieri, K. Bechtol, R. Bellazzini and et al., The spectrum of isotropic diffuse gamma-ray emission between 100 mev and 820 gev, *The Astrophysical Journal* **799**, p. 86 (Jan 2015).
19. A. Gupta, S. Mathur, Y. Krongold, F. Nicastro and M. Galeazzi, A Huge Reservoir of Ionized Gas around the Milky Way: Accounting for the Missing Mass?, *ApJ* **756**, p. L8 (September 2012).
20. Z. Qu, R. Huang, J. N. Bregman and J.-T. Li, An X-ray and SZ bright diffuse source toward M31: A Local Hot Bridge, *arXiv e-prints*, p. arXiv:2011.02125 (November 2020).

A nearly complete census of intergalactic gas using the kinematic Sunyaev-Zel'dovich effect

Chaves-Montero, Jonás

*Donostia International Physics Centre, Paseo Manuel de Lardizabal 4,
20018 Donostia-San Sebastian, Spain
E-mail: jonas.chaves@dipc.org
Webpage: https://jchavesmontero.github.io/jchavesmontero/*

A complete census of baryons in the late universe is a long-standing challenge due to the intermediate temperate and rarefied character of the majority of cosmic gas. To gain insight into this problem, we extract measurements of the kinematic Sunyaev-Zel'dovich (kSZ) effect from the cross-correlation of angular redshift fluctuations maps, which contain precise information about the cosmic density and velocity fields, and CMB maps high-pass filtered using aperture photometry; we refer to this technique as ARF-kSZ tomography. Remarkably, we detect significant cross-correlation for a wide range of redshifts and filter apertures using 6dF galaxies, BOSS galaxies, and SDSS quasars as tracers, yielding a 11 sigma detection of the kSZ effect. We then leverage these measurements to set constraints on the location, density, and abundance of gas inducing the kSZ effect, finding that this gas resides outside dark matter haloes, presents densities ranging from 10 to 250 times the cosmic average, and comprises half of cosmic baryons. Taken together, these findings indicate that ARF-kSZ tomography provides a nearly complete census of intergalactic gas from $z = 0$ to 5. This contribution is a summary of the work already published in Ref. 1.

Keywords: Diffuse radiation; cosmic background radiation; large-scale structure of Universe; cosmology: observations; cosmology: theory

1. Introduction

Over the last decades, precise observations of primordial CMB anisotropies[2] and Big Bang nucleosynthesis studies[3] have set strict constraints on the abundance and distribution of baryons in the early universe. However, a complete census of baryons at late times remains elusive; this is principally due to the intermediate temperature and rarefied character of nearly all cosmic gas, which hinders the detection of baryons outside high-density regions and leaves invisible the majority of cosmological volume. Such is the case that until recently, low redshift studies only detected 70% of the expected amount of baryons.[4–6]

Nonetheless, recent studies have successfully detected baryons outside high-density areas conducting kinematic Sunyaev-Zel'dovich (kSZ) effect observations,[7,8] thermal Sunyaev-Zel'dovich (tSZ) studies,[9,10] low-redshift Lyman-α surveys,[11] and deep X-ray campaigns.[12,13] Despite their success, these works only set constraints on the distribution of baryons at either a few specific redshifts or across a reduced number of line-of-sights, failing to provide a complete picture of cosmic gas in the late universe.

Of the different strategies listed above, throughout this work we set constraints on the properties of intergalactic gas using measurements of the kSZ effect, which refers to the Doppler boosting of CMB photons as these scatter off free electrons moving relative to the CMB rest frame.[14,15] The motivation of using these measurements is that the kSZ effect is sensitive to free electrons independently of the temperature and density of the medium in which these reside, and thus it is uniquely suited to study the large-scale distribution of baryons at low redshift.

Even though the kSZ effect presents significant advantages to observe cosmic gas, it is challenging to extract this signal from observations because the amplitude of kSZ fluctuations is approximately two orders of magnitude smaller than that of primordial CMB fluctuations and the spectral shape of both signals is practically the same. Furthermore, most extraction methods require estimating the peculiar velocity field of intervening matter,[16,17] which is also challenging and adds notable uncertainties. Other approaches circumvent such estimation but require either using cosmological simulations for calibration or modelling and subtracting other effects,[8,18–20] which also introduces substantial uncertainties.

In this scenario, the cross-correlation of angular redshift fluctuations (ARF),[21] which encode precise information about the cosmic density and velocity fields, and CMB observations provides a clean window towards a tomographic detection of the kSZ effect given that systematic uncertainties affecting either of these observables do not present significant correlation. This approach, which we refer to as ARF-kSZ tomography, requires redshift information from either spectroscopic or spectro-photometric surveys as well as theoretical predictions for the large-scale cross-correlation between ARF and the kSZ effect.

2. Results

To extract measurements of the kSZ effect, we start by generating ARF using galaxies from the 6dF Galaxy Survey (6dF),[22] galaxies from the Baryon Oscillation Spectroscopic Survey (BOSS),[23,24] and quasars from the extended Baryon Oscillation Spectroscopic survey (eBOSS)[25] selected at 16 different redshift shells between $z = 0$ and 5. Then, we high-pass filter foreground-reduced *Planck* maps by applying aperture photometry filters of different sizes on the positions given by the aforementioned galaxies and quasars, thereby extracting kSZ signal induced by gas surrounding these sources. This technique also reduces contamination from primordial CMB anisotropies as aperture photometry removes signals that are constant over the size of the aperture. Then, we cross-correlate these maps, finding significant correlation for a wide range of redshifts and filter apertures. After accounting for

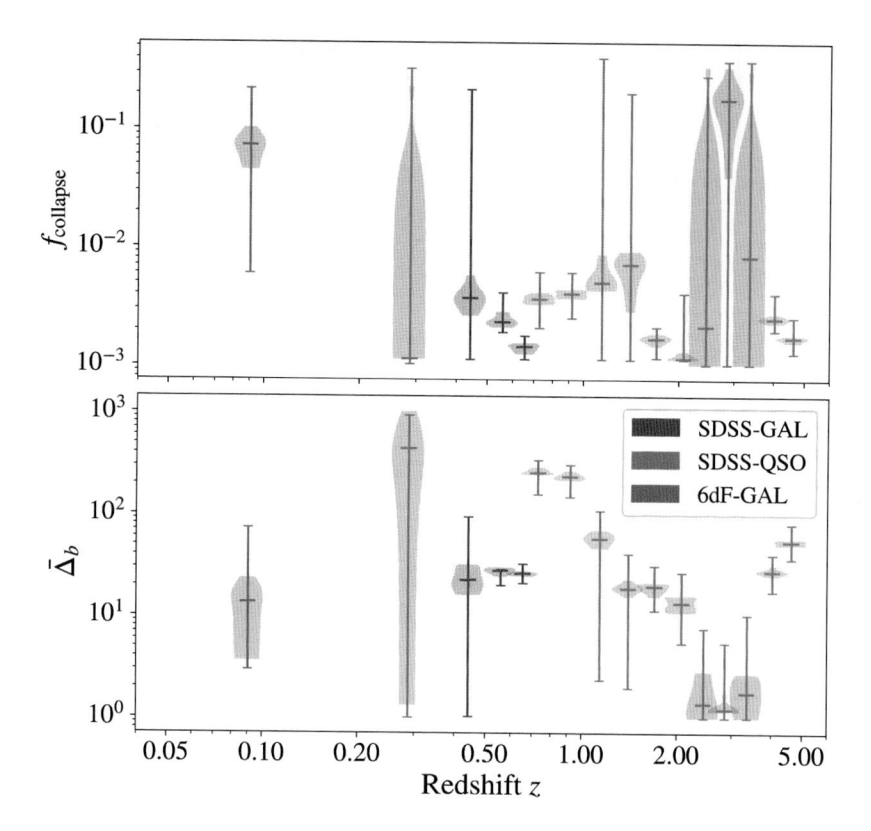

Fig. 1. Fraction of kSZ gas to within dark matter haloes (top panel) and average density of kSZ gas outside these structures (bottom panel). The horizontal bar and size of the shaded regions indicate the average and scatter of results computed using different *Planck* foreground-reduced maps, respectively; green, blue, and orange colours indicate the results for shells containing 6dF galaxies, BOSS galaxies, and SDSS quasars; grey colours denote shells with no significant detection of the kSZ effect; and error bars show 1σ uncertainties for *Planck* COMMANDER map. We find that more than 99% of kSZ gas resides outside haloes and that the density of this gas ranges from 10 to 250 times the cosmic baryon density, which is in agreement with the density of the intergalactic medium according to hydrodynamical simulations.

correlations between different measurements, we find that our measurements yield an 11σ detection of the kSZ effect, which is the highest significance detection of the kSZ effect up to date.

We leverage these measurements to set constraints on the location, density, and abundance of kSZ gas from redshift $z = 0$ to 5. In Fig. 1, we show that more than 99% of kSZ gas resides outside haloes and that the density of this gas ranges from 10 to 250 times the cosmic average, which is in agreement with the density of the gas in filaments and sheets according to hydrodynamical simulations. Then, in Fig. 2 we show that our kSZ measurements are compatible with detecting 50% of

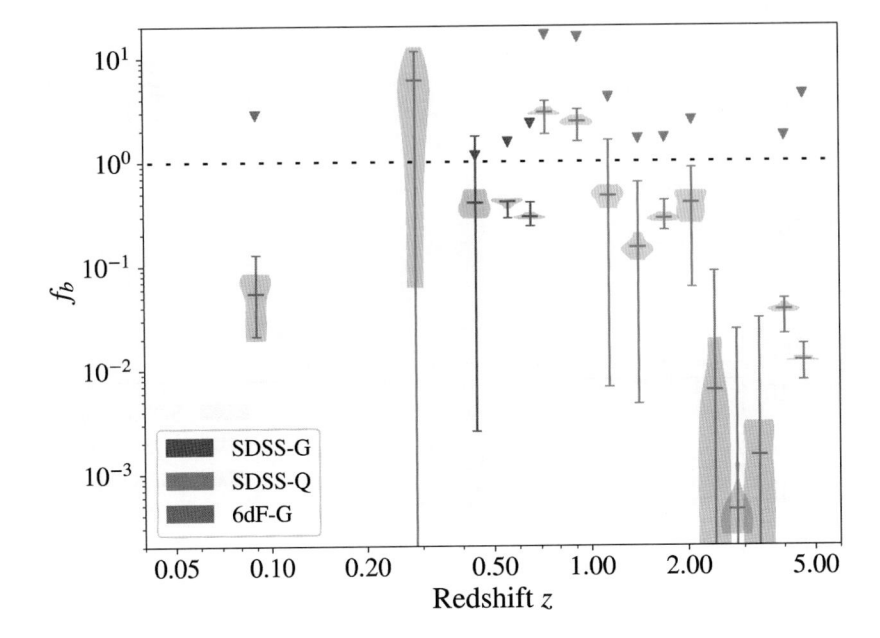

Fig. 2. Fraction of the total abundance of cosmic baryons detected at different redshifts. We use the same coding as Fig. 1. Remarkably, ARF-kSZ tomography is sensitive to approximately 50% of cosmic baryons, which highlights the efficiency of this technique detecting intergalactic gas. The results are well below 50% for the first and last two shells because the number density of sources at these redshifts is very low; in fact, forecasts for f_b when considering an infinite number density of sources (triangles) are compatible among all shells.

cosmic baryons. Taken together, these findings indicate that ARF-kSZ tomography provides a nearly complete census of intergalactic gas from $z = 0$ to 5.

References

1. J. Chaves-Montero, C. Hernández-Monteagudo, R. E. Angulo and J. D. Emberson, Measuring the evolution of intergalactic gas from $z = 0$ to 5 using the kinematic Sunyaev–Zel'dovich effect, *Monthly Notices of the Royal Astronomical Society* **503**, 1798 (March 2021).
2. Planck Collaboration, N. Aghanim, Y. Akrami, M. Ashdown, J. Aumont, C. Baccigalupi, M. Ballardini, A. J. Banday, R. B. Barreiro, N. Bartolo, S. Basak, R. Battye, K. Benabed, J. P. Bernard, M. Bersanelli, P. Bielewicz, J. J. Bock, J. R. Bond, J. Borrill, F. R. Bouchet, F. Boulanger, M. Bucher, C. Burigana, R. C. Butler, E. Calabrese, J. F. Cardoso, J. Carron, A. Challinor, H. C. Chiang, J. Chluba, L. P. L. Colombo, C. Combet, D. Contreras, B. P. Crill, F. Cuttaia, P. de Bernardis, G. de Zotti, J. Delabrouille, J. M. Delouis, E. Di Valentino, J. M. Diego, O. Doré, M. Douspis, A. Ducout, X. Dupac, S. Dusini, G. Efstathiou, F. Elsner, T. A. Enßlin, H. K. Eriksen, Y. Fantaye, M. Farhang, J. Fergusson, R. Fernandez-Cobos, F. Finelli, F. Forastieri, M. Frailis, A. A. Fraisse, E. Franceschi, A. Frolov, S. Galeotta, S. Galli, K. Ganga, R. T. Génova-Santos, M. Gerbino, T. Ghosh, J. González-Nuevo, K. M. Górski, S. Gratton, A. Gruppuso, J. E. Gudmundsson, J. Hamann, W. Handley,

F. K. Hansen, D. Herranz, S. R. Hildebrandt, E. Hivon, Z. Huang, A. H. Jaffe, W. C. Jones, A. Karakci, E. Keihänen, R. Keskitalo, K. Kiiveri, J. Kim, T. S. Kisner, L. Knox, N. Krachmalnicoff, M. Kunz, H. Kurki-Suonio, G. Lagache, J. M. Lamarre, A. Lasenby, M. Lattanzi, C. R. Lawrence, M. Le Jeune, P. Lemos, J. Lesgourgues, F. Levrier, A. Lewis, M. Liguori, P. B. Lilje, M. Lilley, V. Lindholm, M. López-Caniego, P. M. Lubin, Y. Z. Ma, J. F. Macías-Pérez, G. Maggio, D. Maino, N. Mandolesi, A. Mangilli, A. Marcos-Caballero, M. Maris, P. G. Martin, M. Martinelli, E. Martínez-González, S. Matarrese, N. Mauri, J. D. McEwen, P. R. Meinhold, A. Melchiorri, A. Mennella, M. Migliaccio, M. Millea, S. Mitra, M. A. Miville-Deschênes, D. Molinari, L. Montier, G. Morgante, A. Moss, P. Natoli, H. U. Nørgaard-Nielsen, L. Pagano, D. Paoletti, B. Partridge, G. Patanchon, H. V. Peiris, F. Perrotta, V. Pettorino, F. Piacentini, L. Polastri, G. Polenta, J. L. Puget, J. P. Rachen, M. Reinecke, M. Remazeilles, A. Renzi, G. Rocha, C. Rosset, G. Roudier, J. A. Rubiño-Martín, B. Ruiz-Granados, L. Salvati, M. Sandri, M. Savelainen, D. Scott, E. P. S. Shellard, C. Sirignano, G. Sirri, L. D. Spencer, R. Sunyaev, A. S. Suur-Uski, J. A. Tauber, D. Tavagnacco, M. Tenti, L. Toffolatti, M. Tomasi, T. Trombetti, L. Valenziano, J. Valiviita, B. Van Tent, L. Vibert, P. Vielva, F. Villa, N. Vittorio, B. D. Wandelt, I. K. Wehus, M. White, S. D. M. White, A. Zacchei and A. Zonca, Planck 2018 results. VI. Cosmological parameters, *A&A* **641**, p. A6 (September 2020).
3. R. J. Cooke, M. Pettini and C. C. Steidel, One Percent Determination of the Primordial Deuterium Abundance, *ApJ* **855**, p. 102 (March 2018).
4. M. Fukugita and P. J. E. Peebles, The Cosmic Energy Inventory, *ApJ* **616**, 643 (December 2004).
5. F. Nicastro, S. Mathur and M. Elvis, Missing baryons and the warm-hot intergalactic medium, *Science* **319**, 55 (2008).
6. J. M. Shull, B. D. Smith and C. W. Danforth, The Baryon Census in a Multiphase Intergalactic Medium: 30% of the Baryons May Still be Missing, *ApJ* **759**, p. 23 (November 2012).
7. C. Hernández-Monteagudo, Y.-Z. Ma, F. S. Kitaura, W. Wang, R. Génova-Santos, J. Macías-Pérez and D. Herranz, Evidence of the Missing Baryons from the Kinematic Sunyaev-Zeldovich Effect in Planck Data, *Physical Review Letters* **115**, p. 191301 (November 2015).
8. J. C. Hill, S. Ferraro, N. Battaglia, J. Liu and D. N. Spergel, Kinematic Sunyaev-Zel'dovich Effect with Projected Fields: A Novel Probe of the Baryon Distribution with Planck, WMAP, and WISE Data, *Phys. Rev. Lett.* **117**, p. 051301 (Jul 2016).
9. A. de Graaff, Y.-C. Cai, C. Heymans and J. A. Peacock, Probing the missing baryons with the Sunyaev-Zel'dovich effect from filaments, *A&A* **624**, p. A48 (April 2019).
10. H. Tanimura, G. Hinshaw, I. G. McCarthy, L. Van Waerbeke, N. Aghanim, Y.-Z. Ma, A. Mead, A. Hojjati and T. Tröster, A search for warm/hot gas filaments between pairs of SDSS Luminous Red Galaxies, *MNRAS* **483**, 223 (Feb 2019).
11. S. G. Gallego, S. Cantalupo, S. Lilly, R. A. Marino, G. Pezzulli, J. Schaye, L. Wisotzki, R. Bacon, H. Inami, M. Akhlaghi, S. Tacchella, J. Richard, N. F. Bouche, M. Steinmetz and M. Carollo, Stacking the Cosmic Web in fluorescent Ly α emission with MUSE, *MNRAS* **475**, 3854 (April 2018).
12. F. Nicastro, J. Kaastra, Y. Krongold, S. Borgani, E. Branchini, R. Cen, M. Dadina, C. W. Danforth, M. Elvis, F. Fiore, A. Gupta, S. Mathur, D. Mayya, F. Paerels, L. Piro, D. Rosa-Gonzalez, J. Schaye, J. M. Shull, J. Torres-Zafra, N. Wijers and L. Zappacosta, Observations of the missing baryons in the warm-hot intergalactic medium, *Nature* **558**, 406 (Jun 2018).

13. O. E. Kovács, Á. Bogdán, R. a. K. Smith, R. P. Kraft and W. R. Forman, Detection of the Missing Baryons toward the Sightline of H1821+643, *ApJ* **872**, p. 83 (Feb 2019).
14. R. A. Sunyaev and Y. B. Zeldovich, The Observations of Relic Radiation as a Test of the Nature of X-Ray Radiation from the Clusters of Galaxies, *Comments on Astrophysics and Space Physics* **4**, p. 173 (November 1972).
15. R. A. Sunyaev and I. B. Zeldovich, The velocity of clusters of galaxies relative to the microwave background - The possibility of its measurement, *MNRAS* **190**, 413 (February 1980).
16. Planck Collaboration, P. A. R. Ade, N. Aghanim, M. Arnaud, M. Ashdown, E. Aubourg, J. Aumont, C. Baccigalupi, A. J. Banday and R. B. Barreiro, Planck intermediate results. XXXVII. Evidence of unbound gas from the kinetic Sunyaev-Zeldovich effect, *A&A* **586**, p. A140 (Feb 2016).
17. E. Schaan, S. Ferraro, M. Vargas-Magaña, K. M. Smith, S. Ho, S. Aiola, N. Battaglia, J. R. Bond, F. De Bernardis and E. Calabrese, Evidence for the kinematic Sunyaev-Zel'dovich effect with the Atacama Cosmology Telescope and velocity reconstruction from the Baryon Oscillation Spectroscopic Survey, *Phys. Rev. D* **93**, p. 082002 (Apr 2016).
18. P. G. Ferreira, R. Juszkiewicz, H. A. Feldman, M. Davis and A. H. Jaffe, Streaming Velocities as a Dynamical Estimator of Ω, *ApJ* **515**, L1 (April 1999).
19. N. Hand, G. E. Addison, E. Aubourg, N. Battaglia, E. S. Battistelli, D. Bizyaev, J. R. Bond, H. Brewington, J. Brinkmann and B. R. Brown, Evidence of Galaxy Cluster Motions with the Kinematic Sunyaev-Zel'dovich Effect, *Phys. Rev. Lett.* **109**, p. 041101 (Jul 2012).
20. S. Ferraro, J. C. Hill, N. Battaglia, J. Liu and D. N. Spergel, Kinematic Sunyaev-Zel'dovich effect with projected fields. II. Prospects, challenges, and comparison with simulations, *Phys. Rev. D* **94**, p. 123526 (Dec 2016).
21. C. Hernandez-Monteagudo, J. Chaves-Montero and R. E. Angulo, Angular Redshift Fluctuations: A New Cosmological Observable, *arXiv e-prints*, p. arXiv:1911.12056 (November 2019).
22. D. H. Jones, W. Saunders, M. Colless, M. A. Read, Q. A. Parker, F. G. Watson, L. A. Campbell, D. Burkey, T. Mauch, L. Moore, M. Hartley, P. Cass, D. James, K. Russell, K. Fiegert, J. Dawe, J. Huchra, T. Jarrett, O. Lahav, J. Lucey, G. A. Mamon, D. Proust, E. M. Sadler and K.-i. Wakamatsu, The 6dF Galaxy Survey: Samples, observational techniques and the first data release, *MNRAS* **355**, 747 (December 2004).
23. D. J. Eisenstein, D. H. Weinberg, E. Agol, H. Aihara, C. Allende Prieto, S. F. Anderson, J. A. Arns, É. Aubourg, S. Bailey, E. Balbinot and et al., SDSS-III: Massive Spectroscopic Surveys of the Distant Universe, the Milky Way, and Extra-Solar Planetary Systems, *AJ* **142**, p. 72 (September 2011).
24. K. S. Dawson, D. J. Schlegel, C. P. Ahn, S. F. Anderson, É. Aubourg, S. Bailey, R. H. Barkhouser, J. E. Bautista, A. Beifiori, A. A. Berlind, V. Bhardwaj, D. Bizyaev, C. H. Blake, M. R. Blanton, M. Blomqvist, A. S. Bolton, A. Borde, J. Bovy, W. N. Brandt, H. Brewington, J. Brinkmann, P. J. Brown, J. R. Brownstein, K. Bundy, N. G. Busca, W. Carithers, A. R. Carnero, M. A. Carr, Y. Chen, J. Comparat, N. Connolly, F. Cope, R. A. C. Croft, A. J. Cuesta, L. N. da Costa, J. R. A. Davenport, T. Delubac, R. de Putter, S. Dhital, A. Ealet, G. L. Ebelke, D. J. Eisenstein, S. Escoffier, X. Fan, N. Filiz Ak, H. Finley, A. Font-Ribera, R. Génova-Santos, J. E. Gunn, H. Guo, D. Haggard, P. B. Hall, J.-C. Hamilton, B. Harris, D. W. Harris, S. Ho, D. W. Hogg, D. Holder, K. Honscheid, J. Huehnerhoff, B. Jordan, W. P. Jordan, G. Kauffmann, E. A. Kazin, D. Kirkby, M. A. Klaene, J.-P. Kneib, J.-M. Le Goff, K.-G. Lee,

D. C. Long, C. P. Loomis, B. Lundgren, R. H. Lupton, M. A. G. Maia, M. Makler, E. Malanushenko, V. Malanushenko, R. Mandelbaum, M. Manera, C. Maraston, D. Margala, K. L. Masters, C. K. McBride, P. McDonald, I. D. McGreer, R. G. McMahon, O. Mena, J. Miralda-Escudé, A. D. Montero-Dorta, F. Montesano, D. Muna, A. D. Myers, T. Naugle, R. C. Nichol, P. Noterdaeme, S. E. Nuza, M. D. Olmstead, A. Oravetz, D. J. Oravetz, R. Owen, N. Padmanabhan, N. Palanque-Delabrouille, K. Pan, J. K. Parejko, I. Pâris, W. J. Percival, I. Pérez-Fournon, I. Pérez-Ràfols, P. Petitjean, R. Pfaffenberger, J. Pforr, M. M. Pieri, F. Prada, A. M. Price-Whelan, M. J. Raddick, R. Rebolo, J. Rich, G. T. Richards, C. M. Rockosi, N. A. Roe, A. J. Ross, N. P. Ross, G. Rossi, J. A. Rubiño-Martin, L. Samushia, A. G. Sánchez, C. Sayres, S. J. Schmidt, D. P. Schneider, C. G. Scóccola, H.-J. Seo, A. Shelden, E. Sheldon, Y. Shen, Y. Shu, A. Slosar, S. A. Smee, S. A. Snedden, F. Stauffer, O. Steele, M. A. Strauss, A. Streblyanska, N. Suzuki, M. E. C. Swanson, T. Tal, M. Tanaka, D. Thomas, J. L. Tinker, R. Tojeiro, C. A. Tremonti, M. Vargas Magaña, L. Verde, M. Viel, D. A. Wake, M. Watson, B. A. Weaver, D. H. Weinberg, B. J. Weiner, A. A. West, M. White, W. M. Wood-Vasey, C. Yeche, I. Zehavi, G.-B. Zhao and Z. Zheng, The Baryon Oscillation Spectroscopic Survey of SDSS-III, *AJ* **145**, p. 10 (January 2013).
25. A. D. Myers, N. Palanque-Delabrouille, A. Prakash, I. Pâris, C. Yeche, K. S. Dawson, J. Bovy, D. Lang, D. J. Schlegel, J. A. Newman, P. Petitjean, J.-P. Kneib, P. Laurent, W. J. Percival, A. J. Ross, H.-J. Seo, J. L. Tinker, E. Armengaud, J. Brownstein, E. Burtin, Z. Cai, J. Comparat, M. Kasliwal, S. R. Kulkarni, R. Laher, D. Levitan, C. K. McBride, I. D. McGreer, A. A. Miller, P. Nugent, E. Ofek, G. Rossi, J. Ruan, D. P. Schneider, B. Sesar, A. Streblyanska and J. Surace, The SDSS-IV Extended Baryon Oscillation Spectroscopic Survey: Quasar Target Selection, *ApJS* **221**, p. 27 (December 2015).

Searching for Intermediate Mass Black Holes in the Milky Way's galactic halo

A. Franco*, A.A. Nucita, F. De Paolis, F. Strafella and M. Maiorano

Department of Mathematics and Physics "Ennio De Giorgi",
University of Salento, Via per Arnesano, I-73100, Italy,
INFN, Sezione di Lecce, Via per Arnesano, I-73100, Italy
* E-mail: antonio.franco@le.infn.it

Intermediate Mass Black Holes (IMBHs) are a class of black holes with masses in the range $10^2 \div 10^5$ $M_\odot$, which cannot directly derive from stellar evolution. Looking for these objects and estimating their abundance is important not only for a deeper understanding of their origin but also for unveiling the nature and distribution of the dark matter in the galactic halo. Since February 2018 to January 2020, the Large and Small Magellanic Cloud have been intensively monitored by the DECAM instrument, installed on the 4m V. Blanco Telescope (CTIO, Chile) with the main objective to discover microlensing events possibly due to IMBHs.

Here we outline the developed data analysis pipeline. We have tested it versus known variable sources finding many not previously known variables objects. A few sources show a light curve similar to that expected for a microlensing event, but further analysis is required to confirm the microlensing nature of these events.

For these sources, and in particular for the uncatalogued variable stars, we try to determine if they are periodic or not via a periodogram analysis.

Keywords: Intermediate Mass Black Holes, ISIS Subtraction package, Large Magellanic Cloud, Small Magellanic Cloud, DECAM, Microlensing, Variable stars.

1. Introduction

During the last years of XVIII century, the English pastor John Michell and the mathematician Pierre Simon de Laplace imagined the existence of some dark objects, which were called *dark stars*.[1] The given name derived from the fact that if the radius of an object with mass M turns out to be $R = 2GM/c^2$ (where G is Newton's gravitational constant and c is the light speed), it cannot be visible from outside and therefore it would "appear" as *dark*.

The first actual mathematical description was provided in 1916 by Karl Schwarzschild with his solution of Einstein's field equations, representing the gravitational field around a non-rotating, spherical, and electrically neutral mass.

Half a century later, in 1967, John Wheeler coined the term *black hole* (BH) to indicate an object whose gravitational field is so large that does not let anything, even light, escape from its gravitational attraction. Unlike the classical formalization, General Relativity predicts the existence of an event horizon located at $r = r_S = 2GM/c^2$, which is called the Schwarzschild radius.

2. Black Holes Classification

There are three main kinds of black holes: stellar, intermediate, and supermassive BHs. The most common ones are stellar and supermassive BHs: the first one, with a mass less than 30 $M_\odot$, are produced by stellar death, when very massive stars with $M > 25 - 30\ M_\odot$ reach the and of their lives.

Supermassive BHs, with $M \simeq 10^5 \div 10^{10}\ M_\odot$, are located at the center of almost every galaxy in the Universe and are also responsible for the AGN activity.

The most unknown and mysterious intermediate-mass black holes (IMBHs) have a hypothetical mass in the range $30 \div 10^5\ M_\odot$ and might provide the Galactic Halo's dark matter contribution. Their formation and evolution are not well known as we are not able to observe many of these objects. There are four main possible mechanisms for IMBHs[a] formation[11]:

- Evolution of Population III stars
- Stellar collisions in dense star clusters
- Primordial Black Holes[12–17]

3. Gravitational Microlensing

Gravitational microlensing may offer an efficient way to detect BHs if they populate the Galactic Halo. This phenomenon shows up when an object (the lens) stands in the way between the observer and a faraway source. Photons coming from the source are deflected by the gravitational field of the lens (see Ref. 18 for a review). Depending on the phenomenon geometry, we might observe virtual images of the source. If the images are separated by large enough angles, as happens in the case of lensed quasars, one can detect double or multiple images of the same source. In the case of unresolved images, we have a microlensing event. It might be possible to observe the luminosity variation of the source, that is called *amplification*, which follows the *Paczyński law*[19]:

$$\mu(t) = \frac{u(t)^2 + 2}{u(t)\sqrt{u(t)^2 + 4}} \quad (1)$$

where $u(t) = \beta(t)/\theta_E$ is the Lens-Source angular separation ($\beta(t)$) in Einstein's angle (θ_E) unit.

4. Searching for Intermediate Mass Black Holes with DECAM

Searching for IMBHs might be important to obtain significant information regarding the evolution of black holes and constrain their contribution to the halo dark

---

[a]Searches for IMBHs have been attempted recently in dwarf spheroidal galaxies (dSph) where these objects are expected to form (see, e.g., Ref. 2–9). In fact, extrapolating the fundamental M_{BH} - M_{Bulge} relation (see, e.g., Ref. 10, for the supermassive BHs case) down to typical dSph masses, black holes in the typical IMBH mass range arise.

matter. This study could give major contributions about PBHs as dark matter candidates.[20,21] This study can be carried out using the microlensing phenomenon and monitoring some regions in the sky with a very high stellar density, such as the Magellanic Clouds.

The microlensing rate toward the Large Magellanic Cloud (LMC in the following) is estimated to be[22]:

$$\Gamma \approx \frac{1.66 \times 10^{-6}}{(M/M_\odot)^{1/2}} \text{ event/year} \qquad (2)$$

and, given $N_0 \approx 10^7$ the number of LMC stars, the number of expected microlensing events for solar mass lenses is:

$$N_{ev} = N_0\, \Gamma(M)\, t_{exp}\, \varepsilon(M) \approx 50 \text{ events} \qquad (3)$$

where $t_{exp} \simeq 2$ years is the duration of the survey and $\varepsilon \approx 0.1$ is the detection efficiency. Taking into account microlensing events with a duration up to two years, is possible to estimate the detectable mass limit that is $\lesssim 300\, M_\odot$: we can therefore observe lenses in the IMBH mass range.

4.1. *DECAM instrument*

DECAM[23] (Dark Energy CAMera) is a high-performance, wide-field CCD imager mounted at the prime focus of the Victor M. Blanco 4m Telescope (CTIO, Chile). This camera consists of a grid of 62 CCDs (2048×4096 Pixels) which cover a field of view of $\sim 3 \text{ deg}^2$ (~ 2.2 degree wide) with 0.263 arcsecond/pixel resolution. It uses a set of filters similar to those employed in the Sloan Digital Sky Survey (g,r,i,z,Y filters). It is active since September 2012 on behalf of the Dark Energy Survey (DES), finished in January 2019.

4.2. *Blanco/DECAM survey*

The proposal considered for this work, whose Principal Investigator is William Dawson, is related to the current rate of LIGO events that favors such a large abundance that IMBHs would make up the majority of dark matter. A Blanco/DECAM microlensing survey is useful to search for similar IMBHs in our Milky Way.[24] The survey was designed to intensively observe the Magellanic Clouds for two years, from February 2018 to January 2020, acquiring several images toward 23 LMC fields and 6 SMC fields. In particular, the LMC survey, currently under study, has continuously monitored a portion of sky with $4\text{h}\,40\text{m} < \alpha < 6\text{h}\,20\text{m}$ and $-73° < \delta < -65°$. The images have been acquired with a sampling of 7-10 days between each observation night, and a sub-sampling of few hours, acquiring 3-4 images during the same night. The final result is about 40 images acquired for each field and for each filter used (mainly in g and r bands, with just few images obtained in the i band).

In particular, for our aim, we have used 36 resampled images (bias, flat and dark subtracted) in the g band acquired toward the Large Magellanic Cloud.

4.3. Detection method

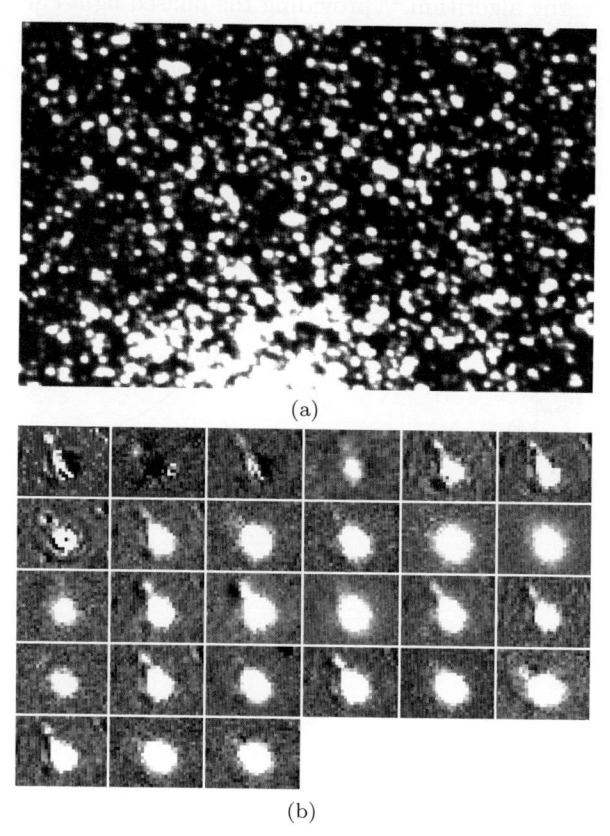

Fig. 1. (a) Small frame within the observed field of view toward LMC. The red dot indicates an identified microlensing candidate at coordinates $\alpha = 84.126\,738°, \delta = -68.797\,069°$. (b) Differential luminosity over time for the microlensing candidate event.

In order to search for microlensing events, it is essential the detection of variable sources in the images. This goal can be achieved using the ISIS 2.2 subtraction package.[25,26] The ISIS software, developed by Christophe Alard since the last years of the 90s, allows to perform the photometry of different objects through images difference, especially in very crowded field like LMC and SMC. The software works in multiple steps:

- Interpolation: images alignment;
- Creation of a reference image (from N selected "good" images from the hole sample) to compute the subtraction process;
- Subtraction between the reference image and each image of the sample, highlighting the brightness difference for variables;
- Detection of variable sources;
- Execution of the photometry for these objects.

Once a variable and potentially interesting source is identified, we use the Schwarzenberg-Czerny algorithm,[27] providing the phased light curve, and attempting an estimate of the period of the source. This algorithm gives more reliable results, in particular for high signal/noise ratio values, where the Lomb-Scargle algorithm is not efficient enough.[28]

4.4. *Microlensing candidate analysis*

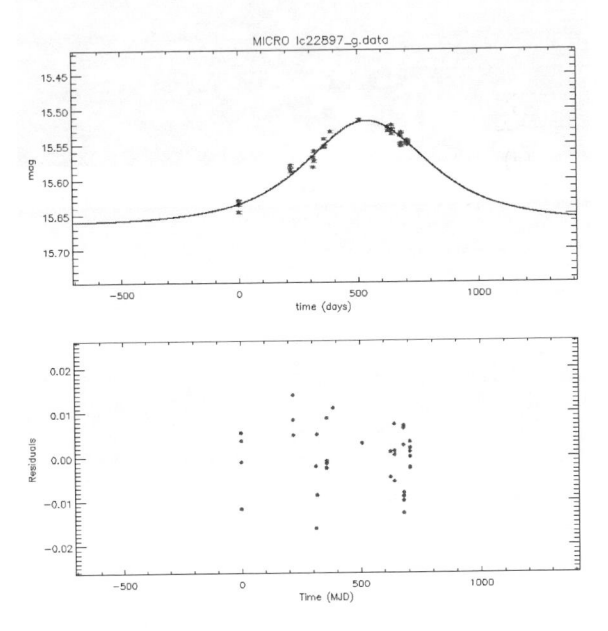

Fig. 2. The upper box shows the magnitude of the variable sources over two years of data (red dots) and the fitted Paczyński curve. The bottom box shows the residuals.

One of the most interesting variable sources detected so far is a microlensing like curve that seems to be associated with an object in the direction of LMC ($\alpha = 84.126\,738°, \delta = -68.797\,069°$). The field of view containing this source is shown in Fig. 1(a).

Using the ISIS software it appears that this source is clearly variable, as shown in Fig. 1(b). The corresponding light curve is shown in Fig. 2 from which it is apparent a Paczynski-like behavior, typical of a microlensing event. The fit and the residuals are shown in the upper and lower panels of Fig. 2, respectively.

The fit returns an estimate of the event Einstein time $t_E = (246.4 \pm 31.7)$ days and the baseline magnitude $m_0 = 15.66 \pm 0.01$. We note that the indicated magnitude represents the instrumental magnitude of the camera, without any photometric correction. In addition, it is important to understand the geometry of the phenomenon in order to estimate the lens mass. For these reasons new images toward

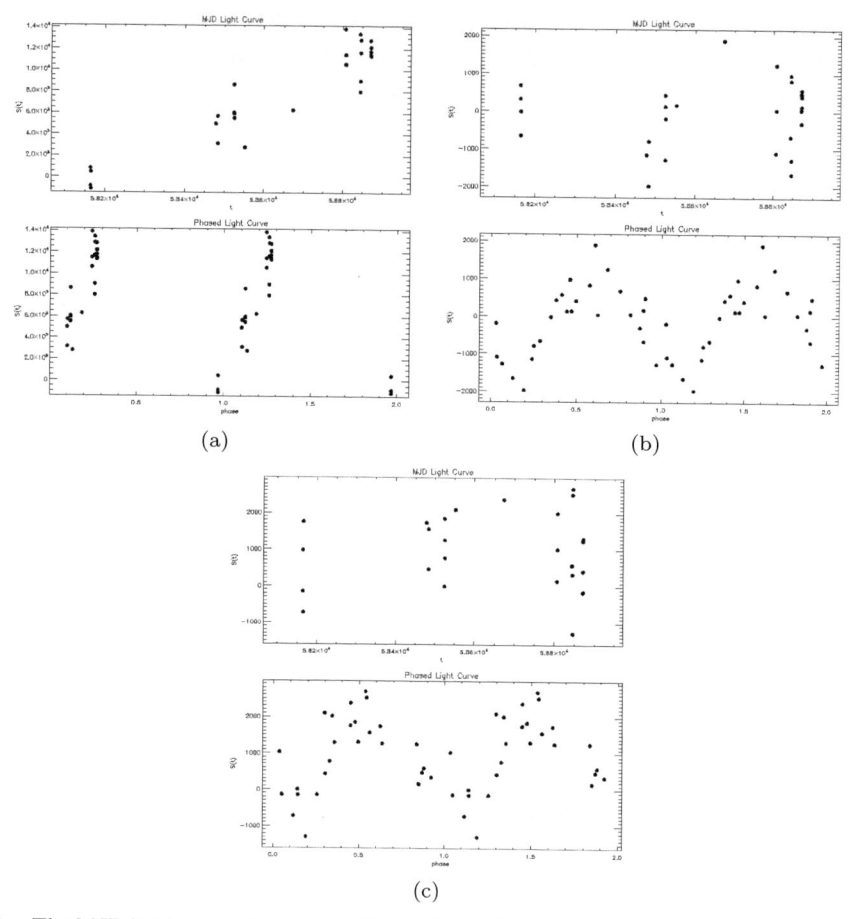

Fig. 3. The MJD light curves (upper panel) and phased light curve (lower panel) for three different variable sources. (a) Non-periodic variable and (b), (c) eclipsing binary candidates.

the particularly interesting fields will be acquired in the next future in order to provide a better and complete results, that will be published after completion of the work.

4.5. Periodic variable sources candidate analysis

ISIS 2.2 and the Schwarzenberg-Czerny algorithm enable the recognition of a few periodic variables and allow to obtain an estimate of their period. This can be used both to confirm previously observed sources and to detect new ones. The observed data for three variable sources toward the LMC are shown in Fig. 3. Panel (a) shows the light curve for non-periodic variable source, at coordinates $\alpha_a = 84.530\,329°, \delta_a = -68.791\,993°$, displaying the increasing flux over time and highlighting the absence of a particular periodicity in the phased light curve. Panels (b) and (c) show two sources, at coordinates $\alpha_b = 84.486\,772°, \delta_b = -68.799\,780°$ and $\alpha_c = 84.303\,917°, \delta_c = -68.741\,760°$, displaying the variation of the flux with respect to the time (upper) and over two phases (bottom), enabling the estimate of the period that is $P_b \simeq 1.69$ days and $P_c \simeq 0.31$ days.

5. Conclusions

The detection of periodic and non-periodic variable sources has allowed confirming the goodness of the developed pipeline. In particular, the two years time window, the sampling and the efficiency of the DECAM instrument have shown the possibility to detect microlensing events. So far, many known variable sources have been identified in four DECAM fields of view - toward LMC - and some unknown variables are waiting to be studied more deeply. A few possible microlensing event candidates (e.g. that shown in Fig. 2), which wait for confirmation, have been also found in the data.

The contents presented in this paper will be discussed in more details in the the paper *"Searching for galactic halo Intermediate Mass Black Holes through gravitational microlensing"*, by A. Franco et al., currently under preparation.

Acknowledgments

We acknowledge the support by the Euclid and TAsP (Theoretical Astroparticle Physics) projects of the Istituto Nazionale di Fisica Nucleare (INFN).

References

1. S. J. CROTHERS, *"A Brief History of Black Holes"*, Progress in Physics, Volume 2, Issue 2, pp.54-57 (2006).
2. L. MANNI ET AL., *"A XMM-Newton observation of a sample of four close dwarf spheroidal galaxies"*, Monthly Notices of the Royal Astronomical Society, Volume 451, Issue 3, p.2735-2749 (2015).
3. A. NUCITA ET AL., *"Hint for a faint intermediate mass black hole in the Ursa Minor dwarf galaxy"*, New Astronomy, Volume 23, p. 107-112 (2013).
4. A. NUCITA ET AL., *"An XMM-Newton search for X-ray sources in the Fornax dwarf galaxy"*, Astronomy and Astrophysics, Volume 550, id.A18, 13 pp. (2013).
5. A. NUCITA ET AL., *"The high energy search for IMBHs in close dSph Milky Way satellites"*, Memorie della Societa Astronomica Italiana, v.84, p.645 (2013).
6. A. NUCITA ET AL., *"The high energy view of NGC 6388: hints for an IMBH?"*, Memorie della Societa Astronomica Italiana, v.84, p.643 (2013).
7. A. NUCITA ET AL., *"The XMM-Newton slew view of IGRJ17361-4441: A transient in the globular cluster NGC 6388"*, New Astronomy, Volume 17, Issue 6, p. 589-593 (2012).
8. A. E. REINES ET AL., *"Dwarf Galaxies with Optical Signatures of Active Massive Black Holes"*, The Astrophysical Journal, Volume 775, Issue 2, article id. 116, 24 pp. (2013).
9. S. M. LEMONS ET AL., *"An X-Ray Selected Sample of Candidate Black Holes in Dwarf Galaxies"*, The Astrophysical Journal, Volume 805, Issue 1, article id. 12, 10 pp. (2015).

10. J. Magorrian et al., *"The Demography of Massive Dark Objects in Galaxy Centers"*, The Astronomical Journal, Volume 115, Issue 6, pp. 2285-2305 (1998).
11. J. E. Greene, J. Strader, L. C. Ho, *"Intermediate-Mass Black Holes"*, Annual Review of Astronomy and Astrophysics, vol. 58, p.257-312 (2020).
12. Y. B. Zel'dovich and I. Novikov, *The hypothesis of cores retarded during expansion and the hot cosmological model*, Astronomicheskii Zhurnal, Vol. 43, p.758 (1966).
13. S. Hawking, *Gravitationally collapsed objects of very low mass*, Monthly Notices of the Royal Astronomical Society, Vol. 152, p. 75 (1971).
14. B. J. Carr, S. W. Hawking, *"Black holes in the early Universe"*, Monthly Notices of the Royal Astronomical Society, Vol. 168, p. 399-416 (1974).
15. P. H. Frampton, *"The Primordial Black Hole Mass Range"*, Modern Physics Letters A, Volume 31, Issue 12, id. 1650064 (2016).
16. J. Garcìa-Bellido, *Massive primordial black holes as dark matter and their detection with gravitational waves*, Journal of Physics: Conference Series, (1) 2017.
17. M. Yu. Khlopov, *"Primordial Black Holes"*, Research in Astronomy and Astrophysics, Volume 10, Issue 6, pp. 495-528 (2010).
18. F. De Paolis et al., *"The Scales of Gravitational Lensing"*, Universe, vol. 2, issue 1, p. 6, https://doi.org/10.3390/universe2010006 (2016).
19. B. Paczyński, *"Gravitational microlensing by the galactic halo"*, Astrophysical Journal v.304, p.1-5 (1986).
20. N. Afshordi, P. McDonald and D. Spergel, *Primordial black holes as dark matter:the power spectrum and evaporation of early structures*, The Astrophysical Journal, Volume 594, Issue 2, pp. L71-L74 (2003).
21. B. Carr, F. Kühnel and M. Sandstad, *Primordial black holes as dark matter*, Physical Review D, Volume 94, Issue 8, id.083504 (2016).
22. K. Griest, *"Galactic microlensing as a method of detecting massive compact halo objects"*, Astrophysical Journal v.366, p.412-421 (1991).
23. R. A. Shaw, *"NOAO Data Handbook (Version 2.2)"*, Tucson: National Optical Astronomy Observatory (2015).
24. W. Dawson, *"Program Information for 2018A-0273"*, Blanco/DECAM survey proposal, https://www.noao.edu/noaoprop/abstract.mpl?2018A-0273.
25. C. Alard, R. H. Lupton, *"A method for optimal image subtraction"*, The Astrophysical Journal, Volume 503, Issue 1, pp. 325-331 (1998).
26. C. Alard, *"Image subtraction using spacially variable Kernel"*, Astronomy & Astrophysics, Astron. Astrophys. Suppl. Ser. 144, 363–370 (2000).
27. A. Schwarzenberg-Czerny, *"Accuracy of period determination"*, Monthly Notices of the Royal Astronomical Society (ISSN 0035-8711), vol. 253, Nov. 15, 1991, p. 198-206 (1991).
28. A. Schwarzenberg-Czerny, *"Fast and Statistically Optimal Period Search in Uneven Sampled Observations"*, Astrophysical Journal Letters v.460, p.L107 (1996).

Virial clouds evolution from the last scattering up to the formation of first stars

Noraiz Tahir[1,2,*], Asghar Qadir[3,†], Muhammad Sakhi[4,‡], and Francesco De Paolis[1,2,§]

[1] *Department of Mathematics and Physics "E. De Giorgi", University of Salento,*
Via per Arnesano, I-73100 Lecce, Italy
[2] *INFN, Sezione di Lecce, Via per Arnesano, I-73100 Lecce, Italy*
[3] *Abdus Salam School of Mathematics, G.C. University, Lahore, Pakistan*
[4] *Department of Physics, Quaid-e-Azam University, Islamabad, Pakistan*
* noraiz.tahir@le.infn.it
† asgharqadir46@gmail.com
‡ sakhi.cosmos@gmail.com
§ francesco.depaolis@le.infn.it

The asymmetry in the cosmic microwave background (CMB) towards several nearby galaxies detected by *Planck* data is probably due to the rotation of "cold gas" clouds present in the galactic halos. In 1995 it had been proposed that galactic halos are populated by pure molecular hydrogen clouds which are in equilibrium with the CMB. More recently, it was shown that the equilibrium could be stable. Nevertheless, the cloud chemical composition is still a matter to be studied. To investigate this issue we need to trace the evolution of these virial cloud from the time of their formation to the present, and to confront the model with the observational data. The present paper is a short summary of a paper.[1] Here we only concentrate on the evolution of these clouds from the last scattering surface (LSS) *up to* the formation of first generation of stars (population-III stars).

Keywords: Dark matter; cosmic microwave background radiations; spiral galaxies; molecular clouds; galactic halos.

1. Introduction

The study of the nature of galactic halos and their dynamics is a task that is difficult to address. Here we present a summary of a more detailed analysis addressing this issue.[1]

The Λ cold dark matter (ΛCDM) model entails that $\sim 5\%$ of our Universe is made of baryonic matter,[2] of which $\sim 60\%$ is detected,[3–7] but $\sim 40\%$ is still undetected at present. This is the so-called "missing baryon problem".

In 1995 it was proposed that a fraction, f, of these missing baryons is present in the galactic halos in the form of *pure* molecular hydrogen (H_2) clouds which are in equilibrium with the CMB.[8] The difficulty was on the observation of such "chameleons" megerd with the background. One of the suggestions was, to look for a Doppler shift effect due to the rotation of galaxies, assuming that the rotation of these clouds is synchronized with the rotation of galactic halos, and hence they should be Doppler shifted, those clouds roatating towards us should give a blue-shift effect while those rotating away from us would give a red-shifted contribution.

In 2011 WMAP data was analyzed for M31. The analysis revelaed a temperature asymmetry in the CMB which was almost frequency independent,[10] which was a strong indication of the Doppler shift effect due to the galactic halo rotation. This opens up a window to observe these clouds and to study the baryonic content of the galactic halos.[11] Soon after WMAP, in 2014 *Planck* data towards M31 was analyzed and the asymmetry was seen at a more precise level.[12] A temperature asymmetry was also detected towards several nearby spiral galaxies.[13–16]

There was more than one item of evidence of the predicted Doppler shift effect, but observing that there is a Doppler shift due to the halo rotation does not reveal the true nature of the effect, i.e. if it is partially or fully due to the molecular clouds in the halos, or, if is there anything else that could give a masking or mimiking effect in the asymmetry. Another unanswered question is the chemical composition of these clouds: are they pure H_2 clouds, or there is some contamination of dust or heavier molecules in them? It is quite obvious that galactic halos contain a significant fraction of dust that *should* contaminate these clouds,[18] so one needs to model the clouds.

As these clouds should survive on acount of the virial theorem, they were called "virial clouds". These clouds were modeled and it was seen that at the current CMB temperature the centeral density of pure H_2 clouds was $\approx 1.60 \times 10^{-18}$kg m^{-3}, similarly the mass and radius were $\approx 1.93 \times 10^{-4} M_\odot$, and ≈ 0.032 pc.[19] The change in their physical parameters with the contamination of heavier molecules and dust were also estimated. It was seen that as the contamination of dust and hevier molecules were increased in the clouds, they became denser, and their mass and radius decreased.[19–21] An objection was raised on the stability of these clouds, as it was believed that molecular clouds can not be stable at this, very low, CMB temperature, as there would be no mode that could be excited by the photons and the cloud might collapse to form stars or other planetary objects,[22] but it was demonstrated that this equilibrium *does* arise on account of the translational mode, despite its extremely small probability, because of the size of the virial clouds and the time scales available for thermal equilibrium to be reached, so that the time required for thermalization is much less than that required for collapse.[19]

Modeling the virial clouds and estimating the change in physical parameters with the contamination of heavier molecules and dust, and observing the CMB temperature asymmetry by *Planck* data still does not answer the question on the nature of virial clouds and the exact cause of the observed asymmetry in the CMB. One has to run the clock back and trace the evolution of virial clouds when they were formed at the LSS to the present. This task needs to be done in two phases: (*i*) from LSS up to the formation of population-III stars; and (*ii*) from the formation and explosion of population-III stars to the present. Here we discuss the first part of evolution, as various qualitative changes took place during the formation of population-III stars.[23] Hence there will be significant changes during the second step, which will be studied more clearly and in more detail later.

2. First epoch of virial clouds evolution

Virial clouds would have formed at $z = 1100$, the last scattering time (LSS) and they evolved in their chemical composition and physical parameters, but in order to maintain their stability they survived the collapse and stayed in quasi-static equilibrium with the CMB since then. It is quite obvious that when they formed they should have had the primordial chemical composition, i.e. $\sim 75\%$ atomic hydrogen and $\sim 25\%$ helium. In addition to H and He there were other atoms and molecules like deuterium, helium-3, lithium and molecular hydrogen, which could have contributed to the virial clouds, but their fraction was negligilble as compared to H and He. Hence these molecules and atoms could not have any significant effect on the virial cloud physical parameters. As a result the ratio of atomic hydrogen and helium would remain the same and these would be the main component to form the virial clouds during the period, but there should be a fast change in their chemical composition after the formation and explosion of population-III stars.

2.1. *Hydrogen-Helium virial clouds*

Since virial clouds must be considered to be in thermal equilibrium because they are embedded in the heat bath of the CMB, we need to use the canonical distribution function for a fixed temperature and use the cooling of the heat bath to provide a quasi-equilibrium. Moreover, these clouds should start to form in the potential well of cold dark matter (CDM). As the clouds are thermalized the potential well will not cause them to collapse to form population-III stars,[24] but will modify the physical parameters of virial clouds.

To obtain a general expressions we consider a virial cloud composed of an arbitrary mixture of H and He, with mass fractions α and β. Then, we use the primordial cosmological fractions of H and He for the final computation. The total mass of the cloud is, obviously, $M_{cl}(r) = \alpha M_H(r) + \beta M_{He}(r)$, with the condition $\alpha + \beta = 1$. The density distribution for two fluids is given by[19]

$$\rho_{cl}(r) = \sqrt{\frac{64}{27} \frac{(G\rho_{c_H}\rho_{c_{He}})^{3/2}}{(k_B T)^{9/2}} (m_H m_{He})^{5/2}}$$
$$exp\left[-\frac{1}{2}\left(\frac{\alpha G M_H(r) m_H}{r k_B T} + \frac{\beta G M_{He}(r) m_{He}}{r k_B T}\right)\right]. \quad (1)$$

and the corresponding differential equation can be written as[19]

$$r\frac{d\rho_{cl}(r)}{dr} - r^2 \left(\frac{2\pi G}{k_B T}\right)[\rho_{cl}(r)(\alpha\rho_{c_H} m_H + \beta\rho_{c_{He}} m_{He})] - \rho_{cl}(r) \ln\left(\frac{\rho_{cl}(r)}{\tau}\right) = 0, \quad (2)$$

where, $\tau = (8/3\sqrt{3})[(G\rho_{c_H}\rho_{c_{He}})^{3/2}/(k_B T)^{9/2}][m_H m_{He}]^{5/2}$, ρ_{c_H} is the central density of H cloud, $\rho_{c_{He}}$ is the central density of He cloud, m_H, the mass of single atom of hydrogen, and m_{He}, the mass of single atom of helium.

We use eq. (2) to estimate the central density of the clouds. We estimated the central density, Jeans mass and radius of the two-fluid virial clouds with primordial fraction of H, and He, i.e. $\alpha = 0.75$, and $\beta = 0.25$. In order to solve eq. (1) numerically, we assumed a guess value of ρ_c, at a fixed temperature, and estimate where the density becomes *exactly* zero at the boundary. We then compare the Jeans radius with that central density with the value available to us. We adjust the central density so that the density becomes zero exactly at the Jeans radius. In this way we get a self-consistent solution of the differential equation subject to the given boundary conditions. Next, we decrease the temperature and repeat the process.

It was seen that with the decrease in temperature and redshift, the density of virial clouds increased, at $z = 1100$ these clouds were $\approx 8.53 \times 10^{-20} kgm^{-3}$ and at $z = 50$ the density of the clouds was $\approx 6.05 \times 10^{-19}$kg m^{-3}. On the other hand the mass decreased with the decrease in temperature and so as the radius of the clouds. These clouds were massive ≈ 50 pc, with a mass $\approx 3.05 \times 10^5 M_\odot$ at $z = 1100$, then at $z = 50$ the clouds were ≈ 3.54 pc with a mass of $\approx 7.54 \times 10^3 M_\odot$.

3. Results and discussion

The first stage of the virial cloud evolution turns out to be quite simple. We have seen that virial clouds became denser with time, and they lost mass and shrunk in size. The physics of the second stage of evolution will not be that simple since there will be cooling due to the formation of molecular hydrogen, turbulence and the angular momentum effects in the virial cloud after the formation and explosion of population-III stars. We need to consider all these things while tracing the second epoch of evolution, and this will be done in the later paper.

One could expect molecular hydrogen to be formed in the first epoch, but during the era of study in the current summarized paper any H_2 molecules formed in the clouds will be unstable and dissociate due to the radiation pressure at that time, since H_2 needs dust particles to remain stable. The molecular cooling of such clouds played a vital role after the recombination and thir cooling rate has been analyzed from $T \sim 120 - 3$ K.[25] Hence, we do not need to consider the effect of cooling from molecular hydrogen till population-III stars exploded. It may also be expected that the electronic transition mode in hydrogen and helium atoms by the CMB photons. One can check that most of the CMB photons at 3000 K do not have enough energy to excite the electrons of a hydrogen atom from its ground state, but the higher energy tail does have sufficient energy to do so. The percentage of such photons is 0.016, which is quite low. Hence, there will be a negligible effect of this mode, but these effects will be more significant in the later stage of evolution.

Acknowledgements

FDP and NT acknowledge support from the TAsP and Euclid INFN projects.

References

1. N. Tahir et al., Evolution of virial clouds-I: From the surface of last scattering up to the formation of population-III stars, *Europ. Phys. J. C* **81**, 827 (2021).
2. A.R.P. Ade, et al., Planck 2015 results-xiii. cosmological parameters, *Astron. Astrophys.* **594**, A13 (2015).
3. A. S. Kassin et al., Dark and baryonic matter in bright spiral galaxies. II. Radial distributions for 34 galaxies, *Astrophys. J.* **643**, 804 (2006).
4. F. Nicastro et al., A decade of warm-hot intergalactic medium searches, where do we stand and where do we go?, *Astron. Nachr.* **338**, 281-286 (2017).
5. R. Dave et al., Baryons in the warm-hot intergalactic medium, *Astrophys. J.* **552**, 473 (2010).
6. J.T. Li et al., Baryon budget of the hot circumgalactic medium of massive spiral galaxies, *Astrophys. J. Letters* **855**, L24 (2018).
7. R. Cen et al., Where are the baryons?, *Astrophys. J.* **514**, 1 (1999).
8. F. De Paolis et al., A Case for a baryonic dark halo, *Pys. Rev. Letters* **74**, 14 (1995).
9. F. De Paolis et al., Observing molecular hydrogen clouds and dark massive objects in galactic halos, *Astron. Astrophys.* **299**, 647 (1995).
10. F. De Paolis et al., Possible detection of the M 31 rotation in WMAP data, *Astron. Astrophys.* **534**, L8 (2011).
11. F. De Paolis et al., CMB as a possible new tool to study the dark baryons in galaxies, *J. Phys.: Conference Series* **354**, 1 (2012).
12. F. De Paolis et al., Planck confirmation of the disk and halo rotation of M 31, *Astron. Astrophys.* **565**, L3 (2014).
13. F. De Paolis et al., Planck revealed bulk motion of Centaurus A lobes, *Astron. Astrophys.* **580**, L8 (2015).
14. V. G. Gurzadyan et al., Planck view of the M 82 galaxy, *Astron. Astrophys.* **582**, A77 (2015).
15. F. De Paolis et al., Triangulum galaxy viewed by Planck, *Astron. Astrophys.* **593**, A57 (2016).
16. V. G. Gurzadyan et al., TMessier 81's Planck view versus its halo mapping, *Astron. Astrophys.* **609**, A131 (2018).
17. F. De Paolis et al., Rotating baryonic dark halos, *Astron. Astrophys.* **629**, A87 (2019).
18. V.N. Yershov et al., Distant foreground and the Planck-derived Hubble constant, *Mon. Not. R. Astron. Soc.* **492**, 5052-5056 (2020).
19. A. Qadir et al., Virial clouds explaining the observed rotational asymmetry in the galactic halos, *Phys. Rev. D* **100**, 4043028 (2019).
20. N. Tahir et al., Constraining Baryons in the M31 galactic halo by Planck data, *Int. J. Mod. Phys.* **28**, 7 (2019).
21. N. Tahir et al., Seeing the halo rotation of nearby spiral galaxies using Planck data, *Arab. J. Math.* **8**, 193-199 (2019).
22. T. Padmanabhan, Statistical mechanics of gravitating systems, *Phys. Rep.* **188**, 285-362 (1990).
23. M. Jeon et al., Recovery from Population III supernova explosions and the onset of second-generation star formation, *Mon. Not. R. Astron. Soc.* **444**, 3288-3300 (2014).
24. R. Barkana et al., In the beginning: the first sources of light and the reionization of the universe, *Phys. Rep.* **349**, 125-238 (2001).
25. P., Denis et al., Thermal equilibrium of molecular clouds in cooling flow clusters, *Astron. Astrophys.* **345**, 723-732 (1999).

Testing Weyl-modified gravity on M31 and Milky Way

Muhammad Bilal* and Asghar Qadir†

Abdus Salam School of Mathematical Sciences, 68-B Model Town,
Government College University, Pakistan
* Email: bilalchughtai799@gmail.com
† Email: asgharqadir46@gmil.com

Lee and Qadir,[1] on the basis of various arguments, suggested using a gravitational Lagrangian with a coupling between the Weyl tensor and two copies of the stress-energy tensor, without testing the suggestion for any actual galaxy. As a first step, they used a constant density in their analysis. However unrealistic the constant density approximation is, here we follow up their first step by using their calculations to obtain the coupling constant for the extra term that fits for M31 and the Milky Way, to check if they are consistent within the crude approximation of the model.

Keywords: Dark matter; flat rotation curves; Weyl-induced gravity.

1. Introduction

While the cosmological constant explains the so-called "dark energy problem",[2] providing the Λ of the standard model of cosmology (SMC), the ΛCDM model, The standard model of particle physics (SMPP) ceased to explain the dark matter required to explain the observed dynamics of galaxies. Various suggestions to modify the law of gravity had emerged since the observations of Vera Rubin,[3] but all needed many parameters to solve a single problem, which is no use. Qadir, Lee and Kim[4] had suggested a modification of the Einstein-Hilbert Lagrangian to include an explicit interaction term, RT, on the grounds that it might also solve the problem of quantum gravity. However, the gravitational field is given by the Weyl tensor, $C^{\mu}{}_{\nu\rho\pi}$ and not the Ricci scalar, which gives the mass-energy.

Lee and Qadir[1] suggested a modification of the Lagrangian by including the interaction term, $\lambda C_{\mu\nu\rho\pi} T^{\mu\rho} T^{\nu\pi}$. They obtained the rotational velocity of particles at arbitrary distances from the centre if the density is known as a function of the radial distance. They went on to approximate it as a constant function as a first step, to simplify the calculation. The idea had been that the same interaction coupling must explain the dark matter for all galaxies and systems, or clusters, of galaxies, and manage to avoid the problem of a non-renormalizable theory of quantum gravity. There had been no basis for the latter, just a pious hope. For the former, on the other hand, it should reasonably work out. The calculations were not applied to any specific galaxy. In this brief note, we compare the results for the value of λ required to obtain the rotational curves for M31 and the Milky Way.

The model takes the Schwarzschild interior metric

$$ds^2 = -e^{\nu(r)}c^2 dt^2 + e^{\mu(r)}dr^2 + r^2 d\Omega^2 , \qquad (1)$$

where $d\Omega^2 = d\theta^2 + \sin^2\theta d\phi^2$. Since the rotation curves are obtained by seeing stars in the outer reaches of the galaxies, the relevant radius is the radius of the visible part of the galaxy, the mass is the total mass contained within that radius and the test particle mass, m, is the mass of a typical star. For definiteness, we take it to be a solar mass.

Using the field equations obtained from the modified Lagrangian[1] we get

$$\mu(r) = F(r) - \ln\left[\left\{\frac{r}{1 - \lambda r c^4 \rho \rho'}\left(\int \frac{e^{F(r)}}{r^2}dr - \kappa c^2 \int \rho(r) e^{F(r)} dr\right)\right\}\right], \qquad (2)$$

where

$$F(r) = \frac{1}{2}\int \frac{4 + \lambda r c^4 \left(r\rho^2 \nu'^2 - 2r\rho\rho'\nu' - 2r\rho'^2 - 2r\rho\rho'' - 8\nu'\rho\rho'\right)}{r(1 - \lambda r c^4 \rho \rho')}dr \qquad (3)$$

and

$$\nu'(r) = \frac{1 + \sqrt{1 + 2\lambda\rho^2 c^4 \left(e^{\mu(r)} - 1\right)}}{2r\lambda\rho^2 c^4} . \qquad (4)$$

The square of the rotational velocity is

$$v^2(r) = \frac{1 + \sqrt{1 + 2\lambda\rho^2 c^4 \left(e^{\mu(r)} - 1\right)}}{2\lambda\rho^2 c^2} , \qquad (5)$$

and hence,

$$\lambda = \frac{2\left(\frac{v}{c}\right)^2 + e^{\mu(r)} - 1}{2\rho^2 v^4} . \qquad (6)$$

Following[1] we assume a constant density. Thus

$$e^{\mu(r)} = \frac{e^{F_{const}(r)}}{r\left(\int \frac{e^{F_{const}(r)}}{r^2}dr - \kappa\rho c^2 \int e^{F_{const}(r)}dr\right)} , \qquad (7)$$

where,

$$F_{const}(r) = 2\ln\left(\frac{rc^2}{2GM(r)}\right) + \frac{\lambda\rho^2 c^4}{2}\int r\nu'^2 dr , \qquad (8)$$

where, M(r) is the mass interior to the radius r. It is worth mentioning that in[1] an r is missing inside the integral which has been corrected here. The square of the rotational velocity is determined numerically, taking r to be the radius of the visible galaxy and thus $M(r)$ to be the mass of the visible galaxy. As required, for positive λ, the "gravitational force" is effectively enhanced.

For M31, the Andromeda galaxy,[5] the radius of the visible halo is $\sim 34.7\ kpc$, and the mass $\sim 3.43 \times 10^{11}\ M_\odot$. The constant density comes out to be $1.97 \times 10^{-3}\ M_\odot/pc^3$. For the Milky Way[6] the radius of the visible halo is $\sim 31.5\ kpc$ and the mass $\sim 6.06 \times 10^{10}\ M_\odot$, yielding a density $\sim 4.66 \times 10^{-4}\ M_\odot/pc^3$. The rotational velocity of the visible halo of M31 is $\sim 226\ km/s$ and of the Milky Way is $\sim 220\ km/s$.

The rotational velocity curve does not come out flat for either galaxies, see Fig. 1. This is due to the crude assumption of a constant density. However the curves for both galaxies match for $\lambda = 1.14 \times 10^{16}\ km^2 s^4/kg^2$, thus verifying that both require the same interaction coupling.

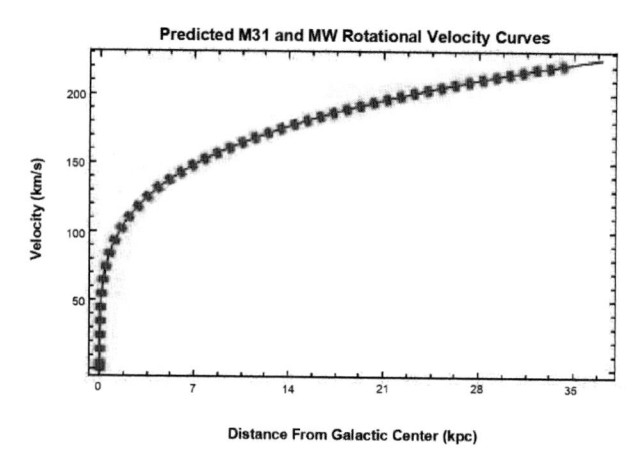

Fig. 1. The black line gives the predicted rotation curve for M31, and the red dotted line the predicted rotation curve for the Milky Way, for $\lambda = 1.14 \times 10^{16}\ km^2 s^4/kg^2$, having taken the rotational velocity at the edge of M31 and the Milky Way as $226\ km/s$, $220\ km/s$ respectively.

For the purpose of checking that the proposal of the Weyl-interaction modification of gravity is viable, it would be necessary to check the proposal for a more realistic model (variable density) for a number of different galaxies, taking into account the baryonic dark matter in that region and distinguishing between the density for the disc matter and the bulge matter.

References

1. A. Qadir, H. W. Lee, *Int. J. Mod. Phys. D* **28**, (2019) 2040014.
2. A. Qadir, *Proc. MG16*, Eds. R. Ruffini, R. Jantzen and G. Vereshchigan (World Scientific 2021).
3. V. C. Rubin, *Ap. J* **451** (1995).
4. A. Qadir, H. W. Lee and K. Y. Kim, *Int. J. Mod. Phys. D* **26** (2017) 1741001.
5. C. Carignan, L. Chemin, W. K. Huchtmeier and F. J. Lockman *ApJ* **641** (2006) L109.
6. P. J. Mcmillan, *MNRAS* **465** (2017) 76.